S0-AUL-962

GEORGIA continued

GAU	Atlanta University, Atlanta.
GAuA	Augusta College, Augusta.
GColuC	Columbus College, Columbus.
GCuA	Andrews College, Cuthbert.
GDC	Columbia Theological Seminary, Decatur.
GDS	Agnes Scott College, Decatur.
GDecA*	Agnes Scott College, Decatur.
GDecCT*	Columbia Theological Seminary, Decatur.
GDoS	South Georgia College, Douglas.
GEU	Emory University, Atlanta.
GHi	Georgia Historical Society, Savannah.
GMM	Mercer University, Macon.
GMW	Wesleyan College, Macon.
GMiW	Woman's College of Georgia, Milledgeville.
GMilvC*	Woman's College of Georgia, Milledgeville.
GOgU	Oglethorpe University, Oglethorpe University.
GSDe*	University of Georgia, DeRenne Library.
GU	University of Georgia, Athens.
GU-De	— DeRenne Georgia Library.
GU-Ex	— Georgia State College of Business Administration Library, Atlanta.

HAWAII

HU	University of Hawaii, Honolulu.
HU-EWC	Center for Cultural and Technical Interchange between East and West, Honolulu.

ILLINOIS

IC	Illinois State Library, Springfield.
	Chicago Public Library.
ICA	Art Institute of Chicago, Chicago.
ICF	Chicago Natural History Museum, Chicago.
ICF-A	— Edward E. Ayer Ornithological Library.
ICHi	Chicago Historical Society, Chicago.
ICIP	Institute for Psychoanalysis, Chicago.
ICJ	John Crerar Library, Chicago.
ICMILC*	Center for Research Libraries, Chicago.
ICMcC	McCormick Theological Seminary, Chicago.
ICN	Newberry Library, Chicago.
ICRL	Center for Research Libraries, Chicago.
ICU	University of Chicago, Chicago.
ICarbS	Southern Illinois University, Carbondale.
IEG	Garrett Theological Seminary, Evanston.
IEN	Northwestern University, Evanston.
IEdS	Southern Illinois University, Edwardsville.
IGK	Knox College, Galesburg.
IHi	Illinois State Historical Library, Springfield.
ILS	St. Procopius College, Lisle.
IMunS	Saint Mary of the Lake Seminary, Mundelein.
INS	Illinois State University, Normal.
IRA	Augustana College Library, Rock Island.
IRivfR	Rosary College, River Forest.
IU	University of Illinois, Urbana.
IU-M	— Medical Sciences Library, Chicago.
IU-U	— Chicago Undergraduate Division, Chicago.

IOWA

IaAS	Iowa State University of Science and Technology, Ames.
IaDL	Luther College, Decorah.
IaDuC	Loras College, Dubuque.
IaDuU	University of Dubuque, Dubuque.
IaDuU-S	— Theological Seminary Library.
IaDuW	Wartburg Theological Seminary, Dubuque.
IaU	University of Iowa, Iowa City.

IDAHO

IdB	Boise Public Library.
IdPI	Idaho State University, Pocatello.
IdPS*	Idaho State University, Pocatello.
IdU	University of Idaho, Moscow.

INDIANA

In	Indiana State Library, Indianapolis.
InAndC	Anderson College, Anderson.
InCollS*	St. Joseph's College, Rensselaer.
InGo	Goshen College Biblical Seminary Library, Goshen.
InHi	Indiana Historical Society, Indianapolis.
InIB	Butler University, Indianapolis.

INDIANA continued

InLP	Purdue University, Lafayette.
InNd	University of Notre Dame, Notre Dame.
InOlH*	St. Leonard College Library, Dayton, Ohio.
InRE	Earlham College, Richmond.
InRenS	St. Joseph's College, Rensselaer.
InStme	St. Meinrad's College & Seminary, St. Meinrad.
InU	Indiana University, Bloomington.

KANSAS

K	Kansas State Library, Topeka.
KAS	St. Benedict's College, Atchison.
KAStB*	St. Benedict's College, Atchison.
KHi	Kansas State Historical Society, Topeka.
KKcB	Central Baptist Theological Seminary, Kansas City.
KMK	Kansas State University, Manhattan.
KStMC*	St. Louis University, School of Divinity Library, St. Louis, Mo.
KU	University of Kansas, Lawrence.
KU-M	— Medical Center Library, Kansas City.
KWiU	Wichita State University, Wichita.

KENTUCKY

Ky-LE	Library Extension Division, Frankfort.
KyBgW	Western Kentucky State College, Bowling Green
KyHi	Kentucky Historical Society, Frankfort.
KyLo	Louisville Free Public Library.
KyLoS	Southern Baptist Theological Seminary, Louisville.
KyLoU	University of Louisville, Louisville.
KyLx	Lexington Public Library.
KyLxCB	Lexington Theological Seminary, Lexington. (Formerly College of the Bible)
KyLxT	Transylvania College, Lexington.
KyMoreT	Morehead State College, Morehead.
KyU	University of Kentucky, Lexington.
KyWA	Asbury College Library, Wilmore.
KyWAT	Asbury Theological Seminary, Wilmore.

LOUISIANA

L	Louisiana State Library, Baton Rouge.
L-M	Louisiana State Museum Library, New Orleans.
LCA	Not a library symbol.
LCS	Not a library symbol.
LHi	Louisiana History Society, New Orleans.
LNHT	Tulane University Library, New Orleans.
LNT-MA	Tulane University, Latin American Library, New Orleans.
LU	Louisiana State University, Baton Rouge.
LU-M	— Medical Center Library, New Orleans.
LU-NO	— Louisiana State University in New Orleans.

MASSACHUSETTS

M	Massachusetts State Library, Boston.
MA	Amherst College, Amherst.
MB	Boston Public Library.
MBAt	Boston Athenaeum, Boston.
MBBC*	Boston College, Chestnut Hill.
MBCo	Countway Library of Medicine. (Harvard-Boston Medical Libraries)
MBH	Massachusetts Horticultural Society, Boston.
MBHo*	Massachusetts Horticultural Society, Boston.
MBM*	Countway Library of Medicine (Harvard-Boston Medical Libraries).
MBMu	Museum of Fine Arts, Boston.
MBU	Boston University.
MBdAF	U.S. Air Force Cambridge Research Center, Bedford.
MBrZ	Zion Research Library, Brookline.
MBrigStJ*	St. John's Seminary, Brighton.
MBtS	St. John's Seminary Library, Brighton.
MCM	Massachusetts Institute of Technology, Cambridge.
MCR	Radcliffe College, Cambridge.
MCSA	Smithsonian Institution, Astrophysical Observatory, Cambridge.
MChB	Boston College, Chestnut Hill.
MH	Harvard University, Cambridge.
MH-A	— Arnold Arboretum.
MH-AH	— Andover-Harvard Theological Library.
MH-BA	— Graduate School of Business Administration Library.
MH-FA	— Fine Arts Library. (Formerly Fogg Art Museum)
MH-G	— Gray Herbarium Library.
MH-HY	— Harvard-Yenching Institute. (Chinese-Japanese Library)

MASSACHUSETTS continued

MH-L	— Law School Library.
MH-P	— Peabody Museum Library.
MH-PR	— Physics Research Library.
MHi	Massachusetts Historical Society, Boston.
MMeT	Tufts University, Medford.
MNF	Forbes Library, Northampton.
MNS	Smith College, Northampton.
MNoeS	Stonehill College Library, North Easton.
MNtcA	Andover Newton Theological School, Newton Center.
MSaE	Essex Institute, Salem.
MShM	Mount Holyoke College, South Hadley.
MU	University of Massachusetts, Amherst.
MWA	American Antiquarian Society, Worcester.
MWAC	Assumption College, Worcester.
MWC	Clark University, Worcester.
MWH	College of the Holy Cross, Worcester.
MWalB	Brandeis University, Waltham.
MWelC	Wellesley College, Wellesley.
MWhB	Marine Biological Laboratory, Woods Hole.
MWiW	Williams College, Williamstown.
MWiW-C	— Chapin Library.

MARYLAND

MdAN	U.S. Naval Academy, Annapolis.
MdBE	Enoch Pratt Free Library, Baltimore.
MdBG	Goucher College, Baltimore.
MdBJ	Johns Hopkins University, Baltimore.
MdBJ-G	— John Work Garrett Library.
MdBP	Peabody Institute, Baltimore.
MdBWA	Walters Art Gallery, Baltimore.
MdU	University of Maryland, College Park.
MdW	Woodstock College, Woodstock.

MAINE

MeB	Bowdoin College, Brunswick.
MeBa	Bangor Public Library.
MeU	University of Maine, Orono.
MeWC	Colby College, Waterville.
MeWaC*	Colby College, Waterville.

MICHIGAN

Mi	Michigan State Library, Lansing.
MiAC	Alma College, Alma.
MiD	Detroit Public Library.
MiD-B	— Burton Historical Collection.
MiDA	Detroit Institute of Arts, Detroit.
MiDU	University of Detroit, Detroit.
MiDW	Wayne State University, Detroit.
MiEM	Michigan State University, East Lansing.
MiEalC*	Michigan State University, East Lansing.
MiGr	Grand Rapids Public Library.
MiH*	Michigan College of Mining and Technology, Houghton.
MiHM	Michigan College of Mining and Technology, Houghton.
MiU	University of Michigan, Ann Arbor.
MiU-C	— William L. Clements Library.

MINNESOTA

MnCS	St. John's University, Collegeville.
MnH*	Minnesota Historical Society, St. Paul.
MnHi	Minnesota Historical Society, St. Paul.
MnRM	Mayo Clinic and Foundation Library, Rochester.
MnSJ	James Jerome Hill Reference Library, St. Paul.
MnSSC	College of St. Catherine, St. Paul.
MnU	University of Minnesota, Minneapolis.

MISSOURI

MoHi	Missouri State Historical Society, Columbia
MoK	Kansas City Public Library.
MoKL	Linda Hall Library, Kansas City
MoKU	University of Missouri at Kansas City, Kansas City.
MoS	St. Louis Public Library.
MoSB	Missouri Botanical Garden, St. Louis.
MoSC*	Concordia Seminary Library, St. Louis.
MoSCS	Concordia Seminary Library, St. Louis.
MoSM	Mercantile Library Association, St. Louis.
MoSU	St. Louis University, St. Louis.
MoSU-D	— School of Divinity Library, St. Louis.
MoSW	Washington University, St. Louis.
MoU	University of Missouri, Columbia.

The National Union Catalog

Pre-1956 Imprints

The National Union Catalog

Pre-1956 Imprints

A cumulative author list representing Library of Congress printed cards and titles reported by other American libraries. Compiled and edited with the cooperation of the Library of Congress and the National Union Catalog Subcommittee of the Resources Committee of the Resources and Technical Services Division, American Library Association

Volume 332

LICHT, WALTER - LIGER, RENÉE

Mansell 1974

Z
018.1
N213

© 1974 Mansell Information/Publishing Limited

© 1974 The American Library Association

*All rights reserved under Berne and Universal Copyright Conventions
and Pan American Union.*

Mansell Information/Publishing Limited
3 Bloomsbury Place, London WC1

The American Library Association
50 East Huron Street, Chicago, Illinois 60611

The paper on which this catalog has been printed is supplied by
P. F. Bingham Limited and has been specially manufactured by the
Guard Bridge Paper Company Limited of Fife, Scotland.
Based on requirements established by the late William J. Barrow
for a permanent/durable book paper it is laboratory certified
to meet or exceed the following values:

Substance 89 gsm
pH cold extract 9.4
Fold endurance (MIT $\frac{1}{2}$kg. tension) 1200
Tear resistance (Elmendorf) 73 (or 67 × 3)
Opacity 90.3%

Library of Congress Card Number : 67–30001
ISBN: 0 7201 0411 4

Printed by Balding & Mansell Limited, London and Wisbech, England
Bound by Bemrose & Sons Limited, Derby, England

Permission is granted to subscribers and users of this Catalog to reproduce
limited copies of individual pages for scholarly and not for commercial purposes.

90937

American Library Association

Resources and Technical Services Division

RESOURCES COMMITTEE

SUBCOMMITTEE ON THE NATIONAL UNION CATALOG

Chairman GORDON R. WILLIAMS
Director CENTER FOR RESEARCH LIBRARIES
5721 Cottage Grove Avenue, Chicago, Illinois 60637

Members

DOUGLAS W. BRYANT *University Librarian*
Widener Library, Harvard University
Cambridge, Massachusetts 02138

VERNER W. CLAPP 1901-1972 *formerly*
Consultant Council on Library Resources, Inc.

JOHN W. CRONIN *formerly*
Director Processing Department
Library of Congress
2129 32nd Place, S.E.
Washington, D.C. 20020

CHARLES W. DAVID *formerly*
Director of Library Development
Marine Historical Association
854 Radnor Road
St. Davids, Pennsylvania 19087

WILLIAM S. DIX *University Librarian*
Princeton University
Princeton, New Jersey 08540

RALPH E. ELLSWORTH *formerly*
Director University of Colorado Libraries
Boulder, Colorado 80302

HERMAN H. FUSSLER *Professor*
Graduate Library School
University of Chicago
Chicago, Illinois 60637

WARREN J. HAAS *Vice President*
for Libraries and Information Services
Columbia University
New York City, New York 10027

RUTHERFORD D. ROGERS *University Librarian*
Yale University
New Haven, Connecticut 06520

GEORGE A. SCHWEGMANN, JR. *formerly*
Chief Union Catalog Division
3534 Porter Street, N.W.
Washington, D.C. 20016

FREDERICK H. WAGMAN *Director*
University of Michigan Libraries
Ann Arbor, Michigan 48104

WILLIAM J. WELSH *Director*
Processing Department
Library of Congress
Washington, D.C. 20540

Publisher's Note

Because of the large number of sources from which the information in the National Union Catalog has been collected over a long period of time an understanding of its scope and an acquaintance with its methods is necessary for the best use to be made of it. Users are therefore earnestly advised to make themselves familiar with the introductory matter in Volume 1. This fully defines the scope of the Catalog and sets out the basis on which the material reported to the National Union Catalog has been edited for publication in book form.

National Union Catalog Designation

Each main entry in the Catalog has been ascribed a unique identifying designation. This alphanumeric combination appears uniformly after the last line of the entry itself and consists of:

1 The letter N, signifying National Union Catalog.
2 The initial letter under which the entry is filed.
3 A number representing the position of the entry within the sequence under its initial letter.

This National Union Catalog designator is sufficient both to identify any main entry in the Catalog and to establish its position within the sequence of volumes. It is, however, recommended that when referring to titles by the National Union Catalog designation a checking element, such as the key word or initials of the title, be added.

Reported Locations

Alphabetic symbols which represent libraries in the United States and Canada follow the National Union Catalog designation. These groups of letters signify which libraries have reported holding copies of the work. The first library so represented usually is the one that provided the catalog information.

Printed on the end sheets of each volume is a list of most frequently used symbols, each followed by the full name of the library. *List of Symbols*, containing a comprehensive list of symbols used, is published as a separate volume with the Catalog. The Library of Congress has also issued *Symbols Used in the National Union Catalog of the Library of Congress*. In cases where a symbol is not identified in these lists the National Union Catalog Division of the Library of Congress will, on enquiry, attempt to identify the library concerned.

Other Developments

Under the terms of their agreement with the American Library Association, the publishers have undertaken to apply, as far as is practicable, new developments in library science and techniques which may have the effect of further enhancing the value of the Catalog. To this end, the publishers will be pleased to receive suggestions and enquiries relating to technical and production aspects of the Catalog and will be glad to consider proposals calculated to improve its utility and amenity. Mansell Information/Publishing Limited will be pleased also to advise libraries on possible applications of the methods and techniques developed for this and similar projects to their own requirements.

J.C.
London, *August 1968*

VOLUME 332

Licht, Walter, Referendar: Verschollenheit und Todeserklärung nach dem Bürgerlichen Gesetzbuche. Mit e. kurzen Überblick über d. histor. Entwicklung. Leipzig 1913: Herrmann. IX, 38 S. 8°

Leipzig, Jur. Diss. v. 25. Juli 1913

[Geb. 3. Mai 86 Leipzig; Wohnort: Bautzen; Staatsangeh.: Sachsen; Vorbildung: Thomassch. Leipzig Reife 06; Studium: Tübingen 2, Leipzig 6 S.; Rig. 30. Juni 10.] [U 13.1035

NL 0341325   ICRL

Licht, Wilhelm.
Das volk ist herz - Hermann Frey. [Von] Wilhelm Licht. Satz: P. Roeder. [Für] Gem. chor.   Berlin, Dionysos-verlag

Photostatic reproduction of manuscript. 1 sheet.

For voice and piano: "Gem. chor."

NL 0341326   NRU NN

Licht, William.
The phase relations existing in the ternary system trichlorethylene, ethyl alcohol, and water as applied to the manufacture of absolute alcohol ... by ... [Cincinnati 1937] 32 l.

NL 0341327   OCU

Licht, William.
Studies of the adsorption wave in beds of granular anhydrous calcium sulphate. [Cincinnati] 1950.
x,110 l. diagrs. 29cm.

Thesis (Ph.D.) - Univ. of Cincinnati, 1950.
Bibliography: l. 96-97.

NL 0341328   OCU

Licht y Sangronis, Carlos Eusebio de.
Oracion politico-moral, qve en el avthorizado concurso opositivo à la lectoral de la santa metropolitana, y patriarchal Iglesia de Sevilla, declamò con estrecho termino de 48. horas el lic. don Carlos Evsebio de Licht, y Sangronis ... Sevilla, I. F. de Blas [1722]
10 p.l.,30 numb. l. 20cm. [Sermones varios. v. 9, no. 7]

F1207 S42 v.9:7 x

NL 0341329   CU-B

Das Licht.
Judaica   Berlin, Philo Verlag.
Bg19   22cm.
L61

NL 0341330   CtY

Das Licht; Missionschrift der Oblaten des heiligen Franz von Sales für die deutschen Länder. 1.-   Jahrg.; 1906-Wien.
v. illus., ports. 25 cm. monthly.

ZP L617

1. Catholic Church - Missions - Period. 2. Oblates of St. Francis de Sales - Period. 3. Missions - Period. 4. Missions, German. I. Oblates of St. Francis de Sales. x General catalogue

NL 0341331   CtY-D

Das Licht; Zeitschrift für praktische Leucht- und Beleuchtungs-Aufgaben.

TK3 .L5

[Berlin]
v. illus., ports. 29 cm. monthly.

Began publication with Oct. 1930 issue. Cf. Union list of serials.
Organ of Deutsche Lichttechnische Gesellschaft E. V. and similar organizations.

1. Electric lighting—Period.   I. Deutsche Lichttechnische Gesellschaft.

50-13009

NL 0341332   DLC

Ein Licht auf meinem Wege; Erlebnisse und Erfahrungen mit der Bibel. Beiträge von: Pierre de Benoit, Marta Wild, Max Ronner [u.a.] ... 3.Aufl. Bern, Christliches Verlagshaus [c1943] 110p. 20cm.

CD50 L699

NL 0341333   NNUT

Licht aus dem dunklen Eck. Waage versus Weiser. 1839.

NL 0341334   PPeSchw

Licht aus dem herzen; briefe und aufzeichnungen eines gefallenen soldaten.   Bonn, H.M. Hieronimi [1947]
174p. 18cm.

940.548 L61

1. World war II, 1939-1945--Personal narratives, German.

NL 0341335   LU NNC MH

Licht aus Osten; eine nützliche, belehrende und unterhaltende Lecture für Freymaurer.   Zweytes Bd. Hof, L. H. Mintzel, 5813 [1813]
vi,186 p. 16cm.

HS 457 L69

No more published?

1. Freemasons--Rituals.

NL 0341336   NIC

Het Licht daalt neder; kerstvertellingen. [Door] Ina Boudier-Bakker, K. van der Geest, K. H. R. de Josselin de Jong [en anderen] ... Zeist, Uitgeverij Ploegsma, 1940.
171 p. 21½ᶜᵐ.

CONTENTS.—Boudier-Bakker, Ina. Het kleed van den heilige.—Geest, K. v. d. Kerstmis thuis.—Josselin de Jong, K. H. R. de. Nieuwe dag.—Man, Herman de. Een kind is verloren, een mensch heeft gevonden.—Pothast-Gimberg, C. E. Het licht daalde neder.—Ridder, Tony de. Haar eenzaam kerstfeest.—Vries, Anne de. Jacht op den strooper.

1. Christmas stories. 2. Dutch fiction.   I. Boudier-Bakker, Ina, 1875-

PT5532.C5L5   A F 47-3853
New York. Public library
for Library of Congress

NL 0341337   DLC NN CU

Das Licht des Buddha
see under [Kuroda, Shinto]

Licht- en schaduwbeelden uit de binnenlanden van Java ...
see under [Junghuhn, Franz Wilhelm] 1809-1864.

Licht; ein märchengedicht
see under [Soyaux, Frida (Schanz)] 1859-

A licht for the ignorant
see   A light for the ignorant.

Licht Gefährten; Tragödie ...
see under [Heizmann, Joseph]

Licht in der finsternis. [Genf, Schweiz, Herausgegeben von der Ökumenischen kommission für die pastoration der kriegsgefangenen] 1945.
79, [1] p. plates. 19 cm.

"Lieder" (with unaccompanied melodies) : p. [65]-79.

1. Christmas.   I. Oekumenische kommission für die pastoration der kriegsgefangenen, Geneva.   II. Title.

BV45.L5   A F 47-5996
Union theol. sem. Library
for Library of Congress

NL 0341343   NNUT DLC MH CoD NN DCU TNV

Licht, mehr licht, psychologisches Sonntagsblatt. Nov.2,9, 1879, Jan. 25, 1880. Paris.

NL 0341344   PPL

Licht muss wieder werden
see under [Nationalsozialistische deutsche Arbeiter-Partei. Reichspropagandaleitung. Haupt-Kulturamt]

Het licht op den kandelaar...
n.p., 1662.

8 p.
William Ames, attributed author.

NL 0341346   PHC

Das **Licht** scheint in der Finsternis; vier Vorträge von der Evangelischen Woche in Stuttgart, 1946.   Stuttgart, Quell-Verlag der Evang. Gesellschaft [1947]   55 p. 19cm.

CONTENTS.—Gibtes eine Rettung aus unserer Not? von W. Lempp. Braucht Christenglaube Gemeinde? von M. Haug.—Der Christ und die letzten Tage, von K. Hutten.—Das Gebot der Nächstenliebe im Lichte unserer Zeit, von W. Lauk.

1. Christianity—Addresses,   essays, lectures. I. Evangelische Gesellschaft, Stuttgart.

NL 0341347   NN

VOLUME 332

Licht übers Land
   see Die **Leuchtrakete.**

Das Licht, und die Lieb der Welt, Jesus Christus der Gecreutzigte, auf dem Schmertzhafften Creutz-Weeg vorgestellt... Mit Lebens-Regeln und Gebettern... Achte Auflag... Bamberg, Gedruckt zu finden bey Johann Georg Klietsch, 1758. 120 p. plates. 14cm. (18°.)

Illustrations: 16 full-page copper engravings (including frontispiece) depicting the Stations of the Cross.
Bound with: Geistliches Schatz-Kästel. Wien, 1718.

1. Cross, Stations of the.
N. Y. P. L.   November 29, 1948

NL 0341349   NN

Licht und Kraft fuer den Tag; Betrachtungen ueber die taeglichen Losungen und Lehrtexte der Bruedergemeine mit Hinweisen auf dazu passende Bibelabschnitte und geistliche Lieder. Moeckmuehl (Wuertt.), im Aue Verlag, 1905-
    v.   19 cm.
    Vol. 1 is 2. Auflage.

NL 0341350   MH-AH

Licht und Kraft für den Tag. Bibellesezettel ... Schwanheim, F. J. Henrich, 1946.
           48
1946 3. Heft.

NL 0341351   CtY NN

Licht und Lampe; Rundschau für die Beleuchtungsindustrie, -installation, Elektrogerät, Sanitäre und Kühlanlagen.

Berlin.
    v. illus. 33 cm. biweekly. (irregular)
"Organ der Einzelhandels-Fachabteilung Beleuchtung und Elektrogerät, Sanitäre und Kühlanlagen und des Verbandes des Geleuchtungs- und Elektroeinzelhandels Deutschland e. V."

1. Electric lighting—Period. 1. Reichsgruppe Handel. Wirtschaftsgruppe Einzelhandel. Fachgruppe Eisenwaren, Porzellan, Elektro- und Hausgerät.

TK3.L53   621.3205   50-40480 ‡

NL 0341352   DLC

Period.   Licht und Leben, evangelisches Monatsblatt.
1074   hrsg. von der Evangelischen Gesellschaft für Deutschland in Wuppertal-Elberfeld und Schriftenmissionsverlag in Gladbeck/Westfalen, 1-   1889/90-
     Gladbeck/Westfalen.
     v. 25cm.

also   _____. Microfilm copy (positive). Chicago,
Mflm.   Dept. of Photoduplication, University of
362P-   Chicago Library for American Theological
374p

     Library Association Board of Microtext.
     reels 35mm.

     1. Inner missions - Periodicals.
     2. Inner missions - Germany. I. Evangelische
Gesellschaft für Deutschland.

NL 0341354   MH-AH

Licht und Leben; evangelisches Wochenblatt. v.1-
1888-   Elberfeld.
       v. weekly.

Micro-   Microfilm. v.31-45; 1919-1933. New Haven, Photographed
film   for the ATLA Microtext Project by Dept of Photoduplication, University of Chicago Library [1967?] 14 reels. 35mm.

     1. Theology--Period.

NL 0341355   CBPac

Licht und liebe. Zur vermählungsfeyer, meiner tochter Cristine Auguste mit J. C. F. Rist
     see under   Westphalen, Frau Christina (von Axen) 1758-1849.

Licht und materie
     see under   Konen, Heinrich Mathias, 1874-   ed.

F050   Licht und Schatten. Jhrg. 1-6; Okt. 1910-16.
L617   Munich, Berlin.
     6v. illus. 25cm. weekly.

     Some issues have subtitle: Wochenschrift für Schwarzweisskunst und Dichtung.
     Vol.5 called Front?

     I. Title: Front.

NL 0341358   KU CtY OrU IU NjP CaBVaU IEN MH MiU NN

Licht und schatten in eines malers leben, vom den verfasser des waisenkindes. Halle, R. Mühlmann, 1858.
     [4], 307, [1] p.

     Bound with Deutsche heldensage. Halle, 1858.

NL 0341359   OCl

Licht und Schatten; Legenden von Martin Beheim-Schwarzbach, Fritz Diettrich [u. a.] Berlin, Eckart, 1935.
     76 p.
     I. Beheim-Schwarzbach, Martin.

NL 0341360   MiD

Licht- und schattenbilder aus dem innern von Java
     see under   [Junghuhn, Franz Wilhelm] 1809-1864.

Licht von Oben
     see under   [Jocundus, Cornelia] b. 1812.

Lichtbehandlung bei schweren und bisher unheilbaren Krankheiten
     see under   Lohse, Dr.

                            50568.27
Lichtbilder aus dem schattenreiche; [poetry]. Berlin, J. Springer, 1842.
     pp. (8), 96.

NL 0341364   MH

Lichtbildlehrbücher. Abt. Wirtschaftslehre und Staatswissenschaft. Bd. 1-   Muenchen, Verlag der Diatypie, 1924-
     v. illus. 22 cm.

NL 0341365   NcD

TT649   **Lichtblau, George.**
.U5
     U. S. *Bureau of Labor Statistics.*
     Case study data on productivity and factory performance, men's bib overalls and men's work jackets [by George Lichtblau] Prepared for Mutual Security Agency, Productivity and Technical Assistance Division. [Washington, 1952]

HD8051   **Lichtblau, George,** joint author.
.A7876
no. 37   **Lentz, Arthur Stanley.**
     Case study data on productivity and factory performance, veneer and plywood, prepared for Mutual Security Agency, Productivity and Technical Assistance Division [by Arthur S. Lentz and George Lichtblau] Washington, 1953.

Lichtblau, Ludwig.

Bačmedjeji, Aleksije, ed.
     Komentar Jugoslovenskog izvršnog postupnika, po komentaru Izvršnog postupnika dr. Georga Neumanna ... i dr. Ludvika Lichtblau ... redigovali: dr. Bačmedjeji Aleksije ... i Branković Stevan ... Novi-Bečej, Vlastito izdanje; U Celju, Štampala Zvezna tiskarna, 1932.

Lichtblau, Ludwig, joint author.
Neumann, Georg.
     Kommentar zur Exekutionsordnung, von dr. Georg Neumann ... im verein mit dr. Ludwig Lichtblau ... 3., neu bearb. aufl. ... Wien, Manz, 1928-29.

Lichtblau, Siegfried Shlomo
Oxidation-reduction phenomena in the fermentation of Streptomyces griseus. [New York] 1954.
     123 l. diagrs., tables. 29cm.

     Thesis, Columbia University.
     Typescript.
     Bibliography: l. 97-99.

NL 0341370   NNC

W 4   **LICHTBLAU,** Stefan, 1923-
M96   Die Appendicopathia oxyurica im Lichte
1950   neuerer Betrachtungen, eigene Beobachtungen. München, 1950.
     30 l.
     Inaug.-Diss.-Munich.
     1. Appendix - Parasitology
     2. Oxyuriasis

NL 0341371   DNLM

VOLUME 332

4QA
519
Lichtblau, W
Mathematisches Unterrichtswerk für
Lehrerbildungsanstalten [von] W.
Lichtblau und B. Wiese. Neubearbei-
tung von B. Wiese, K. Muhs und O.
Teichmann. Breslau, F. Hirt, 1916.
171 p.

NL 0341372 DLC-P4

4QA-70 Lichtblau, W
Methodik des Rechenunterrichts. Zugleich
ein Hilfsbuch für den Unterricht in der ersten
Seminarklasse. Unter Mitwirkung von B. Wiese,
bearb. von W. Lichtblau und A. Knotta.
Breslau, F. Hirt, 1910.
412 p.

NL 0341373 DLC-P4

Der LICHTBOGEN. 1.- Jahrg.; Des./Jan. 1951/
52-
Marl, Kreis Recklinghausen [Germany] v.
illus.(part col.), ports. 30cm.

Monthly, 1951/52-60; irregular, 1961-date
"Werkzeitschrift."
Issued by Chemische Werke Hüls A.G.

Vols. for 1959-60 include separately-paged supplement: Blick vom
Hochhaus.

1. Chemistry--Per. and soc. publ. 2. Plastic materials--Per. and soc.
publ. 3. House organs. I. Chemische Werke Hüls A.G.
II. Blick vom Hochhaus.

NL 0341375 NN

Lichtbote. v.1-2; 1806.
Frankfort, J. C. Hermann.
2v. monthly.

NL 0341376 ICRL

PA4279
f.T38L7 Lichtdrucke des Theaetetpapyros. Neunzehn ta-
feln. Hrsg. von der Generalverwaltung der König-
lichen museen. Berlin, Weidmann, 1905.
cover-title, xix facsim. 53cm.
Running title: Kommentar zum Theaetet.
In portfolio.
The facsimiles have the number of the manuscript:
P.9782.
I. Plato. Theaetetus.

NL 0341377 ICU

Lichte, August.
Untersuchungen an einer anlage für wärme
und stoffaustausch. ... Berlin, n.d.
Inaug. Diss. - Techn. Hochsch. Dresden, [1934].

NL 0341378 ICRL

Lichte (Carl Heinrich) [1879-]. *Der Einfluss des Kochsalzes auf die Blutgerinnung.
23 pp. 8°. Marburg, J. Hamel. 1908.

NL 0341379 DNLM ICRL CtY

Lichte, Egon, 1911-
... Syringomyelie und Unfall ... Werne a.d.
Lippe, 1938.
Inaug.-Diss. - Münster.
Lebenslauf.

NL 0341380 CtY

Lichte, Gustav,
Traumatische tabes.
Inaug. diss. Berlin, 1903.
Bibl.

NL 0341381 ICRL CtY DNLM

Lichte, Hermann F. 669.1 Q710
.... Das Roheisen und seine Darstellung durch den Hochofen-
betrieb. Unter Berücksichtigung sämtlicher Neuerungen allgemein erläutert für die Praxis und das Selbststudium von Herm. F.
Lichte. Mit 76 in den Text und auf 4 Tafeln gedruckten Abbildungen. Hannover, M. Jänecke, 1907.
[2], 308 p. incl. 76 illus., tables. IV fold. pl. (incl. diagrs.) 17½cm. (Bibliothek
der gesamten Technik. 15. Band.)
"Literatur," p. [300].

NL 0341382 ICJ OCl

Lichte, Hugo, 1891-
Physik und technik des tonfilms, von dr. Hugo Lichte und
dr. habil. Albert Narath ... 2., erweiterte aufl. Mit 296 abbildungen. Leipzig, S. Hirzel, 1943.
viii, 411 p. illus., diagrs. 25cm.
"Literaturverzeichnis": p. [372]-401.

1. Moving-pictures, Talking. 2. Sound—Recording and reproducing.
I. Narath, Albert, joint author.
45-16569
Library of Congress TR897.L5 1943
778.5344

NL 0341383 DLC CLU NNC OU

Lichte, Hugo, 1891-
Physik und Technik des Tonfilms, von Dr. Hugo Lichte und Dr.
habil. Albert Narath... 2., erweiterte Aufl... Leipzig, S. Hirzel, 1943 [repr.: Ann Arbor, Edwards bros., 1945] viii, 411 p.
illus. 25cm.
"Literaturverzeichnis," p. [372]-401.

354053B. 1. Moving pictures, Sound. I. Narath, Albert, jt. au.
N.Y.P.L. November 12, 1946

NL 0341384 NN

Lichte, Hugo, 1891- ed.
Fischer, Fritz, 1898-
Tonfilm aufnahme und wiedergabe nach dem klangfilm-
verfahren (system Klangfilm-Tobis) herausgegeben für die
Klangfilm g. m. b. h., Berlin, von der F. Fischer ... [und] dr.
H. Lichte ... Mit 378 abbildungen. Leipzig, S. Hirzel, 1931.

Lichte, H[ugo].
Ueber die Schallintensität des tönenden Lichtbogens. Leip-
zig: J. A. Barth, 1913. 35(1) p. 8°.
Dissertation, Göttingen.

I. Arc (Singing).
N.Y.P.L.

NL 0341386 NN CtY MiU PU MH

Lichte, Lode, pseud.
see
Campforts, Lodewijk.

Lichte, Rudolf: Zur Kenntnis der aus Formaldehyd mit Harnstoff
und Thioharnstoff entstehenden Verbindungen. [Maschinenschrift.]
40 S. 4°. — Auszug: (Kiel 1925: Rößler). 2 Bl. 8°
Kiel, Phil. Diss. v. 3. Aug. 1925 [U 25.5302

NL 0341388 ICRL

Lichte, William Heil, 1911-
Attributes of complex tones, by William H. Lichte ... [Lan-
caster, Pa., Lancaster press, inc., 1941]
cover-title, 455-480 p. incl. tables, diagrs. 24cm.
Main content of thesis (PH. D.)—University of Iowa, 1940.
"Reprinted from Journal of experimental psychology, vol. 28, no. 6 ...
June, 1941."
"References": p. 480.

1. Sound. I. Title. II. Title: Complex tones.
A 41-4785
Iowa. Univ. Library
for Library of Congress QC246.L5
[2] 534.4

NL 0341389 IaU DLC

Lichte Taats, Boudewyn de
... De iure imperantis civilis, obligationem civium naturalem imperfectam com-
mitandi in obligationem civilem perfectam
... submittit Boudewyn de Lichte Taats
... Groningae, P. Doekema, 1778.
2 p.l., 45, [1] p. 23cm.
Diss.- Groningen.

NL 0341390 MH-L

Das Lichte haus. München, K. Röhrig k.-g. [1944]
95, [8] p. incl. pl. 21½ cm.
Prose and verse.

1. German literature—20th cent.
PT1141.L5 830.82 A F 47-5240
Johns Hopkins univ. Libr.
for Library of Congress

CtY CU WU IaU ICRL WU NjP IU MoU NN MH
NL 0341391 MdBJ DLC MiD MnU NRU MdBP IEN MB NNC

LICHTEIKER, Hermann.
Die berichtigungsveranlagung und berichti-
gungsfeststellung auf grund der rechtsprechung
des reichsfinanzhofes. Düsseldorf, G.H.Nolte,
1935.
pp. 4-51+(1). 8°.
Inaug.-diss. --- Köln.

NL 0341392 MH-L CtY

W 4
H47
1609
L.1
LICHTEN, Adam, fl. 1599-1629, praeses
De melancholia, disputatio secunda, in qua de
tertia melancholiae specie, quae ex hypochondriis
originem ducit, agitur ... Helmaestadii, Ex typo-
grapheio Jacobi Lucii, 1609.
[24] p. 20 cm.
Diss. - Helmstädt. (C. Quartus, respondent)

I. Quartus, Christoph, fl. 1605- 1609, respondent

NL 0341393 DNLM

VOLUME 332

Lichten, Frances.
... Decorating the Pennsylvania German chest ...
see her Home craft course in decorating the Pennsylvania German chest.

Lichten, Frances.
Decorative art of Victoria's era. New York, Scribner ₍1950₎
274 p. illus. (part col.) 31 cm.
Bibliography: p. ₍263₎-270.

1. Art, Decorative. 2. Gt. Brit.—Soc. life & cust. 3. U. S.—Soc. life & cust. 4. Gt. Brit.—Hist.—Victoria, 1837-1901. I. Title.

NK1380.L5   745.44   50-9758

KyLx DAU MU MiU CoU CLSU TU
OrSaW OrU Wa WaE WaS WaSp MiU KyLx MdBWA KEmT
MsU FU GU WaSpG WaT CaBVa CaBViP IdB Or OrCS OrP
NL 0341395   DLC PPMoI PP NN TxU MB NcU ViU NcGU

Lichten, Frances.
Folk art motifs of Pennsylvania. New York, Hastings House ₍1954₎
96 p. illus. (part col.) 26 x 31 cm.

1. Folk art—Pennsylvania. 2. Design, Decorative. I. Title.

NK835.P4L48   745.44   54-10701
                                    NcD

PLF WaT PHi NcD
TxU OOxM Or Wa WaS CaBViP CaBVa OrLgE OrMonO PPPL
NL 0341396   DLC RP GU TU NN OC1SA PPPM PJA PPMoI MB

Lichten, Frances, comp.
Pennsylvania art project.
Folk art of rural Pennsylvania. Selected by the Index of American design, Pennsylvania art project, Work projects administration. ₍Philadelphia? 1941₎

Lichten, Frances.
Folk art of rural Pennsylvania ₍by₎ Frances Lichten. New York, C. Scribner's sons; London, C. Scribner's sons, ltd. ₍1946₎
xiv p. 1 l. 276 p. illus. (part col.; incl. facsims.) 31ᶜᵐ.

1. Folk art—Pennsylvania. 2. Art industries and trade—Pennsylvania. I. Title.

NK835.P4L5   745.3   47-1192

IEN CLU TxU CLSU
CaBVa OrP OrU Wa WaE WaS WaT WaSp MU PSt KEmT
MB PPCS ICU PPPM OO NcRS ViU NcD OrCS Or IdU IdB
NL 0341398   DLC N TU PSt PBm PPFr PHC PWcT PPD

Lichten, Frances.
Home craft course in decorating the Pennsylvania German chest ₍by₎ Frances Lichten... Plymouth Meeting, Pa., Mrs. C. Naaman Keyser ₍1944?₎   15 l.   illus.   23cm. (Home craft course series. v. 11.)

1. Chests. 2. Folk art, U.S.—
N. Y. P. L.   Pennsylvania. I. Ser.
                                        June 15, 1945

NL 0341399   NN NNC WaS Or WaSp OC1 PSt MB Mi N

Lichten, H. E., *pseud.*
  see
Riesser, Hans Eduard, 1887- 1965

Lichten, Nicola Hans, 1909-
Der Versuch als umgekehrter Irrtum ... von Nicola Hans Lichten. München, C. Wolf & Sohn, 1935.
39 p. 21cm.
Inaug.-Diss. - Breslau.
"Lebenslauf": p. 39.
"Schrifttum": p. ₍3₎-4.

NL 0341401   MH-L ICRL

PA   Lichtenau, Heinrich von, bp. of Augsburg.
2873   Zur Geschichte der mittellateinischen
L69   Dichtung. Heinrici Augustensis Planctus
       Evae, von J. Huemer. Wien, 1891.
       24 p. 25cm.
       Accompanies "Programm" (Jahresbericht)--
       K. K. Gymnasium, 2d dist., Vienna.

       I. Huemer, Johann.

NL 0341402   NIC

Lichtenau, Karl von Salza und
           see
Salza und Lichtenau, Karl von, 1802-1865.

Lichtenau, Konrad von
       see   Konrad von Lichtenau, provost of Ursperg, d. 1240.

Lichtenau, Wilhelmine (Enke) Gräfin von, 1752-1820.
Apologie der Gräfin Lichtenau gegen die Beschuldigung mehrerer Schriftsteller. Von ihr selbst entworfen. Nebst einer Auswahl von Briefen an sie [hrsg. von J.G. Schummel] Leipzig, W. Heinsius, 1808.
2v. 14cm.

I. Schummel, Johann Gottlieb, 1748-1813, ed.

NL 0341405   IEN CLSU

Lichtenau, Wilhelmine (Enke) *gräfin* von, 1752-1820, *supposed author.*
The confessions of the celebrated Countess of Lichtenau, late Mrs. Rietz, now confined in the fortress of Gloglau ₍!₎ as a state-prisoner. Drawn from original papers, tr. from the German. With an engraved portrait of the countess, after an original painting in the possession of the Countess Matuska. London, Printed by J. W. Myers, 1799.
ix, 68 p. front. (port.) 21½ᶜᵐ.
Dedication signed: Richard B. T. N.
Translation(?) of "Geheime papiere der gräfin von Lichtenau, vulgo München Encken." Charlottenburg ₍Leipzig₎ 1798. A spurious publication. *cf.* Brit. mus. Catalogue.
I. B—t—n, Richard, tr.   II. Title.
                                              17-5276
Library of Congress   DD414.9.L5A4

NL 0341406   DLC

Lichtenau, Wilhelmine (Enke) *gräfin* von, 1752-1820.
Memoiren der Gräfin Lichtenau; ein sittenbild vom hofe der Hohenzollern, herausgegeben von Max Adler. Dresden, C. Reissner ₍1922₎
159, ₍1₎ p.   19ᶜᵐ.
CONTENTS.—Die Gräfin Lichtenau und ihr literarischer ratgeber.—Die memoiren der Gräfin Lichtenau.—Aus dem briefwechsel der Gräfin Lichtenau.

I. ₍1₎ Adler, Max, ed.

NL 0341407   MiU MH

Lichtenau, ₍Wilhelmine (Enke)₎ gräfin von.   Carl 180
Mémoires; contenant des anecdotes secrètes sur la cour de Prusse, et suivis de lettres du comte de Bristol, de Sir Arthur Paget, de Sir William et Lady Hamilton, de Lady Templetown du chevalier de Saxe, &c. Traduits de l'allemand. Londres Colburn, 1809.
2 vol.
Formerly owned by Thomas Carlyle; with his book-plates and autographs.

NL 0341408   MH

Lichtenau, Wilhelmine (Enke) *gräfin* von, 1752-1820.
Mémoires de la Comtesse de Lichtenau, écrits par elle-même en 1808; suivis d'une correspondance relative à ses mémoires et tirée de son porte-feuille. Traduits de l'allemand, par J. F. G. P. ... Paris, Buisson, 1809.
viii, 416 p.   21ᶜᵐ.

I. P., J. F. G., tr.

NL 0341409   MiU WU MdBP ICU

LICHTENAUER, A.
De Isocrate. [Progr]. [Landshut, J. Thomann,1843].
4º. pp.(2).ix.

NL 0341410   MH

Lichtenauer, A.
De Tuscis eorumque origine.   n.p., 1832.

NL 0341411   NjP

LICHTENAUER, Arthur,1898-
Die geographische verbreitung der wasser-. krafte in mitteleuropa. Inaug. diss., Würzburg, 1925.
pp.(8). 52-.   Maps.
"Bücher, " pp. [v-vii]
"Lebenslauf", at end.

NL 0341412   MH ICRL CtY PU

Lichtenauer, Arthur, 1898 —
Die geographische verbreitung der wasserkräfte in Mitteleuropa, von Arthur Lichtenauer; mit 6 abbildungen und 2 wasserkraftkarten. Würzburg, Kabitzsch & Mönnich, 1926.
4 p. l., 62 p. 2 fold. maps, 6 plans on 1 l. 24½ᶜᵐ. (*Added t.-p.:* Mitteilungen der Geographischen gesellschaft zu Würzburg. 2. jahrg.)
"Geschäfts-bericht" (p. ₍55₎-62) signed: Dr. Anton Fries, schriftführer.
"Literaturverzeichnis": 4th prelim. leaf.

1. Water-power—Europe.   I. Title.
                                        CA 31-499 Unrev'd
Library of Congress   TC455.L5   ₍21.312134₎

NL 0341413   DLC NN NIC CtY

VOLUME 332

Lichtenauer, Friedrich Paul, 1908–
... Ein Beitrag zur Chirurgie der arteriellen
Embolie in den grossen Gefässen der Extremitäten
... Hamburg, 1934.
Inaug.-Diss. – Hamburg.
Lebenslauf.

NL 0341414 CtY

PQ1707 Lichtenauer, Hugo.
.V37Z8 Jean Vauquelin sieur de la Fresnaie, der schöp-
L7 fer der klassischen satire in Frankreich...
Dresden, 1889.
xxii p. 24½⁻.

Programm-Gymnasium zum heiligen kreuz, Dresden.

1. Vauquelin, Jean de La Fresnaye, 1536?–1607.

NL 0341415 ICU IU PBm NjP

Lichtenauer, J. M.
Catalogue of the private collection of paintings, water colors
and pastels by American and European artists, collected by the
well-known amateur, the late J. M. Lichtenauer...sold ₍Feb. 22,
1913₎. New York: Amer. Art Assoc., 1913. 46 l. 8°.

1. Paintings.—Collections (Private) Lichtenauer.
N. Y. P. L. May 17, 1913.

NL 0341416 NN

Lichtenauer (Joan. Guilelm.) [1804–]. *De
cicatrisatione. 31 pp. 8°. Berolini, lit. A. Petschli,
[1826]. [Also in: P., v. 329.]

NL 0341417 DNLM PPC

Lichtenauer (Kurt [Leopold 'Hermann])
[1872–]. *Ueber die gutartigen Geschwülste
der Uvula und des weichen Gaumens. 44 pp.
8°. Greifswald, J. Abel, 1895.

NL 0341418 DNLM MiU

DJ411 Lichtenauer, Wilhelm Franz, 1900– joint ed.
.R84C6 Cocheret, Ch A ed.
Bekende Rotterdammers, door hun stadgenoten beschreven. Zes en dertig bijdragen over burgers van Rotterdam,
die in stadsbestuur, bedrijfsleven en op verscheidene gebie-
den van de cultuur hun stadgenoten tot voorbeeld zijn
geweest of mede het leven en streven van hun stad bepaald
hebben. Rotterdam, W. L. & J. Brusse, 1951.

Lichtenauer, Wilhelm Franz, 1900–
De nieuwe regeling van de kamers van koophandel en fabrie-
ken, door mr. W. F. Lichtenauer. 2. druk. 's Gravenhage,
Drukkerij C. Blommendaal n. v. ₍1942₎

1 p. l., xi p., 1 l., 5–96 p. 22½⁻.

1. Boards of trade—Netherlands.
Library of Congress HF316.L5 1942
46–40137

381

NL 0341420 DLC MH

Lichtenauer, Wilhelm Franz, 1900–
De vernietigende verjaring en aanverwante
rechtsfiguren beschouwd naar wezen, begrenzing
en onderlinge verhouding ... door Wilhelm Franz
Lichtenauer ... Wageningen, H. Veenman &
zonen, 1932.
4 p.l., 182, [4] p. 25 cm.
Proefschrift - Leiden.
"Lijst van geraadpleegde werken", p. 172–177.

NL 0341421 CtY-L

Lichtenbaum, J.
Ueber einige derivate des 1-benzoylcumarons.
Inaug. diss. Bern, 1910.

NL 0341422 ICRL PU

PZ90 .H3L46 Hebr Lichtenbaum, Joseph, 1895– ed. and tr.
אגדות הדורות. תל-אביב. הוצאת "יבנה." תשי"ב.
₍Tel-Aviv, 1952₎
143 p. 22 cm. (מאגדות עמי העולם)
Vocalized text.

1. Legends, Indic. Title transliterated: Agadot hodiyot.

PZ90.H3L46 57–51390

NL 0341423 DLC

Lichtenbaum, Joseph, 1895– tr.
Beatah u-Marelah
see under Keyserling, Eduard Heinrich
Nikolaus, graf von, 1855–1918.

Lichtenbaum, Joseph, 1895–
בצל השעות. שירים. ירושלים. "מצפה." תרפ"ח.
₍Jerusalem, 1927/28₎
118 p. 20 cm.
Vocalized text.

I. Title. Title transliterated: Be-tsel ha-sha'o.

53–54920

NL 0341425 DLC

PZ90 .H3L462 (Hebr) Lichtenbaum, Joseph, 1895–
ביבר היות ועופות. אגדות. תל-אביב. נ. מברסקי. תשט"ו.
₍Tel-Aviv, 1955₎
111 p. illus. 21 cm.
Vocalized text.

1. Fables, Hebrew. I. Title.
Title transliterated: Bevar ḥayot ve-'ofot.

PZ90.H3L462 58–51222 †

NL 0341426 DLC

Lichtenbaum, Joseph, 1895– comp.
₍Bitan ha-ḥarsinah₎
ביתן-החרסינה; משירי סין ₍לקט; י. ליכטנבום. ₍תל-אביב₎
הקיבוץ הארצי השומר הצעיר ₍1943₎
46 p. illus. 12 cm. (דורון)
"תרגום השירים נעשה עפ"י באטש, קלבונד, וויילה."

1. Chinese poetry—Translations into Hebrew. 2. Hebrew poetry—
Translations from Chinese. I. Title.

PJ5058.C5L5 72–222255

NL 0341427 DLC

Lichtenbaum, Joseph, 1895– tr.
Dinah weha-meshorer
see under Hofmann, Martha.

NG109 .L5 [Hebr] Lichtenbaum, Joseph, 1895– ed. and tr.
נבעות עולם, מבחר תרגומי שירה. ירושלים, אחיאסף,
תש"ה. ₍Jerusalem, 1945₎
216 p. 19 cm.
Vocalized text.
Translations from Chinese, Japanese, German, French, Serbian,
Russian, and Polish poetry.

1. Hebrew poetry—Translations from foreign literature. I. Title.
Title transliterated: Giv'ot 'olam.

49–14528*

NL 0341429 DLC

PN3491 .L5 ₍Hebr₎ Lichtenbaum, Joseph, 1895–
מספרי העולם. ירושלים. אחיאסף. ₍Jerusalem, 1954–58₎
2 v. ports. 24 cm.
Bibliography : v. 1, p. 331–334 ; v. 2, p. 348–352.
CONTENTS.—סדרה א. מבלוק עד מופסן.—סדרה ב. מפטיבנסון עד טולסטוי.—

1. Fiction—Hist. & crit. 2. Novelists. I. Title.
Title transliterated: Mesapre ha-'olam.

PN3491.L5 56–54101 rev

NL 0341430 DLC

Lichtenbaum, Joseph, 1895–
משני חופים. מבחר שירים. תל-אביב. מוסד ביאליק, תש"ד.
₍Tel-Aviv, 1944₎
214 p. 19 cm.
Vocalized text.

I. Title. Title transliterated: Mi-shene ḥofim.

A 56–506

New York. Public Libr.
for Library of Congress

NL 0341431 NN DLC

PN519 .L5 Hebraic Sect. Lichtenbaum, Joseph, 1895–
מתחום אל תחום. מסות. תל-אביב. צ. ליינמן, תש"ד.
₍Tel-Aviv, 1943/44₎
272 p. port. 18 cm.

1. Literature—Addresses, essays, lectures.
Title transliterated: Mi-teḥum el teḥum.

PN519.L5 52–51718

NL 0341432 DLC

Lichtenbaum, Joseph, 1895– tr.
Ha-sefinah Sobranyeh
see under Berney, Arnold, 1897–1943.

VOLUME 332

Lichtenbaum, Joseph, 1895–
שאול טשרניחובסקי, תולדותיו ויצירתו. ירושלים, המח-
לקה לעניני הנוער של ההסתדרות הציונית, תש"ו.
₍Jerusalem, 1945/46₎
150 p. ports., facsims. 22 cm.
Bibliography: p. ₍148₎–150.

1. Tchernichovski, Saul, 1875–1943.   I. Title.
Title transliterated: Sha'ul Tshernihovski
A 49–7041

*Hebrew Union College Library
for Library of Congress*

NL   0341434   OCH DLC CU OCl

PJ5053
.T3Z7
(Hebr)

Lichtenbaum, Joseph, 1895–
שאול טשרניחובסקי. חייו ויצירתו. תל־אביב, נ. טברסקי.
₍Tel-Aviv, 1953₎ תשי"ג.
160 p. illus., ports. 23 cm.
Bibliography: p. ₍148₎–159.
Includes musical settings (unacc. melodies) of two of Tchernichovski's poems.

1. Tchernichovski, Saul, 1875–1943.   *Title transliterated:* Sha'ul Tshernihovski

PJ5053.T3Z7   56–54129

NL   0341435   DLC

Lichtenbaum, Joseph, 1895–   ed.
הסיפור העברי, אנתולוגיה. הוצאת נ. טברסקי.
₍Tel-Aviv, 1955₎
526 p. 25 cm.

Hebrew.

1. Short stories, Hebrew.   I. Title.
Title transliterated: ha-Sipur ha-'Ivri.

PJ5045.L5   57–50180 ‡

NL   0341436   OCl DLC

Lichtenbaum, Joseph, 1895–   ed.
סופרים, ממאפו עד ביאליק; תולדותיהם, הערכותיהם
ופרקים נבחרים מיצירותיהם. ירושלים, 1950₎
₍Jerusalem, 1950₎
316 p. ports. 25 cm.

1. Hebrew literature, Modern (Selections: Extracts, etc.)   2. Hebrew literature, Modern—Bio-bibl.   *Title transliterated:* Sofrenu.

New York. Public Libr.
for Library of Congress

A 52–10028

NL   0341437   NN FMU MiD

Lichtenbaum, Joseph, 1895–   ed.
סופ. ... ממאפו עד ביאליק; תולדותיהם, הערכותיהם ופרקים
נבחרים מיצירותיהם. מהדורה ב. מתוקנת. ירושלים, הוצאת
"אחיאסף", 1950₎
₍Jerusalem, 1950₎
316 p. ports. 25 cm.

1. Hebrew literature, Modern (Selections: Extracts, etc.)   2.
Hebrew literature, Modern—Bio-bibl.   *Title transliterated:* Sofrenu.
Hist. & crit.
52–58414

NL   0341438   DLC

616.6
L698v   Lichtenbelt, Hendrik van Marken.
Vitamine B₁ en het coma diabeticum; over de
thiamine- en pyrodruivenzuurstofwisseling bij
gezonde personen en lijders aan suikerziekte.
Vitamin B₁ and diabetic coma. (With a summary
in English) Utrecht, Kemink, 1952.
xi,67 p.   diagrs.   24 cm.
Academisch proefschrift—Utrecht.
"Stellingen": ₍2₎ leaves inserted.
Bibliography: p.₍65₎–67.
1.Vitamins. 2.Diabetes.

NL   0341439   MiU DNLM

Lichtenbelt, James William Theodoor.
Die Ursachen des
chronischen Magengeschwürs.   2 p. l., 63
pp., 1 pl.   8°.   Jena, G. Fischer, 1912.

NL   0341440   DNLM PPC

QM471
L52
1918

LICHTENBELT, James William Theodoor.
De invloed van de nervi splanchnici
op de buikingewanden. Utrecht, Gedrukt
bij J. Van Boekhoven [1918]
90p.   illus.   24cm.
Proefschrift – Utrecht.
"Stellingen": p. [89]–90.
acc. no. 7759 cat. * LC * SG *

1. Nerves, Splanchnic 2. Stomach I.
Title Prov. Dusser de Barenne, Joannes
Gregorius, 18   85–1940

NL   0341441   CtY-M ICRL MBCo MiU

[Lichtenberg   ] wood merchant in
Vieselbach.
Den königlichen Hoheiten, Carl Alexander
Johann und Wilhelmine Sophie, in tiefster
Ehrfurcht und Unterthänigkeit die Jünglinge
des Amts-Bezirkes Vieselbach am 22. Oktober
1842.   [n. p., 1842]
2 l.   33. 5 cm.
Title and text within ornamental border.
In verse.

NL   0341442   CtY

Lichtenberg, Abraham ben Aryeh, ed.
Kovets teshuvot ha-Rambam ve-igrotav
see under   Moses ben Maimon, 1135–1204.

Lichtenberg, Alexander von, 1880–   L616.6
Allgemeine Röntgendiagnostik. Von A. v. Lichtenberg ...   S601   v.2
Mit 116 Abbildungen ...
(*In* Handbuch der Urologie. Berlin, 1929. 25½ᶜᵐ. Bd. 2: Allgemeine
Urologie, Teil 2, p. [83]–174. illus.)

NL   0341444   ICJ

Lichtenberg, Alexander von, 1880–   L616.6
Allgemeine urologische Diagnostik und Symptomatologie.   S601   v.2
Von A. v. Lichtenberg ...
(*In* Handbuch der Urologie. Berlin, 1929. 25½ᶜᵐ. Bd. 2: Allgemeine
Urologie, Teil 2, p. 1–82)

NL   0341445   ICJ

B616.6
L617   LICHTENBERG, Alexander von, 1880–
Conferencias pronunciadas en la República argentina...   Buenos Aires, Imprenta Lopez, 1935.
92, ₍2₎ p.   port.   24cm.

1. Genito-urinary organs. Diseases. 2.
Genito-urinary organs. Diseases. Diagnosis.

NL   0341446   MnU

Lichtenberg, Alexander von, ed.
Handbuch der Urologie
see under title

WI
L699u   LICHTENBERG, Alexander von
1909   Über die Kreislaufstörung bei der
Peritonitis und über die Kochsalz-
Suprarenin-Therapie; klinische und
experimentelle Beiträge zur Pathologie
und Therapie der Bauchfellentzündung.
Wiesbaden, Bergmann, 1909.
164 p.   illus.

NL   0341448   DLC ICJ OClW-H

TK
7855   Lichtenberg, Allan J
M33   Helical coupling system.   ₍Cambridge₎
no.290   Massachusetts Institute of Technology, Research Laboratory of Electronics, 1954.
27 p.   diagrs.   (Massachusetts Institut
of Technology. Research Laboratory of Electronics. Technical report, 290)
"Based on a thesis."
Bibliography: p.27.

1.Coupled mode theory.   I. Title.

NL   0341449   UU

Lichtenberg, Anne Marie, 1900–
Die bedeutung des musikalischen für die ästhetische einfüh-
lung in P. B. Shelleys lyrik ... von Anne Marie Lichtenberg ...
Marburg, Universitäts-buchdruckerei J. A. Koch, 1935.
vii, 92 p., 1 l. 23ᶜᵐ.
Inaug.-diss.—Marburg.
Lebenslauf.
"Bücherverzeichnis": p. ₍v₎–vii.

1. Shelley, Percy Bysshe, 1792–1822.   2. Music and literature.   3. Literature—Esthetics.   I. Title.
₍Full name: Hedwig Anne Marie Lichtenberg₎
39–13277

Library of Congress   ML3849.L69B3
780.1

NL   0341450   DLC CSmH CtY

Lichtenberg, Bernard, 1892–1944.
Advertising campaigns, by Bernard Lichtenberg ... in collaboration with Bruce Barton ... New York, Alexander
Hamilton institute ₍*1926₎
xviii, 343 p. diagrs. (1 fold.) 19 cm.   (*Added t.-p.:* Modern
business; a series of texts prepared as part of the modern business
course and service ... Alexander Hamilton institute. ₍v. 13₎)
Short series title on t.-p.

1. Advertising campaigns.   I. Barton, Bruce, 1886–   joint author.   II. Alexander Hamilton institute, New York.

HF5351.M76 1923   26—6339

NL   0341451   DLC NBuC MH PPT OU MiU OCl NcD OClU

VOLUME 332

Lichtenberg, Bernard, 1892–
Advertising campaigns, by Bernard Lichtenberg ... in collaboration with Bruce Barton ... New York, Alexander Hamilton institute [*1930]

xx, 359 p. illus., diagrs. 19^{cm}. (Added t.-p.: Modern business; a series of texts prepared as part of the modern business course and service ... Alexander Hamilton institute)

"Advertising publications": p. 350–352.

1. Advertising. I. Barton, Bruce, 1886– joint author. II. Alexander Hamilton institute, New York. III. Title.

Library of Congress	HF5351.M76 1929 vol. 13	30—23939
— Copy 2.	HF5823.L68	
Copyright A 28063	[n36f5]	(650) 659.1

NL 0341452 DLC NcU WaSp PPD PPFr OCU OCX OCl

LICHTENBERG, BERNARD, 1892–
Has business the right to live? The application of public relations in a changing world. An address delivered before the Association of national advertisers, Hot Springs, Va. [New York, Institute of public relations] 1937. 12 p. 21cm.

1. Publicity. I. Association of national advertisers, inc. II. Institute of public relations, inc., New York.

NL 0341453 NN NNC

Lichtenberg, Bernard, 1892–
Office management, by the editors in collaboration with Geoffrey S. Childs, Edwin J. Clapp and Bernard Lichtenberg ... New York, Alexander Hamilton institute [*1919]

Lichtenberg, Bernard, 1892–
Reselling higher education to America; an address by Bernard Lichtenberg ... before the National war conference of the American college publicity association held at Chicago, May 1944. [New York? 1944] 10 p. 19cm.

1. Publicity, School and college.
N. Y. P. L. January 22, 1948

NL 0341455 NN ICU

Lichtenberg, C. 778.63 L6x
Die indirekte Farbenphotographie in der Hand des Amateurs. 47,[1] p. O Stolp: H. Hildebrandt, 1901.

NL 0341456 ICJ

Lichtenberg, C. *9330-436.73
Der landwirtschaftliche Personalkredit in Elsass-Lothringen. (In Verein fuer Socialpolitik. Schriften. 73. Pp. 337–375. Leipzig, 1896.)

Dec. 17. 1901
E2513 — Alsace. Bus. assoc. — Lorraine. Bus. assoc.

NL 0341457 MB

Lichtenberg, C.
Mittheilungen zur Criminalstatistik des Königreichts Hannover aus den Jahren 1852 und 1853 ... Hannover, 1855. 86 p. 8°

NL 0341458 CtY

Lichtenberg, C.
U.S. Army searchlights. Philadelphia, 1920.

NL 0341459 DAL

Lichtenberg, Carl.
Kollisionen der gesetze ueber den erwerb und verlust der staatsangehoerigkeit. Inaug. diss. Leipzig, 1928. Bibl.

NL 0341460 ICRL

Lichtenberg, Carl, of Weimar.
Die Fettwaaren und fetten Oele. Ausführliche Erörterungen über Herkunft, Eigenschaften, chemisches Verhalten und chemische Zusammensetzung, Gewinnung und Herstellung, Verfälschung, Reinigung und Bleichung, Aufbewahrung und Verwendung aller für den Handel, ingleichen für den Haushalt, für Gewerbe und Künste, für Kosmetik und Pharmacie wichtigen animalischen, wie auch vegetabilischen Fettsubstanzen" Nach den neuesten wissenschaftlichen Erfahrungen. Weimar, B. F. Voigt, 1880.
viii, 187 p. 23 cm. (Neuer Schauplatz der Künste und Handwerke, 56. Bd.)

1. Oils and fats. (Series)
P O 49–54*
U. S. Patent Office. Libr. TP670.L7
for Library of Congress [1]

NL 0341461 DP NN NBuG

Lichtenberg, Carl, of Weimar.
Die seifenfabrikation. Weimar, 1860. 12°

NL 0341462 NN

Lichtenberg, Carl, of Weimar.
Seifenfabrikation ... In 2, gänzlich umgearb. Aufl. hrsg. von N. Graeger und dessen Söhnen, Alexander und Hermann Graeger. Weimar, B. F. Voigt, 1868.
xii, 169 p. and atlas (4 plates) 23 cm. (Neuer Schauplatz der Künste und Handwerke, 245. Bd.)

1. Soap. I. Graeger, Nicolaus, 1806–1873, ed. (Series)
P O 52–222
U. S. Patent Office. Library TP991.L5 1868
for Library of Congress

NL 0341463 DP

Lichtenberg, Carl
see also Lichtenberg, Karl.

Lichtenberg, Carl von.
Die Strafe, die Zuchthäuser und das Zwangs-Erziehungs-System rechtlich entwickelt und practisch dargestellt ... Berlin, 1846. 21 cm.

NL 0341465 CtY

Lichtenberg (Carolus Frider.) [1800–]. *De nonnullis vulgi praejudicatis opinionibus medicis arti obsistentibus. 36 pp. sm. 8°. [Berolini], [ormis Brueschclanis. [1838]

NL 0341466 DNLM PPC

Lichtenberg (Carolus Immanuel.) *De diagnosi sputorum in phthisi. 19 pp. sm. 4°. [Wittenbergae, lit. Tzschiedrichii, [1796].

NL 0341467 DNLM

RM733 M8
Lichtenberg, Christoph, 1921– joint author.

Müller-Gies, Irmtraud, 1921–
Atemübungen mit Kindern, von I. Müller-Gies und Chr. Lichtenberg. Mit einem Geleitwort von B. de Rudder. Stuttgart, G. Thieme [1955]

Lichtenberg, Don Bernett, 1928–
Pion production in proton-proton collisions. Ann Arbor, University Microfilms [1955]
([University Microfilms, Ann Arbor, Mich.] Publication no. 13,513)
Microfilm copy of typescript. Positive.
Collation of the original: iv, 29 l. diagrs.
Thesis—University of Illinois.
Abstracted in Dissertation abstracts, v. 15 (1955) no. 10, p. 1881.
Vita.
Bibliography: leaf 28.

1. Protons. 2. Mesons. 3. Collisions (Nuclear physics)
I. Title.
Microfilm AC-1 no. 13,513 Mic 55–606
Illinois. Univ. Librar.
for Library of Congress

NL 0341469 IU DLC

Lichtenberg, Emil, 1874–
Heinrich Schütz. Irta: Lichtenberg Emil. [Budapest, May János nyomdai műintézet r. t., 1935]
81 p. illus. (music) 20½^{cm}.
Portrait mounted on cover.
"Bibliográfia": p. 81.

1. Schütz, Heinrich, 1585–1672. 39–9610
Library of Congress ML410.S35L7
780.81

NL 0341470 DLC

Lichtenberg, Emil, 1874–
Johann Sebastian Bach élete és művei, irta Lichtenberg Emil. Budapest, Rózsavölgyi és társa [*1940]
2 p. l., [7]–332 p. illus. (music) plates, port., facsims. (music) 20^{cm}.
"Forrásmunkák": p. [330]

1. Bach, Johann Sebastian, 1685–1750. 46–30694
Library of Congress ML410.B1L45

NL 0341471 DLC

W 4 B29 1949
LICHTENBERG, Eva, 1923–
Die Geschichte der intravenösen Injektion im 19. Jahrhundert. [Wien, 1949]
63 p.
Inaug.-Diss. - Basel.
1. Injections - Intravenous - Hist.

NL 0341472 DNLM NIC

Lichtenberg, Eva, 1923–
Die Geschichte der intravenösen Injektion im 19. Jahrhundert. [Wien, 1952]
63 p. 21 cm.
Inaug.-Diss.—Basel.
Vita.
Bibliography: p. 37–62.

1. Injections, Intravenous. I. Title.
RM170.L5 59–27165

NL 0341473 DLC ViU

VOLUME 332

Lichtenberg, Eva Maria, 1909-
Ein Fall von vierfachem Karzinom des Magens.
... 22 p.
Inaug. Diss. - München, n.d.
Lebenslauf.
Literatur-Verzeichnis.

NL 0341474   CtY

Lichtenberg, Friedrich August Hugo
      see Lichtenberg, Hugo, 1877-

Lichtenberg (Fritz Julius Gustav) [1877-].
*Ueber die Beweglichkeit des Beckens von
Neugeborenen. [Strassburg.] 13 pp. 8°. Leip-
zig, G. Thieme, 1906.

NL 0341476   DNLM ICRL

Lichtenberg, Geert Frederik Honnens de
see
Honnens de Lichtenberg, Geert Frederik, 1890-

Lichtenberg, Georg Christoph, 1742-1799.
Schriften. Mit Biographie and Portrait
New York, H. J. Meyer [1851?]
2v. in 1. 11cm. (Meyer's Groschen-
bibliothek der deutschen Classiker. 17.-
18.bd.)

Imperfect: port. wanting.
With this are bound Goethe, J. W.
Genius. New York [1851?] Goethe, J. W.
Sprüche. New York [1851?] Goethe, J. W.
Aphorismen. New York [1851?]

NL 0341478   IEN

PT 2423   Lichtenberg, Georg Christoph, 1742-1799.
L 4   Schriften und Briefe. [München] C.
A 135   Hanser [19
              v.

NL 0341479   MoSW

Lichtenberg, Georg Christoph, 1742-1799.
Georg Christoph Lichtenberg's vermischte schriften,
nach dessen tode aus den hinterlassenen papieren gesam-
melt und hrsg. von Ludwig Christian Lichtenberg ... und
Friedrich Kries ... Göttingen, J. C. Dieterich, 1800-04.
9 v. in 8. fronts. (v. 1, 6 (ports.) 8) 18ᶜᵐ.
Incomplete: v. 9 wanting in L. C. set.
Vol. 2 has imprint: Göttingen, In der Dieterichschen buchhandlung,
1801; v. 3-   : Bey H. Dieterich, 1801-
Vols. 6-   have also special title-pages: Georg Christoph Lichtenberg's
physikalische und mathematische schriften ... 1-   bd.
The author's hitherto unpublished writings are included in v. 1-2.
I. Lichtenberg, Ludwig Christian, ed. II. Kries, Friedrich Christian,
1768-1849, joint ed.
                                        18-1203

Library of Congress   PT2423.L4 1800

NL 0341480   DLC ViW

Lichtenberg, Georg Christoph. 1742-1799.   **4898.11**
Georg Christoph Lichtenberg's Vermischte Schriften nach dessen
Tode aus den hinterlassenen Papieren gesammelt und herausge-
geben von Ludwig Christian Lichtenberg und Friedrich Kries.
Göttingen. Dieterich. 1800-06. 9 v. Portraits. Plates. 16°.

G7648 — Lichtenberg, Ludwig Christia. — Kries, Friedrich Christian, ed. 1768-
1849

NL 0341481   MB CtU OCU ICN NN MH PPG PU PBm MU PSt

333L61 Lichtenberg, Georg Christoph.
IL611   Vermischte schriften, nach dessen tode
Ed.   gesammelt und hrsg. von Ludw. Christ.
1817   Lichtenberg und Friedr. Kries. Wien,
        1817.
        3v. in 1.

        Added t.-p.

NL 0341482   IU CtY OClW

PT   Lichtenberg, Georg Christoph, 1742-1799.
2423   Georg Christoph Lichtenberg's vermischte
L4   Schriften, humoristischen, satyrischen, witz-
1837   igen und ernsten Inhalts; nach dessen Tode
         gesammelt und hrsg. von Ludwig Christ. Lich-
         tenberg und Friedrich Kries. Wien, R. Sammer,
         1837.
         5v.

         ᵗI. Lichtenberg, Ludwig Christian,
         ed. ᵗII. Kries, Friedrich Christian, 1768-1849,
         joint ed.

NL 0341483   UU CtY

Lichtenberg, Georg Christoph, 1742-1799.
Georg Christoph Lichtenberg's vermischte Schriften. Neue
vermehrte, von dessen Söhnen veranstaltete Original-Ausgabe...
Bd. 1-   Göttingen: Dieterich, 1844-   v. in   fronts.
(v. 1, port.; v. 2, fold. facsim.) 16°.
Added t-p. in Bd. 7   : Georg Christoph Lichtenberg's Briefe. Hrsg. von
Chr. W. Lichtenberg. Supplement zu allen früheren Ausgaben...

I. No subject. 2. Lichtenberg, Chris-   toph W., editor.
N. Y. P. L.   November 13, 1919.

NL 0341484   NN CtY MH IaU

838   Lichtenberg, Georg Christoph, 1742-1799.
L617   ... Vermischte Schriften. Neue verm.,
C3   von dessen Söhnen veranstaltete Original-
         Ausg. ... Göttingen, Verlag der Dieterich-
         schen Buchhandlung, 1844-47.
         8v. in 4. illus. 15cm.

         Preface signed: L. Chr. Lichtenberg und
         Fr. Kries.

         I. Lichtenberg, Ludwig Christian, ed.
         II. Kries, Friedrich Christian, 1768-1849,
         joint ed.

NL 0341485   TxU TU PP MH TNJ PU

PT2423   Lichtenberg, Georg Christoph, 1742-1799.
L4   Vermischte Schriften. Neue verm., von dessen
1853   Söhnen veranstaltete Original-Ausg. Göttingen,
         Dieterisch, 1853.
         8 v.in 4. illus.,ports. 16a.
         Vols. 7-8 have special t.p.: Briefe. Hrsg.
         von Chr. W. Lichtenberg. Supplement zu allen
         früheren Ausgaben.

         I.Lichtenberg,   Chr   ed.

NL 0341486   CSt InU CU

Lichtenberg, Georg Christoph, 1742-1799.   **193.50 I**
Georg Christoph Lichtenberg's Vermischte Schriften. Neue
original-Ausgabe. Mit dem Portrait, Facsimile und einer An-
sicht des Geburtshauses des Verfassers. Erster-[achter] Band.
Göttingen, Dieterichsche Buchhandlung. 1867.
8 vol. 2 front. (vol. 1 port., vol. 2), illus., 1 fold. facsim. 15¼ᶜᵐ.
Added t.-p. vol. 7, 8: Georg Christoph Lichtenberg's Briefe. Herausgegeben von
Chr. W. Lichtenberg. Supplement zu allen früheren Ausgaben. Erster-zweiter Band.

NL 0341487   ICJ OU ICRL PSt

PT   Lichtenberg, Georg Christoph, 1742-1799.
2423   Vermischte Schriften, von Georg Chr.
L4A6   Lichtenberg. [Berlin, Erasmus-Verlag,
1923   1923]
         2v. port.(v.1) 21cm.
         Each volume has also special t.-p.
         "Die Durchsicht ... für den Druck be-
         sorgte Lothar Brieger": v.2, p.376.
         CONTENTS. - 1.Bd.Bemerkungen vermisch-
         ten Inhalts. - 2.Bd.Satirische Schriften.

         √I.Brieger, Lothar,   1870-   ed. √II.Title.

NL 0341488   CLSU

Lichtenberg, Georg Christoph, 1742-1799.
Lichtenbergs Werke in einem Band.
Herausgegeben von Rudolf K. Goldschmit.
Stuttgart, Walter Hädecke Verlag, 1924.
435p. 1 fold. facsim. 21cm.
"Von der ersten Auflage wurden einhundert Exemplare numeriert und in Gan-
zleder gebunden. Dieses Exemplar trägt
die Nummer 30."

"Anmerkungen": p. 431-434.

NL 0341489   CaBVaU NN MtU

Lichtenberg, Georg Christoph, 1742-1799.
Lichtenbergs werke in einem band. Herausgegeben von
Rudolf K. Goldschmit. Stuttgart, Walter Hädecke verlag
[1935]
434 p. 1 fold. facsim. 20¼ᶜᵐ.
"Anmerkungen": p. 431-434.
CONTENTS.—Selbstbiographie.—Gott, welt, mensch.—Kunst und wissenschaft.—Briefe und gedanken über das theater.—Politik.—über die
frauen und die liebe.—Epigramme.—Aufsätze, beobachtungen und satiren.—Aus Lichtenbergs briefen.—Lichtenbergs leben und werk.

I. Goldschmit, Rudolf Karl, 1890-   ed.
                                        A C 36-4866
Title from Columbia   Univ. Printed by L. C.

NL 0341490   NNC IdPI

Lichtenberg, Georg Christoph, 1742-1799.
Werke. Hrsg. von Rud. K. Goldschmit-Jentner. Stuttgart, W. Hädecke [1947]
485 p. illus., facsim. 21 cm. (Diotima-Klassiker)
CONTENTS. — Selbstbiographie.—Gott, Welt, Mensch.—Kunst und
Wissenschaft.—Briefe und Gedanken über das Theater.—Politik.—
Über die Frauen und die Liebe.—Epigramme.—Aufsätze, Beobachtungen und Satiren.—Aus Lichtenbergs Briefen.—Lichtenbergs Leben
und Werk.

I. Goldschmit-Jentner, Rudolf Karl, 1890-   ed. (Series)

PT2423.L4 1947   49-17898*

NL 0341491   DLC

Lichtenberg, Georg Christoph, 1742-1799.
...Gesammelte Werke, hrsg. und eingeleitet von Wilhelm
Grenzmann. Frankfurt a. M., Holle Verlag, 1949. 2 v. 20cm.

"Bibliographie," p. 1205-1208.

570401-2B. I. Grenzmann, Wilhelm,   ed.
N. Y. L.   March 21, 1951

      ViU CSt InU NBC NcD CaBVaU IU NRU
NL 0341492   NN PPT IEN NNC CtY CU NcU MH OU MiU NIC

VOLUME 332

Lichtenberg, Georg Christoph, 1742-1799.
Gesammelte Werke; hrsg. und eingeleitet von
Wilhelm Grenzmann. Frankfurt a.M., Holle
Verlag, 1949-1953.
3v. 20cm.; 20x23cm.
"Bibliographie": v.2, p.[1205]-1208.
Fly leaf of v.1 inscribed by donors.
V.3 has note: "Die nachfolgenden Blätter wurden
im Lichtdruckverfahren nach der Erstausgabe von
Riepenhausens Stichen hergestellt als Ergänzungs-
band zu den im gleichen Verlage von Wilhelm Grenz-
mann herausgegebenen gesammelten Werken von Georg
Christoph Lichtenberg".

NL 0341493   NcU

PT Lichtenberg, Georg Christoph, 1742-1799.
2423 Gesammelte Werke. Hrsg. und eingeleitet von
L4 Wilhelm Grenzmann. Baden-Baden, Holle [1953?]
1953 2 v. 21cm.

Bibliography: Bd.2. p.[1205]-1208.
"Register": Bd.2. p.[1211]-1251.
Contents:
Bd.1. Die "Bemerkungen".- Briefe.- Briefe aus
England.- Tagebuchblatter.- Briefe an Lichten-
berg.

Bd.2. Die grossen Streitschriften.- Die
kleinen Schriften.- Fragmente und Gedichte.-
Erklarungen zu Daniel Chodowieckis Monatskupfer
im "Gottinger Taschenkalender" 1778-1783.- Erklärung Hogarthischer Kupferstiche aus dem
Gottingischen Taschenkalender von 1784 und 1785.
Ausführliche Erklärung der Hogarthischen Kupferstiche.

NL 0341495   C NjR CU KMK OrPR

Lichtenberg, Georg Christoph, 1742-1799.
... Aforismos; seleccionados, traducidos y prologados por
Guillermo Thiele. Buenos Aires, "Coni," 1942.
200 p., 3 l. pl., ports. 20cm.
At head of title: Universidad de Buenos Aires. Facultad de filo-
sofía y letras. Instituto de estudios germánicos ...
"Bibliografía y fuentes": p. [191]-200.

1. Aphorisms and apothegms.   I. Thiele, Guillermo, tr.   II. Buenos
Aires. Universidad nacional. Instituto de estudios germánicos.
43-13739
Library of Congress   PT2423.L4A83
838.6

NL 0341496   DLC MoU

Lichtenberg, Georg Christoph, 1724-1799.
... Афоризмы. Переводъ съ нѣмецкаго Н. М. Соколова. С.-Петербургъ, Изд. Л. Ф. Пантелѣева, 1899.
2 p. l., 256 p. 21cm.

1. Sokolov, Nikolaĭ Matvĕevich, 1860-1908, tr.
17-15890

NL 0341497   DLC

Lichtenberg, Georg Christoph, 1742-1799.
... Georg Christoph Lichtenbergs Aphorismen; nach den
handschriften hrsg. von Albert Leitzmann ... Berlin, B. Behr,
1902-08.
5 v. 19cm. (Deutsche literaturdenkmale des 18. und 19. jahrhunderts.
no. 123, 131, 136, 140-141, 3. folge. no. 3, 11, 16, 20-21)
Contents.—1. hft. 1764-1771.—2. hft. 1772-1775.—3. hft. 1775-1779.—
4. hft. 1789-1793.—5. hft. 1793-1799.

1. Aphorisms and apothegms.   I. Leitzmann, Albert, 1867-   ed.
II. Title: Aphorismen.
9—8002
Library of Congress   PT1136.S4   no. 123, 131, 136, 140, 141

NL 0341498   DLC TNJ TU PSt NcU MH MB NcD OrU PBm NjP

Lichtenberg, Georg Christoph, 1742-1799.
... Aphorismen. Ausgewählt und eingeleitet von Albert
Leitzmann. Leipzig, Insel-verlag [1913]
69, [1] p. 18½cm. (On cover: Insel-bücherei, nr. 33)

1. Aphorisms and apothegms.   I. Leitzmann, Albert, 1867-   ed.
43-35303
Library of Congress   PT2423.L4A8 1913

NL 0341499   DLC NN OC1 OKentU MoU CaBVaU CLSU NN

Lichtenberg, Georg Christoph, 1742-1799.
... Aphorismen. Berlin, Deutsche bib-
liothek [192-]
216, [4] p. 17½cm.
"Ausgewählt und mit einer einleitung
versehen von Alexander v. Gleichen-
Russwurm."
Bibliographie: p.[219]

NL 0341500   PSt CLSU OrPR

49554.30.7
Lichtenberg, Georg Christoph, 1742-99.
Aphorismen. Ausgewählt von E.Steffen. Berlin [Maxi-
milian-Gesellschaft] 1922
71 p.
Limited ed.: 300 cop., no.256

NL 0341501   MH CU-S

Lichtenberg, Georg Christoph, 1742-1799.
... Aphorismen; eine sammlung aus Lichtenbergs gedanken-
büchern, in gruppen zeitlich geordnet. Gesammelt, eingeleitet
und erläutert von dr. Ernst Volkmann. Leipzig, P. Reclam
jun. [1944]
289, [1] p. 15½cm. [Reclams universal-bibliothek, nr. 7569-71]
At head of title: G. Chr. Lichtenberg.

1. Aphorisms and apothegms.   I. Volkmann, Ernst, 1881-   ed.
A 46-4904
Columbia univ. Libraries
for Library of Congress   PT2423.L4A8 1944
[2,†]   838.6

ICU TxDaM NN CU MB TxU IU
NL 0341502   NNC DLC NN FU ArU IEN PBL NjR IaU WU

4B-5000 Lichtenberg, Georg Christoph, 1742-1799.
Aphorismen; hrsg. von Max Rychner.
[Zürich] Manesse Verlag [1947]
543 p.   (Manesse-Bibliothek der
Weltliteratur)

NL 0341503   DLC-P4 ICU OCU RPB PSt

398.9 Lichtenberg, Georg Christoph, 1742-1799.
L61ap Aphorismen; Zeichnungen von Fritz Fischer.
1953 München, C. Hanser [1953]
62p. illus. 20cm.

1. Aphorisms and apothegms.   I. Fischer,
Fritz, illus.   II. Title.

NL 0341504   IU NN

Lichtenberg, Georg Christoph, 1742-1799.
... Aphorismen, briefe, schriften, herausgegeben von Paul
Requadt. Mit 8 tafeln und 12 abbildungen. Stuttgart, A.
Kröner [1940]
1 p. l., xiv, 524 p. front. (port.) illus., plates (1 fold.) 18cm. (Half-
title: Kröners taschenausgabe, bd. 154)
At head of title: G. C. Lichtenberg.
"Quellennachweis": p. [511]-516.

1. Requadt, Paul, 1902-   ed.
46-39706
Library of Congress   T2423.L4A16 1940
838.6

NL 0341505   DLC CU ICN

Lichtenberg, Georg Christoph, 1742-1799.
Aphorismen, Briefe und Schriften. [Einführung von H.
Rütter] Zürich, Scientia-Verlag [1946]
114 p. illus., port. 18 cm. (Bleibendes Gut [11])

PT2423.L4A16 1946   50-37204

NL 0341506   DLC OCU

49554.30.8
Lichtenberg, Georg Christoph, 1742-99.
Aphorismen. Hrsg. von M. Rychner. [Zürich] Manesse Verlag [c1947]
543 p.

NL 0341507   MH

838 Lichtenberg, Georg Christoph, 1742-1799.
L617 Aphorismen, Briefe, Schriften, hrsg. von Paul
C4 Requadt. 3. veränderte Aufl. Stuttgart, A.
1953 Kröner [c1953]
xlvii, 474p. illus.,ports. 18cm. (Kröners
Taschenausgabe, Bd.154)

850206   I. Requadt, Paul, 1902-   ed.

NL 0341508   CaBVaU TxDaM NcD CLSU TxU

838 Lichtenberg, Georg Christoph, 1742-1799.
L617ap Aphorismen; ausgewählt von Adolf Haller.
Bern, A. Scherz [c1954]
44 p. (Parnass-Bücherei, Nr.100)

1. Aphorisms and apothegms.

NL 0341509   WaU NN

SPECIAL COLLECTIONS
SPINOZA

Lichtenberg, Georg Christoph, 1742-1799.
Aphorismen und Schriften; sein Werk ausgewählt und eingeleitet, von Ernst Vincent.
Leipzig, A. Kröner [c1931]
xxiii, 299 p. port. 18cm. (Kröners Taschenausgabe. 95)

Includes a reference to Spinoza (p. 155)

NL 0341510   NNC CaBVaU DAU CSt

VOLUME 332

PT2423
.L4A6   Lichtenberg, Georg Christoph, 1742-1799.
    ...Aphorismen und schriften; sein werk
ausgewählt und eingeleitet von Ernst
Vincent.   Leipzig, A. Kröner ₍1935?₎
xxiii,299p. front.(port.)   18cm.
(Kröners taschenausgabe. bd.93)
"Zweiten auflage."
"Zu Lichtenbergs literarischem werk":
p.₍257₎-261.

    I.Vincent, Ernst, ed.   II.Title.

NL   0341511   NNU-W OCU

Lichtenberg, Georg Christoph, 1742-1799.
    Aphorismes; préf. de André Breton. Introd. et traduc-
tion de Marthe Robert. ₍Paris₎ Club français du livre, 1947.
    271 p.   22 cm.

    1. Aphorisms and apothegms.

PT2423.L4A826   57-46158 ‡

NL   0341512   DLC

PT
2423   Lichtenberg, Georg Christoph, 1742-1799
.L4   Aus den Sudelheften. Auswahl und Nachwort
A87   von Wilhelm₍Grenzmann. Stuttgart, Ernst
1949   Klett ₍1949₎
    75p. 19cm. (Anker-Bücherei, 37)

NL   0341513   TNJ

WZ
100   LICHTENBERG, Georg Christoph, 1742-1799
L698   Aus G. C. Lichtenbergs Correspondenz.
1905   Hrsg. von Erich Ebstein. Stuttgart, Enke,
    1905.
    vi, 107 p. illus., port.

    I. Ebstein, Erich Hugo, 1880-1931, ed.

NL   0341514   DNLM DLC-P4 CLSU MH CU WU OCU IU TNJ TxU

PT 2423   LICHTENBERG,GEORG CHRISTOPH,1742-1799
.L4 A6   Aus Lichtenbergs Nachlass; Aufsätze, Ge-
1899   dichte, Tagebuchblätter, Briefe, zur hundert-
    sten Wiederkehr seines Todestages ... hrsg.
von Albert₍Leitzmann. Weimar, H. Böhlaus
Nachf., 1899.
    272 p. port.

    I. Leitzmann, Albert, 1867-   ed.

NL   0341515   InU TxU WaU TNJ MH MB OCU CU-I WU NIC

Zg18   Lichtenberg, Georg Christoph, 1742-179₄
L620   ... Auserlesene Schriften. Mit 24 Kupfern
800   nach D.Chodowiecki. Baireuth,bei I.A.
    Lübecks Erben,1800.
    xvi,440p. mounted plates,diagrs. 18cm.
    Edited by C.S.Krause.

NL   0341516   CtY ICU

Lichtenberg,Georg Christoph, 1742-1799.
    G.C.Lichtenberg's ausführliche erklärung der
hogarthischen kupferstiche,mit verkleinerten
aber vollständigen copien derselben von E.
Riepenhausen ... Göttingen, Dieterich, 1794-
1835.
    14 v.in 4. 16¼cm. and atlas of plates.
    Atlas lacking in U.of M.set.
    Vol.13 by J.P.Lyser; v.14 by Dr.Le Petit,ed.by Karl
Gutzkow.

    1.Hogarth,William,1697-1764. I.Lyser,Johann Peter
Theodor,1803-1870. II.Le Petit,Dr. III.Gutzkow,Karl
Ferdinand,1811-1878, ed.

NL   0341517   MiU DLC NN CtY OCU

LICHTENBERG, GEORG CHRISTOPH, 1742-1799.
    Ausführliche Erklärung der Hogarthischen Kupfer-
stiche, mit verkleinerten aber vollständigen Copien
derselben von E. Riepenhausen.   Göttingen, In der
Dieterich'schen Buchhandlung, 1794-1816.   14 v. in 5.
17cm.
    — Sammlung Hogarthischer Kupferstiche. ₍Radierungen von E. L.
Riepenhausen. Göttingen, 1794-183-₎   1 v. of plates.   35cm.

    Binder's title.
    Issued in parts.
    Imperfect: plates 63 -88 wanting.

    1. Hogarth, William, 1697-1764.   I. Riepenhausen, Ernst Ludwig, 1765-
1840. Sammlung Hogarthischer Kupferstiche.

NL   0341519   NN MdBP CoU IEN OU CU NNC InU MdBP

759.2
H678Lℓ   Lichtenberg, Georg Christoph, 1742-1799.
    Ausführliche Erklärung der Hogarthischen Kup-
ferstiche, mit verkleinerten Copien derselben
von Carl Rahl.   Wien, C. Kaulfuss, 1809-
₍pt.1, 1818₎
    pts. in   17cm.
    Pts. 11-12: Ausführliche Erklärung ... mit
verkleinerten aber vollständigen Copien ... von
E. Riepenhausen. Göttingen, Dieterich, 1809-16.
    Pt.13: J.P. Lyser's ausführliche Erklärung...
mit ... Copien ... von E. Riepenhausen.

       Göttingen, Dieterich, 1833.
    Pt.14: Le Petit's ausführliche Erklärung ...
mit ... Copien ... von E. Riepenhausen. Göttingen, Dieterich, 1835.
    Contains only the descriptions of Lichtenberg
and others; plates published separately?
    Pts. 1-10 have   added title pages, en-
graved.

NL   0341521   TxU InU KU

Lichtenberg, Georg Christoph, 1742-1799.
    Ausführliche Erklärung der Hogarthischen Kupferstiche,
mit verkleinerten aber vollständigen Copien derselben
von E.Riepenhausen. Neue verb. Ausg. Göttingen, Verl.
der Dieterichschen Buchhandlung, 1850-53.

    pt.1-6, 9-10.   (His Vermischte Schriften, 9-11, 13)

NL   0341522   MH DLC CLU

Lichtenberg, Georg Christoph, 1742-1799.
    Ausführliche Erklärung der Hogarthischen Kupfersti-
che. ₍Herausgeber: Helmuth Eggert₎ Erfurt, Gebr. Rich
ters, 1949.
    196 p. 26 plates (in pocket) 31 cm.
    The first four of the 5 Lieferungen completed by the author. Ad-
ditional parts by others were issued until 1833 or 1835.
    Includes the Hogarth engravings commented upon.

    1. Hogarth, William, 1697-1764.   I. Eggert, Helmuth, ed.
II. Title.

NE642.H7L5   769.2   50-27746

NL   0341523   DLC FU IaU NcD

838
L617g   LICHTENBERG, GEORG CHRISTOPH, 1742-1799.
C1   Georg Christ. Lichtenbergs ausgewählte
schriften, hrsg. und mit anmerkungen
versehen, von Eugen Reichel. Leipzig,
P. Reclam [1879?]
    536p. 14cm.

    1. Reichel, Eugen, 1853-1916.

NL   0341524   TxU OCU RPB MH InU

LICHTENBERG, GEORG CHRISTOPH, 1742-1799.
    ...Ausgewaehlte Schriften. Herausgegeben und eingelei-
tet von Adolf Wilbrandt. Stuttgart: J.G. Cotta, 1893.
xii, 368 p. 12°.

568732A. 1. German literature--Misc. I. Wilbrandt, Adolf
von, 1837-1911, editor.

NL   0341525   NN WaU NjP MH

838
L7   Lichtenberg,Georg Christoph,1742-1799.
M58   Ausgewählte Schriften,mit Einleitung und An-
merkungen hrsg.von August Messer. Berlin,
Volksverband der Bücherfreunde,Wegweiser-Verlag
₍1925₎
    475,₍4₎ p. ports. 20 cm.
    Bibliography: p.₍476₎

    I.Messer,August,1867-1937,ed.

NL   0341526   MiU InU CaBVaU

333H29   Lichtenberg, Georg Christoph, 1742-1799.
K1834   ... Auswahl aus Lichtenberg's schriften
    Hildburghausen ₍etc.₎ Bibliographisches insti-
tut, 1834.
    112p. incl.front.(port.)   (Cabinets-biblio-
thek der deutschen classiker. 71.bdchen.)

    Half-title: Neue cabinets-bibliothek der deut-
schen classiker.
    With Hauff, Wilhelm. Anthologie aus den werken
von Wilhelm Hauff. Hildburghausen, 1834.

NL   0341527   IU CLSU OOxM MB PU

Z 9
.L7   Lichtenberg, Georg Christoph,
(Rare)   1742-1799.
    Bibliogenie; oder, Die Entstehung der
Bücherwelt, Gesammelte Aussprüche.
Leipzig, Offizin Haag-Drugulin [1934]
65 p. port.
    "Die hier getroffene Auswahl und
Zusammenstellung sowie die
Überschriften stammen von Ernst
Kellner."

    1. Books--Quotations, maxims, etc. I.
Kellner, Ernst, comp. II. Title.

NL   0341528   ICU

Lichtenberg, Georg Christoph, 1742-1799.
    Die bibliogenie, oder die entstehung der
bücherwelt; eingeleitet und bearb. von Ernst
Volkmann. Weimar ₍Gesellschaft der biblio-
philen₎ 1942.
    107 p. port. 21cm.

    1. Lichtenberg, Georg Christoph, 1742-1799.
2. Books and reading.

NL   0341529   NNC MH CoU

830
L699   Lichtenberg, Georg Christoph, 1742-1799.
d5   Briefe. Hrsg.von Albert Leitzmann und
Carl Schüddekopf. Leipzig, Dieterich,
1901-1904.
    3v. 24cm.

    CONTENTS.- 1.Bd.1766-1781.- 2.Bd.1782-
1789.- 3.Bd.1790-1799. Nachträge.

    I.Leitzmann, Albert, 1867-   , ed. LC.

       NNC OU CtY OO OCU MiU OrPR
NL   0341530   CLSU PBm MH PPT TNJ MoU CU NIC InU IU

VOLUME 332

830
L699
d8
Lichtenberg, Georg Christoph, 1742-1799.
Briefe an die Freunde. [Auswahl von Wilhelm Spohr] Berlin, W.Hoffmann [Vorwort 1938]
284p. 19cm.

NL 0341531   CLSU InU CU MH MiU CU

PT
2423
L4
Z53
Lichtenberg, Georg Christoph, 1742-1799
Briefe an Dieterich, 1770-1798 [von] G. C. Lichtenberg. Zum hundertjährigen Todestage Lichtenberg's hrsg. von Eduard Grisebach. Mit Porträt nach Schwenterley und einem Kupfer von Chodowiecki. Leipzig, Dieterich'sche Verlagsbuchhandlung, 1898.
145 p. illus. 19 cm.

Bibliographical footnotes.

I. Dieterich, Johann Christian, 1712-1800. II. Grisebach, Eduard Rudolf Autor, 1845-1906, ed.

IaU ICarbS IU NjR MH
NL 0341532   WU TNJ MU TU PSt TxU CLSU CaBVaU InU

Lichtenberg, Georg Christoph, 1742-1794.
Lichtenbergs briefe an Johann Friedrich Blumenbach, hrsg. und erläutert von Albert Leitzmann. Leipzig, Dieterich, 1921.
2 p. L, 135, [1] p. illus. 19½ᶜᵐ.

I. Blumenbach, Johann Friedrich, 1752-1840. II. Leitzmann, Albert, 1867- ed.

NL 0341533   MiU CLSU CU MH

Lichtenberg, Georg Christoph, 1742-1799.
Chodowiecki et Lichtenberg
     see under   Focke, Rudolf, 1852-

Lichtenberg, Georg Christoph.
De nova methodo natvram ac motvm flvidi electrici investigandi. Commentatio prior. 1778.
Plates. (Comm. Soc. Goett. t.8, p.168-180)
Bound with other papers.

--- ----- Commentatio posterior. 1778.
Plates. (Comment. mathemat. t.1, p.65-79)
Bound with other papers.

NL 0341535   NNE IU

Lichtenberg (Georgius Christophorus) [1744-99]. De nova methodo naturam ac motum fluidi electrici investigandi commentatio posterior 16 pp., 2 pl. 4°. *Gottingae, J. C. Dieterich,* 1771

NL 0341536   DNLM MdAN

Lichtenberg, Georg Christoph, 1742-1799, attributed author.
Dornenstücke
     see under   Ehrenpreis, Paul.

PN6273
.U8
Lichtenberg, Georg Christoph, 1742-1799.

Usinger, Fritz, 1895-   comp.
Du bist ein Mensch! Worte der Erkenntnis und Besinnung von G. Chr. Lichtenberg, H. P. Sturz und J. H. Merck. Offenbach a. M., W. Kumm [193-?]

QC16
.E7L517
Lichtenberg, Georg Christoph, 1742-1799.

Erxleben, Johann Christian Polykarp, 1744-1777.
Fizyka Jana Polikarpa Erxlebena. Przez G. Lichtenberga nowemi wynalazkami i nayświeższemi odkryciami pomnożona, dla pożytku powszechnego wydana. W Krakowie, w Druk. Szkoły Główney Koronney, 1788.

Lichtenberg, Georg Christoph, 1742-1799.
[G. Ch. Lichtenberg, Th. G. v. Hippel und Al. Blumauer; hrsg. von F. Bobertag. Berlin und Stuttgart, W. Spemann [1886]
2 p. L, 484 p., 1 l. illus. (incl. ports.) 20ᶜᵐ. (Added t.-p.: Deutsche national-litteratur ... hrsg. von J. Kürschner. 141. bd.)
For contents see "Registerband" to "Deutsche national-litteratur".

I. Hippel, Theodor Gottlieb von, 1741-1796. II. Blumauer, Aloys, 1755-1798. III. Bobertag, Felix, 1841-1907, ed.

G—2720
Library of Congress   PT1101.D4 vol. 141

MtBC OrPR
NL 0341540   DLC GU NB ICU NcD PBm PHC PSC PU MH

Lichtenberg, Georg Christoph, 1742-1799.
... Gedanken, satiren, fragmente, herausgegeben von Wilhelm Herzog ... Jena, E. Diederichs, 1907.
2 v. front. (port.) illus., plates. 19ᶜᵐ.
Vol. 2 has title: ... Satiren, fragmente, briefe.
Cover-title: Lichtenberg schriften.
"Literatur": v. 2, p. 355-357.

I. Herzog, Wilhelm, 1884- ed.

34-24065
Library of Congress   PT2423.L4G4 1907   838.6

NL 0341541   DLC NIC GU CLSU PBm NN OCU

Lichtenberg, Georg Christoph, 1742-1799.
... Gedanken und kenntnisse, aphorismen, von Georg Christoph Lichtenberg. Heidelberg und Leipzig, H. Meister [1932]
45 p. 16½ᶜᵐ. (Die Kleinen bücher. [Nr. 8])

1. Aphorisms and apothegms.   I. Title.
PT2423.L4G45   838.6   A F 47-2495
Yale univ. Library for Library of Congress   [3]†

NL 0341542   CtY DLC CU

PT
2423
L4
A16
1871
Lichtenberg, Georg Christoph, 1742-1799.
Gedanken und Maximen; Lichtstrahlen aus seinen Werken. Mit einer biographischen Einleitung von Eduard Grisebach. Leipzig, F. A. Brockhaus, 1871.
226 p. 17 cm.

I. Grisebach, Eduard Rudolf Autor, 1845-1906, ed. II. Title.

NL 0341543   WU NIC

838
L7
G17
Lichtenberg, Georg Christoph, 1742-1799.
Georg Christoph Lichtenberg; Leben und Vermächtnis [hrsg. von] Michael Gallmeier. Hamburg, J. Trautmann Verlag, 1948.
263 p. plates, ports., facsim. 21 cm.
CONTENTS.--Lichtenbergs Leben.--Aphorismen.--Aus den Erklärungen zu Hogarths Kupferstichen.--Briefe Lichtenbergs an.--Literaturangaben (p.261)

I. Gallmeier, Michael, ed.

NL 0341544   MiU MH DLC-P4 TU

Lichtenberg, Georg Christoph, 1742-1799, ed.

Göttingisches magazin der wissenschaften und litteratur. Hrsg. von Georg Christoph Lichtenberg und Georg Forster. 1.-3. jahrg., 4. jahrg., 1.-2. stück; 1780-85. Göttingen, J. C. Dieterich, 1780-85.

Lichtenberg, Georg Christoph, 1742-1799.
Hogarth's werke. Eine sammlung der stahlstiche nach seinen originalen. Mit text von G. Ch. Lichtenberg Revidirt und vervollständigt von dr. Paul Schumann. 3. aufl. Reudnitz bei Leipzig, A. H. Payne [1887?]
xxii, 354 p. front., plates, ports. 31½ᶜᵐ.
Issued in 30 parts, 1886-87.

[1. Hogarth, William, 1697-1764. I. Schumann, Paul, 1855-
20-7393
Library of Congress   ND497.H7L73 1887

NL 0341546   DLC

Lichtenberg, Georg Christoph.
Ideen, mit portrait. Hildburghausen, n.d.
12°

NL 0341547   NN

Lichtenberg, Georg Christoph.
Ideen. Hildburghausen, Bibliographisches Institut, 1844.
174 p.

NL 0341548   PU

LICHTENBERG, Georg Christoph
Ideen, gedanken und einfälle in einer der gegenwart angemessenen auswahl. Cabinetsausg. Hildburghausen, etc., 1829.
9 x 14.

NL 0341549   MH-AH

PN6273
.L5
1835
Lichtenberg, Georg Christoph, 1742-1799.
G. C. Lichtenberg's Ideen, Maximen und Einfälle. Nebst dessen Charakteristik. Hrsg. von Gustav Jördens. 3. Aufl. Wohlfeile Ausg. in Taschenformat. Leipzig, E. Klein, 1835.
iv, 275 p. 13cm.

1. Aphorisms and apothegms. I. Jördens, Gustav, ed.

NL 0341550   ViU

Lichtenberg, Georg Christoph, 1742-1794.
Karrikatur-Allmanach ... Aus Lichtenbergs Nachlass
     see under title

VOLUME 332

Lichtenberg, Georg Christoph, 1742–1799.
Het kleine fundamenten-boek; een Lichtenberg-brevier
Brussel, Uitgeverij De Lage landen, 1942.
3 p. l., 9–82 p., 1 l. 23ᶜᵐ.
"Inleiding, keuze en vertaling van N. de Praetere."
"Bij gelegenheid van de 200ᵉ herdenking der geboorte van Georg
Christoph Lichtenberg ... gedrukt."—leaf at end.
"Beknopte bibliografie": p. 81–82.

1. Aphorisms and apothegms. I. Praetere, N. de, ed. and tr.
II. Title.
PT2423.L4A825   838.6   A F 47–4280
Harvard univ. Library
for Library of Congress

NL   0341552   MH IaU DLC

4B–675   **Lichtenberg, Georg Christoph,** 1742–1799.
Kritik des Lebens. Eine Auswahl aus den
"Bemerkungen." Mit einer Einführung und
Erklärungen hrsg. von Hermann Frasch.
Stuttgart, Schuler-Verlag, 1948.
261 p.

NL   0341553   DLC-P4

Lichtenberg, Georg Christoph, 1742–1799.
Licht und wahrheit: gedanken, satiren, fragmente, von Georg Christoph Lichtenberg. Berlin,
Gustav Kiepenheuer verlag, 1937.
159 p. front. (port.) 2 illus. (incl.port.)
17cm. (Half-title: Kiepenheuer buecherei)
"Nachwort" signed: Helmut Giese.
Contents. - Natur und geist. - Nikolaus Koperni-
kus. - Von deutscher literatur. - Georg Christoph Lichtenberg. - Nachwort.

I. Giese, Helmut. II. Title.

NL   0341554   NRU

Lichtenberg, [Georg Christoph] 1742–1799.
Lichtenberg; ein verkleinertes bild seines
gedankenlebens
see under Friedell, Egon, 1878–1938.

8017   **Lichtenberg, Georg Christoph,** 1742–1799
.5845   Lichtenberg über Naturlehre, Statik, Mechanik,
Hydrostatik und die neue Chemie. Nach seinen
Vorlesungen herausgegeben. Wien, Geistinger,
1808.
564 p. illus. 18 cm.

Edited by G. Gamauf. - cf. Bibliothèque nationale.

NL   0341556   NjP

Lichtenberg, Georg Christoph, 1742–1799.
Lichtenbergs mädchen, mit zwölf ungedruckten briefen Lichtenbergs, seinem porträt in mezzotinto-gravüre, faksimile eines
gedichts, einer abbildung des Weender thors zu Göttingen,
usw., herausgegeben von Erich Ebstein. München, Süddeutsche
monatshefte g. m. b. h., 1907.
90, ₁1₎ p. front. (port.) illus., pl., fold. facsim. 19ᶜᵐ.
Twenty-three letters of Lichtenberg to A. L. F. Meister, with introduction and notes.

I. Meister, Albrecht Ludwig Friedrich, 1724–1788. II. Ebstein, Erich
Hugo, 1880–1931, ed.
Library of Congress   PT2423.L4Z52   44–35269

NL   0341557   DLC PU

Lichtenberg, Georg Christoph, 1742–1799.
Lichtenberg's visits to England as described in his letters
and diaries; translated and annotated by Margaret L. Mare ...
and W. H. Quarrell ... Oxford, The Clarendon press, 1938.
xxiv, 130 p., 1 l. front. (port.) 23ᶜᵐ. (Oxford studies in
modern languages and literature. General editor: H. G. Fiedler)
"The present translation is confined to his letters from England to
friends in Germany, a few fragments of his diary, and the articles on
the English stage which appeared in the 'Deutsches museum' under
the form of letters to H. C. Bole."—Pref.
"Select bibliography": p. ₍125₎

1. England—Descr. & trav. 2. Actors, English. I. Mare, Margaret
Laura, ed. and tr. II. Quarrell, William Henry, 1864– joint ed. and
tr.
                                                    38–83719
Library of Congress   DA620.L7
                                                    914.2

OU OrU
NL   0341558   DLC DAU CaBVaU NcD PHC PU PBm OC1 OCU

Lichtenberg, Georg Christoph, 1742–1799.
Georg Christoph Lichtenberg's Physikalische und
mathematische schriften, nach dessen tode gesammelt
und hrsg. von Ludwig Christian Lichtenberg... und
Friedrich Kries... Göttingen, H. Dieterich,
1803–06.
4 v. diagr.,8 fold.pl. 17cm. (Added t.-p.:
Vermischte schriften ... gesammelt und hrsg. von
Ludwig Christian Lichtenberg... und Friedrich
Kries... 6.–9.bd.)

NL   0341559   WU RPB

Lichtenberg, Georg Christoph, 1742–1799.
The reflections of Lichtenberg; selected and tr. by Norman Alliston. London, S. Sonnenschein & co., lim., 1908.
168 p. 19½ᶜᵐ. (Half-title: Lichtenberg's reflections)

1. Lichtenberg, Georg Christoph, 1742–1799. I. Alliston, Norman,
ed. and tr.
                                                    A 11–1445
Title from Enoch Pratt   Free Libr. Printed by L. C.

NL   0341560   MdBE NIC MB

Lichtenberg, Georg Christoph, 1742–1799.
Schmidt, Friedrich Ludwig, 1772–1841, *ed.*
Sammlung der besten urtheile über Hamlets charakter von
Göthe, Herder, Richardson und Lichtenberg. Hrsg. von F. L.
Schmidt. Leipzig, C. G. Schmidt, 1807.

Lichtenberg, Georg Christoph.
[Schriften] Jena, Diederich, 1907
see his Gedanken, Satiren, fragmente.

Lichtenberg, George Christoph, 1742–99.
Spässe und Probleme. Ausgewählt von Dr. Owlglass. München, Langen, Müller, 1942.

69 p. (Der kleine Bücherei, 239)

NL   0341563   M'

PT 2423   **Lichtenberg, Georg Christoph,** 1742–1799.
L4 A6   Spässe und Probleme ... ₍Ausgewählt von Dr.
1954   Owlglass, pseud.₎ München, A. Langen - G.
Müller, 1954.
67 p. 18 cm. (Langen-Müller's Kleine
Geschenkbücher, 15)

I. Blaich, Hans Erich, 1873–1945, ed.
II. Title.

NL   0341564   OU

Lichtenberg, Georg Christoph, 1742–1799.
... Tag und dämmerung; aphorismen, schriften, briefe, tage
bücher, mit einem lebensbild herausgegeben von Ernst Vincent
Mit 5 zeitgenössischen abbildungen. Leipzig, Dieterich ₍1941₎
4 p. l., ₍8₎–408 p. front., plates, ports. 18ᶜᵐ. (Sammlung Dieterich,
bd. 75)
At head of title: G. C. Lichtenberg.
"Dritte, erweiterte auflage. 1941."

I. Vincent, Ernst, 1887– ed. II. Title.
                                                    46–28778
Library of Congress   PT2423.L4A16 1941
                                                    838.6

NL   0341565   DLC CSt TNV InU TxDaM MH ICU

Lichtenberg, Georg Christoph, 1742–1799.
Taschenbuch zum Nutzen und Vergnügen
see under title

PT 2423   LICHTENBERG,GEORG CHRISTOPH,1749–1799
.L4 T5   Timorus, das ist, Vertheidigung zweyer
1773   Israeliten, die durch die Kräftigkeit Lavaterischen Beweisgründe ... den wahren Glauben
angenommen haben, von Conrad Photorin ₍pseud.₎
Berlin, 1773.
78+16 p.

Nachwort, by Martin Domke, 16 p.

NL   0341567   InU CLSU

Lichtenberg, Georg Christoph.
Timorus, das ist, Vertheidigung zweyer
Israeliten, [die durch die Kräftigkeit
der Lavaterischen Beweisgründe und der
Göttingschen Mettwürste bewogen den wah-
ren Glauben angenommen haben, von C.Pho-
torin, (i.e. G.C.Lichtenberg)]. Hrsg. von
H.Meyer. Mit einem Nachwort von M.Domke.
Berlin: [A.Scholem,] 1926.   4 p.L.,
(1)8–78,xvi p.,2 L.   16.

NL   0341568   OCH CoU

₍Lichtenberg, Georg Christoph₎ 1742–1799.
Ueber physiognomik; wider die physiognomen.
Zu beförderung der menschenliebe und menschen-
kenntniss ... Zweyte verm. aufl. Göttingen,
Johann Christian Dieterich, 1778.
₍8₎, 95 p. 16½cm.

Preface to 2d ed. signed: G. C. L.

1. Physiognomy. I. Title.

NL   0341569   NNC

---

837   LICHTENBERG, GEORGE CHRISTOPHER, 1742–1799.
L617B1 Ungedruckte Briefe. Hrsg. von Martin
Domke. [Frankfurt? Officina Serpentis,
1925]
[16]p. 26cm.

"370 Exemplaren. Dies Exemplar hat die
Nummer 140."

I. Domke, Martin, ed.

NL   0341570   TxU

VOLUME 332

PT2423
L4A6
Lichtenberg, Georg Christoph, 1742-1799.
Unsterblicher Lichtenberg; eine Auslese.
[Auswahl von Wilhelm Spohr] Berlin, W.
Hoffmann [193-?]
152 p. illus.,ports. 20cm.

I.Spohr, Wilhe   lm, 1868-   ed.
II.Title.

NL 0341571   CSt

Lichtenberg, Georg Christoph, 1742-1799.
Vertheidigung des Hygrometers, und der de
Luc'schen Theorie vom Regen. (Göttingen, Dieterich,
1800)

NL 0341572   IU DAS CU

Lichtenberg, Georg Christoph, 1742-1799.
W. Hogarth's zeichnungen, nach den originalen in
stahl gestochen. Mit der vollständigen erklärung derselben von G. C. Lichtenberg, hrsg. und fortgesetzt von dr.
Franz Kottenkamp ... Stuttgart, Literatur-comptoir,
1840.
2 v. in 1. plates, port. 27½ᶜᵐ.
Paged continuously.
CONTENTS.—1. abth. ... Zeichnungen ... Mit der vollständigen erklärung von G. C. Lichtenberg und einer lebensgeschichte Hogarth's von dr.
Franz Kottenkamp.—2. abth. ... Zeichnungen ... Mit der vollständigen
erklärung von dr. Franz Kottenkamp.
1. Hogarth, William, 1697-1764.   I. Kottenkamp, Franz Justus, 1806-
1858.
Library of Congress   ND497.H7L75

10-18163†

NL 0341573   DLC GU PPT NNU-W

Lichtenberg, Georg Christoph.
William Hogarth's Zeichnungen nach den
Originalen in Stahl gestochen ... Stuttgart. Rieger,
1854.
994 p.

NL 0341574   PPG

ND
497
.H7
L75
1857
Lichtenberg, Georg Christoph, 1742-1799
William Hogarth's Zeichnungen. Nach den
Originalen in Stahl gestochen. Mit der vollständigen Erklärung derselben von G. C. Lichtenberg. Herausgegeben mit Ergänzung und Fortsetzung derselben, nebst einer Biographie
Hogarth's von Franz Kottenkamp. 2. Aufl. Stuttgart, Rieger, 1857. 25cm.
725p. illus. 25cm.

1. Hogarth, William, 1697-1764.   I. Kottenkamp, Franz Justus,   1806-1858.

NL 0341575   TNJ OClW NjP

Lichtenberg, G[eorg] C[hristoph], 1742-1799.
William Hogarth's zeichnungen, nach den originalen in stahl gestochen. Mit der vollständigen
erklärung derselben von G.C.Lichtenberg, herausge
geben mit ergänzung und fortsetzung derselben,
nebst einer biographie Hogarth's von Franz Kotten
kamp ... 3.auss neue durchgestehene und verbesserte auflage. Stuttgart, Rieger'sche verlagsbuchhandlung, 1873.
xxxii,600 p. front.(port.)plates. 24cm.

NL 0341576   OrU

Lichtenberg, Georg Christoph, 1742-1799.
William Hogarth's zeichnungen. Nach den originalen
in stahl gestochen. Mit der vollständigen erklärung derselben von G. C. Lichtenberg. Hrsg. mit ergänzung und
fortsetzung derselben, nebst einer biographie Hogarth's
von dr. Franz Kottenkamp. 3. aufs neue durchgesehene
und verb. aufl. Neue ausg. Stuttgart, Rieger, 1882.
3 p. l., iiii-xxxii, 606 p. front., plates, ports. 23ᶜᵐ.
"Vorwort" signed : Ludwig Gantter.

1. Hogarth, William, 1697-1764.   I. Kottenkamp, Franz Justus, 1806-
1858.   II. Gantter, Ludwig, ed.

20-12984

Library of Congress   ND497.H7L75   1882

NL 0341577   DLC CLSU

Lichtenberg, Georg Christoph, 1742-1799.
G. C. Lichtenberg's witzige und launige Schriften, hrsg. von
Johann Schwinghamer...   Wien: Gassler, 1810-11.   5 v. front.
(port.), fold. pl.   12°.
Imperfect: One plate wanting.
v. 4-5 have special title-pages: G. C. Lichtenberg's witzige und launige Sitten-
gemälde nach Hogarth. Für gebildete Leser bearbeitet und hrsg. von Johann
Schwinghamer...   Wien: Gassler, 1811.

1. German literature.—Collected   works. 2. Schwinghamer,
Johann, editor.
N. Y. P. L.   August 22, 1918.

NL 0341578   NN InU CLU CtY OU MH

936A. LICHTENBERG, GEORG CHRISTOPH. Wun-
dercuren der geweihten Ärzte bei einigen ameri-
kanischen Völkern. [1788.] (In his: Vermischte
Schriften. Neue Original-Ausgabe. Goettingen:
Dieterich, 1844-67. 12°. Theil 6, p. 416-417.)
NFG

NL 0341579   NN

838
L7
B42
Lichtenberg,Georg Christoph,1742-1799.
Zeugnisse des Witzes und der Weisheit;
Einbandentwurf nach Motiven der Wiener
Lichtenbergausg. von 1817 von Professor
Josef Behmel. [Klagenfurt; E.Kaiser
[1947]
82 p.   20 cm.

I.Behmel,Josef,ed.   II.Title.

NL 0341580   MiU

Lichtenberg, H. H. Kort veiledning til treplantning og
opelskning af skov. Kjøbenhavn. 1861.   16°.   pp. 29.

NL 0341581   MH-A

Lichtenberg, Heinrich.
Die architekturdarstellungen in der mittelhochdeutschen
dichtung, von Heinrich Lichtenberg. Münster in Westf., Verlag der Aschendorffschen verlagsbuchhandlung, 1931.
118 p. 24½ᶜᵐ. (Added t.-p.: Forschungen zur deutschen sprache und
dichtung ... hft. 4)
Bibliographical foot-notes.

1. German poetry—Middle High German—History and criticism.
I. Title.
A C 33-1493
Title from Columbia   Univ. Printed by L. C.

NL 0341582   NNC PSt MiU

Lichtenberg, Heinrich.
Die architekturdarstellungen in der mittelhochdeutschen
dichtung, von Heinrich Lichtenberg. Münster in Westf., Verlag der Aschendorffschen buchhandlung, 1931.
118 p. 24½ᶜᵐ. (Added t.-p.: Forschungen zur deutschen sprache und
dichtung ... hft. 4)
Bibliographical foot-notes.
Microfilm.

NL 0341583   CaBVaU

Lichtenberg, Heinrich, 1885-   : Akute Osteomyelitis des
oberen Femurendes.   Leipzig 1912: Lehmann.   47 S. 8°
Leipzig, Med. Diss. v. 15. Mai 1912, Ref. Payr
[Geb. 29. Okt. 85 Gronau, Hannover; Wohnort: Hannover; Staatsangeh.:
Preußen; Vorbildung: Gymn. Andreanum Hildesheim Reife O. 05; Studium:
Würzburg 5, Berlin 2, Göttingen 3 S.; Coll. 15. Mai 12; Approb. 19. Sept. 11.]
[U 12. 3100

NL 0341584   ICRL DNLM

Lichtenberg, Hirsch, 1906-
... Hygiène des latrines scolaires ...   Paris,
1933.
Thèse - Univ. de Paris.
"Bibliographie": 1 l. at end.

NL 0341585   CtY

Lichtenberg, Hugo, 1877-
Ueber stoerungen der sensibilitaet bei rheumatischer
peripherischer facialsparalyse.
Inaug. diss. Berlin, 1891
36 p. 1 l. 8°

NL 0341586   ICRL DNLM

Lichtenberg, I. J.
... H. L. Yesler v. Board of Harbor Line Commissioners et al. - No. 9,452. Stimson Mill
Company v. Board of Harbor Line Commissioners
et al. - No. 9,453. Columbia & Puget Sound
Railway Company v. Board of Harbor Line Commissioners et al. - No. 9,457. Motion to quash
alternative writ of prohibition. Opinion of the
court.   [Seattle? n.p., 1891?]
106 p.
In the Superior court of King county, State of
Washington.

NL 0341587   WaU-L

Lichtenberg, Irena, tr.
Némirovsky, Irène.
... Dawid Golder, powieść. Warszawa, Wydawnictwo
współczesne [1930?]

RA
Fiction
Lichtenberg, Isaac Nathan.
The widow's son. A story of Jewish life
of the past. ... Cincinnati, Bloch Publishing and Printing Co.[1884?]
342p.18cm.

I. Title.   II. Bloch Publishing and
Printing Co., Cincinnati. (RA cat. only)

NL 0341589   OC

VOLUME 332

Lichtenberg, Isaac Nathan.
The widow's son. A story of Jewish life of the past.
By I. N. Lichtenberg ... New York, Maccabean publishing co., ʻ1884.
342 p. 18½ᵐ.

Library of Congress   PZ3.L6173W   7-18772†

NL 0341590   DLC NN PPDrop

Lichtenberg, Jacob, freiherr von
  see   Liechtenberg, Jacob, freiherr von.

TX
783
L69   Lichtenberg, J   C
Neuestes Lehrbuch der Conditorei. Stettin,
Hessenland, 1833.
224 p.

1. Confectionery, German. I. Title.

NL 0341592   NIC

Lichtenberg (Joh. Henricus). * De vomitu
cruento plerumque per se non lethali. 26 pp.,
1 l. 4°. Hala Magdeb., typ. J. C. Hilligeri,
[1752].

NL 0341593   DNLM PPC

Lichtenberg, Johannes, 1905-
Die missbildungen der niere und ihre
erkrankungen ... Berlin, 1934.
Diss. - Freiburg i. B.

NL 0341594   MiU

Lichtenberg, Karl.   396.5 Q502
Schriftliche Arbeiten zum häuslichen Nebenerwerb. Ratgeber
für Schreibgewandte von Karl Lichtenberg. ... . Mülheim a. d.
Ruhr, J. Bagel, [1905].
86 p. 20ᵐᵐ.

NL 0341595   ICJ

PR
149
L69e   Lichtenberg, Karl, 1897-
Der Einfluss des Theophrast auf die
englischen Characterwriters des 17. Jahrhunderts. [Weimar] 1921.
viii, 77 p. 23ᶜᵐ.
Inaug.-Diss. - Berlin.
Lebenslauf.
Bibliography: p. [vii]-viii.

NL 0341596   NRU NcU ICRL IU CtY

Lichtenberg, Karl, 1897-
... Kurzgefasste englische sprachlehre, von dr. Karl Lichtenberg ... 7. aufl. Bielefeld und Leipzig, Velhagen & Klasing, 1943.
x, 142 p. 21ᵐ. (Current English für oberschulen für jungen)

1. English language—Text-books for foreigners—Germans.
DLC PE1129.G3L55   A F 47-4924
Newberry library
for Library of Congress

NL 0341597   ICN DLC MH

Lichtenberg, Karl
  see also Lichtenberg, Carl.

WVA
L699o
1888   LICHTENBERG, Kornél
Die Ohrenkrankheiten, deren Verhütung
und hygienische Behandlung. Berlin,
Hampel, 1888.
105 p. illus.

NL 0341599   DNLM

M
787.1
L617C   Lichtenberg, Leopold, 1861-1935, ed.
Compositions for the violin; with
pianoforte acccmpaniment in the first
& third positions. Boston Music Co.,
c1908.
52 p. (piano) 18 p. (violin)

Contains compositions by Henry
Tolhurst and Adolphe Lange.

NL 0341600   WaT

Lichtenberg, Leopold, 1861-   ed.
Rode, Pierre, 1774-1830.
... Concerto no. 8 in E minor for violin. [Op. 13] Edited and fingered by Leopold Lichtenberg; the piano accompaniment arranged by Friedrich Hermann. New York, G. Schirmer, ʻ1901.

Lichtenberg, Leopold, 1861-1935, ed.
Dancla, Charles, 1818-1907.
... Elementary and progressive method for violin, revised and edited by Leopold Lichtenberg, translated from the French by Dr. Th. Baker ... New York, G. Schirmer, ʻ1903.

Lichtenberg, Leopold, 1861-1935, ed.
                    Fantaisie brillante sur des motifs
de l'opéra Faust de Gounod
  see under Gounod, Charles François, 1818-1893.

Lichtenberg, Leopold, 1861-1935.
Scale studies for the violin, by Leopold Lichtenberg... New
York: G. Schirmer [etc., etc., c1902] Publ. pl. no. 16385.   28 p.
35cm.

1. Violin—Exercises and studies.
N. Y. P. L.   February 17, 1941

NL 0341604   NN OC1

Lichtenberg, Leopold, 1861-1935, ed.
... Sonatas for piano and violin
  see under Gade, Niels W[ilhelm] 1817-1890.

Lichtenberg, Leopold, 1861-1935.
Tartini, Giuseppe, 1692-1770.
... Le trille du diable, for violin, edited and fingered by Leopold Lichtenberg, the piano accompaniment by Robert Volkmann, with a biographical sketch of the author by Richard Aldrich. New York, G. Schirmer, ʻ1901.

Lichtenberg, Ludwig, 1908-
Die neuere entwicklung der bauhütten und bauproduktivgenossenschaften ... von Ludwig Lichtenberg ... Quakenbrück, Trute, 1934.
viii, 185 p.

Thesis, Göttingen.
"Literaturverzeichnis": p. 183-185.

1. Housing - Germany. 2. Building trades - Germany.

NL 0341607   NNC MiU CtY ICRL

Lichtenberg, Ludwig Christian, 1738-1812, ed.
Lichtenberg, Georg Christoph, 1742-1799.
Georg Christoph Lichtenberg's vermischte schriften, nach dessen tode aus den hinterlassenen papieren gesammelt und hrsg. von Ludwig Christian Lichtenberg ... und Friedrich Kries ... Göttingen, J. C. Dieterich, 1800-04.

[Lichtenberg, Ludwig Christian] 1738-1812.
Verhaltungs-regeln bey nahen donnerwettern nebst den mitteln sich gegen die schädlichen wirkungen des blitzes in sicherheit zu setzen.
Gotha, Ettinger, 1774.
46 p.

NL 0341609   PPF

Lichtenberg, Ludwig Christian, 1738-1812.
Verhaltungsregeln bey nahen Donnerwettern, nebst den Mitteln sich gegen die schädlichen Wirkungen des Blitzes in Sicherheit zu setzen.
Grätz, Gedruckt bey den Widmanstätterischen Erben, 1776.
45 p. fold. plate. 21 cm.

Bound with Cavallo, Tiberius Vollständige Abhandlung der theoretischen und praktischen Lehre von der Elektricität nebst eignen Versuchen. Grätz [n.d.]

NL 0341610   OkU

*GC7
L6176
774vc   [Lichtenberg, Ludwig Christian, 1738-1812]
Verhaltungs regeln bey nahen Donnerwettern, nebst den Mitteln sich gegen die schädlichen Wirkungen des Blitzes in Sicherheit zu setzen: zum Unterricht für Unkundige. Mit einer Kupfertafel. Dritte vermehrte Auflage.
Gotha, bey Carl Wilhelm Ettinger. 1778.
89, [3] p. fold.-pl. 19.5 cm.

NL 0341611   MH

Lichtenberg, M.
Landwirtschaftliche Haushaltungskunde, ein wirtschaftliches ABC der Bauerfrau und Lehrbuch für Haushaltungschulen. Berlin, Paul Parey, 1902.
x, 352 p. illus.

NL 0341612   MCR

VOLUME 332

Lichtenberg, Martin, tr.

Otto, Ernst, 1870–
The battle at Blanc Mont (October 2 to October 10, 1918) by Lieutenant Colonel Ernst Otto ... translated from the German by Martin Lichtenberg ... Annapolis, Md., United States naval institute, 1930.

HC289
M2L69

Lichtenberg, Martin, 1905–
Entwicklungstendenzen in der Magdeburger industrie... Wolmirstedt, Buchdruckerei A. Grenzau ₍1934₎
4 p.l., 117 p., 1 l.   20½ᶜᵐ.
Inaug.-diss.- Jena.
Lebenslauf.
"Literaturverzeichnis": p.115-117.

1.Magdeburg – Industries.

NL 0341614   CSt-H MiU PU ICRL CtY

Lichtenberg, Niels.
... Dansk teknik, dens udvikling og indsats. København, H. Hirschsprung, 1942.
4 p. l., 316 p. illus. (incl. ports.) diagrs. 24ᶜᵐ. ₍Dansk kultur gennem halvandethundrede aar, redigeret of Kai Flor₎
"1. oplag."
Contents.—Historie og forudsætninger, af Niels Lichtenberg.—Maskin-og skibsbygningsindustrien, af Niels Lichtenberg.—Elktroteknikken, af Sv. Würtz.—Den kemiske teknik, af P. Molde.—Bygningsteknikken, af Sv. Nielsen.
1. Denmark—Indus. 2. Engineering—Denmark. 3. Engineers, Danish. I. Title.
Library of Congress   T26.D4L5   46–36791

NL 0341615   DLC MnU

V
549.4611
L699g

Lichtenberg, Niels.
Det grønlandske mineral kryolit; oparbejdning og anvendelse. Radioforedrag af ...Niels Lichtenberg. ₍København₎ Industriraadet, 1935.
20 p. illus. 22ᶜᵐ. (On cover: Dansk industrier. Nr.1)

Rare Book Room

Title vignette.
Cover-title:...Kryolitindustrien.

1.Cryolite. I.Title.

NL 0341616   CSt

Lichtenberg, Otto Heinrich August, 1889–
Beiträge zur kenntnis der hydrohalogenide der natürlichen kautschukarten ... Kiel, Druck von Schmidt & Klaunig, 1914.
46 p., 1 l. 23½ᶜᵐ.
Inaug.-diss.—Kiel.
Lebenslauf.

1. Halogens. 2. India-rubber.
                                                    Agr 23–866
Library, U. S. Dept. of   Agriculture 387.1L61

NL 0341617   DNAL DLC PU CtY MiU MH

Lichtenberg, Philip.
A content analysis of American motion pictures with special respect to four classes of characters. 174, 3 l. tables.
Thesis (Ph. D.) - Western Reserve University - Dept. of Psychology. - Sept. 24, 1951.

NL 0341618   OC1W

DF76
.L7

LICHTENBERG,REINHOLD,freiherr VON,1865–
...Die ägäische kultur,von prof.dr.R.freiherrn v. Lichtenberg. Leipzig,Quelle & Meyer,1911.
160 p. illus. 19cm. (Wissenschaft und bildung... 83)
Bibliographical foot-notes.

1.Civilization,Greek.

NL 0341619   ICU NcU InU MoU PU NNC MH

LICHTENBERG, R[einhold], freiherr von,1865–
Die ägäische kultur. 2e verbesserte aufl. Leipzig, Quelle & Meyer,1918.

Illustr.
Wissenschaft und bildung,83"

NL 0341620   MH CU IU NcU NjP

Lichtenberg, Reinhold, *freiherr von*, 1865–
Das antike grabporträt besonders bei den Etruskern & Römern ... Strassburg, J. H. E. Heitz (Heitz & Mündel) 1900.
2 p. l., 97 p. 26½ᶜᵐ.
Zur erlangung der venia legendi.—Tech. hochschule, Karlsruhe.
Published in full under title: Das porträt an grabdenkmalen, as "heft" 11 of "Zur kunstgeschichte des auslandes."

1. Sepulchral monuments. 2. Portraits. 3. Sculpture, Ancient.
                                                    1–G–18
Library of Congress   NB1340.L7

NL 0341621   DLC IU NjP PU MiU

DS
41
V95
v.11
no.2

Lichtenberg, Reinhold, Freiherr von, 1865–
Beiträge zur ältesten Geschichte von Kypros. Berlin, Zu beziehen durch W. Peiser ₍1906₎
78 p. 10 plates. 25cm. (Mitteilungen der Vorderasiatischen Gesellschaft, 11. Jahrg. 2)

1. Cyprus--Antiq. 2. Cyprus--Hist.

NL 0341622   NIC OC1 PU ICU PBm CU OCH MH NjP   MB

Lichtenberg, Reinhold, *freiherr von*, 1865–
Cypern und die Engländer; ein beispiel britischer kolonialer willkür, von prof. dr. freiherr v. Lichtenberg. Leipzig, Veit & comp., 1915.
30 p. 24½ᶜᵐ. (On cover: Länder und völker der Türkei ... hft. 3)

1. Cyprus. 2. Gt. Brit.—Colonies—Cyprus. I. Title.
Library of Congress   DS54.8.L5   21–17113

NL 0341623   DLC NNC NN PPDrop NjP

Lichtenberg, Reinhold, Freiherr von, 1865–
Deutsches Land den Deutschen! Ein Beitrag zum Selbstbestimmungsrecht der Völker, von Prof. Dr. R. v. Lichtenberg... Berlin: H. Bermühler ₍1921₎. 77 p. maps. 4°.

1. European war, 1914– —Territorial questions, Germany.
2. Germany. —Historical geography.
N. Y. P. L.   May 26, 1922.

NL 0341624   NN

Lichtenberg, Reinhold, Freiherr von. 1865–   *3043.229.1911
Einflüsse der ägäischen Kultur auf Aegypten und Palästina. Leipzig. Hinrichs. 1911. (1), 104 pp. Illus. [Vorderasiatische Gesellschaft. Mitteilungen. Band 16, Heft 2.] 24 cm., in 8s.

H6168 — Archipelago, Grecian. — Egypt. Civiliz. — Palestine. Civiliz. — S.r.c.

NjP NcD IEG CU NIC
NL 0341625   MB NNUT OC1 OCH PU PBm ICU GEU-T OC1

Lichtenberg, Reinhold, *freiherr von,* 1865–
Haus, dorf, stadt; eine entwicklungs-geschichte des antiken städtebildes von Reinhold freih. von Lichtenberg. Leipzig, R. Haupt, 1909.
ix, 280 p. illus. 26½ᶜᵐ.
"Literaturverzeichnis": p. ₍276₎–280.

Dwellings. 2. Cities and towns, Ancient. I. Title.
Library of Congress   GT150.L5   9–31433

NL 0341626   DLC CU CtY PBm PU ICJ NjP NN

Jdc62
02
907L

Lichtenberg, Reinhold, Freiherr von, 1865–
Hundert Jahre deutsch-römischer Landschaftsmalerei, von Reinhold Freiherrn von Lichtenberg und Ernst Jaffé. Berlin, Oesterheld, 1907.
217 p. and portfolio of 15 plates. 20 cm.
Imperfect: portfolio wanting.

NL 0341627   CtY MH NRU GU NjP IU ICU OCU MH NcD

Lichtenberg, Reinhold, <u>freiherr</u> von, 1865–
Die ionische säule als klassisches bauglied rein hellenischem geiste entwachsen; ein vortrag... Leipzig und New York, R. Haupt, 1907.
71 p. illus. 23½ cm.

NL 0341628   MShM PU OCU

Lichtenberg, Reinhold, *freiherr von,* 1865–
Die landschaftsmalerei bei den Niederländern im XVI. jahrhundert ... Leipzig, Druck von Ramm & Seemann, 1892.
2 p. l., 84 p. illus. 24ᶜᵐ.
Inaug.-diss.—Leipzig.
Lebenslauf.
Published in full, with title: Zur entwickelungsgeschichte der landschaftsmalerei bei den Niederländern und Deutschen im XVI. jahrhundert, as "Beiträge zur kunstgeschichte. Neue folge. XVIII."

1. Landscape painting—Netherlands—Hist. I. Title.
                                                    12–20492
Library of Congress   ND1359.L5

NL 0341629   DLC IaU NjP PPPM

Lichtenberg, Reinhold, *freiherr von,* 1865–
Mehr schutz dem geistigen eigentum: Der kampf um das schicksal des "Parsifal." Dargestellt von R. frhr. v. Lichtenberg und L. Müller v. Hausen. Mit federzeichnung von Franz Stassen. Berlin, K. Curtius ₍1910₎
135, ₍1₎ p. illus. (incl. facsim.) 24½ x 19½ᶜᵐ.

NL 0341630   IEN

VOLUME 332

Lichtenberg, Reinhold, *freiherr von,* 1865–
Mehr schutz dem geistigen eigentum: Der kampf um das schicksal des "Parsifal." Dargestellt von R. frhr. v. Lichtenberg und L. Müller v. Hausen. 3. aufl. Mit federzeichnung von Franz Stassen. Berlin, K. Curtius ₁1914₎

135, ₁1₎ p. illus. (incl. facsim.) 24½ x 19¼ᵐ.

1. Wagner, Richard. Parsifal. 2. Copyright.   i. Müller, Ludwig, 1851–   joint author.   ii. Title.

16–16071

Library of Congress   ML410.W17L5

NL 0341631   DLC

Lichtenberg, Reinhold, *freiherr von,* 1865–
Das porträt an grabdenkmalen, seine enstehung und entwickelung vom alterthum bis zur italienischen renaissance, von dr. Reinhold freiherr von Lichtenberg; mit 44 lichtdrucktafeln. Strassburg, J. H. E. Heitz, 1902.

4 p., 151 p. 44 pl. 29ᵐᵐ. (*Half-title:* Zur kunstgeschichte des auslandes. XI)
Bibliographical foot-notes.
The introduction and first three chapters were issued Strassburg, 1900, as the author's "Habilitations-schrift", Tech. hochschule, Karlsruhe, with title: Das antike grabporträt besonders bei den Etruskern & Römern.

1. Sepulchral monuments. 2. Portraits. 3. Sculpture—Hist.   i. Title.

20–18724

Library of Congress   NB1800.L55

NL 0341632   DLC NcD NcU IaU CSt MU MWiCA MH NN MB

Lichtenberg, Reinhold, *freiherr von,* 1865–
... Ueber den humor bei den deutschen kupferstechern und holzschnittkünstlern des 16. jahrhunderts. Von Reinhold freiherr von Lichtenberg ... Strassburg, J. H. E. Heitz, 1897.

92 p. XVII pl. 24½ᵐᵐ. (Studien zur deutschen kunstgeschichte, 11. hft.)

1. Engraving—Germany—Hist. 2. German wit and humor, Pictorial.   i. Title.

12–8286

Library of Congress   NE651.L7

NL 0341633   DLC NcD IaU PPT CLU CSt CtY MiU NN MB

Lichtenberg, Reinhold, Freiherr von.   8065.179
Über einige Fragen der modernen Malerei.
Heidelberg. Winter. 1903. v, 66 pp. 8°.

F372 — Painting.   Aug. 8,   1903

NL 0341634   MB

Lichtenberg, Reinhold, *freiherr von,* 1865–
Zur entwickelungsgeschichte der landschaftsmalerei bei den Niederländern und Deutschen im XVI. jahrhundert, von Reinhold freiherr von Lichtenberg ... Leipzig, E. A. Seemann, 1892.

4 p. l., 132 p. illus., plates. 24ᵐᵐ. (*Half-title:* Beiträge zur kunstgeschichte. Neue folge. XVIII)

1. Landscape painting—Netherlands—Hist. 2. Landscape painting—Germany—Hist.

6–26554

Library of Congress   ND1348.L7

NL 0341635   DLC MH MB

Lichtenberg, René Ponsul.
Adolfo Hitler e o seu livro Mein Kampf (a Minha luta) 2. ed.   Lisboa, Depositaria editorial Progresso [1939]

NL 0341636   MH

Lichtenberg, Robert M
Great Britain's balance of payments, 1868–1912

Thesis – Harvard, 1953

NL 0341637   MH

Lichtenberg, Rudolf₎
Alt-Osnabrück; 12 Photogravüren nach Original-Aufnahmen von Rudolf und Emil Lichtenberg
see under   Jänecke, Wilhelm, 1872–1928.

Lichtenberg, Rudolf.
Arbeitszeitverhältnisse in den kontinuierlichen betrieben der grosseisenindustrie nordwest-deutschlands. ... Dresden, 1935.   65 p.
Inaug. Diss. – Leipzig, 1935.
Bibliography.

NL 0341639   ICRL

Lichtenberg, Wilhelm. Der schulgarten des realprogymnasiums zu Oldesloe; ₁ein beitrag zur praxis der anlage von schulgärten₎. Oldesloe. 1896. 4°. pp. 1–10. ₎Plan. (Progr. d. realprogym. "1896. nr. 298.")

NL 0341640   MH-A

Lichtenberg, Wilhelm.
Der unterschied der ansprüche aus dem erfolgten rücktritt und aus der bereicherung ... von Wilhelm Lichtenberg ... Zeulenroda, Bernhard Sporn, 1933.

55 p. 21cm.

Inaug.-diss. – Erlangen.
"Literatur": p. 7–10.

NL 0341641   MH-L ICRL

LICHTENBERG, WILHELM, 1892–
Die Dame mit dem schlechten Ruf; Lustspiel in drei Akten. New York, I. S. Richter, [n. d.] 87 l. 29cm.

Typescript.

1. Drama, German.   I. Title.

NL 0341642   NN

LICHTENBERG, WILHELM, 1892–
Die Dame mit dem schlechten Ruf; Schwank.   Wien ₁etc.₎
M. Pfeffer, c1929.   71 p.   20cm.

1. Drama, German.   I. Title.

NL 0341643   NN

Hky   **Lichtenberg, Wilhelm,** 1892–
L617   Eifersucht, Roman.   Zürich, Falken[1952]
E5   340p. 20cm.

NL 0341644   CtY

Lichtenberg, Wilhelm, 1892–
...Fräulein Dr. med. Ruth Keller; Roman.   Zürich, Falken-Verlag ₁1949₎   300 p.   21cm.

515891B. I. Title.   February 24, 1950
N. Y. P. L.

NL 0341645   NN CtY

Hky   **Lichtenberg, Wilhelm,** 1892–
L617   Eine Frau ganz allein; Roman. [1.Aufl.]
F86   Zürich, Falken[c1951]
295p. 21cm.

NL 0341646   CtY

Lichtenberg, Wilhelm, 1892–
...Herr über millionen, komödie in drei akten ...   Wien ₁etc.₎ °1934.

91 p. 19ᵐᵐ.
Reproduced from type-written copy.

I. Title.

Library of Congress   PT2623.I 26H4   43–28804
                                                Brief cataloging

NL 0341647   DLC

Lichtenberg, Wilhelm₎ 1892–
Die Himmelsleiter. Das Leben einer Schauspielerin. Roman. [1.Aufl.] Zürich, Falken-Verlag[1948]
343p.

NL 0341648   CtY

WB   **Lichtenberg, Wilhelm,** 1892–
20580   Das Paradies vor Augen, Roman. [1.Aufl.
Bern₎A.Scher₎[1954]

NL 0341649   CtY NN

Lichtenberg, Wilhelm, 1892–
Schade, dass er ein lump ist! Ein abenteuer in 3 akten ... Berlin, °1932.
140 p. 20ᵐᵐ.
Reproduced from type-written copy.

I. Title.

Library of Congress   PT2623.I 2688   43–28481
                                                Brief cataloging

NL 0341650   DLC

Lichtenberg, Wilhelm, 1892–
Das theater des kaisers; ein Wiener roman aus dem fin de siècle, von Wilhelm Lichtenberg. Zuerich-Bruxelles, F. G. Micha & co. ₁1945₎
4 p. l., 7–440 p. 21ᵐᵐ.

I. Title.

Harvard univ. Library
for Library of Congress

A 47–192

NL 0341651   MH NNC

VOLUME 332

Lichtenberg, Wilhelm, 1892–
Der Trampel; Lustspiel in drei Akten.   Wien, G. Marton,
c1935.   86 p.   21cm.
Film reproduction.   Positive.

  I. Drama, German.   I. Title.

NL 0341652   NN

Lichtenberg, Wilhelm, 1892–
Die Welt in der man verdient.   Roman.   Zürich, Pan
Verlag ₁1953₎
346 p.   21 cm.

  I. Title.

PT2623.I 26W4   833.91   54–15288 ‡

NL 0341653   DLC CtY NN

Lichtenberg, Wilhelm, 1892–
Zu sich selber gesprochen; Ein- und Ausfälle.   Rorschach,
Nebelspalter-Verlag ₁1952₎
68 p.   20 cm.

  I. Title.

PT2623.I 26Z4   54–29279 ‡

NL 0341654   DLC CtY

Lichtenberg, Ger. (District)
Sr. königlichen Hoheit dem durchlauchtigsten
Fürsten und Herrn, Herrn Carl Friedrich,
Grossherzog zu Sachsen-Weimar-Eisenach etc. bei
höchstdessen Regierungs-Antritt in tiefster Ehr-
erbietung gewidmet am 12ten August 1828 von
sämmtlichen treuen Bewohnern der Stadt Ostheim
und übrigen Dörfern des Amtes Lichtenberg.
[n. p.] 1828.
8 p.   24.5 cm.
In verse.

NL 0341655   CtY

JS19   **Lichtenberg, Prussia.** Magistrat.
.L7   Verwaltungs-bericht der stadt Berlin-
Lichtenberg ... 1907
Berlin-Lichtenberg, 19
v.   illus., pl., tables.   28½cm.
Biennial
"Herausgegeben vom Magistrat".
The first report covers the period from
Oct. 15, 1907 to March 31, 1909.
1907–1909–1909–1911 have title:
Verwaltungs-bericht der stadt Lichtenberg
1. Lichtenberg   Prussia—Pol. & govt.

NL 0341656   DLC

Lichtenberg (Principality) Laws, statutes, etc.
Sammlung der für das fürstenthum Lichtenberg vom jahre
1816 bis 1834 ergangenen herzoglich Sachsen-Coburg-Gothai-
schen verordnungen ... Von F. A. Lottner ... Berlin, Sandersche buchhandlung (C. W. Eichhoff) 1836.

vi, 618 p. fold. tab. 20½ᵐ.

  I. Lottner, Friedrich August, 1796?–1836, ed.   II. Saxe-Coburg-Gotha.
Laws, statutes, etc.

48–22522

NL 0341657   DLC

Lichtenberger, André, 1870– 1940.
Eine abenteuerliche reise; roman von André Lichtenberger.   Einzige autorisierte übersetzung aus dem französischen von Alfred Baderle.   Leipzig, P. Reclam jun.
₁1914₎
339 p. 15ᵐ. (On cover: Universal-bibliothek, 5687–5689)   M. 0.60

  I. Baderle, Alfred, tr.   II. Title.

Library of Congress   PQ2623.I 4F65   14–19074

NL 0341658   DLC WU MB

LICHTENBERGER, ANDRE, 1870–
...Amrou, frère des aigles.   Paris: F. Nathan, 1932.
142 p. plates. 16½cm.

654669A. 1. Fiction, French. I. Title.

NL 0341659   NN

Lichtenberger, André, 1870–
... Les André Graffougnat.   Paris, Plon-Nourrit et cⁱᵉ
₁1925₎
2 p. l., 216 p. 18¼ᵐ.

  I. Title.
Library of Congress   PQ2623.I 4A8 1925   25–24801

NL 0341660   DLC GU

Lichtenberger, André, 1870–
... Angomar et Priscilla; illustrations de Mariette Lydis.
Paris, Calmann-Lévy ₁1935₎
32 p. col. illus. 26ᵐ. (On cover: Collection "Pour nos enfants")
At head of title: A. Lichtenberger.

1. Gaul—Hist.—a. c. 58–A. D. 511—Fiction.   I. Lydis, Mariette, illus.
II. Title.   36–17539
Library of Congress   PZ25.L5
Copyright A—Foreign   31109
                                                                      843.91

NL 0341661   DLC NN PPMoI OC1

PQ   Lichtenberger, André, 1870–
2623   L'automne.   Paris, Plon-Nourrit ₁1907₎
I4A9   323 p. 18cm.
1907

NL 0341662   NIC NcD

Lichtenberger, André, 1870–
...Biche; roman.   Paris: Plon-Nourrit et cie ₁1920₎   xv,
233 p. 18½cm.

960429A. 1. Fiction, French.   I. Title.
N. Y. P. L.   March 14, 1939

NL 0341663   NN MtU ScU MH CtY NNC OC1CC PU PPL

Lichtenberger, André, 1870–
Une brouille.   (Annales politiques et littéraires.   Paris,
1921.   f°.   Tome 77, p. 571–573.)
Signed: André Lichtenberger.

1. Drama (French). 2. Title.
N. Y. P. L.   February 9, 1922.

NL 0341664   NN

Lichtenberger, André, 1870–
... Bugeaud, par André Lichtenberger; avec neuf gravures
hors texte et une carte.   Paris, Plon ₁*1931₎
3 p. l., iv, 264 p., 2 l. front., plates, ports., double map. 19ᵐ.
(Les grandes figures coloniales. 5)

1. Bugeaud de la Piconnerie, Thomas Robert, duc d'Isly, 1784–1849.
2. France—Colonies—Algeria. 3. Algeria—Hist.—1830–
Library of Congress   DC269.B9L5   32–4228
Copyright A—Foreign   13949
                                                                      923.544

NL 0341665   DLC IEN NN MH

Lichtenberger, André, 1870–
... Les centaures; roman fantastique.   Paris,
Librairie Baudinière [n. d.]
249 p., 1 l. illus. 18 cm.

NL 0341666   MtU

Lichtenberger, André, 1870–
...Les centaures.   Paris: Calmann-Lévy₁ 1904₎.   324 p.
12°.

272673A. 1. Fiction, French.   2. Title.
N. Y. P. L.   December 28, 1926

NL 0341667   NN

Lichtenberger, André, 1870–
Les centaures; roman fantastique.   Paris,
J. Ferenczi [c1921]
240 p. 19 cm.
On cover: Nouvelle édition.

NL 0341668   NIC CtY

Lichtenberger, André, 1870–
Les centaures, roman, avec vingt-deux compositions gravées sur bois et sur cuivre par
Victor Prouvé.   Paris, Éditions G. Crès, 1924.
218 p. illus., plates. 25cm.

No. 540 of 575 copies.

  I. Prouvé, Victor, 1858–   illus.
II. Title.

NL 0341669   NNC

Lichtenberger, André, 1870–
... Chez les Graffougnat.   Paris, Plon-Nourrit et cⁱᵉ
₁1923₎
2 p. l., 234 p., 1 l. 19ᵐ.

  I. Title.
Library of Congress   PQ2623.I 4C5 1923   23–10724

NL 0341670   DLC OC1 NN

Lichtenberger, André, 1870–
... Le cœur de Lolotte, roman.   Paris, J. Ferenczi et fils
₁1927₎
201 p., 1 l. 18¼ᵐ.

  I. Title.
Library of Congress   PQ2623.I 4C55 1927   27–7916

NL 0341671   DLC PPT

VOLUME 332

844L617
P3
    Lichtenberger, André, 1870–
       ... Le cœur de Lolotte, roman. Bois
    originaux en couleurs de Louise Le Vavasseur.
    Paris, Ferenczi et fils, 1931.
       3 p. l., ₍9₎-160 p. illus. (part col.) 21ᶜᵐ.
    (Le livre moderne illustré. ₍125₎)

       Illustrated t.-p.

    NL 0341672   NNC CtY

Lichtenberger, André.   **F842-L**
    Le cœur est le même.   Paris: Plon-Nourrit et Cie. ₍cop.
1919.₎ 258 p. 12°.

                          CENTRAL CIRCULATION.
1. Title.
N. Y. P. L.   November 10, 1920.

    NL 0341673   NN

    Lichtenberger, André, 1870–
       ...Le cœur est le même.   Paris: Plon-Nourrit et cie ₍c1919₎
258 p. 19cm.
On cover: Treizième édition.

1. Fiction, French. I. Title.
N. Y. P. L.   January 23, 1940

    NL 0341674   NN MH

    Lichtenberger, André, 1870–
       ... Un coin de la guerre; la France au Maroc, par An-
dré Lichtenberger, avec une carte. Paris ₍etc.₎ Berger-
Levrault, 1918.
       63, ₍1₎ p. illus. (double map) 19ᶜᵐ. (Collection "France")

       1. Morocco. 2. French in Morocco. I. Title. II. Title: La France
au Maroc.

       Library of Congress   DT324.L5   21–3433

    NL 0341675   DLC NN IU

    LICHTENBERGER, ANDRÉ, 1870–
       Coliche; roman inédit, par André Lichtenberger.
    (In Les Oeuvres libres. Paris [1929] 18½cm.
v. 100, p. [29]-126)

    NL 0341676   ICU OU

    Lichtenberger, André, 1870–
       ... Coliche, roman. Paris, J. Ferenczi et fils ₍1930₎
    3 p. l., 9–252 p., 1 l. 19ᵐ.

       I. Title.
       Library of Congress   Q2623.I 4C57 1930   30–34117
       Copyright A—Foreign   8729
                          ₍2₎   843.91

    NL 0341677   DLC MB NN

Lichtenberger, André, 1870–
**International congress for protective labour legislation,
Paris, 1900.**
       ... Congrès international pour la protection légale des
travailleurs, tenu à Paris du 25 au 29 juillet 1900.
Compte rendu sommaire par M. André Lichtenberger.
Paris. Imprimerie nationale, 1900.

    Lichtenberger, André, 1870–
       ... Les contes de Minnie: histoires de bêtes, d'enfants,
de fées et de bonnes gens. Paris, Plon-Nourrit et cⁱᵉ
₍1913₎
    2 p. l., 290 p., 1 l. 18½ᶜᵐ.   fr. 3.50

       I. Title.

       Library of Congress   PQ2623.I 4C6 1913   13–7605

    NL 0341679   DLC CtY OO

    Lichtenberger, André, 1870–
       Contes de Minnie; ed. by J. C. Anderson.
    Oxford, At the Clarendon press, 1927.
    96 p.

    (Junior French series)

    NL 0341680   OCl

    LICHTENBERGER, André, 1870–
       Contes héroïques, 1789-1795. Paris, Lib. Fisch-
bacher, 1897.

    18 cm.

    NL 0341681   MH PPL

HD8039
  Lichtenberger, André, 1870–
.D5L7
       ...La crise actuelle de la domesticité...
    Paris, Musée social, 1921.
       cover-title, p. [41]-68. 25ᵐᵐ. (La Musée social
    ... Mémoires et documents [t. 4] no. 2)

       "Conférence donnée au Musée social, le 22 décem
bre 1920".

       1. Servants.

    NL 0341682   ICU

871
  Lichtenberger, André, 1870–
C7.W1
    De Ciceronis re privata ...   Lutetiæ Parisiorum,
    typis mandabat L. Maretheux, 1895.
    90p.

       Thèse--Univ. de Paris.
       Bibliographical foot-notes.

       1. Cicero, Marcus Tullis.

    NL 0341683   IU NcD PBm OU

            Lichtenberger, André, 1870–1940, joint author.
DC126
.L44
  Lemoine, Jean, 1867–
    De La Vallière à Montespan ₍par₎ Jean Lemoine & André
    Lichtenberger. Paris, C. Lévy ₍1902₎

    Lichtenberger, André, 1870–
       ... Des enfants dans un jardin. Paris, Plon ₍1927₎
    2 p. l., 248 p., 1 l. 19ᵐ.

       I. Title.
       Library of Congress   PQ2623.I 4E6 1927   28–6695
                                           36292

    NL 0341685   DLC WaS

    Lichtenberger, André, 1870–
       ... Des enfants dans un jardin, nouvelle. Illustrations de
Carlos S. de Tejada. ₍Paris, Impr. de l'Illustration₎ °1927.
    32 p. illus., plates. 30½ᵐ. (On cover: La Petite illustration ... no.
338, 9 juillet 1927. Roman ₍nouv. sér.₎ no. 151)

       I. Title.

       Title from Newberry   Libr. Printed by L. C.   A 28–1072

    NL 0341686   ICN MiD NN PSt CtY PBm PPT ViU

    LICHTENBERGER, ANDRÉ, 1870–
       Des voix dans la nuit; roman inédit, par André
    Lichtenberger.
    (In Les Oeuvres libres. Paris [1928] 18½cm.
v. 81, p. [5]-104)

    NL 0341687   ICU IaU MH

    Lichtenberger, André, 1870–
       ... Des voix dans la nuit, roman. Paris, J. Ferenczi & fils
₍1929₎
    216 p., 1 l. 19ᵐ.

       I. Title.
       Library of Congress   PQ2623.I 4D4 1929   29–19564

    NL 0341688   DLC MB

    Lichtenberger, André, 1870–
       ... Des voix dans la nuit, roman. Illustrations
de Pierre Mouveau. Paris, J. Ferenczi et fils,
1936.
       5 p. l., [13]-156 p., 1 l. illus. 21 cm.
(Le Livre moderne illustré [252])

    NL 0341689   CtY

    Lichtenberger, André, 1870–
       Deux morts et le vivant; roman inédit, par André Lichten-
berger.
    (In Les Œuvres libres. Paris, 1936. 18ᶜᵐ. v. 181, p. ₍5₎-92)

       I. Title.   A C 37–438
       Northwestern univ. Librar
       for Library of Congress   [PQ1141.O4 vol. 181]
                                     (840.82)

    NL 0341690   IEN OU

    Lichtenberger, André, 1870–
       Le djinn; nouvelle inédite, par André Lichtenberger.
    (In Les Oeuvres libres. Paris ₍1933₎ 18ᶜᵐ. v. 147, p. ₍5₎-42)

       I. Title.
                                A C 34–350
       Title from Northwestern   Univ.
       Library of Congress   [PQ1141.O4 vol. 147]

    NL 0341691   ICN OU

VOLUME 332

Lichtenberger, André, 1870–1940.
La dompteuse des Tamanoir. Illus. de H. Morin. Paris,
Gautier-Languereau, 1939.
125 p. illus. 22 cm. (Bibliothèque de Suzette)

I. Title.

PZ23.L58D6 1939   76–252002

NL 0341692   DLC

Lichtenberger, André, 1870–
L'éléphant Houndji-Poundji, par André Lichtenberger;
illustrations de Henry Morin. Paris, Gautier-Languereau,
1928.
31, [1] p. col. illus. 31½ᶜᵐ.

1. Elephants—Legends and stories.   I. Morin, Henry, illus.
II. Title.
Library of Congress   PZ24.7.L43   29–3406

NL 0341693   DLC

Lichtenberger, André, 1870–
... L'enfant aux yeux de chat, roman. Paris, J. Ferenczi et
fils [*1932]
2 p. l., [9]–250 p., 1 l. 18½ᶜᵐ.

I. Title.
Library of Congress   PQ2623.I 4E6 1932   33–8918
Copyright A—Foreign   *9430
                                                        843.91

NL 0341694   DLC CtY

Lichtenberger, André, 1870–
... La folle aventure. Paris, Calmann-Lévy [1908]
2 p. l., 383 p. 19ᶜᵐ.

. Title.
Library of Congress   PQ2623.I 4F6 1908   8—19175

NL 0341695   DLC NcD

Lichtenberger, André, 1870–
... La folle aventure; couverture de H. Thiriet, illustrations de Robert-Kastor. Paris, P. Lafitte & cⁱᵉ [1913]
122 p., 1 l. incl. front., illus. 24ᶜᵐ. (On cover: "Idéal-bibliothèque."
no. 53) fr. 0.95

I. Title.
Library of Congress   PQ2623.I 4F6 1913   13–19898

NL 0341696   DLC PP

Lichtenberger, André, 1870–
...La folle aventure; roman...   Paris: G. Crès et Cⁱᵉ., 1924.
351 p.   12°.

"Édition définitive."
Printed in Germany.

230409A. 1. Fiction, French.   2. Title.
N. Y. P. L.   August 26, 1926

NL 0341697   NN WU

Lichtenberger, André, 1870–
... La gifle. Roman. Paris, 1920.
15.5 cm. ("Les Œuvres inédites," 6)

NL 0341698   CtY

Lichtenberger, André.
Gorri le forban.   Paris: Calmann-Lévy [19—?].   390 p.
12°.

1. Title.
N. Y. P. L.   June 12, 1924

NL 0341699   NN

Lichtenberger, André, 1870–
Gorri le forban, par André Lichtenberger. Paris, Nelson
[etc., 1925]
372 p. 16ᶜᵐ.
Printed in Great Britain.
"Première édition ... 1906."

I. Title.
                                                42–28000
Library of Congress   PQ2623.I 4G6

NL 0341700   DLC ICU

Lichtenberger, André, 1870–
Grandpa, "Les enfants dans un jardin", by André Lichtenberger; done into English by James C. Jones. [St. Louis] Pub.
priv., 1927.
3 p. l., 74 p. pl. 21½ᶜᵐ.

I. Jones, James Coulter, 1866–   tr. II. Title. III. Title: "Les enfants
dans un jardin."
                                                28–2695
Library of Congress   PQ2623.I 4G7 1927

NL 0341701   DLC

Lichtenberger, André, 1870–   joint author.
                                FOR OTHER EDITIONS
Lichtenberger, Henri, 1864–   SEE MAIN ENTRY
... La guerre européenne & la question d'Alsace-Lorraine,
par Henri et André Lichtenberger. Paris [etc.] Chapelot, 1915.

Lichtenberger, André, 1870–
Hlackova sestrica; poslovenil Niko Kuret.

Slovenian.
Translation of "La petite soeur de Trott".

NL 0341703   OCl

Lichtenberger, André, 1870–
Huit épisodes choisis extraits de
Mon petit Trott ... Edited by Georges
Roth. Édition autorisée. Oxford,
Clarendon press, 1923.
[3]–127p.

NL 0341704   PSt MH

Lichtenberger, André, 1870–
...Huit épisodes choisis: extraits de
Mon petit Trott; ed. by Georges Roth.
Oxford, Clarendon press, 1926.
127 p.

(Junior French series)

NL 0341705   OClh OCl

Lichtenberger, André, 1870–
Iselle; roman inédit et complet, par A. Lichtenberger.
(*In* Les Œuvres libres. Paris, 1939. 18ᶜᵐ. v. 218, p. [199]–287)

I. Title.   A C 40–1929
Northwestern univ. Libr.   [PQ1141.O4 vol. 218]
for Library of Congress
                                                (840.82)

NL 0341706   IEN ICU NRU IU NN NhD OU CSt

Lichtenberger, André, 1870–
...Janine au bois dormant; saynète en un acte. Niort: H.
Boulord [1937] 16 p. 19cm. (On cover: Collection Mon
théatre.)

1. Drama, French. I. Title.
N. Y. P. L.   January 5, 1939

NL 0341707   NN

Lichtenberger, André.
Juste Lobel, Alsacien.   Paris, Plon-
Nourrit et Cie, n.d.
295 p. 19 cm.

NL 0341708   OrPR

PQ2337 **Lichtenberger, André,** 1870–
.L6J8   ... Juste Lobel, alsacien. Paris, Plon-Nourrit et cⁱᵉ [1911]
1911   [5], 295 p. 18½ᶜᵐ.
(Ed)   At head of title: André Lichtenberger.

NL 0341709   ICU MH CSt PPL PBm CtY MiU NjP MtU NjP

Lichtenberger, André, 1870–
...Juste Lobel, Alsacien.   Paris: Plon-Nourrit et Cⁱᵉ. [1911]
3 p.l., 295 p. 16. ed. 12°.

NL 0341710   NN NjR OCU MWelC

Lichtenberger, André.   6698.r79
Juste Lobel, alsacien. [8e édition.]
= Paris. Plon-Nourrit & cie. [1912.] (4), 295 pp. 18½ cm., in 8s.
A novel based on international peace and the political relations of Alsace.

H8627 — T.r. — Peace. — Alsace. Pol. hist.

NL 0341711   MB

VOLUME 332

Lichtenberger, André, 1870–
... Kaligouça, le Cœur-fidèle. **Paris, Calmann-Lévy** ₁1913₎
2 p. l., 334 p. 18½ᶜᵐ.   fr. 3.50

ɪ. Title.

Library of Congress   PQ2623.I 4K2 1913

13–16924

NL 0341712   DLC PPL PP

Lichtenberger, André, 1870–
... Die kleine, von André Lichtenberger; autorisierte übersetzung aus dem französischen von Gertrud Bauer. **Stuttgart, J. Engelhorns nachf.,** 1911.
150 p. 18ᶜᵐ. (Engelhorns allgemeine roman-bibliothek ... 27. jahrg., bd. 11)

ɪ. Bauer, Gertrud, tr. ɪɪ. Title.

Library of Congress   PQ2623.I 4P44

44–14571

NL 0341713   DLC

Lichtenberger, André, 1870–
... Die kleine majestät, roman; einzige berechtigte übersetzung aus dem französischen von A. Ratisbonne. **München, A. Langen** ₁1911₎
268 p. 19ᶜᵐ.   M. 3.50

ɪ. Ratisbonne, A., tr. ɪɪ. Title.

Library of Congress

12–829

NL 0341714   DLC

895.482
L617.

Lichtenberger, André, 1870–
Küçük Trott. Çeviren Esat Onatkut. Istanbul, Millî Eğitim Basımevi, 1949.
109 p. illus.

Translation of Mon petit Trott.

I. Onatkut, Esat,   tr.

NL 0341715   NNC DLC-P4

Lichtenberger, André, 1870–
... Léïla si blanche, roman inédit. **Paris, A. Fayard & cⁱᵉ** ₁1928₎
2 p. l., ₁7₎–258, ₁1₎ p. 19ᶜᵐ. ("Jeunes femmes et jeunes filles")

ɪ. Title.

Library of Congress   PQ2623.I 4L4 1928

29–9616

NL 0341716   DLC WU

PQ1262
.A15
n. s.,
no. 176–
177

Lichtenberger, André, 1870–
... Léïla si blanche, roman. Illustrations de Jean Droi
Paris ₁Impr. de l'Illustration₎ 1928.
59 p. col. plates. 30½ cm. (On cover: La Petite illustration ... no. 394–395, 11–18 août 1928. Roman ₁nouv. sér.₎ no. 176–177)

ɪ. Title.
.ewberry library
for Library of Congress   [PQ1262.A15 no. 176–177]

A 29–890

PBm NcD PSt MB WaS WaTC
NL 0341717   ICN DLC MH CtY ViU MiU OCl OCU ODW OU

Lichtenberger, André, 1870–
... Leurs 400 coups (de tennis) Illustrations de Simone Abadie-Girardet. **Paris, Éditeurs associés, Éditions du Monde moderne** ₁1925₎
3 p. l., ₁9₎–126, ₁2₎ p. ports. 19ᶜᵐ.
At head of title: Lichtenberger (André)—Micard (Étienne)

1. Tennis.   ɪ. Micard, Étienne Jean Phillipe Nicolas, 1889–   joint author. ɪɪ. Abadie-Girardet, Mme. Simone, illus. ɪɪɪ. Title.

Library of Congress   GV995.L48

26–4169

NL 0341718   DLC

Lichtenberger, André, 1870–
... Line. **Paris, Plon-Nourrit et cⁱᵉ** ₁1905₎
2 p. l., 316 p. 18ᶜᵐ.

ɪ. Title.

14–2269

Library of Congress   PQ2623.I 4L5 1905

NL 0341719   DLC NjP WU NIC PSC PU OCl OOxM NN

Lichtenberger, André, *1870–*]
Line. [Roman. 33e édition.]
= Paris. Plon. [1921.] (4), 316 pp. 19 cm.

6698.181

N6664 — T.r.

NL 0341720   MB CtY

LICHTENBERGER, André, ₁870–1940.
The little king; a novel. Tr.by
M.Marrimpouey.
n.d.

NL 0341721   WaS

Lichtenberger, André, 1870–
Lolotte et son vieux roi; roman inédit, par André Lichtenberger.
(In Les Oeuvres libres. Paris [1926] 18½cm. v. 59, p. [105]–202)

NL 0341722   NRU OU

Lichtenberger, André, 1870–
...La main à la pâte; saynète en 1 acte.   Niort: H. Boulord₁, 1926₎.   18 p. 12°.

1. Drama, French. 2. Title.
N. Y. P. L.

December 22, 1927

NL 0341723   NN

Lichtenberger, André, 1870–
... La main de sang, roman; bois originaux de Paul Hannaux ... **Paris, J. Ferenczi et fils,** 1939.
3 p. l., 9–158, ₁2₎ p. incl. illus., plates. 20½ᶜᵐ. (Le livre moderne illustré. ₁315₎)

ɪ. Hannaux, Paul, illus. ɪɪ. Title.

Library of Congress   PQ2623.I 4M3 1939
Copyright A—Foreign   43986

39–24252

843.91

NL 0341724   DLC CtY

Lichtenberger, André, 1870–
... Mano mažasis Trottas; Prancūzų akademijos vainikuotas romanas, iš 196-ojo prancūziškojo leidimo išvertė Vikt. Kamantauskas. Kaunas-Marijampolė, "Dirvos" b-vės leidinys, 1930.
141, ₁1₎ p. 20½ᶜᵐ.

ɪ. Kamantauskas, Viktoras, tr. ɪɪ. Title.

42–26859

Library of Congress   PQ2623.I 4M63

843.91

NL 0341725   DLC WU OCl

Lichtenberger, André, 1870–
Marraine chez Nane, par André Lichtenberger. Illustrations de Henry Morin. Paris, Gautier-Languereau, 1932.
31, ₁1₎ p. col. illus. 32ᶜᵐ.
Illustrated lining-papers.

1. Wit and humor, Pictorial. ɪ. Morin, Henry, illus. ɪɪ. Title.

Library of Congress   PZ24.7.L445
Copyright A—Foreign   21778

33–33111

[847] 741

NL 0341726   DLC

Lichtenberger, André, ₁870–1940₎.
Masza minia; powieść; przekład z francuskiego Wacławy Kiślańskiej. Warszawa. n.d.
₁212 p.₎

NL 0341727   OCl

PQ
1262
I29+
1907
no.3

Lichtenberger, André, 1870–
Minnie. Illustrations de Simont.
₁Paris₎ 1907.
79 p. illus. 30 cm. (Supplément à l'Illustration du 1 juin 1907 ₁romans₎ 3)

NL 0341728   NIC MB MiU OClU NN PBL PP

Lichtenberger, André, 1870–
Moj mali Hlacek; s pisateljevim in zaloznikovin dovoljenjem prevel Jozef Ovca.
Mon petit Trott.

NL 0341729   OCl

Lichtenberger, André, 1870–
Mon petit Trott. Vienne, Larousse, n.d.
208p. (Collection Plon)

NL 0341730   ScU OrPR

Lichtenberger, André.
Mon petit Trott.
— Paris. Plon, Nourrit et cie. [1898.] (3), 252, (1) pp. 16°.

6698.98

E5613 — T.r.

NL 0341731   MB PP PU

VOLUME 332

Lichtenberger, André.
Mon petit Trott. Paris: Plon-Nourrit et Cie. ₁190–?₎ 2 p.l.,
252(2) p. 12°.

ɪ. Title.
N.Y.P.L.   CENTRAL CIRCULATION.
                                        July 14, 1911.

NL 0341732   NN NjP

Lichtenberger, André
  Mon petit Trott. ₍ed. 39₎
Paris, n.d.

NL 0341733   ODW

Lichtenberger, André, 1870-1940.
  ... Mon petit Trott ... ₍61. éd.₎ Paris, Plon-Nourrit et
c^{ie} ₍1913?₎
2 p.l., 252 p., 2 l. 18½ cm.
"Couronné par l'Académie française (prix Montyon)"

ɪ. Title.

PQ2623.I4M6 1913   14—910

NL 0341734   DLC PHC NcD PCC PSC OO NjP CtY WaS Or
     WaTC WaSp CaBVaU MtU

Lichtenberger, André , 1870- Mon petit Trott.

Cardon, Léopold Napoléon, 1872-
  Mon petit Trott; a modern French reader, by Léopold Cardon ... Boston, New York ₍etc.₎ Silver, Burdett and company
₍*1918₎

Lichtenberger, André, 1870-
  ...Mon petit Trott... ₍80. ed.₎ Paris,
Plon-Nourrit et cie. ₍1931?₎
2 p. l., 252 p., 2 l.

NL 0341736   OCU

Lichtenberger, André, 1870-1940.
  ... Mon petit Trott ... [131. éd.]   Paris,
Plon-Nourrit et cie [1921]
2 p.l., 252 p., 2 l. 18.5 cm.
"Couronné par l'Académie française (prix
Montyon)"

NL 0341737   OU

Lichtenberger, André
—Mon petit Trott.—Roman. *Paris, 1928.* 248 p.

NL 0341738   RWoU

Lichtenberger, André, 1870-
  ... Mon petit Trott ... Paris, Plon
et Nourrit ₍1933₎
2 p.l., 245 p., 1 l. 18½ cm.

NL 0341739   PSt

Lichtenberger, André, 1870-
Bachelet, Victor, 1865-
  Mon petit Trott; comédie en 5 actes et 11 tableaux, tirée des
romans d'André Lichtenberger, Mon petit Trott, La petite
sœur de Trott, par Victor Bachelet Paris, Plon ₍1933₎

Lichtenberger, André, 1870-
  ... Monsieur de Migurac; ou, Le marquis philosophe
Éd. définitive. Paris, G. Crès et c^{ie}, 1922.
304 p. 18¼^{cm}.   fr. 6

ɪ. Title.
Library of Congress   PQ2623.I4M65 1922   22-15688

NL 0341741   DLC NN CtY NIC

Lichtenberger, André, 1870-
  ... Montcalm et la tragedie canadienne ... Paris, Plon
₍1934₎
2 p. l., viii, 244 p. front. (port.) fold. map. 19^{cm}.

1. Montcalm-Gozon, Louis Joseph de, marquis de Saint-Véran, 1712-
1759. 2. Canada—Hist.—1755-1763. 3. U. S.—Hist.—French and Indian
war, 1755-1763.
Library of Congress   E199.M367   34-33659
Copyright A—Foreign   25486
                                               973.26

NL 0341742   DLC NcU MiU CaBVaU OCl OU NN

848   Lichtenberger, André, 1870-
L618m   La mort de Corinthe.   Paris, Plon-
      Nourrit ₍1899₎
      304 p. 19 cm.

      1. Corinth, Greece--Hist.--Fiction.
   I. Title.

NL 0341743   LU

Lichtenberger, André, 1870-
  ... La mort de Corinthe ... Paris, Plon-Nourrit et c^{ie}
₍19— ₎
2 p. l., 304, ₍1₎ p., 1 l. 19^{cm}.
On cover: 6. éd.
First edition, 1900.
"Couronné par l'Académie française, Prix Montyon."

1. Corinth, Greece—Hist.—Fiction.   ɪ. Title.
                                               14-3193
Library of Congress   PQ2623.I4M7 19—

NL 0341744   DLC MtU NjP PP

Lichtenberger, André.
  La mort de Corinthe.   Paris: Plon-Nourrit et Cie. ₍cop. 1900₎
2 p.l., 304(2) p. 12°.

ɪ. Title.   CENTRAL CIRCULATION.
N.Y.P.L.   July 14, 1911.

NL 0341745   NN NIC

Lichtenberger, André, 1870-
  ... La mort de Corinthe ...   Paris,
Plon-Nourrit et cie [1920?]
2 p.l., 304, [1] p., 1 l. 19 cm.
On cover: 9. éd.
First edition, 1900.
"Couronné par l'Académie française, Prix
Montyon."

NL 0341746   CtY

Lichtenberger, André, 1870-
  Nane au Maroc, par André Lichtenberger; illustrations de
Henry Morin. Paris, Gautier-Languereau, 1927.
31, ₍1₎ p. col. illus. 31¼^{cm}.

ɪ. Morin, Henry, illus. ɪɪ. Title.
Library of Congress   28-19683

NL 0341747   DLC

Lichtenberger, André, 1870-
  Nane chez les saltimbanques, par André Lichtenberger;
illustrations de Henry Morin. Paris, Gautier-Languereau,
1930.
31, ₍1₎ p. col. illus. 32^{cm}.

ɪ. Morin, Henry, illus. ɪɪ. Title.
Library of Congress   PZ24.7.L455   31-6001
Copyright A—Foreign   9834
                                               843.91

NL 0341748   DLC

Lichtenberger, André, 1870-
  Nane et la vie de château, par André Lichtenberger. illustrations de Henry Morin. Paris, Gautier-Languereau, 1931.
31, ₍1₎ p. col. illus. 31¼^{cm}.
Illustrated t.-p. in colors.

ɪ. Title.
Library of Congress   PZ24.7.L457   32-8464
Copyright A—Foreign   15653
                                               843.91

NL 0341749   DLC

Lichtenberger, André, 1870-
  Nane et sa fille, par André Lichtenberger; illustrations de
Henry Morin. Paris, Gautier-Languereau, 1933.
31, ₍1₎ p. col. illus. 32^{cm}.

ɪ. Morin, Henry, illus. ɪɪ. Title.
Library of Congress   PZ24.7.L462   34-3083
Copyright A—Foreign   22694
                                               843.91

NL 0341750   DLC

Lichtenberger, André, 1870-
  ... Nane et ses bêtes, par André Lichtenberger; illustrations de Henry Morin. Paris, Gautier et Languereau,
1925.
31, ₍1₎ p. col. illus. 31¼^{cm}.
Illustrated lining-papers.
At head of title: Édition de la "Semaine de Suzette".

ɪ. Title.
Library of Congress   PZ24.7.L46   26-19913

NL 0341751   DLC

Lichtenberger, André, 1870-
  Nane policière, par André Lichtenberger, illustrations de
Henry Morin. Paris, Gautier-Languereau, 1929.
31, ₍1₎ p. col. illus. 31¼^{cm}.

ɪ. Title.
Library of Congress   PZ24.7.L464   30-11482

NL 0341752   DLC

VOLUME 332

LICHTENBERGER, André, 1870–
Le naufrage de "la Méduse"; variété inédite.

19 cm.
(In Les OEUVRES libres. Paris, juin 1931,
no.120, pp. [317]-350.)

NL 0341753   MH

Lichtenberger, André.
Notre Minnie.   Paris: Plon-Nourrit et Cie. [1907.]   292 p.
12°.

1. Title.
N. Y. P. L.   September 24, 1924

NL 0341754   NN NcGU NcD NjP

Lichtenberger, André, 1870–
Notre Minnie.   Paris, [1921]
18.5 cm.
On cover: 28. éd.

NL 0341755   CtY

LICHTENBERGER, André, 1870–
Notre Minnie. Paris, Plon-Nourrit et Cie,
[1922].

18 cm.
Cover: 30° éd.

NL 0341756   MH

Lichtenberger, André, 1870–
L'œuvre de la France au Maroc; conférence faite le 26 novembre 1924, par m. André Lichtenberger ... [Paris? 1924?]
18 p. 25°ᵐ.
Caption title.

1. Morocco. 2. French in Morocco.   I. Title.

                                 30–31777
Library of Congress   DT324.L53 1924   916.4

NL 0341757   DLC

Lichtenberger, André, 1870–
... L'œuvre de la France au Maroc, par André Lichtenberger ... Strasbourg, "La Vie sociale en France et dans ses colonies", 1925.
cover-title, 12 p. illus. 27½°ᵐ. (Collection d'études économiques, médicales et sociales; petite encyclopédie de la vie sociale, pub. sous la direction de A. Herrmann ... 35. cahier)

1. Morocco. 2. French in Morocco.   I. Title.

                                 30–31776
Library of Congress   DT324.L53 1925   916.4

NL 0341758   DLC

Lichtenberger, André, 1870–
L'œuvre sociale de la révolution française. Introduction par m. Émile Faguet ... Paris, A. Fontemoing [1901]

Lichtenberger, André.
Ofiara. Przekład z francuskiego M. H.
Warszawa. 1903. 176 pp. 16°.
Issued as a supplement to Tygodnik ilustrowany for 1903.

                              3066.234

F8756 — T.r. — Tygodnik ilustrowany. — H., M., tr. — Poland. Lang. Works in Polish.

NL 0341760   MB

Lichtenberger, André, 1870–
L'oncle d'Afrique, par A. Lichtenberger; illustrations de H. Morin. Paris, Gautier-Languereau, 1938.
125 p., 1 l. incl. illus., plates. 22°ᵐ. (On cover: Bibliothèque de Suzette)

I. Morin, Henry, illus.   II. Title.
                             40–23704
Library of Congress   PZ21.B45L48
Copyright A—Foreign   42859
                     (843.082)   843.91

NL 0341761   DLC

Lichtenberger, André, 1870–
... Pancho, sang de requin. Paris, Plon [1936]
2 p. l., 248 p., 1 l. 19°ᵐ.

I. Title.
                             36–20688
Library of Congress   PQ2623.I4P25 1936
Copyright A—Foreign   32307
                         843.91

NL 0341762   DLC NN

Lichtenberger, André, 1870–
... Un pauvre homme. Paris, J. Ferenczi & fils [*1928]
3 p. l., [5]–227 p., 1 l. 19°ᵐ.

I. Title.
                             28–20593
Library of Congress   PQ2623.I4P3 1928
Copyright A—Foreign   38856

NL 0341763   DLC WaS WaTC NN

Lichtenberger, André.
Père. Paris: Plon-Nourrit et Cie., 1901.   2 p.l., 293(1) p.
12°.

1. Title.   CENTRAL CIRCULATION.
N. Y. P. L.   May 7, 1915.

NL 0341764   NN

Lichtenberger, André.
Père. Paris: J. Ferenczi, 1921.   251 p.   12°.

NL 0341765   NN

Lichtenberger, André, 1870–
... Père. Nouvelle édition. Paris: J. Ferenczi, 1921.   250 p.
19cm.

1. Fiction, French. I. Title.
N. Y. P. L.   January 23, 1940

NL 0341766   NN

Lichtenberger, André, 1870–
Père, roman. D'après les bois gravés par Louis Marc. Paris, J. Ferenczi, 1926.
157p. illus. 21cm. (Le Livre moderne illustré, 35)

              845L61
              Ope

NL 0341767   IU OOxM CtY OClW

PQ2623
.I4P4   Lichtenberger, André, 1870–
1928   ... Père, roman; d'après les bois gravés de Louis Marc. Paris, J. Ferenczi et fils, 1928.
157 p., 1 l. illus. 21½cm. (Le livre moderne illustré)

NL 0341768   OCU OCl OU

Lichtenberger, André, 1870–1940.
... Père, roman d'apres les bois graves de Louis Marc. Paris, J. Ferenczi et fils, 1938.
157 p.

NL 0341769   PPT

Lichtenberger, André, 1870–
... Le petit chaperon vert, suivi d'autres contes. Dessins de Joseph Hémard. Paris: G. Crès et cⁱᵉ, 1922.   81 p.   col'd illus. 22½cm.

845383A. 1. Juvenile literature—   Fiction, French. I. Title.
N. Y. P. L.   May 24, 1937

NL 0341770   NN

Lichtenberger, André.
Le petit roi. Paris: Plon-Nourrit et Cie. [19—?]   2 p.l., 306(1) p.   12°.

NL 0341771   NN

Lichtenberger, André, 1870–
... Le petit roi. Paris, Plon-Nourrit et cⁱᵉ [1910]
2 p. l., 306 p., 1 l. 19°ᵐ.   fr. 3.50

                             10–16135
Library of Congress

NL 0341772   DLC NN NjP OCU MtU WaSp OrPR PP PSC

Lichtenberger, André, 1870–
... Le petit roi. Paris, Plon-Nourrit et cⁱᵉ [1920]
178 p. 18¼°ᵐ. (Half-title: Bibliothèque Plon [18])

I. Title.
                             20–13783
Library of Congress   PQ2623.I4P4 1920

NL 0341773   DLC WaTC WU

Lichtenberger, André, 1870–
... Le petit roi. Paris, Plon-Nourrit et cie, [1927]
2 p.l., 306 p., 1 l. 19 cm.
"39. éd."

NL 0341774   ViU

VOLUME 332

Lichtenberger, André, 1870–
　　Le petit roi; *comédie dramatique*
　　　see under Dubois, Marcel, dramatist.

Lichtenberger, André, 1870–
　　... La petite. Paris, Librairie des Annales ₁1909₎
　　2 p. L, 322 p., 1 l. 19ᶜᵐ.

　　I. Title.

　　Library of Congress　　PQ2623.I 4P43 1909　9—19839

NL　0341776　DLC OC1

Lichtenberger, André.
　　La petite. Paris: Plon-Nourrit et Cie. ₁cop. 1921.₎ 281 p.
　　12°.

　　1. Title.
　　N. Y. P. L.　　　　　　　　　　　　May 12, 1924.

NL　0341777　NN OU

845L61　Lichtenberger, André, 1870–
Op　　　La petite. Paris, Plon-Nourrit ₁cover
　　1924.₎
　　　281p. 19cm.

NL　0341778　IU

Lichtenberger, André, 1870–
　　... Petite madame. Paris, Plon-Nourrit et cⁱᵉ ₁1912₎
　　3 p. L, 308 p. 19ᶜᵐ.

　　I. Title.　　　　　　　　　　　　12—7750
　　Library of Congress　　PQ2623.I 4P45 1912
　　Copyright A—Foreign　　　4833

　　　　　　　　　　OC1 MiU NN
NL　0341779　DLC OrP OCU WaS CoFS CtY MB NcU PP PPL

Lichtenberger, André, 1870–
　　... Petite madame. Paris, Plon-Nourrit et cⁱᵉ ₁1919₎
　　190 p., 1 l. 19ᶜᵐ. (*On cover:* Bibliothèque Plon. ₍2₎)

　　I. Title.

　　Library of Congress　　PQ2623.I 4P45 1919　20-8782

NL　0341780　DLC

PQ2623
.I4P47　Lichtenberger, André, 1870–1940.
1898　　La petite sœur de Trott. Paris, Plon-
　　　Nourrit ₁1898₎
　　　300 p. 19cm.

NL　0341781　ViU MB

Lichtenberger, André.
　　La petite sœur de Trott. Paris: Plon-Nourrit et Cie. ₁190–?₎
　　2 p.l., 300(2) p. 12°.

　　1. Title.　　　　　　　CENTRAL CIRCULATION.
　　N. Y. P. L.　　　　　　　　　　July 14, 1911.

NL　0341782　NN NjP MH

Lichtenberger, André, 1870–
　　... La petite sœur de Trott. Paris, Plon-Nourrit et cⁱᵉ
　　₁1912₎
　　2 p. l., 300 p., 2 l. 19ᶜᵐ.
　　On cover: 36. édition.

　　I. Title.　　　　　　　　　　　12—27443
　　Library of Congress　　PQ2623.I 4P47 1912

NL　0341783　DLC PHC CtY PPT NcD WaSp OrPR WaS MtU

PQ
2623　Lichtenberger, André, 1870–
I4P48　　La petite sœur de Trott. Paris, Plon-
1899　Nourrit ₁c1899₎
　　　301 p. 18cm.

　　On cover: 77ᵉ édition.
　　Couronné par l'Académie Française, prix
　　Montyon.

NL　0341784　NIC

LICHTENBERGER, André, 1870–
　　La petite sœur de Trott. Paris, Librairie
Plon, [1920].

　　19 cm.

NL　0341785　MH

Lichtenberger, André.
　—La Petite sœur de Trott.—Roman. *Paris, 1928.* 304 p.

NL　0341786　RWoU

PQ2337　LICHTENBERGER, André, 1870–
.L6P5　　La petite sœur de Trott, par André Lichtenberger.
1932　Paris ₍etc.₎ Nelson, 1932.
　　　184 p. 16cm. [Collection Nelson]
　　　"Printed in Great Britain."

NL　0341787　ICU

Lichtenberger, André, 1870–1940.
　　La petite sœur de Trott. Paris,
　Nelson, 1934. 184 p. 16cm. (Collection
Nelson)

NL　0341788　NN PP

Lichtenberger, André, 1870–
　　La petite sœur de Trott ... Paris,
　Londres ₍etc.₎ Nelson, 1936.
　　v, 7–184 p. 16 cm.

NL　0341789　OO OC1 PSt

348
L618p　Lichtenberger, André, 1870–
　　　La petite sœur de Trott. Paris, Nelson,
1948.
　　　184 p. 16 cm.

NL　0341790　LU

PQ2623
I 4P5　Lichtenberger, André, 1870–
1923　　Pickles; ou, Récits à la mode anglaise.
　　₁8. éd.₎ Paris, G. Crès, 1923 ₁1922₎
　　　171 p. 19cm.

NL　0341791　CoU MtU

Lichtenberger, André.
　　Portraits d'aïeules. Paris: Plon-Nourrit et Cie. ₁19—?₎
　　312 p. 12°.
　　Lettres. Silhouettes. Dialogues. Nouvelles.

NL　0341792　NN CtY NNU-W

Lichtenberger, André.
　　Portraits de jeunes filles; lettres, dialogues, nouvelles. Paris:
　　Plon-Nourrit et Cie. ₁1900.₎ 320 p. 12°.

NL　0341793　NN NIC MB MWelC

Lichtenberger, André, 1870–
　　... Poupette, fille d'Allah; roman. Paris: Librairie Baudi-
　　nière ₁1924₎ 269 p. 18½cm.

　　1. Fiction, French. I. Title.
　　N. Y. P. L.　　　　　　　　　　　January 23, 1940

NL　0341794　NN

Lichtenberger, André, 1870–
　　... Puip, le petit faune. Illustré par P.-V. Robiquet ...
　　₁Paris, Renaissance universelle₎ °1924.
　　　₁16₎ p. illus. (1 col., double) 27 x 22ᶜᵐ. ₁Collection du Livre d'art de
　　l'enfance et de la jeunesse₎
　　At head of title: A. Lichtenberger.
　　Covers included in paging.

　　I. Title.
　　Library of Congress　　PZ24.7.L47　　26-6998

NL　0341795　DLC

Lichtenberger, André, 1870–
　　... Raramémé; histoire d'ailleurs. Paris, J. Ferenczi
　　₁1921₎
　　　252 p., 2 l. 19ᶜᵐ.　fr. 6.75

　　I. Title.
　　Library of Congress　　PQ2623.I 4R3 1921　21-16100

NL　0341796　NN MH NIC DLC

Lichtenberger, André, 1870–
PQ2623
I4　　... Rédemption. Paris, Plon ₁1902₎
R4　　2 p. l., 289 p., 1 l. 19m.

NL　0341797　RPB

VOLUME 332

Lichtenberger, André.
Rédemption. Paris: J. Ferenczi et fils, 1923.   256 p.
12°.

NL 0341798   NN

Lichtenberger, André, 1870–
...Rédemption; roman. Nouvelle édition.   Paris: J. Ferenczi et fils, 1923.   256 p.   19cm.

I. Fiction, French. I. Title.
N. Y. P. L.   January 23, 1940

NL 0341799   NN MtU

PQ
2623
L71r
Lichtenberger, André, 1870–
Rédemption, roman. 44 bois originaux de Gérard Cochet. Paris, J. Ferenczi, 1924.
157p. illus. 21cm. (Le Livre moderne illustré, 9)

NL 0341800   NRU CtY OOxM

PQ2623
.I4R4 Lichtenberger, André, 1870–
1928
...Rédemption, roman; d'après les bois originaux de Gérard Cochet. Paris, J. Ferenczi et fils, 1928.
157 p., 1 l. illus. 21½cm. (Le livre moderne illustré)

NL 0341801   OCU

Lichtenberger, Andre, 1870–
... Rédemption; roman ...   Paris, J. Ferenczi et fils, 1932.
157 p.

NL 0341802   PPT

Lichtenberger, André, 1870–
... Le règne de Nane, par André Lichtenberger; illustrations de Henry Morin. Paris, Gautier et Languereau, 1926.
31, [1] p. col. illus. 31½cm.
Illustrated lining-papers.
At head of title: Édition de la "Semaine de Suzette".

I. Title.
Library of Congress   PZ24.7.L48   27–18929

NL 0341803   DLC

Lichtenberger, André, 1870–
... Roses de France (récits de la révolution) Éd. définitive. Paris, G. Crès et cⁱᵉ, 1924.
4 p. l., [3]–296 p., 1 l. 19ᶜᵐ.
On cover: 6ᵉ édition.
Previously published under title: Tous héros.

1. France—Hist.—Revolution—Fiction. I. Title.

Library of Congress   PQ2623.I4R6 1924   25–26829

NL 0341804   DLC NN WaS OCl MiU

Lichtenberger, André, 1870–
Sang basque; grande nouvelle inédite, par André Lichtenberger.
(In Les Oeuvres libres. Paris [1925] 18½cm.
v. 53, p. [285]–350)

NL 0341805   NRU OU OOxM

Lichtenberger, André, 1870–
...Sang basque. Paris: La Nouvelle revue critique[, 1926].
158 p. nar. 12°.   (Les maîtres du roman. [no.] 16.)

1. Fiction, French. 2. Title.
N. Y. P. L.   April 13, 1927

NL 0341806   NN

Lichtenberger, André, 1870–
... Le sang nouveau. Paris, Plon-Nourrit et cⁱᵉ [*1914]
3 p. l., 322 p., 1 l. 19ᶜᵐ.

I. Title.
     14—3782
Library of Congress   PQ2623.I4S3 1914

OClW MiU CtY
NL 0341807   DLC IEdS NIC NN PP PPL PSC PU OCl

Lichtenberger, André, 1870–
... Scènes en famille. Faites comme je dis - Maldonne - Le visiteur. Paris, [c1921]
18.5 cm.
On cover: 5. éd.

NL 0341808   CtY

Lichtenberger, André, 1870–
...Scènes en famille... Paris: Plon [1925]   126 p.   19cm.
On cover: 6e édition.
CONTENTS.—Faites comme je dis.—Maldonne.—Le visiteur.

1. Drama, French. I. Title.   II. Title: Faites comme je dis.
III. Title: Maldonne. IV. Title: Le visiteur.
N. Y. P. L.   October 13, 1939

NL 0341809   NN OCl

Lichtenberger, André.
Le socialisme au XVIIIe siècle; étude sur les idées socialistes dans les écrivains français du XVIIIe siècle avant la Révolution. Paris: F. Alcan, 1895.   3 p. l., viii, 471 p., 1 l.   4°.
Dissertation, Paris. Bibliography, p. vii–viii.

1. Socialism.—History, 18th century.   April 1, 1911.

NIC CaBVaU
CtY CSmH NcU NcD N OO NjP MB MH IU ICJ CU TxFTC OrU
NL 0341810   NN KU PBm OU MH–BA InU MWelC CoU MiU ICN

Lichtenberger, André.
Le socialisme et la révolution française. Étude sur les idées socialistes en France de 1789 à 1796 ... Paris, F. Alcan, 1899.
2 p. l., 316 p. 8°.   (Bibliothèque d'histoire contemporaine)

Library of Congress   1–F–802

OCl MiU OClW NcD ICJ
NL 0341811   DLC MeB IU WaU NIC MU IaU MB PPL–R PU

Lichtenberger, André.   9301.44
Le socialisme et la Révolution française.
(In L'œuvre sociale de la Révolution française. Pp. 63–106.
Paris. [1902.])
This is not the same as the author's earlier, longer work, with the same title, on shelf-number 9335.8.

E928⅝ — Socialism.   June 15,   1903

NL 0341812   MB

Lichtenberger, André.   335.1 P800
Le socialisme utopique. Études sur quelques précurseurs inconnus du socialisme, par André Lichtenberger .... Paris, F. Alcan, 1898.
[4], 276, [2] p. 19ᶜᵐ.   (On cover: Bibliothèque d'histoire contemporaine.)
Contents. — Introduction. — 1. Mistress Afra Behn, la première "authoress" et son roman "Oroonoko". — 2. Nicolas Gueudeville, un précurseur de Jean-Jacques Rousseau. — 3. Tiphaigne de la Roche, le roman utopique au XVIIIᵉ siècle. — 4. Beaurieu, les disciples de la nature. — 5. Linguet socialiste. — 6. Charles-Robert Gosselin, un précurseur du socialisme agraire. — 7. Jean-Claude Chappuis, un précurseur inconnu du socialisme et de Malthus. — 8. John Oswald, écossais, jacobin et socialiste. — 9. Un projet communiste en 1795. — 10. Un socialiste inattendu: Le général Caffarelli du Falga.

MB   CU IaU MiDW NNU KU
NL 0341813   ICJ NjP OrCS MnU MH ICN RPB PBm MiU NIC

Lichtenberger, André, 1870–1940.
Tous heros. Paris, Librarie des annales, [1918?]
3 p. l., [3]–296 p., 2 l. 19 cm.

NL 0341814   CaBVaU

Lichtenberger, André, 1870–1940.
Trott, by André Lichtenberger; tr. from the French by Blanche & Irma Weill. With an introduction by Dorothy Canfield Fisher. New York, Island workshop press co-op, 1941.   x, 245 p. 21cm.

342080B. 1. No subject. I. Weill,   Blanche California, 1883–   , tr.
II. Weill, Irma S., tr. III. Fisher,   Dorothea Frances (Canfield), 1879–
N. Y. P. L.   IV. Title.   July 3, 1946

NL 0341815   NN PSt MH OCl ViU

Lichtenberger, André, 1870–
Trott and his little sister, by André Lichtenberger, with an introduction by Dorothy Canfield Fisher; translated from the French by Blanche & Irma Weill. New York, The Viking press, 1931.
x, 245 p. 21½ᶜᵐ.

I. Fisher, Mrs. Dorothea Frances (Canfield) 1879–   II. Weill, Blanche California, 1883–   tr. III. Weill, Irma S., joint tr. IV. Title.
Translation of Mon petit Trott and La petite sœur de Trott.

Library of Congress   PZ7.L5913Tr   31–10761
—— Copy 2.
Copyright A 36632   843.91

PPL OO OU OClh OLak
NL 0341816   DLC NN CaBVaU WaT WaS PBm PPTU PSC PP

Lichtenberger, Andre.
Trottolino mio; tr. de Mario Galo' ... Firenze, Bemporad, 1920.
96 p.

NL 0341817   PP

Lichtenberger, André, 1870–
... Les vacances de Nane, par André Lichtenberger; illustrations de Henry Morin. Paris, Gautier & Languereau [*1924]
2 p. l., 31, [1] p. col. illus. 31½ᶜᵐ.
At head of title: Édition de la "Semaine de Suzette".

I. Morin, Henry, illus. II. Title.
Library of Congress   PZ24.7.L5   25–7582

NL 0341818   DLC NN

VOLUME 332

Lichtenberger, André, 1870– 1940
... Vent du sud ... Paris, A. Fayard & cⁱᵉ ₍ᶜ1932₎
3 p. l., ₍9₎–250 p., 2 l. 18½ᶜᵐ. ("Jeunes femmes et jeunes filles." ₍49₎)
CONTENTS.—Vent du sud.—Idylle d'automne.

I. Title. II. Title: Idylle d'automne.
Library of Congress   PQ2623.I 4V4 1932   33–6237

NL   0341819   DLC

686   LICHTENBERGER, Arthur C   ed.
Eng   The way of renewal; a selection of read-
Box 2   ings for each day in Lent, chosen by
Arthur C. Lichtenberger. [N.p., Church
Congress in the U.S. 1948]
50p. 23.5cm. (Lenten booklet, 1948)

NL   0341820   MH-AH

Lichtenberger (Augustus Ferdinandus). *De
pneumonorrhagia. 32 pp. 4°. *Jenæ, typ. Schrei-
beri et soc.*, [1825]

NL   0341821   DNLM

Lichtenberger, Berthold, 1887–
Lehrbuch der milchwirtschaftlichen maschinenkunde ... von
prof. dr. B. Lichtenberger ... Hildesheim, Molkerei-zeitung,
1932.
369 p. illus., fold. plates (1 col.) fold. tab., diagrs. 21½ᶜᵐ.
"Nachweis der einschlägigen literatur": p. 365–366.

1. Dairying. 2. Agricultural machinery. ₍1, 2. Dairy — Implements
and machinery₎

Library, U. S. Dept. of   Agriculture 44L61L   Agr 33–70

NL   0341822   DNAL CtY

Lichtenberger, Berthold, 1887–
Die milchindustrie der Vereinigten Staaten von Amerika,
unter besonderer berücksichtigung ihrer maschinentechnischen
hilfsmittel, von dr. Berthold Lichtenberger ... Hrsg. von der
Vereinigung der städtischen milchgrossbetriebe Deutschlands
Hildesheim, Molkerei-zeitung, 1926.
275 p. illus., plans (1 fold.) diagrs. 24ᶜᵐ.
"Verzeichnis der benutzten literatur": p. 272–274.

1. ₍Dairy engineering₎ 2. Dairying—U. S. ₍2, U. S.—Dairying₎
                                                    Agr 28–434
U. S. Dept. of agr. Library   44L61
for Library of Congress   ₍a40b1₎

NL   0341823   DNAL DLC

Lichtenberger, Berthold, 1887–
Untersuchungen über die neuzeitliche Entwicklung des land-
wirtschaftlichen Maschinenwesens und ihren Einfluss auf die
Rentabilitätsverhältnisse der deutschen Landwirtschaft, von
Berthold Lichtenberger.   Berlin: P. Parey, 1914.   vii(i), 96 p.
Tables.   4°.

1. Agriculture.—Machinery. 2.   Agriculture.—Economics.
N. Y. P. L.   September 30, 1915.

NL   0341824   NN CtY ICRL

Lichtenberger, Carlo, 1901–
... Klinik und chirurgische Behandlung des
Knochensarkoms mit besonderer Berücksichtigung
der freien Knochenüberpflanzung ...   Char-
lottenburg,[1937]
Inaug.-Diss. - Berlin.
Lebenslauf.
"Literaturverzeichnis": p. [27]–28.

NL   0341825   CtY

Lichtenberger, Carolus Bertholdus.
De calore corporis humani in ictero.
Inaug. Diss.   Leipzig, 1856

NL   0341826   ICRL DNLM

Lichtenberger, Casimir G   F   1927–
Kritische Untersuchung des amerikanischen "Work simpli-
fication"-Programmes. ₍Mannheim?₎ 1952.
63 p.   22 cm.
Inaug.-Diss.—Wirtschaftshochschule, Mannheim.
Vita.
Bibliography: p. 60–62.

1. Industrial management—U. S.   I. Title.

HD70.U5L5   56–18609

NL   0341827   DLC MH-L MiU

Lichtenberger, Charles Ernest

see

Lichtenberger, Ernest, 1847–1913.

Lichtenberger, Ernest, 1847–1913.   13487-55
De carminibus Shakesperi cum nova Thorpianæ inscriptionis
interpretatione. [Thesis.] Parisiis, Hachette, 1877.
pp. 78 +.

Shakespeare-Sonnets||AcS 185604

NL   0341829   MH MiU CtY MB PU

Lichtenberger, Ernest.   47594-35
Étude sur les poésies lyriques de Gœthe.   Paris, Hachette et cie
1878.
pp. (5), 446.

NL   0341830   MH RPB NjP CtY OC1W

PT1904   Lichtenberger, Ernest, 1847–
.L7   Étude sur les poésies lyriques de Goethe, par Ernest
Lichtenberger ... 2. éd. rev. et cor.   Paris, Hachette et
cie., 1882.
₍4₎, 394, ₍1₎ p. 18½ᶜᵐ.
Ouvrage couronné par l'Académie française.

1. Goethe, Johann Wolfgang von.—Criticism and interpretation.

OCU CU
NL   0341831   ICU NcD NIC NcU PU WaU OCU MiU PBm MH

Lichtenberger, Ernest
Étude sur quelques scènes du Faust de
Goethe.   Paris, Hachette, 1899.
53 p.

NL   0341832   OC1W

PT
1926   Lichtenberger, Ernest.
L69   Le Faust de Goethe; esquisse d'une
méthode de critique impersonnelle. ₍Paris,
1905₎
36 p. 25cm.   (In Revue germanique, 1.
année, no. 1)

1. Goethe, Johann Wolfgang von.   Faust.

NL   0341833   NIC

PT2047   Lichtenberger, Ernest Charles, 1847–
C6L69   Le Faust de Goethe; esquisse d'une
méthode de critique impersonnelle. ₍n.p.,
1905?₎
36 p. 23cm.
Caption title.
Detached from Revue germanique, première
année, no. 1, janvier–février 1905.

1.Goethe, Johann Wolfgang von, 1749–1832.
Faust.   NUC

NL   0341834   CSt CLU NNU-W

PT1925   Lichtenberger, Ernest.
L5   Le Faust de Goethe, essai de critique
impersonnelle.   Paris, F. Alcan, 1911.
223 p.   19cm.   (Bibliothèque de philosophie contemporaine)

1. Goethe, Johann Wolfgang von.   Faust.

CU PU CoU OCU OOxM OU ODW OC1 CtY
NL   0341835   CoU NNCoCi RPB NjP MH OrPR CaBVaU MiU

Lichtenberger, Ernest Charles, 1847–1913, ed.
Götz von Berlichingen mit der eisernen Hand;
ein Schauspiel
see under   Goethe, Johann Wolfgang von,
1749–1832.

Lichtenberger, Franz, 1881–
Der abenteuerliche Simplizius Simplizissimus
Nach dem Roman von Hans Jacob Christoffel von
Grimmelshausen erzählt ...
see under   Grimmelshausen, Hans Jacob
Christoffel von, 1625?–1676.

PT1731   Lichtenberger, Franz, 1881–   ed.
.A6
1937   Grimmelshausen, Hans Jacob Christoffel von, 1625–1676.
Abenteuerlicher Simplizissimus; das Erlebnisbuch des
Dreissigjährigen Krieges, neu erzählt von Franz Lichten-
berger. Mit Bildern von Johannes Thiel. Freiburg im
Breisgau. Herder. 1937.

DD396   Lichtenberger, Franz, 1881–   ed.
.N5
1944   Nettelbeck, Joachim Christian, 1738–1824.
Abenteuerliches leben von Nettelbeck, von ihm selbst auf-
gezeichnet. Herausgegeben von Franz Lichtenberger. Breslau, F. Hirt, 1944.

VOLUME 332

Lichtenberger, Franz, 1881–
  Aus alten zeiten; Held Siegfried, Kriemhilds rache, Reineke Fuchs, deutsche sagen, erzählt von Franz Lichtenberger, revised and edited, with introductions, notes, exercises, and vocabulary, by E. P. Appelt ... New York, Prentice-Hall, inc., 1934.
  vii, 324 p. 19½ᶜᵐ.

  1. German language—Chrestomathies and readers.   I. Appelt, Ewald Paul, ed.   II. Title.

Library of Congress	PF3117.L55	34–17952
—— Copy 2.		
Copyright A 72835		438.6

NL   0341840   DLC OC1 OC1JC OC1ND

Lichtenberger, Franz, 1881–
  ... Graf Zeppelin, sein leben und sein werk, der jugend und dem volke erzählt von Franz Lichtenberger. Halle a. S., C. Marhold [1933]
  47, [1] p. 18¼ᶜᵐ. (Marholds jugendbücher, hrsg. von Franz Lichtenberger ... hft. 37)
  "Quellen": p. [48]

  1. Zeppelin, Ferdinand Adolf August Heinrich, graf von, 1838–1917.

| Library of Congress | TL540.Z4L5 | 39–31116 |
| | | 926.2 |

NL   0341841   DLC

PT2623
L1255G8
  Lichtenberger, Franz, 1881–
  Gudrun. Der Jugend erzählt. Halle (Saale), C. Marhold [1935]
  48 p. (Marholds Jugendbücher, hrsg. von Franz Lichtenberger, Heft 19)

NL   0341842   CU

Lichtenberger, Franz, 1881–
  ... Gudrun, der jugend erzählt von Frans Lichtenberger. 56.–85. tausend. Halle (Saale), Carl Marhold, 19—

  48 p.

  (Marholds jugendbücher ... heft 19.)

NL   0341843   NN CU CtY

838
L6991h
Germ.
  Lichtenberger, Franz, 1881–
  ...Held Siegfried, erster teil der Nibelungen-sage. Der jugend erzählt von Franz Lichtenberger... Mit 5 bildern nach holzschnitten von Julius Hübner und Eduard Bendemann. Halle a.S., Marhold [1926?]
  48p. illus. D. (Marholds jugend-bücher, 10.bdchen)

NL   0341844   IaU

Lichtenberger, Franz, 1881–
  ... Kriemhilds Rache. 2. Teil der Nibelungen Sage. Der Jugend erzählt, von Franz Lichtenberger. 64.–74. Taus. Mit 5 Bildern nach Holzschnitten von Adolf Rethel und Eduard Bendemann entnommen dem "Nibelungenlied" (Verlag Otto Wigand, Leipzig) Salle, C. Marhold.

  (Marholds Jugendbücher. 11. Bndchn)

NL   0341845   NN

Lichtenberger, Franz, 1881–
  Das Lumpengesindel, die schönsten Tiermärchen aus den "Kinder- und Hausmärchen" der Gebrüder Grimm
    see under   Grimm, Jakob Ludwig Karl, 1785–1863.

PT875
.L7
  LICHTENBERGER, FRANZ, 1881–
  Der neue weg der deutschen jugendschrift, von Franz Lichtenberger. Halle a.S., C. Marhold, 1930.
  [3]–64 p. 22½cm.
  "Literaturnachweis":p.[54]–55.
  Advertising matter:p.56–64.

  1.Children's literature--Germany.

NL   0341847   ICU

PZ3
2
.R36
  Lichtenberger, Franz, 1881–   ed.
                FOR OTHER EDITIONS
                SEE MAIN ENTRY
  Reinke de Vos. German (Modern) [Lichtenberger]
  Reineke Fuchs, nach Simrock neu erzählt von Franz Lichtenberger. Mit 4 Bildern von Ludwig Richter. Halle (Saale) C. Marhold [193–]

BT
75
L52
  Lichtenberger, Frédéric Auguste, 1832–99.
  Des éléments constitutifs de la sicence dogmatique. Par Frederic Lichtenberger. Strasbourg, Treuttel et Wurtz, 1860.
  183 p. 22 cm.

  1. Theology, Doctrinal.   I. Title.

NL   0341849   NRCR NNUT

Lichtenberger, Frédéric Auguste, 1832–1895.
  L'éducation morale dans les écoles primaires, par F. Lichtenberger.
  (In France. Ministère de l'instruction publique et des beaux-arts. Recueil des monographies pédagogiques. Vol. 4, p. 75–199. Paris. 1889)

NL   0341850   MB

Lichtenberger, Frédéric Auguste, 1832–
  L'éducation morale dans les écoles primaires, par M. F. Lichtenberger ... Paris, Imprimerie nationale, 1889.
  2 p. l., 121 p., 1 l. 24½ᶜᵐ. (Half-title: Mémoires et documents scolaires pub. par le Musée pédagogique. 2ᵉ sér. [fasc. nᵒ 28])

  1. Moral education—Elementary schools—France.

| | | E 12–27 |
| Library. U. S. Bur. of | Education | LC319.F8L6 |

NL   0341851   DHEW

Lichtenberger, Frédéric Auguste, 1832–1899, ed.
  Encyclopédie des sciences religieuses; publiée sous la direction de F. Lichtenberger ... Paris, Sandoz et Fischbacher, 1877–82.

JF2
L617e
  Lichtenberger, Frédéric Auguste, 1832–1899.
  Étude sur le principe du protestantisme d'après la théologie allemande contemporaine. Strasbourg, Treuttel et Würtz, 1857.
  208 p. 23 cm.

  Issued also as thèse, Strasbourg.
  Includes bibliographical references.

  1. Religious thought – Germany.   2. Protestantism.

NL   0341853   CtY-D

Lichtenberger, Frédéric Auguste, 1832–1899.
  Histoire des idées religieuses en Allemagne depuis le milieu du xviiiᵉ siècle jusqu'à nos jours, par F. Lichtenberger ... Paris, Sandoz et Fischbacher, 1873.
  3 v. in 1. 22½ᶜᵐ.

  1. Germany—Religion.   2. Theology—Hist.

NL   0341854   MiU PSt MH

Mnk37
L621
  Lichtenberger, Frédéric Auguste, 1832–1899.
  Histoire des idées religieuses en Allemagne depuis le XVIIIᵉ siècle jusqu'à nos jours ... deuxième éd. ... Paris, Librairie Fischbacher, Société anonyme, 1888.
  3v. 18½cm.

  1.Theology, Doctrinal - History - Germany - 19th cent.   2.Religious thought - Germany.

NL   0341855   CtY CU WU ICMcC

Lichtenberger, Frédéric Auguste, 1832–1899.
  History of German theology in the nineteenth century. By F. Lichtenberger ... Translated and ed. by W. Hastie ... Edinburgh, T. & T. Clark, 1889.
  xxxix, 629, [1] p. 23 cm.

  A study of the evolution of the religious thought of which Germany has been the theatre during the present century, giving a large place to the biographical element. cf. Author's pref.
  "Appendix", p. [611]–624, contains biographical notes taken, for the most part, from Dr. Schaff's Encyclopaedia.
  "General historical works used and referred to by the author": p. xxx.
  Bibliographical foot-notes.

  1. Theology, Doctrinal - Hist. - Germany.   2. Theologians, German.   I. Hastie, William, 1842–1903, ed. and tr.   II. Title: German theology in the nineteenth century.

  CtY-D NjNbS PHC

NL   0341857   ICRL OKEG TxDaM ICMcC PPPD PPL PPLT OO ODW CtY NcD Vi MH ICN CU RP NNG MiU ICU RPB MdBP CU

Lichtenberger, G   E
  Die Ultramarin-Fabrikation, beschrieben nach ihrer Entstehung, Geschichte und gegenwärtigen Ausbildung ... Weimar, B. F. Voigt, 1865.
  viii, 144 p. 19 cm. and atlas (10 plates) 19 x 24 cm. (Neuer Schauplatz der Künste und Handwerke, 273. Bd.)
  Bibliography: p. 142–144.

  1. Ultramarine.   (Series)

| | | P O 52–281 |
| U. S. Patent Office. for Library of Congress | Library | TP936.L5 [2] |

NL   0341858   DP NN

VOLUME 332

Lichtenberger, Hanns Erich.
⊀ Die Operabilität der Collum-Carcinome an der Universitäts-Frauenklinik Heidelberg in den Jahren 1906-30. Heidelberg, 1933.
20 p. 8°.

NL 0341859   DNLM CtY

Lichtenberger, Helmut.
Massüberwachung in der Feinbearbeitung. Stuttgart, Deutscher Fachzeitschriften- und Fachbuch-Verlag ₁1953₁
66 p. Illus. 21 cm. (Schriftenreihe Feinbearbeitung)
Bibliography: p. 65-66.

1. Physical measurements. 2. Measuring instruments.   I. Title.
(Series)
A 54-2574

Illinois. Univ. Library
for Library of Congress

NL 0341860   IU

Lichtenberger, Henri, 1864-₁1941₁
À la gloire de Goethe, par Henri Lichtenberger. Paris, Éditions de la Nouvelle revue critique ₁1939₁
250 p., 1 l. incl. front., illus., plates, ports., facsims. 20ᶜᵐ.
"Bibliographie": p. ₁229₁-241.

1. Goethe, Johann Wolfgang von, 1749-1832.   I. Title.
A C 40-2756

Wesleyan univ. Library
for Library of Congress

NL 0341861   CtW CoU IEN CaBVaU MH OCl

Lichtenberger, Henri, 1864-
... L'Allemagne d'aujourd'hui dans ses relations avec la France. Paris, G. Crès et cⁱᵉ, 1922.
2 p. l., ₁vii₁-viii, 280 p. 19ᶜᵐ. (Le nouveau monde politique, économique et social; enquêtes du Musée social)
"2ᵉ édition."
Published also as Conciliation internationale. Bulletin ₁1923₁ no. 1.
CONTENTS.—L'antagonisme franco allemand.—Les grands courants de l'opinion allemande.—La lutte pour l'exécution du traité de Versailles.—La crise actuelle.
1. Germany—Relations (general) with France. 2. France—Relations (general) with Germany. 3. Versailles, Treaty of, June 28, 1919 (Germany)   I. Title.

Library of Congress   DD249.L48 1922   26-21149

NL 0341862   DLC MiU OU OO NN CU DNW

Lichtenberger, Henri, 1864-
... L'Allemagne moderne; son évolution. Paris, E. Flammarion, 1907.
2 p. l., 399 p. 18½ᶜᵐ. (Bibliothèque de philosophie scientifique)
CONTENTS.—livre I. L'évolution économique.—livre II. L'évolution politique.—livre III. Évolution de la pensée religieuse et philosophique.—livre IV. L'évolution artistique.

1. Germany.

Library of Congress   DD117.L6   7-21290

NL 0341863   DLC NcD PPAmP MiU

Lichtenberger, Henri, 1864-
... L'Allemagne moderne; son évolution. Paris, E. Flammarion, 1908.
2 p. l., 399 p. 19ᶜᵐ. (Bibliothèque de philosophie scientifique)
On cover: 8. mille.
CONTENTS.—Introduction. — livre I. L'évolution économique. — livre II. L'évolution politique.—livre III. Évolution de la pensée religieuse et philosophique.—livre IV. L'évolution artistique.—Conclusion.

1. Germany.
8-29185

Library of Congress   DD117.L62

NL 0341864   DLC ICJ MB

Lichtenberger, Henri, 1864-
... L'Allemagne nouvelle. ₁Paris₁ E. Flammarion ₁1936₁
287 p., 1 l. 19½ᶜᵐ. (Bibliothèque de philosophie scientifique. Directeur: Paul Gaultier)

1. Germany—Pol. & govt.—1933-   2. Nationalsozialistische deutsche arbeiter-partei. 3. Hitler, Adolf, 1889-   4. Germany—For. rel.—1933-   I. Title.
36-28560

Library of Congress   DD253.L5

Copyright A—Foreign   32627

943.085

NL 0341865   DLC NIC MB NcD PPT OCl

Lichtenberger, Henri, 1864-
Les ambitions de l'Allemagne en Europe
see in Les appétits allemands.

Lichtenberger, Henri, 1864-
Ausgleich als aufgabe und schicksal, von ... Henri Lichtenberger ... James Shotwell ... ₁und₁ ... Max Scheler ... Berlin-Grunewald, W. Rothschild, 1929.
vii, 63 p. 24ᶜᵐ. (Added t.-p.: Politische wissenschaft, schriftenreihe der Deutschen hochschule für politik in Berlin und des Instituts für auswärtige politik in Hamburg, hft. 8)
CONTENTS.—Vorwort, von E. Jäckh.—Was ist weltbürgertum? von Henri Lichtenberger.—Stehen wir an einem wendepunkt der weltgeschichte? von James Shotwell.—Der mensch im weltalter des ausgleichs, von Max Scheler.
1. Nationalism and nationality. 2. Peace. 3. Political ethics.   I. Shotwell, James Thomson, 1874-1928.   II. Scheler, Max Ferdinand, 1874-1928.   III. Title.

Library of Congress   JC311.L57   29-29094

NL 0341867   DLC NRU MH-L MiU NN

Lichtenberger, Henri, 1864-
De verbis quæ in vetustissima Germanorum lingua reduplicatum præteritum exhibebant ... Nanceii, typis Berger-Levrault et sodalium, 1891.
viii, 103, ₁4₁ p. 25ᶜᵐ. ₁With his Le poème et la légende des Nibelungen. Paris, 1891₁
Thèse—Faculté des lettres de Paris.
Index librorum quæ ₁!₁ mihi scribenti plurimum profuerunt": p. ₁100₁-101.

1. Germanic languages—Reduplication.
9—12782

Library of Congress   PT1589.L5

NL 0341868   DLC CU MiU MB

DD 249
L482
1924

Lichtenberger, Henri, 1864-
Deutschland und Frankreich in ihren gegenwärtigen Beziehungen. In deutscher Bearbeitung, von Rudolf Berger. Leipzig, E. Oldenburg, c1924.
203 p.
1. Germany - Relations (general) with France. 2. France - Relations (general) with Germany. 3. Versailles, Treaty of, June 28, 1919. I. Title.

NL 0341869   CaBVaU RPB DLC CSt-H

Lichtenberger, Henri, tr.
Divan occidental-oriental
see under Goethe, Johann Wolfgang von, 1749-1832.
West-östlicher Divan. German and French.

Lichtenberger, Henri.
The evolution of modern Germany; translated from the French by A. M. Ludovici. London: Constable & Co., Ltd., 1913. xxv, 440 p. 8°.
Economic evolution. Political evolution. The evolution of religious and philosophical thought. Evolution in art.

1. Ludovici, Anthony Mario, translator. 2. Germany.—History. 3. Germany.—Economic conditions. politics. 5. Germany.—Religion. N. Y. P. L.   lator. 2. Germany.—History. 3. 4. Germany.—Government and 6. Germany.—Art.   August 12, 1913.

NL 0341871   NN

Lichtenberger, Henri, tr.
Faust
see under Goethe, Johann Wolfgang von, 1749-1832. Faust. Parts I and II. German and French.

193
N67
Xz

Lichtenberger, Henri, 1864-
Friedrich Nietzsche; ein Abriss seines Lebens und seiner Lehre. Deutsch von Friedrich von Oppeln-Bronikowski. Dresden, C. Reissner, 1900.
48p. 20cm.

Bound with Ziegler, Theobald. Friedrich Nietzsche.

1. Nietzsche, Friedrich Wilhelm, 1844-1900. ✓LC

NL 0341873   CLSU FTaSU TU NcU IU MH IEN

4B
1614

Lichtenberger, Henri, 1864-
Friedrich Nietzsche; ein Abriss seines Lebens und seiner Lehre. Deutsch von Friedrich von Oppeln-Bronikowski. 3. Aufl. Dresden, C. Reissner, 1905.
48 p.

NL 0341874   DLC-P4 UU PBm MiU

Lichtenberger, Henri, 1864-
Germany and its evolution in modern times, by Henri Lichtenberger ... tr. from the French by A. M. Ludovici. London, Constable & company, ltd., 1913.
xxv, 440 p. 23ᶜᵐ.
CONTENTS.—Introduction.—book I. Economic evolution.—book II. Political evolution.—book III. The evolution of religious and philosophical thought.—book IV. Evolution in art.—Conclusion.

1. Germany.   I. Ludovici, Anthony Mario, tr.
13-13393

Library of Congress   DD117.L64

PPT OU

NL 0341875   DLC CtNh WU InU WaS WU PPCS PP PU PSC

Lichtenberger, Henri, 1864-
Germany and its evolution in modern times ... Tr. from the French by A. M. Ludovici. New York, H. Holt and co., 1913.
xxv, 440 p. 22ᶜᵐ.
CONTENTS.—Introduction.—Economic evolution.—Political evolution.—The evolution of religious and philosophical thought.—Evolution in art.—Conclusion.

1. Germany.   I. Ludovici, Anthony Mario, 1882-   tr.   II. Title.
A 13—1075

New Haven public library
for Library of Congress   DD117.L64 1913 a
₁a40f1₁

ODW OO OCl OClCC ViU DN DLC NN MB ICJ

NL 0341876   CtNh OrP OrPR FMU NjP NN MiU PPL PPCS

Lichtenberger, Henri, 1864-
... Gœthe ... par H. Lichtenberger. Paris, H. Didier ₁1937-
v. 18½ᶜᵐ. (Les grands écrivains étrangers)
CONTENTS.—t. I. La personnalité. Le savant. L'artiste.

1. Goethe, Johann Wolfgang von—Criticism and interpretation.
A C 38-1983

Yale univ. Library
for Library of Congress

NL 0341877   CtY CU NNC LU

VOLUME 332

Lichtenberger, Henri, 1864–
   Goethe ... ₍1929₎
     see his À la gloire de Goethe.

Hkg19 Lichtenberger, Henri, 1864–
967   Goethe. [Freudenstadt] Schwarzwald Verlag
    [1949]
    228p. illus. 24cm.
    Bibliography: p.215-219.

    1. Goethe - Biog. 2. Goethe - Friends and
associates.   cdu

NL 0341879   CtY InU NjP

Lichtenberger, Henri, 1864–
  ... The gospel of superman; the philosophy of Friedrich
Nietzsche, tr. from the French of Henri Lichtenberger, with
an introduction by J. M. Kennedy ... Edinburgh and London, T. N. Foulis, 1910.
  ix, 222 p. 20½ᶜᵐ.
  At head of title: Friedrich Nietzsche.
  "Of the first edition of two thousand copies this is no 902."
  Bibliography: p. ₍217₎-222.
  1. Nietzsche, Friedrich Wilhelm, 1844-1900.   ɪ. Kennedy, John
McFarland, tr. ɪɪ. Title. ɪɪɪ. Title: Superman.
             12–36161
   Library of Congress   ₀3317.L52

   PBm PBa OCl ViU MB
NL 0341880   DLC LU OKentU NIC WaTC Or OrCS CtY PPL

Lichtenberger, Henri.
  The gospel of superman; the philosophy of Friedrich
Nietzsche, translated from the French, with an introduction by
J. M. Kennedy. New York: The Macmillan Co., 1912. 222 p.
12°.
  Works on Nietzsche, p. 220-222.

                  CENTRAL CIRCULATION.
1. Philosophy. 2. Kennedy, John   McFarland, translator.
3. Nietzsche, Friedrich Wilhelm.
N. Y. P. L.   December 11, 1916.

NL 0341881   NN ViU

---

193   Lichtenberger, Henri, 1864–
N67   The gospel of superman; the philosophy of
XLi   Friedrich Nietzsche. Translated from the
1910b French, with an introduction, by J.M.Kennedy.
    London, G.Allen & Unwin [1926]
    xxxiii,219p. 20cm.

    At head of title: Friedrich Nietzsche.
    "First published in 1910."
    Bibliography: p.[217]-219.

    1.Nietzsche, Friedrich Wilhelm, 1844-
1900. I.Title.

NL 0341882   CLSU

Lichtenberger, Henri, 1864–
  ... The gospel of superman; the philosophy of Friedrich
Nietzsche, translated from the French of Henri Lichtenberger,
with an introduction, by J. M. Kennedy ... New York, The
Macmillan company, 1926.
  xxxiii, 219 p. 20ᶜᵐ.
  Printed in Great Britain.
  At head of title: Friedrich Nietzsche.
  "Of the second impression of twelve hundred and fifty copies this
is no. 321."
  "Selected bibliography": p. 217-219.
  1. Nietzsche, Friedrich Wilhelm, 1844-1900.   ɪ. Kennedy, John Mc-
Farland, tr. ɪɪ. Title. ɪɪɪ. Title: Superman. *Translation of* La
philosophie de Nietzsche.
              27–11828
   Library of Congress   B3317.L52 1926

NL 0341883   DLC NN NcD CaBVaU OO OU PSC

Lichtenberger, Henri, 1864–
  ... La guerre européenne & la question d'Alsace-Lorraine, par Henri et André Lichtenberger. Paris ₍etc.₎
Chapelot, 1915.
  132 p. 18ᶜᵐ.   fr. 1
  At head of title: 2. édition.
  Half-title: La question d'Alsace-Lorraine.

  1. Alsace-Lorraine question. 2. European war, 1914–   ɪ. Lichtenberger, André, 1870– joint author. ɪɪ. Title.
               19–8144
   Library of Congress   DD801.A57L6 1915

NL 0341884   DLC RPB PBm NcU OU NN

Lichtenberger, Henri, 1864–
  ... La guerre européenne & la question d'Alsace-Lorraine,
par Henri et André Lichtenberger. Paris ₍etc.₎ Chapelot. 1915.
  132 p. 18ᶜᵐ.
  At head of title: 4. éd.
  Half-title: La question d'Alsace-Lorraine.

  1. Alsace-Lorraine question. 2. European war, 1914-1918. ɪ. Lichtenberger, André, 1870– joint author. ɪɪ. Title. ɪɪɪ. Title: La question d'Alsace-Lorraine.
              34–22488
   Library of Congress   DD801.A57L6 1915 d
            [943.44] 944.38

NL 0341885   DLC CaBVaU DNW NjP CSt-H MB MH ICJ NN

Lichtenberger, Henri, 1864–
  ... La guerre européenne & la question d'Alsace-Lorraine, par Henri et André Lichtenberger. Paris ₍etc.₎
Chapelot, 1918.
  132 p. 18ᶜᵐ.
  At head of title: 7. édition.
  Half-title: La question d'Alsace-Lorraine.

  1. Alsace-Lorraine question. 2. European war, 1914– ɪ. Lichtenberger, André, 1870– joint author. ɪɪ. Title.
               18–16930
   Library of Congress   DD801.A57L6

NL 0341886   DLC CtY ICJ

PT2328 Lichtenberger, Henri, 1864–
.L7   Heinrich Heine als denker. Von Henri Lichtenberger
    ... Autorisierte übersetzung von Friedrich von Oppeln-
    Bronikowski. Dresden, C. Reissner, 1905.
    viii, 312 p. 22½ᶜᵐ.

    1. Heine, Heinrich, 1799-1856.

    CaBVaU PBm OrPR
NL 0341887   ICU NIC OCH PU NN PSC OCU MiU OClW NNU

831.7   Lichtenberger, Henri, 1864–
H46zLic   Heinrich Heine als Denker. Dresden, C.
     Reissner, 1921.
     viii, 312p. 23cm.

     1. Heine, Heinrich, 1797-1856. I. Title.

NL 0341888   IEN CtY NcU NcD

PT2340 Lichtenberger, Henri, 1864–
.L53   Henri Heine penseur. Paris, Félix
    Alcan, 1905.
    250 p. 22 cm.

    1. Heine, Heinrich, 1797-1856.

    MnU CU CLSU InU
NL 0341889   TU CU DLC NcD ViLxW MH NjP RPB OCH CtY

Lichtenberger, Henri, 1864–
  Histoire de la langue allemande, par Henri Lichtenberger...
Paris, A. Laisney, 1895. xiv, 478 p. 22cm.
  "Bibliographie," p. xi-xiv.

521790B. 1. German language—Hist.
N. Y. P. L.   May 26, 1950

NL 0341890   NN NjP ICN PU RPB MH MdBJ NIC NNU CU-S

Lichtenberger, Henri, 1864–
  ... L'impérialisme économique allemand. Paris, E. Flammarion, 1918.
  2 p. l., 280 p. 1 l. 19ᶜᵐ. (Bibliothèque de philosophie scientifique)
  At head of title: ... Henri Lichtenberger ...—Paul Petit ...

  1. European war, 1914-1918—Economic aspects. 2. Germany—Economic policy. 3. Competition, International. ɪ. Petit, Paul, 1862–
ɪɪ. Title.
   Library of Congress   HC286.2.L7   18–10782
   Copyright A—Foreign   15193

NL 0341891   DLC NN PU MiU ICJ MB NjP

Lichtenberger, Henri, 1864–
  ... Impressions of Berlin in 1922, by Professor Henri
Lichtenberger ... New York city, Greenwich, Conn.,
American association for international conciliation ₍1922₎
  27 p. 19½ᶜᵐ. (International conciliation, pub. monthly by the American
association for international conciliation ... August, 1922, no. 177)
  "Lecture delivered March 13, 1922 before the Comité national d'études."

  1. Political parties—Germany. 2. Germany—Pol. & govt.—1918–
3. European war, 1914-1918—Reparations. ɪ. Title.
   Library of Congress   JX1907.A8 no. 177   22–17053

   PHC OU MiU OCl OO
NL 0341892   DLC CaBVaU WaU-L MB NN WaS OrPR PPT

Lichtenberger, Henri, 1864–

Poincaré, Raymond, *pres. France,* 1860–
  ... Inauguration of the Institute of German studies at the
University of Paris; address of M. Raymond Poincaré, address
of M. Henri Lichtenberger ... Worcester, Mass., New York
city, Carnegie endowment for international peace, Division of
intercourse and education ₍1931₎

Lichtenberger, Henri.   2671.161
  L'individualisme de Nietzsche.
  (In Entre camarades. Pp. 341-357. Paris, 1901.)

              July 3,   1902
E4926 — Nietzsche, Friedrich Wilhelm. — Individualism.

NL 0341894   MB

Lichtenberger, Henri, 1864– 1341.

₍Estournelles de Constant, Paul Henri Benjamin, *baron*
d'₎ 1852-1924.
  ... Jaurès et Rathenau, deux victimes du chauvinisme
franco-allemand; introduction de M. d'Estournelles de
Constant ... La Flèche, Dépôt des publications de la Conciliation, 1922.

Lichtenberger, Henri, 1864–
  Das moderne Deutschland und seine Entwickelung, von Henri
Lichtenberger... Autorisierte Übertragung, von Friedrich v.
Oppeln-Bronikowski... Dresden: C. Reissner, 1908. xv,
367 p. 12°.

130811A. 1. Economic history, Ger-   many. 2. Germany—Politics, 19th
century. 3. Religion, Germany, 19th   century. 4. Philosophy, Germany, 19th
century. 5. Art, Germany, 19th cen-   tury. 6. Oppeln-Bronikowski, Friedrich von, 1873– , translator.
N. Y. P. L.   July 15, 1924

NL 0341896   NN PBm OO IaU IEN

VOLUME 332

Lichtenberger, Henri, 1864–
Das moderne Deutschland und seine Entwicklung. Übers.
von Friedrich von Oppeln-Bronikowski. Mit 14 Bildern.
Hamburg, A. Janssen, 1914.
126 p. illus. 20 cm. (Wissenschaftliche Volksbücher für Schule
und Haus, 27)

1. Germany.   (Series)

DD117.L643   49–33535*‡

NL 0341897   DLC

LICHTENBERGER, Henri.
Le mysticisme de Maître Eckart. Genève,
[1921].

Pamphlet.
Cover serves as title-page.
"Vers l'unite. Ire annee, no.1. sept.
1921" pp.6–13.

NL 0341898   MH

Lichtenberger, Henri, 1864–
Nietzsche und sein Werk, von Elisabeth Förster-Nietzsche
und Henri Lichtenberger. Dresden: C. Reissner, 1928. 309 p.
incl. facsim. 8°.
Part 1, by Elisabeth Förster-Nietzsche, p. 7–62, is an introduction to Lichtenberger's work.— cf. p. 7.

413889A. 1. Nietzsche, Friedrich   Wilhelm, 1844–1900. 2. Foerster-
Nietzsche, Elisabeth, 1846–
N. Y. P. L.   June 11, 1929

NL 0341899   NN

Lichtenberger, Henri, 1864–
... Novalis. Paris, Bloud & cᵢᵉ, 1912.
268 p. incl. front. (port.) 19ᶜᵐ. (Les grands écrivains étrangers)
fr. 2.50
"Bibliographie": p. [261]–265.

1. Hardenberg, Friedrich Leopold, freiherr von, 1772–1801.

Library of Congress   12–1737

NL 0341900   DLC InU NcU NcD CU OCU CLSU MB

Lichtenberger, Henri, 1864–
... L'opinion américaine et la guerre. Paris, Bloud et Gay,
1915.
63 p. 19ᶜᵐ. (On cover: "Pages actuelles", 1914–1915. no. 36)

1. European war, 1914–1918—Public opinion.   1. Title.

Title from Univ. of Calif   at Los Angeles D509.P147
Library of Congress   [D509.P2 no. 36]
                                                            A 32–536

NL 0341901   CU MB NN NjP MH IU CtY OO

Lichtenberger, Henri, 1864–
... Où va l'Allemagne? par Henri Lichtenberger ... La
Flèche, Dépôt des publications de la Conciliation, 1925.
1 p. l., [5]–69 p. 19½ᶜᵐ. (Conciliation internationale ... [1925] Bulletin
trimestriel nᵒ 1)

1. Germany—Econ. condit.—1918—   2. European war, 1914–1918—Reparations. 1. Title.
                                                            26–13199
Library of Congress   JX1907.C75 1925 no. 1

NL 0341902   DLC NN PPLas

Lichtenberger, Henri, 1864–   tr.
Pandora
see under   Goethe, Johann Wolfgang von,
1749–1832.
Pandora. German and French.

LICHTENBERGER, Henri.   36
La philosophie de Nietzsche.
Paris. Alcan. 1898. (3), 186, (1) pp. Sm. 8°.

NL 0341904   MB OCU MiU NNC IEN CtY PHC TU

Lichtenberger, Henri, 1864–
La philosophie de Nietzsche, par Henri Lichtenberger
... 4. éd. Paris, F. Alcan, 1899.
2 p. l., 195, [1] p. 18ᶜᵐ.
"Bibliographie": p. [191]–195.

1. Nietzsche, Friedrich Wilhelm, 1844–1900.

                                                            E 9–1781
Library, U. S. Bur. of   Education

NL 0341905   DHEW DLC NIC OU CtY MWelC MH ICU PBm

Lichtenberger, Henri.   193.62 L61
La philosophie de Nietzsche. Sixième édition. [2],195,[1] p.
D. [Bibliothèque de philosophie contemporaine.] Paris: F.
Alcan, 1901.
"Bibliographie," p. 191–195.

NL 0341906   ICJ ICRL

                                                  KD 18552
Lichtenberger, Henri, 1864–
La philosophie de Nietzsche. 7. éd. Paris,
F. Alcan, 1903.

On cover: Bibliothèque de philosophie contemporaine.

NL 0341907   MH

---

193   Lichtenberger, Henri, 1864–
N67   La philosophie de Nietzsche. 8. éd.
XL1   Paris, F. Alcan, 1904.
         196 p. 19 cm. (On cover: Bibliothèque
         de philosophie contemporaine)

         Bibliography: p. [191]–196.

         1. Nietzsche, Friedrich Wilhelm, 1844–
         1900.

NL 0341908   CLSU

Lichtenberger, Henri, 1864–
La philosophie de Nietzsche; 10e ed.
Paris, 1907.

NL 0341909   OCU NjP

LICHTENBERGER, Henri.
La philosophie de Nietzsche. 13e ed.
Paris, F. Alcan, 1912.

(Bibliotheque de philosophie contemporaine)

NL 0341910   MH MoU

Lichtenberger, Henri, 1864–
La philosophie de Nietzsche, suivie d'Aphorismes et
fragments choisis, par H. Lichtenberger ... 12. éd. Paris,
F. Alcan, 1923.
3 p. l., ii, 365 p., 1 l. 18½ᶜᵐ.

1. Nietzsche, Friedrich Wilhelm, 1844–1900.

NL 0341911   MiU ICU UU DCU NIC

B   Lichtenberger, Henri, 1864–
3317   Die Philosophie Friedrich Nietzsches.
L52   Eingeleitet und übers. von Elisabeth Förster-
         Nietzsche. Dresden, C. Reissner, 1899.
         lxix,216p. front.(port.)

         Bibliography: p.[210]–216.

         1. Nietzsche, Friedrich Wilhelm, 1844–
         1900. 1. Förster-Nietzsche, Elisabeth, 1846–
         1935.

NL 0341912   UU NcU

Lichtenberger, Henri, 1864–
Le poème et la légende des Nibelungen ... Paris, Hachette
et cᵢᵉ, 1891.
2 p. l., 442 p. 25 cm.
Thèse—Faculté des lettres de Paris.
With this is bound the author's thesis in Latin (De verbis quæ in
vetustissima Germanorum lingua reduplicatum præteritum exhibe-
bant)
"Les sources de la légende des Nibelungen": p. [415]–422.
"Bibliographie": p. [435]–440.

1. Nibelungenlied. 2. Nibelungen, Legend of the.

PT1589.L5   9—12783

NL 0341913   DLC NjP MH OCl MiU OClW CtY NjP CU NIC

Lichtenberger, Henri, 1864–
Le poème et la légende des Nibelungen ... Paris, Ha-
chette et cᵢᵉ, 1891.
2 p. l., 442 p. 25ᶜᵐ.
Thèse—Faculté des lettres de Paris.
With this is bound the author's thesis in Latin (De verbis quæ in vetus-
tissima Germanorum lingua reduplicatum præteritum exhibebant)
"Les sources de la légende des Nibelungen": p. [415]–422.
"Bibliographie": p. [435]–440.
Photocopy.

NL 0341914   CaBVaU

Lichtenberger, Henri, 1864–   ed.
Poésies lyriques de Goethe et Schiller
see under   Goethe, Johann Wolfgang von,
1749–1832.
Poems.

NL 0341915

Lichtenberger, Henri, 1864–
Le problème autrichien. [Par] M. Lichtenberger ... [Bou-
logne-sur-Seine, 1921.] 26 p. 8°. (Comité national d'études
sociales et politiques. [Rapports et conférences.] Feb. 28, 1921.
Fasc.
Discussion, p. 14–26.

1. Prices and money, Austria, 1921.   2. Finance, Austria, 1921.
N. Y. P. L.   August 25, 1924

NL 0341916   NN

Lichtenberger, Henri, 1864–

Rist, Charles, 1874–
... La prochaine dernière guerre: Les réparations, par
M. le Pᵣ Ch. Rist; La Rhur [!], par M. le Pᵣ Lichtenberger;
une lettre du Pᵣ W. Fœrster ... La Flèche, Dépôt des
publications de la Conciliation, 1923.

VOLUME 332

Lichtenberger, Henri, 1864–
...Le projet allemand de l'Europe centrale, par Henri Lichtenberger... Paris: F. Alcan, 1918. 34 p., 1 l. 12°. (Les appétits allemands.)

1. Europe (Central).—Federation of.
N. Y. P. L.   2. Economic unions. 3. European war, 1914– .—Reconstruction
     December 5, 1919.

NL   0341918   NN

Lichtenberger, Henri, 1864–
Rheinbaben, Werner Karl Ferdinand, *freiherr von*, 1878–
... Que vise l'Allemagne? Adaptation française par Siegfried Floch, suivi de A la recherche d'une transaction finale par Henri Lichtenberger ... Paris-Neufchâtel, V. Attinger, 1928.

Lichtenberger, Henri.
La question d'Alsace-Lorraine
     see his   La guerre européenne.

Lichtenberger, Henri, 1864–
Relations between France and Germany; a report by Henri Lichtenberger ... Washington, The Endowment, 1923.

xvii, 133 p. 25 cm. (*Half-title:* Publications on the Carnegie endowment for international peace. Division of intercourse and education, no. 18)

1. Germany—Pol. & govt.—1918–1933. 2. European war, 1914–1918—Reparations. 3. France—Relations (general) with Germany. 4. Germany—Relations (general) with France. I. Title.
     Library of Congress   DD249.L5
     23—10770

WaU-L MtBC WaWW WaS
NcRS NcC NjN OU OCU DL OCX PV PU OCl PPT IdU-SB
Wa PJB PPL PHC ODW DN ViU DNW ICJ NN MB Ok WaU
NL   0341921   DLC CaBVa CaBVaU OrLgE KEmT OrPR WaSp

Lichtenberger, Henri.
Les revendications autonomistes en Alsace-Lorraine.   (In: Les aspirations autonomistes en Europe.   Paris, 1913.   8°. p. 1–21.)

1. Alsace-Lorraine.—History, 1913.
N. Y. P. L.   September 15, 1913.

NL   0341922   NN

ML410   Lichtenberger, Henri, 1864–
W11474   Richard Wagner, der Dichter und Denker; ein Handbuch seines Lebens und Schaffens. Autorisierte Übersetzung von Friedrich von Oppeln-Bronikowski.   Dresden, C. Reissner, 1899.
     571 p.

     "Bibliographisches": p. [565]–566.

NL   0341923   CU OU

Lichtenberger, Henri, 1864–
Richard Wagner, der dichter und denker. Ein handbuch seines lebens und schaffens von Henri Lichtenberger ... Autorisierte übersetzung von Friedrich von Oppeln-Bronikowski. 2., verb. ausg. Dresden und Leipzig, C. Reissner, 1904.

2 p. l., 571, [1] p., 1 l. 22½ᶜᵐ.

"Preisgekrönt von der Académie des inscriptions."
"Bibliographisches": p. [565]–566.

1. Wagner, Richard, 1813–1883. I. Oppeln-Bronikowski, Friedrich von, 1873– tr.

     19–17379
     Library of Congress   ML410.W11L35

NL   0341924   DLC TxU NcD PU NN

---

838   Lichtenberger, Henri, 1864–
W134F2.Go   Richard Wagner, der dichter und
1913   denker, ein handbuch seines lebens und schaffens... Autorisierte übersetzung von Friedrich von Oppeln-Bronikowski. 2.verb. und erweiterte aufl.   Dresden, Reissner, 1913.
     485p. O.
     Preisgekrönt von der französischen akademie.
     "Bibliographisches": p. [478]–480.

NL   0341925   IaU PPG MiU

Music
ML   Lichtenberger, Henri, 1864–
410   Richard Wagner, poète et penseur. 2. éd.,
W19L69   rev.   Paris, Alcan, 1898.
1898   506 p. 23cm. (Bibliothèque de philosophie contemporaine)

     1. Wagner, Richard, 1813–1883.

NL   0341926   NIC MiU MB IEN MH

Lichtenberger, Henri, 1864–
Richard Wagner, poète et penseur; par Henri Lichtenberger ... 3. éd. rev. ... Paris, F. Alcan, 1902.

2 p. l., 506 p. 23ᶜᵐ. (*On cover:* Bibliothèque de philosophie contemporaine)
"Ouvrage couronné par l'Académie française."
"Les principaux documents à consulter pour l'histoire de Wagner": p. 16–17.

1. Wagner, Richard, 1813–1883.

     Library of Congress   ML410.W13L69
     5—4940

NL   0341927   DLC PBm

ML   Lichtenberger, Henri, 1864–
410   Richard Wagner, poète et penseur. 4 éd.
W13   rev.   Paris, F. Alcan, 1907.
L69   506 p. 23cm.
     Includes bibliography.

     1. Wagner, Richard, 1813–1883

NL   0341928   WU CU

ML
410   Lichtenberger, Henri, 1864–1941.
.W13   Richard Wagner, poète et penseur. 5.éd., rev.
L7   Paris, F.Alcan, 1911.
1911   514 p.
     Includes bibliography.

     1.Wagner,Richard,1813–1883.

NL   0341929   MiU MeB CaBVaU

ML410   Lichtenberger, Henri, 1864–
.W13L69   Richard Wagner, poète et penseur. Nouv.
1931   éd.   Paris, F. Alcan, 1931.
     451 p. 25 cm. (Les maîtres de la musique)

     1. Wagner,   Richard, 1813–1883.

NL   0341930   NjR ICN PPeSchw

Lichtenberger, Henri, 1864–
The Ruhr conflict; a report by Henri Lichtenberger ... Washington, The Endowment, 1923.

vii, 16 p. 25 cm. (*Half-title:* Publications of the Carnegie endowment for international peace. Division of intercourse and education, no. 19)

"Supplementing the report entitled 'Relations between France and Germany,' made by the same author to the Carnegie endowment for international peace."

1. European war, 1914–1918 — Reparations. 2. Ruhr valley. 3. France—For. rel.—Germany. 4. Germany—Hist.—Allied occupation, 1918–1930. I. Title.

     D650.R8I.5
     23—16987

PSC WaS OrP WaU-L
Ok MB OO NcRS ICJ DNW OOxM OCU ODW OU OCl PU PPT PHC
NL   0341931   DLC DAU IdPI ViU KMK OrU OrPR CaBVa WaU

LICHTENBERGER, Henri.
La sagesse de Goethe. Genève, S.A. des Editions Sonor, 1921.

Pamphlet.

NL   0341932   MH PSt

Lichtenberger, Henri. 1864–   2878.214
Schiller jugé par Wagner.
(In Société pour l'étude des langues et des littératures modernes et la Société d'histoire moderne. Études sur Schiller. Pp. 198–242. Paris. 1905.)

G6143 — Wagner, Wilhelm Richard. 1813–1883. — Schiller, Johann Christoph Friedrich von. 1759–1805.

NL   0341933   MB

Lichtenberger, Henri, 1864–
...La tactique allemande en Russie, par Henri Lichtenberger [Paris: Bloud et Gay, 1920?]   8 p.   8°.

At head of title: Prenons garde!

1. France.—Foreign relations: Russia.   1919. 2. Russia—Foreign relations:
N. Y. P. L.   1919. 3. Brest-Litovsk   (Treaty of), 1918.
     January 12, 1922.

NL   0341934   NN

Lichtenberger, Henri, 1864–
The third reich, by Henri Lichtenberger; translated from the French and edited by Koppel S. Pinson; with a preface by Nicholas Murray Butler. New York, The Greystone press, 1937.

xi, 302 p., 1 l. 24 cm.
"The French edition ... appeared in the spring of 1936 under the title, L'Allemagne nouvelle ... The present English version, however, is more than a translation of the French text. Professor Lichtenberger has supplied several additional sections ... The editor has also revised the text and added numerous notes ... Completely new ... is the collection of documents contained in the appendix as well as the bibliography. Both are the work of the editor."—Editor's pref.

1. Germany—Pol. & govt.—1933–1945. 2. Nationalsozialistische deutsche arbeiter-partei.   3. Hitler, Adolf, 1889–   4. Germany—For. rel.—1933–   I. Pinson, Koppel Shub, 1904– ed. II. Title.
     Library of Congress   DD253.L52
     [a48u²2]   37—14255
     943.085

OrStbM OrCS CaBVaU OrMonO WaS WaSp MtBC
PPGi PSC PHC DNW ViU WaU NN MB OrU MnCS KyLxT WaT
NL   0341935   DLC AU MiU MeB WaTC IdU OrP NcD NcRS PU

DD253   Lichtenberger, Henri, 1864–
.L681   The third reich. Translated from the French and edited by Koppel S. Pinson; with a foreword by Nicholas Murray Butler. London, Duckworth, 1938.
     xi, 392 p.

     1. Germany—Pol. & govt.—1933–   2. Nationalsozialistische deutsche arbeiterpartei. 3. Hitler, Adolf, 1889–   4. Germany—For. rel.—1933–

NL   0341936   ICU

VOLUME 332

Lichtenberger, Henri, 1864–
... **Wagner,** par Henri Lichtenberger ...　Paris, F. Alcan, 1909.
2 p. l., 243 p., 2 l.　20½ᵐ.　(Les maitres de la musique)

1. Wagner, Richard, 1813–1883.

9–22929

Library of Congress　　ML410.W1L3

NL　0341937　　DLC ICU ScU MiU

ML410　Lichtenberger, Henri, 1864–
W1L48　　Wagner.　3. éd.　Paris, F. Alcan, 1910.
1910　　243 p. music.　(Les maitres de la musique)

"Catalogue des oeuvres de Wagner": p.[237]–240.
Bibliography: p.[241]–243.

1. Wagner, Richard, 1813–1883.

NL　0341938　　CU MeB

LICHTENBERGER, Henri.
Wagner. 4e ed.,　Paris, F. Alcan, 1912.

At head of title: Les maitres de la musique.

NL　0341939　　MH

Lichtenberger, Henri.
Wagner. 7th. ed.　Paris, Alcan, 1925.
243 p.

NL　0341940　　PPCuP

ML410　Lichtenberger, Henri, 1864–
.W2L74　... Wagner, por Henri Lichtenberger ...　Traducción y
(Ed)　notas de Eduardo L.-Chavarri.　Valencia, M. Villar, 1916.
[3]–217, [1] p.　20½ᵐ.　(Biblioteca Villar ...)
"Catálogo de las obras de Wagner": p. [207]–210.
"Bibliografía": p. [211]–217.

1. Wagner, Richard, 1813–1883.

NL　0341941　　ICU

ML　Lichtenberger, Henri, 1864– 1941.
410　　Wagner Richard, írta Lichtenberger Henrik;
W1　　fordította Esty Jánosné [és] Wagner Richard
L69　　es Magyarország, írta Haraszti Emil.
1916　　Budapest, A Magyar Tudományos Akadémia
　　Kiadása, 1916.
　　493 p. illus. 20cm.　(Magyar Tudományos
Akadémia, Budapest. Könyvkiadó-vállalata.
Uj folyam, 1914–1916, cyclus, 1–2)
　　1. Wagner, Richard, 1813–1883.　I. Haraszti,
Emil, 1885–　　　　　Wagner Richard és
Magyar ország.　　　　III. Series.

NL　0341942　　NIC

Lichtenberger (Henricus Æmilius). * Observationes quædam de spectris objectorum extra fines visus distincti positorum. 24 pp. 4°. *Lipsia*, typ. *Staritzii*, [1829].

NL　0341943　　DNLM

Lichtenberger, James Francis, 1897–　　ed.

Paul, *Mrs.* **Clara Christine (Wernli)** 1882–
From the tabernacle through the temple period; teacher's manual, by Clara W. Paul ... Edited by J. F. Lichtenberger [Minneapolis, ᶜ1941]

Lichtenberger, James Francis, 1897–　　ed.

Paul, *Mrs.* **Clara Christine (Wernli)** 1882–
The tabernacle. An object lesson course, teacher's manual, by Clara W. Paul ... Edited by J. F. Lichtenberger ... [Minneapolis, ᶜ1940]

Lichtenberger, James Pendleton, 1870–
... Concentration of attention by the church on removal of the causes of divorce [by] James P. Lichtenberger ...　[Philadelphia, 1932]　7 f.　28cm.
Reproduced from typewritten copy.
"Paper read before the Church conference of social work, an associate group of the National conference of social work, Philadelphia... May 16, 1932."

1. Divorce—U. S. 2. Marriage　　　　and the church.
N. Y. P. L.　　　　　　　　　November 29, 1938

NL　0341946　　NN

Lichtenberger, James P. 1870– ed.
American academy of political and social science, *Philadelphia*.
Country life ...　Philadelphia, American academy of political and social science, 1912.

Lichtenberger, James Pendleton, 1870–
... Development of social theory, by James P. Lichtenberger ...　New York & London, The Century co., 1923.
xiii, 482 p.　23ᶜᵐ.　(The Century social science series)
Contains bibliographies.

1. Sociology.　I. Title.
Library of Congress　　HM51.L5
23–8284 Revised

MtBC WaSp OrPR OrSaW
PHC PP PPLas CU MtU CtY NIC IU LU CoU NSyU NN MB WaI
NL　0341948　　DLC ViU MiU OO OC1 OC1ND OOxM ODW PSC

HM　Lichtenberger, James Pendleton, 1870–
51　　Development of social theory. London,
L5　　Allen & Unwin [1924]
1924　　482 p. 23cm.

Bibliography: p. 465.

1. Sociology. I. Title.

NL　0341949　　CU-I

LICHTENBERGER, James Pendleton, 1870–
Development of social theory. New York &
London, Century Co., 1925.
482 p.
"The Century social science series."
"Bibliography", at end of each chapter.
Soc 536.43

NL　0341950　　MH WaSpG WaTC PPT OCU PU-PSW

Lichtenberger, James Pendleton, 1870–
...Development of social theory...
New York, D. Appleton-Century company, 1936.
482 p.

(The Century social science series)

Contains bibliographies.

NL　0341951　　OCU

Lichtenberger, James Pendleton, 1870–
... Development of social theory, by James P. Lichtenberger ...　New York, London, D. Appleton-Century company, incorporated, 1938.
xiii, 482 p.　23ᵐ.　(The Century social science series)
Includes bibliographies.

1. Sociology.　I. Title.
Library of Congress　　HM51.L5　1938
38–32191

301

NL　0341952　　DLC PPDrop PU

Lichtenberger, James Pendleton, 1870–
Divorce; a social interpretation, by J. P. Lichtenberger ...　New York and London, Whittlesey house, McGraw-Hill book company, inc., 1931.
xii, 472 p.　22½ᵐ.　$4.00
"First edition."

1. Divorce—U. S.　2. Marriage.
Library of Congress　　HQ814.L68
——— Copy 2.
Copyright A 42773
31–25099

173.1

NcD CU WaTC PHC IdU PU PPPD ViU
GU-L WU-M KEmT Or WaWW CaBVaU OrAshS IU PP OC1 NRCR
NL　0341953　　DLC PP OC1 OCU OU OC1W ODW MH-L WaU NIC

Lichtenberger, James Pendleton, 1870–
Divorce; a study in social causation, by James P. Lichtenberger ...　New York, 1909.
1 p. l., 231 p. incl. illus.　23½ᵐ.
Thesis (PH. D.)—Columbia university, 1909.
Vita.
Published also as Studies in history, economics and public law, v. 35, no. 3.

1. Divorce—U. S.
Title from Columbia
Library of Congress
A 10–2001
Univ. Printed by L. C.
HQ814.L7 1909 a

NL　0341954　　NNC IdU

Lichtenberger, James Pendleton, 1870–
... Divorce; a study in social causation, by James P. Lichtenberger ...　New York, Columbia university, [etc., etc.] 1909.
280 p. diagr., charts.　23ᵐ.　(Studies in history, economics and public law, ed. by the Faculty of political science of Columbia university. vol. XXXV, no. 3)
Published also as thesis (PH. D.) Columbia university.

1. Divorce—U. S.
Library of Congress　　H31.C7　vol. 35, no. 3
——— Copy 2.　　　HQ814.L7
9–29196 Revised

CaBVaU OrP WaS OrU
NcD PU PHC PBm OU OCU OO OOxM I ICJ NN OC1WHi Or
NL　0341955　　DLC DAU MsU NIC MU NjP MH NRCR PU ViU

H1　Lichtenberger, James P., 1870–　ed.
.A4　**American academy of political and social science,** *Philadelphia*.
vol. cxxv, Modern crime: its prevention and punishment ... Editor in
no. 214　charge of this volume: Clyde L. King.　Philadelphia, The American academy of political and social science, 1926.

VOLUME 332

Lichtenberger, James P., 1870-   ed.
    FOR OTHER EDITIONS
    SEE MAIN ENTRY
American academy of political and social science, *Philadelphia.*
    The negro's progress in fifty years ... Philadelphia, American academy of political and social science [c1913]

Lichtenberger, James P., 1870-   joint ed.
American academy of political and social science, *Philadelphia.*
    Prison labor ... Philadelphia, American academy of political and social science, 1913.

Lichtenberger, James Pendleton, 1870-   378.748 UnK5 v.1
    Race-making process in the United States, by J. P. Lichtenber-

    (*In* University of Pennsylvania. University lectures delivered by members of the faculty in the Free public lecture course 1913-1914. Philadelphia, Pa., 1915. 22ᶜᵐ. Vol. 1, p. 398-407.)

NL 0341959   ICJ OU OOxM OCl OO

Lichtenberger, James P., 1870-   ed.
American academy of political and social science, *Philadelphia.*
    War relief work ... Editor in charge of this volume: J. P. Lichtenberger, ph. d. Philadelphia, The American academy of political and social science, 1918.

Lichtenberger, James Pendleton, 1870- ed.

American academy of political and social science, *Philadelphia.*
    Women in public life ... Editor in charge of this volume, James P. Lichtenberger, ph. d. Philadelphia, American academy of political and social science [c1914]

Lichtenberger, Jean Frédéric
    see Lichtenberger, Johann Friedrich, 1743-1831.

Lichtenberger, Johann, 15th century.   **E 542 81
    Practica meyster Johannen Liechtenbergers / so er vor etzlicher Zeit gemacht hat / vonn der grossen Coniunction Saturni vnd Jouis in vergangnen M.cccc.lxxxiiij. Deszgleichē eclipsis d Sonnē in lxxxv werende bisz mā schreibt Mcccccc.lxvij ja re. vff eyn newes getruckt mit seinē vil seltzamē figuren.
    [Leipzig?] 1667. (62) ff. Illus. Portraits. Plates. 18 cm., in 4s.
    Leaf C4 is missing.

D2308 — Saturn. The planet. — Jupiter. The planet. — Astrology.

NL 0341963   MB

   Lichtenberger, Johann, fl.1488
Zg16   Dise Practica vnnd Prenostication ist ge-
L61   druckt wordē zu Mentz im M.CCCC.XCII. Jar
+526   vnd werdt biss man zelt M.D.LXVII. Jar: Dariñ
    ain yeder Mensch abnemen vnd erkennen mag, wie die vergangen Zeit auch yetzt die gegenwertig in diser Practica zu trifft ... [von] Joannes Liechtenberger. [Augsburg, H.Steiner?1526]
    [91]p. illus. 29cm.
    Signatures: A-G⁶,H⁴.
    The woodcuts are ascribed to Jürg Breu, the Elder.

NL 0341964   CtY DNLM

Lichtenberger, Johann, 15th cent.
    Djse Practica vnd Prenostication Johannis Liechtēbergers Jst gedruckt wordē zu Mētz im M.CCCCXcij. Jar. Vnd werdt bisz man zelt. M.D.lxvij. Jar. Darin ein yeder mensch abnemen vnd erkennen mag, wie die vergāgen zeyt auch yetzt die gegenwertig in diser Practica zutrifft, vnd darneben zu besorgen wie hierinn künfftigs zukomen mag, doch Gott ist alle ding möglich. Fleyssig nach dem Latin in das deutsch gebracht, auch von newem Corrigiert [Augsburg, Heinrich Steiner] 1528. 48 l. illus. 28cm. (f°.)

    See: Grässe, IV, 204.   See: Dodgson, v. 2, p. 424.   See: Röttinger:
Zum Holzschnittwerke Jörg Breus d. Ä. 8.
    The same German version as in the Wittenberg, 1527 edition (q. v.), but without the name of Stephan Roth, the translator.
    Printed in type used by Heinrich Steiner.—cf. Götze, Alfred. *Die hochdeutschen Drucker der Reformationszeit.* Strassburg, 1905. pl. 11.

    Illustrations: 46 woodcuts attributed to Jörg Breu the elder, comprising 2 full-page cuts and 44 half-page cuts (including 1 repeat on t.-p.) Ornamental and historiated initials, almost all white on black.
    With bookplate of comte Greffulhe.
    Binding, modern, of half calf.

    1. Prophecies, German.   2. Astrol-   ogy.   3. Wood engravings,
German.   I. Roth, Stephan, 1492-1546,   tr. II. Breu, Jörg, 1480-1537,
illus.   illus.

NL 0341967   NN

WZ   [LICHTENBERGER, Johann] 15th cent.
240   Dise Practica und Prenostication, ist getruckt worden zū
fL699p   Mentz im M. CCCC. XCII. Jar. Und werdt bisz man zelt
1534   M. D. LXVII. Jar ... [n. p.] 1534.
    [95]p. illus. 28 cm.
    Signatures: A-H⁶.
    Cf. Klebs, A. C. Incunabula scientifica et medica, 1938, nos. 606. 6-7 for two Mainz editions of the above.

    I. Title: Practica und Prenostication

NL 0341968   DNLM

BF1790   **Lichtenberger, Johann,** 15th cent. Practica von
.P7   aller Stend der Welt bösen vnd guten Zufällen.
Rosen-   **Propheceien** vnd Weissagungen. Vergangne, gegenwertige,
wald Coll.   vnd künfftige Ding ... als: Doctoris Paracelsi, Johan Liechtenbergers, M. Josephi Grünpeck, Joan. Carionis, der Sibyllen. vnd anderer. [n. p., 1550?]

Lichtenberger, Johann, 15th cent.
    Prenosticatio
      see his Pronosticatio.

Lichtenberger, Johann, *15th cent.*
    Prognosticatio. [n. p., n. pr., after 1 Apr. 1488]
    [88] l., the last blank. woodcuts: illus. f°. 29.8 cm.
    Leaf [1]ᵃ (t. p.): Pronosticatio in Latino ...
    Hain. Repertorium (with Copinger's Supplement) *10080. Brit. Mus. Cat. [xv cent.] II, p. 532 (IB.15483) Stillwell. Second census, L 178. Goff L-204.
    Assigned to the printer Johann Zainer, Ulm, in the Brit. Mus. Cat., to a printer in Strasburg by Copinger, and to Heinrich Knoblochzer, **Heidelberg, by Ernst Weil in Der Ulmer Holzschnitt im 15. Jahrh.,** 1923 (p. 124, note 47)
    Ms. notes on blank leaf.
    1. Astrology.   I. Title.
    Incun. X.L63   Rosenwald Coll.   49-30824 rev

NL 0341971   DLC MH CtY

Lilly   LICHTENBERGER, JOHANN, fl. 1488
BF 1805   [Prognosticatio. Colophon:] Strass-
.L 69.P96   burg [Bartholomaeus Kistler, after] 31
1499a   Dec. 1499.
Vault   [48] p. 45 woodcut illus., 1 historiated initial   4to in eights and fours   (20.1 cm.)
    initial spaces with guides, unfilled

    Title from Goff; fol. [1] begins: Hec practica narrat de presenti āno et seque-

    Continued in next column

Continued from preceding column

1499a   tibus ... annis ...
Vault   BMC 1, p. 165 [IA 2546]; H* 10084; Kristeller, P., Strassburger Bücher-illustration, no. 231; Murray, C. Fairfax, German books, no. 240; Goff L-206. This copy with state of colophon and folding described by BMC as second edition. The plates from earlier editions.

1499a   A few somewhat later ms. marginalia. Bound in modern quarter vellum. Light foxing and stains. Plate at C_{i}, verso rubbed.

    1. Prophecies. I. Printer cd.: Kistler, Bartholomaeus--Strassburg. II. Imprint cd.

NL 0341974   InU DLC

Lichtenberger, Johann.
    Prognosticatio   Modena,
D. Rocociola, [not after 1500].   4to.
    in Latin.
    Sykes-Syston Park-Murray-Dunn copy

    H 10087. BMC.VII.1064; Goff L-207

NL 0341975   MWiW-C

Lichtenberger, Johann.
    Prognosticatio [German:] Practica und Prenostication. [Sine nota] [n.p., n.d.]
    Goff L-208.

NL 0341976   OClW-H

Lichtenberger, Johann.
    Prognosticatio [German] Practica unnd Prenostication. [n.p., n.d.]
    Microfilm.

NL 0341977   CU

Lichtenberger, Johann, 15th cent.
    Prognosticatio [German]   [Heidelberg? Heinrich Knoblochtzer? 1488?]   46 l. illus. 27cm. (f°.)

    Hain 10086. Schreiber 4503. See: Fairfax Murray 239. See: Hind: Introduction to a history of woodcut, II, 308, 345. Weil: Der Ulmer Holzschnitt in 15. Jahrhundert, p. 124. Klebs: Incunabula scientifica et medica, 606.2. Stillwell: Second census, L184. Goff L-210.
    Pronosticatio zu thiutsch

    Gothic type; 44 lines.
    Last leaf (blank) wanting.
    Signed and dated by the pilgrim Ruth [pseud.] April 1, 1488.
    Without imprint. Previously assigned to Johann Zainer at Ulm.
    Illustrations: 45 woodcuts (3 full-page, 42 somewhat smaller). These cuts are the same as those used in the Latin edition of the same year, and all but the last two (Schramm, XV, 1099-1141) were used in the Mainz, 1492 Latin edition printed by Meydenbach. Woodcuts colored by hand. Rubricated.
    With blind impressions in blank spaces on l. 1, 5, 14, etc.

    1. Prophecies, German.   2. As-   trology. I. Title.
N. Y. P. L.   May 13, 1947

NL 0341979   NN

Lichtenberger, Johann, 15th cent.
    Prognosticatio [German]   [Strassburg, Bartholomäus Kistler, 31 Oct. 1497]   66 l. illus. 20cm. (4°.)
    Hain-Copinger 10088. Schreiber 4505. BMC, I, 164. IA. 2427. Schmidt IV, p. 3, no. 2. Hind: Introduction to a history of woodcut, II, 344. Kristeller: Strassburger Bücher-Illustration, 225. Stillwell: Second census, L183. Goff L-209.
    With colophon.
    Gothic type (Proctor 756); 30 lines.
    Last leaf (blank?) wanting.
    Signed and dated by the pilgrim Ruth [pseud.] April 1, 1488.
    Pronosticatio zu tiletsch.

    Continued in next column

VOLUME 332

Continued from preceding column

Illustrations: 44 woodcuts (Schramm, XX², 1754-1755, 1760-1801, 1757), comprising a full-page cut on l. 1ᵇ and 43 half-page cuts (including 1 on t.-p.). Possibly designed by Kistler, the printer.—cf. *Thieme-Becker, XX*, 390. One large pictorial initial and many ornamental initials.
With inscription: Bibl. Panzeri 1807...
Binding, by Zaehnsdorf, of blue morocco, gilt.

1. Prophecies, German. 2. Astro- 4. Bindings, 19th cent., British— logy. 3. Wood engravings, German. Bartholomäus, illus. Zaehnsdorf. I. Title. II. Kistler,

NL 0341981   NN

Lichtenberger, Johann.
　　Prognosticatio [Italian]　　Modena, Dominicus
　　Rocociolus [not after 1500]
　　Goff L-212.

NL 0341982   MdBWA

Lichtenberger, Johann.
　Prognosticatio queda mirabilis ... edita per sanctā ¡Brigidā de Sueuia et sibyllam Cretensem et per Reynardū heremicoiā incipies ab anno dñi. mcccclxxxiiii duratura ad annum dñi. mcccclxvii ... [Lugdinum, 1515].

NL 0341983   MNS

Lichtenberger, Johann, 15th cent.
　Prognosticatio Iohannis Liechtenbergers, Qvam olim scripsit super magna illa Saturni ac Iouis cōiunctione, quæ fuit Anno M. CCCC. LXXXIIII. præterea ad eclypsim Solis anni sequētis uidelicet LXXXV. durans in annum usq¡ue¡ M.D.LXVII. iam iterum, sublatis mendis quibus scatebat pluribus, quandiligentissime excussa. ¡Coloniae, Impensis Petri Quentel, Ciuis Coloniensis, 1526¡　60 l.　illus.　20cm. (4°.)

Panzer, VI, 396, no. 448. Grässe, IV, 204.
Last leaf [blank?] wanting.
Illustrations: 45 woodcuts of various sizes, including 1 full-page and an unframed portrait (?) of the author on t. p. Ornamental and pictorial initials of various sizes, white on black.
Binding 20th(?) century, of red morocco, gilt.

1. Prophecies, German. 2. Astrol-　ogy. 3. Wood engravings, German.

NL 0341985   NN NIC MH ICN

Lichtenberger, Johann, 15th cent.
　Pronosticatio Iohannis Liechtenbergers, iam denuo sublatis mendis, quibus scatebat pluribus, quam diligentissime excussa. ¡Coloniae. Impēsis Petri Quentel, Ciuis Coloniensis¡ 1528.　84 l. illus.　16cm. (8°.)

Panzer, VI, 403, no. 504. Grässe, IV, 204. Merlo: Kölnische Künstler, 987-989, no. 1-38; 1096, no. 126.
Illustrations: 46 small woodcuts of various sizes, including 8 repeats and a por-

trait (?) of the author; attributed by Merlo to Anton von Woensam. Title within four border pieces. Ornamental and pictorial initials, white on black.
Binding, by Cocheu, of red morocco, gilt; with supra-libros with motto Paulatim.

1. Prophecies, German. 2. Astrol　ogy. 3. Wood engravings, German. 4. Bindings, 19th cent., French—　Cocheu. I. Woensam, Anton von, illus.

NL 0341987   NN ICN MB

A2079　Lichtenberger, Johann, fl.1488.
　Prognosticatio Ioannis Liechtenbergers. Quam olim scripsit svper magna illa Saturni ac Iovis coniunctione ... iam iterū sublatis mendis quibus scatebat pluribus, quam diligentissime excusa. Parisiis, apud Collegium Sorbonae, 1530.
　1 reel (unpaged)　¡With Oxford. University Bodleian Library.　Ashmole ms. 1389, 1391, 48, 847, 754, 45, 176. n.d.¡

Microcopy of　　the original.

NL 0341988   WaU

Lichtenberger, Johann, *fl.* 1488.
　Pronosticatio in latino, by John Lichtenberger; a reproduction of the first edition (printed at Strasburg, 1488). Edited by W. Harry Rylands, F. S. A. Manchester, Pub. for the Holbein society by A. Brothers, 1890.
　2 p. l., iii p., facsim.: ¡98¡ p. illus. (part col.) 29ᵐ. ¡The Holbein society's facsimile reprints, vol. XVII?¡
　Eleven illustrations colored by hand, from the copy owned by Owens college, Manchester, are added as specimens of the work of a bookpainter of the period. cf. Introd.

¹ Astrology.　I. Rylands, William Harry, 1847-1922, ed. II. Title.

　　　　　　　　　A 32-381 Revise
Title from New York　　　Univ. NE1240.H7　vol.17
　　　　　　　　　Printed by L. C.

　　　NBuG MB MH NNU-W NNU
NL 0341989   NN PP PPL CtY IU ICN CSmH DLC MdBP

¡Lichtenberger, Johann¡ 15th cent.
　Pronosticatione in uulgare rara & piu non udita laquale expone & dechiara alchuni influxi del cielo...lequale sono state...qllo de male: o de bene demostrano a tepo: & per lo aduenire. Et durera piu anni: cioe insino a lanno.M.CCCCC.LXVII.　¡Venice, Nicolo and Domenico Sandro dal Gesù, 20 Oct. 1511¡　32 l. illus.　21cm. (4°.)

Sar¡der 3969.　Essling 1253. Fava, Domenico. La fortuna del Pronostico di Giovanni Lichtenberger in Italia, 9. (In: Gutenberg-Jahrbuch. 1930. p. 126-148.)

Colophon: ...Impressa in Venetia nel anno.M.CCCCC.XI.adi.xx.Octobrio cauada da unaltra stampada in Modena per maestro Pietro francioso nel anna.M.cccc.lxxxxii. adi.xiiii.de Aprile.
Roman type; 44 lines.
Author's name mentioned on l. 4ᵇ.
Illustrations: 45 woodcuts, including 2 full-page (Essling, II, 498-499) and 25 half-page cuts. Publishers' device (Kristeller 236) on t-p.
With bookplate of Hale, of Alderley, Glos.
Binding (unsigned), by James Macdonald, Inc., New York, of green morocco, gilt.

¡ 1. Prophecies, German. 2. As-　trology. I. Title.
¡ N. Y. P. L.　　　　　　　　November 29, 1948

NL 0341991   NN

Beinecke Library European Tracts
G2 1620 L617

Lichtenberger, Johann, 15 th cent.
　Von dem böhmischen Königreich. Ein Prophezeyhung/ auss dem 20. Capittel Johannis Liechtenbergers Prognostick, die er vor Zeiten vber die grosse Conjunction vnd Zusammenlauffung Saturni vnd Jupiters geschrieben hat/ so gewesen ist Anno 1484. Wie auch vber die Sonnenfinsternuss nachfolgendes nemblich 1485. Jahrs. Von Worten zu Wort transferirt vnnd verteutscht/ durch ein der Antiquitaeten Liebhabern/ auss einer lateinischen edition die

Anno 1526. zu Cöln durch Petrum Quendel in Truck verlegt worden. So sich ansehen lesset/ als solte dieselbige jetziger Zeit varhafftig erfüllet vnd effectuirt werden. [n.p.] Gedruckt jm Jahr Christi/ 1620.
　[6] p.　19 cm.

　1. Bohemia - History - Prophecies. I. Title

NL 0341993   CtY

Lichtenberger, Johann, 15th cent.
　Die weissagunge Johannis Lichtenbergers deudsch, zugericht mit vleys. Sampt einer nutzlichen vorrede vnd vnterricht D. Martini Luthers, Wie man die selbige vnd der gleichē weissagunge vernemen sol. Wittemberg ¡Hans Lufft¡ 1527.　72 l.　illus. 21cm. (4°.)

Brunet, III, 1072.　Grässe, IV, 204.　Mejer: Hans Lufft, 70.　Dodgson, v. 2, p. 360.　Schoeller: Die Kunst im deutschen Buchdruck, 164. With colophon.

Translated by Stephanus Rodt.—cf. l. 72ᵇ.
Illustrations: 45 woodcuts, attributed to Georg Lemberger, comprising title border and 44 illustrations of various sizes. Ornamental initials, white on black.
Binding, by G. Mercier, Sʳ de son père, 1929, of blue morocco, gilt.

1. Prophecies, German. 2. Astrol-　ogy. 3. Wood engravings, German. Bindings, 20th cent.,　French—Mercier.I. Roth, Stephan, 1492-1546, tr. II. Lemberger, Georg,　fl. 1520-1539, illus.

NL 0341995   NN OSW

Lichtenberger, Johann, 15th cent.
　Die weissagunge Johannis Lichtenbergers deudsch, zugericht mit vleys. Sampt einer nutzlichen vorrede vnd vnterricht D. Martini Luthers, Wie man die selbige vnd der gleichē weissagunge vernemen sol.　Wittemberg. ¡Getruckt durch Hans Lufft.¡ 1527. ¡facsim. repr. 1923¡　72 l.　illus. (In: Collectio vaticiniorum ... Nach den alten Drucken um 1500 zusammengestellt. Berlin, 1923. 23cm. ¡Teil 1¡)

See: Brunet, III, 1072. See: Frankfurt am Main. Stadtbibliothek. Flugschriften sammlung Gustav Freytag, 56.
Title within historiated border.
"Verdeutscht durch Stephanum Rodt." — *Verso of l. 72.*

130587B. 1. Prophecies, German.　J. S. BILLINGS MEM. COLL.
Stephan, 1492-1546, tr.　　I. Luther, Martin. II. Roth,
N. Y. P. L.　　　　　　　　May 19, 1942

NL 0341997   NN MiU NNUT

618.9
GF133
Lichtenberger, Johann Friedrich.
　De infantvm recens natorvm mali regiminis correctione, eorvndemque morborvm praecipvervm cvratione Argentorati (Strassbourg) Pavschinger, 1741.
　36 p.
　Dissertatio inauguralis--Strassbourg.

NL 0342001   ICJ DNLM

Lichtenberger, Johann Friedrich, public notary.
　Ausführliche und richtige erzelung aller feyerlichen zurüatungen und lustbarkeiten, welche vor und bey der ankunft, auch hohen anwesenheit, des…herrn Ludwig des Fünfzehenden, königs in Franckreich und Navarra…in der königl.freyen stadt Strassburg, in dem monat September und October MDCCXLIV vorgekehret und angestellet worden… Strassburg, M.Pauschinger ¡1744¡
　50 p. 20 ᶜᵐ.

NL 0342002   NjP MH

Lichtenberger, Johann Friedrich, 1743-63¡respondent¡.
　De creatura vanitati subjecta ad Rom. VIII see under　Beyckert, Johann Philipp, 1713-1787, praeses.

B 4505 824*
Lichtenberger, Johann Friedrich, 1743-1831.
　Geschichte der Erfindung der Buchdruckerkunst zur Ehrenrettung Strassburgs und vollständiger Widerlegung der Sagen von Harlem dargestellt von Johann Friedrich Lichtenberger ... Mit einem Vorberichte von Hrn. Johann Godfried Schweighäuser ... Nebst Gutenbergs Brustbild und sechs Abdrücken von original Holztafeln. Strassburg,bei Johann Heinrich Heitz,Buchdrucker und Buchhändler,1824.
　2p.ℓ.,[iii]-vi,89,[1]p.　front.(port.)illus. 21.5cm.

NL 0342004   MH ICN

Wing Z 3112 .5022
LICHTENBERGER, JOHANN FRIEDRICH, 1743-1831.
　Geschichte der erfindung der buchdruckerkunst zur ehrenrettung Strassburgs und vollständiger widerlegung der sagen von Harlem… Mit einem vorberichte von hrn. Johann Godfried Schweighäuser… Nebst Gutenbergs brustbild und sechs abdrücken von original holztafeln. Strassburg,Heitz,1825.
　89p.

NL 0342005   ICN NNC CtY OO ICJ

VOLUME 332

Lichtenberger, Johann Friedrich, 1743–1831.
　　Histoire de l'invention de l'imprimerie pour servir de défense
à la ville de Strasbourg contre les prétensions de Harlem, par
J. F. Lichtenberger ... Avec une préface de M. J. G. Schweigh-
hæuser ... Accompagnée d'un portrait de Gutenberg et de
huit planches originales gravées sur bois. Strasbourg, J. H.
Heitz, 1825.
　　2 p. l., ₍iii₎–viii, 100 p. incl. facsims. front. (port.) 21ᶜᵐ.
　　Translated from the German.
　　1. Printing—Hist.—Origin and antecedents.　I. Schweighæuser, Johann Gottfried, 1776–1844.
　　　　　　　　　　　　　　　　　　　　　　　6–7837
　　Library of Congress　　　　Z126.L69

NL　0342006　　DLC IaU ICJ

Wing
Z
3112
.5026　LICHTENBERGER, JOHANN FRIEDRICH, 1743–1831.
　　Indulgentiarum literas Nicolai V., P.M., pro
regno Cypri impressas a. MCCCCLIV. matricumque
epocham vindicavit, Initia typogr. supplevit Jo.
Frid. Lichtenberger.　　Argentorati,Treuttel et
Würtz,1816.
　　₍4₎,16p.　24cm.　　(with his Initia typographica 1811)

NL　0342007　　ICN ViU

Lichtenberger, Johann Friedrich, 1743–1831.
　　Initia typographica illustravit Io. Frid. Lichtenberger
... Argentorati, Treuttel et Würtz, 1811.
　　viii, ₍2₎, 259, ₍1₎ p. 22½ᶜᵐ.

　　1. Printing—Hist. 2. Printing—Hist.—Origin and antecedents.
　　　　　　　　　　　　　　　　　　　　　　　6–7838
　　Library of Congress　　　　Z126.L6b

NL　0342008　　DLC ICU MWA ViU NN ICJ MB CU WU NcU

Lichtenberger, Ludwig, 1882–
　　Kindermisshandlung und Strafgesetzgebung
... von Ludwig Lichtenberger. Borna-
Leipzig, R. Noske, 1910.
　　vi, 40 p., 1 l. 22½cm.
　　Inaug.-Diss. - Heidelberg.
　　"Lebenslauf": leaf at end.
　　"Literaturverzeichnis": p. ₍v₎–vi.

NL　0342009　　MH-L ICRL

Lichtenberger, Marguerite, 1900–
　　... Écrivains français en Égypte contemporaine (de 1870 à
nos jours) ... par Marguerite Lichtenberger ... Paris, Les
Presses universitaires de France, 1934.
　　3 p. l., 189, ₍2₎ p. 23ᶜᵐ.
　　Thèse—Univ. de Lyon.
　　"Bibliographie" at end of "Avant-propos" and each chapter.

　　1. French in Egypt. 2. Egypt in literature. 3. French literature—
Hist. & crit. I. Title.
　　Library of Congress　　　PQ145.7.E3L5　　　42–32047

NL　0342010　　DLC CtY

Lichtenberger, Marguerite, 1900 –
　　... Écrivains français en Égypte contemporaine (de 1870 à
nos jours) Paris, Librairie Ernest Leroux, 1934.
　　3 p. l., 189, ₍2₎ p. 22½ᶜᵐ.
　　"Bibliographie" at end of the "Avant-propos" and each chapter.

　　1. Egypt—Description and travel—Bibliography. 2. Egyptology—His-
tory. 3. French in Egypt. 4. French literature—History and criticism.
I. Title.
　　　　　　　　　　　　　　　　　　　　　　　A C 35–2251
　　Title from N. Y. Pub.　　Libr. Printed by L. C.

NL　0342011　　NN WaU

Lichtenberger, Marguerite, 1900 –
　　... Le message de André Lichtenberger. Paris, Calmann-
Lévy ₍1946₎
　　220 p., 3 l. 2 port. (incl. front.) 18½ᶜᵐ.
　　"Ouvrages d'André Lichtenberger": p. ₍4₎

　　1. Lichtenberger, André, 1870–1940.
　　PQ2623.I 4Z7　　　　　　　　　A F 47–1906

　　Harvard univ. Library
　　for Library of Congress　　　　　　　　†

NL　0342012　　MH TxU ICU DLC NN

PR6037
.E16M63　Lichtenberger, Marguerite, 1900–　　tr.
　　Sebastian, Anna.
　　　Le monstre. Tr. de l'anglais par Marguerite Lichtenberger.
Paris, Calmann-Lévy ₍1946₎

Lichtenberger, Maurice.
　　...L'assistance par la terre; colonies agricoles et jardins ouv-
riers... Vals-les-Bains, E. Aberlen et Co., 1904. 52 p. 22cm.
(Petite bibliothèque de la Commission d'action morale et sociale)

　　1. Agricultural colonies.　　　　2. Workingmen's gardens.

NL　0342014　　NN

Lichtenberger, Max, 1878–
　　Ueber behandlung der ulcera cruris.
Inaug. diss. Freiburg, 1904.
　　Bibl.
　　29 p.

NL　0342015　　ICRL DNLM

Lichtenberger, Peter, 1929–
　　Die objektiven Merkmale des pflichtwidrigen Verhaltens
bei fahrlässigen Straftaten im Strassenverkehr nach der
höchstrichterlichen Rechtsprechung. München, 1955.
　　190, vii l. 30 cm.
　　Typescript (carbon copy)
　　Inaug.-Diss.—Munich.
　　Vita.
　　Bibliography: leaves ₍i₎–vii.

　　1. Traffic violations — Germany (Federal Republic, 1949–
　　2. Negligence, Criminal—Germany (Federal Republic, 1949–
　　　　　　　　　　　　　　　　　　　　　　59–30355

NL　0342016　　DLC

Lichtenberger, Philipp.
　　Denkschrift über die lage des tabakbaues in
Süddeutschland. ₍Speyer, 1891₎
　　9 p. 31cm.
　　Caption title.
　　Signed at end: Speyer im mai, 1891. Philipp
Lichtenberger.

　　1.Tobacco manufacture and trade - Germany.
　　2.Tobacco - Taxation - Germany.

NL　0342017　　CU

Lichtenberger, Robert.
　　Contribution à l'étude des sulfates des diols.　Lyon, Imp. A.
Rey, 1943. 83 p.　illus.　24cm.
　　Bibliography, p. ₍81₎–83.

　　1. Sulphates. 2. Diols.　　t. 1943.

NL　0342018　　NN CtY MH

Lichtenberger, Roger, 1897–
　　... Traitement par voie buccale des
nourrissons; hypotrophies hérédo-syphilitiques
... Paris, 1927.
　　23 cm.
　　Thèse - Univ. de Paris.
　　"Bibliographie": p. 119–123.

NL　0342019　　CtY

Lichtenberger, Villers.
　　Sous le vent.　Paris, Beauchesne, 1953.
57 p.　19cm.
　　Poems.

NL　0342020　　NN

Lichtenberger, Walter, 1906–
　　Die besonderheiten des oldenburgischen
verfassungsrechts ... Düsseldorf, 1933.　54 p.
　　Inaug. Diss. -Bonn, 1933.
　　Lebenslauf.
　　Bibliography.

NL　0342021　　ICRL CtY PU

4JN
It.
55　Lichtenberger de Chaimowicz, Doris
　　La posicion de tacito frente al
principado. Bogota, 1955.
　　31 p.

NL　0342022　　DLC-P4 MH

Lichtenbergh, Georg Christoph
　　see　Lichtenberg, Georg Christoph,
1742–1799.

Lichtenbergh, Johannes van der Burcht van
　　see　Burcht van Lichtenbergh, Johann
van der.　[Supplement]

LICHTENBURG, Fritz.
　　Über die Beweglichkeit des Beckens von
Neugeborenen. Leipzig,1902.

NL　0342025　　MBCo

Lichtendorf, Alexander
　　see　Clairville, Alexandre Lichtendorff,
1882–

Lichtendorf, Manfred.
　　Stoff- und Energiewechsel bei der
Fettsucht.　Würzburg, Mayr, 1933.
　　24 p.
　　Inaug.-Diss. - München.

NL　0342027　　PPWI CtY

Lichtendorff, Alexandre
　　see　**Clairville, Alexandre Lichtendorff-,** 1882–

Lichtendorff-Clairville, Alexandre
　　see　**Clairville, Alexandre Lichtendorff-,** 1882–

VOLUME 332

Lichtenecker, Karl, *1882–*

Poincaré, Henri *i. e.* Jules Henri, 1854–1912.
Letzte gedanken, von Henri Poincaré; mit einem geleitwort von Wilhelm Ostwald; übersetzt von dr. Karl Lichtenecker ... Leipzig, Akademische verlagsgesellschaft m.
b. h. (1913)

Lichtenecker, Karl, 1882–   L530.4
  Naturlehre. Mechanik der festen, flüssigen und gasförmigen   L618
  Körper.—Wärmelehre.—Grundriss der Chemie. Bearbeitet von
  Dr. phil. K. Lichtenecker und Dr. techn. P. Artmann ... Heraus-
  gegeben von Emil Burok. Mit 103 Abbildungen im Text.
  Halle a. S., W. Knapp, 1909.
    viii, [2], 168 p. diagrs. 25½ᶜᵐ.   [Der Bahnmeister. Handbuch für den
    Bau- u. Erhaltungsdienst der Eisenbahnen, Band 1, Heft 1.]

NL 0342031   ICJ

Lichtenecker, Norbert.
  Festband Eugen Oberhummer
    see under title

Lichtenecker, Norbert, joint author.

Handel-Mazzetti, Heinrich Raphael Eduard, *freiherr von*,
  1882–
  ... Kartenaufnahmen in Hunan und ihre geographischen
  ergebnisse, von Heinrich Handel-Mazzetti und Norbert Lichtenecker. Mit 2 karten.
  (*In* Akademie der wissenschaften in Wien. Mathematisch-naturwissenschaftliche klasse. Denkschriften. Wien, 1928. 29ᶜᵐ. 101. bd.,
  p. [195]–212. 2 maps (1 fold.))

Lichtenegger, Fritz, 1909–
  Einzelheiten beim ablauf der dithizonreaktion
  mit blei. ... München, 1938.   16 p.
  Inaug. Diss. - München, 1938.
  Lebenslauf.

NL 0342034   CtY

Lichtenfeld (Boleslaw). *Hémiplégie par ra-
  mollissement cérébral central dans la ménin-
  gite tuberculeuse. 23 pp. 8°. Genève, E.
  Meyer, 1919.

NL 0342035   DNLM

Lichtenfeld, Carl, 1909–
  ... Die Differentialdiagnose der Angina mit
  lymphatischer Reaktion und der Angina Plaut-
  Vincenti ... Hamburg [n. d.]
  Inaug. -Diss. - Hamburg.
  Lebenslauf.
  "Literaturverzeichnis", p. 13–14.

NL 0342036   CtY MiU

Lichtenfeld, Gabriel Judah, 1811–1887.
  באו השבון. כולל את כל למודי החשבון המורגל (אריטהמעטיק)
  Bapmaaa, 1895. תרנ"ה.
    iii, 216 p. 23 cm.

  1. Arithmetic.   *Title transliterated:* Bo'u heshbon.

  QA103.L7   54–53764

NL 0342037   DLC

Lichtenfeld, Gabriel Judah, 1811–1887.
  מאמר כהן ללא־אלהים; על דברת המזיה שנדפסה ב"הצפירה"
  משנת תרל"ו. והקונטרס המכונה המזיק ברשות הניזק, שחוברם
  היא אברהם הבן קאפלאן. ווארשא. בדפים נתן שריפטגיססער.
  Bapmaaa, 1876. תרל"ו.
    8 p. 24 cm.

  1. Kaplan, Abraham, 1839–1897.
    Title transliterated: Ma'amar kohen le-lo Elohim.
                                       A 53–3919

New York. Public Libr.
  for Library of Congress

NL 0342038   NN

Hebraic   Lichtenfeld, Gabriel Judah, 1811–1887.
Sect.   ידיעת השיעורים; כוללת מדידת הקוים, השטחים והנפים.
  ווארשא. בדפים יצחק ראמהער, תרכ"ה.
    6, 192 p. 17 fold. diagrs. 22 cm.

  1. Geometry.   *Title transliterated:* Yedi'ot ha-shi'urim.

  QA445.L5   54–54057

NL 0342039   DLC CU

Lichtenfeld, Georg, 1900–
  Ein Fall von Tabes dorsalis mit Herpes zoster
  ... Berlin,[1926]
  Inaug.-Diss. - Berlin.
  Lebenslauf.
  "Literatur": p. [36]–38.

NL 0342040   CtY OU

646.7   Lichtenfeld, Joseph.
L617p   Principles of modern hairdressing. By
  Joseph Lichtenfeld.   London, The author
  [1881]
    33,[1]p. plates. 18½cm.

  1. Hair-dressing.

NL 0342041   TxU PP

Lichtenfeld, Joseph.   391.5 0300
  Principles of physiognomical hairdressing. With illustrations.
  By Joseph Lichtenfeld. London, Published by the author,
  [1883].
    41 p. illus., plates (part fold.), 1 port. 18⅜ᶜᵐ.

NL 0342042   ICJ

Lichtenfeld, Julius.
  A pharmacist's memoirs, fifty years of Ukrainczyk's
  Brighton Pharmacy. New York, Exposition Press [1952]
    108 p. 22 cm.

  1. Brighton Pharmacy, Brooklyn.   I. Title.

  RS73.L5A3   926.1   51–12341 ‡

NL 0342043   DLC OCH NN PPDrop DNLM

Wason   Lichtenfelder, M   W
HV5816   Le pavot a opium. (Méthodes de prépara-
L69+   tion et dosage de MM. Lalande) Appendice
  I: Note sur la production et le commerce de
  l'opium en Chine, par M. H. Brenier.
  Appendice II: Le pavot a opium au Tran-Ninh
  (Laos), par M. R. Pidance.   Hanoi, F.-H.
  Schneider, 1903.
    72 p. map. 28cm.   (Publications de la
  Direction de l'agriculture et du commerce de
  l'Indo-Chine)

  "Extraits du Bulletin économique, nos. 21,
  22 et 23 -- Septembre, Octobre et Novembre,
  1903."

NL 0342045   NIC

Lichtenfeldt, Carolus
  see   Lichtenfeldt, Karl, 1860–

Lichtenfeldt, Karl,   1860–
  De Q. Asconii Pediani fontibus ac fide...
  Inaug. Diss. Breslau, 1887

NL 0342047   ICRL NjP NcD

Lichtenfeldt, Karl, 1860–
  De Q. Asconii Pediani fontibus ac fide, scripsit Carolus
  Lichtenfeldt ... Vratislaviae, apud G. Koebner, 1888.
    3 p. l., 88, [2] p. 23½ᶜᵐ. (Added t.-p.: Breslauer philologische abhand-
    lungen. 2. bd., 4. hft.)

  1. Asconius Pedianus, Quintus.
                                       A C34–2435
  Title from Iowa State   Univ.
  Library of Congress   [PA25.B8 bd. 2, hft. 4]

NL 0342048   IaU DLC CU ViU OCU NcD MB MH

Lichtenfeldt, M   C
  Der Mutter Segen; ein Festgeschenk für die
  reifere Jugend. Bunzlau, Appun, 1854.
    94 p. (His Jugend-Bibliothek, Bd. 1)

NL 0342049   NNC

Lichtenfeldt, M   C
  Ferdinand, der Ziegenhirt; oder, "Bleibe
  fromm und halte dich recht, denn solchen wird
  es zuletzt wohl gehen". Bunzlau, Appun, 1854.
    194 p. (His Jugend-Bibliothek, Bd. 3)

  Bound with Lichtenfeldt. Der Mutter Segen.
  1854.

NL 0342050   NNC

Lichtenfeldt, M   C
  Helene, die edle Wohlthäterin. (Ein Charakter-
  gemälde) Der reiferen Jugend gewidmet. Bunzlau, Appun, 1854.
    173 p. (His Jugend-Bibliothek, Bd. 2)

  Bound with Lichtenfeldt. Der Mutter Segen.
  1854.

NL 0342051   NNC

Lichtenfels, Curt von Dalwigk
  see Dalwigk zu Lichtenfels, Curt von,
       1898–

Lichtenfels, Friedrich Wilhelm Scanzoni von
  see
Scanzoni von Lichtenfels, Friedrich Wilhelm, 1821–
1891.

Lichtenfels, Gustav Franz Karl Ludwig Scanzoni von
  see
Scanzoni von Lichtenfels, Gustav Franz Karl Ludwig, 1885–

Lichtenfels, Hellmut.
  Die christliche religion in ihrer bedeutung
  fuer die charaktererziehung.
  Muenchen. Diss. 1934.

NL 0342055   PU CtY

VOLUME 332

Lichtenfels, Johann Thaddäus Anton Peithner, *ritter von*

    see

Peithner, Johann Thaddäus Anton, *ritter von Lichtenfels*, 1727-1792.

---

109   Lichtenfels, Johann von.
L61a   Auszug des wissenswürdigsten aus der
     geschichte der philosophie. Wien,
     1836.
     232p.

NL 0342057   IU

    Lichtenfels, Johann von
     Lehrbuch der logik. Wien, Heubner, 1842.

NL 0342058   NNC PU

B84   Lichtenfels, Johann von.
L5   Lehrbuch zur Einleitung in die Philosophie.
1855   Allgemeine Einleitung, Psychologie, Logik.
     3. verbesserte Aufl. Wien, W. Braumüller,
     1855.
     iv,264 p.

     Bibliographical foot-notes.

     1. Philosophy. 2. Psychology. 3. Logic.

NL 0342059   CU OC1W

B   Lichtenfels, Johann von.
82   Lehrbuch zur Einleitung in die Philosophie.
L48   5., von Neuem durchgesehene Aufl. Wien, W.
     Braumüller, 1863.
     282p. 24cm.
     Bibliographical footnotes.

     1. Philosophy I. Title: Einleitung
     in die Philosophie

NL 0342060   WU OC1W

    Lichtenfels, Katharina Helene, Freifrau von
     Dalwigk
       see   Dalwigk zu Lichtenfels, Katharina
     Helene (von Tresckow) Freifrau von, 1867-

Lichtenfels, O. von.
    Über ein Cubaturformel.
    (In Kaiserliche Akademie der Wissenschaften, Vienna. Sitzungs-
    berichte. Mathematisch-naturwissenschaftliche Klasse. Band 116,
    Halbband 2, Abteilung 2A, pp. 1190-1202. Wien. 1907.)

G9650 — Cubature.

NL 0342062   MB

PS3523
.I245W3 Lichtenfels, Paul J
1936   War scare, a play in one act, by Paul
     J. Lichtenfels. [Hollywood, Calif.,
     Chapelle & company] c1936.
     8 p. 20cm.

     Caption title.

     I. Title.

NL 0342063   DLC

    Lichtenfels, Reinhard, Freiherr von Dalwigk
       see   Dalwigk zu Lichtenfels, Reinhard,
     freiherr von, 1802-1880.

13545 Lichtenfels, Rudolph, Ritter von, d. 1851.
Y   Beobachtungen über die Gesetze des Ganges
v.3   der Pulsfrequenz und Körperwärme in den
     normalen Zuständen so wie unter dem
     Einflusse bestimmter Ursachen. Von Rud.
     Lichtenfels und Rud. Fröhlich. [Wien, K;K.
     Hof- und Staatsdruckerei, 1852]
     113-154 p. plates. 37cm. (Akademie
     der Wissenschaften, Vienna. Mathematisch-
     naturwissenschaftliche Klasse. Denkschriften,
     Bd. 3, 2. Abth.)

NL 0342065   NIC

Lichtenfels (Rudolph) *Ritter von, d. 1851.* Ueber das Verhalten
des Tastsinnes bei Narkosen der Central-Organe,
geprüft nach der Weber'schen Methode. 14 pp.
8°. [Wien, 1861.]
*Repr. from: Sitzungb.d. k. Akad.d.Wissensch. Math.-
naturw. Cl. Wien 1851.*

NL 0342066   DNLM

---

516   Lichtenfels, Victor, freiherr von
L699u Über die theorie der linearen algebraischen
     gleichungen. [Wien, 1854]
     81p. 23cm.

     Reprint from Sitzungsberichte der mathem.-
     naturw. classe der K. Akademie der wissenschaften
     [Bd.XII, S. 935] Maihefte, 1854.

     1. Geometry, Analytic.

NL 0342067   LNHT

4K Aus.- Lichtenfels, Wolfgang, Freiherr von.
116   Ueber einige Fragen des Binnenversicherungs-
     rechtes, mit besonderer Rücksicht auf Oesterreich.
     Wien, G. J. Manz, 1870.
     68 p.

NL 0342068   DLC-P4

DD901 Lichtenfels, Ger. Stadtarchiv.
L675   Archiv der Stadt Lichtenfels, bearbeitet
+L53   vom Staatsarchiv Bamberg. Bamberg, 1953-
     1v. 29 cm. (Inventare nichtstaatlicher
     Archive Bayerns. 4. Regierungsbezirk Ober-
     franken)
     At head of title: Landkreis Lichtenfels.
     Contents. - 1.T. Urkunden.

NL 0342069   CtY

Lichfenfelt (Hans, 1857-) *W* Anleitung zur Begutach-
tung des Nährwertes der Kost Privater und
der in öffentlichen Anstalten. 26 pp. 8°.
Bonn. F. Cohen. 1903.

NL 0342070   DNLM

Lichtenfelt, Hans, 1857-
    Aus dreissig jahren landwirtschaftlichen betriebes in
Schweden.
    Landw. jahrb. bd. 60, p. 833-846.   Berlin, 1924.

    1. Agriculture—Sweden.
                    Agr 25-749
    Library, U. S. Dept. of   Agriculture 18L23 bd. 60
1

NL 0342071   DNAL

612.39 Lichtenfelt, Hans, 1857-
L699g Die geschichte der ernährung … Berlin, G.
     Reimer, 1913.
     365p. tables, diagrs.

     Bibliographical foot-notes.

     1. Nutrition--Hist.

        NNC ICJ
NL 0342072   IU-M DNLM PPC OU NRU CtY NIC WU-M NN WaU

    Lichtenfelt, Hans, 1857-
     Literatur zur fischkunde. Eine vorarbeit. Von pro-
     fessor Dr. H. Lichtenfelt. Bonn, M. Hager, 1906.
     viii, 140 p. 24½ᶜᵐ.

     1. Fishes—Bibl.

                                      6-40230
     Library of Congress   Z5971.L65

NL 0342073   DLC NjP CU PPAN ICJ NN

Lichtenfelt, Hans, 1857-   547.92 O900
    … Ueber die Bildung des Fettes im Thierkörper. … Von
H. Lichtenfelt. Leipzig-Reudnitz, Druck von M. Hoffmann,
1889.
    56, [3] p. XI (*i.e.* 20) tables (partly fold.) 22½ᶜᵐ.
    Inaug.-dis. — Leipzig.
    At head of title: Aus dem thierphysiolog. Laborat. der landwirtschaftl. Akademie
Poppelsdorf-Bonn.
    "Vita."

NL 0342074   ICJ ICRL

Lichtenfelt, Hans, 1857-
    … I. H. Lichtenfelt: Über die ernährung und deren
kosten bei deutschen arbeitern; II. F. Krömmelbein
Massenverbrauch und preisbewegung in der Schweiz auf
grund Baslerischer wirtschaftsrechnungen. Stuttgart,
W. Kohlhammer, 1911.
    xx p., 2 l., 315 p. incl. tables. 24ᶜᵐ. (Basler volkswirtschaftliche arbeiten.
nr. 2)
    "Massenverbrauch und preisbewegung in der Schweiz" was published also
as the author's inaugural dissertation, Basel, 1910.
    1. Cost and standard of living—Germany. 2. Labor and laboring classes—
Germany. 3. Cost and standard of living—Switzerland. 4. Prices—Switzerland.   I. Krömmelbein, Fritz.

                                  L 12-84 Revised
    Library, U. S. Bur. of   Labor HD7029.L7
    Library of Congress   HD7029.L5

NL 0342075   DL NIC ICJ

    Lichtenfelt, Hans, 1857-
     Ueber Lebensmittelverbrauch, dessen Geldwerth
     und die Lohnhöhe in Bonn während der Jahre
     1809-1903.   Bonn, M. Hager, 1903.
     22 p.   8°.
     Title taken from cover.

NL 0342076   NN

Lichtenfelt, Hans, 1857-
    Der verbrauch von fleisch im deutschen reiche.   2 pl.
    Landw. jahrb. bd. 26, p. 129-144.   Berlin, 1897.

    1. Meat consumption. 2. Meats.
                                Agr 4-1366
    Library, U. S. Dept. of   Agriculture
14

NL 0342077   DNAL

VOLUME 332

Lichtenfelt, Hans, 1857–
Volksernährung und teuerung, eine studie von prof. dr. Lichtenfelt. Stuttgart, W. Kohlhammer, 1912.
61 p. 21 cm.
Bibliographical foot-notes.

1. Nutrition. 2. Dietary studies. 3. Cost of living. 4. Prices.

L 12–183

Library, U. S. Bur. of   Labor HD6979.L5

NL 0342078   DL CtY

Lichtenfelt, Hans Friedrich Wilhelm, 1854–
see Lichtenfelt, Hans, 1857–

Lichtenhahn, Anna.
La storia di ove, dove, onde, donde, di dove, da dove. Bern, A. Francke, 1951.
viii, 158 p. 4 fold. maps. 24 cm. (Romanica Helvetica, v. 38)
Bibliography: p. 149–158.

1. Italian language—Etymology.   (Series)

PC1571.L5   52–22091

CaBVaU OrU
NL 0342080   DLC LU MoU NBuU NBC FTaSU CSt NIC NN CU

Lichtenhahn, Christianus Augustus, respondent.
De fontibus medicatis Lauchstadiensibus
see under Hoffmann, Friedrich, 1660–1742, praeses.

Lichtenhahn, Fritz.
✻Ueber die Krebsmortalität in Kanton Glarus und die Heilerfolge in der kantonalen Krankenanstalt in den Jahren 1881–1922 [Zürich] Basel, 1924.
16 p.   8°.
Also Schweiz. med. Wschr., 1925, 55:

NL 0342082   DNLM CtY

LICHTENHAHN, Fritz.
Über mastitis chronica. cystica. Inaug.-diss., Basel, Leipzig, 1907.

NL 0342083   MBCo DNLM MiU CtY

W 4
329
1946
Lichtenhahn, Hans, 1917–
Beobachtungen über posttraumatische Knochenveränderung (Sudeck) bei Unterschenkelfrakturen. Zürich, Berichthaus, Zürich, 1946.
23 p. illus.

Inaug.-Diss. - Basel.
Reprinted from "Zeitschrift für Unfallmedizin und Berufskrankheiten," 39. Jahrgang, no. 2, 1946.

Summary in French, Italian, English and German.
Bibliography: p. 22–23.

NL 0342085   DNLM

281.178
L61
Ed.2
Lichtenhahn, Paul, 1879–
Landwirtschaftliche Betriebslehre für die Bäuerin; Leitfaden für den Unterricht an bäuerlichen Haushaltungsschulen der Schweiz. 2. Aufl. Frauenfeld, Huber, 1944.
103 p.   (Landwirtschaftliche Lehrbücher)

NL 0342086   DNAL

Lichtenhahn, Paul, 1879–
Unser Fleckvieh. Im Auftrage des Verbandes Ostschweizerischer Fleckviehzucht-Genossenschaften. Thayngen, Buchdr. K. Augustin, 1940.
31 p. illus., fold. map. 21 cm.

1. Cattle—Switzerland. I. Verband Ostschweizerischer Fleckviehzucht-Genossenschaften. II. Title.
SF196.S9L5   A F 49–242*
Iowa. State Coll. Libr.
for Library of Congress   †

NL 0342087   IaU NIC DLC

LICHTENHAHN, Theodor, 1889–
Elektrolyse aliphatischer sulfansäuren und sulfocarbonsäuren. Inaug.-diss., Basel, buchdruckerei E. Birkhäuser, 1915.

pp. 70+. Diagrs.
"Vita", after p. 70.

NL 0342088   MBCo ICRL CtY PU MiU

Lichtenhayn, Carl Ludwig von, respondent.
...De contra vindicatione...
see under Berger, Johann Heinrich von, 1657–1732, praeses.

Lichtenhein (Mauritius) [1816–]. *De vomitu. 30 pp. 18°. Berolini, typ. B. Schlesinger. [1840].

NL 0342090   DNLM

Lichtenheld, Adolf, 1843–1915, ed.
Faust (erster Teil)
see under Goethe, Johann Wolfgang von, 1749–1832. Faust. Part I.

---

ar W
4017
Lichtenheld, Adolf, 1843–1915.
Grillparzerstudien. Wien, 1886.
26 p. 24cm.
Jahresbericht des Staatsgymnasiums im IX. Bezirke in Wien für das Schuljahr 1885/6.

1. Grillparzer, Franz, 1791–1872.

NL 0342092   NIC CU

Lichtenheld, Adolf, 1843–1915.
Grillparzer-studien. Von dr. Adolf Lichtenheld. Wien, C. Graeser, 1891.
vi p.,1 l.,106 p. 22½ cm.
CONTENTS.—Einheit der zeit.—Das entsagungsmotiv.—Cultur und barbarenthum.—Noch ein Bancban.—Die klugen frauen.—Über die schaffensweise Grillparzers.

1. Grillparzer, Franz, 1791–1872.

CaBVaU
NL 0342093   MiU NjP MH NN OClW IaU PBm MiDW NcD OrU

Lichtenheld, Adolf, ed.
Hermann und Dorothea ...
see under Goethe, Johann Wolfgang von, 1749–1832.

Lichtenheld, Adolf, 1843–1915, ed.
... Iphigenie auf Tauris, ein Schauspiel ... [1904]
see under Goethe, Johann Wolfgang von, 1749–1832.

407
L699s
Lichtenheld, Adolf, 1843–1915.
Das Studium der Sprachen, besonders der classischen und die intellectuelle Bildung; auf sprachphilosophischer Grundlage dargestellt. Wien, A. Hölder, 1882.
xvi, 259p.

1. Language and languages—Study and teaching. 2. Classical philology. I. Title.

NL 0342096   IEN NjP MiU MB MH CU

LICHTENHELD, Georg.
Ueber die fertilität und sterilität der echinokokken bei rind, etc., Inaug.-diss., zu Leipzig, Jena, 1904.

NL 0342097   MH OCU ICRL CtY PU

Lichtenheldt, Willibald.
Einfache Konstruktionsverfahren zur Ermittlung der Abmessungen von Kurbelgetrieben. Berlin, VDI-Verlag [*1941]
22 p. illus. 30 cm. (VDI-Forschungsheft 408. Beilage zu "Forschung auf dem Gebiete des Ingenieurwesens," Ausg. B, Bd. 12, Mai/Juni 1941)
Issued also as diss., Technische Hochschule, Berlin, under title: Über das Konstruieren von Gelenkgetrieben in einigen praktisch wichtigen Sonderfällen.
"Schrifttumsverzeichnis": p. 22.
1. Machinery—Design. 2. Cranks and crankshafts.   (Series: VDI-Forschungsheft 408)
[TA3.V515 Heft 408]   A 49–8340*
Illinois. Univ. Library
for Library of Congress

NL 0342098   IU OU

KSE 464(2)
Lichtenklingen. Heppenheim, Verlag Südhessische Post, 1950
31 p. illus. (Schriften für Heimatkunde und Heimatpflege im südhessischen Raum, 2)

NL 0342099   MH

1883–
Lichtenstadt, Leo. Ueber optisch-aktive Verbindungen des Phosphors. (Berlin: Ebering 1912.) 40 S. 8° ¶ (Im Buchh. ebd.)
Berlin, Phil. Diss. v. 12. März 1912, Ref. Gabriel, Nernst
[Geb. 13. Jan. 83 Lodz; Wohnort: Berlin; Staatsangeh.: Rußland; Vorbildung: Friedrichs-Werdersche Oberrealsch. Berlin Reife O. 08; Studium: Berlin Landw. Hochsch. 2, Univ. 8 S.; Rig. 26. Febr. 12.]   [U 12. 293]

NL 0342100   ICRL CtY

Lichtenstadt, Issachar Baer ben Aryeh Loeb
see
Issachar Baer ben Aryeh Loeb Lichtenstein.

VOLUME 332

Lichtenstadter, Ilse, 1907–
Cultural Relations between Jews and Arabs in the Middle Ages. With a Foreword by Arthur Upham Pope. New York, Institute for Arabic and Near Eastern Studies, 1948.
12 p. 22.5 cm.
p. 10-12: Appendix. A Plea for Reconciliation and Lasting Peace in Palestine, signed by William F. Albright, Emmily G. Balch, Will Durant, (and others).
1. Jews and Arabs. 2. Islam - History of. 3. History, Mediaval. 4. Good Will. 5. Pope.

NL 0342102   NNJ

Lichtenstadter, Ilse, 1907–
From Particularism to Unity: Race, Nationality and Minorities in the early Islamic Empire. Reprinted from Islamic Culture, Oct. 1949, p. 1-30.
1. Islam - History of.

NL 0342103   NNJ

Lichtenstadter, Ilse, 1907–   ed.
Kitāb al-muḥabbar
see under   Muḥammad ibn Ḥabib, d. 860.

LICHTENSTADTER, Ilse, 1907–
(Review of) Faris, Nabih Amin, ed. The Arab Heritage...Prineton University Press, 1944.
1.Faris.... 2.Islam.

NL 0342105   NNJ

Lichtenstadter, Ilse, 1907–
... Women in the Aiyâm al-'Arab; a study of female life during warfare in preislamic Arabia, by Ilse Lichtenstädter ... London, Royal Asiatic society, 1935.
4 p. l., 90 p. 22 cm. (Prize publication fund, vol. xiv)

1. Women in Arabia.   i. Title.   ii. Title: Aiyâm al-'Arab.

PJ7701.A53L5   892.709   35–18830 rev

NN NcU
NL 0342106   DLC CaBVaU UU NcD CU PPDrop OCl WaU CLSU

Lichtenstaedt, Jeremias Rudolf, 1792-1849.
Advice to the public for the prevention and cure of Asiatic cholera. London, J. Souter, 1831.
20 p. 8°.
[P., v. 511]

NL 0342107   DNLM

Lichtenstädt, Jeremias Rudolf, 1792-1849.
Die asiatische Cholera in Russland in den Jahren 1829[-1831] Nach russischen amtlichen Quellen bearbeitet von Dr. J. R. Lichtenstädt ... Berlin, Haude und Spenersche Buchhandlung (S. J. Joseephy) 1831-1832.
5 pt. in 1 vol. 1 fold. map, 1 fold. table. 20½ᶜᵐ.
Subtitle varies slightly.
[Pt.] 1829-1830; 1830-1831, issued in 4 parts, paged continuously, as supplement to [pt. 1]

NL 0342108   ICJ MnU PPC DLC MB ICU MBCo IaU DNLM

Lichtenstaedt, Jeremias Rudolph, 1792-1849.
—— De commodis senectutis commentatio. 12 pp. 4°. [Vratislavia], G. T. Korn, [1822].

NL 0342109   DNLM PPC

615.851
L617E   Lichtenstädt, Jeremias Rudolf.
Erfahrungen im Gebiete des Lebens-Magnetismus. Nebst einem Vorworte von Dr. Wolfart. Berlin, in der Sanderischen Buchhandlung, 1819.
xx, 368 p. 21cm.

1. Magnetic healing. 2. Animal magnetism. I. Title

NL 0342110   OO

Lichtenstaedt, Jeremias Rudolph, 1792-1849.
—— Materia medica universe secundum characteres naturales et therapeuticos divisæ prospectus. 1 p. L., 78 pp. 8°. Vratislaviæ, typ. Universitatis, [1826].

NL 0342111   DNLM;

Lichtenstädt (J[eremias] R[udolph]). Meine Erfahrungen über die asiatische Cholera, während ihrer Herrschaft zu St. Petersburg im Sommer 1831. 96 pp. 12°. Berlin, 1831.

NL 0342112   DNLM

WC
264
L699m
1831   LICHTENSTÄDT, Jeremias Rudolph, 1792-1849, ed.
[Mittheilungen über die Cholera-Epidemie zu St. Petersburg im Sommer 1831, von praktischen Aerzten daselbst, hrsg. und redigierte von Lichtenstädt und Seidlitz. St. Petersburg, 1831]
282 p. illus.
Copy imperfect: title-page wanting; title from Heinsius. Allgemeines, 1828-1834.
I. Seidlitz, Karl Johann von, 1798-1885, ed. Title

NL 0342113   DNLM

Lichtenstaedt (Jeremias Rudolph) [1792-1849]. *Nonnulla de medicaminum abusu. 31 pp. 8°. Vratislaviæ, typ. Kreuzero-Scholzianis, [1819].

NL 0342114   DNLM

PA4307
.L7   LICHTENSTÄDT, JEREMIAS RUDOLF, 1792-1849.
Platon's lehren auf dem gebiete der naturforschung und der heilkunde. Nach den quellen bearb. von dr. J. R Lichtenstädt... Leipzig, C. H. F. Hartmann, 1826.
xvi, 180, [1]p. 21cm.

1.Plato.

NL 0342115   ICU PBm

Lichtenstaedt, Jeremias Rudolph, 1792-1849.
—— Rathschläge an das Publikum zur Verhütung und Heilung der herrschenden asiatischen Cholera. 25 pp. 8°. Berlin, Haude u. Spener, 1831. [P., v. 511.]

NL 0342116   DNLM

HB
1323.I4
L699u
1837   LICHTENSTÄDT, Jeremias Rudolph, 1792-1849
Ueber die Ursachen der grossen Sterblichkeit der Kinder des ersten Lebensjahres und über die diesem Uebel entgegenzustellenden Maassregeln. St. Petersburg, Eggers & Pelz, 1837.
xxxii, 111 p.

"Eine von der Kaiserlichen Oekonomischen Gesellschaft mit dem ersten Preise gekrönte Preisschrift."

NL 0342118   DNLM

Lichtenstaedt, Jeremias Rudolph, 1792-1849.
Ueber die Verhütung und Heilung der herrschenden asiatischen Cholera. Für Nichtärzte. St. Petersburg, J. Brieff, 1831.
35 p. 8°.

NL 0342119   DNLM

Rare Book Room
Kqd6
816l   Lichtenstädt, Jeremias Rudolf, 1792-1849.
Untersuchungen über den thierischen Magnetismus, von I. R. Lichtenstädt ... St.Petersburg, Gedruckt bey der Kayserlichen Akademie der Wissenschaften, 1816.
2p.l., [3]-62p. 20cm.
From the library of the imperial palace at Tsarskoe Selo, near Leningrad, with stamp on title-page.

NL 0342120   CtY

Lichtenstädt, Siegfried.
Die Amazonenpapageien; ihre Haltung, Pflege und Abrichtung mit besonderer Berücksichtigung ihrer Krankheiten und deren Heilung, herausgegeben von S. Lichtenstädt. Berlin, S. Mode, [1904]
51 p. 20ᶜᵐ.

NL 0342121   ICJ

Lichtenstädt, Siegfried.   636.6 Q406
Der Graupapagei. Seine Pflege und Abrichtung, sowie Behandlung in Krankheitsfällen. Herausgegeben von S. Lichtenstädt. Berlin, S. Mode, [1904].
53 p. 20ᵐᵐ.

NL 0342122   ICJ

Lichtenstädt, Siegfried.   619.6 Q600
Die Krankheiten der grossen Papageien. Eine kurze Anleitung zur Verhütung und Heilung der hauptsächlichsten Krankheiten der sprechenden Papageien. Von Siegfried Lichtenstädt. Berlin, S. Mode, [1906].
40 p. 20ᵐᵐ.

NL 0342123   ICJ

Lichtenstädter, Benjamin Wolf, 1794–
... אמתחת בנימין: כולל שבלי לקט ועמרי שכחת המפרשים ... וְפִירוּשִים מַבְהִיקִים עַל כַּמָה כְתוּבִים בְּסִפְרֵי תוֹרָה נְבִיאִים וּכְתוּבִים.
Fürth, 1848. תר''ח.
156, 48 p. illus. 20 cm.

1. Bible. O. T.—Commentaries. I. Title.
Title transliterated: Amtaḥat Binyamin.

BS1158.H4L5   55–54232

NL 0342124   DLC

Lichtenstädter, Ilse
see
Lichtenstadter, Ilse, 1907–

[Lichtenstaedter, Siegfried.] 1865–
Antisemitica; Heiteres und Ernstes, Wahres und Erdichtetes, von Dr. Mehemed Emin Efendi [pseud.]. Leipzig: G. Engel, 1926. 126 p. illus. (port.) 21½cm.

283079A. 1. Jews—Anti-Semitic   movement. 2. Jews in Germany —Anti-Semitism. I. Title.
Revised
October 29, 1934

NL 0342126   NN NNC OCH DLC-P4 MH

VOLUME 332

Lichtenstaedter, Siegfried.
Das Ausland-Deutschtum in Europa; seine Kämpfe, seine Ge-
fahren, seine Rettung, von Dr. S. Lichtenstaedter.   Diessen vor
München: J. C. Huber, 1928. 46 p. 22cm.

1. Germans in foreign countries.
February 27, 1940

NL   0342127   NN

₍Lichtenstaedter, Siegfried.₎
Die Balkankrisis in völkerpsychologischer Beleuchtung. Von
Dr. Mehemed Emin Efendi (Pseudonym).   Leipzig: O. Grack-
lauer, 1912. 25 p. 21cm.

633119. 1. Balkan war, 1912-1913.
Revised
October 29, 1934

NL   0342128   NN

[Lichtenstaedter, Siegfried] 1865-
Briefe an einen antisemitischen Freund, von
U. R. Deutsch [pseud.] Leipzig, Engel, 1926.
144 p. 21.5 cm.
1. Jewish question. I. Title.

NL   0342129   NNC MH

Lichtenstaedter, Siegfried.
...Civilisation et humanité; étude de moeurs politiques et de
psychologie sociale.   Traduction de l'allemand.   Paris: G.
Ficker, 1920. iv, 307 p. 17½cm.

Author's pseud., Dr. Mehemed Emin Effendi, at head of title.

969734A. 1. Europe—Civilization.   2. Civilization—Hist.
May 22, 1939

NL   0342130   NN MH

Lichtenstaedter, Siegfried.
Eduard Glaser. Von Dr. Siegfried Lichtenstaedter.   ₍Berlin,
1909₎ p. 136-179. 19½cm.

Cover-title.
"Sonderabdruck aus dem Jahrbuch für jüdische Geschichte und Literatur."

1. Glaser, Eduard, 1855-1908.
September 19, 1939

NL   0342131   NN

DS149   Lichtenstaedter, Siegfried, 1865-
L6992   The future of Palestine; an appeal to Zionis₍
         Jews and the civilised world, by "Dr. Mehemed
         Emin Efendi" (Dr. S. Lichtenstaedter) Authorized
         translation from the German.   London, Luzac &
         co., 1934.
            44 p. 18½ᶜᵐ.
         Translation of the author's Die zukunft
         Palaestinas, published in 1918. -cf.Pref.

         1. Jews - Restoration. 2. Jews in Palestine.
         I. Title.

NL   0342132   CSt-H OCH PPDrop NN InU

Lichtenstädter, Siegfried.   3084.179
The future of Turkey. An essay on the Eastern question and a sug-
gested solution. Translated from the German.
— London. Luzac & Co. 1907. 49 pp. 8°.
An essay against Russian intervention in the internal affairs of Turkey.

G7748 — Turkey. Pol. hist. — Eastern question.—Russia. For. rel. Turkey.—T.r.

NL   0342133   MB NN MH

[LICHTENSTAEDTER, SIEGFRIED]
Geburtenregelung und Judentum, von Ne'man [pseud.]...
Leipzig: G. Engel, 1933. 56 p. 20½cm.

1. Birth control—Jews.

NL   0342134   NN PPDrop OCH

₍Lichtenstaedter, Siegfried₎
"Die grosse Täuschung" in völkerpsychologischer Beleuchtung. Offenes Schreiben an Herrn Geheimrat Friedrich Delitzsch, von Ne'man ₍pseud.₎   Leipzig: G. Engel, 1922. 77 p.
23cm.

1. Delitzsch, Friedrich, 1850-   1922. Die grosse Täuschung.
2. Jews—Hist., to B. C. 332.   3. Bible. O. T.—Criticism.
4. Prophecies, Biblical.
September 15, 1939

NL   0342135   NN OCH

Lichtenstaedter, Siegfried.
Internationale unvernunft und unmoral. Betrachtungen,
warnungen, anregungen. Eine bearbeitung der friedenspreis-
aufgabe E. Filenes: "Wie kann friede und gedeihen für
Deutschland und Europa durch internationale zusammenar-
beit gesichert werden?" Von dr. S. Lichtenstaedter. Diessen
vor München, J. C. Huber, 1925.
   48 p. 19½ᵐ.

1. Peace. 2. Nationalism and nationality. 3. European war, 1914-
1918—Territorial questions. 4. International cooperation.   I. Title.

NL   0342136   DLC OCH PPDrop

₍Lichtenstaedter, Siegfried₎
Jüdische Fragen (Judentum und Judenheit, Lehre und Leben)
...von Ne'man ₍pseud.₎... Leipzig: G. Engel, 1935. 220 p.
21½cm.

969709A. 1. Judaism.
December 28, 1938

NL   0342137   NN

₍Lichtenstaedter, Siegfried.₎
Jüdische Politik; Betrachtungen, Mahnworte, Scheltworte,
Trostworte, von Ne'man ₍pseud.₎. Leipzig: G. Engel₍, 1933₎.
78 p. 21cm.

730377A. 1. Jews in Germany—   Apologetic writings.
October 4, 1934

NL   0342138   NN PPDrop

₍Lichtenstaedter, Siegfried₎
Die jüdische Religion in Gegenwart und Zukunft, offene
Worte an meine Religionsgenossen, von Ne'man (נאמן)
₍pseud.₎ Leipzig, G. Engel, 1921.
   118 p. 21 cm.

1. Jews—Religion.   I. Title.

BM560.L49   49-55504*

NL   0342139   DLC OCH PPDrop

Lichtenstaedter, Siegfried.
Jüdische Sorgen, jüdische Irrungen, jüdische Zukunft; eindring-
liche Worte an meine Religions-Genossen zur Besinnung, von Dr.
S. Lichtenstaedter...   Winnenden b. Stuttgart: Druck von
Lämmle & Müllerschön ₍1937₎ 53 p. 21cm.

"Als Manuskript gedruckt."

1. Jews in Germany. 2. Zionism.
January 4, 1940

NL   0342140   NN OCH

Lichtenstaedter, Siegfried
Der Kampf um Tripolis; ein Mahnruf an das
türkische Volk von Mehemed Emin Efendi (pseud.)
Leipzig, O. Gracklauer, 1912.

   21 p.

NL   0342141   MH DNW

Lichtenstädter, Siegfried, 1865-
Das Kriegsziel. (Völkerpsychologische Ausblicke.) Von
Dr. Mehemed Emin Efendi...   ₍Dresden: R. A. Giesecke,₎
1915. 86 p. 8°.

"Als Manuskript gedruckt."
Bibliographical footnotes.

1. European war, 1914-1918—Ter-   ritorial questions. 2. Title.
August 31, 1926

NL   0342142   NN

D511   ₍Lichtenstaedter, Siegfried₎ 1865-
L702   Das kriegsziel. (Völkerpsychologische aus-
         blicke.) Von dr. Mehemed Emin Efendi ₍pseud.₎
         Als manuskript gedruckt... ₍Winnenden-Stutt-
         gart, Druck von Lämmle & Müllerschön₎ 1915.
            2 p.l.,86 p. 23ᶜᵐ.

         1.European war, 1914-1918 - War aims. I.Title.

NL   0342143   CSt-H

₍Lichtenstadter, Siegfried₎   304 M47
Kultur und Humanität. Völkerpsychologische und politische
87421 Untersuchungen, von Dr. Mehemed Emin Efendi. Würzburg,
   ᵃ   Stahel'sche K. Hof- und Universitäts-Buch- und Kunsthandlung,
      1897.
         [4], 168 p. 23ᶜᵐ.
         Contents. — 1. Begriff der Kultur. — 2. Begriff der Humanität. — 3. Verhältnis der
         Kultur zur Humanität. Die Humanität der Europäer im Verkehre mit den übrigen
         Menschheit. — 4. Die natürlichen Grundlagen und Grenzen der Humanität. — 5. Be-
         trachtungen und Ahnungen über die europäische Kultur.

NL   0342144   ICJ MH

₍Lichtenstaedter, Siegfried₎
Moralische Erzählungen. Zur Erbauung und Fortbildung für
Politiker, von Dr. Mehemed Emin Efendi (Pseudonym). Leip-
zig: O. Gracklauer, 1914. vii, 146 p. 21½cm.

CONTENTS.—Die Pflicht der Friedfertigkeit (Eine Fabel).—Die Pflicht der Dank-
barkeit (Eine zweite Fabel).—Dschingis Chan mit dem Wahlspruch: "Recht muss
Recht bleiben"...(Eine quasi-kolonial-ethische Studie).—Um ein Kunstwerk (Eine
nicht undenkbare Geschichte).—Afrikanisches (Eine sehr glaubwürdige Geschichte).
—Das humane England (Ein Märchen, erzählt im Jahre 4000 n. Chr. G.)

969719A. 1. Satire, German.   I. Title.
March 27, 1939

NL   0342145   NN OCH

Lichtenstaedter, S[iegfried]   *5017.38.8
Nationalität, Religion und Berufsgliederung im Oriente.
(In Beiträge zur Kenntnis des Orients. Band 8, pp. 42-70. Halle.
1910.)

K5883 — Oriental races. Civilization.

NL   0342146   MB

Lichtenstaedter, Siegfried.
Nationalitätsprinzip und bevölkerungs-
austausch; eine studie für den friedens-
schluss, von dr. Mehemed Emin Efendi
(pseudonym) Dresden, R. A. Giesecke,
1917.
   56 p. 21 cm.
   1. Nationalism and nationality. 2. European
war, 1914-1918 - Territorial questions. I. Title.

NL   0342147   CSt-H

VOLUME 332

[LICHTENSTAEDTER, SIEGFRIED]
Natur und Kultur; ein psychologisch-ethischer Versuch. Von Dr. Mehemed Emin Efendi (Pseudonym). Leipzig: O. Gracklauer, 1909. 120 p. 23½cm.

1. Civilization—Hist., 20th cent.

NL 0342148   NN OCH PPDrop ICJ

Lichtenstaedter, Siegfried.
Naturschutz und Judentum; ein vernachlässigtes Kapitel jüdischer Sittenlehre, von Dr. S. Lichtenstaedter. Frankfurt a. M.: J. Kauffmann, 1932. 48 p. 22cm.

1. Nature—Philosophy—Jews.
             September 15, 1939

NL 0342149   NN PPDrop OCH CtY

[Lichtenstaedter, Siegfried]
Das neue Weltreich. (Ein Beitrag zur Geschichte des 20. Jahrhunderts). Psychologische und politische Phantasieen, mit erläuternden Anmerkungen versehen und in 3 Teilen herausgegeben von Dr. Mehemed Emin Efendi. (Pseudonym.) Theil [1]– München: Staegmeyr, 1901– v. 21½ and 23cm.

Vol. 2 has imprint: Berlin [etc.] F. Luckhardt.
"Nachbemerkung aus dem Jahre 1935," 1 typewritten l. inserted in v. 2.
CONTENTS.—Theil 1] Vom chinesischen Kriege bis zur Eroberung Konstantinopels.—Theil 2. Von der Eroberung Konstantinopels bis zum Ende Österreich-Ungarns.

969710A. 1. Prophecies.   2. Twentieth century. 3. Russia—For. rel., 1801–1917. I. Title.
Card revised May 24, 1939

NL 0342150   NN PPDrop

[Lichtenstaedter, Siegfried]
Das neue Weltreich, ein Beitrag zur Geschichte des 20. Jahrhunderts. Psychologische und politische Phantasieen, mit erläuternden Anmerkungen versehen und in 3 Teilen hrsg. von Dr. Mehemed Emin Efendi, Pseud. Berlin, F. Luckhardt [1903]
2 v. 21–23 cm.
Pt. 1 is a reprint of the 1st ed., pub. by C. Staegmeyer, Munich, 1901. Third pt. not pub.
CONTENTS.—1. Th. Vom chinesischen Kriege bis zur Eroberung Konstantinopels.—2. Th. Von der Eroberung Konstantinopels bis zum Ende Österreich-Ungarns.
1. Imaginary wars and battles.

D445.L55   5–22996 rev*

NL 0342151   DLC

[Lichtenstaedter, Siegfried]
Praktisches Judentum (Richtlinien)…von Ne'man [pseud.]… Leipzig: G. Engel, 1931. 174 p. 21cm.

Hebrew title: מדריך נבוכים

969698A. 1. Judaism.
             May 31, 1939

NL 0342152   NN OCH

[Lichtenstaedter, Siegfried] 1865–
Recht oder Unrecht? Ein Disput über den Völkerkrieg zwischen Edward und Mehemed. Von Dr. Mehemed Emin Efendi, *Pseud.* Dresden, A. Giesecke, 1915.
44 p. 22 cm.

1. European War, 1914–1918—Causes.

D511.L38   27–15418 rev*

NL 0342153   DLC NN

BM 720
S63 L5
Lichtenstaedter, Siegfried, 1865–
Schächtfrage und Schächtgegner; ein Beitrag zur Sitten- und Kulturgeschichte des 20. Jahrhunderts, von Ne'man [pseud.] Leipzig, G. Engel, 1931.
60 p. 22 cm.

1. Slaughtering and slaughter-houses—Jews I. Title

NL 0342154   OU OCH

Lichtenstaedter, Siegfried.
Schächtfrage und Tierschutz. Ein Appell an Wahrheit und Gerechtigkeit, von Ne'man pseud. of S. Lichtenstaedter. Leipzig: G. Engel, 1929.
63 p.

NL 0342155   OCH

Lichtenstaedter, Siegfried.
Die siebenbürgische Frage; ein Beitrag zur Revisionsfrage, ein Mahnruf an Magyaren und Deutsche, von Dr. S. Lichtenstaedter. Winnenden bei Stuttgart: J. E. C. Wegner, 1934. 29 p. 22cm.

808253A. 1. Transylvania. I. Title.
            March 25, 1936

NL 0342156   NN CSt-H

[Lichtenstaedter, Siegfried]
"Soll und haben"; Versuch einer unparteiischen Recht- und Schuldbilanz für den Völkerkrieg, von Dr. Mehemed Emin Efendi, *Pseud.* Bad Nassau (Lahn) Zentralstelle zur Verbreitung Guter Deutscher Literatur [1919]
191 p. 21 cm.

1. European War, 1914–1918. 2. Political ethics. I. Title.

D521.L45   26–12369 rev*

NL 0342157   DLC KyLoU NN ICJ

[Lichtenstaedter, Siegfried]
The struggle over Tripoli. A warning to the Turkish nation, by Dr. Mehemed Emin effendi (pseudonym) Authorized translation from the German by Mrs. Ellen Scott. London, Luzac [1912]
cover-title, 16 p. 18½ cm.

NL 0342158   NjP

Lichtenstaedter, Siegfried.
Süd-Tirol und Tessin, zwei national-internationale Fragen mit einer gemeinsamen Lösung. Diessen vor München, J. C. Huber, 1927.
31 p. 22 cm.

1. Bolzano (Province) 2. Ticino (Canton) 3. European War, 1914–1918—Territorial questions.

DB785.B6L5   54–51589 ‡

NL 0342159   DLC CSt NN CSt-H

Lichtenstaedter, Siegfried.
Zionismus und andere Zukunftsmöglichkeiten; Herausforderung zu einer Diskussion, von Dr. S. Lichtenstaedter. Leipzig: G. Engel [1935] 61 p. 21cm.

969717A. 1. Zionism. 2. Jewish question.
            December 28, 1938

NL 0342160   NN PPDrop

[LICHTENSTAEDTER, SIEGFRIED]
Die Zukunft der Juden. Ein Mahnruf an Zionisten und Assimilanten, von Dr. Mehemed Emin Efendi (Pseudonym). Frankfurt a.M.: J. Kauffmann, 1920. 63 p. 18½cm.

DLC: YAR 1045

1. Zionism.

NL 0342161   NN PPDrop MH OCH DLC

956.1
Em47z2
Lichtenstaedter, Siegfried, 1865–
Die Zukunft der Türkei; ein Beitrag zur Lösung der orientalischen Frage, von Mehemed Emin Efendi (Pseudonym) 2. Aufl. Berlin, F. Luckhardt, 1898.
40 p.

1. Turkey. 2. Eastern question. I. Title.

NL 0342162   WaU

[Lichtenstaedter, Siegfried.]
Die Zukunft Palästinas. Ein Mahnruf an die zionistischen Juden und an die ganze Kulturwelt, von Mehemed Emin Efendi (Pseudonym). Frankfurt a. M.: J. Kauffmann, 1918. 40 p. 21cm.
DLC: YAR 1039

BTZE p.v.782, no.4 —— Second copy.

1. Zionism. 2. European war, 1914–1918—Territorial questions—Palestine. I. Title.
Revised October 22, 1934

NL 0342163   NN PPDrop OCH DLC

Lichtenstädter, Wolf
see
Lichtenstädter, Benjamin Wolf, 1794–

Lichtensteger, Georg, 1700–1781.
Die aus der Arithmetic und Geometrie herausgeholten Gründe zur menschlichen Proportion aus das Licht gestellet und verlegt durch… 2 p. l., 24 pp., 14 pl. fol. Nürnberg, J. J. Fleischmann, 1746.

NL 0342165   DNLM PPAN

QH41
.C3
Rare Bk
Coll
Lichtensteger, Georg, 1700–1781, ed.
Catesby, Mark, 1683–1749.
Piscivm, serpentvm, insectorvm, aliorvmqve nonnvllorvm animalivm nec non plantarvm qvarvndam imagines qvas Marcvs Catesby in posteriore parte splendidi illivs operis qvo Carolinae, Floridae et Bahamensivm Insvlarvm tradidit historiam natvralem eivsqve appendice descripsit. Die Abbildungen verschiedener Fische, Schlangen, Insecten, einiger andern Thiere, und Pflanzen, welche Marcus Catesby im zweyten Theil, und im Anhang seines … Wercks, der Natürlichen Historie von Carolina … beschrieben. Mit den Abbildungen der unsrigen und anderer Länder Fische vermehret und in ihren natürlichen Farben vorgestellet von Nicolaus Friedrich Eisenberger und Georg Lichtensteger. Nürnberg, Gedruckt bey J. J. Fleischmann, 1750.

Lichtensteger, Georg, 1700–1781.
Vorstellung der Gebeine und Muskeln des menschlichen Körpers. Wobei dieselben in ihrer natürlichen Farbe dargestellet, in teutsch-, lateinisch und französischer Sprache tabellenförmig beschrieben sind; nebst einer Einleitung von dem was überhaupt von den Gebeinen und Muskeln zu merken ist. Deme auch eine eigene Beschreibung der Proportion einer acht Kopf grossen Figur und die Uebereinstimmung seiner Theile beigefüget worden. Künstlern, Wundärzten und Liebhabern zu Dienst. 9 L., 16 pl. fol. Nürnberg, J. J. Fleischmann, 1774.

NL 0342168   DNLM CtY-M

VOLUME 332

W 4
Z96
1954
LICHTENSTEIGER, Adrian A
1922-
Katamnestische Erhebungen und
Nachuntersuchungen bei 40 Homosexuellen.
Zürich, 1954.
28 p.
Inaug.-Diss. - Zürich.
1. Homosexuality
W4 Z96

NL 0342169   DNLM

Lichtensteiger (Walter). *Die klinische Be-
deutung der Auskultation der kindlichen
Herztöne sub partu. 66 pp. 8°. Zürich,
Gebr. Leemann & Co., 1925.

NL 0342170   DNLM

Lichtenstein. Darmintussusception infolge
von Bauchmassage. 3 pp. 8°. *Berlin,* 189½.
Repr. from: Allg. med. Centr.-Ztg., Berl., 1884, lxiii.

NL 0342171   DNLM

Lichtenstein.
... G. Sumner's (an die Gesellschaft d. d.
Paris, 25. märz 1842 eingesandten) Mittheilungen, den zustand der Indianer Nordamerikas betreffend. [Berlin? 1842]
50-64 p.   23 cm.   [Pamphlets on North
American Indians. v. 1]
Detached from Bulletin of the Geographical
society of Berlin. - note on t.-p.

NL 0342172   CU

Lichtenstein, A.
Der Schachkünstler. Hundert Schach-Kunstspiele, von A.
Lichtenstein. Mit einem Vorwort der Schachgesellschaft.   Ber-
lin: Veit & Co., 1847.   xii, 147 p.   illus.   18cm.

FRANK J. MARSHALL CHESS COLL.
634251A. 1. Chess—Problems, 1847.
October 17, 1933

NL 0342173   NN CaOTP OCl NjP MH PP

QP801 Lichtenstein, Abraham.
.U8L7   Quantitatieve urobilinebepaling en bloedafbraak ... Am-
sterdam, 1924.
[7], 134, [3] p. 23½cm.
Proefschrift—Amsterdam.
"Litteratuur": p. 131-134.

1. Urobilin.

NL 0342174   ICU MiU

Lichtenstein, Abraham, *d.* 1926.
Lotze und Wundt. Eine vergleichende philosophische
studie ... Bern, Druck von Sturzenegger, 1900.
2 p.l., 80, [1] p. 23 cm.
Inaug.-diss.—Bern.

1. *Lotze, Hermann, 1817-1881. 2. Wundt, Wilhelm Max, 1832-
1920.
B3387.L7   G-1998 rev

NL 0342175   DLC NjP OClW IU NN PU ICU

JC75
L617e
Lichtenstein, Adolf
Eusebius von Nikomedien. Versuch einer darstellung seiner persönlichkeit und seines lebens-
unter besonderer berücksichtigung seiner füh-er
schaft im arianischen streit. Halle a.S., M.
Niemeyer, 1903.
104 p. 24 cm.

Includes bibliography.

1. Eusebius,   bp. of Nicomedia, d.ca.342.
2. Arianism.

NL 0342176   CtY-D PPLT DDO MH OO NjPT

Lichtenstein, Adolf, 1884-
... Agranulozytose (typus Schultz) (granulocytopenia mali-
gna) von A. Lichtenstein. Helsingfors [Mercators tryckeri
aktiebolag] 1932.
136 p. illus., tables (1 fold.) diagrs. 23½ᶜᵐ. (*On cover:* Acta medica
scandinavica. Supplementum XLIX)
At head of title: Aus dem Stockholmer epidemiekrankenhause.
"Literaturverzeichnis": p. [130]-136.

1. [Agranulocytosis]   A C 33-2181

Title from John Crerar   Libr. Printed by L. C.

NL 0342177   ICJ OU PPC OClCC MiU

WS
100
L699b
1937
LICHTENSTEIN, Adolf, 1884-
Barnavård. 2. utökade uppl.
Stockholm, Bonnier [1937]
270 p. illus.
1. Children - Care & hygiene

NL 0342178   DNLM

WS
100
L699b
1949
LICHTENSTEIN, Adolf, 1884-
Barnavård. 7. uppl. Stockholm,
Bonnier [1949]
284 p. illus.
1. Children - Care and hygiene

NL 0342179   DNLM

Lichtenstein, Adolf, 1884-   joint author.
Langen, Cornelis Douwe de, 1887-
A clinical text-book of tropical medicine, by Dr. C. D. de
Langen ... and Dr. A. Lichtenstein ... Done into English by
Dr. A. H. Hamilton ... First English edition from the re-
vised third Dutch edition. Batavia-C.-Surabaya-Amsterdam,
Published by G. Kolff & co., 1936.

Lichtenstein, Adolf, 1884 -
.... Hämatologiska studier å för tidigt födda barn under de
184414 första levnadsåren med särskild hänsyn till anämiska tillstånd, av
A. Lichtenstein. Stockholm, I. Marcus' boktryckeri, 1917.
[6], 292, v p. incl. tables, diagrs. 26ᶜᵐ.
At head of title: Från Sachska barnsjukhuset, Stockholm. ....
"Litteraturförteckning," p. [282]-292.

NL 0342181   ICJ OClW-H KU-M DNLM OClW

WS
100
qL699n
1952
LICHTENSTEIN, Adolf, 1884-   ed.
Nordisk laerebog i paediatrie. [3. udg.]
København, Munksgaard, 1952.
xxii, 929 p. illus.
Completed after Prof. Lichtenstein's
death by a committee headed by Preben
Plum.
1. Pediatrics I. Plum, Preben, ed.
Title

NL 0342182   DNLM ICJ

Lichtenstein, Albert
Die Auslobung ... von Albert Lichtenstein ... Danzig, A. W. Kafemann, 1893.
38 p. 23cm.

Inaug.-Diss. - Göttingen.
Bibliographical footnotes.

NL 0342183   MH-L MH

---

*GC9
L6178
913d
Lichtenstein, Alfred, 1889-1915.
Die Dämmerung. Gedichte von Alfred Lichten-
stein (Wilmersdorf).
A.R. Meyer Verlag, Berlin-Wilmersdorf, 1913.
[15]p. 18.5cm., in folder 19.5cm.
Illus. at head of t.-p.

NL 0342184   MH IU IEN

PT
2623
I35A6
1919
Lichtenstein, Alfred, 1889-1915.
Gedichte und Geschichten. Hrsg. von Kurt
Lubasch. [München, G.Müller, 1919]
2v. 24cm.

CONTENTS.- Bd.1.Gedichte.- Bd.2.Geschichten.

I.Lubasch, Kurt, ed.

NL 0342185   CLSU IEN MH CtY InU IaU

Lichtenstein, Alfred, 1889-
Der Kriminalroman; eine literarische und forensisch-medizin-
ische Studie, mit Anhang: Sherlock Holmes zum Fall Hau.
München, E. Reinhardt, 1908.   61 p.   24cm.   (Grenzfragen
der Literatur und Medizin. Heft 7)

Bibliographical footnotes.

1. Detective stories—Hist. and crit.   2. Doyle, Sir Arthur Conan, 1859-
1930. I. Series.

NL 0342186   NN MH CtY DNLM NNNAM

Lichtenstein, Alfred, 1889-1915.
Die rechtswidrige öffentliche Aufführung von Bühnenwerken,
(nach dem Gesetz, betreffend das Urheberrecht an Werken der
Literatur und der Tonkunst)...von Alfred Lichtenstein...
Berlin: H. Walter, 1913.   3 l., 76 p.   8°.

Dissertation, Erlangen.
Bibliography, 1 l. preceding p. 1.

1. Copyright, Dramatic—Germany.   2. Stage—Jurisp.—Germany.
September 11, 1928

NL 0342187   NN ICRL NIC CtY

Lbb81
+II
1926
Lichtenstein, Anni, 1900-
... Über den Wert der Gregorschen Definitions-
methode zur Beurteilung der Intelligenz bei
Kindern von 5 bis 14 Jahren ... Berlin,1926.
Pamphlet
Inaug.-Diss. - Berlin.
Lebenslauf.
"Literaturverzeichnis": p.40.
At head of title: Aus der Universitätskinder-
klinik Berlin.

NL 0342188   CtY PU ICRL DNLM

L
QH45
L53
Lichtenstein, Anton August Heinrich, 1753-1816.
Catalogus rerum naturalium rarissimarum
Hamburgi ... auctionis lege distrahendarum.
Verzeichniss von höchstseltenen, aus allen
Welttheilen mit vieler Mühe und Kosten zusammen
gebrachten, auch aus unterschiedlichen Cabinet-
tern, Sammlungen und Auctionen ausgehobenen
Naturalien welche von einem Liebhaber, als
Mitglied der Batavischen und verschiedener ander-
er Naturforschenden Gesellschaften gesammelt
worden.   Hamburg, Gedruckt bey Gottl. Friedr.
Schniebes [1793-1796]
3 v.   17cm.

CONTENTS. Pt. 1. Mammalia et Aves.- Pt.2.
Conchylia, item Mineralia.- Pt. 3. Insecta.

1.Natural history. I.Title.

NL 0342190   NcRS PPAN

VOLUME 332

FILM
13486
QL
Biology
Library
Lichtenstein, Anton August Heinrich, 1753-1816.
　　Catalogus rerum naturalium rarissimarum ...　Sectio secundus
continens Conchylia, item mineralia, ligna exotica & arte parata.
Hamburg, G.F. Schniebe, 1794.
　　118 p.　On film(negative)

Microfilm.　Original in the British Museum.
Caption title.

1. Mollusks.　2. Mineralogy.　I. Title.

NL　0342191　CU

FILM
13486
QL
Biology
Library
Lichtenstein, Anton August Heinrich, 1753-1816.
　　Catalogus [rerum naturalium rarissimarum] Sectio tertia
continens insecta ...　3. Abschnitt ...　Hamburg. G.F.
Schniebe [1796]
　　222 p.　On film (positive)

Microfilm.　Original in British Museum.
Caption title.

1. Insects - Catalogs and collections.

NL　0342192　CU

Lichtenstein, Anton August Heinrich, 1753-1816.
　　... Lichtenstein's Catalogus rerum naturalium rarissimarum.　Ed. by F. Du Cane Godman ...　London [Print-
ed by Taylor and Francis] 1882.
　　iv, [11], 60 p.　26½ᶜᵐ.

Reprint of ed. of 1793 (Sectio prima continens *Mammalia & Aves*)
including facsim. of original t.-p.
Introduction in Latin and German.
At head of title : The Willughby society.

1. Ornithology.　I. Godman, Frederick Du Cane, 1834-　　ed.

Agr 11-313

Library, U. S. Dept. of　　　　Agriculture 413L61

NL　0342193　DNAL CU CSt CtY PPAN MiU ViU MB ICJ

QL737　Lichtenstein, Anton August Heinrich, 1753-1816.
.P9L7　　Commentatio philologica de simiarum quotquot veteribus
innotuerunt formis earumque nominibus pro specimine
methodi qua historia naturalis veterum ad systema naturae
Linnaeanum exigenda atque adornanda, ab auctore M.
Anton. August. Henr. Lichtenstein ...　Hamburgi, apud B.
G. Hoffmann in commissis, 1791.
　　80 p.　19¼ᶜᵐ.

1. Monkeys.

NL　0342194　ICU CtY PPAN MdBJ

Lichtenstein, Anton August Heinrich.
　　Descriptiones Animalium.　1844
　　　　see under　Forster, Johann Reinhold,
　　　　　1729-1798.

DF
L699
Lichtenstein, Anton August Heinrich,
　　1753-1816, praeses.
　　Paralipomena critica circa textvm
Veteris Testamenti codicvm Hebraicorvm
etiam nvnc svperstitvm ope restitvendvm
e svpellectili Bibliothecae pvblicae
Hambvrgensis havsta ...　Helmstadii,
C.G.Fleckeisen, 1799]
　　4p.l.,c p.　fold.table.　24cm.
　　Diss. - Helmstadt (L.F.A. Hofmeister,
respondent)

NL　0342196　NNUT CtY NNJ

Lichtenstein, Anton August Heinrich.
　　Reise von Orenburg nach Buchara.　1823
　　　　see under　Eversmann, Eduard Friedrich,
　　　　　1794-1860.

PJ3197　Lichtenstein, Anton August Heinrich, 1753-1816.
.L7　　Tentamen palaeographiae assyrio-persicae sive simplicis
compendii ad explicandvm antiqvissima monvmenta popv-
lorvm qvi olim circa mediam Asiam habitarvnt, praesertim
vero cvneatas qvas vocant inscriptiones, avctore d. Anton.
Avgvst. Henric. Lichtenstein ...　Helmstadii, C. G. Fleckei-
sen, 1803.
　　[3], xii, [4], 172 p.　plates (part fold.)　26½x22½ᶜᵐ.

1. Cuneiform inscriptions.

NL　0342198　ICU CU PBm PU MH NN RPB

Lichtenstein, Anton August Heinrich, 1753-1816.
　　Verzeichniss einer sammlung von seltenheiten
aus dem gebiete der natur und kunst, gesammelt
durch C.G. Beireis... . Nebst einem anhange
von theologischen u. andern wissenschaftlichen
büchern, welche am 5. Mai 1816 und an den
folgenden tagen, nach endigung der bücher-
auction, öffentlich versteigert werden sollen.
2. aufl. Helmstädt, Leuckart, Pref. 1810.
　　113-216 p.

NL　0342199　OC1W

Lichtenstein, Arnold, 1878-
　　Ueber den einfluss der koerperhaltung und des blut-
druckes auf die albuminurie ...
　　Inaug. diss. Berlin, 1905

NL　0342200　ICRL CtY DNLM

Lichtenstein, Arthur, 1906-
　　Can attitudes be taught? ...　By Arthur Lichtenstein ...
Baltimore, The Johns Hopkins press, 1934.
　　ix, 89 p., 1 l.　24½ᶜᵐ.

Thesis (PH. D.)—Johns Hopkins university, 1934.
Vita.
"Reprinted from 'The Johns Hopkins university studies in education',
number 21."
Bibliography: p. 79-82.

1. Attitude (Psychology)　2. Child study.　I. Title.

34-34046

Library of Congress　　LB1117.L47 1934 a
Johns Hopkins Univ. Libr.　　[159.943]　158

NL　0342201　MdBJ WaWW PU DLC

Lichtenstein, Arthur, 1906-
　　... Can attitudes be taught?　By Arthur Lichtenstein,
PH. D.　Baltimore, The Johns Hopkins press, 1934.
　　ix, 89 p.　24½ cm.　(The Johns Hopkins university studies in education, no. 21)

Issued also as thesis (PH. D.) Johns Hopkins university.
Bibliography: p. 79-82.

1. Attitude (Psychology)　2. Child study.　I. Title.

LB5.J6　no. 21　　　[159.943]　158　　34-33115

OCU MiU OOxM MB NIC FMU NNC OrU Or Wa
NL　0342202　DLC MtBC MtU PPPL PU-Penn PBm PPT OO OU

Lichtenstein (August. Gerhard Gottfried.
　* De febrium intermittentium theoria et
therapia. cxxiii pp. 8°. *Helmstadii, typ. Fleck-
eisenianis.* [1804].

NL　0342203　DNLM

Lichtenstein, August Gerhard Gottfried.
　　Index alphabeticus generum botanicorum
quotquot a Willdenovio in speciebus plantarum et
a Persoonio in synopsi plantarum recensentur,
concinnatus ab A. G. G. Lichtenstein.
Helmstadii, 1814.
　　viii, 88 p.

NL　0342204　NN

QK91
.S6
1797
L5
[Lichtenstein, August Gerhard Gottfried]
1780-1851.
　　Index alphabeticum filicum, in Caroli a
Linné Specierum plantarum ed. 5. cura
Willdenowii, enumeratarum adjectis varieta-
tibus nominumque genericorum et trivialium
synonymia.　Berolini, Impensis G. C. Nauck,
1821.
　　60 p.　20 cm.

519 B. M.　Hulth p. 91.　Krok p. 433.

NL　0342205　NNBG

Lichtenstein, Ben W
　　A textbook of neuropathology; with clinical, anatomical
and technical supplements.　Philadelphia, W. B. Saunders
Co., 1949.
　　xviii, 474 p.　illus.　26 cm.

Includes "References."

1. Nervous system—Diseases.

RC341.L59　　　　616.8　　　　49-10136*

OC1W DNLM PPJ
NL　0342206　DLC CaBVaU OrU PPPCPh PPT NcU OU ViU

Lichtenstein, C
　　Stammbaum der Mitglieder des Familien-Vereins
　　　see under
　　　Achdus (Familien-Verein)

Lichtenstein, Dagobertus, 1831-
　　De hydrocephalo et encephalitide
　　Inaug. Diss.　Halle, 1856

NL　0342208　ICRL DNLM PPC

Lichtenstein, Carl August Ludwig, freiherr von
　　　see　Lichtenstein, Karl August Ludwig,
　　　　freiherr von, 1767-1845.

Lichtenstein, David.
　　פיתוח התעשיה ומימונה בארץ-ישראל.　ירושלים, המח-
　　לקה לעניני הנער של ההסתדרות הציונית, תש"ו.
　　[Jerusalem, 1946]
　　86 p.　tables.　19 cm.　(ערכים: ספריה המסן למדריכים. ט"ז)

1. Palestine—Indus.　I. Title.　(Series: 'Arakhim. 15)
　　　*Title transliterated: Pituḥ ha-taʻaśiyah u-mimunah
　　　be-Erets-Yiśrael.*

New York.　Public Libr.　　　　A 49-8204*
for Library of Congress

NL　0342210　NN

[Lichtenstein, Edmund] 1864-
　　... Ahlwardt's ende!　Authentische enthüllungen einge-
weihter.　Gesammelt von Ed. Mund [pseud.] ...　Berlin,
"Berliner fanfaren," J. van Groningen & co., 1892.
　　38 p.　22½ᶜᵐ.　("Berliner fanfaren, nr. 3)

At head of title : ... Judenflinten?—Antisemitenflinten.
On cover : 2. aufl.

1. Ahlwardt, Hermann, 1846-　　2. Jewish question.　3. Jews in Germany.　I. Title.

24-9186

Library of Congress　　　DS135.G33A5 1892

NL　0342211　DLC

VOLUME 332

[Lichtenstein, Edmund, 1864– .]
Sibirien in Preussen von Ed. Mund, [pseud. 3. aufl.] Berlin,
[J. van Groningen & co.] 1892.
pp. 36. (Berliner fanfaren, 2.)

NL 0342212   MH NN

[Lichtenstein, Edmund] 1864–
... Sei wahr! roman. Berlin, C. Duncker [*1914]
1 p. l., 349 p. 19ᶜᵐ. mk. 3
Author's pseud., L. Stein, at head of title.

I. Title.
Library of Congress   15–13548 Revised
Copyright A—Foreign   [PT2623.I 3S4 1914
                              11844

NL 0342213   DLC

Lichtenstein (Eduard) 1818– Die Cholera. Das
Wissenswertheste über diese Krankheit, nebst
den gebräuchlichsten Heilmitteln dagegen, sowie neue Vorschläge zur Verhütung und Heilung
derselben. vi, 7–72 pp. 8°. Breslau, A. Schulz
u. Comp., 1853. [P₁₁ v. 170.]

NL 0342214   DNLM

QP101
L613
Lichtenstein, Eduard, 1818–
Historia circulationis sanguinis ante et post
Harvejum ... Vratislaviae, typis Grassii,
Barthii et sociorum [1847]
4 p. l., [5]–35, [1] p.

Diss.-inaug., Breslau, 1847.
"Copia librorum": verso of 4th prel. leaf.
Vita.
From library of W. A. Greenhill.

NL 0342215   NNC PPC

Lichtenstein, Eduard, 1818–
——. Neuer Beitrag zur Cholera. Aetiolo-
gisches und Therapeutisches. (Zur fünfzigjährigen Jubelfeier der Friedrich-Wilhelms-Universität zu Berlin.) vi, 60 pp. 8°. Berlin,
A. Hirschwald, 1860. [P₁₁ v. 170.]

NL 0342216   DNLM

Lichtenstein, Eduard, 1811–
Ueber die fortschritte der neuesten
heilkunde; oder, Zum verständniss der
ärztlichen parteiungen der gegenwart...
von Dr. E. Lichtenstein... Breslau, E.
Aland, 1856.
vi, [7]–52 p.

Bound with Hedden, A. zur, Verderbniss
der zähne.

NL 0342217   MiU

Lichtenstein (Elisabeth). *Influence de la
fatigue sur les accidents du travail. 42 pp.
31. 8°. Montpellier, 1905. No. 9.

NL 0342218   DNLM

Lichtenstein, Ellen, 1899–
...Schlafsucht mit akromegalen erscheinungen
in der pubertät... Frankfurt a. M., Werner u.
Winter, G. m. b. H., 1925.
Cover-title: 14 p.

Inaug.-diss. - Universität zu Frankfurt a. M.
Lebenslauf.
"Literatur": p.12.

NL 0342219   MiDW DNLM

LICHTENSTEIN, ERICH, 1888– , ed.
Briefe an meinen Sohn. Heidelberg, Kemper
[1955] 130 p. illus. 18cm.

An anthology of letters to their children by artists, authors, statesmen,
etc., from Emperor Frederick II to the present day.

1. Letters, German—Collections. 2. Family in literature, German.
I. Title.

NL 0342220   NN

Lichtenstein, Erich, 1888–
Gottscheds ausgabe von Bayles dictionnaire: ein beitrag
zur geschichte der aufklärung, von dr. Erich Lichtenstein.
Heidelberg, C. Winter, 1915.
ix p., 1 l., 151 p. 23 cm. (*Added t.-p.:* Beiträge zur neueren litera-
turgeschichte ... Neue folge ... hft. VIII)
Issued in part (67 p.) as the author's inaugural dissertation,
Heidelberg, 1915.

1. Gottsched, Johann Christoph, 1700–1766. 2. Bayle, Pierre, 1647–
1706. Dictionnaire historique et critique. 3. Enlightenment.

PT2252.Z5L5   23—14058

NL 0342221   NcU NcD OU PPT ICU PU ViU FU NN IU NjP CaBVaU
              DLC NBuU CU GU IaU CtY OCU MiU CSt CLSU

PT
2252
.Z5
L51
Lichtenstein, Erich, 1888–
Die literarischen Anmerkungen Gottscheds zu
Bayles Dictionnaire. Heidelberg, C. Winter,
1915.
67 p.   23cm.

Inaug.-Diss. - Heidelberg.
Issued also under title: Gottscheds Aus-
gabe von Bayles dictionnaire.
Bibliographical footnotes.

NL 0342222   WU ICRL MH PU CtY

Lichtenstein, Erich, 1904–
Die Gesetzgebung im faschistischen Italien. Leipzig, R.
Noske, 1930.
vi, 95 p. 22½ cm. (*Added t.-p.:* Abhandlungen des Instituts für
Politische Auslandskunde an der Universität Leipzig, hrsg. von
Richard Schmidt. Hft. 11)
"Literatur": p. 93–95.

1. Public law—Italy. 2. Fascism—Italy. 3. Italy—Pol. & govt.—
1922–1945. I. Title. (Series: Leipzig. Universität. Institut für
Politik, Ausländisches Öffentliches Recht und Völkerrecht. Abhandlungen, Heft 11)

35–29760 rev

NL 0342223   DLC NN

HQ796
.L5
Lichtenstein, Ernst.
Umrisse einer soziologischen jugendkunde.
Berlin, Duncker [und] Humblot [1955]
111p.

Bibliography: p. 111.

1. Youth. 2. W - Youth. 3. Children.
4. W - Children. 5. Title.

NL 0342224   DS

Lichtenstein, Ernst, 1877–
Zur entstehung der aortenaneurysmen.
Inaug. diss. Freiburg, 1901.
Bibl.

NL 0342225   ICRL DNLM

BS2675
.L7
Lichtenstein, Ernst, 1900–
Die älteste christliche Glaubensformel.
74 p. 25 cm.
Offprint from Zeitschrift für Kirchenge-
schichte, v. 63 (1950)

1. Bible. N.T. 1 Corinthians XV, 3–5--
Criticism, interpretation, etc. 2. Creeds--
Hist. and Crit.

NL 0342226   IEG

Lichtenstein, Ernst, 1900–
... Erfahrungen mit Nitroscleran ...
Charlottenburg [1925]
23 cm.
Inaug.-Diss. - Berlin.
At head of title: Aus der III. Medizinischen
Universitäts-Klinik Berlin. Direktor: Geh. Rat
Prof. Dr. Goldscheider.
Lebenslauf.
Literaturverzeichnis: p. [18] - 19.

NL 0342227   CtY ICRL

Lichtenstein, Erwin, 1901–
Die verkehrs- konferenz von Barcelona.
Inaug. diss. Koenigsberg, 1922

NL 0342228   ICRL

Lichtenstein, Florus, 1878–
Spaetfolgen des entbindungsverfahrens ...
Inaug. diss. Breslau, 1905.
Bibl.

NL 0342229   ICRL

Lichtenstein, Franz, 1852–1884, ed.

Eilhard *von Oberge, 12th cent.*
Eilhart von Oberge. Herausgegeben von Franz Lichtenstein. Strassburg, K. J. Trübner; [etc., etc.], 1877.

Lichtenstein, Franz, 1852–1884, ed.

Müller, Friedrich Max, 1823–1900.
The German classics from the fourth to the nineteenth century, with biographical notices, translations into modern German, and notes, by F. Max Müller ... New ed., rev., enl., and
adapted to Wilhelm Scherer's 'History of German literature',
by F. Lichtenstein ... 2d ed. Oxford, The Clarendon press,
1906.

BF3003 Lichtenstein, Franz, 1852–1884.
.Z6   Das höfische leben zur zeit der minnesinger
v.7   von dr. Alwin Schultz...
              (In Anzeiger für deutsches alterthum und deut-
sche literatur. Berlin, 1881. 23ᶜᵐ. v.VII, p.
[97]–121)

D127 —— —— Separate.
.S4L7
              1. Schultz, Alwin, 1838–1909. Das höfische leben
zur zeit der minnesinger.

NL 0342231   ICU

Lichtenstein, Franz, 1852–1884, ed.

Ottokar von Steiermark, ca. 1265–1320.
Österreichische Reimchronik. Nach den Abschriften
Franz Lichtensteins, herausgegeben von Joseph Seemüller
... Hannover, Hahnsche Buchhandlung, 1890–93.

VOLUME 332

Lichtenstein, Franz, 1852–1884, ed.

Lindener, Michael, *d.* 1562.
Michael Lindeners ¦Rastbüchlein und Katzipori, hrsg. von Franz Lichtenstein. Tübingen, Litterarischer verein in Stuttgart, 1883.

Lichtenstein, Franz, 1852–1884.
Zur Kritik der Prosaromans Tristrant und Isolde. Breslau, R. Nischkowsky, 1877.
36 p.   22 cm.
Diss. - Breslau.

NL   0342234   MdBP CtY NIC PU CU OClW MH

Lichtenstein, Friedrich Wilhelm Jakob, 1826–1875.
Lebensgeschichte des Herrn Jesu Christi in chronologischer uebersicht. Mit erläuternden anmerkungen von dr. F. W. Jakob Lichtenstein ... Erlangen, A. Deichert, 1856.
xiv, 496 p.   22cm.

1. Jesus Christ—Chronology.   I. Title.

33–17444

Library of Congress   BT303.L7   232.9

NL   0342235   DLC OO MH

Lichtenstein, Fritz: Über die Todesursache bei Ileus m. bes. Berücks. d. an d. Königsberg. chirurg. Univ.-Kl. angewandten Absaugeverfahrens nach Kirschner. [Maschinenschrift] 32, v S. 4°. — Auszug: Königsberg i. P. 1922: Kümmel. 2 Bl. 8°
Königsberg, Med. Diss. v. 24. Aug. 1922 [1923]   [U 23. 7547

NL   0342236   ICRL

Lichtenstein, G.
Die schlacht bei Lutter am Barenberge... Braunschweig, Dehme & Mueller, 1850.
190p.   map.

AC931   [Haverford-Bauer pamphlets, v. 117, no. 8]
.H3
v.117

NL   0342237   DLC

Lichtenstein, G   J   A
Der Gesundbrunnen und das Bad bei Helmstädt.
Helmstädt, In der Fleckeisenschen Buchhandlung, 1818
xvi, 157 p.

NL   0342238   MBCo

Lichtenstein, Gaston, 1879–1954.
Early history of Tarboro, North Carolina : also collated colonial public claims of Edgecombe county, and Easter Sunday in Savannah, Ga. By Gaston Lichtenstein. Richmond, W. E. Jones, book and job printer, 1908.
16 p.   23½cm.

1. Tarboro, N. C.—Hist.   2. Edgecombe co., N. C.—Hist.   3. Savannah, Ga.—Descr.

Library of Congress   E264.T17L6   8–31947

NL   0342239   DLC MtU ViN CtY OCH Nc Vi ViU PU NN NcU

Lichtenstein, Gaston, 1879–
Early social life in Edgecombe, also, Early history of Edgecombe, and a Tarborean's experience abroad. Three articles by Gaston Lichtenstein ... Richmond, Va., W. E. Jones, printer, 1904.
16 p.   23½cm.
"Reprinted from the Tarborough southerner, Tarboro, N. C."

1. Edgecombe Co., N. C.

Library of Congress   F262.E2L6   5–3882

NL   0342240   DLC Or NcU NN ViN CtY Nc MWA Vi OU NcD

Lichtenstein, Gaston.
For whom was Edgecombe county named?

(In N.C. booklet.   Oct.1918.   v.18, no.2.)

NL   0342241   NcU

Lichtenstein, Gaston, 1879–
From Richmond to North Cape, by Gaston Lichtenstein. Richmond, Va., William Byrd press, 1922.
viii, [9]–160 p.   front.   20 cm.
"Originally the chapters of this book appeared as a series of articles in the Tarboro (North Carolina) southerner."—Pref.

1. Scandinavia—Descr. & trav.   2. Germany—Descr. & trav.   I. Title.

DL10.L5   22––10259

NL   0342242   DLC MB Nc MiU ViU

Lichtenstein, Gaston, 1879–
George Washington's lost birthday. History of Meridian lodge; also other articles written at various times, by Gaston Lichtenstein. Richmond, Va., The William Byrd press, inc., 1924.
115 p.   front (facsim.) 1 illus., ports.   22 cm.

1. Washington, George, pres. U. S.—Anniversaries, etc.   2. Freemasons, Richmond, Va. Meridian lodge.   I. Title.

E312.6.L63   24––13252

NL   0342243   DLC NcD ViU MB MWA NN NcU OClWHi ViN

Lichtenstein, Gaston, 1879–
History of the Jews of Richmond.   Their progress and prospects.   By Gaston Lichtenstein.   Chicago, Ill., Bloch & Newman [1913]
32 p.   illus. (incl. ports.)   32cm.
Special issue of the Reform advocate, Mar. 8, 1913.

1. Jews in Richmond, Va.   I. The Reform advocate.

13–13694 Revised

Library of Congress   F234.R5L68

NL   0342244   DLC NN Vi

Lichtenstein, Gaston, 1879– joint author.

Ezekiel, Herbert Tobias.
The history of the Jews of Richmond from 1769 to 1917, by Herbert T. Ezekiel and Gaston Lichtenstein. Richmond, Va., H. T. Ezekiel, 1917.

Lichtenstein, Gaston.
Louis D. Wilson, Mexican war martyr, also, Thos. H. Hall, Andrew Johnson as he really was, and Our town common; four articles by Gaston Lichtenstein. Richmond, Va., H. T. Ezekiel, printer, 1911.
20 p.   23cm.

1. Edgecomb co., N. C.   2. Wilson, Louis D., 1789–1847.   3. Hall, Thomas H., 1773–1853.   4. Johnson, Andrew, pres. U. S., 1808–1875.   5. Tarboro, N. C. Town common.

Library of Congress   F262.E2L63   12––2457

NL   0342246   DLC CU OO OCU MiU ViU NcU NN Vi

Lichtenstein, Gaston, 1879–1954.
Recollections of my teacher, Frank S. Wilkinson. Richmond, Va., Masonic Home Press, 1953.
LB
875
W68
L5
[17] p.   24 cm.
"Reprinted from the Daily southerner, Tarboro', North Carolina."
Author's autographed presentation copy to William Moseley Brown.
"Masonic musings": p. [16–17]

1. Wilkinson, Franklin Smith, 1833–1920.   2. Tarboro Male Academy, Tarboro, N. C.   I. Title.

NL   0342247   Vi OCl NcD NIC PBL OCU

Lichtenstein, Gaston, 1879–   *comp.*
Repatriation of prisoners of war from Siberia; a documentary narrative, compiled by Gaston Lichtenstein. Richmond, Va., The William Byrd press, inc., 1924.
177 p.   fold. map, facsims.   23½cm.
Compiled from the records of the Siberian war prisoners repatriation fund, the American Red cross, and the National Catholic war council.   cf. Pref.

1. European war, 1914–1918—Prisoners and prisons, Russian.   I. Siberian war prisoners repatriation fund.   II. Title.

Library of Congress   D627.R8L5   24–14037

NL   0342248   DLC NcD OCH PBm Nc

Lichtenstein, Gaston, 1879–
Thomas Jefferson as war governor, also three travel articles and some North Carolina history, by Gaston Lichtenstein. Richmond, Va., The William Byrd press, inc., 1925.
112 p.   front. (facsim.) plates.   22½cm.

1. Jefferson, Thomas, pres. U. S., 1743–1826.   2. Virginia—Hist.—Revolution.   3. North Carolina—Hist.—Colonial period.

Library of Congress   E332.L7   25–11115 Revised

NL   0342249   DLC NcD OCU MiU ViU PSC NN NcU

Lichtenstein, Gaston, 1879–
The Virginia Lichtensteins; amplified by historical and biographical data, by Gaston Lichtenstein. Richmond, Va., H. T. Ezekiel, printer, 1912.
16 numb. l.   front. (port.)   22cm.

1. Lichtenstein family.   I. Title.

12–15737

Library of Congress   CS71.L697 1912

NL   0342250   DLC OCU OCH NcD NN NcU MWA Vi

Lichtenstein, Gaston, 1879–
A visit to Young's pier at Atlantic City, N. J., also, When Edgecombe was a-borning, The word sheriff, and Products of colonial North Carolina. By Gaston Lichtenstein ... Richmond, Va., W. E. Jones, printer, 1908.
15 p.   23cm.
Reprinted from the Tarborough southerner, Tarboro, N. C.

1. Edgecombe Co., N. C.—Hist.   2. North Carolina—Hist.—Colonial period.   3. Atlantic City, N. J.

Library of Congress   F262.E2L6   9–14747

NL   0342251   DLC NcD OCU Vi TKL Nc NN NcU

Lichtenstein, Gaston, 1879–
When Tarboro was incorporated; also Reverend James Moir, Edgecombe changes her county seat, and Germantown, Pennsylvania. By Gaston Lichtenstein ... Richmond, Va., Capitol printing company, 1910.
27 p.   23½cm.
Reprinted from the Tarborough southerner, Tarboro, N. C.

1. Tarboro, N. C.—Hist.   2. Edgecombe co., N. C.—Hist.   3. Germantown, Pa.

Library of Congress   F264.T17L63   11––6123

MiU NN
NL   0342252   DLC Or OCH OO OCl NcU I MB Vi Nc OCU

VOLUME 332

Lichtenstein, Gaston, 1879–1954, joint comp.

Ezekiel, Herbert Tobias, *comp.*
World war section of The history of the Jews of Richmond, by Herbert T. Ezekiel and Gaston Lichtenstein. Richmond, Va., H. T. Ezekiel, 1920.

Lichtenstein, Georgius Rudolphus, 1745–1807, respondent.
Arithmeticae logarithmicae succinta explicatio
see under   Bunsen, Carl Christian Wilhelm, praeses.

Lichtenstein (Georgius Rudolphus) [1745–1807]. [Pr.] de ratione circuitus sanguinis per cor et pulmones quo lectiones hybernas indicat. 15 pp. 4°. *Helmstadii, lit. vid. B. Pauli, 1777.*

NL 0342255   DNLM

TN144
L69
Corning
Museum of
Glass
Library
Lichtenstein, Georg Rudolph.
Entdekte Geheimnisse oder Erklärung aller Kunstwörter und Redensarten bey Bergwerken und Hütten-Arbeiten nach alphabetischer Ordnung in zween Theilen.   Nebst einem kurzen Vorbericht von D. Georg Rudolph Lichtenstein. Helmstedt, Johann Heinrich Kühnlin, 1778.
122 p.   18 cm.

Contents,–pt. 1. Von Berg-Werken besonders vom Bergbau und dazu gehörigen Künsten.–pt. 2. Vom Puchwerk, Probieren, Schmelzen und Glasmachen.

*C 5521.   1. Mineral industries–Early works to 1800.   2. Manufacture of glass–Early works
I. Title.

NL 0342257   NCornC MH

Lichtenstein, Gustav.
... Vergleichende untersuchung über die jüngeren bearbeitungen der Chanson de Girart de Viane von Gustav Lichtenstein ...   Im anhang: Kapitelüberschriften der Dresdener hs. 081 hrsg. von E. Stengel. Marburg, N. G. Elwert, 1899 [1898]
1 p. l., 72 p. 23½ᶜᵐ. (Ausgaben und abhandlungen aus dem gebiete der romanischen philologie. 97)
Completed and published by E. Stengel after the author's death.
1. Girard de Viane.   2. Bertrand de Bar-sur-Aube, fl. ca. 1220.
I. *Stengel, Edmund, 1845–   ed.

Library of Congress   PC13.A87 hft. 97

22–18351

MB IU
NL 0342258   DLC CU PU CaBVaU PBm OU OClW MiU MdBP

Lichtenstein, Gustav, musician
Odd-Fellow Gruss. Ged. von S. Pniower; componiert von G. Lichtenstein.
Berlin: the composer, 1874.
1 L.

NL 0342259   OCH

Lichtenstein, Gustav, musician
Heiss mich nicht reden. Mignon's Lied von Goethe für eine Alt- oder Baritonstimme mit Begleitung des Harmoniums oder Klaviers. Berlin: C. Simon [by] C. G. Röder [in] Leipzig, [189-?].
3 p.

NL 0342260   OCH

Lichtenstein, Gustav, 1860–   tr.

Päivärinta, Pietari, 1827–1913.
Finnische novellen, von Pietari Päivärinta. Deutsch von Gustav Lichtenstein ... Leipzig, P. Reclam jun. [1889–

Lichtenstein, H.
Geschichte der Israeliten von dem babylonischen exile bis auf die neueste zeit; für die oberklasse israelitischer volksschulen und für die mittelklasse höherer jüdischer lehranstalten bearbeitet von H. Lichtenstein ...   Nebst einem vorworte von B. Wechsler ... Oldenburg, Verlag der Schulzeschen buchhandlung, 1854.
xii, 262 p., 1 l. 21ᶜᵐ.
Bibliography: p. xi.

1. Jews–Hist.

35–23360

Library of Congress   DS118.L6   933

NL 0342262   DLC OCH

Lichtenstein, Hans, 1901–
Die fastenrolle ...
Inaug. Diss. –Berlin, [1932]
Lebenslauf.

NL 0342263   ICRL PU NjP

Lichtenstein, Ḥayah (Weizmann) 1877–
בצל קורתנו. פרקי זכרונות מבית אבא. תל-אביב, "עם עובד"
[Tel-Aviv, 1947/48] תש"ח.
256 p. ports. 22 cm.

1. Zionists–Correspondence, reminiscences, etc.
Title transliterated: Be-tsel koratenu.

DS151.L48A3   54–52262

NL 0342264   DLC

Lichtenstein, Ḥayah (Weizmann) 1877–
אל הגבול הנכסף. תל-אביב, עם עובד, תשי"ג.
[Tel-Aviv, 1952/53]
174 p. ports. 22 cm.
Memoirs.
Continuation of the author's בצל קורתנו

1. Zionists–Correspondence, reminiscences, etc.   I. Title.
Title transliterated: El ha-gevul ha-nikhsaf.

DS151.L48A4   54–55635

NL 0342265   DLC

Lichtenstein, Henry
Travels in southern Africa, in the years, 1803, 1804, 1805, and 1806; translated from the original German, by Anne Plumptre.   London, Printed for Henry Colburn, 1812
383+32p.

NL 0342266   ViHaI ODW

Lichtenstein, Hermann, 1827–1912
see   Lichtenstein, Jechiel Zebi, 1827–1912.

1894–
Lichtenstein, Hermann Zur Klinik der akuten gelben Leberatrophie, mit besonderer Berücksichtigung von vier Fällen. Aus d. Med. Klinik zu Königsberg Pr. Dir.: Mathes. [In Maschinenschrift.] 37 S. 4°(2°). — Auszug: Königsberg i. P. 1920: Kümmel. 2 Bl. 8°
Königsberg, Med. Diss. v. 25. Sept. 1920, Ref. Klewitz
[Geb. 17. Jan. 94 Königsberg i. P.; Wohnort: Königsberg; Staatsangeh.: Preußen; Vorbildung: Kneiphöf. G. Königsberg Reife 12; Studium: Königsberg 10 S.; Coll. 20. Sept. 20; Approb. 26. Juli 20.]   [U 20. 2627

NL 0342268   ICRL

Lichtenstein, Herta, 1905–
Die finanzwirtschaft der deutschen grossstädte von 1925 bis 1931; ein beitrag zu dem problem des finanzausgleichs, von di Herta Lichtenstein ... Jena, G. Fischer, 1933.
x, 112 p. 24½ᵐᵐ. (Added t.-p.: Finanzwissenschaftliche und volkswirtschaftliche studien ... hft. 29)
"Einführung in die literatur des behandelten gebietes": p. [105]–109.

1. Municipal finance–Germany.   I. Title.

Library of Congress   HJ9473.L5   33–32679
                                              352.10943

NL 0342269   DLC ICRL WU ICU IU

Lichtenstein, Hillel, 1815–1891.
עת לעשות; שאלות ותשובות להורות לעם ד' דרך ילכו בת. פערב אויפל. סאטמאר, ח. י. ליכטענשטיין, תרס"ם.
Szatmar, [1908/9]
179 l. 28 cm.
In Yiddish.

1. Responsa.   I. Title.
Title transliterated: 'Et la'asot.

BM522.6.I 3 1908   64–43272

NL 0342270   DLC

Lichtenstein, Hillel, 1815–1891.
מקרי דרדקי. על בראשית-במדבר. לעמברג.
Lemberg, 1888–[99]
4 v. 21 cm.
Vols. 2–4 published in Kolomea.

1. Bible. O. T. Pentateuch–Commentaries.   I. Title.
Title transliterated: Makri dardake.

BS1225.L5   56–50036

NL 0342271   DLC

Lichtenstein, Hillel, 1815–1891.
ספר תשובות בית הילל; חלק ראשון מס' הלכות קטנות. מאת הילל ל"ש. כולל מכתבים במילי דשמיא. סגולות ורפואות הנפש ... כולם נקבצו באו לבית הדפום ע"י חיים יעקב ליכטענשטיין. סאטמאר. בדפום של ז. שווארץ. 1908.
58 l. 23 cm.

1. Responsa–1800–   2. Ethics, Jewish.   I. Title: Teshuvot Bet Hilel.   II. Title: Bet Hilel.
Title romanized: Sefer Teshuvot Bet Hilel.

BM522.6.I 33 1908   78–251662

NL 0342272   DLC

AS
182
B51A31+
1838
no.9
Lichtenstein, Hinrich, 1780–1857.
Beitrag zur ornithologischen Fauna von Californien nebst Bemerkungen über die Artkennzeichen der Pelicane und über einige Vögel von den Sandwich-Inseln.
(In Akademie der Wissenschaften, Berlin. Abhandlungen. Berlin. 27cm. [v. 23] (1838) Physikalische Abhandlungen, p. [417]–451)

NL 0342273   NIC CtY MB

QL31
.N3A4
Lichtenstein, Hinrich, 1780–1857.

Naumann, Johann Friedrich, 1780–1857.
Briefwechsel mit H. Lichtenstein, 1818–1856. Hrsg. und erläutert von Erwin Stresemann und Peter Thomsen. Kopenhagen, E. Munksgaard, 1954.

VOLUME 332

QL
705
.L72   Lichtenstein, Hinrich, 1780-1857.
    Darstellung neuer oder wenig bekannter Säuge-
thiere in Abbildungen und Beschreibungen von
fünf und sechzig Arten auf fünfzig colorirten
Steindrucktafeln nach den Originalen des Zoologischen Museums der Universität zu Berlin.
Berlin, C.G.Lüderitz, 1827-34.
    1 v.   illus.
    1.Mammals--Pictorial works.
                Full name: Martin Hinrich
                Carl Lichtenstein.

NL 0342275   MiU MdBP NN MH ICJ PPAN MdBJ

    Lichtenstein, Hinrich, 1780-1857, ed.
    Descriptiones animalium quae in itinere ad
Maris australis terras ... collegit
    see under Forster, Johann Reinhold,
1729-1798.

Lichtenstein, . Heinrich , 1780-1857.
  Ehrendenkmal des Herrn J. C. W. Illiger.
  (In Koeniglich-preussische Akademie der Wissenschaften. Ab-
handlungen. 1814/1815, pp. 48-64. Berlin. 1818.)
  Verzeichnis von Illiger's Schriften, pp. 63, 64.

G8928 — Illiger, Johann Carl Wilhelm. 1775-1813.

NL 0342277   MB

Lichtenstein . Heinrich 1780-1857.
  Erläuterungen der Nachrichten des Franc. Hernandez von den
vierfüssigen Thieren Neuspaniens.
  (In Koeniglich-preussische Akademie der Wissenschaften. Physikalische Klasse. Abhandlungen. 1827, pp. 89-127. Berlin. 1830.)

G9024 — Hernández, Francisco. 1514-1578. — Mexico. Zool.

NL 0342278   MB DLC

Lichtenstein, Hinrich, 1780-1857.
  Ferdinand Deppe's travels in California in 1837; translated from
the German by Gustave O. Arlt. Los Angeles. Glen Dawson,
1953. 3 p.l., xi-xiii p., 1 l., 27 p., 1 l. 19cm. (Early California
travels series. 15)

"190 copies printed...at the Plantin press."
Introduction signed: Glen Dawson.
"Translated...from...Zeitschrift für Erdkunde ₁1847₎ vol. 7, pp. 383-90. Except

for the first paragraph the same material appeared in 1839 in 'Beitrag zur ornithologischen Fauna von Californiau ₍sic₎' by H. Lichtenstein (Abh. Akad. Wiss., Berlin,
1838, p. 417-51...)."—p. xii.

53R0973. 1. Deppe, Ferdinand.   2. California—Descr. and trav.,
1800-1850. I. Series. II. Arlt,   Gustave Otto, 1895- , tr.
III. Dawson, Glen, 1912-   IV. Title.

    CaBVaU CCamarSJ
NL 0342280   NN OrU IEN ICN CU-B CoD NIC InL CLSU

Lichtenstein,   Heinrich , 1780-1857.
  Die Gattung Dendrocolaptes. Plates.
  (In Koeniglich-preussische Akademie der Wissenschaften. Physikalische Klasse. Abhandlungen. 1818/1819, pp. 197-210, 1820/
1821, pp. 255-266. Berlin. 1820, 1822.)

G8956 — Dendrocolaptæ.

NL 0342281   MB

M912.637
L699k   Lichtenstein, Hinrich, 1780-1857.
    Karte des europaeischen Gebiets am Vorge-
birge der Guten Hoffnung, nach eignen Wahr-
nemungen, nach den neuesten auf Befehl der
holländischen Regierung angestellten Beobachtungen und den besten älteren Materialien zusammengetragen und entworfen. Nie-
dergelegt und ausgeführt von H.H. Gottholdt.
Gestochen von Carl Mare. Berlin, C. Salfeld, 1811.
    21 1/2x28 1/2 inches.

    Gezeichnet von Joseph Jones in der Cap-
stadt und Carl Langner in Berlin.

    1.Africa, South - Maps. 2.Cape of Good
Hope - Maps. I.Gottholdt, H.H.

NL 0342283   CLU

Lichtenstein, Hinrich, 1780-1857.
  [Lectures on zoology. MSS. notes taken by
H.C.L. Barkow] Berlin, 1817.
  4°.
    German script.

NL 0342284   DNLM

LICHTENSTEIN, . Hinrich , 1780-1857.
  Naturhistorischer Anhang [zu Eversmanns Reise].
  (In Eversmann. Reise von Orenburg nach Buchara. Pp. 111-150
Berlin, 1823.)

Sheet D 408:   Oct. 17, 1899

NL 0342285   MB

Lichtenstein, Hinrich, 1780-1857.
  1854. Nomenclator | avium | Musei Zoologici Berolinensis. | Nam-
enverzeichniss | der | in der zoologischen Sammlung der König-
lichen | Universität zu Berlin | aufgestellten Arten von | Vögeln |
nach den in der neueren Systematik am meisten | zur Geltung
gekommenen | Namen der Gattungen | und | ihrer Unterabtheil-
ungen. | Berlin. | Gedruckt in der Buchdruckerei der Königlichen
Akademie | der Wissenschaften. | 1854.
  1 vol. 8vo, pp. I-VIII, 1-123. Berlin.

NL 0342286   PPAN MH

---

              hinrich, 1780 - 1857
Lichtenstein, Hinrich, 1780- 1857.
  Nomenclator reptilium et amphibien Musei
zoologici Berolinensis; namenverzeichniss... Berlin,
1856.
    48 p.

NL 0342287   PU-BZ

        Lichtenstein, Hinrich, 1780-1857.
DT731
.E9   **Eybers, George von Welfling,** 1887-   **ed. and tr.**
  Op die voetspoor van die ou reisigers, stories uit Kolbe,
Barrow, Lichtenstein en Campbell. Oorvertel deur G. W.
Eybers ... Kaapstad, Maskew Miller beperk, 1926.

Lichtenstein, Hinrich, 1780-1857.
  Reisen im südlichen Africa, in den jahren 1803, 1804, 1805
und 1806, von Hinrich Lichtenstein ... Berlin, C. Salfeld,
1811-12.
  2 v. front. (port.) plates (part fold.) 20½ᶜᵐ.

    1. Africa, South—Descr. & trav. I. Title.
           ₍Full name: Martin Hinrich Carl Lichtenstein₎
                           5-15253 Revised
  Library of Congress   DT731.L09

NL 0342289   LDC CtY

DT
731
L617r1   Lichtenstein, Hinrich, 1780-1857.
    Reizen in het zuidelijk gedeelte van Afrika,
in de jaren 1803, 1804, 1805 en 1806. Verkort.
Dordrecht, Blussé & Van Braam, 1818.
    331 p. illus.

    1. Africa, South - Descr. & trav. I. Title.

NL 0342290   CLU

---

        *Lichtenstein, Hinrich, 1780-1857, ed.

  Zimmermann, Eberhard August Wilhelm, von, 1743-1815.
    Taschenbuch der reisen; oder, Unterhaltende darstellung
der entdeckungen des 18ten jahrhunderts in rücksicht der
länder, menschen und productenkunde. Für jede klasse von
lesern, von E. A. W. von Zimmermann ... für das jahr
1802,   Leipzig,
G. Fleischer d. jüng. ₁1802₎–

LICHTENSTEIN, HINRICH, 1780-1857.
    Travels in Southern Africa, in the years
1803, 1804, 1805, and 1806. Translated from
the original German, by Anne Plumptre.
London, H. Colburn, 1812.
    xii, 383, ₍32₎p. front. (port.)plates. 27cm.

NL 0342292   ICN CU MH CtY MnU OU NN MdBP PPL PPAN

Lichtenstein, Hinrich, 1780-1857.
  Travels in southern Africa in the years 1803, 1804, 1805 and
1806, by Henry Lichtenstein. A reprint of the translation
from the original German by Anne Plumptre. Cape Town,
The Van Riebeeck society. 1928-30.
  2 v. plates (1 fold.) port., fold. map. 22ᶜᵐ. ₍Van Riebeeck society.
Publications, 10-11₎
  With reproduction of title-pages of the first edition of this translation.
(London, 1812-15. 2 v.)
  1. Africa, South—Descr. & trav.   I. Plumptre, Anne, 1760-1818, tr.
II. Title.
                  ₍Full name: Martin Hinrich Carl Lichtenstein₎
                            34-6763
  Library of Congress   DT821.V3 no. 10-11
                      (968.0082) 916.8

NL 0342293   DLC CtY MH CSt NcD CU NN NSyU

Lichtenstein,   Hinrich 1780-1857.
  Über äussere Backentaschen an Nagethieren. Plate.
  (In Koeniglich-preussische Akademie der Wissenschaften. Physikalische Klasse. Abhandlungen. 1822/1823, pp. 13-20. Berlin.
1825.)

G9008 — Rodentia.

NL 0342294   MB DLC

Lichtenstein,   Hinrich 1780-1857.
  Über die ägyptische Stachelmaus. Nachträgliche Bemerkungen zu
der Abhandlung über die Stachelratten.
  (In Koeniglich-preussische Akademie der Wissenschaften. Physikalische Klasse. Abhandlungen. 1822/1823, pp. 21-24. Berlin.
1825.)

G9007 — Mouse. — Egypt. Zool.

NL 0342295   MB DLC

Lichtenstein,   Hinrich 1780-1857.
  Ueber die Antilopen des nördlichen Africa, besonders in Beziehung
auf die Kenntniss, welche die Alten davon gehabt haben. Plates.
  (In Koeniglich-preussische Akademie der Wissenschaften. Physikalische Klasse. Abhandlungen. 1824, pp. 195-240. Berlin.
1826.)

G9017 — Africa, North. Zool. — Antelope. — Natural history.

NL 0342296   MB DLC

VOLUME 332

Lichtenstein, H inrich 1780-1857.
Ueber die Gattung Gracula aus der Familie der Krähenvögel Coraces).
(In Koeniglich-preussische Akademie der Wissenschaften. Physikalische Klasse. Abhandlungen. 1816/1817, pp. 143-154. Berlin. 1819.)

G8937 — Gracula. — Crows.

NL 0342297 MB

Lichtenstein, H inrich 1780-1857.
Über die Gattung *Mephitis*. Plates.
(In Koeniglich-preussische Akademie der Wissenschaften. Physikalische Klasse. Abhandlungen. 1836. Pp. 249-313. Berlin. 1838.)

H3249 — Skunk.

NL 0342298 MB PPAN DLC

Lichtenstein, Hinrich i.e Martin Hinrich Carl
Ueber die springmaeuse, oder die arten der gattung Dipus.

(In K. Akademie der wissenschaften. Berlin. Abh. 1825. Berlin, 1825. 4°. Physikalische klasse, p. 133-161. 6 pl.)

AS182
.B33

NL 0342299 DLC CtY

Lichtenstein, Hinrich, 1780-1857
Über die Springmäuse oder die sämtlichen bis jetzt bekannten Arten der Gattung Dipus, von M. H. C. Lichtenstein. Berlin, Druckerei der Königl. Akademie der Wissenschaften, 1828.
29p. 10 col. plates
"Gelesen in der Königl. Akademie der Wissenschaften am 20. Januar 1825."

NL 0342300 MH-Z CtY ICJ

Lichtenstein, H inrich 1780-1857.
Über die Verwandtschaft der kleinen (Insectenfressenden) Raubthiere mit den Nagern.
(In Koeniglich-preussische Akademie der Wissenschaften. Physikalische Klasse. Abhandlungen. 1831, pp. 345-360. Berlin. 1832.)

H3267 — Rodentia. — Insectivora.

NL 0342301 MB DLC

Lichtenstein, H inrich 1780-1857.
Über die weissen Robben. Plate.
(In Koeniglich-preussische Akademie der Wissenschaften. Physikalische Klasse. Abhandlungen. 1822/1823, pp. 1-12. Berlin. 1825.)

G9008 — Seal. The animal.

NL 0342302 MB DLC

Lichtenstein, H inrich 1780-1857.
Über einige Nordamerikanische Hirsch-Arten. Plate.
(In Koeniglich-preussische Akademie der Wissenschaften. Physikalische Klasse. Abhandlungen. 1856, pp. 269-285. Berlin. 1857.)

H3255 — Deer. — America, North. Zool.

NL 0342303 MB NIC DLC

Lichtenstein, H inrich, 1780-1857.
Über neue merkwürdige säugethiere des Königlichen zoologischen museums; von H. Lichtenstein und W. Peters ... Berlin, Druckerei der Akademie der wissenschaften, in commission bei A. Hirschwald, 1855.

1 p. l., 19, 1 p. III col. pl. 29 x 23½ᶜᵐ.

From Abhandl. der K. Preuss. akad. der wiss. 1854.

CONTENTS.—Über die gattung *Centurio* Gray.—Über *Hyonycteris*.—Über *Antilope leucotis* Licht. Pet.

1. Bats. 2. Antilope leucotis. I. Peters, Wilhelm Karl Hartwig, 1815-1883, joint author.

Library of Congress QL708.L6 6-43570†

NL 0342304 DLC NIC CtY

QL71
.B5A2
1818

Lichtenstein, Hinrich, 1780-1857.
Berlin. Universität. *Zoologisches museum.*
Verzeichniss der doubletten des Zoologischen museums der Königl. universität zu Berlin, nebst beschreibung vieler bisher unbekannter arten von säugethieren, vögeln, amphibien und fischen, herausgegeben von dr. H. Lichtenstein ... Berlin, In commission bei T. Trautwein, 1823.

Lichtenstein, Heinrich, 1780-1857.
Von den Sepien mit Krallen.
(In Koeniglich-preussische Akademie der Wissenschaften. Physikalische Klasse. Abhandlungen. 1818/1819, pp. 211-226. Berlin. 1820.)

G8056 — Sepia.

NL 0342306 MB

Lichtenstein, Hinrich, 1780-1857.
Voyage de Henri Lichtenstein dans l'Afrique méridionale, pendant les années 1803, 1804, 1805 et 1806.
Walckenaer, C. A., *baron*. Collection des relations de voyages en Afrique. Paris, 1842. 21ᶜᵐ. v. 17, p. 418-523; v. 18, p. 1-244.

1. Africa, South—Descr. & trav.

Full name: Martin Hinrich Carl Lichtenstein
CA 5—615 Unrev'd

Library of Congress DT1.W16 vol. 17, 18

NL 0342307 DLC

Lichtenstein, Heinrich, 1780-1857.
Die Werke von Marcgrave und Piso über die Naturgeschichte Brasiliens, erläutert aus den wieder aufgefundenen Originalzeichnungen.
(In Koeniglich-preussische Akademie der Wissenschaften. Physikalische Klasse. Abhandlungen. 1814/1815, pp. 201-222, 1816/1817, pp. 155-178; 1820/1821, pp. 237-254, 267-288; 1826, pp. 4 65. Berlin. 1818-1829.)

G8939 — Marcgraff, Georg. 1610-1644. — Piso, Willem. — Brazil. Nat. hist.

NL 0342308 MB DLC PPAN

Lichtenstein, Hinrich, 1780-1857.
Das Zoologische museum der Universität zu Berlin Von Hinrich Lichtenstein ... Berlin, In commission be F. Dümmler, 1816.
108 p., 1 l. fold. plan. 20ᶜᵐ.
[Zoologisches museum, Berlin. Catalogues. 1816-1856. no. 1. 22½ᶜᵐ]
———— 2. ausg. Berlin, 1818.
4 p. l., 120 p. fold. plan. 19½ᶜᵐ.
[Zoologisches museum, Berlin. Catalogues. 1816-1856. no. 2. 22½ᶜᵐ]
1. Berlin. Universität. K. Zoologisches museum.

Library of Congress QL71.B5A2 6-17823-4

NL 0342309 DLC NN

Lichtenstein, Hinrich, 1780-1857.
Zur geschichte der Sing-akademie in Berlin. Nebst einer nachricht über das fest am funfzigsten jahrestage ihrer stiftung und einem alphabetischen verzeichniss aller personen, die ihr als mitglieder angehört haben. Berlin, Trautwein & co., 1843.
xlviii, [2], 47 p. 27ᶜᵐ.
Historical sketch signed: Lichtenstein.

1. Sing-akademie, Berlin. I. Title.

Full name: Martin Hinrich Carl Lichtenstein
Library of Congress ML279.8.B23

5—19802
[a41b1]

NL 0342310 DLC

HD7834
.Z6

Lichtenstein, Howard, joint author.
Zorn, Burton A 1905-
More important provisions of the Labor-management relations act, 1947; an analysis of the Taft-Hartley labor law prepared for the Executive Committee of the New York State Chamber of Commerce by Burton A. Zorn and Howard Lichtenstein. New York, Chamber of Commerce of the State of New York [1946]

Lichtenstein, Hugo.
... Ueber Uterusperforationen bei Abortausräumung ... Höxter a.d. Weser, 1927.
Inaug.-Diss. - Göttingen.
"Literaturverzeichnis": p. 54-55.

NL 0342312 CtY MiU

Lichtenstein, Hugo, d. 1902.
Geschichte des Siegels der Stadt Dorpat. Aus dem Nachlass des weil. Stadtarchivar H. Lichtenstein; bearbeitet und hrsg. von Arnold Feuereisen ... Dorpat: H. Laakmann, 1907. 70 p. plates, port., tables. 8°. (Gelehrte estnische Gesellschaft zu Dorpat. Verhandlungen. Bd. 22, Heft 1.)

1. Seals, Russian—Dorpat. 2. Feu-   ereisen, Arnold, 1868-   , editor.
3. Ser.

September 11, 1925

NL 0342313 NN

LICHTENSTEIN, IGNAC, d. 1908.
Ein Geheimniss aus dem Talmud. [Wien, L. Schönberger, 189-] 41 p. 23cm.

Film reproduction. Positive.

1. Jesus Christ in the Talmud. 2. Jesus Christ--Messiahship.

NL 0342314 NN

Lichtenstein, Isaac, 1888-
Geto motiwn
see under Walkowitz, Abraham, 1880-

Lichtenstein, Isaac, 1888-   illus.
Hillel Gorny
see under Gold, Herman, 1888-

Lichtenstein, Isaac, 1888-
ירושלים. Jerusalem; portfolio of 10 images.
באניט. ניו יארק, 1941,
[2] l., [10] plates. 28 cm.

1. Jerusalem—Descr.—Views. 2. Jews in art.
Title transliterated: Jerusalem.

NC115.L15A44 741.91 51-50192

NL 0342317 DLC OC1 MB

VOLUME 332

Hebraic Sect.

Lichtenstein, Isaac, 1888–
קדושים, לידער פֿון פֿאַרפּיניקטע. מעלאָדיעס–העגער
קאָן, בילדער–יצחק ליכטענשטיין. ניריאָרק, מחמדים
קונסט־פֿאַרלאָ, תש"ח.
32, p. illus., music. 33 cm.
Includes unaccompanied melodies.
CONTENTS.— ...

1. Songs, Jewish (Yiddish).   I. Kon, Henoch.   II. Title.
          Title transliterated: Kedoshim.
M1850.L5K4   48–20418*
Library of Congress

NL 0342318   DLC RPB NN

Lichtenstein, Isaac, 1888–
Niggun. Melody. Paintings by Isaac Lichtenstein. (New York, Machmadim art editions, inc., 1945)
32, p. 31 x 23½ᶜᵐ.
Lithographed.
Includes music (unaccompanied melodies) "by Henech Kon and anonymous composers."
The music is reproduced from manuscript copy.

I. Kon, Henoch. II. Title.
          45–5415
Library of Congress   ND699.L5A5
          759.13

NL 0342319   DLC OC1 NNJ

Lichtenstein, Isaac, 1888–
Oil-paintings, water-colors ...
    see under   Berlin Photographic Company,
New York.   [Supplement]

K
759.13
L617p
Lichtenstein, Isaac, 1888–
Portraits of myself. (New York, Machmadim
Art Editions, 1947)
1 v. (6 ports.) 30cm.

Cover title: The artist himself.
"Artfolio."
"This is number 20 of a limited edition of
two hundred and fifty copies."

I. T: The artist himself.

NL 0342321   MiDW MB OCH

Lichtenstein, Isaac, 1888–
Paris, Éditions "Le Triangle" (1928)
שמואל הירשענבערג.
19 p. plates. 19 cm.
יידן־קינסטלער־מאָנאָגראַפֿיעס)

1. Hirszenberg, Samuel, 1865–1908.   (Series: Yidn-kinstler-monografyes)   *Title transliterated:* Shmuel Hirshenberg.
ND699.H5L5   56–55631

NL 0342322   DLC OC1

Lichtenstein, Isaac, 1888–
Spinoza; eight plates, by Isaac Lichtenstein.
New York, Machmadim Art Editions, Inc., c1946.
(8) ports. (in portfolio) 46cm.

1. Spinoza, Benedictus de, 1632–1677 – Portraits.

NL 0342323   NNC MB ICU Mi

Lichtenstein, Isaac, 1888–   illus.
Der yidisher poyps
    see under   Mark, Yudel, 1897–

Lichtenstein, Isaac, 1888–   illus.
Yosi Loksh fun Khelem
    see under   Glatstein, Jacob, 1896–

Lichtenstein, Issachar Baer ben Aryeh Loeb
    see
    Issachar Baer ben Aryeh Loeb Lichtenstein.

Lichtenstein (Isidorus). *De amblyopia ex
morbo Brightii orta.* 31 pp., 1 pl. 8°. *Regiomonti Pr., typ. Dalkowskianis,* 1857.

NL 0342327   DNLM

Lichtenstein (Jacob) [1889–]. *Beiträge
zur Keuntnis der Nabelhernien der Erwachsenen.* 32 pp., 1 l. 8°. *Berlin, C. Vogt,* 1894.

NL 0342328   DNLM

Lichtenstein, Jacob H
Experimental determination of the effect of horizontal-tail size, tail length, and vertical location on low-speed static longitudinal stability and damping in pitch of a model having 45° sweptback wing and tail surfaces. Washington, U. S. Govt. Print. Off., 1952.
ii, 22 p. illus. 30 cm.   (U. S.) National Advisory Committee for Aeronautics. Report 1096)
Cover title.
Bibliography: p. 22.
1. Stability of aeroplanes, Longitudinal.   2. Aeroplanes—Design and construction.   (Series)
TL521.A33   no. 1096   53–63744
      *629.123   629.13236
      TL574.87L45

NL 0342329   DLC PP

Lichtenstein, Jacob Heinrich Franz von,
respondent.
Dissertatio inauguralis juridica de beneficio
competentiae ex proprio aeque ac tertii jure
    see under   Hellfeld, Johann August,
1717–1782, praeses.

Lichtenstein, Jean L.
... Le comportement des *Polysphincta*, ichneumonides parasites des araignées, par J.-L. Lichtenstein et Étienne Rabaud. Cette, Station zoologique, 1923.
4 p. l., p. (267)–287. illus. 25ᶜᵐ.   (Travaux de l'Institut de zoologie de l'Université de Montpellier et de la Station zoologique de Cette ... 2. sér. no. 33)
"Auteurs cités": p. 286–287.

1. Polysphincta.   I. Rabaud, Étienne, 1868–   joint author.   II. Title.
          24–8126
Library of Congress   QL568.I 2L5

NL 0342331   DLC PU ICJ

Lichtenstein, Jean L.
Étude morphologique et biologique du *Sycosoter lavagnei* Picard et J.-L. Licht., hécabolide parasite de l'*Hypoborus ficus* Er., par Jean-L. Lichtenstein ... et François Picard ... Cette, Station zoologique, 1918.
3 p. l., (1), (40)–474 p. illus. 25ᶜᵐ.   (Travaux de l'Institut de zoologie de l'Université de Montpellier et de la Station zoologique de Cette ... 2. sér.—Mémoire n° 29)

1. Sycosoter lavagnei.   2. Hypoborus ficus.   I. Picard, François, joint author.
          23–1676
Library of Congress   QL568.B8L5

NL 0342332   DLC PU

Lichtenstein, Jean L., joint author.
Brölemann, Henry W.
... Les vulves des diplopodes; mémoire préliminaire, par Henry W. Brölemann ... et Jean L. Lichtenstein ... Cette, Station zoologique, 1919.

Hfc16
95
Lichtenstein, Jéchiel
Racine, poète biblique ... Paris, Librairie
Lipschutz, 1933.
4 p. l., 248p., 1 l. 25½cm.
Thèse - Univ. de Neuchâtel.
"Notice bibliographique": p. [243]–246.

1. Racine, Jean Baptiste, 1639–1699.
2. Bible in litera-   ture.
3. Religion in   literature.

NL 0342334   CtY UU FU PU

Lichtenstein, Jéchiel.
... Racine, poète biblique; préface de Gustave Kahn. Paris,
Lipschutz, 1934.
3 p. l., (ix)–xv, 248 p. 25½ᶜᵐ.
Issued also as thesis, Neuchâtel.
"Notice bibliographique": p. (243)–246.
"Errata": 1 leaf, inserted at end.

1. Racine, Jean Baptiste, 1639–1699.   2. Bible in literature.   I. Title.
          35–6490
Library of Congress   PQ1905.L5 1934
Copyright A—Foreign   27199
          842.45

NNJ
NL 0342335   DLC CU NIC OrU NN PPDrop OO OCU OC1 NcD

Lichtenstein, Jéchiel.
... יהי אור. ללמד בני ישראל קרא וכתב. עם ציורים
מאת ליאון זק. פּריז, "ספר", תרצ"ו.
4 p. l., 5–48 p.; 1 p. l., 36 p. illus. 25 x 20ᶜᵐ.
Added t.-p.: ... Vocabulaire, remarques et lexique alphabétique pour יהי אור "Que la lumière soit!" Préface de m. Julien Weill ... Introduction du grand-rabbin M. Liber.

1. Primers, Hebrew.   I. Zack, Léon, 1892–   illus.   II. Title.
          Title transliterated: Yehi or.
          45–46736
Library of Congress   PJ4569.L54 1936

NL 0342336   DLC

Lichtenstein, Jéchiel.
... יהי אור. ספר למוד הקריאה והכתיבה ברוח התורה
המסורה. מהדורה אמריקאית. עם ציורים מאת ליאון זק.
באשר "ועד החנוך החרדי" ובעזורתו. ניריורק, הוצאת "אבנר",
תש"ב. (New York, 1941)
4 p. l., 5–48 p. illus. 25 x 20ᶜᵐ.
Previously published in Paris, 1936, with an appendix in French.
          PJ4569.L54 1941

—— ... Teacher's guide and vocabulary to יהי אור "Let there be light"; a modern method of Hebrew in the spirit of Torah and tradition. New York, Bloch publishing co. (1944)
31 p. 23ᶜᵐ.

1. Primers, Hebrew.   I. Zack, Léon, 1892–   illus.   II. Title.
          Title transliterated: Yehi or.
          45–46727
Library of Congress   PJ4569.L54 1941 Guide

NL 0342338   DLC

Lichtenstein, Jechiel Zebi, 1831–1912.
Aus Jechiel Lichtensteins Hebräischem
Kommentar
    see under title

BR
158
L5.35
1902
Lichtenstein, Jechiel Zebi, 1831–1912.
Begegnungspunkte zwischen Juden und
Christen. Gesetz und Evangelium. 2.
Ausgabe. London, Hebrew Christian
Testimony to Israel, 1902.
23 p. 23 cm.

1. Jewish Christians. I. Title

NL 0342340   OCH

VOLUME 332

Lichtenstein, Jechiel Zebi, 1827-1912.
Eine Bitte an mein Volk. Budapest:
⟨A. B. Ueberwasser, Hamburg, 189-?⟩
24 p.

NL 0342341 OCH

Lichtenstein, Jechiel Zebi, 1827-1912.
... Commentar zum Matthäus-Evangelium, von
J. Lichtenstein† Nach der Neubearbeitung des
Verfassers herausgegeben von ... H. Laible
und P. Levertoff. Leipzig, 1913.
114 p. 20.5 cm. (Schriften des Institutum
Delitzschianum zu Leipzig, 4. Heft)
Cover-title.
T.-p. and text in Hebrew.

NL 0342342 CtY MH

Lichtenstein, Jechiel Zebi, 1827-1912.
Ein geheimniss aus dem Talmud, von rabbi J. Lichtenstein ... ⟨Wien, L. Schönberger, 189-⟩
41 p. 23ᶜᵐ.

1. Messiah. 2. Talmud. ɪ. Title.
22-21661
Library of Congress BM620.L5

NL 0342343 DLC

Lichtenstein, Jechiel Zebi, 1827-1912.
אגרת פולוס אל הרומיים. מאת י. ליכטענשטיין. יצא לאור ע״י
נ. דאלמאן. לייפציג, תרנ״ח. ⟨Leipzig, 1898⟩
20 l. 23 cm. (His ביאור לספרי ברית החדשה)
Cover title: Römerbrief, von J. Lichtenstein. Hrsg. von G.
Dalman.

1. Bible. N. T. Romans—Commentaries.
Title transliterated: Igeret Polus el ha-Romiyim.

BS2665.L47 57-50253

NL 0342344 DLC

332
L69g
Lichtenstein, Jechiel Zebi, 1827-1912.
Die geschichtliche person Jesu Christi
nach der rationalistischen darstellung
und nach den urkundlichen quellen. Ein
vortrag von J. Lichtenstein. Cincinnati, O., 1880.
24p.

NL 0342345 IU PPG NN

Lichtenstein, Jechiel Zebi, 1827-1912.
Judenspiegel, von Rabbi J. Lichtenstein. ⟨Wien: L.
Schönberger, 1896.⟩ 35 p. 8°.

128702A. 1. Jews.—Conversion. 2. Jesus Christ.
September 2, 1924

NL 0342346 NN OCH

Lichtenstein, Jechiel Zebi, 1827-1912.
Judenthum und christenthum, von J. Lichtenstein ...
Hamburg, A. Scheibenhuber ⟨1892?⟩
vii, 97, ⟨1⟩ p. front. (port.) 19½ᶜᵐ.
On cover: 2. aufl.

1. Jews Religion. 2. Christianity. ɪ. Title.
22-20233
Library of Congress BM535.L45

NL 0342347 DLC OCH NN

Lichtenstein, Jechiel Zebi, 1827-1912.
Der Talmud auf der Anklagebank durch
einen begeisterten Verehrer des Judenthums.
Heft 1- Budapest: V. Bornyánszky, 1886.
1 v.

NL 0342348 OCH

FS25.1
L617t
Lichtenstein, Jechiel Zebi, 1827-1912.
Toledoth Jeschua (Geschichte Jesu) Gründliche erörterung der frage, wer die wahrheit
über die geschichte Jesu Christi erzählt, die
Juden oder die Christen? Aus dem hebräischen
übers. von H.L. Leipzig, Verlag des Ev.-luth.
zentralvereins für mission unter Israel, 1907.
48 p. 24 cm.

Cover title.
"Separatabdruck aus 'Saat auf hoffnung'
1906, heft 4."

NL 0342349 CtY-D

Lichtenstein, Jechiel Zebi, 1827-1912.
התורה והחכמה. פלוסופיא דתית (רעלינידאנס פהילאזאפיע)
יבאר יסודי אמונת תורתינו לפי יסודי החכמה האלהית. נדפס
⟨עם שלישית בהוספות ותקונים בשנת תרמ״ג⟩
Lemberg, Druck v. Pessel Balaban, 1883.
84 (i. e. 80) p. 22 cm.
Incorporates text of his Derekh ha-kodesh.
———— Microfilm copy (positive)
Negative film in the New York Public Library.
1. Judaism—Works to 1900. 2. Cabala. ɪ. Title.
Title transliterated: ha-Torah veha-ḥokhmah.
A 54-7663
New York. Public Libr.
for Library of Congress

NL 0342350 NN

Lichtenstein, Joachim Dietrich, 1706-
1773, praeses
De ivre criminali in terris serenis-
simorvm Dvcvm brvnsvicensivm et lvne-
bvrgensivm in genere ... Helmstadii,
J. Drimborn ⟨1751⟩

3 p.l., 41, ⟨4⟩ p. 18cm.

Diss. - Helmstedt (J.F. Grimmeisen,
respondent)

NL 0342351 MH-L

[LICHTENSTEIN, Joachim Dietrich] 1706-1773.
Epistola [prima-decima] observatiunculas
historico-juridicas ex diplomatibus helm-
stadiensibus sistens. Helmstadii, [1745-56]

NL 0342352 MH-L

Lichtenstein, Joachim Dietrich, 1706-
1773, praeses
Observationes de ivre weichbildico
saxonico ex docvmentis helmstadiensi-
bvs inlvstratas ... Helmstadii, Litteris Schnorrianis ⟨1749⟩

1 p.l., 46 p. 20cm.

Diss. - Helmstedt (J.L.J. Dede-
kind, respondent)

NL 0342353 MH-L NN

Lichtenstein, J[ohn]
Zur Kritik des modernen Materialismus.
Zwei Vorträge. Hrsg. von dem hiesigen
deutschen christlichen Junglingsverein.
Cincinnati, Krehbiel & Moss, pr., 1873.
55 p. 8°.

NL 0342354 NN PPLT PU

Lichtenstein, Joy, 1874-
For the blue and gold; a tale of life at the University
of California, by Joy Lichtenstein. San Francisco, A. M.
Robertson, 1901.
5 p. l., 232 p. front, 12 pl. 20½ᶜᵐ.

1. California university. ɪ. Title.
Library of Congress PZ3.L6176F 1—31750
-A 6821

NL 0342355 DLC CU-S MiU

Lichtenstein, Joy, 1874-
In praise of walking, by Joy Lichtenstein. San Francisco
⟨The Grabhorn press⟩ 1942.
12 p., 1 l. 23ᶜᵐ.
"Five hundred copies printed."

1. Walking. ɪ. Title.
Library of Congress GV1071.L5 42-14229
796.51

NL 0342356 DLC OrU NcRS OKentU

F869
S3
.7
L497
Lichtenstein, Joy, 1874-
"Kelly, Burke and Shea," a romance of the fire insurance
business in the "horse and buggy days" of San Francisco, by
Joy Lichtenstein and A. W. Paynter. [San Francisco,
Kennedy-ten Bosch, Printers, 1945]
29 p. ports. 24cm.

1. Connor, John, 1849-1933. 2. Meherin, Mark Matthew,
1852-1935. 3. Kelly, Harry Michael, 1863-1930. 4. Insurance,
Fire - San Francisco. I. Paynter, A.W., joint author. II. Title.

NL 0342357 CU-B C

Lichtenstein, Jules, 1816-1886.
Les cépages américains, classés et annotés d'après les
auteurs des États-Unis, offert à ses collègues des diverses
sociétés dont il fait partie, par J. Lichtenstein ... Montpellier, Imprimerie centrale du Midi, 1874.
cover-title, 7 p. 24ᶜᵐ.
"Extrait du Messager agricole du 10 juillet 1874."

1. Grape. ɪ. Title.
⟨Full name: Wilhelm Auguste Jules Lichtenstein⟩
11—31704 Revised
Library of Congress SB393.L69

NL 0342358 DLC CU

595.79
L61c
Lichtenstein, Jules, 1816-1886.
Les cynipides. 1ʳᵉ ptie.: Introduction.
La génération alternante chez les cynipides,
par H. Adler, traduit et annoté par J. Lichtenstein; suivi de la Classification des cynipides d'après G. Mayr. Montpellier, C. Coulet, 1881.
xiv, 141p. 3 plates(part col.) 24cm.

No more published?

NL 0342359 IU

Lichtenstein, J[ules]
De l'évolution biologique des pucerons en général et du
phylloxéra en particulier, par J. Lichtenstein ... Paris-
Bordeaux, La librairie vinicole et viticole, 1883.
vii, ⟨9⟩-39 p. 18½ᶜᵐ. (On cover: Librairie vinicole & viticole. sér. E,
n° 1)
"Bibliographie": p. ⟨13⟩-23.

1. Aphididae. 2. Phylloxera.
Agr 4-3565
Library, U. S. Dept. of Agriculture 431.5L61D.

NL 0342360 DNAL CU

VOLUME 332

Lichtenstein, Jules
La generation alternante chez les Cynipides. 1881.

NL 0342361   NIC-A

Lichtenstein, J₍ules₎
Histoire du phylloxéra, précédée de considérations générales sur les pucerons et suivie de la liste des personnes qui se sont occupées de la question phylloxéra, par J. Lichtenstein ... Montpellier, C. Coulet; ₍etc., etc.₎ 1878.
x, ₍11₎–39 p. v pl. (col.) 25ᶜᵐ

1. Phylloxera.

         Agr 4–3566

Library, U. S. Dept. of   Agriculture   431.5L61H.

NL 0342362   DNAL CU

Lichtenstein, Jules, 1816–1886.
Manuel d'entomologie à l'usage des horticulteurs du midi de la France, par Jules Lichtenstein ... Montpellier, Imprimerie centrale du midi, 1872.
vi, ₍7₎–83 p. 22½ᵐ.
"Extrait des Annales de la Société d'horticulture et d'histoire naturelle de l'Hérault."

1. Insects. ₍1. Entomology₎
      ₍Full name: Wilhelm Auguste Jules Lichtenstein₎
         Agr 32–529

Library, U. S. Dept. of   Agriculture   423L61M

NL 0342363   DNAL CU

Lichtenstein, Jules, 1816–1886, joint author.
Planchon, Jules Émile, 1823–1888.
Le *Phylloxera* (de 1854 à 1873) résumé pratique et scientifique; par J.-É. Planchon et J. Lichtenstein ... Montpellier, C. Coulet, 1873.

Lichtenstein, Jules, 1816–1886.
Tableau synoptique et catalogue raisonné des maladies de la vigne, par Jules Lichtenstein ... Montpellier, Impr. Grollier et fils, 1884.
20 p. 24½ᵐ.
Publié dans le Progrès agricole et viticole de Montpellier.

1. Grape—Diseases and pests. ₍1. Vine—Diseases₎
      ₍Full name: Wilhelm Auguste Jules Lichtenstein₎
         Agr 16–147

U. S. Dept. of agr. Library   464.05L61
for Library of Congress   ₍a41b₎

NL 0342365   DNAL OO

Lichtenstein, Julius
Gedichte. Weimar, Böhlau, 1876.
131 p.

NL 0342366   OCIW

Lichtenstein, Julius, 1866–
Hie13   Zur Parzivalfrage ... Halle a.S., E. Karras,
23m   1896.
1p ℓ., 56p., 1ℓ. 22½cm.
Inaug.-Diss. - Leipzig.
Vita.
"Die vollständige Arbeit erscheint in der ...
Zeitschrift: Beiträge zur Geschichte der
deutschen Sprache, Bd.XXII."
A comparison of the versions of Wolfram von
Eschenbach and Chrestien de Troyes.

1. Wolfram von   Eschenbach, 12th cent.
2. Chrestien de   Troyes, 12th cent.

NL 0342367   CtY ICN MH MiU OCl ICRL

Lichtenstein, Karl August Ludwig, freiherr von, 1767–1845, tr.
Arien und Gesänge aus: Das eherne Pferd
see under   Auber, Daniel François, Esprit, 1782–1871.

ML   Lichtenstein, Karl August Ludwig, Freiherr
50   von, 1767–1845
L56   ₍Bathmendi. Libretto. German₎
Bathmendi; eine grosse allegorische Oper
in zwey Aufzügen. ₍Text von Heinrich Wolfgang Behrisch₎ neu bearb. und in Musik
gesetzt vom Freyherrn von Lichtenstein.
Wien, J. B. Wallishausser, 1801.
88p. 18cm.

1. Operas - Librettos   I. Behrisch, Heinrich Wolfgang,   1744–1825 II. Title

NL 0342369   WU PU

PT 2423   LICHTENSTEIN, KARL AUGUST LUDWIG, freiherr von, 1767–1845₎
.L45 B8   Gesänge aus Der Brauer von Preston, komische Oper in drei Akten. Nach dem Französischen der Herren Leuven und Brunswick, zur beibehaltenen Musik von Adam. Berlin, 1839.
48 p.

Without music.
At head of title: Königstädtisches Theater.

I. T₍e₎: Der Brauer von Preston.

NL 0342370   InU

AN   Lichtenstein, Karl August Ludwig, freiherr von, 1767–1845
2   ... Gesänge aus: Königin für einen
C476   tag. Komische oper in drei akten. Nach
dem französischen des Scribe, St. Georges,
von Freiherrn von Lichtenstein. Musik
von Adam. Berlin, 1840.
63p. 16cm. At head of title: Königstädtisches Theater.
Micro-opaque.

NL 0342371   CaBVaU

Lichtenstein, Kurt, 1902–
Ueber die disposition zur pernizioesen anaemie.
Inaug. diss. Berlin 1928
Bibl.

NL 0342372   ICRL CtY

RA857.5P61
L61   Lichtenstein, Ladislaus
Balneologisches handbuch des bades Pistyan
... Leipzig, Deuticke, 1926
v. illus., plate

"Das 'elegische' gedicht des Adam Trajan
über die Pistyaner thermen aus dem jahre 1642":
l. th., p. 89–104.
"Literatur": l. th., p. 104–116.

NL 0342373   NNC

Lichtenstein, Leo.
Die pravatrechtliche behandlung des wucherers.
Inaug. diss. Rostock, n.d.
Bibl.

NL 0342374   ICRL MH

QB351   Lichtenstein, Leon, 1878–1933.
.L7   Astronomie und mathematik in ihrer wechselwirkung; mathematische probleme in der theorie der figur der himmelskörper, von dr. Leon Lichtenstein ... Leipzig, S. Hirzel, 1923.
vi, ₍1₎, 97, ₍1₎ p. diagrs. 23ᶜᵐ.

1. Astronomy—Problems, exercises, etc. 2. Mathematics.

NL 0342375   ICU MH MdBJ PSC NcWsW WU NcU OrCS NN NjP

Lichtenstein, Leon, 1878–
Beiträge zur theorie der kabel untersuchungen über die kapazitätsverhältnisse der verseilten und konzentrischen mehrfachkabel ... München, Druck von R. Oldenbourg, 1908.
40 p. diagr. 32ᵐ.
Inaug.-diss.—Berlin.

1. Electric cables.

Library of Congress   TK3351.L7   9–2441

NL 0342376   DLC ICRL PU ICJ

Lichtenstein, Leon, 1878–   ed.

Hopmann, Josef, 1890–
Beschreibung und untersuchung eines visuellen astrophotometers, von J. Hopmann ... Mit 4 abbildungen. Vorgelegt von herrn Lichtenstein. Leipzig, S. Hirzel, 1931.

Lichtenstein, Leon, 1878–
Beweis des satzes, dass jedes hinreichend kleine, im wesentlichen stetig gekrümmte, singularitätenfreie flächenstück auf einen teil einer ebene zusammenhängend und in den kleinsten teilen ähnlich abgebildet werden kann, von dr. Leon Lichtenstein ... ₍Berlin. K. Akademie der wissenschaften, 1911₎
49 p. 29¼ᶜᵐ. ₍Added t-p.: Abhandlungen der K. Preussischen akademie der wissenschaften. Jahrg. 1911. Physikalisch-mathematische classe. Anhang. abh. vi₎
Series title in part on t-p.

1. Surfaces. Representation of.
         A C 34–10

Title from Cleveland Pub.   Libr.
Library of Congress   ₍A8182.B33 1911, Anhang, abh. 6₎

NL 0342378   OCl NIC PPAmP OCU NN MB

Lichtenstein, Leon, 1878–
Gleichgewichtsfiguren rotierender flüssigkeiten, von Leon Lichtenstein ... mit 4 abbildungen. Berlin, J. Springer, 1933.
vii, ₍1₎, 174, ₍2₎ p. diagrs. 24ᶜᵐ.
"Die vorliegende kleine schrift ist aus einem kolleg über kosmogonische hypothesen hervorgegangen, das ich im sommer-semester, 1928 an der hiesigen universität ₍Leipzig₎ hielt."—Vorwort.

1. Rotating masses of fluid. 2. Mechanics, Celestial. I. Title.
         33–35411

Library of Congress   QB410.L5
Copyright A—Foreign   22247
         521.1

NL 0342379   DLC IaU CU CtY PSC NBuU

Lichtenstein, Leon, 1878–
Grundlagen der hydromechanik, von Leon Lichtenstein ... mit 54 textfiguren. Berlin, J. Springer, 1929.
xvi, 506, ₍2₎ p. diagrs. 24½ cm. ₍Added t-p.: Die grundlehren der mathematischen wissenschaften in einzeldarstellungen ... Bd. xxx₎
"Literaturverzeichnis": p. ₍508₎

1. Fluid mechanics.

QA901.L5   30–3735

     MH ViU IU NN
     PPT OCU MiU OC1W OO OU TxU NNC ICJ NcU NcRS NcD NBC
NL 0342380   DLC WaS OrCS ICU CU PSt MeB PBm NBuU PSC

VOLUME 332

Lichtenstein, Leon, 1878–   joint ed.
Mathematische abhandlungen Hermann Amandus Schwarz zu seinem fünfzigjährigen doktorjubiläum am 6. august 1914 gewidmet von freunden und schülern. Mit dem bildnis von H. A. Schwarz und 53 figuren im text. Berlin, J. Springer, 1914.

Lichtenstein, Leon, 1878–   ed.
Mathematische zeitschrift … 1.–   bd.
29 jan. 1918–
Berlin, J. Springer, 1918–

LICHTENSTEIN, Leon, 1878–1933.
Neue beiträge zur Maxwellschen theorie der Saturnringe. [Berlin, J. Springer, 1924]

pp. [200]–227.
Caption title.
"Untersuchungen über die figur der himmelskörper. Fünfte abhandlung."
"Cover:- Probleme der astronomie. Festschrift für Hugo v. Seeliger, Sonderabdruck.
Astron. Lab.

NL   0342383   MH

Lichtenstein, Leon, 1878–1933.
Neuere entwicklung der potentialtheorie. Konforme abbildung, von L. Lichtenstein …
(*In* Encyklopädie der mathematischen wissenschaften. Leipzig, 1909–21. 25ᶜᵐ. bd. II–3, p. [177]–377)
"Abgeschlossen im mai 1918."
Published December 25, 1919.
"Literatur": p. 179–181.

1. Potential, Theory of.
                                                    A 21–681
Brown univ. Library
for Library of Congress   [QA36.E56 bd. II–3]
                            [a40c1]   (510.3)

NL   0342384   RPB CU OU ODW MiU

Lichtenstein, Leon, 1878–
Neuere entwicklung der theorie partieller differentialgleichungen zweiter ordnung vom elliptischen typus, von L. Lichtenstein … [1924]
(*In* Encyklopädie der mathematischen wissenschaften. Leipzig, 1924–   26ᶜᵐ. bd. II–3, hft. 8, p. [1277]–1334)
"Literatur": p. 1278.

1. Differential equations, Partial.
                                                A 26–644 Revised
Title from Brown Univ.   Printed by L. C.

NL   0342385   RPB CU OU ODW MiU NcD

Lichtenstein, Leon.
Ueber einige neuere Versuche und Erfahrungen mit Hochspannungen v. Torino: V. Bona, 1911.   16 p.   4°.
(Congrès Internat. des Applications d'Électricité, 2. Turin, 1911.)

Cover-title.

1. Electricity.—Transmission, 1911.   2. Off. au.
                                                March 28, 1917.

NL   0342386   NN

Lichtenstein, Leon, 1878–
Vorlesungen über einige klassen nichtlinearer integralgleichungen und integro-differentialgleichungen, nebst anwendungen, von Leon Lichtenstein … Berlin, J. Springer, 1931.
x, 164 p. 24½ᶜᵐ.

1. Integral equations. 2. Differential equations.
Library of Congress   QA431.L65
Copyright A—Foreign   13425
                          31–30941

                                                517.38

NcD WU OrCS
NL   0342387   DLC CU CtY PBm PSC PPT PU-Math OCU MiU

1878–1933.
Lichtenstein, Leon. Zur Theorie der gewöhnlichen Differentialgleichungen und der partiellen Differentialgleichungen zweiter Ordnung. Die Lösungen als Funktionen der Randwerte und der Parameter. (Palermo 1909: Tipogr. Matemat.) 40 S. 8° ¶(Aus: Rendiconti d. Circolo Matem. di Palermo. T. 28.)
Berlin, Phil. Diss. v. 24. Juli 1909, Ref. Schwarz
[Geb. 16. Mai 78 Warschau; Wohnort: Charlottenburg; Staatsangeh.: Rußland; Vorbildung: Friedrichs-Werdersche Oberrealsch. Berlin Reife O. 07; Studium: Berlin Techn. Hochsch. 11, Univ. 7 S.; Rig. 18. Febr. 09.]
                                                    [U 09. 226

NL   0342388   ICRL CtY PU DN-Ob RPB NjP MH MiU IU

Lichtenstein, Leopoldina
see Lichtschein de Bird, Poldy.

Lichtenstein, Louis.
"The practical furrier"; a book for the instruction in the art of fur making and repairing; the first and only publication of its kind in the world, by Louis Lichtenstein … [Norfolk, Va., Atlantic coast printing corporation] 1916.
27 p. illus. 27½ᶜᵐ.
Advertisements: p. 25–27.

1. Fur.   I. Title.

Library of Congress   TT525.L5   16—18921

NL   0342390   DLC ICJ OrP Or NN

Lichtenstein, Louis, 1906–
Bone tumors. St. Louis, Mosby, 1952.
315 p. illus. 26 cm.

1. Bones—Tumors.   I. Title.

RD675.L5   616.71   52—2082 ‡

PPT
NL   0342391   DLC CaBVaU MBCo ICRL DNLM OrU-M NcD ICJ

WO
33354
Lichtenstein, Ludolf
Ueber die Producte der trocknen Destillation von schleimsauren aromatischen Aminen.
Cöthen, 1881.
30 p.

Inaug.-Diss. - Jena.

NL   0342392   CtY ICRL

Lichtenstein, Ludwig, joint ed.

Handbuch des zeugdrucks, herausgegeben von prof. dr. G. Georgievics … prof. dr. R. Haller … [und] dr. L. Lichtenstein … Leipzig, Akademische verlagsgesellschaft m. b. h., 1930.

Lichtenstein, Martin Hinrich Carl.
See
Lichtenstein, Hinrich, 1780–1857.

W 4
B51
1940
Lichtenstein, Martin Werner, 1914–
Über das Auslöschvermögen des Normalserums Erwachsener bei dem Schultz-Charlton'schen Phänomen, nebst Bemerkungen über seine Verwendung beim Wund-und Verbrennungsscharlach. Berlin, Brückner [1940]
21 p.

Inaug.-Diss. - Friedrich Wilhelms Univ., Berlin.
Bibliography: p. 19.

NL   0342395   DNLM

Lichtenstein, Maurice.
La démonstration du théorème de Fermat, par Maurice Lichtenstein. [Paris,] 1927. vi, 51 p. 4°.

420299A. 1. Fermat's theorem.
                                                July 5, 1929

NL   0342396   NN

Lichtenstein, Max, 1860–
De in jure cessionis origine et natura … Auctor Maximilianus Lichtenstein … Berolini, typis expressit G. Schade [1880]
2 p. l., 170, [2] p. 23ᶜᵐ.
Inaug.-diss.—Berlin.
Vita.

1. Possession (Roman law) 2. Land titles—Registration and transfer (Roman law) 3. Inheritance and succession (Roman law) I. Title.
                                                34–4636

NL   0342397   DLC MH

BJ43
L617g
Lichtenstein, Max Manasse, 1889–
Die grundlagen und die entwickelung der bedeutung des wortes *nefesh* im Alten Testament. Teil I. Berlin, Mayer & Müller, 1915.
72 p.   24 cm.

Inaug.-diss. - Rostock.
Lebenslauf.
"Die vollständige arbeit erscheint demnächst in den 'Schriften der lehranstalt

für die wissenschaft des judentums, bd. IV' unter dem titel: 'Das wort *nefesh* in der Bibel.'"
Includes bibliography.

1. Hebrew   language - Terms and phrases.

NL   0342399   CtY-D MH MiU CtY ICRL

Lichtenstein, Max. Manasse, 1889–
…Das Wort נפש in der Bibel; eine Untersuchung über die historischen Grundlagen der Anschauung von der Seele und die Entwickelung der Bedeutung des Wortes נפש, von Max Lichtenstein. Berlin: Mayer & Müller, 1920. 158 p. 4°. (Lehranstalt für die Wissenschaft des Judentums. Bd. 4, Heft 5–6.)

1. Soul. 2. Series.   SCHIFF COLLECTION.
                                                June 21, 1921.

NL   0342400   NN ViRUT MH OCH MH OU

Lichtenstein, Mieczyslaw, 1881–
Ueber Autointoxikation bei hautkrankheiten.
Inaug. diss. Berlin, 1908.
Bibl.

NL   0342401   ICRL DNLM

Lichtenstein, Morris, 1889–1938.
The conquest of fear; a Jewish Science viewpoint. New York, Soc. of Jewish Science, [cop. 1922.]
20 p.

Title taken from paper-cover.

NL   0342402   OCH

Lichtenstein, Morris, 1889–
Cures for minds in distress, by Rabbi Morris Lichtenstein … New York, Jewish science publishing co., 1936.
vii p., 1 l., 11–345 p. 21ᶜᵐ.

1. Mental healing. 2. Nervous system—Diseases. 3. Faith-cure. 4. Prayer. 5. Medicine. 6. Psychoanalysis. I. Title.
                                                36–25545
Library of Congress   RC343.L55

Copyright A 100050   616.8

NL   0342403   DLC DNLM PP OCH OCITem

VOLUME 332

Lichtenstein, Morris, 1889–
How to live; Jewish science essays, by Rabbi Morris Lichtenstein ... New York, Jewish science publishing co., 1929.
4 p. l., 373 p. 19ᵐ.
Published in 1928.

1. Conduct of life.   ɪ. Title.   ɪɪ. Title: Jewish science essays.

Library of Congress   BM729.J4L47   28-30627

NL   0342404   DLC PP OCl OCH OClTem

Lichtenstein, Morris, 1889–
Jewish science and health; text book of Jewish science, by Rabbi Morris Lichtenstein ... New York, Jewish science publishing co., 1925.
334 p. 21ᵐ.

ɪ. Title.
Library of Congress   BM729.J4L5   25-18285

InAndC-T
NL   0342405   DLC MB PP PPDrop OCl OCH OClTem WU

LICHTENSTEIN, MORRIS, 1889-1938.
Jewish science and health; text book of Jewish
science. New York, Jewish science pub. co., 1955.
334 p. 21cm.

1. Jewish science.

NL   0342406   NN NSyU CU-M NNAJHi

Lichtenstein, Morris, 1889–
Joy of life; Jewish science essays, by Rabbi Morris Lichtenstein ... New York, Jewish science publishing company, 1938.
viii p., 1 l., 342 p. 19ᵐ.

1. Jews—Religion—Addresses, essays, lectures. 2. Conduct of life.
ɪ. Title.
                                              38-6301
Library of Congress   BM723.L5
—— Copy 2.
Copyright A 114597   296

NL   0342407   DLC PP OCl InAndC-T

Lichtenstein, Morris, 1889–
Judaism; a presentation of its essence and a suggestion for its preservation, by Rabbi Morris Lichtenstein ... New York city, Jewish science publishing co., 1934.
4 p. l., 11–228 p. 19ᵐ.

1. Jews—Religion.   ɪ. Title.
Library of Congress   BM560.L5   34-6188

Copyright A 69864   296

NL   0342408   DLC MB PP PPDrop OCl OCH OClTem NSyU

Lichtenstein, Morris, 1889–
Peace of mind; Jewish science essays, by Rabbi Morris Lichtenstein ... New York, Jewish science publishing co., 1927.
358 p. 19ᵐ.

1. Conduct of life.   ɪ. Title.

Library of Congress   BM729.J4L57   27-2798
Copyright A 967045

NL   0342409   DLC FMU NcD OCl OCH OClTem PP

Lichtenstein, Morris, 1889– 1938.
ספר רפאת הנפש ... די חידקונע פֿון דער אידישער אמונה
אין זעעליכען לעבען.אויך די מתפֿלל צו זיין וען מען אין
קראנק, און זיי זיך צו פֿירהרען וען מען אין געזונד. מאת רבי
משה ליכטענשטיין ...
New York, Jewish science publishing co., 1934.
133 p., 1 l. 17½ᵐ.
Title (transliterated): Refuath ha-nefesh.

                                              35-4869
Library of Congress

NL   0342410   DLC

Lichtenstein (Moses) [1888–   ]. *Ueber einen Fall von angeborener Bauchspalte. 27 pp., 1 l. 8°. München, M. Ernst, 1913.

NL   0342411   DNLM

Lichtenstein (Nachman Lipa). *Ueber die Morbidität im Wochenbett bei vorzeitigem Fruchttod. 31 pp. 8°. Basel, J. Kohlhapp, 1912.

NL   0342412   DNLM MiU CtY

Lichtenstein, Noah, 1905–
Zur kenntnis des cotoins und anderer oxycarbonylverbindungen
Inaug. Diss. Zürich, 1930.

NL   0342413   ICRL CtY

BF1900
.L699   LICHTENSTEIN, PARKER EARL, 1915–
         Effects of prefrontal lobotomy on the
acquisition, retention, and relearning of a
feeding inhibition in dogs. [Typewritten ms.]
Bloomington, Ind., 1948.   6+139p. Diagrs.
Photos.

         Thesis (Ph.D.)--Indiana university.

NL   0342414   InU

Lichtenstein, Parker Earl, 1915–
Studies of anxiety. [n. p., 1950]
2 pts. diagrs., tables. 26 cm.

Cover title.
Thesis—Indiana University.
Reprinted from the Journal of comparative and physiological psychology, v. 43, no. 1, Feb. and no. 6, Dec., 1950.
Includes bibliographies.

CONTENTS.—1. The production of a feeding inhibition in dogs.—2. The effects of lobotomy on a feeding inhibition in dogs.

1. Anxiety. 2. Inhibition.

BF575.A6L5   A 51-3246
Indiana. Univ. Libr.
for Library of Congress   †

NL   0342415   InU DLC

Lichtenstein (Paul Hellmuth) [1894–   ]. *Beitrag zur Lehre von den Psychosen nach Infektionskrankheiten. (2 Fälle von Amentia nach Grippe.) [Kiel.] 29 pp. 8°. Hamburg, K. Hanf, 1920.

NL   0342416   DNLM ICRL CtY

Lichtenstein, Perry Maurice, 1887–
A doctor studies crime, by Perry M. Lichtenstein ... New York, D. Van Nostrand company, inc. [¹1934]
viii p., 1 l., 263 p. 21ᵐ.

1. Criminal anthropology. 2. Psychology, Pathological. 3. Defective and delinquent classes. 4. Crime and criminals—New York (City)
ɪ. Title.
Library of Congress   HV6080.L6   34-20599
—— Copy 2.
Copyright A 72867   364

NL   0342417   DLC CaBVaU WaS GU CU MB NN PP OrU DNLM

Lichtenstein, Perry Maurice, 1887–
A handbook of psychiatry, by P. M. Lichtenstein ... and S. M. Small ... New York, W. W. Norton & company inc. [1943]
330 p. diagrs. 21ᵐ.
"First edition."
Bibliography at end of each chapter.

1. Psychology, Pathological.   ɪ. Small, Saul Mouchly, 1913– joint author.
Library of Congress   RC341.L6   43-11086
                                                       616.8

       NBuU GAT TU NIC IdU
       PP PPT PPC PV PSt OCU OU OLak OOxM OClh OrPS ICJ Wa
NL   0342418   DLC CaBVaU OCl WaS WaOB OrU-M AAP MB ViU

RC341
.L6   **Lichtenstein, Perry Maurice,** 1887–
1943   A handbook of psychiatry, by P. M. Lichtenstein ... and S. M. Small ... New York, Farrar & Rinehart; distributed by W. W. Norton [c1943]
330 p. diagrs. 21ᵐ.
"First edition."
Bibliography at end of each chapter.

NL   0342419   FMU

Lichtenstein, Perry Maurice, 1887–
Sex and the mind; psychiatric problems in everyday life explained. New York, Simon Publications, 1949.
84 p. 20 cm.

1. Psychiatry—Popular works.   ɪ. Title.

RC605.L52   616.8   50-5103

NL   0342420   DLC DNLM

308t
L6984   **Lichtenstein, Philip Grover**
        Production of protons in carbon by cosmic rays. [Berkeley, 1952]
        11,37 l. diagrs., tables.

        Thesis (Ph.D. in Physics) - Univ. of California, Sept. 1952.
        Bibliography: p.35-36.

        1. Protons. 2. Carbon. 3. Cosmic rays.

NL   0342421   CU

617.16 **Lichtenstein, Richard,** 1881–
L71u
        Über luxationen der patella nach trauma... Halle a.S., Kaemmerer, 1910.
        29p. O.

        Inaug.-diss. - Halle.
        Lebenslauf.
        "Literatur": 1p. at end.
        [Full name: Wilhelm Albert Richard Lichtenstein]

NL   0342422   IaU MH DNLM MiU ICRL

Wing
Z
481   LICHTENSTEIN, RICHARD C.
.5   Early New England and New York heraldic
        book plates. Boston, Clapp, 1886.
        8p.

        "Reprinted, with additions, from the New-England historical and genealogical register for April [i.e.July] 1886."

NL   0342423   ICN OClW MH

Lichtenstein, Richard C
Early southern heraldic book plates. n.p., n.p., 1887. [2]p.

"Reprinted from the New England Historical and Genealogical Register for July, 1887."

NL   0342424   OClW

VOLUME 332

Lichtenstein (Rita) [1883–   ]. *Fünfzehn Fälle von Pylorospasmus der Säuglinge. 38 no. 8°. Berlin, C. Siebert, 1913.

NL 0342425   DNLM CtY

HU 90.6798(2 cop)

Lichtenstein, Robert Bertram
Pejorative personal substantives in German to 1600

Thesis - Harvard, 1954

NL 0342426   MH

LICHTENSTEIN, RUDOLF.
Wohlbekomm's! Gedichte in schwäbischer Mundart. Stuttgart, A. Bonz [1954?]   55 p.   15cm.

1. German language—Dialects—Swabia.

NL 0342427   NN

Lichtenstein, Rudolf, 1904–
Uber Acylverbindungen der Monoaceton-glucose und einige ihrer Umwandlungsprodukte ... Borna-Leipzig, 1931.
Inaug.-Diss. - Berlin.
Lebenslauf.
[Full name: Rudolf Fritz Lichtenstein]

NL 0342428   CtY ICRL OU

QD591 Lichtenstein, S.
.L59   Ueber einige isomere naphtalinderivate.
Karlsruhe, 1896.
32p.
Inaug. diss. Basel.

NL 0342429   DLC

Lichtenstein (Sally) [1861–   ]. * Ueber die Wirkung des circulierenden Harnstoffs auf den tierischen Organismus. Experimente nebst Folgerungen für die Frage von dem Zusammenhang von Herz- und Nierenkrankheiten. 43 pp. 8°. Berlin, G. Schade, 1881.

NL 0342430   DNLM

Lichtenstein, Salomon, 1867–
... Über diffuse gefässgeschwülste der oberen extremität ... Neuwied, Heuser, 1889.
2 p.l., 47, [1] p., 2 l. col. pl. 25 cm.
[Bonn. Universität. Dissertationen. v. 12, no. 7]
Inaug.-Diss. - Bonn.
Vita.
At head of title: Aus der chirurgischen klinik zu Bonn.
"Litteratur": p. [48]
1. Tumors.

NL 0342431   CU PPC DNLM

Lichtenstein, Scheina Kappel
see Kappel-Lichtenstein, Scheina.

Lichtenstein, Schima.
Die Strafzumessung im Anschluss an das russische Strafgesetzbuch von 1903. Borna-Leipzig: R. Noske, 1912.   ix, 59 p., 1 l. 8°.

Dissertation, Giessen. Bibliography, p. vii-ix.

1. Punishment, Russia.   April 17, 1913.

NL 0342433   NN MH-L MH ICRL O

Lichtenstein, Sigmund, ed.

Kunst und handwerk; zeitschrift des Bayerischen kunstgewerbevereins zu München; hrsg. vom Bayerischen kunstgewerbeverein ...

München, R. Oldenbourg; [etc., etc.], 18   –19

Lichtenstein, Stanley.
The effect of frequency and success-failure experiences on recognition thresholds. Ann Arbor, University Microfilms [1954]
([University Microfilms, Ann Arbor, Mich.] Publication no. 8981)
Microfilm copy of typescript. Positive.
Collation of the original: 69 l. illus.
Thesis—Washington University.
Abstracted in Dissertation abstracts, v. 14 (1954) no. 10, p. 1797-1798.
Bibliography: leaves [62]-65.
1. Recognition (Psychology)   I. Title: Recognition thresholds.
Microfilm AC-1 no. 8981   Mic A 54-2662

Washington Univ., St.   Louis. Library
for Library of Congress   †

NL 0342435   MoSW DLC

Lichtenstein, Stefania, 1880–
Methoden zur untersuchung auf mikroorganismen in mikroskopischen präparaten. Von Stefania Lichtenstein ...
(*In* Abderhalden, Emil, ed. Handbuch der biologischen arbeitsmethoden ... Berlin, 1920—   25cm. abt. XII. Leistungen der niederen organismenwelt. t. 1 (1925) p. [363]-460. illus.)
Bibliographical foot-notes.

1. Micro-organisms.
                                         A C 36-4072
Title from Ohio State   Univ.
Library of Congress   [QH324.A3 1920 abt. 12, t. 1]
                                              (574.072)

NL 0342436   OU

LICHTENSTEIN, Tehilla
What to tell your friends about Jewish Science... New York, Society of Jewish Science, 1951.
14p. 17.5cm.

Cover used as title page.

NL 0342437   MH-AH

*GC8   Lichtenstein, Ulrich von, fl. 1255.
T4406   Frauendienst, oder: Geschichte und Liebe des
811f   Ritters und Sängers Ulrich von Lichtenstein, von ihm selbst beschrieben. Nach einer alten Handschrift bearbeitet und herausgegeben von Ludwig Tieck.
Stuttgart und Tübingen, in der J.G.Cotta'schen Buchhandlung.1811.
viii,287p. 19.5cm.,in case 21cm.
Also issued with imprint dated 1812.
Contemporary green wrappers; in cloth case.
Autographed: L. Uhland, 1815.

NL 0342438   MH

Lichtenstein, Ulrich von, *fl.* 1255.
Frauendienst, oder: Geschichte und liebe des ritters und sängers, Ulrich von Lichtenstein, von ihm selbst beschrieben. Nach einer alten handschrift bearbeitet und herausgegeben von Ludwig Tieck. Stuttgart und Tübingen, Cotta, 1812.
viii, 287 p. 19½ cm.
First edition.

I. Tieck, Johann Ludwig, 1773–1853, ed. II. Title.

PT1564.F7 1812   47-41131

NL 0342439   DLC MB NIC OCU ICU KU PHC MdBP MH PHC

PT   Lichtenstein, Ulrich von, fl. 1255.
1564   Frauendienst; oder, Geschichte und Liebe
F7   des Ritters und Sängers Ulrich von Lichten-
1818 stein, von ihm selbst beschrieben. Nach einer alten Handschrift bearbeitet und hrsg. von Ludwig Tieck. Neue verb. Aufl., wörtlich nach dem Originale. Wien, L. Grund, 1818.
340, iv p. front. 18cm.

I. Tieck, Johann Ludwig, 1773–1853, ed. II. Title. III. Title: Geschichte und Liebe des Ritters und Sängers Ulrich von Lichtenstein.

NL 0342440   CoU ICU

Lichtenstein, Ulrich von, fl.1255.

Frauendienst; oder, Geschichte und liebe des ritters und sängers Ulrich von Lichtenstein, von ihm selbst beschrieben. Bearb.von Ludwig Tieck, mit einleitung von Alfred R.Ruhemann. Leipzig, Bruckner, [188–?]
6,247 p. 15½ cm. (Volksbibliothek für kunst und wissenschaft... nr.20. Abt. für varia. hft.2/3)

NL 0342441   NjP OC1

Lichtenstein, Ulrich von, *fl.* 1255.
Ulrich's von Liechtenstein Frauendienst. Herausgegeben von Reinhold Bechstein ... Leipzig, F. A. Brockhaus, 1888.
2 v. 18½ᵐ. (*Added t.-p.:* Deutsche dichtungen des mittelalters. Mit wort- und sacherklärungen. Hrsg. von Karl Bartsch. 6.-7. bd.)

I. Bechstein, Reinhold, 1833–1894, ed. II. Title: Frauendienst.
                                                 1—8114
Library of Congress   PT1564.F7 1888
                               [a44d1]

NL 0342442   DLC TxU CU OO OC1 MiU PHC MH NjP NcU NIC

PT1564 LICHTENSTEIN,ULRICH VON, *fl. 1255.*
.F8   Der Frauendienst des minnesängers Ulrich von
1924   Liechtenstein,frei bearb.von Michelangelo baron Zois. 1.aufl. Stuttgart,R.Lutz[1924]
316,[1]p. 20cm. (Added t.-p.:Memoiren bibliothek. 6.reihe,10.bd.)

NL 0342443   ICU ICN NN MH

PT1564 Lichtenstein, Ulrich von, fl. 1255.
F7   Narr im hohen Dienst. Nach der Textausgabe
1958   von Karl Lachmann ausgewählt, übertragen und eingeleitet von Walter Zitzénbacher. Graz, Stiasny [1598]
127 p. 19cm. (Das Österreichische Wort; Stiasny-Bücherei, Bd. 37)

I. Zitzenbacher, Walter   ed. II. Title.

NL 0342444   CoU

Lichtenstein, Ulrich von, fl. 1255.
Sechs lieder Ulrichs von Liechtenstein. Ins neuhochdeutsche übersetzt von Joseph Strobl. [Wien, A. Holzhausen, 1897?]
[16] p. 28 cm.
I. Strobl. Joseph, 1843–   tr.

NL 0342445   MH

Lichtenstein,Ulrich von,fl.1255.
Ulrich von Lichtenstein,mit anmerkungen von Theodor von Karajan,hrsg.von Karl Lachmann. Berlin, Sandersche buchhandlung,(G.E.Reimer) 1841.
2 p.l.,728 p.,1 l. 19ᶜᵐ.
CONTENTS.—Vrouwen dienest.-Der vrouwen buoch.

I.Karajan,Theodor Georg,ritter von,1810-1873, ed. II. Lachmann,Karl Konrad Friedrich Wilhelm,1793-1851, ed. III.Title: Vrouwen dienest. IV.Title: Der vrouwen buoch.

         OCU CtY ICN ViU NjP ICU CU
NL 0342446   MiU IU MH NNU-W OCU RPB MdBP InU OC1W

VOLUME 332

Microfilm
R3076 Lichtenstein, Ulrich von, fl. 1255.
Ulrich von Lichtenstein. Mit Anmerkungen
von Theodor von Karajan; hrsg. von Karl
Lachmann. Berlin, Sandersche Buchhandlung
(G.E. Reimer) 1841.
728 p.
Microfilm (negative) 1 reel. 35 mm.

ICU
NL 0342447   CaBVaU MH OCU RPB OC1W ICN IU NNU-W MiU

PT   Lichtenstein, Ulrich von, fl. 1255.
1564   Ulrich von Lichtenstein, mit Anmerkungen
F7   von Theodor von Karajan, hrsg. von Karl
1841   Lachmann. Berlin, Sander, 1841.
2 v.

Contains Vrouwen dienest and Der vrouwen
buoch.
Xerox copy of original.

NL 0342448   WaU

LICHTENSTEIN, Walter, 1880 -
At home and abroad; an address before the
Minneapolis chapter of the American Institute
of Banking, May, 13, 1932.

Manifold copy. 4°. ff.13.
Without title-page. Caption title.

NL 0342449   MH

Lichtenstein, Walter, 1880-
Aus der Hohenzollern-sammlung in Harvard
(In Zentralblatt für bibliothekswesen.
Leipzig, 1913. 22 1/2 cm. v. 30, p.228-29]

NL 0342450   DLC

LICHTENSTEIN, Walter.
A banker looks at Europe, by Walter Lichtenstein, before the Institute of Public Affairs,
Charlottesville, Virginia, July 7, 1939. [Char-
lottesville, Va.?, 1939].

Manifold copy. 28 x 22 cm.
Without title-page. Caption title.

NL 0342451   MH

LICHTENSTEIN, WALTER, 1880-
The business outlook for 1926; an address, by Walter Lichtenstein...made before Purchasing Agents Association of Chicago at the Auditorium hotel on Thursday, March 11, 1926.
[Chicago? 1926?] 10 p. 21½cm.

703524A. 1. Commerce--U.S., 1926.
MH
                                            cwa
                                            April 13, 1934

NL 0342452   NN MH

Lichtenstein, Walter, 1880-   L332.04 L61
[Collected papers.]

NL 0342453   ICJ

Lichtenstein, Walter, 1880-
"Concerning old age" (De senectute);
an address ... at the Forum of the
Cleveland chapter, A. I. B., Jan. 21, 1924.
n.p. [1924]
14 p.   O.

An address on economic conditions in the
U.S.

NL 0342454   00 MH

LICHTENSTEIN, Walter.
The date of separation of ecclesiastical
and lay jurisdiction in England. Chicago,
[1908].

1.8°. pp. 8.
"Reprinted from the Illinois law review,
vol. iii. no.6 "

NL 0342455   MH

Lichtenstein, Walter, 1880-
The European situation; an address, by Walter Lichtenstein
...at annual council dinner of the Nebraska Bankers Association,
Omaha, April 16, 1924. [Omaha? 1924?] 20 p. 8°.

411596A. 1. European war, 1914-   1918--Reparations.
                                        May 16, 1929

NL 0342456   NN PU

1511   Lichtenstein, Walter, 1880-
Foreign exchange and the present banking
situation ... Tulsa, Okla., City club (1920)

NL 0342457   DPU

LICHTENSTEIN, Walter.
Foreign trade and the present financial
situation. n.p., [1921]

Pamphlet.
Cover serves as title-page.

NL 0342458   MH

Lichtenstein, Walter, 1880-
The future trend of interest rates; address by Walter Lichtenstein...before the second annual Conference on banking at the
University of Illinois, November 10, 1936. [Chicago? 1936?]
16 p. 23cm.

1. Interest--Rates.
                                        November 18, 1937

NL 0342459   NN

LICHTENSTEIN, WALTER, 1880-
...Inflation... [Chicago? 1936] 13 f. 28cm.

Caption-title.
Reproduced from typewritten copy.
At head of title: Address to be delivered...before the
Michigan bankers association, Mackinac island, Michigan,
Monday, June 29, 1936.

896422A. 1. Inflation and deflation--U.S.

NL 0342460   NN

Lichtenstein, Walter
Joint shipping and purchasing of Chicago libraries.
[Chicago? 1911?]

[7 p.]
Binder's title
Report of a committee of a conference of Chicago
libraries in 1911. Lichtenstein was chairman of the
committee

NL 0342461   MH

Lichtenstein, Walter, 1880-   tr.

Zwingli, Ulrich, 1484-1531.
The Latin works and the correspondence of Huldreich
Zwingli, together with selections from his German works, ed-
ited, with introductions and notes, by Samuel Macauley Jack-
son; translations by Henry Preble, Walter Lichtenstein, and
Lawrence A. McLouth ...
New York [etc.] G. P. Putnam's sons, 1912-

                                        Econ 4842.9
Lichtenstein, Walter, 1880-
Miscellaneous papers and addresses, 1895-1953

4 v.

NL 0342463   MH

Lichtenstein, Walter, 1880-

Bibolotti, Benigno, fl. 1857-1868.
Moseteno vocabulary and treatises, by Benigno Bibolotti,
priest of the Franciscan mission of Inmaculada concepción
de Covendo in Bolivia; from an unpublished manuscript in
possession of Northwestern university library, with an introduction by Rudolph Schuller ... Evanston and Chicago,
Northwestern university, 1917.

LICHTENSTEIN, Walter.
Our present situation; an address. Chicago,
Kimberly-Clark Co., 1921.

Pamphlet.

NL 0342465   MH

LICHTENSTEIN, Walter.
The present financial situation. [Grand
Rapids, Mich., 1921]

Pamphlet.

NL 0342466   MH

Lichtenstein, Walter, 1880-
...Problems in financing the defense program, address by
Walter Lichtenstein...before the Chicago association of com-
merce...on April 23, 1941. [Chicago? 1941] 11 f. 28cm.

Caption-title.
At head of title: ...The First national bank of Chicago.
Reproduced from typewritten copy.

1. Military finance--U.S., 1941.   I. Chicago. First national bank.
                                        October 30, 1941

NL 0342467   NN MH

LICHTENSTEIN, WALTER, 1880-
The problems of American banking; address by Walter
Lichtenstein...before the Commonwealth club of California,
San Francisco, California, September 25, 1936. [Chica-
go? 1936] 20 p. 23cm.

1. Banks and banking--U.S., 1933.

NL 0342468   NN NBuG

HG289   Lichtenstein, Walter, 1880-
L5   Recent literature on the gold problem [by]
Walter Lichtenstein. [No imprint, 1940?]

cover-title[145]-157p. 23cm.

"Reprinted for private circulation from the
Journal of business of the University of Chicago,
vol. XIII, no. 2, April 1940".

1. Gold. 2. Banks and banking. I. Title.

NL 0342469   NBuG

VOLUME 332

Lichtenstein, Walter, 1880–
Relation of exports to imports, by Walter Lichtenstein...
₍Philadelphia? 1922₎   20 p.   22½cm.

Cover-title.
"Address...delivered at the general session of the ninth National Foreign Trade Convention at Philadelphia, on May 12, 1922."

823211A. 1. Commerce, Foreign.
                                              May 26, 1936

NL 0342470   NN MH

Lichtenstein, Walter, '1880–
Report to the president of Northwestern university on the results of a trip to South America, by Walter Lichtenstein, PH. D., librarian of Northwestern university. Evanston and Chicago, Northwestern university press, 1915.
2 p. l., 7–43, ₍1₎ p. 4 facsim. 26¼ᵐ. (*On cover:* Northwestern university bulletin. vol. XVI, no. 1. Sept. 3, 1915)
"Report dealing with the results of my trip to South America made on behalf of the following American institutions: Harvard college library, Harvard law school library, the John Crerar library, Northwestern university library, John Carter Brown library, Northwestern university law school library, and the American antiquarian society."—p. 7.
1. Bibliography—Bibl.—South America. 2. South America—Bibl.

Library of Congress   Z1601.A2L5
                                              15—25895

          NN MB ICJ IU NIC
NL 0342471   DLC OrU MWA PSt DHEW PU OO OClW MiU ViU

Lichtenstein, Walter, 1880–
Report to the president of Northwestern university on the results of a trip to South America, by Walter Lichtenstein, PH. D., librarian of Northwestern university. 2d ed. Evanston and Chicago, Northwestern university press, 1915.
43 p. 1 l. 4 facsim. 26½ cm. (*On cover:* Northwestern university bulletin. vol. XVI, no. 1. Sept. 3, 1915)
"Report dealing with the results of my trip to South America made on behalf of the following American institutions: Harvard college library, Harvard law school library, the John Crerar library, Northwestern university library, John Carter Brown library, Northwestern university law school library, and the American antiquarian society."—p. 7.
1. Bibliography—Bibl.—South America. 2. South America—Bibl.

Z1601.A2L51
                                              16—15830

NL 0342472   DLC IEN ICJ RPJCB

LICHTENSTEIN, Walter.
A review of the financial, industrial and commercial situation of the country as an aftermath of the great war; an address. Mantiowoc, Wis., 1921.

Pamphlet.

NL 0342473   MH PU

LICHTENSTEIN, Walter.
The Turkish peril and the German Reformation.

Curator of the Hohenzollern Collection, Harvard University. Professor of History, and Librarian, Northwestern University. Evanston, Ill,
Official copy of a thesis presented for the doctor's degree at Harvard University. 1907.

NL 0342474   MH

Lichtenstein, Walter, 1880–

American historical association. *Committee on bibliography.*
A union list of collections on European history in American libraries, comp. for the Committee on bibliography of the American historical association, by E. C. Richardson, chairman. Trial ed. Princeton, N. J., 1912.

Lichtenstein, Walter, 1880–   tr.

Coolidge, Archibald Cary, 1866–1928.
Die Vereinigten Staaten als weltmacht; eine betrachtung über internationale politik, von dr. Archibald Cary Coolidge ... Autorisierte übersetzung von dr. Walter Lichtenstein ... Berlin, E. S. Mittler und sohn, 1908.

Lichtenstein, [Wilhelm].
Geschichte des Königlich preussischen Leib-Grenadier-Regiments (1. brandenburgischen) Nr. 8. 1859–1882.   Berlin, E.S. Mittler und sohn, 1883.
Port. of Friedrich Wilhelm III and maps (mostly folded)

NL 0342477   MH

Lichtenstein, Wilhelm Albert Richard
    see Lichtenstein, Richard, 1881–

Lichtenstein, Wilhelm Auguste Jules
    see
Lichtenstein, Jules, 1816–1886.

Lichtenstein, Willy, 1904–
Zur therapie des tetanus des pferdes. Inaug. diss. Leipzig, 1930.
Bibl.

NL 0342480   ICRL DNAL

Lichtenstein, Zevi.
... שעורים בדברי ימי ישראל ... תל-אביב, ,דביר,׳תרצ׳ט-
₍Tel-Aviv, 1939₎
v. maps (part fold.) fold. tab. 22ᵐ.
Includes bibliographies.
CONTENTS.—   :חלק, א׳: מצמיחת מרכז היהדות במערב עד גרוש ספרד.

❧ 1. Jews—Hist.—A. D. 70–
              Title transliterated: Shi'urim be-divre yeme Yiśrael.
                                              45—48704
Library of Congress   DS123.L5

NL 0342481   DLC

833.81 Lichtenstein-Anageton, Edmund,   ed.
C   Den manen Auerbach's unter Mitwirkung der
L61   hervorragendsten Schriftsteller. 2.Aufl.
       Leipzig, Hartmann, 1882.
       72p. 19cm.

       I. Title.   1. Auerbach, Berthold, 1812–1882.

NL 0342482   KU

Lichtenstein de Bird Mosconi, Leopoldina
    see Lichtschein de Bird, Poldy.

Lichtenstein's plural distributive generic names Bubalides ...

see under

Lyon, Marcus Ward, 1875–

Lichtenstern, Eduard, 1900–
Lb85   Das Prinzip der naturgemässen und der kultur-
D57   gemässen Erziehung bei Adolf Diesterweg ...
D935ℓ Hannover,1935.
       65,₍1₎p. 22½cm
       Thesis - Zürich.
       Lebenslauf.
       "Literatur": p.7–8.

       Diesterweg, Friedrich Adolph Wilhelm, 1790–1866.

NL 0342485   CtY NNC

                              1885–
Lichtenstern, Georg, appr. Tierarzt: Lumbalanästhesie beim Pferd und Rind. Hannover: Schaper 1910. 40 S. 8°
Giessen, Veterinär-Med. Diss. v. 25. April 1910, Ref. Pfeiffer
[Geb. 15. Nov. 85 Niederlauterbach; Wohnort: Rottbalmünster; Staatsangeh.: Bayern; Vorbildung: Gymn. Burghausen Reife Juli 04; Studium: Tierärztl. Hochschulen München 5, Stuttgart 2 S.; Rig. 3. Dez. 09.]   [U 10. 1227

NL 0342486   ICRL MH PU

WM   LICHTENSTERN, Hermine
170   Nervosität; ein Lehrbüchlein und
L699n   Wegweiser. Wien, Perles, 1937.
1937   96 p.   WM170 L699n
         1. Neuroses   Title

NL 0342487   DNLM

LICHTENSTERN, Karl,frhr.von.
Die steuerliche belastung der landwirtschaft in Bayern. Inaug.–diss.,München. Kallmünz, M.Lassleben,1929.

"Literaturverzeichnis",pp.[105]–106.

NL 0342488   MH IEN CtY

Lichtenstern,   Karl Reisner *Freiherr* von.   623.5 Q002
       Schiessausbildung und Feuer der Infanterie im Gefecht. Dritte, erweiterte Auflage. xiii,175 p. O. Berlin: E. S. Mittler & Sohn, 1900.

NL 0342489   ICJ DNW

LICHTENSTERM, Karl Anton Reisner, freiherr von.
Geschichte der Reisner, Freiherrn v. Lichtenstern, nebst genealogischen nachrichten aus ihrem familienskreise. Regensburg, J. & K. Mayr 1889.
pp.94, v. 2 geneal tables.
"Separatabdruck aus dem xiii. bde. der Verhandl. des Histor. vereins fur Oberpfalz und von Regensburg."

NL 0342490   MH

          Lichtenstern, Ludwig.
*PGB8   Nur Wahrheit!
V6755R   [Wien]Aus der k.k.Hof= und Staatsdruckerei.
7.14.48   [1848]

          broadside. 38x23cm.
          Dated in contemporary ms. on verso: 14 Juli 848.

NL 0342491   MH

Lichtenstern, Maurizio. Milano, 1897.
Sopra un verso di Dante.
          8 p.

NL 0342492   NIC

VOLUME 332

Lichtenstern, Robert, 1874–　　　　　　L616.03
S800　v.11
Die Beeinflussung der Alterserscheinungen durch chirur-
gische und konservative Behandlung, von Prim. Dr. Robert
Lichtenstern ...

(*In* Neue deutsche Klinik. Berlin, 1933. 26ᶜᵐ. Bd. 11 (Erg. Bd. 1)
p. ₍543₎–555)

"Literatur": p. 555.

NL 0342493　ICJ

Lichtenstern, Robert, 1874–　　　　　　L616.03
S800　v.9
Prostataerkrankungen, von Dr. Robert Lichtenstern ...

(*In* Neue deutsche Klinik. Berlin, 1932. 26ᶜᵐ. Bd. 9, p. 169–225. illus.,
col. pl.)

"Literatur": p. 225.

NL 0342494　ICJ

1874 –
Lichtenstern (Robert). Ueber einen Fall von
selbständiger Endophlebitis obliterans der
Hauptstämme der Venæ hepaticæ. 10 pp. 8°.
Prag, 1900.
Repr. from: Prag. med. Wehnschr., 1900, xxv.

NL 0342495　DNLM

Lichtenstern, Robert.
Die überpflanzung der männlichen keimdrüse, von
primarius dr. Robert Lichtenstern, Wien. Mit 16 textabbildungen. Wien, J. Springer, 1924.

2 p. l., 113, ₍1₎ p. illus. 24ᶜᵐ.

"Literatur": p. ₍110₎–113.

1. Transplantation (Physiology) 2. Testicle.　ɪ. Title.

Library of Congress　　　QP89.L5
25–8683

NL 0342496　DLC CU DNLM

WJ　**LICHTENSTERN, Robert,** *1874 –*
168　　Urologische Operationslehre.
L699u　Berlin, Urban & Schwarzenberg, 1935.
1935　viii, 295 p. illus.
Contains errata slip.
1. Genito-urinary organs - Surgery

NL 0342497　DNLM NNC

Law　**Lichtenstern, Viktor,** ₍joint author₎.

Siebenschein, Rudolf.
Das strafrecht der direkten personalsteuern. Nach dem
Gesetze vom 25. oktober 1896, R. G. B. nr. 220, systematisch
dargestellt von dr. Rudolf Siebenschein ... und dr. Viktor
Lichtenstern ... Wien, Manz, 1904.

Lichtensztul, Józef, 1906–
... Poglądy filozoficzno-prawne Stanisława Orzechowskiego
... Warszawa, Instytut wydawniczy Kasy Mianowskiego,
1930.

vii, 170 p. 22ᶜᵐ. (Prace Seminarjum filozofji prawa Uniwersytetu
warszawskiego ... no. 3)

Thesis—Warsaw.
Życiorys.
Summary in French.
"Źródła": p. 163–166.

1. Orzechowski, Stanisław, 1515?–1566 or 7.　ɪ. Title.

CA 32–580 Unrev'd

Library of Congress
340.1

NL 0342499　DLC NN

DK　**Lichtensztul, Józef,** 1906–
507　The White-Ruthenian problem in Eastern
154　Europe. ₍New York₎ Polish Institute of Arts
and Sciences in America, 1944.
28p. 25cm.

Cover title.
"Reprinted from the Quarterly Bulletin of
the Polish Institute of Arts and Sciences
in America, July, 1944."

1. White Russia - Hist. 2. White Russia -
Relations (Gener　al) with foreign
countries. I.　　Title.

NL 0342500　NBuC CSt-H

Lichtentag, Alexander, 1868–
Dictation and reading practice; paragon shorthand, ₍by₎ A.
Lichtentag. ₍New Orleans, La.?₎ cop. 1915. 85 p. 12°.

O'KEEFE COLLECTION.
168144A. 1. Shorthand—Letters,　　Amer., 1915.
April 8, 1925

NL 0342501　NN ICN CtY

Lichtentag, Alexander, 1868–
Dictation and reading practice; paragon shorthand, ₍by₎ A.
Lichtentag. ₍New Orleans, La.: Paragon Pub. Co.?₎ 1918.
27–85 p. 12°.

O'KEEFE COLLECTION.
1. Shorthand—Dictation.　　June 29, 1925

NL 0342502　NN ICN OCl

Lichtentag, Alexander.
Graded exercises in Paragon shorthand ₍by₎ A. Lichtentag. New Orleans, La. ₍1924₎
1 p. l., 59 p. 19ᶜᵐ.

1. Shorthand—Exercises for dictation.
Library of Congress　　　Z56.L69
24–20147

NL 0342503　DLC

Lichtentag, Alexander, 1868–
...Paragon shorthand...by A. Lichtentag...　　New
Orleans, La.: Hopkins' Prtg. Off.₎, 1895.₎ 18 p. 8°.

Instructions, and key to lessons 1–6, 7 l., inserted.

HOWARD SHORTHAND COLL.
1. Shorthand—Systems, American,　　1895.
May 18, 1926

NL 0342504　NN

Lichtentag, Alexander.
Lichtentag's paragon shorthand; a vast improvement
in the art of shorthand; seven easy lessons ... By A.
Lichtentag. New Orleans, La., The author, 1906.

viii, 88 p. 19ᶜᵐ.

1. Shorthand.
6–25725
Library of Congress　　　Z56.L71

NL 0342505　DLC PPSteph ICJ

Z　**LICHTENTAG, ALEXANDER,** 1868–
201　Lichtentag paragon shorthand; a vast im-
.504　provement in the art of shorthand; seven easy
lessons. New Orleans, La., 1914₍c1906₎
viii,85p. 19cm.
"Reading and writing exercises": p.₍27₎-85.
---- ---- New Orleans, La.,1914₍c1906₎
viii, 26p. 19cm.
Imperfect: p.iii-iv mutilated.
---- ---- New York City, Paragon Institute Home
Study Department,1919.
viii, 26p.　　　　19cm.

---- ---- New York,N.Y.,1919,c1918.
viii,26p. 19cm.

---- ---- New Orleans,La.,1920,c1915.
viii,85p. 19cm.
"Reading and writing exercises": p.₍27₎-85.

NL 0342507　ICN

Lichtentag, Alexander, 1868–
Lichtentag paragon shorthand; a vast improvement in the
art of shorthand; seven easy lessons ... By A. Lichtentag.
New Orleans, La. The author, 1915.

viii, 85 p. 19ᶜᵐ. $1.50

1. Shorthand.
Library of Congress　　Z56.L71　1915
15—18774

NL 0342508　DLC ICJ Wa WaS

Lichtentag, Alexander, 1868–
Lichtentag paragon shorthand; a vast improvement in the
art of shorthand; seven easy lessons ... By A. Lichtentag ...
New York city, Paragon institute home study department,
1918.

viii, 26 p. 19½ᶜᵐ.

1. Shorthand.　ɪ. Title: Paragon shorthand.
33–4799
Library of Congress　　Z56.L71　1918
653.42

NL 0342509　DLC ViU NN ICN OCX

Lichtentag, Alexander.
Paragon shorthand reader and dictator ₍by₎ A. Lichtentag. New Orleans, La., The author, 1920.

1 p. l., vi, 92 p. 20½ᶜᵐ.

1. Shorthand—Readers. 2. Shorthand—Exercises for dictation.
ɪ. Title.
Library of Congress　　Z56.L72
20–4443

NL 0342510　DLC

Lichtentag, Alexander, 1868–
Word hunt; an interesting game for young and old, by
Alexander Lichtentag, containing over one hundred word
hunts. New York, E. P. Dutton & co., inc. ₍1930₎

5 p. l., 117 p. illus. 19½ᶜᵐ.

1. Puzzles.　ɪ. Title.
30–28280
Library of Congress　　GV1507.W83L5
Copyright A 20203　　703.73

NL 0342511　DLC PU

QP177　**Lichtenthaeler, Charles,** 1915–
.L7　Le cytochrome et la respiration cellulaire.
Lausanne, 1944.
30₍ p.
Thèse—Lausanne.

1. Cytochrome. 2. Oxidation, Physiological.

NL 0342512　ICU DNLM ICJ

VOLUME 332

WZ 100
H61f
Lichtenthaeler, Charles, 1915-
La médecine hippocratique. Lausanne, Gonin,
1948-63.
10 pts.in 4 v. 25cm. ([Études hippocrati-
ques, 1.-4.ser.])

Imprint varies: 2.ser., Boudry, La Bacon-
nière. 3.-4.ser. Geneva, E. Droz.
Ser.3-4 issued without title.
Contents:- 1.[ser.]Méthode expérimentale
et méthode hippo-   cratique. Étude comparée
préliminaire.   (Études sur le raison-

nement clinique)- 2.ser.[2.-5.pt.]De l'utilité
actuelle d'un retour à Hippocrate. Introduction
à l'étude de la médecine hippocratique. De
l'étiologie du chaud inné hippocratique. De
l'origine sociale de certains concepts scientifiques et philosophiques grecs. Le premier
aphorisme d'Hippo-   crate et ses prémisses.
(Études sur le   raisonnement clinique)-
[3.ser.]6.pt.   Sur la vocation univer-

sitaire de l'histoire de la médecine; leçon inaugurale. Le troisième épidémique d'Hippocrate,
vient-il vraiment après le premier?- 4.ser.,
7.-10.pt.Sur l'authenticité, la place véritable
et le style de l'"épilogue" du III. épidémique.
De l'économie du pronostic d'Hippocrate. Le lo-
gos mathématique   de la première clinique
hippocratique.   La première clinique
hippocratique;   essai de synthèse.

1.Hippocrates. 2.Medicine, Greek and Roman.
3.Philosophy, Medical. I.Series: Études sur le
raisonnement   clinique.

OU NjP CU-M MiU NNC-M MnU MH
NL 0342516   NcD-MC NBuU WU TxU-M DNLM CU CLU PPC

398.06 LICHTENTHAELER, FRANK E
P387
v.9   Storm blown seed of Schoharie, by Frank E.
Lichtenthaeler.
(In The Pennsylvania German folklore
society. [Allentown,1946] 25cm. vol.9,1944.
p.1-105 double table,fold.maps.)

"Annotations": p.96-105;"References":p.
105.

NL 0342517   PU

W
945   LICHTENTHAL, PETER, 1780-1853.
.504   I capelli considerati sotto varj aspetti e
mezzi per conservarli.   Milano,Presso G.Mei-
ners e Figlio,1835.
63p. 21cm.

NL 0342518   ICN

Lichtenthal, Peter, 1780-1853.
Cenni biografici intorno al celebre maestro Wolfango
Amedeo Mozart, estratti da dati autentici dal dottor Pietro Lichtenthal. Milano, G. Silvestri, 1816.
40 p. 20ᵐᵐ.

1. Mozart, Johann Chrysostom Wolfgang Amadeus, 1756-1791.

10-18278

Library of Congress   ML410.M9L4

NL 0342519   DLC

Lichtenthal, Peter, 1780-1853.
Dictionnaire de musique, par le Dʳ. Pierre Lichtenthal,
traduit et augmenté par Dominique Mondo ... Paris,
Troupenas et cᵉ, 1839.
2 v. 24ᵐᵐ.

Music: 16 p., engr., at end of v. 2.
Translation of v. 1-2 of Lichtenthal's Dizionario e bibliografia della
musica (Milano, 1826. 4 v.)

1. Music—Dictionaries. i. Mondo, D., tr.

23-16258

Library of Congress   ML100.L67

NL 0342520   DLC CaBVaU TU PP OU IEN CU NcGU

Lichtenthal, Peter, 1780-1853.
Dizionario e bibliografia della musica.
Milano, 1820.
4 vols. 8vo.

NL 0342521   NN

Lichtenthal, Peter, 1780-1853.
ML100 Dizionario e bibliografia della musica.
L699   Milano, A. Fontana, 1826.
2 v. diagrs. 22ᵐᵐ.
Musical examples at end of v.1([16] p.)
Vol. 2 is a translation of Forkel's Allgemeine Litteratur der Musik, with additions.
Contents. - v.1. Dizionario e bibliografia
della musica. - v. 2. Letteratura generale
della musica.
1. Music - Dict   ionaries. 2. Music -
Bio-bibl. I. For   kel, Johann Nikolaus,
1749-1818.

NL 0342522   CSt IaU PLatS

Lichtenthal, Peter, 1780-1853.
Dizionario e bibliografia della musica del dottore Pietro
Lichtenthal ... Milano, A. Fontana, 1826.
4 v. diagrs. 22½ᵉᵐ.

Vols. 3-4 are a translation of Forkel's "Allgemeine litteratur der
musik", with additions.
CONTENTS.—v. 1-2. Dizionario di musica.—v. 3-4. Letteratura generale
della musica.

1. Music—Dictionaries. 2. Music—Bio-bibl. i. Forkel, Johann Nikolaus, 1749-1818.

5—38570

Library of Congress   ML100.L69

NIC CU KMK CU-S
NL 0342523   DLC NcU ICU NcU CtY PP PPL MiU MH MB OU

Lichtenthal, Peter, 1780-1853.
Dizionario e bibliografia della musica del dottore Pietro
Lichtenthal ... Milano, A. Fontana, 1836.
4 v. diagrs. 22½ᵉᵐ.

Vols. 3-4 are a translation of Forkel's "Allgemeine litteratur der
musik", with additions.
CONTENTS.—v. 1-2. Dizionario di musica.—v. 3-4. Letteratura generale
della musica.

NL 0342524   ViU WaU MiU

Lichtenthal, Peter, 1780-1853.
Estetica; ossia, Dottrina del bello e delle arti belle, del
dottore Pietro Lichtenthal. Milano, Coi tipi di G. Pirot-
ta, 1831.
xx, 435 p. 18ᵐᵐ.

1. Esthetics.

10-13505

NL 0342525   DLC

WBI   LICHTENTHAL, Peter, 1780-1853
L699i   Idrologia medica; ossia, L'acqua comune
1838   e l'acqua minerale, loro natura, uso
dietetico e medicinale; con una compendiata
descrizione de'bagni di alcuni popoli antichi
e moderni, una generale enumerazione
delle note sorgenti minerali Europee ...
Novara, Ibertis, 1838.
336 p.
Bound with Cavoleau, J. A. OEnologie
française. Paris, 1827.

NL 0342526   DNLM IU

WBI   LICHTENTHAL, Peter, 1780-1853
L699i   Idrologia medica; ossia, L'acqua
1847   comune e l'acqua minerale, loro natura,
uso dietetico e medicinale; con una
compendiata descrizione de'bagni di
alcuni popoli antichi e moderni, una
generale enumerazione delle note sorgenti
minerali Europee ... 2. ed. Novara,
Ibertis, 1847.
336 p.

NL 0342527   DNLM

Lichtenthal, Peter, 1780-1853.
Manuale bibliografico del viaggiatore in Italia concernente località, storia, arti, scienze ed antiquaria, del dottor
Pietro Lichtenthal. Volume unico. Milano, A. Fontana,
1830.
vii, 258 p. 19ᵐᵐ. (Half-title: Collezione di manuali componenti una enci-
clopedia di scienze, lettere ed arti. Letteratura)

1. Italy—Descr. & trav.—Bibl. 2. Italy—History, Local—Bibl.

4-15744

Library of Congress   Z2363.L69

NL 0342528   DLC NcD

Lichtenthal, Peter, 1780-1853.
Manuale bibliografico del viaggiatore in Italia concernente località, storia, arti, scienze, antiquaria e commercio preceduto da un elenco delle opere periodiche letterarie che attualmente si pubblicano in Italia e susseguito
da un' appendice e da tre indici di viaggi, di località, e
d'autori. Del dottor Pietro Lichtenthal. 2. ed. originale,
migliorata ed accresciuta. Milano, L. di Giacomo Pirola,
1834.
1 p. l., xiv, 411, [1] p. 19ᵐᵐ.
1. Italy—Descr. & trav.—Bibl. 2. Italy—History, Local—Bibl.

4-15745

Library of Congress   Z2363.L691

NL 0342529   DLC CLU

Lichtenthal, Peter, 1780-1853.   2162.12
Manuale bibliografico del viaggiatore in Italia concernente località,
storia, arti, scienze, antiquaria e commercio preceduto da un
elenco delle opere periodiche letterarie che attualmente si pubblicano in Italia e susseguito da un appendice e da tre indici
di viaggi di località e di autori. 3a edizione originale notabil-
mente accresciuta e migliorata.
Milano. Silvestri. 1844. xx, 488 pp. 16½ cm., in 8s.

M4304 — Italy. Bibl. — Periodicals. Italian. Bibl. — Italy. Periodicals. Bibl.

NL 0342530   MB ICN CtY PPPM IU NN NRU MH

ML410   Lichtenthal, Peter, 1780-1853.
M9L5   Mozart e le sue creazioni; memoria scritta in
1842   occasione dell'inaugurazione del suo monumento a
Music   Salisburgo in settembre del 1842. Ed.seo. Milano,
Library Ricordi [1842?]
43 p. fold.music.

1. Mozart, Johann Chrysostom Wolfgang Amadeus,
1756-1791. I. Title.

NL 0342531   CU ICU

ML   LICHTENTHAL,Peter,1780-1853
3920   Der musikalische Arzt, oder: Abhandlung
L61   von dem Einfluss der Musik auf den Körper,
und von ihrer Anwendung in gewissen Krahk-
heiten. Nebst einigen Winken, zur Anhörung
einer guten Musik. Von Peter Lichtenthal.
Wien, Bey Christian Friedrich Wapler und
Beck, 1807.
8vo 197 p., 1 l. illus. (music) 15 1/2 cm.
Autograph of Philip Hale.
Disbound.
1. Music--   Physiological effect.
A. Ex libris: Hale,Philip.

NL 0342532   MBCo ICN

Lichtenthal, Peter, 1780-1853.
Nuovo e sicuro metodo di guarire la sifilide in
tutte le sue forme
see under   Dzondi, Karl Heinrich,
1770-1835.

VOLUME 332

L781.6
L699o　Lichtenthal, Peter, 1780-1853.
　　Orphsik, oder Anweisung die Regeln der
　　Composition auf eine leicht facsliche Art
　　gründlich zu erlernen.　Wien, Druckercy am
　　Graben [1813]
　　24,47p.　music.　25 x 35cm.

　　Cover title.

　　1. Composition (Music)　I. Title.

NL 0342534　IEN DLC CtY

WC　　LICHTENTHAL, Peter, 1780-1853
262　　　　Ragguaglio storico terapeutico del
L699r　　cólera-morbo sino alla metà d'ottobre
1831　　1831, secondo fonti autentici ed atti
　　　　governativi.　Milano, Meiners, 1831.
　　　　xv, 271 p.

NL 0342535　DNLM

Lichtenthal, Peter, 1780-1853.
　　Trattato dell'influenza della musica sul corpo umano e del
suo uso in certe malattie, con alcuni cenni come si abbia
ad intendere una buona musica, di Pietro Lichtenthal ...
tradotto dal tedesco e ricorretto dall'autore medesimo.
Milano, Presso G. Maspero, 1811.
　　xvi, 94 p., 1 l.　22½ cm.
　　The original was published in 1807 under title: Der musikalische
arzt.
　　Bibliography: p. 82-83.
　　1. Music, Influence of.　2. Music therapy.

　　ML3920.L69　　　　　　　　　　6—39493

NL 0342536　DLC CSt MBCo DNLM

332　　Lichtenthal, S
L613k　　Das kredithaus; entgegnung auf die
　　　　broschure des amtsgerichtsrats dr. Otto
　　　　Hein, "Abzahlgesetz und kredithäuser",
　　　　im auftrage des verbandes der kredit-
　　　　häuser Deutschlands.　Berlin, 1912.
　　　　320p.

NL 0342537　IU

PT 1450
.L 3　　　　Lichtenthaler Marienklage [1. Aufl.]
1948　　　　Freiburg im Breisgau, Christophorus-Verlag
　　　　[1948]
　　　　[36] p.　illus.

　　　　"Text nach einer Handschrift aus dem 13.
　　　　Jahrh.　Übertragen ins Hochdeutsche und
　　　　handgeschrieben."

NL 0342538　InU MH

Lichtenthurn, Joseph Aschauer, von und zu
　　　　Aschenrain und
　　　　see　Aschauer, Joseph, von [und zu
　　　　Aschenrain und Lichtenthurn] 1782-1843.

Lichtenvoort, Willem Cornelis Star
　　... De pactis emtioni venditioni ad-
　　jectis ... submittit Wilhelmus Cornelius
　　Star Lichtenvoort ... Groningae, T.
　　Spoormaker, 1804.

　　2 p.l., 53, [6] p.　18½cm.

　　Diss.- Groningen.
　　Bibliographical footnotes.

NL 0342540　MH-L

Lichtenvoort, Willem Hendrik Fabricius
　　... De nuptiis prohibitis ... sub-
　　mittit Willem Hendrik Fabricius
　　Lichtenvoort ... Groningae, P. Doekema,
　　1779.

　　2 p.l., 33, [1] p.　23½cm.

　　Diss.- Groningen.

NL 0342541　MH-L

LICHTENWALD, Hans.
　　Das deutsche branntweinmonopol in seiner
　　bedeutung für wirtschaft und fiskus. [Gunzen-
　　hausen, J. Riedel, 1929?].

　　Inaugural-dissertation München.

NL 0342542　MH CtY IEN

Lichtenwallner, William A
　　Problems vital to our religion, by W. A. Lichtenwallner.
Los Angeles, Calif., Times-Mirror printing and binding house,
1920.
　　5 p. l., [7]-183 p.　20ᵐ.

　　1. Christianity—Controversial literature.　I. Title.
　　　　　　　　　　　　　　　　　　　　22-1389
Library of Congress　　BL2775.L43

NL 0342543　DLC OC1 MB

Lichtenwalner, Harry W　　, 1899-
　　Lichtenwalner-Lichtenwalter family history, 1700-1950. Compiled by the committee, arranged and ed. by Harry W. Lichtenwalner. [Easton? Pa., 1951]　424 p.　illus.　24cm.

　　1. Lichtenwalter family.　　　　　　　January 22, 1952

NL 0342544　NN ICN WHi

Lichtenwalner, Norton Lewis, 1889-
　　Report of loss and damage, March 1936,
flood in Pennsylvania.　Philadelphia,
National Emergency Council [1936]
48p.　30½cm.

　　Autographed from type-written copy.
　　Prepared by N.L. Lichtenwalner, State
director for the National emergency
council.

NL 0342545　PSt OC1FRB

LICHTENWALNER family history; compiled and
　　published by the Committee on publication,
　　appointed by the Executive committee of the
　　Pennsylvania branch of the Lichtenwalner family.
　　Allentown, Press of S. J. Brobst, 1900.　198 p.
　　22cm.

　　1. Lichtenwalner family.

NL 0342546　NN

S21　　Lichtenwalter, Rose May (Harsch) 1885-
.A75　　　joint author.
vol. XII,　Long, William Henry, 1867-
no. 2　　Pure cultures of wood-rotting fungi on artificial media. By
W. H. Long ... and R. M. Harsch ...

　　(In U. S. Dept. of agriculture.　Journal of agricultural research.
vol. XII, no. 2, p. 33-82.　26ᶜᵐ.　Washington, 1918)

Lichtenwanger, William, 1915-
　　Instruments of the clarinet type before the modern clarinet,
by William Lichtenwanger ...　(A dissertation submitted in
partial fulfillment of the requirements for the degree of master of music in musicology)　University of Michigan, School
of music. [Ann Arbor, Mich.] 1940.
　　3 p. l., 181 numb. l.　illus. (music)　28½ x 22ᵐ.
　　Type-written (carbon copy)
　　Bibliography : leaves 173-181.

　　1. Clarinet.　I. Title.
　　　　　　　　　　　　　　　　　43-42786
Library of Congress　　ML945.L5 I 6

NL 0342548　DLC

[Hebraic　Lichter, Abraham.
sect.]　מלון חדיש אידיש־עברי, מאדערנער יידישהעברעאיש
ווערטערבוך. מיט א פארווארט פון גרשם באדער. הוצאת
בית מסחר ספרים פרדס. [New York, 1947]
315 p.　15 cm.

　　1. Yiddish language—Dictionaries—Hebrew.
　　　　　　　　Title transliterated: Milon ḥadish idi-'ivr
　　PJ5117.L5　　　　　　　　　　48-13789'

NL 0342549　DLC

Lichter, August, 1860-1925.
　　Durfpum'ranza; lustige bilder aus dem schlesischen volksleben; poesie und prosa in schlesischer
mundart von A. Lichter.　Schweidnitz [1898]
165 p.　19 cm.

NL 0342550　CU

Lichter, August, 1860-1925.
　　Meine muttersproache; lustige bilder aus dem
schlesischen volksleben, poesie und prosa in
schlesischer mundart von A. Lichter. 2. verm.
aufl.　Schweidnitz [1898]
161 p.　19 cm.
　　With author's autograph letter inserted.

NL 0342551　CU

Lichter, August, 1860-1925.
　　Mietebrenge; Erzählungen, Humoresken und Gedichte in
schlesischer Mundart, von August Lichter. Mit dem Bilde des
Verfassers...　Schweidnitz: L. Heege, 1925.　141 p.　18½cm.
　　Without the portrait of the author mentioned on the t.-p.

63564B.　I. German literature—　　Misc.　2. German language—
Dialects—Silesia.　I. Title.　　　　　September 25, 1940

NL 0342552　NN

Lichter, Gerhard, joint author

Walter, Alex Gustav Anton, 1888-
　　Die deutsche eierstandardisierung; erläuterung der verord-
nung über handelsklassen für hühnereier und über die kenn-
zeichnung von hühnereiern—eierverordnung—vom 17. 3. 1932.
Von min.-rat dr. A. Walter u. ober-reg.-rat Gerh. Lichter ...
Berlin, P. Parey, 1932.

Lichter, Hans
　　Fifty responses for choirs ...
　　see under　Gilbert, James L., comp.

Lichter, Hans, ed.
　　Reed organ selections for church use
　　see under title

VOLUME 332

X1.977
.C5L5
Lichter, Hans, comp.
Twenty part-songs for men's voices.
Boston, O. Ditson, c1905.
94 p. 28 cm.

1. Song-books (Men's voices)

NL 0342556 MB

Lichter, Hans, comp.
Twenty part-songs for men's voices.
Boston, Ditson, c1906.
94 p.

Contents:—Selections by Arens, Barri,
Coe, Dressler, Dulcken, Fisher, Froelich,
Geibel, Gumbert, Hatton, Humphries, Jensen,
Jude, Nevin, Noyes, Pike, Pinsuti, Scott,
Steele, Trotère.

NL 0342557 OC1

Lichter, Helmut: Kombination von Schiefhals und Aurikularanhängen.
[Maschinenschrift.] 12 S. 4°. — Auszug: Breslau 1923: Lehmann.
2 Bl. 8°
Breslau, Med. Diss. v. 10. März 1924 [U 24. 1689

NL 0342558 ICRL

Lichter, Helmuth, 1925–
Leistungs- und Soziallohn im Wirtschaftsmechanismus.
Düsseldorf, Triltsch, 1954.
111 p. diagrs. 21 cm.

Inaug.-Diss.—Wirtschaftshochschule, Mannheim.
Vita.
Errata slip inserted.
Bibliography: p. 103–109.

1. Wages. I. Title.

HD4911.L5   56–30301

NL 0342559 DLC

Lichter, Johann August
    see Lichter, August, 1860-1925.

Lichter, Matthias.
EB   Deutsches und ausländisches Staatsangehörig-
ALO keitsrecht, mit Anhang "Reichsbürgergesetz".
QGd Ein Handbuch für den standesamtlichen Gebrauch,
von Matthias Lichter [und] Friedrich A. Knost.
Berlin, Verlag für Standesamtswesen, 1935.
vii, 360 p.

1. Citizenship. 2. Naturalization. 3. Expatriation. I. Knost, Friedrich A   joint author.
II. Title.

NL 0342561 CSt-L MH CSt-H

Lichter, Matthias.
... Deutsches und ausländisches staatsangehörigkeitsrecht ...
von Matthias Lichter ... Berlin, Verlag für standesamtswesen, 1938–
v. 20cm. (Half-title: Handbücherei des standesbeamten, hrsg. von
F. A. Knost und Johann Wagner. bd. VII
Series title in part at head of t.-p.

1. Citizenship. 2. Naturalization. 3. Expatriation. I. Title.
40–36733
Library of Congress   JX4209.L5
323.6

NL 0342562 DLC MH

Lichter, Matthias.
Das Staatsangehörigkeitsrecht im grossdeutschen Reich;
Zusammenstellung der einschlägigen gesetzlichen Bestim-
mungen und Durchführungsanweisungen mit Erläuterungen.
Berlin, C. Heymann, 1943.
viii, 202 p. 24 cm.
"Schrifttum": p. 4–9.

1. Citizenship—Germany. 2. Naturalization—Germany. I. Title
A 51–8830
Northwestern Univ.   Sch. of Law.   Library
for Library of Congress   †

MH-L
NL 0342563 IEN CU-AL IaU IU MH MnU CSt-H DAL NNC

Lichter, Matthias.
Die Staatsangehörigkeit nach deutschem und auslän-
dischem Recht; geltendes und früheres Recht nebst Rechtsver-
gleichung. 2., völlig veränderte Aufl. Berlin, Heymann,
1955.
xx, 947 p. 21 cm.
First ed. published in 1943 under title: Das Staatsangehörigkeitsrecht im grossdeutschen Reich.
"Schrifttum": p. 888–900.

1. Citizenship—Germany (Federal Republic, 1949–   ) 2. Citizenship—Germany. 3. Citizenship.   I. Title.
56–25402

NL 0342564 DLC CtY-L IU MH-L IaU

Lichter (Philipp). * Beitrag zur Statistik der
Chloroform-Narcosen. [Erlangen.] 51 pp. 8°.
Berlin, Fass & Garleb, [1894].

NL 0342565 DNLM CtY

Lichter, William Herman
Shop manual, typographic numbering machine.
[Chicago, General Numbering Machine Service,
a1951]
132 p. illus.

NL 0342566 MiD

Lichter gleiten durch den Schatten

    see under

    Wolter, Gerhard, ed.

Lichterbeck, Hans, 1910–
Kreditausweitung als Mittel krisenbedingter Währungspoli-
tik...von Hans Lichterbeck... Greifswald: H. Adler, 1933.
74 p. 23½cm.

Inaugural-Dissertation — Greifswald, 1933
Lebenslauf.
"Schrifttum", p. [5]–9.

765631A. 1. Credit.
July 15, 1935

NL 0342568 NN MiU CtY PU

Lichterbeck, Karl
Die nominalflexion im gathadialekt.
Inaug. diss. Muenster, 1893 (Guetersloh)

NL 0342569 ICRL MdBP CtY

1894–
Lichterfeld, Arnold; Die Neubildungen der weiblichen Ge-
schlechtsorgane in ihren Beziehungen zu Schwangerschaft,
Geburt und Wochenbett. Aus d. Univ.-Frauenkl. zu Berlin.
[In Maschinenschrift.] 80 S., 10 Tab. 4°(2°). — Auszug:
Berlin (1920): Blanke. 2 Bl. 8°
Berlin, Med. Diss. v. 22. Juli 1920, Ref. Schäfer, Bumm
[Geb. 28. Aug. 94 Berlin; Wohnort: Berlin; Staatsangeh.: Preußen; Vorbildung:
Friedr.-Wilh.-G. Berlin Reife 13; Studium: Berlin 14 S.; Coll. 21. Juli 20;
Approb. 9. März 20.]   [U 20. 1356

NL 0342570 ICRL

Lichterfeld, F., ed.

Hoffmann, Friedrich.
Columbus, Cortes und Pizarro. Geschichte der entdeckung und eroberung von Amerika. Nach den besten
quellen der jugend erzählt von Friedrich Hoffmann.
2. aufl., neu bearb. von F. Lichterfeld ... Mit 12 bildern
in lithographischem farbendruck. Breslau, E. Trewendt,
1866.

ar W   Lichterfeld, Johannes, 1881–
53894   Die Ethik Heinrichs von Gent in ihren
no.6   Grundzügen. [Gräfenhainichen, Druck von
C. Schulze, 1906?]
51 p. 23cm.

Inaug.-Diss.—Erlangen.

1. Henricus Gandavensis, 1217-1293.

NL 0342572 NIC NN NjP CtY MH ICRL

ar V   Lichterfeld, L
2332   Entwickelungsgeschichte der deutschen
Schauspielkunst.   Erfurt, F. Bartholomäus [1882]
286 p. 19cm.

1. Theater--Germany--History.

NL 0342573 NIC MH IU MA

JS19   Lichterfelde, Prussia.
.L75   Verwaltungsbericht der gemeinde Berlin-
Lichterfelde für das jahr 19
[Berlin-Lichterfelde, 19
v. tables. 34x21cm.

NL 0342574 DLC

Lichterfelde, Prussia. Landwirtschaftliche versuchstation.

Eckstein, Oskar.
... Arbeiten über kalidüngung, von prof. dr. dr. h. c. O. Eckstein, dr. A. Jacob und dr. F. Alten. Berlin, Verlagsgesellschaft für ackerbau m. b. h., 1931.

Lichterfelde, Prussia
    see also
Berlin.

Lichterman, Julius.
על הנשר. שירים. ניוורק, הוצאת "נחמיה".
[New York, 1926]
108 p. 21 cm.
Vocalized text.

I. Title.   Title transliterated: 'Al ha-gesher.
PJ5053.L43A7   57–53951 ‡

NL 0342577 DLC

Lichterman, Julius.
המשיה; ספר ראשון לשיחה, למקרא, להשעמה לכתיבה ולדקדוק
מעשי על-פי שמת הדבור הטבעי. עם ציורים מאת רחל כהן.
אינדיאנפוליס, הוצאת "פארן," תשי"ב. [Indianapolis, 1952]
92 p. illus. 23 cm.

1. Hebrew language—Chrestomathies and readers. I. Title.
Title transliterated: ha-Mashiah.
PJ4569.L56   A 55-10068
New York. Public Libr.
for Library of Congress   †

NL 0342578 NN DLC

VOLUME 332

Lichterman, Martin
John Adams Dix: 1798-1879. ₍New York₎
1952.
ii, 778 l. 29cm.

Thesis, Columbia university.
Typewritten manuscript.
Bibliography: l. 770-778.

NL 0342579   NNC

MICROFILM
F378.7CWO
L617

Lichterman, Martin
John Adams Dix: 1798-1879. ₍New York₎
1952.
ii, 778 l. (₍University microfilms, Ann
Arbor, Mich.₎ Publication no. 4210)

Thesis, Columbia university.
Microfilm copy of typewritten manuscript.
Abstracted in Microfilm abstracts.
Bibliography: l. 770-778.

NL 0342580   NNC MiDW CtY PU

Lichterman (*Mlle.* Sophie) [1864-   ]. *De
la forme ascitique de la péritonite tuberculeuse.
72 pp. 4°. Paris, 1890, No. 249.

NL 0342581   DNLM

Lichters, Walter, 1910-
Ich mache mich selbständig. Stuttgart, Fackelverlag
₍1954₎
160 p. 18 cm.

1. Occupations.   I. Title.

HF5382.L5   55-16431 ‡

NL 0342582   DLC

Lichters, Walter, 1910-   *ed.*
Wege zu Wissen und Wohlstand, hrsg. von Walter Lichters und Heinz Reinhardt. Stuttgart, Fackelverlag ₍1955₎
3 v. illus. diagrs. 25 cm.

1. Encyclopedias and dictionaries, German.   I. Reinhardt, Heinz Rainer, 1913-   joint ed. II. Title.

AG27.L5   56-33078

NL 0342583   DLC

Lichtervelde (ALBERT LOUIS DE) *Bishop of Namur.*
Antwoord van den bisschop van Namen, op het depeche aen haer geaddresseert in date 24. Februarii [1789]
door het gouvernement [declining to send the theological students of his diocese to the General Seminary at Louvain] [*Namen?* 1789?]   4 pp. nar. 8°.
In: GAD p. v. 27.

NL 0342584   NN

DT
655
F56

Lichtervelde, B   comte de
Contribution à l'histoire des origines du Congo belge. Note sur les écrits de Luciano Cordeiro, publiciste portugais.
Brussels, M. Hayez, 1936.
pp. 468-487.   maps.

Extrait de Institut Royal Colonial Belge, Bulletin des Séances, vol. VII, pt. 3, 1936

I. Académie   royale des sciences d'outre-mer,   Brussels.

NL 0342585   MBU

Lichtervelde, Gontran Ernest Désiré Aloïs Marie Ghislain, comte de, 1849-
Les légendes de l'inconnu géographique; par le cᵗᵉ G. de Lichtervelde ... Bruxelles, P. Lacomblez, 1903.
81 p.   20½ᶜᵐ.

"Il a été tiré de ce livre 55 exemplaires hors commerce sur papier de Hollande Van Gelder. No. 25."

1. Geographical myths.   I. Title.
3—24135
Library of Congress   G100.L6

NL 0342586   DLC CtY

S
469
.B4
L7

Lichtervelde, Joseph François, comte de, 1772-1840.
Mémoire sur les fonds ruraux du département de l'Escaut. Par J.F.d.L. ... A Gand, De l'impr. de P.F. de Goesin-Verhaeghe, 1815.

3 p.l., 179 p., 2 l.   IV fold.pl., fold.map,
6 fold.tab.   21 cm.

Author's name appears in salutation of letter, p. ₍1₎.

1. Agriculture--Belgium--Scheldt.   I. Title.

NL 0342587   MiU

Lichtervelde, Louis de, *comte,* 1889-
August the fourth, 1914, in the Belgian parliament, by Count Louis de Lichtervelde; tr. from the French. London, Wightman & co., ltd., 1918.
37, ₍1₎ p.   18½ᶜᵐ.

1. European war, 1914-1918—Belgium.
19—123
Library of Congress   D615.L7

NjP PU PHi PPT PPL
NL 0342588   DLC NcD CtY OO OU OC1WHi MiU MB NN IaU

Lichtervelde, Louis de, *comte,* 1889-
... Avant l'orage (1911-1914) Bruxelles, L'Édition universelle, s. a. ₍1938₎
2 p.l., 7-206 p., 1 l.   19½ᶜᵐ.
Bibliographical foot-notes.

1. Belgium—History—Albert I, 1909-1918—Causes.   2. European war, 1914-1918—Causes.   I. Title.
A C 39-2610
New York. Public library
for Library of Congress

NL 0342589   NN CU-S

Lichtervelde, Louis de, *comte,* 1889-
Le comte de Broqueville. Bruxelles, A. Goemaere, 1946.
31 p.   port.   25 cm.
"Il a été tiré 175 exemplaires numérotés de cette étude extraite de la 'Revue générale belge' du 15 mars 1946. Exemplaire no. 120."
"Bibliographie": p. 31.

1. Broqueville, Charles Marie Pierre Albert, baron de, 1860-1940.

DH685.B7L5   923.2493   48-22883*

NL 0342590   DLC

JN
6135
L5

Lichtervelde, Louis, comte, 1889-
Le Congrès national de 1830; études et portraits. Bruxelles, A. Dewit, 1922.
xiii, 209 p.   19 cm.

1. Belgium. Congrès national, 1830-31.
2. Belgium. Constitution.

NL 0342591   CU-S IaU CtY

Lichtervelde, Louis de, *comte,* 1889-
Le Congrès national, l'œuvre et les hommes. Bruxelles, Renaissance du livre ₍1945₎
182, ₍2₎ p. illus. 19 cm. (Collection "Notre passé")
Bibliography: p. ₍183₎

1. Belgium. Congrès national, 1830-1831. 2. Belgium. Constitution.

JN6135.L5   51-36114

NL 0342592   DLC DS CU-S IU CSt NN

PQ3857
.L59G4

Lichtervelde, Louis, de, comte.
...Générations... ₍Bruxelles,
Desclée de Brouwer et cie₎ 1932.
4p.l., 11-171p., 1 l. 18cm. (Collection "Le rond-point". Série "Essais" ₍1₎)

1. Heredity. 2. Intellect. I. Title.

NL 0342593   NNU-W

Lichtervelde, Louis de, *comte.*
Léopold II, par le Cᵗᵉ Louis de Lichtervelde ... Bruxelles, A. Dewit, 1926.
427, ₍1₎ p. front. (port.) fold. map, facsims. 19½ᶜᵐ.
"Ouvrage couronné par la Fondation François Empain."
"Bibliographie": p. 425-426.

1. Léopold II, king of the Belgians, 1835-1909. 2. Belgium—Pol. & govt.—1830-   3. Belgium—Colonies—Kongo.
27-8697
Library of Congress   DH671.L5

NL 0342594   DLC NN IEN CaQML CtY ViU

Lichtervelde, Louis de, comte, 1889-
Léopold II, par le cᵗᵉ Louis de Lichtervelde... Paris: Plon,
1927. 429 p. facsims. (incl. map), front. (port.) 12°.
Bibliography, p. 427-428.

317996A. 1. Leopold II, king of the   Belgians, 1835-1909. 2. Belgium—
Hist., 1865-1909.   August 20, 1927

NL 0342595   NN NjP MB

DH
671
L5
1935

Lichtervelde, Louis, comte de, 1889-
Léopold II. 4. éd., rev. et augm. Paris, Plon, 1935.
453 p. port. 21 cm.

Includes bibliography.

1. Leopold II, King of the Belgians, 1835-1909. 2. Belgium - Pol. & govt. - 1830-1914.

NL 0342596   CU-S NcD PU

Lichtervelde, Louis, de, *comte,* 1889-
Léopold II. Bruxelles, Presses de Belgique ₍1949₎
384 p. port., fold. map. 19 cm. (Présence de l'histoire)
Bibliography: p. ₍383,₎384.

1. Leopold II, King of the Belgians, 1835-1909. 2. Belgium—Pol. & govt.— 1830-1914. 3. Congo (Democratic Republic)—Hist.—Early period to 1908.

DH671.L5 1949   923.1493   50—26516

NL 0342597   DLC IEN NN LU

VOLUME 332

Lichtervelde, Louis de, *comte*, 1889–
Léopold First, the founder of modern Belgium, by Comte Louis de Lichtervelde ... translated by Thomas H. Reed ... and H. Russell Reed. New York, London, The Century co. [1930]

xi p., 2 l., 3–336 p. illus. (map) 2 port. (incl. front.) 22½ᶜᵐ.

1. Léopold I, king of the Belgians, 1790–1865. 2. Belgium—Hist.—Léopold I, 1831–1865. I. Reed, Thomas Harrison, 1881– tr. II. Reed, Howard Russell, 1905– joint tr.

Library of Congress   DH656.L5
                                                30–30114
                                      [a40g1]   923.1493

MB OrPR
NL 0342598   DLC WaSp MtU TU CaBVaU ScU PP ViU NN MH

Lichtervelde, Louis de, *comte*, 1889–
Léopold of the Belgians, by Comte Louis de Lichtervelde, translated by Thomas H. Reed and H. Russell Reed. New York, London, The Century co. [1929]

xi p., 2 l., 3–366 p. front. (port.) fold. map. 23ᶜᵐ.

1. Léopold II, king of the Belgians, 1835–1909. 2. Belgium—Pol. & govt.—1830– 3. Belgium—Colonies—Kongo. I. Reed, Thomas Harrison, 1881– tr. II. Reed, Howard Russell, 1905– joint tr. III. Title.

Library of Congress   DH671.L52
                                                29–11304

OKentU
PBm PU PSC OC1 OCU OOxM ViU MB NN WaSpG OrU OrMonO
NL 0342599   DLC WaT OrPR CaBVaU WaS TU MeB NcU OrP

DH   Lichtervelde, Louis, comte de, 1889–
656   Léopold Ier et la formation de la Belgique
L53   contemporaine, par le Cte L. de Lichtervelde.
         Bruxelles, A. Dewit, 1929.
            384 p. port. 20 cm.

            1. Léopold I, King of the Belgians, 1790–1865.

NL 0342600   CU-S PU CtY

PQ3857   Lichtervelde, Louis de, comte.
.L59M4   Méditations pour le centenaire, par
         le comte Louis de Lichtervelde. Bruxelles, A. Dewit, 1930.
            129p. 18cm.

            Bibliotheca Belgica.

NL 0342601   NNU-W

Lichtervelde, Louis de, *comte*.
... Les méthodes budgétaires d'une démocratie, étude sur le budget suisse, par le Cte Louis de Lichtervelde. Paris, V. Giard & E. Brière; [etc., etc.] 1912.

2 p. l., viii, 177, [2] p. tables. (part fold.) 22½ᶜᵐ. (École des sciences politiques et sociales de l'Université de Louvain. [Publications])

1. Budget—Switzerland. 2. Finance—Switzerland.
                                                12–28422
Library of Congress   HJ2144.A6L5

NL 0342602   DLC PU PP NN

Lichtervelde, Louis de, *comte*.
La monarchie en Belgique sous Léopold Iᵉʳ et Léopold II., par le comte Louis de Lichtervelde ... Bruxelles [etc.] G. van Oest & cⁱᵉ, 1921.

viii, 117, [2] p. 19ᶜᵐ.

1. Belgium—Hist.—Léopold I, 1831–1865. 2. Belgium—Hist.—Léopold II, 1865–1909. I. Title.

Library of Congress   DH656.L53
                                                32–3380
                                                949.3

NL 0342603   DLC NN

Lichtervelde, Louis de, *comte*.
... Le 4 août, 1914, au Parlement belge, par le comte Louis de Lichtervelde. Bruxelles et Paris, G. van Oest et cⁱᵉ, 1918.

61 p. 20½ᶜᵐ.

At head of title: Heures d'histoire.

1. European war, 1914– —Belgium. I. Title. II. Title: Heures d'histoire.

Library of Congress   D615.L6
                                                19–17842

NL 0342604   DLC OC1W

Lichtervelde, Louis de, *comte*, 1889–
... La structure de l'état belge. Louvain, Éditions Rex, 1932.

139 p., 1 l. 19½ᶜᵐ. (On cover: Collection d'études de doctrine politique catholique)

1. Belgium—Pol. & govt. 2. Catholic church in Belgium. I. Title.
                                                35–10816
Library of Congress   JN6165.L5
                                                342.49303

NL 0342605   DLC

Lichtervelde, Pierre de, *comte*.
Un grand commis des ducs de Bourgogne, Jacques de Lichtervelde, seigneur de Coolscamp. Préf. de Léon van der Essen. Bruxelles, Goemaere, 1943.

viii, 340 p. illus. 24 cm.

1. Coolscamp, Jacques de Lichtervelde, seigneur de, d. 1431. I. Title.
                                                50–43504
                  DC611.B78L5

NL 0342606   DLC IEN NN

                        1879–
Lichthardt, Karl] Studien zur Entwicklung der Erbentage und der Amtsverfassung in Cleve-Mark. Ein Beitr. z. Geschichte d. Selbstverwaltung. Witten: Pott [1910] S. 45—128. 8° ¶(Vollst. in: Jahrbuch d. Ver. f. Orts- u. Heimatsk. in d. Grafsch. Mark. 1910.)
Münster, Phil. Diss. v. 18. März 1911, Ref. Spannagel
[Geb. 4. Okt. 79 Mülheim a. R.; Wohnort: Münster i. W.; Staatsangeh.: Preußen; Vorbildung: Realgymn. Oberhausen Reife O. 07; Studium: Freiburg i. B., Berlin, Münster zus. 7 S.; Rig. 30. Juli 10.]   [U 11. 3969]

NL 0342607   ICRL MH PU CtY

M782.6   Lichthardt, Mary.
L617f   [Friendship. Piano-vocal score. English]
         [Friendship] or, In Mozart's time. Operetta for girls [unison and two-part] in one act, three scenes. Book, lyrics and music by Mary Lichthardt (violin ad lib.) Complete with music, dialog, stage and costume directions. Cincinnati, Willis Music Co. [c1932.
            32p. illus. 26cm.

            1. Musical revues, comedies, etc.—Vocal scores with piano.

NL 0342608   IU

Lichthardt, Mary
   Friendship; or, In Mozart's time, operetta for girls; in one act, three scenes. Book, lyrics and music ... Cincinnati, The Willis music co., [c1932]
      32 p.

NL 0342609   OC1

LICHTHARDT, MARY
   A hallowe'en frolic; operetta for boys in one act - 2 scenes. Cincinnati, Willis music co. c1930.
      16 p.

   Contains music.

NL 0342610   Or

BM723   Lichtheim, George, tr.   FOR OTHER EDITIONS
.S35   SEE MAIN ENTRY
1947
     Scholem, Gershom Gerhard, 1897–
        Major trends in Jewish mysticism. [Rev. ed.] New York, Schocken Books [1946]

Lichtheim, George, 1912–
   The pattern of world conflict, by G. L. Arnold [pseud.] New York, Dial Press, 1955.
      250 p. 21 cm.

      1. World politics—1945– 2. Economic policy. I. Title.
D843.L46
                                    55–7670 rev ‡
      *909.82 940.55
Library of Congress

TxU OrP ICU PPULC CoD CoFS CU CoCA CoU KMK OrU CoC PU CaBVaU NN PP TxU NcD OC1 OOxM ODW OO MB MiU TU PSt KT
NL 0342612   DLC Or WaT OrCS OrLgE NNC CaBVa NNR IU MH

Lichtheim, George, 1912–
   Peace or war? [By] G. L. Arnold [pseud.] London, Ampersand Ltd. [1955]
      61 p. 19 cm. (Bellman books, 13)

      1. World politics—1945– I. Title. (Series)
D844.L54
      *909.82 940.55   56–22846 rev
NL 0342613   DLC NNC MH CtY ICU DS OC1W

Lichtheim (Henricus) [1819–   ]. * De gastromalacia infantum. 34 pp. 8°. Berolini, typ. fratrum Schlesinger. [1842].

NL 0342614   DNLM

Lichtheim, Ludwig, 1845–1928.
   Festschrift Herrn Geh. Med.-Rat Prof. Dr. L. Lichtheim in Königsberg i Pr. gewidmet zur Vollendung seines 60. Lebensjahres
      see under title

QP101   Lichtheim, Ludwig, 1845–1928.
L61   Die störungen des lungenkreislaufs und ihr einfluss auf den blutdruck; eine pathologische experimental-untersuchung ... Berlin, Hirschwald, 1876.
            2 p. l., 68 p., 1 l. tables, II fold. diagrs.

            1. Blood - Circulation. 2. Blood - Pressure.

NL 0342616   NNC DNLM MBCo

Film   LICHTHEIM, Ludwig, 1845–1928
1340   Die Störungen des Lungenkreislaufs
no. 17   und ihr Einfluss auf den Blutdruck; eine pathologische Experimental-Untersuchung. Berlin, Hirschwald, 1876.
            68 p. illus.   Film 1340
         Film copy.

NL 0342617   DNLM

Lichtheim (Ludwig) [1845–1928]. * Ueber den Einfluss der Rückenmarksreizung auf die Gallensecretion. 31 pp. 8°. Berlin, G. Schade, 1867.

NL 0342618   DNLM

PJ2193   Lichtheim, Miriam, 1914–   tr.
.S7
     Stefanski, Elizabeth, ed.
        Coptic ostraca from Medinet Habu, by Elizabeth Stefanski and Miriam Lichtheim. Chicago, University of Chicago Press [1952]

VOLUME 332

Lichtheim, Miriam

    Situla no. 11395 and some remarks on Egyptian situlae. ₍Chicago, Univ. of Chicago, 1947?₎
    cover-title, 169-179 p. illus. 25ᶜᵐ. ₍Chicago. University₎ Oriental Institute. Museum notes. no.4)
    "Reprinted from Journal of Near Eastern studies vol. VI, no.3, July, 1947."

    1. Implements, utensils, etc.—Egypt. 2. Egyptians—Implements. 3. Egypt—Antiq. I. Title. II. Ser.

NL 0342620   ViU PU-Mu

Lichtheim, Miriam, 1914–
    ... The songs of the harpers ... by Miriam Lichtheim ... ₍n. p., 1946₎
    ₍1₎, 178-212 p. facsims. 24½ᵐ.
    Thesis (PH. D.)—University of Chicago, 1944.
    "Reprinted from the Journal of Near Eastern studies, vol. IV, no. 3, July, 1945."
    "Bibliography of harpers' songs from monuments of the new kingdom": p. 211-212. Bibliographical foot-notes.

    1. Egyptian ballads and songs. 2. Funeral rites and ceremonies—Egypt. 3. Inscriptions, Hieroglyphic. I. Title.
                    A 46-2677
Chicago. Univ. Library
for Library of Congress   PJ1551.L5
           †

NL 0342621   ICU DLC NNC OrU

Lichtheim, Richard, 1885–1963.
    Der Aufbau des jüdischen Palästina, von Richard Lichtheim. Berlin: Jüdischer Verlag, 1919. 37 p. 8°.

    1. Palestine.—Colonization. 2. Eco-   SCHIFF COLLECTION.
                      nomic history, Palestine.
                      January 14, 1922.

NL 0342622   NN MH OCH

LICHTHEIM, Richard.
    Das Programm des Zionismus. Herausgegeben von der Zionistischen Vereinigung für Deutschland. Berlin-Charlottenburg, 1911.

    22 cm.   pp.52.

NL 0342623   MH NjP

Lichtheim, Richard.
    Das Programm des Zionismus. Von Richard Lichtheim. Hrsg. von der Zionistischen Vereinigung für Deutschland. Berlin: ₍S. Scholem,₎ 1913. 46 p. 2. ed. 8°.

    1. Zionism.
                      July 14, 1924

NL 0342624   NN OCH MiD PPDrop

Lichtheim, Richard, 1885–
    Die Geschichte des deutschen Zionismus. Jerusalem, F Mass ₍1954₎
    285 p. illus. 22 cm.

    1. Zionism—Germany—Hist. 2. Jews in Germany—Hist.

DS149.L467   59–28359 ‡

NL 0342625   DLC LU MH NIC OCH

DS
149
J8L5
Lichtheim, Richard, 1885–1963.
    Kritische Reise durch Palästina (Ein₍ Antwort an Dr. Alfred Wiener, Syndikus des Zentralvereins) ₍Berlin₎ Zionistischen Vereinigung für Deutschland ₍1928?₎
    31 p. 18 cm.

    1. Wiener, Alfred, 1885– Kritische Reise durch Palästina. I. Title

NL 0342626   OCH MH

DS
149
L468
Lichtheim, Richard, 1885– 1963.
    Revision der zionistischen Politik. Berlin, EWER-Buchhandlung, 1930.
    64p.   24cm.

    1. Zionism. I. Title.
               12/68

NL 0342627   UU MH NN OCH NNJ

Lichtheim, Richard, 1885–1963.
    שאר ישוב. זכרונות ציוני מגרמניה ₍תורגם מכת"י ע"י ד. קמחי₎ תל-אביב, הספריה הציונית ליד הנהלה ההסתדרות הציונית. ₍בירושלים בהוצאת ספרים מ. ניומן, תשי"ד₎. ₍Tel-Aviv, 1953₎
    450 p. port. 21 cm. ₍סדרת זכרונות ראשונים, ב₎

    1. Zionists—Correspondence, reminiscences, etc. 2. Zionism—Germany. I. Title.   *Title transliterated:* She'ar yashuv.
DS149.L46   A 54–6248 rev
New York. Public Libr.
for Library of Congress   ₍r60b₎†

NL 0342628   NN DLC

Lichtheim, Richard, 1885– 1945. 1963.
    תולדות הציונות בגרמניה. ₍תירגם מכתבי-יד גרמני: יחיאל חי. נערך בידי ד. קמחי₎ הספריה הציונית בהשתתפות "הכשרת הישוב₎. ₍Jerusalem, 1951₎
    189 p. illus., ports. 22 cm.

    1. Zionism—Hist. 2. Jews in Germany—Hist.
    Title transliterated: Toldot ha-Tsiyonut be-Germanyah.
DS149.L47   52–57364

NL 0342629   DLC

Lichtherz, Carl Wilhelm, 1888–
    Rechte und Pflichten des Mitglieds bei der Aktiengesellschaft und der Gesellschaft mit beschränkter Haftung ... von Carl Wilhelm Lichtherz ... Cöln, Beyer & Schmeisser, 1914.

    2 p.l., 66, ₍4₎ p. 22cm.

    Inaug.-Diss. - Greifswald.
    "Literaturverzeichnis": p.₍67₎-₍68₎

NL 0342630   MH-L PU

Lichthorn, Bruno, 1878–
    Ueber einen fall von rhinosklerom. Inaug. Diss. Berlin, 1903
    Bibl.

NL 0342631   ICRL CtY DNLM

Lichthorn, C.
    Das von Lepsius entdeckte alphabetische lautsystem der hebräischen buchstabenfolge in der vollständig durchgreifenden harmonie seiner organisation erwiesen von C. Lichthorn. ₍Breslau, Druck von C. H. Storch und comp.,₎ 1861₎
    viii, 106 p. 22½ cm.

    1. Hebrew language—Alphabet. 2. Hebrew language—Phonology. 3. *Lepsius, Richard, 1810-1884.
Library of Congress   PJ4589.L6   11—269

NL 0342632   DLC

Lichthorn, C
    Die Erforschung der physiologischen Naturgesetze der menschlichen Geistestätigkeit, auf der Grundlage der neuesten grossen Entdeckungen Dubois Reymond's, Darwin's und Häckel's über die organische Natur und deren vervollkommnende Entwicklung. Der Versammlung der Deutschen Naturforscher Breslau 1874 gewidmet von C. Lichthorn. Breslau, A. Gosohorsky (A. Kiepert), 1875.
    vi, 106 p. 24ᵐ.

NL 0342633   ICJ ICRL CtY MH ICN

Lichti, Eugen, 1902–
    Zur kasuistik des adenoma sebaceum, circumscriptum und disseminatum, kombiniert mit weiteren naevusformen an anderen koerperteilen.
    Inaug. diss. - Erlangen, 1926. (1929)
    Bibl.

NL 0342634   ICRL CtY

Lichti, Hans, 1904–
    Kinetische untersuchung über die einwirkung von stickoxyd auf alkalisulfit, alkalibisulfit und schweflige säure in wässriger lösung. ...Berlin (Auszug)
    Inaug. Diss. - Techn. Hochsch. Berlin, [1934]
    Lebenslauf.

NL 0342635   ICRL

Lichti, Jean Pierre.
    Der Rechtsirrtum, besonders im schweizerischen Obligationenrecht. Zürich, Juris-Verlag, 1950.
    161 p. 21 cm.
    Diss.—Zürich.
    Bibliography : p. 9-13.

    1. Mistake (Law)—Switzerland. I. Title.
                      51–23961

NL 0342636   DLC

Lichtig, Abraham
    ... Cinq observations de thrombophlébite suppurée dans le post-abortum. ... par Abraham Lichtig. ... Lyon, Bosc frères, M. & L. Riou, 1936.

    66 p.

    Thèse.

NL 0342637   DNLM CtY NN

Lichtig, Ignaz.
    Die entstehung des lebens durch stetige schöpfung, von Ignaz Lichtig. Amsterdam, N. v. noord-hollandsche uitgevers maatschappij ₍1938₎
    xx, 371 p. illus. (map) diagrs. 26½ᵐ.
    "Literaturverzeichnis": p. ₍363₎-371.

    1. Life—Origin. 2. Evolution. 3. Phylogeny. I. Title.
                   A C 39–3324 Revised
Iowa. Univ. Library
for Library of Congress   QH325.L602
           ₍r43c2₎†

NL 0342638   IaU CU DNAL CtY DLC

Law
Lichtig, J. G., joint author.

Dyer, Donald B
    Liability in public recreation, by Donald B. Dyer and J. G. Lichtig. ₍Appleton, Wis.₎ C. C. Nelson, 1949.

Lichtig, Lipót.   193.98 L61
    Darstellung und Kritik der Grundprinzipien der Ethik Wundts' von Dr. Lichtig Lipót. Érsekujvár, Buchdruckerei S. Kohn, 1904.
    [8], 127, [1] p. 21½ᵐ.

NL 0342640   ICJ

Lichtigfeld, Adolph, 1904–
    The day of prayer. Sermons by the Rev. Dr. Adolph Lichtigfeld. ₍Germiston?₎ South Africa, Central news agency ₍1942₎ v, 8-34 p. 21cm.

    1. Sermons, Jewish, in English.
                      April 30, 1945

NL 0342641   NN

VOLUME 332

B3279
J33P52
L5
Lichtigfeld, Adolph
Jaspers' metaphysics; based on Karl Jaspers' "Philosophie" (Metaphysik) [1st ed.] With a foreword by Karl Jaspers. London, Colibri Press [1954]
xviii, [7]-120 p.

1. Jaspers, Karl, 1883- / Philosophie.

NL 0342642   CU LU CoU CLSU OrU ICarbS PPDrop IU PHC

Lichtigfeld, Adolph, 1904-
Philosophy and revelation in the work of contemporary Jewish thinkers, by Dr. A. Lichtigfeld; with preface by the Very Rev. Dr. J. H. Hertz ... and foreword by Professor John Macmurray ... London, M. L. Cailingold, 1937.
xii, 163 p. 22½ cm.

1. Philosophy, Jewish. 2. Philosophy and religion. 3. Relevation (Jewish theology) I. Title.

B159.L5   181.3   38-37482

PPDrop MoU
NL 0342643   DLC UU NIC CtY OCH OC1Tem FTaSU TxU WU

Lichtigfeld, Adolph.
Twenty centuries of Jewish thought, by Dr. Adolph Lichtigfeld. London, E. O. Beck, limited [1937?]
168 p. 18½ᶜᵐ.

1. Jews—Religion. I. Title.

Library of Congress   BM40.L5   38-23163

                                              296

NL 0342644   DLC MB TxU OU OCH OC1Tem PPDrop CtY CSmH

LICHTIGFELD, ADOLPH, 1904—
Twenty centuries of Jewish thought, by Dr. Adolph Lichtigfeld... London: Shapiro, Vallentine & co., 1938. 169 p. 18½cm.

36896B. 1. Judaism—Hist. I. Title.

NL 0342645   NN

BM40
.L5
1938
Lichtigfeld, Adolph, 1904-
Twenty centuries of Jewish thought, by Dr. Adolph Lichtigfeld ... 2d impression. London, Shapiro, Vallentine & co., 1938.
168 p. 18.5cm.

1. Jews—Religion. I. Title.

NL 0342646   MB ViU MH

Lichtin, J   Leon, 1924-
The preparation and toxicity of some new organic gold compounds ... 1950.
98 numb. 1.
Thesis (PH.D.) - Ohio state university, 1950.

NL 0342647   OU

Lichtin, Norman Nahum, 1922-
Apparatus for controlled atmosphere research

see under

Boston University.

Lichtin, Norman Nahum, 1922-
The conductivities in liquid sulfur dioxide of some derivatives of triphenylchloromethane.

Thesis - Harvard, 1948.

NL 0342649   MH

Lichtinger (Adolphus Naimsky) [1793-].
*Brevis de cephalalgia tractatus. 35 pp. sm. 8°. [Berolini], formis Bruschckianis, [1822].

NL 0342650   DNLM PPC

Lichtinger, Hedwig.
... Das Hautpigment, seine Entstehung und Bedeutung ... München-Pasing, 1937. Inaug.-Diss. - München. 28 ps.

NL 0342651   CtY

Lichtinghagen, Leo, Arzt: Über ein Papillom des Plexus chorioideus im IV. Ventrikel. Aus d. Universitätskl. f. pathol. Anat. zu Bonn. [In Maschinenschrift.] 32 S. 4°(2°). — Auszug: Bonn 1921: Rost. 8 S. 8°
Bonn, Med. Diss. v. 11. Juli 1921, Ref. Fischer
[Geb. 3. Juli 92 Marienheide; Wohnort: Marienheide; Staatsangeh.: Preußen; Vorbildung: G. Wipperfürth Reife 12; Studium: München 1, Bonn 9 S.; Coll. 11. Juli 21; Approb. 19. Juli 20.] [U 21.2738

NL 0342652   ICRL

Lichtinghagen (Wilhelm). *Ein Beitrag zur Lehre vom Echinokokkos. 26 pp., 1 l. 8°. Würzburg, A. Boegler, 1887. c.

NL 0342653   DNLM

PT287
L5
Der Lichtkreis.   [Sammelausg.]   Berlin-Lichterfelde, E. Runge [1924]
2 v. ports.

Each contribution has special t. p. and separate paging.

Contents.
1. Bd.
Escher, Karl. Bettines Weg zu Goethe. 4.-6. Aufl.
Gleichen-Russwurm, Alexander v. Schillers Reise nach Berlin. 2. Aufl.
Zerkaulen, Heinrich. Theodor Körners Liebesfrühling. 2. Aufl.

Escher, Karl. E. T. A. Hoffmanns Gespensterspiel. 3. Aufl.
Servaes, Franz. Heinrich von Kleists tragischer Untergang. 2. Aufl.
2. Bd.
Preis, Max. Grillparzers ewige Braut. 3. Aufl.
Strecker, Karl. Strindbergs Kindheit. 2. Aufl.
Oppeln-Bronikowski, Friedrich von. Beyle-Stendhals Lebensroman, 1783-1842.
Schaffner, Jakob. Der grosse Seldwyler. 2. Aufl.
Georg, Manfred. Grabbes doppeltes Gesicht.

NL 0342655   CU IU

DQ178
.A5D8
Lichtlen, Fanny, ed.

Durrer, Robert, 1867-1934.
Heinrich Angst, erster Direktor des Schweizerischen Landesmuseums, britischer Generalkonsul. Zu Ende geführt von Fanny Lichtlen. Glarus, Tschudi [1948]

W 4A
qL699b
1944
Lichtman, Aaron Lee, 1914-
Birefringence in tissues and foreign bodies with a study of talc granuloma. [Minneapolis, Minn.] 1944.
142 l. illus.

Thesis (Ph.D. in Surgery) - Univ. of Minnesota.
Typewritten copy.

NL 0342657   DNLM

Lichtman, Aaron Lee, 1914—
Birefringence in tissues. Talc granuloma. [n. p., 1946]
cover-title, 12, 16 p. illus. 26 cm.
Abridgment of thesis—Univ. of Minnesota.
Two articles, the first in collaboration with J. R. McDonald, the second with J. R. McDonald, C. F. Dixon and F. C. Mann, reprinted from the Archives of pathology, v. 42, July 1946, and, Surgery, gynecology and obstetrics, v. 83, Oct. 1946, with cover having thesis statement and Vita.
"References": p. 16.

1. Tumors. 2. Polarizing microscope. 3. Talc — Physiological effect. I. Title. II. Title: Talc granuloma.

RD651.L5   A 49-7902*

Minnesota. Univ. Libr.
for Library of Congress   †

NL 0342658   MnU DLC

W 4
Z96
1954
LICHTMAN, Alvin, 1925-
The effect of demecolcin (des-methyl-colchicine) on the peripheral blood and bone marrow in the rabbit and cat. Zürich, 1954.
23 p. illus.
Inaug.-Diss. - Zürich.
1. Blood - Experimental studies
2. Colchicine

NL 0342659   DNLM

Lichtman, Benzion.
Bene Tsiyon
see under   Caro, Joseph, 1488-1575.

LD3907
.G7
1953
.L8
Lichtman, Irwin Arnold, 1920-
Salt effects in potassium diazomalonate decomposition.
40p. diagrs.
Thesis (Ph.D.) - N.Y.U., Graduate School, 1953.
Bibliography: p.39-40.

NL 0342661   NNU-W

Lichtman, Solomon Sydney, 1898-
Diseases of the liver, gallbladder and bile ducts. Philadelphia, Lea & Febiger, 1942.
906 p. illus. 24 cm.
Includes "References."

1. Liver—Diseases. 2. Gall-bladder—Diseases. 3. Bile-ducts—Diseases.
Library of Congress   RC845.L5   42-23926 rev*
                                [r49i2]   616.36

PPWM PU-M PPAEM
NL 0342662   DLC ViU OU OC1CC DNLM OrU-M NcD PPC PPHa

Lichtman, Solomon Sydney, 1898-
Diseases of the liver, gallbladder, and bile ducts. 2d ed., thoroughly rev. Philadelphia, Lea & Febiger, 1949.
1135 p. illus. 25 cm.
Includes "References."

1. Liver—Diseases. 2. Gall-bladder—Diseases. 3. Bile-ducts—Diseases.
RC845.L5 1949   616.36   49-2944*

PPJ
NL 0342663   DLC PPC PU PPT ICU ViU DNLM ICJ OrU-M

Lichtman, Solomon Sydney, 1898-
Diseases of the liver, gallbladder, and bile ducts. 3d ed., thoroughly rev. Philadelphia, Lea & Febiger, 1953.
2 v. illus. 24 cm.

1. Liver—Diseases. 2. Gall-bladder—Diseases. 3. Bile-ducts—Diseases.
RC845.L5 1953   616.36   53-9571 ‡

ViU ICJ IdU OC1W-H
NL 0342664   DLC CaBVaU DNLM PU-Med OU NcD NcU OC1W

VOLUME 332

DO16.3
L617

Lichtman, William Toby, 1912–
A study of the sociology collection in the City college as compared with the courses offered. 1938.
31, 10 l.

Paper prepared for LS 330, School of library service, Columbia university.
"Sources consulted": 4 l. at end.

NL 0342665   NNC

Lichtman, Ya'akov.
שעת שקיפות. שירים. ירושלים, מסדה, תש"א.
₁Jerusalem, 1940/41₁
76 p. 20 cm.
Vocalized text.

I. Title.   *Title transliterated:* Sha'ot shekufot.

PJ5053.L44S5   57–54411 ‡

NL 0342666   DLC

DS
145
.5   Lichtmann, Otto.
Antisemitisch. Eine Reiseunterhaltung. Reichenberg, 1891.
14 p.   23 cm.
"Separat=Abdruck aus den Zeitschwingen".

1. Antisemitism. I. Title

NL 0342667   OCH

Lichtneckert, Josef.   335.5 R200
Der sozialdemokratische Welt-Staat mit Gemeineigentum und Eigenproduktion als Universalmittel zur Beseitigung aller Armut, Ausbeutung, Kriege, Seuchen, Not, kurz alles Elendes und zur Herbeiführung der dauernden Glückseligkeit und Friedens der Allmenschheit auf Erden. ... Von Josef Lichtneckert. Papiermühle, S.-A., F. Engelke, 1912.
xii, 281, ₂2₁ p. illus., tables. 20 cm.

NL 0342668   ICJ NN ICN

HJ
9925
A9
L5   Lichtnegel, Josef Calasanz
Geschichte der Entwickelung des österreichischen Rechnungs- und Controlwesens. Graz, Im Selbstverlage, 1872.
391p. 24cm.
Bibliographical footnotes.

1. Finance, Public – Austria 2. Finance, Public – Accounting – Hist. I. Title

NL 0342669   WU

834L6175 Lichtneker, Friedrich, 1903–
Ob   Bayrische königstragödie in drei akten ... Stuttgart, Chronos-verlag g.m.b.h. ₁192–?₁
126p.

"Den bühnen gegenüber als manuskript vervielfältigt."
Reproduced from typewritten copy.

1. Ludwig II, king of Bavaria, 1845-1886–-Drama. I. Title.

NL 0342670   IU

834L6175 Lichtneker, Friedrich, 1903–
Obe   ... Beethoven; dramatische biographie ...   Stuttgart, Chronos verlag g.m.b.h. ₁192–?₁
108p.

"Den bühnen gegenüber als manuskript vervielfältigt."
Reproduced from typewritten copy.

1. Beethoven, Ludwig van, 1770-1827--Drama.

NL 0342671   IU

PT 2623 Lichtneker, Friedrich, 1903–
I32 D7   Draga Maschin; Schauspiel in fünf Akten, von
1933   Friedrich Lichtneker und D. M. Brant. Wien, G. Marton, c1933.
113 p. 20 cm.

"Unverkäuzliches Manuskript."

NL 0342672   OU

Lichtneker, Friedrich, 1903–
Draga Maschin, schauspiel in 5 akten, von Friedrich Lichtnecker. Berlin, Ahn & Simrock ₁1935₁
110 p. 20 cm.
Reproduced from type-written copy.

I. Title.
                                  42–28644
                                  Brief cataloging
Library of Congress   PT2623.I 32D7

NL 0342673   DLC

LICHTNEKER, FRIEDRICH.
Eros im Zuchthaus; Schauspiel in drei Akten (neun Bildern) von Friedrich Lichtneker, unter Benutzung des gleichnamigen Buches von Karl Plattner. Berlin, G. Kiepenheuer, c1929. 128 p. 20cm.

1. Drama, German. I. Plättner, Karl. Eros im Zuchthaus. II. Title.

NL 0342674   NN

Lichtneker, Friedrich, 1903–
Fröhliche fastnacht, ein deutsches schelmenspiel mit gesang und tanz in drei aufzügen, von Friedrich Lichtneker und Dora Maria Brandt ... Berlin, Arcadia verlag, °1936.
86 p. 20 cm.
Reproduced from type-written copy.
Without music.

I. Brandt, Dora Maria, joint author. II. Title.
                                  42–28642
                                  Brief cataloging
Library of Congress   PT2623.I 32F7

NL 0342675   DLC

Lichtneker, Friedrich, 1903–
Das geheimnis einer frau, komödie in drei akten (fünf bildern) ... Wien, Eirich ₁°1938₁
₁101₁ p. 28 cm.
Type-written (carbon copy)

I. Title.
                                  43–26085
                                  Brief cataloging
Library of Congress   PT2623.I 32G4

NL 0342676   DLC

Lichtneker, Friedrich, 1903–
Glückliche jugend, lustspiel in drei akten von Friedrich Lichtneker und Dora Maria Brandt. ₁Wien, 1936?₁
118 l. 28 cm.
Reproduced from type-written copy.

I. Brandt, Dora Maria, joint author. II. Title.
                                  43–29859
                                  Brief cataloging
Library of Congress   PT2623.I 32G5

NL 0342677   DLC

Lichtneker, Friedrich, 1903–
Ich will leben! Schauspiel in drei akten ... Berlin, Kiepenheuer, °1930.
120 p. 20 cm.
Reproduced from type-written copy.

I. Title.
                                  42–28643
                                  Brief cataloging
Library of Congress   PT2623.I 32 I 3

NL 0342678   DLC

LICHTNEKER, FRIEDRICH.
Insolvenzen. [Wien, 193–?] 99 p. 23cm.

Film reproduction. Positive.
Imperfect: original t. p. wanting; typewritten t. p. supplied.

I. Drama, German. I. Title.

NL 0342679   NN

Lichtneker, Friedrich, 1903–
Der leuchtende tod, ein stück in sieben bildern ... ₁Wien, °1938₁
103 numb. l. 28 cm.
Type-written (carbon) copy.

I. Title.
                                  43–28568
                                  Brief cataloging
Library of Congress   PT2623.I 32I4

NL 0342680   DLC

4PT   Lichtneker, Friedrich, 1903–
Ger. -   Porzia; Lustspiel in 3 Akten, von Friedrich
367   Lichtneker und Dora Maria Brandt. Berlin, Deutscher Bühnenvertrieb des Zentralverlages der NSDAP. ₁193–?₁
90 p.

NL 0342681   DLC-P4

834L6175 Lichtneker, Friedrich, 1903–
lt   Tiere im busch; schauspiel in fünf bildern ... Berlin, Chronos-verlag g.m.b.h., c1929.
65p.

"Den bühnen gegenüber als manuskript vervielfältigt."
Reproduced from typewritten copy.

NL 0342682   IU

Lichtner, Adolf ₁Karl Georg August₁.
Der Hessen-Casselsche Landtag von 1797/98. Göttingen, 1913. xi(i), 75(1) p. 8°.

Dissertation, Göttingen.
Forms part of a publication entitled: Landesherr und Stände in Hessen-Cassel 1797-1821.

1. Hesse-Cassel—Government, 1797- 98.   February 25, 1914.

NL 0342683   NN MH CtY MiU ICRL

VOLUME 332

JN 3294 H46 L5
Lichtner, Adolf Karl George August.
Landesherr und Stände in Hessen-Cassel, 1797-1821. Göttingen, Vandenhoeck & Ruprecht, 1913.
218p. 24cm.
Includes bibliography.

1. Hessen-Cassel (Electorate) - Constitutional history 2. Upper classes - Germany - Hessen-Cassel (Electorate) I. Title

NL 0342684   WU NjP MH CU

Lichtner, Charles F
Gesellschaftliche Zustände der Vergangenheit und Gegenwart. Eine Erläuterung der Arbeiterbewegungen der Gegenwart und ihre Bedeutung für die Zukunst. Gewidmet den freien Männern von Amerika.   Chicago, 1865.
48 p.   22 cm.

NL 0342685   CtY

Lichtner, Charles F., and brother, *Chicago, pub.*
Address-buch deutscher logen von Chicago der folgenden orden: Bnai Brith, Druiden, Freimaurer, Förster, Hermannssöhne, Harugari, I. sons of Israel, Kesher Shel Barzel, Knights of honor, Knights of Pythias, Odd fellows, Rothmänner und Vereinigte arbeiter, &c. [1.]-ausg. Hrsg. von C. F. Lichtner & bro. ... [Chicago] 1881-
v. 22cm.

1. Secret societies. 2. Germans in Chicago. 3. Chicago—Direct.
8-15815
Library of Congress   F158.9.G3L6 Copyright

NL 0342686   DLC

Lichtner, Charles F., and Brother, Chicago.
Chicago directory of lodges and benevolent societies for the year 1883-1884
see under title

Lichtner, Johann Christoph, 1626-1687, respondent.
Collatio ad Concilium Sirmiense
see under   Dorsch, Johann Georg, 1597-1659, praeses.

Lichtner (Joh. Christoph) 1626-1687. De natura Incis. 11 l. 4º. Lionia, lit. Lankisiana, 1653.

NL 0342689   DNLM

Lichtner, Kurt.
Stahlsaitenbeton [von Kurt Lichtner [und] Erich Jung; eine Unterrichtung über das Gebiet des Stahlsaitenbetons. Hrsg. vom Technischen Büro für Betonsteinerzeugung.   Berlin-Grunewald, Regelien's Verlag [1948-49]
3 v.   illus.   21 cm.
1. Concrete, Prestressed. 2. Reinforced concrete. I. Jung, Erich.

NL 0342690   PSt

Lichtner, Otto, 1923-
Das Hofer Stadtrecht im 14. Jahrhundert, 1319-1436, und seine Rechtsbeziehungen. München, 1952.
104, xxxx l. facsims. 30 cm.
Typescript (carbon copy)
Inaug.-diss.—Munich.
Vita.
Bibliography: leaves 4-12.

1. Law—Hof, Ger.
Full name: Otto Heinrich Walter Lichtner.

54-41365

NL 0342691   DLC

ML 247.8 .P6 H62
LICHTNER, RUDOLF   ,ed.
Památník Zpěváckého spolku Hlaholu v Praze vydaný na oslavu 50tileté činnosti, 1861-1911. V Praze, Nákladem Pražského Hlaholu, 1911.
153+137 p. illus.

1. Hlahol Pražský. I. Title.

NL 0342692   InU

Lichtner, William Otto, 1883-
Plain and reinforced concrete; hand book, by William O. Lichtner ... for use in lectures at evening school of building trades of the Mass. charitable mechanic association ... Boston, Mass., Printed for M. C. M. A. trade school [The Seaver-Howland press] 1914.
ix, 68 p. illus., tables, diagrs. 20cm.

1. Concrete. 2. Concrete, Reinforced.
Library of Congress   TA439.L45   14-6240
Copyright A 369331

NL 0342693   DLC ICJ

Lichtner, William Otto, 1883-
Planned control in manufacturing, by William O. Lichtner ... New York, The Ronald press company, 1924.
xii, 329 p. illus. (forms.) pl., diagrs. 22cm. (Ronald manufacturing management and administration series, ed. by L. P. Alford)

1. Efficiency, Industrial. 2. Factory management.   I. Title.
Library of Congress   TS155.L5   24-4094

NL 0342694   DLC CU PPT PPD PU PSC OCU OU MiU OCIU
OCl OrP ICJ MB NN NcRS CoU

Lichtner, William Otto, 1883-
A simple compression machine for testing structural materials. Illus.
(In American Society for Testing Materials. Proceedings. Vol. 14, part 2, pp. 534-540. [Philadelphia.] 1914.)

K4397 — Testing machines.

NL 0342695   MB

Lichtner, William Otto, 1883-
Time study and job analysis as applied to standardization of methods and operations, by William O. Lichtner ... New York, The Ronald press company, 1921.
xvii, 397 p. incl. illus., tables. diagrs. (1 fold.) 22cm.
"Portions of the material were printed serially in Industrial management from April to September, 1920."—Pref.

1. Efficiency, Industrial. 2. Factory management.   I. Title.
Library of Congress   T58.L5   21-16665

NL 0342696   DLC WaS OrP MtBC DL CU MB PBm PPT PSC
PPD PU MB OU ODW OCU OCl OOxM OO NcD ICJ TU CoU MNU-B

Lichton, Ira Jay, 1928-
Interrelationships between the kidneys and eccrine sweat glands of man in their electrolyte and total osmotic excretions. Ann Arbor, University Microfilms [1955]
([University Microfilms, Ann Arbor, Mich.] Publication no. 10,505)
Microfilm copy of typescript. Positive.
Collation of the original: iv, 66 l. diagrs.
Thesis—University of Illinois.
Abstracted in Dissertation abstracts, v. 15 (1955) no. 1, p. 148. Vita.
Bibliography: leaves 55-59.
1. Excretion. 2. Kidneys. 3. Perspiration.
Microfilm AC-1   no. 10,505   Mic A 55-204

Illinois. Univ. Library
for Library of Congress   †

NL 0342697   IU DLC

Lichtpuntjes
see under   Woud, Elisabeth.

Licht's internationales zuckerstatistisches Jahr- und Adressbuch
see under   Licht, F.O., firm.

Licht's monthly report ...
see under   Licht, F.O., firm.

Licht's sugar report
see   Licht, F.O., firm.
Monthly report on sugar.

Lichtscheid, Ferdinand Helffreich, 1661-1705.
Christliche bedancken ueber das buechlein vom Ewigen evangelio der allgemeinen wiederbringung aller creaturen. Zeitz, M.Hucho, 1700.
624 p. 16½ cm.

NL 0342701   NjP

Lichtscheid, Ferdinand Helffreich, 1661-1707, author and respondent.
... De incrementis in bono et in malo ...
see under   Breithaupt, Joachim Justus, 1658-1732, praeses.

Lichtscheid, Ferdinand Helffreich, 1661-1707.
...Gesamte Geistreiche Schriften, darinnen Miscellan- und Leich- Predigten, Stand-Reden und unterschiedliche Tractate enthalten,... Wie auch Lebens-Beschreibung des auctoris und nöthigen Registern gesammlet und hrsg. von Christoph Albrecht Lösecken. Leipzig, Gottlob Benjamin Frommann, 1733.
1v.(various pagings) 22cm.

1. Lutheran church - Collected works.
2. Theology -   Collected works - 17th century.

NL 0342703   MoSCS

273.7 L699g
Lichtscheid, Ferdinand Helfreich.
Das göttlich-erläuterte Sabbaths-Recht in einer am XVII. Sonntag nach Trinitatis, den 30. Septembr. 1703...vorgestellet nebst einem Anhang dieser Materie vom Recht des Sabbaths, von Ferdinand Helffreich Lichtscheid. Berlin, Johann Christoph Papen, 1704.
32 p.

1. Sabbath.

NL 0342704   TxDaM-P

Lichtscheid, Ferdinand Hel(f)freich, 1661-1707.
Meditatio de iure vocationis ministrorum ecclesiae. [Leipzig, 1697.]. 388 pp.
T.-p. mutilated; imprint from Js.

NL 0342705   OSW

Lichtschein (Louis). Hypnotism as a therapeutic agent. 19 pp. 12º. *New York*, 1896.
Repr. from : N. York M. J., 1896, lxiii.

NL 0342706   DNLM

VOLUME 332

LICHTSCHEIN, Ludwig
...Die 13 Glaubensartikel...
Erläutert in zwanzig...Vorträgen...
1.Lieferung. Brünn. Published by the
Author, 1870. 40p. 20.5cm
    Contains: Sermons I.-III.
1.Sermons-German. 2.Maimonides, Moses:
Thirteen articles.

NL 0342707   NNJ

HQ507
.L7   LICHTSCHEIN,LUDWIG.
    Die ehe nach mosaisch-talmudischer auffassung und
das mosaisch-talmudische eherecht. Von dr.Ludwig
Lichtschein... Leipzig,O.Wigand,1879.
    x,172 p. 21cm.

    1.Marriage--Jews. 2.Marriage law.

NL 0342708   ICU CLI MH OCH NIC

BM
713
L5   Lichtschein, Ludwig
    Die Ehe nach mosaisch-talmudischer Auf-
fassung und das mosaisch-talmudische Eherecht. Leipzig, O. Wigand, 1897.

    x, 172 p. 21cm.

    1. Marriage (Jewish law). 2. Marriage-
Jews. I. Title.
NRCR

NL 0342709   NRCR

Lichtschein, Ludwig.
    Die freiheit unserer Zeit und der Friede.
estpredigt gehalten am ersten Tage des
Pessach-Festes ...(1869) in der Synagoge
zu Austerlitz. Brünn: the auth. 1869.
    14 p.

NL 0342710   OCH

Lichtschein, Ludwig.
    Trauerrede für ... L. Horowitz, gehalten
in der Synagoge zu Austerlitz am ... 28.
Juni, 1868. Brünn: the auth., 1868.
    16 p.

NL 0342711   OCH

Lichtschein de Bird, Poldy.
    El grito en las venas; novela. [1. ed.] Buenos Aires,
Editorial Claridad [1954]
    167 p. 21 cm. (Colección Arco iris, v. 9)

    I. Title.

PQ7797.L484G7   55–38444 ‡

NL 0342712   DLC NN

Lichtschein de Bird, Poldy.
    ... El séptimo velo; versos. Buenos Aires [Impresora de
Plata, s. a., 1943]
    108 p. 2 l. 20½ᵐ.

    I. Title.

                     45–11199
Library of Congress   PQ7797.L484S4

                     861.6

NL 0342713   DLC

Der Lichtschirm
    see under   [Benkert, Charlotte]

LICHTSCHLAG,A.
    Schicksale des klosters Inzigkofen während
des Schwedenkrieges,aus der chronik des klosters. n.p.,[188-].

    pp.[23]-43 of a larger work.

NL 0342715   MH

Lichtschlag (Joseph) [1894-]. Melae-
nae Hippocratica genuinae imago, indoles, et
diagnosis specialior. iv, 5-26 pp., 1 l. 4°.
Bonne, H. Knirenschild, [1828].

NL 0342716   DNLM PPC

Lichtschlag, Josephus.
    De morbis nasi.
    Inaug. Diss.   Berlin, 1864

NL 0342717   ICRL DNLM

Lichtschlag, Margarete, 1905–
    Produktions-, Absatz- und Organisationsfragen der deutschen
Seidenindustrie...von Margarete Lichtschlag... [Heidelberg]
1930.   56 [i. e. 60] p. incl. tables.   22½cm.

    Inaugural-Dissertation — Heidelberg, 1930.
    Lebenslauf.
    "Zusammenstellung der benutzten Literatur," p. [5]

    1. Silk—Trade and stat.—Ger-   many.   May 6, 1938

NL 0342718   NN CtY PU

W 4
M96
1940   **Lichtschlag, Maria,** 1909–
    Über Gastroenterostomie bei
Magen-Ca. München, Mössl, 1940.
    28 p.

    Inaug.-Diss. - Munich.
    Bibliography: p. 27.

NL 0342719   DNLM MnU

             1889-
Lichtschlag, Walter; Das Narbencarcinom. Aus d. Chir.
    Univkl. Breslau. Breslau 1919: Nischkowsky. 38 S. 8°
Breslau, Med. Diss. v. 20. Dez. 1919, Ref. Küttner
   [Geb. 5. Okt. 89 Osnabrück; Wohnort: Breslau; Staatsangeh.: Preußen; Vor-
bildung: G. Baden-Baden Reife 10; Studium: Würzburg 3, Marburg 4, Kiel 7,
Straßburg 1, Freiburg 1 S.; Coll. 11. Juli 19; Approb. 4. Nov. 18.] [U 19. 1181]

NL 0342720   ICRL DNLM

Lichtschlag, Wilhelm, 1901–
    Die gesamtprokura ... 1931.   66 p.
    Inaug. Diss. -Göttingen, 1931.
    Lebenslauf.
    Bibliography.

NL 0342721   ICRL

829.8
L426Fℓ   **Lichtsinn, Peter Hinrich,** 1888-
    Der syntaktische gebrauch des in-
finitivs in Lazamon's Brut... Kiel,
Fiencke, 1913.
    75p. table. O.
    Inaug.-diss. - Kiel.
    "Literatur": p.[vii]-xii.
    Lebenslauf.

NL 0342722   IaU PU MiU PBm CtY MH NjP NNF ICRL

Lichtspielhaus und theater; baupolizeiliche vorschriften
    see under   Grieger, Paul August, ed.

Lichtstein, Abraham.
כנפי נשרים; פירוש התורה ע"פ הרמב"ן ובעל עקרה, מדות
ודעות להרלב"ג, נר מצוה, מנין המצות להרמב"ם, שיורי מצות,
מצות הנוספות להרמב"ן. ווארשא, בדפוס י. אלאפין, תרמ"א.
    Warszawa, 1881.
    5 v. in 1. 22 cm.

    1. Bible. O. T. Pentateuch—Commentaries. I. Title.
                 Title transliterated: Kanfe nesharim.

BS1225.L56   1881   57–52135

NL 0342724   DLC

Lichtstein, Abraham.
כנפי נשרים; פירוש התורה ע"פ הרמב"ן ובעל עקרה, מדות
דעות להרלב"ג, נר מצוה, מנין המצות להרמב"ם, שיורי מצות,
מצות הנוספות להרמב"ן. ווילנא, קאצענעלענבאגען, בדפוס האל-
מנה והאחים ראם, תרנ"ד.   Vilna, 1894.
    5 v. in 1. 24 cm.

    1. Bible. O. T. Pentateuch—Commentaries. I. Title.
                 Title transliterated: Kanfe nesharim

BS1225.L56   1894   57–51249

NL 0342725   DLC

Lichtstein, Abraham.
כנפי נשרים; פירוש התורה ע"פ הרמב"ן ובעל עקרה, מדות
ודעות להרלב"ג, נר מצוה, מנין המצות להרמב"ם, שיורי מצות,
מצות הנוספות להרמב"ן. ווילנא, קאצענעלענבאגען, בדפוס
האלמנה והאחים ראם, תרס"ה.   Vilna, 1905.
    5 v. in 1. 24 cm.

    1. Bible. O. T. Pentateuch—Commentaries. I. Title.
                 Title transliterated: Kanfe nesharim.
                      A 53–1689
New York. Public Libr.
for Library of Congress   [1]

NL 0342726   NN DLC

Lichtstein, Abraham, d. 1926
    see
Lichtenstein, Abraham, d. 1926.

Lichtstein, Abraham Jekuthiel Salman, 18th cent.
    Zeh Sefer Sifre
    see under   Sifre.

          Lichtsteiner, Sigmund
Uzfml8   Die Lumbalanästhesie beim Schwein ...
B45   Zürich,1941.
1941   Inaug.-Diss. - Bern.
    "Separat-Abdruck aus dem 'Schweizer Archiv
für Tierheilkunde', Bd.LXXXIV, Hft.2, Jahrgang 1942."

NL 0342729   CtY

PT   Lichtstrahlen. [Leipzig, F. A. Brockhaus,
1135   1856-1876 (v. 1, no. 1, 1872)]
L69   16 v. in 6. 17cm.

    Cover title.
    Vol. 6, no. 3: Dresden, R. von Zahn.

    1. German literature (Selections, extracts,
etc.) I. Brockhaus, F. A., firm, Leipzig.

NL 0342730   NIC

VOLUME 332

Lichtstrahlen. Blätter für volksverständliche **wissenschaft** und atheistische weltanschauung. Zugleich unterhaltungsblatt und litterarischer wegweiser für das volk. 1.–4. jahrg.; 1. sept. 1890–₍sept.?₎ 1894₎ Berlin, O. Harnisch; ₍etc., etc.₎ 1891–93/94.

4 v. illus. 21½–24ᶜᵐ. biweekly (v. 1: semimonthly)

Vol. 4 in 2 parts (Belehrender theil, Unterhaltender theil) Each part has separate t.-p. and paging.
Title varies slightly.
Vols. 3–4 have imprint: Berlin (v. 4: Berlin-Schöneberg) F. Harnisch & co., 1892/93–1893/94.
No more published.

Library of Congress   AP30.L6   37–6252
                         ₍3₎   053

NL 0342731   DLC

Lichtstrahlen auf lehre und praxis des Lutherthums; ein beitrag zur bessern erkenntniss der christlichen wahrheit. Columbus, Ohio, Gedruckt im "Josephinum", 1898.
324 p.

NL 0342732   OC1ND

LICHTSTRAHLEN moderner naturwissenschaft und geistiger erkenntniss gesammelt aus den werken von Darwin, Häckel, &c., &c., Dresden, 1876.

13 x 18.   And. H.

NL 0342733   MH-AH

Lichttechnik.
Berlin ₍Helios-Verlag₎
v. illus., ports., diagrs., plans. 30 cm. monthly.

Began publication with Aug. 1949 issue. Cf. Deutsche Bibliographie. Zeitschriften, 1945–52.
Organ of Lichttechnische Gesellschaft and other similar organizations.

1. Electric lighting—Period.   I. Lichttechnische Gesellschaft.

TK3.L55   59–40318

NL 0342734   DLC NcRS NNE FU

Lichttechnische Gesellschaft.
Aktuelle Fragen der Strassenbeleuchtung; Aussprache-Veranstaltung der Lichttechnischen Gesellschaft e. V. in Bad Nauheim am 30. Januar 1953. Vorträge und Diskussionen zusammengestellt und bearb. von Dr.-Ing. von der Trappen, Dr.-Ing. Jacob und Ob.-Ing. Pahl. Berlin-Borsigwalde (Westsektor) Helios-Verlag ₍1954₎
46 p. illus. 30 cm.

1. Street-lighting.   I. Trappen, Eberhard von der, ed.   II. Title.

TP741.L5   57–27829 ‡

NL 0342735   DLC NN

Lichttechnische Gesellschaft.
TK3
.L55
Lichttechnik.
Berlin ₍Helios-Verlag₎

Lichttechnische Gesellschaft Karlsruhe.
Die physiologischen, psychologischen u. ästhetischen Grundlagen der Lichttechnik und ihre kulturellen Ziele; Vorträge auf dem VI. Jahrestage der Lichttechnischen Gesellschaft Karlsruhe am 2. Juli 1927; im Auftrage der Lichttechnischen Gesellschaft Karlsruhe herausgegeben von Prof. Dr. J. Teichmüller. Berlin: Union deutsche Verlagsgesellschaft, 1929.   81 p.   diagrs., illus. 8°.

Bibliography, p. 49–50.

Continued in next column

Continued from preceding column

Contents: TEICHMÜLLER, J. Vorwort; Das Bedürfnis der Lichttechnik nach Klärung ihrer nichtphysikalischen Grundlagen. KROH, O. Probleme der physiologischen und psychologischen Optik in ihrer Bedeutung für die Lichttechnik. KRAUSS, S. Die psychologischen Grundlagen der Beleuchtungswahrnehmung und die Bedeutung der psychologischen Beleuchtungslehre für die Lichttechnik. HELLPACH, W. Zivilisation und Kultur des Lichtes und der Farbe. FREESE, H. Gedanken eines Architekten zur Lichttechnik.

506654A. 1. Lighting. 2. Teich-   mueller, Joachim, 1866–
editor.   January 10, 1931

NL 0342739   NN

Lichtträger, Florian.
...Immer wieder Serbien; Jugoslawiens Schicksalsstunde, mit einem Geleitwort von Friedrich Thimme.   Berlin: Verlag für Kulturpolitik, 1933.   203 p.   22½cm.

673019A. 1. Nationality—Yugoslavia.   2. Yugoslavia—Politics. I. Thimme, Friedrich Wilhelm Karl, 1868–   October 21, 1933

NL 0342740   NN InU NNC CSt-H OO DS CLU WaU CtY IU

PT5854 Lichtveld, Lou, 1903–
L5A72   Aansluiting gemist ₍door₎ Albert Helman.   Rotterdam, Nijgh & Van Ditmar, 1936.
         263 p.

NL 0342741   CU MH

₍Lichtveld, Lou₎ 1903–
Afdaling in de vulkaan; roman ₍door₎ Albert Helman ₍pseud.₎ Amsterdam, Amsterdamsche Boek- en Courantmij., 1949.
356 p. 21 cm.

I. Title.

Harvard Univ. Library   A 49–7707 rev*
for Library of Congress   ₍r49b₂₎

NL 0342742   MH NN CtY CU CSt OC1 PU

PT5854 Lichtveld, Lou, 1903–
.L5Z65
Nord, Max.
Albert Helman; een inleiding tot zijn werk. Met enkele teksten, handschriften, foto's, curiosa en een bibliographie. 's-Gravenhage, D. A. Daamen, 1949.

PT
5854   Lichtveld, Lou, 1903–
L69   Albert Helman omnibus.   Amsterdam, Amsterdamsche Boek- en Courantmij., 1947.
A15   605 p. port. 21cm.
1947

NL 0342744   NIC CaBVa NNC MH CU

₍Lichtveld, Lou, 1903–   ₎
*NC9   Aldus sprak Zarathustra, door Friedrich
L6183   Nietzsche ₍pseud.₎
944a   De Twee Fonteinen, Driebergen₍i.e.Amsterdam, F.Hoes,1944₎
       191p.,4ℓ. 24.5cm.
       False imprint.
       Clandestine printing; De Jong 595.
       After the war this book was published (under the author's pseud. "Albert Helman") with title: Teutonen spiegel, een les in literatuur-geschiedenis.

Continued in next column

Continued from preceding column

Colophon: "Aldus sprak Zarathustra" ... werd met de hand gezet uit de Lutetia van Jan v. Krimpen en tijdens de bezetting door de Duitsers, in het verborgene--in een oplage van 275 exemplaren--gedrukt, ergens in Nederland ... 250 exemplaren, genummerd 1–250, werden in de handel gebracht, terwijl 25, genummerd I–XXV, gereserveerd bleven voor de uitgever en zijn vrienden. Dit is no. X.

Page [172] is blank; a printed slip inserted at p.173 explains that the type for that page was pied as a result of a visit by the security police.
Original half japanese vellum & cream boards.

NL 0342747   MH

₍Lichtveld, Lou₎ 1903–
De diepzee-duiker. Verzen van M. Slob ₍pseud.₎ Teekeningen van P. van Luik ₍pseud. van J. Voskuil.
Amsterdam₎ De Distelvink ₍1945₎
23p. illus. 22x25cm.

NL 0342748   IEN

Zeta   ₍Lichtveld, Lou₎ 1903–
Hgk2   De dierenriem; proza van Albert Helman₍pseud.₎
L611   Prenten van Pieter Starreveld. ₍Amsterdam?
+D56   1940₎
         ₍29₎p. col.illus. 38cm.
         Text in black and red.
         Edition limited to 100 copies. This is no.91, signed Albert Helman, Pieter Starreveld.

NL 0342749   CtY

L Du   ₍Lichtveld, Lou₎ 1903–
L699di   De dierenriem. Proza van Albert Helman ₍pseud. en₎ prenten van Pieter Starreveld. ₍Amsterdam, P. Starreveld₎ 1942.
         29₎p. col. illus. 38cm.

         Jong. 374.
         100 copies. No. 59. Signed by the author and the illustrator.

NL 0342750   IEN

PT5854   Lichtveld, Lou, 1903–
L5D6   De dolle dictator; het ondoorgrondelijke leven van Juan Manuel de Rosas ₍door₎ Albert Helman. Rotterdam, Nijgh & Van Ditmar, 1935.
         376 p.

1. Rosas, Juan Manuel José Domingo Ortiz de, 1793-1877 - Fiction. I. Title.

NL 0342751   CU MH

G839.31 Lichtveld, Lou, 1903–
L618rTFt   Don Salustiano ₍par₎ Albert Helman ₍pseud₎ Traduit de néerlandais par W.F.C. Timmermans. Paris, Editions Françaises d'Amsterdam ₍1952₎
         399p. 23cm. (Collection Batave)

         Translation of De Rancho der X mysteries.

NL 0342752   TxU

VOLUME 332

₍Lichtveld, Lou₎ 1903–
Een doodgewone held; de levensgeschiedenis van Gerrit-Jan van der Veen, 1902–1944, door Albert Helman ₍pseud.₎ Amsterdam, Uitgeversbedrijf "De Spieghel," 1946.
254 p. plates, ports. 25ᶜᵐ.

1. Veen, Gerrit Jan van der, 1902–1944. 2. World war, 1939–1945—Underground movements—Netherlands. I. Title.
NB653.V3L5   A F 47–4195
Harvard univ. Library
for Library of Congress   †

NL   0342753   MH NIC MiU NNC CU NN OU CtY DLC

[Lichtveld, Lou] 1903–
De eeuwige koppelaarster [door] Albert Helman [pseud.] Amsterdam, G.A. van Oorschot [1949]
74 p. 21 cm. (De vrije bladen. jaargang 20, schrift 1)

NL   0342754   PBm

PT5854   Lichtveld, Lou, 1903–
L5E8   Het euvel gods [door] Albert Helman. Rotterdam, Nijgh & van Ditmar, 1932.
176 p.

NL   0342755   CU MH

Lichtveld, Lou, 1903–
De geluidsfilm, door Lou Lichtveld... Omslag van Piet Zwart. Rotterdam: W. L. en J. Brusse's uitgeversmij. n. v., 1933. 79 p. illus. (incl. ports.) 22cm. (Serie monografieën over filmkunst. no. 10.)

938694A. 1. Moving pictures,   Sound. I. Ser.   June 21, 1938

NL   0342756   NN WaU

Lichtveld, Lou, 1903–
Hart zonder land [by] Albert Helman [pseud. Illus.: C.Eyck] Utrecht, De Gemeenschap, 1929.
178 p. illus.
Stories

NL   0342757   MH InU

PT5854   Lichtveld, Lou, 1903–
L5H3   Hart zonder land [door] Albert Helman. Amsterdam, E.
1955   Querido, 1955.
168 p. (De Salamander)

NL   0342758   CU MH NN

PT5854   Lichtveld, Lou, 1903–
L5K55   Kleine kosmologie [door] Albert Helman. Amsterdam, Amsterdamsche Boek- en Courantmij, 1947.
251 p.

Essays.

NL   0342759   CU MH

Lichtveld, Lou, 1903–
De laaiende stilte ₍door₎ Albert Helman ₍pseud.₎ Amsterdam, Amsterdamsche Boek- en Courantmij., 1952.
299 p. 21 cm.

I. Title.
            A 52–8793
Harvard Univ. Library
for Library of Congress

NL   0342760   MH CtY CU OC1

Lichtveld, Lou, 1903–
... Leef duizend levens, inleiding tot het lezen van romans, door Lou Lichtveld. ₍Amsterdam₎ N. v. Amsterdamsche boek-en courantmaatschappij, 1941.
384 p. front. 25ᶜᵐ. (Sesam der kunst, 1)
"Literatuur ter verdere oriëntatie": p. 376–377.

1. Fiction. I. Title.
PN3353.L5   47–37347

NL   0342761   DLC MH

PT5854
.L5M5   Lichtveld, Lou, 1903–
Mijn aap lacht; roman ₍door₎ Albert Helman ₍pseud.₎ Amsterdam, Amsterdamsche Boek- en Courantmij, 1953.
270 p. 21 cm.

I. Title.
         A 54–235
Harvard Univ. Library
for Library of Congress   ₍3₎

NL   0342762   MH CU OC1 NN PU DLC

                KD 52810
[Lichtveld, Lou, 1903–]
Millioenen-leed; de tragedie der Joodse vluchtelingen. [By] Albert Helman [psued.] Arnhem, Van Loghum Slaterus 1940

NL   0342763   MH

₍Lichtveld, Lou₎ 1903–
... Ontsporing; verzen. Amsterdam, Amsterdamsche boek en courant maatschappij, 1945.
2 p. l., 7–102 p., 1 l. 21½ᶜᵐ.
Author's pseud., Albert Helman, at head of title.

I. Title.
PT5854.L5O55   A F 47–4466
Harvard univ. Library
for Library of Congress   †

NL   0342764   MH Sc CLU CtY ICU NN DLC CSt

LICHTVELD, LOU, 1903–
Orkaan bij nacht [door] Albert Helman [pseud.]   Amsterdam,
E. Querido, 1953.   256 p.   19cm.   (De Salamander)

1. Fiction, Dutch.

NL   0342765   NN OC1

              Neth 6523.13.125
[Lichtveld, Lou, 1903–]
Overwintering; spel, door Albert Helman [pseud.] Rotterdam, Nijgh & Van Ditmar, 1931
105 p. illus.

NL   0342766   MH

Sp Col
Underground
L Du
L699p   Lichtveld, Lou, 1903–
Proclamatie [door Albert Helman, pseud. Met tekening door J. Voskuil. Amsterdam, M. Oldenboerrichter, 1945]
broadside. illus. 60x30cm.

Jong. 678.
200 copies. No. 39. Signed by the author.

NL   0342767   IEN

₍Lichtveld, Lou₎ 1903–
... De Rancho der x mysteries. Amsterdam, N. v. Amsterdamsche boek- en courantmij, 1941.
352 p. 21½ᶜᵐ.
Author's pseud., Albert Helman, at head of title.

I. Title.
PT5854.L5R3   46–45172

NL   0342768   DLC CU

[Lichtveld, Lou, 1903–]
Ratten [by] Albert Helman [pseud.] Rotterdam, Nijgh & Van Ditmar, 1936
58 p. illus.

NL   0342769   MH

---

*NC9   [Lichtveld, Lou, 1903–]
16183   Rei van smeeckelingen, door Joost van den
944r   Vondel [pseud.]
Ursus Maior, 's Hertogenbosch[i.e.Amsterdam, F.Hoes,1944]
[13]p. col.front.,col.plate. 19cm.,in case 20cm.
Clandestine printing; De Jong 897.
False imprint; false colophon: De "Rei van smeeckelingen" ... werd in den zomer van 1944 ... gedrukt bij A. C. M. Pillot te Tilburg.

No. XXXV of 50 numbered copies; there was also an ordinary edition of 500 copies.
Original printed tan wrappers; in cloth case.

NL   0342771   MH NN IEN DLC

PT 5854   LICHTVELD.LOU,1903–
.L5 S6   's Mensen heen- en terugweg ₍door₎ Albert
Helman ₍pseud.₎ Rotterdam, Nijgh & Van Ditmar, 1937.
235 p.

NL   0342772   InU

₍Lichtveld, Lou₎ 1903–
Sebastiaan. Door Albert Helman ₍pseud.₎ Gesneden en gedrukt door Pieter Starreveld. ₍Amsterdam, P. Starreveld₎ 1944.
₍4₎p. col.illus. 39cm.

NL   0342773   IEN

946.081
L699s   Lichtveld, Lou, 1903–
De sfinx van Spanje; beschouwingen van een ooggetuige. Rotterdam, Nijgh & Van Ditmar, 1937.
189p. 23cm.

1. Spain. Hist. Civil War, 1936–1939. Sources.   I. Title.

NL   0342774   IEN MH

PT5850
.L5S7   Lichtveld, Lou, 1903–
Spokendans ₍door₎ Albert Helman ₍pseud.₎ Amsterdam, Amsterdamsche Boek- en Courantmij., 1954.
123 p. 20 cm.

I. Title.
         A 55–1237
Harvard Univ. Library
for Library of Congress

NL   0342775   MH CU NNC NN PU DLC

VOLUME 332

PT
5854
L69
S8
Lichtveld, Lou, 1903–
   De stille plantage [door] Albert Helman
[pseud.] Rotterdam, Nijgh & Van Ditmar,
1931.
   254 p. 22cm.

NL 0342776   NIC OC1 NNC

839.313
L699s
Lichtveld, Lou, 1903–
   De stille plantage [door] Albert Helman
[pseud.] Rotterdam, Nijgh & Van Ditmar, 1949.
   228p. 21cm. (Nimmer dralend reeks, no.16)

NL 0342777   IEN

[Lichtveld, Lou] 1903–
   De stille plantage. [By] Albert Helman. 9.drik.
's-Gravenhage, Nijgh & Van Ditmar [1955]

   176 p.

NL 0342778   MH

Lichtveld, Lou, 1903–
   Suriname aan de tweesprong. Amsterdam, W. L. Salm,
1945.
   48 p. 19 cm.

   1 Dutch Guiana. I. Title.

F2409.L5   988   51–37608

NL 0342779   DLC NN LU FU

Lichtveld, Lou, 1903–
   Suriname's nationale aspiraties; een aanleiding tot dis-
cussies over de grondslagen van een al-omvattend ontwik-
kelingsplan. Amsterdam, Arbeiderspers, 1953.
   70 p. 20 cm.
   Includes bibliography.

   1. Surinam. 2. Nationalism—Surinam. I. Title.

F2408.L5   62–38484 ‡

NL 0342780   DLC NN FU

Lichtveld, Lou, 1903–
   Teutonen-spiegel; een les in literatuur-geschiedenis [door]
Albert Helman [pseud.] 1. volledige uitg. Amsterdam,
Amsterdamsche Boek- en Courantmij., 1946.
   213 p. 22 cm.

   1. German literature—Hist. & crit. 2. National characteristics,
German. I. Title.

PT111.L5   54–39841

NL 0342781   DLC MH NN CU

[Lichtveld, Lou, 1903–
   Van pij en burnous; een bundel reisschetsen met illustra-
ties van G.Huysser en foto's van de schrijvers [Albert
Helman, pseud.en Albert Kuyle, pseud.] 2.druk. Utrecht,
De Gemeenschap [1931]

NL 0342782   MH

PT5854
L5V4
Lichtveld, Lou, 1903–
   Het vergeten gezicht [door] Albert Helman. Rotterdam,
Nijgh & Van Ditmar, 1939.
   322 p.

NL 0342783   CU MH

PT5854
L5W28
Lichtveld, Lou, 1903–
   Waarom niet [door] Albert Helman. Rotterdam, Nijgh &
Van Ditmar, 1933.
   1043 p.

NL 0342784   CU OrP

LICHTVELD, LOU, 1903–
   Waarom niet [door] Albert Helman [pseud. Opnieuw bewerkt]
Amsterdam, E. Querido, 1948. 475 p. port. 22cm.
(De Reuzensalamander)

   1. Fiction, Dutch. I. Title.

NL 0342785   NN OC1

PT5183
L55
Lichtveld, Lou, 1903–
   Wij en de litteratuur [door] Albert Helman. Utrecht, De
Gemeenschap, 1931.
   104 p.

   1. Dutch literature - 20th century - Addresses, essays, lectures.
2. Authors in literature. I. Title.

NL 0342786   CU MH

[Lichtveld, Lou, 1903–]
   Zuid-Zuid-West. [By] Albert Helman [pseud. Utrecht]
De Gemeenschap, 1926

   117 p.

NL 0342787   MH

PT 5854
.L5 Z45
LICHTVELD, LOU, 1903–
   Zuid-Zuidwest [door] Albert Helman [pseud.
Utrecht] De Gemeenschap, 1932.
   116 p.

NL 0342788   InU

Lichtveld, Lou, 1903–
   Zuid-zuid-west, [door] Albert Helamn;
vierde druk. N. p., De Gemeenschap, n.d.
   118 p. O.

NL 0342789   PP

[Lichtveld, Lou, 1903–
   Zuid zuid west [door Albert Helman, pseud.]
[5. druk] Utrecht, Brussel, Het Spectrum, 1948.

   128 p.
   Dutch.

NL 0342790   OC1 OrP

[Lichtveld, Lou] 1903–
   Zuid-zuid-west [door] Albert Helman [pseud.]
Amsterdam, Querido, 1954.
   206 p. (De salamander; reeks van de beste
oorspronkelijke en veritaalde romans)

NL 0342791   NNC NN

Wason
Pamphlet
JQ
Indonesia
12
Lichtveld, W   H
   Vragen en antwoorden over de Garantiewet
voor burgerlijk overheidspersoneel Indonesië
samengesteld door de vertegenwoordiger der
Samenwerkende Vakorganisaties van Overheids-
personeel in Indonesië. 's-Gravenhage,
Regeringsvoorlichtingsdienst, 1950.
   32 p. 20cm.

   1. Indonesia--Officials and employees.
I. Samenwerkende Vakorganisaties van
Overheidspers.   oneel. II. Title.

NL 0342792   NIC

Lichtwardt, Henry
   A comparative study of piano methods ...
No pub. [1944?]
   44 [2] l.

   Bibliography: 2 l. at end.
   Thesis, Detroit institute of musical art, 1944?]
   Typewritten copy, duplicated.

NL 0342793   MiD

Lichtwardt, Robert William, 1924–
   Morphological, cytological, and taxonomic observations
on species of *Enterobryus* from the hindgut of certain milli-
peds and beetles. Ann Arbor, University Microfilms [1955]
   [University Microfilms, Ann Arbor, Mich.] Publication no. 10,506]
   Microfilm copy of typescript. Positive.
   Collation of the original: v, 241 l. illus.
   Thesis—University of Illinois.
   Abstracted in Dissertation abstracts, v. 15 (1955) no. 1, p. 17–18.
   Vita.
   Bibliography: leaves 238–241.
   1. Enterobryus.

Microfilm AC-1   no. 10,506   Mic A 55–28

Illinois. Univ. Library
for Library of Congress   †

NL 0342794   IU DLC

Lichtwark, Alfred, 1852–1914.
   Alfred Lichtwark; eine auswahl seiner schriften, besorgt
von dr. Wolf Mannhardt. Mit einer einleitung von Karl
Scheffler ... Berlin, B. Cassirer, 1917.
   2 v. 23cm.
   "Verzeichnis der im buchhandel erschienenen schriften Lichtwarks":
v. 2, p. 451.

   1. Art—Collected works. 2. Museums. I. Mannhardt, Wolf, 1864–
ed. II. Scheffler, Karl, 1869–
   [Full name: Friedrich Christian Danger Alfred Lichtwark]

      34–17468

Library of Congress   N37.L5   704

NL 0342795   DLC NcRS NNC ICU MiU

Lichtwark, Alfred, 1852–1914.
   ... Der amateur-photograph und die natur. Vortrag des director prof. dr. Lichtwark in der
Kunsthalle. Hamburg, druck der actien-gesellschaft
"Neue börsen-halle" [1893?]
   16 p. 19cm.
   At head of title: Sonder-abdruck aus dem "Hamb. corres-
pondenten" vom 22. oktober 1893.
   With his Die bedeutung der amateur-photographie. Hamburg [1893?]
   1. Nature photography.

   [Full name: Friedrich Christian Danger Alfred Lichtwark]

NL 0342796   ViU

N6861
.L63
(SA)
Lichtwark, Alfred, 1852–1914.
   ...Aus der praxis. Berlin, Cassirer,
1902.
   170 p. 20 cm. (His Die grundlagen
der künstlerischen bildung)

   1.Art, German. 2.Art in Hamburg.

NL 0342797   NjP NSyU

Lichtwark, Alfred, 1852–1914.
   ... Die bedeutung der amateur-photographie.
Vortrag des director prof. dr. Lichtwark in der
Kunsthalle. Hamburg, druck der actien-gesellschaft "Neue börsen-halle" [1893?]
   15 p. 19cm.
   At head of title: Sonder-abdruck aus dem "Hamb. corres-
pondenten" vom 15. oktober 1893.
   With this are bound his Der amateur-photograph und die
natur. Hamburg [1893?]; Die nationen und ihre vertreter
in der amateur-photographien-ausstellung. Hamburg [1893?]
   1. Photography.

   [Full name: Friedrich Christian Danger Alfred Lichtwark]

NL 0342798   ViU

VOLUME 332

Lichtwark, Alfred, 1852–
***** Die Bedeutung der Amateur-Photographie, von Alfred Lichtwark.
Herausgegeben auf Anregung des Hamburger Amateur-Photo-
graphenvereins. Halle a. S., W. Knapp. 1894.
vi [2], 72 p. illus., XVII pl. incl. front. 28ᶜᵐ.
Contents. — Die Bedeutung der Amateur-Photographie. — Der Amateur-Photograph
und die Natur. — Die Nationen und ihre Vertreter auf der Hamburger Ausstellung 1893.
— Die Geschichte der Ausstellung.

NL 0342799   ICJ

757
qL699b   Lichtwark, Alfred
Das Bildnis in Hamburg, als Manuskript
gedruckt. Hamburg, Der Kunstverein zu
Hamburg, 1889.
2 v. illus. 31cm.

1. Portrait painters, German - History.
I. Title.

NL 0342800   TNJ

FINE ARTS
ND
1300
L61   Lichtwark, Alfred, 1852–1914.
Das Bildnis in Hamburg. Als Manuskript
gedruckt. Hamburg, 1898.
2 v. illus., plates (ports.) 30cm.

At head of title: Der Kunstverein zu Hamburg.

1. Portrait painting - Hamburg. 2. Portraits - Hamburg.   I. Kunstverein in
Hamburg.

NL 0342801   NNC MH NcGU NN NjP

SB
406
.L53   Lichtwark, Alfred, 1852–1914
Blumenkultus; wilde Blumen. Dresden, G.
Kühtmann, 1897.
71p. 20cm.

1. Floriculture. I. Title.

NL 0342802   TNJ NN

Lichtwark, Alfred, 1852–1914.
Blumenkultus; wilde Blumen; 2. erweiterte
Aufl. Dresden, G. Kühtmann, 1901.
90 p. 20 cm.

NL 0342803   PBm

PT
2623
.I35
Z5   Lichtwark, Alfred, 1852–1914.
Briefe an die Kommission für die Ver-
waltung der Kunsthalle. Hamburg, Georg
Westermann [c1923]
2v. 19cm. (Hamburgische Hausbibliothek)

Cover title: Reisebriefe.

NL 0342804   TNJ

N
8375
L61
L613   Lichtwark, Alfred, 1852–1914.
Briefe an die Kommission für die Verwaltung
der Kunsthalle. In Auswahl mit einer Einleitung hrsg. von Gustav Pauli. Hamburg, G.
Westermann, 1924.
2 v. port. 19cm. (Hamburgische Hausbibliothek)

On covers: Alfred Lichtwark, Reisebriefe.

NL 0342805   NNC NN ICU ICarbS

PT
2623
.I35
Z53
1946   Lichtwark, Alfred, 1852–1914
Briefe an Gustav Pauli. Im Auftrage der
Lichtwark-Stiftung herausgegeben von Carl
Schellenberg. Hamburg, Johann Trautmann, 1946.
96p. 19cm.

1. Pauli, Gustav, 1866–1938. I. Schellenberg, Carl, 1898–   ed.

NL 0342806   TNJ IEN MdBJ

Lichtwark, Alfred, 1852–1914. Im Auftrage der Lichtwark-
Stiftung hrsg. von Carl Schellenberg. Hamburg, J. Trautmann, 1947.
349 p. 19 cm.

I. Liebermann, Max, 1847–1935. II. Schellenberg, Carl, 1898–
ed.
Full name: Friedrich Christian Danger Alfred Lichtwark.

N8375.L5A3   A 49–111*
Harvard Univ. Library
for Library of Congress   [a58b¼]†

ICU CtY
NL 0342807   MH CSt IEN TNJ NNC OCl TxU DLC NN WU

Lichtwark, Alfred, 1852–1914.
Briefe an Wolf Mannhardt. Zu Lichtwarks hundertstem
Geburtstag am 14. Nov. 1952 hrsg. von Carl Schellenberg.
Hamburg, J. Trautmann, 1952.
151 p. 20 cm.

I. Mannhardt, Wolf, 1864–1939. II. Schellenberg, Carl, 1898–   ed.
Full name: Friedrich Christian Danger Alfred Lichtwark.

A 53–3498
Harvard Univ. Library
for Library of Congress

NL 0342808   MH NN TNJ

NA
9030
L53
1912   Lichtwark, Alfred, 1852–1914.
Deutsche königsstädte. Berlin-Potsdam-
Dresden-München-Stuttgart. 2. Aufl.
Berlin, B. Cassirer, 1912.
138 p. 20 cm.

1. Cities and towns - Planning - Germany.
2. Cities and towns - Germany.

NL 0342809   CU-I MH TNJ

N
6868
.L5   Lichtwark, Alfred, 1852–1914.
Der Deutsche der Zukunft. Berlin, Bruno
Cassirer, 1905.
243p. 20cm.

1. Art, Modern - 20th century - Germany
(Federal Republic, 1949–   ). I. Title.

NL 0342810   TNJ CSt CtY MH

Lichtwark, Alfred, 1852–
Drei programme. 2ᵉ aufl. Berlin, B. Cassirer, 1902.
pp. 119 +. (His Die grundlagen der künstlerischen bildung,
4.)

NL 0342811   MH NcU

Lichtwark, Alfred.
Die Erziehung des Farbensinnes.
— Berlin. Cassirer. 1901. 64 pp. 8°.
From the artist's standpoint.

         Nov. 6,   1901
E2213 — Color.

NL 0342812   MB TNJ MiU CSmH

ND
1283
L5
1902   Lichtwark, Alfred.
Die Erziehung des Farbensinnes. 2.Aufl.
Berlin, B.Cassirer, 1902.
66 p. (Die Grundlagen der künstlerischen
Bildung: Studien, 2.Bd.)

1.Color. I.Title.

NL 0342813   NSyU

N200
.H3
L5   Lichtwark, Alfred, 1852–1914.
Die Erziehung des Farbensinnes. 3. Aufl.
Berlin, Bruno Cassirer, 1905.
63p. 20cm. (Die Grundlagen der künst-
lerischen Bildung)

1. Art - Study and teaching - Hamburg. I.
Title.

NL 0342814   NcU PHC MH

Lichtwark, Alfred, 1852–1914.
... Die erziehung des farbensinnes. 4. aufl. Berlin,
B. Cassirer, 1914.
3 p. l., 56 p. 19½ᶜᵐ. (*His* Die grundlagen der künstlerischen bildung)

1. Sight. 2. Color-sense.

NL 0342815   MiU OO

N27
.L7   Lichtwark, Alfred, 1852–1914.
Die Grundlagen der künstlerischen Bildung;
Studien. Berlin, B. Cassirer, 1894–
v.
"Aus den Vorträgen an der Kunsthalle."

1. Art--Collected works.

NL 0342816   ICU NN

DD
901
.H24
L53   Lichtwark, Alfred, 1852–1914
Hamburg; Niedersachsen. Dresden, G. Kühtmann, 1897.
76p. 20cm.

1. Hamburg - Description.

NL 0342817   TNJ

N7445
.L52   Lichtwark, Alfred, 1852–1914.
Hamburgische Aufsätze. Hamburg, A. Janssen,
1917.
190 p. (Hamburgische Hausbibliothek. Neue
Reihe zur hamburgischen Kulturgeschichte, Bd.1)

1. Art--Addresses, essays, lectures.

NL 0342818   ICU NNC NjP TNJ

N
6886
.H35
L53   Lichtwark, Alfred, 1852–1914
Hamburgische Kunst. Nach einem Vortrage
über die Frühjahrsausstellung von 1898.
Herausgegeben vom Kunstverein. Hamburg, Als
Manuscript gedruckt, 1898.
88p. 18cm.

1. Art - Hamburg. I. Title.

NL 0342819   TNJ

VOLUME 332

Lichtwark, Alfred.
 Herrmann Kauffmann und die kunst in Hamburg
von 1800-1850. Mün., Verl.- anst. für kunst,
1893.
 104 p.

NL 0342820 PBm

Lichtwark, Alfred, 1852-
 Julius Oldach. Hamburg, Kunsthalle, 1899.
 pp. 146. Ports. and other illus. (His Hamburgische künstler.)

NL 0342821 MH NN NSyU TNJ MdBJ

Lichtwark, Alfred, 1852-
 Die kleinmeister als ornamentisten.
 Inaug. Diss. Leipzig, n.d.

NL 0342822 ICRL

NE
651
L61   Lichtwark, Alfred, 1852-1914.
 Die Kleinmeister als Ornamentisten. Berlin,
 W. Büxenstein [188-?]
 61 p. illus. 23cm.

 Part of thesis, Leipzig.

NL 0342823 NNC

Lichtwark, Alfred, 1852-

Matthies-Masuren, Fritz.
 ... Künstlerische photographie; entwicklung und einfluss in Deutschland, von Fr. Matthies-Masuren; vorwort
und einleitung von Prof. Alfred Lichtwark. Mit einer
gravüre und dreissig tonätzungen. [Berlin] Marquardt &
co. [1907]

Lichtwark, Alfred, 1852-1914.
 Makartbouquet und Blumenstrauss. München: Verlagsan-
stalt für Kunst und Wissenschaft, 1894. 64 p. 12°.
 First published in the Hamburger Weihnachtsbuch, 1892.

 1. Flowers, Germany. 2. Title.
                                           November 5, 1915.

NL 0342825 NN TNJ NSyU

Lichtwark, Alfred, 1852-
 Matthias Scheits als schilderer des Hamburger lebens, 1650-
1700. Hamburg, Kunsthalle, 1899.
 pp. 151. Illus. (His Hamburgische künstler.)

NL 0342826 MH NN NSyU TNJ

LICHTWARK, ALFRED, 1852-1914.
 Meister Bertram, tätig in Hamburg, 1367-1415.
Hamburg, Gedruckt bei Lütcke & Wulff, 1905. 409 p.
127 illus. 23cm. (Hamburgische Lieb-
haber- Bibliothek; hrsg. für die Gesellschaft hamburgischer Kunstfreunde von Alfred Lichtwark)

 "Als Manuscript gedruckt."
1. Bertram, Meister, b. ca. 1345. I. Gesellschaft hamburgischer
Kunstfreunde, Hamburg. Hamburgische
II. Hamburgische Liebhaber-   Liebhaber-Bibliothek.
                                   Bibliothek.

NL 0342827 NN ICU CU TNJ NjP InU MH OU NIC NcU

Fine Arts

Lichtwark, Alfred, 1852-1914.
 Meister Bertram, tätig in Hamburg 1367-1415.
Hamburg, Gedruckt bei Lütcke & Wulff, 1910.
409 p. 127 illus. 23cm. (Hamburgische
Liebhaber-Bibliothek)

NL 0342828 NNC

Lichtwark, Alfred, 1852-1914.
 ... Meister Francke, 1424, von Alfred Lichtwark; mit 22 abbildungen. Hamburg, Kunsthalle, 1899.
 194 p. illus. 20ᵐᵐ. (His Hamburgische künstler)
 "Als manuskript gedruckt für die kreise der Kunsthalle und nicht im
buchhandel."
 "Schriften von Alfred Lichtwark": p. [3]-[4]

 1. Francke, master, 15th cent. I. Hamburg. Kunsthalle.
                                   [Full name: Friedrich Christian Danger Alfred Lichtwark]
                                                          35-21613

Library of Congress   ND588.F7L5   759.3

NL 0342829 DLC NSyU TNJ NIC MH PBm

Lichtwark, Alfred.
 Meister Franckes Einfluss.
 (In Studien aus Kunst und Geschichte Friedrich Schneider ...
 gewidmet ... Pp. 125-128. Freiburg im Breisgau. 1906.)

G4602 — Francke, Meister.

NL 0342830 MB

Lichtwark, Alfred.
 Museum buildings.
 (In Museum of Fine Arts, Boston. Communication to the Trus-
tees. 2. Pp. 76-86. [Boston.] 1904.)
 Translated from his address, Die Museen als Volksbildungsstätten.

G7423 — Museums.

NL 0342831 MB

Lichtwark, Alfred, 1852-1914.
 ... Die nationen und ihre vertreter in der amateur–photographien–ausstellung. Dritter vortrag
des director prof. dr. Lichtwark in der Kunsthalle
am sonntag, den 22. october 1893. Hamburg, druck
der actien-gesellschaft "Neue börsen-halle" [1893?]
29 p. 19ᵐ.
 At head of title: Sonder-abdruck aus dem "Hamb. corres-
pondenten" vom 29. oktober 1893.
 With his Die bedeutung der amateur-photographie. Hamburg [1893?]
 1. Photography.

 [Full name: Friedrich Christian Danger Alfred
                                   Lichtwark]

NL 0342832 ViU

Lichtwark, Alfred, 1852-1914.
 Der Ornamentstich der deutschen Frührenaissance; nach
seinem sachlichen Inhalt, von Alfred Lichtwark. Berlin: Weidmannsche Buchhandlung, 1888. xv, 224 p. illus. 8°.

 1. Decorative art (German). 2. En-   graving (German). August 29, 1919.

NL 0342833 NN ICU

NA7349
L6   Lichtwark, Alfred, 1852-1914.
 Palastfenster und Flügelthür. Berlin,
 B. u. P. Cassirer, 1899.
 181 p. 20cm.

 1. Architecture, Domestic - Germany. 2.
 Architecture - Addresses, essays, lectures.
 L. Title.

NL 0342834 GU OO TNJ

NA3000
L53
1901   Lichtwark, Alfred, 1852-1914.
 Palastfenster und Flügelthür. 2. umgearb.
 Aufl. Berlin, B.und P.Cassirer, 1901.
 x,199 p. 20cm.

 1.Doorways - Germany. 2.Windows - Germany.
 3.Architecture, Modern - 19th cent. -
 Germany. I.Title.

NL 0342835 CSt

Lichtwark, Alfred, 1852-1914
 Palastfenster und Flügeltür. 3.Aufl. Berlin,
Cassirer, 1905

 203 p. (His Die Grundlagen der Künstlerischen
 Bildung)

 1. Windows. 2. Doors

NL 0342836 MH

Lichtwark, Alfred, 1852-1914.
 ... Park- und gartenstudien: Die probleme des Hamburger
stadtparks, Der heidegarten. Berlin, B. Cassirer, 1909.
 121, [1] p. 20ᵐ. (His Die grundlagen der künstlerischen bildung)
 "Schriften von Alfred Lichtwark": p. [1]-[2]

 1. Hamburg—Parks. 2. Parks. 3. Gardens.
                                                          34-20869

Library of Congress   SB485.H3L5   712

NL 0342837 DLC

Lichtwark, Alfred, 1852-1914.
 Philipp Otto Runge, pflanzenstudien mit scheere und papier,
herausgegeben von Alfred Lichtwark. Hamburg, Gedruckt
bei Lütcke & Wulff, 1895.
 24 p. IX pl. 29½ᵐ. (Added t.-p.: Hamburgische liebhaberbibliothek,
hrsg. von der Gesellschaft hamburgischer kunstfreunde. Bd. I)
 "Als manuscript gedruckt."
 "Vertriebsleitung durch die Commetersche kunsthandlung."

 1. Runge, Philipp Otto, 1777-1810.
                                   [Full name: Friedrich Christian Danger Alfred Lichtwark]
                                                          45-27699

Library of Congress   NC910.L5

NL 0342838 DLC

Lichtwark, Alfred, 1852-1914.
 Der rheinische Bismarck, von Alfred Lichtwark und Walther
Rathenau. Berlin: S. Fischer Verlag, 1912. 30 p. 8°.
 "Zum Kampf um das Bismarck-Denkmal."

 398360A. 1. Bismarck-Schoenhausen,   Otto Eduard Leopold, Fürst von, 1815-
 1898. 2. Rathenau, Walther, 1867-   1922.
                                                   January 30, 1929

NL 0342839 NN

Typ
920
22.5229   Lichtwark, Alfred, 1852-1914.
 ... Der Sammler. Sonderdruck aus dem ersten
Band einer Auswahl seiner Schriften.
[Offenbach am Main, 1922]

 35,[1]p. 22cm.
 At head of title: Alfred Lichtwark.
 "Gedruckt im Jahre 1922 von Gebr. Klingspor in
Offenbach am Main, als erster Druck in der von
Rudolf Koch gezeichneten Antiqua. Nr.578."
 Festschrift volume honoring the 50th birthday
of Walter von zur Westen.

 Original half vellum; dove paper boards,
label on front cover.

 Another copy. 21.5cm.
 No.557.
 Original red boards, label on front cover.

NL 0342841 MH NNC

VOLUME 332

ND Lichtwark, Alfred, 1852-1914.
588 Die Seele und das Kunstwerk: Boecklinstud-
B6 ien. Berlin, B. Cassirer, 1899.
L5 60 p.
"Aus den Vorträgen an der Kunsthalle."
"Schlusswort zu den Boecklin-Ausstellungen
in Berlin und Hamburg" (p. [37]-60)

1. Boecklin, Arnold, 1827-1901. I. Hamburg.
Kunsthalle. II. Title.

NL 0342842 NSyU TNJ

ND Lichtwark, Alfred, 1852-1914.
588 Die Seele und das Kunstwerk; Boecklinstudien.
B62L61 3. Aufl. Berlin, B. Cassirer, 1902.
1902 72 p. (Die Grundlagen der künstlerischen
Bildung; Studien [von] Alfred Lichtwark,
Bd.1)

Portrait of artist on cover.

1. Böcklin, Arnold, 1827-1901. I. Title.
II. Series.

NL 0342843 CLU

Lichtwark, Alfred.
Die Seele und das Kunstwerk; Boecklinstudien. Berlin:
Bruno Cassirer, 1911. 72 p. sq. 12°. (Die Grundlagen der
künstlerischen Bildung.)

1. Böcklin, Arnold—Crit. 2. Title.
March 14, 1934

NL 0342844 NN

DL276 Lichtwark, Alfred, 1852-1914.
.L5 Eine Sommerfahrt auf der Yacht
Hamburg. Hamburg, Lütcke & Wulff,
1904.
208p. 23cm. (Hamburgische Liebhaber-Bibliothek)

1. Copenhagen - Descr. I. Title.

NL 0342845 NNU-W TNJ

DK Lichtwark, Alfred, 1852-1914
511 Eine Sommerfahrt auf der Jacht Hamburg.
.B28 2. Aufl. Berlin, B. Cassirer, 1905.
L53 188p. 20cm.

1. Baltic Sea region - Description and
travel. I. Title.

NL 0342846 TNJ

W LICHTWARK, ALFRED, 1852-1914.
O Studien. Hamburg, Lütcke & Wulff, 1896-97.
.505 2v. 23cm. (Hamburgische Liebhaberbibliothek)

Contents.—1.Bd. Vorwort. Musik und bildende Kunst. Publicum. Indische Kunst. Eine ja-
panische Gemäldesammlung. Die Heraldik. Technik.
Eine Concurrenz. Moderne Gartenkunst. Farbige
Sculptur. Die Bebauung der Museumsinsel. Die
beiden neuen Panoramen. Der Neubau der technischen Hochschule. Das Zeughaus. Zur jüngsten
Weltausstellung.—2.Bd. Einleitungen und Ex-
curse. Der Kupferstich. Kopenhagener Museen.
Teppiche. Das Spatenbrau. Rococomöbel. Bil-
lige Einrichtungen. Architektur. Die Kunst im
preussischen Etat. Rembrandt und die holländi-
sche Kunst. Carl Blechen. Böcklin. Hans Thoma.
Adolph Menzel. Marktplatz. Adolph Menzel, das
Fest der Rose. Adolf Hildebrand. Max
Klinger als Wandfion- maler. Eine Festdecora-
tion.

NL 0342848 ICN TNJ NNC

Lichtwark, Alfred, 1852-1914
Taideteoksia oppimassa. Suomentanut Ester
Karilas. Porvoo, Söderström [1926]

141 p. plates

NL 0342849 MH

LICHTWARK, Alfred.
Übungen in der betrachtung von kunstwerken,
nach versuchen mit einer schul-classe herausgegeben von der Lehrervereinigung zur pflege
der künstlerischen bildung. Hamburg, Lütcke
& Wulff, 1897.

sm.8°. Portrs. and plates.

NL 0342850 MH

Lichtwark, Alfred, 1852-
... Übungen in der betrachtung von kunstwerken, nach
versuchen mit einer schulklasse hrsg. von der Lehrervereinigung zur pflege der künstlerischen bildung. 2. aufl.
Mit 16 abbildungen. Dresden, G. Kühtmann, 1898.

143 p. 16 pl. (incl. ports.) 19½ᵐ.

1. Art—Study and teaching—Hamburg. ı. Lehrervereinigung zur pflege
der künstlerischen bildung in der schule, Hamburg.

9–26560

Library of Congress N365.G3L7

NL 0342851 DLC TNJ NjP

Lichtwark, Alfred, 1852-1914.
... Übungen in der betrachtung von kunstwerken, nach versuchen mit einer schulklasse herausgegeben von der Lehrervereinigung zur pflege der künstlerischen bildung. 3. aufl. Mit
16 abbildungen. Dresden, G. Kühtmann, 1900.

143 p. plates. 19½ᵐ.

1. Art—Study and teaching—Hamburg. ı. Lehrervereinigung zur
pflege der künstlerischen bildung in der schule, Hamburg.
[Full name: Friedrich Christian Danger Alfred Lichtwark]
E 11–582 Revised
U. S. Off. of educ. Library N370.L6
for Library of Congress [N365.G3L]

NL 0342852 DHEW

Lichtwark, Alfred. 1852-
Übungen in der Betrachtung von Kunstwerken nach Versuchen mit
einer Schulklasse herausgegeben von der Lehrervereinigung zur
Pflege der künstlerischen Bildung. 6. Auflage.
— Berlin. Cassirer. 1906. 136 pp. Portraits. Plates. [Die Grund-
lagen der künstlerischen Bildung. Studien.] 19 cm., in 8s.

H9526 — Paintings. Criticism. — S.r. — Lehrervereinigung zur Pflege der
künstlerischen Bildung, Hamburg. Publications.

NL 0342853 MB MiU

Lichtwark, Alfred, 1852-1914
Übungen in der Betrachtung von Kunstwerken; nach Versuchen mit einer Schulklasse herausgegeben von der Lehrervereinigung zur Pflege der künstlerischen Bildung. Berlin: Bruno
Cassirer, 1914. 136 p. pl., port. 12°. (Die Grundlagen
der künstlerischen Bildung.)

1. Pictures. 2. Title.
April 13, 1934

NL 0342854 NN

Lichtwark, 1852-1914.
Übungen in der Betrachtung von Kunstwerken.
Nach Versuchen mit einer Schulklasse hrsg. von
der Lehrervereinigung zur Pflege der künstlerischen Bildung. 11. bis 14. Aufl. Berlin, Cassirer, 1918.

NL 0342855 MH

Lichtwark, Alfred, 1852-1914.
... Übungen in der betrachtung von kunstwerken
nach versuchen mit einer schulklasse herausgegeben von der Lehrervereinigung zur pflege
der künstlerischen bildung. Mit 16 abbildungen.
Berlin, B. Cassirer, 1922.
136 p. plates. 19.5 cm.

NL 0342856 WaU MoU CLU

PT Lichtwark, Alfred, 1852-1914
2623 Vom Arbeitsfeld des Dilettantismus. Dres-
.I35 den, Gerhard Kühtmann, 1897.
V65 92p. 20cm.

1. Dilettantism. I. Title.

NL 0342857 TNJ

Lichtwark, Alfred, 1852-1914
Vom Arbeitsfeld des Dilettantismus. Berlin,
Cassirer, 1902

93 p. (His Die Grundlagen der künstlerischen
Bildung)

NL 0342858 MH

N9211 Lichtwark, Alfred, 1852-1914.
L5 ... Vom arbeitsfeld des dilettantismus. 2.
aufl., volksausgabe. Berlin, B. Cassirer, 1907
93 p. 19.3 cm. (Die grundlagen der künstlerischen bildung; studien von Alfred Lichtwark)

1. Folk art—Germany. 2. Art—Germany.
I. Title.

NL 0342859 CSmH

N7477 Lichtwark, Alfred, 1852-1914.
L5 Wege und Ziele des Dilettantismus.
München, Verlagsanstalt für Kunst und Wissenschaft, 1894.
88 p. 19ᵐ.

1. Art - Philos   ophy. I. Title.

NL 0342860 CSt PBm

Lichtwark, Alfred, 1852-1914.
... Die wiedererweckung der medaille ...
Dresden, G. Kühtmann, 1897.
51, iv p. XXII pl. 20 cm.
1. Medals. 2. Medals - Germany.

NL 0342861 CU

Lichtwark, Friedrich Christian Danger Alfred
see
Lichtwark, Alfred, 1852-1914.

VOLUME 332

[Lichtwark, Kar¡] 1859?–1931.
Die drei Orgeln in St. Marien zu Lübeck.
[Lübeck, 1925]
Pamphlet
1. Lübeck. Marienkirche.

NL 0342863   CtY

Lichtwark, Karl, 1859?–1931.
¡Konzertfuge, organ, op. 2, G minor¡

Konzertfuge in G moll für die orgel, componirt von K. Lichtwark ... Op. 2. Leipzig, C. F. Kahnt nachfolger ¡1897¡
11 p.   24 x 32ᶜᵐ.
Publisher's plate no.: 3516.

1. Canons, fugues, etc. (Organ)
45–51011
Library of Congress   M10.L52 op. 2

NL 0342864   DLC

Lichtwark, Karl, 1859?–1931.
Praktische Harmonielehre für Lehranstalten und zum Selbstunterricht.
— Leipzig. Kahnt. 1905. viii, 134 pp. 8°.

G596 — Harmony.

NL 0342865   MB

Lichtwer, Ernst Magnus, 1879–
Ein beitrag zur frage ueber das sehen der schielenden.
Inaug. Diss. Halle, 1903
Bibl.

NL 0342866   ICRL DNLM MH

PT
2423   Lichtwer, Magnus Gottfried, 1719–1783
.L5   Auserlesene verbesserte Fabeln und
A87   Erzählungen. Greifswalde, J. J. Weitbrecht,
1761.
2v. in 1 illus. 20cm.

NL 0342867   TNJ

Beinecke
Library   [Lichtwer, Magnus Gottfried] 1719–1783
Zg18   [Auserlesene, verbesserte Fabeln und Erzählungen. Greifswald und Leipzig, 1761]
L631   136 p.   20 cm.
761   Half-title: Fabeln und Erzählungen. Erstes [–Zweytes] Buch.
In verse.
Edited and corrected, without the author's knowledge, by Karl Wilhelm Ramler. – Allgemeine deutsche Biographie, v.8, 560.
The fables are based on those by Aesopus.
Title-page [and possibly a preface] wanting;

title taken from Meusel, Lexikon der deutschen Schriftsteller, v.8, 1808, p.241.
Most of the tail-pieces are colored by hand in crayon or water-color.
Armorial bookplate of Andrew J. Onderdonk.
Xerox copy of ALS from Kuno Francke to Mr. Onderdonk, June 1, 1912, identifying this work, laid in at end.

NL 0342869   CtY PPAN

Lichtwer, Magnus Gottfried, 1719–1783.

Minor, Jakob, 1855–1912, ed.
Fabeldichter, satiriker und popularphilosophen des 18. jahrhunderts (Lichtwer, Pfeffel, Kästner, Göckingk, Mendelssohn und Zimmermann) Herausgegeben von dr. J. Minor. Berlin und Stuttgart, W. Spemann ¡1884¡

Lichtwer, M¡agnus¡ G¡ottfried¡ 1719–1783.
M. G. Lichtwers ... Fabeln in vier büchern; von dem verfasser selbst hrsg. `3. aufl. Berlin, G. A. Lange, 1762.
xiv, 188, ¡4¡ p. illus., plates. 19½ᶜᵐ.

Library of Congress   5–3824

NL 0342871   DLC MH PHC

Lichtwer, Magnus Gottfried, 1719–1783.
M. G. Lichtwers ... Fabeln in vier Büchern. Von dem Verfasser selbst hrsg. Neue Aufl. Amsterdam, 1765.
xvi, 186, [6] p.   16 cm.
Title vignette.
First published anonymously in 1748 under the title: Vier Bücher aesopischer Fabeln ...
1. Fables, German.

NL 0342872   CtY MH

LICHTWER, Magnus Gottfried, 1719–1783.
Fabeln in vier Büchern. Neueste Aufl. Wien, gedruckt bey J.T.Edl.v.Trattnern, 1767.

17 cm. Engr.plates and title vign.
In verse.

NL 0342873   MH TNJ

LICHTWER, Magnus Gottfried, 1719–1783.
Fabeln in vier Büchern. Wien, gedruckt bey J.T.Edl.v.Trattnern, 1769.

17.5 x 10 cm. Plates.

NL 0342874   MH

PT
2423   Lichtwer, Magnus Gottfried, 1719–1783.
L5   Fabeln in vier Büchern/ M.G. Lichtwern.
F3   Wien: Trattnern, 1773.
1773   219 p.

1. Fables. I. Title.

NL 0342875   KMK NjP

---

331   Lichtwer, Magnus Gottfried, 1719–1783.
L699f   Fabeln in vier Büchern von dem Verfasser selbst herausgegeben. 4. Aufl. Berlin, G. A. Lange, 1775.
188p. illus. 20cm.

Title vignette.
Head and tail pieces.

I. Title. Fabeln.

NL 0342876   NcU InU MH

Lichtwehr, Magnus G.
Fabeln ... Heilbronn, 1825.

NL 0342877   PPL

J
831.61   Lichtwer, Magnus Gottfried, 1719–1783.
26g   Fabeln in drei Büchern. Hildburghausen u. New-York, Bibliographischen Institut, 1830.
124 p. port. 11 cm. (Miniatur-Bibliothek der deutschen Classiker, Lfg. 87.)

Bound with Gellert, C.F. Fabeln. Hildburghausen, 1829.

NL 0342878   N

Lichtwer, Magnus Gottfried, 1719–1783.
Fabeln von Magnus Gottfried Lichtwer. Cabinets-Ausgabe. Hildburghausen: Bibliographisches Institut, 1830. 116 p. 24°.

1989A. 1. Fables (German).   2. Poetry (German).
March 8, 1921.

NL 0342879   NN

Lichtwer, [Magnus Gottfried] 1719–1783.
Lichtwer's Fabeln. Hildburghausen & New York, 1833.
124, (3) p. port. 48°. (Miniatur-Bibliothek der deutschen Classiker)

NL 0342880   MWA

Lichtwer, Magnus Gottfried.
Fabeln. Hildburghausen, Bibliog. institut, 1834.
124 p.

NL 0342881   PU

Lichtwer, Magnus Gottfried, 1719–1783.
...Lichtwer's Fabeln. Hildburghausen: Bibliographisches Institut, 1834. 161 p. front. (port.) 24°. (Cabinets-Bibliothek der deutschen Classiker. Bd. 41.)
Bound with: Neubeck, V. W. Anthologie aus den Gedichten von Neubeck und M. v. Schenkendorf. 1834.

142584A. 1. Poetry, German.   2. Fables, German.
October 31, 1924.

NL 0342882   NN OOxM IU

Lichtwer, Magnus Gottfried.
Fabeln. Hildburghausen, Bibliographisches institut, 1842.
188 p.

NL 0342883   PU

Lichtwer, Magnus Gottfried, 1719–1783.
Fables nouvelles divisées en quatre livres. Traduction libre de l'allemand de Monsieur Lichtwehr. Strasbourg, ¡etc., etc.¡ 1763.
14 p., 1 l., 267, ¡1¡ p. 18ᶜᵐ.
Translated by G. K. Pfeffel.

1. Fables. I. Pfeffel, Gottlieb Konrad, 1736–1809, tr.
18–21742
Library of Congress   PT2423.L5F35 1763

NL 0342884   DLC NjP NN

Lichtwer, Magnus Gottfried, 1719–1783.
Poetische schriften von M. G. Lichtwer ... Wien, F. A. Schræmbl, 1793.
2 v. fronts. (v. 1, port.) 15ᶜᵐ. (Half-title: Sammlung der vorzüglichsten werke deutscher dichter und prosaisten. xxxiv.–xxxv. bd.)
Added title-pages, engraved.

44–38386
Library of Congress   PT2423.L5A17 1793

NL 0342885   DLC CtY WU CU NN OU InU MH CLSU OClW ViU

Lichtwer, Magnus Gottfried, 1719–1783.
Das recht der vernunft, in fünf büchern. Von M. G. Lichtwern ... Leipzig, B. C. Breitkopf, 1758.
7 p. l., ¡3¡–127, ¡1¡ p. 20ᶜᵐ.
In verse.
Head-pieces.

1. Law—Poetry. I. Title.
42–43935

NL 0342886   DLC InU MH CtY OU CLSU NjP NcU CaBVaU

VOLUME 332

LICHTWER, Magnus Gottfried, 1719-1783.
Das Recht der Vernunft, in fünf Büchern.
Wien, bey J.F.Edlen von Trattnern, 1767.

17 cm. Engr. head-pieces.
In verse.

NL 0342887   MH TNJ

LICHTWER, Magnus Gottfried, 1719-1783.
Das Recht der Vernunft, in fünf Büchern; [poem].
Wien, gedruckt bey J.T. Edlen v. Trattnern, 1768.

17.5 x 10 cm. Vigns.

NL 0342888   MH

PT   Lichtwer, Magnus Gottfried, 1719-1783.
2423   Schriften; hrsg. von seinem Enkel Ernst
.L5   Ludwig Magnus von Pott, mit einer Vorrede
1828   und Biographie Lichtwer's von Friedrich
        Cramer.   Halberstadt, Brüggemann, 1828.
           280 p.   14 cm.

        I. Pott, Ernst Ludwig Magnus. von, ed. II.
        Cramer, Friedrich,   1802-1859.

NL 0342889   WU InU MH CtY MdBP MB

PT2423 Lichtwer, Magnus Gottfried, 1719-1783.
.L5F2   Vier bücher Aesopischer fabeln von M. G. Lichtwern ...
1758   2. aufl., nebst einem anhange. Berlin, Bey G. A. Lange,
        1758.
           [8], 200 p. 19½ᶜᵐ.
           Title vignette.

NL 0342890   ICU

Lichtwitz, Alfred.
    Jüdische Politik und ihr Verhalten zur Türkei. Ein Mahn-
ruf.   Guben: der Verfasser, 1911.   16 p.   8°.

1. Zionism.
                                    October 21, 1913.

NL 0342891   NN

W 1   LICHTWITZ, Alfred
SA524   Über die Anwendung der Hyperämie als
Heft 7 Heilmittel in der Zahnheilkunde, mit be-
1911   sonderer Berücksichtigung einer neuen
        Methoden. Leipzig, Dyk, 1911.
           40 p. illus. (Sammlung von Vorträgen
        aus dem Gebiete der Zahnheilkunde,
        Heft 7)

NL 0342892   DNLM

Lichtwitz, Alfred.
    Die zahnpflege in den schulen; vortrag, gehalten im
Gubener lehrerverein am 17. febr. 1912, von zahnarzt
Alfred Lichtwitz ... Osterwieck / Harz, A. W. Zickfeldt,
1912.
    20 p. illus. 24½ᶜᵐ.
    "Bibliographie": p. 20.

1. Teeth—Hygiene.   I. Title.
                                    E 13-1497
Library, U. S. Bur. of   Education   LB3455.L62

NL 0342893   DHEW

Lichtwitz, André, 1899-
    ... Les algies viscérales; études pathogéniques
et thérapeutiques ...   Paris, 1928.
    Thèse - Univ. de Paris.
    "Bibliographie": p. 195-212.

NL 0342894   CtY

WK   LICHTWITZ, André, 1899-
100   Examen clinique et traitement d'un
qL699e endocrinien par A. Lichtwitz & R.
        Parlier. [Paris] L'Expansion scientifique
        française [1954]-
           v. illus.
           Contents. —t. 1. Généralités. Hypo-
        physe, corps Thyroïde, ovaire.
           1. Endocrine glands - Diseases
        I. Parlier, Roger, 1900-   Title

NL 0342895   DNLM MBCo

Lichtwitz, Jacob, 1843-
    Ueber uranoplastik ...   Breslau, Freund,
1867.
    3 p. l., 32 p., 1 l.

    Inaug.-diss., Breslau, 1867.

1. Palate - Surgery.

NL 0342896   NNC

Lichtwitz (Kurt) (1881-   . *Ergebnisse der
Tenotomie und der Muskelverlagerung bei 580
Schieloperationen. 23 pp. 8°. Breslau, 1908.

NL 0342897   DNLM ICRL

WM   LICHTWITZ, Leopold, 1858-1911
L699a   Les anesthésies hystériques des
1887   muqueuses et des organes des sens
        et les zones hystérogènes des muqueuses;
        recherches cliniques.   Paris, Baillière,
        1887.
           182 p.
           Title

NL 0342898   DNLM PPC

Lichtwitz, Leopold, 1858-
    ——. De l'ablation des amygdales avec l'anse
électrothermique. 14 pp., 1 pl. 8°. Paris, G.
Masson, 1895.

NL 0342899   DNLM

Lichtwitz, Leopold, 1858-
    ——. De l'emploi des accumulateurs en méde-
cine, et de la meilleure manière de les charger.
15 pp. 8°. Paris, G. Masson, 1893.

NL 0342900   DNLM

Lichtwitz, Leopold, 1858-
    ——. 1. De l'extirpation rapide des pseudo-
polypes naso-pharyngiens. 2. Un cas de pro-
lapsus double du ventricule de Morgagni, guéri
par l'ablation. 3. Un cas de sarcome pédiculé
de la langue; ablation avec l'anse électro-ther-
mique; guérison. 4. L'orthoforme dans la rhi-
nite vaso-motrice (hydrorrhée nasale, fièvre des
foins). 16 pp. 8°. Paris, Masson & Cie., 1898.

NL 0342901   DNLM PPWD

Lichtwitz, Leopold, 1858-1911.
    Des troubles de la voix articu-
lée (parole) dans les affections du voile du palais,
de la cavité naso-pharyngienne et des fosses na-
sales. 32 pp. 8°. Paris, O. Doin, 1886.
    Repr. from: Rev. mens. de laryngol., etc., Bordeaux,
1886, vi.

NL 0342902   DNLM

Lichtwitz, Leopold, 1858-
    Die Eiterungen der Nebenhöhlen der
Nase und ihre Folgezustände in anderen Körper-
teilen. 16 pp. 8°. Halle a. S., 1895.
    Forms 7. Hft. of: Samml. zwangl. Abhandl. a. d. Geb.
d. Nasen-, Ohren-, Mund- u. Halskr.

NL 0342903   DNLM

Lichtwitz, Léopold, 1858-
    ... Recherches cliniques sur les anesthésies hystériques des
muqueuses et de quelques organes des sens (gout, odorat, ouïe)
et sur les zones hystérogènes des muqueuses. ... Par Léopold
Lichtwitz, ... Bordeaux, Impr. nouvelle A. Bellier & cie, 1887.
    182, [2] p. 27 x 21½ᶜᵐ.
    Thèse—Faculté de médecine et de pharmacie de Bordeaux.
    Bibliographical foot-notes.

NL 0342904   ICJ DNLM

Lichtwitz, Leopold, 1858-1911.
    —— Ueber die Erkrankungen des Sinus oder
Nebenhöhlen der Nase. 35 pp. 8°. Berlin, H.
Kornfeld, 1894.
    Forms 39.-40. Hft. of: Mod. Wander-Vortr., Berl.

NL 0342905   DNLM

Lichtwitz, Leopold, 1876- 1943.
    Functional pathology, by Leopold Lichtwitz ...   New York,
Grune & Stratton, incorporated, 1941.
    3 p. l., iii-xiv, 567 p. incl. illus., tables, diagrs. 23½ᶜᵐ.
    "References" at end of most of the chapters.

1. Pathology.   I. Title.
                                       41-25683
Library of Congress   RB113.L5
                               [15]   616

NL 0342906   DLC MtU OrU-M ICJ ViU PPC OU OClW-H PPHa

Lichtwitz, Leopold, 1876-
    Gallensteinbildung und Gallenblasenkrankheit ...
    (In Neue deutsche Klinik. Berlin, 1929. 26ᶜᵐ. Bd. 3, p. [596]-642. illus.,
diagr.)
    Bibliography: p. 640-642.
    Contents. — Lichtwitz, L. [Gallensteinbildung.— Renner, A. Gallenblasen-
krankheit.

L616.03
S800   v.3

NL 0342907   ICJ

Lichtwitz, Leopold, 1876-
    Klinische Chemie, von Professor Dr. med. L. Lichtwitz, ...
Mit 13 Textfiguren. Berlin, J. Springer, 1918.
    viii, 363, [1] p. 24ᶜᵐ.
    Bibliographical foot-notes.

616.076 R800

NL 0342908   ICJ MH PPC

Lichtwitz, Leopold, 1876-
    Klinische chemie, von professor dr. med. L. Lichtwitz ...
2. aufl., mit 52 abbildungen. Berlin, J. Springer, 1930.
    viii, 672 p. diagrs. 26ᶜᵐ.
    "Literatur" at end of chapters.

1. Physiological chemistry. 2. Pathology. 3. Metabolism.   I. Title.
                                       30-21375
Library of Congress   QP514.L7 1930

NL 0342909   DLC CU PPC NcD CtY ICJ IU DNLM OClW

Lichtwitz, Leopold, 1876-   ed.
    Medizinische kolloidlehre; physiologie, pathologie und the-
rapie in kolloidchemischer betrachtung ... herausgegeben von
prof. dr. L. Lichtwitz ... dr. dr. Raph. Ed. Liesegang ...
prof. dr. Karl Spiro ... Dresden und Leipzig, T. Steinkopff,
1935.

VOLUME 332

Lichtwitz, Leopold, 1876–
Nephritis, by Leopold Lichtwitz ... New York, Grune & Stratton, 1942.
xii, 328 p. incl. illus., tables, diagrs. 22ᶜᵐ.
"References" at the end of each chapter except the fifth.

1. Kidneys—Diseases.
Library of Congress   RC907.L55
42–11260
616.61

ICJ
NL 0342911   DLC OrU-M NcU DNLM PPC OU OC1W-H PPHa

Lichtwitz, Leopold, 1876–
Pathologie der funktionen und regulationen, von prof. dr. L. Lichtwitz ... Leiden, A. W. Sijthoff's uitgeversmaatschappij n. v., 1936.
3 p. l., 332 p. illus., plates, diagrs. 24½ᶜᵐ.
"Literatur" at end of each chapter except chapters II and IV.

1. Pathology. 2. Psychology, Pathological. 3. Metabolism, Disorders of. I. Title.
Library of Congress   RB25.L68
38–25936
616

NL 0342912   DLC NcD OC1W-H

Lichtwitz, Leopold, 1876–1943.
Pathology and therapy of rheumatic fever, by Leopold Lichtwitz ... foreword by William J. Maloney ... edited by Major William Chester ... New York, Grune & Stratton, incorporated, 1944.
xvii, 211 p. illus. 23½ cm.
On spine: Rheumatic fever.
"References" at end of all chapters except chapter 1.

1. Rheumatic fever. I. Chester, William, 1908–   ed.
U. S. Army Medical Libr.   S G 44—42
for Library of Congress   RC182.R4L5
[a49g½]   616.991

PPC OU
NL 0342913   DNLM CaBVaU WaTC OrU-M OC1W-H ICJ PSt

WJ
300
L699P
1921
Lichtwitz, Leopold, 1876–1943.
Die Praxis der Nierenkrankheiten. Berlin, Springer, 1921.
ix, 252 p. illus. 23 1/2 cm.
(Fachbücher für Ärzte, Bd. 8)

1. Kidney Diseases. I. Title. II. Series.

NL 0342914   WU-M OC1W-H N MiU CtY PPC DNLM

Lichtwitz, Leopold, 1876–
... Die praxis der nierenkrankheiten, von professor dr. L. Lichtwitz ... 3. aufl., mit 16 abbildungen und 36 kurven. Berlin, J. Springer, 1934.
viii, 359, [1] p. illus., diagrs. 23½ᶜᵐ. (Fachbücher für Ärzte. bd. VIII)

1. Kidneys—Diseases.
Library of Congress   RC902.L47 1934
Copyright A—Foreign   24314
34–16121
616.61

NL 0342915   DLC CtY ICJ MiU

Lichtwitz, Leopold, 1876–
Ueber beeinflussung der fettresorption im duenndarm durch senfoel.
Inaug. diss. Leipzig, 1901.

NL 0342916   ICRL DNLM CtY

Lichtwitz, Leopold, 1876– *1943.*
Über die bildung der harn- und gallensteine, von professor dr. L. Lichtwitz ... Mit 18 abbildungen im text und auf 8 tafeln. Berlin, J. Springer, 1914.
2 p. l., 81, [1] p. illus., VIII pl. (3 col.) diagr. 25½ᶜᵐ.   M. 3.60
"Literaturverzeichnis": p. [1]–8.

1. Calculi, Urinary. 2. Calculi, Biliary.
Library of Congress   RC921.L6
15–13224

NL 0342917   DLC ICRL ICJ

Lichtwitz, Otto.
Getriebe für aussetzende Bewegung. Berlin, Springer, 1953.
71 p. illus., diagrs., tables. 25 cm.
"Diese Abhandlung ist ursprünglich in der amerikanischen Zeitschrift Machine design und in der englischen Zeitschrift Engineering veröffentlicht worden."

1. Mechanical movements. 2. Machinery, Kinematics of. I. Title. II. Title: Aussetzende Bewegung.
Michigan. Univ. Libr.   A 54–1259
for Library of Congress

NL 0342918   MiU NN OU IEN

Lichtwitz, Otto.
Indexing and spiral milling, for machine tool operators, tool setters and production engineers, by Otto Lichtwitz ... London, G. Newnes limited [1944]
viii, 9–119, [1] p. incl. illus., tables, diagrs. 23ᶜᵐ.
"First published 1944."

1. Indexing (Machine-shop practice) 2. Spiral milling.
Library of Congress   TJ1167.L54
44–51144
621.95

NL 0342919   DLC PPF

Lichtwitz, Otto
621.83
L699M
Mechanisms for intermittent motion ... [Cleveland, Ohio] Machine Design [1952]
cover-title, 50 p. illus., diagrs. 28½ᶜᵐ.

Reprinted from Machine Design.

1. Gearing. 2. Mechanical movements. I. Title

NL 0342920   NcD PHC

Lichtwitz, Otto.
Teilen und Spiralfräsen; Anwendungsmöglichkeiten und Grenzen des Universalteilkopfes. Berlin, Springer, 1955.
iv, 88 p. illus. 25 cm.
"Der grösste Teil des Inhaltes dieses Buches ist ursprünglich in dem Buche 'Indexing and spiral milling' veröffentlicht worden."

1. Indexing (Machine-shop practice) 2. Spiral milling.
Michigan. Univ. Libr.   A 56–647
for Library of Congress   [8]

NL 0342921   MiU NN ICJ

Lichty, Daniel, 1845–
Abraham Lincoln, a comrade's tribute to his comrade commander-in-chief in the war between the states called the civil war for the preservation of the Union and the freedom of all its people. 1861 to 1865 A. D. By Comrade Daniel Lichty ... G. L. Nevins post no. 1, G. A. R. ... 2d printing, November, 1925. Rockford, Ill., 1925.
18, [2] p., 1 l. 21ᶜᵐ.
"Chronology of Lincoln's life": p. [2] at end.

1. Lincoln, Abraham, pres. U. S.—Personality.
Library of Congress   E457.2.L69
27–17070

NL 0342922   DLC

WG
29527
Lichty, David Martin, 1862–
Die chemische Kinetik der Zersetzung der Oxalsäure in konzentrierter Schwefelsäure. Heidelberg, 1906.
55 p. illus.

Inaug.-Diss. - Heidelberg.

NL 0342923   CtY ICRL DNLM PU MH MiU

Lichty, George Maurice, 1905–   *ed.*
Draw cartoons; it's fun to know how. Edited by Lichty. Minneapolis, Minn., General mills inc., ⁺1944.
1 p. l., 5–25 p. illus. 20ᶜᵐ.

1. Caricatures and cartoons. 2. Drawing—Instruction. I. General mills, inc., Minneapolis. II. Title.
Library of Congress   NC1320.L46
45–13440
741.5

NL 0342924   DLC

Lichty, George Maurice, 1905–
Grin and bear it; being a collection ... of 124 very funny and recognition-provoking pictures of the human animal in action. With an introd. by Joseph Henry Jackson. New York, McGraw-Hill [1954]
unpaged (chiefly illus.) 21 cm.

1. American wit and humor, Pictorial. I. Title.
NC1429.L533A47   741.5   54–9712 ‡

NL 0342925   DLC OrLgE WaU NcC TU OC1

Lichty, John Alden, 1866–   L6x6.04 L6xx
[Collected papers on internal medicine.]
Reprinted from various medical serials.

NL 0342926   ICJ

Lichty (John Alden). Intestinal hemorrhage in uremia. 3 pp. 12°. *Philadelphia,* 1896. *Repr. from:* Med. News, Phila., 1896, lxvi.

NL 0342927   DNLM

Lichty, John Alden, 1866–
State care for all the dependent insane in institutions owned and controlled by the state; being a reprint of papers discussing state care, written by John A. Lichty...and by Robert D. Dripps ... Philadelphia: Public Charities Assoc. of Pa., 1916. 20 p. 8°.
Repr.: Assoc. of Trustees and Medical Superintendents of State and Incorporated Hospitals for the Insane and Feeble-Minded of Pa. Proc. Oct., 1915.

1. Insane.—Hospitals and asylums. Public Charities Association of   U. S.: Pa. 2. Dripps, Robert D. 3. Pennsylvania.
January 10, 1917.

NL 0342928   NN PPPE

WA
670
q L699s
1932
LICHTY, Joseph Stoner, 1908–
Sanitary survey of Jamestown, New York. [Boston, Harvard Medical School] 1932.
73 ℓ. illus.
Typewritten copy.
1. Sanitation – New York (State)

NL 0342929   DNLM

VOLUME 332

Lichty, Joy G   1900–
  The chlorine derivatives of vanillin and some of their reactions, by J. G. Lichty ... Easton, Pa., Mack printing company, 1930.

  12 p., 1 l. 23½ cm.

  Thesis (PH. D.)—University of Iowa, 1930.
  Biography.
  "Reprinted from the Journal of the American chemical society, 52 ... (1930)."

  1. Vanillin. 2. Chlorine.

Library of Congress	QD341.A6L67 1930	31–10455
Univ. of Iowa Libr.		
		547.5

NL 0342930   IaU   DLC

ₗLichty, Justin₎ 1890–
  Flags of the United Nations. ₗNew York, S. Gabriel Sons, 1950₎

  57 p. (chiefly illus.) 27 x 31 cm.

  Includes 4 sheets of perforated, gummed, col. illus. to be inserted.

  1. Flags.   ɪ. Title.

| CR109.L5 | 929.9 | 50–1239 |

NL 0342931   DLC IU TxU Or

Lichty, Justin, 1890–
  ... Mississippi moon, a Negro musical comedy; book & lyrics by Justin Lichty. ₗNew York, 1943₎

  3 p. l., 66 numb. l. 28 cm.

  Type-written (carbon copy)
  Scenario; without music.

  ₗ1. Musical revues, comedies, etc.—Librettos₎ ɪ. Title.
                  46–15794

| Library of Congress | ML50.L6895M5 1943 |

NL 0342932   DLC

Lichty, Lester Clyde, 1891–
  ... Carbon monoxide in engine exhaust using alcohol blends, by L. C. Lichty and C. W. Phelps ... ₗNew Haven, Conn., Yale university, 1937₎

  cover-title. 14 p. diagrs.(1 fold.) 23 cm. (Yale university. Publications from the School of engineering. serial no.22, June, 1937)
  "Reprinted from Industrial and engineering chemistry, May, 1937."
  "Literature cited": p.14.

  1. Carbon monoxide. 2. Gas and oil engines. 3. Alcohol as fuel. I. Phelps, C. W., joint author. II. Ser.

NL 0342933   ViU

Lichty, Lester Clyde, 1891–
  ... Engine performance with gasoline and alcohol ₗby₎ L. C. Lichty and E. J. Ziurys ... ₗNew Haven, Conn.₎ Yale university, October, 1936.

  cover-title. 21 p. diagrs. 23½ cm. (Yale university. Publications from the school of engineering. serial no.16, October, 1936)
  "Reprinted from Industrial and engineering chemistry, September, 1936."
  "Literature cited": p.20–21.

  1. Gas and oil engines. 2. Alcohol as fuel. I. Ziurys, E. J., joint author. II. Title. III. Ser.

NL 0342934   ViU

TA1	
.Y3	**Lichty, Lester Clyde,** 1891–
no.180	
1952	Evaluation of flame speed at burner flame tip. ₗNew Haven₎ Yale Univ., 1952.

  ₗ1395₎–1398 p. diagr. 28cm. (Yale University, School of Engineering. Publications serial no. 180)
  Cover title.
  "Reprinted from Industrial and engineering chemistry, vol. 44, page 1395, June, 1952."
  Bibliography: p.1398.

  1. Flame. I. Title: Flame speed at burner flame tip. II. Ser.

NL 0342935   ViU

Lichty, Lester Clyde, 1891–
  ... Gasoline-alcohol blends in internal combustion engines, by L. C. Lichty and C. W. Phelps ... ₗNew Haven, Conn., Yale university₎ 1938.

  cover-title. 24 p. incl. tables, diagrs. 23cm. (Yale university. Publications from the School of engineering. serial no.31, March 1938)
  "Reprinted from Industrial and engineering chemistry, February, 1938."
  "Literature cited": p.24.

  1. Gasoline. 2. Gas and oil engines. I. Phelps, C. W., joint author. II. Title. III. Ser.

NL 0342936   ViU

Lichty, Lester Clyde, 1891–
  Internal combustion engines, by Lester C. Lichty ... 5th ed. New York and London, McGraw-Hill book company, inc., 1939.

  vii, 603 p. illus., diagrs. (part fold.) 23½ cm.

  "This volume is more than a revision of the book by the same title which was first written by the late Robert L. Streeter in 1915 ... The undersigned ₗi. e. L. C. Lichty₎ assumed full responsibility for the third and fourth editions in 1929 and 1933 and now assumes full authorship for this edition."—Pref.

  1. Gas and oil engines.   ɪ. Streeter, Robert Leroy, 1880–1932.

| TJ755.L5 1939 | 621.43 | 39—24312 |

| | NcD NcRS TU ViU PHC PPD PU-Sc WaS OEac IU ICJ IdB |
| NL 0342937 | DLC OrCS OClW OLak OCl OU IdU CU ICRL |

Lichty, Lester Clyde, 1891–
  Internal-combustion engines. 6th ed. New York, McGraw-Hill, 1951.

  ix, 598 p. illus., diagrs. (6 fold. in pocket) 24 cm.
  Bibliographical footnotes.

  1. Gas and oil engines.

| TJ755.L5 1951 | 621.43 | 51–11691 |

| | FTaSU CaBViP CaBVa |
| NL 0342938 | DLC WaT OrCS IdU NIC ViU TxU MB NN CU |

Lichty, Lester Clyde, 1891–   joint author.

Streeter, Robert Leroy, 1880–
  Internal-combustion engines, theory, analysis and design; a treatise on internal-combustion engines for engineers and students in engineering, by the late Robert L. Streeter ... and Lester C. Lichty ... 4th ed. New York and London, McGraw-Hill book company, inc., 1933.

Lichty, Lester Clyde, 1891–   joint author.

Streeter, Robert Leroy, 1880–
  Internal-combustion engines, theory and design; a textbook on internal-combustion engines for engineers and students in engineering, by Robert L. Streeter ... and Lester Clyde Lichty ... 3d ed. New York ₗetc.₎ McGraw-Hill book company, inc., 1929.

Lichty, Lester Clyde, 1891–
  Measurement, compression and transmission of natural gas, by Lester Clyde Lichty ... New York, J. Wiley & sons, inc. ₗetc., etc.₎ 1924.

  2 p. l., iii–v, 523 p. incl. illus., tables, diagrs. maps. 23½ cm.

  1. Gas, Natural. ɪ. Title.
                 24—1821

| Library of Congress | TN880.L5 |

NL 0342941   DLC CU PPD OCl OU MiU OClL OClW ICJ NN

Lichty, Lester Clyde, 1891–   joint author.

Willard, Arthur Cutts, 1878–
  ... A study of the heat transmission of building materials, by A. C. Willard ... and L. C. Lichty ... Urbana, University of Illinois ₗ1917₎

Lichty, Lester Clyde, 1891–
  Thermodynamics; the principles of thermodynamics and their application to engineering processes, by Lester C. Lichty ... 1st ed. New York and London, McGraw-Hill book company, inc., 1936.

  xiv, 281 p. illus., diagrs. (part fold.) 23½ cm.

  1. Thermodynamics.

| Library of Congress | TJ265.L5 | 36–18082 |

  Copyright A 97103   621.101

| | PPD OCU OCl OU MiU OClU MiHM WaU TU CU NN MB |
| NL 0342943 | DLC IdU MtBC OrCS NcRS PHC PV PU-Sc PP |

Lichty, Lester Clyde, 1891–
  Thermodynamics. 2d ed. New York, McGraw-Hill Book Co., 1948.

  xiii, 341 p. diagrs. 24 cm.
  Bibliographical footnotes.

  1. Thermodynamics.

| TJ265.L5 1948 | 621.101 | 48–5383* |

| | PPPM CoU CU OrCS WaS |
| NL 0342944 | DLC CaBVa Wa MiEaIC ICJ TxU ICU ViU MiU |

Lichty, R.J.
  The guaranty clause of the statute of frauds, ₗby R.J. Lichty₎
  267–271 p.   (In Papers in jurisprudence.)
  With Folios.

NL 0342945   WaU–L

Lichty, Stanley S.,   ed.
  Western telephone journal, devoted to independent telephone interests
    see under title

Lichty's pharmacologist.
  Des Moines, Ia.

10
4143

NL 0342947   DLC

Lichy, Johannes, 1892–
  ... De servorum condicione quid senserit L. Annaeus Seneca. ... Monasterii Westfalorum, ex officina Societatis typographicae Westfalae, 1927.

  71, ₗ1₎ p., 1 l. 22½ cm.

  Inaug-diss.—Münster.
  Vita.

  1. Seneca, Lucius Annaeus.

NL 0342948   MiU IU MH

B612.077
L618   **LICHY, Lucien André.**
  ...Qu'est-ce que la vivisection?... Paris, E. Basset et cⁱᵉ, 1912.

  24 p.   20cm.

  At head of title: Lucien-André Lichy et docteur G.-R. Laurent.

  1.Vivisection. 2.Laurent, Gustave René, 1874–   jt. author.

NL 0342949   MnU

VOLUME 332

Lichy, René, 1896-
Exploración por la Región Amazónica de Venezuela por
René Lichy y Marc de Civrieux. ₍Caracas?₎ Tip. "El
Compás" ₍1948?₎
110 p. illus. 24 cm.

At head of title: Comité Ejecutivo. Tercera Conferencia Inter-
americana de Agricultura.
Includes bibliography.

1. Amazonas, Venezuela (Ter.)   I. Civrieux, Marc de, joint
author. II. Title.

F2331.A3L5   58-27795 ‡

NL 0342950   DLC NN InU DNAL DPU ViU

Licia ...
see under [Fletcher, Giles] 1549?-1611.

Licidas, *pseud.*
Licidas veld-zang, ter gelegenheid van de Zeven-en-der-
tigste verjaring van...Willem den vijfden; Prins van
Oranje ..erf-stadhouder...der Vereenigde Nederlanden
...op den 8. Maart 1785. *Rotterdam: P. van Dijk,*
1785. 14 pp. 8°.

NL 0342952   NN

Licini, Gemma
PQ4827   Come te, cipresso ₍poesie₎ ₍Firenze₎
Li27c6   Libreria editrice fiorentina ₍1952₎
76 p.

NL 0342953   CU NN RPB

Licini, Gemma
PQ4827
I235   E presto sarà notte. ₍Versi₎ ₍Roma₎
E13   Il Girasole ₍1950₎
77 p. 18 cm. (Edizioni del Girasole.
Collezione di poesia)

NL 0342954   RPB

Licini, Gemma.
In silenzio. Milano, Gastaldi ₍1953₎ 62 p. 20cm. (Poeti
d'oggi)

NL 0342955   NN

Licini, Gemma
PQ4827
I235   Nudo di noi.   Siena, Maia ₍1952₎
N7   179p. 20 cm. (Quaderni di Ausonia)

NL 0342956   RPB

Licini, Gemma
PQ4827
I235   Poesie dissepolte. Milano, Gastaldi ₍1950₎
P6   59p. 20cm. (Poeti d'oggi, ₍n.s.₎ 68)

On cover: Gemma Lucini.

NL 0342957   RPB

274.531 Licini, Niccolò Antonio.
LG18e   L'esistenza de'sacri corpi delli santi Teonis-
to, Tabra, e Tabrata, martiri, e di s. Liberale
confessore nel duomo di Torcello sostenuta da d.
Niccolò-Antonio Licini ... contro la dissertazione
del signor conte Ranbaldo degli Azzoni Avogaro.
Venezia, L. Baseggio, 1767.
176p.

NL 0342958   IU

Licinianus, Bishop of Carthagena,   *d.*581.
Epistolæ tres.
(In Patrologiæ cursus completus. Scriptores Latini. **Series
prima.** Tomus 72, col. 689-700. Parisiis. 1849.)
Contents. — Epistola ad sanctum Gregorium papam. — Epistola ad Epi-
phanium diaconum. — Epistola ad Vincentium episcopum.

K4595 — Gregory I., the Great, Pope. 540?-604. — Epiphanius, *Diaconus.*

NL 0342959   MB MdBP

Licinianus, bp. of Cartagena, *d.* 581.
Epistulæ Liciniani episcopi Carthaginensis, recensuit P. A. C.
Vega... ₍Escurial₎ Typis Augustinianis monasterii Escurialen-
sis, 1935. 31 p. 24cm. (Scriptores ecclesiastici hispano-
latini veteris et medii aevi. fasc. 3.)

1. No subject. I. Vega, Ángel   Custodio, 1894- , ed. II. Ser.
March 22, 1944

NL 0342960   NN NjP OCU

Licinianus (Gaius?) Granius
see
Licinianus, Granius.

---

871   Licinianus, Granius.
L32   Annalium quae supersunt ex codice ter
1857   scripto Musei Britannici Londinensis nunc
primum edidit Karolus Aug. Frid. Pertz.
Berolini, Typis et impensis G. Reimer, 1857.
xxiii, 49p. facsim. 26cm.

I. Pertz, Karl August Friedrich, 1828-1881,
ed.

ViU ICU
NL 0342962   IU PU PBm IEN CU OCU MdBP InU NN NjP MH

PA6452   LICINIANUS, GRANIUS.
.P4   Grani Liciniani qvae svpersvnt emendatiora
1853   edidit philologorvm bonnensivm heptas. Lipsiae,
in aedibvs B.G.Tevbneri,1858.
xxii,63,₍1₎ p. 22cm. ₍With Livius, **Titus.**
T.Livi Ab vrbe condita librorvm CXLII Periochae
...emendavit Otto Iahn. Lipsiae,1853. cop.2₎

OC1W PBm ViLxW MH IEN IU IaU NjP MH
NL 0342963   ICU PU CU CLSU CtY ViU ICU ViU InU OCU

Licinianus, Granius.
Quae supersunt; recensuit et commentario instruxit Guido
Camozzi. [Pavia], apud I. Galeati et fil, 1900.
pp. x, (1), 67.

NL 0342964   MH PU OCU NN

Licinianus, Granius.
Grani Liciniani quae supersunt; recognovit et apparatu
critico instruxit Michael Flemisch. Lipsiae, in aedibus B. G.
Teubneri, 1904.
xviii, 58 p. 17½ᵐ. (*Lettered on cover:* Bibliotheca scriptorum graecorum et romanorum Teubneriana. ₍8. r.₎)

I. Flemisch, Michael, ed.

Library of Congress   PA6104.L4 1904   4-31899

DDO PHC PU OCU OOxM NjP
NL 0342965   DLC OU NIC CSt TNJ OrPR WaS MH PBL NcD

Licinio Filopatro, pseud.
La aurora de la felicidad nacional, canto
patriótico ... Por Licinio Filopatro.
Valladolid, 1808.

NL 0342966   NNH

Licinio, Publio, pseud.
see Crasso, Niccolo, b. 1586.

Licinio Cardoso, Leontina.
... Almas. São Paulo ₍etc.₎ Comp. melhoramentos de S.
Paulo (Weiszflog irmãos incorporada) ₍1935?₎
4 p. l., ₍7₎-125 p. pl. 18ᵐ.

Contents.—Bibliographia (p. ₍7₎-8) — Teresa de Avila.— Elisabeth
Leseur.—Sophia Swetchine.—Eugénie de Guérin.—Helen Keller.—Nísia
Floresta.

1. Woman—Biog. I. Title.

Library of Congress   CT3202.L5   38-16398
920.7

NL 0342968   DLC

Licinio Cardoso, Leontina.
... Licinio Cardoso, seu pensamento, sua obra, sua vida ...
Rio ₍de Janeiro₎ Z. Valverde, 1944.
231 p. plates, ports., facsim. 22ᵐ.
"Bibliografia": p. ₍229₎-231.

1. Cardoso, Licinio Atanazio, 1852-1926.

Library of Congress   RX66.C3L5   46-12375
926.1

NL 0342969   DLC TxU

Licinio Cardoso, Leontina.
Licinio Cardoso, seu pensamento, sua obra, sua vida. Rio
de Janeiro, Gráfica Editora Souza, 1952.
200 p. illus. 24 cm.

1. Cardoso, Licinio Atanazio, 1852-1926.

RX66.C3L5 1952   54-34520 ‡

NL 0342970   DLC NN

Licinio Cardoso, Vicente
see Cardoso, Vicente Licinio, 1889-1931.

Licinio Cappelli, cavaliere del lavoro
see under Bonuzzi, Guglielmo, 1892-
comp.

Licinio imperatore
see under Noris, Matteo.

Licinius, *pseud.*
The Big 2½. London, St. Botolph Pub. Co., 1947.
99 p. 19 cm.

1. Gt. Brit.—Pol. & govt.—1945-   2. Gt. Brit.—For. rel.—1936-
3. World politics—1945- I. Title.

DA588.3.L5   327.42   47-8322*

NL 0342974   DLC

VOLUME 332

Licinius, *pseud.*
Vote labour? Why? By Licinius. London, V. Gollancz ltd, 1945.
77, [1] p. 19ᵐ.

1. Gt. Brit.—Pol. & govt.—1936— 2. Labor party (Gt. Brit.)
3. Socialism in Gt. Brit. I. Title.

Library of Congress   JN1129.L32L5
                                               45-19178
                                               329.942

NL 0342975   DLC MU CU

Licinius, Marcus
         see Menage, Gilles, 1613-1692.

Licinius Macer Calvus, C.,
                  see
Calvus, C. Licinius Macer.

FILM   Licino, Agostin, 16th cen'
M785.7   Primo [-secondo] libro di dvo cromatici di
L61p   Agostino Licino Cremonese da cantare et sonare
composti una parte sopra laltra con la sua
resolutione da parte nouamente posti in luce.
A dve voci. Venetijs, Apud A. Gardane, 1545-46.

     Microfilm copy, made in 1955, of original in
the Bayerische Staatsbibliothek, Munich.
Negative.

     Collation of original as determined from the
film: 2v. in 3.
For 2 instruments (or voices): superius and
inferius.
Without words.

     1. Canons, fugues, etc.—To 1800. 2. Chamber
music—To 1800. I.   Title: Dvo cromatici.

NL 0342979   IU

VFRT   Licino, Agostin, 16th cent.
FILE
MUSIC   Il secondo libro di duo cromatici. Venetia,
55   A.Gardane, 1546.
39 p.
Photocopy of 1546 ed.

NL 0342980   NSyU

PQ   [Licino, Giovanni Battista] 16th century, comp.
4208   Rime di diuersi celebri poeti dell' età nostra;
L4   nuouamente raccolte, e poste in luce. In Bergamo,
1587   Per Comino Ventura, e compagni, 1587.
Cage
     [40] 42 [i.e. 342] [2] p. a-b⁸, c⁴, A-X⁸, Y⁴
(Y4, probably blank, lacking) 8vo.
Includes poems by Angelo Grillo, Livio Celiano,
Torquato Tasso and others.

NL 0342981   DFo MWelC CtY ICN NIC PU CaOTU

LICINUS, Porcius.
     See **PORCIUS LICINUS.**

Licinus tonsor
      see under [Galante, Aloisius]

NL 0342984   DNLM PU

Slavic-   Liciński, Ludwik Stanisław, 1874-1908.
American   Z pamiętnika wł'óczęgi. Chicago,
Imprints   Polska Ludowa Spolka Wydawnicza [n.d.].
Coll.
425.18   109 p. 19 cm.
L535
     English translation of title: From
the diary of a tramp.

NL 0342985   IEdS

PG7158 Liciński, Ludwik Stanisław, 1874-1908.
.L69   Z pamiętnika włóczęgi. Wyd. 2. Warszawa,
Z15   Nakł. W. Raabego, 1912.
1912   138 p.

NL 0342986   ICU

Licio, Cloneso
        see Cloneso Licio.

GN   **LĪCIS, Janis**
103   **Kraniologische Untersuchungen an**
L711k   **Schädeln altlettischer Stämme.** Rīgā,
1939   **Valtera un Rapas, 1939.**
131 p.   illus.
1. Craniology - Latvia

NL 0342988   DNLM

Licito recreo casero; ó, Coleccion de cincuenta
juegos, conocidos comunmente con el nombre
de juegos de prendas ... Por un aficionado.
Madrid, 1798.

NL 0342989   NNH

PQ   Licito recreo casero; ó, Coleccion de cin-
6171   cuenta juegos, conocidos comunmente con el nom-
.A195   bre de juegos de prendas. Entretenimiento para
L711   pasar divertidas las largas noches del invierno
con diferentes sentencias, adequadas para au-
mentar la diversion. Por Un aficionado. Madrid, Impr. de Alvarez, 1816.
145 p. 15 cm.

     I. Un aficionado

NL 0342990   WU KyU

PQ   Licitra, Ángel.
4390   De la originalidad de la Divina comedia
L618d   y de la leyenda islámica del Isrá y del
Mirach; con prólogo del dr. Enrique E. Riva-
rola. La Plata, Talleres Gráficos Olivieri
y Domínguez, 1921.
118 p. port.

     Bibliographical references included in
Notas, p. [115]-118.

     1. Dante Alighieri. Divina commedia. 2.
Koran. Surat   al-Mi'rāj. I. Title.

NL 0342991   CLU

       Licitra, Carmelo.
DG571   Dal liberalismo al fascismo; con prefazione
L711   di G. Gentile. Roma, L. de Alberti [1925]

     xxi,162 p. 20²⁰.   (Studi politici, II)

     1.Fascism - Italy. 2.Italy - Pol. & govt. -
1922-1945. I.Title.

NL 0342992   CSt-H MH PU

B   LICITRA, CARMELO.
0   La storiografia idealistica dal "programma"
.503   di B. Spaventa all scuola di G.Gentile. Roma,
C.de Alberti,1925.
223p. 21cm.   (Studi filosofici. 4)

NL 0342993   ICN IU

DF77   Licitra, Ducezio.
.M758
     Mondolfo, Rodolfo, 1877-
     ... El genio helénico y los caracteres de sus creaciones espiri-
tuales. [Tucumán] Universidad nacional de Tucumán, Facultad de filosofía y letras [1943]

       Licitra, Salvatore.
     ... I sermoni di S. Antonio da Padova. ...
Rocca S. Casciano, Stabilimento Tipografico
Cappelli, 1907.
80 p. (Estratto da "La Verna").

NL 0342995   DHN

NK2561 Licitra Ponti, Lisa, ed.
.D6
     Domus; l'arte nella casa.
     Mobili e interni di architetti italiani; selezione dalla
rivista Domus, a cura di Lisa Licitra Ponti [ed] Enrichetta
Ritter. Milano, 1952.

Licĭus
     see
Lieh-tzŭ, *4th cent. B. C.*

914.37 Lick, Carl.
L61b   Beiträge zur Geschichte der Stadt Zwittau
und ihrer Umgebung. Zwittau, Im Selbstverlage: B. Lick, 1937.
243p. port. 26cm.

     1. Svitavy, Czechoslovak Republic.

NL 0342998   IU MU

DB879   Lick, Carl.
.S92   Zur Geschichte der Stadt Zwittau und ihrer
L71   Umgebung. Zwittau, Im Selbstverlage, 1910.
xv, 560 p. illus.

     1. Svitavy, Czechoslovak Republic (City)--
Hist. 2. Germans in Svitavy. I. Title.

NL 0342999   ICU

Lick, David E.
     ... Plant names and plant lore among the Pennsylvania
Germans, by David E. Lick ... and Rev. Thomas R. Brendle
... [Lancaster, Pa.] The Society [1923]

     xix, 21-300 p. illus. 25½ᵐ. (*In* Pennsylvania German society.
ceedings and addresses ... Oct. 6, 1922. [Lancaster, Pa.] 1923. v. 33,
pt. 3)

     Bibliography: p. xi-xix.

     1. Plant names, Popular—Pennsylvania. 2. Botany—Pennsylvania.
3. Plant lore. I. Brendle, Thomas R., joint author.

                                               34-21941

Library of Congress   F146.P23 vol. 33

NL 0343000   DLC MoU COU OC1 PU PPLT

VOLUME 332

Lick, David E.
Plant names and plant lore among the Pennsylvania Germans. By David E. Lick ... and Rev. Thomas R. Brendle ... ₍Lancaster, Lancaster press, inc.₎ 1927.
xix, 21-300 p. illus. 25ᶜᵐ.
Issued by the Pennsylvania-German society.
Bibliography: p. xi-xix.

1. Plant lore. 2. Plant names ₍Popular₎, 3. Botany—Pennsylvania. ₍3. Pennsylvania—Botany₎, I. Brendle, Thomas R., joint author. II. Pennsylvania-German society.

Library, U. S. Dept. of   Agriculture 452.14L61

NL 0343001   DNAL PU-B MBH

●HD
266
C2L6
... Catalogue of real estate situated in San Francisco, Santa Clara county, Los Angeles county, and Virginia City, Nev., and the Island de Santa Catalina, to be sold Tuesday, November 17, 1874... per order of trustees James Lick trust. Maurice Dore & co., auctioneers. San Francisco, J. Winterburn & co., printers, 1874.
1 p. 1., 50, [2] p. incl. plans. 28½ᶜᵐ.

At head of title: Maurice Dore [and] H. A. Cobb. Annotated with selling prices.

1. Real property - Calif.

NL 0343002   CLU

Lick, James, 1796-1876.
The currency question
see under Haight, Henry Huntley, 1825-1878.

Lick, James, 1796-1876, plaintiff.

California. *Supreme court.*
Decisions of the Supreme court of California on the currency. Sacramento, J. Anthony & co., printers, 1864.

Lick, James, 1796-1876.
The deed of James Lick. A certified copy of the original. Executed June 2d, 1874, and recorded June 3d, 1874. Printed for the Society of California pioneers. San Francisco, B. F. Sterett, steam book and job printer, 1874.
cover-title, 19 p. 23 cm.

1. Deeds – California. 2. Lick observatory. I. Key, Francis Scott, 1779-1843. II. Society of California pioneers, San Francisco. II. Title.   F863.L5

NL 0343005   Vi DN-Ob CSmH

Lick, James, 1796-1876.
Deed of trust. James Lick to Thomas H. Selby, D.O. Mills, H.M. Newhall, Wm. Alvord, George H. Howard, James Otis and John O. Earl [Trustees] Dated July 16th, A.D. 1874. Recorded at request of James Lick, August 17th, A.D., 1874, at 10 minutes past 2 P.M., in Liber 752, of Deeds, Page I. [Docketed title] ₍San Francisco? 1874₎
10 leaves. Obl. 8vo. Printed in vellum. Lettered on cover: The Lick Deed.

Text begins: This Indenture, made the sixteenth day of July, one thousand eight hundred and seventy-four, by and between, James Lick, party of the first part, Thomas H. Selby, D.O. Mills ... parties of the second part, and the "California Academy of Sciences," and the "Society of California Pioneers," ... parties of the third part ...

NL 0343007   CSmH

★
cF
869
83
L7
Lick, James, 1796-1876.
Deed of trust of James Lick, Esq., of San Francisco, California, dated September 21, 1875, and recorded in the office of the recorder of the County of San Francisco, State of California, in liber 810, of deeds, pp.26, et seq. Nov. 10, 1875. ₍San Francisco, 1887₎
24 p. 24cm.

1. Lick, James, 1796-1876.

NL 0343008   C CLU CSmH PPL MH

RA792.09421
H646L
A lick at 'em all; or, The moderator. A candid consideration of the present controversy between the inspector and his opposers ... London: Printed for W. Reeve, 1753.
₍4₎16p.20cm.

The inspector was Dr. John Hill, who wrote theatrical criticism under that name.

1. Hill, John, 1716?-1775. 2. Actors, English.

NL 0343009   OC MB ICN

x821
L6181
A lick at the country c——y. A satire on the tythe-pig. London, Printed for T. Fox, 1752.
14p. fold.plate. 26cm.

A satire in verse on the clergy.

NL 0343010   IU NIC MB CtY OCU

Lick brook [by H.N.R.]
In, ₍Spencer, Spence₎ The scenery of Ithaca, N.Y., 1866.
150 p. p. 149-150. 17 cm.

NL 0343011   RPB

ffF869
S3
.7
M34
no.17
x
Lick House, San Francisco.
Bill of fare. Tuesday. July 4th, 1865. [San Francisco, F. Eastman, Printer, 1865]
menu 31x20cm. [Menus of early San Francisco hotels and restaurants, no. 17]
In portfolio.
Colored illustrations and ornamental borders.

1. Menus. 2. Fourth of July celebrations. (Series)

NL 0343012   CU-B

Lick House state banquet given by Messrs. Clemens and Pierson
see under ₍Clemens, Samuel Langhorne₎ 1835-1910, supposed author.

Lick observatory.

Moore, Joseph Haines, 1878-
Astronomical photographs taken at the Lick observatory, by J. H. Moore, N. U. Mayall and J. F. Chappell. ₍Mount Hamilton? Calif., 1941₎

522.1
L71Y
Lick Observatory.
A brief account of the Lick Observatory of the University of California. 3d ed. Sacramento, State Print. Off., 1902.
29p. illus. 21cm. (University of California publications)

1. Astronomy. Observations.

NL 0343015   IEN

LICK OBSERVATORY.
A brief account of the Lick Observatory of the University of California, prepared by the director of the observatory. Fourth edition. Berkeley: Univ. of California, 1914.
42 p. front. (port.), illus. 23cm.

"W. W. Campbell, director and astronomer."

1. Astronomy—Observatories—U.S.—Cal.—Berkeley. I. Campbell, William Wallace, 1862-

June 11, 1924

NL 0343016   NN DN-Ob OClWHi

CP. COLL.
Lick Observatory, Mount Hamilton, Calif.
A brief account of the Lick Observatory, of the University of California. Prepared by the Director of the Observatory. 5th ed. Berkeley University of California Press, 1920.
41 p. illus. 23 cm.

W. W. Campbell, director.

I. Campbell, William Wallace, 1862-1938.

NL 0343017   CU-S PPeSchw

QB82
.L53
1924
Lick Observatory.
A brief account of the Lick Observatory of the University of California. Prepared by the Director of the Observatory ₍William Wallace Campbell₎ 6th ed. Berkeley, University of California Press, 1924.
45 p. illus. 23cm.

1. Lick Observatory. I. Campbell William Wallace, 1862-1938.

NL 0343018   ViU OrPR

Lick observatory.
A brief account of the Lick Observatory prepared by the director of the observatory Berkeley, University of California, press, 1931.
By Robert Grant Aitken.

NL 0343019   OLak

Lick observatory.
Bulletins
see its Lick observatory bulletins.

Lick observatory.
Contributions from the Lick observatory ... Printed by authority of the Regents of the University of California. Sacramento, J. D. Young, supt. state printing, 1889-95.
5 v. fronts., illus., plates, diagrs. 23½ᵐ.
Nos. 2-5: A. J. Johnston, supt. state printing.
CONTENTS.
₍no. 1₎ Reports on the observations of the total eclipse of the sun of January 1, 1889. Published by the Lick observatory. 1889. QB543.89L

Continued in next column

VOLUME 332

Continued from preceding column

_[no. 2] Reports on the observations of the total eclipse of the sun, December 21–22, 1889, and of the total eclipse of the moon, July 22, 1888, to which is added a Catalogue of the library. Published by the Lick observatory. 1891. QB543.895L.
  no. 3. Terrestrial atmospheric absorption of the photographic rays of light. By J. M. Schaeberle. 1893. QB121.S27
  no. 4. Report on the total eclipse of the sun, observed at Mina Bronces, Chile, on April 16, 1893. By J. M. Schaeberle. 1895. QB543.93S
  no. 5. Meteors and sunsets observed by the astronomers of the Lick observatory in 1893, 1894, and 1895. 1895. QB746.L69

1. Astronomy—Collected works.   I. Title.

Library of Congress   [35b1]   6—1414

       CLSU CU NN MnU
       MBdAF TU CtY ICJ WaU MtBC IEN CaBVaU TxU C OU IU
NL   0343022   DLC ICU TNJ OC1W MiU ODW NjP OO CU PBL

Lick Observatory.   L524.794
                                C129
    ... Contributions from the Lick Observatory, Mount Hamilton, California. Series II ... [Mt. Hamilton, 1942–]

Library has no. 1 to date.   illus., plates, tables, diagrs. 26^{cm}.

At head of title: The University of California.
Papers relating to the physical division of astronomy, reprinted from the Astrophysical journal.

NL   0343023   ICJ MtBC

Lick observatory.
Description of the astronomical instruments.
    (In Lick observatory. Publications. Sacramento, 1887. 30 x 23½^{cm}. v. 1, p. [59]–77. pl., illus.)

1. Astronomical instruments.

                                     A 14-474

Title from Univ. of Calif.   Library of Congress

NL   0343024   CU OrU OU OO MiU

Lick observatory.
Description of the meteorological instruments.
    (In Lick observatory. Publications. Sacramento, 1887. 30 x 23½^{cm}. v. 1, p. [78]–83. pl.)

1. Meteorological instruments.

                                     A 14-476

Title from Univ. of Calif.   Library of Congress

NL   0343025   CU OU OO MiU

Lick observatory.
Descriptions of the buildings and of the water supply.
    (In Lick observatory. Publications. Sacramento, 1887. 30 x 23½^{cm}. v. 1, p. [34]–41 incl. plan)

                                     A 14-475

Title from Univ. of Calif.   Library of Congress

NL   0343026   CU OrU OU OO MiU

Lick observatory.
    Determination of the solar parallax ...
      see under   Perrine, Charles Dillon, 1867–

Lick observatory.
    Ewing seismograph record. 1906.

NL   0343028   DI-GS

Lick observatory.
    The Lick astronomical department of the University of California
      see under   Shinn, Milicent Washburn, 1858–

Lick observatory.
    ... Lick observatory bulletins. v. 1–
no. 1–
1901/02–
Berkeley, The University press [1902–
    v.   plates, diagrs. 30½ x 24^{cm}.

At head of title: University of California publications. Astronomy.

1. Astronomy—Observations.   I. California. University. Publications. Astronomy.   II. Title.

Library of Congress   QB4.L7   10—33435

      OC1W OO MtBC PBL TNJ Nh MB NN MCSA
NL   0343030   DLC CaBVaU OrCS ICJ LU PSt KU ODW OU

QB
82
.L69   **Lick Observatory.**
A35   Lick Observatory of the University of
1935   California, a brief descriptive account prepared at the Observatory. 9th ed. Berkeley, University of California Press, 1935.
      48 p.   illus.

NL   0343031   MiU

Lick observatory.
    ... Meteors and sunsets observed by the astronomers of the Lick observatory in 1893, 1894, and 1895. Printed by authority of the Regents of the University of California. Sacramento, A. J. Johnston, superintendent state printing, 1895.

    3 p. l., 86 p. XVII pl. (incl. front.) diagrs. 23½^{cm}. (Contributions from the Lick observatory, no. 5)

"Works issued by the Lick observatory": p. [85]–86.

CONTENTS.—The meteor of July 27, 1894, by E. S. Holden.—Simultaneous meteor observations made at Mount Hamilton and Mount Diablo on Aug. 9–10, 1894, by J. M. Schaeberle.—Observations of the August, 1894, meteors at the Lick observatory, by A. L. Colton.—Observations of the August, 1894, meteors at the Lick observatory, by C. D. Perrine.—Sunsets at Mount Hamilton.—Some curious effects of refraction, by A. L. Colton.—Meteor trails photographed in August, 1895, by A. L. Colton and C. D. Perrine.

1. Meteors—August.   2. Sunset phenomena.   I. Holden, Edward Singleton, 1846–1914.   II. Schaeberle, John Martin, 1853–1924.   III. Colton, Allen Lysander, 1857–   IV. Perrine, Charles Dillon, 1867–   V. Title.

Library of Congress   QB746.L69   6—1413
— Copy 2.   QB4.L74
               [3811]

      MH
NL   0343033   DLC CaBViP ICJ GU CU OO OU Nh WaU PSC

QB82
.L799   **Lick observatory**
      Miscellaneous printed matter.

NL   0343034   DLC

QB595
f.L7   **LICK OBSERVATORY.**
      [Moon sets. 1 set of 18 plates, 9 of first and 9 of last quarter moon. Cambridge, Mass., Sky Pub. Corp., 1947]
      [1] l., 18 plates, diagrs. 48cm.

1. Moon—Photographs, maps.

NL   0343035   ICU

QB
595
.L71   **Lick observatory.**
      ... Observatory atlas of the moon. Lick observatory. Published by the gift of W.W.Law ... [Sacramento? 1897?]
      19 plates in portfolio.   51 x 41 cm.
      No t.-p. Title from plates.

NL   0343036   MiU IU ICU MB

QB595   **Lick Observatory.**
.W4
      Weinek, Ladislaus, 1848–1913.
      Photographischer Mond-Atlas, vornehmlich auf Grund von focalen Negativen der Lick-Sternwarte im Massstabe eines Monddurchmessers von 10 Fuss ausgeführt.   Prag, C. Bellmann, 1897–1900.

QB
595   **Lick observatory.**
.L72   [Photographs of the moon reproduced from Lick observatory negatives] [Cambridge, Mass., Sky publishing corporation, 1949]
      1 p. l., 18 pl.   48cm.
      In portfolio.

1. Moon—Photographs, maps, etc.

NL   0343038   MiU

Lick observatory.
    Plate 1, observatory atlas of the moon. Lick Observatory. Published by the gift of W.W.Law. Original negative taken 1896, Oct.10, 16 49^m 10–17^s. Scale 3. Paris feet 38. 36 inches. to the moon's diameter. Mount Hamilton, Cal. [1896]
    By Edward S. Holden

NL   0343039   NN

Lick observatory.
    Plate 2; observatory atlas of the moon. Lick Observatory. Published by the gift of W.W.Law. Original negative taken 1895, Oct.9, 16th 55m 30s–40s. Scale 3. Paris feet 38. 36 inches, to the moon's diameter. Mount Hamilton, Cal., 1896.
    By Edward S. Holden.

NL   0343040   NN

Lick observatory.
    Plate 3; observatory atlas of the moon. Lick Observatory. Published by the gift of W.W.Law. Original negative taken 1895, Oct.2, 16th 9^m 10^s –20^s. Scale 3 Paris feet 38.36 inches, to the moon's diameter. Mount Hamilton, Cal., 1896.
    By Edward S. Holden.

NL   0343041   NN

Lick observatory.
    Plate 4; observatory atlas of the moon. Lick Observatory, published by the gift of W.W.Law... Original negative taken 1895 Oct.9, 16th 53m 2s–12s. Scale 3. Paris feet (38.36 inches) to the moon's diameter. Mount Hamilton, Cal., 1896.
    By Edward S. Holden.

NL   0343042   NN

Lick observatory.
    Plate 5; observatory atlas of the moon. Lick Observatory. Published by the gift of W.W.Law... Original negative taken 1896, Oct.18, 10, 32^m 41s–47s. Scale 3. Paris feet (38.36 inches) to the moon's diameter. Mount Hamilton, Cal., 1896.
    By Edward S. Holden.

NL   0343043   NN

VOLUME 332

Lick Observatory.
Publications. v. 1–
Berkeley ₍etc.₎ University of California Press ₍etc.₎ 1887–19
'⁷. Illus. 31 cm.
At head of title, v. 6–   : University of California publications.

1. Astronomy—Observations.

QB4.L71   7–21759 rev 3*

COMC
TxU PU PPAmP OU PHC PP OCU ODW CaBVaU UU CtY MBdAF
NL 0343044   DLC IdU Nh MH OrCS OO OC1W NjP ICJ

Lick observatory.
Refraction at Mount Hamilton. 1917

37637

NL 0343045   DAS

Lick observatory.
Reports on the observations of the total eclipse of the sun of January 1, 1889. Published by the Lick observatory. Printed by authority of the Regents of the University of California. Sacramento, J. D. Young, supt. state printing, 1889.
x p., 1 l., 210 p. front., 3 pl., diagrs. 23½ᶜᵐ. ₍Contributions from the Lick observatory, no. 1₎

1. Eclipses, Solar—1889.

Library of Congress   QB543.89L.   6–3041

NL 0343046   DLC CU OU PPF PU PSC MH ICJ Nh

Lick observatory.
Reports on the observations of the total eclipse of the sun, December 21–22, 1889, and of the total eclipse of the moon, July 22, 1888, to which is added a Catalogue of the library, published by the Lick observatory. Printed by authority of the Regents of the University of California. Sacramento, A. J. Johnston, supt. state printing, 1891.
2 p. l., 121, 121*, ₍1₎ p. front., illus. 10 pl. 23½ᶜᵐ. ₍Contributions from the Lick observatory, no. 2₎

1. Eclipses, Solar—1889. 2. Eclipses, Lunar—1888.

Library of Congress   QB543.89.L52   6–3042
                           QB4.L74

MB ICJ MH
NL 0343047   DLC CaBViP GU TxU CU ViU NN PPF PU PSC

Lick observatory.
Studies of the nebulae made at the Lick observatory, University of California, at Mount Hamilton, California, and Santiago, Chile. ₍Berkeley, University of California press, 1918₎
6 p. l., 11–268 p. ₁ pl., tables (part fold.) diagrs. 31 cm (*Half-title:* Semicentennial publications of the University of California, 1868–1918)

Issued originally as University of California publications. Publications of the Lick observatory. 1918. vol. XIII.

CONTENTS.—pt. I. Descriptions of 762 nebulae and clusters photographed with the Crossley reflector, by H. D. Curtis.—pt. II. A study of occulting matter in the spiral nebulae, by H. D. Curtis.—pt. III. The planetary nebulae, by H. D. Curtis.—pt. IV. The spectrographic velocities of the brightline nebulae, by W. W. Campbell and J. H. Moore.—pt. V. The radial velocity of the Greater Magellanic cloud, by R. E. Wilson.—pt. VI. The wavelengths of the nebular lines and general observations of the spectra of the gaseous nebulae, by W. H. Wright.

1. Nebulae. I. Curtis, Heber Doust, 1872– II. Campbell, William Wallace, 1862– III. Moore, Joseph Haines, 1878– joint author. IV. Wilson, Ralph Elmer. V. Wright, William Hammond, 1871–

                           A 20–1283

California. Univ. Libr.
for Library of Congress

NL 0343049   CU OrPR OrU CU UU WU ViU PBm MiU OOxM OU

Lick observatory. *Library.*
Catalogue of the library of the Lick observatory of the University of California. Part 1– to July 1, 1890. Prepared by Edward S. Holden. Printed by authority of the Regents of the University of California. Sacramento, State office, A. J. Johnston, supt. state printing, 1891.
121*, ₍1₎ p. 23½ᶜᵐ. (*In* Lick observatory. Reports on the observations of the total eclipse of the sun, December 21–22, 1889 ... Sacramento. 1891)

1. Astronomy—Bibl.—Catalogs.   I. Holden, Edward Singleton, 1846–1914.
                                   6–3043 Revised
Library of Congress   QB543.89L52
—— —— Copy 2.   QB4.L74 no.2
—— —— Copy 3, de-   tached.
                               Z5156.L71
                               ₍r33b2₎   016.52

NL 0343050   DLC CaBViP NN ICN MB MdBP

Lick trustees.
Ceremonies and literary exercises at the unveiling of the Lick bronze statuary by the Lick trustees, assisted by the Society of California pioneers. 1894. ₍San Francisco, The Society of California pioneers₎ 1894.
1 p. l., 48 p. front. 23ᶜᵐ.

1. Lick, James, 1796–1876.   I. Society of California pioneers, San Francisco, joint author.

                                   A 10–1556

Title from Leland Stan-   ford Jr. Univ. Printed by L. C.

NL 0343051   CSt Nh

Lick trustees.
Lick observatory and Lick avenue...2. ed.
₋San Fran. 1884.₎
CL 8451.646.5

NL 0343052   NjP

Lick upon lick; occasion'd by Another occasional letter from Mr. Cibber to Mr. Pope. To which is added, ⟨The third edition.⟩ A blast upon Bays; or, A new lick at the laureat: containing remarks upon that tattling performance, Mr. Cibber's first letter to Mr. Pope, &c. ... London, T. Robbins, 1744.
8, 26 p. 20ᶜᵐ.

1. Cibber, Colley, 1671–1757. 2. Pope, Alexander, 1688–1744.   I. Title: A blast upon Bays.

                                   26–11373

Library of Congress   PR3347.L5

NL 0343053   DLC

---

821   Lickbarrow, Isabella.
L618p   Poetical effusions.   Kendal, Printed for the
         authoress by M. Branthwaite; sold by J. Richardson, London, 1814.
         xii, 131p. 21cm.

NL 0343054   IU NIC MH CtY InU

Lickenstein, Maurus, O.S.B., d. 1709.
   De jure et justitia, contractibus, restitutione in genere et in specie. Praelectiones. ₍1691₎

   535 numbered pages, 20 cm.
   Manuscript.

NL 0343055   PLatS

PT2495 LICKEFETT Y ENGLISH, ENRIQUE
.A2L7   El teatro de Schiller, ensayo crítico. Madrid Imprenta y litografía del depósito de la guerra, 1903. 147p.

NL 0343056   InU

Lickey, Arthur E
Christ forever. Washington, Review and Herald Pub. Association ₍1951₎
122 p. illus. 16 cm. (Little giant pocket series)

1. Jesus Christ—Devotional literature.   I. Title.

BT295.L65   232   51–2120

NL 0343057   DLC

Lickey, Arthur E
Fundamentals of the everlasting gospel. May be used for instructing those desiring baptism and membership in the Seventh-Day Adventist Church. Takoma Park, Washington, D. C., Review and Herald Pub. Assn., *1947.
64 p. illus. (part col.) ports. 24 cm.

1. Seventh-Day Adventists—Doctrinal and controversial works.

BX6154.L5   230.67   48–4977*

OrU IdPI FTaSU
NL 0343058   DLC WaSp WaWW MB ICU ViU PBL KyWAT FMU

Lickey, Arthur E
   God speaks to modern man.   Wash., Review and herald pub.assn.
₋ᶜ1952₎   635p.illus.

   Also pub.under title: Highways to truth.

NL 0343059   WaT CaBVa

Lickey, Arthur E
   Highways to truth; God speaks to modern man. Washington, Review and Herald Pub. Association ₍1952₎
544 p. illus. 22 cm.

1. Seventh-Day Adventists—Doctrinal and controversial works. I. Title.

BX6154.L52   230.67   52–33808 ‡

NL 0343060   DLC CSaT PP TU

Lickey, Arthur E
   Where is God? Washington, Review and Herald Pub. Association ₍1951₎
128 p. illus. 16 cm. (Little giant pocket series)

1. God.   I. Title.

BT101.L49   231   51–20625

NL 0343061   DLC

Lickfold, J   Malcolm
   The Catholic apostolic church, Gordon Square, London; notes on the architectural features and the furniture, with a glossary of technical terms; by J. Malcolm Lickfold, with fourteen photographic plates by W. Wedlake. London, Skinner ₍1935₎
   48 p., 1 l. incl. 14 plates. 28ᶜᵐ.

   The church was designed by Raphael Brandon.

   1.London. Catholic apostolic church, Gordon Square.

NL 0343062   NNC

Licki, Jerzy, ed.
HD7197
.7
.A53   **Poland.** *Ministerstwo Pracy i Opieki Społecznej* (1945–   )
        Osiągnięcia socjalne Polski Ludowej. ₍Wyd. 1.₎ Warszawa, 1951–

VOLUME 332

Law

Licki, Jerzy, ed.

Poland. *Laws, statutes, etc.*
Przepisy prawa pracy. Wyd. 2. uzup. według stanu
prawnego na dzień 1. lip. 1952 r. ₍Opracowali: Eugenia
Pragierowa, Jerzy Licki, Stefan Szymorowski₎ Warszawa,
Wydawnictwo Prawnicze, 1952-

Licki, Jerzy.
Social achievements

see under

Pragierowa, Eugenia.

HD8538
.P7

Pragierowa, Eugenia.
Ten years of People's Poland; social achievements, by
Eugenia Pragierowa and Jerzy Licki. Warsaw, "Polonia"
Foreign Languages Pub. House, 1955.

Licki, Jerzy, joint author.

BX
7675
.B7
L6

Licking, William G., 1857-1912.
Reminiscences of the Redemptorist Father
Rev. John Beil, Rev. Patrick M'Givern, Rev.
John O'Brien, Rev. Leopold Petsch.
Ilchester, Md., Printed at the Redemptorist
college, 1891.
xi, 266 p. ports 19cm.

1. Redemptorists—Biog.

NL 0343067   DCU OrStbM

Licking Association of Particular Baptists
see Baptists. Kentucky. Licking
Association of Particular Baptists.

Licking association of Primitive Baptists
see Primitive Baptists. Kentucky. Licking
association of Primitive Baptists.

Licking County, O. County auditor.
First quadrennial appraisement of
real property, 1910 ... ₍Newark? 1910₎
37 v.

Township lists have title: Real estate
appraisement.
Separate pamphlets for the different
township and corporations.

NL 0343070   OC1WHi

Licking County, O. Society of the
soldiers and sailors

see

Society of the soldiers and sailors of Licking
County, Ohio

Licking County (O.) agricultural society.
Premium list and regulations for the ... annual fair.

Newark, O., 18
v. illus. 21½-22½ᵐ.

CA 16-169 Unrev'd

Library of Congress   S555.L71

NL 0343072   DLC DNAL OC1WHi

Licking County (O.) agricultural society.
Proceedings of the ... annual fair.
Newark ₍O.₎
v. 23ᵐ.

CA 13-793 Unrev'd

Library of Congress   S555.L715

NL 0343073   DLC

Licking County children's home, Newark, Ohio.
By-laws and regulations...adopted
December 20, 1880. Newark, O. Advocate steam
book print. 1881.
8 p.

NL 0343074   OC1WHi

Licking County children's home, Newark, Ohio.
Fifth annual report of the trustees and
superintendent ... to the commissioners of
Licking county for the year ending August
31st. 1885.
37 p.

NL 0343075   OC1WHi

Licking County medical society, Newark, O.
Constitution and by-laws of the Licking
Co. medical society, with fee bill, list
of members and code of ethics. Established
1874. Newark, O., W. D. Morgan, printer,
1878.
23, ₍1₎ p.

NL 0343076   OC1WHi

Licking county pioneer association.

see

Licking County pioneer society.

Licking county pioneer, historical and antiquarian society

see

Licking county pioneer society.

Licking county pioneer society.
An account of the celebration of American independence, at
Clay Lick, by the Licking county pioneers. Together with an
address, by Dr. Coulter, on early times in the Clay Lick settlements. Also, Historical sketches of the townships of Licking, Bowling Green, Franklin and Hopewell, &c. by Isaac
Smucker. Newark, O., Clark & King, printers, 1869.
35 p. 22ᵐ. (On cover: Pioneer pamphlets. no. 3 ... Licking co.
pioneer society)

1. Claylick, O. 2. Fourth of July celebrations.   I. Smucker, Isaac,
1807-1894.

Rc-2199

Library of Congress   F497.L6L6

NL 0343079   DLC MnHi ICN PHi OC1 OC1WHi

Licking County pioneer society, *Newark, O.*
Pioneer pamphlets. ₍no. 1-9₎ Newark, O., 1869-74.
v. in   22-22½ᵐ.
No. 5 printed at Terre-Haute, Ind.
No. 5-6 paged continuously. At head of title of no. 5: Pioneer paper
no. 5.
10 no. were published. No. 10 was written by Isaac Smucker. *cf.*
N. N. Hill, jr., Hist. of Licking County, 1881, p. 236.
CONTENTS.—no. 1₎ Hervey, Rev. H. M.₎ Historical sketches of the
Presbyterian churches. (O. S.) in Licking County, Ohio. ₍1869₎—no. 2₎
Smucker, Isaac. History of the Welsh settlements in Licking County,
Ohio. ₍1869₎—no. 3. Licking County pioneer society. An account of the
celebration of American independence, at Clay Lick, by the Licking
County pioneers ... Also, historical sketches of the townships of Licking,
Bowling Green, Franklin and Hopewell, &c., by Isaac Smucker. 1869.—
no. 4. Winter, Jacob. Historical sketches of the Disciple churches in Licking County, Ohio. 1869.—no. 5-6₎ Park, Samuel. Notes of the early history of Union Township, Licking County, Ohio. American antiquities, by
Samuel Park. 1870.—no. 7. Smucker, Isaac. Our pioneers: being biographical sketches ... 1872.—no. 8. Scott, J. M. Our early times. Historical sketch of St. Albans Township. 1873.—no. 9₎ Licking County, O.
Soldiers' monumental association. Licking County's gallant soldiers ...
1874.

1. Licking Co., O.—Hist.—Societies.

CA 6-2645 Unrev'd

Library of Congress   F497.L6L6

NL 0343081   DLC OC1 OC1WHi OO NN

Licking County soldiers' monumental association, Newark, O.
Licking County's gallant soldiers, who died in defence
of our glorious union, and of human freedom. Pub. by
the Licking County soldier's monumental association.
Newark ₍O.₎ Printed by Clark & Underwood, 1874.
29 p. 22½ᵐ. ₍Licking County pioneer society. Pioneer pamphlets, no. 9₎
Prepared by Isaac Smucker.

1. Licking Co., O. — Hist.—Civil war. 2. Licking Co., O.—Biog.
I. Smucker, Isaac, 1807-1894.

1-21774 Revised

Library of Congress   F497.L6L6

OC1 OC1WHi NN

NL 0343082   DLC MWA NBuHi DNW NjP NcD IU PPL PHi

Licking County ₍O.₎ teachers' institute.
Minutes of the Licking County teachers'
institute, held in Utica, October, 1850;
with a catalogue of officers and members ...
Columbus, Printed by Scott & Bascom, 1850.
36 p.

At head of title on cover: Periodical,
No. IV.

NL 0343083   OC1WHi

335.8
L61

Licking valley.

West Liberty, Ky., Rural Electric Cooperative Corporation.

1. Electric cooperative associations.
Rural. Periodicals. 2. Electricity in
agriculture. Periodicals. I. Rural Electric
Cooperative Corporation (Kentucky)

NL 0343084   DNAL

Licking-Locust Baptist Association
see Baptists. Kentucky. Licking-Locust
Association.

W 1
BE351
Bd. 2
1953

LICKINT, Fritz
Ätiologie und Prophylaxe des Lungen-
krebses als ein Problem der Gewerbe-
hygiene und des Tabakrauches. Dresden,
Steinkopff, 1953.
xv, 212 p. illus. (Beiträge zur
Krebsforschung, Bd. 2)
1. Lungs - Neoplasms 2. Tobacco -
Effects   Series

NL 0343086   DNLM MiU

VOLUME 332

QV
84
L711a
1954
LICKINT, Fritz
    Alkohol und Gesundheit.   Hannover,
Wilkens ₁1954₎
    78 p.
    1. Alcohol - Effects

NL 0343087   DNLM

Lickint, Fritz.
    ... Die krebsfrage im lichte der modernen forschung.   Ber-
lin, F. A. Herbig ₁1935₎
    72 p. illus., 6 pl. (incl. front.) on 3 l. 21ᶜᵐ.

    1. Cancer.

    Library of Congress   45-32891

                            RC261.L693
                                            616.994

NL 0343088   DLC DNLM

Lickint, Frits: Die Leukozytenreaktion nach der modernen Reiz-
therapie und den physikalischen Behandlungsmethoden. [Maschi-
nenschrift.] 79 S. 4° [Lag nicht vor.] — Auszug: o. O. (1923).
4 S. 8°
Leipzig, Med. Diss. v. 17. Mai 1923   [U 23. 8014

NL 0343089   ICRL

RC565
.L53
Lickint, Fritz
    Medikamentöse Therapie des Alkoholismus;
arzneiliche Behandlung der Trunksucht. Leipzig, VEB G. Thieme, 1953.
    x, 118 p.   21 cm.

    Bibliography: p.101-115.

    1. Alcoholism.   2. Alcoholism - Treat-
ment.   I. Title.

NL 0343090   NjR DNLM ICJ

WB
300
L711o
1953
LICKINT, Fritz
    Organismotherapie (Mikrobotherapie,
Zootherapie, Anthropotherapie) Behandlung
mit Lebewesen. Jena, Fischer, 1953.
    iv, 96 p., ports.
    1. Therapeutics 2. Therapeutics -
Hist.

NL 0343091   DNLM ICJ

Lickint, Fritz
    Tabakgenuss und organismus, handbuch der gesamten
tabakkunde ... Stuttgart, Marquardt, 1939.
    1232 p. illus.

    "Schrifttumsverzeichnis": p. 1091-1210.

    1. Tobacco - Physiological effect.
2. Tobacco habit

NL 0343092   NNC-M KyU MH PPC

HV
5733
.L71
1940
Lickint, Fritz.
    Tabakgenuss und gesundheit, von dr. med. Fritz
Lickint ... 6. bis 10. ergänzte aufl. Hannover,
B. Wilken ₁ᶜ1940₎
    92 p. 21ᶜᵐ
    "Das aufklärende schrifttum über den tabak":
p. 92.

    1. Tobacco—Physiological effect. 2. Tobacco
habit. I. Title.

NL 0343093   MiU

W 1
DU732
Heft
11
1954
LICKINT, Fritz
    Wem schaden Alkohol, Tabak und
Kaffee? Berlin, Verlag Volk und
Gesundheit ₁1954₎
    24 p. illus. (Durch Volksgesundheit
zur Leistungssteigerung, Heft 11)
    Cover title.
    1. Alcohol - Effects
    2. Coffee 3. Tobacco - Effects   Series

NL 0343094   DNLM

QV
137
L711z
1953
LICKINT, Fritz
    Die Zigarette; dein Schicksal. Die
Zigarette - des Menschen Feind. 1./2.
Aufl. Wiesbaden, Walther ₁1953₎
    30 p. (Vermögen, Bilanz und Steuer.
Kaufmannsgut - Ebbe und Flut, 28)
    1. Tobacco - Effects

NL 0343095   DNLM

Lickl, Aegidius Ferdinand Karl
    see Lickl, Ferdinand Carl, 1803-1864.

Lickl, Carl Georg, 1801-1877, arr.
    Elégie ... transcrite pour la physharmonica
seule ...
        see under Ernst, Heinrich Wilhelm,
1814-1865.

Lickl, Carl Georg, 1801-1877, arr.
    6 [i. e. Sechs] Lieder ohne Worte von
F. Mendelssohn-Bartholdy für Physharmonica und
Piano oder zwei Pianoforte eingerichtet von
C.G. Lickl
        see under Mendelssohn-Bartholdy, Felix,
1809-1847.

Lickl, Carl Georg, 1801-1877,
    Wiener Salon-Musik. Periodisches Werk für
Physharmonica & Pianoforte [oder 2 Pianoforte.
Op. 51. Nos. 11, 13, 18, 20, 22. Wien,
Ant. Diabelli & Comp. [18-   ]
    5 pms.   f°.
    Op. 51. No. 11. Grosses Septett van L. von
Beethoven. Op. 20. Op. 51. No. 13 Zwei
Potpourri nach Motiven der Oper "Der Prophet"
von G. Meyerbeer. Op. 51. No. 18. Des Geistes
Gesang von Haydn. Op. 51. No. 20. Trio von
W.A. Mozart. Op. 51. No. 22. Allegro und

Romanze aus der Sonate von A. Onslow. Op. 7.

NL 0343100   NN

Lickl, Carl Georg, 1807-1877.
    Zwei Potpourris nach Motiven der Oper "Der
Prophet" von G. Meyerbeer. Für Physharmonika
und Pianoforte (oder 2 Pianoforte) von G. Lickl.
Wien, A. Diabelli & Comp. [18-   ]
    2 pms.   f°. (Wiener Salon-Musik No. 13)

NL 0343101   NN

ML50
L526D5
Music
Library
Lickl, Ferdinand Carl, 1803-1864.
    [La disfida di Barletta. Libretto]
    La disfida di Barletta, melodramma da rappresentarsi nel
Teatro grande di Trieste il carnovale del 1848.   Trieste, Tip.
Weis [1848?]
    37 p.

    The libretto is by A. Gazoletti. Cf. U. Manferrari. Diz.
universale delle opere melodrammatiche.

    I. Gazoletti, A. II. Title.

NL 0343102   CU

Lickl, Ferdinand Carl, 1803-1864.
    Das Grab. Symphonisches Tongemälde, für grosses Orchester.
Partitur.
    N. p. [187-?] (3), 155 pp. L. 8°, obl.

            March 20,   1902

E3196 — T.r. — Symphonic poems.

NL 0343103   MB

Lickl, Ferdinando Carlo Egidio
    see Lickl, Ferdinand Carl, 1803-1864.

ML
50
L5
D8
Lickl, Johann Georg, 1769-1843
    [Der Durchmarsch. Libretto. German]
    Der Durchmarsch; ein ländlich-militärisches
Singspiel in drey Aufzugen, von J. G. Schild-
bach. Die Musik von J. G. Likkel. Wien,
1801.
    107p. 16cm.

    1. Operas - Librettos I. Schildbach, Johann
Gottlieb, fl. 1801. Der Durchmarsch
II. Title

NL 0343105   WU

Lickl, Karl Georg
    see Lickl, Carl Georg, 1801-1877.

Lickleder, Max.
    Die Moosflora der Umgegend von Metten (I.-II. Abteilung
... von P. Max Lickleder ... Landshut, J. Thomann'sche Buch
druckerei ₁1890-1891₎
    2 vol. in 1. 1 pl. 21¼ᶜᵐ.

    Paged continuously.
    Programm—Metten.

NL 0343107   ICJ

Lickley, Ernest J.
    ... Causes of truancy among boys, by Ernest J. Lickley
... Los Angeles, Cal., The Southern California sociolog-
ical society, University of Southern California ₁1917₎
    cover-title, 12 p. tables. 23ᶜᵐ. (Los Angeles. University of Southern
California. Studies in sociology, vol. II, no. 2, November 1917. Total
no. 6)

    1. School attendance.

                                        E 18-38

    Library, U. S. Bur. of   Education LB3081.L6

NL 0343108   DHEW NN CU

Lickley, James Dunlop
    Gray, Henry, 1825-1861.
    Anatomy, descriptive and applied, by Henry Gray ... 23d
ed., edited by Robert Howden ... Notes on applied anatomy
rev. by John Clay ... and James Dunlop Lickley ... London
₁etc.₎, Longmans, Green & co., ltd., 1926.

Lickley, James Dunlop, joint author.
                                    FOR OTHER EDITIONS
                                    SEE MAIN ENTRY
    Dodds, George Robert.
    The control of the breath, an elementary manual for singers
and speakers, by George Dodds ... and James Dunlop Lickley ... 2d ed. London, Oxford university press, H. Milford,
1935.

VOLUME 332

Lickley, James Dunlop
An introduction to gastro-enterology, a
clinical study of the structure and functions
of the human alimentary tube. Baltimore,
Williams, 1947.
viii, 143 p. illus. (part col.)

1. Digestive organs. 2. Digestive organs -
Diseases. I. Title: Gastro-enterology.

NL   0343111   NNC-M DNLM NcU IU-M

Lickley, James Dunlop.
The nervous system: an elementary handbook of the anatomy and physiology of the nervous system for the use of students of psychology and neurology, by James Dunlop Lickley ... With 118 illustrations. London, New York [etc.]
Longmans, Green, and co., 1912.
xii, 180 p. illus. (part col.) diagrs. 21 x 17½ᶜᵐ.

1. Nervous system. 2. Psychology, Physiological.

Stanford univ. Library   A 18—577
for Library of Congress   QM451.L5

OO ICJ ViU DLC MH-M NN NcRS NcD NIC CU ICRL
NL   0343112   CSt MtU PPJ PPPL PPC PU OU OC1ND ODW

Lickley, James Dunlop.
The nervous system. An elementary handbook
of the anatomy and physiology of the nervous
system. For the use of the students of psychology
and neurology.   London, etc., Longmans,
Green and co., 1916.
xii, 130 p.   illus.   8°.

NL   0343113   MH NjP

Lickley, James Dunlop.
The nervous system: an elementary handbook of the anatomy and physiology of the nervous system for the use of
students of psychology and neurology, by James Dunlop Lickley ... With 118 illustrations. New ed. London, New York [etc.]
Longmans, Green, and co., 1919.
xii, 180 p. illus. (part col.) diagrs. 21 x 17½ᶜᵐ.

NL   0343114   ViU PU OU

Lickley, James Dunlop.
The nervous system; an elementary handbook of the anatomy
and physiology of the nervous system for the use of students of
psychology and neurology.   New York: Longmans, Green and
Co., 1920. 130 p.   charts, diagr., illus. (some col'd.)   sq. 8°.

1. Nervous system. 2. Psychology—   Experimental and physiological.
                                      October 8, 1928

NL   0343115   NN PU PSC PPFr OU

Lickley, James Dunlop.
The nervous system; an elementary handbook of the anatomy and physiology of the nervous system, for the use of
students of psychology and neurology, by James Dunlop
Lickley ... with 117 illustrations. New ed. London, New
York [etc.] Longmans, Green and co., 1931.
xii, 144 p. illus. (part col.) diagrs. 21 x 16½ cm.

1. Nervous system.

QM451.L5 1931   611.8   32—1921

          PBa OrAshS MtU OrLgE MtBC
NL   0343116   DLC ViU MiU NIC ICRL CU PU PPT OCU OU

Licklider, Albert Harp, 1874–
Chapters on the metric of the Chaucerian tradition ...
Baltimore, J. H. Furst company, 1910.
v p., 1 l., 241 p., 1 l. 23½ᶜᵐ.
Thesis (PH. D.)—Johns Hopkins university.
Life.

1. Chaucer, Geoffrey, d. 1400. 2. English language—Versification.

                                        A 11–1066

Title from Johns Hopkins   Univ. Printed by L. C.

      PU PBm
NL   0343117   MdBJ NIC TU NjP PPT NcD OU MiU OC1W NN

LICKLIDER, ALBERT HARP, 1874-
Chapters on the metric of the Chaucerian tradition.
Baltimore, J. H. Furst Company, 1910.   241 p.

Film reproduction. Negative.
Thesis--Johns Hopkins university, 1907.
Vita.

1. Prosody, English. 2. Chaucer, Geoffrey.

NL   0343118   NN

Licklider, Charles Marshall, 1862–
Heart throbs, copyright ... by Rev. C. M. Licklider.
[Green Ridge, Mo.] Printed by Green Ridge local news,
ᶜ1925.
2 p. l., 48 p. front. (port.) 18½ᶜᵐ.
Poems.

1. Title.
                                        25–16981
Library of Congress   PS3523.I 25H4 1925

NL   0343119   DLC

Film   Licklider, Joseph   Carl   Robnet
6465   The effects of amplitude distortion upon
.584   the intelligibility of speech. (Relevant to
          project NA-108) [by J.C.R.Licklider] Cam-
          bridge, Harvard University, Psycho-Acoustic
          Laboratory, Research on Sound Control [1944]
          1 reel.
            "OESMsr-658."
            "PB19775."
            At head of title: Office of Scientific

          Research and Development, National Defense
          Research Committee. Division 17, section
          17.3.
            "OSRD Report no.4217, 15 November, 1944."

            1.Speech. 2.Speech - Research. I.U.S.
          Office of Scientific Research and Develop-
          ment. National De-   fense Research Com-
          mittee. II.Har-   vard University.
          Psycho-Acoustic   Laboratory.

NL   0343121   NjP

P90   Licklider, Joseph Carl Robnet   ed.
L53   Paraphrased transcription of a conference
1954   sponsored by the National Science Foundation,
         15-17 June 1954, on problems in human communica-
         tion and control edited by J.C.R.Licklider.
         Cambridge, Mass. [1954]
           203,3ℓ. 28cm.

           1. Communication - Congresses. 2. Information
         theory - Congresses. I. Conference on Problems
         in Human Communication and Control, Massachusetts
         Institute of Technology, 1954. II. Title.
         Human communication and control.

NL   0343122   IaU

G155
.E8L5
         Lickorish, Leonard John.
           American tourists in Europe, by L. J. Lickorish [and] G.
         Anderla. [Brussels] European Travel Commission [195-?]
         60 p. map, tables. 21 cm.

           1. Tourist trade—Europe. 2. Travelers, American. x. Anderla,
         Georges, joint author. II. Title.

         G155.E8L5   64–31005

NL   0343123   DLC

Lickorish, Leonard John.
  Étude critique sur les moyens publicitaires et le développement du tourisme. / [Genève, Alliance internationale de
tourisme, 1955]
  78 p. 21 cm.
  At head of title: Institut international de recherches touristiques.

  1. Tourist trade.

  G155.A1L5   58–42026 ‡

NL   0343124   DLC MH

LICKORISH, LEONARD JOHN.
  Étude critique sur les moyens publicitaires et le
développement du tourisme. [Genève, Institut international de recherches touristiques, 1955] 78 p. 21cm.

  Microfiche (neg.) 2 sheets. 11 x 15cm. (NYPL FSN-3242)

  1. Advertising, Tourist industry.   I. International travel research
institute.

NL   0343125   NN

Lickorish, Leonard John.
  Middle East tourist trends, a survey by L. J. Lickorish
and A. G. Kershaw. Geneva, International Institute of
Scientific Travel Research, 1954.
  96 p. illus. 21 cm.

  1. Tourist trade—Near East. I. Kershaw, Andrew Gabriel, joint
author. II. Title.

  G155.N15L5   59–51361 ‡

NL   0343126   DLC NIC OCH

Lickorish, Leonard John.
  Survey of international motoring in Europe, 1952.
[Geneva, Scientific Commission of the Alliance interna-
tionale de tourisme, 1954]
  94 p. maps, tables. 21 cm. (Alliance internationale de tourisme.
[Monographs] v. 3)

  1. Automobiles—Touring—Stat. I. Title.

  GV1021.L65   62–6094

NL   0343127   DLC MH NN

G   Lickorish, Leonard John
155   Tourist promotion and publicity media; a
.A1   critical survey. [Geneva, International Travel
L55   Research Institute, 1955]
           91 p. illus.

           1. Tourist trade. I. Title.

NL   0343128   MiEM

VOLUME 332

Ličková, Marta.
　　State o spisovateľskej práci

　　see under

　　State o spisovateľskej práci.

Lickroth, G., 1874-
　　Über die abspaltbarkeit von substituenten aus
dem benzolkern. ... Heidelberg, 1900.　　33 p.
Inaug. Diss. - Heidelberg, 1900.
Lebenslauf.

NL　0343130　　ICRL PU

Licks, H　　E.
　　Recreations in mathematics, by H. E. Licks; with 60 illustrations.　New York, D. Van Nostrand company, 1917.
　　v, 155 p.　illus., diagrs.　19½ cm.

　　1. Mathematical recreations.　ɪ. Title.

QA95.L65　　　　　　　　　　17—7557

MiHM ICJ MH NcD MB NjP NcRS OrLgE PPAp
PBa PP PPPL IdU OO OU ODW OLak OC1W OCU OOxM ViU NN
NL　0343131　　　DLC TU MoU FMU NIC IaU CU PPT PU MtBC

Licks, H. E.
　　Recreations in mathematics.
N.Y., Van Nostrand, 1921.
　　155 p.

NL　0343132　　PPF WaTC CaBVaU

QA95
L711r　Licks, H　　E
　　Recreations in mathematics.　New York, Van
Nostrand ₍1928, c1917₎
　　155 p.　illus.　20cm.

　　1. Mathematical recreations.　I. Title.

NL　0343133　　GU NNC NN OC1

QA95
.L65　Licks, H　　E
1929　　Recreations in mathematics.　New York, D.
Van Nostrand Co. [1929]
　　v, 155 p,　illus., diagrs.　20cm.

　　1. Mathematical recreations.　I. Title.

NL　0343134　　MB

Licks, H. E.
　　Recreations in mathematics.　6th printing.
New York, Van Nostrand, 1931.
　　155 p.

NL　0343135　　PPHa

Licks, H. E.
　　Recreations in mathematics, by H. E. Licks.
Seventh printing.　Illustrated.
New York, D. Van Nostrand company, inc. ₍1936₎
　　iii, ₍i₎, 155 p.

NL　0343136　　PU

Licks, H　　E
　　Recreations in mathematics, by H. E. Licks.　8th printing ...
New York, D. Van Nostrand company, inc. ₍1941₎
　　iii, ₍1₎, 155 p.　illus., diagrs.　19½".
　　"First published, January 1917.　Reprinted October 1941."

　　1. Mathematical recreations.　ɪ. Title.

　　　　　　　　　　　　　　　　　　43-6179

Library of Congress　　QA95.L65　1941
　　　　　　　　　　　　　　　　　510.78

NL　0343137　　DLC

QA
95　Licks, H　　E
.L711r　　Recreations in mathematics, by H. E. Licks.　10th printing ...
1946　New York, D. Van Nostrand company, inc. ₍1941₎ ₍1946₎
　　iii, ₍1₎, 155 p.　illus., diagrs.　19½".

NL　0343138　　MiU

Licks, H. E.

　　Sloane, Thomas O'Conor, 1851–
　　Speed and fun with figures ₍by₎ T. O'Conor Sloane ... J. E.
Thompson ... ₍and₎ H. E. Licks.　New York, D. Van Nostrand
company, inc. ₍1939₎

Lickteig, Alfred, tr.

　　Tolstoĭ, Lev Nikolaevich, graf, 1828–1910.
　　... Der lebende leichnam von graf Leo Tolstoi; schau
spiel in 4 akten.　Nach der französischen bearbeitung von
Jean-José Frappa und Georges Silber, übertragen von
Alfred Lickteig.　Strassburg i. E., Treuttel und Würtz,
1911.

Lickteig, Alfred, 1882-
　　Beitrag zur Kenntnis der Geschlechtsorgane
der Knochenfische.　Mit 8 Fig. u. i schemat.
Taf. im Text u. 3 Taf.　Leipzig, W. Engelmann
1913.
　　63 S. , 3 Taf.　8°.
　　Aus: Zeitschrift f. wiss. Zool. Bd. 106.
　　"Literaturverzeichnis": p. 58-60.

NL　0343141　　CtY PU MH

Lickteig, Ernst, 1910 -
　　Schraubenherstellung.
Düsseldorf, Berlag Stahleisen, 1943.
　　253 p.　(Stahleisen-bücher, bd. 4)

NL　0343142　　DBS

Lickteig, Ernst, 1910–
　　Schraubenherstellung.　2. Aufl.　Düsseldorf, Verlag
Stahleisen, 1950.
　　xiii, 244 p.　illus.　24 cm.　(Stahleisen-Bücher, Bd. 4)
　　Bibliography: p. ₍232₎–239.

　　1. Screws.　ɪ. Title.　(Series)

TJ1338.L5　1950　　　　　　　　50–37713

NL　0343143　　DLC ICJ

Lickteig, Eugen, 1879-
　　Über schädigende momente bei uranoplastik
und deren ausschaltung durch Schroeders okklu-
sivprothese ...　Wiesbaden, Bergmann, 1916.
　　19, ₍1₎ p.　illus., II plates.

　　Inaug.-diss., Heidelberg, 1916.
　　Lebenslauf.
　　"Literatur": p. 19.

　　1. Palate - Surgery.

NL　0343144　　NNC ICRL CtY DNLM

Licò, Nigro.　　　　　　　　　　7609A.137
　　Occultismo.
＝　Milano. Hoepli. 1905. xiii, (1), 328 pp. Portraits. Plates. Diagram.
[Manuali Hoepli.] 15 cm., in 8s.

D3439 — S.r. — Occult sciences.

NL　0343145　　MB OC1W

4HV
600　Licò, Nigro
　　Gli orrori del secolo.　Lavagna,
Tip. Artigianelli nell'Ospizio Corde-
viola, 1927.
　　145 p.

NL　0343146　　DLC-P4

Licò, Nigro.
　　Protezione degli animali.　Milano, M.
Hoepli, 1902.
　　1 p. l. , v-viii, 200 p.　16°.　(Manuali
Hoepli)

NL　0343147　　NN OC1W

Lições da escola sabbatina trimensario.　Divisão dos adultos.
no.

São Paulo: Casa publicadora brasileira. 1924—　　　　18cm.
　　nos.　illus., maps.

　　Title varies:　　　– April, 1925, Trimensario das lições da escola sabbatina ;
July, 1925–　　　　Lições da escola sabbatina trimensario.　Divisão dos
adultos.　　　　　　adultos.

　　1. Sunday schools—Lessons—Per. and　　　　soc. publ.　February 8, 1933

NL　0343148　　NN

WB
100　LIÇÕES de clinica, geral e especial ₍por₎
L711　Leonel Gonzaga ₍et al.₎　Rio de Janeiro,
1934　Flores & Mano, 1934.
　　332 p.　(Bibliotheca universitaria
brasileira.　Secção medica, 3)
　　1. Medicine - Collected works
I. Gonzaga, Leonel　Series: Biblioteca
universitaria brasileira.　Medicina, 3

NL　0343149　　DNLM

Lições da vida americana
　　see under　Instituto Brasil — Estados
Unidos, Rio de Janeiro.

Lições sobre neuroses
　　see under　Fernandes, Barahona, ed.

VOLUME 332

Licomati, Carmine.
Vantaggi che il Belgio ritrarrà dalla guerra... Roma: E. Voghera, 1915. 12 p. 8°.
Author's name at head of title.
"Estratto dalla Rivista militare italiana, anno 1915, dispensa ii."

1. European war, 1914–   2. Bel-   gium.—History, 1914–   3. Title
August 30, 1916

NL 0343152   NN IU

Licona, Marcelino
A la memoria de los valientes...
see under title

Licona, R   Aristeo Martínez
see
Martínez Licona, R   Aristeo.

W 4   **LICONA AYALA, Enedina**
M61   Informe médico social de El Susto
1955   municipio de Singuilucan, edo. de
Hidalgo; determinación de la reacción
de Mantoux a los habitantes del mismo.
El problema de la etiopatogenia de la
úlcera péptica.   México, 1955.
35 p.   illus.
Tesis - Univ. de México.
1. Peptic ulcer 2. Public health -
Mexico - Hidalgo (State) 3. Tuberculin

NL 0343155   DNLM

W 4   **LICONA AYALA, Ernesto**
M61   Embarazo ectópico. ¡México¡ 1955.
1955   40 p. illus.
Tesis - Univ. de México.
1. Pregnancy - Ectopic

NL 0343156   DNLM

Licona Morel, José Felipe.
... La confesión judicial como prueba en lo civil y la falsedad en la confesión judicial civil, debe ser punible en la legislación guatemalteca; tesis presentada a la Junta directiva de la Facultad de ciencias jurídicas y sociales de la Universidad de san Carlos por José Felipe Licona Morel en el acto de obtener los títulos de abogado y notario. Guatemala, Tipografía Sánchez & de Guise, 1945.
38, ¡2¡ p. 27ᶜᵐ.
At head of title: Facultad de ciencias jurídicas y sociales de la Universidad de san Carlos de Guatemala. República de Guatemala, Centro América.
"Bibliografía": p. 40.
1. Confession (Law)—   Guatemala.
Library of Congress   46–17665

NL 0343157   DLC

Licona Ruiz, Ruben.
... De los problemas interdictales; tesis que para obtener el título de licenciado en derecho, presenta el pasante Ruben Licona Ruiz. México, D. F., 1940.
47 p. 23ᶜᵐ.
At head of title: Universidad nacional autónoma de México. Facultad de derecho y ciencias sociales.
"Bibliografía": p. 47.

1. Possession—Mexico.

43–41892

NL 0343158   DLC

Liconnet, Norbert.
Traité de laminage à chaud. Paris, A. Lahure, 1952.
159 p. illus. 28 cm.

1. Rolling (Metal-work)   r. Title.

TS340.L5   *671.32   52–68435 ‡

NL 0343159   DLC NN IU

Licopoli, Gaetano, 1833–1897,   joint author.

Pasquale, Giuseppe Antonio, 1820–1893.
... Di un viaggio botanico al Gargano, relazione pel socio ordinario Giuseppe Antonio Pasquale e pel signor professore Gaetano Licopoli.
(*In* R. Accademia delle scienze fisiche e matematiche, Naples. Atti. Napoli, 1873. 31¼ᶜᵐ. vol. v, no. 18. 31 p.)

AS   **Licopoli, Gaetano,** 1833–1897.
222   Gli stomi e le glandole delle piante.
N208   (In Accademia delle scienze fisiche e
A8++   matematiche, Naples. Atti. Napoli, 1878–79.
v. 8   31 cm. v. 8, no. 5. 72 p. plates)
no. 5

NL 0343161   NIC

AS   **Licopoli, Gaetano,** 1833–1897.
222   Ricerche anatomiche e microchimiche sulla
N208   Chamaerops humilis, L., ed altre Palme.
A8++   (In Ac...ia delle scienze fisiche e
v. 9   matematiche, Naples. Atti. Napoli, 1881.
no. 8   31 cm. v. 9, no. 8. 10 p. plate)

NL 0343162   NIC

Licopoli, Gaetano, 1833–1897.
... Storia naturale delle piante crittogame che vivono sulle lave vesuviane. Memoria di Gaetano Licopoli.
(*In* R. Accademia delle scienze fisiche e matematiche, Naples. Atti. Napoli, 1873. 31¼ᶜᵐ. vol. v, no. 2. 58 p. III pl.)

1. Cryptograms. 2. Botany—Italy—Vesuvius.

A C 35–3015

Title from Univ. of Chi-   cago Q54.N23 vol. 5
Library of Congress   [Q54.N2 vol. 5, no. 2]

NL 0343163   ICU NIC OCU

AS   **Licopoli, Gaetano,** 1833–1897.
222   Sul frutto dell'uva e sulle principali
N208   sostanze in esso contenute.
A8++   (In Accademia delle scienze fisiche e
v. 7   matematiche, Naples. Atti. Napoli, 1875–76.
no. 4   31 cm. v. 7, no. 4. 9 p. plate)

NL 0343164   NIC MH-A

1833–1897.
Licopoli, Gaetano, Sull' anatomia e fisiologia del frutto nell' Anona reticulata L., e nell' Asimina triloba Dun.; ricerche. [Napoli. 1884.] 4°. pp. 12. Plate.
"Atti della R. Accademia delle scienze fisiche e matematiche," 1884, ser. 2ª, i, no. 11.

NL 0343165   MH-A

Licorice in the service of mankind. New York, MacAndrews & Forbes co. [n.d.]
18 p. illus. map. Q.

NL 0343166   CaBViP

Liconnet, Norbert
see
Tannstetter von Thannau, Georg, 1482–1535.

*(corrected: **Licoripesis, Georgius** see **Tannstetter von Thannau, Georg,** 1482–1535.)*

M261   **Licorish, David Nathaniel.**
L61   Adventures for today. New York,
Fortuny's publishers ¡c1939¡
111, ¡1¡p, 19½cm.
"First edition"

NL 0343168   DHU

La Licorne.   –3;   –automne 1948. Paris.
no. 28 cm. quarterly.
Began publication with spring 1947 issue.
Directed by S. Soca.

r. Soca, Susana.

AP20.L54   58–21032

NL 0343169   DLC NcU NhD NN

A.6830
.524   La Licorne, recueil de littérature et d'art.
v.1, pts. 1–3; 15 mai – 15 oct. 1911.
Antwerp.
3 pts. in 2. illus. 22 cm.
Edited by Marc S. Villiers, Arthur H. Cornette, Joan Hortie.

1. Periodicals, French.

NL 0343170   MB CU

Licosa, Ermelino Matarazzo di
see
Matarazzo di Licosa, Ermelino.

Licourt (Charles-Théodore). *De l'épistaxis.
22 pp. 4°. Paris, 1837, No. 321, v. 316.

NL 0343172   DNLM

Licourt (Georges) [1884–   ]. *Du traitement abortif pratique de la blennorragie uréthrale chez l'homme. 77 pp. 8°. Nancy, 1911. No. 6.

NL 0343173   DNLM

Licourt (Nicolas). *I. De l'oblitération des bronches. II. [etc.] 26 pp. 4°. Paris, 1843, No. 148, v. 405.

NL 0343174   DNLM PPC

Licques, David de
see
Liques, David de

VOLUME 332

Licquet (Alexandre-Félix). * Sur la gangrène.
19 pp. 4°. Paris, 1812.

NL   0343176   DNLM

Licquet, François Isidore, 1787–1832.
Guide de l'étranger dans Rouen. Extrait de l'itinéraire de Th. Licquet, par Ed. Frère. Orné de cinq vues et d'un plan de Rouen accompagné de la description et de la carte du chemin de fer de Rouen à Paris. Rouen, A. Le Brument, 1851.
2 p. l., viii, 203 p. front., plates, fold. map, fold. plan. 15ᶜᵐ.

1. Rouen—Descr.—Guide-books.   I. Frère, Edouard Benjamin, 1797–1874.

Library of Congress   DC801.R85L7
                                           ᵣ36b1ᵤ
                                                           4—22233

NL   0343177   DLC CtY

Licquet, François Isidore, 1787–1832.
Histoire de Normandie, depuis les temps les plus reculés jusqu'à la conquête de l'Angleterre en 1066; par Th. Licquet ... précédée d'une introduction sur la littérature, la mythologie, les mœurs, des hommes du Nord; par M. G. B. Depping ... Rouen, É. Frère, 1835.
2 v. front. (fold. map) 21ᶜᵐ.

1. Normandy—Hist.—Medieval. 2. Mythology, Norse. 3. Icelandic and Old Norse literature—Hist. & crit. 4. Northmen.   I. Depping, Georg Bernhard, 1784–1853.

                              DC611.N856L7
                                                           4—26395

NL   0343178   DLC MdBP CaBVaU NN PBm

Licquet, François Isidore, 1787–1832, tr.

ᵣDibdin, Thomas Frognallᵤ 1776–1847.
Lettre neuvième relative à la Bibliothèque publique de Rouen, tr. de l'anglais, avec des notes, par M. Thⁿ Licquet ... Paris, Impr. de Crapelet, 1821.

LICQUET, François Isidore, 1787–1832.
Rouen, its History and Monuments Abridged, and translated from the French by M.D.C. Rouen 1840.

NL   0343180   MH OCl Nh

Licquet, François Isidore, 1787–1832.
Rouen; its history and monuments, a guide to strangers by Théod. Licquet ... with a map of the town and five views, abridged and rev. by Ed. Frère, and translated from the French by M.D.C. 2d ed. Rouen, A. Lebrument, 1842.
15.5 cm.

NL   0343181   CtY

LICQUET, François Isidore, 1787–1832.
Rouen, its History and Monuments a Guide to Strangers. Abridge and revised by Ed. Freres and translated from the French by M.D.C. 2d ed. Rouen, 1843.

24°. Plate[ ]. engr. and map.
                              Fr 7082.70.8.5
ROUEN its History, Monuments, and Environs, a Guide to Travellers. 6th ed. revised and annotated by Ed. Treve. Translated from the French by M.D. and H.Banquet. Rouen. 1856.
24°. Vign. front.   6 engr. and 2 maps

NL   0343182   MH PPL PHi

Licquet, François Isidore, 1787–1832.
Rouen; its history and monuments, a guide to strangers by Théod. Licquet ... with a map of the town and five views, abridged and rev. by Ed. Frère and translated from the French by M.D.C. 3d ed.   Rouen, A. Lebrument, 1847.
15.5 cm.

NL   0343183   CtY

914.425
L711r7   Licquet, François Isidore, 1787–1832.
Rouen. Its history, monuments, and environs. A guide necessary to travellers who wish to become thoroughly acquainted with that capital of Normandy. By Th. Licquet. The seventh edition. Revised and annoted by Ed. Frère, illustrated with engravings, and a plan of Rouen. Translated from the French by M.H. Barguet ...   Rouen, A. Lebrument, 1868.
1p.ℓ., ii ₁2₁ iii–viii, 6, 178p. front., plates, fold. plan. 18cm.

NL   0343184   LNHT

Licquet ₍François Isidore₎, 1787–1832.
Rouen; its history, monuments and environs; a guide necessary to travellers who wish to become thoroughly acquainted with that capital of Normandy. By Th. Licquet. 7th ed., revised and annoted by Ed. Frère. Translated from the French by M.H. Barguet. Rouen, A. Lebrument, 1869.
Plates and folded plan.

NL   0343185   MH

ᵣRare
Book
Ip Roomᵤ
H223
Zz871   Licquet, François Isidore, 1787–1832.
Rouen; its history, monuments, and environs, a guide necessary to travellers who wish to become thoroughly acquainted with that capital of Normandy. By Th.Licquet. The seventh edition. Revised and annoted by Ed.Frère, illustrated with engravings, and a plan of Rouen. Translated from the French by M.H.Barguet, professor of languages. Rouen,A.Lebrument,1871.
2p.ℓ.,viii,178p. front.,plates,fold.plan. 17cm.
Original orange paper wrappers.

Thomas Hardy's copy, with bookplate, "From the library of Thomas Hardy, O.M. Max Gate."

NL   0343187   CtY

Licquet, François Isidore, 1787–1832.
Rouen, its history, monuments and environs, by Th. Licquet and Éd. Frère. 9th ed., rev., annotated and enl., with an excursion from Rouen to Havre on the Seine, by S. Frère; translated from the French by J. Walter ... Rouen, C. Métérie, 1879.
2 p. l., ii, 134 p. front., illus., plates, fold. plan. 16½ᶜᵐ.

1. Rouen—Descr.—Guide-books.   I. Frère, Édouard Benjamin, 1797–1874, joint author. II. Frère, Samuel, 1845–   II. Walter, J., tr.
                                                           38–38133
Library of Congress   DC801.R85L74 1879

NL   0343188   DLC

Licquet, François Isidore, 1787–1832.
Rouen; its history, monuments and environs by Th. Licquet and Ed. Frère; 9th ed. rev., annotated and enlarged, with an excursion from Rouen to Havre on the Seine by S. Frère. Tr. from the French by J. Walter ... Rouen, C. Métérie, 1882.
18 cm.

NL   0343189   CtY

DC801   Licquet, François Isidore, 1787–1832.
.R85L7   Rouen; précis de son histoire, son commerce, son industrie, ses manufactures, ses monumens: guide nécessaire pour bien connaître cette capitale de la Normandie. Rouen, Chez Frère, 1827.
4, 348 p. plates, fold. map.

1. Rouen—Descr.—Guide-books.

NL   0343190   ICU

Licquet, François Isidore, 1787–1832.
Rouen; précis de son histoire, son commerce, son industrie, ses monumens. Guide nécessaire ... suivi de notices sur Dieppe, Elbeuf, Le Havre, Bolbec, Tancarville, Lillebonne, Caudebec, Saint-Wandrille, Jumiéges et les endroits les plus remarquables du département de la Seine-Inférieure; par Théod. Licquet ... 2. éd. Rouen, É. Frère, 1830. 372 p. plan. 17cm.

With armorial bookplate of John Gage.
Author's autographed presentation copy to Monsieur Gage.

1. Rouen, France—Guidebooks,   1830. 2. Seine-Inférieure (Depart
ment)—Guidebooks, 1830.   Card retirée
                                                           June 11, 1946

NL   0343191   NN

Licquet, François Isidore, 1787–1832
Rouen; précis de son histoire, son commerce, son industrie, ses manufactures, ses monumens. Ed. 2.
Rouen, 1831.

NL   0343192   PPL

LICQUET, François Isidore, 1787–1832.
Rouen, son histoire et ses monumens; guide nécessaire pour bien connaître cette capitale de la Normandie; suivie de notices sur Dieppe, Argues et le Chatea-Gaillard. 3e éd., Rouen, 1836.   Fr 7082.70.8.2
The same. 3e éd.   Rouen,1839.
Front. plates and plan.

NL   0343193   MH

Licquet, François Isidore, 1787–1832.
Rouen; son histoire, ses monuments, ses environs. Guide nécessaire aux voyageurs pour bien connaître cette capitale de la Normandie et les localités voisines les plus intéressantes. 6. éd., rev. et annotée par Ed. Frère. Rouen, A. Le Brument, 1856.
viii, 188 p. illus., map. 19 cm.
J. P. Kennedy autograph on verso of half title.
1. Rouen - Descr. - Guide-books.

I. Frère, Édouard Benjamin, 1797–1874.
Kennedy, John Pendleton Association fiel.

NL   0343195   MdBP

                                           KC 13959
ᵣLicquet, François Isadore, 1787–1832ᵤ
Rouen; son histoire, ses monuments et ses environs. Guide nécessaire aux voyageurs pour bien connaître cette capitale de la Normandie et les localités voisines les plus intéressantes, par Th.Licquet. 7.ed., rev. et annotée par Ed.Frère. Rouen, A.Lebrument, 1861.

NL   0343196   MH

VOLUME 332

Licquet, François Isidore, 1787–1832.
Rouen; son histoire, ses monuments et ses environs. Guide nécessaire aux voyageurs pour bien connaître cette capitale de la Normandie ... par Th. Licquet. 7. éd., revue et annotée par Ed. Frère ... Rouen, A. Le Brument, 1865.
2 p. l., viii, 200 p. front., plates, fold. map, fold. plan. 16½ᶜᵐ.
₍Hazlitt tracts, v. 16, no. 1₎

1. Rouen—Descr.—Guide-books.   ɪ. Frère, Édouard Benjamin, 1797–1874.

23–1827

Library of Cong. ..   AC911.H3 vol. 16, no. 1

NL 0343197   DLC

DC 801   **Licquet, François Isidore,** 1787–1832.
R85 L7   Rouen; son histoire, ses monuments et ses
1879   environs, par Th. Licquet et Ed. Frère. 9. éd., revue, annotée et augm. d'une excursion de Rouen au Havre par la Seine, par S. Frère.   Rouen, Métérie, 1879.
ii, 136 p. plates, fold. map. 17 cm.

1. Rouen - Description - Guide-books.   I. Frère, Édouard Benjamin, 1797–1874, joint author.   II. Frère, Samuel, 1845–

NL 0343198   OU

Licquet, François Isidore, 1787–1832, tr.
Dibdin, Thomas Frognall, 1776–1847.
Voyage bibliographique, archéologique et pittoresque en France, par le rév. Th. Frognall Dibdin ... Tr. de l'anglais, avec des notes, par Théod. Licquet ... Paris, Crapelet, 1825.

Licquet, Theodore, 1787–1832
see Licquet, François Isidore, 1787–1832.

Licteriis, Francesco de

see

Lettieri, Francesco

326
L618g   **Lictor,** pseud.
Gladstone dissected! Good Templar secession. Duplicate Grand lodges, or the Negrox which is it? A letter to the Rev. Geo. Gladstone, ex G.W.C.T. for Scotland. By Lictor ...   [Glasgow] R. Lindsay [n.d.]
24p. 21cm.

1. Slavery.   2. Templars.   I. Title.

NL 0343202   TxU OClWHi

Licudi, Héctor, tr.

Mussolini, Benito, 1883–
... La amante del cardenal, novela; traducción de Héctor Licudi. Madrid, Editorial España, 1930.

3175   **Licudi, Hector**
.1136   Barbarita; novela. Madrid, Editorial Mundo
.314   latino ₍1929₎
399 p. 19 cm.

NL 0343204   NjP

PQ4827   **Licudis, Argiro,** 1887–1949
I25   Anca cussi; versi dialettali. Venezia, Istituto Tipografico Editoriale, 1952.
A7   170p. illus., port. 22cm.

NL 0343205   RPB ICU NN NNC

Paterno
D855L618   **Licudis, Argiro,** 1887–1949.
U5   Il ponte sul fiume; liriche. Venezia, Istituto Tipografico Editoriale, 1950.
265 p. illus.

NL 0343206   NNC RPB

Licudis, Argiro, 1887–1949.
Il sarcofago d'oro. Venezia, Istituto tip. editoriale, 1951.
256 p. illus. 21 cm.

ɪ. Title.

A 53–1607

Harvard Univ. Library
for Library of Congress

NL 0343207   MH NN RPB

Il Licurgo, overo Il Cieco d'acuta vista; drama per musica da rappresentarsi nel Teatro di S. Angelo, l'anno M.DC.LXXXVI. In Venetia, Appresso Francesco Nicolini, 1686.
57p.

Libretto by Matteo Noris, music by Carlo Francesco Pollaroli.

NL 0343208   MH

Licurgo editorial, Santiago de Chile

see

Editorial Licurgo, Santiago de Chile.

---

851   **Licursi, Domenico**
L618s   Selva d'affenni. Milano, G. Intelisano,
I   1955.
32p. (Nuovi poeti, 16)

NL 0343210   PP

W   **LICURZI, Ariosto,** 1890–
786   La identidad bio-antropológica en
L711i   medicina legal. Buenos Aires, El Ateneo,
1933   1933.
132 p. illus.
1. Identification

NL 0343211   DNLM

Licurzi, Ariosto, 1890–
... Problemas de inmigración y de criminología. Córdoba, República argentina, Imprenta de la Universidad, 1945.
1 p. l., v–viii, 199 p., 2 l. plates. 23½ᶜᵐ.
Summary in English at end of each chapter.
"Fe de erratas": slip inserted.
Bibliographical foot-notes.

1. Crime and criminals—Argentine republic.   2. Argentine republic—Emig. & immig.   ɪ. Title.

Library of Congress   HV6883.L5   46–20384
364.982

NL 0343212   DLC CtY

Licurzi, Ariosto, 1890–
... El suicidio, psicosociología, medicina legal y profilaxis. Buenos Aires, El Ateneo, 1942.
1 p. l., v–xii, 204 p., 1 l. plates. 24ᶜᵐ.

1. Suicide.

Library of Congress   HV6545.L5   43–49721
179.7

NL 0343213   DLC

Licurzi, Ariosto, 1890–
... El suicidio; psicosociología, medicina legal y profilaxis. 2. éd. corr. y ampliada. Con un apéndice sobre "Suicidio y guerra" y el sumario en inglés al pie de cada capítulo. Córdoba ₍Argentina₎ Imprenta de la Universidad, 1946.
xiv, 243 p., 1 l. illus. 24ᶜᵐ.

1. Suicide.

U. S. Army medical library   ₍W864L711s 1946₎   Med 47–823
for Library of Congress

NL 0343214   DNLM

Licurzi, Ariosto, 1890–
... La vagancia disimulada; 20 capítulos de psicología práctica, por el ... dr. Ariosto Licurzi. Buenos Aires, "Orientación integral humana" soc. de resp. ltda. ₍1939₎
141, ₍5₎ p. 18½ᶜᵐ.
"Obras del mismo autor": p. ₍145₎–₍147₎

1. Tramps.   2. Psychology, Pathological.   3. Defective and delinquent classes.   ɪ. Title.

Library of Congress   HV4493.L5   41–20503
339.1

NL 0343215   DLC

LICY, Diodato.
Giuseppe Ferrari.   Torino, 1864.
24°.
(I contemporanei italiani, 68)

NL 0343216   MH

Liczba głów żydowskich w Koronie z taryf roku 1765
see under Kleczyński, Józef, 1841–1900, ed.

Licznerski, Johann, 1886–
Über schädelplastik mit besonderer berücksichtigung der knochenregeneration an der entnahmestelle vom schulterblatt ... Greifswald, Adler, 1919.
2ª p., 1 l.
Inaug.-diss., Greifswald, 1919.
Lebenslauf.
"Literatur": p. ₍27₎–28.

1. Skull - Surgery.   2. Bone-grafting.   3. Scapula.

NL 0343218   NNC MiU CtY

VOLUME 332

Lid, Brita.
Makter og herrevelde. Oslo, Ansgar forlag, 1947.
272 p. 20 cm.

I. Title.

PT9076.L5M3~   50-25411

NL 0343219   DLC

Lid, Brita.
Stormtid. Oslo, Ansgar forlag, 1950.
226 p. 20 cm.

I. Title.

     A 51-3825

Minnesota. Univ. Libr.
for Library of Congress

NL 0343220   MnU

Lid, Dagny Tande.
Ved vinduet, dikt. Oslo, O. Norli, 1947.
93 p. 20 cm.

I. Title.

PT8175.L474V4   48-27412*

NL 0343221   DLC NN

WA   LID, Hallvard
900   Hygieniske problemer under **lofotfisket.**
GN6.1   Oslo, Kirste, 1951.
L8L7h   115 p. illus.
1951   1. Fisheries 2. **Public health -**
Norway - Lofoten

NL 0343222   DNLM

Lid, Johannes, 1886–
Bryophytes of Jan Mayen. Oslo, I kommisjon hos J.
Dybwad, 1941.
13 p. map. 25 cm. (₁Norway₁ Norges Svalbard- og Ishavs-
undersøkelser. Meddelelse₁r₁ nr. 48)
Bibliography : p. 13.

1. Mosses—Jan Mayen Island. 2. Hepaticae—Jan Mayen Island.
(Series)

QK519.L5   588   49–55679*

NL 0343223   DLC NNC

LID, JOHANNES, 1886–
...Crop contents of ptarmigans from Taimyr, by Johannes Lid... Bergen: A. S. J.Griegs boktrykkeri,
1933. 7 p. illus. (chart.) 31cm. (Maud-ekspedi-
tionen, 1918–1925. Scientific results. v. 5, no. 2.)

"Literature," p. 7.

1. Ptarmigans. I. Ser.

NL 0343224   NN

Lid, Johannes, 1886–   joint author.

Dahl, Knut, 1871–
A division of Norway into bio-geographical sectional areas,
agreed upon by botanists and zoologists, by Knut Dahl,
Johannes Lid, and T. Munster. (With 1 map) ... Kristiania,
In commission by J. Dybwad, 1924.

Lid, Johannes, 1866–
Myrtyper og Myrplanter₁[av] Aasulv Lóddesól.
Oslo, Grøndahl, 1950.
95 p.

NL 0343226   CtY

Mann   Lid, Johannes, 1886–
QK   Norsk flora. Med teikningar av Dagny
326   Tande Lid. Oslo, Norske Samlaget ₁c1944₁
L71   637 p. illus. 22 cm.

1. Botany - Norway. I. Lid, Dagny
Tande. II. Title.

NL 0343227   NIC DCU MiEM NIC

581.948   Lid, Johannes, 1886–
L61n   Norsk flora. Med teikningar av Dagny Tande
1952   Lid. 2.utg. Oslo, Norske Samlaget, 1952.
771p. illus. 22cm.

1. Botany—Scandinavia. I. Title.₁

NL 0343228   IU DNAL NNBG MnU

Lid, Johannes, 1886–
... Sphagna from Novaya Zemlya. With an
appendix by E. Jørgensen. Some mosses from
Novaya Zemlya ... Kristiania, A.W. Brøgger,
1924.
7 p. 27 cm. (Report of the scientific results
of the Norwegian expedition to Novaya Zemlya
1921. No. 20)
"Literature cited": p. 7.

NL 0343229   CtY

Lid, Johannes, 1886–
...Vascular plants from South East Greenland, collected on
the "Signalhorn" Expedition in 1931. Oslo: J. Dybwad, 1932.
12 p. illus. (map.) 26½cm. (De Norske Svalbardekspe-
disjoner, 1906– Skrifter om Svalbard og Ishavet... nr. 44.)

1. Botany—Greenland. I. Ser.

     October 2, 1933

NL 0343230   NN CtY

Lid, Johannes, 1886–
... What is *Lepidium groenlandicum* Hornem.? By Jo-
hannes Lid. With 3 figures in the text. København, C. A.
Reitzel, 1933.

9 p. illus. 28ᶜᵐ. (Meddelelser om Grønland, udgivne af Kommissio-
nen for videnskabelige undersøgelser i Grønland, bd. 92, nr. 7)
"Literature cited": p. 9.

1. Lepidium groenlandicum.
     A 45–241

Yale univ. Library
for Library of Congress   Q115.D39 bd. 92, nr. 7

NL 0343231   CtY DLC TxU NNBG ViU OCU

Lid, Jon, *comp.*
Ord for dagen i Norsk rikskringkasting, i utvalg med Jon
Lid og Mentz Schulerud. Oslo, Aschehoug, 1952.
237 p. illus. 21 cm.

1. Quotations, Norwegian. 2. Norwegian literature (Collections)
3. Norwegian literature—Translations from foreign literature. I.
Schulerud, Mentz, 1876– joint comp. II. Title.

     A 53–7232

Minnesota. Univ. Libr.
for Library of Congress

NL 0343232   MnU

LF4514   Lid, Jon, ed.
.A2
1902   **Oslo. Universitet. Students, *1902.***
Studentene fra 1902; Biografiske opplysninger samlet til
50-års jubileet 1952. Redaktører : Jon Lid og Andreas Riis.
Oslo, Aas & Wahls boktr., 1952.

LF4514   Lid, Jon, ed.
.A2
1927b   **Oslo. Universitet. Students, *1927.***
Studentene fra 1927; biografiske opplysninger, statistikk
og artikler samlet til 25 års jubileet 1952. Redaktør: Jon
Lid. Oslo, Bokkomitéen for Studentene fra 1927, 1952.

₁Lid, Nils₁ 1890–
Ein bindetrolldom. ₁Oslo, 1925₁ p. ₁229₁–236. 23cm.

Caption-title.
At head of title in ms.: Or Syn og segn, 1925.
Signed: Nils Lid.
Bibliographical footnotes.

I. Title.

1. Magic, Norwegian.

NL 0343235   NN

Lid, Nils, 1890–

Moe, Moltke, 1859–1913.
... Folke-eventyr frå Flatdal etter uppskrifter av Moltke
Moe. Oslo, Norsk folkeminnelag, 1929.

Lid, Nils, 1890–
... Folketru, utgjeven av Nils Lid ... Stockholm, A. Bon-
nier; ₁etc., etc., 1935₁
3 p. l., 171 p. 25½ cm. (Added t.-p.: Nordisk kultur. ₁xix₁)
Series title also at head of t.-p.
Title on recto of series t.-p.: ... Folketro. København, J. H.
Schultz; ₁etc., etc.₁
Includes bibliographies.
CONTENTS.—Magiske fyrestellingar og bruk, av N. Lid.—Trylle-
formler, af F. Ohrt.—Övernaturliga väsen, av C. W. von Sydow.
1. Magic—Scandinavia. 2. Incantations, Scandinavian. 3. Super-
natural. 4. Folk-lore—Scandinavia. I. Ohrt, Ferdinand Christian
Peter, 1873– II. Sydow, Carl Wilhelm von, 1878– III. Title.

DL3.N6 vol. 19   398.30948   36—28684

NL 0343237   DLC NN TxU ICN OU PU LU IU NcD

Lid, Nils, 1890–
Joleband og vegetasjonsguddom, av Nils Lid;
med 60 tekstbilete ... Oslo, I kommisjon hos
J. Dybwad, 1928.

286 p. illus. 27½ᶜᵐ. (Skrifter utgitt av det
Norske videnskaps-akademi i Oslo. II.Hist.—filos.
klasse. 1928. no.4)
"Utgitt for Fridtjof Nansens fond."
"Litteratur": p.272-282.

1.Christmas. 2.Folk-lore, Scandinavian. 3.Plant lore.

NL 0343238   MiU MoU NIC ICU

VOLUME 332

Lid, Nils, 1890–
Jolesveinar og grøderikdomsgudar, av Nils
Lid. Med 39 tekstbilete ... Oslo, I kommisjon
hos J.Dybwad, 1933.
173,₁₁ p. illus. 27½ᶜᴹ. (Skrifter utgitt av
det Norske videnskaps-akademi i Oslo. II.Hist.-filos.
klasse. 1932,no.5)
"Eit framhald av mi bok Joleband og vegetasjonsguddom
(i Videnskaps-akademiets skrifter 1928)."—Fyreord.
"Utgitt for Fridtjof Nansens fond."
"Litteratur": p.164-169.

1.Christmas. 2.Folk-lore,Scandinavian. 3.Plant
lore.

NL   0343239   MiU MoU NIC ICU

Lid, Nils, 1890–
Light-mother and earth-mother. Oslo ₁Aschehoug₁ 1946.
20 p. 24 cm. (Studia Norvegica, no. 4)
Bibliographical footnotes.

1. Midwives—Norway.   I. Title.   (Series)
GR1.S85   no. 4   65–82193

CaBVaU NIC InU FMU
NL   0343240   DLC CLU MH-P KU NNC MiU OU MH ViU WaU

AS   Lid, Nils, 1890–
283   Norske slakteskikkar, med jamføringar frå
N86H6+ nærskylde umråde. Utgjeve for Benneches fond.
1923   Kristiania, J. Dybwad, 1924–
no.4   v. illus. 27cm. (Videnskapsselska-
          pets skrifter. II. Hist.-filos. klasse.
          1923, no.4

1. Norway—Soc. life & cust. 2. Slaughtering and slaughter-houses--Norway. 3. Folk-
lore--Norway.

NL   0343241   NIC NN ICU MoU IEN

Lid, Nils, 1890–
On the history of Norwegian skis.
Oslo, Foreningen til skiidraettens fremme, 1937.
23 p. (Ski history, no. 1)

NL   0343242   PBm

Lid, Nils, 1890–
Religionshistorie. Stockholm, A. Bonnier ₁1942₁
162 p. 26 cm. (Nordisk kultur, 26)

1. Scandinavia—Religion—Hist. 2. Mythology, Norse.   I. Title.
(Series)
DL3.N6   Bd. 26   293   53–55319

IU NcD
NL   0343243   DLC CU ICN MH NjPT OU TxU NN LU OC1 ViU

Lid, Nils, 1890–
Ein samisk skikk ved bjørnefesten, av Nils Lid.   ₁Oslo, 1926₁
1 l.   23cm.
Caption-title.
"Særtryk av Maal og minne, hefte 4, 1926."

1. Folk lore, Lappish.

NL   0343244   NN

Lid, Nils, 1890–
...Skifundet frå Øvrebø. Med eit tillegg av Erik Granlund...
Oslo, A. W. Brøgger, 1932. 31 p. illus. 24cm.
"Serprent or Universitetets oldsaksamlings årbok, 1930."

1. Ski-running—Norway—   Øvrebø.

NL   0343245   NN NcU

Lid, Nils, 1890–
Stainak og rodno, tvo urnordiske lånord i samisk, av Nils Lid.
₁Oslo, A. W. Brøgger, 1932₁   p. ₁87₁–104.   25cm.
Caption-title.
"Norsk tidsskrift for sprogvidenskap, bind 5, 1932; særtrykk."
Summary in English.

1. Lappish language—Foreign   words and phrases, Norse. 2. Norse
words in foreign languages, Lappish.

NL   0343246   NN

GR221   **Lid, Nils,** 1890–   ed.
.S7
Storaker, Johan Theodor Nilssen, 1837–1872.
Storakers samlinger, ved Nils Lid. Kristiania (Oslo)
Norsk folkeminnelag, 1921–41.

Lid, Nils, 1890–

Nilsson, Martin Persson, 1874–   ed.
... Tideräkningen, utgiven av Martin P:n Nilsson ... Stockholm, A. Bonnier; ₁etc., etc., 1934₁

Lid, Nils, 1890–
Til norsk skihistorie; Dr. Nils Lid forteller om skiforskningens
problemer...   Oslo, Grøndahl og søn, 1931. 11 p.   illus.
22cm.
"Særtrykk av artikkel i 'Skiforeningens årbok' 1931."

1. Ski-running—Norway.

NL   0343249   NN

GR555
.L5
Lid, Nils, 1890–
Trolldom, nordiske studiar. ₁Oslo₁ Cammermeyers bog-
handel ₁1950₁
191 p. illus. 24 cm.

1. Folk-lore—Norway.   I. Title.
                                          A 50–6389
Indiana. Univ. Libr.
for Library of Congress

NL   0343250   InU CU TxU NN DLC

Lid, Nils, 1890–
...Truls-visa, av Nils Lid.   ₁Oslo, 1931₁   32 p.   23cm.
Caption-title.
At head of title: Særtrykk av Maal og minne, 1.hefte 1931.

1. Folk songs, Norwegian—Hist.   and crit. 2. Folk songs, Norwegian.
I. Title: Trulsvisa.

NL   0343251   NN

₁Lid, Nils₁ 1890–
Ullins øyra.   ₁Oslo, 1925₁   p. ₁32₁–48.   25cm.
Caption-title.
In ms.: Særtr. af Heidersskrift til Hægstad 15/7, 1925.
Signed: Nils Lid.
Bibliographical footnotes.

I.Title.

1. Animals—Folk lore—Norway.

NL   0343252   NN

Lid, Nils, 1890–
...Um upphavet til jolehøgtidi; kritikk av dei ymse teoriane...
₁Oslo₁ 1925. 18 p. 23cm.
"Serprent or 'Syn og segn' 1925."

1. Christmas—Hist.

NL   0343253   NN

Lid, Nils, 1890–
Vegetasjonsgudinne og vårplantar, av Nils Lid.   ₁Oslo, A.
W. Brøgger, 1928₁   p. ₁131₁–146. 26cm.
"Serprent or Festskrift til rektor J. Qvigstad, Tromsø museums skrifter, v. 2."

1. Mythology, Lappish. 2. Plant-

NL   0343254   NN

₁Lid, Nils₁ 1890–
...Wilhelm Mannhardt og hans nyskaping av den folkloristiske
metoden. ₁Oslo, 1925₁ 16 p. 23cm.
Caption-title.
At head of title: Serprent or "Syn of segn" 1925.
Signed: Nils Lid.
I. Title.

1. Mannhardt, Johann Wilhelm   Emanuel, 1831–1880. 2. Folk lore—
Study and teaching.

NL   0343255   NN

Lid, Nils, 1890–
... Wilhelm Mannhardt og hans samling av norske folkeminne, ved Nils Lid. Oslo, Norsk folkeminnelag, 1931.
101 p. front. (port.) 23ᶜᵐ. (Norsk folkeminnelag. ₁Skrifter₁ nr. 24)

1. *Mannhardt, Wilhelm, 1831–1880. 2. Folk-lore of agriculture.
3. Folk-lore—Norway.
                                          A C 38–2839
Iowa. Univ. Library
for Library of Congress

NL   0343256   IaU NN ICU NcD

₁Lid, Nils₁ 1890–
...Veideskikkar hjå nord-eurasiatiske folk.   ₁Oslo, 1926₁
8 p.   23cm.
Caption-title.
At head of title: Serprent av "Syn o segn," hefte 7, 1926.
Signed: Nils Lid.
I. Title.

1. Hunting—Lapland.

NL   0343257   NN

VOLUME 332

Lid. v. 1, no. 1-   Oct. 18, 1894-
  Kolfne.
    Bi-weekly.
    With this is bound Zár, Rúda Zár and Ruch,
all incomplete. Zár and Rúda Zár interfiled in
binding.

NL 0343258   PPiU

Lid om Knud Scavenius bogsamling
      see under [Johansen, Th   ]

Lida.
  Le bouquet du jardinier. Images d'Angèle **Malclès.**
[Paris] Flammarion, *1941.
  [24] p. col. illus. 21 cm. (Albums du Père Castor)

    1. Flowers. I. Title. (Series)

  QK49.L65   582.13   48-38142*

NL 0343260   DLC

Lida.
  Bourru, l'ours brun. Texte de Lida,
images de Rojan, [pseud.] [Paris],
Flammarion, c1936.
  35, [1] p., illus., part. col.

  (Albums du père Castor)

  French

NL 0343261   OCl MiD

Lida.
  Bruin, the brown bear; story by Lida; pictures by **Rojan**
[pseud.] translated by Lily Duplaix. **New York, London,**
Harper and brothers, 1937.
  [32] p. illus. (part col.) 26½ x 23½^cm.
  Illustrated t. p. and lining-papers in colors.
  "First edition."

    I. Duplaix, Lily, tr. II. Rojankovsky, Feodor, 1891-   illus. III.
  Title.   37-38861
  Library of Congress   PZ10.3.L61Br

NL 0343262   DLC Or OrP OrLgE PP OCl

Lida.
  Coucou; texte de Lida, illustrations d'après F. Rojankovsky.
Montréal, Les Éditions Variétés [194-]
  [38] p. double col. front., col. illus. 25½ x 23^m.
  "Printed in the United States of America."

    I. Rojankovsky, Feodor, 1891-   illus. II. Title.
                                                A 44-2128
  New York. Public library
    for Library of Congress

NL 0343263   NN

Lida.
  Cuckoo; story by Lida, pictures by Rojan [pseud.] translated by Lily Duplaix. **New York, London, Harper & brothers,**
1942.
  [32] p. col. illus. 26½ x 23½^m.
  "First edition."

    I. Duplaix, Lily, tr. II. Rojankovsky, Feodor, 1891-   illus.
  III. Title.
  Library of Congress   PZ10.3.L61Cu   42-36190

NL 0343264   DLC WaS OrP Or ViU OClh OCl PP PBa

844   **Lida.**
L619f   La ferme du Père Castor; images d'**Hélène**
         Guertik. [Paris] Flammarion, c1937.
           1v. (unpaged) illus. 28cm. (Albums du
         Père Castor)

           I. Guertik, Hélène, illus. II. Title.
         III. Series.

NL 0343265   OrU OrAshS WaS NN PP

Lida.
  Les fleurs que j'aime. Images d'Angèle **Malclès.** [Paris]
Flammarion, *1941.
  [24] p. col. illus. 21 cm. (Albums du Père Castor)

    1. Flowers. (Series)

  QK49.L652   582.13   48-38140*

NL 0343266   DLC

Lida.
  Fluff; the little wild rabbit; story by Lida, pictures by Ro-
jan [pseud.], translated by Georges Duplaix. New York &
London, Harper and brothers, 1937.
  [40] p. illus. (part col.) 26 x 23½^cm.
  Illustrated t.-p. and lining-papers in colors.

    I. Rojankovsky, Feodor, 1891-   illus. II. Duplaix, Georges, tr.
  III. Title.
  Library of Congress   PZ10.3.L61Fl   37-3096 Revised

NL 0343267   DLC WaS Or ViU OCl OClh PWcS PP

Lida.
  ... Froux, le lièvre. Texte de Lida, images de Rojan.
[Paris] Flammarion, *1935.
  35 p. illus. (part col.) 21 x 23^mm. (Albums du père Castor)

    I. Rojankovsky, Feodor, 1891-   illus. II. Title.
                                                37-3267
  Library of Congress   PZ26.3.L5
  Copyright A—Foreign   30147
                                                843.91

NL 0343268   DLC NN WaS

Lida.
  The kingfisher; story by Lida, pictures by Rojan [pseud.]
translated by Lily Duplaix. New York, London, Harper and
brothers, 1940.
  [32] p. illus. (part col.) 26½ x 23½^m. [A Père Castor book]
  Illustrated t-p. and lining-papers in colors.
  "First edition."

    I. Rojankovsky, Feodor, 1891-   illus. II. Duplaix, Lily, tr.
  III. Title.
  Library of Congress   PZ10.3.L61Ki   40-6905

  Copyright   843.91

NL 0343269   DLC OrLgE WaSp Or OOxM OClh PP PBa

Lida.
  The little French farm; story by Lida, pictures by Helene
Guertik; translated by Louise Raymond. New York, London,
Harper and brothers, 1939.
  [26] p. illus. (part col.) 28½^m.
  Illustrated t-p. and lining-papers in colors.
  "First edition."

    I. Guertik, Hélène, illus. II. Raymond, Louise, tr. III. Title.
                                                39-4900
  Library of Congress   PZ10.3.L61Li

  Copyright A 127230   843.91

NL 0343270   DLC NN OrAshS WaS Or CU OCl PP OO OClh

Lida.
  Martin pêcheur, par Lida, images de Rojan
[pseud.] [Paris] Flammarion [1952]
  [34] p. illus. (part col.) (Albums du père
Castor)

  French.

NL 0343271   OCl OKentU PP NN PPPM-I

Lida.
  Panache l'écureuil ... Par Lida, dessins de **Rojankovsky.**
[Paris] Flammarion, *1934.
  35 p. illus. (part col.) 21 x 23^cm. (Album du père Castor)

    I. Rojankovsky, Feodor, 1891-   illus. II. Title.
                                                36-10145
  Library of Congress   PZ26.3.L516
  Copyright A—Foreign   26357
                                                843.91

NL 0343272   DLC PP

Lida.
  Plouf, canard sauvage ... Texte de Lida, images de **Rojan.**
[Paris] Flammarion, *1935.
  35 p. illus. (part col.) 21 x 23^cm. (Album du père Castor)

    I. Rojankovsky, Feodor, 1891-   illus. II. Title.
                                                37-3268
  Library of Congress   PZ26.3.L52
  Copyright A—Foreign   29610
                                                843.9

NL 0343273   DLC Or OrP NN OCl PP

Lida.
  Plouf; the little wild duck ... story by Lida; pictures by
Rojan; translated by G. Duplaix. New York & London, Har-
per and brothers, 1936.
  [40] p. illus. (part col.) 26½^cm. (A Père Castor book)
  Illustrated lining-papers.

    I. Rojankovsky, Feodor, 1891-   illus. II. Duplaix, Georges, tr.
  III. Title.
  Library of Congress   PZ10.3.L61Pl   36-33407
  ———— Copy 2.
  Copyright A 100693   843.91

                                                PBa PP
NL 0343274   DLC OrMonO OrLgE Or OrP OCl OClh PWcS

Lida.
  Pompom; the little red squirrel ... story by Lida; pictures
by Rojan; translated by Georges Duplaix. New York and
London, Harper and brothers, 1936.
  [38] p. illus. (part col.) 26½^cm. (A Père Castor book)
  Illustrated lining-papers.

    I. Rojankovsky, Feodor, 1891-   illus. II. Duplaix, Georges, tr.
  III. Title.
  Library of Congress   PZ10.3.L61Po   36-33406
  Copyright A 100692   [37d2]   843.91

NL 0343275   DLC OrP OrLgE OrMonO WaSp OCl OClh PP

845L615 Lida.
Oq   Quipic, le hérisson ... Dessins de F. Rojankov-
         sky. [Paris] Flammarion, c1937.
           [35] p. illus. (part col.) (Albums du Père
         Castor)

           I. Rojankovsky, Feodor, 1891-   illus. II.
         Title.

NL 0343276   IU PPPM-I OCl

VOLUME 332

ₗLidaₗ
Le royaume des abeilles ... ₗParisₗ Flammarion ₗ1935ₗ
₍82₎ p. incl. covers. illus. (part col.) 16½ x 19ᵐ. (Albums du père Castor)
"Texte de Lida, dessins de Ruda."

    ɪ. Ruda, illus.　ɪɪ. Title.　　　　　　37-2539

Library of Congress　　PZ26.3.L53
Copyright A—Foreign　　27907
　　　　　　　　　　　　　　　843.91

NL　0343277　　DLC OrP

Lida.
Scaf, le phoque ... Texte de Lida,
images de Rojan, (₍pseud.₎ ₍Parisₗ,
Flammarion, c1936.
unp., illus., part. col.

(Album du père Castor)

French

NL　0343278　　OCl

Lida.
Scuff, the seal; story by Lida; pictures by Rojan ₍pseud.₎
translated by Lily Duplaix. New York, London, Harper and
brothers, 1937.
₍33₎ p. illus. (part col.) 26½ x 23½ᵐ.
Illustrated t.-p. and lining-papers in colors.
"First edition."

    ɪ. Duplaix, Lily, tr.　ɪɪ Rojankovsky, Feodor, 1891-　illus.　ɪɪɪ. Title.
　　　　　　　　　　　　　　　37-35652
Library of Congress　　PZ10.3.L618c

NL　0343279　　DLC WaSp Or PBa PP OCl

Lida.
Spiky, the hedgehog; story by Lida, pictures by Rojan
₍pseud.₎ translated by Lily Duplaix. New York, London,
Harper and brothers, 1938.
₍34₎ p. illus. (part col.) 26½ᵐ.
Illustrated t.-p. and lining-papers in colors.
"First edition."

    ɪ. Rojankovsky, Feodor, 1891-　illus.　ɪɪ. Duplaix, Lily, tr.
ɪɪɪ. Title.
　　　　　　　　　　　　　　　38-29787
Library of Congress　　PZ10.3.L618p

NL　0343280　　DLC Or WaSp OCl OO PP

Lida, David
　　see　David ben Aryeh Loeb, of Lida, d. 1696.

Lida, María Rosa
　　see　Lida de Malkiel, María Rosa.

Lida, Raimundo.
... Belleza, arte y poesía en la estética de Santayana. ₍Tucu-
mán₎ Universidad nacional de Tucumán, Facultad de filosofía
y letras ₍1943₎
3 p. l., ₍9₎-157 p., 2 l. 23ᵐ. ₍Universidad nacional de Tucumán.
Facultad de filosofía y letras. Cuadernos de letras. 3₎
Bibliographical foot-notes.

    1. Santayana, George, 1863-　2. Esthetics.　ɪ. Title.
　　　　　　　　　　　　　　　A 44-707
Harvard univ. Library
for Library of Congress　　B945.S24L5
　　　　　　† 　　　　　　　191.9

DPU
NL　0343283　　MH OrU WaU NcU CoU NcD NNC OCU NN DLC

PQ 6424
25 L49　　Lida, Raimundo.
　　　　　　Cartas de Quevedo. Mexico, 1953.
　　　　　　20 p. 24 cm.
　　　　　　"Sobretiro de Cuadernos americanos."

　　　　　　₁. Quevedo y Villegas, Francisco
　　　　Gómez de, 1580-1645　ɪ. Title

NL　0343284　　OU MH

Lida, Raimundo, joint tr.

Schiller, Johann Christoph Friedrich von, 1759-1805.
... De la gracia y la dignidad ... traducción de Juan Probst y
Raimundo Lida, con un estudio preliminar de Juan Probst.
Buenos Aires, Imprenta de la Universidad, 1937.

B945
.S23
D517　　Lida, Raimundo, tr.

Santayana, George, 1863-
... Diálogos en el limbo. Buenos Aires, Editorial Losada,
s. a. ₍1941₎

Lida, Raimundo, joint ed. and tr.

Lenz, Rudolf, 1863-
... El espanol en Chile, trabajos de Rodolfo Lenz, Andrés
Bello y Rodolfo Oroz; traducción, notas y apéndices de Amado
Alonso y Raimundo Lida. Buenos Aires, 1940.

P105
.V617　　Lida, Raimundo, tr.

Vossler, Karl, 1872-
... Filosofía del lenguaje; ensayos. Traducción y notas de
Amado Alonso y Raimundo Lida, con la colaboración del autor.
Prólogo de Amado Alonso. Buenos Aires, Editorial Losada,
s. a. ₍1943₎

Lida, Raimundo, joint author.
　　Geografia Fonética ...
　　　　see under　Alonso, Amado, 1896-1952.

Lida, Raimundo.

... El impresionismo en el lenguaje, por Charles Bally, Elise
Richter, Amado Alonso ₍y₎ Raimundo Lida. Buenos Aires
₍Impr. de la Universidad de Buenos Aires₎ 1936.

Lida, Raimundo, tr.

Geiger, Moritz, 1880-
... Introducción a la estética. Traducción de Raimundo
Lida. La Plata, El Centro estudiantes de humanidades, 1933.

PN803
.V64
1942　　Lida, Raimundo, joint ed and tr.

Vossler, Karl, 1872-
... Introducción a la estilística romance; traducción y notas
de Amado Alonso y Raimundo Lida. 2. ed. Buenos Aires
₍Impr. y casa editora Coni₎ 1942.

Lida, Raimundo, joint ed. and tr.

Hatzfeld, Helmut, 1892-
... La investigación estilística en las literaturas románicas;
traducción y notas de A. Alonso y R. Lida ... Buenos Aires,
1932.

Lida, Raimundo, ed.

Martí, José, 1853-1895.
... Páginas selectas; selección, prólogo y notas de Raimundo
Lida. Buenos Aires, A. Estrada y cía., 1939.

Lida, Raimundo, joint tr.

Schiller, Johann Christoph Friedrich von, 1759-1805.
... Poesía ingenua y poesía sentimental, traducción de Juan
Probst y Raimundo Lida. Buenos Aires, "Coni," 1941.

₍P19
.C27₎　　Lida, Raimundo, joint tr.

Caillois, Roger.
... La roca de Sísifo. Buenos Aires, Editorial sudamericana
₍1942₎

LIDA, Raimundo.
La técnica del relato en "La gloria de don
Ramiro". Buenos Aires, Ed. "Radio revista", 1936.

23 cm. pp. 25.
"De 'Cursos y conferencias', año V, no. 2. "

NL　0343297　　MH ICarbS

[Lida de Malkiel, María Rosa]
　　Bibliografía de Amado Alonso. ...
　　　　see under title

PQ6039
L55　　Lida de Malkiel, María Rosa.
　　　　[Collected papers. 1940-63]
　　　　2 v. of pamphlets.

Title supplied by U. C. Library.
Table of contents in volumes.

1. Spanish literature - Hist. & crit. - Collected works.
2. Romance philology - Collected works.

NL　0343299　　CU

860.9
L61　　Lida de Malkiel, María Rosa.
　　　　₍Collected works and reviews.　Berkeley,
Calif., etc., 1938-1962₎
40 pamphlets in 1v. 27cm.

Reprints from various journals.
Assembled by Yakov Malkiel.

1. Spanish literature—Hist. & crit.—
Collected works.

NL　0343300　　IU

VOLUME 332

Lida de Malkiel, María Rosa.
El cuento popular hispano-americano y la literatura Buenos Aires, 1941.

86 p. 19 cm.

At head of title: Facultad de Filosofía y Letras de la Universidad de Buenos Aires. Instituto de Cultura Latino-Americana.

CONTENTS.—El cuento popular en la literatura grecorromana.—El cuento popular en la literatura española.—El cuento hispanoamericano y la tradición literaria europea.

1. Literature, Comparative—Themes, motives. 2. Folk literature—Themes, motives. I. Title.

PN921.L5   43–32354 rev*

MB CtY TxU CaBVaU OrU
NL 0343301   DLC GU PSt NN OO OU NBuU WU NcU NcD CU

860.9 **Lida de Malkiel, María Rosa.**
L61d   Dido y su defensa en la literatura española. Buenos Aires, Facultad de Filosofía y Letras de la Universidad de Buenos Aires, Instituto de Filología, 1942.
122p. 26cm.

"De la Revista de filología hispánica, año IV, núms. 3 y 4, y año V, no.1."
Author's autograph presentation copy to John van Horne.

NL 0343302   IU MH FU

Lida de Malkiel, María Rosa.
La idea de la fama en la edad media castellana. [1. ed.] México, Fondo de Cultura Económica [1952]

312 p. 22 cm. (Lengua y estudios literarios)

1. Glory in literature. 2. Spanish literature—Early to 1500—Hist. & crit. 3. Classical literature—Hist. & crit. 4. Literature, Medieval—Hist. & crit. I. Title.

PN682.G6L5   809.02   53–4224 ‡

NBuU OC1U CaBVaU PPiU VtMiM MoSU NcD ICU CtY GDS
PHC TxU OCU OU PBm PSt NBC OO AU MiEM OrCS OC1W FU
NL 0343303   DLC ScU TU IaU CLSU ICN NcU NN CU ViU

Lida de Malkiel, María Rosa.
... Introducción al teatro de Sófocles. Buenos Aires, Editorial Losada, s. a. [1944]

4 p. l., 11–205 p., 1 l. incl. front., illus. 20½ cm. (Estudios literarios; colección dirigida por Amado Alonso)

At head of title: María Rosa Lida.

1. Sophocles.

PA4417.L5   882.2   45–11041 rev

NL 0343304   DLC MH DPU ViU InU WaU

PQ6413 **Lida de Malkiel, María Rosa.**
.M2Z8   Juan de Mena, poeta del prerrenacimiento español. [1. ed.] México [Colegio de México] 1950.

589 p. 24 cm. (Publicaciones de la Nueva revista de filología hispánica, 1)

Bibliographical footnotes.

1. Mena, Juan de, 1411–1456. (Series: Nueva revista de filología hispánica. Publicaciones, 1)

A 52–3160

Rochester. Univ. Libr.   PQ6413.M2L5
for Library of Congress

CtY PPT NNC InU NcD DCU PSt DLC
FU DLC AU NN PPiU KMK MU CaBVaU MtU OrU TxU IU ICU
NL 0343305   NRU PBm IEN OU PU OCU NBC ViU OO IaU CU

---

868 **Lida de Malkiel, María Rosa.**
M5330   Juan de Mena, poeta del prerrenacimiento español. [1.
L7?   ed.] México [Colegio de México] 1950.
1950a   589 p. 24 cm. (Publicaciones de la Nueva revista de filología hispánica, 1)

Bibliographical footnotes.
Photocopy. Ann Arbor, Mich., University Microfilms, 1971. 589 p. (on double leaves)

NL 0343306   MiU ICU IU

Lida de Malkiel, María Rosa, ed.

Ruiz, Juan, *arcipreste de Hita, fl. 1343.*
... Libro de buen amor, selección. Buenos Aires, Editorial Losada, s. a. [1941]

Lida de Malkiel, María Rosa.

Horatius Flaccus, Quintus.
... Odas y Epodos. Buenos Aires, Editorial Losada, s. a. [1939]

Lidahl, Olga Møller.
The origin of the Indians

see under

Møller, Fredrik Andreas, 1845–

Lidak, Otto Avgustovich, *ed.*
Рабселькоровские заметки и воспоминания; сборник под редакцией О. А. Лидака. [Ленинград] Огиз, Соцэкгиз, Ленинградское отделение, 1934.

279, [1] p. illus. (incl. ports., facsims.) 17ᵐ.

Half-title: Ленинградский институт истории ВКП(б) Об Ильиче.

1. Lenin, Vladimir Il'ich, 1870–1924. I. Leningrad. Institut istorii Vsesofûznof kommunisticheskof partii (bol'shevikov) II. Title.
Title transliterated: Rabsel'korovskie zametki i vospominanifâ.

37–32849 Revised

Library of Congress   DK254.L4L44 .

NL 0343310   DLC

Lidange (F.) Eaux minérales et thermales du Gers. Mémoire présenté au Conseil central d'hygiène publique et de salubrité du Gers. 5 p. l., 72 pp. 8°. *Auch, J.-J. Portes,* 1854.
[P. v. 1766.]

NL 0343311   DNLM

Lidardi, Cristiano Giuseppe

see

Lidarti, Cristiano Giuseppe, *fl. 1768–1780.*

Lidarti, Cristiano Giuseppe, fl. 1768–1780.
Bever voglic. Glee [T. T. B.].
(In Warren. Collection of Catches. Vol. I, pp. 162–164. London. [1766.])

March 20,   1902
E3196 — T.r. — Part songs.

NL 0343313   MB

Lidarti, Cristiano Giuseppe, fl. 1768–1780.
Bravo chi non falla. Catch [for three voices].
(In Catch Club. Original manuscript collection. Vol. I, p. 9. [London. 1763.])

K5049 — T.r. — Part songs.

NL 0343314   MB

Lidarti, Cristiano Giuseppe, fl. 1768–1780.
Che viva viva. Glee [S. T. B.].
(In Warren. Collection of Catches. Vol. I, pp. 74–77. London. [1764.])

March 20,   1902
E3196 — T.r. — Part songs.

NL 0343315   MB

Lidarti, Cristiano Giuseppe, fl. 1768–1780.
Cure avare. Catch [for three voices].
(In Catch Club. Original manuscript collection. Vol. I, p. 10. [London. 1763.])

K5049 — T.r. — Part songs.

NL 0343316   MB

Lidarti, Cristiano Giuseppe, fl. 1768–1780.
Delitto amoroso. Glee [S. T. B.].
(In Warren. Collection of Catches. Vol. I, pp. 110–113. London. [1764.])

March 20,   1902
E3195 — T.r. — Part songs.

NL 0343317   MB

Lidarti, Cristiano Giuseppe, fl. 1768–1780.
Donna che un falso. Catch [for 3 voices].
(In Catch Club. Original manuscript collection. Vol. I, p. 10. [London. 1763.])

K5049 — T.r. — Part songs.

NL 0343318   MB

Lidarti, Cristiano Giuseppe, fl. 1768–1780.
Hail, mighty wine. Catch [for five voices] with an opening chorus.
(In Catch Club. Original manuscript collection. Vol. 8, pp. 149–151. [London. 1770.])

K5604 — T.r. — Part songs.

NL 0343319   MB

M350 **Lidarti, Cristiano Giuseppe,** fl. 1768–1780.
.M3   [Manuscript collection of trio-sonatas. 17—]
Case

Lidarti, Cristiano Giuseppe, fl. 1768–1780.
Occhi stelle. Catch [for 3 voices].
(In Warren. Collection of Catches. Vol. I, p. 91. London [1764.])

March 20,   1902
E3195 — T.r. — Part songs.

NL 0343321   MB

VOLUME 332

Lidarti, Cristiano Giuseppe, *fl.* 1768–1780.
Preti, frati. Canon [for 3 voices].
(In Catch Club. Original manuscript collection. Vol. I, p. 4. [London. 1763.])

K5056 — T.r. — Part songs.

NL 0343322   MB

Lidarti, Cristiano Giuseppe, *fl.* 1768–1780.
Quartettos [by] Lidarti, &c. [17–]
parts. 23 x 30 cm.
Binder's title.
Manuscript collection in several hands.
For 2 violins, viola and violoncello.
Nos. 1–6 are by Lidarti; 7–24, by F. L. Gassmann (no. 9–10, 19–21 and 23 were pub. by J. J. Hummel as Gassmann's op. 1) An unidentified sinfonia follows the last quartet.

1. String quartets—To 1800—Parts. 2. Music—Manuscripts. I. Gassmann, Florian Leopold, 1729–1774. Quartets, strings. Selections.

M451.L5Q3   48–33988*

NL 0343323   DLC

Lidarti, Cristiano Giuseppe, *fl.* 1768–1780.
Quel bel vermiglio. Glee [S. T. B.].
(In Warren. Collection of Catches. Vol. I, pp. 154–156. London. [1765.])

E3195 — T.r. — Part songs.

March 20,   1902

NL 0343324   MB

M312
.4
.G16T773
Case

Lidarti, Cristiano Giuseppe, fl. 1768–1780.

Galeotti, Salvatore, fl. 1760–1770.
[Trio-sonatas, violins & continuo]
Six sonatas for two violins, with a thorough bass for the organ or harpsichord. Five by Salvatore Galleotti and one by Cristiano Giuseppe Lidardi. London, Printed for P. Welcker [1762]

NL 0343326   DLC FTaSU

Lidarti, Cristiano Giuseppe, *fl.* 1768–1780.
[Sonata, viola pomposa & continuo, Eb major]
Sonata per la Pomposa (Bratsche oder Violine) con Bassi; bearb. und mit Cadenz versehen von Theodor Schulz, Op. 37c. [Leipzig, P. Günther, 19—]
score (8 p.) and part. 35 cm. (Meisterwerke für Viola d'Amore und Bratsche)
Caption title.
Score (viola pomposa and keyboard instrument) and part for violin or viola pomposa.

1. Sonatas (Viola pomposa and harpsichord)—To 1800.

M239.L55 op. 37c   M 55–32

NL 0343326   DLC FTaSU

Lidarti, Cristiano Giuseppe, *fl.* 1768–1780.
Sù cantiamo. Catch a 3 voci.
(In Warren. Collection of Catches. Vol. I, p. 97. London. [1764.])

E3195 — T.r. — Part songs.

March 20,   1902

NL 0343327   MB

Lidarti, Cristiano Giuseppe, *fl.* 1768–1780.
Tremangli spirti. [Glee for three voices.]
(In Catch Club. Original manuscript collection. Vol. I, pp. 12–15. [London. 1763.])

K5049 — T.r. — Part songs.

NL 0343328   MB

M
350
3233

Lidarti, Cristiano Giuseppe, fl. 1768–1780.
Trii, Sei, per due violini è basso...
London: Welcker, [1770?]. 34cm.

NL 0343329   NRU-Mus

Lidarti, Cristiano Giuseppe, *fl.* 1768–1780.
Viva, viva questo Claretto. Glee [T. T. B. B.].
(In Warren. Collection of Catches. Vol. I, pp. 178–180. London. [1766.])

E3195 — T.r. — Part songs.

NL 0343330   MB

Lidback, Dagny.
Att söka den rätte. Stockholm, L. Hökerberg [1948]
319 p. 21 cm.

I. Title.

A 49–5417*

Minnesota. Univ. Libr.
for Library of Congress

NL 0343331   MnU

Lidback, Dagny.
Under vårmånen. Stockholm, Hökerberg [1950]
214 p. 21 cm.

I. Title.

A 50–7767

Minnesota. Univ. Libr.
for Library of Congress

NL 0343332   MnU

LIDBACK, L   P.
The dissolution of governments by greed, crime and wars. By L.P.Lidback. [n.p., 193–?] 26 p. chart. 23cm.

877730A. 1. Industry and state--U.S.

NL 0343333   NN OC1W

Lidbeck, Anders, 1772–1829.
*Almanna aesthetiska anmarkningar
see under   Apelberg, Anund Niclas

Lidbeck, Anders, 1772–1829, praeses.
Dissertatio de Bibliothecae lundensis praecipui incrementis ab anno MDCCLXIX usque ad annum MDCCLXIX... Lundae [1802]
16 p. 23.5 x 18.5 cm.
Diss. - Lund (Respondent, P.E. Bergström).

NL 0343335   CtY

Lidbeck, Anders, 1772–1829, praeses.
De regno Christiani Secundi meditamenta, quae...praeside Andr. Lidbeck...offert Magnus Lagerlöf... Lundae: Litteris Berlingianis[, 1802]. 17 p. 8°.

437122A.   1. Christian II, king of   Denmark, Norway and Sweden, 1481–1559.   2. Sweden—Hist.   3. Lagerlöf, Magnus, 1778–1884, respondent.
October 9, 1929

NL 0343336   NN

Lidbeck, Anders, 1772–1829, praeses.
Memorabilia bibliothecae Lundensis...præside Andr. Lidbeck... Lundæ: Litteris Berlingianis, [1803–]1820.   2 v. in 1. 12°.

Bibliographical footnotes.
Dissertation, Lund.
v. 2, praeses: N. Lovén.
v. 1, part 1, respondent: J. Aurén; part 2: J. Andersson; part 3: M. O. Brisman; part 4: L. Ekman; part 5: S. P. Hanström; part 6: N. P. Westerström; part 7: C. L. Wåhlin; part 8: J. Eneqvist; part 9: J. P. Wåhlin; part 10: A. J. Carlsson; part 11: S. Jutman; part 12: P. N. Anglin; part 13: A. U. Andersson; part 14: J. Lundquist; part 15: J. P. Högman; part 16: A. P. Källström; part 17: N. M. Krok; part 18: N. Lovén; part 19: J. M. Bergman; part 20: L. P. Ståhl. v. 2, part 1, respondent: J. P. Lageman; part 2: J. H. Schreil; part 3: N. H. Lovén; part 4: P. Nyman; part 5: E. O. Gadd.

1. Libraries, Sweden, Lund. 2. Lovén, Nils, 1796–1858, praeses. 3. Aurén, Jacob, respondent. 4. Andersson, Johan, respondent. 5. Brisman, Magnus Olai. respondent. 6. Ekman, Lars, respondent. 7. Hanström, Sven Per, respondent. 8. Westerström, Nils Per, respondent. 9. Wåhlin, Carl Ludvig, respondent. 10. Eneqvist, Johan, respondent. 11. Wåhlin, Johan Peter, 1786–1861, respondent. 12. Carlsson, Anders J., respondent. 13. Jutman, Svante, respondent. 14. Anglin, Per Neosander, respondent. 15. Andersson, Anders U., respondent. 16. Lundquist, Jonas, respondent. 17. Högman, Johan Per, respondent. 18. Källström, Anders Per, respondent. 19. Krok, Nils Magnus, respondent. 20. Bergman, Johan Magnus, 1792–1867, respondent. 21. Ståhl, Lars P., respondent. 22. Lageman,   Johan P., respondent. 23. Schreil, Johan H., respondent. 24. Lovén, Nils   Henrik, 1801–77, respondent. 25. Nyman, Per, 1794–1856, respondent.   26. Gadd, Erik Olof, 1803–76, respondent. 27. Lund. Universitet.—   Bibliothek.
February 8, 1917

NL 0343338   NN

Lidbeck, Andreas,
see Lidbeck, Anders, 1772–1829.

Lidbeck, Carl Johan, ed.
Handledning uti svenska masmästeriet
see under   Garney, Johan Carl, 1740–1808.

1724–1803

Lidbeck, Erik Gustaf, praeses. Dissertatio gradualis de Betula alno, quam sistit Jöran Rooth. Lundae. 1779. sm. 4°. pp. 14.

NL 0343341   MH-A

SD634
.S3
L5

Lidbeck, Eric Gustaf, 1724–1803, praeses.
Dissertatio gradualis de silvicultura Scaniae, quam ... sub praesidio ... Erici Gustavi Lidbeck ... publici examini submittit Ebbe Bring ... Londini Gothorum, C. G. Berling, 1757.
3 p. l., 33, [3] p. 20 cm.

5865 Pritzel.
Avhandling - Lund.

1. Forests and forestry - Scania. 2. Forests and forestry - Sweden. i. Bring, Ebbe, 1733–1804, respondent. ii. t.

NL 0343342   NNBG

Kress
Room

Lidbeck, Eric Gustaf, 1724–1803.
Tal, om skånska plantagerna, hållit den 18 octob. 1755... Stockholm, Tryckt hos L. Salvius, 1755.
1 p.l., 16 p. 18 cm.

"På kongl. Vetenskaps academiens befallning."

1. Agricultural products - Sweden. 2. Manufactures - Sweden.

NL 0343343   MH-BA

VOLUME 332

Lidbeck, Erik Gustaf, 1724-1803.
... De utilitate plantationum arborum fruticum-
que in Scania...   Londini Gothorum [1768]
2 p.l., 16 p.   22.5 cm.
Diss. - Lund   (Olof Hindbeck, respondent).

NL   0343344   CtY

Lidberg, Vilhelm.

See

Liedberg, Wilhelm, 1613-1891.

Lidbetter, Mrs. Elizabeth.
Memoir of Sarah Lidbetter ...
Philadelphia, Tract association of Friends ‹1831?›
20 p.

NL   0343346   PSC-Hi PHC

[Lidbetter, Elizabeth]
Memoir of Sarah Lidbetter, aged nine years and a half, by her
affectionate mother...   London: Harvey and Darton, 1832.
iv, 6-34 p.   17cm.

1. Lidbetter, Sarah, 1822-1831.   I. Title.
                                            January 20, 1944

NL   0343347   NN PHC MH

[Lidbetter, Mrs. Elizabeth]
Memoir of Sarah Lidbetter...   Phila.Tract
association of Friends. 1834.
12p.

NL   0343348   OC1WHi

Lidbetter, Ernest James, 1877-

Eugenics society, *London.*
Family council law in Europe, a study undertaken at the in-
stance of the Eugenics society, 1927-1929 ... [London] The
Eugenics society [1930]

Lidbetter, Ernest James, 1877-
Heredity and the social problem group, by E. J. Lidbetter
... London, E. Arnold & co., 1933-
v. tables. fold. diagrs. 25½cm.
"The purpose of this work is to make available data gathered in investigations which were carried on in the east end of London between
1910 and 1928."—v. 1, p. 11.

1. Heredity. 2. Eugenics. 3. London—Poor.   I. Title. II. Title:
Social problem group, Heredity and the.

                                            34-1847
Library of Congress   HQ753.L5
                                            613.9

NL   0343350   DLC CU CtY OOxM MB NcD

Lidbetter, Ernest James, 1877-
... The Lunacy & Mental treatment act ¡1890 to 1930, by
E. J. Lidbetter ... London, Law & local government publications limited ¡1933]
vi p., 1 l., 181 p., 1 l. 18½cm. (Handbooks for public assistance
officers.—2)
"Appendix on forms": p. ¡139]-174.

Continued in next column

Continued from preceding column

1. Insane—Laws and legislation—Gt. Brit.   2. Forms (Law)—Gt.
Brit.   I. Title.
                                            34-8919
Library of Congress   [347.1] 362.20942

NL   0343351   DLC PPT-L MnU

Lidbetter, Ernest James, 1877-
... Maintenance and desertion, by E. J. Lidbetter ...   London, Law & local government publications limited ¡pref. 1934]
xi, 180 p. 19cm. (Handbooks for public assistance officers.—3)

1. Desertion and non-support—Gt. Brit. 2. Poor laws—Gt. Brit.
I. Title.
                                            35-18121
Library of Congress   362

NL   0343352   DLC

Lidbetter, Ernest James, 1877-
Reconstruction and public health. By E. J. Lidbetter.   ¡Lon-
don, 1918.]   11 p.   8°.
Repr.: Eugenics review. Jan., 1918.

1. Hygiene (Public), Gt. Br.   2. Poor, Gt. Br. 3. Title.
                                            April 28, 1919.

NL   0343353   NN DL

HV248   Lidbetter, Ernest James, 1877-
.L5   Settlement and removal. London, Law and
        Local Government Publications, ltd. ¡1932?]
        164 p. (Handbooks for public assistance
        officers, 1)

        1. Poor laws - Gt. Brit.   I. Title.

NL   0343354   NbU ICU

Lidbetter, Ernest James, 1877-
... Settlement and removal by E. J. Lidbetter ...   2d ed.
London, Law & local government publications, limited ¡pref.
1937]
xii, 168 p. 18½cm. (Handbooks for public assistance officers. 1)

1. Poor laws—Gt. Brit.   I. Title.
                                            38-38050

NL   0343355   DLC

Lidbetter, Hubert.
Quaker meeting houses, 1670-1850.
(In Architectural review. London.
36½cm. May, 1946, p.99-116)

NL   0343356   PSC-Hi

LIDBETTER, HUBERT, ed.
SSA. 14 (Section sanitaire anglaise quatorze) 1915-
1919; an account of the activities in Belgium & Northern
France of a section of the Friends ambulance unit
[edited by H. Lidbetter and N. Monk-Jones]
Manchester, Printed by J.E. Benson, 1919.   viii, 227 p.
illus. (part col.), ports., maps (on lining papers) 21cm.

Title on spine: SSA 14, Motor ambulance convoy, 1915-1919.

1. European war, 1914-1918--Medical and sanitary affairs. 2. European war,
1914-1918--War work--Friends, Society of. 3. European war, 1914-1918--
Regt. hist.--Gt. Br.--Friends ambulance unit. I. Monk-Jones, N., joint
ed.

NL   0343358   NN

Lidblom, Ernst.
Hp36   Lydekinushandskriften i Kongl.biblioteket
L4   (sign. K.B.g.s.B.59) I. Inledning, textkritik,
    substantivets böjningslära: vokalstammarne ...
    Stockholm, Haeggström,1901.
    2p.l.,63p. 23cm.
    Akademisk avhandling - Upsala.
    Also pub. in full in Antiqvarisk tidskrift för
Sverige, pt.17, I.

NL   0343359   CtY ICRL PU MH

Lidborg, Olaf, respondent.
De globo solari
see under   Celsius, Magnus Nicolaus,
1621-1679, praeses.
... Dissertatio physica de globo solari...

Lidborg, Olavus S., resp.
... Dissertatio gradualis de luna disana ...
see under   Burman, Erik, 1692-1729, pr.

Lidbury, C   A
A national wages policy. Leigh-on-Sea, Essex, Thames
Bank Pub. Co. ¡1947]
43 p. 22 cm.
"Reprinted from the Industrial law review, February, 1947."

1. Wages. 2. Job analysis. 3. Wages—Gt. Brit.   I. Title.
HD4909.L5   331.2942   47-28311*

NL   0343362   DLC NNC

Lidbury, Sir Charles, 1880-
...Inaugural address of the President, Sir Charles Lidbury, on
"The economic consequences of the war," delivered on Thursday,
October 4, 1945, in the Beaver hall of the Hudson's bay company.
(With statistical appendix.)   ¡London, 1945]   29 p.   22cm.
At head of title: The Institute of bankers.

1. World war, 1939-1945—Post-   war problems, Economic—Gt. Br.
2. Economic history—Gt. Br., 1918-   . I. Institute of bankers,
London.   January 30, 1948

NL   0343363   NN

Lidbury, Sir David John, 1884-
Report, 1953-54
see under   Gt. Brit. Commission on the
Civil Services of the East African Territories and
the East Africa High Commission.

Lidby, Carl.
Med judar och araber till ruiner och nybyggen; resa
från Nilen till Eufrat. [Stockholm] Förlaget Fila-
delfia [1938]

206 p. illus.

1. Palestine - Descr. - 1919-1948. 2. Near East -
Descr.

NL   0343365   MH

Lidby, Carl.
Skall jag taga vara på min broder; ett ord i jude-
frågan. Stockholm, Lindqvist [1944]

96 p.

1. Antisemitism

NL   0343366   MH

VOLUME 332

Liddall, William John Norbray.
The place names of Fife and Kinross, by W. J. N. Liddall ... Edinburgh, W. Green & sons, 1896.
xii p., 1 l., 58 p. 23ᶜᵐ.

1. Names, Geographical—Scotland—Fife. 2. Names, Geographical—Scotland—Kinross-shire. i. Title.
16-17294

Library of Congress   DA880.F4L6

NL 0343367   DLC OC1

WZ 250 L712a 1608
LIDDEL, Duncan, 1561-1613.
Ars medica, succincte & perspicue explicata ... Hamburgi, Ex Bibliopolio Frobeniano, 1608.
[39], 868, [20] p. 17 cm.

NL 0343368   DNLM PPC

WZ 250 L712a 1617
LIDDEL, Duncan, 1561-1613.
Ars medica, succincte et perspicue explicata ... Alt. ed. emaculatior ... Hamburgi, Ex Bibliopolio Frobeniano, M. CD. XVII [1617]
[15], 868, [18] p. 17 cm.

NL 0343369   DNLM

WZ 250 L712a 1628
LIDDEL, Duncan, 1561-1613.
Ars medica, succincte et perspicue explicata ... Ed. ejus ult. juxta exemplar, quod ipsemet auctor ante obitum ... correxerat et auxerat, recusa ... Accessit ejusdem Tractatus de dente aureo pueri Silesii contra Horstium; ex museo Joach. Morsii nunc primum prolatus. Hamburgi, Ex Bibliopolio Frobeniano, 1628.
[32], 826, [14] p.; 28 p. 17 cm.
"Joannis Jessenii ... historia de rustico Bohemo cultrivorace. Recusa ad exemplar Pragense ... anno 1607": p. 23-28, at end.

1. Horst, Jakob, 1537-1600 2. Jessen, Johann von, 1566-1621 i. Morsius, Joachimus, b. 1593, ed.

NL 0343371   DNLM NNNAM

WZ 250 L712at 1651
LIDDEL, Duncan, 1561-1613.
Artis conservandi sanitatem libri duo, a ... Doctore Liddelio defuncto delineati, atque opera & studio, D. Patricii Dunaei, M. D. ad colophonem perducti, & in apricum prolati. Aberdoniae, Excudebat Jacobus Brounus, 1651.
[16], 471, [1] p. 14 cm.

i. Dun, Patrick, fl. 17th cent., ed.

NL 0343372   DNLM NNNAM

Liddel, Duncan, 1561-1613.
De febribus. Authore Duncano Liddelio. Hamburgae, 1590.

NL 0343373   PPL

---

250 L712df 1610
LIDDEL, Duncan, 1561-1613.
De febribus libri tres ... Hamburgi, Ex Bibliopolio Frobeniano [Excudebat Paulus Langius] 1610.
[16], 830, [2] p. 17 cm.

NL 0343374   DNLM NNNAM PPC CaBVaU

Liddel, Duncan, 1561-1613.
——. De febribus libri tres. 308 pp., 11 l. 4°.
[*Lugduni, A. Chard, 1624.*]
Forms part of the following.

NL 0343375   DNLM

WZ 250 L712 1624
LIDDEL, Duncan, 1561-1613.
... Operum omnium iatro-Galenicorum, ex intimis artis medicae adytis, & penetralibus erutorum tomus unicus ... Repurgatus ... notatiunculis aliquot ... illustratus ... Opera ... Ludovici Serrani ... Lugduni, Sumptibus Antonii Chard, 1624.
[8], 473 p.; 308, [24] p. 26 cm.
Imperfect: wormholes on p. [1-8], 1-28, and 213-304.

i. Serres, Louys de, fl. 1625, ed.

NL 0343376   DNLM MiU ICU

Liddel, Robert.
The seaman's new vade mecum: containing a practical **essay** on naval book-keeping, with the method of keeping the captain's books, and complete instructions in the duty of a captain's clerk ... by R. Liddel ... London: G. G. J. and J. Robinson, 1787. vi, 312 p. diagrs., col'd plates, tables. 8°.

15572A. 1. Seamanship. 2. Naval bookkeeping.   PROUDFIT COLLECTION.
    August 31, 1921.

NL 0343377   NN CtY MdAN

Liddel, Robert.
The seaman's new vade mecum; containing a practical **essay** on naval book-keeping, with the method of keeping the captain's books, and complete instructions in the duty of a captain's clerk ... 2. ed., with considerable additions... By R. Liddel ... London: G. G. and J. Robinson, 1794. vi, 4 l., 280, 32 p. illus. (part col'd.) 22cm.

231276B. 1. Naval accounts.   2. Navy, British—Handbooks, manuals, etc.   June 21, 1943

NL 0343378   NN PPWa NNC PPAmP PPL NNC NjP

Liddel, Robert.
The seaman's new vade mecum; containing a practical essay on naval book-keeping, with the method of keeping the captain's books, and complete instructions in the duty of a captain's clerk ... The third edition, with considerable additions, illustrated with copper plates. By R. Liddel. London: Printed for G. G. and J. Robinson, 1798. 354, 32 p. incl. tables. forms (1 col'd). 8°.

1. Seamanship. 2. Naval book-   keeping.   August 31, 1926

NL 0343379   NN MH

U 5 .507
LIDDEL, ROBERT.
The seaman's new vade mecum; containing a practical essay on naval book-keeping, with the method of keeping the captain's books, and complete instructions in the duty of a captain's clerk. The fourth edition, with considerable additions. London, G. and J. Robinson, 1803.
154, 266, 32p. illus. (part col.)tables. 21cm.

Contents.—Instructions.—Orders.—Abstract[s] of the act[s] of Parliament.

NL 0343380   ICN DSI

Liddel, Robert.
The seaman's New Vade-Mecum; containing a practical essay on naval bookkeeping... and complete instructions in the duty of a captain's clerk.. & c. London, Steel & co., 1811.
xvi, 554 p. 8°.
5 ed.

NL 0343381   NN NcD

Liddel, Urner, 1905-   joint author.
Brackett, Frederick Sumner, 1896–
... Infra-red absorption bands of hydrogen cyanide in gas and liquid, by F. S. Brackett ... and Urner Liddel ... City of Washington, The Smithsonian institution, 1931.

NL 0343...   DNLM

Liddel, Urner, 1905–   joint author.
QC457 .B33
Barnes, Robert Bowling, 1906–
Infrared spectroscopy, industrial applications and bibliography [by] R. Bowling Barnes, Robert C. Gore, Urner Liddel, and Van Zandt Williams ... New York, Reinhold publishing corporation, 1944.

Liddel, Urner, 1905-
... Spectral differentiation of pure hydrocarbons: a near infrared absorption study, by Urner Liddel and Charles Kasper ...
(R P 610, *in* U. S. Bureau of standards. Bureau of standards journal of research. Washington, U. S. Govt. print. off., 1933. 23½ᶜᵐ. November, 1933, v. 11, no. 5, p. 599-618 incl. tab. pl., diagrs. (part fold.))
Running title: Infrared absorption.
"This work is part of project no. 6: The separation, identification, and determination of the constituents of petroleum."—p. 599.
"This paper was presented before the Petroleum division of the American chemical society at Washington, D. C., Mar. 29, 1933."—p. 599.
Bibliography: p. 618.
1. Hydrocarbons. 2. Absorption spectra. i. Kasper, Charles, 1905- joint author. ii. Title. iii. Title: Infrared absorption.
33-26788
Library of Congress   QC1.U52   vol. 11, no. 5
    T1.U42   vol. 11, no. 5
    (506.1)   547.2

NL 0343384   DLC OC1 OU MiU

Liddell,
    The creation
      see under   Haydn, Joseph, 1732-1809.

Liddell,
    La création du monde
      see under   Haydn, Joseph, 1732-1809.

Liddell,
    La creazione del mondo...
      see under   Haydn, Joseph, 1732-1809.

Liddell,
    Haydn's grand oratorio, The creation...
      see under   Haydn, Joseph, 1732-1809.

Liddell,
    Haydn's oratorio, The creation
      see under   Haydn, Joseph, 1732-1809.

Liddell,
    Haydn's sacred oratorio, The creation
      see under   Haydn, Joseph, 1732-1809.

Liddell,
    Libretto of Haydn's oratorio of the creation
      see under   Haydn, Joseph, 1732-1809.

VOLUME 332

Liddell,
   Die Schöpfung
      see under   Haydn, Joseph, 1732-1809.

Liddell,
   Die Schöpfung. Leipzig, Breitkopf ... [n.d.]
      see under   Haydn, Joseph, 1732-1809.

Liddell, A. C., ed.
   The life and adventures of Robinson Crusoe
      see   Defoe, Daniel, 1661?-1731.
      Robinson Crusoe. Part I. 1910.

Liddell, Adolphus George Charles, 1846-
   Notes from the life of an ordinary mortal; being a record
of things done. seen and heard at school. college, and in the
world during the latter half of the 19th century, by A. G. C.
Liddell ... London, J. Murray, 1911.
   xiii, 370 p. front. (port.) 23ᶜᵐ.
   "First edition, March 1911, second edition, April, 1911."

                                                    11—35804
   Library of Congress   DA565.L7A3

      NN PPL
NL 0343395   DLC WaS OrP MiU MH PU NcU OC1W CtY OC1

PA   Liddell, Alfred Crichton.
263   Greek grammar papers. London, Blackie
L71   [1901]
           105 p. 17cm.

           1. Greek language--Grammar--Examina-
        tions, questions, etc.

NL 0343396   NIC

Liddell, Alfred Crichton, comp.
   Latin grammar papers; selected and
arranged by A. C. Liddell, with vocabulary.
London, Blackie, n.d.
   114 p.

NL 0343397   OCX

Liddell, Alix, comp.
   International notebook (Europe)
      see under   Girl guides association.

Liddell, Anna Forbes.
   Alexander's Space, time and deity, a critical consideration [by] Anna Forbes Liddell ... Chapel Hill, N. C.,
The Department of philosophy [1925]
   70 p. 22½ᶜᵐ. (University of North Carolina studies in philosophy, no. 2)

   1. Alexander, Samuel, 1859-   Space, time, and deity. 2. Space and
time. 3. God.
                                                    26-27059
   Library of Congress   BD632.A42

NL 0343399   DLC AAP ScU OC1 NN NcU

Liddell, Anna Forbes.
   The logical relationship of the philosophy
of Hegel to the philosophies of Spinoza and
Kant. Chapel Hill, 1924.

NL 0343400   NcU

Liddell, Arthur R.
   Practical stability information.
   n.p.   n.d.
   8 p.

   (World's Columbian Expos.--Engineering
Cong. Sec. G-Div. of Marine & naval engineering
& naval architecture)

NL 0343401   OO

Liddell, Arthur R., tr.

Gentsch, Wilhelm, 1865-
   Steam turbines; their development, styles of build, con-
struction and uses, by Wilhelm Gentsch ... Tr. from the
German, by Arthur R. Liddell. With numerous illustra-
tions in the text and 19 plates. London, New York and
Bombay, Longmans, Green, and co., 1906.

823   [Liddell, Charles Francis]
L619h   [Hidden links; or, The schoolfellows. A tale.
        London, T. C. Newby, 1857.
        3v. 21cm.

        Author's autograph presentation copy.

NL 0343403   IU

BV   Liddell, Mrs. Christina Catherine Fraser
2.5   (Tytler), 1848-   comp.
L5   Golden censer...a selection from the
        prayers of the saints, A.D. 69-1890;
        with notes and indices...London,
        Longmans, Green, 1890.
           xv, 142 p. 19 cm.

           1. Prayers. I. Title.

NL 0343404   NRCR NNUT

LIDDELL, CHRISTIANA CATHERINE (FRASER-TYTLER), 1848-
   Jasmine Leigh, by C.C.Fraser-Tytler. London: Strahan
& Co., 1871. 293 p. front. 18cm.

   771462A. 1. Fiction, English. I. Title.

NL 0343405   NN MH MB

Liddell, Christina Catherine (Fraser-Tytler) 1848-
   Jasmine Leigh, by C. C. Fraser-Tytler ... 2d ed. London,
S. Sonnenschein & co., 1885.
   2 p. l., [3]-293 p. front. 19½ᶜᵐ.

   I. Title.
                                                    44-44984
   Library of Congress   PZ3.L6193Jas 2

NL 0343406   DLC

Liddell, Christina Catherine (Fraser-Tytler) 1848-
   ... Jonathan; a novel, by C. C. Fraser-Tytler ... New York,
H. Holt and company, 1876.
   1 p. l., 438 p. 17ᶜᵐ. (On cover: Leisure hour series [no.] 58)
   Series title also at head of t.-p.

   I. Title.
                                                    8-31914
   Library of Congress   PZ3.L6193Jo

NL 0343407   DLC NjP MB NN PPL

PZ3   [Liddell, Mrs. Christina Catherine (Fraser-
.L6193   Tytler)] 1848-
Mak   Making or marring, by C. C. Fraser-Tytler (Mrs.
        Edward Liddell) ... Illustrated by Frank Dadd.
        London, M. Ward & co. [etc., etc.] 1879.
        256 p. incl. front., plates. 16ᶜᵐ.
        Head and tail pieces.

NL 0343408   MH

Liddell, Christina Catharine (Fraser-Tytler), 1848-
   Margaret, by C. C. Fraser-Tytler...   New York: Dodd &
Mead [1873]. 3 p.l., 363 p., 4 pl. (incl. front.) 16°.
   "Author's edition."

   1. Fiction (English). 2. Title.
                                                    July 24, 1918.

NL 0343409   NN PPL MB MH

PZ3   Liddell, Mrs. Christina Catherine (Fraser-
.L6193   Tytler) 1848-
Mi   Mistress Judith; a Cambridgeshire story, by
        C. C. Fraser-Tytler ... 2d ed. London, Sampson
        Low, Marston, Low & Searle, 1874.
        2 p. l., [vii]-viii, 344 p. front. 19ᶜᵐ.

NL 0343410   MB GEU

Liddell, Mrs. Christina Catherine Fraser (Tytler) 1848-
   ... Mistress Judith; a Cambridgeshire story, by C. C.
Fraser-Tytler ... New York, H. Holt and company, 1875.
   1 p. l., [vii]-viii, 344 p. front. 17ᶜᵐ. (On cover: Leisure hour series
[no.] 46)
   Series title also at head of t.-p.

                                                    8-31910†
   Library of Congress   PZ3.L6913M 2

NL 0343411   DLC NcD OC1W NN PPL

PZ3   Liddell, Mrs. Christina Catherine (Fraser-
.L6193   Tytler) 1848-
Mi 2   Mistress Judith; a Cambridgeshire story, by
        C. C. Fraser-Tytler. A new ed. London, Chatto
        and Windus, 1884.
        2 p. l., 344 p. 19ᶜᵐ.

NL 0343412   MB

Liddell, Mrs. Christina Catherine Fraser (Tytler) 1848-
   The other half of the world, by Mrs. Edward Liddell
... London, Strahan and company limited [1881]
   vi p., 1 l., 301 p. 18½ᶜᵐ.
   CONTENTS.—pt. I. What it is.—pt. II. What can we do for it.

   1. Poor—Gt. Brit. 2. Social problems.

                                                    15-14274
   Library of Congress   HV4237.A5L5

NL 0343413   DLC

VOLUME 332

Liddell, *Mrs.* **Christina Catherine (Fraser-Tytler)** 1848-
A shepherd of the sheep; the life-story of an English parish-priest, told by his wife, Mrs. Edward Liddell; with a preface by the Rev. Henry Scott Holland ... and a portrait. London, New York [etc.] Longmans, Green and co., 1916.
132 p. front. (port.) 19½ᶜᵐ.

1. Liddell, Edward, 1845-1914. I. Title.

16-22137

NL 0343414   DLC MB PPPD

Liddell, *Mrs.* **Christina Catherine Fraser Tytler,** 1848- Songs in minor keys. 12 pp. (Miles, A. H., *Poets ... of the century,* v. 8, p. 295.)

NL 0343415   MdBP

Liddell, Mrs. Christina Catherine Fraser (Tytler) 1848-
Songs in minor keys... London, 1881.
17 cm.

NL 0343416   CtY

821
L619s   Liddell, Christina Catherine Fraser (Tytler) b.1848.
Songs of the twilight hours, by Mrs. Edward Liddell. London, De la More Press [1909]
48p. 19cm.

"Many of these verses have appeared in the Commonwealth, the Spectator, and Goodwill."

NL 0343417   IU

LIDDELL, Daniel.
Practicability of improving the condition of the Working Classes, addressed, by permission to C.J. Bigge. Newcastle,1836.

12 p.
In vol. backtitlted Pamphlets- Secondary Punishments, Conditions of Labouring Classes, no.,

NL 0343418   MH-L MH NNC

Liddell, Donald Macy, 1879-
Chessmen, by Donald M. Liddell with the collaboration of Gustavus A. Pfeiffer and J. Maunoury. New York, Harcourt, Brace and company [1937]
xii, 171 p. illus., plates. 28½ x 22ᶜᵐ.
"First edition."
"Short bibliography on chessmen and ivories": p. 164-167.

1. Chess. 2. Ivories.   I. Pfeiffer, Gustavus Adolphus. II. Maunoury, Jean. III. Title.

38-708

Library of Congress   GV1318.L5

Copyright A 113189   794.1

NL 0343419   OC1 ODW OU OC1MA   DLC MdBWA PP OrP CaBVa CaBVaU NNC NcD

GV
1318   Liddell, Donald Macy, 1879-
.L72   Chessmen, by Donald M. Liddell, with the collaboration of Gustavus A. Pfeiffer and J. Maunoury. London [etc.] G. G. Harrap & co. [1938]
xii,171p. plates.
Includes bibliography.

NL 0343420   MiU CU OC1 MiU

Liddell, Donald Macy, 1879-   *ed.*
Handbook of chemical engineering, prepared by a staff of specialists, Donald M. Liddell, editor-in-chief ... 1st ed. New York [etc.] McGraw-Hill book company, inc., 1922.
2 v. illus. diagrs. 23½ᶜᵐ. $8.00

1. Chemical engineering.

Library of Congress   TP155.L5   22-20435

WaS MtBC PHC PPD OC1L PU PP PV MB MiHM
NcD OC1 OU OCU MiU OO MH Or WaWW OrCS WaT WaWW OrSaV
NL 0343421   DLC WaT OrP ICJ WaTC CaBVaU KEmT CU ViU

Liddell, Donald Macy, 1879-   *ed.*
Handbook of non-ferrous metallurgy prepared by a staff of specialists, Donald M. Liddell, editor-in-chief ... 1st ed. New York [etc.] McGraw-Hill book company, inc., 1926.
2 v. illus., diagrs. 23½ cm.
Paged continuously.
Contains bibliographies.

1. Nonferrous metals—Metallurgy.

TN665.L6   26—13894

CaBVaU MtU MtBuM
PV PP PU PPT PPD OC1 NcRS OC1U WaTC OrP WaSp WaS
NL 0343422   DLC DN NN CU OU ODW OCU MiU MdBJ MB ICJ

Liddell, Donald Macy, 1879-   *ed.*
Handbook of nonferrous metallurgy ... prepared by a staff of specialists, Donald M. Liddell, editor-in-chief ... 2d ed. New York and London, McGraw-Hill book company, inc., 1945-
2 v. illus., tables, diagrs. 23ᶜᵐ.
First edition published 1926.
Includes bibliographical references.
CONTENTS.—[v. 1] Principles and processes.—[v. 2] Recovery of the metals.

1. Metallurgy.   I. Title: Nonferrous metallurgy.

45-8689 Revised

Library of Congress °   TN665.L815
                        [r46v7]   669

CaBViP CaBVaU IdB OrCS OrP Wa WaS WaT Or MtBC MtBuM
MiHM NIC CU MB OKentU MB PPD PP PPF PU CaBVa WaSpG
NL 0343424   DLC GU NcD NcRS PPT TU DI OCU OU OC1 ICJ

Liddell, Donald Macy, 1879-   *comp.*
The metallurgists and chemists' handbook; a reference book of tables and data for the student and metallurgist, comp. by Donald M. Liddell ... 1st ed. New York [etc.] McGraw-Hill book company, inc., 1916.
vii, 603 p. illus., diagrs. 17½ᶜᵐ. $4.00

1. Metallurgy—Tables, calculations, etc.   I. Title.

16-7926 Revised

Library of Congress   TN671.L5

ICJ MB NjP
NL 0343426   DLC OrPR WaT ICJ CU OC1 OC1W PP OC1L

Liddell, Donald Macy, 1879-   *comp.*
The metallurgists and chemists' handbook; a reference book of tables and data for the student and metallurgist, comp. by Donald M. Liddell ... 2d ed., rev. and enl. New York, McGraw-Hill book company, inc.; [etc., etc.] 1918.
ix, 656 p. diagrs. 17½ᶜᵐ. $4.00

1. Metallurgy—Tables, calculations, etc.

18-15387 Revised

Library of Congress   TN671.L5 1918

OU OCU DN ViU NcRS PBm PP MtBuM OC1W
NL 0343427   DLC IdU CaBVa CaBVaU ICJ CU NjP MiU OC1

Liddell, Donald Macy, 1879-   *comp.*
The metallurgists and chemists' handbook; a reference book of tables and data for the student and metallurgist, compiled by Donald M. Liddell ... 3d ed., rev. and enl. New York [etc.] McGraw-Hill book company, inc., 1930.
vii, 847 p. illus., diagrs. 18ᶜᵐ.

1. Metallurgy—Tables, calculations, etc.

Library of Congress   TN671.L5 1930   30—24753
———— Copy 2.
Copyright A 27738   [m40f2]   669

OU OC1 MiU MH NcRS PU PPF OC1U MtBC MiHM
NL 0343428   DLC ICJ IdU WaS PP OrCS Wa CU TU OEac

Liddell, Donald Macy, 1879-   joint author.
Leith, Kenneth.
The mineral reserves of the United States and its capacity for production. Prepared for the Planning committee for mineral policy by Kenneth Leith and Donald M. Liddell. National resources committee. Washington, D. C., 1936.

Liddell, Donald Macy, 1879-
The principles of metallurgy, by Donald M. Liddell ... and Gilbert E. Doan ... 1st ed. New York and London, McGraw-Hill book company, inc., 1933.
vii, 626 p. illus., diagrs. 23½ᶜᵐ. (*Half-title:* Metallurgical texts)
Bibliography at end of some of the chapters.

1. Metallurgy.   I. Doan, Gilbert Everett, 1897-   joint author.

Library of Congress   TN665.L62   33-29981
———— Copy 2.
Copyright A 65543   669

NcRS MB PPF PP PV
OC1 OCU OU MiU NN DN MtBuM WaS WaSp WaT Wa NcD PPD
NL 0343430   DLC Or OrCS OrU CaBVaU IdU NIC MiHM CU

Liddell, E   M   *comp.*
The coming of the moon; an anthology of quiet verse, comp. by E. M. Liddell; with a foreword by Martin Armstrong. London, Burns, Oates and Washbourne ltd., 1925.
xii, 126 p. 19½ᶜᵐ.

1. English poetry (Collections)   I. Title.

Library of Congress   PR1175.L45   26-14340

NL 0343431   DLC WU NN

Liddell, Mrs. Edward.
    see   Liddell, Mrs. Christina Catherine (Fraser-Tytler).

Liddell, Edward, 1845-1914.
St. Alban's abbey, by the Rev. Edward Liddell ... illustrated by F. G. Kitton. London, Isbister & co. ltd., 1897.
3 p. l., 9-58, [1] p. incl. front., illus., plates. 17½ᶜᵐ. [English cathedrals]

1. St. Albans cathedral.

23-15532

Library of Congress   DA690.S13L5

NL 0343433   DLC OO OC1 DAU

Liddell, Edward George Tandy, joint author.
Sherrington, *Sir* Charles Scott, 1857-
Mammalian physiology; a course of practical exercises. A new edition by E. G. T. Liddell ... and Sir Charles Sherrington ... Oxford, Clarendon press; London, H. Milford, 1929.

VOLUME 332

Liddell, E₍va₎ Louise ₍Barnes₎
Polly Perkins' adventures; a book for girls and boys, by E. Louise Liddell; with illustrations by C. A. Strehlau. Philadelphia, H. Altemus company ₍1902₎
xv p., 1 l., 19-273 p. incl. front., pl. 19ᶜᵐ.

2-26345

NL 0343436   DLC

Liddell, Sir Frederick Francis, 1865-   ed.
Gt. Brit. *War office.*
Manual of military law. War office, 1899. London, Printed for H. M. Stationery off., by Harrison and sons, 1899.

Liddell, George, fl. 1700.
Divine meditations
see under title

Liddell, George, fl. 1700.
A honey-comb to refresh weary travellers gathered by Geor. Liddell in Edinburgh ... London: Printed by R. Janeway, jun. for John Marshall, at the Bible in Grace-church-street. 1700. Price 2 d.
24p. 14cm.
Signatures: A-B⁶.

NL 0343439   CtY

Liddell, George, fl. 1700.
The swan's song: or, Pleasant meditations on the way, by George Liddell, of Edinburgh. The tenth edition, corrected... London, printed for the author, and sold by John and Joseph Marshall, 1710.
48 p. 14.5 cm.

NL 0343440   NNUT

Liddell, George James, joint author.
Jacklin, Harold Madison, 1890-
... Riding comfort analysis, by H. M. Jacklin ... and G. J. Liddell ... Lafayette, Ind., Purdue university, 1933.

Liddell, Georgiana.
See
Bloomfield, Georgiana (Liddell) Bloomfield, baroness. 1822-1905.

Liddell, Glenda L.
McGovern, Elcy.
Social studies. Science. A guide for Kern county teachers. Compiled and edited by Elcy McGovern ₍and₎ Glenda L. Liddell. Bakersfield, Calif. ₍County schools₎ 1943.

LIDDELL, H. T.
Observations on the young of salmon, and some remarks on the migrations of eels. Newcastle, printed by T. and J. Hodgson, n. d.]
5 p. Illustr. 29 cm.
Caption title.
"Read at the Natural History society of Newcastle upon Tyne, August 5, 1835, and published in their Transactions".

NL 0343444   MH

Liddell, Helen.
Education in occupied Germany. L'éducation de l'Allemagne occupée. ₍By₎ Helen Liddell, Edmond Vermeil ₍and₎ Bogdan Suchodolski. Edited by Helen Liddell. Paris, M. Rivière, 1949.
148 p. 22 cm.
"Studies ... prepared ... for a Conference on Some Aspects of the German Problem, held in Holland at Baarn from 6th-11th October, 1947, and at Scheveningen from 11th-17th April, 1948."
CONTENTS.—Introduction, by H. Liddell.—Les Alliés et la rééducation des Allemands, by E. Vermeil.—Notes sur la rééducation en zone française, by E. Vermeil.—Le problème d'une rééducation du peuple allemand, by B. Suchodolski.—Education in occupied Germany: a field survey, by H. Liddell.
1. Education—Germany—1945-   I. Title.   II. Title: L'éducation de l'Allemagne occupée.
LA721.8.L5   370.943   50-1658

DAU PU NcD ICU MB OC1W CtY OU
NL 0343445   DLC NNUN OrU OrP CaBVaU CtY DS NBC NBuU

Liddell, Henry.
... Blaine language from Truthful James. With 30 illustrations by G. Roberty, and numerous "cuts" by Henry Liddell. New York, Pâquet & cᵒ. ₍1888₎
cover-title. 31 l. illus. 14½ x 21ᶜᵐ.
1. Blaine, James Gillespie. 1830-1893—Portraits, caricatures, etc.   I. Roberty, Gabriel, illus.
      11-32626
Library of Congress   JK2263.1888.L6
Copyright 1888: 28010

NL 0343446   DLC OC1WHi

LIDDELL, Henry.
The wizard of the North; The Vampire bride; and other poems. Edinburgh, W. Blackwood, etc., etc., 1833.
pp.(8). 92.

NL 0343447   MH

Liddell, Henry Andrew.
... Oxfordshire, by H. A. Liddell ... With seventy illustrations. Oxford, Clarendon press, 1909.
1 p. 1., ₍5₎-260 p. incl. illus., pl., map. front. 19ᶜᵐ. (Oxford county histories)
Binder's title: History of Oxfordshire.
1. Oxfordshire, Eng.—Hist.
      A 16-910
Title from Enoch Pratt   Free Libr. Printed by L. C.

NL 0343448   MdBE MB

Liddell, Henry Andrew.
School history of Oxfordshire, by H.A. Liddell ... Oxford, Clarendon press, 1908.
256p. incl. front., illus., maps, diagrs., geneal. table. 19½cm.
1.Oxfordshire, Eng. - Hist.

NL 0343449   CtY

---

*
E700
.L54
1888
    Liddell, Henry
The evolution of a Democrat; a Darwinian tale. The jokes interpreted by Henry Liddell; illustrated by G. Roberty. New York, Paquet & Co., ᶜ1888.
47 plates. 21cm.
1. Democratic Party. 2. Tammany Hall. I. Roberty, Gabriel, illus. II. Title.

NL 0343450   ViU NNC OC1WHi RPB MH ICU

Liddell, Henry George, 1811-1898.
The abridged Liddell & Scott's Greek-English lexicon. With an appendix of proper and geographical names, prepared by James M. Whiton. 16th ed. Boston, Ginn brothers, 1876.

NL 0343451   MH NjR IU DN

Lmd81
C49
+1
    Liddell, Henry George, 1811-1898.
A commemoration sermon preached in the Cathedral church of Christ in Oxford on the Sunday after St.Frideswide's day, 1880, being the seven hundredth year after the opening of the present church. By H.G.Liddell ... [Oxford,1880]
16p. 22cm.
"Not for publication."

NL 0343452   CtY

Lmd28
872l
    Liddell, Henry George, 1811-1898.
Correspondence between the Very Reverend Henry George Liddell ... and Mr. Burgon, concerning a privilege of Convocation in respect of the nomination of select preachers. Oxford and London, J.Parker and co.,1872.
12p. 22cm.
Concerns the opposition of Burgon and others to the nomination of A.P.Stanley as one of the select preachers in Oxford university.
1.Stanley, Arthur Penrhyn, 1815-1881. I.Burgon, John William, 1813-1888. 2.Oxford. University - Sermons. Occasional. Madan cd.

NL 0343453   CtY

Liddell, Henry George, 1811-1898, and R. Scott.
A Greek-English lexicon based on the German work of Francis Passow. By Henry George Liddell...and Robert Scott... Oxford: Univ. Press, 1843. xviii, 1584 p. 8°.
411785A. 1. Greek language—   Dictionaries—English. 2. Scott,
Robert, 1811-1887, jt. au. 3. Passow   Franz Ludwig Carl Friedrich.
1786-1833.
      June 14, 1929

NL 0343454   NN CtY ICU MH

Liddell, Henry George, 1811-1898, and R. Scott.
A Greek-English lexicon, based on the German work of Francis Passow. By Henry George Liddell...and Robert Scott ... Oxford: Univ. Press, 1845. xix p., 812 l. 2. ed., rev. and enl. 8°.
408885A. 1. Greek language—   Dictionaries, English. 2. Passow
Franz Ludwig Carl Friedrich, 1786-   1833. 3. Scott, Robert, 1811-1887,
jt. au.   May 27, 1929

NL 0343455   NN ViU MiU ICU MH NjP CtY

VOLUME 332

Liddell, Henry George, 1811–1898.
A Greek-English lexicon, based on the German work of Francis Passow, by Henry George Liddell ... and Robert Scott ... With corrections and additions, and the insertion in alphabetical order of the proper names occurring in the principal Greek authors, by Henry Drisler ... New York, Harper & brothers [¹1846]

xxix, [2], 1705 p. 25¹ cm.

1. Greek language—Dictionaries—English.   I. Scott, Robert, 1811–1887, joint author.   II. Passow, Franz Ludwig Carl Friedrich, 1786–1833.   III. Drisler, Henry, 1818–1897, ed.

PA445.E5L6 1846   483.2   35—22447

OrLgE PHi
PPWe PPL PU ODW OC1 OC1h OO WaS WaWW Or NNBG PPC
NL   0343456   DLC CaBVaU NN NjP MH-L ViU NBB MH MB PPLT

Liddell, Henry George, 1811–1898.
A Greek-English lexicon based on the German work of F. Passow. By H.G. Liddell and R. Scott. Oxford, The University Press, 1848.
xix, 1623 p. 8°.
3d. ed.

NL   0343457   NN

PA
445
E5L6
1848

Liddell, Henry George, 1811–1898.
A Greek-English lexicon, based on the German work of Francis Passow, by Henry George Liddell and Robert Scott. With corrections and additions, and the insertion in alphabetical order of the proper names occurring in the principal Greek authors, by Henry Drisler. New York, Harper, 1848.
xxix, 1705 p. 26cm.

1. Greek language - Dictionaries - English.
I. Scott, Robert, 1811–1887, joint author.
II. Passow, Franz Ludwig Carl Friedrich, 1786–1833. III. Drisler, Henry, 1818–1897, ed. LC

NL   0343459   CLSU OCU MH PPC

Liddell, Henry George, 1811–1898.
A Greek-English lexicon, based on the German work of Francis Passow. By Henry George Liddell ... and Robert Scott ... Oxford, The University press, 1849.
xix, 1623 p. 24 cm.

"Third edition corrected."

1. Greek language - Dictionaries - English.
I. Scott, Robert, 1811–1887, joint author. II. Passow, Franz Ludwig Carl Friedrich, 1786–1833.

NL   0343460   Vi MH PPLT PP CaBVa

Liddell, Henry George, 1811–1898.
A Greek-English lexicon, based on the German work of Francis Passow. By Henry George Liddell ... and Robert Scott ... With corrections and additions, and the insertion in alphabetical order of the proper names occurring in the principal Greek authors, by Henry Drisler ... New York, Harper & brothers, 1850.

xxix, 1705 p. 26ᵐ.

1. Greek language—Dictionaries—English. 2. English language—Dictionaries—Greek.   I. Scott, Robert, 1811–1887, joint author. II. Passow, Franz Ludwig Carl Friedrich, 1786–1833. III. Drisler, Henry, 1818–1897, ed.

Library of Congress   PA445.E5L6 1850   17—31314

NL   0343461   DLC WaTC OrSaW PPC NIC OC1WHi MB ViU

Liddell, Henry George, 1811–1898.
A Greek-English lexicon, based on the German work of Francis Passow, by Henry George Liddell ... and Robert Scott ... With corrections and additions, and the insertion in alphabetical order of the proper names occurring in the principal Greek authors, by Henry Drisler ... New York, Harper & brothers, 1851.

xxix, 2, 1705 p. 26ᵐ.

1. Greek language—Dictionaries—English. I. Scott, Robert, 1811–1887, joint comp. II. Drisler, Henry, 1818–1897, ed. III. Passow, Franz Ludwig Carl Friedrich, 1786–1833.

14—13071

Library of Congress   PA445.E5L6 1856

NL   0343462   DLC ViU NjP

Liddell, Henry George, 1811–1898.
Greek-English lexicon, based on the German work of Francis Passow. With corrections and additions...by H. Drisler. New York: Harper & Bros., 1852. xxix, 1705 p. 4°.
By Henry George Liddell and Robert Scott.

1. Greek language.—Dictionaries   (English). 2. Scott, Robert, jt. au. 3. Drisler, Henry. editor. 4. Passow.   Franz Ludwig Karl Friedrich.   March 4, 1914.

NL   0343463   NN NNBG MiU MB NjP

Liddell, Henry George, 1811–1898.
A Greek-English lexicon, based on the German work of Francis Passow, by Henry George Liddell ... and Robert Scott ... With corrections and additions, and the insertion ... of the proper names occurring in the principal Greek authors, by Henry Drisler ... New York, Harper & brothers, 1854.

xxix, 2, 1705 p. 25¹ᵐ.

1. Greek language—Dictionaries—English.   I. Scott, Robert, 1811–1887, joint author. II. Passow, Franz Ludwig Carl Friedrich, 1786–1833. III. Drisler, Henry, 1818–1897, ed.

Library of Congress   PA445.E5L6 1854   10—23279

NL   0343464   DLC WU DNLM WaT ViU OC1

Liddell, Henry George, 1811–1898.
A Greek-English lexicon, based on the German work of Francis Passow, by Henry George Liddell ... and Robert Scott ... With corrections and additions, and the insertion ... of the proper names occurring in the principal Greek authors ... By Henry Drisler ... New York, Harper & brothers, 1855.

xxix, [2], 3-1705 p. 26ᵐ.

1. Greek language - Dictionaries - English. 2. English language—Dictionaries—Greek. I. Passow, Franz Ludwig Carl Friedrich, 1786-183. II. Scott, Robert, 1811–1887, joint author. III. Drisler, Henry, 1818–1897.

Library of Congre·   PA445.E5L6 1855   22-22203

NL   0343465   DLC CaBVa ViU PCM MB NN MdBF

PA445
.E5L6
1855a

Liddell, Henry George, 1811–1898.
A Greek-English lexicon, compiled by Henry George Liddell and Robert Scott. 4th ed., rev. throughout. Oxford, University Press, 1855.
1617 [1] p. 25 cm.

1. Greek language--Dictionaries--English.
2. English language--Dictionaries--Greek.
I. Scott, Robert, 1811–1887, jt. author.

NL   0343466   T CtY MnHi PPC PBm ICU PPL

Liddell, Henry George, 1811–1898.
A Greek-English lexicon, based on the German work of Francis Passow, by Henry George Liddell ... and Robert Scott ... With corrections and additions, and the insertion in alphabetical order of the proper names occurring in the principal Greek authors, by Henry Drisler ... New York, Harper & brothers, 1856.

xxix, 2, 1705 p. 26ᵐ.

1. Greek language—Dictionaries—English. I. Scott, Robert, 1811–1887, joint comp. II. Drisler, Henry, 1818–1897. III. Passow, Franz Ludwig Carl Friedrich, 1786–1833.

14—13071

Library of Congress   PA445.E5L6 1856

PPLT PPC
NL   0343467   DLC Wa OrStbM NcU NcD OCX MiU MB PPA

Liddell, Henry George, 1811–1898.
A Greek-English lexicon, based on the German work of Francis Passow, by Henry George Liddell ... and Robert Scott ... With corrections and additions, and the insertion in alphabetical order of the proper names occurring in the principal Greek authors, by Henry Drisler ... New York, Harper & brothers, 1857.

xxix, 2, 1705 p. 26ᵐ.

NL   0343468   ViU

QK9
.G7
L5
1858

Liddell, Henry George, 1811–1898.
A Greek-English lexicon, based on the German work of Francis Passow, by Henry George Liddell ... and Robert Scott ... With corrections and additions, and the insertion in alphabetical order of the proper names occurring in the principal Greek authors, by Henry Drisler ... New York, Harper & brothers, 1858.
xxix, 2, 1705 p. 23 cm.

NL   0343469   NNBG MB MH

PA445
.E5L6
1859

Liddell, Henry George, 1811–1898.
A Greek-English lexicon, based on the German work of Francis Passow. By Henry George Liddell ... and Robert Scott ... With corrections and additions, and the insertion in alphabetical order of the proper names occurring in the principal Greek authors, by Henry Drisler ... New York, Harper & brothers, 1859.

NL   0343470   ViU NjP PPRETS

HOUGHTON
READING
ROOM

Liddell, Henry George, 1811–1898.
A Greek-English lexicon, based on the German work of Francis Passow, by Henry George Liddell ... and Robert Scott ... With corrections and additions, and the insertion in alphabetical order of the proper names occurring in the principal Greek authors. By Henry Drisler ...
New York:Harper & brothers, publishers, 329 & 331 Pearl street, Franklin square, 1861.

xxix, 1705(i.e.1707)p. 26cm.
Pages 1*-2*   inserted.

NL   0343471   MH MdBP ODW

Liddell, Henry George, 1811–1898, and R. Scott.
A Greek-English lexicon; compiled by Henry George Liddle ...and Robert Scott... Oxford: Univ. Press, 1861. xi
1644 p. 5. ed., rev. and enl. 4°.

409899A. 1. Greek language—   Dictionaries, English. 2. Scott,
Robert, 1811–1887, jt. au.   May 31, 1929

NL   0343472   NN

Liddell, Henry George, 1811–1898.
A Greek-English lexicon, compiled by Henry George Liddell... and Robert Scott. 5th ed., rev. and augm.
Oxford, Clarendon press, etc. 1863.
1644 p.

NL   0343473   PHC

Liddell, Henry George, 1811–1898.
A Greek-English lexicon, based on the German work of Francis Passow, by Henry George Liddell and Robert Scott. With corrections and additions, and the insertion in alphabetical order of the proper names occurring in the principal Greek authors, by Henry Drisler. New York, Harper & brothers, 1864.

NL   0343474   MH PU-D MB

VOLUME 332

LIDDELL, Henry George, 1811-1898.
A Greek-English lexicon, based on the German work of Francis Passow, by H. G. Lidell and Robert Scott. With corrections and additions, and the insertion in Alphabetical order of the proper names occurring in the principal Greek authors, by Henry Drisler. New York, Harper & Brothers, 1867.

1.8°. pp. xxix. (2). 1705.

NL 0343475   MH

Liddell, Henry George, 1811-1898.
A Greek-English lexicon, based on the German work of Francis Passow. With corrections and additions...by H. Drisler. New York: Harper & Brothers, 1868.   xxix, 1 l., 1705 p.   4°.
By Henry George Liddell and Robert Scott.

1. Greek language.—Dictionaries   (Greek-English). 2. Scott, Robert, jt. au. 3. Drisler, Henry, editor.
December 18. 1911.

NL 0343476   NN MH

LIDDELL, Henry George, 1811-1898.
A Greek-English lexicon, based on the German work of Francis Passow, by H.G.Liddell and Robert Scott. With corrections and additions, and the insertion in alphabetical order of the proper names occurring in the principal Greek authors, by Henry Drisler. New York, Harper & Brothers, 1869.

1.8°. pp.xxix,(2),1705.

NL 0343477   MH OC1W NjP I PPC MB

Liddell, Henry George, 1811-1898.
A Greek-English lexicon compiled by Henry George Liddell ... and Robert Scott ... 6th ed., rev. and augm. Oxford, At the Clarendon press, sold by Macmillan and co. ₁etc.₎ London, 1869.
xvi, 1865 p. 27ᵐ.

1. Greek language—Dict.—English.   I. Scott, Robert, 1811-1887, joint author.
Library of Congress   PA445.E5L6 1869   10-25669

PPC PPT PPPD
NL 0343478   DLC WaU-L NjP MB NN NNUT NBuC CtY ViU

Liddell, Henry George, 1811-1898.
A Greek-English lexicon, based on the German work of Francis Passow, by Henry George Liddell and Robert Scott. With corrections and addition ...by Henry Drisler. New York, Harper & brothers, 1870.

NL 0343479   MH MiU OU ViU

LIDDELL, Henry George, 1811-1898.
A Greek-English lexicon, based on the German work of Francis Passow. By H.G.Liddell and Robert Scott. New York, Harper & Brothers, 1871.

NL 0343480   MH

Liddell, Henry George, 1811-1898.
A Greek-English lexicon, based on the German work of Francis-Passow, by Henry George Liddell ... and Robert Scott ... With corrections and additions, and the insertion in alphabetical order of the proper names occurring in the principal Greek authors, by Henry Drisler ...   New York, Harper & brothers, 1872.
xxix, [2], 1705 p.   26 cm.

NL 0343481   NcA-S

Liddell, Henry George, 1811-1898.
A Greek-English lexicon, based on the German work of Francis Passow, by Henry George Liddell and Robert Scott. With corrections and additions by Henry Drisler. New York, Harper & brothers, 1873.

NL 0343482   MH PU-F

Liddell, Henry George, 1811-1898.
A Greek-English lexicon, based on the German work of Francis Passow, by Henry George Liddell... and Robert Scott... with corrections and additions and the insertion in alphabetical order of the proper names occurring in the principal Greek authors, by Henry Drisler...
N.Y., Harper, 1874.
1698 p.

NL 0343483   PPC OrCS NjP

PA445
.E5
L5
1874
Liddell, Henry George, 1811-1898.
A Greek-English lexicon, based on the German work of Francis Passow, by Henry George Liddell and Robert Scott. With corrections and additions by Henry Drisler. New York, Harper, 1874.
1705 p. 26cm.

NL 0343484   OrCS

Liddell, Henry George, 1811-1898, comp.
Greek-English lexicon. Compiled by Henry George Liddell and Robert Scott. 6th ed., rev. and augmented. Oxford, At the Clarendon Press, 1875.

xvi, 1865 p.

NL 0343485   MH-G MH NcA

Liddell, Henry George, 1811-1898.
A Greek-English lexicon, based on the German work of Francis-Passow, by Henry George Liddell ... and Robert Scott ... With corrections and additions, and the insertion in alphabetical order of the proper names occurring in the principal Greek authors, by Henry Drisler ...   New York, Harper & brothers, 1876.
xxix, ₍2₎, 1705 p. 26 cm.

1. Greek language—Dictionaries—English.   I. Scott, Robert, 1811-1887, joint author. II. Drisler, Henry, 1818-1897, ed.

PA445.E5L6 1876   483.2   4—20108

NL 0343486   DLC OC1W OU OrP WaWW

LIDDELL, Henry George, 1811-1898.
A Greek-English lexicon. Compiled by Henry George Liddell and Robert Scott. 6th ed., revised and augmented. New York, Harper and Bros., 1878.

4°.

NL 0343487   MH ODW PV IU

PA445
.E5L6
1879
Liddell, Henry George, 1811-1898.
A Greek-English lexicon, based on the German work of Francis Passow, by Henry George Liddell and Robert Scott. With corrections and additions, and the insertion in alphabetical order of the proper names occurring in the principal Greek authors, by Henry Drisler. New York, Harper, 1879 ₍c1846₎
xxix, 1705p. 26cm.

1. Greek language—Dictionaries—English. I. Scott, Robert, 1811-1887, joint author. II. Passow, Franz Ludwig Carl Friedrich, 1786-1833. iii.   Drisler, Henry, 1818-1897, ed.

NL 0343488   OrPS

PA445
E5
L6
1880
Liddell, Henry George, 1811-1898.
A Greek-English lexicon compiled by Henry George Liddell...And Robert Scott...6th. ed., rev. and augm. New York, Harper & brothers, 1880.
XVI, 1865p. 27 cm.

1. Greek language--Dictionaries--English. I. Scott, Robert, 1811-1887. II. Title.

NL 0343489   RPJCB CtY ViU

Liddell, Henry George, 1811-1898, and R. Scott.
A Greek-English lexicon; compiled by Henry George Liddell ... and Robert Scott...   New York: Harper and Bros., 1881.
xvi, 1865 p.   6. ed., rev. and enl.   4°.

173681A.   1. Greek languages—Dic-   tionaries—English. 2. Scott, Robert, 1811-1887.
May 28, 1925

NL 0343490   NN WaS CtY MdBP ViU

PA
445
.E5L6
1882
Liddell, Henry George, 1811-1898.
A Greek-English lexicon, compiled by Henry George Liddell ...and Robert Scott. 7th ed., rev. and augm. throughout with the cooperation of Professor Drisler. New York, Harper & brothers, 1882.
xvi, 1776 p. 30 cm.

1. Greek language--Dictionaries--English. I. Scott, Robert, 1811-1887, joint author. II. Drisler, Henry, 1818-1897. III. Title

NL 0343491   OKentU

---

*
PA445
.E5L6
1882
Liddell, Henry George, 1811-1898.
A Greek-English lexicon, compiled by Henry George Liddell and Robert Scott. 8th ed. rev. throughout. New York, American Book Co. ₍1882₎
xiv, 1776 p. 30 cm.
With ms. annotations of R. H. Webb.

I. Scott, Robert, 1811-1887, joint author. II. Drisler, Henry, 1818-1897.

NL 0343492   ViU CtY

Liddell, Henry George, 1811-1898.
A Greek-English lexicon, comp. by Henry George Liddell ... and Robert Scott ... 7th ed., rev. and augm. throughout with the cooperation of Professor Drisler ...   New York, Harper & brothers, 1883.
xvi, 1776 p. 29ᵐ.

1. Greek language—Dictionaries—English.   I. Scott, Robert, 1811-1887, joint comp. II. Drisler, Henry, 1818-1897.
4—13158
Library of Congress   PA445.E5L6 1883
₍a45o1₎   483.2

MB NNBG OrP OrPR MtU IdB WaE
NBB MH MB NjP NNUT ViU DNLM PPC PSC PPLT PPPD PU
NL 0343493   DLC NjP DN OU OCU MiU OC1WHi OC1 DN-Ob

VOLUME 332

Folio
PA445
.E5
L6
1883a
Liddell, Henry George, 1811-1898.
A Greek-English lexicon, comp. by Henry George Liddell and Robert Scott. 7th ed., rev. and augm. throughout. Oxford, Clarendon Press, 1883.
1776p. 30cm.

1. Greek language - Dictionaries - English. I. Scott, Robert, 1811-1887, joint comp.

NL 0343494 NcU

Liddell, Henry George, 1811-1898.
A Greek-English lexicon, compiled by Henry George Liddell ... and Robert Scott ... 7th ed., rev. and augm. throughout with the cooperation of Professor Drisler ... New York, Harper & brothers, 1889.
xvi, 1776 p. 29½cm.

1. Greek language—Dictionaries—English. I. Scott, Robert, 1811-1887, joint author. II. Drisler, Henry, 1818-1897.

35-22459

Library of Congress PA445.E5L6 1889 483.2

PSC PP
NL 0343495 DLC OrU MeB MiU NjP MdBP ODW OOxM ViU

Liddell, Henry George, 1811-1898, and R. Scott.
A Greek-English lexicon, compiled by Henry George Liddell ...and Robert Scott... Oxford: Clarendon Press, 1890. xvi, 1776 p. 7. ed., rev. and enl. 4°.

303275A. 1. Greek language—Dictionaries, English. 2. Scott, Robert, 1811-1887, jt. au.
August 2, 1927

NL 0343496 NN CaBVaU MH ICJ PPC

Liddell, Henry George, 1811-1898.
Greek-English lexicon: 7. ed. New York, 1894.

NL 0343497 NjP OClW

Liddell, Henry George, 1811-1898.
A Greek-English lexicon, comp. by Henry George Liddell ... and Robert Scott ... Rev. and augm. throughout with the cooperation of Professor Drisler ... 8th ed. New York, Cincinnati [etc.] American book company [pref. 1897]
xvi, 1776 p. 29½ cm.
Title-page and pages [v]-viii, 1765-1776 wanting; supplied in photostat.

1. Greek language—Dictionaries—English. I. Scott, Robert, 1811-1887, joint author. II. Drisler, Henry, 1818-1897, ed.

PA445.E5L6 1897a 4-14685

Library of Congress [a54v1]

IdU WaS PPAN PPCCH ViU
PV NN NcRS MoU NcD OrP WaT WaSp CaBVa OrCS OrStbM
NL 0343498 DLC DNLM OLak DDO MH PPT PBm MB NIC PU

Liddell, Henry George, 1811-1898.
A Greek-English lexicon comp. by Henry George Liddell ... and Robert Scott ... Rev. and augm. throughout with the cooperation of Professor Drisler ... 8th ed. New York, Harper & brothers, 1897.
xvi. 1778 p. 30cm.

1. Greek language—Dictionaries—English. I. Scott, Robert, 1811-1887, joint author. II. Drisler, Henry, 1818-1897, ed.

22-14779

PA445.E5L6 1897

DNC
NL 0343499 DLC MB ViU TU OCl DP OO OEac DAU NjP

PA445
E5L6
1901
Liddell, Henry George, 1811-1898.
A Greek-English lexicon, compiled by Henry George Liddell and Robert Scott. 8th ed., rev. throughout. Oxford, Clarendon Press, 1901.
xvi,1776 p. 30cm.

1.Greek language - Dictionaries - English. I.Scott, Robert, 1811-1887.

NL 0343500 CSt TU NjP CtY PU

Liddell, Henry George, 1811-1898.
A Greek-English lexicon, compiled by Henry George Liddell ... and Robert Scott ... A new ed. rev. and augm. throughout by Sir Henry Stuart Jones ... with the assistance of Roderick McKenzie ... and with the co-operation of many scholars ... Oxford, At the Clarendon press [1925-40]
2 v. 30cm.
Paged continuously.
Issued in 10 parts, 1925-40.

1. Greek language—Dictionaries—English. I. Scott, Robert, 1811-1887, joint author. II. Jones, Henry Stuart, 1867-1939, ed. III. McKenzie, Roderick, 1887-1937.

25-20501 Revised

Library of Congress PA445.E5L6 1925

NcD MH-AH NjNbS
OOxM MiU ICJ IU NN ViU MdBWA PPC PPT PSC PBm PU TU
NL 0343501 DLC NjR OClCC CtY OClW OClJC OCX OCl MB

Liddell, Henry George, 1811-1898.
Liddell & Scott Greek-English lexicon abridged. 25th ed., revised and enlarged with an appendix of proper and geographical names prepared by George Ricker Berry ... Chicago, Ill., Follett publishing company, 1927.
2 p. l., 835 p. 19½cm.

1. Greek language—Dictionaries—English. 2. English language—Dictionaries—Greek. I. Berry, George Ricker, 1865-

NL 0343502 MiU IU-M

Liddell, Henry George, 1811-1898.
A Greek-English lexicon, compiled by Henry George Liddell ... and Robert Scott ... 8th ed., rev. throughout. Oxford, The Clarendon press; [etc., etc., 1929]
xvi, 1776 p. 29½cm.
"Impression of 1929; first edition, 1843; eighth edition, 1897."

1. Greek language — Dictionaries — English. 2. English language—Dictionaries—Greek. I. Scott, Robert, 1811-1887, joint author.

30-14625

Library of Congress PA445.E5L6 1929

483.2

NL 0343503 DLC OrPR MBCo NIC CtY OrPR

SSS
2522
.584
.1930
Liddell, Henry George, 1811-1898.
Greek-English lexicon; abridged, 25th ed., rev. and enl. with an appendix of proper and geographical names, prepared by George Ricker Berry. Chicago, Follett, 1930.
835 p. 20 cm.

At head of title: Liddell & Scott.

1. GREEK LANGUAGE - DICTIONARIES - ENGLISH I. Scott, Robert, 1811-1887, joint author.

NL 0343504 NjP

R
483
L712f
Liddell, Henry George, 1811-1898.
Liddell & Scott Greek-English lexicon, abridged. 25th ed., rev and enl. with an Appendix of proper and geographical names, prepared by George Ricker Berry ... Chicago, Ill., Follett publishing company, 1938.

2p. l., 835p. 20cm

On cover: Classic dictionary.

1. Greek language-Dictionaries-English. I. Scott, Robert, 1811-1887, joint author. II. Berry, George Ricker, 1865- III. Title: Classic dictionary.

NL 0343505 CLi

Liddell, Henry George, 1811-1898.
... Greek-English lexicon, abridged. 26th ed. Revised and enlarged, with an appendix of proper and geographical names prepared by George Ricker Berry... Chicago, Illinois, Follett publishing company, 1939 [c1927]
2 p. l., 835 p. 20.5 cm.

NL 0343506 OU

PA
+445
+E5
L6
5
Liddell, Henry George, 1811-1898.
A Greek-English lexicon, compiled by Henry George Liddell and Robert Scott. A new ed. rev. and augm. throughout by Sir Henry Stuart Jones with the assistance of Roderick McKenzie and with the cooperation of many scholars. [9th ed.] Oxford, Clarendon Press [1940]
2 v. in 1. 30cm.
Paged continuously.
1. Greek language - Dictionaries - English I. Scott, Robert, 1811-1887, joint author II. Jones, Henry Stuart, 1867-1939, ed. III. McKenzie, Roderick, 1887-1937

TU OKentU FMU KEmT DSI NIC WaU IaU MH CU NIC
NL 0343507 WU PPDrop ODW PPWe LU CU MH FTaSU OOxM

Liddell, Henry George, 1811-1898.
Liddell & Scott Greek-English lexicon, abridged. 26th ed., rev. and enl. with an Appendix of proper and geographical names, prepared by George Ricker Berry ... Chicago, Ill., Follett publishing company, 1941.
2 p. l., 835 p. 20 cm.
On cover: Classic dictionary.
First published in 1845 under title: A lexicon chiefly for the use of schools, abridged from the Greek-English lexicon.

1. Greek language—Dictionaries—English. I. Scott, Robert, 1811-1887, joint author. II. Berry, George Ricker, 1865- III. Title: Classic dictionary.

PA445.E5L7 1941 483.2 42—16367

NL 0343508 DLC OrStbM

Liddell, Henry George, 1811-1898, comp.
A Greek-English lexicon. Compiled by H.G. Liddell and Robert Scott, a new ed. rev. and augm. throughout by Henry Stuart Jones. Clarendon Press, 1948.
2 v.

NL 0343509 WaSp

483.2
L61g
1941r
Geol
Lib'y
LIDDELL, HENRY GEORGE, 1811-1898.
Liddell & Scott Greek-English lexicon, abridged. 26th ed., rev. and enl. with an Appendix of proper and geographical names, prepared by George Ricker Berry ... Chicago, Ill., Follett publishing company, 1949.
2p.l.,835p. 21cm.
On cover: Classic dictionaries.
"Eighth printing."
1. Greek language - Dictionaries - English. I. Scott, Robert, 1811-1887, joint author. II. Berry, George Ricker, 1865- III. Title: Classic dictionaries.

NL 0343510 TxU PU DLC

PA
445
.E5
L71
1951
Liddell, Henry George, 1811-1898.
A Greek-English lexicon, compiled by Henry George Liddell and Robert Scott. A new [9th] ed., rev. and augm. throughout by Sir Henry Stuart Jones, with the assitance of Roderick McKenzie, and with the co-operation of many scholars. Oxford, Clarendon Press [1951]
2 v. (xlviii, 2111 p.) 30 cm.

1. Greek language - Dictionaries - English. I. Scott, Robert, 1811-1887, joint author. II. Jones, Henry Stuart, 1867-1939, ed. III. McKenzie, Roderick, 1887-1937.

NL 0343511 DCU MH NIC NNC

VOLUME 332

PA
445
.E5
L712
1953

Liddell, Henry George, 1811-1898.
A Greek-English lexicon, compiled by Henry
George Liddell and Robert Scott. A new ed., rev.
and augm. throughout by Sir Henry Stuart Jones
with the assistance of Roderick McKenzie and with
the co-operation of many scholars. Oxford, Clarendon Press ₍1953₎
2 v. in l. 29 cm.

1. Greek language--Dictionaries--English. I.
Scott, Robert, 1811-1887, joint author. II. Jones,
Sir Henry Stuart,   1867-1939, ed. III. McKen
zie, Roderick, 1887-   1927.

NL 0343512   MiU NjR MdBJ MH NjP NN

Liddell, Henry George, 1811-1898.
A history of Rome, from the earliest times to
the establishment of the Empire.
New York, n.d.
751 p.

NL 0343513   PHi PPWe

Liddell, Henry George, 1811-1898.
A history of Rome from the earliest times to the establishment of the empire. By Henry G. Liddell ... London, J.
Murray, 1855.
2 v. plans. 22½ᶜᵐ.

1. Rome—Hist.—Kings, ʙ. ᴄ. 753–510. 2. Rome—Hist.—Republic,
ʙ. ᴄ. 510–30.
                                        4—37244
Library of Congress   DG231.L71

        PPL NjP MdBP
NL 0343514   DLC OrP MeB MH NIC NcU MeB CLSU OCl MiU

LIDDELL, Henry George, 1811-1898.
A history of Rome from the earliest times to
the establishment of the empire, with chapters on
the history of literature and art. Lond., J.
Murray, 1857.

19 cm. pp.x,768. Front., maps, and other
illustr.

NL 0343515   MH OOxM PPL

Liddell, Henry George, 1811-1898.
A history of Rome, from the earliest times to
the establishment of the empire. With chapters
on the history of literature and art. New York,
Harper & brothers, 1858.
768p.

NL 0343516   MH NN DNW PPT NCsC

Liddell, Henry George, 1811-1898.
A history of Rome from the earliest times to
the establishment of the Empire; with chapters on
the history of literature and art. New York,
Harper & Brothers, 1859.
x, 768 p. illus. 20 cm.
Bibliographical footnotes.
1. Rome. Hist. Kings, B.C. 753-510. 2. Rome
Hist. Republic, B.C., 510-30.

NL 0343517   IEG MB NjP MH

Liddell, Henry George, 1811-1898.
A history of Rome, from the earliest times to the establishment of the empire. With chapters on the history of literature and art. By Henry G. Liddell ... New York, Harper
& brothers, 1860.
x, 768 p. incl. front., illus. 19½ᶜᵐ.
First English edition, 1855.

NL 0343518   ViU NjP MB MH OO MiU PPLT

Liddell, Henry George, 1811-1898.
History of Rome from the earliest times
to the establishment of the Empire...
N.Y. 1861.

NL 0343519   ODW WaSpG

Liddell, Henry George, 1811-1898.
A history of Rome, from the earliest times to the establishment of the empire. With chapters on the history of literature and art. By Henry G. Liddell ... New York, Harper
& brothers, 1863.
x, 768 p. incl. front., illus. 19½ᶜᵐ.
First English edition, 1855.

NL 0343520   ViU NcD

LIDDELL, Henry George, 1811-1898.
A history of Rome, from the earliest times to
the establishment of the Empire, with chapters
on the history of literature and art. New York,
Harper & Brothers, 1864.

20 cm. pp.x, 768. Front., maps., plans, and
other illustr.

NL 0343521   MH OCU

Liddell, Henry George, 1811-1898.
A history of Rome, from the earliest times to
the establishment of the empire, with chapters on
the history of literature and art...
New York, Harper, 1865.
768 p.

NL 0343522   PBa

Liddell, Henry George, 1811-1898.
The student's Rome; a history of Rome from the
earliest times to the ... empire with chapters
on the history of literature and art. New ed.
London, 1867.

NL 0343523   PPL

Liddell, Henry George, 1811-1898.
A history of Rome, from the earliest times to the establishment of the empire. With chapters on the history of literature and art. By Henry G. Liddell ... New York, Harper
& brothers, 1868.
x, 768 p. incl. front., illus. 20cm.
First English edition, 1855.

NL 0343524   MeB

2
2913

Liddell, Henry George, 1811-1898.
A history of Rome from the earliest times to
the establishment of the empire. London, J.
Murray, 1869.
676 p. 12°.

NL 0343525   DLC

Liddell, Henry George, 1811-1898.
A history of Rome, from the earliest times to
the establishment of the empire. With chapters
on the history of literature and art. New York,
Harper & brothers, 1870.

Spine: The student's histories.

NL 0343526   MH PSC PU ViU

Liddell, Henry George, 1811-1898.
History of Rome, from the earliest times to
the establishment of the empire. With Chapters
on the history of literature and art. New York,
Harper & brothers, 1871.

"Student's series."

NL 0343527   MH

Liddell, Henry George, 1811-1898.
A history of Rome, from the earliest times to
the establishment of the empire. With chapters
on the history of literature and art. New York,
Harper & brothers, 1872.

Spine: The student's series.

NL 0343528   MH OFH

Liddell, Henry George, 1811-1898.
A history of Rome, from the earliest times to
the establishment of the empire. With chapters
on the history of literature and art. Illustrated by
numerous woodcuts. New York, Harper &
Brothers, 1873.
x, 768 p. 12°.

NL 0343529   NN

Liddell, Henry George, 1811-1898.
A history of Rome, from the earliest times to the establishment of the empire. With chapters on the history of literature and art. By Henry G. Liddell ... New York, Harper
& brothers, 1876.
x, 768 p. incl. front., illus. 19½ cm.
First English edition, 1855.

1. Rome—Hist.—Kings, 753–510 ʙ. ᴄ. 2. Rome—Hist.—Republic,
510–30 ʙ. ᴄ.
DG231.L71 1868   A 12—467
Stanford Univ. Library
for Library of Congress   ₍a56k1₎†

        DLC
NL 0343530   CSt ViU MsU WaTC OrP IdU WaS OrSaW OrU

Liddell, Henry George, 1811-1898.
A history of Rome, from the earliest times
to the establishment of the empire. With
chapters on the history of literature and
art. ... New York, Harper & brothers ₍1876₎
1878.

(Student's ser.)

NL 0343531   OClW

Liddell, Henry George, 1811-1898.
The student's Rome; a history of Rome, from the
earliest times to the establishment of the Empire;
new ed...London, 1879.
12°

NL 0343532   NN

Liddell, Henry George, 1811-1898.
A history of Rome, from the earliest times to
the establishment of the empire. With chapters
on the history of literature and art. By Henry G.
Liddell ... New York, Harper & brothers,
1879.
x, 768 p. incl. front., illus. 19.5 cm.
[The student's series]
First English edition, 1855.
1. Rome-History-Kings, B.C. 753-510.
2. Rome-History-Republic, B.C. 510-530.
I. Ser.

NL 0343533   ViU

VOLUME 332

Liddell, Henry George, 1811–1898.
A history of Rome, from the earliest times to the
establishment of the empire. With chapters on
the history of literature and art. By Henry G.
Liddell ...   New York, Harper & brothers, 1881.
x, 768 p.   incl. front., illus.   19.5 cm.
[The student's series]
First English edition, 1855.
1. Rome-History-Kings, B. C. 753-510.
2. Rome-History-Republic, B. C. 510-530.
I. Ser.

NL   0343534   ViU

Lidell, Henry George, 1811–1898.
History of Rome, from the earliest times
to the establishment of the empire, with
chapters on the history of literature and
art, by ... New York, Harper & bros. 1882.
768 p.

NL   0343535   OClND

Liddell, Henry George, 1811–1898.
The student's history of Rome, from the earl-
iest times to the establishment of the empire.
N.Y., 1883.   12°

NL   0343536   I

LIDDELL, Henry G[eorge], 1811–1898.
A history of Rome, from the earliest times to
the establishment of the empire.... New York,
Harper & Brothers, 1884.

"The student's series."

NL   0343537   MH NjP

LIDDELL, Henry George, 1811–1898.
A history of Rome, from the earliest times to
the establishment of the empire... New York,
Harper & Brothers, 1886.

NL   0343538   MH

Liddell, Henry George, 1811–1898.
A history of Rome from the earliest
times to the establishment of the empire.
With chapters on the history of literature and art. New ed. Lond.,Murray,
1889.   672p.illus.map.(fold.) (The
student's Rome)

NL   0343539   CaBVa

Liddell, Henry George, 1811–1898.
A history of Rome, from the earliest times to the establishment of the empire. With chapters on the history of literature and art. By Henry G. Liddell ... New York, Harper
& brothers, 1890.
x, 768 p. incl. front., illus. 19½cm. The student's series,
First English edition, 1855.

NL   0343540   ViU

Liddell, Henry George, 1811–1898.
A history of Rome, from the earliest times to the establishment of the empire. With chapters on the history of literature and art. By Henry G. Liddell ... New York, Harper
& brothers, 1891.
x, 768 p. incl. front., illus. 19½cm. (The student's series)
First English edition, 1855.
Title vignette

NL   0343541   ViU

DG231
.L71
1893
Liddell, Henry George, 1811–1898.
A history of Rome, from the earliest times to the establishment of the empire. With chapters on the history of literature and art. By Henry G. Liddell ... New York, Harper
& brothers, 1893.
x, 768 p. incl. front., illus. 19½cm.   The student's series,
First English edition, 1855.

NL   0343542   ViU

Liddell, Henry George, 1811–1898.
A history of Rome, from the earliest times to the establishment of the empire. With chapters on the history of literature and art. By Henry G. Liddell ... New York, Harper
& brothers, 1895.
x, 768 p. incl. front., illus. 19½cm. (The student's series)
First English edition, 1855.

NL   0343543   ViU

Liddell, Henry George, 1811–1898.
A history of Rome from the earliest times to
the establishment of the empire. By Henry C.
Liddell ... Harper & brothers, 1896.
768 p. plans. 22½ cm.

NL   0343544   DNW ViU

Liddell, Henry George, 1811–1898.
A history of Rome, from the earliest times to the establishment of the empire. With chapters on the history of literature and art. By Henry G. Liddell ... New York, London,
Harper & brothers, 1899.
x, 768 p. incl. front., illus. 19½cm.   The student's series,
First English edition, 1855.

NL   0343545   ViU

Liddell, Henry George, 1811–1898.
A history of Rome, from the earliest times to the
establishment of the empire. With chapters on the history of literature and art. By Henry G. Liddell ... New
York (etc.) American book company (190-?)
x, 768 p. incl. front., illus. 19½cm.
1st English ed., 1855.

1. Rome — Hist. — Kings, B. C. 753-510. 2. Rome — Hist. — Republic,
B. C. 510-30.
A 12-468
Title from Leland Stan-   ford Jr. Univ. Printed by L. C.

NL   0343546   CSt OrP

Liddell, Henry George, 1811–1898, and R. Scott.
An intermediate Greek-English lexicon founded upon the
seventh edition of Liddell and Scott's Greek-English lexicon.
New York: Amer. Book Co. (1888.)   910 p.   sq. 8°.

118982A. 1. Greek language.—Dic-   tionaries (English). 2. English
language.—Dictionaries (Greek).   3. Scott, Robert, 1811-87, jt. au.
                                                       March 7, 1924.

        MoU OClUr
NL   0343547   NN NcD OOxM CaBVaU MB MtBC OCl TU WaU

Liddell, Henry George, 1811–1898.
An intermediate Greek-English lexicon, founded upon the
seventh edition of Liddell and Scott's Greek-English lexicon.
New York, Harper & brothers, 1889.
2 p. l., 910 p. 22½ x 18cm.

1. Greek language—Dictionaries—English. 2. English language—Dictionaries—Greek.   I. Scott, Robert, 1811-1887, joint author.
                                                       7—13516
Library of Congress   PA445.E5L7 1889

        WaSp IdU
NL   0343548   DLC MiU OU OCU OO NcU FU-HC KU MtBC WaS

PA445
E5L7
1889
Liddell, Henry George, 1811–1898.
An intermediate Greek-English lexicon,
founded upon the seventh edition of Liddell and
Scott's Greek-English lexicon.   Oxford, At
the Clarendon Press c1889,
910p. 23cm.

1. Greek language - Dictionaries - English.
2. English language - Dictionaries - Greek.
I. Scott, Robert, 1811-1887, jt.author.

NL   0343549   IaU MU NIC NjP NcRS DAU

PA445
.E5L7
1890
Liddell, Henry George, 1811–1898.
An intermediate Greek-English lexicon,
founded upon the seventh edition of Liddell
and Scott's Greek-English lexicon. New
York, American Book Co. (189-)
910 p. 23cm.

1. Greek language—Dictionaries—English. I.
Scott, Robert, 1811-1887, joint author.

NL   0343550   ViU

Liddell, Henry George, 1811–1898.
An intermediate Greek-English lexicon, founded
upon the seventh edition of Liddell and Scott's
Greek-English lexicon. New York, Harper & brothers
1892.
2 p.l., 910 p. 22½ x 18cm.
1. Greek language—Dictionaries—English. 2.
English langauge—Dictionaries—Greek. I. Scott,
Robert, 1811-1887, joint author.

NL   0343551   ViU

· Liddell, Henry George, 1811–1898.
An intermediate Greek-English lexicon, founded upon the
seventh edition of Liddell and Scott's Greek English lexicon.
New York, Harper & brothers, 1897 (c1889)
2 p. l., 910 p. 23 cm.
On spine: Liddell & Scott's Greek-English
lexicon, intermediate.

NL   0343552   NcD

Liddell, Henry George, 1811–1898.
An intermediate Greek-English lexicon
founded upon the seventh edition of
Liddell and Scott's Greek-English lexicon.
New York, Harper & brothers, 1900.

NL   0343553   OCl NjP

PA445
E5L6
1900
Liddell, Henry George, 1811–1898.
An intermediate Greek-English lexicon, founded upon
the seventh edition of Liddell and Scott's Greek-English
lexicon. Oxford, Clarendon Press, 1900.
2 p. l., 910 p. 22½ x 18cm.

1. Scott, Robert, 1811-1887, joint author. II. Title. 1. Greek
language - Dictionaries - English.

NL   0343554   CU-B PPYH

Liddell, Henry George, 1811–1898.
A history of Rome to the establishment of the Empire, with chap-
ters on the history of literature and art. A new edition, in part
re-written by P. V. M. Benecke.
— London. Murray. 1901. xxxix, 750 pp. Illus. Plates. Maps.
Sm. 8°.

                                                       1901
E1912 — Rome. Hist. — Benecke, Paul Victor Mendelssohn, ed.

NL   0343555   MB

VOLUME 332

937.02
L71ha Liddell, Henry George, 1811-1898.
A history of Rome, from the earliest times to the establishment of the Empire. With chapters on the history of literature and art. A new ed. thoroughly rev. and in part re-written by P. V. M. Benecke. Lond., J. Murray, 1909.
750p. illus., maps (3 fold. col.)

D5049 1. Rome--Hist.--Kings, B. C. 753-510. 2. Rome--Hist.--Republic, B. C. 510-30. I. Benecke, P V M

NL 0343556 RP OCU MiD

O.R.
483.2
L712I Liddell, Henry George, 1811-1898.
An intermediate Greek-English lexicon, founded upon the 7th ed. of Liddell and Scott's Greek-English lexicon. Oxford, Clarendon Press [1930]
910 p. 23 cm.
This ed. first published 1889.

1. Greek language. Dictionaries. English. 2. English language. Dictionaries. Greek. I. Scott, Robert, 1811-1887, jt. au. II. Title. III. Title: Greek-English lexicon.

NL 0343557 NcD

5980
7433
1955 Liddell, Henry George, 1811-1898.
An intermediate Greek-English lexicon, founded upon the 7th ed. of Liddell and Scott's Greek-English lexicon. Oxford, Clarendon Press, [1955]
910 p. 23cm.

1. Greek language--Dictionaries. I. Scott, Robert, 1811-1887, joint author. II. Title.

NL 0343558 CU-E MiU NNC MB

LIDDELL, Henry George, 1811-1898.
A lexicon abridged from the Greek-English lexicon of H.G.Liddell and R.Scott. 4th ed. Oxford, at the University Press, 1852.

18.5 x 15 cm. pp.iv,804.

NL 0343559 MH

Liddell, Henry George, 1811-1898.
A lexicon abridged from Liddell and Scott's Greek-English lexicon. 7th ed. Oxford, University Press, 1859.
782 p.

NL 0343560 NNC

Liddell, Henry George, 1811-1898.
A lexicon abridged from Liddell and Scott's Greek-English lexicon. 8th ed. Philadelphia, J. B. Lippincott and co., 1860.
782 p.

NL 0343561 OFH PU

Liddell, Henry George, 1811-1898.
A lexicon abridged from Liddell and Scott's Greek-English lexicon; 10th edition. Oxford, Clarendon Press, 1863.

782p. 19cm.

NL 0343562 PLatS

Liddell, Henry George, 1811-1898.
A lexicon abridged form Liddell & Scott's Greek-English lexicon. The 11th ed. Oxford, Clarendon press, 1864.

2 p.l., 782 p.

NL 0343563 OC1W CaBVa CtY

Liddell, Henry George, and Robert Scott, D.D., 1811-1887.
A lexicon abridged from Liddell and Scott's Greek-English lexicon. 12th edition.
Philadelphia. Lippincott & Co. 1868. (4), 782 pp. 18 cm., in 16s.

H3934 — Jt. auth. — Greece. Lang. Dict.

NL 0343564 MB PPF NNC

LIDDELL, [Henry George], 1811-1898
A lexicon abridged from Liddell and Scott's Greek-English Lexicon. 13th ed. Oxford, The Clarendon press, 1869.

sm.4 °. pp.(4).782†.

NL 0343565 MH

Liddell, Henry George, 1811-1898.
A lexicon abridged from Liddell and Scott's Greek-English lexicon. The 13th ed. Boston, Ginn brothers, 1871.

1 p. l., (2), 804 p. 19cm.

1. Greek language — Dictionaries — English. 2. English language — Dictionaries—Greek. I. Scott, Robert, 1811-1887, joint author.

NL 0343566 MiU

Liddell, Henry George, 1811-1898.
A lexicon abridged from Liddell & Scott's Greek-English lexicon; carefully rev. throughout, with an appendix of proper and geographical names arranged by Rev. James M. Whiton, PH. D. New York, American Book Co. [1871]
831 p. 19cm.

CtY
NL 0343567 NIC OrU GEU CLSU TU MH PPLT ViU NjP NcD

Liddell, Henry George, 1811-1898.
A lexicon abridged from Liddell & Scott's Greek-English lexicon. The 24th ed. New York, Economy book house [1871]

804 p. 21 cm.

NL 0343568 MH

483.2
L712ga
1871 Liddell, Henry George, 1811-1898.
A lexicon abridged from Liddell and Scott's Geeek-English lexicon. Oxford, At the Clarendon press [1871]
Science 804p.

On spine: Greek-English lexicon.
"... completely revised ... and considerably enlarged ..."
1. Greek language - Dictionaries-English. I. Scott, Robert, 1811-1887, jt. author. II. Title. III. Gre   ek-English lexicon.

NL 0343569 TxDaM

Liddell, Henry George, 1811-1898.
A lexicon abridged from Liddell and Scott's Greek-English lexicon. The fourteenth edition. Boston, Ginn bros. 1872.
2. p.l., 804 p. D

NL 0343570 OO MH ViLxW PU

Liddell, Henry George, 1811-1898.
A lexicon; abridged from Liddell and Scott's Greek-English lexicon. 15th ed., carefully revised throughout. Oxford, Clarendon press, 1872.

NL 0343571 MH PPDrop PU-L

PA
445
.E5
.L7
1874 Liddell, Henry George, 1811-1898.
A lexicon abridged from Liddell and Scott's Greek-English lexicon. 16th ed., carefully rev. throughout. Oxford, Clarendon Press, 1874.
804 p.
#Greek language--Dictionaries--English.
(A)Scott, Robert, 1811-1887, joint author.

NL 0343572 MoU MB

Liddell, Henry George, 1811-1898.
A lexicon abridged from Liddell & Scott's Greek-English lexicon. The 14th ed. Boston, Ginn brothers, 1875.

2 p. l., 881 p. 19cm.

1. Greek language—Dictionaries—English. I. Scott, Robert, 1811-1887, joint author.

33-31054

Library of Congress PA445.E5L7 1875 483.2

NL 0343573 DLC MtU

Liddell, Henry George, 1811-1898.
A lexicon abridged from Liddell and Scott's Greek-English lexicon. The 17th ed., carefully revised throughout. Oxford, Clarendon press, etc., etc., 1876.

804 p. 19.5 cm.

NL 0343574 MH PU

Liddell, Henry George, 1811-1898.
A lexicon abridged from Liddell and Scott's Greek-English lexicon. 17th ed., carefully rev. throughout. With an appendix of proper and geographical names, prepared by Rev. James M. Whiton ... New York, Harper & brothers, 1878.

1 p. l., 831 p. 19cm.

1. Greek language—Dictionaries—English. I. Scott, Robert, 1811-1887, joint author. II. Whiton, James Morris, 1833-1920.

10—23278

Library of Congress PA445.E5L7 1878

NL 0343575 DLC DSI MsSM CaBVaU NcD

Liddell, Henry George, 1811-1898.
A lexicon abridged from Liddell and Scott's Greek-English lexicon. The 17th ed., carefully revised throughout. With an appendix of proper and geographical names prepared by James M.Whiton. Boston, Ginn & Heath, 1879.

NL 0343576 MH PPCS

VOLUME 332

P A
445
.E3
.L61

Liddell, Henry George, 1811-1898.
   A lexicon abridged from Liddell & Scott's Greek-English lexicon. The 17th ed., carefully rev. throughout. With an appendix of proper and geographical names prepared by Rev. James M. Whiton ... Boston, Ginn & Heath, 1881.
   2 p. l., 831 p.   19cm.

NL   0343577   DNC CtY PSC

Liddell, Henry George, 1811-1898.
   A lexicon abridged from Liddell & Scott's Greek-English lexicon; the 8th ed. carefully rev. throughout, with an appendix of proper and geographical names prepared by the Rev. James M. Whiton, PH. D. New York, Harper & brothers, 1881.
   2 p. l., 831 p. 19cm.

NL   0343578   ViU NN NcD

Liddell, Henry George, 1811-1898.
   A lexicon abridged ... the 19th ed., rev. Oxford, Clarendon Press, 1881.
   804 p.

NL   0343579   CaBVaU

Liddell, Henry George, 1811-1898, and Robert Scott, 1811-1887.
   A lexicon abridged from Liddell and Scott's Greek-English lexicon. 17th edition, revised. With an appendix of proper and geographical names, prepared by James M. Whiton. Boston. Ginn, Heath & Co. 1883. (4), 831 pp. 18½ cm., in 16s.

K2255 — Whiton, James Morris, ed. — Greece. Lang. Ancient Greek. Dict. English. — Jt. auth.

NL   0343580   MB MH

Morrill
PA
445
E5L6
1883

Liddell, Henry George, 1811-1898.
   A lexicon abridged from Liddell & Scott's Greek-English Lexicon. 20th ed. With an appendix of proper and geographical names prepared by James M. Whiton. New York, Harper, 1883.
   831p. 20cm.

   1. Greek language - dictionaries - English. I. Scoot, Robert, 1811-1887. II. Whiton, James M. III. Title.

NL   0343581   MU CU

Liddell, Henry George, 1811-1898, and R. Scott.
   A lexicon abridged from Liddell and Scott's Greek-English lexicon... Oxford: Clarendon Press, 1883. 804 p. 20. ed., rev. 12°.

29886A. 1. Greek language.—Dictionaries: English. 2. Scott, Robert, 1811-87, jt. au.
                                    March 22, 1922.

NL   0343582   NN

Liddell, Henry George, 1811-1898.
   A lexicon abridged from Liddell and Scott's Greek-English lexicon. The 17th ed. carefully rev. throughout. With an Appendix of proper and geographical names prepared by James M. Whiton. Boston, Ginn, Heath, 1884.
   831 p. 19cm.
   1. Greek language—Dictionaries—English. 2. English language—Dictionaries—Greek. I. Scott, Robert, 1811-1887, joint author. II. Whiton, James Morris, 1833-1920.

NL   0343583   ViU MH WaSpG

Liddell, Henry George, 1811-1898.
   A lexicon abridged from Liddell & Scott's Greek-English lexicon; the 21st ed. carefully rev. throughout, with an appendix of proper and geographical names prepared by the Rev. James M. Whiton, PH. D. New York, Harper & brothers, 1884.
   2 p. l., 831 p. 19cm.

   1. Greek language—Dictionaries—English. 2. English language—Dictionaries—Greek. I. Scott, Robert, 1811-1887, joint author. II. Whiton, James Morris, 1833-1920.

Library of Congress   PA445.E5L6   1884   32-9206
                                                       483.2

NL   0343584   DLC WaU

Liddell, Henry George, 1811-1898.
   A lexicon abridged from Liddell and Scott's Greek-English lexicon. 21st ed. carefully rev. throughout.
   Oxford, At the Clarendon press, 1884.
   804 p.

NL   0343585   PPT

Liddell, Henry George, 1811-1898.
   A lexicon abridged from Liddell and Scott's Greek-English lexicon. 17th ed., carefully rev. throughout. With an appendix of proper and geographical names, prepared by Rev. James M. Whiton... Boston, Ginn & company, 1885.
   1 p. l., 831 p.   19 cm.
   1. Greek language-Dictionaries-English. I. Scott, Robert, 1811-1887, joint author. II. Whiton, James Morris, 1833-1920.

NL   0343586   CU

LIDDELL, Henry George, 1811-1898.
   A lexicon abridge from Liddell and Scott's Greek-English lexicon. 17th ed. revised , Boston, Ginn & Co., 1886.

   4°.pp.(4). 831.

NL   0343587   MH

Liddell, Henry George, 1811-1898.
   A lexicon abridged from Liddell and Scott's Greek-English lexicon. 17th ed. carefully revised throughout. With an appendix of proper and geographical names prepared by J.M. Whiton. Boston, Ginn & co., 1887.

NL   0343588   MH

PA445
.E5L87
1887

LIDDELL, HENRY GEORGE, 1811-1898.
   A lexicon abridged from Liddell and Scott's Greek-English lexicon. The 22d ed., carefully rev. throughout. Oxford, The Clarendon press: H. Froude; [etc., etc.] 1887.
   [4], 804 p. 18x14½cm.

   1. Greek language—Dictionaries—English. 2. English language-Dictionaries—Greek.

NL   0343589   ICU

Liddell, Henry George, 1811-1898.
   A lexicon abridged from Liddell & Scott's Greek-English lexicon; the 22d ed. carefully rev. thoughout, with an appendix of proper and geographical names prepared by the Rev. James M. Whiton, PH.D. New York, Harper & brothers, 1888.
   2p. l., 831 p. 19 cm.

NL   0343590   KAS

483.2
L71l
1888
Class

Liddell, Henry George, 1811-1898.
   A lexicon abridged from Liddell and Scott's Greek-English lexicon. [Oxford, The Clarendon press, pref. 1888.]
   910p. O.

   Imperfect: t.-p. lacking; typed t.-p. supplied.

NL   0343591   IaU

Liddell, Henry George, 1811-1898.
   A lexicon, abridged from Liddell and Scott's Greek-English lexicon. 17th ed., carefully revised throughout. With an appendix of proper and geographical names prepared by James M. Whiton. Boston, Ginn & co., 1889.

NL   0343592   MH

Mann
AG
29
L71a
1889

Liddell, Henry George, 1811-1898.
   A Lexicon, abridged from Liddell & Scott's Greek-English Lexicon. 23d ed., carefully rev. throughout, with an appendix of proper and geographical names prepared by the Rev. James M. Whiton, New York, Harper, 1889 [c1871,
   831 p. 20 cm.

   1. Greek language - Dict. - English. I. Scott, Robert, 1811-1887. II. Whiton, James Morris, 1833-1920.

NL   0343593   NIC

Liddell, Henry George, 1811-1898.
   A lexicon abridged from Liddell & Scott's Greek-English lexicon; the 24th ed. carefully rev. throughout, with an appendix of proper and geographical names prepared by the Rev. James M. Whiton, PH. D. New York, Harper & brothers, 1890.
   2 p. l., 831 p. 19cm.

NL   0343594   ViU OClW OCU MiD PP MH PPCCH OCU

LIDDELL, [Henry] George], 1811-1898.
   A lexicon abridged from Liddell and Scott's Greek-English lexicon. 17th ed. carefully revised throughout. With an appendix of proper and geographical names prepared by James M. Whiton. Boston, Ginn & Company, 1891.

   pp.(4).831.

NL   0343595   MH

Liddell, Henry George, 1811-1898.
   A lexicon abridged from Liddell & Scott's Greek-English Lexicon. 24th ed. carefully rev. throughout. With an appendix of proper and geographical names prepared by the Rev. James M. Whiton, Ph. D.   New York, Harper & brothers, 1891.
   831 p.
   1. Greek language. Dictionaries. English. I. Scott, Robert, 1811-1887, joint author. II. Title.

NL   0343596   InAndC-T MH-G

Liddell, Henry George, 1811-1898, comp.
   A lexicon abridged from Liddell and Scott's Greek-English lexicon. The 25th ed., carefully rev. throughout. Oxford, The Clarendon pr.: H. Frowde; [etc., etc.] 1892.

   2p.l., 804p. 18½cm.

NL   0343597   NBB

VOLUME 332

Liddell, Henry George, 1811-1898.
    A lexicon abridged from Liddell & Scott's
Greek-English lexicon. 26th ed., carefully
revised throughout. With an appendix of
proper and geographical names prepared by the
Rev. James M. Whiton.   New York, Harper &
Brothers, 1893.
    831 p. 19 cm.

NL 0343598   PLatS PPT

LIDDELL, Henry George, 1811-1898.
    A lexicon abridged from Liddell and Scott's
Greek-English lexicon. 24th ed., revised. With
an appendix of proper and geographical names
prepared by J.M.Whiton. Boston, Ginn & company,
1894 [cop. 1878].

    sm.4°.pp.(4). 831.

NL 0343599   MH

PA445   Liddell, Henry George, 1811-1898.
E5L6   A lexicon, abridged from Liddell and
1895   Scott's Greek-English lexicon. 24th ed.,
        carefully revised throughout. With an ap-
in   pendix of proper and geographical names pre-
College pared by James M. Whiton. Boston, Ginn,
        1895.
            831 p. 19cm.

        1. Greek language - Dictionaries - English.
        I. Scott, Robert, 1811-1887. II. Whiton,
        James Morris, 1833-1920.

NL 0343600   CoU

Liddell, [Henry George], & Scott, [Robert].
    A lexicon abridged from Liddell & Scott's Greek-English lexicon.
The twenty-sixth edition. ... revised ... . With an appendix of
proper and geographical names, prepared by the Rev. James M.
Whiton. [4],831 p. sq. D. New York: Harper & Brothers,
1895, c. 1878.

NL 0343601   ICJ

Liddell, Henry George, 1811-1898, comp.
    A lexicon abridged from Liddell and
Scott's Greek-English lexicon, Ed. 24,
carefully revised throughout, with an
appendix of proper and geographical
names prepared by Rev. James M. Whiton
... Boston, Ginn, 1896.
    831 p. 19 1/2 cm.

NL 0343602   IdU

Liddell, [Henry George] and [Robert] Scott.
    A lexicon; abridged from Liddell and Scott's Greek-English
lexicon; with an appendix of proper and geographical names, prepared by James M. Whiton. New York: Harper & Brothers,
1896. 2 p.l., 831 p. 27. ed. 12°.

1. Greek language. 2. Dictionaries.   CENTRAL RESERVE.
                              3. Scott, Robert, jt. au.
                                        October 8, 1913.

NL 0343603   NN

Liddell, Henry George, 1811-1898.
    Lexicon, abridged. 26 ed. Oxford, 1896.
    12°.
        By Henry George Liddell and Robert Scott.

NL 0343604   MdBP

Liddell, Henry George, 1811-1898.
    A lexicon, abridged from Liddell & Scott's Greek-English
lexicon. 24th ed., carefully rev. throughout. New York,
Economy Book House; A. Hinds & Co., sole agents [1897?]
    804 p. 19 cm.

    1. Greek language—Dictionaries—English.   I. Scott, Robert,
1811-1887, joint author.

    PA445.E5L7 1897   48-44171

NL 0343605   DLC

Liddell, Henry George, 1811-1898, and Robert Scott, 1811-1887.
    A lexicon abridged from Liddell and Scott's Greek-English lexicon.
27th edition carefully revised throughout. With an appendix of
proper and geographical names, prepared by James M. Whiton.
New York. Harper. 1897. (4), 831 pp. 18½ cm., 16s.

N570 — Whiton, James Morris, ed., 1833-1920. — Greece. Lang. Ancient Greek.
Dict. English. — Jt. auth.

NL 0343606   MB

Liddell, Henry George, and Scott, Robert. A lexicon
abridged from Liddell and Scott's Greek-English lexicon.
With an appendix of proper and geographical names prepared
by J. M. Whiton. 24th ed., revised. Boston. 1898 [cop.
1878]. 4°. pp. [4], 831.

NL 0343607   MH-A MSohG

PA445   Liddell, Henry George, 1811-1898.
.E5L87   A lexicon abridged from Liddell & Scott's
1899   Greek-English lexicon. The 27th ed., carefully
        revised throughout. With an appendix of proper
        and geographical names prepared by the Rev.
        James M. Whiton... New York, Harper & brothers,
        1899.
            [4], 831 p. 19cm.

        1.Greek language--Dictionaries--English. 2.
        English language--Dictionaries--Greek.

NL 0343608   ICU NNC MH

Liddell, Henry George, 1811-1898.
    A lexicon abridged from Liddell and Scott's
Greek-English lexicon. Oxford,
Clarendon press: H.Frowde, etc., etc., 1899.

    804 p. 19 cm.

NL 0343609   MH

Liddell, Henry George, 1811-1898.
    A lexicon, abridged from Liddell & Scott's Greek-English
lexicon. 24th ed., carefully revised throughout. With an appendix of proper and geographical names prepared by George
Ricker Berry ... New York, Economy book house [1901]
    2 p. l., 835 p. 18½ᵐ.

    1. Greek language—Dictionaries—English.   I. Scott, Robert, 1811-
1887. II. Berry, George Ricker, 1865-

                                              1—30608

    Library of Congress   PA445.E5L7 1901

NL 0343610   DLC NjP MH PU DAU MtU OO

Liddell, Henry George, 1811-1898.
    A lexicon abridged from Liddell and Scott's
Greek-English lexicon. 28th ed. Oxford,
at the Clarendon Press, H. Frowde, 1903.
    804 p. 20cm.

NL 0343611   OrPS

Liddell, Henry George, 1811-1898.
    A lexicon abridged from Liddell & Scott's Greek-English
lexicon. The 27th ed., carefully rev. throughout, with an appendix of proper and geographical names prepared by the
Rev. James M. Whiton, ph. d. New York, Cincinnati [etc.
American book company [°1906]
    2 p. l., 831 p. 19ᵐ.

    1. Greek language—Dictionaries—English.   I. Scott, Robert, 181
1887. II. Whiton, James Morris, 1833-1920.

                                              6—29532

    Library of Congress   PA445.E5L7 1906

NL 0343612   DLC CtY TU FMU MoU OC1ND ICU

AC-L   Liddell, Henry George, 1811-1898.
W357L   A lexicon abridged from Liddell & Scott's
L619ℓ   Greek-English lexicon. Oxford, Clarendon press;
        London, Longmans, Green, and co., 1909.
            2 p. ℓ., 804p. 19½cm.
            With autograph and ms. note of E.A.St.J.
        Waugh.
            From the library of Evelyn Waugh.

            I. Scott, Robert, 1811-1887, joint
        author.

NL 0343613   TxU PBa IU OrU DLC

---

*PA445   Liddell, Henry George, 1811-1898.
.E5L7   A lexicon abridged from Liddell and Scott's
1910   Greek-English lexicon, carefully rev. through-
        out with an appendix of proper and geographical
        names, arranged by Rev. James M. Whiton, Ph.D.
        New York, Chicago [etc.] American book company
        [191-?]
            2 p. l., 831 p. 19cm.
            1. Greek language—Dictionaries—English.
        I. Scott, Robert, 1811-1887. II. Whiton, James
        Morris, 1833-1920.

NL 0343614   MB ICU

[Liddell, Henry George, 1811-1898, &
    Scott, Robert].
    A lexicon abridged from Liddell and
Scott's Greek-English lexicon; [rev.ed.]
Oxf.Clarendon press,1920.
    804p.sq.D.
    I.Title.

NL 0343615   CaBViP

Liddell, Henry George, 1811-98, & Scott, R.
    A lexicon abridged from Liddell & Scott's
Greek-English lexicon. Oxford, Clarendon,
1924.
    804 p.

NL 0343616   OC1h

BR44   Liddell, Henry George, 1811-1898.
L71ℓ   A lexicon abridged from Liddell and Scott's
        Greek-English lexicon. [Rev. and enl. ed.]
        Oxford, New York, Clarendon press, 1926.
            804 p. 19 cm.

NL 0343617   CtY-D

Liddell, Henry George, 1811-1898 & Scott,
    Robert.

    A lexicon; abr. from Liddell and Scott's
Greek-English lexicon. Clarendon pr.
[1929]

NL 0343618   OrP

VOLUME 332

Liddell, Henry George, 1811-1898.
A lexicon abridged from Liddell and Scott's
Greek-English lexicon.
Oxford, Clarendon ₍1935₎
804 p.

NL 0343619 PBm

PA445 Liddell, Henry George, 1811-1898.
.E5L87 A lexicon abridged from Liddell and Scott's
1944 Greek-English lexicon. Oxford, Clarendon Press
(Univ ₍1944₎
coll) 804 p.

1. Greek language--Dictionaries--English. 2.
English language--Dictionaries--Greek.

NL 0343620 ICU NcU PU PPPL CtY-M MH

PA Liddell, Henry George, 1811-1898.
445 A lexicon abridged from Liddell and
E5L712 Scott's Greek-English lexicon. Oxford,
1949 Clarendon Press ₍1949₎
804 p. 19cm.

1. Greek language--Dict.--English.
I. Scott, Robert, 1811-1887, joint author.

NL 0343621 NIC MH NRU

PA Liddell, Henry George, 1811-1898.
445 A lexicon abridged from Liddell & Scott's
E5 Greek-English lexicon. Rev. and enlg. ed.
L6 Oxford, Clarendon Press ₍1953₎
1953 804 p. 19cm.

1. Greek language - Dictionaries - English.
2. English language - Dictionaries - Greek.
I. Scott, Robert, 1811-1887, joint author.

NL 0343622 CU-I MH ViU NcU NNC WaS

878 Liddell, Henry George, 1811-1898.
C2Wℓ Life of Julius Caesar. Boston,
Houghton ₍pref.1859₎
247p. S. (On cover: Biographical series)
"Editor's preface" signed: O.W. Wight.

NL 0343623 IaU TU PSt

DG261 Liddell, Henry George, 1811-1898.
.L7 Life of Julius Caesar. By Henry G. Liddell ... New
York, Sheldon & company, 1860.
v, ₍7₎-247 p. 15ᶜᵐ. (On cover: Household library ₍v. 17₎)
"Editor's preface" signed: O. W. Wight.

1. Caesar C. Julius.

NL 0343624 ICU MH IU

DG Liddell, Henry George, 1811-1898.
261 Life of Julius Caesar. New York, Hurd
.L5 and Houghton, 1865.
1865 247p. 16cm.

Extracted from his History of Rome (London,
1855).
Preface signed O₍rlando₎ W₍illiam₎ Wright
and dated 1859.

1.Caesar, C. Julius, 102 or 100-44 B.C.
I.Title: Julius Caesar.

NL 0343625 LLafS

Liddell, Henry George, 1811-1898.
Life of Julius Caesar. N.Y., Hurd, 1870.
247 p. S.

(On cover, Library of biography)

NL 0343626 OO

937.05 Liddell, Henry George, 1811-1898.
C128Bℓ Life of Julius Caesar. New York, Hurd and
Houghton. 1877.
247p.

1. Caesar, C. Julius.

NL 0343627 ICarbS MB

Liddell, Henry George, 1811-1898.
Life of Julius Caesar. N.Y. Amer.
Book Exchange, 1879.
247 p.

NL 0343628 MiU

Liddell, Henry George, 1811-1898.
Life of Julius Caesar. Boston, Houghton,
Mifflin and co., 1881.
247 p. 15.5 cm.
Spine: Biographical series.

NL 0343629 MH

Liddell, Henry George, 1811-1898.
Life of Julius Caesar. (In: Famous biography. New
York, 1883. 12°. 70 p.)

1. Caesar, Caius Julius. April 26, 1911.

NL 0343630 NN

Liddell, Henry George, 1811-1898.
Life of Julius Caesar, by H. G. Liddell...
N.Y., J. B. Alden, 1886.
₍147₎-255 p.

NL 0343631 MiU

Liddell, H₍enry₎ G₍eorge₎, 1811-1898.
Life of Julius Caesar. N.Y. 1887.
147-255 p.

NL 0343632 WaWW

Liddell, Henry George, 1811-1898.
Μέγα λεξικὸν τῆς ἑλληνικῆς γλώσσης ₍ὑπό₎ Henry G.
Liddell καὶ Robert Scott. Ἐπεξεργασθέν, διασκευασθέν καὶ
διὰ πλείστων νέων λέξεων καὶ φράσεων πλουτισθέν ὑπὸ Μιχαήλ
Κωνσταντινίδου. Ἀθῆναι, Ι.Ν.Σιδέρης, 1921
4 v. in 2
1. Greek language - Dict. - Greek (Modern)
I. Scott, Robert, 1811-1887. II. Kōnstantinidēs,
Michaēl ed. Title romanized: Mega lexikon
tēs hellēnikēs glōssēs

NL 0343633 MH PPiU

Liddell, Henry George, 1811-1898, and R. Scott.
...Μέγα λεξικὸν τῆς Ἑλληνικῆς γλώσσης, μεταφρασθὲν ἐκ τῆς Ἀγγλι-
κῆς εἰς τὴν Ἑλληνικὴν ὑπὸ Ξενοφῶντος Π. Μόσχου... Διὰ πολλῶν δὲ
Βυζαντιακῶν ἰδίως λέξεων καὶ φράσεων πλουτισθὲν καὶ ἐκδοθὲν ἐπιστασία
Μιχαήλ Κωνσταντινίδου... Ἀθῆναι: Ι. Ν. Σιδέρης ἐκδότης, 1925.
4 v. in 2. f°.

Printed in double columns.

472875-6A. 1. Greek language— Dictionaries, Greek, Modern.
I. Scott, Robert, 1811-1887, jt. au. II. Moschos, Zenophōn P.,
translator. III. Kōnstantinidēs, Michaēl.
July 16, 1930

NL 0343634 NN DDO MiU

PA441 Liddell, Henry George, 1811-1898.
f.E6 Μέγα λεξικὸν τῆς ἑλληνικῆς γλώσσης; μετά-
φρασθὲν ἐκ τῆς ἀγγλικῆς εἰς τὴν ἑλληνικὴν ὑπὸ
Ξενοφῶντος Π. Μόσχου... διὰ πολλῶν δὲ
Βυζαντιακῶν ἰδίως λέξεων καὶ φράσεων
πλούτισθεν καὶ ἐκδοθεν ἐπιστασία Μιχαήλ
Κωνσταντινίδου... Ἀθῆναι, Ι. Ν. Σιδέρης,
1929.
4 v. in 2. 31 cm.
At head of title: Henry G. Liddell
καὶ Robert Scott.
1. Greek lan- guage - Dictionaries. I. Scott,
Robert, 1811-1887, jt. auth. II. Mosthos, Xenophōn P.,
tr. III. Kōnstantinidēs, Michaēl, ed.

NL 0343635 OCU

q483 Liddell, Henry George, 1811-1898.
L61gGRm ... Μέγα λεξικὸν τῆς Ἑλληνικῆς γλώσσης μεταφρασθὲν ἐκ τῆς Ἀγγλικῆς εἰς τὴν Ἑλληνικὴν ὑπὸ Ξενοφῶντος Π. Μόσχου ... διὰ πολλῶν δὲ Βυζαντιάκων ἰδίως
λέξεων καὶ φράσεων πλουτισθὲν καὶ ἐκδοθὲν ἐπιστασία
Μιχαήλ Κωνσταντινίδου ... Ἀθῆναι, Ι. Σιδερῆς ἐκδότης, ₍1948₎
4v. 31cm.
At head of title: Henry G. Liddell και Robert Scott.
1. Greek language--Dictionaries--Greek, Modern. I. Scott,
Robert, 1811-1887, joint author. II. Moschos, Xenophon, tr.
III. Konstantinides. Michael, ed.

NL 0343636 MiU IU

[Liddell, Henry George] 1811-1898.
The Queen's jubilee; a sermon preached
June 28, 1887 ... in the cathedral of Christ
church, Oxon, by the very rev. the Dean.
Oxford, H. Hart, 1887.
23 p. 22 cm.
Preface signed: H. G. L.
"Printed for private circulation."
I. Title.

NL 0343637 RPB CtY

Liddell, Henry George, 1811-1898.
Vaughan, Charles John, 1816-1897.
Sermons preached in Westminster abbey on Sunday, March
12, 1876, on the death of the Lady Augusta Stanley, by C. J.
Vaughan ... and Henry G. Liddell ... London, Macmillan
and co., 1876.

937 Liddell, Henry George, 1811-1898.
L61hI2 Storia di Roma dai tempi più antichi
fino alla costituzione dell'impero.
Cor. di alcuni capitoli intorno alla
storia delle lettere e delle arti.
Prima traduzione italiana accresciuta
della storia dei primi due secoli dell'
impero, e cor. di una carta geografica.
2.ed. Firenze, 1868.
869p. fold.map.

NL 0343639 IU

VOLUME 332

Liddell, Henry George, 1811–1898.
937
L712HB   Storia di Roma, dai tempi più antichi
fino alla costituzione dell'impero; corredata di alcuni capitoli intorno alla storia
delle lettere e delle arti. Prima traduzione
italiana, accresciuta della storia dei primi
due secoli dell'impero, corredata di una
carta geografica. 7 ed. Firenze, Barbèra,
1880.
    xxxiv, 869 p. fold. map. 20 cm.
    Bibliographical footnotes.
    1. Rome.   History. Kings, B. C.
753–510. 2.   Rome. Hist. Republic,
B. C. 510–30.

NL 0343640   NcD

Liddell, Henry George, 1811–1898.
    The student's Rome. A history of Rome, from the earliest
times to the establishment of the empire. With chapters on
the history of literature and art. By Henry G. Liddell ...
New ed. London, J. Murray, 1877.
    xxvii, (1), 672 p. incl. front., illus. 19ᶜᵐ.
    "This volume contains the history of Rome, slightly abridged from
the larger work by the author."—Pref.

    1. Rome—Hist.—Kings, B. C. 753–510. 2. Rome—Hist.—Republic, B. C.
510–30.   I. Title.
                                            35–25109
    Library of Congress   DG231.L71 1877   937

NL 0343641   DLC

Liddell, Henry Thomas, earl of Ravensworth.

see

Ravensworth, Henry Thomas Liddell, 1st earl of,
1797–1878

Liddell, Howard Scott, 1895–
    ... The comparative physiology of the conditioned motor
reflex, based on experiments with the pig, dog, sheep, goat, and
rabbit, by H. S. Liddell, W. T. James, and O. D. Anderson ...
Baltimore, Md., The Johns Hopkins press (1934)
    cover-title, 89 p. incl. plates, diagrs. 25½ᶜᵐ. (Comparative psychology
monographs. v. 11, serial no. 51, December, 1934)
    Descriptive letterpress on versos facing the plates.
    Bibliography: p. 79–80.
    1. Reflexes. 2. Animal intelligence.   I. James, William Thomas,
1903–   joint author.   II. Anderson, Oscar Daniel, 1903–   joint author.   III. Title.   IV. Title: The conditioned motor reflex.
                                            35–2214
    Library of Congress   QP372.L5

    Copyright A 78783   [159.94363] 158.423

        OC1W PPC PBm ViU
NL 0343643   DLC OrSaW CtY-M CU MU AAP OU MiU OC1

Liddell, Howard Scott, 1895–
    The conditioned reflex.
—   (In Thorndike, Edward L., 1874– , and others. Comparative
psychology. Pp. 247–296. Plates. Diagram. Charts. Tables. New
York. 1934.)
    Bibliography, pp. 295, 296.

    D9806 — Reflexes. Conditional. — Brain.

NL 0343644   MB OC1W

Liddell, Jacques D., joint author.
BF77
.V3
Van den Arend, Guy.
    ... Guide de l'étudiant en psychologie; psychologie géné-
rale, psychologie pathologique, esthétique, psychologie de l'en-
fant, pédagogie. Préface de m. P. Guillaume ... Paris, J.
Vrin (1940)

Liddell (Joannes).   * De febre flava. 4 p. l., 21
pp. 8°. Edinburgi, C. Stewart, 1821.

NL 0343646   DNLM

Liddell, John Robert.
    The Library of Corpus Christi college, Oxford, in the six-
teenth century, by J. R. Liddell.
    (In The Library. London, 1938. 22ᶜᵐ. Fourth ser., vol. XVIII, no. 4,
Mar. 1938, p. (385)–416)
    "Transactions of the Bibliographical society. New ser., vol. XVIII,
no. 4."

    1. Oxford university. Corpus Christi college. Library.
                                            A 40–730
Cleveland. Public library   [Z671.L69 4th ser.—vol. 18, no. 4]
for Library of Congress
                                            (010.5)

NL 0343647   OC1 DLC

Liddell, K   C.
    Contract and plafond bridge self-taught (based on the Cul-
bertson system) by K. C. Liddell ... London, Sir I. Pitman
& sons, ltd., 1936.
    viii, 72 p. 18½ᶜᵐ.
    "Authorities consulted": p. (6)

    1. Contract bridge.   I. Title: Plafond bridge.
                                            36–21163
    Library of Congress   GV1282.3.L48
                                            795.41

NL 0343648   DLC

Liddell, Ken E   1912–   *
E
99   The investiture of James Muir, D.L.C.,
K15L5   President of the Royal Bank of Canada as
Hon. Chief Eagle Ribs in the Blood Indian
Tribe, Blackfoot Confederacy. (Montreal,
Printed for private distribution by the
Royal Bank of Canada, 1954?)
    47 p. illus., ports. (part col.)

    1. Kainah Indians – Rites and ceremonies
    2. Muir, James

NL 0343649   CaOTU

F1076
.5
.L5   Liddell, Ken E   1912–
    Roamin' empire of southern Alberta, by Ken Liddell.
(Calgary, Alberta, Frontiers Unlimited, 195–?)
    64 p. illus. 22 cm. (Frontier book, no. 6)

    1. Alberta—Descr. & trav.   I. Title.

    F1076.5.L5   66–35888

NL 0343650   DLC CaBViP CaBVaU

Liddell, Ken E   1912–
    This is Alberta. Toronto, Ryerson Press (1952)
    190 p. illus. 21 cm. (The Ryerson travel library)

    1. Alberta—Descr. & trav.   I. Title.

    F1076.L5   917.123   53–30335 ‡

        WaS WaT OrU CtY PP NcD LU NN CaOTU
NL 0343651   DLC NcGU MtBC CaBVa CaBViP CaBVaU WaE

xq655.142
L619f   Liddell, Leaton, Burdon, & Co.
    Free trade in novels, forever Liddell, Leaton,
Burdon, & Co. beg to assure their friends and
the public, that they despise the illiberal
menaces of the proprietor of the Minerva Press.
Newcastle, W. Boag, printer (ca. 1815?)
    broadside. 29cm.

    1. Minerva Press, London.   I. Title.

NL 0343652   IU

Z732
.C8W5   Liddell, Leon Morris, joint author.
Wight, Edward Allen, 1899–
    Connecticut library survey, by Edward A. Wight and Leon
Liddell. Hartford, 1948.

Liddell, (Lionel Charles).
    France. Report on the chemical, metal and other industries
of Lyons during the year 1904. London: Harrison and Sons,
1905. 8 p. 8°. (Great Britain. Foreign Office. Diplomatic
and consular reports. Miscellaneous series. no. 638.)

    1. Industries, France: Lyon, 1904.
                                            January 8, 1913.

NL 0343654   NN

Liddell, M. F., ed.
PR6007
.O 8923   Dowhan, S   J
L4   The leaves are scattered, by S. J. Dowhan. Edited by M. F.
Liddell. London, British authors' press, 1944.

Liddell, Mark Harvey, 1866–1936.
    Abstracts of four lectures on "Our English
spelling." (Boston? n.d.)
    (16)p. 23cm.

    Cover title.
    At head of title: Twentieth Century Club,
Education Committee. Tenth season of univer-
sity lectures.
    1. English language—Orthography and spelling.
I. Twentieth Cen-   tury Club of Boston.

NL 0343656   IU

Liddell, Mark Harvey, 1866–1936.
    A brief abstract of a new English prosody, based upon
the laws of English rhythm, by Mark H. Liddell ...
Lafayette, Ind., 1914.
    45 p. 17ᶜᵐ. $0.75

    1. English language—Versification.
                                            14–3133
    Library of Congress   PE1511.L5

NL 0343657   DLC TxU OO MiU ViU PBm PPT PU

Liddell, Mark Harvey, 1866–1936.
    The elements of sound and their relation to language, by
Mark H. Liddell. Urbana, The University of Illinois press,
1940.
    136 p. diagrs. 26½ᶜᵐ. (Added t.-p.: (Illinois. University) Illinois
studies in language and literature. vol. XXVII, no. 1)
    "Biographical sketch" (p. 13–16) signed: Mary S. F. Liddell.

    1. Sound. 2. Phonetics.   I. Title.
                                            40–28889
    Library of Congress   P221.L5
                                            411.5

        PSt PU PSC PPT
NL 0343658   DLC CaBViP CaBVaU OrU MoU CU OCU OO ViU

VOLUME 332

Liddell, Mark Harvey, 1866-1936, ed.

Shakespeare, William, 1564-1616.
The Elizabethan Shakspere ... A new ed. of Shakspere's works, with critical text in Elizabethan English and brief notes illustrative of Elizabethan life, thought and idiom, by Mark Harvey Liddell. ₁v.
New York, Doubleday, Page & co., 1903.

Liddell, Mark Harvey, 1866-1936.
An introduction to the scientific study of English poetry; being prolegomena to a science of English prosody, by Mark H. Liddell ... New York, Doubleday, Page & company, 1902.
xvi, 312 p. 19½ᵐ.

1. English language—Versification.

Library of Congress   PE1505.L7

2—14019

NN MB NjP TU PRosC PPCCH OKentʻU MtU
NL 0343660   DLC PPA PPD PP OC1 OC1W OU OCU MiU OO

LIDDELL, Mark Harvey, 1866-1936.
A new source of the Parson's tale.
[Oxford. 1901]
    pp.(23).
Reprinted from "An English miscellany".

NL 0343661   MH

Liddell, Mark Harvey, 1866-1936.
A new theory of sound, presented in a paper read at the Pittsburgh meeting of the A. A. A. S. on December 29th, 1934, by Mark H. Liddell. New York, Priv. print. ₁F. W. Schmidt, inc., printers₁ 1935.
cover-title, 13, ₁1₁ p. diagrs. 23ᵐ.

1. Sound. 2. Phonetics. 3. Music—Acoustics and physics.

A 38-26

Rochester. Univ. Library   QC229.L7
for Library of Congress

NL 0343662   NRU OU

Liddell, Mark Harvey, 1866-1936
Palladius collated with MS. Bodl. Add. A. 369.
London. Trübner. 1896. 33 pp. [Early English Text Society. Original series. Corrections for nos. 52 & 72: Palladius on husbondrie.] 21½ cm., in 8s.

K7399 — Palladius, Rutilius Taurus Aemilianus. — S.r.c.

NL 0343663   MB OrPU

Liddell, Mark Harvey, 1866-1936.
... The physical characteristics of speech sound. Lafayette, Ind., Purdue university, 1924-1927.
3 v. diagrs. 23ᵐ. (Bulletins no. 16, 23, 28, Engineering experiment station)
On cover: Purdue university. Publications of the engineering departments. vol. VIII, no. 1, vol. IX, no. 10, vol. XI, no. 2.

1. English language—Pronunciation. 2. Phonetics. I. Title.

Title from Purdue Univ.   A 24-744
Library of Congress   QP306.L5

OC1 OC1W OO MiU PPTU NcD
NL 0343664   InLP MH PPDrop WaS WaWW MB DAU OU OCU

LIDDELL, Mark Harvey, 1866-1936.
A plea for the better study of Shakspeare.
[Louisville, 1909.]

NL 0343665   MH

Liddell, Mark Harvey, 1866-1936, ed.

Chaucer, Geoffrey, d. 1400.
... The prologue to the Canterbury tales, the Knightes tale, the Nonnes prestes tale; ed. in critical text, with grammatical introduction, being an elementary grammar of Middle English, notes and glossary, by Mark H. Liddell ... New York, The Macmillan company; London, Macmillan & co., ltd., 1901.

Liddell, Mark Harvey, 1866-1936.
Scientific English scholarship in America.
n.p. [191-].

NL 0343667   NjP

Liddell, Mark Harvey, 1866-1936.
The typography of Shakspere's Midsommer nightes dreame. ₁Indianapolis, Florence & Edwin Grabhorn₁ 1918.
20 p. 20cm.

No. 11 of 100 copies.
Heller & Magee: 14.

                            *
NL 0343668   NNC

Liddell, Mark Harvey, 1866-1936.
The typography of Shakspere's Midsommer nightes dreame, by Mark Harvey Liddell.   San Francisco: John Howell. 1920.
20 p., 1 l.   12°.

Title in red and black; title vignette (portrait of Shakespeare).
Colophon: One hundred copies printed by Edwin & Robert Grabhorn in the city of San Francisco, April, MCMXX.

203292A. 1. Shakespeare, William   —Single plays—Midsummer night's
dream. 2. Shakespeare, William—   Typography.
                                        October 9, 1925

NL 0343669   NN CSmH NcU CSt MH MB ICN

Liddell, Mark Harvey, 1866-1936, ed.
Chaucer, Geoffrey, d. 1400.   FOR OTHER EDITIONS
                                    SEE MAIN ENTRY
... The works of Geoffrey Chaucer; ed. by Alfred W. Pollard, H. Frank Heath, Mark H. Liddell, W. S. McCormick. London, Macmillan and co., limited; New York, The Macmillan company, 1903.

Liddell, Mary, illus.
PZ8
.L887
Ad
14
Lorenzini, Carlo, 1826-1890.
The adventures of Pinocchio, by C. Collodi (Carlo Lorenzini) translated and adapted by Angelo Patri; illustrated by Mary Liddell ... Garden City, N. Y., Doubleday, Doran and company, inc., 1930.

Liddell, Mary.
Little machinery, by Mary Liddell. Garden City, N. Y., Doubleday, Page & co. ₁1926₁
62 p. col. illus. 23ᵐ.

I. Title.

Library of Congress   PZ7.L615Li

26—20633

NL 0343672   DLC OC1h OLak OC1 OO OOxM MB NN

[Liddell, Mary Hannah, ed.]
Poetry: original and select.   York, Robert Sunter, 1850.
xvi, 240 p.   17.5 cm.
Dedication signed: Mary Hannah Liddell.
I. Title.

NL 0343673   NNUT

Liddell, *Mrs.* **Mary Stanley (Field)** 1866-
The Hon. George Gray, 4th, of Philadelphia, his ancestors & descendants, by Mary Stanley Field Liddell ... ₁Ann Arbor, Mich., Lithoprinted by Edwards brothers, inc., 1940.
xxxiv p., 1 l., 228 p. incl. front. (port.) illus. 21½ᵐ.
"Privately printed."

1. Gray family. 2. Gray, George, 1725-1800.
                                    41-4995
Library of Congress   CS71.G78₁ 1940

NL 0343674   DLC OC1WHi

Liddell, Maximilian Friedrich, 1887-
... Irland, von M. F. Liddell ... Leipzig und Berlin, B. G. Teubner, 1931.
3 p. l., 170 p. 24ᵐ. (Handbuch der englisch-amerikanischen kultur)

1. Ireland—Hist.
Library of Congress   DA910.L6
                                    31-11104
                                    911.5

NL 0343675   DLC NN MH ICJ

Liddell, Moses.
Public meeting at Woodville. [115 lines in 2 columns] Moses Liddell, Chairman. F. Davis, Secretary. Woodville, February 25th, 1834. [Woodville, Woodville Republican, 1834.]
Broadside 24.5 x 32 cm.
Text in 2 columns. Meeting to take into consideration the deranged state of the currency and to memorialize Congress.

NL 0343676   Ms-Ar

Liddell, Robert.
One thousand legal facts
    see under   Arnold, Edward W

Liddell, Hon. Robert, 1808-1888, defendant.

Westerton, Charles, 1813-1872, *plaintiff.*
The cases of Westerton against Liddell (clerk), and Horne and others, St. Paul's, Knightsbridge, and Beal against Liddell (clerk), and Parke and Evans, St. Barnabas. Pimlico: as heard and determined by the Consistory court of London, the Arches court of Canterbury, and the Judicial committee of Her Majesty's most honorable Privy council. By Edmund F. Moore ... London, Longman, Brown, Green, Longmans, and Roberts, 1857.

Liddell, Robert, 1808-1888.
The Inspiration of Holy Scripture, as not merely containing, but being, the word of God. A Sermon ... London, 1864.
16 p. 8°. [In v. 699, College Pamphlets].

NL 0343679   CtY

Liddell, Robert, 1808-1888.
"The church an Ordinance of God." A Sermon ... London, 1838.
32 p. 8°. [In College Pamphlets, v. 1755].

NL 0343680   CtY

VOLUME 332

Liddell, Robert, 1808–1888.
"The Commemorative Sacrifice of the Euchar-
ist"; a profession of our faith to be held fast without wavering. A Sermon ... London.
20 p. 8°. [In   colleges Pamphlets].

NL 0343681   CtY

Law
Liddell, Robert, 1808–1888, appellant.
Gt. Brit. *Court of arches.*
The judgment of the Right Hon. Sir John Dodson, knt.,
dean of Arches ... also the Judgment of the Judicial committee
of the Privy council, in the cases of Liddell (clerk) and Horne
and others against Westerton, Liddell (clerk) and Park and
Evans against Beal. Edited by A. F. Bayford, LL. D. (Being
in continuation of the proceedings in these cases already published.) London, Butterworths, 1857.

Law
Liddell, Robert, 1808–1888, defendant.
London (*Diocese*) *Consistory court.*
The judgment of the Right Hon. Stephen Lushington ...
delivered in the Consistory court of the bishop of London in
the cases of Westerton against Liddell (clerk) and Horne and
others, and Beal against Liddell (clerk) and Parke and Evans,
on 5th December 1855. Edited by A. F. Bayford, D. C. L. London, Butterworths [1856]

[LIDDELL, Robert, 1808–1888]
"The lay of the last angler", or A tribute
to the Tweed at Melrose at the end of the season of 1867. By a Sexagenarian, [pseud.] Kelso,
Rutherfurd & Craig, 1871. '70.

24°. 4 vol.
"Printed for private circulation".
"Title page of canto 1 reads "1867, reprinted 1871."
Each canto issued   separately with individual title-pages   Original paper
cover in bound in.

NL 0343684   MH

PR 4889
L34 L3   Liddell, Robert, 1808–1888.
1884   The lay of the last angler; in four cantos.
To which is added Jack's dangers and deli-
berances. Kelso, J. & J.H. Rutherfurd, 1884.
211 p. illus.

1. Fishing. I. Title.

NL 0343685   CaBVaU MH

PR 4889
L34
L3   Liddell, Robert, 1808–1888.
1888   "The lay of the last angler": in five
cantos. Also, Jack's dangers and delibe-
rances with photo. port., and illus.
from original etchings by the author.
Kelso, J. & J. H. Rutherfurd, 1888.
262 p. illus.

1. Fishing. I. Title.

NL 0343686   CaBVaU MH

1808–1888
Liddell, Robert. A letter to the Lord Bishop
of London, on confession and absolution with
special reference to the case of the Rev. Alfred
Poole: . . . with an appendix containing Mr.
Poole's appeal to His Grace the Archbishop of
Canterbury . . . London, Hayes, 1858. 68 p.

NL 0343687   PPPD CtY

Liddell, Robert, 1808–1888.
Plain song, commonly called Gregorian music;
a short sermon on Psalm CL. 6.
London, 1868.

NL 0343688   PPL

Liddell, Robert, 1808–1888.
The Services & Furniture of S. Paul's, Knightsbridge. A Letter to the Bishop of London...
London, 1854.
16 p. 8°. [In v. 633, College Pamphlets.]

NL 0343689   CtY

BV4626
.L71   Liddell, Robert, 1808–1888.
in: The seven deadly sins. Lectures, preached
SWTS   in S. Paul's, Knightsbridge, during Lent
1858: together with three discourses on the
following Good Friday, Easter eve and Easter
day. London, J.T. Hayes [1858]
2, 124p. 17cm.
1. Deadly sins. 2. Lenten sermons.
3. Church of England--Sermons. I. Title.

NL 0343690   IEG

Liddell, Robert, 1908–
Aegean Greece. London, Cape [1954]
284 p. illus. 25 cm.

1. Islands of the Aegean—Descr. & trav.   I. Title.

DS52.L66   914.99   55–70 ‡

CLSU LU MH NIC NN MB PP NcD PBm IEN OCU MiU
NL 0343691   DLC MWiW CaBVa CaBViP CaBVaU Or OrP WaS

Liddell, Robert, 1908–
The almond tree, by Robert Liddell. London, J. Cape [1938]
285 p. 20ᵐ.
"First published 1938."

I. Title.
                                              38–23771
Library of Congress   PZ3.L6194A1

NL 0343692   DLC

Liddell, Robert, 1908–
The Gantillons, by Robert Liddell. London, J. Cape [1940]
3 p. l., 9–258 p. 20ᵐ.
"First published 1940."

I. Title.
                                              41–1475
Library of Congress   PZ3.L6194Ga

NL 0343693   DLC

Liddell, Robert, 1908–
Kind relations, by Robert Liddell. London, J. Cape [1939]
285 p. 20ᵐ.
"First published 1939."

I. Title.
                                              39–8724
Library of Congress   PZ3.L6194Ki

NL 0343694   DLC MH

Liddell, Robert, 1908–
The last enchantments, a novel. London, J. Cape [1948]
221 p. 20 cm.

I. Title.

PZ3.L6194Las   49–16457*

NL 0343695   DLC CLSU IEN PU

Liddell, Robert, 1908–
The last enchantments. New York, Appleton-Century-
Crofts [1949]
273 p. 21 cm.

I. Title.

PZ3.L6194Las 2   49–10771*

NcD OCiU
NL 0343696   DLC OrU Or CaBVaU PP PPL OEac OO PBa

Liddell, Robert, 1908–
The novels of I. Compton-Burnett. London, Gollancz,
1955.
112 p. port. 22 cm.
Bibliography: p. 112.

1. Compton-Burnett, Ivy, 1892–
                                              A 55–5630
Northwestern Univ.   Library
for Library of Congress

CaBVaU OrU OrCS IdU IdPI WU TxU Nc
NIC NNC IU NN TU OKentU IaU AAP ViU TaSU MoSW CaBVa
NL 0343697   IEN NcU AU MB OkU PU OC OC OU PBm MH CU

Liddell, Robert, 1908–
Some principles of fiction. London, J. Cape [1953]
162 p. 21 cm.

1. Fiction.

PN3353.L49   808.3   53–3729 ‡

PBm OU MiU
NN IU TU MH LU FTaSU ScCleA CaBVaU OrCS OrU WaS
NL 0343698   DLC TNJ NjR MU MB TxU OC1 OO CtY NcU

Liddell, Robert, 1908–
Some principles of fiction. Bloomington, Indiana University Press, 1954.
162 p. 21 cm.

1. Fiction.

[PN3353]   808.3   54–11280 ‡
Printed for U. S. Q. B. R.
by Library of Congress

Wa MtBC
NL 0343699   MB OOxM WU PPD PP PU OCU MiU WaU CaBVa

VOLUME 332

Liddell, Robert, 1908–
Take this child ₍by₎ Robert Liddell. New York, The Greystone press ₍°1939₎.
4 p. l., 3–347 p. 20½ᶜᵐ.
Illustrated t.-p.
"First printing."

ɪ. Title.
40-3357

Library of Congress   PZ3.L6194Tak

NL 0343700   DLC WaE GU OEac OLak OOxM OC1 PBa PPL

Liddell, Robert, 1908–
A treatise on the novel. London, J. Cape ₍1947₎
168 p. 21 cm.
Appendices: 1. Classical places. 2. The 'hallucination' theory of The turn of the screw. 3. The novels of I. Compton-Burnett.
Includes bibliographies.

1. Fiction—Technique. 2. Fiction—Hist. & crit. 3. Compton-Burnett, Ivy, 1802–
PN3335.L5   808.3   A 48-1222*
Rochester. Univ. Libr.
for Library of Congress   †

OrU CaBVaU OrStbM MtU WaS MtBC
OC1JC NNC CtY DLC MU MsSM TxU IaU AAP OOxM OrSaW
NL 0343701   NRU KyLoU GU OC1 MiU PV PPT OU ICU TU

808.3
L619t
1947r   Liddell, Robert, 1908–
A treatise on the novel. London, J. Cape [1953]
168p. 21cm.
"First published 1947 ... Reprinted 1953."
Appendices: 1. Classical places. 2. The 'hallucination' theory of The turn of the screw. 3. The novels of I. Compton-Burnett.
Includes bibliographies.
1. Fiction - Techniques. 2. Fiction - Hist. & crit. 3. Compton-Burnett, Ivy, 1892–

NL 0343702   TxU MH PP MB OCU

823.91
L712u   Liddell, Robert, 1908–
Unreal city, a novel. London, Cape [1952]
238p.

NL 0343703   ICarbS KU OC1 IEN MH NN ViU

Liddell, Robert, 1908–
Watering-place, by Robert Liddell ... London, J. Cape ₍1945₎
142 p. 20ᶜᵐ.
"First published 1945."

ɪ. Title.
PZ3.L6194Wat
47-15511

NL 0343704   DLC MH CaBVa

Liddell, Robert B., jt. comp.
Our hymns. Compiled for use in the services of the Baptist Temple
see under   Conwell, Russell Herman, 1843-1925.

Liddell, Robert Scotland.
... A la suite des armées en Belgique Ouvrage enrichi de notes spéciales du capitaine Albert de Keersmaecker... Traduit de l'anglais par Ph. Mazoyer. Paris, P. Lethielleux [1915].
viii, 280 p.   20 cm.
At head of title: S. Scotland Liddell.
Reprinted in part from several periodicals.

NL 0343706   CSt-H WaPS

Liddell, Robert Scotland.
Actions and reactions in Russia, by R. Scotland Liddell ... with 16 illustrations. London, Chapman and Hall, limited, 1917.
v (i. e. viii), 227, ₍1₎ p. plates. 22½ᶜᵐ.
Reprinted in part from the Sphere.

1. European war, 1914–   —Personal narratives, English. 2. European war, 1914–   —Russia. ɪ. Title.
1S—1259
Library of Congress   D551.L445

NL 0343707   DLC CaBVaU WaS ICJ IaU NN PPL NjP ICJ

Liddell, Robert Scotland.
Actions and reactions in Russia, by R. Scotland Liddell... New York: E. P. Dutton & Co., 1918.   vii, 227 p.   plates.   8°.
Printed in Great Britain.

396991A. 1. European war, 1914–   2. European war, 1914–1918—Russia. Campaigns, East. 4. Title.
1918—Personal narratives, English. 3. European war, 1914–1918—
May 31, 1929

NL 0343708   NN MB NNC MH

Liddell, Robert Scotland.
Fifty thousand miles of sun, by R. Scotland Liddell ... With fifteen illustrations from photographs by the author. London, New York ₍etc.₎ Cassell and co., ltd. ₍1925₎
xviii, 283, ₍1₎ p. front., plates. 22ᶜᵐ.

1. Voyages and travels.   ɪ. Title.
26-1987
Library of Congress   G463.L58

NL 0343709   DLC CaBVaU KU NN

Liddell, Robert Scotland.
The gilded sign, by R. Scotland Liddell ... London ₍etc.₎ Cassell and company, ltd. ₍1927₎
ix, 303, ₍1₎ p. 19½ᶜᵐ.

ɪ. Title.
Library of Congress   PZ3.L6196Gi
27-18853

NL 0343710   DLC

Liddell, Robert Scotland.
The memoirs of the Tenth royal hussars
see under   Liddell, Robert Spencer.

Liddell, Robert Scotland.
On the Russian front, by R. Scotland Liddell ... London, Simpkin, Marshall, Hamilton, Kent & co., limited ₍1916₎
x, 273 p. front., plates, ports. 22½ᶜᵐ.

1. European war, 1914–   —Personal narratives. 2. European war, 1914–   —Campaigns—Eastern. ɪ. Title.
16-15304
Library of Congress   D551.L45

NL 0343712   DLC ICJ WaS IU OU CtY OO PPL ICJ MB NN

Liddell, R₍obert₎ Scotland.
Sestra (Sister); sketches from the Russian front.   London: Hodder and Stoughton, 1917.   244 p.   12°.
Sestra. The spy. Olitchka. Five thousand beds. Sunshine and rain. The thief. The colonel's last trick. The little boy who stayed at home. Prayer at even-tide. The gentleman from Berlin. "We brought down one aeroplane." Soldiers home from the war. "After the war." Elegy.

1. European war.—Fiction.
CENTRAL CIRCULATION.
2. Fourteen titles.
November 14, 1917.

NL 0343713   NN MH

Liddell, Robert Scotland.
The track of the war, by R. Scotland Liddell ... with special notes by Captain Albert de Keersmaecker of Belgium. London, Simpkin, Marshall, Hamilton, Kent & co., limited ₍1915₎
xii, 276 p. plates, 2 port. (incl. front.) facsims. 22½ᶜᵐ.
Map on lining-paper.

1. European war, 1914–   —Personal narratives. ɪ. Title.
15-15078 Revised
Library of Congress   D541.L6

NL 0343714   DLC NcU KyLoU MB CtY NjP DNW ICJ NN

Liddell, R₍obert₎ S₍pencer₎.
Lecture on "Modern cavalry on the field of battle," on Monday, August 6th, 1888, in the Prince Consort's and Military Society's Library, South Camp...   Aldershot: Gale & Polden ₍1888₎. 15 p. 8°. (Aldershot Military Society. ₍no. 8₎)

1. Military art and science.
MILITARY SERVICE INST.
2. Aldershot Military Society.
November 28, 1911.

NL 0343715   NN

Liddell, Robert Spencer.
The memoirs of the Tenth Royal Hussars (Prince of Wales' Own) : historical and social. With illus. by Oscar Norie. London, New York, Longmans, Green, 1891.
xvi, 484 p. illus., ports. 26 cm.
Bibliographical footnotes.

1. Gt. Brit. Army. 10th Royal Hussars (Prince of Wales's Own)
UA655 10th.L5   58-53164

NL 0343716   DLC NN

Liddell, Robert Spencer.
The memoirs of the Tenth Royal Hussars (Prince of Wales' Own), historical and social. With illustrations by O. Norie. London: Longmans, Green, and Co., 1891. xvi p., 1 l., 566 p., 3 port. 4°.
Twelve plates removed.

1. Cavalry (British).—History. Regimental histories. 3. Norie,
2. Army (British).—History: Oscar, illus.
October 31, 1911.

NL 0343717   NN ICN MiU MH MB

VOLUME 332

Liddell, T Hodgson, 1860–
R. B. A. China, its marvel and mystery, by T. Hodgson Liddell, R. B. A. With 40 illustrations in colour by the author. London, G. Allen & sons, 1909.
xiii, 202, ₁1₎ p. 40 col. pl. (incl. front.) facsim. 26 x 20½ᶜᵐ.
Plates accompanied by guard sheets with descriptive letterpress.

1. China—Descr. & trav.

10-25378

Library of Congress DS710.L6

NL 0343718 DLC WaS CSt MSaE CtY OCU MiU OCl NcD NN

Liddell, T Hodgson, 1860–
91898 China, its marvel and mystery, by T. Hodgson Liddell, ... , with 40 illustrations in colour by the author. New York, J. Lane Company; London, G. Allen & Sons, 1910.
xiii, 202, [2] p. col. front., 39 col. pl., 1 facsim. 25½ x 19ᵐᵐ.
Each plate has guard-sheet with descriptive letterpress.

NL 0343719 ICJ NIC WaT NcD CSt-H CU OU PU OO NN MB

Liddell, Thomas.
Report of the discussion on the late disruption in the Presbyterian Church which took place in St. Andrew's Church, Galt, on Tuesday, May 27, 1845, between the Rev. Principal Liddell and the Rev. John Bayne. Taken in shorthand, and revised by the speakers. Galt, Printed at the Dumfries Courier Office, by B.C. Hearle, 1845.
60 p.

Pages 57–60 in duplicate.

NL 0343720 CaOTU CaOTP

---

*9338
.0718A3
Liddell, Thomas K
Industrial survey of Newfoundland, September-October, 1933; April-September, 1939; report. St. John's, Robinson, 1940.
142 p. 23 cm.
At head of title: Newfoundland government.

1. Newfoundland—Econ. condit.
I. Title.

NL 0343721 MB CtY

Liddell, Viola Goode.
With a southern accent. ₁1st ed.₎ Norman, Univ. of Oklahoma Press, 1948.
261 p. map (on lining-papers) 21 cm.

1. Alabama—Soc. life & cust. I. Title.

F326.L5 917.61 48-6090*

OOxM ViU
NL 0343722 DLC CU NcD NcGU WaS OrP FTaSU OrU TxU

Liddell, William.

Esquirol, Jean Étienne Dominique, 1772–1840.
Observations on the illusions of the insane, and on the medico-legal questions of their confinement. Tr. from the French of M. Esquirol ... by William Liddell. London, Renshaw and Rush, 1833.

Liddell, William A
The development of science in the American glass industry, 1880–1940. ₁New Haven, Yale University₎ 1953.
292 p. illus. 27½cm.

Thesis (PH.D.) -- Yale University.
Bibliography: p.278–292.

1. Glass manufacture - U. S. I. Title.

NL 0343724 PHC NCorniC

FILM
666.1
L612d **Liddell, William A**
The development of science in the American glass industry, 1880–1940. ₁New Haven₎ 1953.

Microfilm copy (negative) of typescript, made in 1958 by Yale University Photographic Services, Yale University Library.
Collation of the original: 292ℓ. illus.
Thesis—Yale University.
Bibliography: leaves 287–292.

NL 0343725 IU

Liddell, William Andrew.
Stream gaging, by William Andrew Liddell ... 1st ed. New York ₁etc.₎ McGraw-Hill book company, inc., 1927.
xiv, 238 p. illus., diagrs. 23½ᶜᵐ.

1. Stream measurements. I. Title.

Library of Congress TC175.L5 27-15490

MiU MB PU NcD
NL 0343726 DLC OrP IdU WaS OrCS DSI CU OrPS TU OCl

Liddell Hart, Adrian
see
Hart, Adrian Liddell.

Pam.
Coll. **Liddell Hart, Basil Henry,** 1895–1970.

18290 Britain and Spain ... London, Liberal publication department, 1938.
12 p. map. 18½cm.

1. Spain. History. Civil War, 1936–1939.
Foreign public opinion. I. Title.

NL 0343728 NcD

Liddell Hart, Basil Henry, 1895–
The British way in warfare, by Liddell Hart. London, Faber & Faber limited ₁1932₎
311 p. 22¼ᶜᵐ.

1. Military art and science. 2. Strategy. 3. Military history. 4. Gt. Brit.—Defenses. 5. Gt. Brit.—Army—Hist. 6. War. I. Title.

Library of Congress U43.G7L5 32-25257

Copyright A ad int. 16813 355.0942

DN DAL PU NN
NL 0343729 DLC CaBVaU OrU WaS CaBVa TxU MiU CtY

LIDDELL HART, BASIL HENRY, 1895–
The British way in warfare, by Liddell Hart. New York, The Macmillan Company, 1933.
311 p. 22½cm.

644756A. 1. Military art and science—Gt. Br. 2. Military strategy. 3. Defence—Gt. Br. 4. Army, British—Hist. 5. Military history. I. Title.

NL 0343730 NN MB

Liddell Hart, Basil Henry, 1895–
... The British way in warfare, adaptability and mobility, by Liddell Hart. Harmondsworth, Middlesex, Eng., New York, Penguin books ₁1942₎
ix, 11–223, ₁1₎ p. illus. (port.) 18ᵐ.
At head of title: A Penguin special.
"First published in 1932, new edition revised and enlarged March 1935 ... published in Penguin books 1942."
Published in 1935 under title: When Britain goes to war.

1. Military art and science. 2. Strategy. 3. Military history. 4. Gt. Brit.—Defenses. 5. Gt. Brit.—Army—Hist. 6. War. I. Title.

43-1406

Library of Congress U43.G7L5 1942

355

NL 0343731 DLC IEN

Liddell Hart, Basil Henry, 1895–
Colonel Lawrence, the man behind the legend, by Liddell Hart; with illustrations and maps. New York, Dodd, Mead & company, 1934.
ix, 382 p. front., plates, ports., 9 maps. 24ᶜᵐ.
London edition (J. Cape) has title: 'T. E. Lawrence' in Arabia and after.

1. Lawrence, Thomas Edward, 1888–1935. 2. European war, 1914–1918—Arabia.

34-6056

Library of Congress D568.4.L45L5

Copyright A 69862 ₁a3S†1₎ 940.4153

WaSp Or WaS OrSaW MtBC CaBVa
PBm PP PPL MiU DAL NN MB WaTC OrP WaT IdB IdU
OU OLak ViU DN MeB GU KMK MH MsU NcRS PPFr PPA
NL 0343732 DLC CU MB OClJC OClW NcD OEac OCU OCl

Liddell Hart, Basil Henry, 1895–
Colonel Lawrence, the man behind the legend. New and enl. ed. By Liddell Hart ... New York, Dodd, Mead & company, 1935.
ix, 406 p. front., plates, ports., maps. 24ᶜᵐ.
"Published April, 1934 ... Fifth printing November, 1935."

1. Lawrence, Thomas Edward, 1888–1935. 2. European war, 1914–1918—Arabia.

36-300

Library of Congress D568.4.L45L5 1935

Copyright A 89972 940.4153

NL 0343734 DLC CaBViP CaBVaU NcD NN IaU KyLx MB

Liddell Hart, Basil Henry, 1895–
The current of war, by Liddell Hart. London and Melbourne, Hutchinson & co., ltd. ₁1941₎
414 p., 1 l. 22ᵐ.
Maps on lining-papers.

1. European war, 1939– 2. Military art and science. I. Title.

A 41-3658

Harvard univ. Library
for Library of Congress

OKentU IEN CtY
NL 0343735 MH CaBVaU OrU CaBVa OrP NIC FTaSU MiU

VOLUME 332

Liddell Hart, Basil Henry, 1895–
The decisive wars of history; a study in strategy, by B. H. Liddell Hart. Boston, Little, Brown, and company, 1929.
2 p. l., vii–x p., 1 l., 242 p. maps (2 fold.) 22½ᶜᵐ.
Printed in Great Britain.
Part II. The world war of 1914–1918: p. 159–231.
When book was first drafted the author omitted analysis of the war of 1914–18, but was urged by friendly critics to include it. *cf.* p. 159.

1. Military history. 2. Strategy. I. Title.
[D25.L]   A 30–206
Title from Walter Reed   Hospital. Printed by L. C.

PPL PU NN MB IU DAL DNW
NL 0343736   DWR OrCS CaBVa CaBVaU OrU OCl OClW DN

Liddell Hart, Basil Henry, 1895–
The decisive wars of history, a study in strategy, by B. H. Liddell Hart. London, G. Bell & sons, ltd., 1929.
x p., 1 l., 242 p. maps (part fold.) 22½ᶜᵐ.

1. Military history. 2. Strategy. I. Title.
Library of Congress   D25.L45   30–6649

NN
NL 0343737   DLC CaBVaU DNW TxU CtY OCl MiU OO WaU

Liddell Hart, Basil Henry, 1895–
The defence of Britain, by Liddell Hart. London, Faber and Faber limited [1939]
3 p. l., 9–444 p. diagrs. 22½ cm.

1. Gt. Brit.—Defenses. 2. Gt. Brit. Army. 3. Europe—Defenses. I. Title.
UA647.L5 1939a   355.0942   S D 40–77
U. S. Dept. of State.   Library
for Library of Congress   [r49e1]†

FTaSU
NL 0343738   DS DLC CtY MH MnU Wa WaSp CaBVa OrU ICU

Liddell Hart, Basil Henry, 1895–
The defence of Britain, by Liddell Hart. New York, Random house, 1939.
3 p. l., 9–444 p. 22½ cm.
"Printed in Great Britain."

1. Gt. Brit.—Defenses. 2. Gt. Brit. Army. 3. Europe—Defenses. I. Title.
Library of Congress   UA647.L5   39–27865
[r50v³]   355.0942

WaTC OrP IdU CaBVaU IdPI
OO OU OOxM PU PSC OKentU NcD DAU NNC CU IEN WaS
NL 0343739   DLC PPL PP PBm OLak OClh ViU OCl OEac

Liddell Hart, Basil Henry, 1895–
Defence of the West; some riddles of war and peace. London, Cassell [1950]
viii, 300 p. 19 cm.

1. Military art and science. 2. Europe—Politics—1945– I. Title.
U102.L58   355   50–13361
Library of Congress

WaS CaBVaU OClU
NL 0343740   DLC PPA NN ICU TxU OOxM NcD KMK CaBViP

Liddell Hart, Basil Henry, 1895–
Defence of the West. New York, Morrow, 1950.
x, 335 p. 22 cm.

1. Military art and science. 2. Europe—Politics—1945– I. Title.
U102.L58 1950a   355   50–10635

CaBVa Wa WaE WaT Or IdU OrU IdPI
NL 0343741   DLC OrCS OrP OKentU TU AU CtY NcU MB NNC

4JX   **Liddell Hart, Basil Henry,** 1895–
5004   Défense de l'Europe (Defence of the west). Quelques problèmes de la guerre et de la paix; traduit de l'anglais par A. Petitjean et D. Guillet. Paris, Calmann-Lévy [1951]
300 p.
Liberté de l'esprit.

NL 0343742   DLC-P4

Liddell Hart, Basil Henry, 1895–
Dynamic defence, by Liddell Hart. London, Faber and Faber limited [1940]
2 p. l., 7–64 p. 19ᶜᵐ.
"First published in November Mcmxl."

1. Gt. Brit.—Defenses. 2. World war, 1939– I. Title.
41—2255
Library of Congress   UA647.L52 1940
[a42d3]   355.0942

NL 0343743   DLC CaBVaU CaBVa MiU IEN CtY

Liddell Hart, Basil Henry, 1895–
...Escipión el Africano, un hombre más grande que Napoleón, por el capitán B. H. Liddell Hart... Traducido de la versión italiana y cotejada con la inglesa por el general F. Fasola Castaño (con un prefacio del mismo) Buenos Aires, República Argentina [Imp. L. Bernard, 1935] 309 p. front. (port.), 7 maps. 19½ cm. (Biblioteca del oficial. v. 202.)

At head of title: Círculo militar...
Maps in pocket on inside of back cover.

806371A. 1. Scipio Aemilianus   Africanus Minor, Publius Cornelius.
2. Punic war, 2d, B. C. 218–201.   I. Fasola Castaño, Francisco, tr.
II. Ser.   April 27, 1936

NL 0343744   NN TxU KyLoU

Liddell Hart, Basil Henry, 1895–
Europe in arms, by Liddell Hart. London, Faber and Faber limited [1937]
x, 348 p. 22½ cm.

1. Europe—Defenses. 2. Munitions. 3. Military art and science. 4. Europe—Hist.—1918–1945. 5. War. I. Title.
UA646.L5 1937   [940.5] 355.094   37—10984
Library of Congress   [r55f1]

NL 0343745   DLC NBC CtY OU OO DNW UU TxU Or CaBVa

Liddell Hart, Basil Henry, 1895–
Europe in arms [by] Liddell Hart. New York, Random house [1937]
x p., 1 l., 13–287 p. 21 cm.
"First printing."
"Liddell Hart on Spain. This chapter was received by the publishers from Captain Hart after the book was already off press. July 1937": 11 p. inserted between p. viii and ix.

1. Europe—Defenses. 2. Munitions. 3. Military art and science. 4. Europe—Hist.—1918–1945. 5. War. I. Title.
UA646.L5 1937a   [940.5] 355.094   37—27485

NBuC OrP WaS OrU Wa IdU
PPT PBm PU MiHM NcD NcC CLSU OKentU FTaSU NIC
NL 0343746   DLC OCl OClh OOxM MH DN PSC NN PPL PP

Liddell Hart, Basil Henry, 1895–
Europe in arms. [New ed.] Faber, 1938.
362 p.

NL 0343747   MiD IaU

... Der feldherr, die taten des Publius Cornelius Scipio Africanus; mit einem bild und sieben karten. München, Beck [1938]
xl, 210 p., 1 l. front. (port.) illus. (maps) 22½ᶜᵐ.
At head of title: B. H. Liddell Hart.
"Aus dem englischen übertragen von C. von Mayer. Titel der originalausgabe: A greater than Napoleon, Scipio Africanus."
"Bibliographische notiz": leaf at end.

1. Scipio Africanus major, Publius Cornelius. I. Mayer, Catharina von, tr. II. Title.
39–30438
Library of Congress   DG248.S3L53
923.537

NL 0343748   DLC NBuU NN

DC342.8   **Liddell Hart, Basil Henry,** 1895–
F6L713   Foch, der Feldherr der Entente. Berlin, O. Schlegel [193-?]
355 p. illus., fold. maps, ports. 22 cm.

1. Foch, Ferdinand, 1851–1929.

NL 0343749   OU NN CU

355.331 F57 L37
Liddell Hart, Basil Henry, 1895–
Foch, the man of Orleans, by Liddell Hart. Harmondsworth, Eng., Penguin Books Ltd. [1931]
2 v.

1. Foch, Ferdinand, 1851–1929. I. Title.

NL 0343750   CaOTP

Liddell Hart, Basil Henry, 1895–
Foch, the man of Orleans, by Liddell Hart. London, Eyre and Spottiswoode, 1931.
xl p., 1 l., 518 p. fold. maps. 25½ᶜᵐ.
"Printed sources": p. 502–506.

1. Foch, Ferdinand, 1851–1929.
Library of Congress   DC342.8.F6L5   31–33767
Copyright   A ad int. 15655   923.544

NN DNW
NL 0343751   DLC CaBVaU Or OrP MeB FTaSU NcD OCl ViU

Liddell Hart, Basil Henry, 1895–
Foch, the man of Orléans, by Captain B. H. Liddell Hart ... Boston, Little, Brown, and company, 1932.
xii, 480 p. front., illus. (maps) plates, ports. 23 cm.
Bibliography: p. [459]–463.

1. Foch, Ferdinand, 1851–1929.
DC342.8.F6L5 1932   923.544   32—26039

OClh DN DAL PPA PU PV PP CoU MB TU MeB OKentU
NL 0343752   DLC WaTC WaS CaBVaU MiU ViU OU OCl OEac

Liddell Hart, Basil Henry, 1895–
The future of infantry, by Liddell Hart. London, Faber & Faber limited [1933]
83 p. 17½ᶜᵐ.

1. Infantry. I. Title.
Library of Congress   UD145.L5   33–24525
356

NL 0343753   DLC DAL DNW OU CaOTP TxU MiU NN

VOLUME 332

Liddell Hart, Basil Henry, 1895–
  The future of infantry, by Liddell Hart. Harrisburg, Pa.,
Military service publishing co. ₁°1936₁
  91 p. 18ᶜᵐ.

  1. Infantry.   ɪ. Title.
                                                    36–8838
  Library of Congress   UD145.L5 1936

  Copyright A 92789   356

NL 0343754   DLC MtU OrU PU

Liddell Hart, Basil Henry, 1895–
  Los generales alemanes hablan, por B. H. Liddell Hart.
Versión del general J. M. Silva Plazas. Bogotá, Impr. del
Ministerio de Guerra, 1949.
    285 p. 4 maps on 1 fold. leaf (inserted) 23 cm. (Biblioteca del
  oficial, v. no. 28)
    At head of title: República de Colombia. Estado Mayor General
  de las Fuerzas Militares.
    Translation of The German generals talk.
    1. World War, 1939–1945—Campaigns.   2. World War, 1939–
  1945—Germany. 3. Generals—Germany.   ɪ. Title. (Series :
  Biblioteca del oficial (Bogotá), v. no. 28)

  D757.L518   77–236214

NL 0343755   DLC

Liddell Hart, Basil Henry, 1895–
  ...I generali tedeschi narrano... ₁Milano₁ Rizzoli ₁1949₁
  263 p.   22cm.   (La seconda guerra mondiale. 28)
    1. ed.
    "Titolo originale dell'opera: The other side of the hill... Unica traduzione italiana
  autorizzata di Oreste Rizzini."

  516719B. 1. World war, 1939–   1945—Campaigns. 2. Generals,
  German.   July 7, 1950

NL 0343756   NN

D757 **Liddell Hart, Basil Henry,** 1895–
L513   Les généraux allemands parlent. Ascension
      et chute des généraux allemands. Leurs ré-
      cits des événements militaires de 1939–1945.
      Traduit de l'anglais par Lola Tranec.
      Paris, Stock, 1949.
        323 p. maps.

        1. World War, 1939–1945 - Campaigns.
      2. World War, 1939–1945 - Germany. 3. Gen-
      erals - Germany.

NL 0343757   CU

Liddell Hart, Basil Henry, 1895–
  The German generals talk. New York, W. Morrow, 1948.
  xi, 308 p. maps. 22 cm.

  London ed. (Cassell) pub. under title: The other side of the hill.

  1. World War, 1939–1945—Campaigns. 2. World War, 1939–1945—
  Germany. 3. Generals—Germany. ɪ. Title.

  D757.L5 1948a   940.5343   48–4499*

  OrCS MtBC
  PU PBm OrSaW WaT WaS OrP Or OrPR OrU WaSp IdPI
  MH ICU MiU MB NcRS AU CU–I NBuC UU KU MB AAP PSC
NL 0343758   DLC NBuHi MeB Mi ViU OOxM OU TxU OEac

Liddell Hart, Basil Henry, 1895–
  The ghost of Napoleon, by Liddell Hart. London, Faber
& Faber limited ₁1933₁
  199 p. 21 cm.
  "Bibliographical note" : p. 186–193.

  1. Military art and science—Hist. 2. Napoléon ɪ, emperor of the
  French, 1769–1821. 3. War. ɪ. Title.

  U39.L5   355.09   34—213

         WaS CaBVaU
NL 0343760   DLC CtY OCl DN NcRS NcC NN GU TxU ScU

U   **Liddell Hart, Basil Henry,** 1895–
39   The ghost of Napoleon, by Liddell Hart.
L71   New Haven, Yale University Press ₁1934₁
1934   199 p. 21cm. (Yale University. Oliver
       Baty Cunningham Memorial Publication Fund.
       ₁Publications₁)

         1. Military art and science--Hist.
       2. Napoléon I, emperor of the French, 1769–
       1821. 3. War. I. Title. II. Yale Univer-
       sity. Oliver Baty Cunningham Publication
       Fund.

NL 0343761   NIC NcU PSt PP CtY MB OrU WaTC NcD MtBC

355.09 **Liddell Hart, Basil Henry,** 1895–
L712   The ghost of Napoleon, by Liddel Hart.
        New Haven, Yale university press.₁1935₁

          4 p.l., 7–199 p. 21ᶜᵐ.
          "The present volume is the twelfth work
        published by the Yale university press on the
        Oliver Baty Cunningham memorial publication
        fund."
          "First published, September, 1934."
          "Bibliographical note": p.186–193.
        1.Military art and   science - History.
        2.Napoléon I, empe   ᵣor of the French, 1769–
        182₁. 3.War. I.Titl   e.

          OCU MiU PU
NL 0343762   CSt PPD NN WaU OOxM PBm NcD Vi CO OClW

Liddell Hart, Basil Henry, 1895–
  Great captains unveiled, by Captain B. H. Liddell Hart ...
Edinburgh and London, W. Blackwood & sons ltd., 1927.
  5 p. l., ₁3₁–274 p. illus. (maps, plans) 22 cm.
  CONTENTS.—Jenghiz Khan and Sabutai.—Marechal de Saxe—military prophet.—Gustavus Adolphus—founder of modern war.—Wallenstein—the enigma of history.—General Wolfe—grandsire of the United
  States. 1727–1927.
    1. Jenhis Khan, 1162–1227. 2. Sabutai. 3. Saxe, Maurice, comte
  de, 1696–1750. 4. Gustaf II Adolf, king of Sweden, 1594–1632. 5.
  Wallenstein, Albrecht Wenzel Eusebius von, herzog zu Friedland,
  1583–1634. 6. Wolfe, James, 1727–1750.   ɪ. Title.

  D106.L5   28—11239

  DN CtY OO OClh
NL 0343763   DLC WaS OrU IdU TxU PPGi PPA DAL DNW

Liddell Hart, Basil Henry, 1895–
  Great captains unveiled, by Captain B. H. Liddell Hart.
Boston: Little, Brown, and Co., 1928. 274 p. incl. maps. 8°.
  Printed in Great Britain.
  Contents: Jenghiz Khan and Sabutai. Marechal de Saxe, military prophet. Gus-
  tavus Adolphus, founder of modern war. Wallenstein, the enigma of history. General
  Wolfe, grandsire of the United States.

  353304A. 1. Jenghis Khan, 1162–1227.   2. Subutai, fl. 1241. 3. Saxe, Maurice, comte de, marshal of France, 1696–   1750. 4. Gustavus II Adolphus, king of
  Sweden, 1594–1632. 5. Wallenstein,   Albrecht Wenzel Eusebius von, Herzog
  zu Friedland, 1583–1634. 6. Wolfe,   James, 1727–1759. 7. Title.
                                                    April 25, 1928

NL 0343764   NN OKentU OCl PBa

Liddell Hart, Basil Henry, 1895–
  A greater than Napoleon, Scipio Africanus, by Captain
B. H. Liddell Hart ... Edinburgh and London, W. Black-
wood & sons ltd., 1926.
  viii p., 2 l., 281, ₁1₁ p. front. (port.) maps. 22ᶜᵐ.
  Bibliography : p. 281.

  1. Scipio Africanus major, Publius Cornelius. ɪ. Title.
                                                    27—2509
  Library of Congress   DG248.S3L5

  DAL NN NjP PU
NL 0343765   DLC CaBVa CaBVaU WaS WaSp OrP TxU OClW

DG   **Liddell Hart, Basil Henry,** 1895–
248   A greater than Napoleon, Scipio
.S3L5 Africanus, by Captain B. H. Liddell
1927   Hart. Boston, Little, Brown, & co.,
       1927.
         281 p. illus. 22 cm.
         Bibliography: p. 281.

         1. Scipio Africanus Major, Publius
       Cornelius. I. Title

NL 0343766   OKentU KEmT LU NN MB

Liddell Hart, Basil Henry, 1895–
  A greater than Napoleon, Scipio Africanus, by Captain B. H.
Liddell Hart...   Boston: Little, Brown, and Co., 1927. viii.
281 p. front., maps. 8°.
  Printed in Great Britain.
  Bibliography. p. 281.

  340217A. 1. Scipio Africanus Major,   Publius Cornelius. 2. Punic war, 2nd,
  B. C. 218–201.   December 28, 1927

NL 0343767   NN Or MB WaU IU

Liddell Hart, Basil Henry, 1895–
  A greater than Napoleon, Scipio Africanus,
by Captain B.H. Liddell Hart ... Edinburgh and
London, W. Blackwood & sons ltd., 1927.
  viii p., 2 l., 281, (1)p. front.(port.)maps
22₁ cm.

  107316

NL 0343768   DNW OCl MiU OOxM NcGU

Liddell Hart, Basil Henry, 1895–
  A greater than Napoleon, Scipio Africanus.
Boston, Little, Brown, and co., 1928.

  viii, 281 p. port., maps. 22 cm.

NL 0343769   MH OU PPL

Liddell Hart, Basil Henry, 1895–
  A history of the world war, 1914–1918, by Liddell Hart.
London, Faber & Faber limited ₁1934₁
  635 p. maps (2 fold.) 20½ᶜᵐ.
  "First published in MCMXXX under the title of 'The real war' ...
  Second enlarged edition with the new title first published July
  MCMXXXIV."
  Bibliography : p. 594–620.

  1. European war, 1914–1918.
                                              35–299
  Library of Congress   D521.L48 1934
                                              940.4

  NN MiU TU OKentU TxU CtY ViU PPD PPGi
NL 0343770   DLC IdU WaTC OrCS OrU CaBVa CaBVaU OrPR

Liddell Hart, Basil Henry, 1895–
  A history of the world war, 1914–1918, by Liddell Hart.
Boston, Little, Brown, and company, 1935.
  635 p. maps (2 fold.) 22½ᶜᵐ.
  "First published in MCMXXX under the title of 'The real war'."
  Bibliography: p. 594–620.

  1. European war, 1914–1918.
                                              35–7547
  Library of Congress   D521.L48 1935 a
                                              940.4

  ODW OEac OClh OU NN MB OClW WaU MtBC PPT PPL
NL 0343771   DLC WaS Or MtU OrP NcC MiU NIC OOxM OCU

VOLUME 332

940.3   Liddell Hart, Basil Henry, 1895–
L712r   A history of the World War, 1914–1918.
1934   [2d enl.ed.]   London, Faber & Faber
         [1936,c1934]
           635p. maps(2 fold.) 21cm.

           "First published in MXMXXX under the
         title of 'The real war'."
           Bibliography: p.594–620.

           1.European War, 1914–1918.

NL 0343772   CLSU NcD

Liddell Hart, Basil Henry, 1895–
   Infanterie von morgen; Deutsch von Artur Ehrhardt.
Potsdam, L. Voggenreiter [1934]
   80 p. 19 cm.

   1. Infantry.

UD145.L52   356   49–31831*‡

NL 0343773   DLC IEN

Liddell Hart, Basil Henry, 1895–
   The lawn tennis masters unveiled, by B. H. Liddell Hart...
London, Arrowsmith [1926]   263 p.   illus.   19cm.

   1. ed.

459209B. 1. Tennis, Lawn.

                                        July 15, 1949

NL 0343774   NN

Liddell Hart, Basil Henry, 1895–
   Lawrence of Arabia, by Capt. Liddell Hart and
Sir Ronald Storrs.   [London, Corvinus Press,
1936]
   1v.(unpaged) 30cm.

   "The edition comprises 128 numbered copies,
all signed by the authors and distributed as
follows. 24 specially marked copies, printed
for the authors on Barcham Green "Medway" hand
made paper, numbered 1 to 24: 25 copies on Barcham Green "Boswell" paper, numbered 25 to 49:

6 copies on Winchmore Blue paper, numbered 50 to
55: and 70 copies on Barcham Green "Medway" hand
made paper numbered 56 to 125. Also 3 copies on
various papers lettered A to C, printed for the
exclusive use of the printer ... This copy is
number 112. [Signed] B.H. Liddell Hart. Ronald
Storrs."
   CONTENTS.--Lawrence. "The artist in war and
letters," by B.H.   Liddell Hart.--Lawrence.

"Himself," by Sir Ronald Storrs.

   I. Storrs, Sir Ronald, 1881–   joint author.
II. Title.

NL 0343777   TxU MH CSt

Liddell Hart, Basil Henry, 1895–
   The man behind the legend, Colonel Lawrence ⟨of Arabia⟩
New and enl. ed. By Liddell Hart ... New York, Halcyon
house [1937]
   ix, 406 p. front., plates, ports., maps. 24½ cm.

   "Sixth printing January, 1937." Previously printed under title:
Colonel Lawrence, the man behind the legend.

   1. Lawrence, Thomas Edward, 1888–1935. 2. European war, 1914–
1918—Arabia.   I. Title.

D568.4.L45L5 1937   940.4153   37—6330

NL 0343778   DLC IEN OCl OrAshS WaSp OU ODW MB

UD 157   **Liddell Hart, Basil Henry, Sir,** 1895–
L49   1970.
1918a   New methods in infantry training, by
         B. H. L. Hart. Cambridge, Printed at
         the University Press, 1918.
           38 p.   illus.
           "A revised and enlarged edition of
         Outline of the new infantry training,
         adapted to the use of the volunteer
         force."
           Photocopy.   Ann Arbor, Mich.,
         University Microfilms, 1972. 17 cm.

           1. Infantry drill and tactics
         I. Title

NL 0343779   OU

4D-1212   Liddell Hart, Basil Henry, 1895–
         Oberst Lawrence, der Kreuzfahrer des 20.
         Jahrhunderts. Ins Deutsche übertragen von
         Theodor Lücke.   Berlin, Vorhut-Verlag O.
         Schlegel [19
           279 p.

NL 0343780   DLC-P4

Liddell Hart, Basil Henry,1895–
   Oberst Lawrence, der Kreuzfahrer des 20. Jahrhunderts... Aufl.8 Bilder,Karte, 8. Ber.
Schlegel, K.D.
   279 S

NL 0343781   PPG

Liddell Hart, Basil Henry, 1895–
   The other side of the hill; Germany's generals, their rise
and fall, with their own account of military events, 1939–
1945. London, Cassell [1948]
   320 p. maps. 20 cm.

   1. World War, 1939–1945—Campaigns. 2. World War, 1939–1945—
Germany. 3. Generals—Germany.   I. Title.

D757.L5 1948   940.5343   48–3788*

MB ScU FTaSU CaOTP MiU
NL 0343782   DLC CaBViP WaSp CaBVaU CaBVa MB TxU PSt

D757   Liddell Hart, Basil Henry, 1895–
.L5   The other side of the hill; Germany's generals,
1951   their rise and fall, with their own account of
         military events, 1939–1945. Enl. & rev. ed.
         London, Cassell [1951]
           487 p. 19cm.
           "Published in U. S. A. under the title: 'The
         German generals talk'.

           1. World War, 1939–1945—Campaigns. 2. World
         War, 1939–1945—Germany. 3. Generals—Germany.
         I. Title.

NL 0343783   MB MH RPB NIC ViU NcD CaBVa

Liddell Hart, Basil Henry, 1895–
   Paris; or, The future of war, by Captain B. H. Liddell
Hart. London, K. Paul, Trench, Trubner & co., ltd.; New
York, E. P. Dutton & co., 1925.
   92 p. 16½ cm. [To-day and to-morrow]

   1. War. 2. Military art and science.   I. Title.

U102.L6   25—16139

NL 0343784   DLC NNC DSI PWcS OOxM OCl

Liddell Hart, Basil Henry, 1895–
   Paris; or, The future of war, by Capt. B. H. Liddell
Hart. New York, E. P. Dutton & company [1925]
   4 p. l., 86 p. 16ᵐᵒ. [To-day and to-morrow series]

   1. War. 2. Military art and science.   I. Title.
Library of Congress   U102.L6 1925a   25—19548

InU DAU DN DAL DNW NN ICJ MB
NL 0343785   DLC ICJ WaTC WaU MsSM NcU FTaSU OU PSC

Liddell Hart, Basil Henry, 1895–
   The real war, 1914–1918, by Captain B. H. Liddell Hart;
with twenty-five maps. Boston, Little, Brown, and company, 1930.
   xii p., 2 l., [3]–508 p. maps (2 fold.) 23 cm.
   Bibliography: p. [477]–495.

   1. European war, 1914–1918.   I. Title.

D521.L48 1930a   940.4   30–24091

OU MU CoU NcU FTaSU WaS WaT WaTC WaSp CaBVaU
DN OLak MiU OEac OClh NjN WaU PP PPL DNW OKentU KU
NL 0343786   DLC PU PSC PPT PPA MiHM MB NN DAL ViU

Liddell Hart, Basil Henry, 1895–
   The real war, 1914–1918, by B. H. Liddell Hart. London,
Faber & Faber limited [1930]
   539 p. maps (part fold.) 21½ cm.
   Bibliography: p. 509–528.

   1. European war, 1914–1918—Campaigns. 2. European war, 1914–
1918.   I. Title.

D521.L48   940.4   30–19725

OClWHi IU ViU CtY ICU NjP
NL 0343787   DLC WaE IdU OrU CaBVaU KMK TxU MeB NN

D521   Liddell Hart, Basil Henry.
.L478   The real war, 1914–1918, by Captain B. H.
         Liddell Hart; with twenty-five maps.
         Boston, Little, Brown, and Co., 1931.
           508 p. maps.

           Bibliography: p. [477]–495.

           1. European War, 1914–1918. I. Title.

NL 0343788   DS MH OClW

Liddell Hart, Basil Henry, 1895–
   The remaking of modern armies, by Captain B. H. Liddell
Hart ... London, J. Murray [1927]
   xii, 315 p. diagr. 22½ᵐ.

   1. Military art and science. 2. Armies. 3. Gt. Brit.—Army.
4. France—Army.   I. Title.

Library of Congress   U102.L62 1927   27—18673

DNW DAL NN
NL 0343789   DLC WaS OrU Wa CtY TxU NcD OClCC OCl

Liddell Hart, Basil Henry, 1895–
   Reputations, ten years after, by Captain B. H. Liddell Hart
... Boston, Little, Brown, and company, 1928.
   viii p., 3 l., [3]–316 p. front., ports., maps (part fold.) 22ᵐᵐ.

   CONTENTS.--Marshal Joffre, the modern Delphic oracle.--Erich von
Falkenhayn, the extravagance of prudence.--Marshal Gallieni, the real
victor of the Marne.--Haig of Bemersyde, the essence of Britain.--Fer-
dinand Foch, the symbol of the victorious will.--Erich Ludendorff, the
robot Napoleon.--Pétain, military economist.--Allenby of Megiddo, the
evolution of a leader.--Hunter Liggett, a professor of war--and human
nature.--"Black Jack" Pershing, the "100-per-cent American".

   1. European war, 1914–1918—Biog. 2. Generals. 3. Military biography.   I. Title.

D507.L5   28–6416

OrU WaTC OrP WaS
DAL NcGU ViU NjN DN CSt-H NIC MU MeB CoU CaBVaU
OU OOxM OClWHi OClh DN PPFr NN PU WaU PPGi MB PP
NL 0343790   DLC OU MiHM MB NcC NcD NcU OCl OEac

VOLUME 332

D823 Liddell Hart, Basil Henry, 1895–
L58 Reputations, by Captain B. H. Liddell Hart. London, J. Murray [1928]

327 p. maps (part fold.) 22½ᶜᵐ.

CONTENTS.—Marshal Joffre.—Erich von Falkenhayn.—Haig of Bemersyde.—Marshal Gallieni.—Ferdinand Foch.—Erich Ludendorff.—Pétain. Allenby of Megiddo. Hunter Liggett.—"Black Jack" Pershing.

1. European war, 1914–1918—Biog. 2. Military biography.

NL 0343791 ICU TxU CU DAU MH

F
100
.51   Liddell Hart, Basil Henry, 1895–

Reputations… London[1930]

Contents.—Marshal Joffre, the modern Delphic oracle.—Erich von Falkenhayn, the extravagance of prudence.—Haig of Bemerside: the essence of Britain.—Marshal Gallieni, the real victor of the Marne.—Ferdinand Foch, the symbol of the victorious will.—Erich Ludendorff, the robot Napoleon.—Pé-   tain, military economist.—Allenby of Megiddo, the evolution of a leader.—Hunter Liggett, a professor of war and human nature.—"Black Jack" Pershing, the "100-per-cent American."

NL 0343793 ICN IaU NIC

Liddell Hart, Basil Henry, 1895–
The revolution in warfare, by B. H. Liddell Hart. London, Faber and Faber ltd [1946]

99 p. 19½ᶜᵐ.

"First published in Mcmxlvi."

1. War. 2. Military art and science. I. Title.
46–4819
Library of Congress U102.L63
355

ICU TxU NNC CtY
NL 0343794 DLC Wa OrCS NIC MeB CaOTP FTaSU DAL

Liddell Hart, Basil Henry, 1895–
The revolution in warfare, by B. H. Liddell Hart. New Haven, Yale university press, 1947.

x, 125 p. 21ᶜᵐ.

"Published on the foundation established in memory of Oliver Baty Cunningham of the Class of 1917, Yale college."

1. War. 2. Military art and science. I. Title.
U102.L63 1947 355 47–3404

PBL PV PSC NSyU CU MtBC IdPI
NL 0343795 DLC OrPS WaWW WaS WaTC MtU OrU OrP Or

D766
.82
.R57   Liddell Hart, Basil Henry, 1895– ed.
1953   Rommel, Erwin, 1891–1944.   FOR OTHER EDITIONS
                                        SEE MAIN ENTRY
The Rommel papers, edited by B. H. Liddell Hart, with the assistance of Lucie-Maria Rommel, Manfred Rommel, and Fritz Bayerlein. Translated by Paul Findlay. [1st American ed.] New York, Harcourt, Brace, 1953]

Liddell-Hart, Basil Henry, 1895–
A science of infantry tactics. By Capt. B. H. Liddell Hart …
(*In* The Military engineer. Washington, 1921. 30ᶜᵐ. vol. XIII, no. 70, p. 315–320; no. 71, p. 409–414 incl. diagrs.)
"Reprinted from the Royal engineers journal."

1. Infantry drill and tactics. 2. Tactics. I. Title.

U. S. Engineer sch. Library   E S 23–105 Revised
for Library of Congress   [TA1.P85 vol. 13, no. 70]
[r39c2]

NL 0343797 DES DLC OU

UD 157 LIDDELL HART, BASIL HENRY, 1895–
.L712   A science of infantry tactics simplified. With a foreword by Ivor Maxse. 3d rev. and enl. ed. London, W. Clowes, 1926.
108 p.

Founded on lectures given at the Royal United Service Institution, and Institution of Royal Engineers, in 1920.
Photocopy.
1. Infantry drill and tactics. 2. Tactics.
I. Title.

NL 0343798 InU OU CU

937
S418YℓXℱ Liddell Hart, Basil Henry, 1895–
Scipion l'africain [par] B.H. Liddell Hart. Préf. et traduction du Capitaine A. Lageix. Paris, Payot, 1934.
239p. illus. 23cm. (Bibliothèque historique)

Translation of A Greater than Napoleon, Scipio Africanus.

1. Scipio Africanus major, Publius Cornelius. I. Title.

NL 0343799 IEN

Liddell Hart, Basil Henry, 1895–
Sherman; soldier, realist, American, by B. H. Liddell Hart … with maps. New York, Dodd, Mead & company, 1929.

viii p., 2 l., 456 p. front. (port.) maps (part fold.) 24½ᶜᵐ.

London edition (E. Benn, ltd.) has title: Sherman, the genius of the civil war.
"Sources": p. 432–441.

1. Sherman, William Tecumseh, 1820–1891. 2. U. S.—Hist.—Civil war—Campaigns and battles.
E467.1.S55L71 29–27667

PPL WaE OrP MtU WaS CaBVa OrSaW
OEac OLak MiU OClWHi DN MH MB NN WaU PPA PU PHC PP
NL 0343800 DLC WaT NIC IU TU ViU MeB NcD OFH OU OCl

Liddell Hart, Basil Henry, 1895–
Sherman; soldier, realist, American, by B. H. Liddell Hart … New York, Dodd, Mead & company, 1930.

viii p., 2 l., 456 p. front. (port.) maps (part fold.) 24½ᶜᵐ.

"Published, November, 1929 … third printing, June, 1930."
"Sources": p. 432–441.

1. Sherman, William Tecumseh, 1820–1891. 2. U. S.—Hist.—Civil war—Campaigns and battles.
33–16480
Library of Congress E467.1.S55L713
923.573

NL 0343801 DLC OO OClW

Liddell-Hart, Basil Henry, 1895–
Sherman, the genius of the civil war. by B. H. Liddell Hart. [London] E. Benn, ltd.. 1930.

5 p. l., 9–473 p. front. (port.) maps (part fold.) 22ᶜᵐ.

New York edition (Dodd, Mead & company) has title: Sherman: soldier, realist, American.
"Sources": p. 447–456.

1. Sherman, William Tecumseh, 1820–1891. 2. U. S.—Hist.—Civil war—Campaigns and battles.
34–10420
Library of Congress E467.1.S55L72
923.573

NL 0343802 DLC WaSp NjP TxU ICN

Liddell Hart, Basil Henry, 1895–
Sherman, the genius of the civil war, by B. H. Liddell Hart. London, Eyre and Spottiswoode, 1933.

5 p. l., 9–473 p. front. (port.) maps (part fold.) 22ᶜᵐ.

New York edition (Dodd, Mead & company) has title: Sherman: soldier, realist, American.
"Sources": p. 447–456.
"2nd (Cheap) edition."

NL 0343803 ViU

Liddell Hart, Basil Henry, 1895–
Strategy. New York, Praeger [1954]

420 p. illus. 22 cm. (Books that matter)

First published in 1929 under title: The decisive wars of history.

1. Military history. 2. Strategy. I. Title.

D25.L45 1954 355.48 54–9111 rev ‡

OrPR WaSpG WaTC OrCS WaWW IdPI
PPLas OU OClU CaBViP CaBVa IdB MtU OrP WaS WaT
ViU MB TU OClW ODW PPD PBL PCM NcC PPT PLF PU PSC
NL 0343804 DLC NBuC MnU FU WaU ICarbS KEmT CU GU

Liddell Hart, Basil Henry, 1895–
The strategy of indirect approach, by Liddell Hart. London, Faber and Faber limited [1941]

3 p. l., ix–xvii p., 1 l., 316 p. maps (1 fold.) 22½ᶜᵐ.

New and enlarged edition of the author's The decisive wars of history, published in 1929. *cf.* Pref.
"First published in June Mcmxli."

1. Military history. 2. Strategy. I. Title.
41–19906
Library of Congress D25.L45 1941
355.48

NL 0343806 DLC TxU TU FTaSU OU CtY

Liddell Hart, Basil Henry, 1895–
The strategy of indirect approach, by B. H. Liddell Hart, with a foreword by Brigadier E. E. Dorman-Smith … London, Faber and Faber [1946]

xiv, 317 p. maps (1 fold.) 19ᶜᵐ.

"Part of this book was published in Mcmxxix under the title of 'The decisive wars of history.' The present book was first published in June Mcmxli under the title of 'The strategy of indirect approach' … Reprinted under the title of 'The way to win wars' in October Mcmxliii. New and enlarged edition Mcmxlvi."

1. Military history. 2. Strategy. I. Title.
46–6696
Library of Congress D25.L45 1946
355.48

NL 0343807 DLC

Liddell Hart, Basil Henry, 1895–
Strategy, the indirect approach. [3d rev. and further enl. ed.] London, Faber and Faber [1954]

420 p. maps (1 fold.) 23 cm.

"Part of this book was published in Mcmxxix under the title of 'The decisive wars of history.' The present book was first published in June Mcmxli under the title of 'The strategy of indirect approach.' "

1. Military history. 2. Strategy. I. Title.

D25.L45 1954a 355.48 54–4451

NL 0343808 DLC MiU TxU NBC PP NN TxU PSt CaBVaU

VOLUME 332

AC-L
L438&*l*.te
1955
Liddell Hart, Basil Henry, 1895–
T.E. Lawrence, Aldington, and the truth.
[London, 1955?]
9p. 22cm.

"Reprinted from the London magazine, April
1955 (with three additional passages ...)"
Gift of Prof. A.W. Lawrence.

1. Lawrence, Thomas Edward, 1888-1935. 2.
Aldington, Richard, 1892–　I. Title. A.F.:
Lawrence, Arnold　Walter, 1900–

NL 0343809　TxU

Liddell Hart, Basil Henry, 1895–
'T. E. Lawrence'; in Arabia and after, by Liddell Hart
London, J. Cape [1934]
2 p. l., 3-454 p. front., illus. (plan) plates, ports., 9 maps (part fold.)
23ᶜᵐ.

Four of the maps are included in pagination.

1. Lawrence, Thomas Edward, 1888–　2. European war, 1914-
1918—Campaigns—Turkey and the near East.　3. European war, 1914-
1918—Arabia.

Title from Yale Univ.　　Printed by L. C.　　A 34-1444

CtY PHC NN ViU TU CaBViP Wa CaBVa MtU CaBVaU TU
NL 0343810　CtY CaQMM GU InU TxU KMK MtU NcU ScU

D
568.4
L45
L52
1935
Liddell Hart, Basil Henry, 1895–
T. E. Lawrence; in Arabia and after, by
Liddell Hart. London, J. Cape [1935]
454 p. illus., 9 maps (part fold.), plans,
plates, ports. 23 cm.

"First published ... 1934 ... Re-issued in
Academy Books ... 1935."

1. Lawrence, Thomas Edward, 1888-1935. 2.
European War, 1914-1918 - Campaigns - Turkey
and the Near East.　3. European War, 1914-
1918 - Arabia.

NL 0343811　CU-S TxU ViU MH KyLoU NcD FMU CaBVaU

Liddell Hart, Basil Henry, 1895–
'T. E. Lawrence' in Arabia and after, by Liddell Hart.
London, J. Cape [1936]
2 p. l., 3-491 p. front., plates, ports., maps (part fold.) 22½ cm.
[Academy books. no. 20]

"First published March 1934 ... third impression March 1934; re-
issued in Academy books, May 1935; reprinted ... September 1935;
new and enlarged edition, December 1935; reprinted March 1936."
American edition (New York, Dodd, Mead & company) has title:
Colonel Lawrence, the man behind the legend.

1. Lawrence, Thomas Edward, 1888-1935. 2. European war, 1914–
1918—Campaigns—Turkey and the Near East.　3. European war,
1914-1918—Arabia.

D568.4.L45L52 1936　　　　　36-31721
[923.542]　940.4153

NL 0343812　DLC IaU MtBuM NBuU CU MU

Liddell Hart, Basil Henry, 1895–
'T.E.Lawrence' in Arabia and after. London,
J.Cape [1943]

491 p. ports., plates, maps. 20.5 cm.

NL 0343813　MH

Liddell Hart, Basil Henry, 1895–　ed.

Lawrence, Thomas Edward, 1888-1935.
T. E. Lawrence to his biographer, Liddell Hart; information about himself in the form of letters, notes, answers to
questions and conversations. New York, Doubleday, Doran &
company, inc., 1938.

Liddell Hart, Basil Henry, 1895–
This expanding war, by Liddell Hart. London, Faber
and Faber ltd. [1942]
278 p. illus. (maps) 22½ cm.
"First published in Mcmxlii."

1. World war, 1939-1945.　I. Title.
Library of Congress　D743.L52 1942　42-25073
[a50d½]　940.53

NL 0343815　DLC CaBVaU FTaSU OU TxU MiU NcD CtY OCl

Liddell Hart, Basil Henry, 1895–
... Thoughts on war. London, Faber and Faber ltd [1944]
327 p. 22½ᶜᵐ.

At head of title: Liddell Hart.
"First published in Mcmxliv."

1. War. 2. Strategy. 3. Tactics.　I. Title.
Library of Congress　U19.L7　44-5660
355

TxU NIC CtY
NL 0343816　DLC CaBVa MiU CSt FTaSU MU OU CSt-H NcD

Liddell Hart, Basil Henry, 1895–
Through the fog of war, by Liddell Hart. New York,
Random house [*1938]
x, 379 p. 21 cm.
"First printing."
"A selected bibliography": p. 371-372.

1. European war, 1914-1918.　I. Title.
Library of Congress　D521.L483 1938a　38-28966
[50x1]　940.4

InU PSC PP PPL LU
FTaSU MB ViU CtY PU OKentU OU GU NcD OCl OO PPT PPD
NL 0343817　DLC NN Wa OrU WaS OrPR OrP WaE WaTC TxU

UA
647
L57
Liddell Hart, Basil Henry, 1895–
Die Verteidigung Gross-Britanniens; mit
einem Geleitwort von Oberst Dr. Gustav Däniker.
Zürich, Scientia A. G. [1939]
xv, 466 p. 23 cm.
The defence of Britain.

1. Gt. Brit.—Defenses. 2. Gt. Brit.
Army. 3. Europe—Defenses. I. Title.　rw

NL 0343818　IEdS

Liddell Hart, Basil Henry, 1895–
The war in outline, 1914-1918, by Liddell Hart. London,
Faber and Faber, limited [1936]
2 p. l., [vii]-xvii p., 1 l., [9]-259 p. illus. (plans) fold. maps. 19½ᶜᵐ.

1. European war, 1914-1918.　I. Title.
Library of Congress　D521.L485　36-18788
940.3

OClW ViU NNC NBuG NcD CtY NN OO
NL 0343819　DLC IdU CaBVa CaBVaU MiU OU TxU CSt-H

Liddell Hart, Basil Henry, 1895–
... The war in outline, 1914-1918. New York, Random
house [*1936]
xx p., 1 l., 11-285 p. maps (part fold.) 21ᶜᵐ.
At head of title: Liddell Hart.

1. European war, 1914-1918.　I. Title.
Library of Congress　D521.L485 1936 a　36-27463
Copyright A 99416　940.3

NcU WaT WaTC OrP MtU Or WaS OrAshS WaWW Wa
OOxM OU DN MB NN PPPL PPT PPL PP DNW CtY CaOTP OClU
NL 0343820　DLC IaU MH OU NcRS ViU PPA ODW OCl OEac

940.4
H32
Liddell Hart, Basil Henry, 1895–
The war in outline, 1914-1918, by Liddell
Hart. New York, The Modern Library, 1939.
285p. maps. 17cm.

1. European war 1914-1918—Chronology.
I. Title.

NL 0343822　NBuHi

Liddell Hart, Basil Henry, 1895–
The way to win wars; the strategy of indirect approach, by
Liddell Hart. London, Faber and Faber ltd. [1942]
256 p. illus. (maps) 18ᶜᵐ.

"Part of this book was published in Mcmxxix, under the title of 'The
decisive wars of history.' The present book was first published in June
Mcmxli under the title of 'The strategy of indirect approach'."

1. Military history. 2. Strategy.　I. Title. II. Title: The strategy of
indirect approach.
Library of Congress　D25.L45 1942　44-6384
355.48

NL 0343823　DLC NN IEN

U43
G7L7L23
Liddell Hart, Basil Henry, 1895–
Wenn England zu Felde zieht; Betrachtungen
über britische Strategie.　Potsdam, L.
Voggenreiter [1937]
130 p.　19cm.
Translation of When Britain goes to war.

1. Military art and science. 2. Strategy.
3. Military histo　ry. 4. Gt. Brit. -
Defenses. 5. Gt.　Brit. Army - Hist. 6.
War. I. Title.

NL 0343824　CSt-H

Liddell Hart, Basil Henry, 1895–
When Britain goes to war; adaptability and mobility, by
Liddell Hart. London, Faber and Faber limited [1935]
3 p. l., 9-338, [1] p. 21ᶜᵐ.

"First published in Mcmxxxii under the title of The British way in
warfare. New edition revised and enlarged March Mcmxxxv."

1. Military art and science. 2. Strategy. 3. Military history. 4. Gt.
Brit.—Defenses. 5. Gt. Brit.—Army—Hist. 6. War.　I. Title.
Library of Congress　U43.G7L5 1935　35-23275
355.0942

CtY NN
NL 0343825　DLC DNW CaOTP NN CaBVaU WaS NcD CLSU

Liddell Hart, Basil Henry, 1895–
... Why don't we learn from history? By B. H. Liddell
Hart. London, G. Allen & Unwin ltd. [1944]
64 p. 16ᶜᵐ. (P. E. N. books. General editor: Herman Ould)
"First published in 1944."

1. History—Philosophy.　I. Title.
Library of Congress　D16.9.L44　44-5222
901

WaU CSt-H MU CaOTP InU IEN TU NbU CSt NB PPLT LU
NL 0343826　DLC OrPR MH MBAt NBuG CtY IU NjP TNJ

UB
345
.G7
L69
Liddell-Hart, Basil Henry, 1895–
Willing service or compulsion? [London,
Swindon Press, 192-?]
10 p.

1. Military service, Compulsory—Gt. Brit.
I. Title.

NL 0343827　MiU

VOLUME 332

Liddelow, K   P
Clinical dental prosthetics

see under

Fenn, Harold Robert Backwell.

JF515
.C3

Lidderdale, D. W. S., joint author.

Campion, Gilbert Francis Montriou Campion, *baron,* 1882–
European parliamentary procedure, a comparative handbook, by Lord Campion & D. W. S. Lidderdale. With a pref. by the authors and a foreword by Viscount Ruffside. London, Printed and published by the Inter-parliamentary Union on behalf of its Autonomous Section of Secretaries-General of Parliaments, Allen and Unwin ₁1953₎

Lidderdale, D   W   S
Le Parlement français. Préf. d'Émile Blamont. Paris, A. Colin, 1954.

xix, 298 p. 24 cm. (Cahiers de la Fondation nationale des sciences politiques, 54)

1. France. Assemblée nationale, 1946–   I. Title.   (Series: Fondation nationale des sciences politiques. Cahiers, 54)

H31.F6 no. 54   54–2531

NL 0343830   DLC FU PU IU TxU NjP NN NcD ScU DAU

Lidderdale, D   W   S
The Parliament of France. London, Hansard Society ₁1951₎

xix, 296 p. 22 cm.

1. France. Assemblée nationale, 1946–   I. Title.

JN2791.L5   328.44   51–32729

NIC MiU NcU MH NIC CtY IEN ViU TU TxU
NL 0343831   DLC INS CaBVa CaBVaU MtU OrCS WaS WaSpG

Lidderdale, D   W   S
The Parliament of France. New York, F. A. Praeger ₁1952₎

xix, 296 p. 22 cm.

1. France. Assemblée nationale, 1946–   I. Title.
[JN2791.L   ]   A 52–10002
Temple Univ. Library
for Library of Congress   ₁53f5₎

PCM
NL 0343832   PPT CtY WaT WaWW OrP NN PP PV MB OU ODW

H31
.F6
no. 73

Lidderdale, D. W. S., joint author.

Campion, Gilbert Francis Montriou Campion, *baron,* 1882–
La procédure parlementaire en Europe; étude comparée. ₁Par₎ Lord Campion et D. W. S. Lidderdale. Publié avec le concours de l'Union interparlementaire et de sa Section autonome des secrétaires généraux. Paris, A. Colin, 1955.

Lidderdale, Halliday, *d.* 1845.
Disputatio medica inauguralis, quædam de morbis literatorum eorumque de prophylaxi complectens: quam ... ex auctoritate ... d. Georgii Baird ... Academiæ edinburgenæ præfecti ... pro gradu doctoris ... eruditorum examini subjicit Halliday Lidderdale, Scoto-Britannus: Ad diem 12 septembris ₁1800₎ ... Edinburgi, excudebant A. Neill et socii, MDCCC.
3 p. l., 49 p. 21ᶜᵐ.

1. Mental physiology and hygiene. 2. Occupations—Diseases and hygiene.

Library of Congress   RA788.L5   36–36681

NL 0343834   DLC DNAL NNNAM

W 4
L68
v. 9
no. 30

LIDDERDALE, James, *d.* 1761
Disputatio medica inauguralis de inflammatione oculorum
... Lugduni Batavorum, Apud Abrahamum Elzevier. 1708.
21 p. 21 cm.
Diss. - Leyden.

NL 0343835   DNLM

Lidderdale, Kathleen Eleonora, 1894–
Hockey for girls and women, by K. E. Lidderdale .. London, G. Bell and sons, ltd., 1923.

viii, 119 p. plates, diagr. 17½ᶜᵐ.

1. Field hockey.   I. Title.

Library of Congress   GV1017.H7L5   24—2696

NL 0343836   DLC OC1 OLak

Lidderdale, Kathleen Eleonora, 1894–
Hockey for girls and women. [Reprinted.]
— London. G. Bell & Sons Ltd. 1924. viii, 119 pp. Plates. 17 cm., in 8s.

D5689 — Hockey.

NL 0343837   MB OO PSt PP

Lidderdale, Kathleen Eleonora, 1894 –
Hockey for girls and women.   New York: Harcourt Brace & Co. ₁1924₎   119 p. pl. 16°.

1. Hockey.   September 29, 1924.

NL 0343838   NN OU PSC OC1W OOxM

W 4
E23
1796
L 1

LIDDERDALE, Robert.
Dissertatio inauguralis, de imaginatione; et praecipue ejus de viribus in morbis inducendis et sanandis ... Edinburgi,
Alex. Smellie, 1796.
138 p. 21 cm.
Diss. - Edinburgh.

NL 0343839   DNLM

Lidderdale, Thomas William, 1830–1884.

British museum. *Dept. of printed books.*
Catalogue of the books printed in Iceland, from A. D. 1578 to 1880. In the library of the British museum. London, Printed by W. Clowes and sons, 1885.

Liddesdale; or, The border chief
see under [Lawson, James] 1799–188?.

Liddiard, *Mrs.* J   S   Anna (Wilkinson)
Kenilworth and Farley castle; with other poems. By J. S. Anna Liddiard ... Dublin, Printed at the Hibernia-press office, 1813.

2 p. l., xviii, ₁v₎–vii, ₁1₎, 144 p. 19ᶜᵐ.

1. Kenilworth castle, Eng. 2. Farley castle, Eng.   I. Title.
25–25705
Library of Congress   PR4889.L3K4 1813

NL 0343842   DLC CtY

Y
185
.B 61922

LIDDIARD, J   S   ANNA (WILKINSON)
Poems.   Dublin, Hibernia-Press Office, 1810.
100p. front. 17cm.

Binder's title: Farmer's boy.

NL 0343843   ICN

Liddiard, J   S   Anna (Wilkinson)
The sgelaighe; or, A tale of old. With a second ed. of poems, pub. in Dublin, and additions. By Mrs. Liddiard. Bath, printed by Meyler and Son [etc., etc.] 1811.
vi, [1], 184 p. 18 cm.

NL 0343844   NjP

Liddiard, Mabel.

RT91
.R4
1944

Red cross. *Gt. Brit. British Red cross society.*
British Red cross society infant welfare manual ... by Mabel Liddiard ... 5th ed. With 25 illustrations ... London, J. & A. Churchill ltd., 1944.

WS
413
L712m
1924

Liddiard, Mabel.
The mothercraft manual; or, The expectant and nursing mother and baby's first two years. 2d ed. London, Churchill, 1924.
xvi, 175 p. illus.

1. Infants - Care and hygiene
I. Title

NL 0343846   DNLM

Liddiard, Mabel.
The mothercraft manual; or, The expectant and nursing mother and baby's first two years, by Mabel Liddiard ... introduction by J. S. Fairbairn ... London: J. & A. Churchill, 1925.
xvi, 184 p. incl. diagrs., tables.   chart, illus.   3. ed.   12°.

208380A. 1. Mothers. 2. Infants—   Care and feeding.   October 31, 1925

NL 0343847   NN DNLM

Liddiard, Mabel.
The mothercraft manual; or, The expectant and nursing mother and baby's first two years, by Mabel Liddiard ... Introduction by J. S. Fairbairn ... 9th ed., 123d thousand, with 8 plates and 32 text figures. London, J. & A. Churchill ltd., 1934.
xvi, 195, ₁5₎ p. illus., plates, fold. diagr. 19ᶜᵐ.
Blank pages for "Notes" (₁5₎ at end)

1. Infants—Care and hygiene. 2. Infants—Nutrition.   I. Title.
35–8787
Library of Congress   RJ61.L58
649.1

NL 0343848   DLC

VOLUME 332

WS
413
L712m
1940

Liddiard, Mabel.
The mothercraft manual; or. The expectant and nursing mother and baby's first two years. 10th ed. London, Churchill, 1940.
xvi, 199 p. illus.

1. Infants - Care and hygiene I. Title

NL 0343849   DNLM

WS
413
L712m
1948

Liddiard, Mabel.
The mothercraft manual; or, The expectant and nursing mother and baby's first two years. 11th ed. London, Churchill, 1948.
xiii, 176 p. illus.

1. Infants - Care and hygiene I. Title

NL 0343850   DNLM

WS
113
L712m
1954

LIDDIARD, Mabel.
The mothercraft manual; or, The expectant and nursing mother and baby's first two years. 12th ed. London, Churchill ₁1954₎
ix, 178 p. illus.
1. Infants - Care & hygiene
Title

NL 0343851   DNLM

3827
.8
.357

Liddiard, William, 1773-1841.
The legend of Einsidlin; a tale of Switzerland; with poetical sketches of Swiss scenery... London, Saunders, 1829.
14,283 p. 20½ cm.

NL 0343852   NjP

Liddiard, William, 1773-1841.
A three months' tour in Switzerland and France. Illustrated ... and interspersed with poetry; with a route to Chamouni, the Bernese Alps, &c. By the Rev. William Liddiard ... London, Smith, Elder, and co., 1832.
xvi, 263, ₁1₎ p. incl. front. 4 pl., fold. map. 22ᵐ.

1. Switzerland—Descr. & trav. 2. France—Descr. & trav.
4-5894

Library of Congress   DQ23.L7

NL 0343853   DLC NcU PPL

Liddiard, William, 1773-1841.
A short tract upon the expediency of a general establishment of the life boat, but more particularly in the vicinity of the Mortello [i.e. Martello] towers. By the Rev. W. Liddiard ... Dublin, Printed for M. Keene, 1807.
3 p.l., 26 p. 21½cm.

Manuscript corrections on title-page and in text: Mortello to read Martello.

NL 0343854   MdBJ

Liddicoat, J G
Black diamond march, for two banjos and guitar. [Arr. by Charles C. Bertholdt]
St. Louis, C. Bertholdt, 1891.
5 p. 36 cm.
Cover title.

1. Trios (2 banjos, guitar) I. Title.

NL 0343855   MB

Liddicoat, J. G.
Euclid club march ... two mandolins and guitar. Cleveland, Eastman, c1897.

Separate scores for mandolins and guitar.

NL 0343856   OC1

Liddicoat, Richard Thomas, 1918–
Handbook of gem identification, with a foreword by Edward H. Kraus. ₁1st ed.₎ Los Angeles, Gemological Institute of America ₁1947₎
xi, 283 p. illus. 22 cm. (The Jeweler's library, v. 7)

1. Precious stones. 2. Mineralogy, Determinative. I. Title: Gem identification. (Series)

QE392.L5   549   47—31359*

NL 0343857   DLC MiHM NcC Mi WaT WaS CaBViP

QE392
.L5
1948

Liddicoat, Richard Thomas, 1918–
Handbook of gem identification, with a foreword by Edward K. Kraus. ₁2nd ed.₎ Los Angeles, Gemological Institute of America ₁1948₎
xiii, 294 p. illus. 22 cm. (The Jeweler's library, v.7)

1. Precious stones. 2. Mineralogy, Determinative. I. Title: Gem identification. II. Series.

NL 0343858   TU OrCS OrP CU

Liddicoat, Richard Thomas, 1918–
Handbook of gem identification; with a foreword by Edward H. Kraus. ₁3d ed.₎ Los Angeles, Gemological Institute of America ₁1951₎
xiii, 350 p. illus. 22 cm.

1. Precious stones. 2. Mineralogy, Determinative.
I. Title: Gem identification.

QE392.L5 1951   549   51—10568

NL 0343859   DLC OU DI MB CaBVa ICJ OrP OrU MiHM

Liddicoat, Richard Thomas, 1918–
Handbook of gem identification. With a foreword by Edward H. Kraus. ₁4th ed.₎ Los Angeles, Gemological Institute of America ₁1953₎
xv, 350 p. illus. 22 cm.

1. Precious stones. 2. Mineralogy, Determinative. I. Title: Gem identification.

QE392.L5 1953   *549.14   54—367

NL 0343860   DLC Or Wa WaS WaT MiU NcRS PPL MB PP

Liddicoat, Richard Thomas, 1891–
Laboratory manual of materials testing ₁by₎ R. T. Liddicoat ₁and₎ Philip O. Potts. New York, Macmillan ₁1952₎
239 p. illus. 22 cm.

1. Materials—Testing. 2. Engineering—Laboratory manuals.
I. Potts, Philip Orland, joint author. II. Title.

TA412.L5   620.11072   52—14771 ‡

TU OrP OrCS IdU Wa WaSpG
NL 0343861   DLC NSyU WaU IEN MB NN ViU TxU OCU MiHM

Liddicoet, Thomas Herbert, 1927–
The reaction of metals with 1,4-dihalides and some similar compounds. Ann Arbor, University Microfilms ₁1954₎
(₁University Microfilms, Ann Arbor, Mich.₎ Publication 7193)
Microfilm copy of typescript. Positive.
Collation of the original: 3, iv, 108 l. illus.
Thesis—University of Washington.
Abstracted in Dissertation abstracts, v. 14 (1954) no. 3, p. 468.
Vita.
Bibliography: leaves 104-108.

1. Metals. 2. Chemical reactions. I. Title.

Microfilm AC–1 no. 7193   Mic A 54–667

Washington. Univ.,   Seattle. Library
for Library of Congress   ₁1₎†

NL 0343862   WaU DLC

Liddil, Dick
see Liddil, James Andrew, 1852–

Liddil, James Andrew, 1852–

₁Miller, George, jr.₎
The trial of Frank James for murder. With the confessions of Dick Liddil and Clarence Hite, and history of the "James gang." Kansas City, Mo., G. Miller, jr. ₁1898₎

Liddle, Beatrice Boles.
... Three interesting stories featuring Glorified wilderness, a descriptive narrative of Banff national park, and the novelette Path of earthly stars, and a short story, Seaward deluge, by Beatrice Boles Liddle. ₁Calgary, Alta., Printed by Albertan job press limited, 1946₎
cover-title, 54 p., 1 l. 19¼ᵐ.

46–21399

Library of Congress   PZ3.L61965Th

NL 0343865   DLC

Liddle, Carl.
Tunchi, by Carl Liddle and David Thibault. New York, London, The Century co. ₁ᶜ1933₎
v, 312 p. 19¼ᵐ. $2.00
"First printing."

I. Thibault, David, 1892– joint author. II. Title.
Library of Congress   PZ3.L6197Tu   33–7848

NL 0343866   DLC WaSp MB

Liddle, Helen Gordon.
The prisoner: a sketch.
— Letchworth. Garden City Press, Ltd. 1911. xi, 75 pp. 18½ cm.
The cover-title reads: The prisoner: an experience of forcible feeding, by a suffragette.

L3143 — T.r. — Woman suffrage. — Prisons and prison discipline.

NL 0343867   MB

VOLUME 332

Liddle (John). On the moral and physical evils resulting from the neglect of sanitary measures ... To which are added a few remarks on the necessity of appointing district officers of health. Health of Towns Association. 31 pp. 12°. *London, depot of the association, 1847.* [P., v. 754; 808.]

NL 0343868   DNLM

WCB
L713r
1867

LIDDLE, John.
Report on the epidemic of cholera in 1866. London, 1867.
64 p.
I. London. Board of Works, Whitechapel District

NL 0343869   DNLM

Liddle, John.
———. Report upon the necessity of retaining the present staff of four inspectors of nuisances, to the board of works. 7 pp. 8°. *London, 1868.*

NL 0343870   DNLM

Liddle, John T., d. 1909.
In memory of John T. Liddle
see under title

W 4
B92
no. 1272

LIDDLE, Jorge.
Semiología de la carcinosis del estómago. Buenos Aires, 1902.
85 p. (Buenos Aires. Universidad Nacional. Facultad de Ciencias Médicas. Tesis, año 1902, no. 1272)

NL 0343872   DNLM MH

Liddle, R., co., *San Francisco.*
In the field of sports ... Sportsmen's goods ... Catalogue ... San Francisco, R. Liddle co. [18
v. illus. 26 x 20ᶜᵐ.
Cover-title.

1. Sporting goods—Catalogs.

Library of Congress   GV747.L71   CA 5—1846 Unrev'd

NL 0343873   DLC

TN872
.T4B4

Liddle, Ralph Alexander, 1896–
Beede, Joshua William, 1871–
... Further notes on the structure near Robert Lee, Coke county, Texas, by J. W. Beede. The Marathon fold and its influence on petroleum accumulation, by R. A. Liddle ... Austin, Tex., The University [1920]

QE
168
C75
L5

Liddle, Ralph Alexander, 1896–
Geology and mineral resources of Crockett County with notes on the stratigraphy, structure, and oil prospects of the central Pecos Valley, By F.A. Liddle and T.M. Prettyman. Austin [Univ. of Texas] 1918.
97p. diagrs.fold.map. (At head of title: University of Texas bulletin, no. 1857: Oct. 10, 1918)

Folded map in pocket on back cover.

NL 0343875   UU MB PP NN

Liddle, Ralph Alexander, 1896–
... Geology and mineral resources of Crockett county, with notes on the stratigraphy, structure, and oil prospects of the central Pecos valley, by R. A. Liddle and T. M. Prettyman ... Austin, Tex., The University [1920]
97 p. illus., 4 fold. pl. (in pocket; incl. 3 maps) 23ᶜᵐ. (University of Texas bulletin. no. 1857: Oct. 10, 1918)
"Bureau of economic geology and technology. Division of economic geology."

1. Geology—Texas—Crockett co. 2. Mines and mineral resources—Texas—Crockett co. 3. Petroleum—Texas—Pecos valley. 4. Petroleum—Geology. I. Prettyman, Thomas Mann, joint author. II. Texas. University. Bureau of economic geology and technology. Division of economic geology.

Library of Congress   QE168.C75L5   21–27106

MtBuM
NL 0343876   DLC PSt OrAshS ICJ CoU OCl ICJ PU MtBC

Liddle, Ralph Alexander, 1896–
...The geology and mineral resources of Medina county, by R. A. Liddle... Austin, Tex.: The university [1918]. 177 p. diagrs., maps, plates.
At head of title: University of Texas bulletin. no. 1860: October 25, 1918.
"Bureau of Economic Geology and Technology. Division of Economic Geology."

1. Geology, U. S.: Texas: Medina county. 2. Minerals, U. S.: Medina county. 3. Texas. University. Bureau. Economic Geology

Economic Geology and Technology Division.

August 31, 1921.

NL 0343877   NN OU OCU OCl MiU PP

Liddle, Ralph Alexander, 1896–
... The geology and mineral resources of Medina County, by R. A. Liddle ... Austin, Tex., The University [1921]
177 p. illus., 9 (i. e. 10) pl. (part fold.; incl. map) 22½ cm. (University of Texas bulletin. no. 1860: Oct. 25, 1918)
"Bureau of economic geology and technology. Division of economic geology."

1. Geology—Texas—Medina co. 2. Mines and mineral resources—Texas—Medina co. I. Texas. University. Bureau of economic geology and technology. Division of economic geology.

QE168.M4L5   21—27066

MiEM ICJ OrU OrCS
NL 0343878   DLC MtBC MtBuM PU CU PSt ICJ MB MU CoU

Liddle, Ralph Alexander, 1896–
The geology and paleontology of the Cuenca, Azogues, Biblian region provinces of Canar and Azuay, Ecuador, by R. A. Liddle and K. V. W. Palmer. July 7, 1941. Ithaca, N. Y., Paleontological research institution, 1941.
62 p. front. (fold. map) 9 pl. (part fold.) 23¼ cm. (Bulletins of American paleontology. v. 26, no. 100)
Bibliography: p. 30, 53–55.
CONTENTS.—pt. 1. Geology, by R. A. Liddle.—pt. 2. Paleontology, by K. V. W. Palmer.
1. Geology—Ecuador. 2. Paleontology—Ecuador. I. Palmer, Katherine Evangeline Hilton (Van Winkle) 1895–

G S 41—159

U. S. Geol. Survey. Libr.
for Library of Congress   [a59r42h1]

NL 0343879   DI-GS MU CU OU OO

Liddle, Ralph Alexander, 1896–
The geology of Venezuela and Trinidad, by Ralph Alexander Liddle. Fort Worth, Tex., J. P. MacGowan [1928]
xxxix p., 1 l., 552 p. incl. front., illus. plates (part fold.) maps (2 fold., 1 in pocket) 24½ᶜᵐ.
Bibliography: p. 507–511.

1. Geology—Venezuela. 2. Geology—Trinidad. 3. Physical geography—Venezuela.

28—4350

Library of Congress   QE251.L5

OC1W OO OCU MiU ViU MiHM WaU PU PPAN PSt PBm
NL 0343880   DLC CaBVaU WaS IdU MtU NIC IU CU OU OCl

Liddle, Ralph Alexander, 1896–
The geology of Venezuela and Trinidad, by Ralph Alexander Liddle. 2d ed., rev. and enl. Ithaca, N. Y., Paleontological research institution [1946]
xlvii, [2], 890 p. incl. front. plates, maps (part fold.) profiles (part fold.) 24½ᶜᵐ.
Bibliography: p. 795–821.

1. Geology—Venezuela. 2. Geology—Trinidad. 3. Physical geography—Venezuela.

QE251.L5 1946   558.7   47–16444

NNBG TU PU CU NIC ICU TxU MiHM ViU ICJ
NL 0343881   DLC MtU MtBuM CaBVaU OrU OrCS WaS IdU

Liddle, Ralph Alexander, 1896–
The Marathon fold and its influence on petroleum accumulation. 1918. (Texas. University. Bulletin E1847).

NL 0343882   OrU

Liddle, Ralph Alexander, 1896–
Reconnaissance [map] or the areal geology of Venezuela. [n.p., n.d.]
map. 132 x 154 cm. fold. to 40 x 34 cm.
Drawn by Fred W. Sloan.
Scale ca. 1: 393, 600.
This map is based on personal field studies, and on the observations of geologists cited in the preface to the text whose maps have been made available through the generosity of the Servicio Tecnico de Mineria y Geologia, Caracas, Venezuela.

Accompanied by sheet (34 x 60 cm.). Generalized columnar section in Venezuela, not drawn to scale.

NL 0343884   PPT

Liddle, Ralph Alexander, 1896–
... The Rio Cachiri section in the Sierra de Perija, Venezuela, by R. A. Liddle, G. D. Harris and J. W. Wells ... Ithaca, N. Y., Paleontological research institution, 1943.
100 p. 10 pl., 2 maps (incl. front., 1 fold.) 25ᶜᵐ. (Bulletins of American paleontology, v. 27, no. 108)
Bibliography: p. 77–82.

1. Geology — Venezuela. 2. Paleontology — Venezuela. 3. Sierra de Perijá. I. Harris, Gilbert Dennison, 1864– joint author. II. Wells, John West, 1907– joint author. III. Title.

G S 43–94

U. S. Geol. survey. Library
for Library of Congress

NL 0343885   DI-GS CU MU NcD OU OO

Liddle, Ralph Alexander, 1896–
... The Van oil field, Van Zandt county, Texas, by Ralph Alexander Liddle ... Austin, Tex., The University [1936]
82 p. 27 pl. (26 fold. incl. maps, diagrs.) 22ᶜᵐ. (The University of Texas bulletin. no. 3601: January 1, 1936)
"Published in part from the Fort Worth geological society revolving publication fund of the University of Texas."
Plates 2–27 in portfolio.

1. Petroleum—Texas—Van Zandt co. 2. Gas, Natural—Texas—Van Zandt co. 3. Geology—Texas—Van Zandt co. I. Title.

Library of Congress   TN872.T4L5   37–27636
    A836.T4 no. 3601
    553.2809764

NL 0343886   DLC MtBuM OrCS TxU CU GU DI-GS FU

M1619
S69
v.692

Liddle, Samuel, 1868–
[Abide with me; voice, acc. piano]
Abide with me [E major] Words by Henry Francis Lyte. [New York] Boosey & Co., c1896. Pl.no.218 a-2.
3 p. 35ᶜᵐ.
Caption title.
No. 4 in a vol. lettered: Songs, v. 692.

v.668 —— —— Another copy. No. 2 in a vol. lettered: Songs, v.668.

v.611 —— —— Another copy. (Dᵇ. Pl.no.217a-2) No.4 in a vol. lettered:— Songs, v 611.
1. Sacred songs. I. Title.

NL 0343887   CSt OrU

VOLUME 332

Liddle, Samuel, 1868–
Abide with me. [Anthem. S. & A. solos. S.A.T.B.] Words by Henry Francis Lyte. Music by S. Liddle. Arrd. by Sumner Salter. [With organ accompaniment.]
= [New York.] Boosey & Co. 1916. 7 pp. [Sacred quartettes, anthems, etc., for mixed voices. Boosey & Co.'s series. No. 1227.] 26½ cm.

L3366 — Double main card. — Liddle, S.. (M1) — Lyte, Henry Francis. (M2) — T.r. (1) — Church music. Anthems, etc. (1) — Salter, Sumner, ed. (1)

NL 0343888   MB

Liddle, Samuel, 1868–
How lovely are Thy dwellings. Sacred song. No. 3 in D♭. The words taken from Psalm LXXXIV. [With accompaniment for the pianoforte.]
= New York. Boosey & Co. 1908. 6 pp. 31.5 cm.

E1332 — T.r. — Church music. Anthems, etc.

NL 0343889   MB

qM783.4 Liddle, Samuel, 1868–
L619h2   How lovely are Thy dwellings. Sacred song.
         The words taken from Psalm LXXXIV. [New York?] Boosey & Hawkes [c1935].
         6p. 30cm.

         For low voice and piano.

         1. Sacred songs (Low voice) with piano.
         I. Title.

NL 0343890   IU

qM783.4 Liddle, Samuel, 1868–
L619h1   How lovely are Thy dwellings. Sacred song.
         The words taken from Psalm LXXXIV. [New York?] Boosey & Hawkes [c1936].
         6p. 30cm.

         For high voice and piano.

         1. Sacred songs (High voice) with piano.
         I. Title.

NL 0343891   IU

Liddle, Samuel, 1868–
The mermaid, short cantata for female voices and orchestra, the poem by Tennyson…the music by Samuel Liddle. Vocal score with pianoforte accompaniment… London: Boosey & Co., cop. 1899. Publ. pl. no. H. 2612. 2 p.l., 23 p. 4°.

Vocal score.

JULIAN EDWARDS COLL.
Tennyson, 1st baron, 1809–92.

1. Cantatas. 2. Tennyson, Alfred 3. Title.

April 25, 1916.

NL 0343892   NN

M   Liddle, Samuel, 1868–
2114.5   An old French carol. Quelle est cette odeur
.L71   agréable? The English version by Faith Liddle.
04   The music arr. by Samuel Liddle. [New York] Boosey & Hawkes [c1923].
         5 p. 31 cm.
         Cover title.
         For voice and piano.

         1. Carols, French. I. Title. II. Title: Quelle est cette odeur agréable?

NL 0343893   DCU

Liddle, Samuel, 1868–
To tell thee how I love, and In my garden; two short love songs. New York, Boosey, °1904.
7p. 35½cm.

NL 0343894   OrU

Liddle, W. E., editor.
Aunt Milly. A popular Virginia melody. [Song with accompaniment for the pianoforte.]
= Boston. Prentiss. 1844. 4 pp. 32 cm.

D8713 — T.r. Song. — Songs. With music.

NL 0343895   MB

Liddle, W. M.

Industrial survey associates.
Aircraft trade schools in California; a study of private and public training programs, by Industrial survey associates … Field research for this survey by Robert A. Trow [and] W. M. Liddle. Los Angeles, 1941.

Liddle, Warren
Men on a rocky hill; poems. Boston, B. Humphries [1948, °1947]
80 p. 20 cm.

I. Title.

PS3523.I 26M4   811.5   49–7146*

NL 0343897   DLC

Liddle, William.
… Sweden, by … Wm. Liddle … and Mrs. Liddle, with twelve full-page illustrations in colour by Anders Zorn, Carl Larsson and others. London, A. and C. Black, 1911.
vii, [1], 87, [1] p. col. front., col. plates, map. 20ᶜᵐ. (Peeps at many lands)
Title within ornamental border.
Illustrated end-paper.

1. Sweden—Descr. & trav.   I. Liddle, Mrs.

A 12–376

Title from Cincinnati   Pub. Libr. Printed by L. C.

NL 0343898   OCU OrP OEac OClh OLak PPFr NN MB

Liddle, William.
… Sweden, by Rev. Wm. Liddle … and Mrs. Liddle; with eight full-page illustrations in colour by Anders Zorn, Carl Larsson, and others. London, A. & C. Black, ltd., 1920.
vii, [1], 87, [1] p. incl. map. col. front., col. plates. 20ᶜᵐ. (Peeps at many lands)

1. Sweden—Descr. & trav. 2. Sweden—Soc. life & cust.   I. Liddle, Mrs. William.

Library of Congress   DL611.L5   21–7566

NL 0343899   DLC

Liddle, William.
… Sweden, by Rev. Wm. Liddle … and Mrs. Liddle, and Finland, by M. Pearson Thomson; with sixteen full-page illustrations in colour. New York, The Macmillan company, 1921.
viii, 87, [1], ii, 87, [1] p. incl. maps. 16 col. pl. (incl. front.) 19½ᶜᵐ. (Peeps at many lands)

1. Sweden—Description and travel. 2. Sweden—Social life and customs. 3. Finland—Description and travel. 4. Finland—Social life and customs. I. Liddle, Mrs. William. II. Thomson, M. Pearson.

Kansas City, Mo. Pub. libr.
for Library of Congress   [DL611.L]

A 24–1057

NL 0343900   MoK WaE Or WaSp OLak OO PWcS PP MtBC

Liddle, William.
… Sweden, by Rev. Wm. Liddle and Mrs. Liddle, with eight full-page illustrations in colour by Anders Zorn, Carl Larsson, and others. London, A. & C. Black, 1922. 87 p. illus., map. (Peeps at many lands)
"First published in November 1911; reprinted, with slight textual emendations, in February 1922."

1. Sweden — Trav. and descr.   2. Sweden — Soc. life and cust.
I. Liddle, Mrs. William, jt. au.

June 16, 1939

NL 0343901   NN

Liddle, Mrs. William.

Liddle, William.
… Sweden, by Rev. Wm. Liddle … and Mrs. Liddle, and Finland, by M. Pearson Thomson; with sixteen full-page illustrations in colour. New York, The Macmillan company, 1921.

Bon.   LIDDLE, WILLIAM, fl. 1821.
Coll.   Poems on different occasions, chiefly in
No.12087   the Scottish dialect… Edinburgh, The author,
         1821.
         248p. 18cm.

         Bookplate of T. Bell, 1797.

NL 0343903   ICN RPB

Liddle, William F.
A catalogue of law books, in the different libraries in Rochester, on the 31st day of August, 1847, with references to the several owners of each. By William F. Liddle. Rochester, N. Y., Printed by Shepard & Reed, 1847.
55 p. 22¼ᶜᵐ.

1. Law—Bibl.—Catalogs. 2. Libraries, Private—Rochester, N. Y.

Library of Congress   Z6459.L53   7–18323

NL 0343904   DLC

Liddo, Salvatore.
Le grotte di S. Andria in Andria; inchiesta d'igiene sociale del Prof. Salvatore Liddo. [Molfetta, 1953] 36 p. plates. 25cm.

At head of title: Amministrazione comunale di Andria.

1. Housing for the working class—Italy—Andria. I. Andria, Italy. t. 1953.

NL 0343905   NN MH

Liddon, Benjamin Sullivan, 1853–1909.

Florida. *Laws, statutes, etc.*
The general statutes of the state of Florida; prepared under authority of and adopted by the Legislature of the state of Florida. B. S. Liddon, T. F. West, J. C. B. Koonce, commissioners. St. Augustine, Fla., The Record company, 1906.

VOLUME 332

Liddon, Eloise S   1897–
The riddle of the Florentine folio; a case for Peggy Fairfield, by E. S. Liddon ... Garden City, N. Y., Published for the Crime club, inc., by Doubleday, Doran & company, inc., 1935.

vii p., 2 l., 299 p. 20ᶜᵐ.

"First edition."

I. Title.

Library of Congress   PZ3.L61973R1   35–4876

NL 0343907   DLC MB

Liddon, Eloise S   1897–
The riddle of the Russian princess, by E. S. Liddon. Garden City, N. Y., Pub. for the Crime club, inc., by Doubleday, Doran & company, inc., 1934.

3 p. l., v–vi p., 2 l., 297 p. incl. plan. 19½ᶜᵐ.

"First edition."

I. Title.

Library of Congress   PZ3.L61973R1   34–12084

NL 0343908   DLC MB

Liddon, Eloise S   1897–
Some lose their way, by Eloise Liddon ... New York, E. P. Dutton & co., inc., 1941.

352 p. 20½ᶜᵐ.

"A Virginia quarterly review book."
"First edition."

I. Title.

Library of Congress   PZ3.L61973So   41–17613

OLak AU ViU

NL 0343909   DLC OrU WaTC NcD OCl OU OEac PU PP PPD

BV
4254.5
.L5
1899
Liddon, Henry Parry, 1829–1890.
Advent in St. Paul's. Sermons bearing chiefly on the two comings of our Lord, by H.P. Liddon. New and cheaper ed. London, New York, Longmans, Green, 1899.
613p.

1. Advent sermons. I. Title.

NL 0344001   TxFTC PPL

BV
4254
.5
.L5x
Liddon, Henry Parry, 1829–1890.
Advent in St. Paul's; Sermons bearing chiefly on the two comings of Our Lord. London, Rivingtons, 1889.
2 v. 19 cm.

1. Advent sermons. 2. Second advent. I. Title

NL 0344002   OKentU

BX5133
.L713a
Liddon, Henry Parry, 1829–1890.
Advent in St. Paul's; sermons bearing chiefly on the two comings of Our Lord. By H. P. Liddon. New York, E. P. Dutton. 1889.
2v. 19cm.

1. Church of England—Sermons. 2. Advent sermons. I. Title.

NL 0344003   IEG MdBP CtY PPA PBm NjNbS MH

Liddon, Henry Parry, 1829–1890.
Advent in St. Paul's; sermons bearing chiefly on the two comings of Our Lord. New and cheaper ed. London, Longmans, Green, 1891.
xx, 613 p. 20ᶜᵐ.

1. Advent sermons. 2. Second advent. I. Title.

NL 0344004   ViU PPPD PPWe MH

Liddon, Henry Parry, 1829–1890.
Advent in St. Paul's; sermons bearing chiefly on the two comings of Our Lord... new ed. London, Longmans, 1892.
613 p.

NL 0344005   PPT PPLT

Liddon, Henry Parry, 1829–1890.
Advent in St. Paul's; sermons bearing chiefly on the two comings of our Lord. Longmans, 1912.

NL 0344006   OrP

Liddon, Henry Parry, 1829–1890.
The aim and principles of Christian Missions. A sermon preached in substance on the anniversary of S. George's mission at S. Mary Magdalene's Munster Square, November 27, 1860. London, Masters, 1860.
23 p.

NL 0344007   OO

Liddon, Henry Parry, 1829–1890.
Bishop Wilberforce: a Sermon preached at the Parish Church of Graffham, Sussex... London, 1875.
31 p. 8°. [In "College Pamphlets", v. 2007].

NL 0344008   CtY

BX5133
.L713chr
1869
in:
SWTS
Liddon, Henry Parry, 1829–1890.
Christ and education: a sermon, preached at St. James's, Piccadilly, on the third Sunday after Trinity, 1869. London, Rivingtons, 1869.
28p. 22cm.

1. Church of England—Sermons. I. Title.

NL 0344009   IEG RPB

Liddon, Henry Parry, 1829–1890.
Christmastide in St. Paul's; sermons bearing chiefly on the birth of Our Lord and the end of the year, by H. P. Liddon ... London, Rivingtons, 1889.
xv, 426 p. 19cm.

1. Christmas sermons. 2. Jesus Christ—Nativity. 3. Sermons, English. 4. Church of England—Sermons. I. Title.

NL 0344010   ViU OCl MiU NjNbS MdBP PPPD

BX5133
.L713ch
SWTS
Liddon, Henry Parry, 1829–1890.
Christmastide in St. Paul's; sermons bearing chiefly on the birth of Our Lord and the end of the year. By H. P. Liddon. New York, E. P. Dutton, 1889.
xv, 426p. 19cm.

1. Christmas sermons. 2. Church of England--Sermons. I. Title.

NL 0344011   IEG

Liddon, H[enry] P[arry], 1829–1890.
Christmastide in St. Paul's. Sermons bearing chiefly on the birth of our Lord... London, Longmans, Green & Co., 1890.
xv, 426 p., 1 l. 12°.
2d. ed.

NL 0344012   NN

BX
5133
L5C5
Liddon, Henry Parry, 1829–1890.
Christmastide in St. Paul's; sermons bearing chiefly on the birth of our Lord and the end of the year, by H. P. Liddon. 3d ed. London, Longmans, Green & Co., 1891.
xv, 426 p. 19 cm.

1. Jesus Christ - Nativity - Sermons.
2. Church of England - Sermons. 3. Sermons, English.   I. Title.

NL 0344013   NRCR

Liddon, Henry Parry, 1829–1890.
Christmastide in St. Paul's; sermons bearing chiefly on the birth of our Lord the end of the year. 4th ed.
London, Longmans, 1893.
426 p.

NL 0344014   PPLT

BQT
2994
.L5
S.R.
Liddon, Henry Parry, 1829–1890.
Christmastide in St. Paul's; sermons bearing chiefly on the birth of Our Lord and the end of the year. 5th ed. London, Longmans, Green, 1898.
xv, 426 p. 20 cm.

1. Christmas sermons. 2. Church of England - Sermons. I. Title.

NL 0344015   NBuCC CLamB

BX5133
L5
C48
Liddon, Henry Parry, 1829–1890.
Christmastide in St. Paul's; sermons bearing chiefly on the birth of our Lord and the end of the year, by H. P. Liddon. London, New York, Longmans, Green, 1903.
xv, 426 p.

1. Christmas sermons. 2. Church of England - Sermons. 3. Sermons, English. I. Title.

NL 0344016   ODaU MB

Liddon, H[enry] P[arry], 1829–1890.
Clerical life and work, a collection of sermons with an essay. London and N. Y., Longmans, Green & co., 1894.
11, 377 p.

DNC IEG TxDaM
NL 0344017   MiD InAndC PBm PPL MB CtW GEU NjNbS NcD

VOLUME 332

BV4017
.L7   LIDDON,HENRY PARRY,1829-1890.
   Clerical life and work,a collection of sermons with an essay,by H.P.Liddon ... 2d ed. London and New York,Longmans,Green,and co.,1895.
   xi,377,[1]p. 20cm.

   1.Theology,Pastoral. 2.Church of England--Clergy 3.Sermons,English.

NL 0344018   ICU MBtS PPPD CtY-D KKcB

Liddon, Henry Parry, 1829-1870.
   Clerical life and work; a collection of sermons with an essay.
   N.Y., Longmans, 1903.
   377 p.

NL 0344019   PPLT

Liddon, Henry Parry, 1829-1890.
   Clerical life and work; a collection of sermons with an essay... 4th impression. London, Longmans, 1907.
   377 p. 20 cm.

NL 0344020   CtY

BX5149
.C6L71 Liddon, Henry Parry, 1829-1890.
1883   Confession. A letter. [n.p., 1883?]
   [4]p. 21cm.

   1. Confession--Anglican Communion. I. Title.

NL 0344021   IEG

           1829-1890.
Liddon, Henry Parry.^ Devotion to the Church of Christ: a sermon . . . . Oct. 28th, 1888 . . . London. Rivingtons. 1889. 33 p.

NL 0344022   PPPD

Liddon, Henry Parry, 1829-1890.
   The divinity of Our Lord and Saviour Jesus Christ; eight lectures preached before the University of Oxford, in the year 1866, on the foundation of the late Rev. John Bampton ... By Henry Parry Liddon ... London [etc.], Rivingtons, 1867.
   xix, 776 p. 22ᵐ. (*Half-title:* The Bampton lectures for M.DCCC.LXVI)

   1. Jesus Christ—Divinity. ɪ. Title.

| | | 38-16273 |

Library of Congress   BR45.B3 1866
     D   [2]   (230.082)   232.8

               ViU PPL
NL 0344023   DLC OrP MB DNC NN ODW PPT PPLT PPPD RPB

Liddon, Henry Parry, 1829-1890.
   The divinity of Our Lord and Saviour Jesus Christ; eight lectures preached before the University of Oxford, in the year 1866, on the foundation of the late Rev. John Bampton, M.A., canon of Salisbury. By Henry Parry Liddon ... New edition. New York, Scribner, Welford, and co., 1868.
   xxix, 1 l., 535, [1] p. 19½ᶜᵐ. (Half-title: The Bampton lectures for M.DCCC.LXVI)

   1. Jesus Christ--Divinity. I. Title. II. Ser.

NL 0344024   ViU NNUT MH OO PPPD MB NcU

BR45
.B3 Liddon, Henry Parry, 1829-1890.
1866   The divinity of our Lord and Savior
1869 Jesus Christ. 4th ed. London, Rivingtons, 1869.
in: xxix, 1, 552p. 19cm. (Bampton.lectures,
SWTS   1866)

   1. Jesus Christ--Natures. 2. Jesus Christ--Divinity. I. Title. (Series)

267877

NL 0344025   IEG

Liddon, Henry Parry, 1829-1890.
The divinity of our Lord and Saviour Jesus Christ; eight lectures preached before the University of Oxford, in the year 1866. New York: Scribner, Welford, and Co., 1869.   549 p.   4. ed. 12°. (The Bampton lectures.)

1. Jesus Christ. 2. Series.   CENTRAL RESERVE.
N. Y. P. L.   February 2. 1917.

NL 0344026   NN CtY CU MiU OClW MH

BR45
.09 Liddon, Henry Parry, 1829-1890.
1866   The divinity of Our Lord and Saviour Jesus Christ; eight lectures preached before the University of Oxford, in the year 1866, on the foundation of the late Rev. John Bampton, M. A., canon of Salisbury. By H. P. Liddon ... 5th ed. London, Oxford and Cambridge, Rivingtons, 1871.
   xxix p., 1 l., 552 p. 19ᶜᵐ. (*Half-title:* The Bampton lectures for 1866)

NL 0344027   ViU OO PPLT PPWe

Liddon, Henry Parry, D. D. 1829-. Divinity of Our Lord and Saviour Jesus Christ. Eight lectures preached before the University of Oxford in the year 1866, on the foundation of the late Rev. John Bampton. ² ed. London, 1872. 12°. (Rev. of in *London Quart. Rev.* v. 29, 1868, p. 489.)
           —4226

NL 0344028   MdBP

Liddon, Henry Parry, 1829-1890.
   The divinity of Our Lord and Saviour Jesus Christ; eight lectures preached before the University of Oxford, in the year 1866, on the foundation of the late Rev. John Bampton, M. A., canon of Salisbury. By H. P. Liddon ... 6th ed. New York, Scribner, Welford and Armstrong, 1873.
   xxix p., 1 l., 552 p. 19½ᶜᵐ.

   1. Jesus Christ--Divinity. ɪ. Title.

Library of Congress   BT215.L5 1873   20—17712
                   [26b1]

NL 0344029   DLC NN PPPD

Liddon, Henry Parry, 1829-1890.
   The divinity of Our Lord and Saviour Jesus Christ; eight lectures preached before the University of Oxford, in the year 1866, on the foundation of the late Rev. John Bampton, M. A., canon of Salisbury. By H. P. Liddon ... 7th ed. London, Oxford and Cambridge, Rivingtons, 1875.
   xxix p., 1 l., 552 p. 19ᶜᵐ. (*Half-title:* The Bampton lectures for 1866)

   1. Jesus Christ—Divinity. ɪ. Title.

Library of Congress   BT215.L5 1875   22—7793

NL 0344030   DLC OrCS NcD NN

Liddon, Henry Parry, 1829-1890.
   The divinity of our Lord and Saviour Jesus Christ. New York, 1878. 16°

   Bampton Lectures, 1866.

NL 0344031   NNUT

BR45
.09 Liddon, Henry Parry, 1829-1890
1866   The divinity of Our Lord and Saviour Jesus
1882 ed. Christ; eight lectures preached before the University of Oxford, in the year 1866, on the foundation of the late Rev. John Bampton, M.A., canon of Salisbury by H. P. Liddon ... 9th ed., revised London and Oxford, Rivingtons, 1882.
   xxix p., 1 l., 584 p. 19ᶜᵐ. (Half-title: The Bampton lectures for MDCCCLXVI)

   1. Jesus Christ—Divinity. I.Title. II.Ser

NL 0344032   ViU

Liddon, Henry Parry, 1829-1890.
   The divinity of Our Lord... 10th ed. London, Rivingtons, 1884.
   584 p. (Bampton lectures for M.DCCC.LXVI)
   ---- --- 22d imp. Lond., Longmans, 1908.

NL 0344033   PPEB

Liddon, Henry Parry, 1829-1890.
The divinity of Our Lord and Saviour Jesus Christ. 11th ed.
London, Oxford and Cambridge, Rivingtons, 1885.
552 p. (The Bampton lectures 1866)

NL 0344034   PPT PU

Liddon, Henry Parry, 1829-1890.
   The divinity of Our Lord and Saviour Jesus Christ; eight lectures preached before the University of Oxford in the year 1866, on the foundation of the late Rev. John Bampton, M.A., canon of Salisbury, by H. P. Liddon...13th edition. London, Rivingtons, 1889.
   xxiii p., 1 l., 584 p. 19 cm. (The Bampton lectures for 1866).

   1. Jesus Christ-Divinity. I. Title. II. Ser.

NL 0344035   ViU RP MH-AH OOxM

Liddon, Henry Parry, 1829-1890.
   The divinity of Our Lord and Saviour Jesus Christ; eight lectures preached before the University of Oxford in the year 1866 on the foundation of the late Rev. John Bampton, canon of Salisbury. 16th ed. London, Longmans, Green and Co., 1892.

NL 0344036   MH

Liddon, Henry Parry, 1829-1890.
   The divinity of Our Lord and Saviour Jesus Christ. Eight lectures preached before the University of Oxford in the year 1866. 17th ed. London, Longmans, Green, 1894.
   xii,585p. 20cm.

NL 0344037   PSC

Liddon, Henry Parry, 1829-1890.
   The divinity of Our Lord and Saviour Jesus Christ; eight lectures preached before the University of Oxford in the year 1866, on the foundation of the late Rev. John Bampton ... by H. P. Liddon ... 18th ed. London, New York [etc.], Longmans, Green, and co., 1897.
   xii, 1 l., 585 p. 19½ᶜᵐ.

   1. Jesus Christ—Divinity. ɪ. Title.

                             30-13588
Library of Congress   BT215.L5 1897

NL 0344038   DLC NjP DCU-H

VOLUME 332

Liddon, Henry Perry, 1829-1890.
The divinity of Our Lord and Saviour Jesus
Christ; eight lectures preached before the
University of Oxford in the year 1866. 19th
impression.   London, New York, Longmans,
Green, and Co., 1900.
xli, 585 p. 20 cm.
First published 1867.

NL 0344039   PLatS OKentU

Liddon, Henry Parry, 1829-1890.
The divinity of Our Lord and Saviour
Jesus Christ; eight lectures preached be-
fore the University of Oxford in the year
1866, on the foundation of the late Rev.
John Bampton-- by H.P. Liddon-- ₍14th ed.₎
London, Longmans, 1903.
xli, 585 p., 20ᶜᵐ.

NL 0344040   NjPT OCX

Liddon, Henry Parry, 1829-1890.
The divinity of Our Lord and Saviour, Jesus Christ; eight
lectures preached before the University of Oxford in the year
1866, on the foundation of the late Rev. John Bampton, M. A.,
canon of Salisbury; by H. P. Liddon ... Twentieth impression. London, New York ₍etc.₎ Longmans, Green, and co.,
1903.
xii p., 1 l., 585 p. 20ᵐ.

NL 0344041   ViU

Liddon, Henry Parry, 1829-1890.
The divinity of Our Lord and Saviour, Jesus Christ; eight
lectures preached before the University of Oxford in the
year 1866, on the foundation of the late Rev. John Bampton.
M. A., canon of Salisbury. London, New York, Longmans,
Green, 1906.
xii, 585 p. 20 cm.

1. Jesus Christ—Divinity.   I. Title.

BT215.L5 1906   W 8-105 rev*

Washington, D. C. Pub.   Library
for Library of Congress   ₍r57h1₎†

NL 0344042   DWP PHC NcD DLC

Liddon, Henry Parry, 1829-1890.
The Divinity of our Lord and Saviour Jesus Christ;
eight lectures preached before the University of
Oxford in the year 1866 on the foundation of the
late Rev. John Bampton... 21st impression...
London, Longmans, 1908.
585 p.

NL 0344043   PBa

Liddon, Henry Parry, 1829-1890.
Easter in St. Paul's; sermons bearing chiefly
on the resurrection of Our Lord...
N.Y., Dutton, 1885.
2 v.

NL 0344044   PU PPL PPPD

Liddon, Henry Parry, 1829-1890.
Easter in St. Paul's. Sermons bearing chiefly
on the resurrection of Our Lord ... By H. P. Liddon ... New York, E. P. Dutton and company, 1886.
2 v. 19½ᶜᵐ.

1. Easter—Sermons. 2. Church of England—Sermons. 3.
Sermons, English. 4. Jesus Christ—Resurrection. I.
Title.

NL 0344045   ViU

Liddon, Henry Parry, 1829-1890.
Easter in St. Paul's. Sermons bearing chiefly
on the resurrection of our Lord. v. 1-2. London, Rivington, 1887-1890.
2 v.   12°.
2d. ed.
v. 1, pub. by Londmans, Green, & Co., London
1890.

NL 0344046   NN

BX5133
.L713ea   Liddon, Henry Parry, 1829-1890.
          Easter in St. Paul's; sermons bearing chief-
SWTS   ly on the Resurrection of Our Lord. By H. P.
          Liddon. 2d ed. New York, E. P. Dutton, 1889.
          2v. 19cm.

          1. Easter sermons. 2. Church of England--
          Sermons. I. Title.

NL 0344047   IEG NRCR PPC

Liddon, Henry Parry, 1829-1890.
Easter in St. Paul's; sermons bearing chiefly
on the resurrection of Our Lord... New ... ed.
London, Longmans, 1891.
459 p.

NL 0344048   PPPD

Liddon, Henry Parry, 1829-1890.
Easter in St. Paul's, sermons bearing chiefly
on the resurrection of Our Lord. New and cheaper
ed. London, Longmans, 1892.

NL 0344049   MH PPD

B X   Liddon, Henry Parry, 1829-1890.
5133   Easter in St. Paul's; Sermons chiefly on the Res-
.L62   urrection of Our Lord... new & cheaper ed. Lond.,
          Longmans, Green & co., 1895.
          459 p. 19½cm.

NL 0344050   DNC PPWe

BV   Liddon, Henry Parry, 1829-1890.
4259   Easter in St. Paul's; sermons bearing chiefly on the resur-
L5   rection of our Lord. New and cheaper edition. London, New
1897   York, Longmans, Green, 1897.
          xvi, 459 p. 20cm.

          1. Easter--Sermons. 2. Resurrection--Sermons. 3. Church
          of England--Sermons. I. Title.

NL 0344051   CBDP OCl NNUT

Liddon, Henry Parry, 1829-1890.
Easter in St. Paul's... New and cheaper edition
New impression.
London, 1901.
459 p.

NL 0344052   PPWe

BV4259
L5   Liddon, Henry Parry, 1829-1890.
      Easter in St. Paul's; sermons bearing
chiefly on the resurrection of Our Lord.
London, New York, Longmans, Green, 1914.
459 p.

1. Easter - Sermons. I. Title.

NL 0344053   ODaU MB OrP

Liddon, Henry Parry, 1829-1890.
Essays and addresses, by H. P. Liddon ... London and
New York, Longmans, Green, and co., 1892.
4 p. l., 212 p. 19½ᵐ.
CONTENTS.—Lectures on Buddhism.—Lectures on the life of St. Paul.—
Papers on Dante.

10-12689

NL 0344054   DLC MsU NcD OCl OCU PPPD MH PPL PHC

1689
₍Liddon, Henry Parry₎ 1829-1890.
Evening communions contrary to the teaching
and practice of the church in all ages, with
additional notes.
34 p.
Reprinted from The Christian Remembrancer,
for April, 1860.
Bound with 1679.
I. Title.

NL 0344055   TxDaM

Liddon, Henry Parry, 1829-1890.
Examination of Canon Liddon's Baonpton lectures
on the divinity of Our Lord and Saviour Jesus Christ
see under ₍Voysey, Charles₎ 1828-1912.

Liddon, Henry Parry, 1829-1890.
Explanatory analysis of St. Paul's Epistle to the
Romans.   not published   Oxford Printed by
E. Baxter, 1876.
2 p. l., 200 p. 22 cm.
"[This work] is composed of a series of papers
which were distributed to students who attended
the author's lectures in 1875-1876."
1. Bible. N. T. Romans ₍stamped₎.

NL 0344057   CtY

BS3666 Liddon, Henry Parry, 1829-1890.
.L7   Explanatory analysis of St. Paul's Epistle to the Romans,
        by H. P. Liddon ... London and New York, Longmans,
        Green, and co., 1893.
        vi, ₍2₎, 309, ₍1₎ p. 23ᵐ.

        1. Bible. N. T. Romans—Commentaries.

        OCH PPC PPPD NRCR
NL 0344058   ICU IEG MB MH PPL PHC CtY OO NcC CtY-D

BS2665
.L71   Liddon, Henry Parry, 1829-1890.
1897   Explanatory analysis of St. Paul's
        Epistle to the Romans. 3d. ed. New York,
        Longmans, Green, 1897.
        vi, 309p. 23cm.
        First printed 1892, from manuscripts
        written 1876-80.

        1. Bible. N. T. Romans--Criticism,
        interpretation, etc. I. Title.

NL 0344059   IEG

*BS   Liddon, Henry Parry, 1829-1890.
2665   Explanatory analysis of St. Paul's
L71   epistle to the Romans, by H.P. Liddon,
1899   D.D...4th ed. London, Longmans, Green,
        1899.
        vi, 309p. 23 cm.

        1. Bible. N.T. Romans - Criticism, inter-
        pretation, etc.

NL 0344060   IMunS NIC

VOLUME 332

Liddon, Henry Parry, 1829–1890.
M£z805   Explanatory analysis of St.Paul's First
877£   epistle to Timothy ... Oxford,Printed by E.
Baxter,1877.
2p.£.,62p. 21cm.
"This analysis was drawn up for the use of
the author's pupils in Michaelmas term 1876,
and Lent term 1877. It is not published."

1.Bible. N.T. I.Timothy.

NL   0344061   CtY

BS3746 Liddon, Henry Parry, 1829–1890.
.L7   Explanatory analysis of St. Paul's First epistle to Timothy,
by H. P. Liddon ... London ₍etc.₎ Longmans, Green, and
co., 1897.
₍7₎, 93, ₍1₎ p. 23ᶜᵐ.

1. Bible. N. T. I Timothy—Commentaries.

NL   0344062   ICU PPWe PPPD MB IEG

Liddon, Henry Parry, 1829–1890.

—— Fatalism and the living God: a sermon preached ... Sept. 23, 1866. 2nd ed.
London, Rivingtons, 1866. 42 p.

NL   0344063   PPPD CtY

Liddon, Henry Parry, 1829–1890.

—— A father in Christ: a sermon preached
... at the consecration of the Rt. Rev.
Edward King, D.D. ... and of the Rt. Rev.
Edward Henry Bickersteth, D.D. ... 1885.
2nd ed. with a notice of the Rev. Dr. Hatch's
paper in the "Contemporary Review." June,
1885. London, Rivingtons, 1885. xlii–34 p.

NL   0344064   PPPD

---

237   Liddon, Henry Parry, 1829–1890.
L61f   The first five minutes₎after death
and the future crown. 2d ed. ...
London, 1911.
42p.   (Churchman's penny library,
no.12)

NL   0344065   IU

Liddon, Henry Parry, 1829–1890.
Forty sermons on various subjects, by the Rev. H. P.
Liddon ... London, F. Davis ₍1872₎
₍332₎ p. 22ᶜᵐ.
Issues of the Penny pulpit, with a collective t.-p.
Various pagings.

I. The Penny pulpit.

23-14342

Library of Congress   BX5133.L5F6

NL   0344066   DLC PPPD PPLT IEG ViU

Liddon, Henry Parry, 1829–1890.
Forty sermons on various subjects, preached in
the cathedral church of St. Paul, London, by the
Rev. H. P. Liddon ... First series. London, C.
Higham, 1886.
iv, ₍356₎ p. 22ᶜᵐ.
Issues of the Penny pulpit, with a collective
t.-p.
Binder's title: Canon Liddon's sermons.
Imprint on cover: New York, James Pott & co.
With this are bound his Forty-one sermons.
Second series. London, 1886; Forty-two sermons.
Third and fourth se₋ ries. London, 1886.
1. Sermons, Eng₋   lish. 2. Church of Eng-
land—Sermons. I.   The Penny pulpit.

NL   0344067   ViU NcD

Liddon, Henry Parry, 1829–1890.
Forty-one sermons on various subjects, preached
in the cathedral church of St. Paul, London, including two lectures on St. Paul. By the Rev. H.
P. Liddon ... Second series. London, C. Higham,
1886.
iv, ₍352₎ p. 22ᶜᵐ.
Issues of the Penny pulpit, with a collective
t.-p.
Various pagings.
With his Forty sermons. First series. London
1886.
1. Sermons, English. 2. Church of England—
Sermons. 3. Paul,   Saint, apostle. I. The
Penny pulpit.

NL   0344068   ViU

Liddon, Henry Parry, 1829–1890.
Forty-two sermons on various subjects, preached
in the cathedral church of St. Paul, London, by
the Rev. H. P. Liddon ... Third ₍and fourth₎ series. London, C. Higham, 1886.
iv, 340, iv, 338 p. 22ᶜᵐ.
Each series has special t.-p., and is paged
separately with various pagings.
"The incredulity of Thomas" has special t.-p.,
and has imprint: London, F. Davis.
Issues of the Penny pulpit, with a collective
t.-p.
With his Forty sermons. First series. London,
1886.
1. Sermons, Engl₋   ish. 2. Church of England—Sermons. I.   The Penny pulpit.

NL   0344069   ViU

Liddon, Henry Parry, 1829–1890.
Life and letters of Henry Parry Liddon... by
J. O. Johnston. With a concluding chapter by the
Lord Bishop of Oxford. With portraits. London,
Longmans, Green, & Co., 1904.
ix, 1 l., 424 p., 1 pl., 4 port. 2. impression.
8°.

NL   0344070   NN

L872   Liddon, Henry Parry, 1829–1890.
H18   Life in death: a sermon, preached in Salis-
xL61   bury cathedral, on the 11th Sunday after Trinity
August 8, 1869, being the day after the funeral
of Walter Kerr Hamilton, D.D., Lord Bishop of
Salisbury. London, Rivingtons, 1869.
32 p. 22 cm.

1. Hamilton, Walter Kerr, bp. of Salisbury,
1808–1869. 2. Funeral sermons. I. Title.

NL   0344071   CtY-D CtY TxU

Liddon, Henry Parry, 1829–1890.
Life of Edward Bouverie Pusey, doctor of divinity, canon of
Christ church; regius professor of Hebrew in the University
of Oxford, by Henry Parry Liddon ... Edited and prepared
for publication by the Rev. J. O. Johnston ... and the Rev.
Robert J. Wilson ... London and New York, Longmans, Green,
and co., 18
v.   fronts. (ports.) illus. 23ᶜᵐ.
Vol. 4 edited and prepared for publication by J. O. Johnston, Robert
J. Wilson and W. C. E. Newbolt.
Vol. 2: 3d ed.;   v. 4: 3d impression.
"A bibliographical list of the printed works of Dr. Pusey": v. 4,
p. ₍395₎–446. "Dr. Pusey's sermons arranged in order of the texts":
v. 4, p. ₍447₎–453.
1. Pusey, Edward Bou-   verie, 1800–1882. I. Johnston,
John Octavius, 1852–   1923, ed.
BX5199.P9L52   46-43851

NL   0344072   DLC

Liddon, Henry Parry, 1829–1890.
Life of Edward Bouverie Pusey, doctor of divinity, canon of
Christ church; regius professor of Hebrew in the University of
Oxford, by Henry Parry Liddon ... Edited and prepared for
publication by the Rev. J. O. Johnston ... and the Rev. Robert J.
Wilson ... London and New York, Longmans, Green, and co.,
1893–97.
4 v. fronts., illus., ports., facsim. 22½ᶜᵐ.
Vol. 4, edited and prepared for publication by J. O. Johnston, R. J.
Wilson and W. C. E. Newbolt.
Vols. 1, 3–4, 2d ed.
"A bibliographical list of the printed works of Dr. Pusey": v. 4,
p. ₍395₎–446. "Dr. Pusey's sermons arranged in order of the texts":
v. 4, p. ₍447₎–453.
1. Pusey, Edward Bou-   verie, 1800–1882. I. Johnston,
John Octavius, 1852–1923,   ed.
BX5199.P9L5   46-43585

    MiU OrP ViU CaBVaU WaTC MB IU ICN OCl
    MiD TxDaM NjPT NcU TU PPPD NN FU ScU NjPT InU WaSpG
NL   0344073   DLC PP PPA PPFr PPL MdBP ViU CU NcD CtY

Liddon, Henry Parry, 1829–1890.
The life of faith and the Athanasian Creed;
a sermon preached before the University of Oxford
in the Church of St. Mary the Virgin on the 21st
Sunday after Trinity, 1872.
35 p. 20 cm.
"Printed by request."

NL   0344074   MB

BX5133
.L713m Liddon, Henry Parry, 1829–1890.
SWTS   The Magnificat; sermons in St. Paul's August,
1889. By H. P. Liddon. London, Rivingtons,
1889.
viii, 111p. 19cm.

1. Magnificat. 2. Church of England. Sermons.

NL   0344075   IEG MH MB

232.93 Liddon, Henry Parry, 1829–1890.
L713m   The Magnificat. Sermons in St. Paul's,
1890   August, 1889. 2d ed. London, Rivington's, 1890.
x,111p. 20cm.

1.Mary, Virgin. I.Title.

NL   0344076   CLSU PPL

B V   Liddon, Henry Parry, 1829–1890.
469   The Magnificat. Sermons in St. Paul's, August,
.M3   1889... 3d ed. London, N.Y., Longmans, Green
.L62   & co., 1891.
x, 111. 19½cm.

NL   0344077   DNC MBtS PPLT PPPD NN

Liddon, Henry Parry, 1829–1890.
The magnificat; sermons in St. Paul's
August, 1889. Ed. 4.
London, 1895.
111 p.

NL   0344078   PPPD

Liddon, H₍enry₎ P₍arry₎ 1829–1890.
The Magnificat. Sermons in St. Paul's, August, 1889.
By H. P. Liddon ... 5th ed. London, New York & Bombay, Longmans, Green, and co., 1898.
x, iii, [1] p. 20ᶜᵐ.

NL   0344079   DLC

VOLUME 332

BV199
C32
M3
1910

Liddon, Henry Parry, 1829-1890.
The Magnificat. Sermons in St. Paul's, August, 1889, by H. P. Liddon. [2d ed.] New York, Longmans, Green, 1910.
111 p.

1. Magnificat. I. Title.

NL 0344080   ODaU MB

Liddon, Henry Parry, 1829-1890, ed.
A manual for the sick with other devotion...
see under Andrewes, Lancelot, bp. of
Winchester, 1555-1626.

Ap
L619
870m

Liddon, Henry Parry, 1829-1890.
The model of our new life. A sermon preached at the special evening service in St. Paul's cathedral on Easter day, 1870, by H. P. Liddon ...
Rivingtons London, Waterloo Place Oxford, High Street; Cambridge, Trinity Street 1870. 15p. 21½cm., in case 27cm.

NL 0344082   TxU

BR759
.A1P12
no. 13

SWTS

Liddon, Henry Parry, 1829-1890.
The moral groundwork of clerical training; a sermon preached at the anniversary festival of Cuddesdon College on Tuesday, June 10, 1873. London, Rivingtons, 1873.
28p. 21cm. (Pamphlets. no. 13)

1. Theological education. I. Cuddesdon College. II. Title.

NL 0344083   IEG

BX5133
.L713mo
1868

in:
SWTS

Liddon, Henry Parry, 1829-1890.
The moral value of a mission from Christ; a sermon. preached in Christ Church Cathedral, at the general ordination of the Lord Bishop of Oxford, on the 4th Sunday in advent, Dec. 22 1867. London. Printed by command, Rivingtons. 1868.
32p. 22cm.

1. Church of England—Sermons. I. Title.

NL 0344084   IEG

Liddon, Henry Parry, 1829-1890.
Motives and methods in modern missions. A sermon preached in St. Paul's Cathedral, in behalf of the Society for the Propagation of the Gospel, on Sunday, Dec. 22, 1889, by the Rev. Canon Liddon. London, Printed for the Society for the Propagation of the Gospel by Spottiswoode, 1890.
Microfilm copy. Negative.
Collation of the original, as determined from the film: 13 p.
"Reprinted from the Mission field, February 1890."
1. Missions—Sermons. 2. Church of England—Sermons.
I. Title.

Microfilm BV-1517 reel 16   Mic 54-381

NL 0344085   DLC

Liddon, Henry Parry, 1829-1890.

Imitatio Christi.

Musica ecclesiastica. The imitation of Christ, by Thomas Kempis, now for the first time set forth in rhythmic sentences according to the original intention of the author. Preface by the late H. P. Liddon ... London, R. Scott [1911?]

Ap
L619
870o

Liddon, Henry Parry, 1829-1890.
... Newness of life. A sermon by the Rev. H. Parry Liddon, (canon of St. Paul's,) preached in St. Paul's cathedral, on Easter Sunday evening, April 17th, 1870.
[London] Published by J.Paul,1,Chapter-house court,North Side of St. Paul's,1870. p.[9]-16. 22cm.,in case 27cm. (The penny pulpit, n.s. no. 429)
Caption title.

NL 0344087   TxU

Ap
L619
871n

Liddon, Henry Parry, 1829-1890.
"The night cometh." A funeral sermon on the death of the Very Rev. Dr. Mansel, D.D. (dean of St. Paul's), preached in St. Paul's cathedral, on Sunday afternoon, August 6th, 1871, by the Rev. H. P. Liddon ...
[London] Published by J.Paul,1,Chapter-house Court,North side St. Paul's,[1871] p.[269]-276. 22½cm.,in case 27cm. (The penny pulpit, n.s. 518)
Caption title.

NL 0344088   TxU

BX5133
.L713o
1873

in:
SWTS

Liddon, Henry Parry, 1829-1890.
The one salvation; a sermon preached in St. Paul's Cathedral on the fifth Sunday after Easter, 1873, at the anniversary service of the Bishop of London's fund. London, Publishe by desire of the committee, Rivingtons, 1873.
27p. 22cm.

1. Church of England—Sermons. I. Title.

NL 0344089   IEG

Liddon, Henry Parry, 1829-1890.
Our Founder's Vow: A Sermon, preached...at the dedication of the chapel of St. John's College, Hurstpierpoint... Oct. 17, 1865... London, 1865.
24 p. 8°. [In v , College Pamphlets].

NL 0344090   CtY

Liddon, Henry Parry, 1829-1890.
—— Passiontide sermons. London, Longmans, 1891. xii-299 p.

NL 0344091   PPPD PPL PPLT NN CtY IEG

WV10
L713
P

Liddon, Henry Parry, 1829-1890.
Passiontide sermons. 2d ed. London, Longmans, Green, 1891.
xii, 299 p.

NL 0344092   KyLxCB MH

Liddon, Henry Parry, 1829-1890.
Passiontide sermons, by H. P. Liddon. London, New York, Longmans, Green, 1906.
xii, 299 p.

1. Good Friday sermons. 2. Church of England - Sermons. 3. Sermons, English. I. Title.

NL 0344093   ODaU MB

Liddon, Henry Parry, 1829-1890.
Practical reflections on every verse of the Psalter... London, 1891
see under Bible. O. T. Psalms.
English. 1891. Coverdale.

Liddon, Henry Parry, 1829-1890.
The priest in his inner life.
London, Masters, 1891.
52 p.

NL 0344095   PPPD

Liddon, Henry Parry, 1829-1890.
Profit and loss: a Sermon, preached...at St. Paul's... on the 3d. Sunday after Epiphany, 1865. 4th ed. London, 1865.
24 p. 8°. [In v. 681, College Pamphlets].

NL 0344096   CtY

Liddon, Henry Parry, 1829-1890.
The Purchas judgment; a letter of acknowledgment to the Right Hon. Sir J. T. Coleridge. Together with a letter to the writer by E. B. Pusey. London .etc., Rivingtons, 1871.
71p. 21cm.

1. Purchas, John, 1823-1872. I. Pusey, Edward Bouverie, 1800-1882.

NL 0344097   IEG PPPD

BX5121
.P98L7
1871

SWTS

Liddon, Henry Parry, 1829-1890.
The Purchas judgment. A letter of acknowledgment to the Rt. Hon. Sir J. T. Coleridge...Together with a letter to the writer by the Rev. E. B. Pusey. New York, Pott & Amery [1871?]
48p. 22cm.

1. Purchas, John, 1823-1872. I. Pusey, Edward Bouverie, 1800-1882. II. Title. III. Coleridge, Sir John Taylor, 1790-1876.

NL 0344098   IEG TxDaM PPD PPL CtY

Liddon, Henry Parry, 1829-1890.
—— Religion and arms: a sermon preached in St. Paul's Cathedral . . . April 28, 1889. London, Rivingtons, 1889. 27 p.

NL 0344099   PPPD

Liddon, Henry Parry, 1829-1890.
The Secret of Clerical Power: a Sermon, preached...at the General Ordination of the Lord Bishop of Salisbury...1865...2d. ed. London, 1865.
26 p. 8°. [In v. 700, College Pamphlets].

NL 0344100   CtY

208
L713a

Liddon, Henry Parry, 1829-1890.
Selections from the writings of H.P. Liddon. London, Rivington, 1882.
224 p. 19 cm.

1. Theology. Collections.

NL 0344101   N NNUT

VOLUME 332

208
L713
Liddon, Henry Parry, 1829-1890.
Selections from the writings of H.P.
Leddon. New York, Dutton, 1883.
224 p. 18 cm.

1. Theology. Collections.

NL 0344102   N PPL

Liddon, Henry Parry, 1829-1890.
Sermons.
N.Y., Whittaker, 1888.
192 p.

NL 0344103   PP PPPD

BX5133 Liddon, Henry Parry, 1829-1890.
.L48S3   Sermons, by H. P. Liddon. 2d ed. London, S.
Sonnenschein, Lowrey, 1888.
192 p.

1. Church of England - Sermons.
2. Sermons, English.

NL 0344104   GEU-T

252.03
L619s
Liddon, Henry Parry, 1829-1890.
Sermons ₁1st- ser.₎ London, Sonnenschein
1890-
v. (The Contemporary pulpit library)

Vol.1 "Fourth edition"
Vols. 2,3 published in New York by Thomas
Whittaker.

1. Church of England--Sermons. 2. Sermons,
English.

NL 0344105   TxFTC

Liddon, Henry Parry, 1829-1890.
Sermons. New York, Thomas Whittaker, 1890.
188 p.
YA. 26998
[The contemporary pulpit library.]

NL 0344106   DLC PPWe

Liddon, Henry Parry, 1829-1890.

Sermons. 2d ed. London, S. Sonnenschein,
1890.
2 l., 188 p. 20ᶜᵐ. (The contemporary pulpit library)

1. Church of England—Sermons. 2. Sermons, English.
I. Ser.

NL 0344107   ViU

L372
L619se
Liddon, Henry Parry, 1829-1890.
Sermons. 4th ed. London, S. Sonnenschein,
1890.
192 p. 20 cm. (Contemporary pulpit library
₁1₎)

1. Sermons, English. I. Series

NL 0344108   CtY-D CtY

BX5133
.L5S44
Liddon, Henry Parry, 1829-1890.

... Sermons, by H. P. Liddon ... New York, T
Whittaker, 1891.
2 p.l. 188 p. 19½ᶜᵐ. (The contemporary
pulpit library.)
Series note lettered also on cover.

1. Sermons, English. I. Ser.

NL 0344109   ViU CLamB

BX
5133
L5
Liddon, Henry Parry, 1829-1890.
Sermons. London, S. Sonnenschein, 1892.
188 p. 20cm. (The contemporary pulpit library)

1. Church of England--Sermons. 2. Sermons, English.

NL 0344110   CBDP

Liddon, H₍enry₎ P₍arry₎, 1829-1890.
Sermons. New York: Thomas Whittaker, 1892. 2 p.l.,
188 p. 12°.

Solomon's sin. The parting of two friends. Naaman the Syrian. Christ the
pattern man. Christ the enlightener of mankind. Christ the deliverer from sin.
Christ the giver of grace. The risen Lord. The sudden conversion of St. Andrew.
The teaching of the Holy Spirit. Social responsibility. Saint Paul at Ephesus.
The body of humiliation. Patient submission to undeserved wrong.

NL 0344111   NN

Liddon, Henry Parry, 1829-1890.
Sermons on Old Testament subjects. London
and New York, Longmans, Green, and co., 1891.
xiv, 379 p. 18 cm.

1. Bible. O.T.--Sermons. 2. Sermons,
English. I. Title.

NL 0344112   IEG MH ViU PPLT PPPD OCH MB

Liddon, Henry Parry, 1829-1890.
Sermons on Old Testament subjects, by H. P. Liddon ...
4th impression. London, New York and Bombay, Longmans,
Green, and co., 1898.
xiv, 379 p. 19¼ᶜᵐ.

I. Title.

Library of Congress   BS1171.L5 1898
2-21451

NL 0344113   DLC

Liddon, Henry Parry, 1829-1890.
— Sermons on some words of Christ ...
4th impression. London, Longmans, 1892.
xii-356 p.

NL 0344114   PPPD PPL PPLT PV

Liddon, Henry Parry, 1829-1890.
Sermons on some words of Christ... 3d ed.
London, New York, and Bombay, Longmans, Green
and co., 1895.
356 p.

NL 0344115   PHC

Liddon, Henry Parry, 1829-1890.
Sermons on some words of Christ, by H. P. Liddon ... 4th
impression. London, New York ₍etc.₎, Longmans, Green, and
co., 1899.
xii, 356 p. 20ᵐ.

1. Jesus Christ—Words—Sermons. 2. Church of England—Sermons.
3. Sermons, English.

Library of Congress   BT306.L5 1899   2-12008 Revised
₍r43e2₎   232.9

NL 0344116   DLC OO PV

Liddon, Henry Parry, 1829-1890.
Sermons on some words of Christ. 6th impression.
— London. Longmans, Green & Co. 1915. xii, 356 pp. 19 cm.,
in 8s.

L787 — Christ. Words. — Sermons. Colls.

NL 0344117   MB

Liddon, Henry Parry, 1829-1890.
Sermons on some words of St. Paul, by H. P. Liddon ...
London, New York and Bombay, Longmans, Green and co.,
1898.
xii, 290 p. 19¼ᵐ.

1. Bible. N. T. Epistles of Paul—Sermons. 2. Church of England—
Sermons. 3. Sermons, English. 4. Bible—Sermons—N. T. Epistles of
Paul. I. Title.

Library of Congress   BS2650.L5   39-32779
₍2₎   227

NL 0344118   DLC MB PPPD PBm PPWe DNC

Liddon, Henry Parry, 1829-1890.
— ... Sermons on various subjects,
preached in the cathedral church of St. Paul,
London ... selected from "The Penny Pulpit." Four series. London, Higham, 1886. 4 v.

NL 0344119   PPPD CtY

Liddon, Henry Parry, 1829-1890.
Sermons preached before the University of
Oxford,
N.Y., 1866.   12°

NL 0344120   I

Liddon, Henry Parry, 1829-1890.
Sermons preached before the University
of Oxford. 2d ed. London ₍etc.₎, Riving
tons, 1866.
513p. O.

NL 0344121   PPLT NjP RPB PPPD

WV10
L713u
1868
Liddon, Henry Parry, 1829-1890.
Sermons preached before the University of
Oxford, chiefly during the years 1863-1865.
By H.P. Liddon ... Boston, E.P. Dutton and company,
1868.
2p.l., [vii]-x, [11]-291p. 19.5 cm.

NL 0344122   NNUT PPL PU OO CtY

VOLUME 332

ar V
8470
Liddon, Henry Parry, 1829-1890.
Sermons preached before the University of Oxford. 2d ed., rev. London, Rivingtons, 1869.
xvi, 350 p. 20cm.

1. Church of England--Sermons

NL 0344123   NIC

Liddon, Henry Parry, 1829-1890.
Sermons preached before the University of Oxford. By H. P. Liddon ... 3d ed., rev. London [etc.] Rivingtons; Oxford, James Parker & co., 1869.
xvi, 350 p. 19½cm.
on spine: Liddon's university sermons.

1. Church of England—Sermons. 2. Sermons, English. 3. Universities and colleges—Sermons.

NL 0344124   ViU PPT CtY PPLT ODW OO NRU CU OrPR

Liddon, Henry Parry, 1829-1890.
Sermons preached before the University of Oxford. 3d ed., rev. New York, Scribner, Welford, & co., 1870.

NL 0344125   GEU PPC

BX5133
.L5S47
1876
Liddon, Henry Parry, 1829-1890.
Sermons preached before the University of Oxford, by H. P. Liddon ... 6th ed., London, Oxford, and Cambridge, Rivingtons; Oxford, J. Parker & co., 1876.
xvi, 350 p. 19½cm.
Binder's title: Liddon's University sermons.

1. Sermons, English. I. Title. II. Title: University sermons

NL 0344126   ViU PPWe

Liddon, Henry Parry, 1829-1890.
Sermons preached before the University of Oxford, by H. P. Liddon ... Second series, 1869-1879. London, Oxford [etc.] Rivingtons, 1879.
xiii, 331 p. 19½cm.
on spine: Liddons University sermons ... E. P. Dutton & co

1. Church of England—Sermons. 2. Sermons, English. 3. Universities and colleges—Sermons.

NL 0344127   ViU CLSU MH

Liddon, Henry Parry, 1829-1890.
Sermons preached before the University of Oxford, by H. P. Liddon. [First-] second series... New York, E. P. Dutton and company, 1880, '79.

2v. 19cm.
Vol. 2 published in London by Rivingtons.
Vol. 1, 3d American ed.

Printed by the Wesleyan   University Library, 1936

NL 0344128   CtW MH ODaU IaU ICRL NNUT OO

WV10
L713u
1883
Liddon, Henry Parry, 1829-1890.
Sermons preached before the University of Oxford ... by H.P.Liddon ... 8th ed. London, Rivingtons[etc.,etc.]1884,'83.
2v. 19.5cm.
Vol.2: 3d ed. London,Rivingtons,1883.
Contents.- [v.1] First series, 1859-1868. - [v.2] Second series, 1868-1882.

NL 0344129   NNUT CtY

Liddon, Henry Parry,1829-1890.
Sermons preached before the University of Oxford. Second series, 1868-1882, by H.P. Liddon. 4th ed. London, Rivingtons, 1887.

NL 0344130   GEU NNUT

Liddon, Henry Parry, 1829-1890.
Sermons preached before the University of Oxford. 1st series, 1859-1868. 9th ed. London, Rivingtons, etc., etc., 1889.

NL 0344131   MH

BM
5133
L5
Liddon, Henry Parry, 1829-1890.
Sermons preached before the University of Oxford. London Longmans, Green & Co. 1895.
2 v. in 1. 19 cm.
Title on spine: University Sermons.

1. Church of England - Sermons

NL 0344132   IMunS PPPD

252.03
L619se
Liddon, Henry Parry, 1829-1890.
Sermons preached on special occasions, 1860-1889. London, New York, Longmans, Green, 1897.
359p.

1. Church of England--Sermons. 2. Sermons, English. I. Title.

NL 0344133   TxFTC NcD OKentU MB PPL PPPD PPWe KyLxCB

BX5133
.L5S4
Liddon, Henry Parry, 1829-1890.
Sermons to the people, preached chiefly in St. Paul's cathedral, by H. P. Liddon ... with a preface by the American editor. New York, E. & J. B. Young & co., 1881.
xiv, 347 p. 19½cm.

1. Sermons, English. I. Title.

NL 0344134   ViU MiU OKentU

Liddon, Henry Parry, 1829-1890.
The sights & sounds of Christendom. A sermon ... London [1870]
[193]-200 p. 22.5 cm. (Penny pulpit. Part 75. New series, no. 452).

NL 0344135   CtY

BX5133
.L713si
1869
in:
SWTS
Liddon, Henry Parry, 1829-1890.
A sister's work: a sermon, preached in substance at All Saints', ...on the second Sunday after Trinity, 1869. London, Published by desire of the Mother and Community of All Saints', Rivingtons, 1869.
32p. 22cm.

1. Church of England—Sermons. I. Title.

NL 0344136   IEG RPB

Liddon, H[enry] P[arry], 1829-1890.
Some elements of religion. Lent lectures 1870. London, etc., Rivingtons, 1872.
pp. x, 241.

NL 0344137   NN CtW IMunS   MH PPPD MB ViU ICN WaPS GEU NcD IEG ODaU

BX5133
.L5S6
1872
Liddon, Henry Parry, 1829-1890.
Some elements of religion: Lent lectures, 1870, by H. P. Liddon ... New York, Scribner, Welford, & Armstrong, 1872.
x, 241 p. 19½cm.

1. Religion. 2. Sermons, English. I. Title.

NL 0344138   NRCR PPLT PPPD   ViU MB NN NNUT GEU OO ODW MiU ICN PPC

BX5133
.L5S6
1873
Liddon, Henry Parry, 1829-1890.
Some elements of religion: Lent lectures, 1870, by H. P. Liddon ... 2d ed. London, Oxford, and Cambridge, Rivingtons, 1873.
xxiv, 243 p. 19½cm.

1. Religion. 2. Sermons, English. I. Title.

NL 0344139   ViU IEG OC1W OO NN

Liddon, Henry Parry, 1829-1890.
Some elements of religion. Lent lectures, 1870. 4th ed. London, Rivingtons, 1883.
248 p. D.

NL 0344140   NcD

LIDDON, H[enry] P[arry], 1829-1890.
Some elements of religion; Lent lectures, 1870. 10th and cheaper ed. London, Longmans, Green, & Co., 1894.

NL 0344141   MH IMunS

Liddon, Henry Parry, 1829-1890.
Some elements of religion, Lent lectures, 1870. Ed. 11.
London, 1896.
240 p.

NL 0344142   PBm

VOLUME 332

Liddon, Henry Parry, 1829-1890.
Some elements of religion; Lent lectures,
1870; 14th impression (6th ed.)
London, Longmans, Green and co., 1898.
240 p.

NL 0344143   PHC OOxM NjP

283.0852
L713s   Liddon, Henry Parry, 1829-1890.
1899   Some elements of religion. Lent lectures, 1870.
Theol.   [3d ed.] 14th impression. London, New York
               [etc.] Longmans, Green, and co., 1899.
               xxvi, 248p. 20cm.

1. Lenten sermons. I. Title.

NL 0344144   TxDaM

RC75   Liddon, Henry Parry, 1829-1890.
L71   Some elements of religion. Lent lectures, 1870.
1904   By H.P.Liddon ... 20th impression (6th ed.)
               London,New York[etc.]Longmans,Green,and co.,1904.
               xxviii,240p. 18.5cm.

NL 0344145   NNUT

BX   Liddon, Henry Parry, 1829-1890.
5133   Some elements of religion. Lent lectures,
L71   1870. 6th ed. London, Longmans, Green,
               1910.
               xxviii, 240 p. 18cm.

1. Church of England--Sermons.

NL 0344146   NIC OrP

252.5
L619s   Liddon, Henry Parry, 1829-1890.
               Some words for God; being sermons preached
               before the University of Oxford, chiefly during
               the years 1863-1865. London, Rivingtons, 1865.
               313p.

1. Universities and colleges--Sermons.
2. Sermons, English. I. Title.

NL 0344147   TxFTC NRCR

Liddon, Henry Parry, 1829-1890.
Teaching and healing; a sermon preached before
the International Medical Congress, at St. Paul's
Cathedral, on the eighth Sunday after Trinity, August 7th, 1881. London, Rivington, 1881.
22 p. 8°.

NL 0344148   DNLM

Ap   Liddon, Henry Parry, 1829-1890.
L619   The ten lepers. A sermon on behalf of the
870t   National society for aid to the sick and
               wounded in war, preached in St. Paul's
               cathedral, on Sunday afternoon, Sept. 18th,
               1870, by the Rev. H. P. Liddon ...
               London:J.Paul,1,Chapter House Court,North
               Side of St.Paul's;and Paternoster Row.1870.
               p.[217]-224. 22½cm.,in case 27cm. (The penny
               pulpit, n.s. no. 455)

NL 0344149   TxU

BX5133   Liddon, Henry Parry, 1829-1890.
.L713t   There is a holy ghost; a sermon, preached
1868   before the University of Oxford, in the
in: Church of St. Mary the Virgin on Whitsunday
SWTS   1867. 2d ed. London, Rivingtons, 1868.
               32p. 22cm.

1. Church of England--Sermons. I. Title.

NL 0344150   IEG ICJ

LIDDON, HENRY PARRY, 1829-1890.
Thoughts on present church troubles occurring in four
sermons preached in St. Paul's cathedral in December, 1880.
With a preface by H. P. Liddon... London [etc.] Rivingtons, 1881.
xliv, 87, [1]p. 19½cm.

Printed by Wesleyan   University Library

NL 0344151   CtW

Liddon, Henry Parry, 1829-1890.
Thoughts on present church troubles occurring
in four sermons preached in St. Paul's Cathedral
in December 1880, with a preface by H.P. Liddon.
New York, E. P. Dutton, 1881.
xliv, 87 p. 19 cm.
1. Church of England. Doctrinal and controversial works. 2. Church of England. Sermons.
I. Title.

NL 0344152   IEG PPPD

Liddon, Henry Parry, 1829-1890.
Thoughts on present church troubles, occurring in four sermons preached in St. Paul's cathedral in December, 1880, with
a preface, by H. P. Liddon ... 2d ed. Oxford and London,
Rivingtons, 1882.
xlvi, 87, [1] p. 19¾ᵐ.

1. Church of England—Doctrinal and controversial works. 2. Church
of England—Sermons. 3. Sermons, English. I. Title.

Library of Congress   BX5132.L5 1882
                                            39—16022
                          [2]

NL 0344153   DLC

Liddon, Henry Parry, 1829-1890.
Twelve sermons preached in St.Paul's
Cathedral... London, Reeves, 1871.
separately paged. 22cm.

NL 0344154   MeWC

Liddon, H[enry] P[arry], 1829-1890.
The vision at Corinth. A sermon...on behalf
of the Christ Church mission at Poplar, East
London...May 12, 1889. London, Rivingtons,
1889.
28 p. 8°.

NL 0344155   NN

Liddon, H[enry] P[arry], 1829-1890.
Walter Kerr Hamilton, bishop of Salisbury; a sketch, reprinted
with additions and corrections from "the Guardian." 2d ed
London, etc., Rivingtons, 1869.
pp. viii, 151 +.

Hamilton, Walter Kerr, bp. of Salisbury

NL 0344156   MH PPPD MB CtY IEG NN

Liddon, Henry Parry, 1829-1890.
"Witness for Jesus:" a sermon preached...at
St. Paul's Cathedral, ... April 17, 1864. London,
1864.
16 p. 8°. [In v. 1318, College Pamphlets].

NL 0344157   CtY

Liddon, Henry Parry, 1829-1890.
The Whole Counsel of God: or, The duty of the
clergy as teachers..., with reference to the...
judgment in The case of "Essays & Reviews" A
Sermon... Oxf'd, 1864.
iii, 43 p. [In College Pamphlets, v. 699].
The same with slip inserted in   , fl. 1318.

NL 0344158   CtY

BX5133   Liddon, Henry Parry, 1829-1890.
.L713w   The work and prospects of theological
1868   colleges: a sermon, preached at the Cuddesdon
in: anniversary festival, on June 10, 1868.
SWTS   London. Rivingtons, 1868.
               32p. 22cm.

1. Church of England--Sermons. I. Title.

NL 0344159   IEG

LIDDON, Henry Parry, 1829-1890.
The worth of the Old Testament. A sermon. New [2d] ed.
Lond. Longmans, G., & co. 1891. 41 pp. Sm. 8°.

NL 0344160   MB

Liddon, John.
Cruelty the natural and inseparable consequence of slavery, and
both diametrically opposite to the doctrine and spirit of the Christian religion: represented in a sermon, preached on Sunday,
March 11th, 1792, at Hemel-Hempstead, Herts. By John Liddon.
London, Sold by C. Dilly, M. Gurney, T. Knott; and by Mr. Chapman, Hemel-Hempstead, 1792.   32 p.   21cm. (8°.)

Sabin 40971.

55R0457. 1. Slavery and the church.

NL 0344161   NN RPB

PR   Liddy, James.
6019   Esau, my kingdom for a drink; homage to James
O9Z51   Joyce on his LXXX birthday; a memorial address
               delivered at King's Inns, Dublin on 13th Feb.,
               1962. Dublin,Dolmen Press,1962.
               15p. 21cm.

1. Joyce, James, 1882-1941. I. Title.

NL 0344162   MU

[Liddy, Lewis Wagener] 1884–
Photoplay instructions; embracing the technical features of
the photoplay. [Chicago?] Western photoplay association,
°1913.
3 p. l., 9–46 p. 22¾ᵐ.

1. Moving-picture plays. I. Title.
                                            13—19436
Library of Congress   PN1996.L5

NL 0344163   DLC

VOLUME 332

Liddy, Lewis W[agener], 1884–
Photoplay instructions, embracing the technical features of the photoplay.   San Francisco: Western Photoplay Assoc., 1913.   46 p.   8°.

1. Photo-plays.
N. Y. P. L.   June 4, 1914.

NL 0344164   NN

Liddy, Roy Balmer, 1885–
The relation of science and philosophy ... by Roy Balmer Liddy ...   Toronto, University press [1914]

3 p. l., 3–129 p., 1 l.   23ᶜᵐ.
Thesis (PH. D.)—University of Toronto, 1914.
Vita.

1. Philosophy.   2. Science.   I. Title.
                                                          A 16–371
Title from Leland Stan-   ford Jr. Univ. Printed by L. C.

NL 0344165   CSt NjP NIC ICJ PU

Liddy, William L   1887–1924.
Shakespeare's key to the human heart, by Very Rev. Msgr. Wm. L. Liddy, PH. L.   [Chicago, Paul H. Fieberg co., ᶜ1925]

23, [1] p.   illus. (port.)   17½ᶜᵐ.

1. Shakespeare, William, 1564–1616.
Library of Congress   PR2976.L45
                                                        25–22486

NL 0344166   DLC

Lide, Mrs. Alice (Alison) 1890–1956.
Aztec drums, by Alice Alison Lide, illustrated by Carlos Sanchez M.   New York, Toronto, Longmans, Green and co., 1938.

142 p. incl. front., illus., plates.   20ᶜᵐ.
Illustrated lining-papers.
"First edition."

1. Aztecs—Fiction.   I. Title.
Library of Congress   PZ7.L616Az
                                                        38–27738
———————— Copy 2.

NL 0344167   DLC CaBVaU Or WaSp WaS OrP NN OCl OClh
OEac PSt PP PPT

Lide, Mrs. Alice (Alison) 1890–1956.
Dark possession, by Alice Alison Lide and Margaret Alison Johansen.   New York, London, D. Appleton-Century company incorporated, 1934.

3 p. l., 330 p.   19½ᶜᵐ.
Illustrated lining-papers.

I. Johansen, Mrs. Margaret (Alison) joint author.   II. Title.
Library of Congress   PZ3.L6198Dar
                                                        34–6713

NL 0344168   DLC OU NN

Lide, Alice (Alison) 1890–1956.
History of St. Paul's Parish, Carlowville, by Alice Alison Lide and Margaret Lee Alison Johansen.   Montgomery, Ala., The Paragon Press, 1923.
22 p.

1. Carlowville, Ala.   St. Paul's Parish—Hist.

NL 0344169   AAP

Lide, Mrs. Alice (Alison) 1890–1956.
Inemak, the little Greenlander, by Alice Alison Lide, illustrated by W. W. Clarke.   Chicago, New York, Rand, McNally & company [ᶜ1927]

148 p.   illus.   20ᶜᵐ.

I. Title.
                                                        27–17551
Library of Congress   PZ9.L619 In

NL 0344170   DLC CaBVaU OrMonO OrP Or PWcS

Lide, Mrs. Alice (Alison) 1890–1956.
Johnny of the 4-H club, by Alice Alison Lide, with illustrations by C. E. B. Bernard.   Boston, Little, Brown and company, 1941.

xi, 210, [1] p. incl. front., illus., plates.   19½ᶜᵐ.
"First edition; published March 1941."
"Part of Johnny of the 4-H club appeared in Junior weekly under the title of Adventures in friendship and part appeared in the Ambassador under the title of Swamp venture."

I. Title.
                                                        41–4378
Library of Congress   PZ7.L616Jo

NL 0344171   DLC PP Or

Lide, Alice (Alison) 1890–1956.
Lapland drum [by] Alice Alison Lide and Margaret Alison Johansen.   Illustrated by Ursula Koering.   Nashville, Abingdon Press [1955]

128 p.   illus.   22 cm.

1. Johansen, Margaret (Alison) 1896–   joint author.

PZ7.L616Lap   55–14248 ‡

NL 0344172   DLC WaSp WaS OrP Or ScU NcD OCl PP

Lide, Alice (Alison) 1890–1956.
Mystery of the Mahteb, a tale of thirteenth-century Ethiopia, by Alice Alison Lide and Margaret Alison Johansen, illustrated by Avery Johnson.   New York, Toronto, Longmans, Green and co., 1942.

x p., 1 l., 237 p. incl. illus., plates.   21 x 16ᶜᵐ.
Map on lining-papers.
"First edition."

1. Ethiopia—Hist.—Fiction.   I. Johansen, Margaret (Alison) 1896– joint author.   II. Title.
                                                        42–21564
Library of Congress   PZ7.L616My

NL 0344173   DLC OCl PPGi PP

Lide, Mrs. Alice (Alison) 1890–1956.
Ood-le-uk the wanderer, by Alice Alison Lide and Margaret Alison Johansen, illustrated by Raymond Lufkin.   Boston, Little, Brown, and company, 1930.

6 p. l., [3]–265 p. incl. illus., plates.   col. front.   21ᶜᵐ.
Maps on lining-papers.

1. Johansen, Mrs. Margaret (Alison) joint author.   II. Title.
                                                        30–21773
Library of Congress   PZ3.L6198Oo

NL 0344174   DLC WaS Or WaSp OKentU IEdS CoU OO OEac
OClh MB NN PWcS PPGi PP

Lide, Alice (Alison) 1890–1956.
Pearls of fortune, by Alice Alison Lide and Margaret Alison Johansen, illustrated by Philip Cheney.   Boston, Little, Brown, and company, 1931.

viii p., 2 l., [3]–276 p. incl. illus., plates.   col. front.   20½ᶜᵐ.

1. Mobile, Ala.—Hist.—Fiction.   I. Johansen, Margaret Alison, joint author.   II. Title.
                                                        31–23960
Library of Congress   PZ7.L616Pe

NL 0344175   DLC WaS WaSp Or CoU NN OO PP OEac OClh
OLak MB

Lide, Alice (Alison) 1890–1956.
Princess of Yucatan, by Alice Alison Lide; illustrated by Carlos Sanchez M.   New York, Toronto, Longmans, Green and co., 1939.

6 p. l., 187 p. incl. front., illus., plates.   19½ᶜᵐ.
Illustrated lining-papers.
"First edition."

1. Mayas—Fiction.   I. Title.
                                                        39–22089
Library of Congress   PZ7.L616Pr

NL 0344176   DLC WaSp WaS Or OrP LU OCl PP

Lide, Alice (Alison) 1890–1956.
Secret of the circle, by Alice Alison Lide and Margaret Alison Johansen; illustrated by Vera Bock.   London, New York [etc.] Longmans, Green & co., 1937.

223 p. incl. double front., illus., plates (part double)   19½ cm.
"Printed in the United States of America."
"First edition."

I. Johansen, Margaret (Alison) joint author.   II. Title.
PZ7.L616Se   37–28567

NL 0344177   DLC Or WaSp OrP OLak OEac OClh OCl

Lide, Mrs. Alice (Alison) 1890–1956.
Tambalo and other stories of far lands, by Alice Alison Lide and Annie H. Alison.   Chicago, Beckley-Cardy company [ᶜ1930]

160 p.   col. front., illus.   19½ᶜᵐ.

I. Alison, Annie H., joint author.   II. Title.
                                                        31–1277
Library of Congress   PZ9.L619Tam

NL 0344178   DLC WaSp PPT OEac OCl MB

Lide, Mrs. Alice (Alison) 1890–1956.
Thord Firetooth, by Alice Alison Lide and Margaret Alison Johansen; illustrated by Henry Pitz.   Boston, New York, Lothrop, Lee and Shepard company, 1937.

ix, 13–226 p. incl. front., plates.   20½ᶜᵐ.
Illustrated lining-papers.

I. Johansen, Mrs. Margaret (Alison) joint author.   II. Title.
Library of Congress   PZ3.L6198Th
                                                        37–13966

NL 0344179   DLC OrP WaSp Or OLak OEac OO OClh OCl
PP PPGi PBa

Lide, Alice (Alison) 1890–1956.
The wooden locket [by] Alice Alison Lide and Margaret Alison Johansen; illustrated by Corydon Bell.   New York, Viking Press, 1953.

127 p.   illus.   24 cm.

I. Johansen, Margaret (Alison) 1896–   joint author.   II. Title.
PZ7.L616Wo   53–8723 ‡

NL 0344180   DLC WaS OrP Or CaBViP PPT PPi PBa OCl
OOxM OO TxU MoU WaSp WaWW ScU PWcS

Lide, Alice (Alison) 1890–1956.
Yinka-tu the yak, by Alice Alison Lide; illustrated by Kurt Wiese.   New York, The Viking press, 1938.

63 p.   col. illus.   28ᶜᵐ.
Illustrated t.-p. and lining-papers in colors.
"First published August 1938."

I. Wiese, Kurt, 1887–   illus.   II. Title.
                                                        38–27807
Library of Congress   PZ7.L616Yi

NL 0344181   DLC WaSp OrAshS OrLgE Or NIC NN OCl OEac
OClW OO OClh PWcS PP

VOLUME 332

Lide, Anne Ayers.
Robert Alexander and the early Methodist church in Texas
... by Anne Ayers Lide. ₁La Grange, Tex., Press of La Grange
journal, ʰ1935₎

5 p. l., 176, ₍2₎ p. port. 22½ᶜᵐ.
Thesis (M. A.)—University of Texas.
Bibliography : p. 106-108.

1. Alexander, Robert, 1811-1882. 2. Methodist Episcopal church,
South, in Texas.

Library of Congress   BX8495.A5L5   35-14984
———— Copy 2.
Copyright A 83698   ₍3₎   922.773

NL 0344182   DLC NcD

Lide, David Reynolds, Jr.
Molecular structure studies with microwave spectroscopy.

Thesis - Harvard, 1952.

NL 0344183   MH-C

Lide, Edwin Scott, 1893–
... Constitutional basis of public school education, by Edwin S. Lide, United States Office of education. United
States Department of the interior. Ray Lyman Wilbur,
secretary. Office of education, William John Cooper, commissioner. Washington, U. S. Govt. print. off., 1931.
1 p. l., 11 p. 23 cm. (U. S. Office of education. Leaflet no. 40.
July, 1931)

1. Education—U. S. 2. Educational law and legislation—U. S.
3. Public schools—U. S. I. Title.
U. S. Office of Education.   Library L111.A53 no. 40   E 31—692
———— Copy 2.   L12523.L6
for Library of Congress   [L111.A73 no. 40]
₍a50k1₎   (370.61) 379.1473

OrU
NL 0344184   DHEW OC1BE MiU PP OU NcD WaWW OrSaW

Lide, Edwin Scott, 1893–
... Instruction in mathematics, by Edwin S. Lide ...
Washington, U. S. Govt. print. off., 1933.
vi, 72 p. 23 cm. (U. S. Office of education. Bulletin 1932, no. 17)
At head of title : United States Department of the interior. Ray
Lyman Wilbur, secretary. Office of education, William John Cooper,
commissioner.
National survey of secondary education. Monograph no. 23,
William John Cooper, director; Leonard V. Koos, associate di-
rector; Carl A. Jessen, coördinator.
1. Mathematics—Study and₍ teaching₎—Secondary schools₎ I.
Cooper, William John, 1882-1935. II. Koos, Leonard Vincent, 1881–
III. Jessen, Carl Arthur, 1887–   IV. Title. V. Title: National sur-
vey of secondary education.
[L111.A6 1932, no. 17]   E 33—707

U. S. Off. of Education.   Library
for Library of Congress   ₍a57v1₎

PP MB PPPL PBm PBa NcRS OC1U
NL 0344185   DHEW CaBVaU WaS WaWW WaTC OU OOxM OC1 OCU

Lide, Edwin Scott, 1893–
Legal basis of the organization, support, and control o
city schools. Chicago, 1930.
xii, 340 l. tables. 29 cm.
Thesis—University of Chicago.
Typescript (carbon copy)
Bibliography : leaves 337-340.

1. Educational law and legislation—U. S.—States. I. Title.

53-52613

NL 0344186   DLC ICU

Lide, Edwin Scott, 1893–
Mathematics in the changing curriculum of the high school
₍by₎ Edwin S. Lide.
(*In* National education association of the United States. **Addresses
and proceedings, 1933.** p. 491)

1. Mathematics—₍Study and₎ teaching—₍High schools₎ I. Title.

E 34—145

Library, U. S. Office of   Education L13.N212 1933
Library of Congress   [L13.N4 1933]

NL 0344187   DHEW

Lide, Edwin Scott, 1893–
... Procedures in curriculum making, by Edwin S. Lide ...
Washington, U. S. Govt. print. off., 1933.
vii, 98, ₍1₎ p. 23 cm. (U. S. Office of education. Bulletin, 1932,
no. 17)
At head of title : United States Department of the interior. Harold
L. Ickes, secretary. Office of education. William John Cooper, com-
missioner.
National survey of secondary education. Monograph no. 18.
William John Cooper, director; Leonard V. Koos, associate director; Carl A. Jessen, coördinator.
1. Education—Curricula. ₍1. Course of study₎   I. Cooper, William John, 1882-1935. II. Koos, Leonard Vincent, 1881–   III. Jessen, Carl Arthur, 1887–   IV. Title. V. Title: National survey of
secondary education.
[L111.A6 1932,   no. 17] (370.6173) E 33—1159
———— Copy 2.   LA222.A14 no. 18
U. S. Office of Education   Library L111.A6 no. 17
for Library of Congress   ₍a51b2₎

OC1 OOxM MB PPPL PBm PBa PP DAU
NL 0344188   DHEW CaBVaU WaTC WaWW OC1U OCU OU ODW

Lide, Florence E
The home story book
see under title

Lide, Lanneau Du Rant, 1876–1953.
The trial judge in South Carolina.   Columbia, University
of South Carolina Press, 1953.
114 p. illus. 24 cm.

1. Trial practice—South Carolina.   I. Title.

347.9   53-12517 ‡

Library of Congress   ₍5₎

TU NN NcD MsU
NL 0344190   DLC WaU-L NcGU ViU IaU MU NBuU-L NcU

Lide, Martin J
Protection of Alabama's water rights. An open
letter to the legislature Birmingham. n.p. 1915.
12 p. O.

NL 0344191   NcD

Lide, Robert Wilkins, 1852–1940.
Loyalties in black and white, by R. W. Lide. ₍Columbia,
S. C., R. L. Bryan company, ʰ1940₎
9 p. l., 3–116 p. ports. 19½ᶜᵐ.
CONTENTS.—Relations between former slaves and their owners, by
Marion E. Wilson.—Character sketches, by Mrs. R. W. Lide and R. W.
Lide.—"Old Faithful" ; or, Faithful to the end, by E. C. Dargan.—The
slave owners concern for the religious teaching of their slaves, by R. W.
Lide.—The old southern colored folk reflected in 1938, by Dora L. Lide.—
Hopewell saves his master's life, by J. S. Plowden.—Nannie and Grannie
in the Norwood family.—An enemy raid, by Mrs. W. C. Wilson.—Some
notable instances of the affection that existed between the whites and
the blacks, by R. W. Lide.—Instances of generous devotion, by Herbert
Bucks.—"The Negroes in Richmond history," by D. S. Freeman.—A
chapter of the ludicrous, by R. W. Lide.
1. Negroes. 2. U. S.—   Race question.   I. Title.
Library of Congress   E185.61.L55   41-22893
₍2₎   325.260973

NL 0344192   DLC NcD

PF5656 **Lide, Sven** ₍Alfred Larsson₎
.L7   Das lautsystem der niederdeutschen kanzleisprache Ham-
burgs im 14. jahrhundert mit einer einleitung über das
hamburgische kanzleiwesen ... ₍Oldenburg i. O., Druck von
G. Stalling, 1922₎
₍1₎, xi, ₍1₎, 132 p. 21½ᶜᵐ.
Akademische abhandlung—Upsala.
Added t.-p. with imprint: Uppsala, Appelbergs boktryckeri, 1922.
"Literaturverzeichnis" : p. ₍vii₎-xi.

1. Low German language—Dialects—Hamburg.

NL 0344193   ICU MH IU PBm PU CtY ICRL

830.8   **Lide, Sven** Alfred Larsson.
L714vn   Von Heine bis Hauptmann, mit Anmerkungen. 4.
1952   Aufl., 4 Druck. Stockholm, Bonnier ₍1952₎
151 p.   19 cm.
Bibliography: p.₍121₎

1.German literature--19th cent. 2.German
literature--20th cent. I.Title.

NL 0344194   MiU MH

D765.1   Lidé První armády ze země Sovětu do Varšavy a
L9486   na Berlín. ₍Z polského originálu Ludzie Pierw-
szej armii, přeložil a poznámkami opatřil
Rudolf Kozák,   Praha, Naše vojsko, 1948.
188 p. illus.,ports. 21cm.

Hoover
Library

1. Poland - Army - 1. armia. 2. World War,
1939-1945 - Regimental histories - Poland - 1.
armia. 3. World   War, 1939-1945 - Campaigns
I. Kozák, Rudolf,   ₍ed. II. Naše vojsko (Peri
odical₎

NL 0344195   CSt-H

Lidegaard, Kresten Holger, 1895-
... Af Abraham-sønnernes saga. Kjøbenhavn,
Nyt Nordisk forlag,A.Busck, 1933.
144 p. 22ᶜᵐ.
At head of title: Kresten H.Lidegaard.
Colored illustration on cover.
CONTENTS.—Den jydske hedes tatere.—Tater-sind.—
Hans Abrahams flyttedag.—Staerke kvinder.—Den sidste
tater.—Glint fra gamle slaegter.—Frederik ve ae
spaeng.—Tatermoderns traengsel og juleglaede.—Fra
tæterkongens ungdom.—Taterkongens søn.
1.Gipsies—Denmark. 2.Jørgensen family (Abraham
Jørgensen,fl.1760) I.Title.

NL 0344196   MiU

Lidegaard, Kresten Holger, 1895–
... Den bette kumpen. København, Gyldendal, 1943.
8 p. l., ₍5₎-115 p. 21½ᶜᵐ.
At head of title: Kresten H. Lidegaard.

I. Title.
PT8175.L475B4   47-37250

NL 0344197   DLC

Lidegaard, Kresten Holger, 1895–
Graabonden fortæller. København, Gyldendal, 1948.
86 p. 21 cm.

1. Tales, Danish. I. Title.

GR210.L5   52-1571₈

NL 0344198   DLC

VOLUME 332

Lideks, Osvalds, 1906-1952, *comp.*
Jāņu dziesmas. Rediģējis P. Smits; sakartojis O. Lideks. Rīgā, Latviešu folkloras krātuve, 1937.
182 p. 18 cm.

1. Folk-songs, Lettish.   i. Smits, Pēteris, 1869-1938, ed.   ii. Title.

PG9015.L5   63-57602

NL 0344199   DLC NN

Lideks, Osvalds, 1906-1952.
Latviešu svētki. K. Strauberga redakcijā. Rīgā, Latviešu folkloras krātuves izdevums, 1940.
107 p. 21 cm. (Latviešu folkloras krātuves materiāli, B 8)
Summary in German.
"Saīsinājumi" (bibliographical): p. 102.

1. Festivals — Latvia.   i. Straubergs, Kārlis, 1890-   ed.
ii. Title.   (Series: Latvia. Latviešu folkloras krātuve. Materiāli, B 8)

GT4871.L3L5   64-29178

NL 0344200   DLC

Lidel, Andreas
see
Lidl, Andreas, *ca.* 1740-*ca.* 1788.

Lidell, Hilding, 1904-
Studier i Johannes Messenius dramer ... av Hilding Lidell ... Uppsala, Wretmans boktryckeri a.-b., 1935.
316 p. 24 cm.
Akademisk avhandling—Uppsala.
"Litteraturförteckning": p. (291)-307.

1. Messenius, Johannes, 1579-1636.
(Full name: Karl Hilding Kristoffer Lidell)

Library of Congress   PT9697.M5L5 1935   36-30110
                                              (2)   839.7221

NL 0344202   DLC CU CtY NjP NN PU

Lidell, John A.
A case of neuroma of the optic nerve, with remarks and illustrations. By John A. Lidell ... 2d ed. New York, Holman, printer, 1863.
15 p. pl. 23 cm.

1. Optic nerve—Diseases.

Library of Congress   RE701.L71   7-14212†

NL 0344203   DLC DNLM MB

Lidell, John A.
——— A memoir on osteomyelitis. Read before the New York Academy of Medicine. 33 pp. 8°. *New York,* 1866. [P., v. 194.]

NL 0344204   DNLM OC1W-H CtY

Lidell, John A.
On gunshot wounds of arteries, traumatic hemorrhage and traumatic aneurism. By John A. Lidell ... Washington, D. C., McGill & Witherow, printers, 1863.
cover-title, 24 p. 23 cm.

1. Arteries—Wounds and injuries.

Library of Congress   RD156.L71   7-1146†

NL 0344205   DLC DNLM

Lidell, John A.
i. On the wounds of blood-vessels, traumatic hemorrhage, traumatic aneurism, and traumatic gangrene. ii. On the secondary traumatic lesions of bone: namely, osteo-myelitis, periostitis, ostitis, osteo-porosis, caries, and necrosis. iii. On pyæmia. By John A. Lidell ... Ed. by Prof. Frank Hastings Hamilton. New York, U. S. sanitary commission, 1870.
xi, 586 p. illus., 10 col. pl. 24 cm. (U. S. sanitary commission. Surgical memoirs of the war of the rebellion. (New York, 1870. v. 1))

1. Traumatism.   2. Bones—Diseases.   3. Pyemia.

Library of Congress   E631.A65 vol. 1   2—20532

NL 0344206   DLC NN MdBP

Lidell, John A.
A treatise on apoplexy, cerebral hemorrhage, cerebral embolism, cerebral gout, cerebral rheumatism, and epidemic cerebro-spinal meningitis. By John A. Lidell ... New-York, W. Wood & co., 1873.
xix, 395 p. 24 cm.

1 Brain—Diseases.   2. Apoplexy.
                                                 7-35767

Library of Congress   RC383.A7L7

          PP PPC DNLM
NL 0344207   DLC OC1W-H OC1 MiU Nh NNC ICJ NN MB PU

Lidell, Karl Hilding Kristoffer
see
Lidell, Hilding, 1904-

Lidell & Williams, *Chicago.*
Catalogue of Lidell & Williams. Chicago,
v. illus. 26 cm.
Cover-title.
Catalogue of corner blocks, head blocks, base blocks, balusters, etc.

1. Woodwork—Catalogs.
                                          ca 8-355 Unrev'd
Library of Congress   TH1155.L7

NL 0344209   DLC

Lidemann, Henrik.
"Betzy", Farce i 1 Akt, frit efter Eugene Labiche ved Henrik Lidemann. (In: Theater nips. Kjøbenhavn, 1889-1890. 12°. pt. 1 p. 31-65.)

NL 0344210   NN

Lidemark, Arne, ed.

VM81
.N6
Norwegian shipbuilding; an illustrated propaganda publication.
Oslo, Smiths publishing office (19

DS126
.4
.L5
(Hebraic
Sect.
לדמותם; קובץ זכרון לבני תל־יוסף וחבריה לעולים והחנ־
כים שנפלו במלחמת העצמאות תש׳׳ח-׳ט. תל־יוסף,
תש׳׳י. (Tel Yosef, 1949/50)
359 p. illus., ports. 23 cm.

1. Israel-Arab War, 1948-1949.   2. Palestine—Biog.
Title transliterated: Li-demutam.

DS126.4.L5   52-48945

NL 0344212   DLC

Liden, A. J.
Bidrag till kaennedomen om skulderapparatens och vingens ben hos svenska roffoglar.
Inaug. diss. Upsala, 1875.

NL 0344213   ICRL

Lidén, Arne, 1897-
Den norska strömningen i svensk litteratur under 1800-talet ... av Arne Lidén ... Uppsala, Almqvist & Wiksells boktryckeri-a.-b., 1926-
v. 24 cm.
Vol. 1 is the author's thesis, Uppsala.
"Litteraturförteckning": v. 1, p. (294)-302.
Contents.—i. Traditionen om Norge. Före Björnson. Synnøve Solbakken. Brand. Norskt og svenskt under 70-talet. Strindberg.
1. Literature, Comparative—Swedish and Norwegian.   2. Literature, Comparative—Norwegian and Swedish.
(Full name: Arne Holger Lidén)
                                                 36-30114
Library of Congress   PT9286.N6L5 1926
                                 (2)   839.70908

NL 0344214   DLC CU PU CtY IU MH ICU

Lidén (Carolus Olav(us))
De legatione Gallica Hugonis Grotii. Upsaliae, 1808.
1 p.l., 8 pp.   12°.
In: GFD p. v. 3.

NL 0344215   NN

Lidén, E   O   R
Kölingared; sockenbeskrivning. (Ulricehamn) Ulricehamns Tidn. a.-b:s tr., 1948.
37 p. illus., ports. 22 cm.

1. Kölingared, Sweden.

DL991.K65L5   50-17220

NL 0344216   NN MnU DLC

Lidén, Evald, 1862-
Äldre nordiska tillnamn. Tydningar och härledningar. (Helsingfors, 1910.) 52 p. 8°. (Svenska Litteratursällskapet i Finland. Skrifter. (v.) 92, (no.) 1.)
Signed by Evald Lidén.
Pipping, H. Studier i nordisk filologi. Band 1, (no.) 1.

1. Names.—Surnames (Norse).
N. Y. P. L.   August 31, 1915.

NL 0344217   NN NIC

PK8007
.L7
LIDÉN, EVALD, 1862-
Armenische Studien. Göteborg, Wald. Zachrissons, 1906.
149 p.

1. Armenian language.   i. Title.

NL 0344218   InU RPB NN OC1 MH NRU NjP DDO TxU

VOLUME 332

Lidén, Evald, 1862–
 Baltisch-slavische Worterklärungen, von Evald Lidén.
₍Uppsala: Almqvist & Wiksell, 1911.₎ p. ₍195–₎203. 4°.
 Caption-title.
 Repr.: Le monde oriental, ₍v.₎ 5. 1911.
 Bibliographical footnotes.

1. Slavonic languages.—Etymology.
N. Y. P. L.   August 29, 1922.

NL 0344219   NN

491.8
L619b   Lidén, Evald, 1862–
 Ein baltisch-slavisches Anlautgesetz, von
Evald Lidén.   Göteborg, Zachrissons Boktryck-
eri, 1899.
 31p. 25cm.

1048262   1. Balto-Slavic languages – Phonology. I.
Title.

NL 0344220   TxU NN PBm PU RPB NIC

Lidén, Evald, 1862–
 Blandade språkhistoriska bidrag, af Evald Lidén ... Göteborg, W. Zachrissons boktryckeri a.-b., 1903–34.
 2 v. 24½ᵐ. (Göteborgs högskolas årsskrift ₍x.₎ 1904: 1₎; ₍xl. 1934: 3)
 Series title at head of v. 2.
 Vol. 2 (Nordiska ordstudier) published by Elanders boktryckeri
aktiebolag.

 1. Aryan languages—Etymology. 2. Scandinavian languages—Ety-
mology. I. Title.
                                                       A C 35–318
 Title from Univ. of Mich.   AS284.G6842 vol. 40
 Library of Congress   [AS284.G6 vol. 10, no. 1;
                               vol. 40, no. 3]
                                   ₍2₎

NL 0344221   MiU PU OU TxU PBm NN

Lidén, Evald, 1862–

 Germanska namnstudier tillägnade Evald Lidén den 3 oktober 1932. Uppsala, A.-b. Lundequistska bokhandeln ₍1932₎

439.7   Lidén, Evald, 1862–
L610   ... Ordstudier ...   Göteborg, Elanders boktryckeri aktiebolag, 1937.
 cover-title, 145p. front.(port.)   (Meijer-
bergs arkiv för svensk ordforskning. 1)

 Bibliographical foot-notes.

 1. Swedish language--Words--Hist.

NL 0344223   ICU OU PU NcD

AS   Lidén, Evald, 1862–
284   Studien zur altindischen und vergleich-
H912S6   enden Sprachgeschichte. Upsala, Almqvist
v.6   & Wiksell, 1897.
no.1   107 p. 24cm. (Skrifter utg. af K.
Humanistiska vetenskapssamfundet i Upsala,
VI, 1)

 1. Indo-Aryan languages--Etymology.

NL 0344224   NIC MH NjP MiU

AS284
G7   Lidén, Evald, ¹⁸⁶²–
22   Studien zur tocharischen Sprachgeschichte.
Göteborg, Elanders boktryckeri aktiebolag,
1916.
 37 p. 25 cm.   (Göteborgs högskolas årsskrift XXII bd., 1916, nr. 2)

 1. Tokharian language.   (Series)

NL 0344225   RPB NcU

P
291   Lidén, Evald, 1862–
.L5   Vermischtes zur Wortkunde und Grammatik,
von Evald Lidén.   Upsala, Berling, 1893.
 1v.(various pagings) 24cm.
 "Aus Upsala Universitets Årsskrift 1894".
 Bound with author's other essays, Studien
zur altindischen und vergleichenden Sprachgeschichte (1897) and Ein baltisch-slavisches
Anlautgesetz (1899)
 1. Grammar, Comparative and general –
Syntax. I. Title.

NL 0344226   NNU

Lidén, Gunnar Knut Oskar, 1918–
 Speech audiometry; an experimental and clinical study
with Swedish language material. Stockholm, 1954.
 145 p. illus. 27 cm. (Acta oto-laryngologica. Supplementum
114)
 Akademisk avhandling—Karolinska institutet.
 Without thesis statement.

 1. Audiometry. 2. Speech.   (Series)
                                               A 57–3966
 John Crerar Library
 for Library of Congress   ₍2₎

NL 0344227   ICJ DNLM ViU ICU PSt MoU

Liden, Johan Henrik, 1741–1793, respondent.
 Auxiliante summo numine. Tentamen
historico-literarium de favore sereniss.
domus mediceae in migrantes ab oriente
in occidentem literas ...
   see under Ekerman, Petrus, 1696–1783, pr

45055
.S79M3   Lidén, Johan Henrik, 1741–1793.

Marklin, Gabriel, 1777–1857.
 Catalogus disputationum in academiis Scandinaviæ et Fin-
landiæ Lidenianus continuatus a Gabr. Marklin ... ₍1778–
1819₎ Upsaliæ, excudebant Reg. academiæ typographi, 1820.

Lidén, Johan Henrik, 1741–1793.

Marklin, Gabriel, 1777–1857.
 Catalogus disputationum in academiis Sveciæ et Fenniæ
habitarum Lidenianus iterum continuatus a Gabr. Marklin ...
₍1820–1855₎ Stockholm, 1874.

Lidén (Johan Henrik) 1741–1793.
 *De favore sereniss. domus Mediceæ, in migrantes ab
Oriente in Occidentem literatos et literas. *Upsaliæ,*
1760. 2 p.l., 44 pp. 12°.
 In: BTE p. v. 8.

NL 0344231   NN

Lidén, Johan Henrik, 1741–1793.
 ... Historiola litteraria poëtarum svecanorum
 ... exhibet Johannes Henricus Lidén ₍et alii₎ ...
Upsaliae ₍1764–1803₎
 1 v. 20.5 cm.
 Issued in a series of 7 academic dissertations,
Upsala.
 Each diss. has it's own t.p.
 In the first diss. Karl Aurivillius is named as
praeses; diss. 2–4 were presented by Lidén, in
collaboration with others, no praeses being named;
diss. 5–6, with Erik Mikael Fant named as praeses

 form a continuation of Lidén's work, partly
elaborated from his papers, partly composed
by the respondents (cf. pref. to pars 5a, p. ₍109₎)

NL 0344233   CtY

Lidén, Johan Vilhelm, 1797–1862, ed.

 Diplomatarium dalekarlicum. Urkunder rörande lan-
skapet Dalarne, samlade och utgifne af C. G. Krönings-
svärd och J. Lidén. Stockholm, Nordströmska boktryckeriet, 1842–46.

Lidén, Johan Vilhelm, 1797–1862, respondent.

QH9
.T6
no.232– Thunberg, Karl Peter, 1743–1828, praeses.
233   ... Examen classis monoeciae ... Upsaliæ, excudebant Palm-
Rare Bk. blad et c. ₍1825₎
Coll.

Lidén, Johan Vilhelm, 1797–1862, ed.

Sweden. Riksarkivet.
 Svenska riks-archivets pergamentsbref från och med
år 1351 förtecknade med angifvande af innehållet ...
Stockholm. P. A. Norstedt & söner, 1866–72.

Lidén, Karl, ed.

 De ungas sånger, 181 en- och tvåstämmiga sånger samt 20
kanons, samlade och utgivna av Karl Lidén. Gävle, Skol-
förlaget ₍1940₎
 2 p.l., 188, ₍5₎ p. 19½ᵐ.
 "Rättelser" slip inserted.
 Songs for one or two parts, unaccompanied.

 1. School song-books, Swedish. I. Title.
                                               42–5043
 Library of Congress   M1581.L7U6
                                               784.62

NL 0344237   DLC

R10   Lidén, Kurt.
Lu949   Studies on the arc spectrum of fluorine: wave-
length measurements and term analysis; hyperfine
structure; stark effect. Lund, 1949.
 Thesis - Lund.
 Without thesis statement.

NL 0344238   CtY

BV45   Liden, O E   ed.
 Christmas tidings; a Christmas service of
Scripture reading, recitation and song for
Sunday schools. Rock Island, Ill., Augustana
Book Concern, 1923.
 35 p. illus., music. 23 cm.

 Cover title.

 1. Christmas--Prayer-books and devotions.
2. Christmas music. I. Title.

NL 0344239   MnHi

VOLUME 332

Lidén (OLAVUS) [and] **Hultström** (C. S.)
  *Monumenta litteraria historiam Johannis Skytte, senioris,
  illustrantia... *Upsaliae*, 1813-30. 2 parts. 12°.
  In: GFD p. v. 2.

NL 0344240   NN

WD   **Lidén, Oskar Linus,** 1870-
3828   Akademisk övertro; kommentarer till en
    student-afton. Lund,C.Bloms boktr.,1951.
    72p. illus. 24cm.

  1. Occult sciences. I. Title (1)

NL 0344241   CtY NN

Lidén, Oskar Linus, 1870-
  Aktuella sydsvenska stenåldersproblem; Jonstorp, Sjö-
  holmen och Barumsgraven. [Lund, Gleerupska univ.-bok-
  handeln, 1948]
  104 p. illus., maps. 24 cm.

  1. Stone age—Sweden. I. Title: Sydsvenska stenåldersproblem.

  GN776.S2L37   49-14746*

NL 0344242   DLC MnU

DL991   **Lidén, Oskar Linus,** 1870-
.A538L5   Bilder från det gamla Alingsås. Lund, Gleerupska univ.-
    bokhandeln [1953]
    83 p. illus., ports. 25 cm.

  1. Alingsås, Sweden—Hist. I. Title.

  Minnesota Univ. Libr.   A 54-5525
  for Library of Congress   [3]

NL 0344243   MnU DLC NN

Lidén, Oskar Linus, 1870-
  Bland prästmän och skolfolk; bilder från mitt småländska
  arbetsfält. Lund, C. Bloms boktr., 1947.
  131 p. illus. 24 cm.

  1. Teachers—Sweden—Småland. I. Title.

  LA2375.S8L5   52-68273 ‡

NL 0344244   DLC

Lidén, Oskar Linus, 1870-
  De flinteggade benspetsarnas nordiska kulturfas, studier i
  anslutning till nya sydsvenska fynd, av Oskar Lidén. Lund,
  C. W. K. Gleerup [1942]
  142 p. illus. (incl. maps) 24½ᶜᵐ. (Half-title: Skrifter utgivna av
  Kungl. humanistiska vetenskapssamfundet i Lund ... XXXIII)
  "Tryckt med understöd av Längmanska fonden."
  Summary in German.
  "Litteraturförteckning": p. [124]-129.

  1. Stone age—Sweden—Scania. 2. Scania—Antiq. I. Title.
                                  46-39071
  Library of Congress   GN776.S2L4
                        [2]   571.15

NL 0344245   DLC MoU CSt PU CU ICU MnU NcU

Lidén, Oskar Linus, 1870-
  Från sagornas ö; bilder från bondekulturens slutskede.
  Lund, Gleerupska universitetsbokhandeln [1946]
  171 p. illus., ports., map. 24 cm.

  1. Iceland—Civilization. I. Title.

  DL326.L5   52-3501

NL 0344246   DLC NN MnU

913.485 **Lidén, Oskar Linus,** 1870-
L619h   Hällgröpningsstudier i anslutning till nya
    sydsvenska fynd. [Lund, Gleerup, 1938]
    158p. illus., maps. 24cm.

  Bibliography, p.[155]-158.

  1. Stone age—Scania. 2. Scania—Antiq.
  I. Title.

NL 0344247   IU MH

914.85 **Lidén, Oskar Linus,** 1870-
L619s   Smålandskt. Lund, Gleerupska Univ.
    Bokhandeln [1945-1952?]
    2 v. illus., ports.

  1. Småland, Sweden - Description and
  travel. 2. Småland, Sweden - Social life
  and customs. I. Title.

NL 0344248   WaU NN MnU PU

Lidén, Oskar Linus, 1870-
  Striden om tro och sed kring sekelskiftet; kulturbilder
  och personteckningar. Lund, C. Bloms boktr., 1950.
  100 p. illus., ports. 23 cm.

  1. Sweden—Civilization. 2. Sweden—Biog. I. Title.

  Minnesota. Univ. Libr.   A 52-4716
  for Library of Congress   [3]

NL 0344249   MnU NN

Lidén, Oskar Linus, 1870-
  Svältorna och livet i Svältbygden förr och nu. [Lund,
  Gleerupska univ.-bokhandeln, 1949]
  222 p. illus., ports., maps. 24 cm.
  Bibliography: p. 35.

  1. Älvsborg, Sweden (Province)—Civilization. I. Title.

  DL971.A4L5   914.86   50-28078

NL 0344250   DLC MnU NN DNAL

GN776 **Lidén, Oskar Linus,** 1870-
.S2L67   Sydsvensk stenålder belyst av fynden på bop-
    latserna i Jonstorp... I.Skivyxkulturen. Lund,
    1938.
    210 p.

  Akademisk avhandling--Lund.

  1.Stone age--Sweden.

NL 0344251   ICU OrU MH ICRL CtY NjP ViU DLC-P4

Lidén, Ragnar.
  ... Geokronologiska studier öfver det finiglaciala skedet
  i Ångermanland, af Ragnar Lidén, med 7 taflor. Stockholm, Kungl. boktryckeriet, P. A. Norstedt & söner, 1913.
  39 p. illus., maps (1 fold.) diagrs. (part fold.) 32ᶜᵐ. (Sweden)
  Sveriges geologiska undersökning. Ser. Ca. Afhandlingar och uppsatser
  i 4: o. n: o 9)
  Has English summary of contents.

  1. Glacial epoch.

                                  G S 14-591

  Library, U. S. Geol.   survey (583) qCa no. 9

NL 0344252   DI-GS NIC

Lidén, Ragnar.
  ... Kalkstensförekomster utefter inlandsbanan mellan
  ströms Vattudal och Pite älf, af Ragnar Lidén. Med en
  karta. Stockholm, Kungl. boktryckeriet, P. A. Norstedt
  & söner, 1911.
  45 p. illus., fold. map, fold. tab. 25ᶜᵐ. (Sveriges geologiska undersökning. Ser. C. Afhandlingar och uppsatser. n: o 235. Årsbok 4 (1910
  n: o 7)

  1. Mines and mineral resources—Sweden. 2. Limestone—Sweden.

                                  G S 12-581

  Library, U. S. Geol.   survey (583) D 1910 no. 7

NL 0344253   DI-GS

Rare Book En liden artig oc konstrig fiske-bog / om
Room   adskillige fiskefang / hvorledis mand med
Uzk23   største lyst / fordeel / konst oc behendighed
649l   kand fange alle slags fiske ... Aff tydsken /
    paa danske / saa vel som udaff egen forfarenhed
    oc daglige experientz sammen skreffven / oc
    nu til trycken forfoerdiget. J Kiøbenhaffn hos
    Jørgen Holst / B.tilkiøbs tryckt Aar 1649.
    1p.l.,46p. 18½cm.
    Signatures: 1l. unsigned, A-E⁴F³.
    Title-woodcut (fishing scene)

  From Oeconomia nova paa danske, edited by
  Jørgen Holst.
  Title-page and p.9-10 supplied from another,
  smaller, copy.

NL 0344255   CtY MH

En liden samling   adskillige vers og sange,
  til opmuntring og opbyggelse sammenskreven.
  3. opl. formeret. Kiøbenhavn, Trykt hos Niels
  Hansen Møller, 1748. 1 p.l., 207, [7]p. 14 cm.
  A Moravian hymn-book in Norwegian translation.
  ———— Kiøbenhavn, Trykti de Berlingske arvingers
  bogtrykkerie ved J. C. og G. C. Berling, 1760.
  324, [12]p. 14 cm.
  A Moravian hymn-book in Norwegian translation.

  Luther College Library, Decorah, Iowa.

NL 0344256   IaDL

Lidenius, John Abr.
  Works by this author printed in America before 1801 are available
  in this library in the Readex Microprint edition of Early American
  Imprints published by the American Antiquarian Society.
  This collection is arranged according to the numbers in Charles
  Evans' American Bibliography.

NL 0344257   DLC

VOLUME 332

Ayer
183
L66
1756

LIDENIUS, JOHN ABR.
The lawfulness of defensive war. A sermon preached before the members of the church, at Chiechester ⟨!⟩ in the county of Chester, and Province of Pennsylvania, upon their association for defence, February 14, 1756. Philadelphia, Printed by J.Chattin,1756.
16p.

Photostat reproduction (negative) from the Library company of Philadelphia copy.
Evans. Amer.   bibliog. no.7697.

NL   0344258   ICN PPL PHi

Lidenius, Johan Abr.
Sveriges Allmaenna Nytta Och Enshildta Trefnad Fundne Uti Hans Kunglige Hoghets Dyra Person... Underdaenigast Af Johan Abr. Lidenius Americano-Stockholmiensis.   Stockholm, Trycht hos Lars Salvius [1748]
24 p.
cf. Larsen (Swed. Comm.) 414.

NL   0344259   RPJCB

4U
644

Lider, Julian.
Czynniki zwycięstwa; o stałych czynnikach decydujących o wyniku wojny. 2. wyd. [Warszawa] Wydawn. Ministerstwa Obrony Narodowej [1952]
207 p.

NL   0344260   DLC-P4

Lider, Julian.
Nasza Konstytucja; materiały pomocnicze do nauki o konstytucji dla szkoły ogólnokształcącej. Opracowali J. Lider i E. Słuczański. ⟨Wyd. 1.⟩ Warszawa, Państwowe Zakłady Wydawn. Szkolnych, 1952.
251 p. illus. 22 cm.

1. Poland—Constitutional law.   I. Słuczański, E., joint author.   II. Title.

54-28400 ‡

NL   0344261   DLC MH

335.411
L714p
IN:
main

Lider, Julian.
Pogadanki o dialektyce i materializmie.
Wyd. 2.   Warszawa Państwowy Instytut Wydawn., 1949.
150p.   21cm.

1. Dialectical materialism.   I. Title.

NL   0344262   IEN DLC-P4 NN

146.3
L61p
1949

Lider, Julian.
Pogadanki o dialektyce i materializmie.
Wyd. 4., przejrzane i uzup. ⟨Kraków⟩ Państwowy Instytut Wydawn., 1949.
162p. 21cm.

1. Dialectical materialism.   I. Title.

NL   0344263   IU

Lider, Julian.
Pogadanki o dialektyce i materializmie. Wyd. 6. przejrz. i rozsz. ⟨Warszawa⟩ Państwowy Instytut Wydawniczy ⟨1951⟩
257 p.   21 cm.

1. Dialectical materialism.   I. Title.

B809.8.L5 1951   54-28456 ‡

NL   0344264   DLC

SB608
G7L55

Lider, Lloyd Arthur, 1921-
Inheritance of resistance to root-knot nematode (Meloidogyne incognita, Kofoid and White) in Vitis spp. ⟨Davis, 1952⟩
11,65 l.   illus.,tables.

Thesis (Ph.D. in Genetics) - Univ. of California, Davis, June 1952.
Bibliography: p.54-56.

NL   0344265   CU

PJ5126
.L49
Hebr

לידער. .2. אופל. רינע, פארלאג "קאמף." ⟨Riga⟩ 1940.
39 p. 18 cm.

1. Yiddish poetry (Collections) 2. Russian poetry—Translations into Yiddish.   *Title transliterated: Lider.*

PJ5126.L49   57-57236 ‡
Library of Congress   ⟨8⟩

NL   0344266   DLC

El líder máximo de China.
see under   [Martin, Juan Luis].

לידער צום זינגען. מים די נאטן, א מתנה מיינע פריינם ... ⟨פון⟩ אברהם רייזען. ניו יארק, ארויסגענעבן פון דעם א. רייזען יובל-קאמימעם. 1947.
64 p. port. 22 cm.
Unacc. melodies; Yiddish words (romanized); also printed as text (Hebrew characters) before each song.

1. Songs, Jewish (Yiddish)   I. Reisin, Abraham, 1876-1953.
Title romanized: Lider tsum zingen.

M1619.5.R53L5   79-279307
[M1852]

NL   0344268   DLC

לידער וועגן סמאלינען. זאמלונג. מעליכע-פארלאג "דער עמעם." ⟨Москва⟩ 1940.
29 p. 16 cm.
———— Microfilm copy (positive)
Negative film in the New York Public Library.

1. Stalin, Iosif Vissarionovich, 1879-1953—Poetry.   I. Title.
Title transliterated: Lider vegn Stalinen.

A 56-4488

New York. Public Libr.
for Library of Congress

NL   0344269   NN

PJ5126
.L5
Hebr⟩

לידער-זאמלונג ⟨פון⟩ כ. נורעוויימש. אי. בארוכאוויטש. מ. לעלמשוק. פ. פלאמקין. מינסק, מעליכע-פארלאג באם ראמפמאלקאם פון ווסר. ⟨Минск⟩ 1940.
91 p. 18 cm.

1. Yiddish poetry (Collections) 2. Yiddish literature—Russia.
Title transliterated: Lider-zamlung.

PJ5126.L5
OCAT   56-51809

NL   0344270   DLC

Liderkranz of the city of New York. History committee.
History of the Liederkranz of the city of New York, 1847 to 1947, and of the Arion, New York ... New York, Drechsel printing co., 1948.
xiv, 161 p. illus., ports.

Bibliography: p. 159.

NL   0344271   NNC

TF240
.D82

Liders, Georgiĭ Vladimirovich.

Durnovo, Pavel Sergeevich.
Восстановление железнодорожного пути. Москва, Гос. трансп. жел.-дор. изд-во, 1943.

Liders, Georgiĭ Vladimirovich.
Железнодорожный путь. Допущено в качестве учебника для учащихся жел.-дор. училищ. Москва, Гос. трансп. жел.-дор. изд-во, 1946.
321 p. illus. 20 cm.

1. Railroads—Russia—Track.   I. Title.
Title transliterated: Zheleznodorozhnyĭ put'.

TF240.L49 1946   54-42158

NL   0344273   DLC

Liders, Georgiĭ Vladimirovich.
Железнодорожный путь. 2. перер. изд. Допущено в качестве учебника для жел.-дор. училищ. Москва, Гос. трансп. жел.-дор. изд-во, 1950.
331 p. illus. 23 cm.

1. Railroads—Russia—Track.
Title transliterated: Zheleznodorozhnyĭ put'.

TF240.L49 1950   50-38200

NL   0344274   DLC

Liders, Georgiĭ Vladimirovich.
Железнодорожный путь; устройство, ремонт и текущее содержание. 3., перер. изд. Одобрено в качестве учебника для жел.-дор. училищ. Москва, Гос. трансп. жел.-дор. изд-во, 1953.
364 l. illus. 23 cm.
Photocopy (negative)
Collation of the original, as determined from the photocopy: 363 p. illus.

1. Railroads—Russia—Track.   I. Title.
Title transliterated: Zheleznodorozhnyĭ put'.

TF240.L49 1953a   62-38178 ‡

NL   0344275   DLC

VOLUME 332

Lidervald (A[leksandr] K[arolovich]). *K
voprosu o mochepolovikh aviahtshakh u zhen-
shtshin i ikh operativnou llechenii. [Uro-geni-
tal fistulu in women and their operative treatment.] 99 pp., 2 l. 8°. *S.-Peterburg, S.
Dobrodieyeff, 1894.*

NL 0344276   DNLM

Lidforss, Bengt, 1868–1913.
August Strindberg och den litterära nittiotaletsreklamen, av
Bengt Lidforss. 2. uppl. med ett tillägg: Filosofisk Levertin-
kult. Malmö, Aktiebolaget Framtiden. 1910.

90 p. 19½ᶜᵐ.

1. *Strindberg, August, 1849–1912. 2. Levertin, Oscar Ivar, 1862–1906.
3. Swedish literature—Hist. & crit.   I. Title.

33–21992

Library of Congress   PT9816.L45 1910 a   928.397

NL 0344277   DLC MnU ICU IEN NcU NcD NN MiU

PT9815
L5
Lidforss, Bengt, 1868–1913.
August Strindberg och den litterära
nittiotalsreklamen. Malmö, Aktiebolaget
Framtidens förlag, 1918.
81 p.

1. Strindberg, August, 1849–1912.

NL 0344278   CU

PT
9875
.08
Z72
Lidforss, Bengt, 1868–1913.
Barbarskogens skald; recensioner och pole-
miker. Malmö, Framtidens förlag [1908]
119 p.   20 cm.

1. Ossian-Nilsson, Karl Gustaf, 1875–
I. Title.

NL 0344279   WU WaU MH CU

1868–1913.
**Lidforss, Bengt.* Batologiska iakttagelser. [i], ii. [Stock-
holm. 1899–1901.] 8°.
*Öfvertryk af Kongl. svenskape-akademiens förhandlingar, 1899–1901
[v], 21–35; [viii, 59–90.

NL 0344280   MH–A

Lidforss, Bengt, 1868–1913.
... Dagsbilder. Malmö, Aktiebolaget Framtidens bokförlag
[1917]
242, [4] p. 19½ᶜᵐ.

At head of title: Ur Bengt Lidforss' litterära kvarlåtenskap.
On cover: Andra upplagan.
"Innehållet i föreliggande volym ... har förut varit publicerat som
artiklar i tidningen 'Arbetet'."—p. 242.

1. Social sciences—Addresses, essays, lectures.   I. Title.

35–31505

Library of Congress   H35.L62   304

NL 0344281   DLC MH

Lidforss, Bengt, 1868–1913.
Fragment och miniatyrer, av Bengt Lidforss. 2. förändrade
uppl. Malmö, Framtidens bokförlag [1912]
255, [1] p. 19½ᶜᵐ.

1. Europe—Descr. & trav.   I. Title.

33–21432

Library of Congress   D921.L47 1912   91

NL 0344282   DLC MH

Lidforss, Bengt, 1868–1913.
Kristendomen förr och nu; en populärvetenskaplig framställning. Malmö, Framtidens förlag, 1911.
487 p. 20 cm.

1. Christianity—20th cent.   I. Title.

BR121.L499   55–45943 ‡

NL 0344283   DLC

BR
121
L5
Lidforss, Bengt, 1868–1913.
Kristendomen förr och nu; en populär-
vetenskaplig framställning. 2. uppl.
Malmö, Aktiebolaget Framtidens bokförlag,
1923.
374p.   20cm.
Bibliographical footnotes.

1. Christianity   2. Church history –
Primitive and early church   3. Theology,
Doctrinal   I. Title

NL 0344284   WU

PT9875
.LAZ8L7
Lidforss, Bengt, 1863–1913.
Levertinkultens apologet. En vidräkning med doc. Fredrik Böök av Bengt Lidforss   Malmö, Aktiebolaget Framtidens förlag, 1910.
47 p. 20ᶜᵐ.
"Efterföljande artikelserie har   varit publicerad i tidningen 'Arbetet' ... 26
och 27 sept. samt den 1 okt. som svar på tvänne inlägg av docenten Böök i 'Svenska dagbladet' ... 20 och 2¹ sept."—Pref. note.

NL 0344285   ICU MH NcU NcD

Lidforss, Bengt, 1868–1913.
Litteraturkritik. Ur Bengt Lidforss' kvarlåtenskap.
(2. genomsedda uppl.) Malmö, Aktiebolaget Framtiden
[°1920]
268, [3] p. 19½ᶜᵐ.

1. Swedish literature—Hist. & crit.   I. Title.

33–18331

Library of Congress   PT9275.L5 1920   839.704

NL 0344286   DLC

230
L61m
Lidforss, Bengt, 1868–1913.
Modärna apologeter; en antikritik.   Malmö,
Aktiebolaget Framtidens förlag, 1911.
110p. 20cm.

NL 0344287   IU MH

Lidforss, Bengt, 1868–1913.
Naturvetenskapliga kåserier av Bengt Lidforss. [Första–tredje
samlingen. Andra upplagan.] Malmö, A.-B. Framtidens bokförlag, [1918]
3 vol. in 1. 20½ᶜᵐ.
Vol. 2, third edition.

NL 0344288   ICJ

LIDFORSS, Bengt, 1868–1913.
Onda makter och goda. Uppsatser i blandade
ämnen.   Malmö,   Framtidens förlag,
[1909].

NL 0344289   MH

WB
23650
Lidforss, Bengt, 1868–1913.
Polemiska inlägg. Malmö, Framtidens Bokförlag [1913]
266p.

NL 0344290   CtY MH

Lidforss, Bengt, 1868–1913.
Samlade skrifter. [Malmö, Aktiebolaget
Framtidens bokförlag, 1908–25]
18 v. in 8. 19ᶜᵐ.
Binder's title. Each volume has special t.-p.only.
Imprint varies slightly.
Editions vary. Vol.1,3d ed.,1925.

NL 0344291   MiU

Lidforss, Bengt, 1868–1913.
Socialistisk journalistik, af Bengt Lidforss. Stockholm, A.
Bonnier [1907]
5 p. l., [3]–261 p. 19½ᶜᵐ.

1. Social sciences—Addresses, essays, lectures.   I. Title.

33–19874

Library of Congress   H35.L63   304

NL 0344292   DLC ICJ WU

Lidforss, Bengt, 1868–1913.
Socialistisk journalistik, ur Bengt Lidforss' efterlämnade
skrifter... Del 1–3   Malmö: Aktiebolaget Framtidens Bokförlag [1921–1923] 3 v. in 2. 12°.

Del 1–2, 2. ed.
Contents: Del 1. Sociala, politiska och blandade spörsmål. Del 2. Dagsbilder.
Del 3. Från universitetslivet och lärdomsstaden.

1. Essays (Swedish). 2. Socialism.   —Essays.
N.Y.P.L.   October 9, 1924

NL 0344293   NN

Lidforss, Bengt, 1868–1913.
Studier öfver elaiosferer i örtbladens mesofyll och epidermis.
Af Bengt Lidforss...   Lund: Berlingska boktryckeri- och
stilgjuteri-aktiebolaget, 1893.   35 p.   4°.   (Lund. Universi-
tet. Acta Universitatis Lundensis. Lunds universitets årsskrift.
Tomus 29, afdelning 2[, no. 11].)

Bibliography, p. 34–35.

1. Botany, Physiological and structural.
N.Y.P.L.   December 23, 1923

NL 0344294   NN ICRL

Lidforss, Bengt, 1868–1913.
... Studier öfver pollenslangarnes irritationsrörelser, af
Bengt Lidforss... Lund, E. Malmströms boktryckeri, 1901–
1906.
2 v. 29½ᶜᵐ. (Lunds universitets årsskrift. bd. 37, afd. 2, n:r 4; n.f.,
afd. 2, bd. 1, n:r 6)
K. Fysiografiska sällskapets handlingar. [n. f.] bd. 12, n:r 4; bd. 16,
n:r 6.
Vol. 2 has imprint: Lund, H. Ohlssons boktryckeri.
Bibliographical foot-notes.

1. Pollen. 2. Plants—Irritability and movements.   I. Title.

A 31–630

Title from John Crerar   Libr. 058
Library of Congress   [AS284.L8]
                             [2]

NL 0344295   ICJ IaU NN MoU LU NcU PU

VOLUME 332

Lidforss, Bengt, 1868–1913.
Ueber die Wirkungsphäre der Glycose- und Gerbstoff-Reagentien. Von Bengt Lidforss. Lund: Berlingska boktryckeri- och stilgjuteri-aktiebolaget, 1892. 14 p. 4°. (Lund. Universitet. Acta Universitatis Lundensis. Lunds universitets årsskrift. Tomus 28, afdelning 2₍, no. 9₎.)

Bibliographical footnotes.

1. Tannin. 2. Glucose.
N. Y. P. L.   December 29, 1925

NL   0344296   NN PU

Lidforss, Bengt, 1868–1913.
... Ueber kinoplasmatische verbindungsfäden zwischen zellkern und chromatophoren, von Bengt Lidforss. Lund, H. Ohlssons buchdruckerei, 1908.
38, ₍2₎ p. iv pl. 29½ᶜᵐ. (Lunds universitets årsskrift. n. f., afd. 2, bd. 4, nr. 1)
K. Fysiografiska sällskapets handlingar. n. f., bd. 19, nr. 1. Bibliographical foot-notes.

1. Plant cells and tissues. 2. Chromatophores.
Title from John Crerar   Libr. 058   A 31–730
Library of Congress   [AS284.L8 n. f., afd. 2, bd. 4, nr. 1]

NL   0344297   ICJ MoU NcU NN

Lidforss, Bengt, 1868–1913.
Ur Bengt Lidforss' kvarlåtenskap; litterära uppsatser och recensioner. Malmö: Aktiebolaget Framtidens Bokförlag ₍1916₎. 268 p., 2 l. 2. ed. 12°.

1. Authors (Swedish). 2. Essays   (Swedish).
N. Y. P. L.   November 14, 1916.

NL   0344298   NN NjP MH

Lidforss, Bengt, 1868–1913.
Ur Bengt Lidforss' litterära kvarlåtenskap. Vetenskap och världsåskådning. Malmö: Framtidens Bokförlag ₍1917₎. 244 p., 2 l. 12°.

1. Science and religion. 2. Philos-   ophy (Swedish). 3. Rydberg,
Viktor, 1828–95. 4. Philosophy.—   Essays and misc.
N. Y. P. L.   September 25, 1918.

NL   0344299   NN NcU

Lidforss, Bengt, 1868–1913.
Ur Bengt Lidforss' litterära kvarlåtenskap. Dagsbilder. Malmö: Aktiebolaget Framtiden ₍1917₎. 242 p., 2 l. ₍2. ed₎ 12°.

1. Sociology.—Essays.
    October 7, 1918

NL   0344300   NN

Lidforss, Bengt, 1868–1913.
Utkast och silhuetter, av Bengt Lidforss. Malmö, Tryckeri-a.-b. Framtidens förlag, 1909.
3 p. l., ₍3₎–218 p., 1 l. 19½ᶜᵐ.
"Efterföljande uppsatser utgöra andra delen av ... 'Onda makter och goda'."
CONTENTS.—Barbariets renässans.—Sociala framtidsfrågor.—Gammal radikalism och ny.—Den döda punkten.—Karl Marx' livsverk.—En omvänd optimist.—Idéer och makter.—Arisk världsåskådning.—Charles Darwin.—F.° W. C. Areschoug.—David Bergendal.—Magnus Blix.—Oscar Levertin.—Emil Kléen.—Vid Victor Larssons grav.—Proletärpsykologi.
1. Swedish essays. 2. Social problems—Addresses, essays, lectures. I. Title.
    33–22001
Library of Congress   PT9875.L46U7 1909   839.746

NL   0344301   DLC CtY MH

Lidforss, Bengt, 1868–1913.
Utrikespolitiska vyer, av Bengt Lidforss. Malmö: Aktiebolaget Framtidens bokförlag₍, 1915₎. 99 p. 19½cm.

617006A.   1. Scandinavianism.
N. Y. P. L.   December 16, 1932

NL   0344302   NN

Lidforss, Bengt, 1868–1913.
... Vetenskap och världsåskådning. 2., förändrade uppl. Malmö, Aktiebolaget Framtiden ₍1917₎
274, ₍3₎ p. 20ᶜᵐ.
At head of title: Ur Bengt Lidforss' litterära kvarlåtenskap.

1. Science—Philosophy. I. Title.
Library of Congress   Q175.L5   21–4437

NL   0344303   DLC WaS ICJ

Lidforss, Bengt, 1868–1913.
Weitere beitraege sur kenntnis der psychroklinie. Lund., Phlesson, 1903.
73 p.

NL   0344304   PU

Lidforss, Bengt, 1868–1913.
... Weitere beiträge zur kenntnis der psychroklinie, von Bengt Lidforss. Lund, H. Ohlssons buchdruckerei, 1908.
18 p., 1 l. illus., iii pl. 29½ᶜᵐ. (Lunds universitets årsskrift. n. f., afd. 2, bd. 4, nr. 3)
K. Fysiografiska sällskapets handlingar. n. f., bd. 19, nr. 3. Bibliographical foot-notes.

1. Plants, Effect of temperature on. 2. Geotropism. 3. Growth (Plants) I. Title.
Title from John Crerar   Libr. 058   A 31–732
Library of Congress   [AS284.L8 n. f., afd. 2, bd. 4, nr. 3]

NL   0344305   ICJ MiU NcU NN

Lidforss, Bengt, 1868–1913.
... Die wintergrüne flora; eine biologische untersuchung, von Bengt Lidforss. Mit 4 tafeln. Lund, H. Ohlssons buchdruckerei, 1907.
76, ₍2₎ p. iv pl. 29½ᶜᵐ. (Lunds universitets årsskrift. n. f., afd. 2, bd. 2, nᵣr 13)
K. Fysiografiska sällskapets handlingar. n. f., bd. 2 ₍i. e. 17₎ nᵣr 13. Bibliographical foot-notes.

1. Evergreens. 2. Acclimatization (Plants) 3. Plants—Metabolism. I. Title.
Title from John Crerar   Libr. 058   A 31–642
Library of Congress   [AS284.L8 n. f., afd. 2, bd. 2, nr. 13]

NL   0344306   ICJ PU MoU NcU NN

Lidforss, Bengt, 1868–1913.
Zur physiologie des pflanzlichen Zellkernes. I. Über das Sichelstadium des Nucleolus. II. Über die Chromatophilie der Sexualkerne. Lund: E. Malmström, 1897. 1 p.l., 26 p., 2 l., 1 pl. (col'd). 4°. (Lund. Universitet. Acta universitatis Lundensis. Lunds universitets årsskrift. Tom. 33, afdeln. 2, ₍no. 11₎ 1897.)

One page of bibliography.

1. Botany (Physiological and   structural).
N. Y. P. L.   December 15, 1911.

NL   0344307   NN

Pamphlet
P
1576
Lidforss, Edvard, 1833–1910.
Anatole France; en studie. Stockholm, P. A. Norstedt ₍1904₎
47 p. 23cm. (Svenska humanistiska förbundets skrifter, 8)

1. France, Anatole, 1844–1924. I. Series: Svenska humanistiska förbundet. Skrifter, 8.

NL   0344308   NIC ICN

Bonaparte
Collection
No. 9410
Lidforss, Edvard, 1833–1910.
Beiträge zur kenntnis von dem gebrauch des konjunktivs im deutschen. Ein sprachgeschichtlicher versuch, der, als akademische lehrfähigkeitsprobe... öffentlich wird verteidigt werden. Mit einwilligung einer weit berühmten filosofischen fakultät der Universität Uppsala findet die verteidigung mittwoch den 26 februar 1862...im ökonomischen hör saale statt. Uppsala, 1862.

NL   0344309   ICN CU ICRL IU OCIW OU NcD

Lidforss, Edvard, 1833–1910, ed.
Los cantares de myo Cid. 1895
see under El Cid Campeador.

PC2825 **Lidforss, Edvard,** 1833–1910, ed.
.L7   Choix d'anciens textes français pub. par Eaouard Lidforss. Lund, F. Berling, 1877.
₍4₎, 96 p. 26x22ᶜᵐ.

1. French language—Old French—Texts.

NL   0344311   ICU IU

Lidforss, Edvard, 1833–1910.
... Dante, af Edvard Lidforss. Stockholm, H. Geber ₍1907₎
72 p. 19½ᵐ. (De största märkesmännen. vi)
Portrait on cover.

1. Dante Alighieri, 1265–1321.
₍Full name: Volter Edvard Lidforss
    33–22003
Library of Congress   PQ4340.L5   928.5

NL   0344312   DLC

Pamphlet
P
1779
Lidforss, Edvard, 1833–1910.
Gaston Boissier; en studie. Stockholm, P. A. Norstedt ₍1909₎
28 p. 23cm. (Svenska humanistiska förbundets skrifter, 15)

1. Boissier, Gaston, 1823–1908. I. Series: Svenska humanistiska förbundet. Skrifter, 15.

NL   0344313   NIC

Lidforss, Edvard, 1833–1910, ed.

Isla, José Francisco de, 1703–1781.
... Historia del famoso predicador fray Gerundio de Campazas, alias Zotes. 1. ed. entera, hecha sobre la ed. príncipe de 1758 y el manuscrito autógrafo del autor, por D. Eduardo Lidforss ... Leipzig, F. A. Brockhaus, 1885.

VOLUME 332

Lidforss, Edvard, 1833–1910.
Le mémorie di Giorgio Pallavicino giudicate
dal professore V.E. Lidfortt. Traduzione dallo
svedese. Torino, V. Bona, [188–?]
24 p.

NL 0344315 MH

Lidforss, Edvard, 1833–1910.
Observations sur l'usage syntaxique de Ronsard et de ses
contemporains, par W. Édouard Lidforss ... Avec une appendice contenant La defense et illustration de la langue françoise
de Ioachim du Bellay. Lund, Gleerup & c°. [1865]

2 p. l., 60, 36 p. 22ᶜᵐ.

1. Ronsard, Pierre de, 1524–1585. 2. French language—Hist.—16th
cent. I. Du Bellay, Joachim, 1525 (ca.)–1560. La defense et illustration de la langue françoise.
[Full name: Volter Edvard Lidforss]

Library of Congress   PQ1678.L5
                                        44–37862

NL 0344316 DLC MH MB PHC OClW PSC LU CtY ICN

[Lidforss, Edvard, 1833–1910, editor.]
VII anciens textes français, publiés d'après les meilleures leçons.
Lund, H. Ohlsson, 1866.
pp. (2), 45 +.
"Tirés à 150 exemplaires."
Signed "W. É. L."
Contents:— Serments de Strasbourg. — Cantilène en l'honneur de Sainte Eu-
lalie. — Fragment de Valenciennes. — Chanson de St. Alexis. — Lois de Guillaume
le Conquérant. — Li primiers livres des reis. — L'image dou monde.

[L., W. E.]

NL 0344317 MH

PQ6332
.S23A2
1905a

Lidforss, Edvard, 1833–1910, ed.

Cervantes Saavedra, Miguel de, 1547–1616.
Den sinnrike junkern Don Quijote af la Mancha. Öfvers.
och försedd med upplysande noter af Edvard Lidforss.
Jubileumssuppl. Stockholm, Fahlcrantz [1905]

[Bonaparte
Collection   Lidforss, Edvard, 1833–1910.
No. 9410
            A survey of the English conjugation...
With permission of the philosophical
faculty of the University of Uppsala,
to be publicly discussed at the econom-
ical auditory on Wednesday the 26:th
February 1862... Uppsala, 1862. (with
his Beiträge zur kenntnis von dem gebrauch des konjunktivs im deutschen...
1862)

NL 0344319 ICN OClW MH

PQ4204
.A3C6
vol. 127

Lidforss, Edvard, 1833–1910, ed.

Riva, Bonvesin da, 1240 (ca.)–1314?
Il tractato dei mesi, dato in luce per cura di Eduardo Lidforss. Bologna, G. Romagnoli, 1872.

PF3109   LIDFORSS, Edvard, 1833–1910.
.L7   Tysk grammatik för elementar-undervisningen af
         Wolter Edward Lidforss. Örebro, N.M.Lindh, 1860.
         viii,259,[1]p. 19½cm.

1.German language--Grammar.

NL 0344321 ICU

Lidforss, Volter Edvard, 1833–1910
    see Lidforss, Edvard, 1833–1910.

Lidforss af Geijerstam, Gärda
    see Geijerstam, Gärda (Lidforss) af.

Lidgate, John.

see

Lydgate, John, 1370?–1451?

QK
525.5   Lidgate, John M
.H3   A short synopsis of Hawaiian ferns.
L72   [n.p.,] 1873.
          14 p.

1.Ferns--Hawaii. I.Title.

NL 0344325 MiU MBH MB

LIDGE, Tchantchès d', pseud.

See TCHANTCHÈS D'LIDGE, pseud.

Lidgerwood manufacturing company

Bulletin.

Library has

NL 0344327 OrP

Lidgerwood manufacturing company.
Cableway sketches (2. ed.)... Hoisting and conveying devices
employed in construction of dams, piers, walls and sewers, also
for open pit mining, quarrying, logging, handling coal or packages
... New York, Lidgerwood mfg. co., 1894. 104 p. illus.
15 x 24cm.

1. Hoisting and conveying   machinery.
N.Y.P.L.   April 10, 1946

NL 0344328 NN

Lidgerwood manufacturing company.
... Cableways for hoisting and conveying...
employed in coaling at sea discharging vessels,
saving life at sea, quarrying, open pit mining,
log handling, logging by steam. N.Y. Lidgerwood mfg. co., 1908.
il. sq. Q.

NL 0344329 OrP

Lidgerwood manufacturing co.
... [Catalogue of] Lidgerwood manufacturing co., manufacturers of improved hoisting engines and boilers, suspension
cableways ... [New York, The Winthrop press] 1892 –1900.

v. illus. 30ᶜᵐ.

Title varies slightly.
Imprint varies.

1. Hoisting machinery—Catalogs.

Library of Congress   TJ1353.L69   0–4205 Revised

NL 0344330 DLC PPF

Lidgerwood manufacturing Co.
Catalogue of manufacturers of improved hoisting
engines "L" horisontal engines and superior
stationary and marine boilers.
n.p., 1889.
88 p.

NL 0344331 PU

LIDGERWOOD MANUFACTURING CO.
Hoisting engines and boilers, cableways, log
hauling machinery, hoisting and conveying appratus,
ballast unloaders. New York, 1902. 168 p. illus.
31cm.

Microfilm (master negative)
Positive in *ZV-95

NL 0344332 NN

Lidgerwood manufacturing co.
An illustrated description of a new device known as the
rapid unloader ...   New York, Lidgerwood manufacturing company
2. v. fronts., illus. 15 x 23–14 x 23ᶜᵐ.

1. Conveying machinery—Catalogs.

Library of Congress   TJ1353.L71   CA 7–6032 Unrev'd

NL 0344333 DLC

Lidgerwood Manufacturing Co.
An illustrated description of approved devices,
Logging by steam; employing improved systems...
    see under   Lidgerwood manufacturing
co. Logging machinery department.

Lidgerwood manufacturing co.
An illustrated description of approved devices for logging by steam ... manufactured exclusively by Lidgerwood manufacturing company ... [New York, Bartlett
& company, printers, 1893]
40 p. illus. 16 x 24ᶜᵐ.

1. Hoisting machinery—Catalogs. 2. Lumbering.

Library of Congress   TJ1353.L7   CA 7–6033 Unrev'd

NL 0344335 DLC

VOLUME 332

Lidgerwood manfacturing co.
Improved hoisting engines and boilers.
catalogue.
N.Y., 1884.
15 p.

NL 0344336   PPF

Lidgerwood Manufacturing Co.
.... Improved hoisting engines and boilers, cableways, log hauling machinery, hoisting and conveying apparatus, ballast unloaders. ... . New York, 1903.
168 p. illus. 30 x 23½ᶜᵐ.
At head of title: Lidgerwood Manufacturing Co.

NL 0344337   ICJ

Lidgerwood manufacturing co.
... The Lidgerwood cableway; a hoisting and conveying device employed in construction of canals, dry docks ... etc. ... New York, Lidgerwood manufacturing co., 1904.
1 p. l., 5–160 p., 1 l. illus. 29½ x 23ᶜᵐ.

1. Wire rope transportation.   6–23722

Library of Congress   TJ1385.L72 Copyright

NL 0344338   DLC

Lidgerwood Manufacturing Co.
Lidgerwood cableways, hoisting and conveying devices employed in canal and trench excavation, construction of dams, piers, walls, etc. Also for open pit mining, quarrying, logging, handling coal or packages. Manufactured under patents of Locke, Miller, Butters, North, Harris, Covell, Dickinson, Baptist, Delaney and others. ... . 107,[3] p. il. 1 pl. ob. S. New York 1895.

NL 0344339   ICJ

Lidgerwood Manfacturing co.
Lidgerwood cableways, hoisting and conveying devices.
N.Y., The company, 1898.
109 p.

NL 0344340   PPF

TJ385   Lidgerwood manufacturing co.
.L75   Lidgerwood cableways for hoisting and conveying
New York, 1912.

NL 0344341   DLC

Lidgerwood Manufacturing Co.
The Lidgerwood derrick. Derrick fittings and derrick engines. Lidgerwood Manufacturing Co. ... . New York, 1902.
64 p. illus. 30 x 23½ᶜᵐ.
——. The Lidgerwood cableway; a hoisting and conveying device employed in construction of canals, dry docks, locks, filter beds, piers, log handling, fortifications, open pit mining, quarrying, discharging vessels, etc. coaling at sea and logging by steam, cane hoists and the Lidgerwood transfer. Lidgerwood Manufacturing Co., ... New York, 1904.
160, [2] p. illus. 30 x 23½ᶜᵐ.
Bound together.

NL 0344342   ICJ

Lidgerwood Manufacturing Co.
Lidgerwood Manufacturing Co. Manufacturers of improved hoisting engines and boilers, suspension cableways, log hauling machinery, hoisting and conveying apparatus and Temperley transporters. 141,[1] p. il. sq. F. New York 1898, c. 1892.

NL 0344343   ICJ

Lidgerwood Manufacturing Co.
The Lidgerwood-Miller marine cableway for coaling in a seaway. New York, 1907. (1)4–48 p. illus. 4°.

1. Coaling of ships at sea.
N.Y.P.L.   March 21, 1912.

NL 0344344   NN

Lidgerwood manufacturing company.
Lidgerwood overhead cableway skidders of the tree rigged type. Bulletin no. 58. New York, N. Y., Chicago [etc.] Lidgerwood manufacturing company [ᶜ1917]
31 p. illus. 30ᶜᵐ.

1. Hoisting machinery—Catalogs. 2. Conveying machinery—Catalogs. 3. Lumbering.   I. Title.

Library of Congress   TJ1353.L714   17–13627

NL 0344345   DLC

Lidgerwood manufacturing co.
Lidgerwood portable high spar skidders for overhead skidding. Bulletin no. 55. New York, N. Y., Chicago [etc.] Lidgerwood manufacturing company [ᶜ1915]
15, [1] p. illus. 30ᶜᵐ.

1. Hoisting machinery—Catalogs. 2. Conveying machinery—Catalogs. 3. Lumbering.
     15–22716

Library of Congress   TJ1353.L715

NL 0344346   DLC

Lidgerwood Manufacturing Co.
.... Rapid unloader for discharging dirt, ballast, ore, etc., from flat cars in railroad work ... . Manufactured exclusively by Lidgerwood Manufacturing Company under an exclusive license from the Rapid Unloader & Equipment Co. of New York City. ... . Second edition, June, 1903. [New York, The Duyster Press, 1903.]
48 p. illus. 15½ x 24ᶜᵐ.
At head of title: The Lidgerwood Manufacturing Company.

NL 0344347   ICJ

[Lidgerwood manufacturing co.]
Sketches of the hoisting and conveying devices employed in open pit mining, quarrying and construction work ... [New York, Bartlett & company, printers, 1892]
40 p. illus. 16 x 24ᶜᵐ.
Copyright by the Lidgerwood manufacturing co.

1. Conveying machinery—Catalogs. I. Title.

Library of Congress   TJ1353.L72   CA 7–6034 Unrev'd
     (Copyright 1892: 12653)

NL 0344348   DLC PPF

[Lidgerwood manufacturing co.]
Sketches of the hoisting and conveying devices employed in phosphate mining ... [New York, Lidgerwood manufacturing co., ᶜ1891]
32 p. illus. 15½ x 24ᶜᵐ.

1. Wire rope transportation. I. Title.

Library of Congress   TJ1385.L73   6–36501†

NL 0344349   DLC

[Lidgerwood Manufacturing Company.]
The traveling cableway, and some other devices employed by contractors on the Chicago main drainage canal. [New York, cop. 1895.] 72 p. front., diagrs., illus., plan. ob. 24°.

1. Chicago Drainage Canal. 2. Title.
N.Y.P.L.   May 14, 1919.

NL 0344350   NN

SD538   **Lidgerwood Manufacturing Company.**
qL48   Skidding logs. New York [ᶜ1918–19]
     1 v. (various pagings) illus. 30cm.
VAULT   (Its Bulletin, no.59–63)

     1. Lumbering – Machinery. I. Title.
Series.

NL 0344351   OrCS

Lidgerwood manufacturing co. *Logging machinery department.*
An illustrated description of approved devices. Logging by steam; employing improved systems under the patents of Baptist, Beekman, Miller, Dickinson and others. New York [etc.] The Logging machinery department of the Lidgerwood manufacturing company, 1905.
1 p. l., 5–127 p. illus. 29½ᶜᵐ.

1. Lumbering.   5–26961

Library of Congress   SD538.L7

NL 0344352   DLC MH NN NjP OrP NIC ICJ MB

Lidgerwood manufacturing co., *Chicago.*
Lidgerwood-Crawford scraper bucket excavator [catalog]
Chicago, Lidgerwood manufacturing co.
1 v. illus. 31ᶜᵐ.
Only latest number received is kept on shelf.

1. Excavating machinery—Catalogs.   CA 11–1335 Unrev'd

Library of Congress   TA737.L6

NL 0344353   DLC

TN870
L42   **Lidgett, Albert**
     Petroleum. London, Pitman [1919?]
     vii, 168 p. illus., diagrs., tables.
     18 cm. (Pitman's common commodities and industries)

     1. Petroleum. 2. Petroleum industry and trade.

NL 0344354   DI NN ICRL

VOLUME 332

Lidgett, Albert.
... Petroleum, by Albert Lidgett ... London, New York ⌜etc.⌝ I. Pitman & sons, ltd. ⌜1919⌝
vii, 168 p. front., illus., diagrs. 19cm. (Pitman's common commodities and industries)

1. Petroleum.
G S 19—345
U. S. Geol. survey. Library 467 L6
for Library of Congress [TN870.L]

NL 0344355 DI-GS CU NIC OU OLak OCU OCl ICJ MB PPFRB

Lidgett, Albert.
... Petroleum, by Albert Lidgett ... London, New York ⌜etc.⌝ Sir I. Pitman & sons, ltd. ⌜192-⌝
vii, 166 p. front., illus. 18½cm. (Pitman's common commodities and industries)

1. Petroleum. 2. Petroleum—Gt. Brit.
26-1891
Library of Congress TN870.L45

NL 0344356 DLC

Lidgett,Albert
Petroleum. London.1928.

NL 0344357 NjN DN

Lidgett, Albert, 1876–
Petroleum, by Albert Lidgett ... 3d ed., rev. and enl. London, New York ⌜etc.⌝ Sir I. Pitman & sons, ltd., 1928.
xii, 160 p. incl. front., illus. 21½cm.

1. Petroleum. 2. Petroleum engineering.
28-31200
Library of Congress TN870.L45 1928

NL 0344358 DLC DI NcD MiU OClh OClW NN PU PV PBm

Lidgett, Albert, ed.
The **Petroleum** times. v. 1– Jan. 11, 1919–
⌜London, A. Lidgett, 1919–

Lidgett, Albert
Vanstone, John Henry.
The raw materials of commerce; a descriptive account of the vegetable, animal, mineral and synthetic products of the world and of their commercial uses, by J. Henry Vanstone ... with contributions by J. P. Gilmour ... Albert Lidgett ... John Roberts ... J. C. Sachs ... London, New York ⌜etc.⌝ Sir I. Pitman & sons, ltd., 1929.

Lidgett, Elizabeth S.
An ancient people; a short sketch of Armenian history, by Elizabeth S. Lidgett. London, J. Nisbet & co., limited, 1897.
xi, ⌜1⌝, 64 p. incl. front., illus. (map.) 17½cm.

1. Armenia—Church history.

NL 0344361 MiU PPT NNUN PPL

Lidgett, Elizabeth S. Poor law children and the departmental committee. 16 pp. (*Contemp. Rev.* v. 71, 1897, p. 205.)

NL 0344362 MdBP

RD5 **Lidgett, John Scott,** 1854–1953.
L619c The Christian religion, its meaning and proof, by J. Scott Lidgett. London, R. Culley ⌜1907⌝
xv, 516 p. 23 cm.

"This book forms the sequel to my former work, entitled The fatherhood of God in Christian truth and life."—Pref.
Bibliographical footnotes.

1. Christian evidences. 2. Experience (Religion) I. Title.

NL 0344363 CtY-D MH

Lidgett, John Scott, 1854–
The Christian religion, its meanings and proof, by J. Scott Lidgett ... New York, Eaton & Mains; Cincinnati, Jennings & Graham ⌜c1907⌝
xiv p., 2 l., 3–516 p. 23½cm.
"This book forms the sequel to my former work, entitled The fatherhood of God in Christian truth and life."—Pref.

1. Christianity—Essence, genius, nature. 2. Apologetics—20th cent. I. Title.
7-37982
Library of Congress BR121.L5

NL 0344364 DLC OrSaW OrP OO ODW NN PPC PPLT

Lidgett, John Scott, 1854–
The fatherhood of God in Christian truth and life, by J. Scott Lidgett ... Edinburgh, T. & T. Clark, 1902.
xxiv, 427 p. 23½ cm.

1. God—Fatherhood. I. Title.
BT101.L5 3—7792

NL 0344365 DLC CtY OO ODW NNUT NcD NjNbS

Lidgett, John Scott, 1854-1953.
The fatherhood of God in Christian truth and life...
[2d ed.] London, Charles H. Kelly [1913]
427 p.

NL 0344366 PPEB

Lidgett, John Scott, 1854–
God and man, by Dr. J. Scott Lidgett. London, The Epworth press (E. C. Barton) ⌜1944⌝
85, ⌜1⌝ p., 1 l. 19cm.
"First published in 1944."

1. God. 2. Religion—Philosophy. I. Title.
45-14645
Library of Congress BT165.L5
⌜3⌝ 231

NL 0344367 DLC NjPT

BL200
.L5
Lidgett, John Scott, 1854–
God and the world; essays in Christian theism, by Dr. J. Scott Lidgett. London, The Epworth press ⌜1943⌝
156 p. 19½cm.
"First published in 1943."

1. Theism. I. Title.
44-33467
Library of Congress BL200.L5
⌜2⌝

NL 0344368 DLC NcD NjPT PPWe

Lidgett, John Scott, 1854–
God, Christ and the church, by J. Scott Lidgett ... London, Hodder and Stoughton limited, 1927.
320 p. 20cm.

1. God. 2. Jesus Christ. 3. Christian union. I. Title.
28-16249
Library of Congress BR121.L52
⌜3⌝

NL 0344369 DLC

Lidgett, John Scott, 1854–
God in Christ Jesus; a study of St. Paul's Epistle to the Ephesians, by J. Scott Lidgett ... London, C. H. Kelly ⌜1915⌝
xi, 388 p. 21½cm.

I. Title.
17-5706
Library of Congress

NL 0344370 DLC OO

Lidgett, John Scott, 1854–
The idea of God and social ideals...by J. Scott Lidgett... London: The Epworth press ⌜1938⌝ 111 p. 22cm. (The social service lecture, 1938.)

970845A. 1. Sociology, Christian. 2. Kingdom of God. 3. Prophecies, Biblical. I. Title. II. Ser.
N. Y. P. L. December 23, 1938

NL 0344371 NN

Div.S. Lidgett, John Scott, 1854-1953.
232 Jesus Christ is alive, by J. Scott
L714J Lidgett. London, Epworth Press ⌜1948⌝
72 p. 19 cm.

1. Jesus Christ. Person and offices. I. Title.

NL 0344372 NcD

Lidgett, John Scott, 1854-
Compton-Rickett, Arthur, 1869– *ed.*
Joseph Compton-Rickett; a memoir, ed. by Arthur Compton-Rickett, with a foreword by the Rt. Hon. David Lloyd George, O. M. Bournemouth, E. Cooper, 1922.

Lidgett, John Scott, 1854– *ed.*
Methodism in the modern world, by members of the Methodist churches. Edited by J. Scott Lidgett ... and Bryan H. Reed, B. D. London, The Epworth press ⌜etc., 1929⌝
286 p. 22½cm.
"First edition."
CONTENTS.—The rise and progress of Methodism, by W. T. A. Barber.—God and man, by E. S. Waterhouse.—The person of Our Lord Jesus Christ, by J. S. Lidgett.—The atonement, by W. F. Lofthouse.—The work of the Holy Spirit, by A. L. Humphries.—Religious experience, by Atkinson Lee.—The church, by A. W. Harrison.—Methodist evangelism, by J. E. Rattenbury.—Methodism and modern society, by E. C. Urwin.—Methodism and the world missionary task, by C. P. Groves.—Methodism and modern youth, by J. Rounsefell.—Methodism today and tomorrow, by Richard Pyke.
1. Methodism—Addresses, essays, lectures. I. Reed, Bryan H., joint ed. II. Title.
32-9246
Library of Congress BX8215.L5
⌜2⌝ 287.08

CtY NcD
NL 0344374 DLC KyLxCB MH-AH NN CSaT IaU IEG MBrZ

VOLUME 332

Lidgett, John Scott.
The modern social problem.
(In Christ and civilization ... Pp. 3-42. London. 1910.)

H3856 — T.r. —Sociology

NL   0344375   MB 00

Lidgett, John Scott, 1854-
My guided life, by J. Scott Lidgett ... London, Methuen & co., ltd. [1936]
vii, 279 [1] p. front. (port.) 22½ᶜᵐ.

I. Title.

Library of Congress   BX8495.L49A3 1936
Copyright A ad int. 2130⁹   [2]   922.742

36-9461

NL   0344376   DLC NN

LU70   **Lidgett, John Scott,** 1854-1953.
L619r   Reminiscences. London, Epworth press
[pref. 1928]
95 p. port. 22 cm.

"The following pages have already appeared in a series of articles contributed to the Methodist magazine." - Pref.

NL   0344377   CtY-D NcD NN CtY

FX93   **Lidgett, John Scott,** 1854-1953.
L619s   Salvation as proclaimed by prophets, apostles
and by Our Lord Jesus Christ. London, Epworth press [1952]
54 p. 18 cm.

NL   0344378   CtY-D

Lidgett, John Scott, 1854-1953.
The social teaching of the Bible
see under   Keeble, Samuel Edward, 1853-

Lidgett, John Scott, 1854-
Sonship and salvation; a study of the Epistle to the Hebrews, by J. Scott Lidgett ... London, The Epworth press [1921]
275 p. 23ᶜᵐ.

1. Bible. N. T. Hebrews—Criticism, interpretation, etc.   I. Title.

Title from General Theol.   Sem. Printed by L. C.   A 22-357

NL   0344380   NNUT IEG PPPD

Lidgett, John Scott
The spiritual principle of the Atonement...
The 27th Fernley lecture.
London, 1897.
498 p.

NL   0344381   PPWe PPEB

Lidgett, John Scott, 1854-1953.
The spiritual principle of the atonement... 4th ed.
London, Charles H. Kelly [pref. 1897]
xxiii, 498 p.   21 cm.

NL   0344382   NcD NRCR

BT265   LIDGETT,JOHN SCOTT,1854-
.L72   The spiritual principle of the atonement as a satis-faction made to God for the sins of the world; being the twenty-seventh Fernley lecture delivered in Leeds, July,1897,by John Scott Lidgett... 2d ed. London,C. H.Kelly,1898.
xxiii,498 p. 22½cm.

1.Atonement.

NL   0344383   ICU NRCR CtY-D CtY

---

241   Lidgett, John Scott, 1854-
117   The spiritual principle of the Atonement
L634   as a satisfaction made to God for the sins of
p3ed   the world; being the 27th Fernley lecture, delivered in Leeds, July, 1897.   3d ed.
London, Charles H. Kelly, 1901.
498p 22cm

NL   0344384   MnCS PPPD 00

Lidgett, John Scott, 1854-
The spiritual principle of the atonement as a satisfaction made to God for the sins of the world ... by John Scott Lidgett. Fourth edition. Cincinnati, Jennings & Graham; New York, Eaton & Mains. [1907]
xxiii, 498 p. 22cm. (The 27th Fernley lecture)

Atonement. I.   le.

NL   0344385   DAU TxFTC NcD PPT InAndC-T

232.3   Lidgett, John Scott, 1854-
L619s   The spiritual principle of the atonement as
1907   a satisfaction made to God for the sins of
the world. 4th ed.   London R. Culley [1907]
498p.   (The 27th Fernley lecture)

1. Atonement. I. Title.

NL   0344386   TxFTC

Lidgett, John Scott, 1854-   **joint ed.**

Carlyle, Alexander James, 1861-   ed.
Towards reunion; being contributions to mutual understanding by Church of England and Free church writers ... London, Macmillan and co., limited, 1919.

Lidgett, John Scott, 1854-1953.
The Victorian transformation of theology.
Foreword by W. Foxley Norris. [1st ed.]
London, Epworth Press [1934]
96 p. 19ᶜᵐ. (Maurice lectures, 1934)

1.Theology, Doctrinal - Hist. - 19th cent. I.Title. ser.: London. University. King's College. Maurice lectures, 1934)
NUC

IU TxU
NL   0344388   CSt CaBVaU CLSU CtY-D PPWe IaU MWelC

Lidgey, Charles Albert, d. 1924.
Album of ten songs, composed by C. A. Lidgey... [Op. 1, no. 1-5. Op. 2, no. 1-5]   London: Pitt & Hatzfeld [188-?]   48 p. 27½cm.

For 1 voice with piano acc. English words.
Composer's autographed presentation copy to David Bispham.
CONTENTS.—In absence (Goethe).—Lullaby; The starlings (Charles Kingsley).—Dream-fancies (Dora Beck).—The constant lover.—"A widow bird state mourning;" "One word is too often profaned;" I arise from dreams of thee; Music, when soft voices die (Shelley).—To Constance (Richard Garnett).

BISPHAM BEQUEST.
1. Songs, English.
N.Y.P.L.   December 15, 1939

NL   0344389   NN

Lidgey, Charles Albert, d. 1924.
A lover's moods; a song cycle. The words by Herrick, Sir Thomas Wyatt, Francis Davison, and others. The music composed by C. A. Lidgey... London: Boosey & Co., cop. 1903.
Publ. pl. no. H. 3902.   34 p.   f°.

English words; music for 1 voice with piano acc.
CONTENTS: The lover singeth in praise of his ladye. He entertaineth hope of her favour. He complaineth that he is forsaken. He professeth indifference. He craveth his ladye's forgiveness. He protesteth his constancy.

1. Songs, English. 2. Songs—Song   cycles. 3. Title.
N.Y.P.L.   October 5, 1928

NL   0344390   NN

LSette of
Odd Volumes
L4   Lidgey, Charles Albert, d. 1924
[Ye marche of ye Odd Volumes]
Marche of ye Odd Volumes. London, 1898.
7p.   33cm.

For piano.

I.Title.

NL   0344391   IEN

Lidgey, Charles Albert, d. 1924.
Richard Wagner and 'Der ring des Nibelungen'. A paper read before ye Sette of odd volumes January 28th, 1908, by Charles A. Lidgey, gleeman and secretary of ye Sette ... [London], 1908.
71, [1] p. illus. (music) 15 x 10½ᵐ. (Half-title: Privately printed opuscula issued to members of the Sette of odd volumes. no. 57 [i. e. 58])

"This edition is limited to 249 copies and is imprynted for private circulation only."

1. Wagner, Richard. Der ring des Nibelungen.
20-19634 Revised
Library of Congress   ACI.85 no. LVIII

NL   0344392   DLC MH

Lidgey, Charles Albert, d. 1924.
A song of life; cycle of seven songs. The words by W. E. Henley... The music by C. A. Lidgey... London: Boosey & Co., cop. 1909.   Publ. pl. no. H. 6315.   27 p.   f°.

English words; music for 1 voice with piano acc.
CONTENTS: A sigh sent wrong. The wind on the wold. All in a garden green. Sing to me. Gray hills. Out of the night. Dearest, when I am dead.

1. Songs, English. 2. Songs—Song   cycles. 3. Henley, William Ernest, 1849-1903. 4. Title.
N.Y.P.L.   October 5, 1928

NL   0344393   NN

Lidgey, Charles A.
Wagner.   London: J. M. Dent & Co., 1899.   xv, 268 p., 1 fold. fac., 5 pl., 2 port.   fac.   12°.   (The master musicians.)

Music in text.

CENTRAL RESERVE.
I. Wagner, Wilhelm Richard. 2. Se-   ries.
N.Y.P.L.   August 27, 1914.

NL   0344394   NN OO NcC OCl OCU MH NIC IU

VOLUME 332

Lidgey, Charles Albert, *d.* 1924.
Wagner, by Charles A. Lidgey; with illustrations and portraits. London, J. M. Dent & co.; New York, E. P. Dutton & co., 1904.

xv, 287, ₁₁ p. front., illus., plates, ports., double facsim. 19 cm. (*Half-title:* The master musicians; ed. by F. J. Crowest)

"First edition December, 1899 ... third edition May, 1904."
"Chronological list of Wagner's compositions": p. 247-252.
"Literary works": p. 253-255.

1. Wagner, Richard, 1813-1883.

ML410.W1L5   5—41732

NL 0344395   DLC OrU CaBVaU

Lidgey, Charles Albert, *d.* 1924.
Wagner, by Charles A. Lidgey; with illustrations and portraits. London, J. M. Dent & co.; New York, E. P. Dutton & co., 1907.

xv, 287, ₁₁ p. front., illus., plates, ports., double facsim. 19ᶜᵐ. (*Half-title:* The master musicians; ed. by F. J. Crowest)

"First edition December, 1899 ... third edition November, 1907."
"Chronological list of Wagner's compositions": p. 247-252.
"Literary works": p. 253-255.

NL 0344396   NjR CU Or

780.923 Lidgey, Charles Albert, d.1924.
W12ℓi   Wagner, by Charles A. Lidgey; with illustra-
1911   tions and portraits.   London, J. M. Dent &
          sons, ltd.; ₁etc., etc.₁ 1911.
          267p. front., illus., plates, ports., double
          facsim.   (Half-title: The master musicians;
          ed. by F. J. Crowest)
          "First edition December, 1899 ... Fourth edition
          April, 1911."
          Chronological list of Wagner's compositions":
          p.247-252.
          "Literary works": p.253-255.
          1. Wagner, Richard, 1813-1883.

NL 0344397   IU CaBViP ViU

Lidgey, Charles Albert, d. 1924.
      Wagner. [5th edition.]
—   London. J. M. Dent & Sons Ltd. 1921. xv, 267, (1) pp. Portraits. Plates. Facsimiles. Tables. [The master musicians.] 18 cm., in 8s.

N7595 — S.r. — Wagner, Wilhelm Richard, 1813-1883.

NL 0344398   MB

Lidgey, E.

Victoria, *Australia. Dept. of mines.*
... Report of lecture on the deep leads of Victoria, and some indications of ore deposits, by E. Lidgey, field geologist. Melbourne, R. S. Brain, government printer ₁1898₁

Lidg'i, Sofia
      see
      Lidji, Sofia.

Lidhja së Artistëve të Shqipërisë.
      Nëndori; revistë letrare, artistike, shoqërore
politike
      see under title

Lidhja së Artistëve të Shqipërisë
      see also
      Lidhja së Shkrimtarëve dhe Artistëve të Shqipërisë.

AP95   Lidhja së Shkrimtarëve dhe Artistëve të
.A3N4   Shqipërisë.

Nëndori; revistë letrare, artistike, shoqërore, politike. 1.–
      Jan. 1954–
      ₁Tiranë₁

Lidhja së Shkrimtarëve dhe Artistëve të Shqipërisë
      see also
      Lidhja së Artistëve të Shqipërisë.
      Lidhja së Shkrimtarëve të Shqipërisë.

AP95   Lidhja së Shkrimtarëve të Shqipërisë.
.A3N4

Nëndori; revistë letrare, artistike, shoqërore, politike. 1.–
      Jan. 1954–
      ₁Tiranë₁

Lidhja së Shkrimtarëve të Shqipërisë
      see also
      Lidhja së Shkrimtarëve dhe Artistëve të Shqipërisë.

Lidhjes së Artistëve të Shqipërisë
      see Lidhja së Artistëve të Shqipërisë.

Lidhjes së Shkrimtarëve dhe Artistëve të Shqipërisë
      see Lidhja së Shkrimtarëve dhe Artistëve
të Shqipërisë.

Lidhjes së Shkrimtarëve të Shqipërisë
      see Lidja së Shkrimtarëve të Sqipërisë.

PT   Lidholm, A
9993   Karl femtonde och vallehärsbonden; eller,
.0515   Kungsskjutsen till Varnhems kyrka. Skildring
          ur verkligheten, af A. Lidholm. Chicago,
          Engberg-Holmberg Pub. Co., 1901.
          45 p. illus. 17 cm.

          1. Karl XV, King of Sweden, 1826-1872--
          Fiction. 2. Children's stories, Swedish. I.
          Title.

NL 0344410   MnHi

Lidholm, Andreas, respondent.
      Vindiciae verae patriae Normannorum ...
          see under Lagerbring, Sven, 1707-1787,
praeses.

Lidholm, Benjamin.
      Medelplana och Västerplana kyrkor, jämte kortfattad beskrivning av församlingens kyrkogårdar och prästboställe m. m., av Benjamin Lidholm.   Lidköping, Författarens förlag ₁1950₁
102 p.   illus.   23cm.

"Källor," p. 100.

1. Västerplana. Sweden—Churches.   2. Medelplana, Sweden—Churches.

NL 0344412   NN

Lidholm, Ingvar, 1921–
      ₁Concerto, string orchestra₁
      Concerto för stråkorkester. Partitur. ₁n. p., ᵗ1949₁
score (28 p.) 36 cm.
Reproduced from ms.

1. String-orchestra music—Scores.

M1145.L717C6   49—54621*

NL 0344413   DLC

Lidholm, Ingvar.
      ₁Concerto, string orchestra₁
      Concerto för stråkorkester. Stockholm, C. Gehrman ₁1951₁
score (24 p.) 32 cm.
Cover title.
Duration: 14 min.
Lacks the 3d movement, Molto tranquillo, of the unpublished version.

1. String-orchestra music—Scores.

M1145.L717C6 1951   52—67433

NL 0344414   DLC ICN IU

Lidholm, Ingvar.
      ₁Songs₁
      Fem ₁i. e. sex₁ sånger ... ₁Stockholm₁ Föreningen svenska tonsättare ₁1946₁
9 p. 34 cm. (Svenska sånger, tryckta som manuskript, ser. 2)

CONTENTS.—För vilsna fötter sjunger gräset (Hjalmar Gullberg)—Vid medelhavet (Hjalmar Gullberg)—Den sista kvällen (Hjalmar Gullberg)—Saga (Erik Härninge)—Jungfrulin (Erik Härninge)—Madonnans vaggvisa (Lope de Vega, tr. by K. A. Hagberg)

1. Songs (Medium voice) with piano.

M1621.L   48—12601*

NL 0344415   DLC

LIDHOLM, INGVAR, 1921–
[STYCKEN, VIOLONCELLO & PIANO]
Frya stycken för cello och piano. Quattro pezzi per violoncello e pianoforte, 1955. [1955?] score (16 p.) and part. 33cm.

Reproduced from holograph.

1. Violoncello and piano.

NL 0344416   NN

Lidholm, Ingvar, 1921–
      Trios, strings (1953)
      Liten stråktrio (1953) för violin, viola och celle. Stockholm, Gehrman [c1955] Pl.no.C.G.4982

Score (6 p.)

NL 0344417   MH

VOLUME 332

M23
L712
Lidholm, Ingvar
[Sonata, piano (1947)]
Sonata per pianoforte.   Stockholm, C.
Gehrmans [c1948]
20 p.   31cm.

1. Sonatas (Piano)

NL   0344418   CoU MH

M25
L54M5
Lidholm, Ingvar.
[Miniatures, piano]
10 [i.e. tia] miniatyrer för piano.
Stockholm, C. Gehrmans Musikförlag [c1948]
10 p   31cm.
Cover title.

1. Piano music.

NL   0344419   CoU MH

LIDHOLM, INGVAR, 1921-

Toccata e Canto för orkester.   [Stockholm,
C. Gehrmans musikförlag, c1948]   score(23 p.)   31cm.
(Nordiska toner för orkester)

For chamber orchestra.

1. Chamber orchestra.

NL   0344420   NN MH

Lidholm de Oliveira, Oscar.
Os dizimos eclesiásticos do Brasil, nos
períodos da Colonia e do Império.   [Roma,
1939]
157 p.   illus.   24cm.
Diss. - Pont. Univ. Gregoriana, Rome.
"Fontes & Bibliografia": p. [153]-157.

1. Tithes--Brazil.   2. Church and state
in Brazil.   I. Title.

NL   0344421   DCU

Lidholm de Oliveira, Oscar.
... Trabalhos em madeira, Caderno n. 1[-8]   S. Paulo, Em-
prêsa editora brasileira [1940]

8 v.   illus. diagrs. 26½ᵐ.   (Série técnica de trabalhos manuais: artes
industriais e domésticas ... organizada com a colaboração de J. T. Araujo
... e J. B. Salles da Silva)
Cover-title.

1. Woodwork.   I. Title.

Library of Congress   TT180.L5
                              [2]   43-21909
                                                              684

NL   0344422   DLC

Lidia, Palmiro de, pseud.
See
Valle, Adrian del, 1872-

La Lidia; revista gráfica taurina.   año 1-
(núm. 1-   ) ; nov. 27,1942-
México, D. F., 1942-
v. in   illus. (incl. ports.)   32ᵐ.   weekly.

1. Bull-fights—Period

GV1107.A145   791.8   46-45249

NL   0344424   DLC NN

La LIDIA; revista taurina ilustrada.   Año 1-19; abr.
1882-nov. 1900.   Madrid.   19 v. in 10.   col. illus.
(part fold.)   29-42cm.

Weekly (Apr.-Nov.)
Subtitle varies.
DLC: YA 2986
1. Bull-fights—Per. and soc. publ.

NL   0344425   NN DLC

Lidia.   Dramma per musica...
see under   Trento, Vittorio, 1761?-1833?

Lidice.   [Prague, 1945?]
[11] p.   plates.   34 cm.
"Speech delivered by President E. Beneš at Lidice, June 10th, 1945":
p. [7]-[11]

1. Lidice, Czechoslovak Republic.   2. World War, 1939-1945—Atrocities.   3. World War, 1939-1945—Pictorial works.   I. Beneš, Edvard,
Pres. Czechoslovak Republic, 1884-

D804.G4L48   940.54056   47-28366*

NL   0344427   DLC NNC NjP

Lidice, čin krvavého a porušeni žákonu...
see under   Czechoslovak Republic.   Odbor
pro politické zpravodajstvi.

Lidice memorial committee, inc., New York.
Lidice; a memorial from the people of the United States to the
people of Czechoslovakia.   [New York, Lidice memorial committee, 1942]   8 l.   illus.   23 x 31cm.

1. Lidice, Czecho-Slovakia.   2. World war, 1939-1945—Atrocities
—Czecho-Slovakia—Lidice.
N. Y. P. L.   June 15, 1948

NL   0344429   NN

D 804
.G4 L 7
LIDICE SHALL LIVE; MEMORIAL TO THE MARTYRED
and monument to victory.   Prague, Společnost
pro Obnovu Lidic, Association for the Restoration of Lidice, 1947.
28 p.   16 plates.
TRANSLATORS: M. Pichová
F. E Keary.

1. World War,1939-1945--Czechoslovak Republic--
Lidice.   2. World War,1939-1945--Atrocities.
I. Společnost pro   Obnovu Lidic,Prague.

NL   0344430   InU CU

Lidie von Wendlant; ein bürgerliches Trauerspiel in
fünf Aufzügen.   Wien, Gerold, 1781
94 p.
Photoreproduction of copy in the Österreichischer
Nationalbibliothek, Vienna

NL   0344431   MH

Lidin, pseud.
see
Liadov, Martyn Nikolaevich, 1872-1947.

Lidin (Georges) [1852-   ].   *Coup d'œil sur la
climatologie et la pathologie du Sénégal.   70
pp., 1 l.   4°.   Paris, 1882, No. 172.

NL   0344433   DNLM PPC

TN305
.G3
Lidin, Georgiĭ Dmitrievich, ed.
Газообильность каменноугольных шахт СССР.   Ответствен-
ный редактор А. А. Скочинский.   Москва, Изд-во Ака-
демии наук СССР. 1949-

Lidin, Georgiĭ Dmitrievich.
Газовыделения в угольных шахтах и меры борьбы с
ними.   Из цикла лекций "Новости горной техники."
Под общей ред. А. М. Терпигорева.   Москва, Угле-
техиздат, 1952.
58, [5] p.   illus.   22 cm.
At head of title: Министерство угольной промышленности
СССР. Дом инженера и техника им. Ф. Э. Дзержинского.   Г. Д.
Лидин.
Bibliography: p. [55]
1. Mine gases.   2. Mine ventilation.   I. Title.
Title romanized: Gazovydeleniia
v ugol'nykh shakhtakh.

TN305.L5   54-27888

NL   0344435   DLC

AC
855
Lidin, Olavus, resp.
...Dissertatio academica de conjugationibus
Graecis ...
see under
Dahl, Christoph, pr.

AC
855
Lidin, Olavus   resp.
Dissertatio de ecclesia graeca ejusque a
romano-catholica dissensu ...
see under
Fant, Erik Mikael, 1754-1817.   pr.

Lidin, Vladimir Germanovich, 1894-
(Sobranie sochineniĭ)
Собрание сочинений.   Москва, Гос. изд-во, 1929-
v.   27 cm.
At head of title, v.   : Вл. Лидин.

PG3476.L56 1929   73-336384

NL   0344438   DLC

VOLUME 332

Lidin, Vladimir Germanovich, 1894–   ed.

Актеры и режиссеры, "театральная Россия." Составлена при ближайшем участии С. Кара-Мурза и Ю. Соболева редакция В. Лидина. Москва, "Современные проблемы" Н. А. Столляр, 1928–

Lidin, Vladimir Germanovich, 1894–
The apostate, by Vladimir Lidin; translated by Helen Chrouschoff Matheson. London ¡etc.¡ J. Cape ¡1931¡

4 p. l., 11–336 p. 20^{cm}.

American edition (New York, London, Harper & brothers) has title: The price of life.

ɪ. Matheson, Elena Nikolaevna (Khrushchova) 1872–   tr.   ɪɪ. Title.
¡Name originally: Vladimir Germanovich Gomberg¡
31–16914 Revised

Library of Congress   PZ3.L6199Ap
¡r43d2¡   891.73

NL 0344440   DLC CtY MU CaBVaU

Lidin, Vladimir Germanovich, 1894–
Azure cities; stories of new Russia
see under title

Lidin, Vladimir Germanovich, 1894–
¡Bol'shaíà reka¡
Большая река. Москва, Худож. лит-ра, 1938.

278 p. 17 cm.

At head of title: Вл. Лидин.

ɪ. Title.

PG3476.L56B6   73–206071

NL 0344442   DLC

PG3476
.L56D9

Lidin, Vladimir Germanovich, 1894–
Две жизни; роман. Москва, Советский писатель, 1950.

189 p. 21 cm.

ɪ. Title.   *Title transliterated:* Dve zhizni.
Name originally: Vladimir Germanovich Gomberg.

PG3476.L56D9   50–55863

NL 0344443   DLC

D811
.L44

Lidin, Vladimir Germanovich, 1894–   ed.
... Говорят документы. ¡Казань¡ Советский писатель, 1941.

39, ¡1¡ p. 16^{cm}.

At head of title: Вл. Лидин.

1. World war, 1939–   —Personal narratives, German.   ɪ. Title.
Title transliterated: Govorîàt dokumenty.
¡Name originally: Vladimir Germanovich Gomberg¡
44–16555

Library of Congress   D811.L44

NL 0344444   DLC

PG3476
.L56V48
Hebraic
Sect.

Lidin, Vladimir Germanovich, 1894–
גרױסער אָדער שטילער, ראָמאַן ¡פֿון רוסיש. י. פֿרידמאַן,
מינסק, מעלוכע־פֿאַרלאַג פֿון װײסרוסלאַנד. נאַצסעקסיע.
¡Minsk¡ 1936.

363 p. 18 cm.

ɪ. Title.   *Title transliterated:* Groyser oder shtiler.
Name originally: Vladimir Germanovich Gomberg.

PG3476.L56V48   53–47927

NL 0344445   DLC

PG3476
L56
I3

Lidin, Vladimir Germanovich, 1894–
Idut korabli; roman. Riga, "Gramatu draugs", 1930.

198 p. 20 cm.   (Biblioteka novieĭsheĭ literatury, tom 91)

NL 0344446   RPB

Lidin, Vladimir Germanovich, 1894–
¡Iskateli¡
Искатели; роман. Изд. 3., перер. автором. Москва, Сов. писатель, 1935.

207 p. 18 cm.

At head of title: Вл. Лидин.

ɪ. Title.

PG3476.L56 I 7   1935   73–202960

NL 0344447   DLC

PG3476
.L56A6
1948

Lidin, Vladimir Germanovich, 1894–
Избранное. ¡Москва¡ Советский писатель, 1948.

353 p. 21 cm.

Title transliterated: Izbrannoe.
Name originally: Vladimir Germanovich Gomberg.

PG3476.L56A6 1948   51–40146

NL 0344448   DLC

Lidin, Vladimir Germanovich, 1894–
¡Izbrannye rasskazy¡
Избранные рассказы. Москва, Худож. лит-ра, 1935.

283 p. 20 cm.

At head of title: Вл. Лидин.

PG3476.L56A6 1935   72–228118

NL 0344449   DLC CSt

PG3476
.L56 I 8

Lidin, Vladimir Germanovich, 1894–
Изгнание; роман. ¡Москва¡ Советский писатель, 1947.

319 p. 20 cm.

ɪ. Title.   *Title transliterated:* Izgnanie.
Name originally: Vladimir Germanovich Gomberg.

PG3476.L56 I 8   48–20974*

NL 0344450   DLC

Lidin, Vladimir Germanovich, 1894–
¡Mogila neizvestnogo soldata¡
Могила неизвестного солдата. Москва, Худож. лит-ра, 1935.

234 p. 20 cm.

At head of title: Вл. Лидин.

ɪ. Title.

PG3476.L56M55   73–200899

NL 0344451   DLC

Lidin, Vladimir Germanovich, 1894–
... Моря и горы ¡рассказы 1917–18¡ Москва, "Северные дни," 1922.

3 p. l., 9–107 p., 2 l. 21^{cm}.

At head of title: Вл. Лидин.

Contents.—Моря и горы.—Посох.—Свиданье.—Князь.—Звездная буря.—Последнее плаванье.—Прялка.

ɪ. Title.   *Title transliterated:* Morîà i gory.
¡Name originally: Vladimir Germanovich Gomberg¡
43–20071

NL 0344452   DLC

PG3476
.L56M6

Lidin, Vladimir Germanovich, 1894–
... Морской сквозняк; повесть. Москва, Петроград, Издательство Л. Д. Френкель, 1923.

161, ¡1¡ p. 19^{cm}.

At head of title: Вл. Лидин.

ɪ. Title.   *Title transliterated:* Morskoĭ skvoznîàk.
¡Name originally: Vladimir Germanovich Gomberg¡
43–20134

NL 0344453   DLC

Lidin, Vladimir Germanovich, 1894–
¡Myshinye budni¡
Мышиные будни; ¡рассказы¡. Москва, Геликон, 1923.

92 p. 19 cm.

At head of title: В. Лидин.

CONTENTS: Ковчег.— Китай.— Королева бразильская.— Проходным двором.—Еврейское счастье.—Будда.— Звероловы.— Евражка.

ɪ. Title.

PG3476.L56M9 1923b   73–205505

NL 0344454   DLC

PG3476
L56M9

Lidin, Vladimir Germanovich, 1894–
... Мышиные будни; рассказы. Москва, Петроград, Издательство Л. Д. Френкель, 1923.

113 p., 1 l. 18½ x 14^{cm}.

At head of title: Вл. Лидин.

CONTENTS.— Ковчег.—Китай.—Королева Бразильская.—Проходным двором.—Еврейское счастье.—Звероловы.—Будда.—Роза Шираза.—Евражка.

ɪ. Title.   *Title transliterated:* Myshinye budni.
¡Name originally: Vladimir Germanovich Gomberg¡
43–20078

NL 0344455   DLC

Lidin, Vladimir Germanovich, 1894–
¡Obychaĭ vetra¡
Обычай ветра; рассказы 1926–1928. Москва, Гос. изд-во, 1929.

202 p. 20 cm. (His Собрание сочинений, т. 5)

At head of title: Вл. Лидин.

CONTENTS.— Младость.— Звенит золотая пшеница.— Обычай ветра.—Возвращение "Гелы."—Волхвы.—Порфира.—Белые ночи.—Магнитные бури.— Ледники.— Степь.—Полевые цветы.—Приморская тишина.—Люксембургский сад.

ɪ. Title. ɪɪ. Series: Lidin, Vladimir Germanovich, 1894–   Sobranie sochineniĭ, t. 5.

PG3476.L56 1929, t. 5   73–336385

NL 0344456   DLC

VOLUME 332

Lidin, Vladimir Germanovich, 1894–
(Otstupnik)
Отступникъ; романъ. Вступ. статья Петра Пиль-
скаго. Портретъ автора работы А. П. Апсита. Рига,
Лит-ра, 1928.
240 p. port. 21 cm. (Наша библіотека, 27)
At head of title: Вл. Лидинъ.

I. Title.   II. Series: Nasha biblioteka, 27.
PG3476.L56O8 1928   73–216674

NL 0344456–1   DLC

Z2500
.L6
1928
Lidin, Vladimir Germanovich, 1894–   *ed.*
Писатели; автобиографии и портреты современных рус-
ских прозаиков, под ред. Вл. Лидина. Изд. 2, доп. и
испр. Москва, Современные проблемы, 1928.
395 p. ports. 18 cm.

1. Russian literature—20th cent.—Bio-bibl.   2. Russian prose literature—Bio-bibl.   I. Title.   *Title transliterated:* Pisateli.
Name originally: Vladimir Germanovich Gomberg.

Z2500.L6 1928   48–34713*

NL 0344457   DLC

Lidin, Vladimir Germanovich, 1894–
The price of life, by Vladimir Lidin, translated by Helen
Chrouschoff Matheson. New York, London, Harper &
brothers [1932]
4 p. l., 11–336 p. 19¼ᶜᵐ.
"First edition."
London edition (J. Cape) has title: The apostate.

I. Matheson, Elena Nikolaevna (Krushchova) 1872–   tr.   II. Title.
[Name originally: Vladimir Germanovich Gomberg]
32–5354 Revised
Library of Congress   PZ3.L6190Pr
[r43f3]   891.73

NL 0344458   DLC NNC

PG3476
.L56P7
Lidin, Vladimir Germanovich, 1894–
... Простая жизнь. Москва, Советский писатель, 1943.
122, [2] p. 14 x 11ᶜᵐ.
At head of title: Вл. Лидин.
CONTENTS.— Учитель.— Простая жизнь.— Хирург.— Письмо.—
Братья.— Дочь.— Наборщик.— Школа.— Старик.— Таинственный
остров.—Из дневника: Земля. Уголь. Мир и война.

I. Title.   *Title transliterated:* Prostaia zhizn'.
[Name originally: Vladimir Germanovich Gomberg]
Library of Congress   PG3476.L56P7
[2]   44–10415

NL 0344459   DLC

PG3476
.L56P8
Lidin, Vladimir Germanovich, 1894–
Пути и версты. Ленинград, Прибой [1927]
187 p. 17 cm.

I. Title.   *Title transliterated:* Puti i versty.
Name originally: Vladimir Germanovich Gomberg.

PG3476.L56P8   48–37918*

NL 0344460   DLC

Lidin, Vladimir Germanovich, 1894–
(Rasskazy)
Рассказы. Москва, Сов. писатель, 1939.
174 p. 17 cm.
At head of title: Вл. Лидин.
CONTENTS: Мать.—Наследник.—Берег моря.—"Соловей."—
Сад.— Ваня.— Гамлет.— Рылеев.— Аддажио.— Мечтатель.— Весен-
няя охота.—Март.—Ливень.—Утро.

PG3476.L56A6 1939   73–201868

NL 0344461   DLC

PG3476
.L56A15
1954
Lidin, Vladimir Germanovich, 1894–
Рассказы, повести, воспоминания. Москва, Гос. изд-во
худож. лит-ры, 1954.
590 p. illus. 21 cm.

Title transliterated: Rasskazy, povesti, vospominaniía.
Name originally: Vladimir Germanovich Gomberg.

PG3476.L56A15 1954   55–25079 ‡

NL 0344462   DLC

891.74
L61
OcFm
1933
Lidin, Vladimir Germanovich, 1894–
Le renégat. Traduit du russe par Thérèse
Monseaux. 3.éd. Paris, Gallimard, 1933.
269 p. 19 cm. (Les Jeunes Russes)

Translation of Отступник (transliterated:
Otstupnik)

NL 0344463   IU

Lidin, Vladimir Germanovich, 1894–
The sixth door. (In Transition stories, ed. by
Eugene Jolas and Robert Sage. 1929.)

NL 0344464   OU

PG3476
.L56S9
Lidin, Vladimir Germanovich, 1894–
Свежий ветер. Москва, Советский писатель, 1952.
383 p. 21 cm.

I. Title.   *Title transliterated:* Svezhii veter.
Name originally: Vladimir Germanovich Gomberg.

PG3476.L56S9   53–31671 ‡

NL 0344465   DLC

Lidin, Vladimir Germanovich, 1894–
(Syn)
Сын; роман. Москва, Худож. лит-ра, 1936.
223 p. 20 cm.
At head of title: Вл. Лидин.

I. Title.

PG3476.L56S93   72–228153

NL 0344466   DLC

Lidin, Vladimir Germanovich, 1894–
(Syn cheloveka)
Сын человека; рассказы. Изд. 2. Москва, Гос. изд
-во, 1927.
152 p. 17 cm. At head of title: Вл. Лидин.
CONTENTS: Марина Веневцева.— Сын человека.— Салазга.—
Волчок.—Зацветает жизнь.—Свирель.—Голубое руно.—Друг.

I. Title.

PG3476.L56S94 1927   73–215892

NL 0344467   DLC

PG3476
.L56V4
1934
Lidin, Vladimir Germanovich, 1894–
Великий или Тихий; роман. Москва, Советская литература, 1934.
227 p. 20 cm.

I. Title.   *Title transliterated:* Velikii ili Tikhii.
Name originally: Vladimir Germanovich Gomberg.

PG3476.L56V4 1934   50–53193

NL 0344468   DLC

PG3476
.L56V4
1935
Lidin, Vladimir Germanovich, 1894–
Великий или Тихий; роман. Изд. 3. Москва, Худо-
жественная литература, 1935.
216 p. 21 cm.

I. Title.   *Title transliterated:* Velikii ili Tikhii.
Name originally: Vladimir Germanovich Gomberg.

PG3476.L56V4 1935   50–53195

NL 0344469   DLC

Lidingö, Sweden. Högre Allmänna Läroverket.
Redogörelse.

NL 0344470   DLC

Lidingö, Sweden. Millesgården.
Millesgården
see under   Milles, Carl, 1879–

Lidingö, Sweden. Stadsbiblioteket.
Årsberättelse.
[Stockholm]
v. 24 cm.

Z828.L52   55–39833 ‡

NL 0344472   DLC

Lidington, F. W.
Practical share transfer work; a handbook for the use of com-
pany clerks, by F. W. Lidington. London: Sir I. Pitman & Sons,
Ltd., 1921. vii, 116 p. forms. 12°.

22984A. I. Stocks.—Transfer, Gt.   Br. 2. Corporations, Gt. Br.
N. Y. P. L.   October 13, 1921.

NL 0344473   NN

VOLUME 332

Lidingtone, William Maitland, Laird
  see Maitland, Sir William, Laird of
Lethington, 1528-1573.

D804
.G4L49

Лидицы будут жить; сборник памяти мучеников и памятник победы. Перевод В. Озерецковского и Л. Александровой. ₁Прага₎ Изд. Общества по восстановлению Лидиц ₁1947₎

28 p., 16 p. of illus. and ports. 21 cm.

1. Lidice, Czechoslovak Republic. 2. World War, 1939-1945—Czechoslovak Republic—Lidice. 3. World War, 1939-1945—Atrocities. I. Společnost pro obnovu Lidec, Prague.
Title transliterated: Lidiísy budut zhit'.

D804.G4L49   54-18627

NL 0344475   DLC

Lidji, David I.
  see
Lidzhi, David I.

Lidji, Jacques.
  Manuel de l'étranger en France. La naturalisation selon la loi du 10 août 1927. Droits et devoirs de l'étranger avant et après sa naturalisation. Déchéance. Formules. Renseignements pratiques. Textes et projets de loi. Jacques Lidji ... A. Le Moal ... Préface par M. Charles Lambert ... Paris, Librairie du Recueil Sirey ₁1928₎

2 p. l., ₍7₎-174 p., 1 l. 16½ᶜᵐ.

1. Naturalization—France. I. Le Moal, A., joint author. II. France. Laws, statutes, etc. III. Title.

Library, U. S. Dept. of   Labor
                                 ₍2₎   L 28-148

NL 0344477   DL MH-L

Lidji, Jacques.
  ... La propriété commerciale; commentaire de la Loi du 30 juin 1926 et les modifications votées par la Chambre des députés, le 18 décembre 1926 ... Préface de Bertrand Nogaro ... Paris, Les Presses universitaires de France, 1927.

1 p. l., ₍v₎-xviii, 190 p. 24ᶜᵐ. (Bibliothèque de la Revue de jurisprudence commerciale de Paris)

At head of title: Jacques Lidji ... ₍et₎ A. Le Moal ...

1. Landlord and tenant—France. I. Le Moal, A., joint author.

                                               44-16902

NL 0344478   DLC MH

Ngd90   Lidji, Maurice
929l   ... Le chèque en Bulgarie ... Paris, Jouve
          & Cie, 1929.
          2p. ₍.l.₎,212p. 25½cm.
          Thèse - Univ. de Paris.
          "Bibliographie": p.[1]-2.

          1.Checks. 2.Law, Comparative.

NL 0344479   CtY MH-L

Lidji, Maurice.
  ... Le chèque en Bulgarie, d'après la législation bulgare et en droit comparé: législations anglo-saxonnes, allemande, française, italienne et suisse. Paris, Dalloz, 1929.

2 p. l., 212 p. 25½ᵐ.

"Bibliographie": p. ₍1₎-2.

1. Checks. 2. Law, Comparative. ₍2. Comparative law₎ ₍3. Checks—Bulgaria₎ I. Title.

                                               30-9699

NL 0344480   DLC CtY NN

M219
.R383S6   Lidka, Maria, ed.
           Reizenstein, Franz.
           ₍Sonata, violin & piano, G♯₎

           Sonata in G sharp, for violin and piano. London, A. Lengnick ₍1947₎

---

*ML283
.8
.W4L5   Lidke, Wolfgang.
           Das Musikleben in Weimar von 1683-1735. Weimar, Stadtmuseum [1954?]
           95 p. music. 21 cm. (Weimar. Stadtmuseum. Schriften zur Stadtgeschichte und Heimatkunde, Heft 3)

           1. Music—Germany—Weimar.

NL 0344482   MB MH

Lidköping, Sweden. Lägre allmänna läroverket.

Skara, Sweden. Högre allmänna läroverket.

  Den allmänna undervisningens ... vänner inbjudas härigenom till åhörande af de offentliga årsexamina vid Skara Högre allmänna läroverk ... ₍Skara, 1887-

---

WX
2
GS8
L7L2a   LIDKÖPING, Sweden. Länslasarettet
           Årsberättelse.
           Lidköping ₍1867?₎-
           v.

NL 0344484   DNLM

Lidl, Andreas, ca. 1740-ca. 1788.
  ₍Duets, violin & viola, op. 6₎

  A second sett of six duettos, three for violin and tenor, and three for violin and violoncello. Composed ... by And. Lidel. Op. vi. London, The author ₍1785?₎

2 pts. 32ᵐ.

Parts: violin, and viola and violoncello.

1. Violin and viola music—To 1800. 2. Violin and violoncello music—To 1800.

Library of Congress   M287.L7 op. 6   46-42020

NL 0344485   DLC ViU

Lidl, Andreas, ca. 1740-ca. 1788.
  ₍Quartets, strings, op. 7₎

  A second sett of six quartetto's, five for two violins, tenor and violoncello and one for a flute or oboe, violin, tenor and violoncello, composed by A. Lidel. London, W. Forster ₍1785?₎

4 pts. 31½ x 24ᵐ.

"Op. vii."
Publisher's plate no.: 15.
There is no separate flute part. The caption title of quartet no. 4 in first violin part reads "Flute or oboe."

1. String quartets—To 1800—Parts. 2. Quartets (Flute, violin, viola, violoncello)—To 1800.
                                               46-33449
Library of Congress   M452.L714 op. 7

NL 0344486   DLC NRU-Mus

Lidl, Andreas, ca. 1740 - ca. 1788.
  ₍Duets. Violin & viola. Op. 3₎

  Six duettos, for the violin and tenor, with a separate part for the violoncello, to be play'd occasionally instead of the tenor... by A. Lidel. Opera 3d. London: The author ₍1779₎   1 v. 35cm.

Parts for violin, viola and violoncello.
With autograph of composer.

223918B. 1. Violin and viola—To
3. Autographs—Signatures, etc.—
N. Y. P. L.

                        JUILLIARD FOUNDATION FUND.
                        1800. 2. Viola and violin—To 1800.
                        Lidl, A.
                                        April 16, 1943

NL 0344487   NN

Lidl, Andreas, ca. 1740-ca. 1788.
  Quartets, op.2
  Six quartettos, three for two violins, tenor, & violoncello, and three for flute, violin, tenor, & violoncello obligato. Opera 2da. L, Forster [177-?]

  4 pts.
  Pts. for violino I (flauto o violino), violino II, viola & violoncello

NL 0344488   MH NRU-Mus

Lidl, Andreas, ca. 1740 - ca. 1788.
  ₍Sonatas. 3 strings. Op. 4, no. 1-6.₎
  Six sonatas for violin, tenor, & violoncello... Compos'd by A. Lidel. Opera 4ᵗᵃ... London: Printed for W. Forster₍, ca. 1780₎. 3 parts. 34cm.

Parts only.
In portfolio.
Violoncello part has imprint: London, Printed & sold by the author.

701236A. 1. Chamber music.   18th cent.—Trios. 2. Violin—
Trios—Violin, viola and violoncello.   3. Sonatas—Trios.
N. Y. P. L.   June 27, 1934

NL 0344489   NN CU

LIDL, ANDREAS, ca. 1740-ca. 1788.

  Six trios for a violin (or flauto) violino secondo and violoncello obligato... Composed by Andrew Lidel. Opera 1. London, Printed by Longman, Lukey and Broderip [ca. 1776] 3 parts.

  Microfilm.

1. Chamber music, 18th cent.--Trios. 2. Violin in trios (2 violins, violoncello)--To 1800. 3. Flute in trios (Flute, violin, violoncello)--To 1800.

NL 0344490   NN

Lidl, Andreas, ca. 1740-ca. 1788.
  ₍Trios, 2 violins & violoncello, op. 1₎

  Six trios for a violin (or flauto) violino secondo, and violoncello obligato ... Composed by Andrew Lidel. Opera 1ˢᵗ. London, Printed by Longman, Lukey and Broderip ₍1778₎

3 pts. 32ᵐ.

Part for violin 1 has caption "violino primo e flauto" and is occasionally divided into two parts indicated respectively as "violino" and "flauto."

1. String trios (2 violins, violoncello)—To 1800. 2. Quartets (Flute, 2 violins, violoncello)—To 1800.
                                               46-42460
Library of Congress   M351.L7 op. 1

NL 0344491   DLC ViU

[Lidl, Bernhard]
  Chronicon Lunaelacense juxta seriem abbatum trina rerum memorabilium genera recensens
    see under Mondsee, Austria. (Benedictine monastery)

VOLUME 332

⌐Lidl, Ildefons; 1750-1815.
B802   Meine Zweifel über das unredlich seyn sol-
Z3   lende Betragen der vorgeblichen Feinde der
Aufklärung, dem redlich seyn wollenden Ver-
fasser, Judas Thaddäus Zauner, beyder Rechte
Lizentiaten in Salzburg zur Wissenschaft vor-
gelegt. ⌐Augsburg; 1791.
64 p. 16cm.
Bound with Zauner, J.T. Ueber das unredliche
Betragen der Feinde der Aufklärung. Frank-
furt, 1791.
1.Enlightenment.   I.Title.

NL 0344493 CSt

[Lidl, Ildephons, 1736-1806]
Rede auf das Fest des Heiligen Lorenz, Leviten und
Martyrers. [Augsburg, Merz] 1790

72 p. (In Gesammelte Schriften unserer Zeiten zur
Vertheidigung der Religion und Wahrheit, 6)

NL 0344494 MH

Wing
ZW   LIDL, JOHANN JACOB, 1696-1771.
756   ⌐Goldener Gnaden Fluss. ⌐Welcher das kost-
.L 612   bahre Perl der Andacht einer Gott liebenden
Seele ausgiesset in gegenwärtigen⌐Gebett-Buch⌐
Viennae,J.J.et J.A.Lidl sculps.et excud.⌐1753⌐
⌐19⌐,266,⌐8⌐p. illus. 16cm.

Engraved after handwritten copy.

NL 0344495 ICN

LIDL,Johann Jacob.
Nova et accurata mappa geographica in qua
totum S.R. Imperium et Italia cum magna parte
confinium regnori Hungariae , nimirum Poloniae,
et Borussiae, exhibentur singuli circuli impe-
riales, electoratus, ducatus, principatus et
comitatus exactissime designantur; postae seu
stationes veredariae per universum imperium
annotantur et distantiae locoru per adjectas
miliarium scalas diligentissime exprimuntur.⌐
⌐Vienna? 1750?⌐
183/4 x 27 1/2 in.
Also with title In   German "Neue und

accurate general postland-kartur. " etc.,
Printed on satin.
At one time this map belong to Willem V,
Prince of Orange.

NL 0344497 MH

LIDL, Johann Jacob.
Novissimum Silesiae Theatrum, id est exac-
tissimus superioris et inferioris Silesiae,
comitatus Glacensis, et confinium regnorum
schmatismus in quo non solum singulae amplis-
simi hujus ducatus provinciae, principatus dy-
nastiae districtus, territoria, verum etiam
singulae, civitates oppida, arces pagi, statione⌐
et viae veredariae, montes, sijlvae lacus
flumina , etc., ex originalibus et probatis-
simis topographiis depormpta exhibentur.
"Vienna? 1750?]
31 1/4 x 35 in.At one time this map
belonged to Willem V. prince of Orange.

NL 0344498 MH

LIDL, Joh[ann] Jacob, 1696-1771.
Novum belli theatrum, seu Geographica descriptio utriusq archiducatus Austriae supra et
infra anasium siti cui accedit major pars superioris et inferioris Bavariae,cum reliquis omnibus con finibus Regnis et provincijs,nec non
exacta designatione viarum et stationum veredar-
iarum;ppera et studio. Ioh. Iacob Lidl. ⌐Vien-
na?1750?⌐
18 1/2 x 41 3/4 in.
Also with title in German: Neu und accurat
eröffentes kriegs thea   trum. Printed on
satin. At one time th   is map belonged to
Willem V, prince of Orange. X 87.48*

NL 0344499 MH

Lidl, Max Beiträge zur kenntniss des bayerischen waldes.
Freysing. 1856. 8°. pp. 41-80. (Progr. d. Königl.
landwirthschaftlichen centralschule zu Weyhenstephan.)

NL 0344500 MH-A

99.76
L61   Lidl, Otto.
Ed.6   Der kleine Holzrechner. 6. ergänzte
und verb. Aufl. München, Bayerischer
Landwirtschaftsverlag [1951]
23 p.

1. Lumber trade. Tables and ready
reckoners.

NL 0344501 DNAL

Lidl, Walter, 1918-
Die Bedeutung von Tatbestand und Rechtswidrigkeit für
die Häufigkeit des Zustandekommens freisprechender Urteile
im Strafverfahren. ⌐München? 1949?⌐
xi, 148 l. 29 cm.
Photocopy (positive) of typescript.
Inaug.-Diss.—Munich.
Vita.
Bibliography : leaves ⌐v⌐-vi.
1. Acquittals—Germany (Federal Republic, 1949-   ) 2. Corpus
delicti—Germany (Federal Republic, 1949-   ) 3. Illegality—
Germany (Federal Republic, 1949-   )   I. Title.

62-39004

NL 0344502 DLC

Lidle, Helmut
Über die natur des bei der elektrolytischen
reduktion wässriger chromsäurelösungen entstehenden
kathodenfilms. ... 76 p.
Inaug. Diss. - Techn. Hochschule Dresden, [1936]

NL 0344503 ICRL

QR133
S515   Lidle, Herbert, 1927-
Kritische veterinär-medizinische betrachtung
der landwirtschaftlichen abwasserverwertung mit
speziellen untersuchungen über die einwirkung
verschiedener drucke auf wurmeier und wurmlarven.
München, 1954.
[4], 35 p. tables. 21 cm.
Inaug.-Diss. - Ludwig Maximilian-Universität,
München.
Lebenslauf.
At head of title: Aus dem Zoologisch-Parasi-
tologischen Institut der Tierärztlichen Fakul-
tät der Univer-   sität München...

Bibliography: p. 30-34.

1. Sewage - Bacteriology. 2. Worms, Intestinal
and parasitic. 3. Sewage disposal. I. Title.

NL 0344505 DI

Lidle, Wilhelm
Untersuchungen ueber die trennung von antimon und
sinn auf trockenem wege. (Auszug.)
Inaug. Diss. Freiberg, 1925

NL 0344506 ICRL

Lidle, Wilhelm, ed. and tr.

Mantell, Charles Letnam, 1897-
Zinn; berg- und hüttenmännische gewinnung, verarbeitung
und verwendung, von C. L. Mantell ... Ins deutsche übertragen und bearbeitet von dr.-ing. W. Lidle ... Mit 113 abbildungen und 52 zahlentafeln. Halle (Saale) W. Knapp, 1937.

Lidley,
Celebrated oratorio of The creation
see under   Haydn, Joseph, 1732-1809.

Lidley,
Complete book of words of Joseph Haydn's
oratorio The creation...
see under   Haydn, Joseph, 1732-1809.

Lidley,
The creation
see under   Haydn, Joseph, 1732-1809.

Lidley,
La création du monde
see under   Haydn, Joseph, 1732-1809.

Lidley,
La creazione del mondo...
see under   Haydn, Joseph, 1732-1809.

Lidley,
Haydn's grand oratorio, The creation...
see under   Haydn, Joseph, 1732-1809.

Lidley,
Haydn's oratorio, The creation
see under   Haydn, Joseph, 1732-1809.

Lidley,
Haydn's sacred oratorio, The creation
see under   Haydn, Joseph, 1732-1809.

Lidley,
Libretto of Haydn's oratorio of the creation
see under   Haydn, Joseph, 1732-1809.

VOLUME 332

Lidley,
   Die Schöpfung
      see under Haydn, Joseph, 1732–1809.

Lidley,
   The vocal and orchestral parts to the Creation
      see under Haydn, Joseph, 1732–1809.

Lidley,
   The words of the Creation
      see under Haydn, Joseph, 1732–1809.

#BS
2695
.L5
   Lidman, Adam, 1849–1933.
      Tankar öfver Efesierbrefvets första kapitel; jemte tvenne predikningar, af A. Lidman. Buffalo, Minn., 1897.
      111 p. port. 18 cm.

      1. Bible. N.T. Ephesians I—Criticism, interpretation, etc. 2. Bible. N.T. Matthew XXV—Criticism, interpretation, etc. 3. Bible. O.T. Isaiah IX— Criticism, interpretation, etc. I. Title.

   NL 0344520   MnHi

#BX
8039
.L5A3
   Lidman, Adam, 1849–1933.
      Ur minnets fatabur; minnen och erfarenhetsrön från en kort tjenstgöringstid inom Svenska statskyrkan, af A. Lidman. Minneapolis, 1916.
      102 p. illus., ports. 18 cm.

      1. Svenska kyrkan—Clergy—Correspondence, reminiscences, etc. I. Title.

   NL 0344521   MnHi DLC-P4 MnU WaU

Lidman, Brita.
   "Hedningen" fra Vargön; Brasilpioneren Daniel Berg. Til norsk ved Osvald Orlien. Oslo Filadelfiaforlaget, 1946.
   207 p. 20 cm.

      1. Berg, Daniel. 2. Missions—Brazil. 3. Missions, Swedish. I. Title.

   BV2853.B7B46   63–35094 ‡

   NL 0344522   DLC

Lidman, Carl Hindrik Sven Rudolphsson
   see Lidman, Sven, 1882–1960.

Lidman, Erik Torsten, 1875–

Sweden. *Automobiltrafikkommittén.*
   Betänkande med förslag till ändrad lydelse av vissa delar av förordningen om automobiltrafik den 30 juni 1916 m. m. avgivet av därtill utsedda sakkunniga. Linköping, Billstens boktryckeri, 1919.

DL991
.E2L5
1949
   Lidman, Hans Gustav Otto, 1910–
      Edsbyn i bild, av Hans Lidman ¡och¡ Stig Elvén. 2. omarb. uppl. Lund, C. Bloms boktr., 1949.
      99 p. illus., ports. 22 cm.

      1. Edsbyn, Sweden.   I. Elvén, Stig, joint author.

                                   A 50–861

   Minnesota. Univ. Libr.
   for Library of Congress   ¡2¡

   NL 0344525   MnU

PT9875
.L485F3
   Lidman, Hans Gustav Otto, 1910–
      Fäbodnatt; berättelser från Hälsingland. Stockholm, LTs förlag ¡1951¡
      211 p. 20 cm.

      I. Title.

                                   A 52–1192

   Minnesota. ¡Univ. Libr.
   for Library of Congress   ¡2¡

   NL 0344526   MnU DLC

48H
28
   Lidman, Hans Gustav Otto, 1910–
      Fiskefeber. Stockholm, LTs förlag [1952]
      205 p.

   NL 0344527   DLC-P4 MnU

SK35
.L47
   Lidman, Hans Gustav Otto, 1910–
      En¡ jägares ungdomssynder. Stockholm, P. A. Norstedt ¡1950¡
      211 p. illus. 22 cm.

      1. Hunting—Sweden.   I. Title.

                                   A 51–4148

   Missouri. Univ. Libr.
   for Library of Congress   ¡2¡

   NL 0344528   MnU NN

   Lidman, Hans Gustav Otto, 1910–
      Nappatag i Hälsinglands älvar och sjöar, i lappländska forsar och fall, och havet vid Varanger. [1955]
      221 p.

   NL 0344529   MoU

   Lidman, Hans Gustav Otto, 1910–
      Den sjungande dalen. ¡Stockholm¡ LTs förlag ¡1954¡
      162 p. illus. 27 cm.

      1. Hälsingland, Sweden—Descr. & trav. 2. Natural history—Sweden—Hälsingland.   I. Title.

                                   A 55–7493

   Minnesota. Univ. Libr.
   for Library of Congress   ¡2¡

   NL 0344530   MnU OrCS NN

   Lidman, Hans Gustav Otto, 1910–
      Skogsvandringar. Stockholm, P. A. Norstedt ¡1947¡
      244 p. illus. 23 cm.

      I. Title.

   PT9875.L485S5   839.786   48–27411*

   NL 0344531   DLC NN

   Lidman, Hans Gustav Otto, 1910–
      Sommardagar. Stockholm, LTs förlag ¡1951¡
      227 p. illus. 21cm.

   NL 0344532   MnU

   Lidman, Hans Gustav Otto, 1910–
      Vinterdagar. ¡Stockholm¡ LTs förlag ¡1953¡
      151 p. illus. 21 cm.

      I. Title.   A 54–5526

   Minnesota. Univ. Libr.
   for Library of Congress   ¡2¡

   NL 0344533   MnU

   Lidman, Karl Hindrik Sven Rudolfsson

                  see

   Lidman, Sven, 1882–1960.

   Lidman, Nicolaus Rudolphus, respondent.
      Rationem sacrificii et sacerdotii sanctissimi salvatoris
         see under Hagberg, Fredrik Theodor, praeses.

   Lidman, Sam, 1923–
      Tryggare kan ingen vara, roman. Stockholm, Bonnier ¡1955¡
      199 p. 20 cm.

      I. Title.

   PT9875.L488T7   55–34970 ‡

   NL 0344536   DLC MnU

   Lidman, Sara, 1923–
      Hjortronlandet. Stockholm, Bonnier ¡1955¡
      274 p. 20 cm.

      I. Title.
   PT9875.L489H5   A 56–1159
   Minnesota. Univ. Libr.
   for Library of Congress   ¡2¡†

   NL 0344537   MnU OrP OrU CoU C NN OCl CU DLC

VOLUME 332

Lidman, Sara, 1923–
Tjärdalen. Stockholm, Bonnier [1953]
207 p. 20 cm.

I. Title.

PT9875.L489Tᴵ   53-31201 ‡

NL 0344538   DLC OrP WU MnU OCl NN MH

Lidman, Sven, 1882–*1960*
Blodsarv; försök till ett människoödes förhistoria, av Sven
Lidman. Stockholm, A. Bonnier [1937]
346 p. incl. geneal. tab. 19½ᶜᵐ.

1. Lidman family.   I. Title.
[Full name: Karl Hindrik Sven Rudolfsson Lidman]

Library of Congress	CS929.L5 1937	38-33355
Copyright A—Foreign	37075	
	[3]	929.2

NL 0344539   DLC

PT   **Lidman, Sven,** 1882–
9875   Carl Silfverståhls upplefvelser; roman.
L5   Stockholm, A. Bonnier [1912]
C3   340p. 19cm.

NL 0344540   WU ICU MH

Lidman, Sven, 1882–
Dikter. Stockholm, Natur och kultur [1953]
107 p. 22 cm.
"Ett urval, verkställt i samråd av författaren och Bengt Holmqvist,
ur samlingarna Pasiphaë 1904, Primavera 1905, Källorna 1906, Elden
och altaret 1907 samt Oroligt var mitt hjärta 1933."

Full name: Carl Hindrik Sven Rudolphsson Lidman.
A 53-6573
Minnesota. Univ. Lib
for Library of Congress   [2]

NL 0344541   MnU NN

PT9875 **Lidman, Sven,** 1882–
.L5   Elden och altaret; dikter af Sven Lidman. Stockholm,
1907   A. Bonnier [1907]
137, [4] p. 22ᶜᵐ.

NL 0344542   ICU MH NcD

Lidman, Sven, 1882–
Fjäril och vilddjur, en bok om liv och nåd. Stockholm,
A. Bonnier [1947]
282 p. 20 cm.

1. Devotional literature.   I. Title.
Full name: Karl Hindrik Sven Rudolfsson Lidman.

BV4836.L5   49-13613*

NL 0344543   DLC

BV   **Lidman, Sven,** 1882–
4836   Förgängelsens trälar och frihetens söner;
L619f   tankar om nöd, nad och nödvändighet. An-
1928   dra upplagan. Stockholm, A. Bonnier [1928]
307 p.

1. Devotional literature.   I. Title.

NL 0344544   CLU

Lidman, Sven, 1882–
Från Coventry till Bethlehem; en bok om
frälsning i stormen. Stockholm, Bonnier
[1942]
276 p.

1. Devotional literature.   I. Title.

NL 0344545   WaU MnU

PT9875
.L5Z53
Lidman, Sven, 1882–
Gossen i grottan; [memoarer] Stockholm, Natur och kul-
tur [1952]
808 p. illus., ports. 22 cm.

1. Authors—Correspondence, reminiscences, etc.   I. Title.
A 53-739
Harvard Univ. Library
for Library of Congress   [1]

NL 0344546   MH DLC ICU NNC NN MnU NcU NcD OCl CU OrP

BV4836 **Lidman, Sven,** 1882–
L5   Guds eviga nu; en bok om vägen, sanningen
och livet. Stockholm, A. Bonnier [1947]
328 p.

1. Devotional literature 2. Christian life
I. Title

NL 0344547   CU

839.7872 **Lidman, Sven,** 1882–
L714HR   Härskare; två dramer om makt och vanmakt.
Stockholm, A. Bonnier [1908]
1 v. (unpaged) 23 cm.

NL 0344548   NcD MH

Lidman, Sven, 1882–
Huset med de gamla fröknarna; en
berättelse om helgon och hjältar… Stockholm, Bonnier [1918]
333 p. 18 ᶜᵐ.

NL 0344549   NjP

Lidman, Sven, 1882-1960.
Huset med de gamla fröknarna; en berättelse om
helgon och hjältar. Stockholm, Bonnier [1934]
256 p. [Vår egen tids bästa]

NL 0344550   WaS

PT9875 **Lidman, Sven,** 1882-1960.
.L5H8   Huset med de gamla fröknarna; en berättelse
1937   om helgon och hjältar. Stockholm, A. Bonnier
[1937]
256 p. 20 cm.

NL 0344551   MB

PT9875 Lidman, Sven, 1882–
L5H8   Huset med de gamla fröknarna, en berättelse
1939   om helgon och hjältar. Stockholm, Åhlén &
Åkerlund [1939]
200 p. 19cm.

NL 0344552   CU

Lidman, Sven, 1882–
Huset med de gamla fröknarna; en berättelse om helgon
och hjältar. Stockholm, Bonnier [1940]
256 p. (Moderna svenska berättare)

NL 0344554   MH ICU

PT9875 Lidman, Sven, 1882–
L5H8   Huset med de gamla fröknarna; en berättelse
1948   om helgon och hjältar. Stockholm, A. Bonnier [1948]
256 p.

NL 0344555   CU

Lidman, Sven, 1882–
839.7872
L714H   Huset med de gamla fröknarna. Stockholm,
A. Bonnier [1955]
314 p. 20 cm. (Bonnierbiblioteket)

NL 0344556   NcD ICU NN TxHR

Lidman, Sven, 1882–
839.7872
L714I   Imperia; dramatiska situationer. Stockholm, A. Bonnier [1907]
137 p. illus. 23 cm.

NL 0344557   NcD NN

Lidman, Sven, 1882–
Ingen lurar Gud; sett, tänkt och talat.
Stockholm, Bonnier [1945]
244 p.

NL 0344558   NNC

Lidman, Sven, 1882-1960.
Ingen lurar Gud. Sett, tänkt och
talat. Stockholm, Bonnier [1946]
244 p. 19 cm.

NL 0344559   MnU

Lidman, Sven, 1882–
839.7872
L714K   Källorna; dikter. Stockholm, A. Bonnier
[1906]
125 p. illus. 23 cm.

NL 0344560   NcD NN ICU

VOLUME 332

Lidman, Sven, 1882–
Köpmän och krigare, roman af Sven Lidman. Stockholm, A. Bonnier ₁1911₎
436 p. 18½ᶜᵐ. kr. 5.50

11–32262

Library of Congress

NL 0344561 DLC ICU MnU WaS

Lidman, Sven, 1882–
Köpmän och krigare, roman af Sven Lidman. Stockholm, A. Bonnier, *1925*
436 p. 18½ᶜᵐ. kr. 5.50

NL 0344562 CaBVa

PT9875 **Lidman, Sven,** 1882–
L5K6 Köpmän och krigare, roman. Stockholm, Vårt
1930 hems förlag ₁1930₎
284 p. 19cm. (Svenskt liv och leverne ...
av de förnämste samtida berättarna)
Vårt hems gyllene bibliotek.

NL 0344563 CU

Lidman, Sven, 1882–
Lågan och lindansaren. Stockholm, Natur och kultur
₁1952₎
271 p. illus. 22 cm.
Autobiography.

I. Title.
Full name: Carl Hindrik Sven Rudolphsson Lidman.

PT9875.L5Z52 54–42519 ‡

NL 0344564 DLC NcD OC1 MH MnU ICU NN

Lidman, Sven, 1882– *ed.*
Det lefvande fäderneslandet, en bok om svensk aktivism
1916; utg. af Sven Lidman. Stockholm ₁Bröderna Lagerström i distribution₎ 1916.
3 p. l., 224 p., 1 l. 24ᶜᵐ.
Articles reprinted from Svensk lösen.
CONTENTS.—Svenska tankar.—Svensk utrikespolitik.—Svensk inrikespolitik.—Dagspolitiska situationsbilder.—Kritik och polemik.
1. Sweden—Pol. & govt.—1907– I. Title.
₁Full name: Karl Hindrik Sven Rudolfsson Lidman₎
23–1592

Library of Congress JN7799.L5

NL 0344565 DLC IU

Lidman, Sven, 1882–
Människan och tidsandan, av Sven Lidman... Andra upplagan. Stockholm: A. Bonnier ₁ 1932₎. 236 p. 19½cm.
Reprinted from various sources.

659827A. 1. Christian life.
N.Y.P.L. November 14, 1933

NL 0344566 NN

Lidman, Sven, 1882–
Människan och tidsandan. Stockholm, A. Bonnier ₁1943₎
236 p. 19cm.
Contents.– Människan och tidsandan.– Gemenskapens hemlighet.– Den eviga bryggan.– Den eviga gränslinjen.

NL 0344567 MnU

Lidman, Sven, 1882–
Mandoms möda; ₁memoarer₎ Stockholm, Natur och kultur ₁1954₎
357 p. 22 cm.

1. Authors, Swedish—Correspondence, reminiscences, etc.
I. Title.
Full name: Carl Hindrik Sven Rudolphsson Lidman.
A 54–6475

Minnesota. Univ. Libr.
for Library of Congress ₁₃₎

NL 0344568 MnU NcD WaU OC1 NN

Lidman, Sven, 1882–
På resan genom livet; sett och tänkt, av Sven Lidman. Sjätte upplagan... Stockholm: A. Bonnier ₁1936₎ 320 p. 19½cm.

896118A. 1. No subject. I. Title.
N.Y.P.L. August 25, 1937

NL 0344569 NN

BV4836 **Lidman, Sven,** 1882–
I515 På resan genom livet, sett och tänkt av
Sven Lidman. Stockholm, A. Bonnier ₁1947₎
320 p.

1. Devotional literature 2. Christian life
I. Title

NL 0344570 CU

Lidman, Sven, 1882–1960.
Pasiphaë, och andra dikter. Stockholm, A.
Bonnier [1904]
98 p. 12°.

NL 0344571 NN

PT 9875 **Lidman, Sven,** 1882–
.L5P7 Primavera. Dikter. Stockholm, A.
1905 Bonnier [1905]
136 p.

NL 0344572 ICU

---

921 **Lidman, Sven,** 1882–
L619Lic Resan till domen. Stockholm, Natur och
kultur ₁1949₎
210 p.
3. upplagan.

1. Pethrus, Lewi, 1884– 2. Pentecostal
churches – Sweden. I. Title.

NL 0344573 WaU NcU NNUT

LIDMAN, Sven, 1882–
Sasom genom eld. 5e uppl. Stockholm, A.
Bonnier, [1920].

NL 0344574 MH

Lidman, Sven, 1882–
Stensborg; roman af Sven Lidman. Stockholm: A. Bonnier ₁1910₎. 290 p. 12°.

1. Fiction (Swedish). 2. Title.
N.Y.P.L. May.6, 1915.

NL 0344575 NN MH

Lidman, Sven, 1882–
Stensborg; roman. Stockholm, Bonnier ₁1924₎
186 p. 20cm. (his Valda berättelser)

NL 0344576 WU ICU WaS

Lidman, Sven, 1882–
... Stjärnan som tändes på nytt. Stockholm,
Natur och kultur₁1950₎
211,₁1₎p. 20cm.

NL 0344577 NNUT

PT9875 **Lidman, Sven,** 1882–
.L5T5 Thure-Gabriel Silfverstååhl; roman. Stockholm, A. Bonnier ₍1910₎
1910 341 p.

NL 0344578 ICU WaS WU MH NN

Lidman, Sven, 1882–
Tulen läpi; suomentanut Sisko Wilkana.

NL 0344579 OC1

Lidman, Sven.
Tvedräktens barn; roman. Stockholm: A. Bonnier ₁1913₎.
357 p. 12°.

1. Fiction (Swedish). 2. Title.
N.Y.P.L. July 2, 1914.

NL 0344580 NN

Lidman, Sven, 1882–
Uppenbarat; en bok om andlig verklighet... Stockholm, A. Bonnier
₁1943₎
253 p., 1 l. 19cm.

NL 0344581 MnU

VOLUME 332

Lidman, Sven, 1882–
Ur Sven Lidmans skrifter; valda
stycken samlade och utgivna till
hans sextiofemårsdag. Av Zander
Åberg.   Stockholm, Förlaget Fila-
delfia ₍1947₎

142 p.   port.   19cm.

I. Åberg, Zander, ed.

NL 0344582   MnU

Lidman, Sven, 1882–
Utvald av Gud; en själs lovsång...
Stockholm, A. Bonnier ₍1940₎

269 p., 1 l.   19cm.

NL 0344583   MnU

BV4836   Lidman, Sven, 1882–
L52   Utvald av Gud; en själs lovsång.
Stockholm, A. Bonnier ₍1948₎
272 p.

1. Devotional literature. 2. Christian
life. I. Title.

NL 0344584   CU NNUT

Lidman, Sven, 1882–1960.
Valda berättelser...   Stockholm, A. Bonnier
[1924–25]
4 v. in 2   19.5 cm.
Each volume has also special t.-p.
Contents. – [v. 1] Stensborg. – [v. 2] Köpman och
krigare. – [v. 3] Huset med de gamla fröknarna. –
[v. 4] Såsom genom eld.

NL 0344585   CtY

Lidman, Sven, 1882–
Valda berattelser.   2.uppl.
Stockholm, A. Bonnier ₍1944–

v.   19cm.

Contents.–₍1₎ Såsom genom eld.–

NL 0344586   MnU

Lidman, Sven, 1882–
Vanhojen neitien talo; kertomus pyhi istä
ja sankareista. ₍1928₎

NL 0344587   OC1

Lidman, Sven, 1882–
Var inte förskräckt! Sett, tänkt och talat av Sven Lidman
... Stockholm, A. Bonnier ₍1939₎
301 p., 1 l. 19½ᵐ.

1. Religion—Philosophy.   I. Title.
₍Full name: Karl Hindrik Sven Rudolfsson Lidman₎
41–414
Library of Congress   BL51.L475
Copyright A—Foreign   44797
₍2₎   201

NL 0344588   DLC

BV4836   Lidman, Sven, 1882–1960
L525   Var inte förskräckt! Sett, tänkt och talat
av Sven Lidman ... Stockholm, A. Bonnier
₍1948₎
301 p.

1. Devotional literature 2. Christian
life

NL 0344589   CU NNUT

Lidman, Sveno Fredricus, respondent.
Dissertatio mathematica de trigometria e sectioni-
bus conicis...
see under Cronstrand, Simon Andreas,
praeses.

Lidman, Ulla, 1910–
Min dotter far till Kina; Ulla Lidmans
brev fran Kina och Mongoliet, samman-
ställda och utgivna av Sven Lidman.
Stockholm, A. Bonniers förlag ₍1935₎

215 p., 1 l. plates, ports.   19cm.

1.Missionaries, Women. 2.Missions in
China. I.Lidman, Sven, 1882–
II.Title.

NL 0344591   MnU

Lidmanowski, Wacław.
Technika wysokich napięć. ₍Wyd. 1.₎   Warszawa,
Państwowe Wydawn. Techniczne, 1953.
203 p. illus. 22 cm.
Includes bibliography.

1. Electric engineering.   I. Title.

TK153.L5   59–20076 ‡

NL 0344592   DLC NN

Lidmark, Tore.
Kalix i närbild. Kalix, Distribution: Blomquists bok-
handel, 1954.
102 p. (chiefly illus., ports.) 23 cm.

1. Kalix, Sweden—Descr.—Views.
A 55–2679
Minnesota. Univ. Libr.
for Library of Congress   ₍3₎

NL 0344593   MnU NN

Lidmila, Saint, duchess of Bohemia
see Ludmilla, Saint, duchess of Bohemia,
860?–921?

Lidner, Bengt, 1757–1793.
Samlade arbeten. Stockholm, Tryckt hos J.C. Holmberg,
1788–89.

2 v.in 1

NL 0344595   MH

Lidner, Bengt, 1757–1793.

Samlade arbeten af Lidner ... Andra uplagan,
mycket tillökt och förbättrad. Stockholm, Johan
Christopher Holmberg, 1796–1800.
2 v. in 1. 20½cm.

NL 0344596   ViU

LIDNER, Bengt.
Samlade arbeten. Ny uppl. 2d a. Stockhl.
1812–14.

NL 0344597   MH NN

Lidner, Bengt, 1757–93.
Samlade arbeten. [5.uppl. ombesörjd af G.J.Billberg]
Götheborg, Backman, 1836

2 v.

NL 0344598   MH

PT9696   Lidner, Bengt, 1757–1793.
A1   Samlade arbeten. [Stockholm, Tryckta hos A.G. Hellsten,
1836   1836]
2 v. in 1. port. (Utmärkta och klassiska arbeten af svenska
författare, 1.–2. delen)

NL 0344599   CU

PT   Lidner, Bengt, 1757–1793
9696   Samlade arbeten. 7. uppl. Stockholm, A.
A1   Bonnier [1859]
1859   569p. illus. 22cm.

NL 0344600   WU NdU CU

LIDNER, Bengt, 1757–1793.
Samlade skrifter af Bengt Lidner. 8. upplagan. Stockholm, A. Bonnier ₍1878₎
xxxvi, 2 l., ₍43₎–532p. front. (port.) illus., pl. 17cm.

Printed by Wesleyan   University Library

NL 0344601   CtW MB NNC MiU CtY

839.708   Lidner, Bengt, 1757–1793.
Sv25   Samlade skrifter. Utgivna av Harald Elovson.
v.14   Stockholm, A. Bonnier, 193–
v. 24cm. (Svenska författare, XIV)

I. Elovson, Harald, ed. Series (contents)

NL 0344602   TxU IU

Lidner, Bengt, 1757–1793.
Hpf   Samlade skrifter av Bengt Lidner, utgivna av
L70   Harald Elovson ... Stockholm, A.Bonnier[1932–
932   v. 24½cm. (Svenska författare, utg. av
Svenska vitterhetssamfundet. XIV)
Issued in parts, 1930–
Contents. – 1. Första perioden (1772–1780).
Andra perioden (1781–1787). –

NL 0344603   CtY CU IEN MnU NcU PU

VOLUME 332

Lido, Serge.
Ballet.
New York, Macmillan [19

Lido, Serge.
Les Ballets américains de Ruth Page, Bentley Stone, José Limón; photos. de Serge Lido. [Paris, 1951?]
unpaged. illus. 30 cm.

1. American Ballet Company. I. Title.

GV1787.L436   52-33912 ‡

MiU
NL 0344605   DLC PPMoI NN CLSU MB OC1 CoGrS NcGU FMU

GV1787
.M355
Masques; revue internationale d'art dramatique.
La danse ... The dance. Préf. de Jean Cocteau. Photos. de Serge Lido. Hommage à la danse, par Roger Lannes. Commentaires d'Irène Lidova. [Paris, °1947]

Lido, Serge.
Danse; numéro hors série: sauts
see his Sauts.

Lido, Serge.
17 [i. e. Dix-sept] visages de la danse française
see under Lidova, Irène.

q
792.8
L715p   Lido, Serge
Theol.   Panorama de la danse. Préface de Jean Cocteau. Texte de Irène Lidova. [Paris] Art et industrie, distribué par La Société Française du livre [n.d.]
          1 v. (chiefly illus.) 31cm.

1. Ballet—Pictures, illustrations, etc. I. Title.

NL 0344609   TxDaM

LIDO, SERGE.
    Revanche, de Ruth Page. Photographies de Serge Lido. [Paris, Impr. E. Destossés-Néogravure, 1951] [12] p. (chiefly illus.) 30cm.

Includes reviews from Le Monde and Le Combat of Paris.

1. Ballet. Revanche.   Page, Ruth. I. Title.

NL 0344610   NN

GV
1595
L5   Lido, Serge.
1950   Sauts. Danse, numéro hors série. Photographies de Serge Lido, preface de Olivier Merlin. [Paris, Masques, 1950]
          1 v. (unpaged) illus.

          A special number of the French magazine, Danse.

          1. Dancing – Pictorial works. 2. Ballet dancing. 3. Jumping. I. Title. II. Danse, Paris

NL 0344611   NGenoU OrU NN CS

Lido, Serge.
Le secret de la ligne par la danse; 6 leçons par 6 étoiles
see under Lidova, Irène, ed.

Lido, Italy   Ospedale al mare.
Archivio. anno 1, fasc. 1-   giugno
1949-   Lido di Venezia.

NL 0344613   ICJ

Lidoe, Christopher, 1690-1739.
Judaica   Dissertatio I[-posterior] philologico-
Mc16   historico-critica de publicanis [Judaeorum]
3   ... Hafniae, Ox officina Ovidii Lynnowii
2   [1713-14]
             2v. in 1. 19cm. [Dissert. Jud. histor-
             iae]
             Diss. - Copenhagen.
             Defendents: diss. 1, Johannes Adolphus
             Bröerson; diss. 2, Olaus Hannibal Andreae
             Hoff.
             Paged contin-   ously.

NL 0344614   CtY

Lidofsky, Leon Julian
A study of the radioactive decay of Br^{80} and Tl^{204}. [New York] 1952.
vi, 81 l. diagrs. 29cm.

Thesis, Columbia university.

NL 0344615   NNC

MICROFILM
F378.7CZO
L619
Lidofsky, Leon Julian
A study of the radioactive decay of Br^{80} and Tl^{204}. 1952.
vi, 81 l. diagrs. ([University microfilms, Ann Arbor, Mich.] Publication no. 4580)

Thesis, Columbia university.
Abstracted in Microfilm abstracts.

NL 0344616   NNC

Li Donni, Carmelo
... Il matrimonio e il divorzio dal lato etico-giuridico. Palermo, Fratelli Marsala, 1902.
14 p. 23½cm.
With author's autograph.

NL 0344617   MH-L

4K   Li Donni Ferro, Ferdinando.
Ital.-   Azione-contestazione della lite-giudicato sommi
539   lineamenti, storico-giuridici. 1. ed. Palermo,
          A. Amenta, 1887.
          240 p.

NL 0344618   DLC-P4

Lidonnici, Giacomo, ed.
Boccaccio, Giovanni, 1313-1375.
... Il "Buccolicum carmen"; trascritto di su l'autografo Riccardiano e illustrato per cura di Giacomo Lidonnici. Città di Castello, S. Lapi, 1914.

---

*PQ   Lidonnici, Giacomo.
4311   La corrispondenza poetica di Giovanni del
E4L61   Virgilio con Dante e il Muscato, e le postille
          di Giovanni Boccaccio. Firenze, L. S.
          Olschki, 1914.
          39 p.
          Bibliography: p. 37-39.

          1. Dante Alighieri, 1265-1321. Eclogae.
          2. Giovanni del Virgilio, fl. 1319. 3. Mussato, Albertino, 1261-1329. I. Title.

NL 0344620   CLU

Z253
.L7
Hebr   Lidor, Ephraim.
          המברכת. העדיכה והמונחים העבריים על ידי מרדכי וייס
          וגרשון זילברברג. הוצאת מדות על ידי עם עובד.
          [Tel-Aviv, 1954]
          184 p. illus. 23 cm.
          Added t. p.: The linotype composing machine.

          1. Linotype. I. Title.   Title transliterated: ha-Misderet.

Z253.L7   59-55906

NL 0344621   DLC

Lidorie ancienne chronique allusive
see under Gorjy, Jean Claude, 1753-1795.

4 PA   Lidōrikēs, Alekos M
Greek-   Ένας ιππότης στον καιρό μας... Σε 4 πρά-
168   ξεις. Αθήνα, Αετός, 1943.
          119 p.
          (Θεατρική βιβλιοθήκη Αετού)

          Title transliterated: Henas ippotēs ston kairo mas.

NL 0344623   DLC-P4

4 PA   Lidōrikēs, Alekos M
Greek-   Καινούργιοι άνθρωποι και άλλα διηγήματα.
37   Αθήναι, Πυρσός, 1938.
          160 p.

          Title transliterated: Kainourgoi anthrōpoi.

NL 0344624   ICU NNC DLC-P4

Lidōrikēs, Miltiadēs Geōrgiou, 1871-1951
Άσπρο, κόκκινο, κίτρινο· Αθηναϊκον
μυθιστόρημα. Αθήναι, Ι. Ν. Σιδέρης
[1922]   216 p.   21cm.

Title transliterated: Aspro, kokkino, kitrino· Athēnaïkon mythistorēma.

1. Fiction. Greek,   Modern.

NL 0344625   NN OC1 OCU

Lidōrikēs, Miltiadēs Geōrgiou, 1871-1951
Κοντά στή φωτιά· δράμα. Έκδ. 2. Αθήναι, Σιδέρης [1925]
45 p. (Εταιρεία Ελλήνων θεατρικών συγγραφέων)

NL 0344626   MH NN

VOLUME 332

Lidōrikēs, Miltiades G
Πολεμικαὶ ἐντυπώσεις εὐζώνου. [New York, Βιβλιοπω-λεῖον 'Ατλαντίδος, 1913;]

151 p. (Πολεμικὴ βιβλιοθήκη 'Ατλαντίδος, 1)

NL 0344627   MH

Lidōrikē, Miltiades G.
Πολεμικαὶ ἐντυπώσεις εὐζώνου, 20 σεπτεμβρίου 1912 — 20 μαρτίου 1913.
n. p. ¿1914?₎   1 p.l., (1)8–131 p.   8°.   (Πολεμικὴ βιβλιοθήκη. 'Αριθμὸς 1.)

Author's name at head of title.
Cover-title.

1. Balkan war, 1912-13. 2. Series.
N. Y. P. L.   February 28, 1917.

NL 0344628   NN OCU

DR585 Lidorikis, Miltiadis G.
.L7   ... Πολεμικαὶ ἐντυπώσεις εὐζώνου 20 σεπτεμβρίου 1912–20 μαρτίου 1913. Ἐν 'Αθήναις, ἐκδοτικὸς οἶκος Γ. Δ. Φέξη, 1914.
151, ₍1₎ p. 21ᶜᵐ.   (Βιβλιοθήκη τῶν βαλκανικῶν πολέμων 1912–1913)
At head of title: Μιλτιάδου Γ. Λιδωρίκη.

1. Balkan Peninsula—Hist.—War of 1912-1913—Personal narratives.

NL 0344629   ICU OCU

Lidors, Volter Edvard
    see   Lidforss, Edvard, 1833-1916.

Lidorss, Edvard, 1833-1910
                see
Lidforss, Edvard, 1833-1910

Lidov, Arthur

    ... Pencil portraits of famous writers,
with teaching suggestions based on the
Literature and life books. ₍New York,
Scott, Foresman and company, 1944₎
    cover-title, ₍4₎p. 12 plates 26 cm.

    At head of title: Drawings by Arthur
Lidov.
    Contents.- Carl Sandburg. - Edgar Allan
Poe.-Charles Dickens.-Stephen Vincent Benet.-
Willa Cather.-G.K. Chesterton.-George Bernard
Shaw.-Mark Twain.-Bobby Burns.-The Brownings.-
Benjamin Franklin.-Shelley.

    1. Authors--Portraits. I. Title.

NL 0344633   RPB ICarbS OCH

PR6045   Lidov, P.
.I 575M8
         Wilson, Andrew P
           ... My daughter Tanya, a play by Andrew P. Wilson ...
         Glasgow, Scoop books limited ₍1943?₎

DK268   Lidov, P
.K6L5
1942   Таня. ₍Москва₎ Воениздат, 1942.
          18 p. illus. 15 cm. (Библиотека красноармейца)

          1. Kosmodem'ianskaia, Zoiя Anatol'evna, 1923-1941. I. Title.
                                              Title transliterated: Tania.

          DK268.K6L5 1942   53-54143 ‡

NL 0344635   DLC

DK268   Lidov, P
.K6L5
          ... Таня (герой Советского союза Зоя Анатольевна Космо-
          демьянская) Москва, Огиз, Государственное издательство
          политической литературы, 1942.

          1 p. l., 5-20, ₍2₎ p. illus. 20ᶜᵐ.
          At head of title: П. Лидов.
          Portrait on cover.

          1. Kosmodem'ianskaia, Zoiя Anatol'evna, 1923-1941.   *Title*
                                                      transliterated: Tania.
          Library of Congress   DK268.K6L5   43-22376

NL 0344636   DLC

DK268   Lidov, P
.K6L5
1943   ... Таня, герой Советского союза Зоя Анатольевна Космо-
          демьянская. ₍Москва₎ Огиз, Госполитиздат, 1943.

          19, ₍1₎ p. illus. 19ᶜᵐ.
          At head of title: П. Лидов.
          Portrait on cover.

          1. Kosmodem'ianskaia, Zoiя Anatol'evna, 1923-1941.
                                            Title transliterated: Tania.
          Library of Congress   DK268.K6L5 1943   44-14114

NL 0344637   DLC

Lidov, P
    ... Tanja, die verhaal van 'n vryheidsheldin, deur P. Lidov,
vertaal deur Frans Wessels. ₍Johannesburg, S. A. Vriende van
die Sowjet-unie, 1942?₎

    1 p. l., 13 p. illus. (port.) 21½ᶜᵐ. (Soviet life-pamflet, no. 2)

    1. Kosmodem'ianskaia, Zoiя Anatol'evna, 1923-1941. I. Wessels,
Frans, tr.   *Translation of* Таня (*transliterated:* Tania)
                                                            46-28338
    Library of Congress   DK268.K6L513

NL 0344638   DLC

Lidov, P
    Tanya; the story of a heroic Russian partisan ₍by₎ P. Lidov.
Moscow, Foreign languages publishing house, 1942.

    1 p. l., 5-35, ₍1₎ p. ports. 14 x 11ᶜᵐ.

    1. Kosmodem'ianskaia, Zoiя Anatol'evna, 1923-1941.   I. Title.
    Translation of Таня (*transliterated:* Tania)
                                                        44-24811
    Library of Congress   DK268.K6L52
                                             ₍2₎   920.7

NL 0344639   DLC CSt-H NN

Lidov, Rex Everett, 1913–
    ... Studies toward the synthesis of 4-methyl-5, 5-diethyl-
uracil ... by Rex Everett Lidov ... ₍Chicago₎ 1939.

    ii numb. l., 38 p., 24ᶜᵐ.
    Thesis (PH. D.)—University of Chicago, 1936.
    Lithoprinted.
    "Private edition, distributed by the University of Chicago libraries,
Chicago, Illinois."

    1. Uracil.
                                                        40-4635
    Library of Congress   QD401.L68 1936
    Univ. of Chicago Libr.
    —— Copy 2.   ₍2₎   547.8

NL 0344640   ICU NIC CU NcD OCU DLC

GV 1785   Lidova, Irène.
A1 L47   17 ₍i. e. Dix-sept₎ visages de la
          danse française. 80 photos. de Serge
          Lido. Préf. par Philippe Heriat.
          Paris, Art et industrie, 1953.
            61 p. ports. 25 cm.
          "La première version des 'Visages de
          la danse française' a été publiée dans
          le 'Ballet annual', édition A. and C.
          Black, Londres."

            1. Dancers I. Title

NL 0344641   OU NN MiD

Lidova, Irene.
    Panorama de la danse
    see under Lido, Serge.

Lidova, Irène, ed.
    Le secret de la ligne par la danse; 6 leçons
par 6 étoiles. ₍Photographies par Serge Lido.
Composition du numéro par Irène Lidova. Paris,
Rester Jeune, 1948₎
    1 v. (unpaged) chiefly illus. (Rester Jeune,
no. 67)

    Cover-title.

NL 0344643   MiD

LT 360   LIDOVÁ ČÍTANKA SVAZU OSVĚTOVÉHO. NA DOPLNĚNÍ
.L 72   všeobecného vzdělání školského pokračovacím
         školám a kursům, dospívající mládeži i kaž-
         dému, to touží po dalším sebevzdělání
         sestavili Josef Horčička ₍a₎ Jiří V. Klíma.
         V Praze, J. Otto ₍1908₎
           387 p. illus.,ports.,plan,scores.

NL 0344644   InU

AN181   Lidová demokracie, roč.1-   Prague
f.P89L7 12.květ.1945-
         Praha.

         Daily.
         Organ Československé strany lidové.

         I. Československá strana lidová.

NL 0344645   ICU NSyU

LIDOVÁ demokracie, Prague. Květ. 12, 1945-
    Praha.   v.   illus.,ports.   46cm.

    Film reproduction. Positive.

    Daily.
    "Organ Československé strany lidové."

    I. Československá strana lidová.

NL 0344646   NN MH

AY1039   Lidová demokracie Prague.
.C95L5
         Lidový kalendář.
         Praha, Lidová demokracie.

VOLUME 332

Lidová knihovna Aventina. Praha, Aventinum

MH *

4 (1924) - Čapek, Josef, 1887-1945
Umělý člověk.

NL 0344648   MH

Lidová kultura.
Ročník

Praha, 194   v.   illus.   48cm.

Weekly (slightly irreg.)
Published by the Revoluční odborové hnutí, ročník
by the Ústřední kulturní komise Ú. R. O., ročník   ;

Ročník   , various issues have supplement: Vše pro zdar dvouletého plánu!

1. Periodicals—Czecho-Slovakia.   I. Revoluční odborové hnutí.
II. Ústřední rada odborů. Kulturní   komise.
N. Y. P. L.   January 6, 1950

NL 0344649   NN

LIDOVA kultura. roč. 1, čís. 16, roč. 2, čís. 5-roč. 4, čís.
16; září, 1945, led. 30, 1946-dub. 29, 1948
Praha.   v.   illus.   48cm.

Film reproduction. Positive.
Weekly (slightly irregular).
Published by the Revoluční odborové hnutí, Jan. 30-June 13, 1946; by the
Ústřední kulturní komise Ú.R.O., Oct. 18, 1946-Apr. 29, 1948.
1. Periodicals--Czechoslovakia. I. Revoluční odborové hnutí. II. Ústřední
rada odborů. Kulturní komise.

NL 0344650   NN

Lidová píseň v Československé republice: Krajové sbírky z
Moravy a Slezska.
Praha, Nakl. Československé akademie věd, 195
v.   24 cm.

Issued by Kabinet pro ethnografii a folkloristiku ČSAV in Brno.
Melodies.

1. Folk-songs, Czech. I. Československá akademie věd. Kabinet
pro ethnografii a folkloristiku, Brünn.

M1704.L5   M 60-1306
                              M: **

NL 0344651   DLC MH MiU

DB 541 LIDOVÁ REVUE MOR.-SLEZSKÁ; ČASOPIS VĚNOVANÝ
.L72   otazkám Moravy a Slezska. Rediguje a vydává
        Otakar Skýpala. roč. 1-
        Mor. Ostrava, Nákl. J. Richtra v Příboře. 1905-

        v. illus., monthly

x1. Moravia,--Period. x2. Silesia, Austria --
Period. xI. Skýpala, Otakar, 1877-1943, ed.

NL 0344652   InU

JS 4721 LIDOVÁ SPRÁVA--Ústřední komise
.S6   -/Slovník; rukověť pro funkcionáře národnich
        výborů./ Sestavil pracovní kolektiv Ústřední
        komise Lidové správy při ÚV KSČ. ₍Praha₎ 1947.
        659 p. (Knihovna Lidové Správy, čis. 17.)

1. Local government--Czechoslovac Republic--
Handbooks, manuals, etc.

NL 0344653   InU

Lidová strana
see Československá strana lidová.

Lidová strana československá.

See

Ceskoslovenska strana lidová.

AP52
.L53 **Lidová tvořivost;** časopis pro hudbu a zpěv, společenský a
      lidový tanec.
      Praha, Orbis.
      v. in   illus., ports. 29 cm. monthly.

Subtitle varies slightly.
Issued by Ministerstvo školství a kultury and other agencies.

I. Czechoslovak Republic. Ministerstvo školství a kultury.

AP52.L53   65-31652

NL 0344656   DLC

Lidová umělecká tvořivost v SSSR. ₍Výbor ze sovětských časo-
pisů Klub a Kulturno prosvětitělnaja rabota uspořádal Josef
Stýblo. Přeložili Jiřina Bartošová et al. Ilustroval a obálku
navrhl Karel Teissig. 1. vyd.₎ Praha, Práce—Vydavatelstvo
Roh, 1955. 85 p. illus. 21cm. (Život v klubech₎)

1. Russia—Social life, 20th cent. I. Stýblo, Josef, ed. II. Stýblo,

NL 0344657   NN

Lidová universita. V Praze, Melantrich

MH*

11 (1924) - Trávníček, František, 1888-
O českém jazyce

NL 0344658   MH

LA
688   **Lidová výchova v demokracii;** sborník prací o
.C95   lidové výchově, vyšších lidových školách,
L5   školském a poučném filmu, lidovýchovném
        rozhlasu knihovnické propagaci a správě.
        ₍Pro 1. celostátní sjezd lidovýchovných
        pracovníků a knihovníků veřejných knihoven
        v Brně r. 1928. Red. V. Patzak. V Praze,
        Vyd. péčí ministerstva školství a národní
        osvěty₎ 1928.
        469p. 22cm.
        Title also i·   Slovak and German;
        German title: Die Volksbildung in der
        Demokratie.

        Papers in Czech and German.

        1. Education - Czechoslovak Republic. I.
        Patzak, Václav, 1891-   ,ed. II. Czechoslo-
        vak Republic. Ministerstvo školství a osvety.
        III. Title: Die   Volksbildung in der
        Demokratie.

NL 0344660   NNCU-G IU

GR159 **Lidové balady karpatoruské.** Přeložil Jan
.R87   Vondráček. v Bratislavě, Podkarpatorusské
L59   nakladatelství, 1938.
        84p.

1. Folk-songs, Ruthenian. I. Vondráček, Jan,
1882-1953, ed.

NL 0344661   NcU

Lidové hry českého jeviště. V Praze

MH *

275(1936) - Lounský, H   G
            K.H.Mácha

NL 0344662   MH

Lidové knihovny vídeňské. Ve Vídni
MH*

3 (1926) - Machar, Josef Svatopluk, 1864-1942
           Machar

NL 0344663   MH

Lidové kroje Československé
see under Kazimour, Josef, 1881-1933, ed.

391.094372
L619 **Lidové kroje na Moravě** před 100 lety; 24
      tabulek krojů podle originalů litografa
      Viléma Horna z roku 1838. Nově vydal
      Archiv pro krojový výzkum v Praze.
      Praha, Taussig & Taussig, 1938.
      24 col.plates. 14cm. (Československé
      obrázkové slovníčky lidových krojů, sv.1)

      1. Costume--Moravia. I. Horn, Vilém.
      (Series)

NL 0344665   IU

Lidové Noviny.
roč.

v Brně: Tiskne Lidová tiskárna s. z. s. v. o., 19   47cm.
v. illus.

Issued twice daily (morning and afternoon) on weekdays, once on Sundays.
Editor : 19   , Jaroslav Rejzek.
Includes special Saturday section with children's page.

1. Newspapers—Czecho-Slovakia   —Brno. I. Rejzek, Jaroslav, ed.
N. Y. P. L.   May 17, 1940

NL 0344666   NN

LIDOVÉ Noviny, Brno. září 26, 1929-září 30, 1951
(incomplete)
Brno ₍etc.₎   v.   illus., ports.
47cm.

Film reproduction. Positive.

Twice daily (morning and afternoon) on weekdays,
once on Sundays, Sept. 28, 1929-Nov. 1939: daily.

Continued in next column

VOLUME 332

Continued from preceding column

May 13, 1948–Sept. 1951.
   File for 1929-39 includes special Saturday
section with children's page.
   "List Svazu československých spisovatelů," May 13,
1948–Sept. 1951.

1. Newspapers--Czechoslovakia--Brno. I. Svaz
československých spisovatelů.

NL 0344668   NN

Lidové novíny, Brünn.

ML60
J265
   Janáček, Leoš, 1854–1928.
    Janáčkovy feuilletony z L. N.; ve prospěch chudých
dětí českých škol brněnských. Uvodní studie napsali: Arne
Novák a Vladimír Helfert. Uspořádala Hana Humlová.
V. Brně, Nakl. Pokorný a spol., 1938.

Lidové novíny, *Brünn*.
   President mezi svými; druhý zájezd na Moravu a návštěva
Slezska v roce 1924. Články a zprávy Lidových novin. V
Praze, F. Borový, 1924.
   154 p. illus., port. 22 cm.

   1. Masaryk, Tomáš Garrigue, Pres. Czechoslovak Republic, 1850-
1937. I. Title.

DB217.M3L48   56–53145

NL 0344670   DLC MH

AS
142
C44
v.70
   Lidové povídky jiho-makedonské z rukopisu st.
verkovičových. Vydali Petr A. Lavrov a Jiří
Polívka. Praha, Nakl. České akademie věd a
umění, 1932.
   595 p.   (Rozpravy České akademie věd a umění.
Trida 3, čís. 70)
   Bibliography included.

   1. Tales, Macedonian. 2. Short stories, Macedonian. I. Lavrov, Petr A., 1856-1929. II. Polívka,
Jiří, 1858-   (Series: Česka akademie věd a
umění, Prague. Trida 3. Rozpravy, čís. 70)

NL 0344671   NSyU

Lidové povídky z českého Podkrkonoší;
podhoří západní
see under   Kubín, Josef Stefan,
1864-1965.

W 1
LI248
   LIDOVÉ rozpravy lékařské.
     čís. 1-   1901-
   Praha.
     v.

   1. Medicine - Collected works

NL 0344673   DNLM

D802
.R8L52
Hebraic
Sect.
   Lidovsky, Abraham.
   ביערות, רשימות של פרטיזן יהודי. תרגם מכתב־יד. ח.
ש. בדאברם. הוצאת הקיבוץ המאוחד, תש"ז.
   [Tel-Aviv, 1946]
    160 p. 17 cm.

   1. World War, 1939-1945--Underground movements--Russia.
2. World War, 1939-1945--Personal narratives, Jewish. I. Title.
          Title transliterated: Ba-ye'arot.

D802.R8L52   50–54571

NL 0344674   DLC

AY1039
.C95L5
   Lidový kalendář
   Praha, Lidová demokracie.
    v. illus., ports. 23 cm.

   1. Almanacs, Czech.   I. Lidová demokracie Prague.

AY1039.C95L5   58–16005

NL 0344675   IEdS DLC

Lidový nábytek východočeský. [Pořádá Karel V.
Adámek. Chrudim] Průmyslové Museum pro
Východní Čechy [1906]
   2 v. 10 col. plates.

   1. Furniture, Czech.
   2. Folk art--Czechoslovak Republic.
   3. Design, Decorative--Czechoslovak Republic.
   I. Adámek, Karel Václav, 1868-1944.

NL 0344676   CaOTP

Lidový sborník modliteb a bohoslužebných zpěvů
   Pravoslavné církve
     see under   [Prague. (Archdiocese, Orthodox)]

Lidový zpěvník
   see under   Horčička, Josef, comp.

Lidovýchovná knihovna Melantricha. V Praze, Melantrich

21 ([19-?]) - Strejček, Ferdinand, 1878-
            Eliška Krásnohorská.

NL 0344679   MH

... The Lid's off
   see under   Newberry, Cammann.

DK511
.L2L4
Hebraic
Sect.
   Lidski, N., tr.
   Lechem, G
   דברי ימי לימא; עם פרק מיוחד. המומנטים האופיים של קורות
היהודים בלימא מאת ג. ל. ספר למוד ומקרא. קובנה, הוצאת
            "ספר," תרפ"ג [Kaunas, 1922/23]

PJ4701
.L5
Hebraic
Sect.
   Lidski, N
   סנטכסיס הלשן העברית, אנב דגמאות ותרגילים. ספר
למוד בשביל תלמידי בתי־ספר תיכונים ולומדים מעצמם.
        קובנה, הוצאת "ספר," תרפ"ד [Kaunas, 1923]
    76 p. 21 cm.
    Added t. p.: Hebraju kalbos sintaksis.
   (LC copy: Cover title: Ebraju kalbos sintakse)

   1. Hebrew language--Syntax.
         Title transliterated: Sintaksis ha-lashon ha-'ivrit.

PJ4701.L5   A 52–1663

New York. Public Libr.

NL 0344682   NN DLC

Lidskii, Arkadiĭ Timofeevich.
   Инфицированный огнестрельный перелом; огнестрельный остеомиэлит. [Свердловск] Медгиз, Свердловское
отд-ние, 1946.
   98 p. illus. 20 cm.

   1. Gunshot wounds. 2. Fractures.   I. Title.
       Title transliterated: Infiŝirovan-
nyĭ ognestrel'nyĭ perelom.

RD96.3.L5   65–52796

NL 0344683   DLC

Engin.
QA
255
F6
1952
   Lidskiĭ, Viktor Borisovich
   The proper values of the sum and product
of symmetric matrices, by V. B. Lidskiĭ.
Translated from the Russian by Curtis D.
Benster. Edited by Wallace Givens and
George E. Forsythe. [n.p.] 1953.
   8p. 27cm.

   Bound with Four articles on numerical
matrix methods.
   At head of title: 1101-10-5100, February
5, 1953, 2248.

   "Preprint. This translation was sponsored
in part by the Office of Naval Research."
   Bibliography: p.8.

   1. Numbers, Complex. I. Title. II. Title:
Symmetric matrices.

NL 0344685   CLSU ViU CSt

Lidskjalf, et Ugeblad for Dannekvinder
og Dannemænd i fem Nummere, udgivet
fra [.Reitzels Boghandling. København,
1825. 4°. pp. (2) + 40.   IcA41L716
   Contains a few poems on Old Norse subjects
by Rask and others, and a series of articles on
Danish orthography by Porl. G. Repp, etc.

NL 0344686   NIC

Lidský (Anna). *Ueber die Beeinflussung der
Blutgerinnung durch die Schilddrüse. [Bern.]
20 pp. 8°. Berlin. L. Schumacher. 1910.

NL 0344687   DNLM

LIDSTONE, G   H   , ed.
   On guard! a history of the 10th (Torbay) battalion Devonshire home
guard. [n. p.] Battalion publication committee; designed and printed
by the Torquay Times & Devonshire press. [1945] illus., ports. 22 cm.

   Includes roster.

   1. Home guards--Gt. Br.--Eng.--Devonshire. I. Great Britain. Home
guard. 10th Devon battalion. II. Title.   1. 1945.

NL 0344688   NN

Lidstone, G   J
   Notes on Everett's interpolation formula.
[Edinburgh, 1922]
   21-26 p. 29 cm.
   Reproduced from Edinburgh mathematical society.
Proceedings. v. 40, p. 21-26.

NL 0344689   OCU

VOLUME 332

Lidstone, James Torrington Spencer.
The Bostoniad : giving a full description of the principal establishments, together with the most honorable and substantial business men, in the Athens of America. By the Hon. James Torrington Spencer Lidstone ... Boston, Pub. under universal patronage ₍Hollis & Gunn, prs.₎ 1853.
1 p. l., ₍5₎–62 p. 18¼ᶜᵐ.
In verse.

1. Boston—Descr. ɪ. Title.
6—4454
Library of Congress   F73.44.L71

NL 0344690   DLC MB

Lidstone, James Torrington Spencer.
The Bostoniad: giving a full description of the principal establishments, together with the most honorable and substanial business men, in the Athens of America. By the Hon. James Torrington Spencer Lidstone... Boston, Pub. under universal patronage [Hollis & Gunn, prs.] 1853.
86 p.   19 cm.
In verse.
Parts 1-2.

NL 0344691   RPB MWA

Lidstone, James Torrington Spencer.
The Bostoniad: [poems] giving a full description of the principal establishments, together with the most honorable and substantial business men, in the Athens of America. [Part 1-3.] Boston. [Hollis & Gunn.] 1853. 122 pp. 12°.

G358 — T.r. — Boston, Mass. Bus. assoc.

NL 0344692   MB RPB MH

Lidstone, James Torrington Spencer.
The Londoniad (complete): Giving a full description of the principal establishments, together with the most honourable and substantial business men, in the capital of England, &c., &c. [Verse.]
— London. Published under universal patronage. 1856. iv, 112 pp. 17½ cm., in 8s.

T ₅₈R₄ — T.r. — London. Bus. assoc.

NL 0344693   MB

Lidstone, James Torrington Spencer
The sixth Londoniad: (complete in itself.) being the poem on Parliamentary character, giving an account of Members eminent in literature, science, and art; ...and pieces on some of the most celebrated personages in the Kingdom, and in the provinces of British North America; forming altogether episodes in a grand national poem on the arts. London, Published by the Author, 1859.
iv, 116p.   18 cm.

With his: The   Torontiad.... 1850.

NL 0344694   RPB CaBVaU

76
L715t   Lidstone, James Torrington Spencer
850   The Torontiad; a complete business directory for Toronto, giving a splendid description of the most celebrated establishments in that famous city, together with illustrations of its most eminent personages. Toronto, Published under universal patronage, 1850.
35 p.   19 cm.

In verse.

NL 0344695   RPB

Lidstone, Ronald A.
The art of fencing; a practical manual for the foil, épée and sabre, by Ronald A. Lidstone ... With photographs and text figures ... London, H. F. & G. Witherby ₍1930₎
224 p. front., illus., plates.   22½ᶜᵐ.   (The sports and pastimes library)

1. Fencing.

Library of Congress   U860.L5   31-17172
₍3₎   796.86

NL 0344696   DLC OrP OrCS OCl OClh PP NN

Lidstone, Ronald A.
Bloody bayonets; a complete guide to bayonet fighting, by Squadron Leader R. A. Lidstone ... Sketches by L./Cpl. M. C. Clifford ... Aldershot, Gale & Polden limited ₍1942₎
vii, 68 p. incl. illus., 2 forms.   18¼ᶜᵐ.

1. Bayonets.   ɪ. Title.
42-19881
Library of Congress   UD400.L5   796.86
₍2₎

NL 0344697   DLC

Lidstone, Ronald A
Fencing; a practical treatise on foil, épée, sabre. London, H. F. & G. Witherby, 1952.
384 p.   illus.   21 cm.   (The Sports and pastimes library)

1. Fencing.   ɪ. Title.
U860.L52   796.86   53-29220 ‡

NL 0344698   DLC CaBVa AU IU MiD OO

133
L61s   Lidstone, Ronald Alexander.
Studies in symbology. London, Theosophical Pub. House ₍1926₎
93p. illus., diagrs. 23cm.

1. Symbolism. I. Title.

NL 0344699   IU MH NN

TJ
461
L715   Lidstone, Thomas.
Notes on the model of Newcomen's steam-engine (1705). Exhibited in the "Special loan collection of scientific apparatus," South Kensington museum, 1876. By Thomas Lidstone. London, New York, E. & F. N. Spon, 1876.
6, ₍1₎ p. illus. 21 cm.

1. Steam-engines. I. Title: Newcomen's steam-engine   (1705).

NL 0344700   DSI

Lidstone, William, joint author.

Brown, Charles Barrington.
Fifteen thousand miles on the Amazon and its tributaries. By C. Barrington Brown ... and William Lidstone, c. ᴇ. With map and wood engravings. London, E. Stanford, 1878.

Lidstone, William.
Map of a part of the Republic of Colombia.
— London. Stanford. 1899. 2 sheets. Size, when joined, 61 × 28 inches. Scale, 1:810000 (or, 12.8 miles to 1 inch).

L5716 — Colombia. Geog. Maps.

NL 0344702   MB

HV
5538
B39   Lidström, A   E
Alkoholismens utbredning hos de gamla nordborna. Bidrag till kännedomen om alkoholismens historia. [Stockholm] Svenska Nykterhetsförlaget [1907]
40 p. [With: Berglund, Aug. Hindren för ett rusdrycksförbud och medlen för deras undanrödjande, 1904]

1. Alcoholism.   I. Title.

NL 0344703   WaU NIC

4UG
193   Lidström, Erik, 1903-
Den svenska graniten i försvarets tjänst; en översikt över nutida befästningskonst. Stockholm, Riksförbundet för sveriges försvar [1943]
55 p.

(Medborgarkunskap om riksförsvaret, 14)

NL 0344704   DLC-P4

Lidström, Fritz.
Clinical and experimental studies on intravenous nutrition with a dialyzed enzymatic casein hydrolysate. ₍Translated from the Swedish by Erica Odelberg₎ Stockholm, 1954.
60 p. illus. 24 cm. (Acta chirurgica Scandinavica. Supplementum 186)
At head of title: From the Department of Surgery, Sabbatsbergs sjukhus, Stockholm, Sweden.
Includes bibliographies.

1. Protein metabolism. 2. Amino acids. ɪ. Title: Intravenous nutrition with a dialyzed enzymatic casein hydrolysate. (Series)
A 57-7584
Wisconsin. Univ. Libr.
for Library of Congress   ₍2₎

NL 0344705   WU OkU-M PPJ ViU DNLM PPT

QH9
.T6
no. 260-26   **Thunberg, Karl Peter,** 1743-1828, praeses.
Rare Bk.   De ipecacuanha dissertatio ... Upsaliæ, excudebant Regiæ academiæ typographi ₍1824₎

Lidströmer, Joh. Otto, respondent.

NA7373
L5   Lidt om danske murstenshuse.   [Udg. af A/B Mälardalens tegelbruk, Stockholm; A/S Frederiksholms tegl- og kalkvaerker, København; A/S Hedehus- teglvaerket, Hedehusene; Kählers tegl-vaerk, Korsør.   København, 1953]
31 p.   illus.

Leaf, containing French, German and English translations of preface, tipped in.

1. Architecture, Domestic - Denmark.   2. Building, Brick.

NL 0344707   CU

LIDT om Öhlenschlaegers Nordens guder og Heibergs Nordiske mythologie. [Lund, Berlingska boktrycheriet, 1868].

pp.22.
Without title-page, Caption title.

NL 0344708   MH

VOLUME 332

W 4
U92
1952

LIDTH DE JEUDE, Albert Hendrik van
Trichomonas vaginalis heeft geen
pathogene betekenis; trichomonas
vaginalis leeft aan de oppervlakte van
het slijmvlies zonder haar gastvrouw
te benadelen. Trichomonas vaginalis
is not pathogenic ... Ziest, Dijkstra's
Uitgeverij, 1952.
135 p.
Proefschrift - Utrecht.

Summary and conclusion in Dutch
and English.
1. Trichomonas vaginalis
AFML54-11087

NL 0344710   DNLM

Lidth de Jeude, Albert Peter, *jonkheer* **van,** 1884–
Quantitatieve onderzoekingen over het antagonisme van
sulfas atropini tegenover hydrochloras pilocarpini, salicylas
physostigmini en hydrochloras muscarini (Grübler) op over-
levende darmen van zoogdieren ... door Albert Peter van
Lidth de Jeude ... Amsterdam, A. H. Kruyt, 1916.
5 p. l., 157 p. pl., fold. tab., diagrs. (part fold.) 27 x 19½ᶜᵐ.
Plate and diagrams in pocket.
Proefschrift—Utrecht.
"Stellingen" (3, p.) laid in.
1. Alkaloids—Physiological effect. 2. Intestines. 3. Medicines, An-
tagonism of.
37-9593

Library of Congress   QP921.A1L5 1916
(2,   [615.52] 612.398195

NL 0344711   DLC MBCo

Wason
PT5854
L71B8

Lidth de Jeude, E   van
Brieven zonder antwoord.   Maastricht,
Boosten & Stols (1930)
125 p.   20cm.

NL 0344712   NIC

Lidth de Jeude, Jan Lambert van
... De domicilio ... defendet Janus
Lambertus van Lidth de Jeude ... Tra-
jecti ad Rhenum, ex offic. Paddenburgii
et soc., 1833.
2 p.l., 51 p. 20½cm.
Diss.- Utrecht.
Bibliographical footnotes.

NL 0344713   MH-L

Lidth de Jeude, Karel Willem Hendrik van, 1863–
De "zaak" (affaire) rechtskundig beschouwd ... door Karel
Willem Hendrik van Lidth de Jeude ... Utrecht, Stoom-
boek- en steendrukkerij "De Industrie", J. van Druten, 1888.
4 p. l., 120 p., 1 l. 23ᶜᵐ.
Proefschrift—Utrecht.
"Stellingen": p. (115)–120.

1. Commercial law—Netherlands.   I. Title.
34-37858

NL 0344714   DLC MB

Lidth de Jeude (LAMBERT JOHAN ADRIAAN VAN)
*De terugwerkende kracht van het vonnis van scheiding
van goederen ... . 7. Juli 1886 ... *Leiden: P. Somer-
will*, 1886. 3 p.l., pp. 9–53, 1l. 8°.

NL 0344715   NN

Lidth de Jeude, Martinus Elisa Johannes Jacobus van, *jonk-
heer,* 1853–1916.
De levering van schepen en scheepsaandeelen ... door
Martinus Elisa Johannes Jacobus van Lidth de Jeude ...
Utrecht, P. J. Diehl, 1882.
3 p. l., 111 p. 22½ᶜᵐ.
Proefschrift—Utrecht.
"Stellingen": p. (105)–111.

1. Maritime law—Netherlands. 2. Sales—Netherlands.   I. Title.
34-37738

NL 0344716   DLC MH NN

387.12972986
L715h

Lidth de Jeude, O   C   A
van
De haven van Curaçao. 'sHertogenbosch
[Neth.] Typ. Lutkie & Cranenburg [1910]
xii, 100 p. illus., maps (19 fold. col.
plates in portfolio) 31cm.

University of Florida copy imperfect:
plate IV wanting.

1. Willemstad, Curaçao - Harbor.
2. Harbors - Curaçao. I. Title.

NL 0344717   FU

Lidth de Jeude, Theodor Gerard van, 178ᵦ
1863.
Catalogue du Musée zoologique de Th.G.van
Lidth de Jeude. Partie 1ᵉ 11ᵉ 1vᵉ contenant les
collections de mammifères, d'oiseaux et de
poissons. ... Arnhem, 1858.

(4), 155 p.   8°.

NL 0344718   MH-Z PPAN

LIDTH DE JEUDE, Th. G. VAN.
Recueil de figures des vers intestinaux ouvrages présentant une distribution methodique de
ces animaux, les caractères de leurs familles et
de leurs genres, et la description de quelques
espèces les plus remarquable. Leide, 1827.

obl.4°.pp.(29). 11 plates.

NL 0344719   MH

QL387
L5

Lidth de Jeude, Theodor Gerard van, 1788-1863.
Recueil de figures des vers intestinaux,
ouvrage, présentant une distribution
méthodique de ces animaux, les caractères
généraux et particuliers de leurs familles
et de leurs generes, principalement suivant
le système de Mr. le professeur C.A.
Rudolphi et la description de quelques
espèces les plus remarquables. Leide, S. et
J. Luchtmans, 1829.
1 v. (unpaged) illus. 27 x 40cm.

1.Worms, Intest   inal and parasitic.
I.Rudolphi, Karl   Asmund, 1771-1832.

NL 0344720   OrCS DNLM

568
L61c

Lidth de Jeude, Theodorus Willem van, 1853-
Catalogue ostéologique des poissons,
reptiles et amphibies par T.W. van Lidth
de Jeude. Leide, E.J. Brill, 1898.
54, 52, 11 p. 25 cm.

Cover title.
Muséum d'Histoire naturelle des Pays-Bas,
t. X². Cf. Zoological record, v. 35, 1898,
sec. 4, p. 7.

1. Fishes, Fossil. 2. Reptiles, Fossil.
I. Leyden. Rijks Museum van Natuurlijke
Historie. II. Title.

NL 0344722   LU

Lidth de Jeude, Theodorus Willem van, 1853–
De spijsverteringsorganen der phytophage lamellicor-
nienlarven ... Utrecht, Kemink & zoon, 1882.
4 p. l., 56 p. fold. pl. 23½ᶜᵐ.
Proefschrift—Utrecht.

1. Digestive organs—Insects. 2. Lamellicornia.

Library of Congress   QL856.L7
7-1739

NL 0344723   DLC CU

Lidth de Jeude, Wilhelmus Albertus van, respondent
Disputatio juridica inauguralis de occupatione
rerum hostilium
see under   Irhoven, Willem van, 1698-1761,
praeses.

Lidth de Jeude, Willem Frederik Carel
van
... De effectu emtionis venditionis rei
alienae, jure francico ... defendet
Guilielmus Fredericus Carolus van Lidth
de Jeude ... Tielae, A. van Loon, 1828
(i.e. 1838)
3 p.l., 36 p. 22cm.

Diss.- Leiden.

NL 0344725   MH-L

Lidu českému. V Praze, Nakl. spisovatelovým

Řada 2 (1890) - Košut, Bedřich Vilém, 1819-93
Historie kalicha v Čechách a na
Moravě.

NL 0344726   MH

Slavic-
American
Imprints
Coll.
420.17
M88

Lidumil; povídka od K. New York, Česko-americká
knihovna [1887]
44 p. 20 cm. (Česko-americká knihovna číslo 1. Oddělení I.
English translation of title: The philantropist; a novel by
K.
Bound with Kužáková, Johana: Poslední poustevnice. New York,
1888; Doležal, Karel: Žena ve společnosti lidské. New York,
1888; Volney, C. F.: Zříceniny; úvahy o převratech říší. New
York, 1888; Almanach na rok 1887. New York, 1887; Doležal,
Karel: Naše republika. New York, 1887. rw

NL 0344727   IEdS

Lidvall, Nils, *ed.*
Gatan, praktisk handledning i gatubyggnad. (Utarb. av
ingenjörer vid Stockholm stads gatukontor. Redigerad av
Nils Lidvall. Stockholm; Svenska kommunal-tekniska fö-
reningen (1953)
581 p. illus., col. plate, diagrs., forms, plans. 25 cm.
Includes bibliographies.
CONTENTS.—Planläggning.—Utförande.

1. Streets. 2. Cities and towns—Planning. 3. Traffic engineering.
4. Pavements. 5. Road construction.
A 54–1258

Michigan. Univ. Libr.
for Library of Congress   (3)

NL 0344728   MiU NN

VOLUME 332

Lidwell, George,   defendant.
A report of the trial of George Lidwell and
Thomas Prior, esqrs. upon an information, filed
ex officio, by His Majesty's Attorney general,
for sending and delivering a challenge to Chol-
meley Dering, esq. colonel of the Romney fencibles.
By William Ridgeway, esq. barrister at law. Dublin, Printed by J. Exshaw, 1800.
1 p.t., 51 p.   22ᶜᵐ.
No. ₍6₎ in v.5 of set lettered: Pamphlets on Irish
affairs.

I. Prior, Thomas, defendant.   II. Ridgeway, William, d. 1817.

NL 0344729   MiU

Lidwell, Thomas,   defendant.
Lidwell's trial. An authentic report of the
trial of Thomas Lidwell, esq. on an indictment
for a rape committed upon the body of Mrs. Sarah Sutton, wife of Jacob Sutton, esq. of Portar-
lington, Queen's County. Tried at Naas, Lent assizes, 1800, before the Right Honourable Lord
Viscount Carleton, lord chief justice of the
Court of common pleas, and a respectable jury
of the county of Kildare ... By permission of
the Court. Dublin, Printed by R. Marchbank, for
W. Wilson, 1800.
2 p.t., viii, 91 p.   front.   22ᶜᵐ.
No. ₍5₎ in v.5 of set lettered: Pamphlets on Irish
affairs.
I. Sutton, Mrs. Sarah   (Reed ?) b. 1774?

NL 0344730   MiU

Lidy, J   1886-
... Contribution à l'étude de la thérapeutique des
cancers inopérables par les métaux colloïdaux...
Alger, 1914.
24.5 cm.
Thèse - Univ. d'Alger.

NL 0344731   CtY

Lidy (Paul-Antoine-Joseph) [1885-   ]. *Car
diopathies valvulaires et aptitude militaire
158 pp. 8°   Paris. 1918.   No. 82.

NL 0344732   DNLM CtY

Lidyat, Thomas

see

Lydiat, Thomas

Lidzbarski, Marcellus, 1868-1928.

see

Lidzbarski, Mark, 1868-1928.

Lidzbarski, Mark, 1868-1928.
Altaramäische urkunden aus Assur, mitgeteilt und untersucht von Mark Lidzbarski; mit 2 lichtdrucktafeln und 4
abbildungen im text. Leipzig, J. C. Hinrichs, 1921.
20 p.   II pl.   35½ cm.   (Added t-p: Ausgrabungen der Deutschen
Orient-gesellschaft in Assur.   E: Inschriften.   V)
On verso of t.-p.: 38. Wissenschaftliche veröffentlichung der Deutschen Orient-gesellschaft.

1. Aramaic language—Texts.   2. Assyria—Antiq.   I. Title.

DS41.D44   hft. 38   22—21830

OCl PU PPAmP
NL 0344735   DLC CU IEG KyLoS NN MB MH-AH MiU OCH

PJ3085   Lidzbarski, Mark, 1868-1928, ed.
.L59   Altsemitische Texte, hrsg. und erklärt von
Mark Lidzbarski. Erstes Heft; Kanaanäische
Inschriften (Moabitisch, Althebräisch, Phöni-
zisch, Punisch) Mit 8 Abbildungen.   Giessen,
A. Töpelmann, 1907.
64 p. illus.

1. Inscriptions, Semitic.   I. Title.

NjP NcD ICMcC PU TNJ-R
NL 0344736   GEU-T CtY CU PP NNUT DCU-H ICU OCl MH MiU

₍Lidzbarski, Mark₎ 1868-
Auf rauhem wege, jugenderinnerungen eines deutschen
professors. Giessen, A. Töpelmann, 1927.
2 p. l., 215 p.   21½ᵐ.

I. Title.

Library of Congress   PJ3009.L5A2   28-18143

NL 0344737   DLC OCl OCH NN PPDrop PPiPT MH CU CtY

Lidzbarski, Mark, 1868-
De propheticis, quae dicuntur, legendis arabi-
cis prolegomena.   [4], 64, [2] p.   Lipsiae, typis
G. Drugulini, 1893.

Inaug.-diss. - Berlin.
Vita.

CtHC
NL 0344738   MH PPDrop NjP CtY NIC MiU MH ICRL CU OCl

Lidzbarski, Mark, 1868-   ed.

Ephemeris für semitische epigraphik ...   1. bd.: 1900-
Giessen, J. Ricker, 1902-   FOR OTHER EDITIONS
                                 SEE MAIN ENTRY

Lidzbarski, Mark, 1868-
Geschichten und lieder aus den neu-aramäischen handschriften der Königlichen bibliothek zu Berlin.   Von
Mark Lidzbarski.   Weimar, E. Felber, 1896.
xvi, 312 p., 1 l.   22ᵐ.   (Added t.-p.: Beiträge zur volks- und völker-
kunde.   4. bd.)
"Verzeichnis der mit abgekürzten titeln zitierten schriften": p. ₍xiii₎-xvi.

                                               10-20234

NL 0344740   DLC NIC CU CtY OU PPDrop NN MB OCl

Lidzbarski, Mark, 1868-   tr.

Ginzā.
Ginzā, der Schatz, oder das Grosse buch der Mandäer übersetzt und erklärt von Mark Lidzbarski. Göttingen, Vandenhoeck & Ruprecht; Leipzig, J. C. Hinrichs, 1925.

Lidzbarski, Mark, 1868-
Handbuch der nordsemitischen epigraphik, nebst aus-
gewählten inschriften, von Mark Lidzbarski ...   Weimar,
E. Felber, 1898.
2 v.   XLVI pl.   23½ᵐ (v. 2: 33½ᵐ)
Vol. 1, text; v. 2, plates (in portfolio)
"Bibliographie": v. 1, p. ₍4₎-88; "Nachträge. Zur bibliographie": p.
₍493₎-499.

1. Inscriptions, Semitic.   2. Inscriptions, Semitic—Bibl.

Library of Congress   PJ3085.L6   11—13643

MH-AH MoSCS TNJ-R
OCl ODW OCH PHC PPDrop PBm PP PU OO CU PPiPT CtY-D
NL 0344742   DLC MiU CtY DC DCU-H NcD NNUT NjNbS NjP

Lidzbarski, Mark, 1868-1928.
Das Johannesbuch der Mandäer
see under   Drasia d lahia, German and
Mandean. [supplement]

B13   Lidzbarski, Mark, 1868-1928, ed.
L619k   Kanaanäische inschriften (moabitisch, althebräisch, phönizisch, punisch) Giessen, A.
Töpelmann, 1907.
64 p. facsims. 21 cm. (His Altsemitische
texte, 1. heft)

Includes bibliographical references.

1. Canaanite literature.   I. Author series.

NL 0344744   CtY-D ICMcC

AS182   Lidzbarski, Mark, 1868-1928, ed.
.G812
N. F.   Mandaeans. Liturgy and ritual.
Bd. 17,   Mandäische Liturgien, mitgeteilt, übers. und erklärt von
Nr. 1   Mark Lidzbarski. Berlin, Weidmannsche Buchhandlung,
1920.

Lidzbarski, Mark, 1868-1928.
Ein mandäisches Amulett.   (In: Florilegium; ou,
Recueil de travaux d'érudition dédiés à Monsieur le
marquis Melchoir de Vogüé.   Paris, 1910.   4°.
p. 349-373, 1 p. l.)

NL 0344746   NN

Lidzbarski, Mark, 1868-1928.
Die Namen der Alphabetbuchstaben. Gieszen,
1906.

NL 0344747   NjP

PJ3104   Lidzbarski, Mark, 1868-1928, ed. and tr.
251   Die neu-aramäischen Handschriften der
v.4-9   Königlichen Bibliothek zu Berlin, in
Auswahl, hrsg. übersetzt und erläutert von
Mark Lidzbarski.   Weimar, E. Felber, 1894-
1895.
2v. illus. 24cm. (Semitistische
Studien, Hft.4-9)

1. Manuscripts, Aramaic.   I. Berlin.
Preussische Staatsbibliothek.

NL 0344748   IaU

492.008   Lidzbardki, Mark, 1868-1928, ed. and tr.
Se525   Die neu-aramäischen Handschriften der König-
Heft 4-9   lichen Bibliothek zu Berlin; in Auswahl hrsg.,
übers. und erläutert von Mark Lidzbarski.
Weimar, E. Felber, 1896.
2 v. 24cm. (Semitistische Studien
Ergänzungshefte zur Zeitschrift für
Assyriologie, Heft 4/9)

1. Syriac language, Modern - Texts.
I. Berlin. Preussische Staatsbibliothek. Mss.
II. T.   III. Ser: Semitistische Studien,
Heft 4/9.

NL 0344749   MiDW MiU OCl MH MoU NIC NNUT PPDrop OCH

VOLUME 332

Lidzbarski, Mark, 1868–1928.
Paradigmen und register zu Gesenius' Kautzsch Hebräischer grammatik. Nebst zwei facs. der Siloahinschrift und einer neuen schrifttafel von M. Litzbarski. 27. auflage.   Leipzig, Vogel, 1902.
518–591 p.   O.

NL 0344750   DCU-H NcD

Lidzbarski, Mark, 1868–1928.
Phönizische und aramäische krugaufschriften aus Elephantine. Von prof. dr. Mark Lidzbarski ... ₁Berlin, Verlag der Königlichen akademie der wissenschaften, in commission bei Georg Reimer, 1912₎

20 p. illus., vi pl. (facsims.) 29½ᵐ. (Abhandlungen der Königlich preussischen akademie der wissenschaften, Phil₁osophisch₎-hist₁orische₎ klasse. ₁Jahrg.₎ 1912. Anhang, abh. 1)

Bibliographical foot-notes.

1. Inscriptions, Phenician. 2. Inscriptions, Aramaic. 3. Elephantine (Island)—Antiq.   I. Title.
                                                A 41-1549
Princeton univ. Library
for Library of Congress   [AS182.B34 1912]
                      ₍3₎   (063)

NL 0344751   NjP NNC ICMcC OCU OCl MH PU PPDrop

Lidzbarski, Mark. 1868–
Phönizische und aramäische Krugaufschriften aus Elephantine. 20 pp. 6 plates.
(In Koeniglich-preussische Akademie der Wissenschaften, Berlin. Philosophisch-historische Classe. Abhandlungen. 1912. Nichtmitgliederabhandlung I. Berlin. 1912.)

K c80 — Elephantine. island. Antiq. — Aramaean language. Works in Aramaean.

NL 0344752   MB

Lidzbarski, Mark. 1868–
Eine punisch-altberberische Bilinguis aus einem Tempel der Massinissa. Plate.
(In Koeniglich-preussische Akademie der Wissenschaften, Berlin. Sitzungsberichte. Jahrgang 1913, Halbband 1, pp. 296–304. Berlin. 1913.)

K5132 — Carthage. Lang. — Inscriptions. Punic.

NL 0344753   MB OCl

Lidzbarski, Mark. 1868–
Uthra und Malakha. Von Mark Lidzbarski.
(In Orientalische Studien Theodor Nöldeke . . . gewidmet. Vol. I, pp. 537–545. Giessen. 1906.)

G5630 — Mendaites. Myth. — T.r. -

NL 0344754   MB

Lidzsbarski, Mark, 1868–1928.
Gesenius, Friedrich Heinrich Wilhelm, 1786–1842.
Wilhelm Gesenius' Hebräische grammatik. 29. aufl. Hebräische grammatik, mit benutzung der von E. Kautzsch bearb. 28. aufl. von Wilhelm Gesenius' Hebräischer grammatik, verfasst von G. Bergsträsser. Mit beiträgen von M. Lidzbarski ... Leipzig, F. C. W. Vogel, 1918–

Lidzelius, Nicol. D.   resp.
Commenatationum s toicarum ...

see under

Biberg, Nils Fredrik, 1776–1827   pr.

Lidzhi, David I., joint author.

Mevorakh, Nissim.
Законъ за гражданското съдопроизводство; текстъ, мотиви, библиография и съдебна практика. София ₁Печатница С. Василевъ₎ 1935–

Lidži, David I.
see
Lidzhi, David I.

Lidzki-Śledziński, Stefan
see
Śledziński, Stefan, 1897–

AS283 Lie, Arthur Gotfred, 1887–
.C56   Gamle assyriske love transkriberet og oversat med bemerk-
1923   ninger til de forskjellige paragrafer, av A. G. Lie ... Utgit for H. A. Benneches fond. Kristiania, I kommission hos J. Dybwad, 1924.

iv, 66 p. 27ᵐ. (Videnskapsselskapets skrifter. II. Hist.—filos. klasse. 1923. no. 5)

"Literatur": p. 66.

1. Law, Assyro—Babylonian.

NL 0344760   ICU MoU NIC NN

Lie, Arthur Gotfred, 1887–
Om Assyriens historie og sproget i de assyriske indskrifter fra den ældste tid og ned til Tiglatpileser I. (ca. 1100 f. Kr.) af A. G. Lie. København, M. P. Madsen, 1921.

116 p. 22ᵐ.

Thesis—Copenhagen.
"Literatur": p. ₁115₎–116.

1. Assyria—Hist. 2. Assyro-Babylonian language. 3. Cuneiform inscriptions.
                                                25-6364
Library of Congress   DS71.L55

NL 0344761   DLC ICU IU NN CtY

Lie, Arthur Gotfred, 1887–
Ordalet i Hammurabis lov og i de gamle assyriske love, av Arthur Gotfred Lie.   (In: Studier tilegnede Professor, Dr. Phil. & Theol. Frants Buhl. København, 1925. 8°. p. 103–111.)

1. Hammurabi, king of Babylon.
N. Y. P. L.   December 17, 1926

NL 0344762   NN

Lie, Bergliot.
Møteteknikk; Veien fra studiesirklen til de Forente nasjoner. Oslo, Enersens trykkeri, 1946.

47 p. 21 cm. (Kvinnen og tidens studiesirkler)

1. Discussion. 2. Leadership.   I. Title.

BF637.D5L5   55–39559

NL 0344763   DLC NN

Lie, Bernt ₁Bessesen₎, 1868–1916
... Samlede verker, mindeutgave. Kristiania, H. Aschehoug & co. ₁1917₎ 10 vols. 19cm

NL 0344764   NdU MH

Lie, Bernt Bessesen, 1868–1916
Diáktörténetek (Kalandok a fjordok földjén); magyarra átdolgozta Tábori Kornel. Budapest, Lampel R. kk., 1911. ₍159 p.₎

NL 0344765   OCl

Lie, Bernt Bessesen, 1868–
... Gabriel Selje: roman fra første halvdel av forrige aarhundrede. Kristiania, H. Aschehoug & co. (W. Nygaard) 1912.

2 p l, 242 p. 20ᵐ.   kr. 3.75

I. Title.

Library of Congress   13–1662
Copyright A—Foreign 6682

NL 0344766   DLC CaBVa

Lie, Bernt ₁Bessesen₎.
Gabriel Selje: roman fra første halvdel av forrige aarhundrede. Kristiania: H. Aschehoug & Co., 1912. 2 p.l., 242 p. 4. thousand.   12°.

1. Fiction (Norwegian). 2. Title.
N. Y. P. L.   January 15, 1914.

NL 0344767   NN MH

Lie, Bernt.
Guttedage; syv smaafortællinger. Kristiania: H. Aschehoug & Co., 1905. 2 p.l., 162 p.   12°.

NL 0344768   NN WaS

Lie, Bernt Bessesen, 1868–
... Guttedage, med illustrationer av S. Segelcke. 4. oplag. Kristiania, H. Aschehoug & co. (W. Nygaard) 1920.

152 p. illus. 19ᵐ. (His Guttefortaellinger IV)
"1. oplag., 1905."

I. Title.

NL 0344769   MiU

Lie, Bernt Bessesen, 1868–
... Helle. Kristiania, H. Aschehoug & co. (W. Nygaard) 1909.

3 p. l., ₁3₎–201 p. 20ᵐ.   kr. 3.00

                                    10–1054
Library of Congress

NL 0344770   DLC

Lie, Bernt ₁Bessesen₎ 1868–
... Hildr; illustreret af Thorolf Holmboe. ₁2. opl.₎ København og Kristiania, E. Bojesen, 1902.

167 p. incl. illus., 1 col. pl. 18ᵐ. (Half-title: Nordisk bibliotek ₁IX₎)
"Trykt ialt 6000 eksempl."

                                    3-30068

NL 0344771   DLC NdU

VOLUME 332

Lie, Bernt Bessesen, 1868-1916.
... I Knut Arnebergs hus. Kristiania, H. Aschehoug & co., 1899.
2 p. l., 326 p. 18ᶜᵐ.
A novel.

ɪ. Title.
3-18509
Library of Congress   PT8950.L5 I 2 1899

NL 0344772   DLC

PT8950 **Lie, Bernt Bessesen,** 1868-1916.
.L5I16   ... I eventyrland, fortælling fra det nordlige Norge. Illus.
1898   af Thorolf Holmboe. 2. opl. ¡Kristiania¡ A. Cammermeyer
Rare   ¡1898¡
bk.   ¡8¡, 304 p. illus. 15ᶜᵐ.
Room   At head of title: Bernt Lie.
Author's autograph presentation copy.

NL 0344773   ICU CLU NdU

839.82372 **Lie, Bernt Bessesen,** 1868-1916.
L716l   I eventyrland; fortælling fra det nordlige Norge.
København, Gyldendalske boghandel, Nordisk forlag,
1912.
190 p. 19 cm.

NL 0344774   N CU NcD

Lie, Bernt Bessesen, 1868-
...I eventyrland; fortælling.   Kristiania: Gyldendalske Bok-
handel, 1923. 129 p.   8°.

1. Fiction, Norwegian. 2. Title.
N.Y.P.L.   January 7, 1925

NL 0344775   NN

Lie, Bernt ¡Bessesen¡ 1868-
... I Knut Arnebergs hus.   Kristiania, H. Aschehoug
& co., 1899.
2 p. l., 326 p. 18ᶜᵐ.
3-18509

NL 0344776   DLC NdU

Lie, Bernt Bessesen, 1868-1916.
I Knut Arnebergs Hus. 2. ed.   Kristiania, H.
Aschenhoug & Co., 1902.
2 p. l., 315 p.   12°.

NL 0344777   NN

Lie, Bernt Bessesen, 1868-
I Marjastilla.   Kristiania: H. Aschehoug, 1914.   2 p.l.,
220 p.   12°.
Author's name at head of title.

1. Fiction (Norwegian). 2. Title.
N.Y.P.L.   October 25, 1915.

NL 0344778   NN NBC

Lie, Bernt Bessesen, 1868-
... I Marjastilla.   4. tusen.   Kristiania, H. Aschehoug
& co. (W. Nygaard) 1914.
2 p. l., 220 p. 20ᶜᵐ.   kr. 3.50

ɪ. Title.
15-16637
Library of Congress   11566

NL 0344779   DLC NcD

Lie, Bernt Bessesen, 1868-1916.
Im kampf gegen die übermacht; roman.   Leipzig
Grunow, 1910.

NL 0344780   OrP

Lie, Bernt Bessesen, 1868-1916.
... Im Märchenland. Erzählung aus dem nörd-
lichsten Norwegen. Autorisierte Uebersetzung aus
dem Norwegischen von Ottilie von Harling. Stuttgart, Engelhorn, 1901.
158p. 18cm. (Engelhorns allgemeine Romanbibliothek. Eine Auswahl der besten modernen Romane
aller Völker. 17.Jahrg.,¡Bd.19)

NL 0344781   NBC PPG NN

Lie, Bernt Bessesen, 1868-1916.
... In 't wonderland; uit het Noorsch door A. van Oosterzee.
¡Amsterdam: Maatschappij voor Goede en Goedkoope Lectuur,¡
1922. 169 p. 12°. (Wereld bibliotheek. ¡no.¡ 429.)

1. Fiction, Norwegian. 2. Oosterzee,   A. van, translator. 3. Title.
4. Ser.
N.Y.P.L.   November 29, 1927

NL 0344782   NN

PT8950 **Lie, Bernt Bessesen,** 1868-1916.
.L8J92   ... Justus Hjelm, fortælling.   Kristiania, H. Aschehoug &
1894 co., 1894.
Rare   ¡2¡, 349 p. 18ᶜᵐ.
bk.   At head of title: Bernt Lie.
Room   Author's autograph presentation copy.

NL 0344783   ICU WU NdU

LIE, Bernt Bessesen.
Justus Hjelm; fortælling.
Kristiania. H. Aschehoug. 1908.
249p.

NL 0344784   WaS

PT8950 **Lie, Bernt Bessesen,** 1868-1916.
.L5K2   ... Kasper Bugge.   Kristiania, H. Aschehoug & co., 1898.
¡4¡, 168 p. 18ᶜᵐ.
At head of title: Kasper Bugge.
Author's autograph presentation copy.

NL 0344785   ICU OrP WaS NN NdU

Lie, Bernt Bessesen, 1868-1916.
Lektor Hauch.   1907.

NL 0344786   WaS

Lie, Bernt.
Lofoten og Lofotfisket; omslagstegning og titelvignet av
Th. Holmboe, fotografierne av A. B. Wilse.   Kristiania: Nar-
vesens Kioskkompani, 1910. 44 p. illus. 4°.

NL 0344787   NN

Lie, Bernt Bessesen, 1868-
... Mot overmagt, fortælling fra midten av forrige aarhundrede. Kristiania, H. Aschehoug & co. (W. Nygaard)
1907.
3 p. l., ¡3¡-279 p. 20ᶜᵐ.

8-13699
Library of Congress

NL 0344788   DLC OC1

PT8950 **Lie, Bernt Bessesen,** 1868-1916.
.L5M6   Mot overmagt; fortælling fra midten av
1907b   forrige aarhundrede. 2.opl. Kristiania, H.
Aschehoug (W. Nygaard) 1907.
279p. 19cm.

NL 0344789   NBC

Lie, Bernt Bessesen, 1868-1916.
... Mot overmagt; fortælling fra midten av
forrige aarhundrede. 3. oplag. Kristiania,
H. Aschehoug & co. (W. Nygaard) 1907.
3 p.l., ¡3¡-279 p. 19cm.

NL 0344790   WU CU

PT8950 **Lie, Bernt Bessesen,** 1868-1916.
.L5N8   ... Nordover, fortællinger og billeder. Kristiania, H.
1896   Aschehoug & co., 1896.
Rare   ¡5¡, 209 p. 17¾ᶜᵐ.
bk.   At head of title: Bernt Lie.
Room   Author's autograph presentation copy.
CONTENTS.—Nordover.—Lissiva.—Spitsberggast.—Metje Kajsa.—Cecilie Røn-
now.—I den gamle Præstegaard.

NL 0344791   ICU OrP NdU

3352 **Lie, Bernt Bessesen,** 1868-1916.
.54   ...Nordwärts. Erzählungen und bilder...
.368   Autorisierte übersetzung aus dem norwe-
.7   gischen von Ottilie von Harling. Stuttgart, Engelhorn, 1903.
144 p. 18½ ᶜᵐ. (Engelhorns allgemeine roman-bibliothek.. 19.Jahrg.,
bd.20)

I.Harling,Ottilie von,   tr.

NL 0344792   NjP PPG

PT8950 **Lie, Bernt Bessesen,** 1868-1916.
.L5N95   ... Nye kræfter, fortælling. Kristiania, H. Aschehoug &
1895 co., 1895.
¡4¡, 215 p. 18ᶜᵐ.
At head of title: Bernt Lie.
Author's autograph presentation copy.

NL 0344793   ICU NdU MH

VOLUME 332

Lie, Bernt Bessesen, 1868–
Nye Kræfter...   Kristiania: H. Aschehoug & Co., 1915.
149 p.   2. ed.   12°.

1. Fiction, Norwegian.   2. Title.
N. Y. P. L.   October 31, 1924

NL 0344794   NN

Lie, Bernt Bessesen, 1868–1916.
... Overlærer Hauch. Kristiania, H. Aschehoug & co.
(W. Nygaard) 1906.
3 p. l., ¡3¡–296 p., 1 l. 20ᵐᵐ.

ı. Title.

Library of Congress   PT8950.L5O8 1906   16–18017

NL 0344795   DLC OC1 NN

PT8950 **Lie, Bernt Bessesen,** 1868-1916.
.L5P4   ... Peter Napoleon, historier om en gut. Kristiania, H.
1900   Aschehoug & co. (W. Nygaard) 1900.
¡3¡, 162 p. 18ᵐᵐ.
At head of title: Bernt Lie.
Author's autograph presentation copy.

NL 0344796   ICU MnU

Lie, Bernt.
Peter Napoleon; historier om en gut, med tegninger af Jacob
Sømme. Kristiania: H. Aschehoug & Co., 1905. 2 p.l., 163 p.,
11 pl. 12°.

1. Title. 2. Sømme, Jacob, illus-   CENTRAL CIRCULATION.
N. Y. P. L.   trator.   June 15, 1914.

NL 0344797   NN WaS OrP

Lie, Bernt Bessesen, 1868–
... Peter Napoleon, med tegninger av Jacob Sømme. 4.
oplag. Kristiania, H. Aschehoug & co. (W. Nygaard)
1920.
159, ¡1¡ p. illus. 19ᵐᵐ. (*His* Guttefortaellinger III)
"1. oplag, 1900."

ı. Title.

NL 0344798   MiU

Lie, Bernt Bessesen, 1868–
... En racekamp; skuespil i 3 akter. Kristiania, H.
Aschehoug & co. (W. Nygaard) 1915.
4 p. l., ¡3¡–121 p. 20ᵐᵐ.

ı. Title.

Library of Congress   PT8950.L5R2 1915   16–11414

NL 0344799   DLC

Lie, Bernt Bessesen, 1868–
... Raklev i Simavaag. Kristiania, H. Aschehoug & co.
(W. Nygaard) 1911.
3 p. l., ¡3¡–212 p. 20ᵐᵐ.   kr. 3.50

ı. Title.

Library of Congress   12–2493

NL 0344800   DLC CaBVa NN

Lie, Bernt
Særsyn   3 det ed.

NL 0344801   NdU

PT8950 **Lie, Bernt Bessesen,** 1868-1916.
.L5S2   ... Et særsyn. Kristiania, H. Aschehoug & co. (W. Ny-
1903   gaard) 1903.
Rare   ¡7¡, 210 p. 18ᵐᵐ.
bk.   At head of title: Bernt Lie.
Room   Sequel to "Søster Judit'.
Author's autograph presentation copy.

NL 0344802   ICU WU CU CLU MB

Lie, Bernt Bessesen, 1868–1916.
Et særsyn. 3. ed.   Kristiania, H. Aschehoug
& Co., 1903.
4 p. l., 210 p. 12°.

NL 0344803   NN

Lie, Bernt Bessesen, 1868–1916.
... Samlede fortællinger. Ny utgave ...   Oslo, H.
Aschehoug & co. (W. Nygaard) 1927-28.
7 v.   3 fronts. (ports., v. 1, 3, 6) 19½ᶜᵐ.
CONTENTS.—ı. I eventyrland. Justus Hjelm.—ıı. Nye kræfter. Nordover.
Kasper Bugge.—ııı. I Knut Arnebergs hus. Hildr.—ıv. Søster Judit. Et særsyn.
Underveis.—v. Vildfugl. Overærer Hauch.—vı. Mot overmagt. Helle. Thalja.
—vıı. Raklevisimavaag. Gabriel Selje. I marjastilla.

NL 0344804   MiU

PT8950 **Lie, Bernt Bessesen,** 1868–1916.
.L5S65   ... Søster Judit. Kristiania, H. Aschehoug & co. (W. Ny-
1901   gaard) 1901.
¡2¡, 271 p. 18ᵐᵐ.
At head of title: Bernt Lie.
Sequel: Et særsyn.
Author's autograph presentation copy.

NL 0344805   ICU

PT   Lie, Bernt Bessesen, 1868-1916.
8950   Søster Judit. 4. opl. Kristiania, H.
L62S68   Aschehoug, 1901.
1901   271 p.

NL 0344806   CLU WaS NdU

Lie, Bernt Bessesen, 1868–
... Søster Judit. 5. oplag. Kristiania,
H. Aschehoug & co. (W. Nygaard) 1902.
1 p.l., 271 p. 18½cm.

NL 0344807   WU CaBVa

PT8950 **Lie, Bernt Bessesen,** 1868-1916.
.L5S7   Sorte ørn, guttefortællinger af Bernt Lie. Ny, forøget udg.
1898   med tegninger af S. Segelcke. Kristiania, H. Aschehoug &
co., 1898.
¡3¡, 175 p. incl. illus., plates. 20ᵐᵐ.
Author's autograph presentation copy.
CONTENTS.—Magnus.—Sorte ørn.—Pengesorger.—Fin-Marja.—Skaarungen.—
Hr. Finsd.l.—Laras og Hanas.—Ruona.—En landsgut.—Det første bud.—Sidste
dag før juleferien.

NL 0344808   ICU NdU

Lie, Bernt.
Sorte ørn; guttefortællinger, med tegninger av S. Segelcke.
Kristiania: H. Aschehoug & Co., 1912. 2 p.l., 162 p.   illus.
12°.

NL 0344809   NN WaS

Lie, Bernt Bessesen, 1868–
...Sorte ørn; med vignetter og illustrationer av S.
Segelcke. 5. oplag. Kristiania, H. Aschehoug & co.
(W. Nygaard) 1920.
159, ¡1¡ p. illus. 19ᵐᵐ. (*His* Guttefortaellinger 1) .

ı. Title.

NL 0344810   MiU

Lie, Bernt, 1868-1916.
Svend Bidevind; skolehistorier. 2ᵈᵉᵗ opl. Kristiania, H.
Aschehoug & co. 1897.
pp. (2), 142.

NL 0344811   MH NdU

PT8950 **Lie, Bernt Bessesen,** 1868–1916.
.L5S92   ... Svend Bidevind, skolehistorier. 3. opl. Kristiania, H.
1901   Aschehoug & co. (W. Nygaard) 1901.
Rare   144 p. 18ᵐᵐ.
bk.   At head of title: Bernt Lie.
Room   Author's autograph presentation copy.

NL 0344812   ICU

Lie, Bernt.
Svend Bidevind; skolehistorier, med omslagstegning av S.
Segelcke og vignetter av Jac. Sømme. Kristiania: H. Aschehoug
& Co., 1911. 2 p.l., 144 p. 12°.

Svend Bidevind. Fusk. Slagsmaal. Eksamen.

1. Four titles.   CENTRAL CIRCULATION.
N. Y. P. L.   June 20, 1914.

NL 0344813   NN

Lie, Bernt Bessesen, 1868–
... Svend Bidevind, med vignetter og illustrationer av
S. Segelcke. 7. oplag. Kristiania, H. Aschehoug & co.
(W. Nygaard) 1920.
142 p., 1 l. illus. 19ᵐᵐ. (*His* Guttefortaellinger II)
"1. oplag, 1897."

ı. Title.

NL 0344814   MiU

VOLUME 332

Lie, Bernt ₍Bessesen₎.
Thalja.   Kristiania: H. Aschehoug & Co., 1910.   2 p.l.,
217 p.   12°.

1. Fiction (Norwegian). 2. Title.
N. Y. P. L.   July 17, 1911.

NL 0344815   NN

Lie, Bernt Bessesen, 1868–
... Thalja. 4. tusen. Kristiania, H. Aschehoug & co.
(W. Nygaard) 1910.
2 p. l., 217 p. 20ᶜᵐ.   kr. 3.50

                                                11–1102

Library of Congress

NL 0344816   DLC

Lie, Bernt Bessesen, 1868–1916.
... Underveis, skitser og novelletter. Kristiania, H.
Aschehoug & co. (W. Nygaard) 1906.
3 p. l., ₍3₎–162 p., 1 l. 20ᶜᵐ.
Contents.— Figenskjæret.—To kys.— Fjeldet.—Jack og jeg.— Et lidet
jagtbrev.—Alfer.—Indian outfitted.—Fru Drude.—Videnskabens triumf.—
Et baal i julenatten.—Hvide roser.—Ridderspranget.

1. Title.

Library of Congress   PT8950.L5U5 1906
                                                16–18018

NL 0344817   DLC

PT   Lie, Bernt Bessesen, 1868–1916.
8950   Vildfugl. Kristiania, H. Aschehoug, 1905.
L62V71   237 p.

NL 0344818   CLU WaS

Lie, Bernt Bessesen, 1868–1916.
... Vildfugl. 6. oplag. Kristiania, H. Aschehoug & co. (W. Nygaard) 1905.
2 p.l., 237 p. 18½cm.

NL 0344819   WU CU

Wason   Lie, Bo Thay.
PL   Ichtisar paramasastera bahasa
5107   Indonesia untuk sekolah menengah, oleh
L71   Lie Bo Thay. ₍Djakarta₎ Djambatan, 1952
            39 p. 19cm.

1. Indonesian language--Grammar.

NL 0344820   NIC

Lie, Edvarda.
...Sirkus i byen...   ₍Oslo₎ NKL forlag ₍1950?₎   1 v.
col. illus. 30cm.
Cover-title.
At head of title: Originallitografier av Edvarda Lie. Rim og regler av Louis
Kvalstad.

1. Juvenile literature—Picture   books, Norwegian. I. Kvalstad,
Louis, 1905–   December 6, 1951
N. Y. P. L.

NL 0344821   NN

Lie, Erik Røring Møinichen, 1868–
Af første generation.   Kjøbenhavn, 1906.
251 p.

NL 0344822   WaS

PT9070 Lie, Erik Røring Møinichen, 1868–
.Z8L7   ... Arne Garborg, en livsskildring, med billeder og breve.
Kristiania, H. Aschehoug & co. (W. Nygaard) 1914.
₍7₎, 247 p. front., illus. (incl. facsims.) ports. 19½ᶜᵐ.
At head of title: Erik Lie.

1. Garborg, Arne, 1851–

NL 0344823   ICU CU IU NIC NcU NdU

Lie, Erik Røring Møinichen, 1868–
... Arne Molviks ungdom; roman. Kristiania og Kjøbenhavn, Gyldendal, Nordisk forlag, 1913.
223 p. 20ᶜᵐ.   kr. 3.75

1. Title.

Library of Congress   14–395

NL 0344824   DLC

Lie, Erik.
Arne Molviks ungdom; roman.   Kristiania: Gyldendal,
1913. 223 p.   2. ed.   12°.

1. Fiction (Norwegian). 2. Title.
N. Y. P. L.   July 2, 1914.

NL 0344825   NN

PT   Lie, Erik Røring Møinichen, 1868–
8906   Bibliografiske oplysninger til Jonas Lie's
1902   samlede vaerker.
14   (In Lie, Jonas. Samlede vaerker. v.14
(1904) p.227-287)

1. Lie, Jonas Lauritz Idemil, 1833–1908 –
Bibliography. I.   Title.

NL 0344826   WU

Lie, Erik Røring Møinichen, 1868–
... Blandt sigøinere; en liten guts oplevelser. Kristiania, H. Aschehoug & co. (W. Nygaard) 1915.
3 p. l., 136 p. 20ᶜᵐ.   kr. 2.20

1. Title.

Library of Congress   PT8950.L55B5 1915
                                                16–17173

NL 0344827   DLC

Lie, Erik Røring Møinichen, 1868–

Z2560   Paris. Bibliothèque Sainte-Geneviève. *Bibliothèque nor-*
.P23   *dique.*
Catalogue du Fonds scandinave de la Bibliothèque Sainte-
Geneviève. Châlon-sur-Saône, E. Bertrand, 1908.

Lie, Erik Røring Møinichen, 1868–
... Direktør Lyngs hjem; fortaelling. Kjøbenhavn, Gyldendal (F. Hegel & søn) 1903.
2 p.l., 283 p. 18½cm.

NL 0344829   WU NN NdU CU

Lie, Erik Røring Møinichen, 1868–
... Erindringer fra et dikterhjem. Oslo, H. Aschehoug &
co., 1928.
5 p. l., ₍3₎–205 p. illus. 20ᶜᵐ.
At head of title: Erik Lie.
Contents.—Rom.—Berchtesgaden.—Paris.—Hjemme 1 Norge.

1. Authors—Correspondence, reminiscences, etc. 2. Lie, Jonas Lauritz
Idemil, 1833–1908. 3. Ibsen, Henrik, 1828–1906. 4. Bjørnson, Bjørn-
stjerne, 1832–1910. I. Title.
Library of Congress   PT8950.L55Z5 1928
                                                29–5774

NL 0344830   DLC MB NIC ICU NN

Lie, Erik Røring Møinichen, 1868–
Eurooppalainen kirjallisuus; kulttuurihistoriallisia
kuvia. Suomentanut Helmi Krohn. Tr. into Finnish.
1914.

NL 0344831   RP

Lie, Erik Røring Møinichen, 1868–
... Den europæiske litteratur i kulturhistoriske billeder.
Kjøbenhavn, Gyldendal, 1896.
3 p. l., 505 p. 21½ᶜᵐ.
Imperfect: p. 497-498 wanting.
"Kilder": p. 493-496.

1. Literature—Hist. & crit.
                                                1–21863
Library of Congress   PN573.L5

NL 0344832   DLC NdU

Lie, Erik Røring Møinichen, 1868–
... Farsarven; roman. Kristiania og Kjøbenhavn,
Gyldendal, Nordisk forlag, 1912.
226 p. 20ᶜᵐ.   kr. 3.50

1. Title.

Library of Congress   13–4794

NL 0344833   DLC WaS NN

Lie, Erik Røring Møinichen, 1868–
... Finn, Jan og Ola Smørbuk, guttefortælling; med
omslagstegning av Jacob Sømme. Kristiania og Kjøbenhavn, Gyldendalske boghandel, Nordisk forlag, 1910.
91 p. 20ᶜᵐ.

                                                11–1659
Library of Congress

NL 0344834   DLC NN

Lie, Erik Røring Møinichen, 1868–
Finn Urædd; guttefortælling, av Erik Lie; med omslagstegning av Marie Hauge. Kristiania, Kjøbenhavn,
Gyldendalske boghandel, Nordisk forlag, 1908.
2 p. l., 91 p. 20ᶜᵐ.

                                                9–1587
Library of Congress

NL 0344835   DLC NN

VOLUME 332

Lie, Erik Røring Møinichen, 1868–
    ... Fra skolebenken til Pampasslettene, guttefortelling. Kristiania, H. Aschehoug & co. (W. Nygaard) 1924.
2 p. l., 126 p., 1 l.   20ᶜᵐ.
At head of title: Erik Lie.

    ɪ. Title.
    Library of Congress   PT8950.L55F7 1924   25–4240

NL 0344836   DLC NdU

Lie, Erik Røring Møinichen, 1868–
    Gerda Wolmer; Fortælling...   København: Gyldendal, 1905.   2 p. l., 128 p.   12°.
    Author's name at head of title.

    1. Fiction (Norwegian). 2. Title.   August 14, 1917.

NL 0344837   NN WaS

Lie, Erik Røring Møinichen, 1865–
    ... Hans Ulrichs død; fortælling. København, Kristiania, Gyldendal, 1904.
2 p. l., 197 p.   18½ cm.

NL 0344838   WU CU

PQ2178 **Lie, Erik Røring Moinichen,** 1868–
.L7   ... Honoré de Balzac, mennesket og kunstneren, en kildestudie. København, Gyldendal (F. Hegel & søn) 1893.
[12], 275 p.   front., ports.   18¼ᶜᵐ.

    1. Balzac, Honoré de, 1799–1850.

NL 0344839   ICU OrU

Lie, Erik Røring Møinichen, 1868–
    ... Indenfor fæstningens mure; skildringer fra det beleirede Tyskland. Kristiania, H. Aschehoug & co. (W. Nygaard) 1918.
2 p. l., 184 p.   20ᶜᵐ.
At head of title: Erik Lie.

    1. European war, 1914–   —Germany.
    Library of Congress   D515.L55   19–13301

NL 0344840   DLC PU

Lie, Erik Røring Møinichen, 1868–
    Jonas Lie; en livsskildring, av Erik Lie. Med portretter og illustrasjoner. Oslo, Gyldendal norsk forlag, 1933.
210, [1] p.   illus. (incl. ports., facsims.)   21¼ᶜᵐ.
    "Boken er bygget på og delvis omarbeidet efter mitt arbeide 'Jonas Lies oplevelser', som kom ut i 1908. Meget er tatt ut og adskillig nytt er tilføiet."—Forord.

    1. Lie, Jonas Lauritz Idemil, 1833–1908.
    Title from N. Y. Publ.   Libr.   A C 34–2277
    Library of Congress   [PT8914.L   ]

NL 0344841   NN ICU MH NcD NcU CU

Lie, Erik Røring Møinichen, 1868–
    Jonas Lie, oplevelser fortalt af Erik Lie; med breve, illustrationer og portrætter. Kristiania og København, Gyldendal, Nordisk forlag, 1908.
5 p. l., [9]–306 p.   front., illus., ports., 11 fold. facsim.   22ᶜᵐ.
Half-title: Jonas Lies oplevelser.
Issued in 10 parts.

    1. Lie, Jonas Lauritz Idemil, 1833–1908.
    Library of Congress   PT8914.L5   8–29632 Revised

NL 0344842   DLC NcD PU CtY NN

---

4 Music   **Lie, Erik Røring Møinichen,** 1868–
880   Jonas Lie's Erlebnisse.   [Übers. von Mathilde Mann]   Leipzig, Haupt & Hammon, 1909.
315 p.

NL 0344843   DLC-P4 OC1 MiU MH

Lie, Erik Røring Møinichen, 1868–
    ... Kurt Adeler Klinge; en fortelling om vor tids børn. Kristiania, H. Aschehoug & co. (W. Nygaard) 1916.
2 p. l., 206 p.   20ᶜᵐ.   kr. 3.75

    ɪ. Title.
    Library of Congress   PT8950.L55K8 1916   17–21870
         14454

NL 0344844   DLC

Lie, Erik Røring Møinichen, 1868–
    Med Blyanten.   Christiania, A. Cammermeyer, 1890.
3 p. l., (1) 4–187 p.   12°.

NL 0344845   NN

PT8950   **Lie, Erik Røring Møinichen,** 1868–
L53   Minnen från ett diktarhem.   Översättning av Eva Berg.
Z514   Stockholm, Bonnier [1929]
    206 p.   illus., ports.

    1. Authors, Danish - Correspondence, reminiscences, etc.
    2. Lie, Erik Røring Møinichen, 1868–

NL 0344846   CU

Lie, Erik Røring Møinichen, 1868–
    ... Mirakeldoktoren. Kristiania, H. Aschehoug & co. (W. Nygaard) 1922.
2 p. l., 198 p.   20ᶜᵐ.
At head of title: Erik Lie.
A story.

    ɪ. Title.
    Library of Congress   PT8950.L55M5 1922   23–2489

NL 0344847   DLC

Lie, Erik Røring Møinichen, 1868–
    ... Mogens Møllendamm & sønner. Kristiania og København, Gyldendalske boghandel, Nordisk forlag, 1909.
3 p. l., [3]–183 p.   20ᶜᵐ.   kr. 3

    Library of Congress   10–1051

NL 0344848   DLC NN

Lie, Erik Røring Møinichen, 1868–
    ... Naadigherren, et billede fra gamle dage. Kristiania, H. Aschehoug & co. (W. Nygaard) 1921.
2 p. l., 207 p.   20ᶜᵐ.
At head of title: Erik Lie.

    ɪ. Title.
    Library of Congress   PT8950.L55N3 1921   22–2620

NL 0344849   DLC

Lie, Erik Røring Møinichen, 1868–
    ... Den nye lykke, Kristiania-roman. Kristiania og Kjøbenhavn, Gyldendalske boghandel, Nordisk forlag, 1911.
157 p.   20ᶜᵐ.

    ɪ Title.
    Library of Congress   12–2202

NL 0344850   DLC NN

Lie, Erik Røring Møinichen, 1868–
Lie, Jonas Lauritz Idemil, 1833–
    ... Samlede værker ... [Folkeudgave] Kjøbenhavn og Kristiania, Gyldendalske boghandel, Nordisk forlag, 1902–04.

Lie, Erik Røring Møinichen, 1868–
    ... Tønne storskryter og hans venner; fortelling for gutter. Kristiania, H. Aschehoug & co. (W. Nygaard) 1923.
2 p. l., 107 p.   20ᶜᵐ.
At head of title: Erik Lie.

    ɪ. Title.
    Library of Congress   PT8950.L55T6 1923   24–4007

NL 0344852   DLC

Lie, Erik Røring Møinichen, 1868–
    Tolv procent.

NL 0344853   NdU

Lie, Finn, 1893–
    Naar krigsfaklen luer. Kristiania, H. Erichsen, 1915.
125 p.   18 cm.   (Helge Erichsen & co.s ukeserie nr. 45)

    1. European War, 1914–1918—Fiction.   ɪ. Title.
    PT8950.L56N2 1915   22–25559 rev*

NL 0344854   DLC

Lie, Finn.
    Et nordisk grenseland; Sønderjyllands kamp for sin frihet. Oslo, Roséns forlag, 1945.
117 p.   21cm.

    1. Schleswig-Holstein question.

NL 0344855   MnU

VOLUME 332

Lie, Finn, 1893–
...Sørover med Stella; reisebrev fra en Middelhavstur...
Oslo: Steenske forlag, 1931.   175 p.   plates.   24cm.

Plates printed on both sides.

603815A. 1. Mediterranean sea—   Descr. and trav. I. Title.
N. Y. P. L.   February 27, 1933

NL 0344856   NN

Lie, Haakon, 1884–
Ekorn, by Haakon Lie, illustrations by Kurt Wiese; a
translation from the Norwegian by Claes Leonard Hultgren.
Chicago, New York, Laidlaw brothers, 1931.

5 p. l., 150 p. incl. illus., col. plates. col. front. 20½ᶜᵐ.

  I. Hultgren, Claes Leonard, tr. II. Title.
  Library of Congress   PZ10.3.L62Ek   31–23460
  ——— Copy 2.
  Copyright A 41302   ₍2₎   839.8236

NL 0344857   DLC WaSp MB PWcT PPFr OO OLak OEac OC1

Lie, Haakon, 1884–
Ekorn; illustrations by Kurt Wiese; a translation
from the Norwegian by Claes Leonard Haltgren.
Chicago, Whitman, 1939.
150 p.

NL 0344858   PP

Lie, Haakon, 1884–
Elva, ætta og eventyret. Oslo, Noregs boklag, 1955.

219 p. 20 cm.

  I. Title.
  PT9076.L52E4   A 56–6454
  Minnesota. Univ. Libr.
  for Library of Congress   ₍8₎†

NL 0344859   MnU DLC

Lie, Haakon, 1884–
...Gjester på jordi.   Oslo: H. Aschehoug & co., 1934.
120 p.   20cm.

786587A. 1. Animals—Legends   and stories. I. Title.
N. Y. P. L.   November 6, 1935

NL 0344860   NN

Lie, Haakon, 1884–
Laerebok i skogbotanik.   Kristiania, 1911.
72 p.   23 cm.

NL 0344861   CtY

Lie, Haakon, 1884–
Laerebok i skogbotanik; naermest til bruk
ved de lavere skogskoler. ₍2. opl.₎
Kristiania, Grøndahl & Søns forlag, 1920.
105 p. illus.

  1. Botany. I. Title.

NL 0344862   WaU

Lie, Haakon, 1884–
... Naar gamle skjold brister. Kristiania, Grøndahl &
søn, 1920.
179 p. 20ᶜᵐ.
A story.

  I. Title.
  Library of Congress   PT8950.L57N3 1920   21–2096
                            17609

NL 0344863   DLC MH

Lie, Haakon, 1884–
Skog-Noreg; prologar, helsingar, dikt. ₍Oslo₎ Noregs
boklag ₍1954₎
80 p. 26 cm.

  I. Title.
                                         A 55–6810 rev
  Minnesota. Univ. Libr.
  for Library of Congress   ₍r56b½₎

NL 0344864   MnU

Lie, Haakon, 1884–
Skogens fulger og insekter.   Kristiania, 1912.
23 cm.

NL 0344865   CtY

Lie, Haakon, 1884–
Det skuggar over hei. Oslo, Noregs boklag, 1946.
100 p. 22 cm.

  I. Title.
  PT9076.L52S55   839.8216   50–25962

NL 0344866   DLC

Lie, Haakon, 1884–
Vegen til livet; roman. Oslo, Grøndahl, 1950.
414 p. 20 cm.

  I. Title.
                                         A 51–3852
  Minnesota. Univ. Libr.
  for Library of Congress   ₍3₎

NL 0344867   MnU NN

Lie, Haakon, 1884–
Villmark og villdyr. Illustrert av Omar Andreen. Oslo,
Tiden ₍1949₎
188 p. illus. 26 cm.

  1. Hunting—Norway. I. Title.
  SK529.L5   50–26743

NL 0344868   DLC MnU NN

Lie, Haakon, 1905–
Arbeiderbevegelsen i de Forente stater. ₍Oslo₎ Arbeidernes opplysningsforbund, Tiden norsk forlag ₍1947₎
146 p. illus. 20 cm.

  1. Labor and laboring classes—U. S.—1914–   2. Trade-unions—
  U. S. I. Title.
  HD8072.L53   55–56273 ‡

NL 0344869   DLC MH–IR NN MnU

Lie, Håkon, 1905–
...De faglige kampmidlene. 4. oppl. Utgitt av Arbeidernes
opplysningsforbund. ₍Oslo₎ Det Norske arbeiderpartis forlag,
1939. 48 p. 19cm. ₍Småskrifter i fagforeningskunnskap.
2₎

  1. Capital and labor. I. Ser.
  N. Y. P. L.   December 20, 1951

NL 0344870   NN

HX56
.S416

Lie, Håkon, 1905–   ed.

Selznick, Philip, 1919–
Kaderpartiet; kommunistisk strategi og taktikk ₍utg. av
Haakon Lie₎ Oslo, Fram forlag, 1954.

Lie, Haakon, 1905–
De kommunistiske dekkorganisasjonene; Dagbladet og
Kaderpartiet. Oslo, Fram forlag, 1954.
48 p. 18 cm.
"Foredrag ... holdt i Oslo journalistklubb 26. oktober 1954."

  1. Communist strategy. I. Title.
  HX518.S8L5   62–49239 ‡

NL 0344872   DLC NIC NN

Lie, Haakon, 1905–
Nazi i Norge. Utg. av Arbeidernes faglige landsorganisasjon, Norsk sjømannsforbund. ₍London, Victoria house
printing co., ltd., 1942₎
79 p. 21 cm.

  1. Norway—Hist.—German occupation, 1940–1945. 2. Norway—Pol.
  & govt.—1905–   I. Norsk sjømannsforbund. II. Title.
  DL532.L5   948.1   42–50881 rev

NL 0344873   DLC

Lie, Håkon, 1905–
...Produksjonsutvalgene i De Forente Stater under krigen.
Utgitt av Arbeidernes opplysningsforbund. ₍Oslo₎ Det Norske
arbeiderpartis forlag ₍1945₎ 32 p. illus. 19cm. (Småskrifter
i fagforeningskunnskap. 11)

  1. Production—U. S. 2. World   war, 1939–1945—Economic aspects—
  U. S. I. Ser.
  N. Y. P. L.   December 6, 1951

NL 0344874   NN

Lie, Haakon, 1905–
Søkelys på Sovjet. ₍Oslo₎ Fram forlag ₍1953₎
110 p. illus. 19 cm.

  1. Russia—Econ. condit.—1945–1955. I. Title.
  HC336.L48   62–25790 ‡

NL 0344875   DLC NN

VOLUME 332

Lie, Håkon, 1905–   comp.

Norsk sjømannsforbund.
Vi synger. ₍Brooklyn, N. Y.? 1942₎

Lie, Haakon, 1905–
Vi synger; ei sangbok for heim og lag. Oslo, Tiden norsk
forlag, 1946.
285 p. 16 cm.
Without the music.

1. Song-books, Norwegian.   ɪ. Title.

M1772.L72V5 1946   M 57–378 ‡

NL 0344877   DLC MnU

Lie, Haakon, 1905–   *ed.*
Vi synger; sangbok for heim og lag. 2. utg. ₍Oslo₎
Norske arbeiderpartis forlag ₍1951₎
288 p. 14 cm.
"Denne sangboka er en ny utgave av 'Vi synger' som første gang
ble gitt ut i 1946. 'Vi synger' bygger på 'Arbeidersangboka som før
krigen kom ut i en rekke opplag, og på sangbøkene 'Det frie Norge
synger' og 'Vi synger' som ble trykt i Stockholm og London under
krigen."
Without the music.

1. Song-books, Norwegian.   ɪ. Title.

M1772.L72V5 1951   M 54–855 rev

NL 0344878   DLC

Lie, Hallvard, 1905–   , ed.
Ibsen og Grimstad. [Utg. av Hallvard Lie]
see under   Eitrem, Hans Thure Smith,
1871–1937.

Lie, Hallvard, 1905–   *ed.*
Islandske ættesagaer. Oslo, Aschehoug, ₍1951–54₎
4 v. illus. 22 cm.
CONTENTS.—1. Egils saga. Sagaen om Gunnlaug Ormstunge.
Sagaen om Hallfred Vandrådaskald. Sagaen om Bjørn Hitdøls-
kjempe. Sagaen om fostbrødrene. Kormaks saga.—2. Grettes saga.
Viga-Glums saga. Sambandsmennenes saga. Sagaen om vatsdølene.—
3. Sagaen om laksdølene.—Sagaen om øyrbyggjene. Eirik Raudes
saga. En saga om grønlendingene. Grønlendingetåtten. Sigmund
Brestesons saga.—4. Njåls saga. Gisles saga. Sagaen om Ravnkjell
Frøysgode. Sagaen om Hønsa-Tore. Tre sagatåtter.

1. Sagas.   ɪ. Title.

PT7269.A2L5   56–21382

NL 0344880   DLC ICU NIC OU CU MnU

Lie, Hallvard, 1905–
Jorvikferden; et vendepunkt i Egil Skallagrimssons liv.
Oslo, Mallingske boktr., 1946.
248 p. 25 cm.
"Utmitt av Edda; årg. 33 (1946)"
Bibliographical footnotes.

1. Egill Skallagrímsson, ca. 900–ca. 983.

PT7269.E4L5   50–18867

NL 0344881   DLC

Z6621   Lie, Hallvard, 1905–   comp.
.O 75
Oslo. Universitet. *Bibliotek.*
Norske og danske dikteres originalmanuskripter; katalog
ved Hallvard Lie. Oslo, Grøndahl & søns boktr., 1948.

Ic   Lie, Hallvard, 1905–
F44   Skaldestil-studier. Oslo, Det
L561   Mallingske Boktrykkeri, 1952.
            92 p. 23cm.

"Særtrykk av Maal og Minne 1952."
Cover title.
1. Icelandic and Old Norse literature—
Hist. & crit. 2. Scalds and scaldic
poetry. I. Title.

NL 0344883   NIC

Lie, Hallvard. Snorres dramatiske dialog.
In Norvegica. Minneskrift til femti-års-
dagen for oprettelsen av Universitets Biblio-
tekets Norske Avdeling, 1933. pp. 45–61.
                                                2969A84

NL 0344884   NIC

AS283   LIE, HALLVARD, 1905–
.C56   Studier i Heimskringlas stil; dialogene og talene,
1936   av Hallvard Lie ... Oslo,I kommisjon hos J.Dybwad,
v.2   1937.
            136 p. illus. 27½cm. (Skrifter utgitt av det
Norske videnskaps-akademi i Oslo. II.Hist.-filos.
klasse. 1936,no.5)
"Utgitt for Oslo kommunes fond."
"Bibliografi":p.134–136.

1.Snorri Sturluson,1178–1241. Heimskringla.

NL 0344885   ICU NIC PU RPB NbU MnU MoU

                        Ellingsen
616.998 Lie, Hans Peter, 1862–
L716ℓ   Lepra im rückenmark und den peripheren nerven .
Wien ₍etc.₎ W. Braumüller, 1904.
            180p. plates(part col.)

"Erweiterter sonderabdruck aus dem Archiv für
dermatologie und syphilis."

1. Leprosy. 2. Nervous system—Diseases.

NL 0344886   IU-M

Lie, Hans Peter Ellingsen, 1862–
[Proceedings] Mitteilungen und Verhandlungen
see under   International Congress of
Leprosy. 2d, Bergen, 1909.

Lie, Herman, 1884–
... Bankreform und zentralbankproblem in Amerika.
Von Herman Lie. ₍Jena, G. Fischer, 1910₎
p. 179–199. 23½ᶜᵐ.
Caption title.
"Abdruck aus den Jahrbüchern für nationalökonomie und statistik ...
dritte folge. band ₍40₎"

1. Banks and banking—U. S.
                                                13–35301

Library of Congress   HG2481.L49

NL 0344888   DLC

Lie, I., *tr.*

Lie, Jonas, 1899–
The devil's birthday, by Jonas Lie. London, B. Cassirer
₍1940₎

Lie, J., joint author.

Hjort, Johan, 1869–
... Norwegian pelagic whaling in the Antarctic ... Oslo, I
kommisjon hos Jacob Dybwad, 1932–

Lie, Jo.
Huset som fikk ben. Illustrert av Vinni Okolow Moa.
Oslo, N. W. Damm ₍1955₎
118 p. illus. 16 cm. (Damms barnebibliotek, nr. 12)

ɪ. Title.

PZ53.L45H8   58–19980

NL 0344891   DLC

Lie, Joek Koey.
中華印尼大辭典 Kamus baharu bahasa Tionghoa-
Indonesia. 李鍼愷編 椰城 國民書局 Djakarta,
Kuo min, 1933.
332, 208 p. fold. col. map. 16 cm.

1. Chinese language—Dictionaries—Indonesian.   ɪ. Title.
ɪɪ. Title: Kamus baharu bahasa Tionghoa-Indonesia.
                Title romanized: Chung-hua Yin-ni ta tsʻû tien.

PL5077.L48   C 65–780

NL 0344892   DLC

Wason   Lie, Joek Koey.
PL5077   Kamus ketjil bahasa Indonesia-Tionghoa, oleh
L69   Li Joek Koey. 袖珍印華字典 ₍Tjetakan 2.₎
1949   Batavia, Kuo Min Book Co. ₍1949?₎
            v. 15 cm.

1. Indonesian language—Dictionaries—
Chinese.

NL 0344893   NIC

Lie, Joek Koey.
綜合華巫荷英大辭典 國語注音 李鍼愷編 A
classified dictionary of Chinese-Malay-Dutch-English with
Chinese pronunciation, by Li Joek Koey. 增訂第 3 版
Batavia. 國民書局 Kuo Min Book Co., 1948.
xxxxix ₍sic₎, 163, 208 p. 16 cm.
Cover title: 華印荷英四國文大辭典
On spine: 華巫荷英大辭典 上下部 合訂本
Some numbers are omitted in prelim. paging.
1. Chinese language—Dictionaries—Polyglot. ɪ. Title. ɪɪ.
Title: A classified dictionary of Chinese-Malay-Dutch-English with
Chinese pronunciation. ɪɪɪ. Title: Hua Yin Ho Ying ssŭ kuo wên ta
tsʻû tien. ɪv. Title: Hua Wu Ho Ying ta tsʻû tien.
                        Title romanized: Tsung ho Hua
                                Wu Ho Ying ta tsʻû tien.

PL1441.L5   C 68–1313

NL 0344894   DLC

Lie, Johan Herman
see
Lie, Herman, 1884–

Microfilm Lie, Johanne Eleonora (Vogt) 1870–   tr.
11131
PQ   **Flaubert, Gustave,** 1821–1880.
... Fru Bovary, roman fra det franske provinsliv; over-
sat af fru Johanne Vogt Lie med en indledning af Carl
Nærup. ₍Kristiania₎ A. Cammermeyer ₍1898₎

VOLUME 332

Lie, Johanne Eleonora (Vogt) *1870–*
Kunstnerliv i Nord og Syd. Kristiania og Kjøbenhavn, Gyldendalske boghandel, Nordisk forlag, 1910.
160 p. 20ᶜᵐ.   kr. 2.50

11–1541

Library of Congress

NL 0344897   DLC

Lie, Johannes, 1831–
see Lie, Lars Johannes, 1831–

PT9076 **Lie, John,** 1846–1916.
.L6A64   Aarolilja, av John Lie ...   Kristiania, Norske samlag,
1879 1879.
₍3₎, 84 p. 18ᶜᵐ.
Poems written in dialect.

NL 0344899   ICU

Lie, John
Aarolilja   2 dre utg.

NL 0344900   NdU

Lie, John, 1846–1916.
Bondekvelder.   Minneapolis, Minn.,
K.K. Rudie, 1909.
264 p.   19cm.

NL 0344901   MnU

Lie, John, 1846–1916.
Egil Bakken; fortælling om en gut, av John Lie.   Kristiania,
P. Omtvedt ₍1911₎   64 p.   20cm.

NL 0344902   NN

PT   **Lie, John,** 1846–1916.
8950   Egill á Bakka, saga af ungum manni,
L58   Bjarni Jónsson íslenzkaði. Reykjavík,
E415   Bókaverzlun Sigurjóns Jónssonar, 1926.
104 p. (Bókasafn Æskunnar, III)

Translation of Egil Bakken.

NL 0344903   WaU NIC

Lie, John
Fille-Værn; fortællinger fra Telemarken.
Kristiania, Bertrand Jensen, 1896.
64 p.   port.   19 cm.

"Særtryk af "Fra fjeldbygden"."

NL 0344904   WU

PT8905 **Lie, John,** 1846–1916.
.L71F6   Fra fjeldbygden; fortaellinger.
Decorah, Iowa, Decorah-postens bogtr., 1890.
136 p.   port.   18 cm.

Cover title.
"Decorah-postens praemiebog
for 1890–1891."

NL 0344905   MnHi

GR220 **Lie, John,** 1846–1916.
.N86   ... Gaamaalt etti bestemor, av John Lie og Hallvor Lie.
1924 Risør, Kosta av "Norsk folkekultur," 1925.
43 p. incl. front. (port.) 20½ᶜᵐ. (Norske folkeminnesamlarar II, 5)
Tilleggsbok til Norsk folkekultur. 1924.
Edited by Rikard Berge.

1. Legends—Norway.   2. Folk-lore—Norway.

NL 0344906   ICU OC1

Lie, John.
En Gaardmandssön; Fortælling fra Thelemarken.   Dram-
men: D. Steen, 1888.   290 p.   12°.

1. Fiction (Norwegian).   2. Title.
N. Y. P. L.   August 5, 1914.

NL 0344907   NN

PT8905 **Lie, John,** 1846–1916.
.L71H4   Helsing til Amerika; song-leik.
Hillsboro, N.D., Banner Pub. Co.,
1898.
32 p.   15 cm.

Cover title.
Poems.

NL 0344908   MnHi

PT9036 **Lie, John,** 1846–1916.
.L7   Hugaljo, av John Lie.   Kristiania, Norske samlaget
1874.
101, ₍14₎ p. 18ᶜᵐ.
"Hugaljo, av Hallvor Lie": p. ₍73₎–101.
"Digtsamling i Molands dialekt."—Halvorsen.   Norsk forfatter-lexikon.

NL 0344909   ICU

839.81623 **Lie, John,** 1846–1916.
OHu   Hugaljo. Av John Lie og Hallvor Lie. Nytt
uppl.   ₍Minneapolis₎ K.K. Rudie, 1913.
103 p.   18cm.

I. Lie, Hallvor, jt.author.   II. Title.

NL 0344910   MnU IU

Lie, John, 1846–1916.
Knut Trondsen; fortælling fra Telemarken, av John Lie.
Kristiania: P. Omtvedt ₍1921₎.   256 p.   12°.

86328A.   1. Fiction (Norwegian).   2. Title.
N. Y. P. L.   June 18, 1923.

NL 0344911   NN

Lie, John, 1846–1916.
Paradiset paa jorden—eller—Det sande hjem, dets
grundvold og velsignelser. Af John Lie ... Chicago,
John Anderson publishing company, 1893.
2 p. l., 3–291 p.   illus., plates.   19½ᶜᵐ.
"Skandinavens præmiebog for 1894."

I. Title.

Library of Congress   PT8905.L8P3   17–18439

NL 0344912   DLC

Lie, John, 1846–1916.
Signe og Hermod, fortælling fra Telemarken af John
Lie. Chicago, John Anderson publishing co., 1892.
136 p.   17ᶜᵐ.
Cover dated 1893.

I. Title.

Library of Congress   PT8905.L8S5   17–18440

NL 0344913   DLC MnU OO

Lie, John, 1846–1916.
...Ståle Storli.   Oslo, Fonna forlag, 1946.   180 p.   port.
19cm.
"På Nynorsk ved Haakon Lie."

378582B.   1. No subject.   I. Lie,   Haakon, 1884–   , tr.   II. Title.
N. Y. P. L.   March 21, 1947

NL 0344914   NN WaT OrP

Lie, John, *1846–*
Staali Storli. En Fortælling fra Telemarken.
Hamar. Arvesen. 1880. 475, (1) pp. 18 cm., in 8s.

D8669 — T.r. Fortælling. — Norway. Lang. Works in Norwegian.

NL 0344915   MB NdU

PT8905 **Lie, John,** 1846–1916.
.L71S7   Staali Storli; fortaelling fra
Telemarken. Decorah, Iowa, Decorah-
postens damp-trykkeri, 1891.
332 p.   17 cm.

NL 0344916   MnHi

HQ796 **Lie, Jon Aage,** joint ed.
.L9
Lynau, Kjell, *ed.*
Våken ungdom; boken om ungdomsproblemer. Redak-
tører: Kjell Lynau ₍og₎ Jon Aage Lie. Sekretærer: Rigmor
Lütcherath Luihn ₍og₎ Gro Bagn. Oslo, Aschehoug, 1949.

Lie, Jonas, 1833–1908.
see Lie, Jonas Lauritz Idemil, 1833–1908.

VOLUME 332

Lie, Jonas, 1899–
   The devil's birthday, by Jonas Lie. London, B. Cassirer ₍1940₎

296 p. 19ᵐ.

"Translated from the Norwegian by I. Lie and E. H. Campion."
"First published in England 1940."

   ɪ. Lie, I., tr.   ɪɪ. Campion, E. H., joint tr.   ɪɪɪ. Title.   *Transla-tion of* Natten til fandens geburtsdag.
                                         40–31879

Library of Congress   PZ3.L6202De

NL   0344919   DLC

₍Lie, Jonas₎ 1899–
   ... Natten før fandens fødselsdag, kriminalroman. Køben-havn, Det Schønbergske forlag ₍1935₎

183 p. 21½ᶜᵐ.

Author's pseud., Max Mauser, at head of title.

   ɪ. Title.   44–46704

Library of Congress   PT8950.L574N32
                               ₍2₎   839.8236

NL   0344920   DLC

[LIE, JONAS] 1899–
   ...Natten til fandens geburtsdag. [Oslo] Steenske forlag [1934] 190 p. 20cm.

Author's pseud., Max Mauser, at head of title.

82520B.   1. Fiction, Norwegian.   I. Title.

NL   0344921   NN

Lie, Jonas, 1899–
   ... Der todesdiamant, polizei-rapport über den Orlow, krimi-nalroman ... Nürnberg, J. L. Schrag ₍1938₎

234, ₍2₎ p. illus. (plans) 18ᶜᵐ. (Turmbücher)

"Aus dem norwegischen übertragen von Amico W. Schilling."

   ɪ. Schilling, Amico W., tr.   ɪɪ. Title.

PT8950.L574D64   839.8236   47–36775

NL   0344922   DLC MnU

Lie, Jonas Lauritz Idemil, 1833–1908.
   Samlade berättelser, af Jonas Lie; af författaren autoriserad och med särskildt förord försedd öfversättning. Stockholm: Z. Haeggström, 1877.   555 p.   front. (port.)   18cm.

   CONTENTS.—Vid Enare träsk.—Visionären; eller, Bilder från Nordland.—Söndmörs-ottringen.—Tremastaren "Fremtiden."—Nordfjordshästen.—Fanfulla.—Lotsen och hans hustru.—Antonio Banniera.—Lapp-blod.

642175A.   1. Norwegian literature—   Collected works.
N.Y.P.L.   April 2, 1934

NL   0344923   NN

PT8906
1920   **Lie, Jonas Lauritz Idemil,** 1833–1908.
     Samlede digterverker ₍av₎ Jonas Lie. Standardutg. Indledning av Valborg Erichsen; oplysninger og varianter ved Paula Bergh. Kristiania, Gyldendal, 1920-21.
     10 v. ports. 19cm.

     CONTENTS.—1. bd. Den fremsynte. Fort-aellinger og skildringer. Tremasteren "Fremtiden."—2. bd. Lodsen og Hans Hustru. Faustina Strozzi.—3. bd. Thomas Ross.

Continued in next column

Continued from preceding column

Adam Schrader. Grabows kat.—4. bd. Rutland. Ole Bull. Gaa paa!—5. bd. Livsslaven. Familien paa gilje. En malstrøm.—6. bd. Otte fortaellinger. Stemninger. Kommandørens døttre.—7. bd. Et samliv. Maisa Jons. Onde magter.—8. bd. Trold I-II. Niobe. Lystige koner.—9. bd. Naar sol gaar ned. Dyre rein. Lindelin. Faste Forland.—

10. bd. Wulffie & Comp. Naar Jernteppet falder. Ulfvungerne. Østenfor Sol, vestenfor Maane. Eventyr. Digte.
   ɪ. Bergh, Paula   ed.

NL   0344926   ViU NcD PP IaU IU

Lie, Jonas Lauritz Idemil, 1833–
   ... Samlede værker ... ₍Folkeudgave₎ Kjøbenhavn og Kristiania, Gyldendalske boghandel, Nordisk forlag, 1902-04.

14 v. ports., facsim. 19½ᶜᵐ.
Imprint varies: v. 1-12, Kjøbenhavn. Gyldendalske boghandel.—v. 13-14, Kjøbenhavn og Kristiania, Gyldendalske boghandel, Nordisk forlag.
Cover dates: 1906-1907.
Issued in 61 parts.
CONTENTS.—1. bd. Indledningsdigt. Den fremsynte, eller Billeder fra Nordland. Tremasteren "Fremtiden," eller Liv nordpaa.—2. bd. Lodsen og hans hustru. Faustina Strozzi.—3. bd. Thomas Ross. Adam Schrader.—

4. bd. Grabows kat. Rutland.—5. bd. Gaa paa! Livsslaven.—6. bd. Fami-ljen paa Gilje. En malstrøm.—7. bd. Fortaellinger og skildringer.—8. bd. Kommandørens døttre. Et samliv.—9. bd. Maisa Jons. Onde magter.—10. bd. Digte og sange. Trold, 1.-2. samling.—11. bd. Niobe. Lystige ko-ner.—12. bd. Naar sol gaar ned. Dyre Rein.—13. bd. Lindelin. Faste For-land.—14. bd. Wulffie & comp. Naar jernteppet falder. Erik Lie: Biblio-grafiske oplysninger til Jonas Lie's Samlede værker.

   ɪ. Lie, Erik Røring Møinichen, 1868–
                                   8–5364

Library of Congress

NL   0344928   DLC OrU NdU NcU CtY MiU PPT

839.82
L62
A3   **Lie, Jonas Lauritz Idemil,** 1833–1908.
   ... Samlede vaerker ... [Folkeudgave] Kjøbenhavn, Gyldendalske boghandels forlag, 1902-[05]
   15v. ports.,facsim. 19cm.
   Imprint varies: v.12-14, Kjøbenhavn og Kristiania, Glydendalske boghandel, Nordisk forlag.
   CONTENTS.—1.bd. Indledningsdigt. Den frem-synte, eller Billeder fra Nordland. Tremas-teren "Fremtiden," eller Liv nordpaa.—2.bd.

Lodsen og hans hustru. Faustina Strozzi.—3. bd. Thomas Ross. Adam Schrader.—4.bd. Gra-bows kat. Rutland.—5.bd. Gaa paa! Livsslav-en.—6.bd. Familjen paa Gilje. En malstrøm.—7.bd. Fortaellinger og skildringer.—8.bd. Kom-mandørens døttre. Et samliv.—9.bd. Maisa Jons. Onde magter.—10.bd. Digte og sange.

Trold, 1.-2. Samling.—11.bd. Niobe. Lystige koner.—12.bd. Naar sol gaar ned. Dyre Rein.—13.bd. Lindelin. Faste Forland.—14.bd. Wulffie & comp. Naar jernteppet falder. Erik Lie: Bibliografiske oplysninger til Jonas Lie's Samlede vaerker.—[15.bd.] Ulfvungerne. Østen-for sol, vesten for maane og bagom Babylons taarn. 1903-05.

NL   0344931   TxU MH

PT8906
1902   **Lie, Jonas Lauritz Idemil,** 1833–1908.
     ... Samlede værker ... ₍Folkeudgave₎ Kjøbenhavn og Kristiania, Gyldendalske boghandel, Nordisk forlag, 1902-09.
     15 v. ports., facsim. 19½ᶜᵐ.
     Imprint varies: v. 1-12, Kjøbenhavn, Gyldendalske boghandel.—v. 13-15, Kjøbenhavn og Kristiania, Gyldendalske boghandel, Nordisk forlag.

     CONTENTS.—1. bd. Indledningsdigt. Den fremsynte, eller Billeder fra Nordland. Tremasteren "Fremtiden," eller Liv nordpaa.—2. bd. Lodsen og hans hustru. Faustina Strozzi.—3. bd. Thomas Ross. Adam Schrader.—

4. bd. Grabows kat. Rutland.—5. bd. Gaa paa! Livsslaven.—6. bd. Fami-ljen paa Gilje. En malstrøm.—7. bd. Fortaellinger og skildringer.—8. bd. Kommandørens døttre. Et samliv.—9. bd. Maisa Jons. Onde magter.—10. bd. Digte og sange. Trold, 1.-2. samling.—11. bd. Niobe. Lystige ko-ner.—12. bd. Naar sol gaar ned. Dyre Rein.—13. bd. Lindelin. Faste For-land.—14. bd. Wulffie & comp. Naar jernteppet falder. Erik Lie: Biblio-grafiske oplysninger til Jonas Lie's Samlede værker.— 15. Ulfvungern Østenfor sol, vesten for maane og bagom Babylons taarn!

NL   0344933   CU OrU WaSp

Lie, Jonas Lauritz Idemil, 1833–1908.
   Samlede værker. Mindeudgave. Kristiania og København, Gyldendal, 1908-09.
   5v. port. 23cm.

   Contents. - 1. bd. Den fremsynte eller billeder fra Nordland. Tremasteren "Fremtiden"; eller, Liv nordpaa. Faustina Strozzi. Thomas Ross. - 2.bd. Adam Schrader. Grabows kat. Rutland. Gaa paa! Livsslaven. - 3. bd. Familien paa Gilje. En

malstrøm. Fortaellingerog skildringer. Kommandørens døtre. Et samliv. - 4. bd. Maisa Jons. Onde magter. Digte og sange. Trold. Niobe. - 5. bd. Lystige koner. Naar sol gaar ned. Dyre rein. Lindelin. Faste Forland. Wulffie & Comp. Naar jernteppet falder. Ulfvungerne. Østenfor sol, vestenfor maane og bagom Babylons taarn!

NL   0344935   IEN MB TxU CU-I NcU OU CU ViU WaU

PT8906
1914   **Lie, Jonas Lauritz Idemil,** 1833–1908.
     Samlede vaerker. Kristiania, Gyldendal, 1914.
     10 v.

NL   0344936   ICU CaBVaU CoU

839.82
L62
A1
1914   **LIE, JONAS LAURITZ IDEMIL,** 1833–1908.
     Samlede vaerker [3. udgave] Kristiania og København, Gyldendalske boghandel, Nordisk forlag, 1914.
     10v. port.,facsim. 19½cm.
     CONTENTS.—bd.1. Den fremsynte. Tremasteren "Fremtiden". Lodsen og hans hustru.—bd.2. Rutland. Gaa paa!—bd.3. Thomas Ross, Adam Schrader.—bd.4. Livsslaven. Familien paa Gilje.—bd.5. En malstrøm. Kommandørens døtre. Et samliv.—bd.6. Grabows kat. Lystige koner.

Lindelin. Wulffie & comp. Faustina Strozzi.—bd.7. Fortaellinger og skildringer. Trold.—bd.8. Maisa Jons. Onde magter. Niobe.—bd.9. Naar sol gaar ned. Dyre Rein. Faste Forland.—bd.10. Naar jernteppet falder. Ulfungerne. Østenfor sol, vestenfor Maane. Digte og sange.

NL   0344938   TxU PU CtY InU MH CU NcD NjP WaT OrP

Lie, Jonas, 1833–1908.
   Samlede værker. Oslo, Gyldendal, 1941.

   5 v. 21 cm.
   "5.udg."

NL   0344939   MH

VOLUME 332

Lie, Jonas, 1833-1908.
Aaweiden nakija, eli Kuwauksia Norlandista.
Suomentanut Hj. Hietala. Jywäskylässä, Keski-
Suomen kustantama, 1877

71 p.

NL 0344940   MH

Lie, Jonas Lauritz Idemil, 1833-1908.
Adam Schrader. Fortælling af Jonas Lie. Kjøbenhavn, Gyldendal (F. Hegel & søn) 1879.

287 p. 18ᶜᵐ.
First edition.

I. Title.

17-24584

Library of Congress   PT8911.A6 1879

NL 0344941   DLC CU CtY ICU IU MB MnU

Lie, Jonas Lauritz Idemil.
Arne Garborg
    see under Lie, Erik Røring Møinichen,
1868-

LIE, JONAS LAURITZ IDEMIL, 1833-1908.
Auf Irrwegen; Roman. [Autorisierte Übersetzung
aus dem Dänischen von Mathilde Mann] Berlin, S.
Fischer [1921] 189 p. 18cm. (Fischers Bibliothek zeitgenössischer
Romane)

I. Mann, Mathilde (Scheven). 1859-1925. tr.   II. Title.

NL 0344943   NN CtY TNJ

Lie, Jonas Lauritz Idemil, 1833-1908.
... Aus urgrossvaters haus. Roman. München,
[1920]
    19 cm. (Die skandinavische bibliothek, begründ
von Gustaf af Geijerstam, fortgeführt von Else von
Hollander)

NL 0344944   RPB

Lie, Jonas Lauritz Idemil, 1833-
    The barque Future; or, Life in the far North. By
Jonas Lie. Tr. by Mrs. Ole Bull. Chicago, S. C. Griggs
and company, 1879.

253 p. 19¼ᶜᵐ.

I. Bull, Sara Chapman (Thorpe) "Mrs. Ole Bull," 1850-   tr.

Library of Congress   PZ3.L6203B   7-18774†

NL 0344945   DLC PPD MiU OCl OClW IaU IEdS MA MB

Lie, Jonas Lauritz Idemil, 1833-1908.
Bilder aus Norwegen. Drei Erzählungen. Aus
dem Norwegischen von Philipp Schweitzer. Jena,
O. Deistung, 1878.
    18.5 cm.
    Contents. - Der Graue. - Die Geschichte eines
Bootes. - Finnenblut.

NL 0344946   CtY

Lie, Jonas Lauritz Idemil, 1833-1908.
The commodore's daughters, by Jonas Lie; tr. from the
Norwegian by H. L. Brækstad and Gertrude Hughes.
London, W. Heinemann, 1892.

xii, 276 p. 19ᶜᵐ. (On cover: Heinemann's international library, ed.
by E. Gosse. (9))

I. Brækstad, Hans Lien, 1845-   tr. II. Hughes, Gertrude, tr. III. Ti-

A 14-1120

Title from Leland Stan-   ford Jr. Univ. Printed by L. C.

MiU MB PPL
NL 0344947   CSt WaS OrPR N NIC MoU NjP OC1 ODW

Lie, Jonas Lauritz Idemil.
The commodore's daughters. Translated from the Norwegian by H.
L. Brækstad and Gertrude Hughes.
New York. United States Book Co. [1895.] 12°.

△1067 — T.r. — Brækstad, Hans Lien, tr. — Hughes, Gertrude, tr.

NL 0344948   MB

LIE, JONAS, 1833-1908.
Davíð skygni. Reykjavík, ísafoldarprentsmiðja
1909.

24°.
"Sérprentun úr ísafold".

NL 0344949   MH NIC

PT   Lie, Jonas Lauritz Idemil, 1833-1908.
8911   Davíð skygni. Thýðing eftir Guðmund
F715   Kamban. Reykjavík, Sigfús Eymundsson, 1934.
        152 p.

        Translation of: Den fremsynte.

NL 0344950   WaU NIC

Lie, Jonas Lauritz Idemil, 1833-1908.
Digte, af Jonas Lie. Kjøbenhavn, Gyldendal (F. Hegel &
søn) 1889.
4 p. l., 165 p. 18½ᶜᵐ.

40-22540

Library of Congress   PT8910.A1 1889

NL 0344951   DLC IU

Lie, Jonas Lauritz Idemil, 1833-1908.
Der dreimaster "Zukunft". Erzählung aus dem nördlichen
Norwegen von Jonas Lie. Deutsch von H. Denhardt. Leipzig, P. Reclam jun. [1890]
202 p. 15ᶜᵐ. (On cover: Universal-bibliothek, 2704, 2705)

I. Denhardt, H., tr. II. Title.

31-20583

Library of Congress   PT8911.T7G4   839.8236

NL 0344952   DLC RPB IEN MB

Lie, Jonas Lauritz Idemil, 1833-1908.
... Dyre Rein; en historie fra oldefars hus. Kjøbenhavn, Gyldendal (F. Hegel & søn) 1896.

2 p. l., 256 p. 17¼ᶜᵐ.
First edition.

I. Title.

17-24585

Library of Congress   PT8911.D8 1896

NL 0344953   DLC IU

839.83 **Lie, Jonas Lauritz Idemil,** 1833-1908.
L62d   Dyre Rein; en historie fra oldefars hus.
1896   Kjøbenhavn, Gyldendal (F. Hegel & søn) 1896.
        1 p.l., 256p. 18cm.

        2. opl.

NL 0344954   IU

        Lie, Jonas Lauritz Idemil, 1833-1908.
Hol   ... Dyre Rein; en historie fra oldefars hus. Kjøben-
L61   havn, Gyldendal (F. Hegel & søn) 1896.
D8   2 p. l., 256 p. 17½ᶜᵐ.

        3. opl.

NL 0344955   CtY CU

LIE, Jonas Lauritz Idemil.
Dyre Rein. Eine Geschichte aus Urgrossvaters Hause.
    Leipzig. Göschen. 1897. (2), 239 pp. 16°.

NL 0344956   MB

        LIE, Jonas Lauritz Idemil. 1833-
        ...Dyre rein; en historie fra oldefars
hus; tredie oplag.
        Kjøbenhavn. 1910. 190p.

NL 0344957   WaS

Lie, Jonas Lauritz Idemil, 1833-1908.
Eine ehe, roman von Jonas Lie. Berlin, S. Fischer [1908]
x p., 1 l., 191, [1] p. 18ᶜᵐ. (Half-title: Fischers bibliothek zeitgenössischer romane. [Jahrg. I, bd. 8])

I. Title.

44-18479

Library of Congress   PT8911.S3G4

NL 0344958   DLC TNJ PPG

        Lie, Jonas Lauritz Idemil, 1833-1908.
HX531   Az életfogytiglan elitélt; regény, irta
A1V69   Jonas Lie. Norvég eredetiből forditotta Ritoók
v.55-63   Emma. Budapest, A Népszava-könyvkereskedés
        kiadása, 1919.
            192 p. 15ᶜᵐ. (On cover: Világosság könyv-
        tár, 55-63)
            On cover: A Magyarországi szocialista párt
        kiadása.

            I.Ritoók, Emma, tr. II.Title.

NL 0344959   CSt-H

VOLUME 332

Lie, Jonas Lauritz Idemil, 1833–1908.
... Eventyr. Kristiania og Kjøbenhavn, Gyldendalske
boghandel, Nordisk forlag, 1909.
79 p. 20ᶜᵐ.   kr. 1.70
CONTENTS.—Impromptu.—Jomfru Maria.—Fjæsingen.—Mor Øfsti—
Havets fantasier.—Aand.—Moder natur.—Finmarksvidden.—Første kapitel af Lies paabegyndte bog.

Library of Congress   10-813

NL 0344960   DLC CaBVaU NcU

Lie, Jonas Lauritz Edemil, 1833–1908.
Die familie auf Gilje--Ein roman aus dem
leben unserer zeit.   Übertragen von Mathilde Mann.
Leipzig, n. d.
18 cm.   (Bibliothek der romane)

NL 0344961   RPB

LIE,Jonas,1833-1908.
Die Familie auf Gilje;Roman aus dem Leben unserer Zeit. Rechtmässige Übersetzung von Mathilde Mann. Leipzig,P.Reclam,Jun.,[1896].

15 cm.
Paper-cover:Universal-Bibliothek,3554,3555.

NL 0344962   MH MB

Lie, Jonas [Lauritz Idemil].
Die Familie auf Gilje; ein Roman aus dem Leben unserer
Zeit; übertragen von Mathilde Mann.   Leipzig: Insel [19—?].
246 p.   12°.

NL 0344963   NN

Lie, Jonas Lauritz Idemil, 1833–1908.
Familjen paa Gilje. Et interieur fra firtiaarene af
Jonas Lie. Kjøbenhavn, Gyldendal (F. Hegel & søn)
1883.
2 p. l., 282 p. 18ᶜᵐ.
First edition.

I. Title.

                                                  17-24586
Library of Congress   PT8911.F3 1883

NL 0344964   DLC

Lie, Jonas Lauritz Idemil, 1833-1908.
Familjen paa Gilje. [Fortælling.] Et interieur fra firtiaarene.
2. oplag.
Kjøbenhavn. Gyldendal. 1887. 286 pp. 17 cm., in 8s.

E2009 — T.r. — Norway. Lang. Works in Norwegian.

NL 0344965   MB

Lie, Jonas Lauritz Idemil, 1833–1908.
... Familjen paa Gilje, et interieur fra firtiaarene. 3. opl.
Kjøbenhavn, Gyldendal, 1898.
286 p. 18½ᶜᵐ.

I. Title.

                                                  3—22715
Library of Congress   PT8911.F8 1898

NL 0344966   DLC

Lie, Jonas [Lauritz Idemil] 1833–
... Familjen paa Gilje, et interieur fra firtiaarene. 3.
opl. Kjøbenhavn, Gyldendal, 1907.
197p. 18½ᶜᵐ.

NL 0344967   WaS

Lie, Jonas [Lauritz Idemil] 1833–1908.
Familjen paa Gilje et Interiør fra Firtiaarene. 4.ed
Kjøbenhavn, Gyldendalske Boghandel, 1903.
184 p.   12°.

NL 0344968   NN

PT   Lie, Jonas Lauritz Idemil, 1833–1908.
8911   Familjen paa Gilje; et interiør fra
F3   firtiaarene. Kristinia, Gyldendal, 1907.
1907   197 p.

          "Efter Fortaellingens 4de Udgave."

NL 0344969   WaU NdU

Lie, Jonas Lauritz Edemil.
Familjen paa Gilje; et interior fra
firtiaarene; tiende udgave. Kristiania
Gyldendalske Boghandel,1919.

NL 0344970   WaE

Lie, Jonas Lauritz Edemil, 1833–1908.
Familjen paa Gilje et interior fra firtaarene.
Kristiania, Gyldendalske, 1923.
Ellevte utgave.

NL 0344971   CaBVa

839.823   Lie, Jonas Lauritz Idemil, 1833-1908.
L716f   Familjen paa Gilje. [Oslo] Gyldendal [1928]
1928   200p. 20cm. (Norges national litteratur
          [9])

NL 0344972   IEN

PT8911   Lie, Jonas Lauritz Idemil, 1833-1908.
F8   Familjen paa Gilje; interiør fra firtiaarene.
1929   Med tegninger av Erik Werenskiold. [2. utg.]
          Oslo, Gyldendal, 1929.
          226 p. illus. 26cm.

NL 0344973   CoU

PT8911   Lie, Jonas Lauritz Idemil, 1833–1908.
F4   Familien på Gilje. Et interiør fra firti-
1942   årene. Med tegninger av Erik Werenskiold. Os-
          lo, Gyldendal Norsk Forlag, 1942.
          241 p. illus.

NL 0344974   ICU

Lie, Jonas Lauritz Idemil, 1833–1908
**Familien på Gilje; et interiør fra
firtiaarene.** Oslo, Gyldendal [1953]
169p.

Norwegian.

NL 0344975   OC1

Lie, Jonas Lauritz Idemil, 1833–1908.
The family at Gilje; a domestic story of the forties, by
Jonas Lie; tr. from the Norwegian by Samuel Coffin Eastman, with an introduction by Julius Emil Olson. New
York, The American-Scandinavian foundation; [etc., etc.]
1920.
3 p. l., [v]–xxxi, 245 p. 19½ cm. (Half-title: Scandinavian classics,
vol. XIV)

I. Eastman, Samuel Coffin, 1837–1917, tr. II. Title.

PZ3.L6203Fa   21–26552
Library of Congress

CU MB OrP WaTC Wa OrMonO
NBuC NIC AAP NBuU NcGU WaT IdPI OU MH CoU Or WaS OrU
NL 0344976   DLC OEac OCU OC1h OC1 PP PU PPT PHC MiU

839.83   Lie, Jonas Lauritz Idemil, 1833–1908.
L62fE   The family at Gilje; a domestic story
1920   of the forties, translated from the
          Norwegian by Samuel Coffin Eastman, with
          an introduction by Julius Emil Olson.
          New York, Doubleday [c1920]
          xxxi, 245 p.

NL 0344977   WaU

Lie, Jonas Lauritz Idemil, 1833–1908.
The family at Gilje; a domestic story of the 'forties, by
Jonas Lie; translated from the Norwegian by Samuel Coffin
Eastman, with an introduction by Julius Emil Olson ...
Garden City, N. Y., Doubleday, Page and company, 1923.
xxxi, 245 p. 19½ cm.
"Originally published by the American-Scandinavian foundation as
volume XIV of the Scandinavian classics."

I. Eastman, Samuel Coffin, 1837–1917, tr. II. Title.

                                                  A 24—244
Chicago. Public Library
for Library of Congress   [a51d½]

NL 0344978   ICU OrU OrCS TxU MB NN PPD

Lie, Jonas, 1833–1908.
Faste Forland. Kjøbenhavn, Gyldendalske boghandels forlag,
1899.
pp. (2), 257.

NL 0344979   MH FU IU

Lie, Jonas Lauritz Idemil, 1833–1908.
Faustina Strozzi. Af Jonas Lie. Kjøbenhavn, Gyl-
dendal (F. Hegel) 1875.
148, [2] p. 17ᶜᵐ.
First edition.
Drama, in verse.

I. Title.

                                                  17–24588
Library of Congress   PT8909.F3 1875

NL 0344980   DLC IU InU MnU

VOLUME 332

PT
8911
K6514
1895

Lie, Jonas Lauritz Idemil, 1833–1908.
Les filles du Commandant [par] Jonas Lie;
roman traduit du norwégien par Mademoiselle
Aline Toppélius. Paris, Albert Savine, 1895.
xii, 275 p.

Translation of Kommandørans døttre.

NL 0344981   WaU

PT8911
F6
1872

Lie, Jonas Lauritz Idemil, 1833–1908.
Fortaellinger og skildringer fra Norge, af Jonas
Lie. Kjøbenhavn, Gyldendal, 1872.
123 p.

NL 0344982   CU

Lie, Jonas Lauritz Idemil, 1833–1908.
· Fortaellinger og Skildringer fra norge ...
Chicago, Standinaven's boghandel, 1886.
89 p.   D.

NL 0344983   OO

Lie, Jonas Lauritz Idemil.
Fortællinger og Skildringer fra Norge. 4. Oplag.
Kjøbenhavn. Gyldendal. 1892. (3), 223 pp. Sm. 8vo.
Contents. — Nordfjordhesten, en liden Fortælling fra Skydskariolen.
Søndmørs-Ottringen. — Finneblod. — Svend Føyn og Ishavsfarten.

D866s — T.r. — Norway. Lang. Works in Norwegian.

NL 0344984   MB MH RPB NdU CtY WaS

Lie, Jonas Lauritz Idemil, 1833–1908.
Den fremsynte, eller Billeder fra Nordland. Af Jonas
Lie. 2. opl. Kjøbenhavn, Gyldendal (F. Hegel) 1871.
143 p. 17¼ᶜᵐ.

ɪ. Title.

17-22503

Library of Congress   PT8911.F7 1871

NL 0344985   DLC NdU CU

LIE, Jonas, 1833–1908.
Den fremsynte, eller Billeder fra Nordland.
5e opl. Kjobenhavn, boghandel, Gyldendalske, 1875.

pp.146.

NL 0344986   MH

839.8L62
OFrb

Lie, Jonas Lauritz Idemil, 1833–1908.
Den fremsynte; eller, Billeder fra Nordland.
7. opl. Kjøbenhavn, Gyldendal, 1882.

146p.   18cm.

NL 0344987   MnU

PT8911
.F7

Lie, Jonas Lauritz Idemil, 1833–1908.
Den fremsynte; eller, Billeder
fra Nordland. Chicago, C. Rasmussen
₁1883₎
34 p. 23 cm. (Skandinavisk
national-bibliothek, 2.aarg. (nr.10))

NL 0344988   MnHi

Lie, Jonas ₁Lauritz Idemil₎ 1833–
... Den fremsynte; eller, Billeder fra Nordland. 9. opl.
Kjøbenhavn, Gyldendal, 1896.
146 p. 18¼ᶜᵐ.   3-22730

NL 0344989   DLC CtY

PT8906
.F6
1901

Lie, Jonas Lauritz Idemil, 1833–1908.
Den fremsynte; eller, Billeder fra Nordland.
10. opl. Kjøbenhavn, Gyldendal, 1901.
146 p.

I. Title. II. Title: Billeder fra Nordland.

NL 0344990   ICU

Lie, Jonas Lauritz Idemil, 1833–1908.
... Den fremsynte; eller, Billeder fra Nordland.
9. opl. Kjøbenhavn, Gyldendal, 1903.
120 p. 18.5 cm.

NL 0344991   WaS

Lie, Jonas Lauritz Idemil, 1833–1908.
Den fremsynte; eller, Billeder fra Nordland. 12. udg. Kjøbenhavn, Gyldendal, 1905.

121 p. 19cm.

I. Title.

NL 0344992   MnU

Lie, Jonas Lauritz Idemil, 1833–
... Den fremsynte; illustreret af Thorolf Holmboe. København, Kristiania, Gyldendal, 1906.
148 p. illus. (1 col.) 20ᶜᵐ. (*Half-title:* Nordisk bibliotek (xxxiii))
On verso of t.-p.: 1ste illustrerede udgave. 13de oplag.

Library of Congress   7-18130

NL 0344993   DLC CU

Lie, Jonas Lauritz Idemil, 1833–1908.
Den fremsynte; eller, Billeder fra Nordland.
Chicago, J. Anderson, 1911.
146 p.   20 cm.

NL 0344994   MnU Or WaT

Lie, Jonas Lauritz Idemil, 1833–1908.
Gaa paa! Sjøfortælling af Jonas Lie. Kjøbenhavn,
Gyldendal (F. Hegel & søn) 1882.
344 p. 18ᶜᵐ.
Added t.-p., illus.
First edition.

ɪ. Title.

17-24589

Library of Congress   PT8911.G3 1882

NL 0344995   DLC NdU CtY

Lie, Jonas Lauritz Idemil.
Gaa paa! Sjøfortælling. 2. Oplag.
Kjøbenhavn. Gyldendal. 1882. 344 pp. Engraved title-page.
Sm. 8vo.

D866s — T.r. — Norway. Lang. Works in Norwegian.

NL 0344996   MB IU

Lie, Jonas Lauritz Idemil, 1833–1908.
Gaa paa! Sjøfortaelling. Chicago,
Kølling, 1883.
215p. 18cm.

NL 0344997   IEN

LIE, Jonas, 1833–1908.
Gaa paa! Sjøfortaelling. 3 die opl., Kjøbenhavn, Gyldendalske boghandels forlag, 1898.

pp. 344. Vign.
With added half-title illustrated.

NL 0344998   MH

Lie, Jonas Lauritz Idemil, 1833–1908.
Gaa paa! sjofortaelling. Kjøbenhavn, 1911.
222 p.

NL 0344999   WaS

Lie, Jonas Lauritz Idemil, 1833–1908
... Gaa paa 1920

NL 0345000   NdU

839.83
L62g
1941

Lie, Jonas Lauritz Idemil, 1833–1908.
Gaa paa! Sjøfortaelling. ₁12 opl.₎   Oslo,
Gyldendal, 1941.
174p. 20cm. ₁Norges nasjonal litteratur, 11₎

NL 0345001   IU

Lie, Jonas Lauritz Idemil, 1833–1908.
Gå på; sjøfortelling. Oslo, Gyldendal, 1951.
190 p. 19 cm. (Hjemmenes boksamling)

ɪ. Title.
PT8911.G3N6 1951   52-22705

NL 0345002   DLC

PT8125
.B8Z542

Lie, Jonas Lauritz Idemil, 1833–1908.
Brandes, Georg Morris Cohen, 1842–1927.
Georg og Edv. Brandes' brevveksling med Bjørnson, Ibsen, Kielland, Elster, Garborg, Lie. Utg. av Francis Bull
under medvirkning av Morten Borup. Oslo, Gyldendal₁
1939–41.

VOLUME 332

Lie, Jonas Lauritz Idemil, 1833–1908.
Grabows kat. Skuespil i tre akter af Jonas Lie. Kjøbenhavn, Gyldendal (F. Hegel & søn) 1880.
162 p. 18ᶜᵐ.
First edition.

I. Title.

17-24587

Library of Congress   PT8909.G7 1880

NL 0345003   DLC CtY MB ICU IU

Lie, Jonas Lauritz Idemil, 1833–1908.
Grossvater. Berlin, 1896.

NL 0345004   NjP

Lie, Jonas ₍Lauritz Idemil₎.
Grossvater. Berlin: Richard Taendler, 1904.   247 p.
12°.

NL 0345005   NN

PT1679
W4A36
Lie, Jonas Lauritz Idemil, 1833–1908
Der Hellseher; oder, Bilder aus Norwegen.
Aus dem Norwegischen von Wilhelm Lange.
Vom Verfasser autorisirte Übersetzung.
Leipzig, Reclam ₍187-?₎
120p. 14cm.

Bound with Wernher der Gartenaere, 13th
cent. Meier Helmbrecht. Leipzig ₍1878?₎

I.Title. Bd with ₍no shelf cd.₎

NL 0345006   IaU IEN RPB

Lie, Jonas Lauritz Idemil, 1833–1908.
Der hellseher oder Bilder aus Norwegen, von
Jonas Lie. Aus dem norwegischen von Wilhelm
Lange. Leipzig, P. Reclam jun. [1881]
120 p. 15 cm (On cover: Universal-Bibliothek
[no] 1540)
Translation of Den fremsynte, eller Billeder fra
Nordland. - cf. Brockhaus.

NL 0345007   RPB

839.88
L72f
₍J6₎
Lie, Jonas Lauritz Idemil, 1833–1908.
Der hellseher; oder, Bilder aus Nordland
von Jonas Lie. Aus dem norwegischen von
Dr.Otto Jiriczek. Halle, O.Hendel, [1891]
96 p. 18cm.

NL 0345008   MiU NN PPG

Hop
L63
NF21
Lie, Jonas Lauritz Idemil, 1833–1908.
... Hof Gilje. Eine Familiengeschichte, von
Jonas Lie. Aus dem Norwegischen übersetzt von
F.Mangold. Stuttgart,J.Engelhorn,1894.
160p. 18½cm. (Engelhorns Allgemeine Roman-
bibliothek ... 10.Jahrg.,Bd.20)

I. Mangold, F   tr. x.ser.^

NL 0345009   CtY ICRL

Lie, Jonas ₍Lauritz Idemil₎.
Hof Gilje; eine Familiengeschichte, aus dem Norwegischen
übersetzt von F. Mangold. Stuttgart: J. Engelhorn ₍19—?₎.
160 p. 12°.

I. Title.   CENTRAL CIRCULATION.
N. Y. P. L.   December 3, 1918.

NL 0345010   NN

Lie, Jonas Lauritz Idemil, 1833–1908.
Jonas Lie; et festskrift i anledning af hans
60-aarige fødselsdag
see under title

839.82369
L716J
Lie, Jonas Lauritz Idemil, 1833–1908.
Jonas Lie og hans samtidige; breve i ud-
valg ved Carl Naerup. ₍Kristiania (Oslo)₎
Gyldendal, 1915.
292 p. 19 cm.

I. Naerup, Carl Georg Nicolai Hansen,
1864-1937, ed.

NL 0345012   NcD IEN NcU CU MH TxU

PT
8914
A6
Lie, Jonas Lauritz Idemil, 1833–1908.
Jonas Lie og hans samtidige; breve i
udvalg, ved Carl Naerup. ₍Kristiania₎
Nordisk forlag, 1915.
292 p. 19cm.

I. Naerup, Carl Georg Nicolai Hansen,
1864-1931, ed. II. Title.

NL 0345013   NIC NN CtY

Lie, Jonas Lauritz Idemil, 1833–1908.
... Kommandørens døtre.
(*In* Juuls store nordiske bibliothek ... Chicago, 1891. 20ᶜᵐ. v. 4.
204 p. port.)

I. Title.

17-8153

Library of Congress   PT7090.J8 vol.4

NL 0345014   DLC

Lie, Jonas Lauritz Idemil, 1833–1908.
Kommandørens døtre. Roman af Jonas Lie. Kjøbenhavn, Gyldendal (F. Hegel & søn) 1886.
323 p. 18ᶜᵐ.

I. Title.

17-22510

Library of Congress   PT8911.K6 1886

NL 0345015   DLC NdU NjP

Lie, Jonas Lauritz Idemil.
Kommandørens Døtre. Roman. 2. Oplag.
Kjøbenhavn. Gyldendal. 1893. 323 pp. Sm. 8vo.

D8665 — T.r. — Norway. Lang. Works in Norwegian.

NL 0345016   MB IU NN

Lie, Jonas ₍Lauritz Idemil₎ 1833–
Kommandørens døtre. Roman af Jonas Lie. 3. opl.
Kjøbenhavn, Gyldendal, 1899.
323 p. 18¼ᵐ.

3-22712

Library of Congress, no.

NL 0345017   DLC

PT8911
K6
1905
Lie, Jonas Lauritz Idemil, 1833–1908.
Kommandørens døttre; roman. 4. udg. København.
Gyldendal, 1905.
238 p.

NL 0345018   CU WaS N

Lie, Jonas Lauritz Idemil, 1833–1908.
Lebenslänglich verurtheilt; erzählung von Jonas
Lie. Aus dem norwegischen von M. von Borch.
Leipzig, P. Reclam jun. [1884]
188 p. 15 cm. (On cover: Universal-bibliothek
[no] 1909, 1910)
Translation of Livslaven.

NL 0345019   RPB

Lie, Jonas ₍Lauritz Idemil₎ 1833–
... Lindelin, eventyr-spil i fire akter. Kjøbenhavn,
Gyldendal, 1897.
3 p. l., 233 p. 18¼ᵐ.   3-22707

Library of Congress, no.

NL 0345020   DLC CU CtY NN MB

Lie, Jonas Lauritz Idemil, 1833–1908.
... Lindelin, novellen; einzig autorisierte Übersetzung aus dem norwegischen ₍von Ernst Brausewet-
ter₎ Umschlagzeichnung von Georg Tippel. Berlin,
Bard, Marquardt & co., 1904.
3 p. l., 3-207 [1] p. 19 cm (Half-title:
Bibliothek Bard, bd. 12-13)

NL 0345021   RPB

PT
8911
.O672x
Lie, Jonas Lauritz Idemil, 1833–1908.
Little Grey, the pony of Nordfjord;
or, The story of Gjermund and Sigrid.
Tr. by permission from the Norwegian by
Hon. Mrs. Arbuthnott. Edinburgh, T.C.
Jack; London, Hamilton, Adams 1873.
xiii, 84 p. 18 cm.
Translation of Nordfjordhesten.

NL 0345022   OKentU OC1

Lie, Jonas Lauritz Idemil, 1833–1908.
Livsslaven. Af Jonas Lie. Kjøbenhavn, Gyldendal
(F. Hegel & søn) 1883.
223 p. 18ᶜᵐ.
A novel.

I. Title.

17-22507

Library of Congress   PT8911.L5 1883

NL 0345023   DLC MnHi NN NdU

Lie, Jonas Lauritz Idemil, 1833–1908.
Livsslaven. Chicago, Skandino vens boghandel,
1889.

NL 0345024   OrP

Lie, Jonas Lauritz Idemil, 1833–1908.
Livsslaven. Af Jonas Lie. 2. opl. Kjøbenhavn, Gyldendal
(F. Hegel & son) 1894.
223 p. 18¼ᵐ.
A novel.

I. Title.

3-22709 Revised

Library of Congress   PT8911.L5 1894

NL 0345025   DLC IU MB

VOLUME 332

PT8123
B4Al5
1905
Scandi-
navian
Dept.

Lie, Jonas Lauritz Idemil, 1833-1908.
Livsslaven. [Efter fortaellingens 2. opl., 1894] København,
Gyldendal, 1906.
168 p. port. [Bound with Bauditz, S.G. Fortaellinger.
1905]

NL 0345026   CU KU

TR

Lie, Jonas Lauritz Idemil, 1833-1908.
Lodsen og hans hustru. Af Jonas Lie.
Kjøbenhavn, Gyldendal (F. Hegel) 1874.
298 p. 18 cm.

Added t.-p., illustrated.
I. Title.

NL 0345027   VtU NN MB IU NdU

Lie, Jonas Lauritz Idemil, 1833-1908.
Lodsen og hans hustru. Af Jonas Lie. 2. opl. Kjøbenhavn, Gyldendal (F. Hegel) 1874.
2 p. l., 301 p. 17½ᶜᵐ.
Added t.-p., illus.

I. Title.

17-25699

Library of Congress   PT8911.L6 1874

NL 0345028   DLC

Lie, Jonas Lauritz Idemil, 1833-1908.
... Lodsen og hans hustru.

(In Juuls store nordiske bibliothek ... Chicago, 1891. 20ᶜᵐ. v. 2.
227 p. pl.)

I. Title.

17-8152

Library of Congress   PT7090.J8 vol.2

NL 0345029   DLC

Lie, Jonas Lauritz Idemil, 1833-1908.
Lodsen og hans hustru, af Jonas Lie. 7. opl.
Kjøbenhavn, gyldendal (F. Hegel & søn) 1891.
1 p. l., 303 p. 18 cm.
Added t.-p., illus.

NL 0345030   RPB MH

Lie, Jonas [Lauritz Idemil] 1833-
... Lodsen og hans hustru. 9. opl. Kjøbenhavn,
Gyldendal, 1899.
1 p. l., 303 p. 18½ᶜᵐ.
Added t.-p., illus.

8-23711

Library of Congress, no.

NL 0345031   DLC

PT8911
L6
1903

Lie, Jonas Lauritz Idemil, 1833-1908.
Lodsen og hans hustru. 10. udg. Kjøbenhavn, Gyldendal,
1903.
245 p.

Added t.-p., illus.

NL 0345032   CU

PT8911
L8
1912

LIE, JONAS LAURITZ IDEMIL, 1833-1908.
...Lodsen og hans hustru. København og Kristiania,
Gyldendal, Nordisk forlag, 1912.
254 p. 18½cm.
"Efter 10.de udgave. 1903(...Samlede værker II")

NL 0345033   ICU KU CU WaS

Lie, Jonas Lauritz Idemil, 1833-1908.
Lodsen og hans hustru. Cedar Rapids, Iowa.
N. Fr. Hansen, 1918.

NL 0345034   WaE

Lie, Jonas Lauritz Idemil, 1833-1908.
...Lodsen og hans hustru; ed. with introd., notes, and vocabulary by Nils Flaten... Minneapolis, Augsburg pub. house,
1924. 358 p. 20cm.

336834B. 1. No subject. I. Flaten, Nils, ed. II. Title.
N. Y. P. L.   November 22, 1946

NL 0345035   NN OU MnU

PT8911
L58
1950

Lie, Jonas Lauritz Idemil, 1833-1908.
Losen og hans hustru [av] Jonas Lie. Oslo, Gyldendal, 1950.
205 p. (Hjemmenes boksamling)

NL 0345036   CU

Lie, Jonas Lauritz Idemil, 1833-1908.
... Der lotse und sein weib, von Jonas Lie.
Autorisierte ueberstzung aus dem norwegischen von
Marie Herzfeld. Stuttgart, J. Engelhorn, 1889.
164 p. 18 cm (Engelhorns Allgemeine roman
bibliothek, V, 24)
Translation of Lodsen og hans hustru.

NL 0345037   RPB CtY PP ICRL

Lie, Jonas [Lauritz Idemil].
Der Lotse und sein Weib; autorisierte Uebersetzung aus dem
Norwegischen von Marie Herzfeld. Stuttgart: J. Engelhorn
[19—?]. 164 p. 12°.

NL 0345038   NN

LIE, Jonas Lauritz Idemil.
Der Lotse und seine Frau. Uebersetzt aus dem Norwegischen durch
Edzard Brons.
Emden. Haynes. 1897. viii, 318 pp. 16°.

Sheet D 754   Oct. 21, 1898

NL 0345039   MB

3352
.55
.359
.5

Lie, Jonas Lauritz Idemil, 1833-1908.
Lotsen och hans hustru... Svensk
upplaga. Stockholm, Norstedt [1909]
174 p. 21½ ᶜᵐ.

Translation of his Lodsen og
hans hustru.

NL 0345040   NjP

Lie, Jonas [Lauritz Idemil,] 1833-1908.
Luotsi ja hänen vaimonsa; suomentanut.
J. Hollo.

NL 0345041   OC1

Lie, Jonas, 1833-1908.
Lystige koner; skuespil i tre akter. Kjøbenhavn, Gyldendalske
boghandels forlag, 1894.
pp. (6), 110.

NL 0345042   MH WU CtY InU NN IU

Lie, Jonas Lauritz Idemil, 1833-1908.
Ein Mahlstrom, Erzählung. Autorisierte
Übertragung aus dem Norwegischen von Erich
Holm [pseud.] Leipzig, P. Reclam [183-]
179p. 14cm. [With his Der Hellseher.
Leipzig [188-]

I. Prager, Mathilde (Lucca) d.1921, tr.
II. Title.

NL 0345043   IEN RPB

PT8911
M3
1888

Lie, Jonas [Lauritz Idemil] 1833-1908
Maisa Jons. Af Jonas Lie. Kjøbenhavn, Gyldendal,
1888.
2 p. l., 286 p. 18½ᶜᵐ.

Library of Congress, no.

NL 0345044   DLC MB CU

PT8911
M3
1889

Lie, Jonas Lauritz Idemil, 1833-1908
Maisa Jons. La Crosse, Wis., Foedrelandet
og Emigrantens Officin, 1889.
203 p. 17 cm.

NL 0345045   MeB

Lie, Jonas [Lauritz Idemil].
Maisa Jons. Leipzig: O. Gracklauer, 1900. 290 p. 12°.

NL 0345046   NN

Lie, Jonas, 1833-1908.
En malstrøm; fortælling. Kjøbenhavn, Gyldendalske bog
handels forlag, 1884.
pp. (3), 243.

NL 0345047   MH RPB IU

Lie, Jonas Lauritz Idemil.
En Malstrøm. Fortælling. Andet Oplag.
Kjøbenhavn. Hegel. 1885. 248 pp. 16mo.

D8666 — T.r. — Norway. Lang. Works in Norwegian.

NL 0345048   MB

Lie, Jonas Lauritz Idemil.
Na manowcach. Powieść norweska. Przekład C. N.
Warszawa. 1904. 72 pp. 17 cm., in 8s.
Supplement to Tygodnik illustrowany.

M78x6 — T.r. — Niewiadomska, Cecylia, tr. — Poland. Lang. Works in Polish.

NL 0345049   MB

VOLUME 332

PT 8911 N3   Lie, Jonas Lauritz Idemil, 1833-1908
Naar jernteppet falder. Af livets komedie
[af] Jonas Lie. Kjøbenhavn, Gyldendal, 1901
263p. 18cm.
A novel.

NL 0345050   WU ViU MH WaE

PT8911 .N16 1901   LIE,JONAS LAURITZ IDEMIL,1833-1908.
...Naar jernteppet falder. Af livets komedie. 2.
oplag. Kjøbenhavn,Gyldendal,1901.
[4],263 p. 19cm.

NL 0345051   ICU NN

HoL L61 N3 1901   LIE,JONAS LAURITZ IDEMIL,1833-1908.
...Naar jernteppet falder. Af livets komedie.3.
oplag. Kjøbenhavn,Gyldendal,1901.
[4],263 p. 19cm.

NL 0345052   ICU IU CtY

PT8911 N3 1895   Lie, Jonas Lauritz Idemil, 1833-1908.
Naar Sol gaar ned, fortaelling [af] Jonas Lie.
Kjøbenhavn, Gyldendal, 1895.
241.p.

NL 0345053   CU PPAmSwM NdU IU CtY MH WaE

839.83 L62na 1896   Lie, Jonas Lauritz Idemil, 1833-1908.
Naar sol gaar ned, fortælling. 3. oplag.
Kjøbenhavn, F. Hegel & søn, 1896.
241p.

At head of title: Jonas Lie.

NL 0345054   IU IaU

Lie, Jonas Lauritz Idemil, 1833-1908.
Nioba doby naši. Roman, Jejž napisal Jonaš Lie.
Z norského přeložil V. P. Praha, J. Otto, n. d.
284 p.
Bohemian.

NL 0345055   OC1

Lie, Jonas Lauritz Idemil, 1833-1908.
Niobe. Nutidsroman af Jonas Lie. Kjøbenhavn, Gyldendal, 1893.
2 p. l., 345 p. 18½cm.

I. Title.

Library of Congress   PT8911.N5 1893   3-22714

NL 0345056   DLC CU NdU

PT 8911 N5 1897   Lie, Jonas Lauritz Idemil, 1833-1908.
Niobe; translated from the Norwegian
by H. L. Braekstad. London, W. Heinemann,
1897.
xii, 290 p. 19cm. (Heinemann's
international library)

NL 0345057   NIC NN MiU OC1 PPT IU CtY WaS OrPR

Lie, Jonas Lauritz Idemil, 1833-1908.
Niobe. Translated from the Norwegian by
H. L. Braekstad. New York, G. H. Richmond,
1898.
xii, 290 p. 20 cm.

A novel.

I. Braekstad, Hans Lien, 1845-1915, tr. II.
Title.

NL 0345058   NcD NBuG OO WU NN

Lie, Jonas Lauritz Idemil, 1833-1908.
... Østenfor sol, vestenfor maane og bagom Babylons
taarn! Streif paa jagtgebetet. Kjøbenhavn og Kristiania, Gyldendal, Nordisk forlag, 1905.
159 p. 20cm.
On verso of half-title: 1ste-12te tusind.

I. Title.

Library of Congress   PT8911.O4 1905   16-18019

NL 0345059   DLC InU MH CU IU NN

Lie, Jonas Lauritz Idemil, 1833-
Bull, Ole [Bornemann] 1810-1880.
Ole Bulls breve i uddrag udgivne af hans søn Alexan-
der Bull. Med en karakteristik og biografisk skitse af
Jonas Lie. Kjøbenhavn, Gyldendal, 1881.

Lie, Jonas, 1833-1908.
Onde magter. Kjøbenhavn, Gyldendalske boghandels forlag,
1890.
pp. (4), 322.

NL 0345061   MH CtY NN IU

Lie, Jonas Lauritz Idemil, 1833-1908.
Onde magter; roman. Minneapolis [etc.]
C. Rasmussen's forlagsboghandel [19--?]
205 p. 18cm.

NL 0345062   MnU CtY WaE

Lie, Jonas Lauritz Idemil, 1833-1908.
One of life's slaves, by Jonas Lie ... translated from the
Norwegian by Jessie Muir. London, Hodder brothers, 1895.
vi p., 1 l., 176 p. 19½cm.

I. Muir, Jessie, tr. II. Title.

   34-37782
Library of Congress   PZ3.L6203On   839.8236

NL 0345063   DLC CtY OC1 PPL

Lie, Jonas, 1833-1908
Oplevelser. Fortalt af E.Lie. Kristiania, Gyldendal,
1908
306 p. illus.

NL 0345064   MH

WA 18894   Lie, Jonas, 1833-1908.
Otte fortaellinger. Chicago, Skandinavens
Boghandel, 1885.
159 p.

NL 0345065   CtY

Lie, Jonas Lauritz Idemil.
Otte Fortællinger.
Kjøbenhavn. Hegel. 1885. (3), 252 pp. 16mo.
Contents. — Alligatoren. — Jon Sunde. — Paa Kirkegaarden. — Fanfulla.
— Improvisatoren. — Susamel. — Slagter-Tobias. — Stemninger: Fra
Fjeldbygden; Ved Enaresjøen.

D8666 — T.r. — Norway. Lang. Works in Norwegian.

NL 0345066   MB IU MH NN

Lie, Jonas Lauritz Idemil, 1833-1908
Pahuuden voimia; norjankielestä
suomensi I. K. Inha.

NL 0345067   OC1

Lie, Jonas Lauritz Idemil, 1833-
... The pilot and his wife [a Norse love story] Tr. by
Mrs. Ole Bull. Chicago, S. C. Griggs and company, 1876.
336 p. incl. front. 19cm.

I. Bull, Sara Chapman (Thorpe) "Mrs. Ole Bull," 1850-   tr.

Library of Congress   PZ3.L6203P·   7-18773†

NL 0345068   DLC Or IU OC1 OO MH NdU

PZ3 .L6203 P   Lie, Jonas Lauritz Idemil, 1833-1908.
The pilot and his wife; tr. from the
Norwegian of Jonas Lie, by G. L. Tottenham.
Edinburgh and London, W. Blackwood and sons,
1877.
2 p. l., 355, [1] p. 19cm.

I. Tottenham, G   L   tr. II.
Title.

NL 0345069   MB RPB IU

839.82 L62utb 1877   Lie, Jonas Lauritz Idemil, 1833-1909.
... The pilot and his wife. By Jonas Lie.
Translated by Mrs. Ole Bull. 2d ed. Chi-
cato, S.C. Griggs and company, 1877 [c1876]
336p. incl. front. 19½cm.

At head of title: a Norse love story.
Translation of Lodsen og hans hustru.

I. Bull, Sara Chapman (Thorp) 1850-1911,
tr. II. Title.

NL 0345070   TxU MB

PT 8911 A3 B8 1891   Lie, Jonas Lauritz Idemil, 1833-1908.
...The pilot and his wife [a Norse love
story] Tr. by Mrs. Ole Bull. Chicago, S. C.
Griggs and company, 1891.
336 p.

NL 0345071   KMK

Lie, Jonas Lauritz Idemil, 1833-1908.
...The pilot and his wife. By Jonas Lie. Translated by Mrs.
Ole Bull. Chicago: S. C. Griggs and Co., 1891. 336 p. front.,
illus. 3. ed. 12°.

At head of title: A Norse love story.

505868A. 1. Fiction, Norwegian.   I. Bull, Sara Chapman (Thorp),
1850-1911, translator. II. Title.
N. Y. P. L.   July 17, 1931

NL 0345072   NN NcU MiU MB

Lie, Jonas, 1833-1908
Rutland; eine seegeschichte.
Leipzig, Merseburger, 1911.
240 p.

NL 0345073   PP

VOLUME 332

Lie, Jonas Lauritz Idemil, 1833–1908.
Rutland. Fortælling af Jonas Lie. Kjøbenhavn, Gyldendal (F. Hegel & søn) 1880.
3 p. l., ₅5₁–293 p. 18ᶜᵐ.

I. Title.
17–22508

Library of Congress   PT8911.R8 1880

NL 0345074   DLC IU

Lie, Jonas Lauritz Idemil.
Rutland. Fortælling. 2. Oplag. Kjøbenhavn. Gyldendal. 1881. 297 pp. Engraved title-page. Sm. 8vo.

D8669 — T.r. — Norway. Lang. Works in Norwegian.

NL 0345075   MB

Lie, Jonas, 1833–1908.
Rutland; fortælling. 3ᵈⁱᵉ opl. Kjøbenhavn, Gyldendalske boghandels forlag, 1897.
pp. 296.
With added half-title illustrated.

NL 0345076   MH CtY

Lie, Jonas Lauritz Idemil, 1833–1908.
Rutland; fortælling; fjerde udgave. Kjøbenhavn, 1906.
200 p.

NL 0345077   WaS

Lie, Jonas Lauritz Idemil, 1833–1908.
...Samlede romaner. Bind 1–   Oslo: Gyldendal, 1933–
₅34₁.   v.   front. (v. 1, port.)   19½cm.

"Hundreårsutgave."
CONTENTS.—Bind 1. Den fremsynte. Tremasteren "Fremtiden."—Bind 2. Lodsen og hans hustru.—Bind 3. Rutland.—Bind 4. Gaa paa.—Bind 5. Familien paa Gilje.—Bind 6. Livsslaven. En malstrøm.—

I. Norwegian literature—Collected   works.
N.Y.P.L.   July 19, 1934

NL 0345078   NN CU NcU

PT8911 **LIE, JONAS LAURITZ IDEMIL, 1833–1908.**
.S2   Et samliv. Af Jonas Lie. Kjøbenhavn, Gyldendal,
1887   1887.
Rare bk [3],255 p. 18¼cm.
room   First ed.

NL 0345079   ICU NdU

839.83 **Lie, Jonas Lauritz Idemil, 1833–1908.**
L62s   Et samliv. Af Jonas Lie.   Chicago, Ill.,
1888   Skandinaven's boghandel, 1888.
178p.

NL 0345080   IU

Lie, Jonas Lauritz Idemil, 1833–1908.
Et Samliv. 2. ed.   Kjøbenhavn, Gyldendal, 1888.
2 p. l., 255 p.   12°.

NL 0345081   NN

Lie, Jonas Lauritz Idemil, *1833–1908.*
Et Samliv. 3. oplag.
Kjøbenhavn. Gyldendal. 1896.   (3), 255 pp.   16 cm., in 8s.

E2009 — T.r. — Norway. Lang. Works in Norwegian.

NL 0345082   MB MH

Hol **Lie, Jonas Lauritz Idemil, 1833–1908.**
L61   Et samliv. 4. opl. Kjøbenhavn, Gyldendal,
S3   1901.
1901   255 p.   18 cm.

NL 0345083   CtY

Lie, Jonas Lauritz Idemil, 1833–1908.
... Selected stories and poems; ed., with English notes and vocabulary, by I. Dorrum ... Minneapolis, Minn., The Free church book concern, 1914.
177, ₅1₁ p.   front. (port.)   19ᶜᵐ. $0.75

I. Dorrum, Ingebret, ᵉd.
15–1828

Library of Congress

NL 0345084   DLC NcU MnHi MnU

Lie, Jonas Jaurits Idemil, 1833–1908.
Sklave des lebens; roman. ₅Aus dem norwegischen übertragen von Georg Daub₎ Berlin, Morawe & Scheffelt ₅1909?₎
179 p.   (Nordland-bücher)

I. Daub, Georg   tr.   II. Title.

NL 0345085   NNC

Lie, Jonas Lauritz Idemil.
Staali Stori
see under   Lie, John, 1846–1916.

LIE, Jonas, 1833–1908.
Susamel und andere Geschichten. Einzig autorisierte Uebersetzung von C.Brausewetter. Mit Illustrationen von A.v.Schrötter. Berlin, etc., H.Hillger, [1898].

17 cm. Facsim.and other illustr.
"Kürschners Bücherschatz,118."

NL 0345087   MH

Lie, Jonas Lauritz Idemil, 1833–1908.
Thomas Ross. Fortelling af Jonas Lie. Kjøbenhavn, Gyldendal (F. Hegel & søn) 1878.
2 p. l., 322 p. 18ᶜᵐ.

I. Title.
17–22509

Library of Congress   PT8911.T5 1878

NL 0345088   DLC CtY InU IU MB NdU CU

PT8911 **Lie, Jonas Lauritz Idemil, 1833–1908.**
T6G5   Die Töchter des Commandeurs; Roman.
1887   Autorisierte Uebersetzung aus dem Norwegischen von M. Ottesen. Stuttgart, J. Engelhorn, 1887.
159 p.   (Engelhorn's Allgemeine Romanbibliothek, 4. Jahrg., Bd.8)

Translation of: Kommandørens døttre.

NL 0345089   CU RPB

Lie, Jonas ₅Lauritz Idemil₎.
Die Töchter des Commandeurs; autorisierte Uebersetzung aus dem Norwegischen von M. Ottesen.   Stuttgart: J. Engelhorn ₅19—?₎.   159 p.   12°.

CENTRAL CIRCULATION.
I. Title.
N. Y. P. L.   December 3, 1918.

NL 0345090   NN

Hol **Lie, Jonas ₅Lauritz Idemil₎ 1833–1908.**
L61   Tremasteren „Fremtiden"; eller, Liv nordpaa, en fortælling af Jonas Lie. 6. udg. Kjøbenhavn, Gyldendal,
T6   1902.
1902   198 p.   19 cm.

NL 0345091   CtY CaBVa

Lie, Jonas Lauritz Idemil, 1833–1908.
Tremasteren "Fremtiden" eller Liv nordpaa. En fortælling af Jonas Lie. Kjøbenhavn, Gyldendal (F. Hegel) 1872.
3 p. l., 287 p. 18ᶜᵐ.
Added t.-p., illus.
On verso of t.-p.: Tredje tusinde.

I. Title.
17–22506

Library of Congress   PT8911.T7 1872

NL 0345092   DLC CU PSC

839.8L62 **Lie, Jonas Lauritz Idemil, 1833–1908.**
OTra   Tremasteren "Fremtiden"; eller, Liv nordpaa. En fortaelling. 4. udg. Kjøbenhavn, Gyldendal 1885.

287 p.   18cm.

NL 0345093   MnU

Lie, Jonas Lauritz Idemil, 1833–1908.
Tremasteren "Fremtiden"; eller Liv nordpaa ... Chicago, 1888.
17 cm.
Added t.p. illus.

NL 0345094   RPB

Lie, Jonas Lauritz Idemil, 1833–1908.
Tremasteren "Fremtiden"; eller, Liv nordpaa, en for tælling af Jonas Lie. 5. udg. Kjøbenhavn, Gyldendal (F. Hegel & søn) 1895.
3 p. l., 287 p. 18¼ᵐ.
Added t.-p., illustrated.

I. Title.
3–22713

Library of Congress   PT8911.T7 1895

NL 0345095   DLC

PT8911 **Lie, Jonas Lauritz Idemil, 1833–1908.**
T7   Tremasteren "Fremtiden", eller, Liv nordpaa; en fortaelling.
1914   Kjøbenhavn, Gyldendal, 1914.
219 p.

"Efter fortaellingens sjette udgave (1902)"

I. Title: Tremasteren "Fremtiden".   II. Title: Liv nordpaa.

NL 0345096   CU

VOLUME 332

Lie, Jonas ¡Lauritz Idemil¡ 1833–
Trold. En tylft eventyr af Jonas Lie. Kjøbenhavn,
Gyldendal, 1891.
2 p. l., 236 p., 1 l. 18½ᶜᵐ.
8-22717

Library of Congress, no.

NL 0345097   DLC OrP KyU CtY CU

PT8911
T7
1892
Lie, Jonas Lauritz Idemil, 1833–1908
Trold: en tylvt eventyr. Chicago,
Skandinavens Boghandel, 1892.
168 p. port. 17 cm.

NL 0345098   MeB

Lie, Jonas ¡Lauritz Idemil¡ 1833–
Trold. En tylft eventyr. Af Jonas Lie. Ny samling.
Kjøbenhavn, Gyldendal, 1892.
2 p. l., 202 p., 1 l. 18½ᶜᵐ.
8-22718

Library of Congress, no.

NL 0345099   DLC CaBVaU OrP CU CLU KyU NN

Lie, Jonas Lauritz Idemil, 1833–1908
Troll; märchen, mit vorwort des verfassers;
einzig autorisierte übers. von E. Brausewetter,
illus. von Rich. Scholz. 1.–4. tausend.
130,[1]p. il. Leipzig, A. Dieckmann [1897]
(Illustrierte diamant-bibliothek, v.1)

NL 0345100   OC1

Lie, Jonas Lauritz Idemil, 1833–1908
Ulfvungerne; et blad af lidenskabernes
bog. Kjøbenhavn, Gyldendal, 1903.
221 p. 20 cm.

NL 0345101   WU MH IU IEN CaBVaU

Lie, Jonas Lauritz Idemil, 1833–1908.
The visionary; or, Pictures from Nordland, by Jonas
Lie; tr. from the Norwegian by Jessie Muir, with a preface and portrait of the author. London, Hodder brothers, 1894.
xiv p., 2 l., ¡3¡–165 p. incl. front. (port.) 19¼ᶜᵐ.

I. Muir, Jessie, tr. II. Title.

13-17721
Library of Congress   PZ3.L6203V

NL 0345102   DLC WaTC CU CtY MB MH MiU NcU OC1 PPL IEN

Lie, Jonas Lauritz Idemil, 1833–1908.
Weird tales from northern seas, from the Danish of
Jonas Lie, by R. Nisbet Bain. With twelve illustrations
by Laurence Housman. ¡London¡ K. Paul, Trench, Trubner & co., ltd., 1893.
vi p., 2 l. ¡3¡–201 p. front., plates. 22½ᶜᵐ.
Nos. 1 and 3 are from Den fremsynte; Finn blood is from Fortællinger
og skildringer, published in 1872; the remaining eight stories are from Trold,
first published in 1891. cf. Pref.
CONTENTS.—The fisherman and the draug.—Jack of Sjöholm and the
Gann-finn.—Tug of war.—"The earth draws."—The cormorants of Andvær.—Isaac and the parson of Brönö.—The wind-gnome.—The huldrefish.—
Finn blood.—The homestead westward in the Blue Mountains.—"It's me!"
I. Bain, Robert Nisbet, 1854–1909, tr. II. Title.

22-16032
Library of Congress   PZ3.L6203We

OC1 OC1W PPL MB NN WaS CaBVaU
NL 0345103   DLC NcU OKentU WU NcD MdBP TxU CtY MiU

Lie, Jonas Lauritz Idemil, 1833–
Weird tales from northern seas, from the Danish of
Jonas Lie, by R. Nisbet Bain. With twelve illustrations
by Laurence Housman. ¡London¡ K. Paul, Trench, Trübner & co., ltd., 1898.
vi p., 1 l., 201 p. 12 pl. (incl. front.) 21¼ᶜᵐ.
Title in red and black.

I. Bain, Robert Nisbet, 1854–   tr. II. Housman, Laurence, 1867–
illus.

W 10-145
Washington, D. C.   Public Library

NL 0345104   DP DWP

PT
8911
H3
1896
Lie, Jonas Lauritz Idemil, 1833–1908.
Wenn der Vorhang fällt, aus der Komödie des
Lebens; Roman. Berlin, R. Taendler ¡1896¡
219 p. 19 cm.

Translation of Naar sol gaar ned.

I. Lie, Jonas Lauritz Idemil, 1833–1908.
Naar sol gaar ned—German. II. Title.

NL 0345105   NIC

Lie, Jonas ¡Lauritz Idemil¡.
Wenn der Vorhang fällt; aus der Komödie des Lebens. Berlin: Richard Taendler's Verllag ¡19—?¡. 207 p. 12°.

NL 0345106   NN

PT 8909
.W9
LIE, JONAS LAURITZ IDEMIL, 1833–1908
Wulffie & Comp.; drama i tre akter.
Kjøbenhavn, Gyldendalske Boghandels Forlag,
1900.
132 p.

NL 0345107   InU IU NN

832.08
D763
v.14
Lie, Jonas Lauritz Idemil, 1833–1908.
Wulffie & Comp.; einzig berechtigte
Übersetzung von Cläre Mjöen. München,
A.Langen, 1901.
105p. 18cm.

Bound with Das rote Horn, von A.Eisert.

NL 0345108   CLSU

LIE, KARI.
...So gifter vi oss; folkekomedie i 2 akter. Oslo:
Noregs boklag, 1937. 55 p. illus. (plan.) 19cm.
(On cover: Skodespel for ungdomelag.)

Music, p. 46–55.

1. Drama, Norwegian. I. Title.

NL 0345109   NN

Lie, *Fru* Kathrine (Dons) 1876–
... Gyllemburgslottet, fortælling for unge piker. Kristiania, H. Aschehoug & co. (W. Nygaard) 1922.
1 p. l., 134 p. 20ᶜᵐ.
At head of title: Kathrine Lie.

I. Title.
Library of Congress   PT8950.L58G8 1922   23-2488

NL 0345110   DLC

Lie, Kathrine (Dons), 1876–
...Munkegårdsdøttrene. Oslo: Gyldendal norsk forlag,
1931. 135 p. 19½cm.

597818A. 1. Fiction, Norwegian.   I. Title.
N.Y.P.L.   September 12, 1932

NL 0345111   NN

Lie, Kathrine (Dons), 1876–
...De tre i Paradiset. Oslo: H. Aschehoug & Co., 1928.
148 p. 8°.

427963A. 1. Fiction, Norwegian.   2. Title.
N.Y.P.L.   September 3, 1929

NL 0345112   NN

Lie, *Fru* Kathrine (Dons) 1876–
... Den vemmelige lange gutten, fortelling for unge
piker. Oslo, H. Aschehoug & co. (W. Nygaard) 1925.
2 p. l., 121 p. 20ᶜᵐ.

I. Title.
Library of Congress   PZ53.L47V4 1925   26-4823

NL 0345113   DLC

W 1
LE986
v.27
1955
LIE, Khing-ting
Onderzoekingen over het kweken van
Mycobacterium tuberculosis in het
bebroede kippenei. Leiden, Stenfert
Kroese, 1955.
106 p. illus. (Verhandelingen van het
Nederlands Instituut voor Praeventieve
Geneeskunde, 27)
Issued also as thesis, Leyden.

1. Mycobacterium tuberculosis
Series: Leyden. Nederlands Instituut
voor Praeventieve Geneeskunde. Verhandelingen, 27

NL 0345115   DNLM

Lie Kian Joe
see Joe, Lie-kian.

TG400
.K55
Lie, Kuo-hao, joint author.

Klöppel, Kurt.
Nebeneinflüsse bei der Berechnung von Hängebrücken
nach der Theorie II. Ordnung. Modellversuche. Allgemeine Grundlagen und Anwendung. Von K. Klöppel und
K. H. Lie. Berlin, Springer-Verlag, 1942.

WO
fL716c
1884
LIE, Lars Johannes, 1831–
Chirurgisch-anatomischer Atlas mit
autografischen colorirten Abbildungen
in Lebensgrösse für practische Ärzte und
Studierende. Christiania, Gundersen,
1880–84.
¡48¡ l., 40 plates (in portfolio)

NL 0345118   DNLM

Lars
Lie, Johannes, 1831–
Lærebog i descriptiv anatomie. Udarbeidet efter "Traité d'anatomie descriptive par Cruveilhier," af J. Lie, ... Første[andet] bind. ... . Christiania, J. Dahl, 1867–1869.
2 vol. in 1. illus. 23ᶜᵐ.
Paged continuously.

NL 0345119   ICJ

VOLUME 332

Lie, Marie Leskien-
see
Leskien-Lie, Marie

Lie, Marius Sophus
see
Lie, Sophus, 1842–1899.

Lie, Michael, 1862–
... Fra mit liv som diplomat. Oslo, Gyldendal, norsk forlag, 1929.
296 p. illus. (facsims.) plates, ports. 24½ᶜᵐ.

1. Norway—For. rel. 2. Mexico—Pol. & govt.—1910– ɪ. Title.
ₜFull name: Michael Strøm Lieₗ
Library of Congress   D413.L5A3   30–12127
Copyright A—Foreign   6338

NL 0345122   DLC NN MnU

Lie, Mikael H
see Lie, Mikael Strøm Henriksen, 1873–1926.

Lie, Mikael Strøm Henriksen, 1873–1926.
... Betenkning angaende grunnlovens 97 og 105 og om damstolenes myndighet, av Mikael H. Lie. (Kristiania, 1923)
68 p.   27 cm.
At head of title: Dokument nr. 13 (1923)

NL 0345124   DL

Lie, Mikael Strøm Henriksen, 1873–1926.
Domstolene og Grunnloven. Kristiania, O. F. Arnesens bok- og akcidenstr., 1923.
68 p.   28 cm.
Includes bibliographies.

1. Retroactive laws—Norway.   ɪ. Title.
48–32585*

NL 0345125   DLC

Lie, Mikael Strøm Henriksen, 1873–
Havens frihet; av jur. dr. Mikael H. Lie. Översat efter författarens manuskript ... ₜLund, H. Ohlssons boktryckeri, 1916ₗ
31, ₗ1ₗ p. 21ᶜᵐ. (Svenska fredsförbundets skriftserie. xvɪɪ)
"Litteraturförteckning": 1 p. at end.

1. Freedom of the seas.   ɪ. Title.
Library of Congress   JX4425.L5   23–1591

NL 0345126   DLC

Lie, Mikael Strøm Henriksen, 1873–1926.
Legitimation ved traktat. Kristiania, 1912.

NL 0345127   MH-L

Lie, Mikael Strøm Henriksen, 1873–1926.
... Lensprincipet i Norden; udgivet med understøttelse af det Finneske legat, Kjøbenhavn, og den Stangske stiftelse, Kristiania. Kristiania, Mallingske bogtrykkeri, 1907.
2 p. l., 102 p.   23ᶜᵐ.
At head of title: Mikael H. Lie.
"Bilag til 'Tidsskrift for retsvidenskab' 1907, første hefte."

1. Feudalism—Scandinavia. 2. Feudalism.   ɪ. Tidsskrift for retsvidenskap. Supplement. ɪɪ. Title.
28–4260 Revised
Library of Congress   D131.L5

NL 0345128   DLC NIC NN

Lie, Mikael Strøm Henriksen, 1873–
... Luxemburg eller Belgien. Kristiania, H. Aschehoug & co. (W. Nygaard) 1915.
3 p. l., 71 p.   20ᶜᵐ.
At head of title: Mikael H. Lie.
"Henvisninger": p. ₗ70ₗ–71.

1. Luxemburg—Neutrality. 2. Belgium—Neutrality.
Library of Congress   D621.L8L5   21–15675

NL 0345129   DLC NN

Lie, Mikael Strøm Henriksen, 1873–1926.
Minister-ansvaret ute og hjemme. Oslo, A. W. Brøggers boktrykkeris forlag, 1926.
148 p.   20 cm.
Bibliography: p. 148.

1. Ministerial responsibility—Norway. 2. Ministerial responsibility.   ɪ. Title.
JN7501.L5   50–44720

NL 0345130   DLC IaU

Lie, Mikael Strøm Henriksen, 1873–
ₗBerggrav, Eivind Josefₗ 1884–
Paa korsveien, bidrag til en nøgtern drøftelse av Norges stilling til krig og fred. Kristiania, Steenske bogtrykkeri ₗ1917ₗ

Lie, Mikael Strøm Henriksen, 1872–1926.
... Randbemerkninger til Hagerups Panteret. Kristiania, A. W. Brøggers boktrykkeris forlag i kommission, 1918.
119 p.   23ᶜᵐ.
At head of title: Mikael H. Lie.

1. Mortgages—Norway. 2. *Hagerup, Francis, 1853–1921.   Den norske panteret.   ɪ. Title.
36–3734
Library of Congress   332.700481

NL 0345132   DLC

Lie, Mikael Strøm Henriksen, 1873–
... Rets- og freds-problemer. Kristiania, H. Erichsen & co., 1917.
119 p.   24ᶜᵐ.
At head of title: Mikael H. Lie.
Contents.—Folkerettens natur.—Det individualistiske system.— Samfolkelige bestræbelser.—Organisationsproblemet og Haag-konferancerne.— Imperialisme og nationalitetsidé.—Seierherrens ret.—Nyere organisationsideer.—Det kollektive system.—A league to enforce peace.

1. International law and relations. 2. Peace.   ɪ. Title.
23–1590
Library of Congress   JX1953.L5

NL 0345133   DLC

Lie, Mikael Strom Henriksen, 1873–1926.
Stormagterne og de smaa nationer, av Mikael H. Lie. Kristiania, H. Uschehoug & co. (W. Nygaard) 1912.
1 p. l., 95 p.   20ᶜᵐ.
"Kilder og studieanvisninger": p. ₗ93ₗ–95.

1. States, Small. 2. Europe—Politics.   ɪ. Title.
13–15665
Library of Congress   JC365.L5

NL 0345134   DLC WaS

Lie, Mons, 1864–
Adam Ravn

NL 0345135   NdU

Lie, Mons
(Det) brede humør

NL 0345136   NdU

Lie, Mons, 1864–
Don Juans Død. Tragedie i tre Akter. Kjøbenhavn, Gyldendal, 1899.
3 p. l., 109 p.   12°.

NL 0345137   NN

Lie, Mons.
En drømmers bog; fortælling. Kjøbenhavn, Gyldendalske boghandels forlag, 1895.
pp. (3), 321.

NL 0345138   MH NdU

Lie, Mons, 1864–
En Forbryders Bekjendelser. Kjøbenhavn: Gyldendalske Boghandel, 1896. 85 p.   12°.

428737A.
N.Y.P.L.   1. Fiction, Norwegian.   2. Title.   September 25, 1929

NL 0345139   NN NdU

Lie, Mons
Høstnoveller

NL 0345140   NdU

Lie, Mons, 1864–
... I kvindens net; fortaelling. Kristiania, H. Aschehoug & co. (W. Nygaard) 1903.
2 p. l., 174 p.   17½cm.

NL 0345141   WU NdU CU

Lie, Mons, 1864–
Livet paa Eventyrslottet; Roman. København: Gyldendal, 1905. 2 p. l., 256 p.   12°.
Author's name at head of title.

1. Fiction (Norwegian). 2. Title.
N.Y.P.L.   July 11, 1917.

NL 0345142   NN WU

Lie, Mons.
Lombardo og Agrippina; tragedie i tre akter. [Kristiania?] J. M. Stenersen & co. [1898].
pp. 177 +.

NL 0345143   MH NN

VOLUME 332

Lie, Mons, 1864–
Mand overbord! En søvngjængers underlige skjæbne, roman af Mons Lie. Andet oplag. København, Kristiania, Gyldendal, 1904.
2 p.l., 171 p. 18½cm.

NL 0345144   WU NN CtY CU

Lie, Mons, 1864–
Ræmeni. Forvaagede nætter; en fortælling fra Paris. Kristiania, Aschehoug, 1895.
107 p. 19 cm.

NL 0345145   WU NdU

Lie, Mons
Sjøfareren

NL 0345146   NdU WaS

Lie, Mons, 1864–
Ved Hotellets doe kkede Bord. Somrens Roman. Kristiania, Gyldendal, 1906.
253 p. 12°.

NL 0345147   NN CtY

Lie, Nils Aars Nicolaysen, 1902–   ed.
PT8950
.H58Z75   Festskrift til Sigurd Hoel på 60 årsdagen. ¡Redaksjonskomité: Nils Lie, Arnulf Ursin-Holm ¡og¡ Arnulf Øverland¡ Oslo, Gyldendal, 1950.

Lie, Nils Aars Nicolaysen, 1902–
… Trekløveret, en guttefortælling. Kristiania ¡etc.¡ Gyldendal, 1924.
133 p., 1 l. 20ᵐᵐ.
At head of title: Nils Lie.

I. Title.
Library of Congress   PZ53.L5T7
25–7885

NL 0345149   DLC

PL5099   Lie, Oen Hock
.54   Peraturan² tjatatan sipil (burgerlijke stand) di Indonesia.
R4L5   ¡Apa jang harus diketahui tiap orang djika: nikah, tjerai,
1954   melahirkan anak, kematian famili, ganti nama, dsb., berikut
tjontoh² surat permohonan¡ Tjetakan 2. Djakarta, Keng Po ¡1954¡
96 p. forms.

1. Indonesia - Statistics, Vital. 2. Recording and registration - Indonesia. I. Indonesia (Country) Laws, statutes, etc.

NL 0345150   CU

Lie, Olaf.
Slægtsundersøkelser og erindringer, med mere, væsentlig vedrørende min fars og mors familie. Arendal, P. M. Danielsens trykkeri, 1949.
167 p. illus., ports. 21 cm.

1. Lie family.   I. Title.
CT1308.L48A3
51–30125 rev

NL 0345151   DLC MnU

Lie, Olaf, 1891–
Etiopia. Bergen, Lunde, 1954.
157 p. illus. 21 cm.

1. Ethiopia—Hist.

DT381.L5
56–33031

NL 0345152   DLC NN

Lie, Pok Liem, 1921–
Enkele aspecten van de persoonlijkheidsdiagnostiek en de toepassing van de mozaïektest. Leiden, Lectura ¡1954¡
140 p. illus. (part col.) 24 cm.
Proefschrift—Leyden.
Summary in English.
"Errata": slip inserted.
"Stellingen": ¡2¡ p. inserted.
Bibliography: p. 135–139.

1. Personality tests.

RC469.L5
55–38382

NL 0345153   DLC CtY DNLM

Wason   Lie, Sek Hiang.
E185.6   Bangsa negro di Amerika serikat.
L71   Djakarta, "Quick" ¡1954¡
122 p. illus. 23cm.

1. Negroes.   2. U. S.—Race question.   3. Negroes—Social life & cust.   I. Title.

NL 0345154   NIC

---

qM787.1 Lie, Sigurd, 1871–1904.
L621s   Snow (Sne) Norwegian song. Concert ed.
1937   ¡Transcribed by¡ Joseph Szigeti.   New York, C. Fischer ¡c1937¡
score (5p.) and part. 31cm. (Sheet music edition B2404)

1. Violin and piano music. I. Szigeti, Joseph, 1892– arr.

NL 0345155   IU DLC

Lie, Sigurd, 1871–1904.
Soft-footed snow.   London, Lucas [c1904]
6 p. 35 cm.
English text, with German and Norwegian words on a separate page.

NL 0345156   OrU

Wason   Lie, Sim Djwe, tr.
PL5093   Tjerita Theng Gwat Lauw, atawa Gloembang-
C5L71   aja pertjinta'an; tjerita jang benar telah kedjadian di Tiongkok pada djaman Beng Tiauw. Ditjeritakan oleh Lie Sim Djwe. Soerabaia, Ang Sioe Tjing, 1923–
v. 16cm.

I. Title. II. Title: Theng Gwat Lauw.   III. Title: Gloembangnja pertjinta'an.

NL 0345157   NIC

Lie, Sophus, 1842–1899.
Bestimmung aller Raumcurven, deren Krümmungsradius, Torsionsradius und Bodenlänge durch eine beliebige Relation verknüpft sind. . . . . 6 p. O. Christiania: J. Dybwad, [1882].
Reprinted from *Christiania Videnskabsselskabs Forhandlinger* 1882, no. 10.
No title-page. Title taken from inside cover.

NL 0345158   ICJ

Lie, Sophus, 1842–1899.
Classification der flächen nach der transformationsgruppe ihrer geodätischen curven, von Sophus Lie. Universitätsprogram für das erste semester 1879. Kristiania, Gedruckt bei Grøndahl & søn, 1879.
1 p. l., 45 p. 30 x 24ᵐᵐ.

1. Surfaces. 2. Transformations. Infinitesimal.
¡Full name: Marius Sophus Lie¡
3–22981 Revised
Library of Congress   QA603.L71

NL 0345159   DLC GU CtY MiU NjP PPAmP PU WaU

Lie, Sophus, 1842–1899.
Discussion aller Integrations-Methoden der partiellen Differential-Gleichungen I. O. Pt. i, ii, [Christiania, 1875]
8°.
"Besonderer Abdruck nach der Verh, der Gesellschaft d. W. zu Chr. a 1875."
Pt. ii. has the title: —"Allgemeine Theorie partielle Differential-Gleichungen I. O."

NL 0345160   NIC

Lie, Sophus, 1842–1899.
… Geometrie der berührungstransformationen. Dargestellt von Sophus Lie und Georg Scheffers … 1. band. Mit figuren im text. Leipzig, B. J. Teubner, 1896.
xl, ¡1¡, 693, ¡1¡ p. diagrs. 25ᶜᵐ.
No more published.
CONTENTS.—I. Berührungstransformationen der ebene.—II. Geometrie er linienelemente des raumes.—III. Einführung in die geometrie der flächenelemente. Partielle differentialgleichungen erster ordnung. — sachregister.—Namenverzeichnis.
1. Contact transformations.   I. Scheffers, Georg Wilhelm, 1866–
¡Full name: Marius Sophus Lie¡
5–26857
Library of Congress   QA385.L66

CtY CU OU MB ICJ NBuU MiU OClW OCU OU NBC
NL 0345161   DLC PPF PBm PSC PU TU CLSU NjP ICJ NcD

516.55   Lie, Sophus, 1842–1899.
L716g   … Geometrie der berührungstransformationen. Darge-
1968   stellt von Sophus Lie und Georg Scheffers … 1. band. Mit
ENGINEERS   figuren im text. Leipzig, B. J. Teubner, 1896; [Ann Arbor,
& PHYSICS   Mich., University Microfilms, 1968;
LIBRARY   xl, ¡1¡,693, ¡1¡ p. diagrs. 25 cm.
No more published.

NL 0345162   FU

Lie, Sophus, 1842–1899.
… Gesammelte abhandlungen auf grund einer bewilligung aus dem Norwegischen forschungsfonds von 1919 mit unterstützung der Videnskapsakademi zu Oslo und der Akademie der wissenschaften zu Leipzig, hrsg. von dem Norwegischen mathematischen verein durch Friedrich Engel … ¡und¡ Poul Heegaard … Leipzig, B. G. Teubner; Oslo, H. Aschehoug & co., 1922–
v. in   front. (port.) diagrs. 24 cm.
Added t-p. in Norwegian (bd. 3 and bd. 5 have t.-p. in Norwegian and added t-p. in German) Text in German or French.
"Anmerkungen" to accompany bd. 1, bd. 4 and bd. 6 issued as separate volumes with cover-title and continuous paging.

Bibliographical foot-notes.
Contain "Druckfehler, berichtigungen und zusätze."
CONTENTS.—1. bd. Geometrische abhandlungen, 1. abt. 1934.—2. bd. Geometrische abhandlungen, 2. abt., 1-2. t. 1937.—3. bd. Abhandlungen zur theorie der differentialgleichungen, 1. abt. 1922.—4. bd. Abhandlungen zur theorie der differentialgleichungen, 2. abt. 1929.—5. bd. Abhandlungen über die theorie der transformationsgruppen, 1. abt. 1924.—6. bd. Abhandlungen über die theorie der transformationsgruppen, 2. abt. 1927.

1. Mathematics—Collected works. 2. Geometry—Foundations. 3. Surfaces, Minimal. 4. Differential equations. 5. Groups, Theory of. 6. Transformations (Mathematics)   I. Engel, Friedrich, 1861–ed.   II. Heegaard, Poul, 1871–ed.   III. Norske videnskape-akademi i Oslo. IV. Sächsische akademie der wissenschaften, Leipzig. v. Norsk matematisk forening, Oslo.

Full name: Marius Sophus Lie.

QA3.L5   510.81   N O 32–2
U. S. Naval Observatory.   Library
for Library of Congress   ¡a62r38p3¡†

MiDW DLC RPB
PU CU PSt ICJ CtY MiU ViU OCU NcRS NBuU OClW LU MoU
NL 0345165   DN-Ob NN PSC OrCS MiEM NcD MH CLSU OU

VOLUME 332

Lie, Sophus.
Mathematiske Meddelelser af Sophus Lie til Videnskabs-selskabet fra Aarene 1869-1871.   Ved L. Sylow.   Christiania: J. Dybwad, 1899.   15 p.   4°.   (Videnskabs-Selskabet i Christiania.   Skrifter.   I.   Mathematisk-naturvidenskabelig Klasse. 1899, no. 9.)

1. Mathematics.—Collected essays. 2. Sylow, Ludvig.
N. Y. P. L. December 5, 1911.

NL 0345166   NN

Lie, Sophus
Neue Integrations-Methode eines 2n-gliedrigen
Pfaff'schen Problems.
(Christiania) n.d.
26 p.   23cm.

Christiania, Forhandlinger, 15, 1873, p. 321-343.

NL 0345167   DN-Ob

Lie,   Sophus, 1842-1899, ed.
Oeuvres completes
see under   Abel, Niels Henrik, 1802-1829.

(510.4 Lie, Sophus, 1842-1899.
L62o   OEuvres mathématiques.   (n.p., 1870-98)
4v.   23-30cm.

Binder's title.
A collection of reprints and monographs in
German, Norwegian and French, by Sophus Lie,
F. Klein and others.

1. Mathematics—Collections.

NL 0345169   IU

Lie, Sophus i. e. Marius Sophus, 1842-1899,
ed.
Holst, Elling Bolt, 1849-1915.
Om Poncelet's betydning for geometrien.   Et bidrag
til de modernegeometriske ideers udviklingshistorie af
Elling Holst ...   Udgivet som universitets-program for
1ste halvaar 1879 ved Sophus Lie.   Christiania, Trykt hos
A. W. Brøgger, 1878.

Lie, Sophus
Partielle Differential-Gleichungen I.O., in
denen die unbekannte Funktion explicite vorkommt.

36 p.   23 cm.

Christiania, Forhandlinger, 15, 1873, p. 52-85.

NL 0345171   DN-Ob

Lie, Sophus, 1842-1899.
Theorie der Transformationsgruppen ... unter mitwirkung
von dr. Friedrich Engel bearb. von Sophus Lie ...   Leipzig,
B. G. Teubner, 1888-93.

3 v.   25ᶜᵐ.

CONTENTS.—1. abschnitt. Allgemeine eigenschaften der endlichen continuirlichen transformationsgruppen.   1888.—2. abschnitt. Theorie der
berührungstransformationen und der gruppen von berührungstransformationen.   1890.—3. abschnitt. I. Die endlichen continuirlichen gruppen
der geraden linie und der ebene.   II. Die endlichen continuirlichen gruppen
des gewöhnlichen raumes.   III. Die projectiven gruppen des gewöhnlichen
raumes.   IV. Untersuchungen über verschiedene arten von gruppen des

Continued in next column

Continued from preceding column

n-fach ausgedehnten raumes.   v. Untersuchungen über die grundlagen
der geometrie.   vi. Allgemeine betrachtungen über endliche continuirliche
gruppen.   1893.

1. Groups, Continuous.   2. Contact transformations.   I. Engel,
Friedrich, 1861-
(Full name: Marius Sophus Lie)
3-5189
Library of Congress   QA385.L68

              WaU ICJ NjP PU PBm NcD NcU CLSU KU OrPR OrCS MH
NL 0345174   DLC CU PBL CtY OU OCU MiU OO NBC ViU

Lie, Sophus, 1842-1899.
Theorie der Transformationsgruppen.   Unter
Mitwirkung von Friedrich Engel bearb. von Sophus
Lie.   [Neue Ausg.]   Leipzig, B. G. Teubner, 1930.
3 v.   26 cm.
Content. -1. abschnitt. Allgemeine Eigenschaften
der endlichen continuirlichen Transformationsgruppen. -2. abschnitt. Theorie der Berührungs-
transtrionationen und der Gruppen von Berührungs-
transfromationen. -3. abschnitt. I. Die endlichen
continuirlichen Gruppen der geraden Linie und der

Ebene. II. Die endlichen continuirlichen Gruppen
des gewöhnlichen Raumes. III. Die projectiven
Gruppen des gewöhnlichen Raumes. IV. Untersuchungen über verschiedene Arten con Gruppen des
n fach ausgedehnten Raumes. V. Untersuchungen
über die Grundlagen der Geometrie. VI. Allgemeine
Betrachtungen über endliche continuirliche Gruppen.

NL 0345176   NcRS

Lie, Sophus. Ueber eine darstellung des imagi-
naeren in der geometrie. 8 pp. (Journ. f. d. reine u.
angewn. math. v. 70, 1869, p. 346.)

NL 0345177   MdBP

Lie, Sophus, 1842-1899.
Über integralinvarianten und differential-
gleichungen, von Sophus Lie ...   Christiania,
J. Dybwad, 1902.
2 p.l., 73 p.   27½ᶜᵐ.
"Udgivet for Fridtjof Nansens fond."
"Videnskabsselskabets skrifter. I. Mathematisk-
naturv.klasse. 1902. no.1."
"Diese bildet eine fortsetsung sweier früherer abhandlungen über integralinvarianten, die in den berichten
der Kgl.Säch.gesellschaft der wiss.su Leipsig 1897
publicirt sind." cf.Vorwort, signed: Alf Guldberg.
(Continued on next card)

1.Differential forms.   I.Guldberg, Alf Victor
Emanuel, 1866-   ed. II.Størmer, Carl, 1874-   joint ed.
(Full name: Marius Sophus Lie)

NL 0345179   MiU DLC CoU NN IU MH

Lie, Sophus
Ueber partielle Differential-Gleichungen I.O.
Christiania,
38 p.   23cm.

Christiania, Forhandlinger, 15, 1873, p. 16-51.

NL 0345180   DN-Ob

LIE, Sophus.
Untersuchungen über differentialgleichungen. I-IV.   4 pt. in 2 vol.   Christiania,
[1882-83]

"Christiania videnskabsselskabs forhandlinger
1882. No. 21, 22. 1883."

NL 0345181   MH

Lie, Sophus, 1842-1899.
Untersuchungen über unendliche continuirliche gruppen, von
Sophus Lie.
(In K. Sächsische gesellschaft der wissenschaften. Mathematisch-
physische klasse. Abhandlungen. Leipzig, 1895. 28½ᶜᵐ. bd. XXI,
p. (43)-150)

1. Groups, Continuous.
(Full name: Marius Sophus Lie)
A C 33-4165
Title from Wisconsin   Univ.
Library of Congress   [A8182.S21 bd. 21]

NL 0345182   WU IU NN NjP MoU PU

Lie, Sophus, 1842-1899.
... Vorlesungen über continuierliche gruppen mit geometri
schen und anderen anwendungen.   Bearb. und hrsg. von dr.
Georg Scheffers ...   Mit figuren im text. Leipzig, B. G. Teubner, 1893.
xii p., 2 l., 810 p. diagrs. 25ᶜᵐ.
"Die aufgabe des unterzeichneten bestand in der hauptsache in der
anordnung und bearbeitung des reichen stoffes, wobei ihm zu einem
grossen teil knappgehaltene manuscripte von Lie sowie eigene nach-
schriften zur verfügung standen.   In stärkerem masse hat er das kapitel über complexe zahlen beeinflusst."—Editor's pref.
1. Groups, Continuous.   I. Scheffers, Georg Wilhelm, 1866-   ed.
(Full name: Marius Sophus Lie)
3-378 Revised
Library of Congress   QA385.L7

          CtY ICJ CtY OCU OU MiU OC1W NBC ViU PBm PHC PU
NL 0345183   DLC OrU OrCS GU MoU NcRS NcU CU PBL TU

QA
365   Lie, Sophus, 1842-1899.
.L7   Vorlesungen über continuierliche gruppen
mit geometrischen und anderen anwendungen.
Bearb. und hrsg. von dr. Georg Scheffers.
Leipzig, B. G. Teubner, 1893.
810 p.   diagrs.

Photo reproduction, Cleveland, Bell & Howell,
Micro Photo Division [1968?]

1. Groups, Continuous.   I. Scheffers, Georg
Wilhelm, 1896-   ed. II. Title.

NL 0345184   MiEM

Lie, Sophus, 1842-1899.
... Vorlesungen über differentialgleichungen mit bekannten
infinitesimalen transformationen.   Bearb. und hrsg. von dr.
Georg Scheffers. Leipzig, B. G. Teubner, 1891.
xiv p., 1 l., 568 p. diagrs. 25ᶜᵐ.

1. Differential equations.   2. Transformations, Infinitesimal.
I. Scheffers, Georg Wilhelm, 1866-   ed.
(Full name: Marius Sophus Lie)
3-377
Library of Congress   QA372.L72

          CU CtY OrCS AU MU MoU ICRL PPF PHC PSC PBm OC1W NBC
NL 0345185   DLC NjP MH ICJ OC1W MiU OCU OU NcRS LU

Lie, Sophus
Vorlesungen über differentielgleichungen
mit bekannten infinitesimalen transformationen
bearbeitet und herausgegeben von Georg
Scheffers. Leip. 1894.

NL 0345186   ODW

QA372
.L72   Lie, Sophus, 1842-1899.
1912
Vorlesungen über Differentialgleichungen
mit bekannten infinitesimalen Transformationen.   Bearb. und hrsg. von Georg
Scheffers.   Anastatischer neudruck. Leipzig,
B. G. Teubner, 1912.
xv, 575 p.   diagrs.   25cm.

1. Differential equations.   2. Transformations,
Infinitesimal.   I. Scheffers, Georg Wilhelm, 1866-
ed.
Full name: Marius Sophus Lie.

NL 0345187   ViU OrPR TxU PSt CU

VOLUME 332

Lie, Sophus
Zur analytischen Theorie der Beruhrungs-Transformationen.
(Christiania, 1873)
1 f.+ 26 p.   23cm.

Christiania, Forhandlinger, 15, 1873, p. 237-256.

NL 0345188   DN-Ob

AS
182
S22M+
v.14
no.12

Lie, Sophus, 1842-1899.
Zur Theorie der Berührungstransformationen.
Leipzig, S. Hirzel, 1888.
(537)-562 p. 27cm. (Abhandlungen der
Mathematisch-physischen Classe der Königl.
Sächsischen Gesellschaft der Wissenschaften,
14. Bd., No. 12)

1. Contact transformations.

NL 0345189   NIC NN MH

Lie, Sophus, 1842-1899
see also
Séminaire "Sophus Lie."

284.3
L62

Lie, Sverre.
Prisavtalen for jordbruket; utviklingen fram
til avtalen, og forhandlingene inntil 1955 m.v.
(Oslo) Norges bondelag, 1955.
134 p.

1. Prices. Norway. I. Norges bondelag.

NL 0345190   DNAL

Lie Tjien Tjong, 1911-
...Die Krankheiten der Glandula parotis...
Bonn, 1935.
Inaug.-Diss. - Bonn.
Lebenslauf.
"Literatur-Verzeichnis": p. 85-86.

NL 0345191   CtY

Lie, Trygve, 1896-
De Forente nasjoner. (Utg. i samarbete med Förente nationernas informationskontor för Danmark, Island, Norge och Sverige. Stockholm, 1949)
39 p. 19 cm. (Upplysningsskrifter om Förenta nationerna, n:r 4)

1. United Nations.
Full name: Trygve Halfdan Lie.
JX1977.L462   57-24344 ‡

NL 0345192   DLC MH MH-L

Lie, Trygve, 1896-
Leve eller dø; Norge i krig. Oslo, Tiden norsk forlag (1955)
300 p. illus.,ports. 25 cm.

1. World War, 1939-1945 — Personal narratives, Norwegian.
2. World War, 1939-1945—Norway. I. Title.
Full name: Trygve Halfdan Lie.
A 56-3641
Minnesota. Univ. Libr.
for Library of Congress

NL 0345193   MnU CU IU OC1 C MH MnU DS NN IEN DLC

Lie, Trygve, 1896-
Den nye arbeidsvistlov; boikottbestemmelsene; en juridisk
utredning utarbeidet på foranledning av Arbeidernes faglige
landsorganisasjons sekretariat, av Trygve Lie og Viggo Hansteen ... (Oslo, Det Norske arbeiderpartis forlag, 1933)
24, 22 p., 1 l. 21½ᶜᵐ.
"Lov om arbeidstvister av 5. mai 1927 med endringslover av 19 juni
og 6 juli 1933": 22 p. at end.
1. Strikes and lockouts—Norway. 2. Boycott—Norway. 3. Labor
laws and legislation—Norway.   I. *Hansteen, Viggo, 1900-   joint
author. II. Arbeidernes faglige landsorganisasjon i Norge. III. Norway.
Laws, statutes, etc. IV. Title.
(Full name: Trygve Halfdan Lie)
36-5549

331.8909481

NL 0345194   DLC

Lie, Trygve, 1896-
In the cause of peace; seven years with the United Nations.
New York, Macmillan, 1954.
473 p. illus. 22 cm.

1. United Nations. 2. World politics—1945-   I. Title.

JX1977.L47   341.13   54—12462 ‡

OrP OrSaW OrU Wa WaE WaS WaSpG WaWW WaTC WaT WaSp
NcC NcRS CaBVa CaBVaU CaBViP IdB IdPI IdU MtU MtBC
OC1 PPT PU-L NIC OCH PLF PHC PSt PBL PWcS PSC PJB
Or OrAshS OrCS NcU KyLxT KyU NcU MiU NNJ PCM PPA OU
OC1W OC1U ODW OOxM OO PPD OrLgE OrMonO OrPR MSohG
NL 03415195   DLC KEmT NNC MoU GU-L ViU TU MB NN TxU

JX1977
L716

Lie, Trygve Halvdan, 1896-
Mr. Trygve Lie speaks at Winnipeg.   Winnipeg
(1947)
18 p.   25ᵐ.   (Winnipeg free press pamphlet, 16)
"Included _ are the articles which appeared on
the editorial page of the Winnipeg free press to
mark the occasion of the first official visit to
Canada of _ Mr. Trygve Lie, together with the
text of addresses delivered at a public meeting
June 11, 1947 _ by Mr. Lie, Premier Stuart
Garson, and Dr. A. W. Trueman."

1.United Nations   I.Title.

NL 0345197   CSt-H

JX1977
.P42

Lie, Trygve, 1896-
Peace on earth (by) Trygve Lie (and others) Introd. by
Robert E. Sherwood. New York, Hermitage House, 1949.

NL 0345198   (no location)

Lie, Trygve, 1896-
The road to peace; a twenty-year United Nations program;
text of address to the General Assembly on the development
of a twenty-year program for achieving peace through the
United Nations. [Lake Success] United Nations, Dept. of
Public Information, 1950.

12 p.

NL 0345199   MH

JX1977
.L466

Lie, Trygve, 1896-
Syv år for freden. Oslo, Tiden norsk forlag (1954)
438 p. illus.,ports. 25 cm.

1. United Nations. 2. World politics—1945-   I. Title.
Full name: Trygve Halfdan Lie.
A 55-6848
Minnesota. Univ. Libr.
for Library of Congress

NL 0345200   MnU MH WU IEN CU OCU C DLC

Lie, Trygve, 1896-
see also United Nations. *Secretary-General, 1946-1953*
(Lie)

Lie, Ying-Chen, 1898-
Ueber den einfluss parenteral zugefuehrter
Proteinkörper auf die Phagozytose gegenüber
pathogenen Microorganismen.   Berlin, 1922.
Inaug. diss. Berlin.

NL 0345202   ICRL

Lie-Pettersen, O. J.
...Beiträge zur Kenntnis der marinen Rädertier-Fauna Norwegens. Von O. J. Lie-Pettersen... (Bergen: J. Grieg, 1906.)
44 p. illus. plates. 8°. (Bergens Museum, Bergen, Norway. Bergens Museums aarbog. 1905, no. 10.)

1. Rotifera, Norway. 2. Series.
N. Y. P. L.   May 9, 1923.

NL 0345203   NN

Lie-Pettersen, O. J.
...Entomologiske bidrag til skjærgaardsfaunaen i det vestlige Norge. Af O. J. Lie-Pettersen. (Bergen: J. Grieg, 1905.)
25 p. incl. tables. 8°. (Bergens Museum, Bergen, Norway. Bergens Museums aarbog. 1904, no. 11.)

1. Insects, Norway. 2. Series.
N. Y. P. L.   April 26, 1923.

NL 0345204   NN

Lie-Pettersen, O. J.
Entomologiske Undersøgelser i nordre Bergenhus amt. 1. Lepidoptera iagttagne i Lærdal Sommeren 1897.
[Bergen. 1898.] 29 pp. [Bergens Museums Aarbog 1897. No. 13.] 8°.

G7170 — Bergen District. Norway. Entom. — Lepidoptera.

NL 0345205   MB

Lie-Pettersen, O. J.
...Neue Beiträge zur Biologie d. norwegischen Hummeln. Von O. J. Lie-Pettersen. (Bergen: A/S J. Grieg, 1907.)   41 p. 8°.   (Bergens Museum, Bergen, Norway. Bergens Museums aarbog. 1906, no. 9.)
Bibliography, p. (42.)

1. Bumblebees, Norway. 2. Series.
N. Y. P. L.   May 9, 1923.

NL 0345206   NN

Lie-Pettersen, O. J.
...Zur Kenntnis der Süsswasser-Rädertier-Fauna Norwegens. Von O. J. Lie-Pettersen... (Bergen: A/S J. Grieg, 1910.)
99 p. incl. tables. plates. 8°. (Bergens Museum, Bergen, Norway. Bergens Museums aarbog. 1909, no. 15.)
Bibliography, p. 95-99.

1. Rotifera, Norway. 2. Series.
N. Y. P. L.   May 9, 1923.

NL 0345207   NN

Lié Sou, G.
... T'seu-hsi, impératrice des Boxers, par G. Lié Sou.
Paris, Éditions d'Art et de littérature (1911)
2 p. l., 204 p. front. 19ᵐᵐ. (Les femmes illustres)   fr. 2.50

1. Tzŭ-hsi, empress dowager of China, 1834-1908.

Library of Congress   DS763.T8L5   11-15609

NL 0345208   DLC IaU MB

VOLUME 332

Lie algebras and Lie groups

see under

American Mathematical Society. Summer
Mathematical Institute, Colby College,
Waterville, Me. 1st, 1955.

The lie of the 3rd of August, 1914
see under [Puaux, René] 1878-

Lie-sien tchouan
see under Liu, Hsiang, 77?-6? B.C.,
supposed author.

Lieb (Albert) [1881-]. *Ueber einen Fall
von Glaukom nach Ammoniakverätzung.
[Tübingen.] 23 pp. 8°. Freudenstadt, O.
Kaupert. 1912.

NL 0345212 DNLM CtY

Lieb, Alfred, 1900–
Deutsche Kolonialarbeit und zehn Jahre Mandatsherrschaft in
Kamerun (eine kolonialwirtschaftliche Betrachtung)...von Alfred
Lieb... Schwarzenbach a. d. Saale: W. Weigand, 1932. 50 p.
incl. tables. 22½cm.

Dissertation — Nürnberg, 1931.
Lebenslauf.
"Literaturverzeichnis," p. [53]–[54]

1. Economic history—Cameroons.   I. Title.
N. Y. P. L.   July 10, 1940

NL 0345213 NN MH-L

**W 6
P3**   LIEB, Anton
Unter dem Pantoffel der Mode: schuh-
geschichtliche Betrachtungen eines Arztes.
[München, 1951.]
48 p. illus.
1. Shoes - hist.   Title

NL 0345214 DNLM

Lieb, Anton, 1910–
... Die Zustandsbilder und Schicksale der
Abszesse bei tuberkulöser Wirbelsäulenentzündung
unter besonderer Berücksichtigung der
Röntgenbefunde .   München, 1935.
Inaug.-Diss. - München.
Lebenslauf.

NL 0345215 CtY

Lieb, C.
Eine beschreibung der stadt Chattanooga und umgegend,
nebst karte. Ein wichtiges gebiet zur niederlassung für kapi-
talisten, geschäftsleute, geschickte arbeiter und landwirthe.
Herausgegeben zur förderung deutscher einwanderung nach
dem süden der Vereinigten Staaten von Nord-Amerika, von
C. Lieb ... Cincinnati, Druck von S. Rosenthal & co., 1885.
27 p. illus. (incl. map) 21½cm.

1. Chattanooga—Descr.

Library of Congress   F444.C4L7   Rc-1302

NL 0345216 DLC

Lieb, C.
Eine beschreibung der stadt Chattanooga und umgegend, nebst karte. Ein gebiet unbegrenzter möglichkeiten, oder : das kommende neunte wunder der Neuen welt ...
Verfasst, zur förderung deutscher einwanderung nach
genanntem südlichen teile der Vereinigten Staaten von
Nord Amerika, von C. Lieb, geschäftsführer des Chattanooga distrikt bureau für einwanderung. [Chattanooga?
1904?]
cover-title, [56] p. illus., map. 23½cm.
Advertisements interspersed.
Much enlarged from his pamphlet issued under same-title, Cincinnati,
1885.
1. Chattanooga, Tenn.—Descr.   2. Tennessee—Descr. & trav.   3. Alabama—Descr. & trav.   4. Georgia—Descr. & trav.   5. Chattanooga district bureau of   immigration, Chattanooga, Tenn.

Library of Congress   F444.C4L72   5-40524

NL 0345217 DLC

Lieb, Charles, 1852–
The president's international policy.
Speech of Hon. Charles Lieb, of Indiana,
in the house of representatives, Tuesday,
July 18, 1916. [Wash., Govt. pr. off.,
1916.]
6 p.

NL 0345218 OO

**SF
287
.L5**   Lieb, Christoff Jacob.
Gebissbuch; oder, Kurtzer und gründlicher
Bericht von Gebiss und Zeumung der Pferd sampt
deroselben unterschiedlichen Würckung auch wie
dieselben nützlich und nach gelegenheit der
Pferdt zugebrauchen sein... Dressden, Gedruckt
bey Gimel Bergen, 1616.
[4] ℓ. 19 p. illus., plates.

Author's autograph presentation copy.
Bound with the author's Practica et arte di
cavalleria.   Dressden, 1616.
1. Bridle. I.   Title.

NL 0345219 INS

**SF
287
.L5**   Lieb, Christoff Jacob
Practica et arte di cavalleria. Ubung und
Kunst des Reitens in welcher die Bereuter die
Pferd nach ihrer Art und Natur zu unterweisen
und abzurichten erfahren und geubt sein sol...
Dressden [Gedruckt bey Gimel Bergen, in vor-
legung des Authoris] 1616.
60 p. [1] ℓ., 61 p. illus.

Author's autograph presentation copy.

Contents.-1. Buch. Vom Anfang und erster
unterweisung der Pferdt.-2. Buch. Von vollkommener unterweisung und abrichtung der Pferdt.
Bound with the author's Gebissbuch. Dressden, 1616.
1. Horse-training. 2. Horsemanship. I.
Title. II. Title: Übung und Kunst des Reitens.
anals.

NL 0345221 INS

LIEB, CLARENCE WILLIAM, 1885–
Diet for booksellers; being a special edition of Eat,
drink & be healthy, by Clarence W. Lieb... New York:
The J. Day Co.[, 1928.] xix, 180 p. 19cm.

One of an edition of 250 copies printed.

596707A. 1. Diet. 2. Food.

NL 0345222 NN

Lieb, Clarence William, 1885–
Eat, drink & be healthy; an outline of rational dietetics, by
Clarence W. Lieb ... New York, The John Day company
[*1928]
xix, 180 p. 19½cm.

1. Diet. 2. Food.   I. Title.

Library of Congress   RM216.L73   28-20124
Copyright A 1083162

OC1 OC1U MB
NL 0345223 DLC Or PPT PPD PPA KMK NcRS IU OCX OC1h

Lieb, Clarence William, 1885–
Eat, drink and be slender; what every overweight person
should know and do, by Clarence W. Lieb ... New York,
The John Day company [1929]
xi, 194 p., 1 l. incl. illus., tables. 20cm.

_ 1. Corpulence. 2. Diet. 3. Exercise. 4. Food.   I. Title.

Library of Congress   RC813.L5   29-16095

NN
NL 0345224   DLC PPGi PPC NNC-M OEac OC1 OC1h ICJ MiU

LIEB, Clarence William, 1885–
Effect of an exclusive meat diet on chemical
constituents of the blood,[by] Clarence W.Lieb
and Edward Tolstoi. n.p.,[1929].

26 cm. pp.(3).
Paper cover serves as title-page.
"Reprinted from the Proceedings of the Society
for Experimental Biology and Medicine,1929,xxvi,
pp.324-325.

NL 0345225 MBCo

LIEB, Clarence William, 1885–
The effects on human beings of a twelve
months' exclusive meat diet,based on intensive
clinical and laboratory studies on two Arctic
explorers living under average conditions in a
New York climate. Chicago,American Medical
Association,1929.

21.5 cm. pp.9.
Paper cover serves as title-page.
"Reprinted from The Journal of the American
Medical Association, July 6,1929,Vol.93,
pp.20-22."

NL 0345226 MH

Lieb, Clarence William, 1885–
Meat diet in health and in disease ... Chicago, American
medical association, °1927.

Lieb, Clarence William, 1885–
Outwitting your years. [1st ed.] New York, Prentice-
Hall [1949]
viii, 278 p. 21 cm.

1. Old age.   I. Title.

BJ1691.L48   618.97   49-2296*

WaSp
DNLM CaBVa CaBViP IdB Or OrCS OrP WaE WaS Wa WaOB
NL 0345228   DLC WU-M PP PSt PPT OU MB NcU OO TxU KyL

Lieb, Clarence William, 1885–
Outwitting your years. Kingswood, Surrey, World's
Work [1950]
viii, 318 p. 19 cm.

1. Old age.   I. Title.

BJ1691.L48 1950   618.97   51-29432

NL 0345229 DLC

Lieb, Clarence William, 1885–
Outwitting your years.   New York, Prentice-
Hall, Inc. [1951, c1949]
viii, 278 p. 21 cm.
1. Old age. I. Title.

NL 0345230 NcD

VOLUME 332

Lieb, Clarence William, 1885–
Safer smoking; what every smoker should know and do. ₁1st ed.₁ New York, Exposition Press ₁1953₁
106 p. 22 cm.
"A Banner book."

1. Tobacco habit. 2. Tobacco—Physiological effect.   I. Title.

HV5733.L5   *613.86 613.84   53–7368 ‡

NcD PSt DSI
NL 0345231   DLC WaT CaBVa DNLM OU OOxM OC1 OC1U NN

Lieb, Eduard: Über ungleichförmige Bewegungen eines Fadens, bei denen er seine Gestalt nicht ändert. Leipzig 1912: Teubner. 35 S. 8°
Tübingen, Naturwiss. Diss. v. 18. Nov. 1911, Ref. v. Brill
₁Geb. 18. April 87 Leutkirch; Wohnort: Ludwigsburg, Württ.; Staatsangeh.: Württemberg; Vorbildung: Oberrealsch. Ravensburg Reife Juli 05; Studium: Tübingen 8 S.; Rig. 18. Nov. 11.₁   ₁U 12. 4507₁

NL 0345232   ICRL CtY

                    Lieb, Franz, 1875–   ed.
Law   FOR OTHER EDITIONS
                                   SEE MAIN ENTRY
Germany. *Laws, statutes, etc.*
Arbeitsgerichtsgesetz in der vom 1. Mai 1934 an geltenden Fassung, mit Einleitung, Erläuterungen und Sachverzeichnis von Franz Lieb und Hugo Gift. 3., neubearb. Aufl. München, C. H. Beck, 1934.

          ₁875–
Lieb, Franz, ed.
Arbeitsgerichtsgesetz nebst ergänzendem anhang; mit einleitung, erläuterungen und sachverzeichnis von dr. Franz Lieb... und Hugo Gift ... 2. neubearb. aufl. München, C. H. Beck, 1931.
xix, 534 p.   16ᵇᵐ.

NL 0345234   MiU-L

LIEB, Franz, 1875–
Die Arbeitstarifverträge. Unter besonderer Berücksichtigung der Münchener Verhältnisse. München [1910] 85 S.

Tübingen, Jur. Diss.

NL 0345235   MH CtY

Lieb, Franz Xaver.
Vierstimmige Messe für gemischten Chor zur Advent- oder Fasten zeit.
Offenbach a/M. André. [185–?] 14 pp. L. 8°, obl.

E3194 — Masses.

NL 0345236   MB

Lieb, Frederick George, 1888–
The Baltimore Orioles; the history of a colorful team in Baltimore and St. Louis. New York, Putnam ₁1955₁
246 p. illus. 21 cm. ₁Putnam sports series. The Big league library₁

1. Baltimore. Baseball club (American League)

GV875.B2L5   796.357062752   55–5777 ‡

CaOTP MsU OrCS WaT
NL 0345237   DLC FU NN MB ViU OC1 PP PBL PJA OOxM IEN

Lieb, Frederick George, 1888–
The baseball story. New York, Putnam ₁1950₁
xiv, 335 p. illus., ports. 22 cm. ₁Putnam pennant series. The big league library₁

1. Baseball—Hist.   I. Title.

GV863.L528 1950   796.35709   50–9863

NcRS NcGU OrP WaE WaS WaT
NL 0345238   DLC Or IdU CaBVa InU LU MB TU OC1 TxU

Lieb, Frederick George, 1888–
The Boston Red Sox, by Frederick G. Lieb ... New York, G. P. Putnam's sons ₁1947₁
xiii, 257 p. front., ports. 21½ᵐ.

1. Boston. Base-ball club (American league)

GV875.B62L5   796.357   47–2943

Library of Congress

WaSp WaT
NL 0345239   DLC WaS OrP Or CaBVa FU ViU TxU MB PP

Lieb, Frederick George, 1888–
Connie Mack, grand old man of baseball, by Frederick G. Lieb. New York, G. P. Putnam's sons ₁1945₁
xi, 276 p. front., ports. 21½ᵐ.

'. McGillicuddy, Cornelius, 1862–

Library of Congress °   GV865.M27L5   45–3796
                                                    927.96357

CaBVaU CaBViP IdB Or WaS WaSp WaT
NL 0345240   DLC ViU PP OC1 OEac OO OU NcC PPPL CaBVa

GV865
.M27L5   **Lieb, Frederick George,** 1888–
1948   Connie Mack, grand old man of baseball.
             [Rev. ed.] New York, G. P. Putnam's Sons
             [1948]
             xi, 284 p. illus. 21cm.

1. McGillicuddy, Cornelius, 1862–

NL 0345241   MB NRU

---

*
AC8
.A6   **Lieb, Frederick George,** 1888–
no.1260   The Detroit Tigers. New York, Editions
1946   for the Armed Services ₁1946₁
             384 p. 16cm. (Armed Services ed. 1260)

NL 0345242   ViU

Lieb, Frederick George, 1888–
The Detroit Tigers ₁by₁ Frederick G. Lieb. New York, G. P. Putnam's sons ₁1946₁
xii, 276 p. front., ports. 21ᵐ.

1. Detroit. Base-ball club (American league)

                                              46–6583
Library of Congress   GV875.D6L5
                                              796.357

PP PPGi Or IdB WaS OrU
NL 0345243   DLC FU MiU TxU MH MB NcC NcRS PWcS PSt

134.6
L621h   Lieb, Frederick G
           Healing mind, body and purse. ₁1st ed.₁
           St. Petersburg, Fla., Priv. print. ₁1941₁
           120p.

           Author's autograph presentation copy.

           1. Mental suggestion. I. Title.

NL 0345244   TxFTC

Lieb, Frederick George, 1888–
The Philadelphia Phillies ₁by₁ Frederick G. Lieb and Stan Baumgartner. New York, Putnam ₁1953₁
246 p. illus. 21 cm. ₁Putnam sports series. The big league library₁

1. Philadelphia. Baseball club (National League)   I. Baumgartner, Stan, joint author.   II. Title.

GV875.P45L5   796.357   53–5328 ‡

NL 0345245   DLC CaBVa IdB Or WaE WaS WaT FU

Lieb, Frederick George, 1888–
The Pittsburgh Pirates. New York, G. P. Putnam's Sons ₁1948₁
xii, 290 p. ports. 22 cm.

1. Pittsburgh. Base-Ball Club (National League)

GV875.P5L5   796.357   48–6739*

WaSp WaT
NL 0345246   DLC MH MB Mi MiEM FU IdB OrP Or WaE WaS

---

*
AC8
.A6   **Lieb, Frederick George,** 1888–
no.S–25   The St. Louis Cardinals. New York,
1945   Editions for the Armed Services, °1945.
             287 p. 11 x 17cm. (Armed Services ed.
             S–25)

NL 0345247   ViU

Lieb, Frederick George, 1888–
The St. Louis Cardinals, the story of a great baseball club, by Frederick G. Lieb ... New York, G. P. Putnam's sons ₁1944₁
ix, 218 p. front., ports. 21½ cm.

1. St. Louis. Baseball club (National league)   I. Title.

GV875.S3L5   796.357   44–6951

PPGi WaS WaT WaTC CaBVa Or OrP
NL 0345248   DLC TU OC1W OOxM OLak OC1 ViU PSt PP

Lieb, Frederick George, 1888–
The St. Louis Cardinals, the story of a great baseball club, by Frederick G. Lieb ... New York, G. P. Putnam's sons ₁1945₁
4 p. l., 3–218 p. front., ports. 21ᵐ.
"Fourth Impression."

1. St. Louis. Base-ball club (National league)   I. Title.

                                                    45–2557
Library of Congress   GV875.S3L5 1945
                                                    796.357

NL 0345249   DLC WaSp NIC

VOLUME 332

GV875
.S3L5
1947
Lieb, Frederick George, 1888–
The St. Louis Cardinals, the story of a great baseball club. New York, G. P. Putnam's Sons [c1947]
239 p. illus. 22cm.
"Revised through 1946."—Dust jacket.

1. St. Louis. Base-ball Club (National League) I. Title.

NL 0345250 MB PP

Lieb, Frederick George.
Sight unseen; a journalist visits the occult. New York, Harper [c1939] 257 p.

1. Occult sciences I. Title.
N. Y. P. L.   June 21, 1939

NL 0345251 NN

Lieb, Frederick George, 1888–
Sight unseen, a journalist visits the occult, by Frederick G. Lieb. New York, London, Harper & brothers [1939]
x p., 1 l., 257 p. 21½ᶜᵐ.
"First edition."

1. Occult sciences. I. Title.
Library of Congress   BF1031.L47   39–10231
—— Copy 2.
Copyright A 127922   [150.961] 133

NL 0345252 DLC Or FTaSU PWcS PP OKentU OCl OO

Lieb, Frederick George, 1888–
The story of the World Series, an informal history. New York, G. P. Putnam's Sons [1949]
xi, 333 p. ports. 22 cm.

1. Base-ball—Hist.
GV863.L53   796.357   49–8520*

CaBVa WaS WaT OrP
NL 0345253 DLC MiD MB OCl OClU PSt KMK PV PP GU MB

Lieb, Frederick George, 1888–
The story of the world series, an informal history. New York, Putnam [1950]
342 p. illus. 22 cm.

1. Baseball—Hist. I. Title: The world series.
GV863.L53 1950   796.357   51–7142 ‡

NL 0345254 DLC NN CU-I OrU OrAshS

Lieb, Fritz, 1892–
... Christ und Antichrist im dritten reich; der kampf der deutschen bekenntniskirche. Paris, Éditions du Carrefour, 1936.
277, [3] p. 23½ᶜᵐ.

1. Germany—Religion—1933– I. Title. 2. Church and state in Germany—1933–
Library of Congress   BR856.L48   38–31142
274.3

NL 0345255 DLC WU NN NNUT CtY

Lieb, Fritz, 1892–
Christentum und Marxismus; die Kirche im Übergang von kapitalistischer zu proletarischer Diktatur. Berlin, G. Spielberg [1949]
47 p. 24 cm. (Akademische Reihe)

1. Socialism and religion. I. Title.
HX536.L65   A 51–4850
New York. Public Libr.
for Library of Congress

NL 0345256 NN DLC DWT

B2953
.L7
Lieb, Fritz, 1892–
Franz Baaders frühentwicklung. 1. abschnitt: Jugendgeschichte bis 1792 ... München, C. Kaiser, 1924.
vi, 72 p.
Habilitationsschrift—Basel.

1. Baader, Franz von, 1765–1841.

NL 0345257 ICU

Lieb, Fritz, 1892–
Franz Baaders jugendgeschichte; die frühentwicklung eines romantikers, von Fritz Lieb ... München, C. Kaiser, 1926.
xxiv, 258 p. 23½ᶜᵐ.
Published in part (vi, 73 p.) as the author's "habilitationsschrift", under title: Franz Baaders frühentwicklung. Abschnitt 1: Jugendgeschichte bis 1792. München, C. Kaiser, 1924.
"Benützte bücher und abkürzungen" p. [xxi]–xxiv.

1. *Baader, Franz von, 1765–1841.
          31–22728
Library of Congress   B2953.L5   921.3

NL 0345258 DLC CU MH NjP NIC PU TU ICU OU

Lieb, Fritz, 1892–
Glaube und offenbarung bei J. G. Hamann. Erweiterte habilitationsrede in Basel von Fritz Lieb. München, C. Kaiser, 1926.
28 p. 23ᶜᵐ.
Bibliographical foot-notes.

1. Hamann, Johann Georg, 1730–1788.

NL 0345259 MiU

Lieb, Fritz, 1892–
Der "Mythos" des nationalsozialistischen Nihilismus; Vortrag gehalten auf dem Kongress der Tschechoslowakischen Akademischen Y. M. C. A. [Strassburg] Sebastian Brant-Verlag, 1938.
[20] p. 21 cm.
Originally published in E. J. Gumbel's Freie Wissenschaft, 1938.

1. Rosenberg, Alfred, 1893–1946. Der Mythus des 20. Jahrhunderts. I. Title.
CB425.R74L5   62–55548 ‡

NL 0345260 DLC

Lieb, Fritz.
...Revolution, Kirche und Christentum. Basel: Neue Jugend [1921?] 8 p. 8°. (Kommunistische Jugendbibliothek. Nr. 25.)

1. Church and state. 2. Bolshevism. 3. Series.
N. Y. P. L.   April 18, 1922.

NL 0345261 NN NNC

Lieb, Fritz, 1892–
... La Russie évolue, le peuple russe entre le communisme et le christianisme. Neuchâtel, Paris, Delachaux & Niestlé s. a. [1946]
270 p. 18½ᶜᵐ. (Collection "Civilisation et christianisme")
"L'édition originale de cet ouvrage a paru en 1945 ... à Berne, sous le titre Russland unterwegs, der russische mensch zwischen christentum und kommunismus. Adaptation française de Eugène Porret avec la collaboration de W. Lepp, Ch. Kastler, P. Uldry."
Bibliographical foot-notes.

1. Russia—Civilization. 2. Russia—Religion. I. Porret, Eugène, tr. II. Title.
DK267.L4615   947.084   A 47–3615
New York. Public Library
for Library of Congress

NL 0345262 NN CtY DLC

Lieb, Fritz, 1892–
... Russland unterwegs; der russische mensch zwischen christentum und kommunismus. Bern, A. Francke [1945]
474 p. 21½ᶜᵐ. (Half-title: Mensch und gesellschaft, hrsg. von Konrad Farner. Bd. IV)
Bibliographical references included in "Anmerkungen und hinweise" p. [451]–474)

1. Russia—Civilization. 2. Russia—Religion. I. Title.
DK267.L46   A 47–2706
Harvard univ. Library
for Library of Congress

PU DLC MnU NcD
NL 0345263 MH NIC IU CU TxU CLU PSC OCU ICN ICU NNC

Lieb, Fritz, 1892–
Die Selbsterfassung des russischen Menschen im Werke Dostojewskijs und Solowjews. Aus dem Buch: Russland unterwegs. Berlin, Chronos Verlag [1947]
38 p. 24 cm.

1. Dostoevskiĭ, Fedor Mikhaĭlovich, 1821–1881. 2. Solov'ev, Vladimir Sergeevich, 1853–1900. 3. National characteristics, Russian. I. Title.
PG3328.Z6L5   *891.733   52—65215

NL 0345264 DLC CSt CSt-H ICRL IaU OU

Lieb, Fritz, 1892–
... Das westeuropäische geistesleben im urteile russischer religionsphilosophie, von Fritz Lieb ... Tübingen, J. C. B. Mohr (P. Siebeck) 1929.
39 p. 23 cm. (Sammlung gemeinverständlicher vorträge und schriften aus dem gebiet der theologie und religionsgeschichte. [nr.] 136)
"Anmerkungen" (bibliographical): p. [36]–39.
1. Religion - Philosophy.

NL 0345265 CU NNUT

Me21
T34
TT.31
Lieb, Fritz, 1892–
Wir Christen und der Kommunismus. München, C.Kaiser, 1952.
36p. 23cm. (Theologische Existenz heute, n.F. Nr.31)

NL 0345266 CtY ICU MH NcD TNJ-R KyLxCB CPFT DWT

Lieb, Hans, 1887–
Anleitung zur Darstellung organischer Präparate mit kleinen Substanzmengen von Hans Lieb und Wolfgang Schöniger. Wien, Springer, 1950.
xl, 161 p. illus. 21 cm.

1. Chemistry, Analytic—Quantitative. 2. Chemistry, Organic. I. Schöniger, Wolfgang, joint author.
QD101.L65   51–3041

CU OrU
NL 0345267 DLC PU-Sc NBC NcD ICU ICJ CSt TxU OU

VOLUME 332

Lieb, Hans, 1887–
Der gerichtlich-chemische nachweis von giften. Von Hans Lieb ... (Mit 21 abbildungen.)

(*In* Abderhalden, Emil, ed. Handbuch der biologischen arbeitsmethoden ... Berlin, 1920– 25ᶜᵐ. abt. IV, Angewandte chemische und physikalische methoden. t. 12, 1. hälfte, bd. 2 ₍hft. 6₎ (1938) p. ₍1301₎–1506. diagrs.)

Bibliographical foot-notes.

1. Poisons.   I. Title.

Ohio state univ. Library   A C 39–711
for Library of Congress   [QH324.A3 1920 abt. 4, t. 12]
    ₍4₎   (574.072)

NL 0345268   OU DLC

Lieb, Hans, 1887–
Manuel pratique de préparations organiques avec de petites quantités de substances ₍par₎ H. Lieb et W. Schöniger. Traduction française de R. Specklin. Préf. du Pʳ. R. Locquin. Paris, Masson, 1953.

181 p. illus. 23 cm.

1. Chemistry, Analytic—Quantitative. 2. Chemistry, Organic.
I. Schöniger, Wolfgang, joint author.

QD101.L654   57–23668 ‡

NL 0345269   DLC

Lieb, Hans, 1887–
Mikrochemische Analyse, von Professor Dr. H. Lieb ... und Priv.-Dozent Dr. A. Benedetti-Pichler ...

(*In* Chemisch-technische Untersuchungsmethoden. Achte Auflage. Berlin, 1931. 24ᶜᵐ. Bd. I, p. ₍1120₎–1211 incl. illus., tables, diagrs.)

Bibliographical foot-notes.

NL 0345270   ICJ

Lieb, Hans, 1887–
Mikroelektrolytische bestimmung des kupfers. (Nach F. Pregl, mit besonderer berücksichtigung der kupferbestimmung in gemüsekonserven, drogen und ähnlichen organischen produkten.) Von Hans Lieb ...

(*In* Abderhalden, Emil, ed. Handbuch der biologischen arbeitsmethoden ... Berlin, 1920– 25ᶜᵐ. abt. I, Chemische methoden. t. 3 (1921) p. ₍871₎–876. illus.)

1. Copper. 2. Electrochemical analysis.   I. Title.

    A C 36–4225
Title from Ohio State   Univ.
Library of Congress   [QH324.A3 1920 abt. 1, t. 3]
    (574.072)

NL 0345271   OU

Lieb, Hans, 1887–
Die mikroelementaranalyse nach Fritz Pregl. (Bestimmung von C, H, N, Cl, Br, J, S, P, As und metallen.) Von Hans Lieb ...

(*In* Abderhalden, Emil, ed. Handbuch der biologischen arbeitsmethoden ... Berlin, 1920– 25ᶜᵐ. abt. I, Chemische methoden. t. 3 (1921) p. ₍325₎–392. illus.)

Bibliographical foot-notes.

1. Microchemistry. 2. Chemistry, Analytic. 3. Pregl, Fritz, 1869–1930.

    A C 36–4211
Title from Ohio State   Univ.
Library of Congress   [QH324.A3 1920 abt. 1, t. 3]
    (574.072)

NL 0345272   OU

Lieb, Hans, 1887–
Mikromethoxyl- und methylimidbestimmung. Von Hans Lieb ...

(*In* Abderhalden, Emil, ed. Handbuch der biologischen arbeitsmethoden ... Berlin, 1920– 25ᶜᵐ. abt. I, Chemische methoden. t. 3 (1921) p. ₍535₎–546. illus.)

Bibliographical foot-notes.

1. ₍Imides₎ 2. Methoxy-group.   I. Title.

    A C 36–4218
Title from Ohio State   Univ.
Library of Congress   [QH324.A3 1920 abt. 1, t. 3]
    (574.072)

NL 0345273   OU

Lieb, Hans, 1887–
Mikromolekulargewichtsbestimmung nach Fritz Pregl. Von Hans Lieb ... (Mit 4 abbildungen.)

(*In* Abderhalden, Emil, ed. Handbuch der biologischen arbeitsmethoden ... Berlin, 1920– 25ᶜᵐ. abt. III, Physikalisch-chemische methoden. t. A, 1. hälfte (1928) p. ₍723₎–728. illus.)

1. Molecular weights. 2. Pregl, Fritz, 1869–1930.   I. Title.

    A C 36–3125
Title from Ohio State   Univ.
Library of Congress   [QH324.A3 1920 abt. 3, t. A]
    (574.072)

NL 0345274   OU

Lieb, Hans, 1887–
Praktikum der physiologischen Chemie ... Graz, Kienreich, 1946.

215 p. illus. 20 cm.

1st ed.

1. Physiological chemistry. ₍1. Biochemistry₎

    Med 47–2025
U. S. Army medical library   [QU4L716p 1946]
for Library of Congress   ₍2₎

NL 0345275   DNLM OU

Lieb, Hermann.
Emperor William I., the founder of the new German empire. With an historical sketch of the German people from the earliest times to the foundation of the Hohenzollern dynasty. By Hermann Lieb ... Fully illustrated. Chicago, New York ₍etc.₎ Belford, Clarke & co., 1888.

₍3₎–482 p. incl. front., plates, ports. 20½ᶜᵐ.

A German edition was issued the same year.

1. Wilhelm I, German emperor, 1797–1888.

Library of Congress   DD223.L7   4–27100

NL 0345276   DLC IU WaTC OrU WaSp WaT I

943.083
W678zL   **Lieb, Hermann.**
Emperor William I, the founder of the new German empire. With an historical sketch of the German people from the earliest times to the foundation of the Hohenzollern dynasty. Chicago ₍etc.₎, Belford, Clarke, 1888.
492p. illus. 21cm.

A German edition was issued the same year: Kaiser Wilhelm I.
1. Wilhelm I, German emperor, 1797–1888. I. Title.

NL 0345277   NcU

Lieb, Hermann.
Emperor William I., the founder of the new German empire. With an historical sketch of the German people from the earliest times to the foundation of the Hohenzollern dynasty. By Hermann Lieb... Chicago: Amer. Mutual Library Assoc., 1890.
2 p.l., 9–516 p. front., illus. (incl. ports.) 12°.

1. William I, German emperor,   1797–1888 2. Germany.—History.
N. Y. P. L.   October 11, 1920.

NL 0345278   NN

Lieb, Hermann.
The foes of the French revolution, centralization and anarchy, by Hermann Lieb ... Chicago, New York ₍etc.₎ Belford, Clarke & co., 1889.

vii, ₍4₎, 9–331 p. incl. front. 15 pl., 32 port. 19½ᵐ.

1. France—Hist.—Revolution—1789–1794.

    4–11113
Library of Congress   DC161.L71

NL 0345279   DLC WaTC WU

Lieb, Hermann.
Fürst Bismarck und das deutsche volk ... Mit einer genauen lebensbeschreibung des fürsten Otto von Bismarck ... nebst dem leben und der regierung des kaisers Wilhelm I ... n. p., 1898₎

526 p. illus. 20½ cm.

An enlarged edition of the author's Kaiser Wilhelm I, published in Chicago, 1888.

1. Wilhelm I, German emperor, 1797–1888. 2. Bismarck, Otto, fürst von, 1815–1898.

DD220.L7   98–1989 rev

NL 0345280   DLC MiA1bC

DD89
L5   **Lieb, Hermann.**
Geschichte des deutschen Volkes von den frühesten Zeiten bis zur Thronbesteigung Kaiser Wilhelm II. Einschliesslich einer vollständigen und ausführlichen Lebensbeschreibung Kaiser Wilhelm I, des Schöpfers des neuen deutschen Reiches. Von Hermann Lieb und Emil Dietzsch. Chicago, Donohue & Henneberry ₍1888₎
498 p. illus. 21cm.

1. Wilhelm I, German Emperor, 1797–1888. 2. Germany – Hist. I. Dietzsch, Emil, b. 1829, jt. a.   II. Title.

NL 0345281   OrCS

Lieb, Hermann
Geschichte des deutschen volkes von den frühesten Zeiten bis zur Thronbesteigung Kaiser Wilhelm II; einschliesslich einer vollständigen und ausführlichen Lebensbeschreibung Kaiser Wilhelm I, des Schöpfers des neuen Deutschen Reiches, ... und Emil Dietzsch. Chicago, Donohue, Henneberry & co., 1890.
498 p. illus. port.

NL 0345282   OCl

Lieb, Hermann.
History of the German people from the earliest times to the accession of Emperor William II. Chicago, Belford, Clarke & Co., 1889.
9–516 p. incl. plates. 21cm.

1. Germany—Hist.

NL 0345283   ViU MiU

Lieb, Hermann.
History of the German people from the earliest times to the accession of Emperor William II. Including a full and complete life of Emperor William I, founder of the new German empire. By Hermann Lieb ... with over 50 full-page illustrations. Chicago: American mutual library ass'n, 1890. 516 p. incl. front. plates, ports. 21cm.

Published also with title: Emperor William I., the founder of the new German empire.

997458A. 1. William I, German   emperor, 1797–1888. 2. Germany
—Hist.
N. Y. P. L.   December 15, 1939.

NL 0345284   NN WaT

DD89 **Lieb, Hermann.**
.L7   History of the German people from the earliest times to the accession of Emperor William II., including a full and complete life of Emperor William I., founder of the new German empire. By Hermann Lieb ... Chicago, S. C. Knowles, 1896.

₍3₎–516 p. incl. front., plates, ports. 20ᵐ.

1. Germany—Hist. 2. Wilhelm I, German emperor, 1797–1888.

NL 0345285   ICU

VOLUME 332

Lieb, Hermann.
The initiative and referendum, by Hermann Lieb ... Chicago, H. Lieb, jr., & co., 1902.
141 p. 18½ᶜᵐ.

1. Referendum. 2. U. S.—Pol. & govt.   ɪ. Title.

Library of Congress   JF493.U6L52   3—26115

NL 0345286   DLC NjP

Lieb, Hermann.
The initiative and referendum, by Hermann Lieb ... Chicago, H. Lieb, jr. & co., 1902.
178 p. front. (port.) 20ᶜᵐ.

1. Referendum. 2. U. S.—Pol. & govt.   ɪ. Title.

Library of Congress   JF493.U6L5   3—5950

MB PP PU
NL 0345287   DLC Or Wa OrP CU MU OO OCU ODW ICJ NN

Lieb, Hermann.
Kaiser Wilhelm ɪ., der schöpfer des neuen Deutschen Reiches. Mit einem blick in die geschichte des deutschen volkes, von den frühesten zeiten bis auf die heutigen tage, von Hermann Lieb ... und Emil Dietzsch ... Chicago, New York ₍etc.₎ Belford, Clarke & co., 1888.
3 p. l., ₍11₎–498 p. incl. plates, ports. front., pl., port. 20¼ᶜᵐ.
An English edition was issued the same year.

1. Wilhelm ɪ, German emperor, 1797–1888. ɪ. Dietzsch. Emil, b. 1829. ɪɪ. Title.

Library of Congress   DD223.L72   4—27099

NL 0345288   DLC ICN

HF
1755
.L68
1887
Lieb, Hermann.
The protective tariff. What it does for us! By Hermann Lieb. 4th and rev. ed. Chicago, Hermann Lieb ₍c1887₎
204 p. 18 cm.

1. Free trade and protection--Free trade. 2. Tariff--U. S. I. Title

NL 0345289   OKentU

Lieb, Hermann.
The protective tariff. What it does for us! By Hermann Lieb. Chicago, The author, 1888 ₍ᶜ1887₎
232 p. 20ᶜᵐ.

1. Free trade and protection—Free trade. 2. Tariff—U. S.

Library of Congress   HF1755.L68   5—42666

NL 0345290   DLC MtU WaS OFH MiU PPL ICJ

HF1755
.L683
LIEB, HERMANN.
The protective tariff. What it does for us! By Hermann Lieb... 4th and rev.ed. Chicago₍etc.₎Belford,Clarke & co.,1888.
₍2₎,242 p. 20cm.

1.Free trade and protection--Free trade. 2.Tariff--U.S.

ICU MH PU
NL 0345291   ICU PU FU ICRL NIC MiD-B MiD OU OCIW

Lieb, Hermann.
The Protective Tariff. What it does for us"! [4th and rev. ed.] Chicago, Hermann Lieb. 1890.

NL 0345292   ScU

Lieb (Hermann).A ⋆Ein Fall von Exophthalmus infolge Mucocele der Stirnhöhle, operiert durch Kombination von "Kroenlein" und "Killian." [Zürich.] 20 pp. 8°. Schaffhausen, Nohl ₍n. d.₎

NL 0345293   DNLM

Lieb, Joh. Wilhelm Friedrich, 1730-1807.
Diss. de dormientibus secunda agens de justa somni salutaris quantittate et mensura
see under   Handtwig, Gustavus Christian.

Lieb (Joh. Wilhelm Friedrich) [1730–1807]. Die Eispflanze als ein fast specifisches Arzneimittel. 16 pp. 12°. *Hof, Vierling,* 1785.
Bound with: CɴNA (S.) Abhandlung vom Lazarethfieber ₍etc.₎ 12°. *Wien. 1784.*

NL 0345295   DNLM

Lieb, Johann. Miscellanea historica Schlierseensia. 2 pp. (Œfele, A. F. von, *Rer. Boicar. script.* v. 1, p. 386.)

NL 0345296   MdBP

Lieb, John S.
Marquette University Law School: patent law course. Milwaukee? 1955. 1 v. (various pagings) 28 cm.

Includes bibliographies.

1. Patent laws and legislation.
(1) Marquette University, Milwaukee. Law School. (2) TITLE: Patent law course. (TITLE)

NL 0345297   NN

Lieb, John William, 1860-1929.
Collection of books and pamphlets on Leonardo da Vinci, library of John W. Lieb, at New Rochelle, N. Y. ₍New Rochelle?₎ 1929. 63 l. 4°.
Cover-title.
Typewritten.

510734A. 1. Vinci, Leonardo da,   1452-1519—Bibl.
N. Y. P. L.   February 21, 1931

NL 0345298   NN

Lieb, John William, 1860-
The contribution of the electric light and power industry to the safety movement, by John W. Lieb. New York city, 1928.
16 p. 20 cm.
"Paper presented at the seventeenth Annual safety congress of the National safety council October 1, 1928, New York city."

NL 0345299   DL

₍**Lieb, John William**₎ 1860-
The East River generating station of the New York Edison company ₍New York, New York Edison co., c1927₎
32 p. illus., map, diagrs.

"Address ... delivered before the joint luncheon of the New York electrical league and the Electrical board of trade of New York ... January 27, 1927."

NL 0345300   NNC MH NN

Lieb, John William, 1860–
The Edison system of electric lighting; presidential address by John W. Lieb... ₍New York: The Marchbanks Press,₎ 1920.
23 p. 8°.
Cover-title.
Presented at the third annual meeting of the Edison Pioneers, held at the Edison Laboratories, Orange, N. J., in celebration of the seventy-third birthday of Thomas Alva Edison, Feb. 11, 1920.

1. Electricity.—Lighting : History.
N. Y. P. L.   August 16, 1920.

NL 0345301   NN

Lieb, John William, 1860–
The historic Pearl street, New York, Edison station. By the first electrician of the station ⟨Mr. John W. Lieb⟩... ₍New York, 1927?₎ 8 l. diagrs., illus. 8°.
Cover-title.
Repr.: Edisonia. 1904.

387088A. 1. New York (city)—   Power plants, Electric.
N. Y. P. L.   December 19, 1928

NL 0345302   NN

Lieb, John William, 1860–
Leonardo da Vinci, natural philosopher and engineer, by John W. Lieb ... ₍n. p., 1921₎
64 p. incl. illus., port. 23ᶜᵐ.
"Presented at the annual meeting of the Franklin institute ... January 19, 1921; reprinted from the Journal of the Institute, June–July, 1921."

1. Leonardo da Vinci, 1452–1519.

Library of Congress   ND623.L5L5   22–3815

NL 0345303   DLC OrPR NN CoU PPF PU-FA

Lieb, John W₍illiam₎ 1860-
... The organization and administration of national engineering societies. By John W. Lieb, jr. ... ₍New York? 1905₎
16 p. 23ᶜᵐ.
At head of title : Monday, June 19, 1905. Presidential address. American institute of electrical engineers ... Twenty-second annual convention, Asheville, N. C.
Advance copy, subject to revision.

1. Engineering—Societies.

Library of Congress   TA155.L71   7-8924

NL 0345304   DLC

Lieb, John William, 1860–
The philosophy of invention; an address by Dr. John W. Lieb, presented before the International Congress on Illumination, September 23, 1928, at Saranac Inn, New York. ₍New York? 1928.₎
19 p. 8°.

531817A. 1. Inventions.
N. Y. P. L.   September 3, 1931

NL 0345305   NN

Lieb, John William, 1860-1929.
Progress of the central station industry in America, by Dr John W Lieb... ₍New York₎ New York Edison co. ₍1928₎ 1 v. illus. 25cm.

1. Electric power plants—U. S.   ɪ. New York Edison company.
N. Y. P. L.   March 10, 1948

NL 0345306   NN

Lieb, John William, 1860–
Review of power resources and their development in the northeastern states of the United States, including statistics and information relating to the New England and Middle Atlantic states, Delaware, Maryland, West Virginia, District of Columbia, and Virginia and interconnections with eastern Ohio. By John W. Lieb. The World power conference, London, England, June 30–July 12, 1924. ₍New York, The Marchbanks press, ᶜ1924₎
42 p. illus. (incl. maps) diagrs. 25ᶜᵐ.
Bibliographical foot-notes.
1. Electric engineering—Atlantic states. 2. Electric power-plants—Atlantic states. ɪ. World power conference. 1st, London, 1924.

Library of Congress   TK23.L4   24–15995

NL 0345307   DLC WaS PPPR OU

VOLUME 332

Lieb, Julia Christina, 1887–
Broken glass, by Julia C. Lieb. Philadelphia, Dorrance and company [*1938]
340 p. 20⁰ᵐ.

    ɪ. Title.

Library of Congress   PZ3.L621Br   38–6349

NL 0345308   DLC

[Lieb, Julia Christina] 1887–
Steel under velvet [by] Vance Carmichael [pseud.] New York, Margent press, 1939.
5 p. l., 3–497 p. 22½ᵐ.

    ɪ. Title.

Library of Congress   PZ3.L6218t   39–24573

NL 0345309   DLC WaE OU

Lieb, Ludwig.
...Die Entwicklung der Augsburger Effenktenbörse. (1816–1896.) Augsburg: Selbstverlag der Stadt, 1930. 86 p. 24cm. (Augsburg. Stadtarchiv. Abhandl. zur Geschichte der Stadt Augsburg. Heft 3.)
Bibliography, p. 85–86.

1. Stock exchange—Germany—
N. Y. P. L.   Augsburg. I. Ser.
September 12, 1932

NL 0345310   NN

Lieb, Margaret.
Forward and reverse mutation in a histidine-requiring strain of *Escherichia coli*. [n. p., 1951]
[460]–477 p. diagrs., tables. 25 cm.
Cover title.
Thesis—Columbia University.
"Reprinted from Genetics, vol. 36, no. 5, September, 1951."
"Literature cited": p. 476–477.

    1. Variation (Biology) 2. Bacillus coli communis. 3. Histidine.
ɪ. Title.
QH401.L58   A 55–8547
Columbia Univ.   Libraries
for Library of Congress   [3]†

NL 0345311   NNC DLC

Lieb, Michael Leo.
See
Munkácsy, Mihály , 1844–1900.

Lieb, Mihály
    see
Munkácsy, Mihály, 1844–1900.

RK58
.F69
    Lieb, Myron M., joint author.
    Friend, David.
The dentist and his patient; a new concept of dental practice, by David Friend ... George D. Kudler ... Myron M. Lieb ... [and others] New York city, Revere publishing company, 1944.

RK58
.F69
1945
    Lieb, Myron M., joint author.
    Friend, David.
The dentist and his patient, correlating diagnosis and treatment planning with patient education and practice management for optimum control of dental disease, by David Friend ... George D. Kudler ... Myron M. Lieb ... [and others] With foreword by Harold J. Leonard ... New York city, Revere publishing company, 1945.

Lieb, Norbert, 1907–
Allgäuer Kunst; Grundlagen ihrer Entwicklung und Eigenart ihrer Leistung. München, Schnell & Steiner [1941]
40 p. illus., 16 plates. 25 cm.
"Sonderdruck aus dem 'Allgäuer Geschichtsfreund.' Kempten, n. F., Nr. 48/1941."

    1. Art—Allgäu.

N6886.A4L5   A F 49–761*
Harvard Univ. Library
for Library of Congress

NL 0345316   MH ICA DLC

Lieb, Norbert, 1907–
    Augsburg
    see under title

Lieb, Norbert, 1907–
Das Augsburger Rathaus. [Berlin, Deutscher Kunstverlag, 1944]
14 p. illus. 18 cm. (Führer zu grossen Baudenkmälern, Heft 37)
Caption title.

    1. Augsburg. Rathaus. ɪ. Series.
NA4435.G4A83   A F 48–3464*
Columbia Univ.   Libraries
for Library of Congress [1]†

NL 0345318   NNC CtY IU CoD GAT WU DLC

Lieb, Norbert, 1907–
    Augsburger Renaissance
    see under
    Augsburg. Städtische Kunstsammlungen.

Lieb, Norbert, 1907–
Barockkirchen zwischen Donau und Alpen. Aufnahmen von Max Hirmer. München, Hirmer [1953]
174 p. illus., 178 plates, plans. 28 cm.
Includes bibliographies.

    1. Architecture, Gothic. 2. Church architecture—Bavaria.
3. Church architecture—Swabia. ɪ. Hirmer, Max. ɪɪ. Title.
            A 54—1499
Harvard Univ. Library
for Library of Congress [55f3]

DLC
NIC MH MB RPB OClMA WaS OrU MiU OOxM PSt TxU PBm ICU
NL 0345320   MH CLU NIC PP IaU NN OClSA NjP NNC CtY

Lieb, Norbert, 1907–
    Benediktinerabteikirche Ottobeuren
    see under
    Hirmer, Max.

Lieb, Norbert, 1907.
    Benediktinerabteikirche St. Alexander und Theodor
    see under Hirmer, Max.

Lieb, Norbert, 1907–
Führer durch die Städtischen Kunstsammlungen, Augsburg. [Augsburg] 1953.
63 p., 8 plates on 4 l., 21 cm.

    ɪ. Augsburg. Städtische Kunstsammlungen.

NL 0345323   DNGA

Lieb, Norbert, 1907–
Die Fugger und die Kunst. Mit einem Exkurs: Die Bildhauer der Fugger-Kapelle bei St. Anna zu Augsburg; Stilkritische Bemerkungen zu Sebastian Loscher und Hans Daucher, von Karl Feuchtmayr. München, Schnell & Steiner, 1952–
    v. plates. 25 cm. (Studien zur Fuggergeschichte, Bd. 10)
Schwäbische Forschungsgemeinschaft bei der Kommission für Bayerische Landesgeschichte. [Veröffentlichungen] Reihe 4. Bd. 1. Includes bibliographies.
    Contents.—[1] Im Zeitalter der Spätgotik und der frühen Renaissance.—[2] Im Zeitalter der hohen Renaissance.

    1. Art patronage. 2. Fugger family. (Series: Studien zur Fuggergeschichte, Bd. 10 [etc.] Series: Akademie der Wissenschaften, Munich. Kommission für Bayerische Landesgeschichte. Schwäbische Forschungsgemeinschaft. Veröffentlichungen. Reihe 4, Bd. 1 [etc.]
HF442.F788 Bd. 10, etc.   54–44413 rev

    MCM PBm PU NN MdBWA NIC ICN NjP OCU FTaSU
NL 0345325   DLC LU MH UU MiU CU ViU NcD CSt CU–S IaU

Lieb, Norbert, 1907–
    Fugger und Welser
    see under title

Lieb, Norbert, 1907–
Jörg Seld, Goldschmied und Bürger von Augsburg, ein Meisterleben im Abend des Mittelalters. München, Schnell & Steiner [1947]
46 p. plates. 19 cm.

    1. Seld, Jörg, 1454 (ca.)–1527.
NK7198.S4L5   48–15509*

NL 0345327   DLC MH IaAS NN

Lieb, Norbert.
Jörg Seld, Goldschmied und Bürger von Augsburg; ein Meisterleben im Abend des Mittelalters. München, Schnell & Steiner [1947]
46 p. plates. 19 cm.
Microfiche (Negative). 2 sheets. 11 x 15cm. (NPYL FSN 188.)

NL 0345328   NN

Lieb, Norbert, 1907–
Madonnen, Hauptwerke der italienischen und nordischen Malerei, 10 Farbtafeln, mit Einführung von Norbert Lieb. [Augsburg, J. P. Himmer, 1948]
5 p., 10 col. plates (in portfolio) 40 cm. (Meisterwerke; Herausgeber Georg Biermann)
Cover title.

    1. Mary, Virgin—Art. ɪ. Title. (Series)
N8070.L47   755.5   48–24950*‡

NL 0345329   DLC WaT

DD901
.M77L5
    Lieb, Norbert, 1907–
München; Lebensbild einer Stadtkultur. München, G. D. W. Callwey, 1952.
307 p. illus., plates. 24 cm.

    1. Munich—Descr. 2. Munich—Intellectual life. 3. Art—Munich.
4. Architecture—Munich.   A 53–1252
Rochester. Univ. Libr.
for Library of Congress

NL 0345330   NRU NN NjP DLC

VOLUME 332

Lieb, Norbert, 1907–
Münchener Barockbaumeister; Leben und Schaffen ir
Stadt und Land. Archivalische Vorarbeiten von Adolf A
Lieb. München, Schnell und Steiner, 1941.
301 p. 80 plates. 25 cm. (Forschungen zur deutschen Kunst-
geschichte, Bd. 35)
Bibliography: p. 217.

1. Architecture—Munich. 2. Architecture—Bavaria. 3. Architecture, Baroque. I. Title. (Series)

NA1086.M8L5　　　　　　　　　55–51488

MiU MWiCA PBm CtY
NL 0345331　　DLC CSt OC1MA CU NNC NN IU InU MH NjP PU

Lieb, Norbert, 1907–
Ottobeuren und die barockarchitektur Ostschwa-
bens ... von Norbert Lieb ... Augsburg, Rösler,
1933.
vii, 221 p. 23 cm.

Thesis, München.

1. Architecture, Baroque. 2. Architecture.- Swabis
3. Church architecture - Ottobeuren. I. Title.

NL 0345332　　NNC PU CtY MiU NjP PBm

NA1086　　Lieb, Norbert, 1907–
W515.25　　Wessobrunn; Geschichte, Bedeutung,
B4　　Führung, von Norbert Lieb, Hugo
L5　　Schnell, [und] J. Klem. Stadler.
München, Schnell & Steiner. [1953]
25 p.　illus., facsims., 22 plates.
24cm. (Grosse Kunstführer, 13)

"Wichtigstes Schrifttum": p. [2].

NL 0345333　　MWiCA MH NN

Lieb, Norman.
Münchener Barockmeister:
see under Lieb, Norbert, 1907–

Lieb, Paul , 1906–
Die rechtskraft im strafprozess.
Inaug. diss. Tuebingen, 1930
Bibl.

NL 0345335　　DLC ICRL OU MH-L

Lieb, Richard.
Die moderne Sisalspinnerei; ausführlicher Lehrgang in 12
Kapiteln und einem Anhang "Wirtschaftskunde für den Spinnerei-
praktiker"...von Richard Lieb... Berlin: Berg & Schoch,
1930. 254 p. incl. tables. illus. (incl. map, plans.) f°.
Repr.: Deutsche Seiler-Zeitung, 1930?

530112A. 1. Sisal hemp.　　　　　　　　　June 17, 1931
N.Y.P.L.

NL 0345336　　NN

Lieb, Sarah.
History of Michigan . . . Chicago, New York [etc.]
Belford, Clarke & co., 1889.
194 pp. front., illus., port. 8°.
In words of one syllable.

F566.L71　　　　　　　　　1–6092–M 1

NL 0345337　　DLC Mi

Lieb, Thomas John.
Line coaching; a text of detailed football instruction, by
Thomas J. Lieb ... Menomonie, Wis., Athletic supply co.
inc. [°1927]
111 p. incl. front. (port.) illus. 20 cm.

1. Line play (Football)　I. Title.

GV959.L6　　　　　　　　　27—18786

NL 0345338　　DLC OrCS WaWW NcD OU OO OOxM

797　　Lieb, Thomas John
L71ℓ　　Line coaching; a text of detailed
Ed.2　　football instruction. 2d ed. rev.
Los Angeles, Calif., Lieb [1930]
158p. front.(port.) illus.,diagrs. D.

NL 0345339　　IaU OC1 OO PWcS PHC MiU WaWW

AC　　Lieb, Viktor A.
851　　Über die bildung substituierter hydantoine aus
aldehyden und ketonen. ... n.p., [1932?] 64 p.
Inaug. Diss. Techn. Hochsch. München, [1932]

NL 0345340　　ICRL

Lieb Heimatland, ade! Volksweise. [Männerchor.]
(In Das Rütli. Pp. 229, 230. St. Gallen, 1873.)

E3194 — Part songs.　　Mar. 8,　　1902.

NL 0345341　　MB

844L621　　Lieb-Rose, ou l'épreuve de la vertu, histoire
Oℓ　　scythe, traduite de l'Allemand, par M. le
Chevalier de ***. Bouillon, Société
Typographique, 1770.
3v. in 1. 14cm.

NL 0345342　　IU

Lieb vaterland...feldbriefe unserer offiziere, aerzte und soldaten ... Mit genehmigung des stellv. generalkommandos.
Heilbronn, E. Salzer, 1914.
2 v. 19½ᵐᵐ.
Edited by Eugen Salzer.

1. European war, 1914–1918—Personal narratives, German.
I. Salzer, Eugen, 1866–　ed.

　　　　　　　　　　　　　　37–35207
Library of Congress　　D640.A2L5
　　　　　　　　　　　　　940.48243

NL 0345343　　DLC DNW CtY

Lieb vaterland; kriegslesebuch. Berichte
über erlebnisse in feld und heimat. Ergänzungen zu den lesebüchern der schulen
see under Thiene, Ernst, ed.

Lieb vaterland magst ruhig sein![Berlin ... 1914]
see under [Pickardt, Ernst]

Lieb vaterland magst ruhig sein! Würzburg, 1915.
see under Heuler, Felix, 1877–　ed.

Lieba, Saint
see Lioba, Saint, 8th cent.

Liebach, Hildegard, 1908–
... Malignes Adenom der Cervix uteri ...
Gütersloh i. Westf. [n. d.]
Inaug. -Diss. - Berlin.
Lebenslauf.
"Literaturverzeichnis": p. 15–17.

NL 0345348　　CtY

Liebach, Johannes.
Bataillonsführung nach den neusten dienst-
vorschriften bearbeitet von Liebach. 2. erweit.
aufl. Berlin, Vossische buchhandlung, 1908.
118 p. 21 cm.

9181

NL 0345349　　DNW

4UD-　　Liebach, Johannes.
42　　Bataillons-, Regiments- und Brigade-Uebungen
und Besichtigungen der Infanterie in praktischen
Beispielen, ein Beitrag zur kriegsmässigen
Ausbildung, Besichtigung und Verwendung der
Infanterie im Gefecht. Aus der Praxis für die
Praxis. Berlin, Vossische Buchhandlung, 1914.
138 p.

NL 0345350　　DLC-P4

Liebach, Johannes.
...Ejemplos prácticos de ejercicios de servicio en campaña
y de guarnición para oficiales; contribución a la preparación y
al perfeccionamiento táctico de los oficiales por Liebach...
Revisado por el mayor A. F. Sabella. Buenos Aires: Ferrari
hnos., 1921. 151 p. diagr., forms, maps. 12°. (Biblioteca del oficial. v. 39.)

644636A. 1. Military tactics.　　I. Sabella, A. F., editor. II. Ser.
N.Y.P.L.　　　　　　　　　　　　May 31, 1933

NL 0345351　　NN

Liebach, Johannes.
...Ejercicios de batallón. Regimiento y brigada e inspección
de la infanteria. Ejemplos practicos. Contribución a la instruc-
ción de guerra, inspección y empleo de la infantería en el combate.
Por Liebach... Traducido de la 1ª. edición alemana del año 1914
por el teniente coronel de estado mayor Julio C. Costa. Buenos
Aires: Ferrari hnos., 1921. xiii, 145 p. map, plans. 12°.
(Biblioteca del oficial. v. 30.)
Map and plans in pocket.

568618A. 1. Infantry—Drill and　　tactics. I. Costa, Julio C., translator.
II. Ser.
N.Y.P.L.　　　　　　　　　　　　February 2, 1932

NL 0345352　　NN

Liebach, Johannes.
Taktische wanderungen über die schlacht-
felder um Metz 1870... Berlin, Mittler und
sohn, 1894.

NL 0345353　　DNW

Liebach, Johannes.
Taktische wanderungen über die schlachtfeld-
er um Metz 1870- Auf veranlassung der general
inspektion des militar-erziehungs- und bildungs-
swesens, bearbeitet von Liebach...2d auflage,
Berlin, Mittler und sohn, 1903.
vi, 141 p. 6 maps, 4 plans (fold.inpocket)
21 cm.

NL 0345354　　DNW

VOLUME 332

**4D
-708** Liebach, Johannes.
Volkstümlicher Überblick über den Weltkrieg
1914-1918, bearb. von Liebach.   Berlin-Schönberg
P. J. Oestergaard [Vorwort 1932]
218 p.

NL 0345355   DLC-P4

Liebach, Johannes.
Volkstümlicher Überblick über den Weltkrieg 1914-1918,
bearbeitet von Liebach...   Berlin-Schöneberg: P. J. Oester-
gaard₍, 1933₎.   218 p.   illus. (charts), map.   21cm.

"Quellen," p. 218.

673137A.   1. European war, 1914–   1918—Germany.
N.Y.P.L.   October 17, 1933

NL 0345356   NN

Liebaers, F.
... Quinze jours en Russie soviétique
see under   Centrale nationale du vêtement
et parties similaires de Belgique.

Liebaers, Herman.
Exposition Thierry Martens ...
see under   Brussels. Bibliothèque royale de
Belgique.

LIEBAERS, HERMAN.
The information and documentation service of the
European council for nuclear research. Provisional
arrangements and tentative programme. [Brussels,
1954]   12 l.   28cm.

1. Libraries, Research.   2. European council for
nuclear research

NL 0345359   NN

·Liébaert, Jacques.
La doctrine christologique de saint Cyrille d'Alexandrie
avant la querelle nestorienne. Lille, Facultés catholiques,
1951.

252 p. 26 cm. (Mémoires et travaux publiés par des professeurs
des Facultés catholiques de Lille, fasc. 58)

"Bibliographie": p. ₍5₎–7.

1. Cyrillus, Saint, Patriarch of Alexandria, 370 (ca.)–444. 2.
Arianism.   i. Title.   (Series: Lille. Facultés catholiques.
Mémoires et travaux, fasc. 58)

                                                         A 53–14
Catholic Univ. of   America. Library
for Library of Congress

       CtY-D NN MH MoSU-D DDO OWorP CLSU GEU-T
NL 0345360   DCU IEG WaSpG NcD ICU NjPT NNUT MH-AH

Liebaert, Paul, *d.* 1915.
Inventaire inédit de la Bibliothèque capitulaire de Novare,
dressé en 1175.

(*In* Revue des bibliothèques. Paris. 1911. 25ᶜᵐ. v. 21. p. ₍105₎–113)

Signed: Paul Liebaert.

1. Novara. Duomo. Biblioteca capitolare. Mss. (XXXIX) 2. Manu-
scripts. Italy—Catalogs.
                                                         A C 34–1247
Title from Cleveland   Pub. Libr.
Library of Congress   ₍Z671.R45   vol. 21₎

NL 0345361   OCl MiU

Liebaert, Paul, *d.* 1915.
The Liebaert collection of photographs from Latin mss.
₍n. p., 19—?₎ folder of 6 p.   33½cm.

Caption-title.
Edited by W. M. Lindsay.

1. Manuscripts, Latin—Bibl. I. Lind-   say, Wallace Martin, 1858–   ,
editor.   editor.
N.Y.P.L.   August 28, 1933

NL 0345362   NN MH OO OU DLC

Liebaert, Paul, d. 1915.
Ehrle, Franz, *cardinal,* 1845–1934.
Specimina codicvm latinorvm Vaticanorvm collegervnt Fran-
ciscvs Ehrle, s. j., et Pavlvs Liebaert. Bonnae, A. Marcvs et
E. Weber; ₍etc., etc.₎ 1912.

Liebaldt, Hermann.
... C. Licinius Macer. Abhandlung von dr.
Liebaldt ...   Naumburg z/S., F. W. A. Littfas,
1848.
1 p.l., 19 p.   25 cm.
Programm - Domgymnasium, Naumburg.

NL 0345364   CU NjP PBm

LIEBALDT, Hermann.
De L.Risone, annalium serixtore. Naumberg
a/S., K.A.Klaffenbach, 1836.

4°. pp.(2), 15.

NL 0345365   MH NjP PU

LIEBALDT,[Hermann].
De Valerio Antiate, annalium scriptore.
Naumburg a.S., gedruckt bei K.A.Klaffenbach, 1840

4°. pp.(2), 22.
Progr.

NL 0345366   MH NjP MdBP PBm

Liebaldt, Hermann
Historicorum Roma... norum reliquiae demis
collectae et illustratae.
Halis, Saxonum, 1833.
23 p. Halle univ. Ph.D. diss.

NL 0345367   PU

Liebaldt, Herman
Historicum Romanorum reliquinae denus collectae
et illustratae Cuius opeqis specimen De La.
Cincio Alimento defendet H. Liebaldt.
Halis, 1833.
8 p.

NL 0345368   PU

₍Lieban, J   ₎

Notgeld.
1 v.   30 x 37½ ᶜᵐ.

An album of German and Austrian
paper currency issued during the period
following the first world war.

1. Paper money in Germany.

NL 0345369   NjP

Lieban Córdova, Olivo de.
... 7 años con Muñoz Marín (diario íntimo de un taquígrafo)
prólogo del lcdo. Armando A. Miranda ... San Juan de
Puerto Rico, Editorial Esther, 1945.

197 p., 1 l. illus. (incl. music) plates, ports. 23½ᵐᵐ.

"Misterio," song with music: p. 141–142.

1. *Muñoz Marín, Luis, 1898–   2. Puerto Rico—Pol. & govt.—
1898–
                                                         46–14071
Library of Congress   F1975.M76L5
                                                         972.95

NL 0345370   DLC WU CSt CU NNC MnU

Liébana, Juan Fernández
see
Fernández de Liébana, Juan.

LIÉBANA, Pérez de.
See PÉREZ DE LIÉBANA.

Liébana y Trincado, Evaristo.
Apuntes sobre el camino militar emprendido desde la
provincia de Abra á la de Cagayan, en la isla de Luzon.
Por el comandante D. Evaristo Liébana y Trincado ...
Madrid, Impr. del Memorial de ingenieros, 1882.

96 p. fold. map. 23½ᵐᵐ.

Deals largely with the social and political life of the Igorrotes.

1. Roads—Philippine Islands. 2. Igorrotes.
                                                         12–19304
Library of Congress   HE365.P6L5

NL 0345373   DLC

Liébana (Monastery)
see   Santo Toribio de Liébana (Benedictine
Monastery) Spain.

Liébant (Marcel). *Du volvulus de l'S iliaque
du colon. [Paris, No. 166.] 1 p. l., 85 pp. 4°.
Versailles. 1882.

NL 0345375   DNLM

LIÉBARD, Theodore
Étude historique et économique de la Foire
de Guibray. Paimboeuf, F.Covaud, 1904.

NL 0345376   MH

LIÉBARD, Theodore.
Les pêcheurs et la prévoyance sur les côtes
françaises. Ce qui est, ce qui devrait être.
Paimboeuf, Impr.-libr. F.Coyaud, 1903.

60 p. 22 cm.

NL 0345377   MH

LIEBAU, Friedrich Weinedel.
See WEINEDEL-LIEBAU, Friedrich, 1897–

VOLUME 332

Liebau, Friedrich Wilhelm, 1802-1843.
Die Pfade zur Gottheit: Oratorium in drei
Abthielungen. 1 ste Abth. In Musik gesetzt.
[Libretto] Quedlinburg, 1834.
15 p. 8°. (In "Librettos," 25)

NL 0345379   CtY

Liebau, Friedrich Wilhelm, *1802- 1843.*
Die Reue des Petrus. Oratorium in 2 Abtheilungen [von H. Bode].
Componirt von F. W. Liebau. [Partitur.]
Quedlinburg. Basse. [183-?] (8), 252 pp. F°.

E3384 — Bode, H. — Oratorios.

Mar. 21,   1902

NL 0345380   MB DLC

Liebau, Friedrich Wilhelm.
Der LXXXIV Psalm nach M. Luthers Uebersetzung für vier Solo-
stimmen und Chor mit Orgelbegleitung. Op. 15.
= Magdeburg. Heinrichshofen. [184-?] 13 pp. L. 8°, obl.

Mar. 21,   1902
E3385 — Church music. Anthems. &c.

NL 0345381   MB

Liébau (G.-Victor). * De la dysenterie épidémique. 52 pp. 4°. Paris, 1862, No. 60.

NL 0345382   DNLM

Liebau, Gerhart, 1905-
... Die Berechnung des Grundumsatzes aus
Kreislauffunktionen (Readsche Formel) ...
Charlottenburg.[1934]
Inaug.-Diss. - Berlin.
Lebenslauf.
"Literatur": p. [23]

NL 0345383   CtY

Liebau, Gustav, ed.
Das Medizinal-Prüfungswesen im Deutschen
Reiche
          see under   Germany. Laws, statutes, etc.

Liebau, Gustav, 1846-1902.
Abhandlung über der Kaufmann von Venedig.
(The merchant of Venice) für Verehrer des
Dichters. Berlin,C.Salewski,1877. 30p.
18cm. (Shakespeare-Galerie. [2.lfg.])

1. Shakespeare, William. Merchant of Venice.
Series.

NL 0345385   MWelC MB

Liebau, Gustav, *1846-1902.*
Abhandlung über Hamlet, Prinz von Dänemark ...
Berlin. Salewski. 1877. 38p. [Shakespeare-Galerie.] 16°.

This card was printed at the Boston   Public Library, October 8, 1917.
L2566 — S.r.c. — Shakespeare, William. Hamlet.

NL 0345386   MB MWelC

Liebau, Gustav, 1846-1902.
Abhandlung über Hamlet, Prinz von Dänemark,
(Hamlet, Prince of Denmark) für Verehrer des
Dichters. 2 durchgesehene Aufl.   Berlin,C.
Salewski,1877.   38p. 19cm. (Shakespeare-
Galerie [3.lfg.])

1. Shakespeare, William. Hamlet. Series.

NL 0345387   MWelC

Liebau, Gustav, 1846-1902.
Abhandlung über König Lear, (King Lear) für
Verehrer des Dichters. Berlin,C.Salewski,1877.
24p. 20cm. (Shakespeare-Galerie [5.lfg.])

1. Shakespeare, William. King Lear. Series.

NL 0345388   MWelC MB

Liebau, Gustav, *1846- 1902.*
Abhandlung über Romeo und Julia. . . .
Berlin. Salewski. 1877. 31 pp. [Shakespeare-Galerie.] 16°.

G9769 — S.r. — Shakespeare, William. Romeo and Juliet.

NL 0345389   MB

Liebau, Gustav, 1846-1902.
Abhandlung über Romeo und Julia (Romeo and
Juliet) für Verehrer des Dichters. 2 durchgesehene Aufl.   Berlin,C.Salewski,1877.
31p. 18cm. (Shakespeare-Galerie [1.lfg.])

1. Shakespeare, William. Romeo and Juliet.
Series.

NL 0345390   MWelC

Liebau, Gustav, 1846-1902.
Abhandlungen über Die bezähmte Widerspenstige
([Taming of the shrew]) und Das Wintermärchen
([The winter's tale]) für Verehrer des Dichters.
Berlin,C.Salewski,1877.   47p. 18cm. (Shake-
speare-Galerie [4.lfg.])

1. Shakespeare, William. The taming of the
shrew. 2. Shakespeare, William. The winter's
tale. Series.

NL 0345391   MWelC MB

Liebau, Gustav, 1846-1902.
Abhandlungen über ein Sommernachtstraum
([A midsummer night's dream]) und Viel Lärm
um Nichts ([Much ado about nothing]) für
Verehrer des Dichters.   Berlin,C.Salewski,
1877.   40p. 18cm. (Shakespeare-Galerie
[6.lfg.])

1. Shakespeare, William. A midsummer night's
dream. 2. Shakespeare, William. Much ado about
nothing. Series.

NL 0345392   MWelC MB

Liebau, Gustav, *1846- 1902.*
Erzählungen aus der Shakespeare-welt.
Für die deutsche jugend bearbeitet von Gustav
Liebau... Lerlin,C.Salewski,1876.
150 p. 17cm.

Contents. — Shakespeare's leben.— Der sturm.—
Die bezähmte widerspenstige.— Das wintermärchen.—
Hamlet, prinz von Dänemark.— König Lear.— Romeo
und Julia.

1. Shakespeare — Paraphrases, tales, etc.

NL 0345393   PU-F PU MB

Liebau, Gustav, 1846-1902.
... König Eduard III. von England im lichte europäischer
poesie; von Gustav Liebau. Heidelberg, C. Winter, 1901.
viii, 100 p. 22½ᶜᵐ. (Anglistische forschungen hrsg. von J. Hoops.
hft. 8)
"Gestalten aus der englischen geschichte und litteraturgeschichte als
dichterische vorwürfe in der deutschen litteratur": p. [79, 99].

1. Edward III, king of England, 1312-1377.

[Full name: Johann Heinrich Gustav Liebau]
                                   3-9270 Revised
Library of Congress   PE25.A5 hft. 6
                           DA233.L7

MiU MB NN PSC PU-F
NL 0345394   DLC FTaSU MoU MoSU NcU NcD OU OCU OClW

Liebau, Gustav, 1846-1902.
König Eduard III. von England und die gräfin von Salis-
bury. Dargestellt in ihren beziehungen nach geschichte, sage
und dichtung, unter eingehender berücksichtigung des pseudo-
Shakespeare'schen schauspiels "The raigne of king Edward
the Third ...." Berlin, Druck von E. Felber, 1900.
vi, 60 p. 21ᶜᵐ.
Inaug.-diss.—Heidelberg.
Vita.
1. Edward III, king of England, 1312-1377. 2. Salisbury, Catharine
(Grandison) de Montacute, countess of, ca. 1310-1349. 3. Edward III
(Drama)

[Full name: Johann Heinrich Gustav Liebau]
                                   3-10418 Revised
Library of Congress   DA233.L72

NL 0345395   DLC CU CoU NcD MiU ICRL CtY PU

Liebau, Gustav, 1846-1902.
König Eduard III. von England und die gräfin von Salisbury; dargestellt in ihren beziehungen nach geschichte, sage
und dichtung, unter eingehender berücksichtigung des pseudo-
shakespeare'schen schauspiels "The raigne of King Edward
the Third"; von dr. Gustav Liebau. Berlin, E. Felber, 1900.
xii, 201 p. fold. tables. 21½ᶜᵐ. (Added t.-p.: Litterarhistorische
forschungen. XIII. hft.)
Published in part as the author's inaugural dissertation, Heidelberg.
The Countess of Salisbury is confused with Joan, countess of Kent, later
wife of the Black prince.
1. Edward III, king of England, 1312-1377. 2. Salisbury, Catharine
(Grandison) de Montacute, countess of, 1310-1349? 3. Joan, princess
of Wales, 1328-1385. 4. Edward III (Drama)

                                   1-12929 Revised
Library of Congress   PN35.L6 vol. 13

NL 0345396   DLC NjP OU MiU PSC PU CaBVaU

Liebau, Gustav, 1846-1902.
Shakespeare-galerie. Abhandlung...
Für verehrer des dichters hrsg. von Gustav
Liebau... Berlin, C.Salewski, 1877.
6 pts. 17½-18½cm.

Lieferung 1,3: 2.durchgesehene aufl.
Published 1878 in one vol.(220p.), wit
subtitle: Eine sammlung literar-ästhetischer abhandlungen über acht der bedeutenderen dramen Shakespeare's...
"Eine fortsetzung meiner schrift 'William Shakespeare's leben und dichten.'"
—Vorwort(lfg.1)

Bibliography: 1.lfg., p.4-5.
Contents.— 1.lfg. Abhandlung über Romeo
und Julia.— 2.lfg. Über Der kaufmann vor
Venedig.— 3.lfg. Über Hamlet.— 4.lfg.Über
Die bezähmte widerspenstige und Das wintermärchen.— 5.lfg. Über König Lear.— 6.
lfg. Über Ein sommernachtstraum und Viel
lärm um nichts.

I.Title.

NL 0345398   MWelC MB

Liebau, Gustav, *1846-1902.*

Die Shakespeare-galerie. Eine sammlung
literar-ästhetischer abhandlungen über acht der
bedeutenderen dramen Shakespeare's. Für verehrer
des dichters hrsg. von Gustav Liebau... Berlin,
C. Salewski, 1878.
219, (1) p. 19cm.
A continuation of his William Shakespeare's
leben und dichten.
Contents.—Romeo und Julia.—Der Kaufmann von
Venedig.—Hamlet, prinz von Dänemark.—Die bezähmte

widerspenstige.—Das wintermärchen.—König
Lear.-Ein sommernachtstraum.—Viel lärm um nichts
Chronologische tabelle der werke Shakespeare's

1. Shakespeare, William — Criticism and
interpretation. 2. Shakespeare, William —
Chronology of the plays. I.Title.

NL 0345400   PU-F PU

VOLUME 332

PT
1899
Z9U22
Liebau, Gustav, 1846-1902.
"Ueber allen Gipfeln ist Ruh';" ein
Gedenkblatt zur Erinnerung an Goethe's
Aufenthalt in Ilmenau.　Ilmenau, A.
Schröter, 1884.
48 p.　illus.　20cm.

1. Goethe, Johann Wolfgang von, 1749-1832.
Ueber allen Gipfeln ist Ruh'. 2. Ilmenau,
Germany--Descr.

NL　0345401　　NIC CSt MiU

PR
2899
.L72
Liebau, Gustav, 1846-1902.
William Shakespeare's leben und dichten.
Von Gustav Liebau.　Gera, Issleib & Rietz-
schel, 1873.

4 p.ℓ.,55,[1] p.　22½cm.

1.Shakespeare,William,1564-1616.　a.Shakespeare,
William--Appreciation--Germany.

NL　0345402　　MiU MB PU-F

Liebau, Hans, 1905-
Defensivzeichen defensivwarenverzeichnisse
und defensivfirmen.
Inaug. diss.　Jena, 1929.
Bibl.

NL　0345403　　DLC MiU ICRL CtY PU

Liebau, Helmut.
Die Lungentuberkulose

see under

Hirsch, Wolfgang, M.D.

Liebau, Helmut, 1909-
... Über die Behandlung des Erysipels im
Säuglings- und Kleinkindesalter mit Röntgenstrahlen,
ultravioletten Strahlen und Rotlicht ...　[Zeulen-
roda i. Thür., 1937]
Inaug.-Diss. - Leipzig.
Lebenslauf.

NL　0345405　　CtY

Liebau (Henricus). *De hypertrophia cordis.
10½ pp., 1 l.　8°.　Petropoli, C. Kray, 1847.

NL　0345406　　DNLM

Liebau, J. H. G.
see　Liebau, Gustav, 1846-1902.

Liebau, Kurt: 100 Faelle von Gesichts- und Stirnlagen der Koenigs-
berger Univ.-Frauen-Kl. in ihrer Bedeutung fuer Mutter und Kind.
[Maschinenschrift.]　40 S.　4°.　— Auszug: Königsberg i. Pr.
[1923]: Kgsb. Allg. Zeitung.　1 Bl.　8°
Königsberg, Med. Diss. v. 10. April 1924 [1925]　　[U 25.5875

NL　0345408　　ICRL

616.203　Liebau, Oskar, 1884-
L71i　　...Infektionsdelirien nach influenza...　Kiel, Fiencke, 1913.
16p. O.

At head of title: Aus der Königl. psychiatr.
und nervenklinik der Universität Kiel.
Inaug.-diss. - Kiel.
Lebenslauf.
"Literatur": 1p. at end.

NL　0345409　　IaU MBCo ICRL DNLM

Liebau, Otto, 1887- Beiträge zur Anatomie und Morphologie der
Mangrove-Pflanzen insbesondere ihres Wurzelsystems.
Halle a. S. 1913: (Nischkowsky, Breslau).　33 S.　8°　¶Aus:
Beiträge z. Biol. d. Pflanzen.　Bd 12.
Halle, Phil. Diss. v. 5. Mai 1913, Ref. Karsten
[Geb. 9. Okt. 87 Annarode; Wohnort: Halle a. S.; Staatsangeh.: Preußen;
Vorbildung: G. Eisleben Reife 08; Studium: Halle 1, Göttingen 4, Halle 4 S.;
Rig. 28. Jan. 13.]　　　　　　　　　　　　　　[U 13. 3615

NL　0345410　　ICRL CtY MH

Liebau, Walter.
.... Autokauf, von Walter Liebau, ... Mit 83 Abbildungen.
Berlin, R. C. Schmidt & Co., 1920.
130 p. incl. illus., tables, diagrs.　17cm.　(Autotechnische Bibliothek, Band 51.)

NL　0345411　　ICJ

Liebau, Werner, joint ed.

Die Stadt Hagen (Westf.): herausgegeben von oberbürger-
meister Alfred Finke, dr. Werner Liebau ... und Erwin
Stein ... in verbindung mit bibliotheksdirektor dr. Anger-
mann ... [u. a.]　Mit zahlreichen abbildungen.　Berlin-Frie-
denau, Deutscher kommunal-verlag, g. m. b. h., 1928

Liebau, Werner: Theorie und Praxis der wirtschaftlichen Demokratie.
[Maschinenschrift.]　147 S.　4°.　— Auszug: Inaug.-Dissertationen
d. R.- u. Staatswiss. u. Phil. Fak. Königsberg Pr. — o. O. [1922].
S. 68—71.　8°
Königsberg, R.- u. staatsw. Diss. v. 10. März 1922　　[U 22.6722

NL　0345413　　ICRL

Liebang, Hans, 1895- Die Ursachen der Agrarkrisis der zwanziger Jahre
des 19. Jahrhunderts im Urteil der Zeitgenossen.　[Maschinen-
schrift.]　71 S.　4°　[Lag nicht vor.] — Auszug: Giessen 1924.
3 Bl.　8°
Gießen, Phil. Diss. v. 8. April 1924　　　　　　　[U 24.3335

NL　0345414　　ICRL

Liébault,　　abbé.
Exercice littéraire de la pension de M. l'Abbé
Liébault
see under title

Liébault, Georges Alexandre Marie René, 1881-
... Notions élémentaires d'oto-rhino-laryngologie à
l'usage des praticiens.　Paris, G. Doin & cⁱᵉ, 1926.

236 p., 1 l.　24cm.

1. Ear--Diseases. 2. Nose--Diseases. 3. Throat--Diseases.　ɪ. Title.
Library of Congress　　RF46.L5　　　　　　26-16695

NL　0345416　　DLC DNLM ICJ PPC

Liébault, Georges Alexandre Marie René, 1881-
joint author.
Moure, Jean Gabriel Émile, 1855-
Pathologie de guerre du larynx et de la trachée, par
E. J. Moure ... G. Liébault ... [et] G. Canuyt ... avec 128
gravures dans le texte et 8 planches en couleurs hors texte
contenant 17 figures.　Paris, F. Alcan, 1918.

Liébault, Georges Alexandre Marie René.
...Les sténoses inflammatoires chroniques
de la région cardiaque de l'oesophage.
Bordeaux, Imprimeries Gounouilhou, 1913.
132 p. illus.

Bibliographie: p. [125]-132.
Thèse - Paris.

NL　0345418　　OO DNLM MBCo

SB99
.F7E8
1668
Rare Bk.
Liébault, Jean, ca. 1575-1596.

FOR OTHER EDITIONS
SEE MAIN ENTRY
Estienne, Charles, 1504-1564.　L'agriculture et maison rustique, de maistres Charles
Estienne, et Iean Liébault ...　Reueuë & augm. de beau-
coup, dont le contenu se voit en la seizième page.　Auec
vn bref recueil des chasses du cerf, du sanglier, du lieure,
du renard, du blereau, du connil, du loup, des oyseaux, &
de la fauconnerie; comme pourrez voir à la fin de ce liure,
auec les figures.　Y joint la fabrique & vsage de la iauge,
ou diapason.　Plus a esté adjouté en cette derniere edition, vne instruction pour sçauoir en quels temps, mois,

lune & saison on doit semer & replanter selon le pays
froid, pour faire auancer & retarder les semences, &
toutes sortes de graines.　Derniere ed.　London, Chez
I.-B. Gimeaux, 1668.

SB99
.F7E83
1592
Rare Bk.
Coll.
Liébault, Jean, d. 1596.

FOR OTHER EDITIONS
SEE MAIN ENTRY
Estienne, Charles, 1504-1564.
xv. [i. e. Fünfzehn] Bücher von dem Feldbaw vnd recht
vollkommener Wolbestellung eines bekömmlichen Landsitzes,
vnnd geschicklich angeordneten Meierhofs oder Landguts,
sampt allem was demselben Nutzes vnd Lusts halben anhän-
gig.　Deren etliche vorlängst vō Carolo Stephano vnd Joh.
Libalto frantzösisch vorkomen.　Welche ... theyls vom Herrn
Melchiore Sebizio, theyls auss letzten Libaltischen Zusetzen
durch Nachgemelten inn Teutsch gebracht seind.　Etliche
aber an jetzo auffs new erstlich auss dem Frantzösischen
letstmahls ernewertem vnd gemehrtem Exemplar ... 1592

Liébault, Jean, ca. 1535-1596, joint author.

Estienne, Charles, 1504-1564.
De landtwinninghe ende hoeue.　Van M. Kaerle
Steuens, ende M. Ian Liébaut ...　Wt de Fransoische
spraecke in de Nederduytsche ouergheset.　Den laetsten
druck, ouersien ende vermeerdert, waer af het in-houdt
in de naeuolghende pagie cortelijck begrepen staet.　Ant-
vverpen, By C. Plantijn, 1582.

Liébault, Jean d. 1596, joint author.

FOR OTHER EDITIONS
SEE MAIN ENTRY
Estienne, Charles, 1504-1564.
Maison rustique, or, The covntrey farme.　Compyled
in the French tongue by Charles Stevens, and Iohn Lie-
bavlt ... and tr. into English by Richard Svrflet ...　Now
newly reuiewed, cor., and augm., with diuers large additions, out of the works of Serres his Agriculture, Vinet
his Maison champestre, French.　Albyterio in Spanish,
Grilli in Italian; and other authors.　And the husbandrie
of France, Italie, and Spaine, reconciled and made to
agree with ours here in England: by Gervase Markham
London, Printed by A. Islip for J. Bill, 1616.

Liébault, Jean, d. 1596.
Quatre livres des secrets de médecine et de
la philosophie chimique
see under　[Gesner, Konrad] 1516-1565.

Liébault, Jean, d. 1596.
Secrets de medecine et de la philosophie
chimique
see under　[Gesner, Konrad] 1516-1565.

VOLUME 332

16th cent
LIEBAULT, Jean, ca. 1535-1596.
Thesavrvs sanitatis paratv facilis.
Selectvs ex variis authoribus ... per
Ioannem Liebavltivm ... Parisiis, Apud
Iacobum du Puys, 1577.
8p. ℓ., 422, [8]ℓ. 12cm.
Bound with Le Bon, Jean. Therapia
pverperarvm. Parisiis, 1577.
acc. no. 29267 cat. ~ LC ~ NLM ~~~

1. Medicine - Early works to 1800 I.
Title

NL 0345426   CtY-M NNNAM

Liébault, Jean. ca 1535-1596.
Thresor des remedes secrets povr les maladies
des femmes. Pris du Latin, & faict François.
A Paris, chez Iacques du Puys à la Samaritaine,
1587.
8 l., 924 p. 17.2 cm. (8°).
Title at head of table of contents reads:
"Trois livres de la santé, foecundité & maladies
des femmes".

NL 0345427   NNNAM

Liébault, Jean, 1535-1598.
Thresor vniversel des pavvres et des
riches, ov recveil de remedes faciles, pour
toute sorte de maladies qui suruiennent au
corps humain; depuis la plante des pieds,
insqu'au sommet de la teste, tant interieures
qu'exterieures. Fidelement tirez des plus
excellens medecins Grecs, Arabes, & Latins;
Anciens & modernes, par M. Iean Liebaut, ...
A plantâ pedis vsque ad verticem, erit in te
sanitas. A Paris, chez Gervais Clovsier,
1651.

Microfilm copy, made in 1960 of the
original in Vatican. Biblioteca vaticana.
Positive.
Negative in Vatican. Biblioteca vaticana.
Collation of the original as determined
from the film: [6], 371, [36] p.
1. Medicine--15th-18th centuries. (Series:
[Manuscripta, microfilms of rare and out-of-
print books. List 15, no. 48])

NL 0345429   MoSU OU NcU NcD

[Liebault, Jean, ca.1535-1596]
16th cent.   Tresor des remedes secrets povr les maladies
des femmes. Pris du Latin ... [from the Italian
of Giovanni Marinelli, translated, altered, and
augmented by Jean Liebault] A Paris, Chez Iacques
du Puys à la Samaritaine, 1585.
8p. ℓ., 924p., 8ℓ. 17cm.
Title page reads: Thresor des remedes ...

1. Woman - Diseases. I. Marinelli, Giovanni.
II. Title: Tresordes   remedes secrets ...

NL 0345430   CtY-M PPJ

[Liébault, Jean] d. 1596.
Tresor des remedes secrets povr les maladies des femmes
Pris du latin, & fait françois. Paris, M. Sonnivs, 1617.
7 p. l., 924, [16] p. 18½cm.
Original edition appeared in 1582 under title: De sanitate, fecunditate
et morbis mulierum. cf. Barbier, Dict. des ouvrages anonymes, v. 4, col.
825.

1. Woman—Diseases.   I. Title.
6—42802
Library of Congress   RG91.L5

NL 0345431   DLC

Liébault, Jean. ca. 1535-1596.
Trois libres de l'embellissement et ornement
du corps humain. Pris du latin ... & faict
françois. A Lyon, par Benoist Rigavd. 1595
586 p., 11 l.   11.8 cm. (16°).

NL 0345432   NNNAM

Liébault, Jean, d.1596.
Trois livres appartenans avx infirmitez
et maladies des femmes. Pris dv latin de
m. Iean Liebavt ... & faicts françois. Lyon,
Iean Veyrat,1597.
8 p.ℓ.,923,[16]p. 16 1/2cm.

1.Woman - Diseases.

NL 0345433   CtY-M

16th cent
Liebault, Jean, ca.1535-1596.
Trois livres appartenans avx infirmites.
et maladies des femmes. Pris dv Latin de M.
Iean Liebavt. . . A Lyon, Par Iean Veyrat,
1598.
8p.ℓ., 923p., 8ℓ. 17cm.
Translated from a work by Giovanni Marinello,
and altered and augmented by Liebault.

I. Marinello, Giovanni

NL 0345434   CtY-M DNLM

Liebaut, Jean
Trois livres appartenans aux infirmites et
maladies des femmes...
Rouen, Petit Val, 1609.
923 p.

NL 0345435   PPC

WZ   LIÉBAULT, Jean, d. 1596
240   Trois livres de l'embellissement et ornement du corps humain.
L716dcF   Pris du latin ... & faict francois. Paris, Jacques du Puys, 1582.
1582   [16], 463, [14] p. 17 cm.
A translation of HIS De cosmetica seu ornatu et decoratione,
published in Paris the same year. The work is chiefly compiled
from Giovanni Marinelli's Ornamenti delle donne. Cf.
British Museum catalogue.

1. Marinelli, Giovanni, 16th cent. Ornamenti delle donne

NL 0345436   DNLM PPiU-D NNC-M

Liébault, Jean ca. 1535-1596.
Trois livres de la sante foecvndite ...   Paris,
1582.

NL 0345437   NNNAM

Liebaut. Die Regenerationskur nach 40jähri-
gen Erfahrungen and Erfolgen in Hospitälern,
Kliniken, etc., festgestellt. vi, 50 pp. 12°.
Brüssel [n. d.]

NL 0345438   DNLM

Liebaut (A.-G.) *Considérations générales sur
le tétanos. 29 pp. 4°. Paris, 1816, No. 124, v.
123.

NL 0345439   DNLM

LIEBAUT, Jean.
See LIÉBAULT, Jean, ca. 1535-1596

Liébaut, Achille Pierre
Lamourette, prêtre et évêque assermenté, 1742-94.
Nancy, 1894.

66 p., illus.

NL 0345441   MH

LIÉBAUT, Ange Edmond.
Recherches sur le tabac; son histoire, son
action physiologique, taxique, et thérapeutique.
[Thèse.] Paris, Rignoux, 1851.

4°. pp. 32.

NL 0345442   MH DNLM

Liébaut (Eugène). *Influence des émotions
morales, chez l'homme sain ou malade, et des indications qu'elles fournissent au médecin. 42
pp. 4°. Paris, 1852, No. 320, v. 528.

NL 0345443   DNLM

Liébaut, Nicole.
Les miseres de la femme mal mariee. Où se peuuent
voir les peines & tourmens qu'elle reçoit durant sa vie, mis
en forme de stances par Madame Liebavt. Augmenté
d'vn Discours de l'excellence de la femme, par Mademoiselle Marie de Romieu Viuaroise. Auec vn trophee des
dames. Roven, C. Le Villain, 1618.
3 p. l., 42 p. 13cm. [With Olivier, J. Alphabet de l'imperfection ... des
femmes. Paris, 1617]

"Le trophee des dames," by Joaquin Blanchon, is composed of 38 son-
nets; followed by "Stances du mariage" (2 p.) and a chanson.

1-22182
Library of Congress

NL 0345444   DLC

Liebbald-Ljubojević, Julij.
Katoličko ženitbeno pravo obzirom na gradjanske zakone.
2. izdanje. U Osieku, Brzotiskom D. Šandora (I. V.
Hamanna) 1878.
221 p. illus. 25 cm.
L. C. copy imperfect: p. 218 incorrectly numbered: 212.

1. Marriage (Cannon law) 2. Marriage law—Austria. I. Title.
59—58306

NL 0345445   DLC

Liebe, Alexander, 1852-1931
FMA1131.2   Ueber die Analogie der aus der Entwickelung
Film   von $(1--2ax+a^2)-2$ entspringenden Funktionen
Copy   mit den Kegelfunktionen. (II. Teil) Borna,
Physical   R. Noske, 1901.
Sciences
Library   Microfilm copy--Negative, made 1943.
Collation as determined from film: 24p.
At head of title: Wissenschaftliche Beilage
zum SSVIII. Jahresbericht des stadtischen
Realgymnasiums   zu Borna. Ostern
1901.

NL 0345446   RPB NjP

Liebe, Annelise, 1911-
Ka94   Die Xsthetik Wilhelm Diltheys. Halle,
D5   C.Nieft,1938.
938ℓ   79p. 21cm.
Inaug.-Diss. - Halle-Wittenberg.
Bibliography: p.77.
Vita.
Cover title.

NL 0345447   CtY NIC

VOLUME 332

Liebe, Arthur.
Zwei fälle von hermaphroditismus verus bilateralis beim schwein. Ein beitrag zur lehre von der zwitterbildung der säugethiere ... Berlin, Druck von L. Schumacher, 1904.
38 p. II pl. 22½ᶜᵐ.
Inaug.-diss.—Bern.
"Sonder-abdruck aus dem Archiv für wissensch. u. prakt. tierheilkunde. bd. 30. 1904."
"Literatur-verzeichnis": p. 36-37.

1. Hermaphrodites. 2. Swine.

Library of Congress   QL991.L7   6-43432

NL 0345448   DLC CU DNLM DNAL

Liebe (Bernhard Walther) [1874-]. *Ueber Blutveränderung nach Blutverlusten. 54 pp. 2 l. 8°. Halle a. S. R. Nietschmann. 1896

NL 0345449   DNLM MBCo ICRL

Liebe, Bruno, [1876-]. *Ein Fall von Aneurysma arterio-venosum der rechten Femoralgefässe durch Stichverletzung. 47 pp. 8°. Halle a. S., C. A. Kaemmerer & Co. 1906.

NL 0345450   DNLM MBCo ICRL

Diss.
378
Halle
1907

Liebe, Carl, 1880-
Der Arzt im elisabethanischen Drama.
Halle a.S., R. Espehahn, 1907.
50p. 22cm.

Inaug.-Diss. - Halle.
Lebenslauf.

1. Physicians in literature. 2. Medicine in literature. 3. English drama. Early modern and Elizabethan. Hist. & crit.

CtY NcU

NL 0345451   IEN PU MH ICRL NjP NcD NN NNU-W MiU OC1

Liebe (Carl Friedrich Wilhelm) [1840-]. *Bemerkungen über Staphyloma scleroticæ posticum incipiens und progressive Myopie. 14 pp. 1 l. 8°. Leipzig. L. Schnauss, 1862.

NL 0345452   DNLM PPC

Liebe, Carl Julius Otto

    see

Liebe, Otto .

Liebe, Christian Frederik Julius Hegelund,
1815-1883.

Denmark. *Stænderforsamling, Viborg.*
Tidende for forhandlingerne ved Provindsialstænderne for Nørre-Jvlland ... 1836[-1848] Viborg. H. Wissing [1836-

---

Liebe, Christian Frederik Julius Hegelund,
1815-1883.

Denmark. *Stænderforsamling, Roskilde.*
Tidende for forhandlingerne ved Provindsialstænderne for Sjællands, Fyens og Lollands-Falsters stifter samt for Island og Færøerne. 1835-1836—   Kjøbenhavn, Brøderne Berling, 1836-

---

Liebe, Christian Sigismund, 1687-1736.
Gotha nvmaria, sistens thesavri fridericiani nvmismata antiqva avrea, argentea, ærea ... auctore Christiano Sigismvndo Liebe. Accedunt ex Andreæ Morellii Specimine vniversæ rei numariæ antiquæ excerpta, & Epistolæ tres Ez. Spanhemii, quibus rariores eiusdem thesauri numi illustrantur. Amstelædami, apud R. & J. Wetstenios & G. Smith, 1730.
7 p. l., xxvi, [28] p. front., illus., port. 39ᶜᵐ.
Title vignette; head-pieces.

1. Numismatics, Ancient.   I. Gotha. Herzogliches münzkabinett. II. Morel, Andreas, 1646-1703. III. Spanheim, Ezechiel, freiherr von, 1629-1710.

                   10-30777†

Library of Congress   CJ215.G7

NL 0345455   DLC NN NjP CtY DSI

[Liebe, Christian Sigismund] 1687-1736.
[Lebens-beschreibungen der vornehmsten theologorvm sowohl evangelischer als päbstischer seite, welche an. 1530. den Reichs-tag zu Augspurg besucht, und an denen wegen ubergabe der Augspurgischen confession angestellten religions-handlungen theil genommen, nebst einem vorbericht von denen übrigen sowohl evangelischen als päbstischen gottes-gelahrten, welche allda zugegen gewesen. Gotha, J. A. Reyher, 1730.
28, 75, [1] p. 20ᶜᵐ. [With Beaumont, J. Historisch- physiologisch- und theologischer tractat von geistern. Halle, 1721. copy 2]

1. Augsburg, Diet of. 2. Reformation—Germany—Biog. 3. Theologians. I. Title.

                   20-17858

Library of Congress   BF1445.B3   Copy 2

NL 0345456   DLC MoSCS ICU

Liebe, Curt.
Wörterbuch für kakteenliebhaber, von Curt Liebe; mit 8 abbildungen. Berlin-Kaulsdorf, Selbstverlag des verfassers [1928]
cover-title, 40 p. illus. 14ᶜᵐ.
"Abkürzungen der bekanntesten autorennamen": p. 34-38.
Advertising matter: p. 39-40.

1. Cactus. 2. Botanists.   I. Title.
Library of Congress   QK495.C11L5   29-19612

NL 0345457   DLC CtY MH-A

Liebe, Dieudonné.
Johann Bochelen; ein elsässischer Märtyrerpriester der Grossen Revolution. Ein Spiel in 5 Bildern. Mulhouse, Editions Salvator, 1955.   64 p.   21cm.   (Salvator-Theater. nr. 740)

1. Bochelen, Johann, 1763-1798—Drama. 2. German language—Dialects—Alsace. 3. Drama.   German

NL 0345458   NN

Liebe, Dieudonné.
Maria Goretti, die Heilige; religiöses Drama in 4 Akten, Nachspiel und Apotheose. Mulhouse, Editions Salvator, 1952.   59 p.   21cm.   (Salvator-Theater. No. 717)

1. Maria Goretti, Saint, 1890-1902—Drama. 2. Drama, German. I. Title.

NL 0345459   NN

Liebe, Eduard Ludwig, 1819 - 1900,
Abendlied [T. T. B. B.]
(In Abt. Leichte Männerchöre. Heft 14, pp. 17, 18. Schleusingen. [1860.])

E3384 — T.r. — Part songs.   Mar. 21,   1902

NL 0345460   MB

LIEBE, Eduard Ludwig.
Der Choral von Leuthen. (After the battle.) [T. T. B. B.] Op. 112. Berlin. Luckhardt. [1888.] II pp. [Neue Männer-Chöre L. 8°.
The words are in German and English.

Sheet D 2994   Aug. 23, 1839

NL 0345461   MB

M1
.S44
v.135
no.25

Liebe, Eduard Ludwig, 1819-1900.
[Gertruds Traumwalzer]

Gertrude's dream. Figure 2½ in five pointed star. New York, S. T. Gordon, 706 Broadway [after 1858?]
4 p. 35cm. [Sheet music collection, v.135, no. 25]
The celebrated waltzes, by Beethoven, no. 2.
1. Waltzes (Piano). I. Title. II. Title: Gertruds Traumwalzer.

NL 0345462   ViU

Liebe, Eduard Ludwig, 1819-1900.
[Gertruds Traumwalzer]

Gertrude's dream, a much admired waltz composed for the piano forte, by Liebe. Boston, G. P. Reed, ᶜ1842.
[2] l. 33 cm.
Later editions erroneously ascribed to Beethoven.

1. Waltzes (Piano). I. Title.

M1.A13L   68-35104/M

NL 0345463   DLC ViU ICN MB MH

M1
A13L
no.16

Liebe, Eduard Ludwig, 1819-1900.
[Gertruds Traumwalzer]
Gertrude's dream waltz. Composed for the piano forte by Beethoven. Boston, Published by E.H.Wade, 197 Washington Street [n.d.]
2 l. 34cm. (In [Music for piano, v.p., ca. 1840-1858] no.16)

Caption title.
Erroneously ascribed to Beethoven. Cf. Kinsky, p.728.

NL 0345464   IaU

M1
.S444
v.76
no.30

Liebe, Eduard Ludwig, 1819-1900.
[Gertruds Traumwalzer]
Gertrude's dream waltz (Thranen Waltzer)
[n. p.], 18—   Pl. no. 275.
[2] p. 36cm. [Sheet music collection, v. 76, no. 30]
Caption title.
Advertisement of melodeons for sale by W. W. Whitney, 151 Summit St., Toledo, Ohio, on back cover.
Blind stamp of Blackmar & Co., pianos, music, &c., 74 Camp St. New   Orleans, on p. [1]
Also attributed   to Liebe.
1. Waltzes (Piano) I. Title. II.Title: Thranen Waltzer.

NL 0345465   ViU

Liebe, Eduard Ludwig, 1819-1900.
[Gertruds Traumwalzer]

Gertrude's dream waltz. Composed for the piano, by Beethoven. Louisville, Peters, Webb [18—] Pl. no. 393.
2 l. 32cm.
Caption title.
Erroneously ascribed to Beethoven. Cf. Kinsky, Anh. 16, Nr. 2. An earlier ed. (Boston, G. P. Reed, ᶜ1842) has title: Gertrude's dream ... by Liebe.

1. Waltzes (Piano) I. Title.

M1.A13L   68-35101/M

NL 0345466   DLC

VOLUME 332

⌐Liebe, Eduard Ludwig₎ 1819–1900.
⌐Gertruds Traumwalzer₎

Gertrude's dream waltz. Composed for the piano forte,
by Beethoven. Philadelphia, A. Fiot ⌐between 1844 and 49₎

⌐2₎ l. 35 cm.

Caption title.
Erroneously ascribed to Beethoven. Cf. Kinsky, Anh. 16, Nr. 2.
An earlier ed. (Boston, G. P. Reed, ⌐1842) has title: Gertrude's dream
... by Liebe.

1. Waltzes (Piano)   I. Title.

M1.A13L   68–35105/M

NL 0345467   DLC

⌐Liebe, Eduard Ludwig₎ 1819–1900.
⌐Gertruds Traumwalzer₎

Gertrude's dream waltz. Composed for the piano forte,
by L. v. Beethoven. Boston, O. Ditson ⌐between 1844 and
1857₎ Pl. no. 1336.

2 l. 34 cm.

Caption title.
Erroneously ascribed to Beethoven. Cf. Kinsky, Anh. 16, Nr. 2.
An earlier ed. (Boston, G. P. Reed, ⌐1842) has title: Gertrude's dream
... by Liebe.

1. Waltzes (Piano)   I. Title.

M1.A13L   68–35103/M

NL 0345468   DLC IU

M1
.A13L
Case   ⌐Liebe, Eduard Ludwig₎ 1819–1900.
         ⌐Gertruds Traumwalzer₎

Gertrude's dream waltz. Composed for the piano forte,
by Beethoven. Boston, A. & J. P. Ordway ⌐between 1848
and 1851₎

2 l. 35 cm.

Caption title.
Erroneously ascribed to Beethoven. Cf. Kinsky, Anh. 16, Nr. 2.
An earlier ed. (Boston, G. P. Reed, ⌐1842) has title: Gertrude's dream
... by Liebe.

1. Waltzes (Piano)   I. Title.

M1.A13L   68–35102/M

NL 0345469   DLC

M1
.S444
v.81   Liebe, Eduard Ludwig, 1819–1900.
no.27   ⌐Gertruds Traumwalzer₎

Gertrude's dream waltz. Thranen Waltzer.
Composed for the piano forte by Beethoven.
Redd pr 8? New York, Horace Waters, 333
Broadway ⌐185–?₎

⌐2₎ p. 35cm. ⌐Sheet music collection, v. 81,
no. 27₎
Caption title.
Also claimed by Liebe.

NL 0345470   ViU

Liebe, Eduard Ludwig, 1819–1900.
Gertrude's dream waltz. Thränen Waltzer.) Composed for the
piano forte.
= New York. Hall. ⌐185–?₎ (2) pp. 33½ cm.

NL 0345471   MB

⌐Liebe, Eduard Ludwig₎ 1819–1900.
⌐Gertruds Traumwalzer₎

Gertrude's dream waltz. Composed for the piano forte,
by Beethoven. New York, J. E. Gould ⌐1850 or 51₎

⌐2₎ l. 33 cm.

Caption title.
Erroneously ascribed to Beethoven. Cf. Kinsky, Anh. 16, Nr. 2.
An earlier ed. (Boston, G. P. Reed, ⌐1842) has title: Gertrude's
dream ... by Liebe.

1. Waltzes (Piano)   I. Title.

M1.A13L   M 58–1302 rev

NL 0345472   DLC

Liebe, Eduard Ludwig.
Heimatlied [T. T. B. B.].
(In Das Rütli. Pp. 239, 240. St. Gallen, 1873.)

                    Mar. 21,   1902
E3384 — T.r. — Part songs.

NL 0345473   MB

Liebe, Eduard Ludwig, 1819–1900.
Ludwig Liebe–Album
    see under   Claassen, Arthur, 1859–1920,
editor.

Liebe, Eduard Ludwig.
Mein Heimatthal. [Männerchor.]
(In Das Rütli. Pp. 220, 221. St. Gallen, 1873.)

                    Mar. 21,   1902
E3384 — T.r. -- Part songs.

NL 0345475   MB

Liebe, Eduard Ludwig.
O mein Herz so warm! [Männerchor.] Op. 101, No. 5.
= Berlin. Luckhardt. [1887.] 5 pp. [Neue Männer-Chöre.] L.8°.

                    Mar. 21,   1902
E3384 — T.r. -- Part songs.

NL 0345476   MB

Liebe, Eduard Ludwig.
Sterne sind schweigende Siegel. Solo-Quartett [T. T. B. B.].
(In Abt. Deutsche Sängerhalle. Vol. 1, pp. 87, 88. [Leipzig,
187–?])

                    Mar. 21,   190–
E3384 — T.r. — Part songs.

NL 0345477   MB

Liebe, Eduard Ludwig, 1819–1900.
Vier Lieder für eine Singstimme mit Begleitung
des Pianoforte von L. Liebe. Op. 34 no. 3 & Op. 52
No. 1. Cassel, Carl Luckhardt, [18–]
No. 3 (Op. 34) Mein Heimaththal (Für Alt)
No. 1 (Op. 59) Auf Wiedersehn! (Für Sopran)

NL 0345478   NN

Liebe, Eduard Ludwig.
Walzer [T. T. B. B.].
(In Abt. Deutsche Sängerhalle. Vol. 1, pp. 33–36. [Leipzig,
187–?])

                    Mar. 21,   1902
E3384 — T.r. — Part songs.

NL 0345479   MB

Liebe, Eduard Ludwig.
Wanderlied [T. T. B. B.].
(In Abt. Deutsche Sängerhalle. Vol. 3, pp. 26–30. [Leipzig,
187–?])

E3385 — T.r. — Part songs.

NL 0345480   MB

Liebe, Eduard Ludwig.
We meet above. (Auf Wiedersehn.) Song. Soprano.
Boston. Ditson & Co. 1867. 5 pp. F°.

G4083 — T.r. (2). — Songs. With music.

NL 0345481   MB

M1619   Liebe, Eduard Ludwig, 1819–1900.
S69   ⌐Auf Wiedersehn₎ acc. piano₎
v.648   We meet again (Auf Wiedersehn) Op. 52.
         Soprano. ⌐New York₎ G.Schirmer, c1874. Pl.
         no.1622.
         5 p. 35ᵐ. (New series of Gems of German
         songs, no.120)
         Caption title.
         English and German text.
         No. 5 in a vol. lettered:Songs, v.648.

         1.Title.   II.Title: We meet again.

NL 0345482   CSt

Liebe, Eduard Ludwig.
We meet again. [Part song.] Op. 106, no. 3.
Berlin. Luckhardt. 1889. 3 pp. [Collection of quartets and
choruses for male voices. I.] L. 8°.

                    Mar. 21,   1902
E3385 — T.r. — Part songs.

NL 0345483   MB

---

q784.3   Liebe, Eduard Ludwig, 1819–1900.
Sh37   We'll meet again. ⌐By₎ Louis Liebe. ⌐Chica-
v.12   go, Root & Cady₎ c1866.
no.31   5p. (Gems of German song, with English and
         German words. no.145)

         ⌐Sheet music printed in Chicago prior to 1871.
         v.12,no.31₎
         Caption title.
         Plate no.: 5170.

         I. Title.

NL 0345484   IU

LIEBE, Friedrich. Gottlob August von, 1809-1885
Die emancipation der wissenschaft auf dem
gebiete der theologie. Leipz.,1835.

NL 0345485   MH-AH

Liebe, Friedrich Gottlob August von, 1809–1885.
Entwurf einer wechselordnung für das herzogthum Braunschweig, sammt motiven. Braunschweig,
1843.

NL 0345486   MH-L

JU411   Liebe, Friedrich Gottlob August von, 1809–1885.
.L7   Der grundadel und die neuen verfassungen. Von
         dr.Friedrich Liebe... Braunschweig,G.C.E.Meyer
         sen.,1844.
         ⌐3₎,355,⌐1₎p. 21½cm.

         1.Aristocracy. 2.Land tenure.

NL 0345487   ICU CU NNC

VOLUME 332

Liebe, Friedrich Gottlob August von, 1809–1885.
Die Stipulation und das einfache Versprechen; eine
civilistische Abhandlung. Braunschweig, G. C. E. Meyer,
1840.

xvi, 400 p.   GDB•••

Includes bibliographical references.
Photo-offset. Frankfurt a. M., F. Keip, 1970. 21 cm.

1. Contracts (Roman law) 2. Contracts—Germany. I. Title.

70–573446

NL   0345488   DLC MH–L CtY NjP

Liebe, Georg, 1859–1912
    see Liebe, Georg Hermann Theodor,
1859–1912.

Liebe (Georg). Alkohol und Tuberculose mit
besonderer Berücksichtigung der Frage: Soll in
Volksheilstätten Alkohol geg-ben werden? 63
pp. 8°. *Tübingen, Osiander,* 1899.

NL   0345490   DNLM

Liebe, Georg, 1865–   *ed.*
Handbuch der krankenversorgung und krankenpflege;
hrsg. von Dr. Georg Liebe, Dr. Paul Jacobsohn, Dr.
George Meyer ... Berlin, A. Hirschwald, 1899 [1898]–
1903.

2 v. in 3. illus. 24½ᶜᵐ.

"Anhang: Bibliographie der gesammten krankenpflege. Von ... Dr. Ernst
Roth": II. bd., 2. abth." p. [456]–1332.

Contents.—1. bd. 1. abth. Geschichtliche entwicklung der krankenpflege ... von Dr. Dietrich. 1898. 2. abth. 1. lfg. Specialkrankenhäuser.
Reconvalescenten- und siechenanstalten. 1898. 2. lfg. Allgemeine krankenhäuser. 1899.—II. bd. 1. abth. 1. Fürsorge auf dem gebiete des kranken-
comforts. Von Dr. Paul Jacobsohn. II. Fürsorge auf dem gebiete der
krankenwartung. Von Dr. Paul Jacobsohn. III. Fürsorge auf dem gebiete
des krankenpflege-unterrichts. Von Dr. Paul Jacobsohn. IV. Fürsorge auf
dem gebiete des krankentransportweens. Von Prof. Dr. George Meyer.
v. Fürsorge auf dem gebiete des rettungswesens. Von Prof. Dr. George
Meyer. VI. Fürsorge für kranke durch die gesetzgebung (krankenpflegege-
setzgebung. Von ... Dr. Dietrich. 1902. II. abth. Specielle krankenversorgung. Anhang. Nachträge. 1903.

NL   0345492   DLC DNLM

Liebe, Georg, 1865–1924.
... Der klinische betrieb in den lungenheilanstalten, von san.-
rat dr. Georg Liebe ... Leipzig, J. A. Barth, 1922.

25 p. 22½ᶜᵐ. (Tuberkulose-bibliothek; beihefte zur Zeitschrift für
tuberkulose, hrsg. von prof. dr. Lydia Rabinowitsch. nr. 9)

1. Tuberculosis—Hospitals and sanatoriums.

A C 35–536

Title from Univ. of Mich.   Printed by L. C.

NL   0345493   MiU DNLM PPC

RC306   Liebe, Georg, 1865–1924.
.B402   ...Die lichtbehandlung (heliotherapie) in den
no.8   deutschen lungenheilanstalten. Denkschrift auf
     veranlassung der Vereinigung der lungenheilan-
     staltsärzte,bearb.von...Georg Liebe... Leipzig
     und Würzburg,C.Kabitzsch,1919.
     [5,]61 p. illus. 26cm. (Beiträge zur klinik
     der tuberkulose und spezifischen tuberkulose-
     forschung... VIII.supplementbd.)
     At head of title:Klinische beiträge.

     1.Sun-baths. 2.Tuberculosis.

NL   0345494   ICU

Liebe, Georg, 1865–1924.
Die Lichtbehandlung (Heliotherapie) in den
deutschen Lungenheilanstalten; denkschrift auf
Veranlassung der Vereinigung der Lungenheilan-
stalts-Ärzte. Mit einem Geleitwort von Dr. Kirchner und mit Beiträgen von Dr. Bacmeister [et al.]
3. neubearb. Aufl. von Hans H. Meiners. Leipzig,
C. Kabitzsch, 1926.

44 p. illus.

I. Meiners, Hans H., ed. 1. Tuberculosis –
Therapy.   615.831   616.246

NL   0345495   ICJ

Liebe, Georg, 1865–1924, ed.
Der Stand der Volksheilstätten-Bewegung im In- und Auslande.
V. Bericht unter Mitwirkung von Basilio Bonardi [et al.] Mün-
chen, Seitz & Schauer, 1900.

85 p.
Contains bibliographies.

NL   0345496   ICJ

Liebe, Georg, 1865–
Vorlesungen über die mechanische und psychische behandlung der tuberkulösen besonders in heilstätten, von
dr. Georg Liebe ... München, J. F. Lehmanns verlag,
1909.

viii, 267 p. 23½ᶜᵐ. (Added t.-p.: Vorlesungen über tuberkulose, hrsg.
von dr. G. Liebe ... 1)

1. Tuberculosis.

Library of Congress   RC311.L69   9–3740
                     (Copyright 1908 Res. no. 2373)

NL   0345497   DLC MiU DNLM CtY-M

WFA   LIEBE, Georg, 1865–1924, ed.
L717v   Vorlesungen über Tuberkulose.
     München, Lehmann, 1909–
     v.

NL   0345498   DNLM ICJ

Liebe, Georg, 1876–
    see Liebe, Kurt Georg, 1876–

LIEBE, Georg Hermann Theodor, 1859–1912.
Die französische besatzung im herzogtum
Magdeburg, 1808–1811. Halle a.S.,O.Hendel,1911.

pp.43.
(NEUJAHRSBLÄTTER,35.)

NL   0345500   MH

Liebe, Georg Hermann Theodor, 1859–1912.
... Das Judentum in der deutschen vergangenheit; mit 106
abbildungen und beilagen nach originalen, grösstenteils aus
dem fünfzehnten bis achtzehnten jahrhundert. Leipzig, E.
Diederichs, 1903.

127, [1] p. illus. (incl. ports., facsims.) plates. 28½ᶜᵐ. (Half-title:
Monographien zur deutschen kulturgeschichte. 11. bd.)

Series title also at head of t.-p.
Illustrated t.-p. In parallel columns. Text begins on verso of t.-p.

1. Jews in Germany.

Library of Congress   DD65.M7   3–23571
               [a29d1]

MoU PBm PPG OU OCU MH OC1W UU
NL   0345501   DLC FU NN MU MH ICJ NcD KyLxCB NIC IEdS

DS   Liebe, Georg Hermann Theodor, 1859–1912.
135   Das Judentum in der deutschen vergangenheit.
G3L62   Zweite Aufl. Jena, Eugen Diederichs, 1924.
1924   127 p. 103 illus. (Die deutschen Stände in
     Einzeldarstellungen, Bd. 2)
     "Neuausgabe der früheren Monographien zur
     deutschen Kulturgeschichte."

     1. Jews in Germany. I. Title. II. Series.

NL   0345502   CLU OU CtY NNC NRU NN IU OO MH

Liebe, Georg, 1859–
Die kommunale bedeutung der kirchspiele in den deutschen
städten. Berlin, W. Weber, 1885.
pp. 55.

NL   0345503   MH NN

LIEBE, Georg Hermann Theodor.
Die mittelalterlichen siechenhäuser der
provinz Sachsen. Halle,druck und verlag von O.
Hendel,1905.

pp.35.
(NEUJAHRSBLÄTTER,29.)

NL   0345504   MH

Liebe, Georg Hermann Theodor.
Die rechtlichen und wirtschaftlichen Zustände der Juden im Erzstift Trier. [Trier,189-.]
[311]–374 p. 23 cm.

Excerpt: Westd. Zeitschr. f. Gesch. u.Kunst
12 4.

NL   0345505   OCH

Liebe, Georg Hermann Theodor, 1859–
Mülverstedt, George Adalbert von, *comp.*
Regesta Archiepiscopatvs magdebvrgensis. Sammlung
von auszügen aus urkunden und annalisten zur geschichte
des erzstifts und herzogthums Magdeburg. Nach einem
höhern orts vorgeschriebenen plane in gemeinschaft mit
dr. Ed. Jacobs ... dr. K. Janicke ... dr. F. Geisheim ...
und dr. C. Sattler ... bearb. und auf kosten der Landstände der provinz Sachsen hrsg. von George Adalbert
v. Mülverstedt ... Magdeburg, E. Baensch jun., 1876–86.

Liebe, Georg Hermann Theodor, 1859–1912.
... Der soldat in der deutschen vergangenheit, mit ein-
hundertdreiundachtzig abbildungen und beilagen nach
den originalen aus dem 15.–18. jahrhundert. Leipzig, E.
Diederichs, 1899.

2 p. l. 7–157, [1] p. illus., plates (part double) 28½ᶜᵐ. (Monographien
zur deutschen kulturgeschichte. [bd. 1])

Illus. t.-p.

1. Military art and science. 2. Germany—Army—Hist. 3. Soldiers.
i. Title.

     G–1205

Library of Congress   DD65.M7 bd. 1

CaOTP NcD NIC OCU OU PP–W PBm PU PPG MB ICJ IdU
NL   0345507   DLC MH PSt TU DNW NcU ICU MiU OKentU

     Liebe, Georg Hermann Theodor, 1859–1912.
943.02   Der Soldat in der deutschen Vergangenheit.
qD486   2. Aufl. Jena, E. Diederichs, 1924.
84.1   157 p. illus., facsims. 29 cm. (Die
     Deutschen Stände in Einzeldarstellungen, Bd. 1)
     1. Military art and science. 2. Germany.
     Army. Hist. 3. Soldiers. I. Title.

NL   0345508   NcD NN OO InU

VOLUME 332

DD Liebe, Georg Hermann Theodor, 1859-1912.
61 Soziale Studien aus deutscher Vergangen-
L71 heit. Berlin, H. Costenoble, 1901.
vi, 119 p. 20cm.

1. Germany--Soc. life & cust. I. Title.

NL 0345509 NIC

LIEBE, Georg Hermann Theodor
Die universität Erfurt und Dalberg. Halle,
druck und verlag von O.Hendel,1898.

pp.44.
(NEUJAHRSBLÄTTER,22.)

NL 0345510 MH

Liebe, Georg Hermann Theodor, 1859-1912, comp.
Zur Geschichte deutschen Wesens von 1300-1848; kul-
turhistorische Darstellungen aus älterer und neuerer Zeit.
Berlin, Vossische Buchhandlung, 1912.
319 p. 24 cm.
Bibliographical footnotes.

1. Germany—Civilization. 2. Germany—Intellectual life.
I. Title.

DD61.L5   67-52295

NL 0345511 DLC IU

Liebe, Georgius Guilelmus, respondent.
Dubitationes de augmento lactis ex anastomosi
vasori mammorium ...
see under Bose, Ernest Gottlob, 1723-1788.
praeses [supplement]

Liebe, Georgius Henricus, respondent.
Clariss. virorvm ad Georg. Casp. Kirchmaiervm
... epistolae qvae svpersvnt ...
see under Kirchmayer, Georg Kaspar,
1635-1700.

Liebe, Georgius Henricus, respondent.
De vomitu simplici
see under Sperling. Paul Gottfried,
d. 1709, praeses.

Liebe, Gottfried.
Wind-Elektrizität, ihre Erzeugung und Verwendung für ländliche
Verhältnisse. Von Dr.-Ing. Gottfried Liebe, ... Mit 47 Textabbildungen. Berlin, P. Parey, 1915.
vii, 124 p. illus., tables, diagrs. 19cm. (On cover: Thaer-Bibliothek, Band 114.)

NL 0345515 ICJ DAS

Liebe, H   comp.
Russian marches performed by the most
distinguished regiments in the service of Alexander,
Emperor of all the Russias ... and arranged for
the pianoforte by H. Liebe ... London, Printed &
sold by Preston [182-?]
12 p. 33.5 cm.

NL 0345516 CtY

Liebe, Hans.
... Italiens gartenbau, erzeugung und aussenhandel, von dr.
Hans Liebe ... Berlin, P. Parey, 1935.
104 p. diagrs. 26cm. (On cover: Germany, Reichsministerium für
ernährung u. landwirtschaft. Berichte über landwirtschaft. n. f., 103.
sonderheft)
At head of title: Untersuchungen des Instituts für konjunkturfor-
schung Berlin.

1. Fruit trade—Italy. 2. Produce trade—Italy.

Agr 35-281

Library, U. S. Dept. of   Agriculture 18G31A hft. 103
[HD9240   ]

NL 0345517 DNAL MoU MiU

Liebe, Hans.
... Preisbildung bei gemüse und obst, von dr. Hans Liebe.
Mit 36 textabbildungen. Berlin, P. Parey, 1931.
70 p. diagrs. (part fold.) 26cm. (On cover: Germany, Reichsministerium für ernährung u. landwirtschaft. Berichte über landwirtschaft.
n. f., 52. Sonderheft)
At head of title: Arbeiten der Reichsforschungsstelle für landwirt-
schaftliches marktwesen, leiter: dr. F. Baade.

1. Fruit trade—Germany. [1. Fruit—Prices] 2. Vegetables—[Prices]
3. [Prices—Germany] 4. [Farm produce—Marketing]

Agr 32-440 Revised

U. S. Dept. of agr. Library   18G31 sonderheft, 52
for Library of Congress   HD9253.6.L5

NL 0345518 DNAL MoU CU MiU DLC

Liebe, Hapsburg.
The clan call, by Hapsburg Liebe; frontispiece by
Ralph Pallen Coleman. Garden City, New York, Doubleday, Page & company, 1920.
vii, 239, [1] p. col. front. 19½cm.

I. Title.
Library of Congress   PZ3.L622Cl   20-19762

NL 0345519 DLC PP MB

Liebe (Hermannus Augustus). * De diversis la-
probandi methodis. 25 pp. 8°. Lipsia, Stur-
et Koppe. 1857.

NL 0345520 DNLM ICRL

Liebe, I.
see Liebe, Christian Frederik Julius
Hegelund, 1815-1883.

---

6 Liebe, Karl Leopold Theodor, 1828-1894.
Die faerbenden mineralien der diabase des
Voigtlands und Frankenwalds. Gera, Iszleib &
Rietzschel [1869]
15 p. 4°.

NL 0345522 DLC

Leopold
Sy4 Liebe, Karl Theodor, 1828-1894.
893L Ornithologische Schriften. Gesammelt und
hrsg. von Carl R. Hennicke. Leipzig, W.
Malende [1893]
724 p. port. 23 cm.

1. Birds. I. Hennicke, Carl Richard,
1865- ed.

NL 0345523 CtY

Leopold
Liebe, Karl Theodor, 1828-1894.

Geinitz, Hanns Bruno, 1814-1900.
Ueber ein aequivalent der takonischen schiefer Nord-
amerika's in Deutschland und dessen geologische stel-
lung. Von dr. H. B. Geinitz und dr. K. Th. Liebe ... Der
Akademie übergeben am 5. februar 1866. Dresden,
Druck von E. Blochmann & sohn [1867]

Leopold
Liebe, Karl Theodor, 1828-1894.
Uebersicht über den schichtenaufbau Ostthüringens
von K. Th. Liebe ... Hrsg. von der Königlich preussischen geologischen landesanstalt. Berlin, In commission
bei der S. Schropp'schen hof-landkartenhandlung (J. H.
Neumann) 1884.
vi, 130 p. 2 fold. maps. 26cm. (Added t.-p.: Abhandlungen zur geologischen specialkarte von Preussen und den thüringischen staaten. bd. v,
hft. 4)

1. Geology—Thuringia.

G S 10-193

Library, U. S. Geol.   survey (530.1) C vol. 5, pt. 4

NL 0345525 DI-GS MoU

Liebe, Karl Theodor
see
Liebe, Karl Leopold Theodor, 1828-1894

Liebe (Kurt Georg) [1876-]. *Ueber einen
Fall von Littlescher Starre mit corticaler
Amblyopie. 27 pp. 8°. Leipzig, A. Edel-
mann, 1907.

NL 0345527 DNLM ICRL CtY

Liebe, Louis
see Liebe, Eduard Ludwig, 1819-1900.

Liebe, Martin
Beitraege zur lehre von der traumatischen ent-
stehung der sarcome und enchondrome.
Inaug. diss. Strassburg, 1881 (Berlin)

NL 0345528 ICRL MBCo DNLM

FILM Liebe, Matthias
4333 Cato pastoralis; nonnullas ministrorum ecclesiasti-
PT corum censuras morales continens: bono animo satyris
Reel aliquot conscriptus a Matthia Libio Bipontino ...
9 Oppenheimii, typis H. Galleri, sumtibus viduae L.
Hulsii, 1615.
43p. 17cm.
(German Baroque Literature, reel 9 , No. 48
Research Publications)
Microfilm.

NL 0345529 CU

Liebe, Max, 1913–
Die internationale Gewerkschaftsbewegung in ihrer Ausein-
andersetzung mit dem Nationalsozialismus ... von Max Liebe...
Berlin: "Szaro," 1937. 150 p. 21cm.
Inaugural-Dissertation — Berlin, 1935.
Lebenslauf.
"Literaturverzeichnis," p. [149]-150.

1. Trade unions—Internat. rel.   2. Trade unions—Germany.
3. Socialism, 1933– 4. Fascism   —Germany.
N. Y. P. L.   September 30, 1938

NL 0345530 NN CtY CSt-H ICRL

LIEBE, Otto.
Die auf der universitäts-ohrenklinik in Halle
während des letzten decenniums beobachteten
fälle von erysipelas. Inaug.-diss. Halle
a.S.,1894.

NL 0345531 MBCo DNLM

VOLUME 332

Liebe, Otto.
Über die respiration der tracheaten, besonders über den mechanismus derselben und über die menge der ausgeathmeten kohlensäure ... Chemnitz, Druck von J. W. Geidel, 1872.
2 p. l., 28 p. 22^{cm}.
Inaug.-diss.—Jena.
Bibliography on verso of 2d prelim. leaf.

1. Respiration. 2. Tracheae in arthropoda.
                         S—21902
Library of Congress   QP121.L72

NL 0345532   DLC

Liebe, Paul
Die Konzentrationsmöglichkeiten in deutschen Sortimentsbuchhandel. Dresden, Jocken & Oltmanns, 1955.
86 p.

Also published as thesis, Handelshochschule, Leipzig.
Bibliography: p. 84-86.

1. Booksellers and bookselling - Germany.

NL 0345533   NNC

Liebe, Paul W
Deutsch-Englisches und Englisch-Deutsches Fachwörterbuch für das Bauwesen. Stuttgart, Franckh [1949]
viii, 215 p. 17 cm.

1. Building—Dictionaries. 2. Building—Dictionaries—German. 3. English language—Dictionaries—German. 4. German language—Dictionaries—English.

TH9.L5   690.3   50–13357

NL 0345534   DLC

193   Liebe, Reinhard, 1878–
F31Y11   Fechners metaphysik.   Greifswald, 1903.
89p.
By Reinhard Ernst Liebe.
Inaug.-diss.—Strassburg.
Vita.

NL 0345535   IU ICRL PU CtY MH

4BD   Liebe, Reinhard, 1878–
245   Fechners Metaphysik im Umriss dargestellt und beurteilt. Leipzig, Dieterichsche Verlags-Buchhandlung, 1903.
89 p.

NL 0345536   DLC-P4 OC1W NN MH

Liebe, Reinhard, 1878–
Gottwirklichkeit und religion; briefe über die innere not, von Reinhard Liebe. Tübingen, Mohr, 1935.
92 p. 22^{cm}.
CONTENTS.—Die lage.—Die alte religion.—Die "Gottwirklichkeit."—Die deutsche aufgabe.—Immer noch christentum?—Deutscher glaube.—Die "neue lehre."—Die deutsche kirche.—Die stimme des volkes.

1. Germany—Religion—1933–   I. Title.
                         36–15276
Library of Congress   BR856.L5
                         274.3

NL 0345537   DLC MH-AH CtY-D

621   LIEBE, Reinhard, 1878–
L716ne   Die Neugeburt des Christentums.
1926   Zweite, umgearbeitete Auflage. Freiburg, Ernst Mauckisch, 1926.
293p. 23cm.

NL 0345538   MH-AH

Liebe, Reinhard Ernst
     see Liebe, Reinhard. 1878–

Liebe, Rudolf
Ueber die haemophilie und ueber ihre beziehungen zur zahnheilkunde
Inaug. Diss. Breslau, 1923

NL 0345540   ICRL

Liebe, Siegfried.
*Beiträge zur Epidemiologie der Infektionskrankheiten: Scharlach, Masern, Diphtherie und Keuchhusten [Leipzig] 63p. 8°.
[Zeulenroda i. Thür., 1930]

NL 0345541   DNLM CtY

Liebe, Siegfried.
Lehrbuch für die Kinderpflegerin und Kinderkrankenschwester Hrsg. von Siegfried Liebe. Leipzig, Thieme, 19

v. illus. (part col.) 25 cm. 35.00 (v. 2)
                      GDB 68-A41-496 (v. 2)
Vol. 2 reprinted from first ed.

1. Pediatric 2. Pediatric nursing. I. Title.
[DNLM: 1. Pediatric Nursing. WY 159 L716L 1969]
[RJ45]   77–450874
Shared Cataloging with   DNLM
Library of Congress   70 [2]

NL 0345542   DNLM

QK641 Liebe, Theodor.
.L7   Die elemente der morphologie. Ein hilfsbuch für den ersten unterricht in der botanik von dr. Theodor Liebe ... Berlin, A. Hirschwald, 1868.
viii, 60 p. illus., fold. pl. 22^{cm}.

1. Botany—Morphology.

NL 0345543   ICU ICJ NjP

QK641 Liebe, Theodor.
.L71   Die elemente der morphologie. Ein hilfsbuch für den unterricht in der botanik, von prof. dr. Th. Liebe .. 3. aufl. ... Berlin, A. Hirschwald, 1881.
viii, 62 p. illus., pl. 22^{cm}.

1. Botany—Morphology.

NL 0345544   ICU

Liebe, Theodor.
Grundriss der speciellen botanik für den unterricht an höheren lehranstalten, von dr. Theodor Liebe ... Berlin, A. Hirschwald, 1866.
2 p.l., 132 p. 22½^{cm}.

1. Botany—Classification.

NL 0345545   ViU ICU

QK97 Liebe, Theodor.
.L71   Grundriss der speciellen botanik für den unterricht an höheren lehranstalten, von dr. Theodor Liebe ... 2. aufl. ... Berlin, A. Hirschwald, 1879.
iv, 144 p. pl. 21½^{cm}.
Interleaved; manuscript notes and drawings.
Plate preceded by leaf with explanatory letterpress.

1. Botany.

NL 0345546   ICU

QK671 Liebe, Theodor.
.L7   Grundzüge der pflanzen-anatomie und -physiologie. Zur unterstützung des unterrichts an höheren lehranstalten und einführung in das privat-studium, entworfen von dr. Theodor Liebe ... Berlin, A. Hirschwald, 1878.
vii, 63 p. illus. 23^{cm}.

1. Botany—Anatomy. 2. Botany—Physiology.

NL 0345547   ICU CU

Liebe, Theodor. Ueber die geographische verbreitung der schmarotzerpflanzen. 2 abth. (in 1 vol.). Berlin. 1862-[69]. 4°.

NL 0345548   MH-A

Liebe, V   von.
Der besitz als recht in thesi. Civilistische abhandlung von V. v. Liebe ... Braunschweig, C. A. Schwetschke und sohn, 1876.
2 p. l., 172 p. 22^{cm}.

1. Possession (Roman law) 2. Real property (Roman law)
                       40–21760

NL 0345549   DLC CU-AL MU CtY

Liebe, Walter: Die Fälle von Extra-Uterin-Gravidität [an d. Univ.-Frauen-Klin. u. am Diakonissenhaus zu Halle] i. d. J. 1914—1918. [Maschinenschrift] 87 S. 4°. — Auszug: Halle, Saale o J. 2 Bl. 8° Halle, Med. Diss. v. 9. Okt. 1919 [1923]   [U 23.5022]

NL 0345550   ICRL

Liebe, Walther, 1874–
Ueber blutveraenderungen nach blutverlusten
     see under Liebe, Bernhard Walther, 1874–

Liebe, Walther, 1889– a. Beuthen, Oberschlesien: Das männliche Begattungsorgan der Hausente. Jena 1914: Kämpfe. 70 S. 8° ¶ Aus: Jenaische Zeitschrift f. Naturwiss. Bd 51. Jena, Phil. Diss. v. 10. Febr. 1914, Ref. Plate
[Geb. 15. Juli 89 Oppeln; Wohnort: Jena; Staatsangeh.: Preußen; Vorbildung: G. Beuthen Reife 08; Studium: Tübingen 3. Jena 7 S.; Rig. 14. Juni 13.]   [U 14. 3984]

NL 0345552   ICRL CtY MH

Liebe, Wilhelm: Über die Ergebnisse der postoperativen Mammakarzinombestrahlung. [Maschinenschrift] 24 S. 4°. — Auszug: Halle a. d. S. 1922: Wolff. 2 Bl. 8° Halle, Med. Diss. v. 19. Okt. 1922 [1923]   [U 23.5023]

NL 0345553   ICRL

Liebe, Wilhelm Bruno, 1876–
     see Liebe, Bruno, 1876–

Liebe, Wilhelm, 1840–
     see Liebe, Carl Friedrich Wilhelm, 1840–

Liebe, Wolfgang.
Danziger Hochschulführer
     see under Danzig. Technische Hochschul.

VOLUME 332

Liebe-Harkort, Ellen.

   See

Soeding, Ellen (Liebe-Harkort), 1904-

Liebe. [Männerchor.]
   (In Orpheus. Band 7, pp. 26, 27. Leipzig. [184-?])

               Mar. 21,   1902
E3386 — Part songs.

NL 0345558   MB

     Der Liebe Augustin, hrsg. von der Öster-
*fGC9   reichischen Verlags-Anstalt F.& O. Greipel.
R4574   1.Jahrg., Nr.1-24; 1904.
LL621   Wien,1904.
     24 nos.in 1v. illus.(part col.) 30.5cm.
3 times a month.
Chief editor: Gustav Meyrink.
No more published?

NL 0345559   MH

225.92   Die Liebe der Magdalena, ein französi-
M189L7 scher sermon, gezogen durch den abbé Jo-
seph Bonnet aus dem manuskript Q I 14 der
Kaiserlichen bibliothek zu St.Petersburg;
übertragung durch Rainer Maria Rilke.
Leipzig, Insel-verlag, 1912.
    50p. 21cm.

   1.Mary Magdalene, Saint. I.Rilke, Rainer
Maria, 1875-1926, tr. II.Bonnet, Joseph.

NL 0345560   CLSU NN IU IEN ICU

    Die liebe der Magdalena, ein französischer sermon, gezogen
durch den abbé Joseph Bonnet aus dem manuskript Q I 14 der
Kaiserlichen bibliothek zu St. Petersburg; übertragung durch
Rainer Maria Rilke. Leipzig, Insel-verlag, 1919.

   50 p., 1 l. 21ᶜᵐ.

   "Zweite auflage."

   1. Mary Magdalene, Saint. i. Rilke, Rainer Maria, 1875-1926, tr.
i. Bonnet, Joseph.
                         42-46760
  Library of Congress   BS2485.L5

NL 0345561   DLC NBC CtY OrPR WU MH CtW

    Die liebe der Magdalena, ein französischer sermon, gezogen
durch den abbé Joseph Bonnet aus dem manuskript Q I 14 der
Kaiserlichen bibliothek zu St. Petersburg; übertragung durch
Rainer Maria Rilke. Leipzig, Insel-verlag, 1921.

   51 p., 1 l. 21ᶜᵐ.

   "Dritte auflage."

NL 0345562   CLSU

    Die liebe der Magdalena; ein französischer sermon
gezogen durch den abbé Joseph Bonnet aus dem manuskript Q I 14 der Kaiserlichen bibliothek zu St. Petersburg. Übertragung durch Rainer Maria Rilke. Leipzig,
Im Insel-verlag, 1922.

   50 p. 21ᶜᵐ.

   7. bis 10. tausend.

   1. Bonnet, Joseph. ii. Rilke, Rainer Maria, 187$- 2tg. iii. Title

NL 0345563   MiU CU OCl

     Liebe Freunde und Mitbürger! Grosses ist
*GB8   gewonnen, die feste Grundlage nämlich, auf
V6755R welcher sich das Glück der Völker und der
3.14.48 Einzelnen allmählich aber sicher aufbauen lässt
   ...
   [Wien,1848]
    broadside. 29x23cm.
    Reschauer-Smets (I.356) print this document
with the date: Wien, am 14. März 1848.
    Signed: A. Auersperg (Anastasius Grün). Ferd
Colloredo-Mannsfeld [& 3 others].

NL 0345564   MH

    Die Liebe in Pannonien; oder, Der Sieg der
      Pflichten
       see under [Ayrenhoff, Cornelius Hermann
von] 1733-1819.

    Liebe Kindlein, kauft ein! Alte und neue
Gedichte für unsere Kinder. Bilder von Karl
Nussbaumer. Wien, C. Ueberreuter [°1950,
26 p. illus.

NL 0345566   MiD

    Liebe, Eine, mit Dampf; Schwank in einem Act. Frei nach dem
Französischen von Bernard. Hamburg: C. A. Sachse [1851?].
22 p. 8°

   1. Drama (German). 2. Bernard.
N. Y. P. L.   February 21, 1911.

NL 0345567   NN

---

sE   Liebe Reime für die Kleinen! Bilder von El-
L622 friede Reinhardt. Wiesbaden, J. Scholz-
Mainz [194-?]
   [6]p. col.illus. 19cm.

   Cover title.

   I. Reinhardt, Elfriede, illus.

NL 0345568   IU

    Liebe, terra incognita
      see under [Martin, Maurice Léon] 1887-

392.5
L621   Liebe und Ehe in der Narrenkappe und im
    Philosophenmantel. Von einem Greise.
Breslau, Brieg und Leipzig, bey Christian
Friedrich Gutsch, 1786.
   255, [1] p. engr. 18 cm.

   Small engraved illus. on title page.
   Provenance: Maryland Diocesan Library.

   1. Love. 2. Marriage. I. Greis, ein.

NL 0345570   NNG

    Liebe und Hass
      see under [Auer, Ludwig] 1839-1914.

    Liebe und Liebelei
      see under [Deinhardstein, Johann Ludwig]
1794-1859.

    LIEBE und rechtschaffenheit; ein schauspiel
in einem aufzuge. 1789.

    (In DEUTSCHE schaubühne,1789,vii,pp.[305]-
328.)

NL 0345573   MH

    Liebe und Sehnsucht (German air)
      Am I not fondly thine own?
      see under title

---

   750. Liebe und Tugend. (Magazin für Frauen-
      zimmer. Strasburg, 1783. 12°. Jahrg. 2, Bd. 3,
      p. 279-282.)   *DF
      Anecdote of the Revolutionary War.

NL 0345574   NN

M1021   Liebe und sehnsucht (German air)
.B67
op. 22   Böhm, Theobald, 1794-1881.
    [Variations brillantes sur un air allemand; arranged]

   Variations brillantes sur un air allemand: Du, du liegst mir
am herzen. Pour la flûte avec accompagnement d'orchestre
ou de piano, composées ... par Th. Boehm ... Op. 22 ...
Mayence [etc.] Les Fils de B. Schott; [etc., etc., 184-?]

    Liebe und Vaterland. Ein Nachspiel.
      see under [Bilderbeck, Ludwig Benedict
Franz, Freiherr von] b. 1766?

PT   Liebe wirkt schnell; ein Lustspiel in einem
1799   Aufzuge. Wien, 1782.
A1   63p. 19cm.
L48

NL 0345577   WU NN

    Die liebe zeit; oder, die Jamim Noraim und der
    Jom Ha-kippurim, nach ihrer liturgischen,
rituellen und historischen bedentung aus den
quellen dargestellt. Berlin, Sittenfeld, 1869.
46 p. D.

NL 0345578   NcD

    Die liebe zu Maria; oder, Betrachtungen zur ehre der
Gottesmutter Maria nebst den allgemeinen andachts-
übungen ... Einsiedeln, Wyss, Eberle & co. [1890]

   1 p. l., 383 p. front., pl. 12½ᶜᵐ.

   Added t.-p., engr.

                                   5-19192†
  Library of Congress   BX2160.L47

NL 0345579   DLC

Liébeault, Ambroise Auguste, 1823-1904.
   Du sommeil et des états analogues, considérés surtout au
point de vue de l'action du moral sur le physique, par A.-A.
Liébeault ... Paris, V. Masson et fils; Nancy, N. Grosjean,
1866.

   535 p. 22ᶜᵐ.

   Bibliographical foot-notes.

NL 0345580   ICJ OClW-H DNLM MdBP MH

Liebeault, Ambroise Auguste
   Ébauche de psychologie. xvi, 202 pp.
8°. Paris. G. Masson 1873.

NL 0345581   DNLM

VOLUME 332

Liébeault (Ambroise - Auguste) [1823 - 1904].
*Étude sur la désarticulation fémoro-tibiale.
1 p. l., 32 pp. 4°. Strasbourg, 1850, 2. s.,
No. 205.
For biography see Gaz. méd. de Par., 1904, 12. s., iv, 101.
Also J. I. Frychol. u. Neurol., Leipz., 1904, iii, 97-100 (A.
Forel). Also Lancet, Lond., 1904, i, 693. Also Psychol.
en Neurol. Bl., Amst., 1904, viii, 205-209 (A. W. van Ren-
terghem). Also Rev. de Phypnot. et psychol. physiol.,
Par., 1903-4, xviii, 235-290 (Bérillon). Also Rev. méd. de
l'est, Nancy, 1904, iii, 19-24 (G. Michel).*

NL 0345582   DNLM

LIÉBEAULT, Ambroise Auguste.
    Étude sur le zoomagnétisme. Paris, etc., 1883.
    pp. 29.

NL 0345583   MH

BF
L716s
1892
    LIÉBEAULT, Ambrose Auguste, 1823-1904
      Der künstliche Schlaf und die ihm
ähnlichen Zustände. Autorisirte deutsche
Ausg. von Otto Dornblüth. Leipzig,
Deuticke, 1892.
      vii, 203 p.
      Translation of Le sommeil provogué
et les états analogues.

NL 0345584   DNLM

Liébeault, Ambroise Auguste, 1823-1904.
    Pour constater la réalité du magnétisme.
Confession d'un hypnotiseur, extériorisation
de la force neurique ou fluide magnétique
par le docteur A.-A. Liébeault. 2. ed. avec
notes biographiques, un portrait et trois
lettres inédites de l'auteur ... Paris,
H. Durville e1904,
    35 p.
    cover-title,

NL 0345585   MiU

Liébeault, Ambroise Auguste, 1823-1904.
    Le sommeil provoqué et les états analogues, par dr.
A.-A. Liébeault. Paris, O. Doin, 1889.
    xii, 310 p. 19ᶜᵐ.
    First published in 1866 with title: Du sommeil et des états analogues, con
sidérés surtout au point de vue de l'action du moral sur le physique.

    1. Hypnotism.

NL 0345586   MiU CU DCU DNLM MH PPC

Liébeault, A(mbroise) A(uguste), 1823-1904.
    Thérapeutique suggestive, son mécanisme, propriétés diverses
du sommeil provoqué et des états analogues. Paris, O. Doin, 1891.
    pp. vii, 308.

    Hypnotism|Suggestion (Mental)||AcS 185704

NL 0345587   MH DNLM NcD OC1W MB

Liébeault, Antoine August
      see   Liébault, Ambroise Auguste, 1823-1904

B3287
.L5W5
1928
   Liebeck, Adolf.
     ... Welterwachen; der weg zu einer neuen kultur
des Abendlandes ... Stuttgart, Strecker und Schröder, 1928-
     v.
     "Die kritik der sinne ist der kernbestandteil
dieses ersten bandes ... in sich vollkommen abgeschlossen ... dient er als fundament für den zweiten band."--Vorwort.

     1. Civilization--Philosophy. 2. Phenomenology.

NL 0345589   ICU MH

W 4
G82
1913
    LIEBECK, Adolf, 1886-
      Das Tentamen abortus provocandi
deficiente graviditate und seine
rechtliche Bedeutung. Berlin, Karger,
1913.
      65 p.
      Inaug.-Diss. - Greifswald.

NL 0345590   DNLM MiU CtY

Liebeck, Oskar.
    Currency to come; the way to permanent prosperity and security,
by Dr. Oskar Liebeck...including authentic ordinance chart of
Great Britain's economic development from 1800-1937 (June).
¡London: Printed by R. M. Rohrer, 1937; 64 p. chart. 24cm.

    Chart in pocket.

29728B. 1. Money, 1933-   I. Title.
N.Y.P.L   January 4, 1940

NL 0345591   NN CtY

Liebeck, Oskar.
    Das unbekannte und die angst, von Oskar Liebeck. Leipzig,
F. Meiner, 1928.
    vi, 138 p. 23½ᶜᵐ.
    "Literatur": p. ¡136,-138.

    1. Knowledge, Theory of. 2. Fear.   I. Title.

Library of Congress   BD201.L5   44-50021

NL 0345592   DLC CaBVaU MH

Liebeck, Oskar.
    Vernunft statt Tradition; das Wesen der Demokratie.
Stuttgart, F. Mittelbach ¡1949;
    206 p. 23 cm.
    CONTENTS.--Die falsche Grundhaltung: Der Aberglaube.--Pla-
nung--die Wahnidee des 20. Jahrhunderts.--Demokratische, das heisst
freie Wirtschaft.--Parteipolitik, der Todfeind der Demokratie.--Die
Lehren aus der Geschichte Amerikas.--Grundzüge einer demokratischen Verfassung.

    1. Democracy.   I. Title.

JC423.L52   321.8   50-33337

NL 0345593   DLC NBuU

Liebeck, Siegfried.

Kliemke, Ernst, 1870-
    ... Esperanto und recht, eine vortragsfolge; beiträge von
rechtsanwalt Kliemke: rechtsanwalt Liebeck; patentanwalt
Schiff; rechtsanwalt Tichauer. Berlin, R. L. Prager, 1928.

---

ar W
53463
no.3
    Liebeck, Siegfried.
      Das Versprechen der Herstellung einer
Eigenschaft beim Kauf. Ein Beitrag zur
Lehre von den gemischten Verträgen. Berlin, Frensdorf, 1913.
      57 p. 22cm.

      Inaug.-Diss.--Erlangen.

NL 0345595   NIC NN ICRL

LIEBECKE, Johann Christian Gotthilf.
   Magdeburg während der blockade in den jahren
1813 und 1814; ein beitrag zur geschichte jener
denkwürdigen zeit. Nach den tagebuch-aufzeich-
nungen bearbeitet und herausgegeben von Paul
Wendt. Magdeburg, J. Neumann, 1913.

   Plates and plan.

NL 0345596   MH

Liébecq, Claude.
    ... Conception actuelle du catabolisme de l'hémoglobine.
Paris, Masson ¡etc.¡ 1946.
    63, ¡1¡ p. Illus. 26 cm. (Actualités biochimiques, no. 7)
    "Bibliographie": p. 56-63.

    1. Bilirubin. 2. Hemoglobin.   I. Series.
QP91.L695   612.11111   Med 47-3581*
U. S. Army Medical Library   [W1AC9897 no. 7]
for Library of Congress   ¡2¡†

NL 0345597   DNLM MoU ICU DLC

Liébecq, Claude, ed.
    Proceedings

      see under

    International Congress of Biochemistry.
    3d, Brussels, 1955.

4K
Ger
608
    Liebegott, A
      Die Bearbeitung der Grundbuch-
sachen. Handbuch für Grundbuch-
beamte und Notare. Berlin, J.
Guttentag, 1910.
      156 p.

NL 0345599   DLC-P4

LIEBEGOTT, Albert Konrad Martin,

    See LIEBEGOTT, Martin, 1882-

Liebegott, Martin, 1882-
    Der brandenburgische Landvogt als Jus-
tizbeamter bis zum 16. Jahrhundert ...
¡von¡ Martin Liebegott ... Opponenten: ...
Curt Genzmer ... Walter Holfeld. Halle a.
d.S., E. Karras, 1906.
    2 p.l., 37, ¡2¡ p. 21½cm.
    Inaug.-Diss. - Halle-Wittenberg.
    Part of the author's larger work with
title: Der brandenburgische Landvogt.

NL 0345601   MH-L ICRL

Oqn31
906l
    Liebegott, Martin, 1882
      Der brandenburgische Landvogt bis zum
XVI. Jahrhundert. Halle a.S., M.Niemeyer,
1906.
      179p. 23cm.

      1. Brandenburg - Pol. & govt.

NL 0345602   CtY MH-L

Liebeherr (Bogislaus Frederic von)
    A...Florimond comte de Mercy d'Argenteau, ambassa-
deur de sa Majesté Impériale à la cour de France & ministre plénipotentiaire au gouvernement des Pays Bas
Autrichiens...[B. F. von Liebeherr, Dutch refugee, re-
siding in Austrian Flanders, requests that a chance be
given him to defend his honor and reputation from the
attacks of powerful enemies and to prove his innocence
Bruxelles ?, 1791 ?] 16 pp. nar. 8°.

NL 0345603   NN

Liebeherr, Max von.
   Ueber Hexerei: ein Vortrag gehalten am 21. Novbr. 187
   Rostock, 1871.

NL 0345604   NIC MH

VOLUME 332

Liebel, Fridolin.
Die württembergische torfwirtschaft; eine wirtschafts-
geschichtliche studie unter besonderer berücksichtigung
Oberschwabens nach den ergebnissen einer privaterhe-
bung, von Fridolin Liebel ... Stuttgart und Berlin. J. G.
Cotta, 1911.

viii, 288 p. incl. tables. fold. tab. 23ᶜᵐ. *(Added t.-p.: Münchener volks-*
wirtschaftliche studien ... 114. stück)

"Quellen": p. [287]–288.

1. Peat—Württemberg.

12–6240

Library of Congress   HD9559.P5G4 1911

NL   0345605   DLC ICJ NN

PQ   **Liebel, Frieda.**
2623   Confessions de Frieda. Paris, Éditions du
I44   Vert-Logis [1948]
C6   227p. 18cm.
             Cover title: Les confessions d'une saphiste.

I. Title II. Title: Les confessions d'une
saphiste

NL   0345606   WU

Liebel, Ignatius
    see   Liebel, Ignaz, 1754-1820.

Liebel, Ignaz [1754-1810] ed
    Archilochi iambographorum principis reli-
quiae...
    see under Archilochus.

PT 2433 LIEBEL, IGNAZ, 1754-1820.
.L6 E6   Epistel über poetische Stümper und Stümpe-
             rey. Wien, Gedruckt bey A. Strauss, 1817.
             39 p.

NL   0345609   InU

PT2423 Liebel, Ignaz, 1754-1820.
L6   Gedichte. 2., verb. und verm.
A17   Aufl. Wien, A. Pichler, 1814.
1814   392 p. port.
                 I. Title.

NL   0345610   CaBVaU

Liebel, Leonard.
    ... Die wirtschaftliche struktur der gesellschaft mit be-
schränkter haftung, von diplom-kaufmann dr. Leonard Liebel
... Berlin [etc.] Industrieverlag Spaeth & Linde, 1931.

141 p. 22½ᶜᵐ. (Betriebs- u. finanzwirtschaftliche forschungen ... II.
ser., hft. 55)
The author's dissertation.
"Literaturverzeichnis": p. [135]–141.

1. Private companies—Germany.   I. Title.

32–25519

Library of Congress   HD2741.L5
                             [a44d1]   658.11440943

NL   0345611   DLC

Liebel, Willy.
    Fünf Jahre Stadt der Reichsparteitage Nürnberg, ein
Bericht über die nationalsozialistische Aufbauarbeit in der
Stadt der Reichsparteitage Nürnberg. [Nürnberg, K. Ulrich,
1938]

169 p. illus., ports., maps. 21 x 25 cm.

1. Nuremberg—Descr.—Views. 2. Nationalsozialistische Deutsche
Arbeiter-Partei.   I. Title.

DD901.N94L5   50–52433

NL   0345612   DLC ICU

4PT   **Liebel-Monninger, Anna.**
Ger.   Gertrud, ein Wille und ein Weg; eine
248   Geschichte um den Reichsparteitag. [2. Aufl.]
             Langensalza, J. Beltz [1943]
             85 p.

NL   0345613   DLC-P4

W   **LIEBEL-FLARSHEIM Company, Cincinnati**
26   [Catalogs of X-ray, electrosurgical and
[L716   physiotherapy apparatus]

             A file of these publications will be
           found on the shelves under the above call
           number.
             1. Radiography - Apparatus - Catalogs
             2. Surgical instruments & apparatus -
           Catalogs

NL   0345614   DNLM

WO   **LIEBEL-FLARSHEIM Company, Cincinnati**
162   [Collection of publications]
qL716
             The library has a collection of miscel-
           laneous publications of this organization
           kept as received. These publications are
           not listed nor bound separately.
             1. Surgical instruments & apparatus

NL   0345615   DNLM

Liebeler, Jean (Mayer)
    You, the jury, by Jean Mayer Liebeler. Toronto, New
York, Farrar & Rinehart, inc. [1944]

4 p. l., 3-306 p. 19ᶜᵐ.

I. Title.
                                          44–6667
Library of Congress   PZ3.L62203Yo

NL   0345616   DLC WaS WaT OLak OOxM PU PPL PP

608.2 **LIEBELT, Christian Daniel, 1734-1807.**
L97.9   Predigten zur Befoerderung christlicher
C357ca   Erkenntnisse und der Gottseligkeit
1780   besonders unter den Landleuten. Leipzig,
             Johann Friedrich Langenheim, 1776.
             4p.l., 310p. 20.5cm.

             Bound with: Der Catechismus Lutheri...
           1776.

NL   0345617   MH-AH

Liebelt, Friedrich Wilhelm , 1884-
    Die besonderheiten der verpfaendung...
    Inaug. diss. Breslau, 1908.
    Bibl.

NL   0345618   ICRL

4JX Liebelt, Herbert.
576   Die völkerrechtliche Regelung der
           Luftfahrt im Kriege. Würzburg, [
           ] 1935.
                 51 p.

NL   0345619   DLC-P4 MH

Liebelt, Karl Paul
    see Liebelt, Paul, 1887-

Liebelt, Otto.
    Ueber die bitterstoffe des bitterklee's (*Menyanthes tri-*
foliata) und der barbados-aloë (*Aloë hepatica*) ... Halle,
Gebauer-Schwetschke'sche buchdruckerei, 1875.

40 p. diagr. 21ᶜᵐ.

Inaug.-diss.—Jena.

1. [Bitter principles]   I. Title.

Agr 32–689

Library, U. S. Dept. of   Agriculture 387.1L62

NL   0345621   DNAL

Liebelt [Paul] [1887-   ]. *Zur Frage
der Beziehungen der Hysterie zu den funk-
tionellen Psychosen. [Bonn.] 101 pp., 2 l.
8°. Riess, Langer & Winterlich. 1914.

NL   0345622   DNLM CtY MBCo ICRL

Liebelt, Paul Albert, 1880-
    Creation! Why? How? What for? By Paul A. Liebelt.
[Brooklyn, N. Y., George W. Green printing co., inc., ᶜ1933]

16 p. 23ᶜᵐ.

1. Creation. 2. Redemption.

Library of Congress   BS652.L5   33–33096
————— Copy 2.
Copyright AA 131668   [2]   213

NL   0345623   DLC

Liebelt, Paul Albert, 1880-
    The master-key for life's problems, by Paul A. Liebelt ...
Boston, The Christopher publishing house [ᶜ1936]

vii, 9-176 p. 19½ᶜᵐ.

1. Title.
                                          36–360
Library of Congress   PZ3.L62204Mas

NL   0345624   DLC

Lieben, Adolf.
    Festschrift Adolf Lieben zum fünfzigjährigen
Doktorjubiläum und zum siebzigsten Geburtstage
    see under title

Lieben (Adolf). Ueber die Gährung. 48 pp.
12°. *Wien, C. Gerold's Sohn, 1863.*

NL   0345626   DNLM PPAmP

QD   **Lieben, Adolf.**
22   Rede zum Gedächtniss an Ludwig Barth von
+B2   Barthenau; gehalten im Namen der philosophischen
L5   Facultät am 25. April 1891 in der K. K. Uni-
           versität Wien, von Ad. Lieben. Wien, 1891.
           29p. illus. 26cm.

           1. Barth von Barthenau, Ludwig

NL   0345627   WU

Lieben, Albert.

FOR OTHER EDITIONS
SEE MAIN ENTRY

Wauwermans, Paul, 1861-
    Manuel pratique des sociétés anonymes; commentaire des
lois des 18 mai 1873 et 22 mai 1886 modifiées par la Loi du 25
mai 1913, interprétées par les travaux parlemantaires, la doctrine et la jurisprudence, par Paul Wauwermans ... suivi de
formules d'actes de sociétés, par Albert Lieben ... Bruxelles,
É. Bruylant; Paris, Librairie générale de droit et de jurisprudence, 1913.

VOLUME 332

SF
309
.L48
1665

Lieben, Christoff Jacob.
(Christoff Jacob Liebens ...) Kurtz gefasstes Reit-Buch, in welchem angewiesen, wie ein Pferd nach seiner Art und Natur zu erkennen, vollkömlich abzurichten, und zu schönen wolanständigen Geberden zu gewehnen ... Nebst den Gebiss-Buch ... In Leipzig, zu finden bey Christian Kirchnern, 1665.
    ᶜ4₎, 181ᶜ1.ᵉ. 179₎ p. illus. 16 x 20 cm.
    Added title page, engraved.
    "Gedruckt zu Hall   in Sachsen".
    Bookplate of   "G. C. G. V. P."

NL   0345629   MiEM PU CtY

Beinecke
Library
Uzfe45
+671L

Lieben, Christoff Jacob.
Practica et arte di cavalleria, of Oeffeningh en konst des rydens ... in twee deelen vervat, met byvoegingh van een Gebit-Boeck ... Door Christophorus Lieb. Nu vertaelt door Simon de Vries. Utrecht, J. Ribbius, 1671.
    4 p.ℓ., 150p., 1ℓ., 20, [24] p. incl. illus., plates. 37½ cm.
    Added engr. illus. t.-p.
    Plates printed on both sides.
    "Gebit-Boeck" has special t.-p. and separate pagination.

Translation of Christoff Jacob Liebens ... Kurtz gefasstes Reit-Buch ... Halle, 1665.

I. Vries, Simon de, b. 1630, tr.

NL   0345631   CtY

PA6507
.L7

Lieben, Eugen.
Zur biographie Martials. Von dr. Eugen Lieben ... Prag, 1911-12.
    2v. in 1. 23½ᶜᵐ.

Separatabdruck aus dem Jahresberichte des Staatsgymnasiums ... in Prag-Altstadt für das jahr 1910-1911[-1911-1912]

NL   0345632   ICU PU IU NjP

Lieben, Fritz, 1890-
Geschichte der physiologischen chemie, von dr. Fritz Lieben ... Leipzig und Wien, F. Deuticke, 1935.
    ix, ₎1₎, 741, ₎1₎ p., 1 l. diagrs. 24ᶜᵐ.
    Includes bibliographies.

    1. Physiological chemistry—Hist.
    Stanford univ. Library   A C 35-1947
    for Library of Congress
                        QP511.L5
                        ₎a46c1₎†   612.01509

NL   OrU-M
    0345633   CSt NIC CU ICJ NcD-MC NcD CtY-M MiU DLC

Lieben, Fritz, 1890-
Vorstellungen vom Aufbau der Materie im Wandel der Zeiten; eine historische Übersicht. Wien, F. Deuticke, 1953.
    384 p. 25 cm.

    1. Matter. 2. Science—Philosophy. 3. Science—Hist.   I. Title.
    Q175.L52   55-17214₎‡

NL   0345634   DLC WaU UU IEN NIC NNC NN CtY

Lieben, Guilelmus
De verborum *iambicorum ... synaloephis*

see

Lieben, Wilhelm, 1885-

Lieben, Henning von.
... Deutsche in Afrika, von Henning von Lieben. Leipzig, Lühe & co., 1938.
    45 p. map. 21 cm. (Deutsche in Übersee)

    1. Germans in Africa.   I. Title.

NL   0345636   NcD CU NN

Lieben, Henning von.
... Deutsche in Afrika, von Henning von Lieben. Leipzig, Lühe & co., 1938.
    (Deutsche in übersee, hrsg. von E. Barth von Wehrenalp)
    Film copy made in 1943 by the Library of Congress. Negative.

    Collation of the original, as determined from the film: 45 p. map.
    1. Germans in Africa.   44-11402
    Library of Congress   Film DD-1   reel 30, no. 9

NL   0345637   DLC CSt-H IaU RPB CtY NcD NN

Lieben, Koppelmann, 1811-1892, ed.
[Hebrew text]
[Hebrew text]
[Hebrew text]
[Hebrew text]
[Hebrew text] ₎Prag, 1856₎.
    liv, 84 p.; xx, 71 p. 17 cm.
    Added t. p.: Gal-ed; Grabsteininschriften des Prager Isr. alten Friedhofs, mit biographischen Notizen.
    Hebrew and German.

    1. Epitaphs—Prague. 2. Epitaphs—Jews. 3. Jews in Prague.
    I. Rapoport, Salomon Judah Löb, 1790-1867. II. Title.
                        Title transliterated: Gal 'ed.
    DS135.C96P74   55-55435

NL   0345638   DLC MH NNJ NNC

Lieben, Richard, joint author.
... Recherches sur la théorie du prix
    see under   Auspitz, Rudolf, 1837-1906.

Lieben, Richard, joint author.
Auspitz, Rudolf, 1837-1906.
Untersuchungen über die theorie des preises. Von Rudolf Auspitz und Richard Lieben. Leipzig, Duncker & Humblot, 1889.

Lieben, Richard, joint author.
Auspitz, Rudolf, 1837-1906.
Zur theorie des preises. Von Rudolf Auspitz und Richard Lieben. Mit vier steintafeln. Leipzig, Duncker & Humblot, 1887.

Lieben, Ruth von, 1895-   Über die Ätiologie und Symptomatologie der in den jahren 1903-1910 in der Universitätsklinik für innere Medizin zu Königsberg Pr. beobachteten Fälle von primärer Polyzythaemie. [In Maschinenschrift.] 21 S. 4°(2°). — Auszug: ₎Königsberg i. P.₎ 1920: Hartung. 2 Bl. 8°
Königsberg, Med. Diss. v. 6. Juni 1920 [1921], Ref. Matthes
    [Geb. 9. Dez. 95 Neuhausen, Kr. Königsberg; Wohnort: Königsberg i. P.; Staatsangeh.: Preußen; Vorbildung: RG. StA. Königsberg Reife 13; Studium: Königsberg 11 S.; Coll. 7. Nov. 19; Approb. 1. Okt. 20.]   [U 21. 4673]

NL   0345642   ICRL CtY

Lieben, Salomon, 1884-1942
Shechitah, by S. Lieben... New York: Union of Orthodox Jewish Congregations of America₎, cop. 1929₎. 24 p. 16°.
(The Jewish library. Second ser. v. 3.)
    Bibliography, p. 23-24.

    529904A. 1. Slaughtering—Jewish   method.
    N. Y. P. L.   May 27, 1931

NL   0345643   NN NNJ PPDrop

DS
135
P75

Lieben, Salomon Hugo, 1881-1942
Briefe von 1744-1748 über die Austreibung der Juden aus Prag, von S.H. Lieben. Prag, 1932.
    127p.
"Sonderabdruck aus dem Jahrbuch der Gesellschaft für Geschichte der Juden in der Cechoslovakischen Republik. 4. Jahrgang."

    1. Jews in Prague. I. Title. II. Title: Die Austreibung der Juden aus Prag.

NL   0345644   UU

Lieben, Salomon Hugo, ed
Handschriftliches zur geschichte der Juden in Prag in den Jahren 1744-1754. Frankfurt a.M. T. Kauffmann, 1905-6.
    2 v.

NL   0345645   DCU-H NNC OCH

DS 135
.C95 L 7

LIEBEN, SALOMON HUGO, 1881-1942, ed.
Handschriftliches zur Geschichte der Juden in Prag in den Jahren 1744-1754. Frankfurt a.M., J. Kauffmann, 1905.
    66 p.
"Sonderabdruck aus dem Jahrbuch der Jüdisch-Literarischen Gesellschaft, 1904." Text and free translation of Hebrew manuscript 'Be-yamin ha-eleh' in the Israelitische. Gemeindebibliothek, Prague.
    1. Jews--Prague--   Hist. I. Tc.

NL   0345646   InU OU

Lieben, Salomon Hugo, 1881-1942.
Das jüdische Museum in Prag
    see under   Prague. Státní Židovské Museum.

PA
6608
L71

Lieben, Wilhelm, 1885-
De verborum iambicorum apud Plautum synaloephis. Marburg, 1915.
    70 p. 23cm.

    Inaug.-Diss.--Marburg.

    1. Plautus, Titus Maccius--Versification.

NL   0345648   NIC CtY NcD PU OClW ICRL MH IU NjP CU

622.14
L62

Liebenam, Adolf.
Lehrbuch der markscheidekunst und praktischen geometrie. Für bergschulen und andere technische lehranstalten, sowie zum selbstunterrichte bearbeitet von Ad. Liebenam ... Leipzig, A. Mentzel, 1876.
    xvi, 406 p. illus., 2 fold. plates, diagrs. 22ᶜᵐ.

    1. Mine surveying.

NL   0345649   NNC PBL NIC

QA55
.L7

Liebenam, Adolf.
Tafel der vielfachen sinus und cosinus sowie der einfachen tangenten und cotangenten. Für geometer, markscheider und techniker überhaupt, sowie zum gebrauch für bergschulen etc., berechnet und zusammengestellt von Adolf Liebenam ... Eisleben, G. Reichardt (W. Hasenpflug) 1873.
    26, ₎1₎ p. 26½ᶜᵐ.

    1. Trigonometry—Tables, etc.

NL   0345650   ICU

VOLUME 332

Liebenam, Guilelmus
see Liebenam, Wilhelm, 1859–1918.

Liebenam, Leonore, 1897–
... Über das Vorkommen des Trachoms in
Thüringen ... Borna-Leipzig, 1931.
Inaug.-Diss. - Jena.
Lebenslauf.
"Literatur": p. 69–81.
[Full name; Leonore Mary Liebenam]

NL 0345652   CtY ICRL MiU

Liebenam, *Frau* **Lore (Holzhausen)** 1894–
Anschauungen über stadt und land in der englischen litera-
tur des achtzehnten jahrhunderts (mit ausschluss des romans)
... von Lore Liebenam, geb. Holzhausen ... Oberviechtach
(Opf.) Druck I. Forstner, 1928.
viii, 125 p. 22½cm.
Inaug.-diss.—Halle-Wittenberg.
Lebenslauf.
"Literaturverzeichnis": p. 109–124.

1. English literature—18th cent.—Hist. & crit. 2. City and town life.
3. Country life—Gt. Brit. 4. Pastoral poetry, English.
36-30399

Library of Congress   PR449.S6L5 1928
820.903

NL 0345653   DLC ICRL CtY DSI IU MH PU

942
L621   LIEBENAM, *Frau* Lore (Holzhausen) 1894–
Eigenart englischer kultur, von dr. Lore
Liebenam. A holiday in the country, by
Reg. W. Ford, Reading. Engländertum und
Gottesgedanke, von dr. Lore Liebenam...
Halle, Gebauer-Schwetschke verlag nachf.
kg. [c1938]

3 p.l., 9–44 p. illus. 22cm.
(Added t.-p.: Schriften des Deutsch-
englischen kulturaustausches. The Deka
series, hft.1)

1. England. Civilization. 2. National
characteristics, English. I. Ford, Reg-
nald W. II. Title.III.Title:
A holiday in the country. IV. Title:
Engländertum und Gottesgedanke.

NL 0345654   MnU

Liebenam, *Frau* **Lore (Holzhausen)** 1894–   *ed.*
G. F. Handel and Halle; in memory of the 250th anniversary
of the composer's birth, edited by dr. Lore Liebenam. Halle
(Saale) [Deutsch-englischer kulturaustausch] 1935.
[20] p. incl. front., illus. 21ᶜᵐ.
Contents on p. [3] of cover.
Contents.—Handel, the mediator between two peoples, by Lore
Liebenam.—Halle's tribute to Handel, by Newman Flower.—Handel's
mission, by Arnold Schering.—Handel's early youth at Halle, by Walter
Serauky.

1. Händel, Georg Friedrich, 1685–1759. 2. Music—Germany—Halle.
36-32713

Library of Congress   ML410.H13L47
[2]   927.8

NL 0345655   DLC NN

LIEBENAM, Wilhelm 1859–1918.
Aus dem vereinswesen im Römischen Reiche.
2 pt.in 1 vol. [Berlin,1893-04.]

pp.(51)
Zeitschrift für kulturgeschichte,neue (H.)
folge,1893,etc. i.112–138,172–195.

NL 0345656   MH

JC
83
L71   Liebenam, Wilhelm, 1859–1918.
Beiträge zur Verwaltungsgeschichte des
römischen Kaiserreichs. 1. Die Laufbahn
der Procuratoren bis auf die Zeit Diocletians. Jena, E. Frommann, 1886.
160 p. 24cm.

No more published?

1. Rome—Pol.   & govt.

NL 0345657   NIC NjP MH ICU

Liebenam, Wilhelm, 1859–   *comp.*
... Fasti consulares Imperii romani von 30 v. Chr. bis 565
n. Chr., mit kaiserliste und anhang bearb. von Willy Liebenam ... Bonn, A. Marcus und E. Weber's verlag, 1909.
128 p. 20 cm. (Kleine texte für theologische und philologische
vorlesungen und übungen, hrsg. von H. Lietzmann. 41–43)
Cover dated 1910.

1. Rome—Hist.—Chronology.   I. Fasti consulares.

DG202.L5   10—11861

MiU DDO ODW OCU MiU OC1W
NL 0345658   DLC OO NcD NjP PSC PHC PV NIC NNC CaBVaU

DG87
.L7   LIEBENAM, WILHELM, 1859–1918.
Forschungen zur verwaltungsgeschichte des römischen
kaiserreichs, von W.Liebenam... I.bd. Die legaten in
den römischen provinzen von Augustus bis Diocletian.
Leipzig,B.G.Teubner,1888.
v,[1],482 p. 23cm.
No more published.
"Fortsetzung meiner im jahre 1886 erschienenen Bei-
träge theil I."--Vorwort.
Bibliographical foot-notes.
1.Rome—Provinces   --Administration.

OC1W PPL
NL 0345659   ICU MH PU KU NIC WU NjP MdBJ NNC OCU

DG83
.5
P3L5   Liebenam, Wilhelm, 1859–1918.
Die Laufbahn der Procuratoren bis auf die
Zeit Diocletians. Erster Teil. Der Philosophischen Facultät zu Jena zur Erlangung
der Venia Docendi, eingereicht von W. Liebenam. Jena, A. Neuenhahn, 1886.
102 p.

"Bemerkung: Der zweite Teil erscheint zugleich mit dem ersten vereinigt unter dem
Titel: Beiträge zur Verwaltungsgeschichte
des römischen Kaiserreichs."
Bibliographical footnotes.

NL 0345660   CU ICRL MH NjP

Liebenam, Wilhelm 1859–1918.
Qvaestionvm epigraphicarvm de imperii romani
administratione capita selecta.
Inaug. Diss. Bonn, 1882.

NL 0345661   ICRL NjP NBuU OCU

Liebenam, W[ilhelm] 1859–1918.
Städteverwaltung im Römischen kaiserreiche. Von
W. Liebenam. Leipzig, Duncker & Humblot, 1900.
xviii, 577, [1] p. 22½ᶜᵐ.
Contents.—Einnahmen und ausgaben der städte.—Städtische vermö-
gensverwaltung.—Staat und stadt.

1. Cities, Ancient.

Library of Congress   DG81.L71
1-G-1071

NjP
NL 0345662   DLC NSyU NIC DDO CtY OU MiU PBm PU ICJ

DG109
.G46L7   LIEBENAM, WILHELM, 1859–1918.
(C1)   Zur geschichte und organisation des römischen ver-
einswesens. Drei untersuchungen von W.Liebenam ...
Leipzig,B.G.Teubner,1890.
viii,334,[1]p. 23cm.

1.Gilds--Rome.

NL 0345663   ICU PBm PU MiU CtY NjP NcD NIC CU DDO

Liebenam, Willy
see Liebenam, Wilhelm, 1859–1918.

230.06
T390
v.51   [Liebenau, von]
Beurtheilung des Gutachtens, betreffend die
Uebergabe der höhern Lehranstalt des Kantons
Luzern an die Gesellschaft Jesu. Luzern, X.
Meyer, 1842.
28 p.
"Vorwort" signed: Dr. v. Liebenau.
Bound with other pamphlets.

1. Lucerne (Canton)--Education. 2. Jesuits in
Lucerne (Canton) I. Title.

NL 0345665   TxDaM-P

Hoehn
Collection   Liebenau, A. von
Charakterbilder aus Luzern's vergangenheit ...
Nach geschichtlichen quellen von A. von Liebenau.
Luzern, C. F. Prell's buchhandlung, 1884–1891.
2v. 24cm.

Contents: v.1. Petermann Feer, Kaspar Pfyffer,
Hans Schürpf. – v.2. Hesso von Rynach, Anna Russ,
Marschall Jost von Durler.

NL 0345666   LNHT MH OU

Liebenau, Alix Rohde-
see
Rohde-Liebenau, Alix.

---

ar X
750   Liebenau, Ed   von
Ein Ausflug nach dem Sinai.
Wiesbaden, J. F. Bergmann, 1896.
66 p. illus. 26cm.

1. Sinaitic Peninsula--Descr. & trav.
I. Title.

NL 0345668   NIC NjP MB

Liebenau, Erich, 1902–
Der grundbesitz der stadt Stralsund
Inaug. Diss. Greifswald, 1930.

NL 0345669   ICRL MiU CtY PU

Liebenau Eugen, 1870–
Die photogrammetische beurteilung des tier-
koerpers.
Inaug. diss. Leipzig, 1904.
58 p. 21[1]. 26 cm

NL 0345670   ICRL MH PU

VOLUME 332

Liebenau, Eugen, 1870-
Die photogrammetrische beurteilung
des tierkörpers. Von Eugen Liebenau ...
Berlin, P. Parey, 1904.
58p. 21pl. 26cm.

NL 0345671   PSt

Liebenau, Eugen, 1882-
Ist die Bevollmächtigung nach dem Bürgerlichen Gesetzbuch ein kausales oder
ein abstractes Rechtsgeschäft? Worin bestehen die Konsequenzen der einen und
der anderen Auffassung? ... von Eugen
Liebenau ... Greifswald, J. Abel, 1905.
vi p., 1 l., 84 p. 22½cm.
Inaug.-Diss. - Greifswald.
"Literatur": p.[v]-vi.

NL 0345672   MH-L ICRL NN

Hoehn Collection Liebenau, Hermann von, 1807-1874.
Arnold Winkelried, seine zeit und seine that.
Ein historisches bild nach neuesten forschungen ...
Aarau, H. R. Sauerländer, 1862.
xiv, 232 p. fold. table. 21cm.

With this is bound: Meyer von Knonau, G. Die
sage von der befreiung der Waldstätte ... 1873.

1. Winkelried, Arnold. 2. Switzerland —
Hist. I. Title.

NL 0345673   LNHT OrU MH

LIEBENAU, Hermann VON.
Förderung der Eidgenossenschaft durch des
Hauses Habsburg innere Verhältnisse. Lucern,
1857.
4°. pp.56. Colored plate.

NL 0345674   MH

LIEBENAU, Hermann VON.
Die geschichtlichen Ursachen der Entstehung
einer schweizerischen Eidgenossenschaft.
Dargestellt nach quellen. Lucern, 1857.
4°. pp.42. Fac-simile.

NL 0345675   MH

Liebenau, Hermann von.
Hundert Urkunden zu der Geschichte der Königin
Agnes, Wittwe von Ungarn, 1288-1364. Regensburg,
G. J. Manz, 1869.
xii, 192 p.

1. Agnes, consort of Andrew III, King of
Hungary, 1281-1364.

NL 0345676   WaU CaBVaU

Liebenau, Hermann von.
Lebens-Geschichte der Königin Agnes von
Ungarn, der letzten Habsburgerin des erlauchten
Stammhauses aus dem Aargone. Regensburg,
G. J. Manz, 1868.
lvi, 590 p. 22cm.

1. Agnes, consort of Andrew III, King of
Hungary, 1288-1364.

NL 0345677   WU CaBVaU

DQ 92 L71 Liebenau, Hermann von, 1807-1874.
Die Tell-Sage zu dem Jahre 1230; historisch nach neuesten Quellen beleuchtet.
Aarau, H. R. Sauerländer, 1864.
x, 171 p. 19cm.

1. Tell, Wilhelm.

NL 0345678   NIC OC1 OO CU KU MH MdBP PU

LIEBENAU, Hermann von, 1807-1874.
Die Winkelriede von Stans bis auf Arnold
Winkelried, den helden von Sempach nach urkunden.

(In MITTHEILUNGEN der Antiquarischen gesellschaft in Zürich, 9er bd., 1853. 4°. pp. 29-63.)

NL 0345679   MH

Liebenau, Theodor von, 1840-1914.
Das alte Luzern topographisch-kulturgeschichtlich geschildert.
Mit vier bildern nach Diebold Schilling's Chronik vom jahre 1512.
Luzern, C. F. Prell, 1881.
pp. (2), 323 +. Plates.

Lucerne-Descr.||

NL 0345680   MH PU LNHT

DQ 309 .8 L71 Liebenau, Theodor von, 1840-1914.
Burg Wildeck und ihre Bewohner; nach
alten Dokumenten bearb. Brugg, 18 -19
v. illus. 19cm.

1. Wildeck Castle. I. Title.

NL 0345681   NIC

Hoehn Collection Liebenau, Theodor von, 1840-1914.
Die chronisten des stiftes Neuchâtel.
n.p., n.p., n.d.
23p. 22cm.

Caption title.

1. Neuchâtel — Biog. I. Title.

NL 0345682   LNHT

Liebenau, Theodor von, 1840-1914.
Die Familie Schnyder von Wartensee in Sursee und
Luzern; historische Notizen. Bearb. von Th. von Liebenau. Luzern, J. Schill's Erben, 1906.
158 p. illus.

1. Schnyder von Wartensee family

NL 0345683   MH

Liebenau, Theodor von, 1840-1914.
Der franziskaner dr. Thomas Murner, von dr. Theodor
von Liebenau ... Freiburg im Breisgau [etc.] 1913.
viii, 266 p. 23ᶜᵐ. (Added t.-p.: Erläuterungen und ergänzungen zu
Janssens Geschichte des deutschen volkes ... IX. bd., 4. u. 5. hft.)

I. Murner, Thomas, 1475-1537.
                                               20-22127
Library of Congress   DD176.J26 1x. bd., 4.-5. hft.

NL 0345684   DLC IEN DHN MiU OU GU

Liebenau, Theodor von, 1840-
Das gasthof- und wirthshauswesen der Schweiz in ael-
terer zeit. Von Dr. Theodor von Liebenau ... Zürich,
J. A. Preuss, 1891.
x, 347 p. front., illus., pl. (partly fold.) 23½ᶜᵐ.

                                               6-4090

NL 0345685   DLC LNHT ICJ MB

Hoehn Collection [Liebenau, Theodore von] 1840-1914.
Das geleit am Gotthard. Ein beitrag zur
erklärung der Tellsage. n.p., n.p., n.d.
9p. 23cm.

Caption title.

1. Tell, Wilhelm. I. Title.

NL 0345686   LNHT

LIEBENAU, Theodor von, 1840-
Geschichte der fischerei in der Schweiz...
Erworben und veröffentlicht vom eidgenössischen
Departement des innern... Bern, Buchdruckerei
Michel & Büchler, 1897.
V p., 1 l., 207 p. front, 23 1/2 cm.

NL 0345687   MH

LIEBENAU, Theodor VON.
Geschichte der Freiherren von Attinghusen und
von Schweinsberg. Ein Beitrag zur Geschichte
der Urkantone. Aarau, 1860.
The name subscribed to the "Vorwort] is "Dr.
H. v. Liebenau."

NL 0345688   MH

Liebenau, Theodor von, 1840-
Geschichte des Klosters Königsfelden. Hrsg. im
historischen Theil der Katholischen Schweizerblätter
für christliche Wissenschaft und Kunst. Luzern, In
Kommission von Gebr. Räber, 1868
192 p.

NL 0345689   MH

NK5304 .L62q (SA) Liebenau, Theodor von, 1840-1914.
Die Glasgemälde der ehemaligen Bene-
diktinerabtei Muri im Aargauischen Museum für
Kunst und Gewerbe in Aarau. Hrsg. von der
Mittelschweizerischen Geographisch-Kommerziellen Gesellschaft in Aarau. 2., verm. und
verb. Aufl. Aarau, Verlag der Mittelschweizerischen Geographisch-Kommerziellen Gesellschaft,
1892.
28 p. illus., plates. 38 cm.
In portfolio.
"Separat-Ausgabe aus "Völkerschau",
Band I, II and III."

NL 0345690   MB NjP MiD

Hoehn Collection Liebenau, Theodor von, 1840-1914.
Hans Holbein d. J. Fresken am Hertenstein-
Hause in Luzern nebst einer geschichte der familie
Hertenstein ... Luzern, C. F. Prell, 1888.
236 p. front., photographs. 24cm.

1. Holbein, Hans, the younger, 1497-1543.
2. Hertenstein family. 3. Switzerland — Genealogy.
I. Title.

NL 0345691   LNHT

VOLUME 332

Liebenau, Theodor von, 1840-1914.
... Das Kloster Königsfelden. Geschichtlich
dargestellt von Th. von Liebenau, kunstgeschichtlich von Wilhelm Lübke. Hrsg. von der
antiquarischen Gesellschaft in Zürich. Zürich,
In Commission bei Ebner & Seubert in Stuttgart,
1867.
2 f., 50, 8 p. plans. (Denkmäler des
Hauses Habsburg in der Schweiz. III).

NL 0345692 DHN

Hoehn Collection
Liebenau, Theodor von, 1840-1914.
Eine münzgenossenschaft der Urschweiz,
1548-1552 ... Basel, Emil Birkhäuser, 1887.
22 p. plate. 22cm.

Separat-abdruck aus dem Bulletin de la
Société suisse de numismatique. Bd. 6.

1. Numismatics – Switzerland. I. Title.

NL 0345693 LNHT

[Liebenau, Theodor von] 1840-
Oberst Joseph Amrhyn und der fall von Turin
n.p., [18?]
29 p.
Without title-page. Caption title.
Signed: Th. v. Liebenau.

NL 0345694 MH

Liebenau, Theodor von, 1840-1914
Ritter Melchior Russ von Luzern; Vortrag, gehalten
im Historischen Verein in Luzern.

p.[299]-314, [343]-356, [384]-393
Extracts from Katholische Schweizer-Blätter, 12.
Jahrgang, oder Neue Folge, 2.Band, 6.Heft, 1870

1. Russ, Melchior, Ritter von Lucern

NL 0345695 MH

Hoehn Collection
Liebenau, Theodor von, 1840-1914.
Die schlacht bei Sempach. Gedenkbuch zur
fünften säcularfeier. Im auftrage des h.
Regierungrathes des kantons Luzern ... Luzern,
C. F. Prell, 1886.
2 p.ℓ., 468p. front., plates, facsims., fold.
maps. 23cm.

1. Sempach, Battle of. I. Title.

NL 0345696 LNHT CU MU ICN NN MH ICU PU

4DQ-
50
Liebenau, Theodor von, 1840-1916.
Die Schlacht bei Sempach; Gedenkbuch zur
fünften Säcularfeier. Im Auftrage des h.
Regierungrathes des Kantons Luzern.
Luzern, C.F. Prell, 1886.
80 p.

NL 0345697 DLC-P4

Liebenau, Theodor von, 1840-
Ueberblick über die geschichte der buchdruckerei der stadt
Luzern, verfasst von dr. Th. von Liebenau, Luzern. Gedenkblatt zur 500-jahrigen Gutenberg-feier. Luzern, H. Keller,
1900.
2 p. l., 5-62 p. 23cm.
Head and tail pieces.

1. Printing—Hist.—Lucerne.
3—27012
Library of Congress Z176.L9L7

NL 0345698 DLC MH ICJ

Liebenau, Theodor von, 1840-
Urkundenbuch des stiftes Bero-münster
see under Beromuenster, Switzerland. Bero
Münster (abbey).

Hoehn Collection
Liebenau, Theodor von, 1840-1914.
Zum schrätteliglauben. Zürich, Emil Cotti
1899.
p.248-249. 25cm.

Separat-abdruck, Schweizerisches archiv für
volkskunde. 3. jhrg. Heft 3.

1. Superstitions.

NL 0345700 LNHT

Liebenau, Theodor von Huber-
see Huber-Liebenau, Theodor von.

Liebenberg, Adolph, *ritter von*, 1851-
Ueber das verhalten des wassers im boden ... Halle,
Buchdr. des Waisenhauses, 1873.
2 p. l., 34, (2) p. fold. tables. 23cm.
Inaug.-diss.—Halle.
Vita.

1. Soil moisture.
12–14380
Library of Congress S594.L6

NL 0345702 DLC

Liebenberg, Adolph, *ritter von*, 1851-
Untersuchungen über die bodenwärme ... Halle, 1875.
41 p. 23cm.
Habilitationsschrift—Halle.

1. Agricultural physics.
12–11296 Additions
Library of Congress S589.L7

NL 0345703 DLC

Liebenberg, Adolf, *ritter von*.
... Die versuchsthätigkeit des praktischen landwirthes
auf grund der erfahrungen des Vereines zur förderung
des landwirthschaftlichen versuchswesens in Oesterreich,
erörtert von dr. Adolf, ritter v. Liebenberg ... Wien,
K. u. K. Hofbuchhandlung W. Frick, 1895.
39 p. 19½cm. (Kurze berichte des Vereines zur förderung des landwirthschaftlichen versuchswesens in Oesterreich ... 2. hft.)

1. Agriculture. Experimentation.
Agr 10–1669
Library, U. S. Dept. of Agriculture 30L621

NL 0345704 DNAL

PT8152
.A5A63
1893
Liebenberg, Frederik Ludwig, 1810-1894, ed.
FOR OTHER EDITIONS
SEE MAIN ENTRY
Oehlenschläger, Adam Gottlob, 1779-1850.
Aladdin; eller, Den forunderlige lampe, dramatisk eventyr
af Adam Oehlenschläger, udgivet ved F. L. Liebenberg, illus-
treret af Hans Nik. Hansen. Kjøbenhavn, P. G. Philipsen,
1893.

Liebenberg, Frederik Ludvig, 1810-1894, ed.
Baldur hiin Gode
see under Oehlenschläger, Adam Gottlob,
1779-1850.

Liebenberg, Frederik Ludvig, 1810-1894.
Betænkning over den holbergske orthographi. For det Holbergske samfund. Af F. L. Liebenberg. Kjøbenhavn, Trykt
hos L. Klein, 1845.
32, (4), 6 p. 23½cm.
"Prøve paa den forehavende (Holberg-)udgaves orthographiske for-
hold til udgaven af 1731" (facsimile reprint) : 10 pages at end.

1. Holberg, Ludvig, baron—Language. I. Holbergske samfund.
30–20436
Library of Congress PT8094.L5

NL 0345707 DLC NIC CtY

Liebenberg, Frederik Ludvig, 1810-1894.
Oehlenschläger, Adam Gottlob, 1779-1850.
Bidrag til den Oehlenschlägerske literaturs historie.
(Kjøbenhavn) Samfundet til den danske literaturs fremme,
1868.

Liebenberg, Frederik Ludvig, 1810-1894, ed.
FOR OTHER EDITIONS
SEE MAIN ENTRY
Holberg, Ludvig, *baron*, 1684-1754.
Den danske skueplads, eller Holbergs comedier. Udgivne
ved F. L. Liebenberg. 3. opl. Kjøbenhavn, Forlagsbureauet,
1884.

Liebenberg, Frederik Ludvig, 1810-1894, ed.
Holberg, Ludvig, *baron*, 1684-1754.
Ludvig Holbergs comedier, udgivne for det Holbergske
samfund af F. L. Liebenberg ... Kjøbenhavn. Berlingske
bogtrykkeri, 1848-54.

Liebenberg, Frederik Ludvig, 1810-1894.
Holberg, Ludvig, *baron*, 1684-1754.
Ludvig Holbergs comoedier i urval; utgifna på originalsprå-
ket samt språkligt og estetisk belysta af Carl R. Nyblom och
Helena Nyblom ... Stockholm, Fahlcrantz & co., 1888-(90)

Liebenberg, Frederik Ludvig, 1810-1894, ed.
Staffeldt, Adolph Wilhelm Schack von, 1769-1826.
Schack Staffeldts digte, udgivne af F. L. Liebenberg. Med
en charakteristik af digteren ved Georg Brandes. Kjøbenhavn, P. G. Philipsen, 1882.

Liebenberg, Frederik Ludvig, 1810-1894, ed.
Bredahl, Christian Hviid, 1784-1860.
Dramatiske scener. Af C. Bredahl. 2. forkortede udg.
... Kjøbenhavn, Samfundet til den danske litteraturs
fremme, 1855.

Liebenberg, Frederik Ludvig, ed.
Helge. 1894
see under Oehlenschläger, Adam Gottlob,
1779-1850.

Liebenberg, Frederik Ludvig, 1810-1894, ed.
Holberg, Ludvig, *baron*, 1684-1754.
Ludvig Holbergs Helte-historier. Udg. af F. L. Liebenberg ... Kjøbenhavn, Samfundet til den danske litteraturs
fremme, 1864-65.

VOLUME 332

Liebenberg, Frederik Ludvig, 1810-1894, ed.
Holberg, Ludvig, *baron*, 1684-1754.
Jubeludgave af Ludvig Holbergs samtlige comoedier ved F. L. Liebenberg ... Med 4 bilag, ornamenterede af Arnold Krog. I. Georg Brandes: Ludvig Holberg som komedieforfatter. II. Edgar Collin: Holbergske skuespillere. III. Axel Grandjean: Traditionel musik til komedierne. IV. Otto Zinck: Holbergsk theaterstatistik. Illustrationernes historiske troskab under medvirkning af Bernh. Olsen. Kjøbenhavn. E. Bojesen ₁1883-88₁

Liebenberg, Frederik Ludvig, 1810-1894, ed.
Holberg, Ludvig, *baron*, 1684-1754.
Ludvig Holbergs kirke-historie. Udg. ved F. L. Liebenberg. Med en indledning af R. Nielsen ... Kjøbenhavn, Samfundet til den danske literaturs fremme, 1867-68.

Liebenberg, Frederik Ludvig, 1810-1894, ed.
Holberg, Ludvig, *baron*, 1684-1754.
Ludvig Holbergs mindre poetiske skrifter. Udg. af F. L. Liebenberg. Kjøbenhavn, Samfundet til den danske literaturs fremme, 1866.

4PT   Liebenberg, Frederik Ludvig, 1810-1894.
Den.   Nogle Optegnelser om mit levned.
409   Kjøbenhavn, Gyldendalske Boghandels Forlag, 1894.
       143 p.

NL   0345719   DLC-P4 MdBJ KU

Liebenberg, Frederik Ludvig, 1810-1894, ed.
Staffeldt, Adolph Wilhelm Schack von, 1769-1826.
Schack Staffeldts samlede digte ... Udg. af F. L. Liebenberg ... Kjøbenhavn, Samfundet til den danske literaturs fremme, 1843.

Liebenberg, Frederik Ludvig, 1810-1894, ed.
Ewald, Johannes, 1743-1781.
Johannes Ewalds samtlige skrifter. Udg. ved understøttelse af Samfundet for den danske litteraturs fremme ... Kjøbenhavn, E. L. Thaarup, 1850-55.

Liebenberg, Frederik Ludvig, 1810-1894.
Holberg, Ludvig, *baron*, 1684-1754.
Tegner udgave af Ludvig Holbergs samtlige comoedier; Liebenbergs textudgave. Kjøbenhavn, E. Bojesen, 1896.

Liebenberg, Frederik Ludvig, 1810-1894, ed.
Oehlenschläger, Adam Gottlob, 1779-1850.
Oehlenschlägers tragoedier i udvalg ved F. L. Liebenberg ... Kjøbenhavn, Selskabet til udgivelse af Oehlenschlägers skrifter, 1879.

Leibenberg, Hans, 1906-
    ... Der Einfluss des Kaufflächenreliefs der Zähne auf die mechanische Zerkleinerung von Speisen ...   Speicher [1930]
    Inaug.-Diss. - Bonn.
    Lebenslauf.
    "Literaturverzeichnis": p. 19.

NL   0345724   CtY ICRL

Ltfj77   Liebenberg, Johannes Jacobus, 1890-
B5   Die Geschichte des Berufs- und Fachschulwesens
933ℓ   in Südafrika ... Kallmünz,M.Lassleben,1933.
           vii,171,[1]p. 23cm.
           Inaug.-diss. - München.
           Lebenslauf.
           "Literatur-Verzeichnis": p.[166]-171.

NL   0345725   CtY PBm MiU PU

HA40   Liebenberg, Maurice,
15L5   Constructing an income size distribution from income tax
Social   data, 1944 [by] Maurice Liebenberg and Hyman Kaitz.   [n. p.,
Sciences 1949?]
           94 ℓ. illus.

       At head of title: Conference on Research in Income and
       Wealth, April 1949.
       "Preliminary and confidential. "

       1. Income - Stat. I. Kaitz, Herman, joint author. II. Title.

NL   0345726   CU

LIEBENBERG, Michael Frederik, 1767-1828.
   Turandot,prindsesse af China; tragikomisk skuespil i fem optog efter Schillers bearbeidelse af Gozzis original. Kjøbenhavn,J.F. Schultz,1815.

NL   0345727   MH

---

40   Liebenberg, Otto.
L622   Die Besamung der Haustiere, insbesondere
         des Rindes.   Radebeul, Neumann [1952]
         80 p.

         1. Impregnation, Artificial.

NL   0345728   DNAL

Liebenberg, Otto.
    Der Einfluss verschiedener Umweltfaktoren auf die Befruchtungsfähigkeit der Vatertiere unter besonderer Berücksichtigung des Spermabildes. Radebeul, Neumann ₁1953₁
    87 p. illus. 25 cm.
    Includes bibliography.

    1. Fecundity. 2. Spermatozoa. 3. Stock and stock-breeding. I. Title.
    SF105.L5   55-18303 ‡

NL   0345729   DLC DNAL MoU NIC IU

Liebenberg, Richard.
    Berufsberatung; methode und technik. Ein handbuch für die praxis, von dr. Richard Liebenberg ... Leipzig, Quelle & Meyer, 1925.
    viii, 234 p. incl. forms. 22ᶜᵐ.
    "Handbücherei für den berufsberater (zugleich literaturnachweis zur berufsberatung)": p. 138-145.

    1. Profession, Choice of. ₁1. Vocational guidance₁   I. Title.
    Library, U. S. Dept. of   Labor   L 26-59

NL   0345730   DL PU ICRL

Liebenberg, Richard, 1888-
    Über das Schätzen von Mengen ...
Leipzig, 1914.
    Pamphlet.
    Inaug.-Diss. - Berlin.
    Lebenslauf.
    Full name: Richard Paul Franz Liebenberg.

NL   0345731   CtY RPB

Liebenberg, Richard, 1888-
   Über das schätzen von mengen ...
Leipzig, J.A. Barth, 1914.
   2 p. l., 75, [1] p.
   Film copy of the original at Harvard.
Negative.
   Thesis - Berlin.
   Lebenslauf.

NL   0345732   RPB

Liebenberg, Richard Paul Franz
    see Liebenberg, Richard, 1888-

Liebenberg, Skalk, 1905-
    Die dromer, en ander Bybelverhale, deur Skalk Liebenberg.
    Herdruk.   Stellenbosch, Die Christen-studentevereniging van Suid-Afrika, 1946.   167 p.   19cm.

426624B. 1. Bible—Hist. of events,   Juvenile.
N. Y. P. L.   March 19, 1948

NL   0345734   NN

Liebendörfer (G. Eugen). "Ueber den Einfluss des Tropenklimas auf den Europäer, mit besonderer Berücksichtigung Ostindiens. 50 pp. 8°. *Basel, Schultze*, 1886.

NL   0345735   DNLM

PN1664   Liebeneiner, Wolfgang, 1906-
.M8   Müller, Gottfried, 1908-
         Dramaturgie des theaters und des films, von dr. Gottfried Müller; mit einem beitrag von professor Wolfgang Liebeneiner ... Würzburg, K. Triltsch, 1944.

Liebener, Heinrich Richard Ottocar
    see   Liebener, Ottocar, 1844-

Liebener, Leonhard.
    Die mineralien Tirols nach ihrem eigenthümlichen vorkommen in den fundorten, beschreiben von Leonhard Liebener ... und Johann Vorhauser ... Innsbruck. Im verlage der Wagner'schen buchhandlung, 1852.
    xii p., 2 l., 303, ₁1₁ p. 18½ᶜᵐ.

    1. Mineralogy—Tyrol. I. Vorhauser, Johann, joint author.
                                               G S 33-223
    Libr., U. S. Geol. Surv.,   Geo. F. Kunz Collection
                                  K103 (533) L62

NL   0345738   DI-GS MH

Liebener   , Ottocar) [1844-
    ]. Ueber Sternopagen mit besonderer Berücksichtigung der inneren Organisation. 28 pp. 2 l., 1 pl. 8°. *Halle, Plötz,* [1870].

Full name: Heinrich Richard Ottocar Liebener

NL   0345739   DNLM ICRL

Liebenfels, Jörg Lanz von
    see Lanz-Liebenfels, Jörg.

VOLUME 332

Liebenmeister (C.) Ueber Hysterie und deren Behandlung.
In: SAMML. klin. Vortr., Leipz., 1883, No. 236 (Inn. Med., No. 82, 2129-2158).

NL 0345741 DNLM

Liebenow, Carl
see Liebenow, Karl Heinrich Joachim Bernhard, 1855-1905.

W 4
B51
1939
Liebenow, Erwin, 1915-
Kryptorchismus und maligne Entartung.
Jena, Werkstätte, 1938 [i.e. 1939?]
43 p.

Inaug.-Diss. - Berlin.
Bibliography: p. 39-43.

NL 0345743 DNLM

Liebenow (Franz Moritz Conrad) [1859-].
* Ueber ausgedehnte Epidermis-Bekleidung der Schleimhaut der Harnwege mit Bildung eines metastatischen Cholesteatoms am Zwerchfell. 23 pp. 8°. *Marburg, R. Friedrich*, 1891.

NL 0345744 DNLM

Liebenow, Guilelmus Heinricus Ferdinandus
see Liebenow, Wilhelm Heinrich Ferdinand, 1821-

Liebenow, Karl Heinrich Joachim Bernhard, 1853-1906
Der elektrische widerstand der metalle, von C. Liebenow... Halle a. S., W. Knapp, 1897.
63 p. tables, diagrs. 21½cm. (Encyclopädie der electrochemie. bd. 10)

Errata sheet attached.

NL 0345746 NNC OU CU

Liebenow, Karl Heinrich Joachim Bernhard, 1853-1906.
Ueber die abhängigkeit der kapazität der bleiakkumulatoren von der stromstärke ... Berlin, Druck von O. Elsner, 1905.
1 p. l., 32 p., 1 l. diagrs. 21½cm.
Inaug.-diss.—Göttingen.
Vita.

1. Storage batteries.

6—46806

Library of Congress QC605.L7

NL 0345747 DLC CU CtY ICJ NN

Liebenow, Karl Richard Franz, 1898-
Spätwirkungen erschöpfender muskelarbeit auf den sauerstoffverbrauch. IV. Mitteilung. Der verlauf der erholungskurve unmittelbar nach der anstrengung. Berlin, 1927.
40-60 p.
Inaug.-Diss. - Universität zu Berlin.
From Zeitschrift für die gesamte experimentelle Medizin, Bd. 59.

NL 0345748 OU DNLM ICRL

WO
278
C5
L716
Liebenow, Roland Rudolph,
A clinical evaluation of the effects of chloroform on the cardiovascular system, by Roland R. Liebenow, O. Sidney Orth, Clayton P. Wangeman and Ralph M. Waters.
15l., illus., 28 cm.

Xerox copy of M. D. Thesis, Wisconsin, 1948.

1. Chloroform. 2. Cardiovascular system. Effect of anesthesia I. Orth, Sidney O. II. Wangeman, Clayton P. III. Waters, Ralph H.

NL 0345749 IParkA

WO
278
C5
L716
Liebenow, Roland Rudolph.
A laboratory re-evaluation of the hepatic renal and cardiovascular effects of chloroform. II. A clinical evaluation of the effects of chloroform on the cardiovascular system.
28l., illus., 28 cm.

Xerox copy of Thesis, University of Wisconsin, 1948.

1. Chloroform. 2. Kidneys. Effect of anesthesia. 3. Cardiovascular system. Effect of anesthesia.

NL 0345750 IParkA

Liebenow, Wilhelm.
Die promulgation. Von dr. Wilhelm Liebenow. Berlin, E. Ebering, 1901.
xv, 124 p. 22½cm.
"Litteratur": p. [vii]-xv.

1. Legislation. I. Title.

38-33796

NL 0345751 DLC MH-L ICRL NN

Liebenow, Wilhelm, 1822-1897.
Eisenbahn- und Reise-Karte von Mittel-Europa.
= Berlin. Berliner lithographisches Institut. 1890. Size, 27¾ × 29¾ inches. Scale, 1:2,000,000 (or, 189.4 miles to 1 inch.) Folded.

G9411 — Europe, Central. Geog. Maps.

NL 0345752 MB

Liebenow, Wilhelm, 1822-1897.
Karte der europäischen Türkei.
= [Berlin.] Berliner lithographisches Institut. [1876.] Size, 24¾ × 34¼ inches. Scale, 1:1250000 (or, 19.7 miles to 1 inch).
Submap.—Constantinopel u. der Bosporus.

K8391 — Turkey. Geog. Maps.

NL 0345753 MB

Liebenow, Wilhelm, 1822-1897.
W. Liebenow's Karte der Rheinprovinz und der Provinz Westfalen. Section III. (Trier.)
Berlin. Berliner lithogr. Institut. [187-?] Size, 21 × 20¾ inches. Scale, 1:240000 (or, 3.8 miles to 1 inch).

H2461 — Rhine Province. Geog. Maps.

NL 0345754 MB

Liebenow, Wilhelm, 1822-
Karte der Umgegend von Düsseldorf.
= Berlin. Schropp. [1866?] Size, 20¼ × 25⅜ inches. Scale, 1:80000 (or, 1.07 miles to 1 inch). Folded.
The title is on the cover.

F4118 — Duesseldorf, Germany. Descr. Maps.

NL 0345755 MB

Liebenow, Wilhelm, 1822-
Karte vom Deutschen Reiche zur übersicht der Eisenbahnen, einschl. der Linien, der Gewässer und hauptsächlichsten Strassen. Berlin, 1891.
col. map on 2 sheets 67 x 104 cm.
Scale 1:1, 250,000.
1. Railroads - Germany - Maps.
2. Germany - Maps.

NL 0345756 NIC

Liebenow, Wilhelm, 1822-
Prof. W. Liebenow's Kriegs-Karte von Frankreich... Berlin: Gea Verlag, G. m. b. H. [1915.]
Scale: 1 = 1 250 000. Approx. 20 m. = 1 in.
Size within border: →27½ × ↑39½ in.
Printed in color.
1 sheet, folded.
The map has his "Kriegs-Karte von Mitteleuropa" printed on verso.

1. European war, 1914- —Maps. 2. France.—Maps, 1915.
N. Y. P. L. September 21, 1915.

NL 0345757 NN

Liebenow, Wilhelm, 1822-
Prof. W. Liebenow's Kriegs-Karte von Mitteleuropa... Berlin: Gea Verlag G. m. b. H. [1915.] (Map on verso of his: Kriegs-Karte von Frankreich... Berlin, 1915.)
Scale: 1 = 2 000 000. Approx. 31½ m. = 1 in.
Size within border: →30 × ↑27¾ in.
Printed in color.
Inset map: Mittel-Italien.
Maps on left margin: Britische Inseln. Scale: 1 = 6 000 000. Approx. 95 m. = 1 in. Size, 7⅛ × 7¼ in.
Frankreich. Scale: 1 = 6 000 000. Size, 7⅛ × 7¼ in.
Russland. Scale: 1 = 10 000 000. Approx. 158 m. = 1 in. Size, →7⅛ × ↑10¼ in.

1. European war, 1914- —Maps. 2. Europe.—Maps, 1915. 3. Great Britain.—Maps, 1915. 4. Russia.—Maps, 1915.
N. Y. P. L. September 13, 1915.

NL 0345758 NN

G6060s
300
.L5
Liebenow, Wilhelm, 1822-
Mittel-Europa. Hannover, Hermann Oppermann [1900-
col.maps 28x38cm.

Scale 1:300,000.
Indexed with Germany--Reichsamt für Landesaufnahme, Übersichtskarte von Mitteleuropa G6060s 300 G411.

1. Europe, Central--1900-

NL 0345759 IU

Liebenow, Wilhelm, 1822-
Special-karte von Mittel-Europa. Verlag von Herm. Oppermann in Hannover...Berlin [186- ?-76]
79 sheets.

NL 0345760 NN

Liebenow, Wilhelm, 1822-
1822-1897.
1877047 W. Liebenow's Special-Karte von Mittel-Europa im Massstabe von 1:300 000. Hannover, H. Oppermann, [1871-1875].
Library has sheet no. 30, 42, 47, 54, 55, 60, 67-69, 74, 81-83, 88-91, 95-97, 100-105, 109-119, 123-125, 130-133, 137-139, and 2 index maps. 27 x 36cm.
These are the sheets issued during the above years, with the exception of no. 35 and 75. *cf.* Heinsius' Bücher-Lexikon.
Complete in 164 sheets.
Title taken from index map.

NL 0345761 ICJ

VOLUME 332

Liebenow, Wilhelm, 1822-
Übersichtskarte der deutschen Nord u. Ost-See Küste.
Berlin. Berliner lithographisches Institut. 1870. Size, 16½ ×
40½ inches. Scale, 1:1250000 (or, 19.7 miles to 1 inch).
Reprinted from his Eisenbahnkarte von Deutschland.

H3461 — Germany. Geog. Maps.

NL 0345762   MB

Liebenow, Wilhelm, 1822-
Übersichts-Karte der Länder zurischen Berlin u. Paris.
Berlin. Berliner lithogr. Institut. 1870. Size, 23⅜ × 28¾
inches. Scale, 1:1250000 (or, 272½ miles to 1 inch).
Besonderer Abdruck aus W. Liebenow's Eisenbahnkarte von Central-
Europa.
To illustrate the Franco-German War.

H2667 — Franco-German War, 1870, 1871. Maps.

NL 0345763   MB

Liebenow, Wilhelm 1822-1897.
Verkehrs-Karte von Oesterreich-Ungarn, nebst den angrenzenden
Ländern des deutschen Reiches, von Russland und der Europäi-
schen Türkei. Bearbeitet von W. Liebenow. . . . Berlin, Ber-
liner Lithographisches Institut, 1891.
1 fold. map. 128×133ᶜᵐ.
Scale, 1:1 250 000
The various systems of state and private railways are indicated by color.
—— [Another issue of the same map, bringing the railway
development up to about the year 1883.]
Systems not distinguished as in   the foregoing map.

NL 0345764   ICJ

Liebenow (Wilhelm Heinrich Ferdinand)
[1821-]. *De morbo Brightii. 31 pp. 8º.
Berolini, G. Schade, [1819]

NL 0345765   DNLM

554.321 Liebenroth, Friedrich Ernst Franz von.
162g   Geognostische Beobachtungen und Entdeckungen
in der Gegend von Dresden.   Weissenfels, F.
Severin, 1798.
viii, 120p. 22cm.

1. Geology--Dresden area. I. Title.

NL 0345766   IU OkU

Liebenson, Joseph, joint author
Mo'ade Yiśrael
see under Marenof, Shlomo.

Liebenson, Joseph, tr.
ha-'Olam ha-zavu'a
see under Komaiko, Solomon Baruch,
1879-

557.95 Liebenstein, Charles.
L621   The Sumpter gold fields, their history;
OrP   big mines and the opportunities they offer
for profitable investment. [Sumpter, Ore.?
c1902]
[52]p. illus. 21cm.

Cover title.

1. Oregon.   Mines and mineral resources.
Gold. I. Title.

NL 0345769   OrU OrHi OrP

Liebenstein, Clemens Zedtwitz-
see Zedtwitz [Liebenstein], Clemens,
Graf von, 1814-1896.

Liebenstein, Eliezer
see
Livneh, Eliezer, 1902-

LIEBENSTEIN, Gebhardt Orland, Freiherr von.
Wer haftet für den vom gerichtsvollzieher bei
der pfändung schuldhaft verursachten schaden?
Freiburg-Elbe,1908.

53+(10) p.
Inaug.-diss. - Münster.

NL 0345772   MH-L

Liebenstein, Georg Ernst Ludwig, *freiherr* von Preuschen von und zu
see
Preuschen von und zu Liebenstein, Georg Ernst Ludwig, *freiherr* von, 1727-1794.

Liebenstein, Joannes Franciscus Meler von
see Meler von Liebenstein, Johann
Franz, fl. 1719.

Liebenstein, Ludwig August Friedrich, Freiherr von, 1781-1824.
Der Krieg Napoleons gegen Russland in den Jahren 1812
und 1813. Dargestellt von Ludwig August Friedrich von Liebenstein... Frankfurt am Main: Hermannsche Buchhandlung,
1819. 2 v. 8º.

1. Napoleonic wars, 1812-13. 2. Rus-   sia.—History.
N.Y.P.L.   August 16, 1916.

NL 0345775   NN

Liebenstein, Werner, 1925-
Gerhart Hauptmann und das Reformationszeitalter.
München, 1950.
92 l. 30 cm.
Typescript (carbon copy)
Inaug.-Diss.—Munich.
Vita.
Bibliography : leaves 91-92.

1. Hauptmann, Gerhart Johann Robert, 1862-1946.

PT2616.Z9L5   56-21225

NL 0345776   DLC CaBVaU

FILM   Liebenstein, Werner, 1925-
7477   Gerhart Hauptmann und das Reformationszeitalter.
.1950.
1. 30 cm.
Typescript
Inaug.-Diss.—Munich.
Vita.
Bibliography : leaves -85-86.
Microfilm (negative) 1 reel.

1. Hauptmann, Gerhart Johann Robert, 1862-1946.

NL 0345777   MiU

Liebenstund, F.
Coblence on Rhine and Moselle ... short
guide through the town and its sights...
Coblence, Krabbensche Druckerei (1920)
16p. 23cm.

NL 0345778   DNW

Der liebenswürdige alte
see under [Dyck, Johann Gottfried] 1750-1815.

Der liebenswürdige mensch
see under [Marin, François Louis
Claude] 1721-1809.

932.7
An13
v.25-28
Liebental, Nikolaus, father, d. 1518?
Nikolaus Liebental und seine Chronik der
Aebte des Breslauer St. Vinzenzstiftes.
Tongerloo, Sint Norbertusdrukkerij P.V.B.A.
[1949-52]
202 p. 25ᶜᵐ. (Analecta Praemonstratensia,
t. 25-28)

At head of title: Leo Santifaller.
Bibliography: p. [5]-8.

NL 0345781   NNC NjPT OCU

Liebental, Gross-
see Grossliebental, *Ukraine.*

Liebentantz, Michael, 1636-1678, praeses.
... Disqvisitio philologica de manna Israelita-
rum ... sub praesidio ... Michaelis Liebentantz
... Wittebergae, 1667.
12 l. 19 cm.
Diss. - Wittebergae. (Christophorus Bresler,
author)

NL 0345783   CtY

A30   Liebentantz, Michael, 1636-1678, praeses.
W7   Ex grammaticis de Scheva Ebraeorum.
1660L Wittebergae,1660.
[14] p.
Diss. - Wittenberg (C.Ritter, respondent)

I. Ritter, Caspar   respondent.

NL 0345784   CtY

Judaica Liebentantz, Michael, 1636-1678, praeses.
Mc16   Exercitationem philologicam, de facie
5   Mosis, qvam pingunt, cornutâ, ad Exod. cap.
8   XXXIV. comma 29. ex parte ... submittunt ...
praeses M. Michael Liebentantz & respondens
Martinus Hoffmannus ... Ed. 3. VVitenbergae,
Ex officina Christiani Schroederi,1696.
[32]p. 19cm. [Dissert. jud. historiae]
Diss. - Wittenberg.

NL 0345785   CtY

A30   Liebentantz, Michael, 1636-1678, praeses.
A2   Exercitationem philologicam De facie Mosis,
209   quam pingunt Cornutâ, ad Exod. XXXIV. comma
29. ... submittunt examini praeses M.Michael
Liebentantz & respondens Martinus Hoffmannus.
Ed.4. Wittebergae,1678.
[30] p. 20cm. [Miscellaneous dissertations,
v. 209]
Diss. - Wittenberg, 1659 (M.Hoffmann, respondent)

1. Hoffmann, Martin,   respondent.

NL 0345786   CtY

VOLUME 332

JN3249 Liebenthal, Christian, 1586-1647.
.L72   Collegium politicum, in qvo de societatibus,
Rare   magistratibus, juribus majestatis, et legibus
Bk   fundamentalibus, item de universa ac summa Repvb.
       Romana, vtpote, de imperatore, rege Romanorum &
       statibus Romani Imperii... Giessae Hessorum,
       Typis N. Hampelii, 1619.
       ‹14› 420 p.

       1. Holy Roman Empire--Pol. & govt. I. Title.

NL 0345787   ICU

Liebenthal, Christian, 1586-1647.
   Collegium politicum, in qvo de societatibus, magistratibus, juribus majestatis, et legibus fundamentalibus. Item de universa ac summa repvb. romana, vtpote, de
imperatore, rege romanorum & statibus romani imperii: ut et de nobilitate, eques-
tri dignitate, consiliariis, legatis,
officiariis, legibus, earundemq́; execu-
tione: nec non de pace religiosa, jure
episcopali et patronatus, jure belli, &

subditorum officiis ac oneribus ... de
quibus praeside & auctore Christiano
Liebenthal ... Giessae Hessorum, typis
Nicolai Hampelii, 1620.

   8 p.l., 420 p. 20cm.

NL 0345789   MH-L

Liebenthal, Christian, 1586-1647.
   Collegivm politicvm in qvo de societatibus, magistratibus, juriribus ‹!› majestatis, & legibus, fundamentalibus. Item
de universa ac summa republ. Romana, utpote,
de imperatore, rege Romanorum, & statibus
Romani imperii ... de quibus praeside et
auctore Christiani Liebenthal ... Ed. post-
rema correctior. Amstelodami, apud
Joannem Janssonium juniorem, 1652.
   481 p. 13½cm.

   Added engraved t.-p.

NL 0345791   MH-L

Liebenthal, Christian, 1586-1647.
   ... Collegium politicum, in qvo tum
in genere rerumpublicarum omnium con-
stitutio, tum in specie status imperii
romano-germanici hodiernus per theses
et communiores quaestiones ... explicat-
ur ... Ed. 10, nova, & ab innumeris ...
erratis emendata ... aucta, opera Hieronymi Thomae ... Giessae Hassorum, typis
& sumptibus Josephi Dieterici Hampelii,
1668.
   2 p.l., 731 p.   16cm.

NL 0345792   MH-L

370.9401 Liebenthal, Christian, praeses.
L62d   De privilegiis studiosorum, eorumque, qui stu-
1636   diosis adjumento sunt et inserviunt. Ex authent.
         habita c. Ne filius pro patre, & aliis tâm pris-
         cis quàm recentioribus privilegiorum tractatibus,
         jurisq̄ canonici & civili praeceptis: De quibus
         preside & auctore Christiano Liebenthal ... Re-
         spondit Georgius von Dassel ... Editio secunda.
         Rintelij, typis exscripsit P. Lucius, 1636.
         ‹54›p.

         Diss.--Giessen.
         Title vignette.

NL 0345793   IU

Liebenthal, Emil, 1859-
   Die Bahnkurven des Combe'schen Apparates. Hamburg:
Hammerich & Lesser in Altona, 1887. 1 p.l., 18 p., 3 charts. 4°.
(Germany. Seewarte, Direktion der. Aus dem Archiv der deut-
schen Seewarte. Jahrg. 10, 1887, Heft 4.)

1. Chronometer.--Rating, 1887.
N. Y. P. L.   March 15, 1912.

NL 0345794   NN

Liebenthal, Emil, 1859-
   Praktische photometrie, von dr. Emil Liebenthal ... mit 201
eingedruckten abbildungen. Braunschweig, F. Vieweg und
sohn, 1907.
   xv, 445 p. incl. illus., tables, diagrs. 23½cm.
   "Abkürzungen der berücksichtigten literatur": p. ‹xiii›-xiv.

1. Photometry.

Library of Congress   QC391.L6   7-36114

NL 0345795   DLC OrP CU NIC OC1W CtY ICJ NN PU OC1L

Liebenthal, Emil, 1859-
   Untersuchungen über die attraction zweier homogener
körper ... Greifswald, Druck von J. Abel ‹1880›
   26 p. 26ᵐ.
   Inaug.-dis.--Greifswald.
   Vita.

1. Attractions.
                                             4-24145†
Library of Congress   QA827.L7

NL 0345796   DLC DNLM

Liebenthal (Ernst) [1887-   ]. *Statistische
Mitteilung über die Frage nach der Ätiologischen Bedeutung der Lues für Augener-
krankungen. 1 p. l., 32 pp., 1 l. 8°. München. C. Wolf & Sohn. 1912.

NL 0345797   DNLM

Liebenthal, Frank, 1888-
   Ueber die Wiedergabe kleiner Geschichten bei
Fällen von Pseudologia   phantastica.
Berlin, Ebering, 1917.
   53 p. 8°.
   Inaug.-Diss. - Berlin, Ebering.
   Bibl.

NL 0345798   ICRL DNLM CtY

Liebenthal, Gerhard F
   Andra världskrigets spioner ‹av› Gerhard Liebenthal
‹och› Sven Ingemansson. Södertälje, Fants nordiska förlag
‹1940›
   133 p. illus. 20 cm.

   1. World War, 1939-1945--Secret service.   I. Ingemansson, Sven,
joint author. II. Title.

D810.S7L48   63-28963 ‡

NL 0345799   DLC

LIEBENTHAL, GERHARD F.
   Andra världskrigets spioner [av] Gerhard Liebenthal
[och] Sven Ingemansson. [Stockholm] Fants nordiska
förlag [1946] 133 p. illus., ports. 21cm.

   1. World war, 1939-1945--Secret service. 2. World war, 1939-1945--
Secret service--Germany. I. Ingemansson, Sven.

NL 0345800   NN

Liebenthal, Gerhard F
   Domen; ett dokument i bild och skrift om krigsförbrytarprocessen i Nürnberg. Med introduktion av Hugo Lindberg. Stockholm, Åhlén & Åkerlund, 1946.
   64 p. (chiefly illus.) 29 cm.

   1. Nuremberg Trial of Major German War Criminals, 1945-1946.
I. Title.

D804.G42L45   66-87092 ‡

NL 0345801   DLC

LIEBENTHAL, GERHARD F.
   Domen; ett dokument i bild och skrift om
krigsförbrytarprocessen i Nürnberg. Med introd. av
Hugo Lindberg. Stockholm, Åhlén & Åkerlund, 1946.
   64 p. illus., ports. 29cm.

   Microfilm.

   1. World war, 1939-1945--   Trials--Germany.

NL 0345802   NN

Liebenthal, Gerhard F
   De stora krigs- förbrytarna och deras agärnin-
gar. Oversättning fran engelskan av S. Nordfeldt.
[2.uppl.] Södertälje, Fants nordiska förlag,
1945.

NL 0345803   MH

Liebenthal, lte.   1921, Jena.
   Gedichte.

NL 0345804   NjP

Liebenthal, Kurt: Der derzeitige Stand der Wurzelbehandlung bei
Milchzähnen. [Maschinenschrift.] iv, 78, v S. m. Tab. 4°. —
Auszug: Greifswald (1923): Adler. 1 Bl. 8°.
Greifswald, Med. Diss. v. 12. Dez. 1923   [U 23. 4696

NL 0345805   ICRL

Liebenthal (Leopold) [1868-   ]. *Ueber das
Weber'sche Syndrom. [Leipzig.] 62 pp. 8°.
Berlin, J. S. Preuss. 1894.

NL 0345806   DNLM CtY

B2790 Liebenthal, Robert.
.A7   Kantischer Geist in unserm neuen bürgerlichen
       Recht. Königsberg in Pr., F. Beyer, 1897.
       20 p. ‹With Arnoldt, Emil. Beiträge, 1898.
       Tischrede--Königsberg (173. Geburtstag Imma-
       nuel Kants)
       "Separat-Abdruck aus der Altpreuss. Monats-
       schrift, Bd.XXXIV, Heft 3 u.4."

       1. Kant, Immanuel, 1724-1804.

NL 0345807   ICU

Liebenthal, Walter, 1886-
   The book of Chao
   see under   Seng-chao, 384-414.

AC   Liebenthal, Walter, 1886-
831   Satkarya in der darstellung seiner
       buddhistischen gegner. ... Stuttgart-Berlin,
       1933. 152 p.
       Inaug. Diss. - Breslau, 1933.
       Lebenslauf.
       Bibliography.

NL 0345809   ICRL MiU CtY

VOLUME 332

Liebenthal, Walter, *1886 -*
Satkārya in der darstellung seiner buddhistischen gegner. Die prakṛti-parīkṣā im Tattvasaṃgraha des Śāntirakṣita zusammen mit der Pañjikā des Kamalaśīla, übers. und ausführlich interpretiert von Walter Liebenthal. Stuttgart-Berlin, W. Kohlhammer, 1934.

xvi, 152 p. 22½ᶜᵐ. (*Added t.-p.:* Beiträge zur indischen sprachwissenschaft und religionsgeschichte, 9. hft.)

"Literatur-verzeichnis und abkürzungen": p. ix-xvi.

1. Buddha and Buddhism. 2. Philosophy, Hindu. 3. Śāntirakshita. 4. Kamalasīla.   I. Title.   II. Title: Tattvasaṃgraha.

A C 35—482

Cleveland. Public library
for Library of Congress   ₍a40d1₎

NL 0345810   OCl WaU TNJ-R TxU CSt CtY CBPac PU

Liebenthal, Werner, 1888-
Ursprünge und Entwickelung des römischen **Testaments** in den Grundzügen ... von Werner Liebenthal ... Berlin, H. S. Hermann, 1914.

188 p. 22½cm.

Inaug.-Diss. – Greifswald.
"Literaturverzeichnis": p.₍5₎-7.

NL 0345811   MH-L

Liebenthal, Gross-
see **Grossliebental,** *Ukraine.*

Liebenzeller mission.
Im land der aufgehenden sonne; aus der arbeit der Liebenzeller mission in Japan.   Bad Liebenzell (Württ.) Liebenzeller mission [1936?]
46 p., 1 l.   illus. (incl. port.)   19.5 cm.
A collection of articles by missionaires and ministers on the history and work of the Liebenzeller mission in Japan.

NL 0345813   CtY-D

Liebenzeller Mission.
Short history of the work of the Liebenzeller Mission, now Evangelical Mission on the Admiralty Islands, Territory of New Guinea. [Schooley's Mountain, New Jersey, n.d.]

20 p.   illus.

NL 0345814   CLamB

4QP   **Lieber, Adolf,** 1909–
98   1. Der Aa-bach. 2. **Untersuchung des Seewassers und des Abwassers von Pfäffikon (Zürich).   Frauenfeld, 1935.**
             52

NL 0345815   DLC-P4 CtY ICRL

Lieber, Albert Carl, 1895–
Engineers in the 1923 rifle matches. ₍By₎ A. C. Lieber, jr. ...

(*In* The Military engineer. Washington, 1923. 30ᶜᵐ. vol. XV, no. 84, p. 548-551. illus.)

1. Shooting contests, ₍Military₎   I. Title.

E S 28-58

Title from U. S. Engi-   neer School Libr.   Printed by L. C.

NL 0345816   DES OU

Lieber, Albert Carl, 1895–
Use of plank in floating foot-bridges. ₍By₎ A. C. Lieber, jr. ...

(*In* The Military engineer. Washington, 1925. 30ᶜᵐ. vol. XVII, no. 94, p. 334-335. illus.)

1. Military bridges.   I. Title : Floating foot-bridges, Use of plank in.

E S 28-208

Title from U. S. Engi-   neer School Libr.   Printed by L. C.

NL 0345817   DES OU

Lieber, Alfred.
Frühmittelalterliche Weltwirtschaft.

xxv, 311 *l.*   col.map (in pocket)
Typescript

NL 0345818   MH

HF395   **Lieber, Alfred.**
.L54   Frühmittelalterliche weltwirtschaft.
             ₍Amsterdam? 1938?₎
             xxv, 40 *l.*   30cm.

             Proefschrift – Amsterdam.
             Bibliography: *l.* xi-xxv.

             1. Commerce – History.   I. Title.

NL 0345819   OCU

834L6185 Lieber, Alfred von, 1884?-1921.
Oh   ... Hortus animae, gedichte.   München ₍etc.₎ G. Müller, 1908.
             83p.

NL 0345820   IU

Lieber, Alfred von, 1884?-1921.
... Orphische küste; ₍gedichte, mit originallithographie von Erich Godal₎ Potsdam, Tillgner, 1920.
42 p.   incl. front.   26 cm.
No. 16 of an edition of 30 copies, signed by the author.

NL 0345821   NjP

Lieber, Arnulf.
Das helgilied, Helgakwida.   Berlin, Vaterländische verlagsanstalt, ₍1894₎.
pp. 104.   Illus.

||Edda Saemundar. Ger. :1894: Lieber|AcS 185712

NL 0345822   MH OCl CU

LIEBER, ARTHUR.

Ashes.   St. Louis, Mo., Foster bros. [c1900]

Song with piano accompaniment.
First line: We found the gate to Folly's estate.

1. Songs, U.S. 2. Songs, Secular—1870-

NL 0345823   NN

LIEBER, ARTHUR.

...My love.   St. Louis, Mo. Foster bros. [c1900]

Song with piano accompaniment.
Words by Charles Mackey.
First line: I send a message by the rose.

1. Songs, U.S. 2. Songs, Secular—1870-   I. Mackey, Charles.

NL 0345824   NN

Lieber, Asta Alice, 1902-
Zur Oogense einiger Diopatra-Arten ... Leipzig, 1931.
Inaug.-Diss. - Tübingen.
Lebenslauf.
"Diese Arbeit erschien in der 'Zeitschrift für wissenschaftliche Zoologie', Band 138, Heft 4, 1931."
"Literaturverzeichnis": p. 646-649.

NL 0345825   CtY

Lieber (August). Die erste ärztliche Hilfeleistung bei Erkrankungen und Unglücksfällen **auf Alpenwanderungen.** 49 pp. 8°. *München, J. Lindauer,* 1887.
—— *Repr. from:* Ztschr. d. deutsch. u. öster. Alpenver.
—— The same. 2. Aufl. 83 pp. 12°. *Innsbruck. Wagner.* 1889.

NL 0345826   DNLM

Lieber, Auguste-Henri, 1914-
... États paranoïdes après commotion cérébrale ...   Strasbourg.-Neudorf, 1939.
Thèse - Univ. de Strasbourg.

NL 0345827   CtY

Lieber, Ben Seev.
It is never too late to mend; a play by Ben Seev Lieber. Jerusalem: Head off. of the Keren Kayemeth Leisrael (Jewish national fund), 1935.   21 p., 3 l.   illus. (incl. music.)   29½cm.

Cover-title.
Reproduced from typewritten copy; cover printed.
Incidental songs, 2 l. at end.

1. Drama, English—Palestinian authors. 2. Zionism—Drama.
I. Jewish national fund. II. Title.
N. Y. P. L.   June 9, 1939

NL 0345828   NN

Lieber, Benjamin Franklin, 1853–1915, *comp.*
Lieber's bankers' and stockbrokers' code and merchants' and shippers' blank tables ... compiled by B. Franklin Lieber and Charles J. Dawson ...   New York, London, Lieber code company, 1905.

6 p. l., 10-487 p.   20ᶜᵐ.

Text runs parallel with the back.

1. Cipher and telegraph codes.   I. Dawson, Charles Joseph, 1865-
Joint comp.

Library of Congress   HE7677.B2L7   5-39511 Revised

NL 0345829   DLC

Lieber, Benjamin Franklin, 1853–1915.
Code télégraphique de Lieber, par B. Franklin Lieber ... New York ₍etc.₎ The Lieber code co., 1901.

xlvi, 806 p.   25½ cm.

Pages i-xv, 802-806, advertising matter.

1. Cipher and telegraph codes.

1—15195

Library of Congress   HE7678.F8L7

NL 0345830   DLC

Lieber, Benjamin Franklin, 1853–
Lieber's ₍five letter American telegraphic code ... by B. Franklin Lieber ...   New York, The Lieber code co. ₍°1915₎

xx, 802 (i. e. 956) p.   25½ᶜᵐ. $10.00

Includes advertisements.
"Published also in French, Spanish and German (and pocket edition in English)"

1. Cipher and telegraph codes.

Library of Congress   HE7676.L74   16—5081

NL 0345831   DLC DN WaS OCl MB ICJ PPSteph

VOLUME 332

Lieber, Benjamin Franklin, 1853–1915, *comp.*
A general telegraphic cipher adapted to the use of whole-sale liquor dealers, importers, merchants and merchandise brokers. Comp. by B. F. Lieber ... ₍New York, C. S. Nathan, printer₎ 1883.
116 p. 22½ᶜᵐ.

1. Cipher and telegraph codes—Liquor trade.

CA 7—3706 Unrev'd

Library of Congress   HE7677.L75L7

NL   0345832   DLC PP

Lieber, Benjamin Franklin, 1853–1915.
Lieber's latest code ... New York, Lieber code co. ₍ᶜ1926₎
xvi, 815 p. 25ᶜᵐ.
Issued in 1915 under title: Lièber's five letter American telegraphic code.
——— Copy 2.
Copyright A 958385
—— Analytical index for Lieber's latest code ... New York, Lieber code co. ₍ᶜ1926₎
90 p. 25ᶜᵐ. $2.50
1. Cipher and telegraph codes.   I. Lieber code co., New York.
II. Title.
Library of Congress   HE7676.L74 1926   CA 27—120 Unrev'd

NL   0345833   DLC MB OC1 ICJ

25.9   **Lieber, Benjamin Franklin**, 1853–1915.
Lieber's manual. Containing the sailing of the ocean steamers from New York, postal information. [etc.] Circulated bi-monthly. Oct. 1884. April, 1885, Oct. 1885, Feb. 1886. [New York, 1884–1886]
no. 4, 7, 1–. 12. 4 v.   8°.

NL   0345834   DLC

Lieber, Benjamin Franklin, 1853–1915
Mutilation detector for Lieber's latest code...
New York, [c1926]

HE7676
.L75

NL   0345835   DLC OC1 ICJ MiD

Lieber, Benjamin Franklin, *comp.*
100,000,000 combination ciphers admitting variations fr 00000000 to 99999999. .... Compiled by B. Franklin Lie .... New York, London, Lieber Code Company, ᶜ1906.
16, [48] p. 30¼ᶜᵐ.
[48] p. blank.

NL   0345836   ICJ

Lieber, Benjamin Franklin, 1853–1915.
Lieber's standard telegraphic code. By B. Franklin Lieber ... New York, Lieber publishing co., 1896.
3 p. l., ₍xvii₎–xxvi, 800 p. 25½ᶜᵐ.

1. Cipher and telegraph codes

CA 7–4962 Unrev'd

Library of Congress   HE7676.L73

NL   0345837   DLC OrP OC1 MH PPF PP

Lieber, Benjamin Franklin, 1853–1915.
Lieber's Standard telegraphic code. By B. Franklin Lieber ... New York, Lieber publishing co., 1898.
xxii, 804 p. 25½ᶜᵐ.
Includes advertising matter.

1. Cipher and telegraph codes.

44–50411

Library of Congress   HE7676.L73 1898

NL   0345838   DLC ICJ ICRL MH ViU WaSp

Lieber, Benjamin Franklin.
Lieber's telegraphen-schlüssel, auch in englisch, französisch und spanisch herausgegeben, aus dem englischen übersetzt von C. C. Beyer ... Hamburg, Lieber code co., 1910.
xxxvi, 800 p. 25½ᶜᵐ.   M. 43
p. ii–x, advertising matter.

1. Cipher and telegraph codes.   I. Beyer, C. C., tr.

10–13857

Library of Congress   HE7678.A2L7

NL   0345839   DLC

Lieber, Benjamin Franklin, 1853-   comp.

General electric company.
Telegraphic cipher of the General electric company, New York and Boston ... Comp. by B. Franklin Lieber. New York, 1892.

Lieber, Benjamin Franklin, 1853–1915.
Lieber's terminal index for the detection of mutilations of the ciphers of Lieber's code, handy tables and appendix. By B. Franklin Lieber... London: Lieber Code Co.₍, 189–?₎   350 p. 4°.

567424A.   1. Telegraphy—Codes.
N. Y. P. L.   HASTINGS COLLECTION.
                               April 14, 1933

NL   0345841   NN MiD CtY

Lieber, Benjamin Franklin, 1853–1915.
Lieber's universal telegraphic cipher. Adapted to the use of bankers, stock brokers, merchandise brokers, importers and merchants. By B. Franklin Lieber ... ₍New York₎ 1888.
250 p. 25½ᶜᵐ.

1. Cipher and telegraph codes—Bankers and brokers.

CA 7–4956 Unrev'd

Library of Congress   HE7676.L72

NL   0345842   DLC

Lieber, Bernhard, 1853–
Ueber einen fall von lumbalhernie ... Berlin, Schade ₍1887₎
30, ₍2₎ p.

Inaug.-diss., Berlin, 1887.
Lebenslauf.

L. Hernia.

NL   0345843   NNC DNLM

Lieber, Carl
Das Deutsche Patentgesetz vom 7. April 1891 und das Gesetz betreffend den Schutz von Gebrauchs-mustern vom Juni, 1891 für die Praxis erlautert. Berlin, 1892.

NL   0345844   PU-L

Lieber, Carl, ed.
Gesetz betreffend das Diensteinkommen der Lehrer und Lehrerinnen an den öffentlichen Volksschulen Preussens
see under   Prussia. Laws, statutes, etc.

Lieber, Carl.
Justizverwaltung in zweiter auflage neubearbeitet von Carl Lieber ... 2. aufl. Berlin, F. Vahlen, 1929.
xiii, 111 p. 24ᶜᵐ.   (Added t.-p.: Die gerichtspraxis ... XI)

1. Justice, Administration of—Germany.   I. Title.

31–16946

NL   0345846   DLC

L₍ieber₎, C₍arl₎ H₍erman₎ *comp.*
Lieber's price tables for picture frames; being a book of ready computed prices of frames made from mould-ings of various widths at prices ranging from one cent a foot upward. Comp. by C. H. L. Indianapolis, Ind., The H. Lieber co. ₍1901₎
[121] pp. 23ᶜᵐ.
Subject entries: Picture-frames and framing.

2–1093—M 2

NL   0345847   DLC

Lieber, D.
Über Indolinone.
(In Kaiserliche Akademie der Wissenschaften, Vienna. Mathe-matisch-naturwissenschaftliche Klasse. Sitzungsberichte. Band 117, Abteilung 2B, pp. 169–177. Wien. 1908.)

H2222 — Indolinons.

NL   0345848   MB

Lieber, Emma (Rappaport) 1874–
From boyhood to manhood, by E. Lieber. Pub. by Indiana State board of health, Indianapolis, Indiana, co-operating with the United States Public health service ... ₍Indianapolis, ᶜ1920₎
8 p. 19ᶜᵐ.

1. Sex instruction.   I. Indiana.   State board of health.   II. U. S. Public health service.   III. Title.

HQ56.L36   25–18456 rev

NL   0345849   DLC

Lieber, Emma (Rappaport) 1874–
From girlhood to womanhood, by Emma Lieber. Pub. by Indiana State board of health, Indianapolis, Indiana, co-operating with the United States Public health service ... ₍Indianapolis, ᶜ1919₎
8 p. 9ᶜᵐ.

1. Sex instruction.   I. Indiana.   State board of health.   II. U. S. Public health service.   III. Title.

HQ56.L38   25–18457 rev

NL   0345850   DLC

Lieber, Emma (Rappaport) 1874–
God's children, by Emma Lieber, illustrated by Will Vawter. Kansas City, Mo., Burton publishing company ₍ᶜ1921₎
2 p. l., 7–61 p. 23½ᶜᵐ.

1. Sex instruction.   I. Title.

HQ56.L4   22–1015 rev

NL   0345851   DLC

Lieber, Emma (Rappaport) 1874–
Richard Lieber, by his wife, Emma. ₍Indianapolis, ᶜ1947.
170 p. illus., ports. 24ᶜᵐ.
Copyright date from label mounted on t.-p.

1. Lieber, Richard, 1869–1944.

CT275.L43L5   920   47–22535*

NL   0345852   DLC

VOLUME 332

5
M
1941
4
    Lieber, Eric E.
        What to eat and why. London, John
Bale Medical Pub., 1941.
        xvi, 126 p. illus.
        I. Title

NL 0345853   MBCo

Lieber, Eric E
What to eat and why, by Dr. Eric E. Lieber. With a fore-
word by Lord Horder. London, Staples books limited ₁1941₎
xvi, 126 p. incl. tables, diagr. 22ᶜᵐ.
"Errata" slip inserted.
Bibliography: p. 122.

1. Nutrition. 2. Food. ɪ. Title.
                          A 43–879

Harvard univ. Library
   for Library of Congress

NL 0345854   MH

Lieber, Eugene, 1907–
    Reduction of nitroguanidine, the reduction of nitroguani-
dine by catalytic hydrogenation. Brooklyn ₁Polytechnic
Institute of Brooklyn₎ 1937.
    ₁39₎ p. 23 cm.
    E. Lieber's thesis—Polytechnic Institute of Brooklyn.
    Six articles by Eugene Lieber and G. B. L. Smith, reprinted from
the Journal of the American Chemical Society, v. 57–59, 1935–1937
(Contribution no. 28, 31, 32, 36, 38 and 39 from the Dept. of Chemistry
of the Polytechnic Institute of Brooklyn)
    "Biographical and professional note": p. ₁39₎

    1. Nitroguanidine. 2. Hydrogenation. 3. Catalysis. ɪ. Smith,
Gilbert Brown Lorenzo, 1894– joint author.

QD305.A8L549   547.8   49–41141*

NL 0345855   DLC CtY

Lieber, Francis, 1800–1872.
    Dr. Lieber's address [at dedication of
monument to Alexander Humboldt] [New York,
The New York printing company, 1871]
    p. 24–33. 22.7 cm.
    Caption title.
    In: New York (City) Board of commissioners
of Central park. 14th report ... 1871.
    1. Humboldt, Alexander, freiherr von,
1769–1859.

NL 0345856   CSmH

Lieber, Francis, 1800–1872.
    Address by Francis Lieber, chairman of the
Council's committee on addresses, read at the
meeting by their request. [New York? 1863]
    broadside, 45. 35.9; text, 42.1 x 31.9 cm.
    I. Loyal national league of the state of
New York.

NL 0345857   CSmH PPL

Lieber, Francis. 1800–1872.
    An address on secession.
    (In Lieber. What is our Constitution? Pp. 39–48. New York,
1861.)

F3870 — United States. Hist. Civil War, 1861–1865. Disc. of prin.

NL 0345858   MB DLC

Lieber, Francis, 1800–1872.
    ... An address on secession. Delivered in South Caro-
lina in the year 1851, by Francis Lieber ... New York,
Loyal publication society, 1865.
    12 p. 22ᶜᵐ. (Loyal publication society ... ₁Pamphlets₎ no. 77)
    Address read at Greenville, S. C., July 4, 1851.

    1. Secession. 2. Fourth of July orations.

Library of Congress   E458.L92 no. 77   18–10831
                      E458.L93 vol. 3

NL 0345859   DLC NcU NIC NjP CSmH MB ScU OU OCU CU

Lieber, Francis, 1800–1872.
    Address to the people of the United States in
behalf of the American copyright club adopted
Oct. 18th, 1843...
New York, Published by the club, n.d.₎
    20 p.

NL 0345860   PPL

Lieber, Francis, 1800–1872.

Columbia university.
    Addresses of the newly-appointed professors of Columbia
college, with an introductory address by William Betts, ʟʟ. ᴅ.
February, 1858. New York, By authority of the Trustees,
1858.

₁Lieber, Francis₎ 1800–1872.
    ... Amendments of the Constitution, submitted to the
consideration of the American people ... New York,
1865.
    39 p. 22ᶜᵐ. (Loyal publication society ... ₁Pamphlets₎ no. 63)
    Errata slip attached to t.-p.
    Preface signed: Francis Lieber.
    Note on verso of t.-p. signed: Jas. McKaye, ch. pub. com.

    1. U. S. Constitution—Amendments. ɪ. Title.
                                19–1319

Library of Congress   E463.L97 vol. 3

NL 0345862   DLC ViU NIC TU

₁Lieber, Francis₎ 1800–1872.
    ... Amendments of the Constitution, submitted to the
consideration of the American people ... New York, 1865.
    39 p. 22ᶜᵐ. (Loyal publication society ... ₁Pamphlets₎ no. 83)
    Preface signed: Francis Lieber.
    Corrected edition, with note by chairman of Publication committee, on
p. ₁4₎

    1. U. S. Constitution—Amendments. ɪ. Title.

Library of Congress   E463.L96 no. 83   19–1318
—— Copy 2.   ₁Miscellaneous pamphlets, v. 474, no. 13₎
                           AC901.M5 vol. 474

NL 0345863   DLC CU OU

Lieber, Francis, 1800–1872.
    The ancient and the modern teacher of politics. An intro-
ductory discourse to a course of lectures on the state. Delivered on the 10th of October, 1859, in the law school of
Columbia college. By Francis Lieber ... Pub. by the Board
of trustees. New York, 1860.
    35 p. 22½ᶜᵐ.

    1. Political science—Study and teaching.

Library of Congress   JA86.L6   9–21248
                       JA87.L72

        PU PPB PPL DHEW
NL 0345864   DLC NcD ScU PHi NIC CtY MiU ViU MB NN ICN

Lieber, Francis, 1800–1872.
    ... The arguments of secessionists. A letter to the Union
meeting, held in New York, September 30, 1863. By Francis
Lieber ... New York, Holman, printer, 1863.
    7 p. 22½ᶜᵐ. (Loyal publication society. ₁Pamphlets₎ no. 35)

    1. U. S.—Pol. & govt.—Civil war. 2. Secession.
Library of Congress   E463.L96 no. 35   12–26613
                       E463.L97

NL 0345865   DLC NIC MnHi NcU OU CSmH MB ViU PU

Lieber, Francis, 1800–1872.
    Aus den Denkwürdigkeiten eines Deutsch-
Amerikaners
        see his   Franz Lieber: Aus den
Denkwürdigkeiten eines Deutch-Amerikaners...

Lieber, Francis, 1800–1872.
    Bruchstücke über Gegenstände der Strafkunde,
besonders über das Eremitensystem ...
Hamburg, Agentur des Rauhen Hauses, 1845.
    48 p. 20.5 cm.
    Lieber collection.

NL 0345867   CSmH

1800–1872.
₁Lieber, Francis₎ comp₎ ₁California scrap-book.
1848–49₎ 1v. 28cm.

NL 0345868   CU-B

Lieber, Francis, 1800–1872.
    The character of the gentleman: an address to the stu-
dents of Miami university, on the evening before commencement day, in the month of August, 1846. By Francis Lieber ... Cincinnati, J. A. James, 1846.
    31 p. 21ᶜᵐ.

    1. Conduct of life. 2. Courtesy.
                              9–33715†

Library of Congress   BJ1521.L7 1846

NL 0345869   DLC NIC PPPrHi OCl MeE NN MB

B
692
.513
    LIEBER, FRANCIS, 1800–1872.
        The character of the gentleman: an address to
the students of Miami university, on the evening
before commencement day, in the month of August,
1846   Cincinnati, J.A.James, 1847.
        31p. 21cm.

NL 0345870   ICN

Lieber, Francis, 1800–1872.
    The character of the gentleman. An address to the stu-
dents of Miami university, Ohio, on the evening before
commencement day, in the month of August, ᴍᴅᴄᴄᴄxʟᴠɪ.
2d and enl. ed. By Francis Lieber ... Columbia and
Charleston, S. C., Allen, McCarter & co., 1847.
    110, ₁1₎ p. 18½ᶜᵐ.

    1. Conduct of life. 2. Courtesy.
                              9–33713†

Library of Congress   BJ1521.L7 1847

        PU
NL 0345871   DLC ViW ViU OOxM MWA NcD ScU ViU MB PPL

Lieber, Francis, 1800–1872.
    The character of the gentleman. By Francis Lieber ...
3d and much enl. ed. Philadelphia, J. B. Lippincott &
co., 1864.
    121 p. 17½ᶜᵐ.

    1. Conduct of life. 2. Courtesy.
Library of Congress   BJ1521.L7 1864   9–33745

NL 0345872   DLC ODW NcD NIC CU MB Njp PU PPL WaU-L

Lieber, Francis, 1800–1872.

U. S. *War dept.*
    A code for the government of armies in the field, as
authorized by the laws and usages of war on land.
Printed as manuscript for the Board appointed by the
secretary of war. ⟨Special orders, no. 399.⟩ "To pro-
pose amendments or changes in the Rules and articles of
war, and a code of regulations for the government of
armies in the field, as authorized by the laws and usages
of war." By Francis Lieber, member of the Board.
February, 1863. ₁New York? 1863₎

VOLUME 332

Lieber, Francis. 1800–1872.
Columbia Athenæum lecture. A lecture on the history and uses of Athenæums, delivered . . . the seventeenth of March, 1856.
Columbia. Gibbes. 1856. 32 pp. 8°.

F4226 — Libraries. Hist. — T.r.

NL 0345874   MB NN

Lieber, Francis, 1800–1872.
A constitution and plan of education for Girard college for orphans, with an introductory report, laid before the Board of trustees. By Francis Lieber ... Printed by order of the board. Philadelphia, Carey, Lea and Blanchard, 1834.
227, [1] p. 23cm.

1. Girard college, Philadelphia.

Library of Congress   LD7501.P5G55   7—12905

NL 0345875   PU PHi PPAN PPL
DLC ICN TxU NIC OrU NcD NIC MiU NN NIC

Lieber, Francis. 1800–1872.
Contributions to political science, including lectures on the Constitution of the United States, and other papers.
Philadelphia. Lippincott & Co. 1881. 552 pp. [Miscellaneous writings. Vol. 2.] 22 cm., in 8s.
The writings of Francis Lieber, pp. 531–535.

H8460 — S.r.c. — Political science. — United States. Const. 1789. Works about. about.

NL 0345876   MB NjN LU

Lieber, Francis, 1800–1872.
... De l'idée de la race latine et de sa véritable valeur en droit international ... [Ghent, Belgium, 1871]
6 p. 24.6cm.

At head of title: "Extrait de la Revue de droit international, 3e livraison, 1871."

NL 0345877   CSmH

Lieber, Francis, 1800–1872
...De l'unité des mesures et étalons dans ses rapports avec le droit des gens et avec le droit et les rapports privés de nation à nation.
[Bruxelles, 1871]

QC88
.L6

NL 0345878   DLC

Lieber, Francis, 1800–1872.
... De l'unité des mesures et étalons dans ses rapports avec le droit des gens et avec le droit et les rapports privés de nation à nation. Lettre au rédacteur-en-chef de la Revue, par François Lieber. [Londres, Williams et Norgate: New York, Westerman et cie., 1871]
10 p. 25 cm.
Caption title.
"Notice additionnelle a l'article qui précède.--La réforme monétaire en Allemagne": p. 8–10, signed, G.R.-J.
"Extrait de la Revue de droit international et de législation comparée, 4e livraison, 3e année."
I. Rollin-Jaequemyns, Gustave, 1835–1902. La réforme monétaire en   Allemagne. II. Title.

NL 0345879   CSmH

Lieber, Francis, 1800–1872.
... De l'unité des mesures et étalons dans ses rapports avec le droit des gens et avec le droit et les rapports prives de nation a nation. Lettre ... par François Lieber ...   [Paris, 1871]
10 p.   22.5 cm.   [His Writings; collected pamphlets]
Extrait de la Revue de droit international et de legislation comparée, 4e livraison, 3e année.
Caption title.

NL 0345880   CU

FOR OTHER EDITIONS SEE MAIN ENTRY
Lieber, Francis, 1800–1872, tr
Ramshorn, Johann Gottlob Ludwig, 1768–1837.
Dictionary of Latin synonymes, for the use of schools and private students, with a complete index. By Lewis Ramshorn. From the German, by Francis Lieber. Boston, Little, Brown and company, 1856.

Lieber, Francis, 1800–1872.

E415.9   Franz Lieber: Aus den Denkwürdigkeiten eines
L7A35   Deutsch-Amerikaners (1800–1872) Auf grundlage des englischen textes von Thomas Sorgeant Perry und in verbindung mit Alfred Jachmann, herausgegeben von Franz v. Holtzendorff ...   Berlin & Stuttgart, W. Spemann, 1885.

viii, 317 p. front. (port.) 22cm. 3|4 gray calf.
1. U. S.—Pol. & govt.—1849–1877. I. Perry, Thomas Sorgeant, 1845–1928. II. Jachmann, Alfred. III. Holtz   endorff, Franz von, 1829–1889, ed.

NL 0345882   CSmH NIC OClWHi MdBP DLC-P4 MnU MH

Lieber, Francis, 1800–1872, ed.
FOR OTHER EDITIONS SEE MAIN ENTRY
Encyclopædia americana. A popular dictionary of arts, sciences, literature, history, politics and biography, brought down to the present time; including a copious collection of original articles in American biography; on the basis of the 7th ed. of the German Conversations-lexicon. Ed. by Francis Lieber, assisted by E. Wigglesworth ... Philadelphia, Carey, Lea & Carey, 1829–33.

Lieber, Francis, 1800–1872.
... Englische und französische freiheit ... [Heidelberg, 1849]
p. 286–303 21.8cm.
In a complete number of: Kritische zeitschrift fur rechtswissenschaft und gesetzgebung des auslandes ... v. 21, no. 2.

NL 0345884   CSmH

Lieber, Francis, 1800–1872.
Dr. Francis Lieber's English version of his German address at the Humboldt celebration in the Central park, New York, September 14, 1869 ... ⟨Manuscript⟩ [n. p., 1869]
8 p. 23cm.
Caption title.

1. Humboldt, Alexander i. e. Friedrich Wilhelm Heinrich Alexander, freiherr von, 1769–1859.
5–22465†
Library of Congress   Q143.H9L6

NL 0345885   DLC

33   Lieber, Francis, 1800–1872.
Ein erguss von Franz Lieber. Printed at St. Louis for private circulation by an old friend of Dr.Francis Lieber, 1872.
[St. Louis, J. Bechtlof & co. 1872]
3 p. unp. 12°.

NL 0345886   DLC NcD MH CSmH

Lieber, Francis, 1800–1872.
Erinnerungen aus meinem zusammenleben mit Georg Berthold Niebuhr, dem geschichtschreiber Roms.
Heidelberg, 1837.
1 p.l., 251, 1 l.   18 cm.

NL 0345887   CSmH

Lieber, Francis, 1800–1872.
Essay on penal lay & solitary confinement...
Phila., 1838.

NL 0345888   PPL

Lieber, Francis, 1800–1872.
Essays on property and labour as connected with natural law and the constitution of society. By Francis Lieber. New-York, Harper & brothers, 1841.
xx p., 1 l., [15]–225 p. 16cm. (On cover: Harper's family library. no. CXLVI)
"Introduction. By Rev. A. Potter": p. [iii]–xx.

1. Property.   I. Potter, Alonzo, bp., 1800–1865. II. Title.
A 31–34
Minnesota. Univ. Library
for Library of Congress   [a38c1]

NL 0345889   MB MH WaU CaBVaU
MnU NcD NjNbS DLC FU MH-BA PSC PU ODW

Lieber (Francis) 1800–1872
Essays on property and labour as connected with natural law and the constitution of society. *New York: Harper & brothers.* 1842. xx, 1l., 15–225 pp. 16°. (Harper's Family Library, No. 146.)
Gift of Mrs Henry R. Hoyt.

NL 0345890   NN MB DLC ICJ RP ViU ScU

335.01   Lieber, Francis, 1800–1872.
L621e   Essays on property and labour as connected
1843   with natural law and the constitution of society. By Francis Lieber. New York, Harper & brothers, 1843.
xxp.,1l.,[15]–225p. 16cm.
Binder's title: Labour and property.
"Introduction. By Rev. A Potter ...": p. [111]–xx.

1. Property. I. Potter, Alonzo, bp., 1800–1865. II. Title. Labour and property.

NL 0345891   TxU MiU NN MB DLC

Lieber, Francis, 1800–1872.
Essays on property and labour as connected with natural law and the constitution of society. By ...
New York, Harper & brothers, 1854.

NL 0345892   OClW OCU PMA

Lieber, Francis, 1800–1872.
Essays on property and labour as connected with natural law and the constitution of society. New York, Harper & brothers, 1856.
xx p., 1 l.,[15]–325 p. 16cm.

NL 0345893   OClWHi OO

Lieber, Francis, 1800–1872.
A festive song for the celebration of Washington's birth-day in the South Carolina college chapel, MDCCCXLVIII ... [n.p., 1848]
broadside, 24.3 x 20; text, 19.2 x 15 cm.

NL 0345894   CSmH CU

VOLUME 332

Lieber, Francis, 1800–1872.
Fragmentos de ciencia politica sobre nacionalismo e internacionalismo. Opúsculo de Francis Lieber ... Tr. del ingles y precedido de una breve noticia acerca del autor ... New York, M. M. Zarzamendi, impresor, 1870.
24 p. 23 cm.

1. Nationalism. 2. Nationalism—U. S.

JX4211.L5 10—23605

NL 0345895 DLC CU

Lieber, Francis, 1800–1872.
Fragments of political science on nationalism and internationalism. By Francis Lieber ... New York, C. Scribner & co., 1868.
23 p. 23cm.

1. Nationalism and nationality. 2. U. S.—Nationality.

Library of Congress JX4211.L48 9—23689

NL 0345896 DLC NIC MnHi OFH NcD NjP MB NN PHi PPL

[Lieber, Francis] 1800–1872.
France: a series of articles reprinted from the Encyclopædia americana ... Philadelphia, Carey & Lea, 1831.
[79] p. 22cm.
CONTENTS.—Part of the article France.—Department.—Codes, Les cinq.—Election.—Charles x.—Louis Philip I.
NN
1. France. 2. France—Pol. & govt.
Library of Congress DC5.L71 4-13529
——— Copy 2.
——— Copy 3. [With Napoleon his own historian. London, 1818]
Library of Congress DC203.9.N22
——— Copy 4. 23cm. [Miscellaneous pamphlets, v. 877, no. 12]
Library of Congress

NL 0345897 DLC PPAmP NN MiU MB

[Lieber, Francis] 1800-1872.
Free trade and other things. A philosophical tutti frutti. [New Orleans, 1853]
p. [53-65] 18.9 cm.
Caption title.
Excerpted from De Bow's review, v. 15, no. 1, July, 1853, and mounted with ms. additions and corrections as preparation for reprinting.
Lieber collection.

NL 0345898 CSmH

Lieber, Francis, 1800-1873.

U. S. *War dept.*
... Government of United States armies in the field. Letter from the secretary of war, relative to "Instructions for the government of armies of the United States in the field" ... [Washington, Govt. print. off., 1874]

Lieber, Francis, 1800–1872, comp.
Great events described by distinguished historians, chroniclers, and other writers. Collected and in part translated by Francis Lieber. Boston. Crosby & Nichols. [184-?] 415 pp. 12°. 2218.30 2218.31
Contents. — The battle at Thermopylæ [B. C. 430], by Herodotus. — The death of Socrates [B. C. 399], by Plato. — The surrender of the Roman army at the defile near Caudium [B. C. 319], by Livy. — Impeachment of Publius Cornelius Scipio, surnamed Africanus, and of Lucius Cornelius Scipio, surnamed Asiaticus [B. C. 187], by Livy. — Delivery of the four Swiss forest districts (Waldstädte) [A. D. 1303], by Tschudi. — The battle at Sempach [A. D. 1386], by John von Muller. — The death of Huss [A. D. 1415], by Theobald. — The conquest of Constantinople [A. D. 1453], by Gibbon. — Martin Luther's appearance before the diet of the German Empire, at Worms [A. D. 1522], by the Abbé Vertot. — The sack of Rome [A. D. 1527], by James Bonaparte,

Continued in next column

Continued from preceding column

an eyewitness. — Henry VIII., King of England, and Catharine of Aragon, his Queen, before the Legatine court, consisting of Cardinals Wolsey and Campeggio [A. D. 1527], by George Cavendish. — The sieges of Leyden [A. D. 1574], and Ostend [A. D. 1601], by Bentivoglio. — The destruction of the Invincible Armada [A. D. 1588], by John Stone — The siege of Zaragoza [A. D. 1808], by Southey and Napier. — Glossary. — Index.

NL 0345902 MB MH OO

Bf4 57 Lieber, Francis, 1800-1872, comp.
Great events, described by distinguished historians, chroniclers, and other writers. Collected and in part translated by Francis Lieber. Boston, Marsh, Capen, Lyon, and Webb, 1840.
415p. 19cm.

NL 0345903 CtY ScU RP MB

Lieber, Francis, 1800-1872, comp.
Great events, described by distinguished historians, chroniclers and other writers. Collected and translated by F. Lieber. New York, 1847.

NL 0345904 PPL KyLx

Lieber (FRANCIS), 1800-1872, comp.
Great events, described by distinguished historians, chroniclers, and other writers, Collected and in part translated by Francis Lieber. *New York: Harper Brothers*, 1855. 2 p.l., 5-415 pp. 12°.

NL 0345905 NN

Lieber, Francis, 1800–1872, *comp.*
Great events, described by distinguished historians, chroniclers, and other writers. Collected and in part translated by Francis Lieber. New York, Harper & brothers, 1856.
415 p. 19½cm.
First edition published at Boston, 1840.

1. History—Addresses, essays, lectures. 2. Battles. I. Title.

26-2959

Library of Congress D24.L5

NL 0345906 DLC KyU MB

Lieber, Francis, 1800-1872, comp.
Great events, described by distinguished historians, chroniclers, and other writers. Collected and in part translated by Francis Lieber. New York, Harper & brothers, 1862.
415 p. 19½cm.
First edition published at Boston, 1840.

NL 0345907 NNC OCX MiU

D6 .L7 **Lieber, Francis, 1800–1872, *comp.***
Great events, described by distinguished historians, chroniclers, and other writers. Collected and in part tr. by Francis Lieber. New York, Harper & brothers, 1871.
415 p. 19½cm.
CONTENTS.—The battle at Thermopylae, by Herodotus.—The death of Socrates, by Plato.—The surrender of the Roman army at the defile near Caudium, by Livy.—Impeachment of Publius Cornelius Scipio and of Lucius Cornelius Scipio, by Livy.—Delivery of the four Swiss forest districts (Waldstädte) by Tschudi.—The battle at Sempach, by John von Müller.—The death of Huss, by Theobald.—The conquest of Constantinople, by Gibbon.—Martin Luther's appearance before the Diet of Worms, by Marheinecke.—The siege and surrender of Rhodes, by the Abbé Vertot.—The sack of Rome, by James Bonaparte.—Henry VIII and Catharine of Aragon, before the Legatine court, by George Cavendish.—The sieges of Leyden and Ostend, by Bentivoglio.—The destruction of the invincible Armada, by John Stowe.—The siege of Zaragoza, by Southey and Napier.
1. History—Collections.

NL 0345908 ICU DNW I

Lieber, Francis, 1800-1872, comp.
Great events, described by distinguished historians, chroniclers and other writers.
N.Y. Harper, 1887.
415 p.

NL 0345909 OCl

Lieber, Franz, 1800-1872.
Ein Gruss von Franz Lieber, 1843.
(St. Louis, 1872.) [Presentation of Washington's Sword to Congress.]

NL 0345910 M

Lieber, Francis, 1800–1872.
Guerrilla parties considered with reference to the laws and usages of war. Written at the request of Major-Gen. Henry W. Halleck ... by Francis Lieber ... New York, D. Van Nostrand, 1862.
22 p. 18½cm.

1. Guerrillas. I. Title.

6—42276

Library of Congress UB485.L71
——— Copy 2. [Diplomatic pamphlets, v. 14, no. 6]

NL 0345911 DLC MnHi OrU C NIC ICU MB MnU ViU NcD MiU

Lieber, Francis, 1800–1872.
History and political science, necessary studies in free countries. An inaugural address, delivered on the seventeenth of February, 1858, by Francis Lieber ... New York [Wynkoop, Hallenbeck & Thomas, printers] 1858.
62 p. 22cm.

1. History—Study [and teaching] 2. Political science—Study [and teaching]

Library, U. S. Office of Education D16.L6 E 9-1782

NL 0345912 DHEW ViU MB NN

Lieber, Francis, *1800-1872.*
History and political science, necessary studies in free countries. An inaugural address, . . . 17th of Feb., 1858 . . . Columbia College New York.

(*In* Columbia College. Addresses of the newly-appointed professors. Pp. 55-116. New York. 1858.) 4495.6

N1403 — History. Study and teaching. — Columbia University. Addresses.

NL 0345913 MB NN DLC

UB500 .A2 1863 c Rare bk. Coll. Lieber, Francis, 1800-1872.
FOR OTHER EDITIONS SEE MAIN ENTRY
U. S. *War dept.*
... Instructions for the government of armies of the United States, in the field. Prepared by Francis Lieber, LL. D., and revised by a board of officers. New York, D. Van Nostrand, 1863.

Lieber, Francis, 1800-1872.

[Davis, George Breckenridge] 1847–1914.
Doctor Francis Lieber's instructions for the government of armies in the field.
(*In* American journal of international law. New York, 1907. v. 1, p. [13]-25)

Lieber, Francis, 1800-1872.
International Arbitration. A letter to Hon. Wm. H. Seward... [From the New York Times, Sept. 22, 1865. Mounted on 8 leaves of 16° size.]
[In U.S. Civil War Pamphlets, v. 23]

NL 0345916 CtY

VOLUME 332

Lieber, Francis, 1800-1872.
U.S. *Naval war college, Newport.*
... International law discussions, 1903. The United States
naval war code of 1900 ... Washington, Govt. print. off., 1904.

Lieber, Francis, 1800-1872, comp.
Items of political economy.   [n. p., n. d.]
23 cm.
Mounted clippings.
1. Economic conditions. 2. Statistics.

NL   0345918   CU

Lieber, Francis, 1800-1872.
Latin synonymes.   Philadelphia, 1881.

NL   0345919   OClStM

Z
901.9
L621ℓ
Lieber, Francis, 1800-1872.
A lecture on the origin and development of the
first constituents of civilisation.   Columbia,
S.C., I.C. Morgan, 1845.
18p. 22cm.   ₍YA 10090₎

1. Civilization.

PPL RPB MH MdBJ DLC MB GU-L
NL   0345920   TxU ViW NjP ICN CU NcD CtY ScU DLC CSmH

Lieber, Francis, 1800-1872.
... A lecture on the history and uses of athenaeums, delivered at the request of the Columbia athenaeum on the seventeenth of March 1856, by Francis Lieber. Columbia, S. C.,
Press of R. W. Gibbes, 1856.

32 p. 23 cm. (Columbia athenaeum lecture)

1. Learned institutions and societies.

AS5.L5   A 13-641
Chicago. Univ. Libr.
for Library of Congress   ₍a61b¼₎†

NL   0345921   ICU DLC PPAmP PPL TU ViU

Lieber, Francis, 1800-1872.
Legal and political hermeneutics; or, Principles of interpretation and construction in law and politics, with remarks on
precedents and authorities. Enl. ed. By Francis Lieber. Boston, C. C. Little and J. Brown, 1839.

xii, ₍13₎-240 p. 19¼ᶜᵐ.

1. Law—Hist. & crit. 2. Political science.   I. Title.

Library of Congress   JF423.L48   5—2789

MdBP NN ViU PPDrop PPB PPC
NL   0345922   DLC DN GU NcD MU NcA-S OCl OO MiU ICRL

Lieber, Francis, 1800-1872.
Legal and political hermeneutics, or, Principles of interpretation and construction in law and politics, with remarks
on precedents and authorities. By Francis Lieber ... 3d ed.,
with the author's last corrections and additions, and notes
by William G. Hammond ... St. Louis, F. H. Thomas and
company, 1880.

xiv, 352 p. 24½ cm.

1. Law—Hist. & crit. 2. Political science.   I. Hammond, William
Gardiner, 1829-1894.

JF423.L5 1880   9-33647

ViU NcD FU NIC CU-AL WaU-L MtU
NL   0345923   DLC NBuU-L UU OCU OU PP PHC PU-L ICJ

320
L6233
Lieber, Francis, 1800-1872.
Legal and political hermeneutics, or, Principles of interpretation and construction in
law and politics, with remarks on precedents
and authorities. Enl. ed. ... Boston, Little,
1889.
xii, ₍13₎-240 p.

1. Law - History and criticism. 2. Political
science.

NL   0345924   NNC

Lieber, Francis, 1800-1872.
Letter to His Excellency Patrick Noble, governor of South
Carolina, on the penitentiary system, by Francis Leiber. ₍n. p.,
1839₎
1 p. l., ₍85₎-62 p. 24¼ᵐ.
Signed: Francis Lieber.

1. Punishment. 2. Prisons.   I. Title.   18—22006

Library of Congress   HV8728.L5

NL   0345925   DLC CU NcU MB NN ScU

Lieber, Francis, 1800-1872.
... A letter to Hon. E. D. Morgan ... on the amendment of
the Constitution abolishing slavery. Resolutions, passed by
the New York Union league club, concerning conditions of
peace with the insurgents. By Francis Lieber ... New York,
1865.
4 p. 22½ᵐ. (Loyal publication society. ₍Pamphlets₎ no. 79)

1. Slavery in the U. S.—Emancipation. 2. U. S.—Pol. & govt.—Civil
war.   I. New York. Union league club.   12—26331

Library of Congress   E463.L96 no. 79
—— —— Copy 2.   E463.L97

NL   0345926   DLC NIC OU MB

Lieber, Francis, 1800-1872.
[Letter to Rev. Sydney Algernon McMaster, about the
college commons. Columbia, S. C.] South Carolina College, 10th February, '47. 2 leaves. 8°. Note: Mss. presented to the South Carolina College Library, June 15,
1905, by the Rev. Dr. S. S. Gilson, through Rev. Dr. J. W.
Flinn.

NL   0345927   ScU

Lieber, Francis, 1800-1872.
Letters to a gentleman in Germany, written after a
trip from Philadelphia to Niagara. Ed. by Francis Lieber. Philadelphia, Carey, Lea & Blanchard, 1834.

2 p. l., ₍9₎-356 p. 23ᵐᵐ.

Reissued, 1835, under title: The stranger in America; or, Letters to a
gentleman in Germany ... By Francis Lieber.

1. U. S.—Soc. life & cust.   I. Title.

Library of Congress   E165.L71   1-26557

NjP OU OClL PPA PHi PPL MdBP NN AU
NL   0345928   DLC NBuHi NcU MiU-C InU MoSU TU MdBP NcD

Lieber, Francis, 1800-1872.
Letters to a gentleman in Germany, written after a trip
from Philadelphia to Niagara. Philadelphia, Carey, Lea,
& Blanchard, 1834.
(American culture series, 104 : 2)
Microfilm copy (positive) made in 1960 by University Microfilms,
Ann Arbor, Mich.
Collation of the original : 356 p.

1. U. S.—Soc. life & cust.   I. Title.

Microfilm 01291 reel 104, no. 2 E   Mic 60-7508

NL   0345929   DLC ICRL KEmT FTaSU

MIC
US
904
LIE
Lieber, Francis, 1800-1872
₍Letters to Prof. Carl Joseph Anton
Mittermaier of Heidelberg, between Feb. 9, 1838
and Dec. 29, 1860. Boston ₍etc.₎ 1838-1860.₎

2 reels. 35mm.

Microfilm (negative) of manuscript letters.
Contents.- reel 1. Aug. 23, 1832-Oct. 14, 1837.-
reel 2. Feb. 9, 1838-Dec. 29, 1860.

NL   0345930   MH-L

LIEBER, Francis, 1800-1872.
Lettre sur l'arbitrage international. ₍Dated
Washington, 17 sept. 1865.₎

(BLUNTSCHLI, J.C. Opinion impartiale, etc. 1870.
pp. 33-38.)

NL   0345931   MH

Lieber, Francis, 1800-1872.
...La libertà civile e l'autogoverno. Prima traduzione
italiana...di Pietro Fea. (Biblioteca di scienze politiche e
amministrative. Torino, 1890. 8°. ₍ser. 1,₎ v. 5, p. 105-
488.)

1. Liberty, Civil. 2. Democracy.   3. Fea, Pietro, 1849- , trans-
N. Y. P. L.   lator.   February 9, 1929

NL   0345932   NN

Lieber, Francis, 1800-1872.
La libertad civil y el gobierno propio, por el doctor Francisco
Lieber. Traducida del ingles al español por Florentino Gonza-
lez ... Con apéndices que contienen las constituciones de Ingla-
terra, Francia, Estados Unidos, etc., etc. ... Paris, Librería de
Rosa y Bouret, 1872-

v. 22½ᵐ.

1. Political science. 2. Democracy.   I. González, Florentino, 1805-
1874, tr.   *Translation of* On civil liberty and self-government.
                                                     44—44286

Library of Congress   JC212.L75

NL   0345933   DLC TxU MH

Micro-
film
2
LIEBER, FRANCIS, 1800-1872.
The life and letters of Francis Lieber;
ed. by Thomas Sergeant Perry.   London,
Trübner & co. ₍18—?₎
439 p. front. 24cm. negative microfilm.
1 reel.

NL   0345934   ICN

Lieber, Francis, 1800-1872.
The life and letters of Francis Lieber; ed. by Thomas Sergeant Perry ... Boston, J. R. Osgood and company, 1882.
iv, 439 p. front. (port.) 23½ᶜᵐ.

1. U. S.—Pol. & govt.—1844-1877.   I. Perry, Thomas Sergeant,
1845-1928.   11—27392

Library of Congress   E415.9.L7L7

ScU RPB OFH OU MiU DNW OrU OrPS MeB MoU OOxM MdBP DN
NL   0345935   DLC PU PSC PBm NjP NN MH MB ICJ MWA NjN

JC
212
.L6
1882a
Lieber, Francis, 1800-1872.
The life and letters of Francis Lieber.
Edited by Thomas Sergeant Perry. Boston,
J.R.Osgood, 1882.
iv, 439 p. illus.
Photocopy. Ann Arbor, Mich., University
Microfilms, 1971. iv, 439 p. (on double leaves)

1. U.S.--Pol.& govt.--1844-1877.   I. Perry,
Thomas Sergeant,   1845-1928, ed.

NL   0345936   MiU

VOLUME 332

E
415.9
L7L7
Lieber, Francis, 1800–1872.
    The life and letters of Francis Lieber; ed.
by Thomas Sergeant Perry. Boston, Osgood,
1882.
    iv, 439 p. 20 cm.

    Xerox copy.

    1. U. S. - Pol. & govt. - 1844-1877. I.
Perry, Thomas Sergeant, 1845-1928.

NL 0345937   NBuU

Lieber, Francis, 1800–1872.
    ... Lincoln oder McClellan? Aufruf an die Deutschen in
Amerika, von Franz Lieber. ₍New York₎ Gedruckt bei H. Ludwig, 1864.
    4 p. 22½ᶜᵐ. (Loyal publication society. ₍Pamphlets₎ no. 59)
    Caption title.

    1. Campaign literature, 1864—Republican.
                                                    12–26580
    Library of Congress   E463.L96 no. 59
    ———— Copy 2.   E463.L97 no. 59

NL 0345938   DLC NIC

₍Lieber, Francis₎ 1800–1872.
    ... Lincoln oder McClellan? An die Deutschen in Ame-
rika ... ₍New York, 1864₎
    1 l. 29½ x 23½ᵐᵐ. (₍Loyal publication society. Pamphlets₎ no. 59)
    At head of title: No. 59. The seal of the Loyal publication society fol-
lows the title.
    Signed: Franz Lieber.

    1. Campaign literature, 1864—Republican. I. Title.
                                                    16–25457
    Library of Congress   E458.4.L69

NL 0345939   DLC NIC OU PPL

₍Lieber, Francis₎ 1800–1872.
    Lincoln oder McClellan? An die Deutschen in Ameri-
ka. ₍Philadelphia, King & Baird, printers, 1864₎
    4 p. 23ᶜᵐ.
    Caption title.
    Signed at end: Franz Lieber.

    1. Campaign literature, 1864—Republican.
                                                    11–11810
    Library of Congress   E458.4.L692
    ———— Copy 2.   ₍Union league of Philadelphia. ₍Pam-
                     phlets₎ v. 3, no. 97₎

NL 0345940   DLC

Lieber, Francis, 1800–1872.
    ... Lincoln of McClellan? Oproep aan de Hollanders in
Amerika. Van Francis Lieber. ₍New York, Loyal publication society₎ 1865₎
    4 p. 22½ᵐᵐ. (Loyal publication society ... ₍Pamphlets₎ no. 71)
    Caption title.

    1. Campaign literature, 1864—Republican.
                                                    18–10825
    Library of Congress   E463.L96 no. 71
    ———— Copy 2.
    ———— Copy 3.   E463.L97 no. 71

NL 0345941   DLC NIC OU MiU-C

Lieber, Francis, 1800–1872.
    ... Lincoln or McClellan. Appeal to the Germans in
America. By Francis Lieber. Tr. from the German by
T. C. ₍New York, 1864₎
    8 p. 22½ cm. (Loyal publication society. ₍Pamphlets₎ no. 67)
    Caption title.

    1. Campaign literature, 1864—Republican. I. C., T. II. T. C.
    E463.L96 no. 67   12—26335
    ———— Copy 2.   E463.L97
    ———— Copy 3.   E458.4.L694

NL 0345942   DLC OC1WHi OU NIC

Lieber, Francis, 1800–1872.
    Manual of political ethics, designed chiefly for the use
of colleges and students at law ... By Francis Lieber.
Boston, C. C. Little and J. Brown, 1838–39.
    2 v. 22½ᵐᵐ.

    1. Political ethics.

    Library of Congress   JC212.L6 1838   1–13076

        NN ICJ MH MdBP KyLx PMₐ WaU-L NWM-V
NL 0345943   DLC OU NcD OC1W OO PBa PU PPB ScU CtY

Rare   Lieber, Francis, 1800–1872.
JC   Manual of political ethics ... Part I.
212   ... London, William Smith, 1839.
L71M2   xv, 413 p. 24cm.
1839
            This copy belonged to Henry Thomas
        Buckle.

NL 0345944   NIC MeB NjP PSC

Lieber, Francis, 1800–1872.
    Manual of political ethics, designed chiefly
for the use of colleges and students at law.
Boston, 1847.
    2 vols.

NL 0345945   PPL OO CtY

Lieber, Francis, 1800–1872.
    Manual of political ethics, designed chiefly for the use of
colleges and students at law. By Francis Lieber ... 2d ed.
rev. Ed. by Theodore D. Woolsey. Philadelphia, J. B. Lippincott & co., 1875.
    2 v. 23ᵐᵐ.

    1 1. Political ethics. I. Woolsey, Theodore Dwight, 1801–1889, ed.

    Library of Congress   JC212.L6 1875   1–13077

NL 0345946   DLC NcD TU OFH OU OO I ICN Nh NjP NN MH

Lieber, Francis, 1800–1872.
    Manual of political ethics, designed chiefly for the use of
colleges and students at law ... By Francis Lieber ... 2d ed.,
rev. Edited by Theodore D. Woolsey. Philadelphia, J. B.
Lippincott & co.; London, Trübner & co., 1875.
    2 v. 23ᵐᵐ.
    On spine: Political ethics.

    1. Political ethics. I. Woolsey, Theodore Dwight, 1801–1889, ed.

    Library of Congress   JC212.L6 1875 a   44–34158

NL 0345947   DLC WaTC OrCS IU PHC

Lieber, Francis. 1800–1872.
    Manual of political ethics, designed chiefly for the use of colleges
and students at law. 2d edition, revised. Edited by Theodore
Woolsey.
= Philadelphia. ·Lippincott & Co. 1876. 2 v. 8°.

F6800 — Woolsey, Theodore Dwight, ed. 1801–1889. — Political ethics.

NL 0345948   MB MsSM OU MiU MH MH-L

Lieber, Francis, 1800–1872.
    Manual of political ethics, designed chiefly for the use of
colleges and students at law ... By Francis Lieber ... 2d
rev. Ed. by Theodore D. Woolsey. Philadelphia. J. B. Lippincott & co. **London, Trübner & co., 1876.**
    2 v. 23ᵐᵐ.

    1. Political ethics. I. Woolsey, Theodore Dwight, 1801–1889, ed.

NL 0345949   ViU

Lieber, Francis, 1800–1872.
    Manual of political ethics, designed chiefly for the use of colleges
and students at law. ... . By Francis Lieber, LL.D., ...
Vol. I–[II]. Second edition, revised. Edited by Theodore D.
Woolsey. Philadelphia, London, J. B. Lippincott & Co., 1881,
[°1874].
    2 vol. 23ᵐᵐ.
    First edition: Boston 1838–1839.

NL 0345950   ICJ CtY NjP

JC
212
.L6
1885
Lieber, Francis, 1800–1872.
    Manual of political ethics, designed
chiefly for the use of colleges and students
at law. 2d ed. rev. Ed. by Theodore D.
Woolsey. Philadelphia, J.B. Lippincott
[1885?]
    2 v.

    1. Political ethics. I. Woolsey, Theodore
Dwight, 1801–1889, ed.

NL 0345951   NBuU NjNbS

JC212
.L6
1888
Lieber, Francis, 1800–1872.
    Manual of political ethics, designed
chiefly for the use of colleges and
students at law. Edited by Theodore D.
Woolsey. 2d ed., rev. Philadelphia,
Lippincott, 1888.
    2 v. 23cm.

NL 0345952   OCU

Lieber, Francis, 1800–1872.
    Manual of political ethics ... edited
by T. D. Woolsey. ed. 2, rev. Phila.
1890.

NL 0345953   ODW

Lieber, Francis, 1800–1872.
    Manual of political ethics, designed
chiefly for the use of colleges and
students at law ... by ... 2d. ed., rev.
and ed. by Theodore D. Woolsey. Philadelphia and London, J. B. Lippincott company,
1892.

NL 0345954   OC1W PPD PP

Lieber, Francis, 1800–1872.
    Manual of political ethics, designed chiefly for the use
of colleges and students at law ... By Francis Lieber ...
2d ed., rev. and ed. by Theodore D. Woolsey, with an introduction by Nicholas Murray Butler. Philadelphia and
London, J. B. Lippincott company, 1911.
    2 v. 23½ cm.

    1. Political ethics. I. Woolsey, Theodore Dwight, 1801–1889, ed.

    JC212.L6 1911   11–9303

NL 0345955   DLC IdU PU NN FU

Lieber, Francis, 1800–1872.
    ... Memorial from Francis Lieber ... relative to pro-
posals for a work on the statistics of the United States.
April 18, 1836. Referred to the Committee on the Library, and ordered to be printed ... ₍Washington₎ Gales
& Seaton print ₍1836₎
    17 p. 22½ᵐᵐ. (₍U. S.₎ 24th Cong., 1st sess. Senate. ₍Doc. no.₎ 314)
    Caption title.

    1. U. S.—Stat. I. U. S. Congress. Joint committee on the Library.
                                                    2–27103
    Library of Congress   HA37.U5 1836

NL 0345956   DLC MiU CtY MB

VOLUME 332

Lieber, Francis, 1800–1872.
... Memorial from Dr. Francis Lieber relative to verdicts of jurors. New York, June 26th, 1867. [Albany, 1867]

4 p. 23 cm. (State of New York. No. 26. In convention, July 12, 1867)

Caption-title.

1. Jury.

NL 0345957   CSmH

Lieber, Francis, 1800–1872.
... Memorial from Dr. Francis Lieber, relative to verdicts of jurors, New York, June 26th 1867. [New York? 1867]

[2] p.   24 x 20.3 cm.
At head of title: A reprint, with some additions of Document: State of New York, no. 26. In convention, July 12, 1867.
Caption-title.

NL 0345958   CSmH LU NN

Lieber, Francis, 1800–1872.
Memorial to Congress, praying a modification of the tariff in regard to the duties on books. [Washington] 1842. O. 8p.

NL 0345959   RPB CSmH

Lieber, Francis, 1800–1872.
... Memorial of Francis Lieber ... praying a revision of the law regulating postage on printed matter to the territories of the United States, June 12, 1868. Referred to the Committee on the post offices and post roads and ordered to be printed. [Washington, D. C., 1868]

2 p.   23.9 cm. ([U. S.] 40th Cong. 2d sess. Senate. Mis. doc. no. 92)
Caption title.

I. U. S. Congress. Senate. Committee on post offices and post roads.

NL 0345960   CSmH

Lieber, Francis, 1800–1872. The metaphysical religion of Hegel.
Haushalter, Walter Milton, 1889–
Mrs. Eddy purloins from Hegel; newly discovered source reveals amazing plagiarisms in Science and health, by Walter M. Haushalter. Boston, A. A. Beauchamp, 1936.

JC212   Lieber, Francis, 1800–1872.
L7   The miscellaneous writings. [Edited by Daniel C. Gilman] Philadelphia, Lippincott [1880]
        2v. 23cm.

Contents.– v.1. Reminiscences, addresses, and essays.– v.2. Contributions to political science, including lectures on the Constitution of the United States, and other papers.

NL 0345962   IaU MU WaSpG

Lieber, Francis, 1800–1872.
The miscellaneous writings of Francis Lieber ... Philadelphia [etc.] J. B. Lippincott & co., 1881.
2 v. front. (port.) 23ᶜᵐ.
Half-title: each volume has special t-p.
Edited by Daniel C. Gilman.
"The life, character, and writings of Francis Lieber. A discourse delivered before the Historical society of Pennsylvania, January 13, 1873. By Hon. M. Russell Thayer": v. 1, p. 13–44.
"Lieber's service to political science and international law. By Dr. J. C. Bluntschli": v. 2, p. 7–14.
Contents.–v. 1. Reminiscences, addresses, and essays.–v. 2. Contributions to political science, including lectures on the Constitution of the United States, and other papers.
1. Political science—Collected works. I. Gilman, Daniel Coit, 1831–1908, ed.
Library of Congress   JC212.L7
10–30501

MdBP NN MB NjP KEmT CaBVaU OrPR OrCS
NL 0345963   DLC Vi NcD NBuU NjNbS MH MWA ScU OClW

Lieber, Francis, 1800–1872.
Miscellaneous writings. [Philadelphia, Lippincott, 1881]
(American culture series: 180: 1)
Microfilm copy (positive) made in 1961 by University Microfilms, Ann Arbor, Mich.
Collation of the original: 2 v. port.
"The writings of Francis Lieber": vol. 2, p. 531–535.
Contents.—1. Reminiscences, addresses, and essays.—2. Contributions to political science.

1. Political science—Collected works.
Microfilm 01291 reel 180, no. 1 E   Mic 62–7469

NL 0345964   DLC MiU FTaSU ICRL CSt

Lieber, Francis, 1800–1872.
La moral aplicada á la política, por Francisco Lieber ... Versión directa del inglés por Cárlos Casares y Federico Saenz de Urraca bajo la dirección del doctor Enrique Azarola. Montevideo, Tipo-lit. la Minerva, 1887.
vii, xv, 327 p., 1 l., 195, [13] p.   29ᶜᵐ.

1. Political ethics.   I. Casares, Cárlos, tr.   II. Saenz de Urraca, Federico, tr.   III. Azarola, Enrique, ed.
1–17171
Library of Congress   JC212.L65

NL 0345965   DLC

Lieber, Francis, 1800–1872.
...The Mormons. Shall Utah be admitted into the Union?... [N.Y., 1855]
p.[225]–236.
Caption title.
Detached from Putnam's Monthly; a magazine of Literature, Science, and Art. Vol.V, March, 1855, No.XXVII.

NL 0345966   NcD-L

Lieber, Francis, 1800–1872.
The national polity is the normal type of modern government. ⟨A fragment⟩ [n.p., 18––?]
broadside, 19.8 x 10.3; text, 19.3 x 9.6 cm.
Three other variant copies included.

NL 0345967   CSmH

Lieber, Francis, 1800–1872.
Nationalism. A fragment of political science. By Francis Lieber ... [New York. Press of Fisher & Field, 186–]
6 p. 22ᶜᵐ.
Caption title.

1. Nationalism and nationality.
10–4282
Library of Congress   JC311.L6

NL 0345968   DLC PHi NN

Lieber, Francis, 1800–1872.
The necessity of continued self-education. An address to the graduating class of S. C. college, at commencement, on the first of December, MDCCCLI. By Francis Lieber ... Printed by order of the governor. Columbia, Press of A. S. Johnston, 1851.
17 p.   23ᶜᵐ.

I. South Carolina college, Columbia.
7—16584
Library of Congress   LD5037.2 1851

NL 0345969   DLC PP NN PPL MB

LIEBER, Francis, 1800–1872.
The necessity of religious instruction in colleges. n.p., [1850?]

Pamphlet.
Without title-page. Caption title.

NL 0345970   MH CSmH

Lieber, Francis, 1800–1872.
... The necessity of religious instruction in colleges. By the late Francis Lieber ... [San Francisco, 1872]
[4] p.   22.5 cm.   [His Writings; collected pamphlets]
Newspaper clipping.

NL 0345971   CU

[Lieber, Francis] 1800–1872.
No party now, but all for our country. [Address by Francis Lieber ... read at the meeting of the Loyal national league ... New York, on the 11th of April, 1863] Philadelphia, Crissy & Markley, printers, 1863.
cover-title, 12 p. 22ᶜᵐ.

1. U. S.—Hist.—Civil war—Addresses, sermons, etc.   I. Title.
Library of Congress   E458.3.L7   4–33418
———— Copy 2.
———— Copy 3.   (In Philadelphia. Union league.
[Pamphlets] 1863–66.   v. 1, no. 19)
                                   E458.P54 vol. 1

PPL PU PP CaBVaU
NL 0345972   DLC NIC KyU NjP NNC NN MnHi MWA OClW

Lieber, Francis, 1800–1872.
... No party now; but all for our country. By Dr. Francis Lieber. New York, May, 1863. New York, C. S. Westcott & co., printers, 1863.
10 p. 23ᶜᵐ. (Loyal publication society. [Pamphlets] no. 16)

1. U. S.—Hist.—Civil war—Addresses, sermons, etc.
Library of Congress   E458.L93   12–27533
———— Copy 2.   E458.3.L71

NL 0345973   DLC NIC NNC NcU MB

Lieber, Francis, 1800–1872.
... No party now but all for our country. By Francis Lieber. New-York, May, 1863. Rev. ed. New York, C. S. Westcott & co., printers, 1863.
cover-title, 8 p. 23ᶜᵐ. (Loyal publication society. [Pamphlets] no. 16)
"Address read at the inaugural meeting of the Loyal national league, by the request of the League, in Union square, New York, on the 11th of April, 1863."

1. U. S.—Hist.—Civil war—Addresses, sermons, etc.
Library of Congress   E458.L93   12–27534
- Copy 2.   E458.3.L711

NL 0345974   DLC NIC OU MiU OO ViU MB NN CSmH

Lieber, Francis, 1800–1872.
... No party now but all for our country. By Francis Lieber. New-York, May, 1863. Rev. ed. New York, Loyal publication society, 1864.
cover-title, 8 p. 22ᶜᵐ. (Loyal publication society. [Pamphlets] no. 16)

1. U. S.—Hist.—Civil war—Addresses, sermons, etc.
12–27535
Library of Congress   E458.L92 vol. 1

NL 0345975   DLC MiU MB PU

240478

Lieber, Francis, 1800–1872.
A Northern tribute to Southern loyalty. Resolutions offered by Francis Lieber, and seconded by C. E. Detmold, concerning the demise of James L. Petigru, of South Carolina, and unanimously approved at the great mass meeting of the Loyal national league and other loyal citizens, on occasion of the Sumter anniversary, in New York, April 11th, 1863. [New York, 1863]
broadside, 24.1 x 15.2; text, 13.6 x 5.9 cm.
Lieber collection.
1. Petigru, James Louis, 1789–1863.   I. Loyal national league of the state of New York.
II. Title.

NL 0345976   CSmH

VOLUME 332

Lieber, Francis, 1800–1872.
Notes on fallacies of American protectionists. **4th ed.**
... By Francis Lieber. New York, American free-trade
league, 1870.
48 p. 18½ᵐ.

1. Tariff—U. S. 2. Free trade and protection—Free trade.

16–24669

Library of Congress   HF1755.L72 1870

NL 0345977   DLC CtY PPL PHi NN MB MH NcD

Lieber, Francis, 1800–1872.
Notes on fallacies peculiar to American protectionists,
or chiefly resorted to in America. By Francis Lieber.
New York, American free trade league, 1869.
39 p. 23ᵐ.

1. Free trade and protection—Free trade.

Library of Congress   HF1755.L72   5–42667†

NL 0345978   DLC OFH OU MiU PPL ICU MB

Lieber, Francis, 1800–1872.
On civil liberty and self-government. By Francis Lieber
.. London, R. Bentley, 1853.
xv, 552 p. 23ᵐ.

1. Political science. 2. Democracy.

33–33177

Library of Congress   JC212.L72 1853 a   320.1

NL 0345979   DLC OC1W ICJ MiU OO NcU ViHaI MiU-C

Lieber, Francis, 1800–1872.
On civil liberty and self-government. By Francis Lieber ... In two volumes. Philadelphia, Lippincott, Grambo and co., 1853.
2 v. 18½ᵐ.

1. Political science. 2. Democracy.

CA 10—4517 Unrev'd

Library of Congress   JC212.L72

    PPA PSC PPL MB NN PHi PU WaU-L Or CaBVaU
NL 0345980   DLC TNJ WaU PMA GU NcA-S NcD NjN ViU ScU

FILM
321.8
L62o
1853

Lieber, Francis, 1800–1872.
On civil liberty and self-government.
Philadelphia, Lippincott, Grambo, 1853.

Microfilm copy (negative) made in 1958 by
the University of Illinois Library of the original in the University of Pennsylvania Library.
Collation of the original: 2v.
Bibliographical footnotes.

1. Political science. 2. Democracy.

NL 0345981   IU

Lieber, Francis, 1800–1872.
On civil liberty and self-government. By Francis Lieber
... Enl. ed. in one volume. Philadelphia, J. B. Lippincott
and co.; ₁etc., etc., 1859.
xiv p., 1 l., ₁17₁–629 p. 23 cm.

1. Political science. 2. Democracy.

JC212.L73 1859   10—29461

    NN OO MB NjP MdBP WaWW MnHi CSmH
NL 0345982   DLC NcD PP MoS MiU OOxM OU MeB MWA CtY

Lieber, Francis, 1800–1872.
On civil liberty and self-government. By Francis Lieber
... 3d ed., rev. Ed. by Theodore D. Woolsey. Philadelphia,
J. B. Lippincott & co., 1874.
622 p. 23ᵐ.

1. Political science. 2. Democracy. ɪ. Woolsey, Theodore Dwight,
1801–1889, ed.
10—4278

Library of Congress   JC212.L72 1874

    OC1WHi NN MH PHC PP IaAS OrCS
NL 0345983   DLC FU DAU NIC NBuU NcD TU OC1 OFH MB

JC212
.L72
1875

Lieber, Francis, 1800–1872.
On civil liberty and self-
government. Edited by Theodore D.
Woolsey. 3d ed. rev. Philadelphia,
Lippincott, 1875.
622 p. 23 cm.
Includes bibliographical references.

NL 0345984   OCU MB NjNbS OU

Lieber, Francis, 1800–1872.
On civil liberty and self-government. By Francis Lieber ...
3d ed., rev. Edited by Theodore D. Woolsey. Philadelphia,
J. B. Lippincott & co.; London, Trübner & co., 1877.
622 p. 23ᵐ.

1. Political science. 2. Democracy. ɪ. Woolsey, Theodore Dwight,
1801–1889, ed.
45–26159

Library of Congress   JC212.L72 1877

NL 0345985   DLC MnHi MiU-C ScU CtY OC1W MtU OrPR ViU

JC 571
.L6
1880

LIEBER, FRANCIS, 1800–1872.
On civil liberty and self-government.
Edited by Theodore D. Woolsey. 3d ed., rev.
Philadelphia, Lippincott, 1880.
622 p.

1. Liberty. I. Tc.: Civil liberty and self-
government. UGL cds.

NL 0345986   InU

Lieber, Francis, 1800–1872.
On civil liberty and self-government. By Francis Lieber ...
3d ed., rev. Edited by Theodore D. Woolsey. Philadelphia,
London, J. B. Lippincott & co., 1881.
622 p. 23ᵐ.

1. Political science. 2. Democracy. ɪ. Woolsey, Theodore Dwight,
1801–1889, ed.
45–26158

Library of Congress   JC212.L72 1881

NL 0345987   DLC WaSpG WaTC ICJ OO

Lieber, Francis, 1800–1872.
On civil liberty and self-government.
By ... 3d ed., rev. ed. by Theodore D.
Woolsey. Philadelphia, ₁etc.₁ J. B.
Lippincott company, 1888.
622 p.

NL 0345988   MiU OC1W PBm

M-film
300
Am3
344–8

Lieber, Francis, 1800–1872.
On civil liberty and self-government. Ed. by
Theodore D. Woolsey. 3d ed., rev. Philadelphia, J. B. Lippincott, 1891.
622 p.

Microfilm (positive) Ann Arbor, Mich.,
University Microfilms, 1967. 8th title of 9.
35 mm. (American culture series, 344.8)

1. Political science. 2. Democracy.
I. Title.

NL 0345989   KEmT PSt

Lieber, Francis, 1800–1872.
On civil liberty and self-government.
3rd ed. rev. Philadelphia, J. B.
Lippincott, 1894.

NL 0345990   OC1W PP

Lieber, Francis, 1800–1872.
On civil liberty and self-government. Ed. 3, rev.
by Theodore D. Woolsey.
Phila., Lippincott, 1901.
622 p.

NL 0345991   PPSteph CtY WaS WaSp

Lieber, Francis, 1800–1872.
On civil liberty and self government by
Francis Lieber, edited by Theodore D. Woolsey
with an introductory note by Daniel C. Gilman.
4th edition. Philadelphia, J.B. Lippincott Co.,
1901.

NL 0345992   MsU

Lieber, Francis.
On civil liberty and self-government, ed. by
T. D. Woolsey. ed. 3.
Phila., Lippincott, 1911.
622 p.

NL 0345993   PU

Lieber, Francis, 1800–1872.
On history and political economy, as necessary branches of
superior education in free states. An inaugural address, delivered in South Carolina college, before ... the governor and
the legislature of the state, on Commencement day the 7th of
December, 1835. By Francis Lieber, ʟʟ. ᴅ. ... Printed by
order of ... the Board of trustees. Columbia, S. C., Printed
by A. S. Johnston, 1836.
26 p. 21½ᵐ.

1. History—Study and teaching. 2. Economics—Study and teaching.
ɪ. South Carolina. University.
2—29514

Library of Congress   D16.L71

NL 0345994   DLC MiU-C TxU CSmH MB ScU NcD PPAmP PP

Lieber, Francis, 1800–1872.
On international copyright, in a letter to the Hon. W. C.
Preston ... By Francis Lieber ... New York, Wiley &
Putnam, 1840.
67 p. 23ᵐ.

1. Copyright, International.

Library of Congress   Z552.L71   6–42488

NL 0345995   DLC CtY-L MiU NN PHi PP

Lieber, Francis, 1800–1872.
On the idea of the Latin race and its real
value in international law. An article in the
Revue de droit internationale ... translated
from the French by W.W.S. [New York] Printed
for private circulation, November, 1871.
[4] p. 23.4cm.

NL 0345996   CSmH

Lieber, Francis, tr.
On the penitentiary system in the United States...
see under   Beaumont de La Bonninière,
Gustave Auguste de, 1802–1866.

VOLUME 332

Lieber, Francis, 1800–1872.
On the relation between education and crime.
Phila., 1836.

NL 0345997   PPL

Lieber, Francis, 1800–1872.
On the subjects of penal law. Philadelphia, 1838.
8°

NL 0345998   NN

Lieber, Francis, 1800–1872.
... On the vocal sounds of Laura Bridgeman, the blind deaf-mute at Boston; compared with the elements of phonetic language. By Francis Lieber. ₍Washington, Smithsonian institution, 1850₎

31 p. 31½ cm. (Smithsonian contributions to knowledge, vol. II, art. 2)

Smithsonian institution publication 12.

1. Bridgeman, Laura Dewey, 1829–1889.

[Q11.S68 vol. 2, art. 2]   S 13—3

Smithsonian Institution.   Library
for Library of Congress   ₍a50d½₎

WaS OrU CaBVaU MnHi PPWa
NL 0345999   DSI OCl OO OCU MiU OU NN ICJ DNLM PPAN

Lieber (Francis) 1800–1872. A paper on the vocal sounds of Laura Bridgman, the blind deaf-mute at Boston; compared with the elements of phonetic language. 31 pp., 1 l. 4°. Washington, 1851.
Repr. from : Smithsonian Contrib. to Knowledge, ii.

NL 0346001   DNLM NN ICJ DSI

Lieber, Francis, 1800–1872.
Plantations for slave labor the death of the yeomanry. ₍n.p., n.d.₎

NL 0346002   CtY NcD NhD MnHi NN

Lieber, Francis, 1800–1872.
Plantations for slave labor the death of the yeomanry. ₍New York, 186–?₎
8 pp. 8°

NL 0346003   DLC

Lieber, Francis, 1800–1872.
Plantations for slave labor, the death of the yeomanry.
N.Y., 1863.

NL 0346004   PPL

Slavery
E   Lieber, Francis, 1800–1872.
441   Plantations for slave labor the death of the yeomanry.
M46   By Francis Lieber. New York, W.C. Bryant,
v.136   printers, 1863.
no.21   8 p. 24 cm. (Loyal publication society.
        ₍Pamphlets₎ no. 29)

May anti-slavery pamphlets, v. 136.

1. Slavery in the U. S.—Controversial literature—1863.   I. Title.

NL 0346005   NIC TU

Lieber, Francis, 1800–1872.
Plantations for slave labor the death of the yeomanry.
By Francis Lieber, LL. D. ₍Philadelphia, C. Sherman, son & co., 1863₎

cover-title, 8 p. 21½ᶜᵐ.

1. Slavery in the U. S.—Controversial literature—1863.
Library of Congress   E449.L71   12–20627
———— Copy 2.   ₍Philadelphia. Union league. Pamphlets. v. 2, no. 61₎
                E458.P54 vol.2

NNC CSmH ICN RPB OO ICU
NL 0346006   DLC NcU KyU TxU PPL PHi NIC PU PPAmP MH

Lieber, Francis, 1800–1872.
Plantations for slave labor. The death of the yeomanry.
By Francis Lieber... New York, Oct., 1863.   New York, 1865.
8 p.   8°.   (Loyal Publ. Soc. ₍Pamphlets.₎ no. 29.)

Cover-title.
Also published under title: Slavery, plantations and the yeomanry.

1. Slavery, U. S., 1863. 2. Series.
N. Y. P. L.   July 22, 1918.

NL 0346007   NN CU OO NSchU NBuG

Lieber, Francis, 1800–1872.
[Poems by Lieber, together with an article on him by Gustav Körner, excerpted from Der Deutsche pionier. Cincinnati, 1879–1880]

various paging 23cm.

Excerpts from v. 11, nos. 1, 9; v. 12, nos. 1,9.

NL 0346008   CSmH

SPECIAL COLLECTIONS
B12L62
L
        Lieber, Francis, 1800–1872.
        Poems ₍and letters by₎ Francis Lieber.
        ₍1826–1854₎
        2 v. 18cm. (v. 2, 19cm)

Manuscript.
Title from covers.
Principally in German, with a few passages in English. The dated portions are mostly 1826 and 1827, with a few dated 1847, 1848, 1852 and 1854.

NL 0346009   NNC

Lieber, Francis, 1800–1872
Polgári szabadság és önkormányzat. Dr. Lieber hasonczímü könyve után szabadon magyarítsák Scholcz Viktor és Vajda János.
Pest, Heckenast G., 1869.

2 p.l., vii, 158, ₍2₎ p. 24cm.

NL 0346010   MH-L

Lieber, Francis, 1800–1872.
Political hermeneutics; or On political interpretation and construction; and also on precedents. By Francis Lieber ...
Boston, C. C. Little & J. Brown, 1837.

1 p. l, 78 p. 24ᶜᵐ.

"Reprinted from the American jurist, for October, 1837."
Originally intended as a chapter for the author's Manual of political ethics, but later rewritten and published separately, in 1839, under title: Legal and political hermeneutics. cf. Pref. to 1839 ed.

1. Law—Hist. & crit. 2. Political science.   I. Title.
                                38–6624
Library of Congress   JF423.L5 1837

NL 0346011   DLC PPL ScU

Lieber, Francis, 1800–1872.
A popular essay on subjects of penal law, and on uninterrupted solitary confinement at labor, as contradistinguished to solitary confinement at night and joint labor by day, in a letter to John Bacon ... president of the Philadelphia society for alleviating the miseries of public prisons. By Francis Lieber ... Philadelphia, Pub. by order of the Society, 1838.

iv, ₍5₎–94 p. 23½ᶜᵐ.

1. Punishment. 2. Prisons.

Library of Congress   HV8675.L7   10—21550

PU PHC NN OO MdBP
NL 0346012   DLC IaU DNLM MiU-C TU NcU PPB PSC PHi

Lieber, Francis, 1800–1872.
Prison discipline. Mrs. Elizabeth Fry and F. Lieber ... upon the separate confinement of prisoners. From the Manchester guardian of ... 24th June, 1848. Manchester ₍Eng.₎ Cave and Sever, printers, 1848.

8 p. 20.3cm.

Includes a letter of Lieber to J. Adshead, with comments on quotations from Mrs. Fry's life, purported to be her "views of solitary confinement."

NL 0346013   CSmH

Lieber, Francis, 1800–1872.
Reflections on the changes which may seem necessary in the present constitution of the state of New York, elicited and published by the New York Union league club. By Francis Lieber ... New York, 1867.
50 p. 27½ᶜᵐ.

1. New York (State) Constitution.
                                9–34914
Library of Congress   JK3425.1867.L5

NL 0346014   DLC ICRL NIC ICU NcD NN ICJ Nh PHi CtY

CT   Lieber, Francis, 1800–1872.
211   Remarks ₍concerning J. A. Andrew.
B61   Boston? ca. 1867₎
v.6   broadside. 15 x 49cm. (fold. and
no.2   bound in 23cm. vol.)

1. Andrew, John Albion, 1818–1867.

NL 0346015   NIC

AC901
.M5 Lieber, Francis, 1800–1872.
        Remarks on the final adjournment of the Loyal publication society. ₍1866₎
        12 p.

(Miscellaneous pamphlets, 474; 5)

NL 0346016   DLC

Lieber, Francis, 1800–1872.
Dr. Lieber's ₍remarks on the final adjournment of the Loyal Pub. Socy.
N.Y., 1865.

NL 0346017   PPL

Lieber, Francis, 1800–1872.
Dr. Lieber's remarks on the final adjournment of the Loyal publication society. ₍New York? 1866?₎
3 p. 23ᶜᵐ.
Caption title.

I. Loyal publication society.

                        CA 30–1524 Unrev'd
Library of Congress   E463.L71   973.7114

NL 0346018   DLC NN NcD CU

VOLUME 332

Lieber, Francis, *1800-1872*.
Remarks on the post establishment of the U.S.
New York, 1841.

NL 0346019   PPL

Lieber, Francis, 1800–1872.
Remarks on the relation between education and crime,
in a letter to the Right Rev. William White ... By Francis Lieber ... To which are added, some observations by
N. H. Julius ... Philadelphia, 1835.

24 p. 22½ᵐ.

Pub. by order of the Philadelphia society for alleviating the miseries of
public prisons.

1. Crime and criminals. 2. Education.   I. Julius, Nicolaus Heinrich,
1783-1862.

Library of Congress   HV6166.L7   10–17418†
———— Copy 2   (Educational pamphlets, v. 5, no. 11;
                      LB7.A2 vol. 5

            PPL PU PPAmP PHi CtY MWA NN MB
NL 0346020   DLC NIC MiU-C CtY-M OKentU CU PPPrHi

Lieber, Francis, 1800–1872.
Reminiscences, addresses, and essays.
Philadelphia. Lippincott & Co. 1881. 534 pp. Portrait. Auto-
graph facsimile. [Miscellaneous writings. Vol. 1.] 22 cm., in 8s.
Contains the life, character, and writings of Francis Lieber, by M. Russell
Thayer, catalogued separately.

H8500 — S.r.c.

NL 0346021   MB MdBP LU MH PPL PPFr

E
5   LIEBER, FRANCIS, 1800-1872.
.N 5525   Reminiscences of an intercourse with George
            Berthold Niebuhr, the historian of Rome...   Lon-
            don,Bentley,1835.
            231p.

NL 0346022   ICN CaBVaU OrU ScU MdBP PU PPL CtY

Lieber, Francis, 1800–1872.
Reminiscences of an intercourse with Mr. Niebuhr, the historian, during a residence with him in Rome, in the years 1822
and 1823. By Francis Lieber ... Philadelphia, Carey, Lea &
Blanchard, 1835.

xii, (13,–192 p. 18½ᵐ.

1. Niebuhr, Barthold Georg, 1776-1831.   16–8331 Revised

Library of Congress   DG206.N5L5
                             (r39b2;

            NjP PPA PHi
NL 0346023   DLC TU MeB PU CtY MiD MdBP MiU I MB

Lieber, Francis, 1800-1872.

... Professor F. Lieber's Schreiben über die
Nationalität der Deutschen in den Vereinigten
Staaten von Nord-Amerika. [n.p., 1847?]

p. 20-25.   27.8 cm.

Caption title.
Excerpt from unidentified periodical.

NL 0346024   CSmH

E469
L5   [Lieber, Francis] 1800-1872, comp.
❋
            [Scrapbook of newspaper clippings per-
            taining to the Trent case, 1861-1862]
            1 v.   23 cm.

            Compiled by Francis Lieber; cf. origin-
            al bookplate.

            1. Trent affair, Nov. 8, 1861.

NL 0346025   RPB

Lieber, Francis, 1800-1872.
Secession. By Francis Lieber, LL.D. [New
York, 1861]

8 l.   19.5 cm.

Caption title.
Mounted newspaper clippings from the
Independent of January 10, 1861.

NL 0346026   CSmH

Lieber, Francis, 1800–1872.
... The ship Jamestown. Sonnet tr. by the
Rev. C.T.B. from the German of Francis
Lieber.   [n.p. 1848?]
1 l.   24 cm.   [His Writings: collected
pamphlets]
Newspaper clippings.

NL 0346027   CU

Lieber, Francis. 1800–1872.
[Slavery in point of social economy.]
[New York, 1863.]   Newspaper cutting.
Cut from the New York Evening Post, September 19, 1863.

F3974 — Slavery. — United States. Slavery.

NL 0346028   MB

Lieber, Francis, 1800–1872.
... Slavery, plantations and the yeomanry. By Francis Lieber. New-York, Oct. 1863. New York, C. S. Westcott & co., printers, 1863.

cover-title, 8 p. 23ᵐ.   (Loyal publication society. (Pamphlets; no. 29)

1. Slavery in the U. S.—Controversial literature—1863.
                                                    12–27329
Library of Congress   E458.L92 vol. 1

NL 0346029   DLC PPPrHi KyU OU ViU CSmH PPL

Lieber, Francis, 1800–1872.
Some truths worth remembering, given, as a recapitu-
lation, in a farewell lecture to the class of political economy of 1849, by Prof. Francis Lieber ... (n. p., 1849?;

6 p. 23½ᵐ.

Caption title.

1. Economics—Addresses, essays, lectures.

                                                    5–21697†
Library of Congress   HB172.L7

NL 0346030   DLC CU ScU

Lieber, Francis, 1800–1872.
A song on our country and her flag. By Francis Lieber.
Written in 1861, after the raising of the flag on Columbia
college, New York. Printed by the students ... (New York,
Baker & Godwin, printers, 1861?;

(2; p. 21ᵐ.

Caption title.
Without music; tune indicated by title.

1. U. S.—Hist.—Civil war—Poetry.   I. Title.

                                        CA 32–217 Unrev'd
Library of Congress   PS2246.L39S6   811.49

NL 0346031   DLC NNC CU MH NN CtY

Lieber, Francis, 1800-1872.
The Stranger in America. Mariner's Society,
etc., of the United States. London, 1834.

NL 0346032   AU

E
165   **Lieber, Francis**, 1800–1872.
L71   The stranger in America; or, Letters to a gentleman
1834   in Germany: comprising sketches of the manners, soci-
               ety, and national peculiarities of the United States. By
               Francis Lieber. Philadelphia, Carey, Lea & Blanchard
               (c1834;

               356 pp. 23½ᵐ.

Issued, 1834, under title: Letters to a gentleman in Germany.'

1. U.S.—Social life and customs. 2. U.S.—
Description and travel--1783-1848. I. Title.
II. Lieber, Francis, 1800-1872. Letters to
a gentleman in Ge   many.

NL 0346033   NIC

Lieber, Francis, 1800–1872.
The stranger in America: comprising sketches of the manners, society, and national peculiarities of the United States,
in a series of letters to a friend in Europe. By Francis Lieber
... London, R. Bentley, 1835.

2 v. 20ᵐ.

1. U. S.—Social life and customs. 2. U. S.—Description and travel.

                                                    A 11—2656
Chicago. Univ. Library   E162.L716
for Library of Congress   (a40b1;

            NN PPF PPL
NL 0346034   ICU ScU MH PP CU-S DN NcD OCl MdBP MB

Lieber, Francis, 1800–1872.
The stranger in America; or, Letters to a gentleman
in Germany: comprising sketches of the manners, society, and national peculiarities of the United States. By
Francis Lieber. Philadelphia, Carey, Lea & Blanchard,
1835.

356 p. 23½ᵐ.

Issued, 1834, under title: Letters to a gentleman in Germany.

Library of Congress   E165.L72   1–26858

            NN NjP PU PP PLF NcWsW GASC
NL 0346035   DLC WaS TxU NcU OO Vi MiU MB PMA AU

Lieber, Francis, 1800–1872, supposed author.
Thoughts for the times ...
    see under   Americus, pseud.

(Lieber, Francis; 1800–1872.
The unanimity of juries ... (Philadelphia, 1867;

cover-title, p. (727;–732. 22½ᵐ.

"Reprinted from the American law register, October, 1867."
"A letter from Dr. Francis Lieber to a member of the New York constitutional convention, revised with additions by the author."—p. (727;

1. Jury—New York (State)   I. Title.

                                                    33–20991

NL 0346037   DLC CU CSmH

DF806   Lieber,Francis,1800-1872.
.L7   Tagebuch meines aufenthaltes in Griechenland
         während der monate januar,februar und märz im
         jahre 1822. Von d.Franz Lieber... Leipzig,
         F.A.Brockhaus,1823.
         x,186 p. 15½cm.

NL 0346038   ICU CSmH NN

Lieber, Francis, 1800–1872.
The true character of the gentleman. By Francis Leiber (sic
... With preface by E. B. Shuldham... Edinburgh: W. G.
Patterson, 1862. viii, 12–90 p. 2. ed., enl. 16°.

543862A. 1. Conduct of life.
N. Y. P. L.   September 15, 1931

NL 0346039   NN CLSU

VOLUME 332

Lieber, Francis, 1800-1872.
Two lectures on the Constitution of the United
States. New York, 1861.

'25.7
5127a

NL 0346040   DLC DS MnHi NN PU PHi

JC
212
.L725   Lieber,Francis,1800-1872.
Ueber bürgerliche freiheit und selbstverwaltung,
von dr.Franz Lieber ... Nach der 2.aufl.aus dem
englischen übersetzt von dr.Franz Mittermaier.
Heidelberg, J.C.B.Mohr, 1860.
xiv p.,1 ℓ.,477,[1] p. 22cm.

NL 0346041   MiU CtY

Lieber, Francis, 1800-1872.
Ueber die Lancasterische lehrweise, von Dr.
Franz Lieber ... Hamburg, Gedruckt bei C.W.
Carstens & comp., 1826.

17 p.   20 cm.

"Aus no. 122 und 123 der Literarischen blätter
der börsen-halle."
Another copy, with Lieber's ms. notes, and
lacking p. 7-10.

NL 0346042   CSmH

Lieber, Francis, 1800-1872.
Ueber hinrichtungen auf offenem felde, oder
über extramuran- und intramuran-hinrichtungen
... [Heidelberg? 1844]
30 p.   20.5 cm.
Caption-title.
Lieber collection.
Ms. notes and clippings at end.
Reprinted from Kritische zeitschrift für
rechtswissenschaft und gesetzgebung des
auslandes.
I. Title.   XVII. B.1.H.

NL 0346043   CSmH

Lieber, Francis, 1800-1872.
 Okk15   Ueber die Unabhängigkeit der Justiz oder die
1   Freiheit des Rechtes in England und den Verein-
1848   igten Staaten, in einem Briefe aus Amerika von
Franz Lieber ... Heidelberg,1848.
16 p

NL 0346044   CtY MH-L MH CSmH

[Lieber, Francis] 1800-1872.
Vierzehn wein- und wonnelieder.   [von Arnold
Franz, pseud.]   Berlin, 1826.
34p.
Manuscript copy for H. A. Rattermann.
Appended to: Rattermann, H. A. Deutsch-
amerikanische gedichte des 18. jahrhunderts.

NL 0346045   IU

SPECIAL COLLECTIONS
B312L62
L   [Lieber, Franz] 1800-1872.
1826a   Vierzehn wein- und Wonnelieder, von Arnold
Franz [pseud.] Berlin, T. H. Riemann, 1826.
32 p. 16cm.

Author's autograph on title-page, and his
manuscript notes throughout the text.
Five preliminary leaves inserted, containing
the author's autobiographical sketch in manuscript. Nine pages bound in at end, plus one
folded leaf tipped in, contain additional
manuscript poems by the author.

NL 0346046   NNC

837.081   Lieber, Francis, 1800-1872.
R18d   Vierzehn wein- und wonnelieder von Arnold Franz
[pseud.] Berlin 1826. Bei T. H. Riemann.
p.175-212.
Transcribed by an unidentified scribe, in H. A.
Rattermann's copy book, Deutsch-amerikanische
gedichte des 18. jahrhunderts. Aus den deutsch-
amerikanischen zeitungen entnommen.
"Dedikation, ms. auf der ersten und zweiten um-
schlagseite. Seiner theuren schwester, Mathilde
Hermann Friedrich Lieber. Berlin den 21ten oktober 1828" transcribed by H. A. Rattermann.- p.212.

NL 0346047   IU NNC

[Lieber, Francis] 1800-1872.
Washington and Napoleon. A fragment ... New York,
1864.
12 p. 20½ x 15½cm.
"Two hundred copies printed for the Metropolitan fair, held in behalf
of the Sanitary commission, in the month of April."
"By Francis Lieber."—Ms. note on t.-p.

1. Washington, George, pres. U. S., 1732-1799. 2. Napoléon I, emperor
of the French, 1769-1821.   I. Title.
18—7511

Library of Congress   E312.17.L7

NL 0346048   DLC MiU-C CU ScU NcD MWA MB CtY NIC

---

*
PS2246
.L5W4   Lieber, Francis, 1800-1872.
1848   The West, a metrical epistle. New York,
Putnam, 1848.
30, [2] p. 15cm.

NL 0346049   ViU ScU CSmH NNC ICN

Lieber, Francis, 1800-1872.
What is our Constitution,—league, pact, or government? Two lectures on the Constitution of the United
States ... delivered in the Law school of Columbia college,
during the winter of 1860 and 1861, to which is appended
an address on secession written in the year 1851. By
Francis Lieber ... New York, Printed by direction of the
Board of trustees, 1861.
48 p. 21½cm.

1. U. S. Constitution. 2. State rights. 3. Secession.

Library of Congress   JK320.L65
9–23586†

PP NN MB
NL 0346050   DLC NIC TU NNC CSt-Law ViU NcD PPL MiU

Lieber, Francis, 1800-1872.
Writings of Francis Lieber. 1845-1872.
32 v. in 1. 22 cm.
Binder's title.
A collection of pamphlets by F. Lieber,
including S. Tyler's De Tocqueville and Lieber
as writers on political science.

NL 0346051   CU

Lieber, Francis, 1800-1872.
U. S. *War dept.*
Ynstrucciones para el gobierno de los ejercitos de los
Estados Unidos, en campāna. Formadas de orden del
gobierno de los Estados Unidos del Norte America, por
el profesor Francis Lieber. Tr. del ingles por un mexicano. Washington, Powell, Ginck y ca., 1870.

Lieber, Frank.
America's natural wealth, a story of the use
and abuse of our resources. [1st ed.]
New York, 1942.

NL 0346053   PU

Lieber, Franz
see
Lieber, Francis, 1800-1872.

Lieber, Friedrich.
Aus der Werkstatt der Kunst. [Leipzig, Jugendbuchver-
lag E. Wunderlich [1954]
108 p. illus. 20 cm. (Jugendbuchreihe "Erlebte Welt," Bd. 28)

1. Art—Juvenile literature.   I. Title.

N7440.L5
56–29727 ‡

NL 0346055   DLC

Lieber, Fritz, 1905-
Die Friedenspflicht im Tarifvertrege...
von Fritz Lieber... Ohlau i.Schl., H.
Eschenhagen, 1931.
vi, 65, [1] p. 20½cm.

Inaug.-Diss. - Halle-Wittenberg.
"Lebenslauf": p.[66]
"Literaturverzeichnis": p. v-vi.

NL 0346056   MH-L MiU ICRL PU

Lieber, Gabriele von, ed.
Frauen-zukunft ...
München und Leipzig, Frauen-verlag, 19

Liebermann, Gerald J   joint author.
The problem of the isolated lot
see under
Grant, Eugene Lodewick, 1897-

Lieber, Gertrude.
References to 20th century typewriting, compiled by Gertrude Lieber ... Cincinnati, New York [etc.] South-western
publishing company, 1941.
33 p. 24cm.

1. Typewriting. 2. English language—Composition and exercises.
I. Lessenberry, David Daniel, 1896-   20th century typewriting. 3d ed.
II. Title.

Library of Congress   Z49.L63 1938 r   42–362
[4]   652

NL 0346059   DLC OrU

Z49
.A3L5   Lieber, Gertrude,   comp.
Typewriting style manual; with references
to 20th century typewriting, sixth edition,
by Lessenberry and Crawford. Compiled by
Gertrude Lieber. Cincinnati [etc.] South-
Western Pub. Co., [1952]
45 p. 23 cm.

1. Typewriting. I. Title.

NL 0346060   TU

LIEBER, Gisbert.
Ueber das wachsthum Jesu in der weisheit.
Exegetisch-dogmengeschichtliche erörterung der
stelle Luc II,52. Mainz,1850.

NL 0346061   MH

VOLUME 332

LIEBER, Guido Norman, *1837-1923*.
Cashiering and dismissal.
N. p. [1865.] 14 pp. 12°.

NL 0346062   MB CSmH

Lieber, Guido Norman, 1837-1923.
The justification of martial law. By G. Norman Lieber ...
Washington, Govt. print. off., 1898.
25 p. 24½ᵐ.
On verso of t.-p.: War dept., Document no. 79.
"Reprint from the North American review."

1. Martial law—U. S.   I. U. S. War dept.
46–34598

Library of Congress   JK349.L5

OClWHi
NL 0346063   DLC MdBP ICN RPB PP MiU-L OO OOxM

Lieber, Guido Norman, 1837-1923.
Leyes de la guerra, instrucciones del doctor Lieber para el
ejercito en campaña. Mexico, J. S. Ponce de Leon, 1871.
40 p. 18ᵐ.

1. Military law. 2. War (International law)   I. Title.
27–8609

NL 0346064   DLC

Lieber, Guido Norman, 1837-1923.
Leyes de la guerra, instrucciones del doctor Lieber para el
ejercito en campaña. Mexico, 1872. 40 p. 8°.

1. Military law.
N. Y. P. L.
November 27, 1925

NL 0346065   NN

F   Lieber, Guido Norman,   1837-1923.
8321   ...Martial law during the revolution.
.32   [New York, 1877?]   (with Gardiner, A.B.
Martial law during the revolution.
[1877?])
Caption title.
Reprinted from the Magazine of American history, v.1, p.[538]-541.

NL 0346066   ICN

[Lieber, Guido Norman] 1837-1923.
Meaning of the term martial law as used in the Petition of
right and the preamble to the Mutiny act. [New York? 1877?]
19 p. 20½ᵐ.
Caption title.
Signed: G. Norman Lieber, judge advocate, U. S. army.
Bibliographical foot-notes.

1. Martial law—U. S.   I. Title.
45–31587

Library of Congress   JK347.L5

NL 0346067   DLC CSmH

Lieber, Guido Norman, 1837-1923.
Observations on the origin of the trial by council of war,
or the present court-martial. By G. Norman Lieber, judge
advocate, U. S. Army. New York, 1876.
1 p. l., 16 p. 17ᵐ. [With Fry, J. B. A sketch of the Adjutant general's department, U. S. Army, from 1775 to 1875 ... New York city,
1875]

1. Courts-martial and courts of inquiry.   I. Title.
29–3868

Library of Congress   UB173.F7

NL 0346068   DLC ViU NBuU NN

Lieber, Guido Norman, 1837–
Remarks on the army regulations, by G. Norman Lieber, judge-advocate general. Washington, Govt. print.
off., 1897.
111 p. 23ᵐ.

1. U. S.—Army—Regulations.   I. U. S. Judge-advocate-general's dept.
(Army)
9–8226†

Library of Congress   U1:501 1897

NL 0346069   DLC NN

Lieber, Guido Norman, 1837–
Remarks on the army regulations and executive regulations in general. By G. Norman Lieber, judge-advocate
general, U. S. army. Washington, Govt. print. off., 1898.
189 p. 24½ᵐ.
On verso of t.-p.: War dpartment. Document no. 63. Office of the
judge-advocate general.

1. U. S.—Army—Regulations.   I. U. S. Judge-advocate general's
dept. (Army)
9–1717

Library of Congress   UB501 1898 d

MiU DNW ICJ NjP NN PPB PHi PP PU WaWW
NL 0346070   DLC KMK DI DNLM MdBP DN OCl OClWHi OO

Lieber, Guido Norman, 1837-1923.
The use of the army in aid of the civil power. By G. Norman
Lieber, judge-advocate general, U. S. army. Washington,
Govt. print. off., 1898.
86 p. 24½ᵐ.
On verso of t.-p.: War department. Document no. 64. Office of the
judge-advocate general.
Appendices: a. Extract from speech of H. B. Banning, delivered March
2, 1877, "The object of our army."—b. Army regulations, Article LII. Employment of troops in the enforcement of the laws.—c. Governor Altgeld's
protest against the use of United States troops in Illinois.

1. U. S.—Army.   I. U. S. Judge-advocate-general's dept. (Army)
II. Title
CA 10—2004 Unrev'd

Library of Congress   UB770.L7
——— Copy 2.   JK355.L5

MdBP PU PHC PP
NL 0346071   DLC NIC DI OCl OO OClWHi MiU I ICJ MB

Lieber (Gustavus) [1796-   ].   * Monstri molæ
speciem præ se ferentis descriptio anatomica.
24 pp., 2 pl. 4°. *Berolini, form. Brueschkiana,*
[1821].

NL 0346072   DNLM

Lieber, Hans.
Die wirkung der temperatur der muskeln auf die
beantwortung vom zentrum kommender erregungen.
Inaug. diss. - Freiburg, 1926. (Muenchen)
Sonderabdruck aus der Zeitschrfft fuer biologie,
Band 85, heft 2.

NL 0346073   ICRL MiU CtY

Lieber, Hans Joachim.
Wissen und Gesellschaft; die Probleme der Wissenssozio-
logie. Tübingen, M. Niemeyer, 1952.
166 p. 25 cm.
Bibliography: p. 162–166.

1. Sociology—Methodology. 2. Knowledge, Theory of.   I. Title.
A 52–8666

Chicago. Univ. Libr.
for Library of Congress   [1]

NL 0346074   ICU DLC NN PU OCU NIC

Lieber, Heinrich *Wilhelm*.
Aufgaben über kubische und diophantische Gleichungen, Deter-
minanten und Kettenbrüche, Kombinationslehre und höhere
Reihen. iv,[2],129 p. O. Berlin: L. Simion, 1898.

Joint author: C. Müsebeck.

NL 0346075   ICJ DLC-P4

QA497   LIEBER, HEINRICH WILHELM, 1835-1896.
.L7   Geometrische constructions-aufgaben, hrsg. von dr.
H. Lieber... und F. von Lühmann... 4. aufl. ... Berlin,
L. Simion, 1878.
xii,185 p. fold. pl. 22cm.

1. Geometrical drawing.

NL 0346076   ICU

Lieber, Heinrich Wilhelm, 1835-1896, ed.
Geometrische konstruktions-aufgaben.
Hrsg. von prof. dr. H. Lieber ... und F.
von Lühmann ... 8. aufl. ... Berlin,
L. Simion, 1887.
xii, 206 p. diagrs. on fold. pl. 23 cm.
1. Geometry, Plane. I. Lümann, F
von, joint ed.

NL 0346077   CU

Lieber, Heinrich Wilhelm, 1835-1896, *ed.*
Geometrische konstruktions-aufgaben. Hrsg. von prof.
dr. H. Lieber ... und F. von Lühmann ... 8. aufl. ...
Berlin, L. Simion, 1889.
xii, 206 p. 22 diagr. on fold pl. 22½ᵐ.
With this is bound his Stereometrische aufgaben. 1888.

1. Geometry, Plane—Problems, exercises, etc.   I. Lühmann, Friedrich von,
d. 1899, joint ed.

NL 0346078   MiU NjP

Lieber, Heinrich Wilhelm, 1835-1896
Geometrische konstructions-aufgaben.
Herausgegeben von dr. H. Lieber... und F. von
Lühmann... 10. aufl. Mit einer figurentafel.
Berlin, L. Simion, 1893.

NL 0346079   PU

LIEBER, *Heinrich Wilhelm*
Geometrische konstructions-aufgaben. Herausgegeben von H. Lieber und F. von Lühmann.
13e aufl. Berlin, L. Simion nf., 1908.

NL 0346080   MH

Lieber, Heinrich Wilhelm, 1835-1896.
Leitfaden der Elementar-Mathematik
hrsg. von Dr. H. Lieber ... und F. von
Lühmann ... I. Theil: Planimetrie. 2.
Aufl. Berlin, L. Simon, 1879.
2 p.l., 99 p. diagrs. on 6 fold. pl.
21 cm.
With Müller, Johannes, Oberlehrer, Ritter-
Akademie, Brandenburg. Lehrbuch der elemen-
taren Planimetrie. 1870.

NL 0346081   RPB

Lieber, Heinrich *Wilhelm*.
Leitfaden der elementar-mathematik
von . . . und F. von Lühmann. Ed. by
Carl Müsebeck. Berlin, Simion, 1899-
1902.
3 v.   v. 1. is ed. 16
v. 2 is ed. 7
v. 3 is ed. 9

Contents. 1. Planimetrie. 2. Arithmetic.
3. Erweiterung der Planimetrie, ebene
trigonometrie, Stereometrie, ...

NL 0346082   OO

VOLUME 332

Lieber, Heinrich. Wilhelm, 1835-1896.
Leitfaden der Elementar-Mathematik. Von Dr. H. Lieber, ... und F. von Lühmann, ... Nach den Bestimmungen der preussischen Lehrpläne vom Jahre 1901 neu bearbeitet von Carl Müsebeck, ... Erster-[dritter] Teil. .... In neuer Rechtschreibung. .... Berlin, L. Simion Nf., 1902-1904.
3 vol. 22cm.
Contents.—1. Teil. Planimetrie. Ausgabe A für Gymnasien, Realgymnasien und Oberrealschulen. Achtzehnte unveränderte Auflage. 1904. v, [2], 155 p. 176 diagr.—2. Teil. Arithmetik. Ausgabe A für Gymnasien, Realgymnasien und Oberrealschulen. Achte Auflage. 1902. iv, [2], 186 p.—3. Teil. Ebene Trigonometrie, Stereometrie, Sphärische Trigonometrie, Grundlehren von den Koordinaten und Kegelschnitten. Elfte Auflage. 1903. v, [2], 180 p. 124 diagr.

NL 0346083 ICJ

Lieber, Heinrich. Wilhelm
Leitfaden der Elementar-Mathematik, von H. Lieber und F. von Lühmann. Nach den Bestimmungen der preussischen Lehrpläne vom Jahre 1901 neu bearbeitet von Carl Müsebeck. 3.Teil. 13.unveränderte Aufl. Berlin, L.Simion Nf., 1907.

Contents. - 3.Teil. Ebene Trigonometrie, Stereometrie, Sphärische Trigonometrie, Grundlehren von den Koordinaten und Kegelschnitten.

NL 0346084 MH

QA453   LIEBER,HEINRICH WILHELM,1835-1896.
.L66   ...Planimetrie... 8.aufl. Berlin,L.Simion,1892.
[5], 124 p. VII fold.pl. 22cm. (Leitfaden der elementar-mathematik,hrsg.von prof.dr.H.Lieber...und F.von Lühmann... 1.t.)

1.Geometry.

NL 0346085 ICU

Lieber, Heinrich Wilhelm, 1835-
Stereometrische aufgaben. Hrsg. von prof. dr. H. Lieber ... Berlin, L. Simion, 1888.
vi, 141 p. 22½cm.
With his Geometrische konstruktions-aufgaben ... 1889.

1. Geometry, Solid. 2. Geometry—Problems, exercises, etc. I. Title.

NL 0346086 MiU PBL

Lieber, Heinrich Wilhelm, 1835-1896, ed.
Trigonometrische aufgaben. Hrsg. von dr. H. Lieber ... und F. von Lühmann ... 3. aufl. Berlin, L. Simion, 1889.
vii, 298 p. incl. tables. fold. diagr. 22½cm.

1. Trigonometry—Problems, exercises, etc. I. Lühmann, Friedrich von, d 1899, joint ed.

NL 0346087 MiU

Lieber, Heinrich Wilhelm, 1835-1896.
QA3   Über den Brocardschen Kreis. (Fort-
-M39   setzung der Abhandlung in den Programmen
6   von 1886 und 1887) Stettin, R. Grass-
Physical   mann, 1888.
Sciences   11p. 25 cm.
Library
Programm-Friedrich-Wilhelms-Schule zu Stettin, 1888.
No. [15] of v.6 of Mathematical pamphlets.

NL 0346088 RPB

Lieber, Heinrich Wilhelm.
Ueber den Unterricht in der mathematischen Geographie. Pyritz, 1867.

NL 0346089 NjP

QA3   Lieber, Heinrich Wilhelm, 1835-1896.
-M39   Über die Gegenmittellinie und den Grebe-
6   schen Punkt. Stettin, R. Grassmann, 1886.
Physical   14 p. 25cm.
Sciences
Library   Programm—Friedrich-Wilhelms-Schule zu
Stettin, 1886.
No. [13] of v. 6 of Mathematical pamphlets.

NL 0346090 RPB

QA3   Lieber, Heinrich Wilhelm, 1835-1896.
-M39   Über die Gegenmittellinie und den Grebe-
6   'schen Punkt. Über den Brocardschen Kreis.
Physical   Stettin, R. Grassmann, 1887.
Sciences   16 p. diagrs. 25cm.
Library
Programm—Friedrich-Wilhelms-Schule zu Stettin, 1887.
No. [14] of v. 6 of Mathematical pamphlets.

NL 0346091 RPB

Lieber, Heinrich Wilhelm, 1835-1896.
Ueber die isogonischen ... punkte des dreiecks. Stettin, 1896-97.
2 pt.

NL 0346092 NjP

Lieber, Hertha.
Die dynamik als erklärungsprinzip des kapitalismus (kritische untersuchungen zur statischen theorie)... [Frankfurt a.M., Lehrberger, 1937]
77 p. 21 cm.

Inaug.-diss. - Munich.
"Literaturverzeichnis": p.73-77.

1.Capitalism. 2.Economics.

NL 0346093 NjP NNC CtY

Lieber, Hugh Gray, 1896-
Comédie internationale; a book of symbols. With a foreword by Lillian R. Lieber. Brooklyn, Long Island University Press [n.d.] [38] p. (chiefly illus.)

1. American wit and humor, Pictorial. I. Title.

NL 0346094 DGU

Barnard
D741   Lieber, Hugh Gray, 1896-
L623   Comédie internationale, a book of symbols.
With a foreword by Lillian R. Lieber. Brooklyn, N. Y., Long Island University Press [1954]
1 v. (chiefly illus.) 22cm.

1. Satire. 2. Drawings. 3. Symbolism in art. I. Title. II. Lieber, Lillian (Rosanoff) 1886-

NL 0346095 NNC PBL KEmT

QA39   Lieber, Hugh Gray, 1896-   illus.
.L488
1944   FOR OTHER EDITIONS
SEE MAIN ENTRY
Lieber, Lillian (Rosanoff) 1886-
The education of T. C. Mits. Drawings by Hugh Gray Lieber, words by Lillian R. Lieber. New York, W. W. Norton & company, inc. [1944]

QC6   Lieber, Hugh Gray, 1896-   illus.
.L416
Lieber, Lillian (Rosanoff) 1886-
The Einstein theory of relativity. Part 1: Theory of relativity. Text by Lilian R. Lieber, drawings by Hugh Gray Lieber. [Lancaster, Pa., The Science press printing company, 1936]

QC6   Lieber, Hugh Gray, 1896-   illus.
.L415
Lieber, Lillian (Rosanoff) 1886-
The Einstein theory of relativity; text by Lillian R. Lieber, drawings by Hugh Gray Lieber. New York, Toronto, Farrar & Rinehart, inc. [1945]

Lieber, Hugh Gray, 1896-
Good-bye Mr. Man. Hello, Mr. NEWman; with an introd. by Lillian R. Lieber. Brooklyn, Long Island University Press [1951, *1949]
13 p. illus. 38 cm.

I. Title.

NC139.L5L5   741.91   52-35549 ‡

NL 0346099 DLC NNC NN

BC135   Lieber, Hugh Gray, 1896-   illus.
.L5
Lieber, Lillian (Rosanoff) 1886-
Mits, wits and logic; drawings by Hugh Gray Lieber. [1st ed.] New York, W. W. Norton [1947]

QA39   Lieber, Hugh Gray, 1896-   illus.
.L488
1946   Lieber, Lillian (Rosanoff) 1886-
Modern mathematics for T. C. Mits, the celebrated man in the street; drawings by Hugh Gray Lieber, words by Lillian R. Lieber. London, G. Allen & Unwin ltd [1946]

QA39   Lieber, Hugh Gray, 1896-   illus.
.L489
Lieber, Lillian (Rosanoff) 1886-
Take a number; mathematics for the two billion. Words by Lillian R. Lieber, drawings by Hugh Gray Lieber. Lancaster, Pa., The Jaques Cattell press [1946]

Lieber, Hugo, 1867-
Blaugas, the new illuminating agent, by Dr. Hugo Lieber... [New York, 1917?] 4 p. 4°.

Cover-title.
Repr.: Engineers' list.

1. Blau gas.
N. Y. P. L.   March 5, 1919.

NL 0346103 NN

VOLUME 332

Lieber, Hugo, 1867–
Modern uses and applications of radium, by
Hugo Lieber ... Reprinted from The Journal
of the Franklin Institute, December, 1911.
[New York], J.B. Lippincott Company, 1911.
p. 579–590.   illus.
Cover-title.
Skinner Collection.
(Orig. paper wraps)
Bound in: Radium Pamphlets (Black cardb.).
1. Radium - Therapeutic.

NL 0346104   KU-M

Lieber, Hugo, 1867–
Radium and its use in therapy, by Hugo Lieber.
Reprinted from Homoeopathic Eye, Ear and
Throat Journal, July, 1907.
8 p.
Cover-title.
Skinner Collection.
(Orig. paper wraps)
Bound in: Radium Pamphlets (Black cardb.)
1. Radium - Therapeutic.

NL 0346105   KU-M

Lieber, Hugo, 1867–
The use of coal tar colors in food products, by Hugo
Lieber.   New York, H. Lieber & co., 1904.
150 p. 20¼ᶜᵐ.

1. Coal-tar colors, Physiological effect of. 2. Food adulteration.

Library of Congress   TX571.C7L7 Copyright   5–78.

NL 0346106   DLC DNLM ICJ WaU

Lieber, Hugo, 1890–1915.
Beiträge zur Geologie des Rimberggebietes
bei Marburg. Nach dem Tode des Verfassers
hrsg. vom Geologisch-Paläontologischen Institut
der Universität Marburg. Bamberg, C.C. Buchner, 1917.
vi, 98 p. illus., 10 pl., 2 fold. col.
profiles, fold. col map. 27cm.
Map in pocket.
1. Prussia - Geology - Marburg. I. Marburg.
Universität. Geologisch-Paläontologisches Institut.

NL 0346107   CtY DI-GS

Lieber, Hyacinth Maximilian, 1882–
Kapitaene und Konsuln nach der Seemannsordnung. Leipzig, 1909.
viii, 63 p. 8°.
Inaug.-Diss. - Leipzig.
Bibl.

NL 0346108   ICRL

Lieber (Joannes Carolus Otto) [1839–]. *De
concrementis systematis uropoetici. 32 pp. 8°.
Berolini, G. Lange, [1863].

NL 0346109   DNLM

Lieber (Julius). *De radice rhei. 30 pp. 8°.
Dorpat, typ. H. Laakmanni, 1853.

NL 0346110   DNLM

Lieber, Julius Wilhelm Bernhard
see   Lieber, Bernhard, 1853–

Lieber (Karl) [1890–]. *Ueber die Myome
der Haut. [Frankfurt a. M.] 40 pp., 1 l. 8°.
Jena, G. Fischer, 1915.

NL 0346112   DNLM

Lieber, Leslie.
Fashion's folly [by] Leslie Lieber and Toni Miller.
Photos. by Carl Perutz. New York, Vanguard Press [1954]
unpaged (chiefly illus.) 28 cm.

1. American wit and humor, Pictorial.   I. Miller, Toni (Bauer)
1926–   joint author. II. Title.

NC1429.L534A45   741.5   54–11507 ‡

NL 0346113   DLC IdPI PPD OCU PP

MT86
.W48   Lieber, Leslie, joint author.
1948   FOR OTHER EDITIONS
          Whiteman, Paul, 1890–   SEE MAIN ENTRY
               How to be a bandleader, by Paul Whiteman and Leslie
          Lieber. New York, R. M. McBride [1948]

Lieber, Lillian (Rosanoff) 1886–
The education of T. C. Mits. Drawings by Hugh Gray
Lieber, words by Lillian R. Lieber. Brooklyn, N. Y., The
Galois institute press, Long island university, 1942.
2 p. l., 186 (i. e. 195) p. incl. illus., tables, diagrs. 21ᶜᵐ.

In verse.
T. C. Mits, "the celebrated man in the street." cf. Introd.

1. Mathematics.   I. Lieber, Hugh Gray, 1896–   illus. II. Title.
                                                      43–5011
Library of Congress   QA39.L488
                          [3]   510

NL 0346115   DLC KyWA OrU OCU PSt

*
AC8
.A6   Lieber, Lillian (Rosanoff) 1886–
no.Q–4
1944   The education of T. C. Mits.   Drawings
          by Hugh Gray Lieber. New York, Editions
          for the Armed Services, ©1944.

            157 p.   10 x 14cm. (Armed Services
          ed. Q–4)

NL 0346116   ViU

Lieber, Lillian (Rosanoff) 1886–
The education of T. C. Mits. Drawings by Hugh Gray
Lieber, words by Lillian R. Lieber. New York, W. W. Norton
& company, inc. [1944]
230 p. illus., diagrs. 21ᶜᵐ.

In verse.
T. C. Mits, "the celebrated man in the street." cf. p. 9.
"Revised and enlarged edition. First printing."
"Suggested reading": p. 230.

1. Mathematics.   I. Lieber, Hugh Gray, 1896–   illus. II. Title.
                                                      44–40067
Library of Congress   QA39.L488 1944
                          [18]   510

WaWW WaS WaE
MtBuM Or OrCS OrLgE OrP OrPR OrPS OrSaW Wa WaT
PSC PWcS PPT IdPI CaBViP CaBVaU CaBVa MtBC MtU
KyLx KyU-A AU CoAlC NcC NcRS LN OrPS GAT ViU PP
OOxM DNAL NcD KEmT IEN OCU TNJ KyMdC NcU NIC AU
NL 0346117   DLC KyU-H MiU CU MB NBuG OO OC1W OU

Lieber, Lillian (Rosanoff) 1886–
The Einstein theory of relativity. Part 1: Theory of relativity. Text by Lillian R. Lieber, drawings by Hugh Gray
Lieber. [Lancaster, Pa., The Science press printing company, 1936]
2 p. l., 73 p. col. front., illus. (part col.) col. plates, diagrs. 21½ cm.

Part 2 was first published and issued with pt. 1 in 1945 (New York,
Toronto, Farrar & Rinehart, inc.)
"Some interesting reading" on front end-paper and text on back
end-paper.

1. Relativity (Physics) 2. Einstein, Albert, 1879–   I. Lieber,
Hugh Gray, 1896–   illus.

QC6.L416   530.1   38–30771

ViU NcD PU PSt IEN OrU WaS
NL 0346119   DLC AU CU TxU OCU IaU OC1U OU OC1W MiU

PHYSICS
MATH
QC   Lieber, Lillian (Rosanoff) 1886–
6   The Einstein theory of relativity; text by
L416   Lillian R. Lieber, drawings by Hugh Gray
1945   Lieber. New York, Holt, Rinehart and Winston
           [c1945]
              x, 324 p. illus. 22cm.
              "Part I of this book was published in
           1936. Part II is now (1945) being published for
           the first time."
              "Some interesting reading." p. 324.
              1. Relativity (Physics) 2. Science -
           Philosophy I. Lieber, Hugh Gray, 1896–   illus.
           II. Title

NL 0346120   WU WaU NN CoU

Lieber, Lillian (Rosanoff) 1886–
The Einstein theory of relativity; text by Lillian R. Lieber, drawings by Hugh Gray Lieber. New York, Toronto,
Farrar & Rinehart, inc. [1945]
x, 324 p. illus., diagrs. 21 cm.

"Part I of this book was published in 1936. Part II is now (1945)
being published for the first time."
"Some interesting reading": p. 324.

1. Relativity (Physics) 2. Einstein, Albert, 1879–1955.   I. Lieber,
Hugh Gray, 1896–   illus.

QC6.L415   530.1   45–9563

Or OrCS OrP OrPS OrSaW OrU Wa WaT WaTC WaE OrSaW
CaBVa CaBVaU IdB IdPI IdU MtBC MtU MtBuM OrAshS
NIC KEmT NcD OC1 CSt OU OC1CC MH PPT PP PU PWcS
NL 0346121   DLC NcD NcRS NcC MB CU TU TxU ViU AU

Lieber, Lillian (Rosanoff) 1886–
The Einstein theory of relativity; drawings by Hugh
Gray Lieber. London, D. Dobson [1949]
xii, 324 p. illus. 23 cm.
Bibliography: p. 324.

1. Relativity (Physics) 2. Einstein, Albert, 1879–

QC6.L415 1949   530.1   50–32337

NL 0346123   DLC NBuU TxU

Lieber, *Mrs.* Lillian (Rosanoff) 1886–
Galois and the theory of groups: a bright star in mathesis.
Text by Lillian R. Lieber; drawings by Hugh Gray Lieber.
[Lancaster, Pa., The Science press printing company, °1932]
4 p. l., 58, [4] p. col. front., col. illus., col. plates, diagrs. 21½ᶜᵐ.
Text on end-papers, including "A few interesting books".

1. Groups, Theory of. 2. Galois theory.
Library of Congress   QA171.L75   34–2290 Revised
——— Copy 2.
Copyright A 68238   [r39d2]   512.86

OC1W OC1U PSC PHC PBa PV
NL 0346124   DLC MiU TNJ CtY CU OU OCU MiU OC1CC PBm

VOLUME 332

LIEBER, Lillian (Rosanoff),1886–
Galois and the theory of groups:a bright star
in Mathesis. Drawings by Hugh Gray Lieber.
[Lancaster,Pa.,Science Press Printing Co.,1941.]

21.5 cm. pp.(8),61. (i.e.64),(2). Plates and
illustr.(part colored) and diagrs.
Their "Modern mathematical series,2."
Text on end-papers.

NL 0346125 MH

512.2 Lieber, Lillian (Rosanoff) 1886–
L621g   Galois and the theory of groups: a bright
1932r1 star in mathesis. Text by Lillian R. Lieber;
drawings by Hugh Gray Lieber. [Ann Arbor,
Mich., Edwards brothers, inc., 1947, c1932]
4p.ℓ.,61p. front.,illus.,plates, diagrs.
21½cm.
"Second printing 1941. Photo-lithoprint
reproduction ... 1947."
Text on end-papers, including "A few interesting books".
1. Groups, Theory of. 2. Galois theory.

NL 0346126 TxU DLC

Lieber, Lillian (Rosanoff), 1886–
Galois and the theory of groups: a bright star in mathesis. Text
by Lillian R. Lieber; drawings by Hugh Gray Lieber. [Ann
Arbor, Edwards bros., 1947, 61 p. illus. 22cm. (hglrl
modern mathematical series. no. 2)

Text on end papers, including "A few interesting books."

1. Groups. 2. Galois theory.
N.Y.P.L.   October 26, 1949

NL 0346127 NN NBuU IU MH

Lieber, Lillian (Rosanoff) 1886–
Infinity; with drawings by Hugh Gray Lieber. New
York, Rinehart [1953]
359 p. illus. 21 cm.

1. Infinite. I. Title.

QA9.L5   510   53–5355 ‡

MtBC OrMonO Wa WaT Or OrCS OrP OrU WaS OrPR
TxU ViU KyU-N OViND KEmT CaBVa CaBVaU IdPI OC1W IdU
NL 0346128   DLC TU FMU MsSM OU NcRS MB PPT PU NcD IU

Lieber, Lillian (Rosanoff) 1886–
Mits, wits and logic; drawings by Hugh Gray Lieber.
[1st ed.] New York, W. W. Norton [1947]
240 p. illus. 21 cm.

1. Logic, Symbolic and mathematical. 2. Science—Philosophy.
I. Lieber, Hugh Gray, 1896–   illus. II. Title.
BC135.L5   164   47–11623*

WaU CU IaU IdPI OrU MtBC OrCS OrPS OrSaW
NL 0346129   DLC TNJ KEmT ICU OU TxU NcRS NcD PU MH

Lieber, Lillian (Rosanoff) 1886–
Mits, wits, and logic. Drawings by Hugh Gray Lieber.
[Rev. ed.] Brooklyn, Galois Institute Press [1954]
240 p. illus. 23 cm.

1. Logic, Symbolic and mathematical. 2. Science—Philosophy.
I. Title.
BC135.L5 1954   164   55–16783 ‡

NL 0346130 DLC CU MiU MsSM MsU

Lieber, Lillian (Rosanoff) 1886–
Modern mathematics for T. C. Mits, the celebrated man in
the street; drawings by Hugh Gray Lieber, words by Lilian R.
Lieber. London, G. Allen & Unwin ltd [1946]
230 p. illus., diagrs. 18½½.

In verse.
First edition (Brooklyn, N. Y., 1942) has title: The education of T. C.
Mits.
"First published in [London] 1946."
"Suggested reading": p. 230.

1. Mathematics.   I. Lieber, Hugh Gray, 1896–   illus. II. Title.

Library of Congress   QA39.L488 1946   46–7147
[5]   510

NL 0346131   DLC MH CU NcU NBuU MiU

Lieber, Lillian (Rosanoff) 1886–
Non-Euclidean geometry; or, Three moons in mathesis, by
Lillian R. Lieber, with drawings by Hugh Gray Lieber.
[New York, Academy press, c1931]
1 p. l., 34 (i. e. 41) p. col. illus., col. pl. 21½ cm.

1. Geometry, Non-Euclidean.   I. Title.

QA685.L65   513.8   31—19994

PSC PHC CU RPB NBuU NcU WaWW
NL 0346132   DLC OCU OC1 OO OC1W MiU WaU PPPL PBm

513.8 Lieber, Lillian (Rosanoff) 1886–
L621n   Non-Euclidean geometry; or, Three moons in mathesis;
text by Lillian R. Lieber, drawings by Hugh Gray Lieber.
[Lancaster, Pa., The Science press publishing company,
c1940, Brooklyn, N.Y., The Galois Institute of
Mathematics and Art.
1 p. l. 40 (i. e. 48) p. col. illus., col. plates. 22 cm.
Includes 8 unnumbered pages (illustrations)
Illustrated lining-papers.
"Second edition."

NL 0346133 MsSM

Lieber, Lillian (Rosanoff) 1886–
Non-Euclidean geometry; or, Three moons in mathesis; text
by Lillian R. Lieber, drawings by Hugh Gray Lieber. [Lan-
caster, Pa., The Science press printing company, c1940]
1 p. l., 40 (i. e. 46) p. col. illus., col. plates. 22cm.
Includes six unnumbered pages (illustrations)
Illustrated lining-papers.
"Second edition."

1. Geometry, Non-Euclidean.   I. Title.   II. Title: Three moons in
mathesis.
40—29551
Library of Congress   QA685.L65 1940
[a43e1]   513.8

IdPI WaSp
ViU PPT PSt OrPS MtU KEmT OrCS NN OrPR CaBVaU WaS
NL 0346134   DLC WaU Or PWcS TxU CU MB ICU OC1 OU NcD

QA685 Lieber, Lillian (Rosanoff) 1886–
.L65   Non-Euclidean geometry; or, Three moons
1940a in mathesis. Drawings by Hugh Gray Lieber.
2d ed. Brooklyn, N.Y., Galois Institute
of Mathematics and Art c1940a
40 p. illus. 22 cm.

1. Geometry, Non-Euclidean. I. Title.
II. Title: Three moons in mathesis.

NL 0346135   TU AAP ICU IU NN ODW

Lieber, Lillian (Rosanoff) 1886–
Take a number; mathematics for the two billion. Words by
Lillian R. Lieber, drawings by Hugh Gray Lieber. Lancaster,
Pa., The Jaques Cattell press [1946]
vii, [2], 221 p. incl. front., illus., diagrs. 21½½.

1. Mathematics.   I. Lieber, Hugh Gray, 1896–   illus. II. Title.
QA39.L489   510   47–1469

WaSp CaBVa CaBVaU IdPI Or OrCS WaWW OrU
NL 0346136   DLC NSyU GAT PPD ICU TxU PU MH OrPR WaS

510   Lieber, Lillian (Rosanoff) 1886–
L622t   Take a number; mathematics for the two
1946   billion. Words by Lillian R. Lieber, drawings
by Hugh Gray Lieber. New York, Ronald Press
Co. sc1946s
vii, 221p. illus., diagrs. 24cm.

1. Mathematics. I. Lieber, Hugh Gray,
1896–   illus. II. Title.

MiU OKentU CU CoGrS
NL 0346137   IU FU CoA1C OrPS OrP CaBVaU OrPS ViU

Lieber (Ludwig Clemens) [1880–]. Die
primäre fibrinöse Pneumonie in der Göttinger
medizinischen Klinik von 1. April 1900 bis
1. April 1905. 58 pp., 2 l. 8°. Göttingen,
L. Hofer, 1906.

NL 0346138 DNLM

Lieber, Martin.
Étude critique du traitement du psoriasis.
Pari, L. Rodstein, 1937.
63
Thèse.

NL 0346139 DNLM CtY NNC

Lieber, Max.
Untersuchung des drehfeldes eines asynchronen ...
Inaug. Diss Berlin, Techn. Hoch, 1904.

NL 0346140 ICRL

Lieber, Max,1900–
Ueber die durch den erfolg qualifizierten delikte.
Inaug. diss. Zuerich, 1925.
Bibl.

NL 0346141 ICRL CtY

Lieber, Maxim, joint comp.
Great short stories of the world...
see under Clark, Barrett Harper, 1890–
1953, comp.

Lieber, Maxim, comp.
Great stories of all nations: one hundred and
fifty eight complete short stories from all
periods and countries; selected by Maxim Lieber
and B.C. Williams. Lond. Harrap [1927]
1121 p.

Williams, Bianca Colton, joint comp.
Short stories – Collections

NL 0346143 CaBVa

Lieber, Maxim, ed.
Great stories of all nations; one hundred sixty complete
short stories from the literatures of all periods and countries,
edited by Maxim Lieber & Blanche Colton Williams ... New
York, Brentano's, 1927.
xii, 1121 p. 22½½.

1. Short stories.   I. Williams, Blanche Colton, 1879–1944, joint ed.
II. Title.
27—19408
Library of Congress   PZ1.L62Gr

NN ViU NcD PPD PWcS KMK OrP IdU Or OrSaW WaWW
NL 0346144   DLC FU OrPS NcC OC1h OEac OC1 OC1W OCX

VOLUME 332

Lieber, Maxim, 1897–   *ed.*
    Great stories of all nations; one hundred sixty complete
short stories from the literatures of all periods and countries,
edited by Maxim Lieber & Blanche Colton Williams ...   New
York, Tudor publishing co. ₍1934₎
    2 p. l., vii–xii, 1132 p.   23½ cm.

    1. Short stories.   I. Williams, Blanche Colton, 1879–1949, joint
ed.   II. Title.
    PZ1.L62Gr 5   38–9840

NL 0346145   DLC OC1ND MB ViU

Lieber, Maxim, ed.
    Great stories of all nations; one hundred sixty
complete short stories from the literatures of
all periods and countries, edited by Maxim
Lieber & Blanche Colton Williams ...   N.Y.,
Tudor pub. co., [1936]
    1132 p.

NL 0346146   NcRS

PN6014
L52   **Lieber, Maxim,** ed.
1942   Great stories of all nations; one hundred
    sixty complete short stories from the literatures
    of all periods and countries, edited by Maxim
    Lieber & Blanche Colton Williams ...   New York,
    Tudor Publishing Co., 1942.
        xii, 1132 p.   24cm.

        1. Short stories.   I. Williams, Blanche Colton,
    1879–1944.   II. Title.

NL 0346147   GU PJB PSt ViU LU

Lieber, Maxim, joint ed.

Williams, Blanche Colton, 1879–   *ed.*
    A panorama of the short story, selected and edited by
Blanche Colton Williams ... and Maxim Lieber ...   Boston,
New York ₍etc.₎ D. C. Heath and company ₍ᶜ1929₎

[Lieber, Moritz] supposed author.
    Die Gefangennehmung des Erzbischafs von
Köln ...
        see under title

Lieber, Norman, 1906–
    Untersuchung von Hochspannungs-Stossanlagen
mit dem Kathodenstrahl-Oszillographen zur
Erzeugung normgerechter Spannungsstösse. ...
1935.   Braunschweig, 1935.
    Inaug.-Diss. - Techn. Hochsch. Braunschweig,
Lebenslauf.

NL 0346150   ICRL

Lieber, Oscar Montgomery, 1830–1862, tr.

Wöhler, Friedrich, 1800–1882.
    The analytical chemist's assistant: a manual of chem-
ical analysis, both qualitative and quantitative of natural
and artificial inorganic compounds, to which are appended
the rules for detecting arsenic in a case of poisoning.   By
Friederich Woehler ...   Tr. from the German, with an
introduction, illustrations, and copious additions, by
Oscar M. Lieber ...   Philadelphia, H. C. Baird, 1852.

Lieber, Oscar Montgomery, 1830–1862.
    The assayer's guide; or, Practical directions to assayers,
miners and smelters, for the tests and assays, by heat and
by wet processes, of the ores of all the principal metals, and
of gold and silver coins and alloys.   By Oscar M. Lieber ...
Philadelphia, H. C. Baird, 1852.
    117 p. pl. 17½ᵐ.

    1. Assaying.
    Library of Congress   TJ543.L71   4–34033
    ———— Copy 2.   Lettered on cover: Practical series.

NL 0346152   DLC TNJ OCU PPF ViU MdBP NN ScU OrSaW

LIEBER, Oscar M[ontgomery], 1830–1862.
    The assayer's guide; or, Practical directions
to assayers, miners, and smelters, for the tests
and essays by heat and by wet processes, of
the ores of all the principal metals, of gold
and silver coins and alloys, and of coals &c.
Philadelphia, H.C.Baird, 1856.

    Plates and tables.
    (Practical series.)

NL 0346153   MH-C NcD

Lieber, Oscar Montgomery, 1830–1862.
    The assayer's guide; or, Practical directions
to assayers, miners, and smelters for the tests
and assays, by heat and by wet processes, of the
ores of all the principal metals, of gold and
silver coins and alloys, and of coal &c.   By
Oscar M. Lieber ...   Philadelphia, H.C.
Baird & co., 1869.
    133 p. incl. tables.-plates.   19.5 cm.
    1. Assaying.

NL 0346154   PKsL

TN550   Lieber, Oscar Montgomery, 1830–1862.
L717   The assayer's guide; or, Practical direc-
    tions to assayers, miners, and smelters, for
    the tests and assays, by heat and by wet
    processes, of the ores of all the principal
    metals, of gold and silver coins and alloys,
    and of coal &c.   Philadelphia, H.C. Baird,
    1875 [1852]
        133 p.   illus.   20cm.

        1. Assaying.

NL 0346155   CoU

Lieber, Oscar Montgomery, 1830–1862.
    The assayer's guide; or, Practical directions to assayers,
miners, and smelters, for the tests and assays, by heat and by
wet processes, of the ores of all the principal metals, of gold
and silver coins and alloys, and of coal &c.   By Oscar M.
Lieber ...   Philadelphia, H. C. Baird & co., 1877.
    133 p. incl. tables, plates.   19½ᵐ.

    1. Assaying.
    Library of Congress   TN550.L717   4–34034

NL 0346156   DLC

Lieber, Oscar Montgomery.
    The assayer's guide; or, Practical directions
to assayers, miners and smelters, for the tests
and assays, by heat and by wet processes, of the
ores of all the principal metals, of gold and
silver coins and alloys, and of coal, &c.   By
Oscar M. Lieber ...   Philadelphia, H.C.
Baird & co., 1884.
    5–133 p. 5 pl.,   diagrs.

NL 0346157   MiHM OrP

Lieber, Oscar Montgomery, 1830–1862.
    The assayer's guide; or, Practical directions to assay-
ers, miners and smelters, for the tests and assays, by heat
and by wet processes, of the ores of all the principal metals, of gold and silver coins and alloys, and of coal, &c.
By Oscar M. Lieber ...   New, rev. and enl. ed.   Philadelphia, H. C. Baird & co., 1893.
    xvi, 17–283 p. 5 pl., diagrs.   19ᵐ.

    1. Assaying.
    Library of Congress   TN550.L72   5–2385

NL 0346158   DLC CoU OCl MtBC WaS

M-film
600   Lieber, Oscar Montgomery, 1830–1862.
Am3   The assayer's guide; or, Practical directions
325-8   to assayers, miners, and smelters, for the tests
    and assays, by heat and by wet processes, of the
    ores of all the principal metals, of gold and
    silver coins and alloys, and of coal &c.   A
    new, rev. and enl. ed.   Philadelphia, H. C.
    Baird, 1899.
        283 p. illus.

        Microfilm (positive) Ann Arbor, Mich.,
    University Microfilms, 1966.   8th title of 9.

        35 mm. (American culture series, reel 325.8)

        1. Assaying.

NL 0346160   KEmT PSt

Lieber, Oscar Montgomery.
    The assayer's guide; or, Practical directions to assayers, miners
and smelters, for the tests and assays, by heat and by wet processes, of the ores of all the principal metals, of gold and silver
coins and alloys, and of coal, &c.   A new, revised and enlarged
edition.   283 p. il. 5 pl. D. Philadelphia: H. C. Baird & Co.,
1902, c. 1892.

NL 0346161   ICJ ICRL WaWW

Lieber, Oscar Montgomery.
    Assayer's guide; or, Practical directions to
assayers, miners & smelters for the tests... of
the ores of all the principal metals... New ed.
rev. & enl.
Phila., Baird, 1907.
    283 p.

NL 0346162   PP CU

Lieber, Oscar Montgomery, 1830–1862.
    The itacolumite and its associates, comprising observations on
their geological importance and their connection with the occurrences of gold : a contribution to the geologic chronology of the
southern Alleghanies, supplementary to reports 1, 2 & 3.   By O.
M. Lieber, ... Columbia, S. C., R. W. Gibbes, state printer,
1859.
    [75]–223 p. xv–xvii fold. pl. (incl. 2 maps).   25ᵐ.   (*In* Report III on the Sur-
vey of South Carolina, Supplement.)

NL 0346163   ICJ PPL

Lieber, Oscar Montgomery, 1830–1862.
    ... Notes on the geology of the coast of
Labrador, by Oscar M. Lieber, esq., August 1860.
(Sketch no. 38) [Washington, 1861]
    p. 402–408   fold pl.   29 x 23 cm.
    Caption title.
    United States Coast survey report for 1860.
Appendix no. 42.
    1. Geology - Labrador.

NL 0346164   CU

VOLUME 332

Lieber, Oscar Montgomery, 1830–1862.
... Notes on the geology of the coast of Labrador, by Oscar M. Lieber, esq., August 1860. (Sketch no. 38) ₁Washington. 1860?₁

7 p. fold. pl. 29 x 23ᵐ.

Caption title.
From the United States Coast survey report for 1860. Appendix no. 42.
Plate (sketch no. 38) wanting.

1. Geology—Labrador.

9—3265

Library of Congress   QE196.L3L7

NL   0346165   DLC PPAmP

Lieber, Oscar Montgomery, 1830–1862.
Petrology and metamorphism. By Oscar M. Lieber. [n. p., 1859]
15 p.   23 cm.   [Pamphlets on geology. v. 5, no. 10]
Caption title.
From Mining magazine and journal of geology. 2d ser. v. 1, Dec. 1859.
1. Rocks, Crystalline and metamorphic.

NL   0346166   CU

Lieber, Oscar Montgomery, 1830–1862

South Carolina. *Mineralogical, geological and agricultural survey.*
Report on the survey of South Carolina: being the first₁–fourth₁ annual report to the General assembly of South Carolina, embracing the progress of the survey during the year 1856₁–1859₁ ... by Oscar M. Lieber, mineralogical, geological and agricultural surveyor of South Carolina ... Columbia, R. W. Gibbes, state printer, 1856–60.

NL   0346168   DLC MB

Lieber, Oscar Montgomery..
Report upon Dr. Homer Holland's patented process for the desulphurization of metalliferous sulphurets. Springfield, (Mass.), 1854.
10p.

YA 12922

NL   0346168   DLC MB

LIEBER, OSCAR MONTGOMERY
Reports on the geognostic survey of South Carolina, 1, 2, 3, 4, 1856–1860. Columbia, S. C., R. W. Gibbes, 1860.
v. p. Il. 8°.

NL   0346169   ScU

Lieber, Oscar Montgomery.
Reports on the Survey of and of the Geognostic Survey 1856–1866. Columbia, 1858–9.

NL   0346170   AU

s.c.
p557.57
L62r

Lieber, Oscar Montgomery, 1830–1862.
A sketch of the geology of the state of Mississippi. (In: The Mining and Statistic Magazine, vol. III, no. 1, July, 1854. P. ₍39₎ –47, incl. map.)

Imperfect: p. 43–46 missing.
Detached copy in pamphlet binder.
In binder with his Report on the survey of South Carolina. 1858.
1. Geology – Mississippi.

NL   0346171   ScU

Lieber, Oscar Montgomery, 1830–1862.
Vocabulary of the Catawba language, with some remarks on its grammar, construction and pronunciation. By Oscar M. Lieber ... Charleston, S. C., James and Williams, printers, 1858.

18 p.   21½ᵐ.

From Collections of the South-Carolina historical society, vol. II.

1. Catawba language—Glossaries, vocabularies, etc.

13–10435

Library of Congress   PM751.L5

NL   0346172   DLC NBu CU MnHi OCl

Lieber, Otto.
22 years of hustling; a story of successful retail lumber yard management, by Otto Lieber, jr. ... Neenah, Wis. ₍*1941₁

86 p., 1 l. incl. front. (port.) illus., tables, forms. 28 x 21½ᵐ.

1. Lumber trade—U. S.   I. Title.

41–16976

Library of Congress   HD9755.L5
                          ₍2₁   658.974

NL   0346173   DLC OrP OCl

Geology
D551.2
L62

Lieber, Paul.
Studies on the propagation of seismic waves in visco-elastic media, by Paul Lieber, K. T. Yen, and H. C. Mattice. Contract no. Nonr 511 (01) Troy, N. Y., Dept. of Aeronautical Engineering, Rensselaer Polytechnic Institute, 1952.
iii, 22 l. diagrs.

"Approved by: R. P. Harrington, Head of the Department."
"RPIAL no. 102."
Bibliography: l. 22.

NL   0346174   NNC

Lieber, Richard, joint author.

Buss, Hans.
Deutscher mais auf deutschem boden; erfahrungen und anregungen in 1000 worten und 100 bildern, von Hans Buss ... und dr. Richard Lieber ... Berlin ₍Reichsnährstand verlagsges. m. b. h., ₍1937₁

Lieber, Richard.
Morphologische und pflanzenzüchterische betrachtungen über die luzerne.
Landw. jahrb. bd. 68, p. 117–141.   Berlin, 1928.
"Literatur": p. 141.

1. Alfalfa.

Agr 29–1254

Library, U. S. Dept. of   Agriculture 1SL23 bd. 68

NL   0346176   DNAL

Lieber, Richard, 1869–1944.
America's natural wealth; a story of the use and abuse of our resources, by Richard Lieber. New York and London, Harper & brothers, 1942.

xiv p., 1 l., 245 p. front., illus. (map) plates, facsim., diagrs. 22ᵐ.
"First edition."

1. Natural resources—U. S. 2. U. S.—Econ. condit.—1918–   I. Title.
42–50713

Library of Congress   HC106.4.L58
                          ₍a45z*10₁

CaBVaU OrStbM PBm PU PWcS PHC PP
OrCS OrSaW OrU IdB NcD NcRS IdU MtU MtBuM MtBC
ODW OEac DI MU KEmT WaT WaS WaTC WaWW Or OrP OrPR
NL   0346177   DLC TU NIC CoU OCl OClJC OOxM MiHM ViU

1869–1944.
Lieber, Richard, Democracy, the heritage of all. N. Y. 1918.

NL   0346178   NjP

Lieber, Richard, 1869–1944.
Indiana. *Laws, statutes, etc.*
Laws of Indiana relating to the conservation of natural resources, including the laws relating to geology, natural gas, entomology, forestry, lands and waters and fish and game. Prepared under the supervision of Richard Lieber, director of the Department of conservation, by Charles Kettleborough, director of the Legislative reference bureau ... 1919. ₍Indianapolis, W. B. Burford, contractor for state printing and binding, 1919₁

Lieber, Richard, 1869–1944.
One hundred years of Indiana's resources.
Fort Wayne, Ind. Fort Wayne Printing Co. 1920. 45 pp. Plates. [Indiana. Department of Conservation. Publication no 11.] 22.5 cm.

D4995 — S.r.c. — Natural resources. — Indiana. Pol. econ.

NL   0346180   MB

Lieber, Richard, 1869–1944.
Using our abandoned farms, by Richard Lieber, director, Indiana Department of conservation ... ₍July 1, 1930₁

11 p. incl. illus. ports. 22½ cm. (Indiana. Dept. of conservation. ₍Publication no. 95₁ Division of forestry. ₍Forestry circular no. 7₁)
Reprint from National republic, vol. XVIII, no. 1, Washington, D. C., May, 1930.

1. Farms—Indiana. 2. Natural resources—Indiana. 3. Indiana—Econ. condit.   I. Title.

SD12.I 43 no. 7   31–20281

NL   0346181   DLC OrCS MiU PPAN

Lieber, Robert.
Qualitative chemische Analyse nach dem Schwefelnatriumgang. Unter Mitarbeit von Hofrat Dr. tech. h. c. et phil. Georg Vortmann...bearbeitet und herausgegeben von Ing. Robert Lieber... Wien₍, etc.₁: E. Haim & Co., 1933.   viii, 184 p. incl. tables. 23½cm.

Bibliographical footnotes.

736687A. I. Chemistry, Analytical,   Qualitative, 1933. I. Vortmann,
Georg, 1854–1932.   Georg, 1854–1932.
N. Y. P. L.   January 7, 1935

NL   0346182   NN CtY

Lieber, Thomas
        see Erastus, Thomas, 1524–1583.

Lieber, Walter, 1885–   Das Nachindossament des präjudizierten Wechsels. Borna-Leipzig 1913: Noske. IX, 63 S. 8°
Leipzig, Jur. Diss. v. 23. Mai 1913
₍Geb. 9. Okt. 85 Stroga; Wohnort: Borna b. Leipzig; Staatsangeh.: Sachsen; Vorbildung: Fürstensch. Grimma Reife 05; Studium: Leipzig 4, Freiburg 1, Leipzig 3 S.; Rig. 12. Febr. 10.₁   [U 13. 1036]

NL   0346184   ICRL

BF
1548
L71

Lieber, William.
Devil & devilry.   London, R. & T. Washbourne, 1917.
v, 81 p. 17cm.

1. Devil. 2. Spiritualism. I. Title.

NL   0346185   NIC

VOLUME 332

235
L71d
   Lieber, William
   Devil & devilry.   New York,
   Benziger, 1917.
   81p. D.

NL 0346186   IaU

Lieber, William.
  The 'new theology,' or the Rev. R. J. Campbell's main conclusions
refuted.
— London. Washbourne. 1907. (5), 53 pp. Sm. 8°.
  The Rev. R. J. Campbell's The new theology may be found on shelf-
number 3459.268.

G5918 — T.r. — Theology. Doctrinal. — Roman Catholic Church. Doctr. and
contr. works. — Campbell, Reginald John. 1867–

NL 0346187   MB MBtS OClStM

BT
78
C2L5
  Lieber, William.
    The 'new theology'; or R. J. Campbell's main conclusions
  refuted.   London, R. & T. Washbourne; New York, Benziger,
  1907.
    53 p. 19cm.

      1. Campbell, Reginald John, 1867–   The new theology.
    2. Catholic Church—Doctrinal and controversial works—Catholic
    authors. I. Title.

NL 0346188   COSA

Lieber and Niebuhr
   see under   [Howland, M   ]

Lieber code co., New York

Lieber, Benjamin Franklin, 1853–1915.
  Lieber's latest code ... New York, Lieber code co. [c1926]

4DC
1157
   Lieber Micha; dreizehn Briefe aus
   Paris mit Bildern von Oleg Zinger.
   Berlin, Kinderbuchverlag [c1951]
   44 p.

NL 0346191   DLC-P4

Lieberberg, Joseph
  see Liberberg, Iosif.

Lieberberg, Ruwin,
  Ueber angeborene klitorishypertrophie.
  Inaug. diss. Bern, 1912
  Bibl.

NL 0346193   ICRL

808.21
L716a
  Lieberenz, Paul Karl, 1893–
   Abenteuer mit der Filmkamera. Berlin,
   Minerva-Verlag, 1946.
   236p. illus. 19cm. (Die Haus- und
   Jugendbücher)

    1. Moving-pictures. I. Title.

NL 0346194   IEN

Lieberenz, Paul Karl, 1893–
  ...Im Lande der Renntiere; mit 48 Kupfertiefdruckbildern
nach den Aufnahmen des Verfassers.   Berlin: R. Hobbing[,
1933]. 154 p. 2 maps, plates. 24cm.

667188A. 1. Lapland—Descr. and   trav.   September 30, 1933
N.Y.P.L.

NL 0346195   NN

Lieberenz, Paul Karl, 1893–
  Mit der Flimmerkiste ins Affenland...
   see under   Angebauer, Karl.

Lieberenz, Paul Karl, 1893–
  Mit Sven Hedin durch Asiens wüsten, nach dem tagebuch
des filmoperateurs der expedition, Paul Lieberenz, bearb. von
dr. Arthur Berger; mit 16 abbildungen. Berlin, Volksverband der bücherfreunde, Wegweiser-verlag g. m. b. h. [c1932]
  383, [1] p. plates, ports. 18¼cm.

    "Dieses werk ist als vierter band der dreizehnten (allgemeinen)
jahresreihe für die mitglieder des Volksverbandes der bücherfreunde
hergestellt worden und wird nur an diese abgegeben."

    1. Gobi. 2. Mongolia—Descr. & trav. 3. Hedin, Sven Anders, 1865–
I. Berger, Arthur, 1871– ed. II. Volksverband der bücherfreunde,
Berlin. III. Title.

   Library of Congress   \DS793.G6L5   32–21321

                                     915.17

NL 0346197   DLC CaOTP NIC

Lieberenz, Paul Karl, 1893–
  ... Das rätsel Abessinien; mit 22 kupfertiefdruckbildern
nach den aufnahmen des verfassers. Berlin, R. Hobbing
[c1935]
  119, [1] p. incl. illus. (map) plates, ports. 23¼cm.

  At head of title: Paul Lieberenz.

    1. Ethiopia—Descr. & trav. I. Title.   35–19581

   Library of Congress   DT378.L5
   Copyright A—Foreign   29150
                    [2]
                                 916.3

NL 0346198   DLC CtY ICRL ICU NN

B
430
.L5
  Lieberg, Godo.
   Die Lehre von der Lust in den Ethiken
   des Aristoteles. München, C.H. Beck, 1958.
   130p. 25cm. (Zetemata; Monographien
   zur klassischen Altertumswissenschaft, Heft.
   19)

    Bibliography: p.[125]-126.

    1. Aristoteles.   Ethica. I. Title.
    II. Series.

NL 0346199   OrU

Lieberg, Walter: Die deutsche Glasindustrie im 20. Jahrhundert,
ihre Entwicklung und ihre weltwirtschaftlichen Beziehungen
unt. Berücks. der während d. Krieges entstandenen Konkurrenz-
industrien d. feindl. Auslandes. [Maschinenschrift.] 268, v S.
m. Taf. 4°. — Auszug: o. O. (1923). 8 S. 8°
Göttingen, R.- u. staatswiss. Diss. v. 5. März 1923   [U 23.3981

NL 0346200   ICRL

Liebergen (Antoine Joseph Hubert) van
Over febris puerperalis. [Utrecht.] 2 p. l., 44
pp. 8°. *Breda, K. G. Oukoop,* 1875.

NL 0346201   DNLM

Liebergen (D.)
  Godsdienst en vryheit herstelt, in Europa uit de banden
van slaverny verlost, door . . . Wilhem den derden, en
zyn . . . gemalin Maria Stuart, koning en koningin van
Engeland, . . . *'s Gravenhage : G. van Limburg,* [1690?]
30 pp. 4°.

NL 0346202   NN

Liebergius (Didericus). Fasciculus poematum.
Arn. Henr. Westerhovius collegit et coll curavit.
9 p. l., 181 pp., 1 l., 1 pl. 12°. *Gouda, J. & A.
Endenburg, 1718.*

NL 0346203   DNLM

[Lieberherr, Christian Gottfried]   ed.
  Concordia. Einhundert Chorgesänge für
  Christliche Gesang-Vereine, nebst einer
  ausführlichen Gesanglehre. Cincinnati,
  Chicago, [etc.], Walden & Stowe, 1881,
  [c. 1881, pref. 1881]
    151, [1] p. 17 x 25 cm.
    100, [1] pieces, with music.
    Bound with His: Der evangelische Zionssänger
  ... 1881.

NL 0346204   NNUT

VM
2132.G3
L 71e
1866
  LIEBERHERR, CHRISTIAN GOTTFRIED,   ed.
   Der evangelische Zionssänger. Eine sammlung
  von zweihundert dreiundneunzig choral- und siebenundfünfzig chor-gesängen, nebst einer kurzen anleitung zum gesang-unterrichte... Cincinnati,
  Poe & Hitchcock, 1866.
    240p. 17x25½cm.

NL 0346205   ICN NNUT

Lieberherr, Christian Gottfried,   ed.
  Der evangelische Zionssänger. Eine Sammlung
  von zweihundert dreiundneunzig Choral-Gesängen,
  nebst einer KurzenAnleitung zum Gesang-
  Unterrichte bearbeitet von Christian Gottfried
  Lieberherr.   Cincinnati, Chicago, [etc.],
  Walden & Stowe, 1881, [c. 1866, pref. 1865]
    165 p.   17 x 25 cm.
    Tunes number 1-278 (some numbers repeated)
    I. Title

NL 0346206   NNUT

M2132
L716
Theol.
  Lieberherr, Christian Gottfried.
   Der evangelische Zionssänger. Eine Sammlung
  von zweihundert dreiundneunzig Choral- und
  siebenundfünfzig Chor-Gesängen, nebst einer
  kurzen Anleitung zum Gesang-Unterrichte. Cin-
  cinnati, Chicago und St. Louis, Cranston &
  Stowe, 1888.
    151p. 17 x 25cm.

    1. Protestant churches—Hymns. 2. Hymns,
  German.

NL 0346207   TxDaM

Lieberherr, E.
  A few notes on Indian groundnuts. By E. Lieberherr ...
[Bombay, Times press, 1928]
  2 p. l., 54 p. illus., plates, diagrs. 25cm.

  Bibliography: p. 54.

    1. Peanuts.
                               Agr 29–98
  Library, U. S. Dept. of   Agriculture 77L62

NL 0346208   DNAL

VOLUME 332

Lieberherr, Martha.
...Eine Frauenkorrespondenz. ₁Basel, 1946₁ 128 p. 17cm.

At head of title: Martha Lieberherr / M. E. Gysin.

1. Letters, Swiss-German.
N.Y.P.L.   I. Gysin, M. E.   April 23, 1948

NL 0346209   NN

Lieberherr, Richard, 1920-
Synthese einiger lokalanästhetisch und tuberkulostatisch wirksamer Derivate des 2-Oxy-4-aminochinolins. Zürich, Juris-Verlag, 1950.

150 p. illus. 23 cm.

Promotionsarbeit—Eidgenössische Technische Hochschule, Zürich. Vita.
Bibliography: p. 146–149.

1. Choline. 2. Local anesthesia. 3. Tuberculosis.

RD86.C54L5   56–21415

NL 0346210   DLC CtY DNLM

Lieberherr, Werner, 1907-
... Zur Therapie der Febris undulans Bang ... Zürich, 1933.
Inaug.-Diss. - Zürich.
Curriculum vitae.
"Aus dem 'Wiener Archiv für innere Medizin,' 24. Band, Heft 1 vom 15. August 1933."
"Literatur": p. 27-28.

NL 0346211   CtY

Lieberich, Ernst, 1904-
Kritische Betrachtung uber die Hexabromidzahl ... [München, 1937]
Inaug.-Diss. - München.
Lebenslauf.
Text reproduced from typewritten copy.

NL 0346212   CtY

Lieberich, Heinrich.
Die russische handelsvertretung in Deutschland, ihre stellung im deutschen recht ... Von Heinrich Lieberich ... München, Druck von V. Hofling, 1928.

66 p. 20ᶜᵐ.

Inaug.-diss.—Erlangen.
"Literaturverzeichnis": p. 5–6.

1. Russia—Comm.—Germany. 2. Germany—Comm.—Russia. 3. Corporations, Foreign—Germany. I. Title.

35–37547

NL 0346213   DLC CtY CSt-H NN PU NIC

LIEBERICH, Heinrich, 1864-
Studien zu den proömien in der griechischen und byzantinischen geschichtsschreibung. 2 teile (In 1 vol.) München, 1898-1900.

G 804
The same. Teil I. Inaug.-diss. München, 1899.
Life, p.2.

NL 0346214   MH NjP

Leiberich, Heinrich, 1864-
Studien zun den Proömien in der griechischen und byzantinischen Geschichtsschreibung. München, Joh. Gg. Weiss'sche Buchdruckerei (Josef Olbrich) . 1899-1900.
2 v.
Pt. 1.- Inaug.-Diss. München. Pt. 2.-
Programm des Kgl. Realgymnasiums München für das Schuljahr 1899/100.
Contents. - 1. Theil. Die griechischen Geschichtsschreiber. - 2. Theil Die byzantinischen Geschichtsschreiber und Chronisten.

NL 0346215   DDO MH NIC

Lieberich, Rudolf, 1911-
Fragen der rationalisierung im einzelhandel ... von Rudolf Lieberich ...   Landau, Pfalz, Kausslersche verlagsanstalt, 1931.
90 p.

Thesis, Heidelberg.
Bibliography: p. ₁5-7₁

1.Retail trade. 2.Rationalization.

NL 0346216   NNC CtY PU

Liebering, Wilhelm.
Beschreibung des bergreviers Coblenz i. bearbeitet im auftrage des Königlichen oberbergamts zu Bonn von Wilhelm Liebering ... Bonn, A. Marcus, 1883.

2 p. l., 113 p. 25ᶜᵐ.

"Druckschriften und ausarbeitungen": p. 100–111.

1. Mines and mineral resources—Germany—Koblenz I.   I. Prussia. Oberbergamt zu Bonn.

Library of Congress   TN74.P9L7   6—21435

NL 0346217   DLC MiHM

S22
0350
21
Lieberkind, Ingvald, 1897-
Asteridae der Deutschen Tiefsee-Expedition.
1.Porcellanasteridae ...
(In Wissenschaftliche Ergebnisse der Deutschen Tiefsee-Expedition. Jona,1932. 34½cm. v.21, p.[269]-299,3ℓ. illus.,pl.XI-XVII.)
Double pagination.

NL 0346218   CtY

Lieberkind, Ingvald, 1897-
... *Asteroidea* ... by Ingvald Lieberkind ...   Copenhagen, Printed by B. Luno a/s., 1935-
Library has pt. 1+ illus. (incl. maps) plates. 34ᶜᵐ. (The Danish Ingolf-expedition. vol. IV: 10   )

NL 0346219   ICJ CU NIC CSt

Lieberkind, Ingvald, 1897-
... Da Gysse fo'r vild, og andre fortællinger om vore husdyr fortalt for børn. ₁København₁ S. Hasselbalch, 1942.
110 p. illus. 22½ᵐ. (*On cover:* Lieberkind fortæller)

I. Title.
PZ56.3.L5   47–38942

NL 0346220   DLC

Lieberkind, Ingvald.
Da maaren fik bersærkergang og andre fortællinger om dyr, fortalt for børn af I. Lieberkind; med tegninger af Oscar Knudsen. København, H. Koppel, 1929.
72 p., 1 l. incl. plates. 23ᶜᵐ.
Head and tail pieces.
CONTENTS.—Da husmaaren fik bersærkergang.—Hvad gøgen saa Sct. Hans nat.—Paa maaneskinstur med et pindsvin.—Foraarspassiar med en regnorm.

1. Animals, Legends and stories of.   I. Title.
Library of Congress   PZ53.L54D2   30–7527

NL 0346221   DLC

Sy4
939L
Lieberkind, Ingvald, 1897-
Dyrenes verden: Fugle 1-3. København, Standard Forlaget, 1939.
3 v. illus. 25 cm.

1. Birds.

NL 0346222   CtY

RC115
.L5
1928
Lieberkind, Ingvald.
Farliga gäster; djur som smittbärare och sjukdomskällor; till svenska av Robert Larsson. Stockholm, A. Bonniers ₁1928₁
213p. illus. 24cm.

1. Insects as carriers of disease. 2. Parasites. I. Title.

NL 0346223   AAP

Lieberkind, Ingvald.
... Farlige gæster; dyr som smittebærere og sygdomskilder. København, H. Koppel, 1927.
214, ₂₁ p., 2 l. illus. 24ᶜᵐ.
At head of title: I. Lieberkind.
"Litteraturliste": p. ₂215₁-₂217₁

1. Insects as carriers of contagion. 2. Parasites.
Library of Congress   RC115.L5   28–13262

NL 0346224   DLC

Lieberkind, Ingvald, 1897-
... Guldsmeden, dens liv og levned fortalt for børn. ₁København₁ S. Hasselbalch, 1942.
95 p. illus. 22½ᵐ. (*On cover:* Lieberkind fortæller)
Title on cover: Om guldsmeden.

I. Title. II. Title: Om guldsmeden.
PZ56.3.L53   47–38940

NL 0346225   DLC

Lieberkind, Ingvald.
Haletudsen og andre vand- og landstrygere, af magister I. Lieberkind. Illustrator af Vilh. Sandstrøm. København, Eget forlag, 1926.
60 p. illus. 22ᶜᵐ.
"Radioforedrag."
CONTENTS.—Haletudsens oplevelser.—Hvordan dagen gaar for en søstjerne.—Et besøg hos gedehamsene.

1. Toads. 2. Starfishes. 3. Wasps. 4. Zoology—Juvenile literature. I. Title.
Library of Congress   QL49.L5   27–11417
34144-

NL 0346226   DLC

Lieberkind, Ingvald.
Mens aalen vandrer—; historier om dyr fortalt for børn, af I. Lieberkind, med tegninger af Oscar Knudsen. København, H. Koppel, 1928.
75, ₁1₁ p., 1 l. incl. plates. 23ᶜᵐ.
Head and tail pieces.
CONTENTS.— Aalens livseventyr. — Et besøg i myretuen. — Storkens rejseeventyr.—Edderkoppens liv.

1. Animals, Legends and stories of.   I. Title.
Library of Congress   PZ53.L54M4   30–14125
5291

NL 0346227   DLC

Lieberkind, Ingvald, 1897-
... Mikkeline og ungerne. ₁København₁ S. Hasselbalch, 1942.
77 p. illus. 22½ᵐ. (*On cover:* Lieberkind fortæller)

I. Title.
PZ56.3.L55   47–38941

NL 0346228   DLC

VOLUME 332

QL
669
.L723 Lieberkind, Ingvald, 1897-
    Vergleichende Studien über die Morphologie und
Histogenese der larvalen Haftorgane bei den Am-
phibien. København, C.A.Reitzel, 1937.
    180 p. illus., 28 fold.pl. 26 cm.
    Thesis-- Copenhagen.
    Translated from the Danish by Dr. Knopf. cf.
Vorwort.
    "Resumé" (in Danish): p.₍160₎-163.
    "Literaturverzeichnis": p.₍164₎-180.
    1. Embryology--Amphibia.

NIC CU
NL   0346229   MiU CtY ICRL CaBVaU CSt ICJ OCU NcD IU

Lieberknecht (August) [1882-]. *Ueber
Rippendefecte und anderweitige Missbildungen bei angeborenem Hochstand des
Schulterblattes. 42 pp. 1 pl. 8°. Marburg,
1906.

NL   0346230   DNLM ICRL CtY

Lieberknecht, Fritz, 1910-
    ... Ueber die Bedeutung der Uterus-Doppelbil-
dungen in Verlauf von Schwangerschaften und
Geburten an Hand von 30 Fällen der Universitäts-
Frauenklinik Marburg während der letzten
10 Jahre ... Marburg (Lahn) 1937.
    Inaug.-Diss. - Marburg.
    Lebenslauf.
    "Literatur": p. 41-42.

NL   0346231   CtY

Lieberknecht, Herbert, 1896-
    Das altpreussische Zuchtauswesen bis zum
Ausgang des 18. Jahrhunderts, insbesondere
in den Provinzen Pommern und Ostpreussen ...
Charlottenburg, 1921.
    Inaug.-Diss. - Göttingen.
    Literatur- und Quellenangabe, p. [9]-10.
    Lebenslauf.

NL   0346232   CtY ICRL MiU

W 4   LIEBERKNECHT, Hilde, 1911-
M31   Zur Behandlung der sogenannten
1937   Ohr-Tubenentzündung. Marburg,
    Bauer, 1937.
    20 p.
    Cover title.
    Inaug.-Diss. - Marburg.
    1. Eustachian tube

NL   0346233   DNLM

TEXT.   Lieberknecht (Karl), Inc.
TT685   Full-fashioned knitting machine primer.
.L71   Reading, Pa., c1947.
    47 p. illus. 24cm.

    1. Knitting-machines. I. Title. II.Title:
Knitting machine primer.

NL   0346234   ScCleU

Lieberknecht, Klaus, 1907-
    Über die änderung der eigenschaften von
stahldraht durch lagerung bei raumtemperatur und
durch kälte. ... Dortmund, 1934.
    Inaug. Diss. - Techn. Hochsch. Braunschweig,
1934.
    Lebenslauf.

NL   0346235   ICRL

Lieberknecht, Otfried.
    Patente, Lizenzverträge und Verbot von Wettbewerbsbe-
schränkungen. Eine vergleichende Darstellung der Rechtslage in Deutschland, Grossbritannien und den Vereinigten
Staaten. Frankfurt am Main, V. Klostermann ₍°1953₎
    335 p. 23 cm. (Schriften des Instituts für Ausländisches und In-
ternationales Wirtschaftsrecht, Frankfurt am Main, Bd. 4)
    Bibliography: p. ₍317₎-323.
    1. Patent licenses. 2. Trusts, Industrial—Law. 3. Restraint of
trade. (Series: Frankfurt am Main. Universität. Institut für
Ausländisches und Internationales Wirtschaftsrecht. Schriften, Bd. 4)

    54—24037

NL   0346236   DLC ICU CU MH-L

Lieberknecht, Paul Ernst, 1886–
    Geschichte des Deutschkatholizismus in Kurhessen...von
Paul Lieberknecht... Marburg: N. G. Elwert, 1915. viii,
116 p. 8°.
    Dissertation, Göttingen.
    Bibliography, p. 3-4.
    Lebenslauf, p. (v.)

    1. Catholic Church (Roman).—   History, Germany.
    N.Y.P.L.   May 26, 1922.

NL   0346237   NN MiU MH CtY

Lieberkuehn, Adolf.
    De fractura colli femoris.
    Inaug. Diss. Halle, 1863
    26, 8°

NL   0346238   ICRL DNLM

Lieberkühn, Christian Gottlieb, respondent.
    ... De indole
    see under   Baumgarten, Siegmund Jakob,
1706-1757, praeses.

832
L6211   Lieberkühn, Christian Gottlieb.
    Die Insel der Pucklichten; ein Lustspiel
von einer Handlung. [Berlin, 1767]
    [381]-412p. 18cm.

NL   0346240   TxU

LIEBERKÜHN, CHRISTIAN GOTTLIEB,
    Lieder, erzählungen, sinngedichte u. ernsthafte
stücke. Leipzig, Junius, 1755.

NL   0346241   MiU

[Lieberkuehn, Christian Gottlieb]
    Die Lissabonner; ein bürgerliches Trauerspiel, und
die Insel der Pucklichten; ein Lustspiel. Breslau,
Meyer, 1758

    127 p.
    Photoreproduction of copy in the Staatsbibliothek der
Stiftung Preussischer Kulturbesitz

NL   0346242   MH CLU

LIEBERKÜHN, Christian Ludwig.
    Dissertatio antiquaria de off. judiciali anglo-
sexonibus corsned. Halae,1771.

NL   0346243   MH

LIEBERKÜHN, Ernst.

    See LIEBERKÜHN,Wilhelm Ernst Ferdinand,
    (1810-1861)

Lieberkühn (Joannes Samuel.) *De abscessi-
bus hepatis. 36 pp. 4°. Lipsia, ex off. Langenhemia, [1761].

NL   0346245   DNLM

Lieberkühn, Johann Nathanael, 1711-1756.
    Dissertatio anatomico-physiologica de fabrica et actione
villorum intestinorum tenuium hominis. Iconibus aeri incisis
illustrata. Lugduni Batavorum, C. et G. J. Wishof, 1745.
    36 p. illus., plates. 26 cm.

    1. Intestines—Early works to 1800. I. Title.

    QM345.L5 1745   61-57542

NL   0346246   DLC NIC DNLM

Adelmann
QM
345
L71   Lieberkühn, Johann Nathanael, 1711-1756.
1760   Dissertatio anatomico-physiologica de
    fabrica et actione villorum intestinorum
    tenuium hominis. Iconibus aeri incisis
    illustrata. Amstelaedami, Apud Joannem
    Schreuder et Petrum Mortier, 1760.
    36 p. illus. 25cm.

    Apparently sheets left from 1745 ed.
    were used, with change only of t.p.

    1.Intestines.

NL   0346247   NIC

W 6   LIEBERKÜHN, Johann Nathanael, 1711-1756.
P3   Dissertatio medica inauguralis, de valvula
v.1365   coli et usu processus vermicularis ...
no.13   Lugduni Batavorum, Apud Conradum Wishoff, 1739.
    22 p. 23 cm.
    Diss. - Leyden.

NL   0346248   DNLM PPC

MN
611.34
L71   Lieberkühn, Johann Nathanael, 1711-1756.
    ...Dissertationes quatuor;nimirum,De
    valvula coli et usu processus vermicularis;
    De fabrica et actione villorum intestino-
    rum tenuium hominis;Sur les moyens propres
    à découvrir la construction des viscères;
    Description d'un microscope anatomique;
    omnia nunc primum in unum collecta & edi-
    ta cura et studio Joannis Sheldon... Lon-
    don,T.Cadell,1782.
    10+25+₍1₎,;,2,+36p. il.5pl.(2 fold.)
    25x19½cm.

    Stained.
    In this is-   sue the second disserta-
    tion follows   the fourth.

    The French dissertation "Sur les
    moyens propres à découvrir la construc-
    tion des viscères" is taken from "Mé-
    moires de l'Academie Royale des sciences
    & belles lettres de Berlin",1748.

    1. Intestines. 2. Microscope and microscopy.
    I. Sheldon, John, 1752-1808, ed.

NL   0346250   N ICJ DNLM

QL
374
L5   Lieberkühn, Nathanael, 1822-1887.
    Beiträge zur Anatomie der Kalkspongien,
    von N. Lieberkühn. [Berlin, C. Unger, 1865?]
    19p. illus.,plate(fold.)

    "Besonderer Abdruck aus Reichert's und
    du Bois-Reymond's Archiv 1865, Heft 6."

    1. Sponges--Anatomy.

NL   0346251   UU

VOLUME 332

QL931
L62
Lieberkühn, Nathanael, 1822-1887.
De structura gangliorum penitiori. Auctore
Nathanael Lieberkuehn. Commentatio ab amplis-
simo medicorum ordine Berolinensi aureo praemio
ornata ... Berolini, Schade, 1849.
17, [1] p. plate.

1. Nerves.

NL 0346252   NNC DNLM

Lieberkühn, Nathanael, 1822-1887.
Évolution des Grégarines.
46 p. 11 pl. 4°. (In: Academie royale ...
de Belgique. Mémoires couronnés et mémoires
des savants étrangers. Bruxelles, 1850.
4°. tome 26 [no. 1])

NL 0346253   NN

---

12   Lieberkühn, Nathanael, 1822-1887.
Notice sur les psorospermies. (extrait)
[Bruxelles, 1854]
3 p. 1 pl. 8°. [Zoological pamphlets
v. 19.]

NL 0346254   DLC

Lieberkühn (N[athanael]) [1822-]. Rede
zur Feier des neun und sechzigsten Stiftungstages des medicinisch-chirurgischen Friedrich-
Wilhelms-Instituts am 2. August 1863. 27 pp.
8°. Berlin, Gebr. Unger, [1863?]

NL 0346255   DNLM

Adelmann
QH   Lieberkühn, Nathanael, 1822-1887.
581   Ueber Bewegungserscheinungen der Zellen.
L71   Mit fünf Tafeln... Marburg, N. G. Elwert,
1870.
51 p. 5 plates. 24cm.

"Abgedruckt aus den Schriften der Gesellschaft zur Beförderung der Gesammten Naturwissenschaften zu Marburg, Band IX."

1. Cells. 2. Cells--Motility.

NL 0346256   NIC ICJ NNC DNLM

W1   Lieberkühn, Nathanael, 1822-1887.
GE798V   Ueber Bewegungserscheinungen der Zellen.
Bd.9   [Marburg, Elwert, 1872]
Abh.11   p. [335]-385, illus. (Gesellschaft zur Beförderung
1872   der Gesammten Naturwissenschaften. Schriften, Bd. 9
[Abh. 11])
I. Title II. Series

NL 0346257   DNLM

Lieberkühn, Nathanael, 1822-1887.
Ueber das Auge des Wirbelthierembryo ...
Cassel, 1872.
cover-title, 80 p. 11 pl. 24.5 cm.
[Schriften der Gesellschaft zur Beförderung der
gesammten Naturwissenschaften zu Marburg.
Bd. 10, 5. Abh.)

NL 0346258   CtY

W1   Lieberkühn, Nathanael, 1822-1887.
GE798V   Ueber das Auge des Wirbelthierembryo. [Cassel,
Bd.10   Kay, 1872]
Abh.5   p. [299]-381. illus. (Gesellschaft zur Beförderung
1872   der Gesammten Naturwissenschaften. Schriften, Bd.
10, Abh. 5)
Film S2469.1.
I. Title II. Series

NL 0346259   DNLM

Lieberkühn, [Nathanael] 1822-1887.
... Ueber die keimblätter der säugethiere ... Marburg,
Universitäts-buchdruckerei (R. Friedrich) 1879.
3 p. l., 26 p. pl. 31ᶜᵐ.

At head of title: Zu der funfzigjährigen doctor-jubelfeier des Herrn
Hermann Nasse ... bringt ... glückwünsche dar die Medicinische facultät
zu Marburg.

1. Embryology.
8-27320†

Library of Congress   QL971.L72

NL 0346260   DLC ICJ PU PPAN

Lieberkühn, Nathanael, 1822-1887.
Ueber resorption der knochensubstanz, von N. Lieberkühn
und J. Bermann. Mit 8 tafeln ... Frankfurt a. M., C. Winter,
1877.
1 p. l., 68 p. viii col. pl. 27½ x 23ᶜᵐ.
"Abdruck a. d. Abhandl. d. Senckenb. naturf. gesellschaft. xi. bd."

1. Bone.   I. *Bermann. Isidor, 1845-1918, joint author.
36-31168

Library of Congress   QP88.2.L5

NL 0346261   DLC

Lieberkuehn, Philipp Julius, 1754-1788.
Kleine Schriften; nebst dessen Lebensbeschreibung und einigen Briefen an Prof. Stuve,
herausg. von L. F. G. E. Gedike. Züllichau.
Frommann. 1791.
xxiv, 592 p. 16°.

NL 0346262   MB

JC393   LIEBERKÜHN, PHILIPP JULIUS, 1754-1788.
.D3L7   Versuch über die mittel in den herzen junger leute,
die zu hohen würden oder zum besiz grosser reichthümer
bestimmt sind, menschenliebe zu erwekken und zu unterhalten... Züllichau, Waysenhaus und Frommannische
buchhandlung, 1784.
viii, 112 p. 16½cm.
Preisschrift.

1.Education of princes. 2.Love(Theology)

NL 0346263   ICU IU

---

377   Lieberkühn, Philipp Julius, 1754-1788.
Z7a   Versuch über die mittel in den herzen junger
1788   leute, die zu hohen würden oder zum besitz grosser reichthümer bestimmt sind, menschenliebe zu
erwecken und zu unterhalten. Eine von der Akademie der wissenschaften und künste in Padua gekrönte preisschrift ... Wien, 1788.
95p. [With Zollikofer, G. J. Abhandlung
über die moralische erziehung. Wien, 1788]

1. Moral education. 2. Education of princes.
3. Humanity.

NL 0346264   IU

Lieberkühn, Richard, 1867-
Die historische entwicklung der operativen
behandlung der gallensteine ... Berlin, Vogt
[1894]
31, [1] p.

Inaug.-diss., Berlin, 1894.
Lebenslauf.
"Litteratur": p. 31.

1. Calculi, Biliary. 2. Gall-bladder - Surgery.

NL 0346265   NNC DNLM

Lieberkühn, Samuel, 1710-1777.
The acts of the days of the Son of Man
see under Bible. N. T. Gospels.
English. Harmonies. 1771. (London, Lewis)
Also: 1808 (... from the Passion-week to his
ascension. Philadelphia, Zentler) 1814 (dtto.)

Lieberkühn, Samuel, 1710-1777.
Die Geschichte der Tage des Menschen-Sohns
auf erden... Barby, 1759
see under Bible. N. T. Gospels.
German. Harmonies. 1759.

Lieberkühn, Samuel, 1710-1777.
Die Geschichte unsers Herrn und Heilandes
Jesu Christi... Barby, 1769
see under Bible. N. T. Gospels.
German. Harmonies. 1769. (also 1780)

C   [LIEBERKÜHN, SAMUEL] 1710-1777.
6591   Der Hauptinhalt der Lehre Jesu Christi zum
.505   Gebrauch bey dem Unterricht der Jugend in den
Evangelischen Brudergemeinen. 2.Ausg. Barby,
1778.
80p. 18cm.

NL 0346269   ICN NN

[Lieberkühn, Samuel]
Der Hauptinhalt d. Lehre Jesu Christi zum
Gebrauch bey dem Unterricht der Jugend in den
evang. Brüdergemeinen. 3te. Ausg. Barby,
1794.
80 p. 8°.

NL 0346270   CtY

[Lieberkuehn, Samuel] 1710-1777.
Hauptinhalt der lehre Jesu Christi.
Barby, 1809
Moravian.

NL 0346271   PPeSchw

Lieberkühn, Samuel, 1710-1777.
The history of Our Lord and Saviour Jesus Christ:
comprehending all that the four evangelists have
recorded concerning Him ... by the Rev. Samuel
Lieberkuhn ... Tr. into the Delaware language ...
New York, Fanshaw, 1821
see under Bible. N. T. Gospels. Delaware.
Harmonies. 1821. Zeisberger.
The same title, issued by the Shawanoe Baptist
Mission [Kan.] in 1837, is a new translation; see
under Bible. N. T. Gospels. Delaware. Har-
monies. 1837. Blanchard.

Lieberkühn, Samuel, 1710-1777.
The history of Our Lord and Saviour Jesus
Christ ... tr. into the language of the Otoe,
Ioway, and Missouri tribes ... [Rochester,
N.Y., 1888]
see under Bible. N. T. Gospels. Oto.
Harmonies. 1888. Merrill.

BX   [Lieberkühn, Samuel] 1710-1777.
8070   Die hoofd-inhoud van die leering van Jesus
H6   Christus, tot gebruk voor die Neger-gemeenten,
van die Evangelische broeer-kerk. Barby, 1785.
78p. 18cm.

1. Lutheran church—Doctrinal and controversial
works. 2. Lutheran church in the Netherlands.

NL 0346274   CU ICN

---

686   [LIEBERKUEHN, Samuel] 1710-1777.
Mora.5   Die Lehre Jesu Christi und seiner
L717Ie   Apostel zum Unterricht der Jugend in den
1774   evangelischen Brüdergemeinen. Barby, 1774.
72p. 17.5cm
Title vignette.

NL 0346275   MH-AH

VOLUME 332

Lieberkühn, Samuel, 1710–1777.
Rlathemwakunek wtclawswakun nrvlalkwf
krthwvalkwf Nhesus Klyst ...   Jawanouf, 1837
see
Bible. N.T. Gospels. Delaware.
Harmonies. 1837. Blanchard.
The history of Our Lord and Saviour
Jesus Christ ... tr. into the Delaware language ...
Shawanoe Baptist Mission, 1837.

₍Lieberkühn, Samuel₎ 1710–1777.
A summary of the doctrine of Jesus Christ, to be used
for the instruction of youth in the congregations of the
United brethren. 2d ed. London, 1788.
vi, ₍7₎-64 p. 16¼ᶜᵐ.
Author's name in preface.
Translated from the author's "Hauptinhalt der lehre Jesu Christi," Barby, 1774.

5-30963

NL   0346277   DLC MB NcU

Mtk75
1
1795ℓ
[Lieberkühn, Samuel] 1710–1777.
A summary of the doctrine of Jesus Christ, to
be used for the instruction of youth in the
congregations of the United Brethren. The 3rd
ed. Bath, Printed by S.Hazard, 1795.
vi, [7]-64p. 17cm.
Author's name in preface.
Translation of his "Der Hauptinhalt der Lehre
Jesu Christi zum Gebrauch bey dem Unterricht der
Jugend in den Evangelischen Brüdergemeinen",

published in the province of Barby, 1778. cf.
J.G.Meusel, Lexikon der vom Jahr 1750 bis 1800
verstorbenen teutschen Schriftsteller ...
Leipzig, 1808, v.8, p.248.
Pamphlet

NL   0346279   CtY NcU

Mtk75
1
1804ℓ
[Lieberkühn, Samuel] 1710–1777.
Summary of the doctrine of Jesus Christ, to
be used for the instruction of youth in the
congregations of the United brethren. The 4th
ed. Manchester[Eng.]Printed by R.& W.Dean &
co.,1804.
vi,[7]-64p. 14½cm.
Author's name in preface.
Translation of his "Der Hauptinhalt der Lehre
Jesu Christi zum Gebrauch bey dem Unterricht
der Jugend in den Evangelischen Brüdergemeinen",

published in the province of Barby, 1778. cf.
J.G.Meusel, Lexikon der vom Jahr 1750 bis 1800
verstorbenen teutschen Schriftsteller ...
Leipzig, 1808, v.8, p.248.

NL   0346281   CtY

₍Lieberkühn, Samuel₎ 1710–1777.
Summary of the doctrine of Jesus Christ, to be used for the
instruction of youth in the congregations of the United brethren. Philadelphia : Printed by Conrad Zentler, in Second, below Race street. 1812.
vi, ₍7₎-68, 22 p. 14½ᶜᵐ.
"Done by ... Samuel Lieberkühn": p. ₍111₎
"Extract of the twenty-one doctrinal articles of the Augustan or Augsburg confession ... Philadelphia, 1812": 22 p. at end.
Translation of the author's "Der hauptinhalt der lehre Jesu Christi
zum gebrauch bey dem unterricht der jugend in den Evangelischen
Brüdergemeinen", published in the province of Barby, 1778. cf. J. G.
Meusel, Lexikon der vom Jahr 1750 bis 1800 verstorbenen teutschen
schriftsteller ... Leipzig, 1808, v. 8, p. 248.
1. Moravians—Doctrinal   and controversial works.   I. Augsburg confession. II. Title.
Library of Congress   BX8571.L5
                                ₍t25b2₎
4-1395 Revised

NL   0346282   DLC

LIEBERKÜHN, Wilhelm Ernst Ferdinand, 1810-1861.
Commentatio de conjunctis negationibus mḗ oὐ.
Vimariae, 1853.

4°. pp.18.

NL   0346283   MH PBm

Gna20
840ℓ
Lieberkuehn, Wilhelm Ernst Ferdinand, 1810-
... Commentatio de diurnis romanorum Actis.
Vimariae, 1840.
1p.ℓ.,17p. 24½cm.
Programm - Gymnasium Guilielmo-Ernestinum,
Weimar.

NL   0346284   CtY NjP PU MH

Lieberkühn, Wilhelm Ernst Ferdinand.
De auctore vita₍o₎rum, quae sub₍nomine₎ Cornelii
Nepotis feruntur, quaestiones criticae.
Leipzig, 1837.
8 p.

NL   0346285   PU IEN

Lieberkühn, Wilhelm Ernst Ferdinand
De auctore vitarum, quae sub nomine Cornelii
Nepotis feruntur, quaestiones criticae.
Lipsiae, 1837.
179 p.

NL   0346286   PBm NjP

Lieberkuehn, Wilhelm Ferdinand Ernst.
De diuvrnis Romanorum actis
see his ....Commentatio de diurnis
Romanorum actis.

LIEBERKÜHN, Ernst   Ferdinand.
De Erasmi Roterodami ingeniu ac doctrina
quid valuerint ad restaurationem errorum.
Jenae, [1836].

NL   0346288   MH-AH

Lieberkühn, william Ernst Ferdinand.
De negationibus conjunctis, mḗ oὐ.
Vimariae, 1853.
18 p. O.

NL   0346289   OCU NjP

LIEBERKÜHN, Wilhelm Ernst Ferdinand.
De negationibus mḗ oὐ cum infinitivis et parti-
cipiis conjunctis. Weimar, 1860.

4°. pp.(2),15ℓ.
Progr.d.Wilhelm-Ernstische gym.

NL   0346290   MH NjP PBm PU

LIEBERKÜHN, Wilhelm Ernst Ferdinand.
De negationum graecarum cumulatione. Weimar,
[1840].

4°. pp.20.
Progr.d.Wilhelm-Ernstische gym.

NL   0346291   MH NjP PU

Lieberkühn, Wilhelm Ferdinand Ernst, 1810-1861.
Vindiciae librorum iniuria suspectorum.
Insunt: I. Epistola critica de vetere diurnorum
actorum fragmento Dodwelliano data ad virum
emplissimum Victorem Le Clericum,
Parisiensem; II. Defensio Cornelii Nepotis contra
Aemilium Probum, librarium. Scripsit G.E.F.
Lieberkuehnius ... Lipsiae, F.C.W. Vogelii,
1844.
ix p., 1 l., 236 p. 22 cm.

NL   0346292   CU MH PBm NjP PU

Lieberkuhn, Samuel
see   Lieberkühn, Samuel, 1710-1777.

Lieberman, Abraham I.
Labor law. Rules of the Board of standards
and appeals; rules of the Labor relations board
see under   New York (State) Laws,
statutes, etc.

Law   Lieberman, Abraham I.

New York (State) Laws, statutes, etc.
... Workmen's compensation law and Industrial board rules,
with amendments to December 31, 1938, and annotations to
January 1, 1938. Issued under the direction of Elmer F. Andrews, industrial commissioner. Prepared by Division of statistics and information ... ₍Albany, N. Y., J. B. Lyon company, printers, 1938₎

NL   0346285   PU IEN

Lieberman, Abraham I.

New York (State) Laws, statutes, etc.
... Workmen's compensation law. Rules of Industrial board.
Rules of industrial commissioner relative to medical care of in-
jured employees. With amendments and annotations to July 1,
1941. State Department of labor, Frieda S. Miller, industrial
commissioner ... The Industrial board, Richard J. Cullen,
chairman ... Division of statistics and information, Eugene B.
Patton, director ... ₍Albany? 1941₎

Lieberman, Abraham Moses, 1896-
₍New York₎ 1947.
יונג-בראזיל. לידער און פאעמסעם. ניו-יארק.
128 p. illus. 29 cm.
Added t.-p.: Yung Brasil

I. Title.   *Title transliterated:* Yung-Brazil.

PJ5129.L527Y8   57-57141 ‡

NL   0346297   DLC MH

Lieberman, Arnold Leo, 1903-
... Comparative studies on calcium gluconate and other
calcium salts ... by Arnold Leo Lieberman ... ₍Chicago, 1931₎
1 p. l., 7 p. diagrs. 21ᶜᵐ.
Thesis (PH. D.)—University of Chicago, 1931.
"Private edition, distributed by the University of Chicago libraries,
Chicago, Illinois."
"Reprinted from the Journal of the American medical association,
July 4, 1931, vol. 97."

1. Calcium gluconate. 2. Calcium salts.

Library of Congress   QP913.C2L5 1931   32-13675
Univ. of Chicago Libr.
——— Copy 2.   ₍2₎   612.014463

NL   0346298   ICU OU MiU DLC

Lieberman, B. B.
... Torts in Jewish law, by B. B. Lieberman...   ₍London,
1927.₎   p. 231–240. 8°. (Soc. for Jewish Jurisprudence,
London. Publ. no. 3.)
Cover-title.
Repr.: Jour. of comparative legislation. Nov., 1927.

1. Torts, Jewish.
N. Y. P. L.   October 19, 1929

NL   0346299   NN MH-L WaU-L CU-L

Lieberman, Barnet, 1903-   joint ed.

Dunlap, James D.   FOR OTHER EDITIONS
                    SEE MAIN ENTRY
A book of forms for practice in the courts and for convey-
ancing, by James D. Dunlap. 9th ed., completely rev. and enl.,
by Milford J. Meyer and Barnet Lieberman ... to which are
appended a new note on title searches, by Henry R. Robins ...
and a glossary of law terms ... Philadelphia, George T. Bisel
company, 1934.

VOLUME 332

Law

Lieberman, Barnet, 1903–   joint ed.

Meyer, Milford Joseph, 1907–   *ed.*
Dunlap-Hanna Pennsylvania forms. Editor: Milford J. Meyer; associate editor: Barnet Lieberman. Philadelphia, G. T. Bisel Co., 1948–53.

Lieberman, Barnet.
Local administration and enforcement of housing codes: a survey of 39 cities. Washington, D. C., National Association of Housing and Redevelopment Officials. Publication no. N531)

1. Housing – U. S. – Law and legislation.
I. Title.

NL 0346302   NcU

LIEBERMAN, BERNARD.
Accounting system for retail stores, by Bernard Lieberman ... [New York] Accounting Systems and Forms Co., cop. 1932. 26 p. incl. forms. 17½cm.

796601A. 1. Accounting and bookkeeping for retail trade.

NL 0346303   NN ICU OC1

Lieberman, Chaim
   see
Lieberman, Herman, 1889–1963

Slavic Div.
PG 3549
.L5 N3

[Lieberman, Clara]
... На жизненном пути; собрание рассказов. Нью Иорк [Radio printing corp.] 1943.
xii p., 1 l., 206 p. port. 23cm.
Author's pseud., Клара Маркова, at head of title.
"Собрание ... рассказов, которые были напечатаны в газете ‘Русский голос,’ а некоторые из них в ‘Новом мире,’ за подписью Клары Марковой (Либерман)"–p. xi.

I. Title.   *Title transliterated:* Na zhiznennom puti.

43–45358

NL 0346305   DLC

Lieberman, David S
Cubic to orthorhombic diffusionless phase change; experimental and theoretical studies of AuCd, by D.S. Lieberman, M.S. Wechsler and T.A. Read. [New York, 1955]
cover-title, 473–484 p. illus., diagrs. 28 cm.
D.S. Lieberman's thesis, Columbia University.
"Reprinted from Journal of applied physics, vol. 26, no. 4 ... April, 1955."
Bibliographical footnotes.

NL 0346306   NNC

Lieberman, Elias, 1883–
The American short story; a study of the influence of locality in its development, by Elias Lieberman ... Ridgewood, N. J., The Editor, 1912.
xvi, 183 p. 19½cm.
The author's thesis (PH. D.)–New York university, 1911.
Bibliography: p. 169–175.

1. Short story. 2. American fiction—Hist. & crit. I. Title.

13–4458

Library of Congress   BS374.S5L5
New York Univ. Libr.   [n21s27d1]

OC1W MiU PPT MsU IU NN WaS Or OrCS IEN DLC
NL 0346307   NNU AU MB DAU ViU NcD OEac OU OC1 PU

PS
374
S5L5
1912a

Lieberman, Elias, 1883–
The American short story; a study of the influence of locality in its development, by Elias Lieberman ... Ridgewood, N. J., The Editor, 1912. [Ann Arbor, Mich., University Microfilms, 1968]
xvi, 183 p. 19].
The author's thesis (PH. D.)—New York university, 1911.
Bibliography: p. 169–175.

NL 0346308   CoU

Lieberman, Elias, 1883–   ed.

Coleridge, Samuel Taylor, 1772–1834.
The ancient mariner, by Samuel Taylor Coleridge, with a collection of supplementary poems of the sea, edited by Elias Lieberman ... Chicago, New York, Lyons and Carnahan [1926]

Lieberman, Elias, 1888–
The collective labor agreement; how to negotiate and draft the contract, by Elias Lieberman ... New York and London, Harper & brothers, 1939.
xii, 233 p. 24cm.
"First edition."
Bibliography: p. 220–221.

1. Labor contract—U. S. 2. Trade-unions—U. S. 3. Labor laws and legislation—U. S. I. Title.

39–27866

Library of Congress   HD7811.U6L54
——— Copy 2.
Copyright A 133232   [15]   331.110973

WaU-L OrPR PPT PP PU PHC PBm
OC1W MU OrPS GU OrP WaT IdU WaWW OrCS CaBVa Or WaS
NL 0346310   DLC MH NNC ICJ TU NcRS OCU OC1 OU NcD MH

Business

Lieberman, Elias, 1888–
The collective labor agreement; how to negotiate and draft the contract. [3d ed.] New York, Harper [c1939]
xii, 233 p.

Bibliography: p. 220–221.

1. Collective labor agreements – U. S.
2. Labor contract – U. S.

NL 0346311   NNC

Lieberman, Elias, 1883–
The hand organ man by Elias Lieberman. New York, Saga press, 1930.
116 p. incl. plates. 23cm.
Poems.

I. Title.
Library of Congress   PS3523.I 27H3 1930
——— Copy 2.
Copyright A 23726   [2]   811.5

NL 0346312   DLC NcD

Lieberman, Elias, 1883–   ed.
Magazine essays of today, edited by Elias Lieberman ... New York, Prentice-Hall, inc., 1935.
xv, 488 p. 20cm.
"Suggestions for reading" at end of each selection.

1. American essays. I. Title.

35–6149

Library of Congress   PS688.L5
——— Copy 2.
Copyright A 82751   [3]   814.50822

OCU OC1 MH PPT PP
NL 0346313   DLC PRosC OrP OrU Or WaS IdPI OrCS WaU

Lieberman, Elias, 1883–
Man in the shadows, by Elias Lieberman. New York, Liveright publishing corporation [c1939]
xi, 102 p. 19½cm.
Poems.

I. Title.

39–24483

Library of Congress   PS3523.I 27M3 1939
——— Copy 2.
Copyright A 133343   [2]   811.5

NL 0346314   DLC PSt FMU CU OU

Lieberman, Elias, 1883–
Paved streets, by Elias Lieberman. Boston, The Cornhill company [1917]
xiii p., 1 l., 107, [1] p. 19½cm.
Poems reprinted in part from various periodicals.

I. Title.

18–10299

Library of Congress   PS3523.I 27P3

NL 0346315   DLC FU MB NN OU

PR1175
L7

Lieberman, Elias, 1883–   ed.
Poems for enjoyment. New York, McGraw-Hill [1931]
xxv, 510 p. front. 20cm.

1. English poetry (Collections) 2. American poetry (Collections) I. Title.

NL 0346316   GU WaU ViU InU

Lieberman, Elias, 1883–   ed.
Poems for enjoyment, edited by Elias Lieberman ... New York and London, Harper & brothers, 1931.
xxv, [1], 510 p. front. 20 cm.
"First edition."
"Suggested readings for selected poets": p. 421–460.

1. English poetry (Collections) 2. American poetry (Collections)
I. Title.

PR1175.L46   821.08   31—10193

OC1U
PP NmU OrP Wa CaBVa Or WaS OrMonO WaSp OrSaW OrCS
NL 0346317   DLC NN MB NcC OC1 OC1h OEac PWcS PV PPT

Lieberman, Elias, 1883–   ed.
Poems for enjoyment; edited by Elias Lieberman. New York, London: Harper & Bros., 1932 [cop. 1931] 398 p. 12°.
CONTENTS.—Poetry and prose. The music of poetry: Rhythm. The lyric. Narrative verse. Condensed forms. The sonnet. French verse forms. Light and humorous verse. Free verse. Some great themes of poetry.

1. English poetry. 2. Title.

N. Y. P. L.   August 14, 1936

NL 0346318   NN RPB

808.1
L62po

Lieberman, Elias, 1883–   ed.
Poems for enjoyment. New York, McGraw-Hill [1952]
xxv, 510p. map. 20cm.
"Suggested readings for selected poets": p. 421–460.

1. English poetry (Collections) 2. American poetry (Collections) I. Title.

NL 0346319   IU FTaSU

VOLUME 332

Lieberman, Elias.
Poetry for junior high schools, book one; edited by Elias Lieberman.   New York: Charles Scribner's Sons₍, cop. 1926₎.
198 p.   8°.

1. English poetry. 2. American   poetry. 3. Poetry—Collections and selections.
N. Y. P. L.   February 24, 1927

NL 0346320   NN

Lieberman, Elias.
Poetry for junior high schools, book two; edited by Elias Lieberman.   New York: Charles Scribner's Sons₍, cop. 1926₎.
164 p.   12°.

1. English poetry. 2. American   poetry. 3. Poetry—Collections
and selections.
N. Y. P. L.   February 16, 1927

NL 0346321   NN

Lieberman, Elias, 1883–   *ed.*
Poetry for junior high schools ... edited by Elias Lieberman ... New York, Chicago ₍etc.₎ C. Scribner's sons ₍*1926₎
2 v. 20¹⁄₂ᵐ.

1. American poetry (Collections) 2. English poetry (Collections)
Library of Congress   PS586.L45   26—11161

        ViU CaBVa
NL 0346322   DLC WaT Or WaS KyLx OU OC1h OEac OC1

Lieberman, Elias, 1883–
To my brothers everywhere. ₍Poems. 1st ed.₎ New York, Dutton, 1954.
96 p. 21 cm.

I. Title.

PS3523.I 27T6   811.5   54–10933 ‡

NL 0346323   DLC FTaSU NN ViU OC1 PP OC1Tem MB

Lieberman, Elias, 1888–
Unions before the bar; historic trials showing the evolution of labor rights in the United States. ₍1st ed.₎ New York, Harper ₍1950₎
x, 371 p. 24 cm.
Bibliography: p. 355–362.

1. Labor laws and legislation—U. S.—Cases. 2. Trade-unions—U. S. I. Title.
                                         50–7184

        Or OrPR OrU-L IdU-L IdPI OC1U
        WaU-L PBL NcGU CaBVa CaBYiP OrU PBm OrPS CaBVaU WaWW
        TxU TU PP NBuU-L UU MiU NIC Wa NcD WaS WaT WaSpG
NL 0346324   DLC MB NNC ICU ODW NcU OU OC1 OC1CC ViU

PZ7
.B6687   **Lieberman, Frank Joseph,** 1910–   illus.
Fat
Boutell, Clarence Burley, 1908–
The fat baron, written by Clip Boutell; pictures by Frank Lieberman. Boston, Houghton Mifflin, 1946.

Lieberman, Frank Joseph, 1910–   illus.
₍**Ershov, Petr Pavlovich**₎ 1815–1869.
The little hunchback horse, by Ireene Wicker, illustrated by Frank Lieberman. New York, G. P. Putnam's sons ₍1942₎

Lieberman, Frank Joseph, 1910–   illus.
Rostron, Richard.
The sorcerer's apprentice, by Richard Rostron, illustrated by Frank Lieberman. New York, W. Morrow and company, 1941.

Lieberman, Frank Joseph, 1910–   illus.
Urbahns, Estelle.
The tangled web, by Estelle Urbahns; illustrations by Frank Lieberman. New York, E. P. Dutton & co., inc. ₍1943₎

Lieberman, Frank Joseph, 1910–   illus.
₍**Platt, Samuel C** ₎ 1888–
Where are you? By Sam See ₍*pseud.*₎ illustrated by Frank Lieberman. New York, Simon and Schuster, 1941.

423
L623   **Lieberman, Frank V   1911–**
Aerial spraying and dusting short course, Logan, Utah, February 15-16, 1954.
[Logan? 1954]
3 p.

1. Insecticides. 2. Airplanes in insect control. I. Knowlton, George Franklin, joint author.

NL 0346330   DNAL

Lieberman, George L
Student government movement in American education, 1920–1930 ...
Philadelphia, Pa., 1933.
118 p.

NL 0346331   PPT

3781
S78   **Lieberman, Gerald J.**
L716   Contributions to sampling inspection.
₍Stanford, Calif.₎ 1953.
48 l. tables.
Thesis (Ph.D.) - Dept. of Statistics, Stanford University.
Bibliography: l.47.

1. Sampling (Statistics)

NL 0346332   CSt

M09.67
L716e   **Lieberman, Gerald J**
An evaluation of the 1951–1952 cloud seeding experiment in Santa Clara County.
Stanford, Calif., Stanford University, ₍1953?₎
21 numb. ₍. illus., tables   28cm.

"Bibliography":p.21.

NL 0346333   DAS

Lieberman, Gerald J., joint author.
HA40
.I 6B6   **Bowker, Albert Hosmer,** 1919–
Handbook of industrial statistics ₍by₎ Albert H. Bowker and Gerald J. Lieberman. Englewood Cliffs ₍N. J.₎ Prentice-Hall, 1955.

QA
276.5   **Lieberman, Gerald J**
.L72   Multistage inspection schemes. Stanford, Calif. ₍1951₎
20 ℓ.   28 cm. (Technical report no.4, Applied Mathematics and Statistics Laboratory, Stanford University)
"Prepared under contract N6onr–25126 ₍NR–042–022₎ for Office of Naval Research."
"Preliminary draft for comment."
1.Sampling (Statistics) I.Title.

NL 0346335   MiU

Lieberman, Harry, 1892–   *ed.*
Fourth American tourney at Cedar Point, Ohio, August 8th to 15th, 1920, for the checker championship of America and $1000 in prizes, annotated by America's leading checker experts; Harry Lieberman, editor-in-chief ... Hannibal, Mo., E. H. Greene ₍1921₎
250 p. illus. (incl. ports.) 23¹⁄₂ᵐ.

1. Checkers.

Library of Congress   GV1463.A5 1921   21–2118

NL 0346336   DLC CaOTP OC1

Lieberman, Harry, 1892–
Jordan vs. Banks match games for a purse of $1,000.00 and the restricted world's checker championship, annotated by the principals and arranged for publication by H. Lieberman. ₍Kansas City, Mo., Printed by Burd & Fletcher, ᵗ1914₎
2 p. l. 3–75 p. illus. (incl. ports.) 19ᶜᵐ. $1.00

1. Jordan, Alfred, 1870– 2. Banks, Newell W., 1887– 3. Checkers.
                                         15–1241
Library of Congress   GV1463.L5

NL 0346337   DLC OKentU NN OC1

Lieberman, Harry, 1892–
The third American tourney at Chicago, Illinois, January 11th to 15th, 1915, for the checker championship of America and $500.00 in prizes, annotated by Harry Lieberman and Louis C. Ginsberg, assisted by Newell W. Banks; editorial arrangement by Harry Lieberman; Edinburgh consolation tourney by Louis C. Ginsberg ... Kansas City, Mo., E. H. Greene ᵗ1915₎
358 p. illus. (incl. ports.) 20ᶜᵐ.

1. Checkers. I. Ginsberg, Louis Charles, 1893–   II. Banks, Newell W., 1887–
Library of Congress   GV1463.A5 1915   15–0685

NL 0346338   DLC OC1

Lieberman, Hayyim
        see
Lieberman, Herman, *1884–1963*

Lieberman, Herman
see **Lieberman, Herman.**

                1884 M
DK440   **Lieberman, Herman,** ₍1870–   *defendant.*
L716a   Sprawa brzeska. Przedrukowano w Londynie. ₍London, Drukarnia Polska₎ 1941.
247 p. 24cm.
Hoover   Trial of Herman Lieberman, Wincenty Witos
Library   and other leaders of the opposition accused of conspiracy against the government of Poland held before Sąd Okręgowy, Warsaw, Oct.26, 1931–Jan. 13, 1932.

1. Trials (Political crimes and offenses) - Poland. 2. Poland - Pol. & govt. - 1918–1945. I. Witos, Wincenty,   1874–1945, defendant. II. Poland. Sąd Ok   ręgowy (Warsaw) III. Title.

NL 0346341   CSt-H CtY-L

VOLUME 332

Lieberman, Herman, 1869 or 70–   *defendant.*
Sprawa brzeska, 1930–32. ₍Katowice₎ Wydawca: Śląskie
zakłady graf. i wyd. "Polonia" s. a., 1932.

384 p. plates, ports. 20½ᶜᵐ.

Lieberman, Barlicki, Dubois, Mastek, Pragier, Ciołkosz, Witos, Kiernik, Bagiński, Putek, and Sawicki were accused of having attempted to provoke insurrection against the government and were tried before the District court of Warsaw.

I. Barlicki, Norbert, 1880–   defendant. II. Dubois, Stanisław, 1900 or 01–   defendant. III. Poland. Sąd okręgowy (Warsaw) IV. Title.
43–42552

NL 0346342   DLC

Lieberman, Herman, 1889–1963.
ביכער און שרייבער. פון חיים ליבערמאן. ניױארק.
₍New York₎ 1933.

300 p. 22½ᶜᵐ.

1. Yiddish literature—Hist. & crit.   I. Title.
Title transliterated: Bikher un shreiber.
A 45–4552

New York. Public library
for Library of Congress   ₍2₎

NL 0346343   NN DLC

Lieberman, Herman, 1889–
The Christianity of Sholem Asch, an appraisal from the Jewish viewpoint. ₍From the Yiddish, by Abraham Burstein₎ New York, Philosophical Library ₍1953₎

276 p. 24 cm.

Translation of שלום אש און קריסטענטום (transliterated: Shalom Ash ...)

1. Asch, Shalom, 1880–1957.   I. Title.

PJ5129.A8Z783   *838.99 892.493   53—11659 ‡

        MB ICU NN OCH NNJ PPDrop MoSW MU TU WaS OrPR
NL 0346344   DLC MoU PPWe OU PBa PPT NcD NcC PP ViU

Lieberman, Herman, 1889–
... דיכטער און וועלטען. ₍Berlin, 1923₎

210 p., 1 l. 21½ᶜᵐ.
At head of title: חיים ליבערמאן

1. Yiddish literature—Addresses, essays, lectures. 2. Literature—Addresses, essays, lectures.   I. Title.
Title transliterated: Dichter un welten.
45–46140

Library of Congress   PJ5124.L5
₍2₎

NL 0346345   DLC CBM

Lieberman, Herman, 1889–1963.
Discussion Regarding Rabbi Yehiel Mikhel Epstein. Reprinted from Yiddish Scientific Institute, Annual, vol.VII. 1952, p.296–304.
Pertains to the article by Shlomo Noble on "Rabbi Yehiel Mikhel Epstein..." in Yivo Bleter, vol.35 (1951) in Hebrew and in Yivo Annual VI. in English translation. The original Hebrew version of the present Discussion in Yivo Bleter,36, 1952.
1.Epstein, Yehiel Mikhel. I.Noble, Shlomo, jt.author. Noble, Shlomo: Rabbi Yehiel Epstei...

NL 0346346   NNJ

Lieberman, Herman, 1889–1963.
דר. חיים זשיטלאװסקי און זײנע פאלעמידיקער; נאך א וװארם
װועגן דעם ניוספיקן באנקראם פון א דור. ניד-יארק.
₍New York₎ 1944.

156 p. 22 cm.

Contents.—ד. ת. זשיטלאװסקי—דיכמער און דענקער—דער גרעסטער פארזוכןן אין א נ־יו—דער ארדװאקעט גם גלות—זשיטלאװסקי צװוישן איר און נ־יו...

1. Zhitlowsky, Chaim, 1865–1943.
Title transliterated: Dokter Hayim Zehitlovski.

PJ5129.Z54Z72   64–42188

NL 0346347   DLC OCl

Lieberman, Herman, 1889–
ערנסט טאלער; די טראגעדיע פון א זוכענדען גײסט, פון
חיים ליבערמאן. ניו יארק, פארלאג "פעדער," 1924.
₍New York₎

100 p. 18½ᶜᵐ.

1. Toller, Ernst, 1893–1939.   *Title transliterated:* Ernst Toler.
45–40146

Library of Congress   PT2642.O65Z75

NL 0346348   DLC CBM

Lieberman, Herman, 1889–
...Ernst Toller; la tragedia de un espiritu inquieto. Buenos Aires: Ediciones Iman, 1936. 80p. 18cm. (Cuadernos económicos. no. 23 ₍1936₎)
"Traducción directa del original idisch de Samuel Kaplan."

1. Toller, Ernst, 1893–1939.   I. Kaplan, Samuel, tr.
N. Y. P. L.   July 24, 1939

NL 0346349   NN

FILM **Lieberman, Herman,** 1889–
PT   Ernst Toller: La tragedia de un espíritu
no.42   inquieto. Buenos Aires, Iman, 1936.
           80p. (Cuadernos econ6micos, 23)

           Microfilm (negative). New York, New York Public Library, 1965. 1 reel. 35mm.

           1.Toller, Ernst, 1893–   I.Title.

NL 0346350   CLSU

Lieberman, Herman, 1889–1963.
... די אידישע ערציהונג אין אמעריקע. 2. גענדערטע
אויפל. פון "דאס פראבלעם פון אידישער ערציהונג." ניו
יארק, כ. מייועל, 1916.

58 p. 20ᶜᵐ.
At head of title: ח. ליבערמאן

1. Jews in the U. S.—Education.   I. Title.
Title transliterated: Di idishe erzihung in Amerike.
45–44060

Library of Congress   LC741.L5

NL 0346351   DLC

Lieberman, Herman, 1889–1963.
אידן און אידישקײם אין די שריפטען פון ח. זשיטלאװסקי;
געדאנקען וװעגן א פארבלאנדזשעטן דור. פון חיים ליבערמאן.
ניד-יארק, תש"ה, 1944.

117 p. 22 cm.

1. Zhitlowsky, Chaim, 1865–1943.   I. Title.
Title transliterated: Idn un Idishkayt.

PJ5129.Z54Z73   A 55–2616 rev
New York. Public Libr.
for Library of Congress   ₍r68b2₎†

NL 0346352   DLC NN

Lieberman, Herman, 1889–1963.
אין קאמף פאר אידישער דערציאונג; וװעגן די אידישװעלטלאכע
שולן אין זײער אידישקײם. פון חיים ליבערמאן. ניו יארק.
הױפטם פארקויף אין פארלאג פרדס. תש"א ₍1941₎

116 p. 22 cm.

1. Jews in the U. S.—Education.   I. Title.
Title transliterated: In kamf far idisher dertsiung.

LC741.L52   A 50–7834 rev
New York. Public Libr.
for Library of Congress   ₍r68b2₎†

NL 0346353   NN UU DLC

DS143   **Lieberman, Herman,** 1889–
.L47   אין טאל פון טויט. געדאנקען וװעגן אומער צײט און אידיש
Hebr   שיקואל אין איר, פון חיים ליבערמאן. ניױארק, 1938.

₍New York, 1938₎
36 p. 23 cm.

I. Title.
Title transliterated: In tol fun toit.
A 47–4161

New York. Public library
for Library of Congress

NL 0346354   NN DLC

PN779   **Lieberman, Herman,** 1889–1963
.L5   ליטעראארישע סילועטן, פון חיים ליבערמאן. ניױארק, פאר
לאג "אידיש לעבן," 1927. ₍New York₎

160 p. 22ᶜᵐ.

1. Literature, Modern—20th cent.—Addresses, essays, lectures.
I. Title.   *Title transliterated:* Literarishe siluetn.
44–53506

Library of Congress   PN779.L5

NL 0346355   DLC

Lieberman, Herman, 1889–
... ממעמקים, פון די טיפעניס. ניױארק, אוױסמעעכבן פון
א גרופע, תש"ב. ₍New York, 1942₎

24 p. 22ᶜᵐ.
At head of title: חיים ליבערמאן

I. Title.   *Title transliterated:* Mi-ma'amakim.
45–13907

Library of Congress   PJ5129.L53M5

NL 0346356   DLC MH

Lieberman, Herman, 1889–
נצרותו של שלום אש. תנובה על כתבי הנסיוניים. ערך, צבי
הרכבי ₍תרגם מאידיש ומאנגלית, דוד יוספון₎ תל-אביב. הוצאת
"נצח" ₍Tel-Aviv, 1954₎

240 p. 23 cm.
Translation of שלום אש און קריסטענטום (transliterated: Shalom Ash un Kristentum)

1. Asch, Shalom, 1880–
Title transliterated: Natsruto shel Shalom Ash.

PJ5129.A8Z785   A 55–6731
New York. Public Libr.
for Library of Congress

NL 0346357   NN DLC MH

Lieberman, Herman, 1889–1963
אויב איך וועל עס דיר פארגעסן, ענגלאנד, פון חיים
ליבערמאן. ניו יארק, תרצ"ט. ₍New York, 1939₎

16 p. 23ᶜᵐ.

1. Gt. Brit. Colonial office. Palestine. Statement of policy ... 1939.
I. Title.
Title transliterated: Oib ich well es dir fargesn, England.
45–43845

Library of Congress   DS126.L46

NL 0346358   DLC

- Lieberman, Herman, 1889–1963.
Rabbi Nakhman Bratslaver and the Maskilim of Uman. Reprinted from YIVO Annual of Jewish Social Science, vol.6, 1951, p.287–301; Originally published in the Yivo Bleter, vol.29, 1947.

1.Nahman ben Simhah of Bratslav. 2.Hassidim. 3.Maskilim.

NL 0346359   NNJ

VOLUME 332

.A8Z78
(Hebraic
Sect.)

Lieberman, Herman, 1889–1963

שלום אש און קריסטנטום, אן עטטפער אויף זײנע מיסי
אנערישע שריפטן. ניו־יארק, אום פאב. קא., תש״א.

(New York, 1950)

256 p. 23 cm.

1. Asch, Shalom, 1880–*1957*   *Title transliterated:* Shalom Ash ...

PJ5129.A8Z78   51–46405

NL 0346360   DLC OC1

HX86
.L695
(Hebr)

Lieberman, Herman, 1889–1963

(New York) 1937.

שדים אין מאסקװע

173 p. 22 cm.

1. Communism.   I. Title.
          Title transliterated: Sheydim in Moskve.

HX86.L695   57–57503 ‡

NL 0346361   DLC

DS112
.L63

Lieberman, Herman, 1889–1963

די שטימע פון טאל. זאמלבוך פון בריװ און ארטיקלען פון
רבנים, שריפטשטעלער ... און מענשן פון פאלק װעגן דער
אידישער פראגע אין דער הינטיגער צײט געשריבן אין שײכות
מיט'ן ביכל "אין טאל פון טויט." צוזאמען געשטעלט פון
טויט." צוזאמענגעשטעלט מיט באאמרקונגען פון חיים ליבער־
מאן. ניו יארק, ת״ש.

(New York, 1940)

349 p. 23½ .

"אין טאל פון טויט" has special t.-p. dated תר״צ.
1. Jews—Civilization. 2. Jewish question. 3. Jews—Hist.—Philosophy.   I. Title.   *Title transliterated:* Di shtime fun tol.

Library of Congress   DS112.L63

               45–43866

NL 0346362   DLC

Lieberman, Herman, 1889–

Strangers to glory; an appraisal of the American Council
for Judaism. New York, Rainbow Press, 1955.

125 p. 22 cm.

1. American Council for Judaism.   I. Title.

BM21.L5   296   55–11036 ‡

NL 0346363   DLC OrPR PPDrop OCH NcD NN MB TxU

Lieberman, Herman, 1889–

צען קאפיקעס; אן אמת'ע מעשה מים דרײ אינגעלאך ... ניו
יארק, אום פאב. קא. תשי״ג.

(New York, 1953)

62 p. 22 cm.

I. Title.   *Title transliterated:* Tsen kopikes.

PJ5129.L53T7   53–53207 ‡

NL 0346364   DLC

PJ5129
.L53W4
Hebraic
Sect.

Lieberman, Herman, 1889–1963

װען די װעלט האט געברענט. 1946–1939. ניו יארק, "פאר־
יערמס."

(New York, 1947–

v. 24 cm.

"אין קאפושלען ... זײנען אפגעקליבן געװארן פון דער אפסי״לט אין "מאראװערס" װאס
איז אין די ארק פון דער מלחמה געקומען אנטקין נאמען; די מלחמה.

1. World War, 1939–1945—Addresses, sermons, etc.   I. Title.
       Title transliterated: Wen di welt hot gebrent.

PJ5129.L53W4   47–26455*

NL 0346365   DLC

DS117
.D86
Hebraic
Sect.

Lieberman, Herman, 1889–1963, tr.

Dubnov, Semen Markovich, 1860–

... די אידישע געשיכטע פאר שולע און פאלק איבער־
זעצט פון חיים ליעבערמאן און מיטע ליוושיץ ... ניו־
יארק, מאקס נ. מיזעל (17)–1915.

3 v. illus. (ports.) 21 cm.
Contents.

NL 0346366

PS3529
.N5Z685
(Hebraic
Sect.)

Lieberman, Herman, 1889–1963

יודשין אמיל, אן אמעריקאנער דראמאטורג. פארלאג א.
בידערמאן, New York (1930)

162 p. 23 cm.

Added t. p.: Eugene O'Neill, American dramatist.

1. O'Neill, Eugene Gladstone, 1888–   *Title transliterated:* Yudshin Onil.

PS3529.N5Z685   51–53913

NL 0346367   DLC

Lieberman, Irving.

Audio-visual instruction in library education. New York,
School of Library Service, Columbia University, 1955.

213 l. illus. 28 cm.

1. Audio-visual library service.   I. Title.

Z717.L5   025.177   55–13833 ‡

MtU OrU WaS
OOxM NNC IU TU TxU PPD CaBVa IdPI OrAshS Wa CaBVaU
NL 0346368   DLC CU MB PV IaU AU MoU KEmT OKentU OU

Z
717
L5
cu.
Se.
Lab.

Lieberman, Irving

Audio-visual instruction in library education. New York, School of Library Service,
Columbia University, 1955.

x, 213 l. illus. 27 cm.

This is an authorized facsimile of the
original book, and was prodcued in 1969 by
microfilm-xerography by University Microfilms,
A Xerox Company, Ann Arber, Mich.

Includes bibliographies.

1. Audio-visual library service.
I. Title.

NL 0346369   NBuU

LB1043
.A82
1953

Lieberman, Irving.

Audio-Visual Workshop, *University of Southern California,*
1953.

Proceedings (of the) Audio-Visual Workshop, prior to the
1953 conference of the American Library Association. Prepared by Irving Lieberman. Berkeley, 1953.

NL 0346371   CU

QR82
C6L5

Lieberman, Irving, 1921–

Studies on the nutrition and enzyme systems
of Clostridium kluyveri. (Berkeley, 1952)

vi,218 l. illus.,diagrs.,tables.

Thesis (Ph.D. in Bacteriology) - Univ. of
California, June 1952.

Bibliography: p.215-218.

NL 0346371   CU

Lieberman, Jack.

Fort Benning, Georgia; book of photographs by S/Sgt. Jack
Lieberman. (Fort Benning, 1944)

(61) p. illus. 15½ x 20 cm.

1. U.S. Infantry school, Fort Benning, Ga.

                   45–36419

Library of Congress   U428.1 6L5

           (2)   356.071173

NL 0346372   DLC

Lieberman, Jacob, joint author.

Brundage, Milton B.

Basic assignments in chemistry for parallel use with any
textbook, by Milton B. Brundage and Jacob Lieberman (!) ...
New York, Globe book company (*1928)

Lieberman, Jacob, *writer on botany*
see
Lieberman, Jacob.

3781
S78
L716

Lieberman, Jay Benjamin.

Changing concepts of freedom of the press.
(Stanford, Calif.) 1952.

iv,332 l.

Thesis (Ph.D.) - Dept. of Political Science,
Stanford University.

Bibliography: l.319-332.

1. Liberty   of the press.

NL 0346375   CSt

Lieberman, Joseph, ed.

Best Stage for action plays. [New York?
195–] 1 v. (various pagings) illus. 29 cm.

Contents.—The Salem story, by S. Alexander.—
Untitled, by N. Corwin.—The soldier who became
a great Dane, by J. Shore and R. Lincoln.—Dream
job, by A. Perl.—A wee bit of corruption, by L.
Pine.—All aboard, by B. Bengal.—Talk in
darkness, by M. Wald.—Room for a crib, by L.
Gilbert.—Hiccuping Mr. Higgins, by A. Miller.—
Freedom 1948, by J. Jacobs.—Family crossroads,
by A. Weingarten.—Who are the weavers, by J.
Shore and S.G. Williamson.—Open secret, by R.
Adler, G. Bellak and L.N. Ridenour.

1. Drama, American—Collections. I. Stage for
action. II. Title.   III. Lieberman,
Joseph.

NL 0346376   NN

KF2265
.Z9B74

Lieberman, Joseph Almyk, 1909–   joint author.

Brodsky, David, 1908–

Handbook of interstate motor carrier law; a practical handbook of state and federal requirements affecting interstate
common, contract and private motor carriers, together with
an analyses (!) of the practical application of the Motor carrier
act, 1935, by David Brodsky ... (and) J. Almyk Lieberman ...
New York, N. Y., Milbin publishing co., 1937.

Lieberman, Joshua.

Creative camping; a coeducational experiment in personality development and social living, being the record of six
summers of the national experimental camp of Pioneer youth
of America. By Joshua Lieberman ... Introduction by
Prof. William Heard Kilpatrick. New York, Association
press, 1931.

xvii, 251 p. illus. plates. 19½ cm.

1. Pioneer youth of America, inc. 2. Camping. 3. Education—Experimental methods.   I. Title.

Library of Congress   SK605.P5L5

                   31–15283

—— Copy 2.

Copyright A 38626   (3)   796.54

OO OrP IdU OrCS OrU Or WaTC PV PPT WaU PPC
NL 0346378   DLC CU NSyU NcD TU MB OU OEac OOxM OC1

LIEBERMAN, Joshua.

Educating American Jewish Children-
a New Approach. n.pl., n.publ. n.d.

30p 23cm

1.Education-Jewish. 2.Education-U.S.

NL 0346379   NNJ

VOLUME 332

Lieberman, Joshua.
   Layman's guide to Jewish reading
      see under title

LC
741
L5
Lieberman, Joshua.
   A new approach to the education of American Jewish children. Introduction by Alan M. Stroock. Prepared for the Commission on New Approaches to American Jewish Education. New York, The Jewish Education Committee of New York [194-]
   40p.

   1. Jews--Education. 2. Jews in the U.S. I. Title.

NL 0346381   UU TxU NNU-W N IaU ICU OCH

Lieberman, Joshua, *ed.*
   New trends in group work, edited by Joshua Lieberman. New York, Association press, 1938.
   xii, 229 p. diagr. 21 cm.
   "Published under the auspices of the National association for the study of group work."

   1. Social group work.   I. American Association of group workers. II. Title.
   HV45.L5   374   39—15551
   Library of Congress   [a51n1]

      OO PP PBm OCU Or OrU CaBVaU NcD
NL 0346382   DLC OrP OrSaW OC1W OC1 OU OLak NN PU

Lieberman, Joshua, ed.
   New trends in group work, edited by Joshua Lieberman. New York, Association press, 1939. xii, 229 p. diagr. 21cm.
   "Published under the auspices of the National association for the study of group work."

   1. Group work, Educational and social.   I. American association of group workers.

NL 0346383   NN CU TU

Lieberman, Judith Berlin
      see Berlin-Lieberman, Judith, 1904–

Lieberman, Julius.
   Jakob Wasserman's social, philosophical, and ethical views against a historical background with special consideration of his final trilogy: Der fall Maurizius, Etzel Andergast, and Kerkhovens dritte existenz ... [by] ... [Cincinnati, 1943]
   3 p.l., viii, 175 [i. e. 178] numb. l.
   3 half-titles not included in pagination.
   Thesis (Ph.D.) University of Cincinnati. 1943.
   Typewritten.
   Bibliography; l. 171–175.

NL 0346385   OCU

LIEBERMAN, Leo.
Co-operative research in the development of a guidance program.

   Typewritten. 28 x 21 cm.
   Thesis, Ed.D.- Harvard University, 1941.

NL 0346386   MH

LIEBERMAN, M., ed.
   Tunes and songs of the rabbis; collected and arranged by M. Lieberman. London, 1948. 20 p. 22cm.

   Unacc. melodies.
   Title in Hebrew and English; words in Hebrew or Yiddish, with transliteration.

   1. Hasidism. 2. Synagogue   music. I. Title.
   II. Lieberman, M.

NL 0346387   NN

Lieberman, Max.
   Building construction contracts and mechanics' lien law, by Max Lieberman ... New York, The Court press, 1939.
   1 p. l., v, iv p., 1 l., 159 p. 23½ᵐ.

   1. Building laws — U. S. 2. Building — Contracts and specifications. 3. Mechanics' liens—U. S.   I. Title.
   Library of Congress   TH425.L5   39–13079
   ———— Copy 2.
   Copyright A 126466   [2]   692.4

NL 0346388   DLC GU

Lieberman, Max.
   Gersoniana; a Latin sermon on the Immaculate Conception of the Virgin Mary, ascribed to Jean Gerson. New York, 1951.
   74 l. 28 cm.

   1. Gerson, Joannes, 1363–1429. 2. Immaculate Conception.
   BT620.G43L5   *232.93 232.1   52–22791 ‡

NL 0346389   DLC NNUT

Lieberman, Menachem Mendel, joint author.
   Safah ḥayah
      see under Fischman, Pesach Leib.

Lieberman, Milton Nathaniel, 1905–
   Abstracts and titles; a practical annotated treatise on the law and practice pertaining to abstracts and titles, with forms. 2d ed. Newark, N. J., Soney & Sage Co., 1951.
   xxx, 907 p. 27 cm. (New Jersey practice, v. 13)
   First ed. published under title: New Jersey abstracts and titles.
   To be kept up to date by pocket supplements.

   1. Abstracts of title—New Jersey. 2. Land titles—Registration and transfer—New Jersey. 3. Real property—New Jersey.   (Series)
                  333.34   52–3855

NL 0346391   DLC NNC

Lieberman, Milton Nathaniel, 1905–
   Effective drafting of contracts for the sale of real property, with check list and suggested forms. Newark, N. J., Gann Law Books [1954]
   365 p. 24 cm.

   1. Vendors and purchasers—U. S.—Forms.   I. Title.
                  333.3   54–31462 ‡

   OU PPT-L
NL 0346392   DLC NcU OrU-L WaU-L CaBVaU TxU TU NcD

Lieberman, Milton Nathaniel, 1905–
   New Jersey abstracts and titles; the New Jersey law complete with reference to abstracts and examination of titles, with annotations, by Milton N. Lieberman ... Newark, N. J., Soney & Sage co., 1931.
   xxxi, 759 p. illus. (plans) diagrs. 24 cm.
   References : p. [501]–605.
   —— Supplement 1940 to New Jersey abstracts and titles; the New Jersey law complete with reference to abstracts and examination of titles with thorough annotations. Keyed to

Continued in next column

Continued from preceding column

New Jersey statutes of 1937 to 1939 incl. By Milton N. Lieberman ... Newark, N. J., Soney & Sage co., 1940.
   xxii, 223 p. 23½ cm.
   On cover : Abstracts and titles, New Jersey.
   "Table of cases": p. [167]–183.

   1. Abstracts of title—New Jersey. 2. Title examinations—New Jersey.   I. Title.
                           31—12111

NL 0346394   DLC PPT MH-L

Lieberman, Milton Nathaniel, 1905–
   New York abstracts and titles; the New York law complete with reference to abstracts and examination of titles, with annotations, by Milton N. Lieberman ... Newark, N. J., Soney & Sage co., 1937.
   xxxi, 754 p. illus. (plans) diagrs. 24ᵐ.
   "Table of cases": p. [559]–643.

   1. Abstracts of title—New York (State) 2. Land titles—New York (State) 3. Real property—New York (State) 4. Forms (Law)—New York (State)   I. Title.
   Library of Congress   37–451

NL 0346395   DLC

Lieberman, Morris.
   The use of fiction in Jewish education, by Morris Lieberman ... [Cincinnati] 1934.
   5 p. l., 108 numb. l. 27½ cm. (On cover: Dept. of Jewish religious education. Publication no. 17)
   Reproduced from type-written copy.
   "Thesis submitted in partial fulfillment of the requirements for graduation from the Hebrew union college."
   Published also without thesis note under title: The use of fiction in Jewish religious education.
   "An annotated and classified bibliography of Jewish fiction": p. 30–108.
   1. Jews—Education. 2. Religious education—Jews. 3. Jews in literature—Bibl. 4. Fiction—Bibl.   I. Title.
   LC719.L5   1934   377.96   49–30571

NL 0346396   DLC

Lieberman, Morris.
   The use of fiction in Jewish religious education, by Rabbi Morris Lieberman, containing a classified and annotated bibliography of works of fiction in the English language suitable for religious school use ... Cincinnati, Dept. of Jewish religious education, Hebrew union college, 1935.
   4 p. l., 108 numb. l. 27½ x 21½ cm. (On cover: Dept. of Jewish religious education, Hebrew union college. Publication no. 17)
   Reproduced from type-written copy.
   Issued also as thesis, Hebrew union college, under title: The use of fiction in Jewish education.
   1. Jews—Education. 2. Religious education—Jews. 3. Jews in literature—Bibl. 4. Fiction—Bibl.   I. Title.
   LC719.L5   1935   377.96   49–30570

NL 0346397   DLC OCH PPDrop PGratz NN

Lieberman, Morris, 1919–
   The effect of reduced oxygen levels on respiration, the production of volatiles, and the keeping quality of broccoli (*Brassica oleracea* var. *italica*) [College Park, Md.] 1952.
   79 l. mounted illus. (1 col.) tables. 30 cm.
   Typescript (carbon)
   Thesis—University of Maryland.
   Vita.
   "Literature cited": leaves [76]–79.

   1. Vegetables—Storage. 2. Broccoli.   I. Title.
   SB333.L5   A 54–3837
   Maryland. Univ. Libr.
   for Library of Congress   [3]†

NL 0346398   MdU DLC

FILM
370.1
L621a
Lieberman, Myron, 1919–
   Axiological aspects of selected themes of intellectual discipline. Ann Arbor, University Microfilms, 1953.

   ([University Microfilms, Ann Arbor, Mich.] Publication no.5239)

   Microfilm copy of typescript. Positive.
   Collation of the original: v, 156l.
   Thesis—University of Illinois.
   Vita.
   Bibliography: leaves 152–156.

NL 0346399   IU

VOLUME 332

Lieberman, Nathaniel.
A study of mottos of outstanding contemporary individuals in relation to their biographies. Phila., 1930.
210 p.

NL 0346400   PPT

Lieberman, Norman.
Widening bridge over Big Walnut Creek on route 16 ... by ... Columbus, The Chio state university, 1937.
4 p. 43 [i.e. 44] numb.

NL 0346401   OU

LD
3907
.G7
1972
.L53

also
Film
T8597
Film

Lieberman, Ralph E   1939-
The church of Santa Maria dei Miracoli in Venice.
3v.
Thesis (Ph.D.) - N.Y.U., Graduate School.

1. Dissertations, Academic - N.Y.U. - 1972.
2. Venice. Santa Maria dei Miracoli (Church)
I. Title.

NL 0346402   NNU

Lieberman, Rosalie.
Heaven is so high. [1st ed.] Indianapolis, Bobbs-Merrill [1950]
288 p. 21 cm.

I. Title.

PZ3.L62205He   50-5520

NL 0346403   DLC WaE WaT PP OC1ND

Lieberman, Rosalie.
The man who sold Christmas. [1st ed.] New York, Longmans, Green [1951]
128 p. 20 cm.

I. Title.

PZ3.L62205Man   51-13800 ‡

NL 0346404   DLC Or OrU MiU WU NN

Lieberman, Samuel,
Contact between Rome and China. [New York] 1953.
ix, 337 l. 29cm.

Thesis, Columbia university.
Typescript.
Bibliography: l. 328-337.

NL 0346405   NNC

Lieberman, Mrs. Samuel D.
See
Strode, Muriel.

Lieberman, Saul, 1898-
על חירושלמי. ירושלים. "דרום." תרפ"מ. [Jerusalem, 1929]
84 p. 25 cm.
Added t. p.: On the Yerushalmi.
CONTENTS.—לתקון נוסח חירושלמי.—גובהאות כח"י רומא לסס' סוטה עם־־ פתיחות, חערות וחשואות.

1. Talmud Yerushalmi — Criticism, Textual. 2. Talmud Yerushalmi. Soṭah—Criticism, Textual.
Title transliterated: 'Al ha-Yerushalmi.

BM498.8.L5   57-54251

NL 0346407   DLC CU

EY54
M319
L621d

Lieberman, Saul, 1898-
The discipline in the so-called Dead Sea. Manual of discipline. [Philadelphia, 1952]
199-206 p. 24 cm.

Caption title.
"Reprint from Journal of Biblical literature, volume LXXI, part IV, 1952."
Bibliographical footnotes.

1. Manual of discipline. I. Title.

NL 0346408   CtY-D

Lieberman, Saul, 1898-
Greek in Jewish Palestine; studies in the life and manners of Jewish Palestine in the II-IV centuries C. E., by Saul Lieberman ... New York, The Jewish theological seminary of America, 1942.
ix p., 1 l., 207 p. 23½ cm.

Bibliographical foot-notes.

1. Jews in Palestine. 2. Jews—Soc. life & cust. 3. Talmud. 4. Hellenism. 5. Hebrew language—Foreign words and phrases—Greek. 6. Aramaic language—Foreign words and phrases—Greek. I. Jewish theological seminary of America. II. Title.

DS112.L64   296   42—9927

NL 0346409   DLC OrU TNJ PPWe DDO OCU OU OC1W OCH

Lieberman, Saul, 1898-
Hellenism in Jewish Palestine; studies in the literary transmission, beliefs and manners of Palestine in the I century B. C. E.–IV century C. E. New York, Jewish Theological Seminary of America, 1950.
xiv, 231 p. 24 cm. (Texts and studies of the Jewish Theological Seminary of America, v. 18)

Bibliographical footnotes.

1. Jewish literature—Hist. & crit. 2. Bible. O. T.—Criticism, Textual. 3. Aramaic language—Foreign words and phrases. 4. Jews—Hist.—586 B. c.–70 A. D. 5. Jews—Hist.—70–1789. I. Title. (Series: Jewish Theological Seminary of America. Texts and studies, v. 18)

BM497.L5   296   51-2776

NL 0346410   DLC NN TU DDO MH TxU PPDrop OO CoU NNJ

Lieberman, Saul, 1898-   ed.
Hilkhot ha-Yerushalmi
     see under   Moses ben Maimon, 1135-1204.

EY50
L621l

Lieberman, Saul, 1898-
Light on the cave scrolls from rabbinic sources. New York, 1951.
395-404 p. 25 cm.

Cover title.
"Reprinted from Proceedings of the American Academy for Jewish Research, vol. XX, 1951."
Bibliographical footnotes.

1. Dead Sea scrolls. I. Title.

NL 0346412   CtY-D

---

g
DS
122.9
L5

Lieberman, Saul, 1898-
The martyrs of Caesarea [by S. Lieberman]. [New York, Éditions de l'Institut: H.Grégoire, 1944]
[395]-446 p. 24 x 31 cm.
Caption title.
Photocopy from Annuaire de l'Institut de Philologie et d'Histoire Orientales et Slaves, t.7 (1939-1944)
1.Jews in Caesarea--Persecutions. 2.Jews in Palestine--Hist.--70-638 C.E. I.Title.

NL 0346413   OCH

Lieberman, Saul, 1898-
מדרשי תימן; הרצאה על מדרשי תימן על מהותם וערכם. ירו־שלים. במברנר את וואהרמן. תרנ"ן. [Jerusalem, 1940]
42 p. illus. 25 cm.
Added t. p.: Yemenite Midrashim; a lecture on the Yemenite Midrashim, their character and value.

1. Midrash—Addresses, essays, lectures. I. Title.
Title transliterated: Midreshe Teman.

BM514.L5   57-54331

NL 0346414   DLC UU MH

DS 122.9
.L716

LIEBERMAN, SAUL, 1898-
Palestine in the third and fourth centuries. Philadelphia, The Dropsie College for Hebrew and Cognate Learning, 1946.
329-370+31-54 p.

Reprinted from the Jewish quarterly review, new series, v. 36, no. 4, and v. 37, no. 1

1. Palestine--History. 2. Jews--History--70-1789. I. Title.

NL 0346415   InU DDO CLU

BM700
L5

Lieberman, Saul, 1898-
שקיעין; דברים אחדים על אגדות, מנהגים ומקורות ספרותיים של היהודים שנשתקעו בספרי הקראים והנוצרים (בצרוף מפתח לספרי היהודים חמובאים בספר פנין האמונה של ריימונד מרמיני) ירושלים. במברנר את וואהרמן. תרצ"מ. [Jerusalem, 1939]
96 p.; vi p. 25 cm.
Added t. p.: Shkiin; a few words on some Jewish legends, customs and literary sources found in Karaite and Christian works (including an index of the Jewish books cited in Pugio fidel of Raymund Martini)
1. Jews—Rites and ceremonies. 2. Martini, Raimundo, 13th cent. Pugio fidel. I. Title. *Title transliterated:* Sheki'in.

BM700.L5   55-46177

NL 0346416   DLC CU OU OC1 CtY ICU

Lieberman, Saul, 1898-
Shkiin; a few words on some Jewish legends
     see his   Sheki'in.

Lieberman, Saul, 1898-
The Talmud of Caesarea
     see his   Talmudah shel Kisrin.

Lieberman, Saul, 1898-
[Talmudah shel Kisrin]
תלמודה של קיסרין. ירושלמי מסכת נזיקין. ירושלים. תרצ"א. [Jerusalem, 1931]
viii, 108 p. 24 cm. (מוסף־התרבין, 2)
Added t. p.: The Talmud of Caesarea, Jerushalmi tractate Nezikin.

1. Talmud Yerushalmi. Nezikin. I. Title. II. Title: The Talmud of Caesarea. III. Series: Tarbits. Musaf, 2.

BM506.N63L5   A 53–6602

NL 0346419   DLC OU CU OC1

BM508
.2
.L5
[Hebr]

Lieberman, Saul, 1898-
תוספת ראשונים. פירוש מיוסד על כתבי יד התוספתא וספרי ראשונים ומדרשים בכתבי יד ודפוסים ישנים. ירושלים. במברנר את וואהרמן. תרצ"ז–צ"מ. [Jerusalem, 1937–39]
4 v. facsim. 27 cm.
Added t. p.: Tosefeth rishonim, a commentary based on manuscripts of the Tosefta and works of the rishonim and Midrashim in manuscripts and rare editions.
CONTENTS.—חלק א. זרעים מועד.—חלק ב. נשים נזיקין קדשים.—חלק ב. מקואות־עוקצין.

1. Tosefta—Commentaries. I. Title.
Title transliterated: Tosefet rishonim

BM508.2.L5   57-56238

NL 0346420   DLC CtY ICU

Lieberman, Saul, 1898-   ed.
Tosefta
     see under title

VOLUME 332

Lieberman, Saul, 1898–
(Tosefta ki-feshutah)
תוספתא כפשוטה; באור ארוך לתוספתא. נויארק, סמון מאיר
ליב רבינוביץ ע"י בית המדרש לרבנים שבאמריקה. 715–
1955–
v. 27 cm.
Added t. p.: Tosefta ki-fshuta; a comprehensive commentary on
the Tosefta.
Vol. 8– published by בית המדרש לרבנים שבאמריקה
—— קונטרס תיקונים והשלמות. סדר מועד. נויארק, בית
המדרש לרבנים שבאמריקה. 722 ,2 or 1961.
14 p. 27 cm.
1. Tosefta—Commen-   BM508.2.L48 Suppl
taries. I. Title.
BM508.2.L48   55–12504

NL 0346422   DLC MH-AH IaU NcD CU MH NjPT

BM514 Lieberman, Saul, 1898–
.L7   Yemenite midrashim; a lecture on the Yemenite
midrashim, their character and value ... Jerusalem, Bamberger & Wahrmann, 1940.
42, 2 p. pl.
Added t.-p. in Hebrew: Midrashe Teman.
Text in Hebrew.

1. Midrash.

NL 0346423   ICU NcU

Lieberman, Saul, 1898–
הירושלמי כפשוטו. פירוש מיוסד על כתבי יד של הירושלמי
וספרי רבותינו הראשונים ומדרשים בכתבי יד ודפוסים עתיקים.
חלק ראשון כרך א. שבת עירובין פסחים. ירושלים, הוצאת
"דרום" תרצ"ד, Jerusalem, 1934.
826 p. facsim. 27 cm.
Added t. p.: Hayerushalmi kiphshuto; a commentary based on
manuskripts (sic) of the Yerushalmi.
No more published.
1. Talmud Yerushalmi. Mo'ed—Commentaries. I. Title.
Title transliterated: ha-Yerushalmi ki-peshuto.
A 55–751
New York. Public Libr.
for Library of Congress   [1]

NL 0346424   NN OU

Lieberman, Seymour, 1926–
The relationship between attitudes and roles: a natural
field experiment. Ann Arbor, University Microfilms [1955]
([University Microfilms, Ann Arbor, Mich.] Publication no. 11,311)
Microfilm copy of typescript. Positive.
Collation of the original: viii, 185 l. form, tables.
Thesis—University of Michigan.
Abstracted in Dissertation abstracts, v. 15 (1955) no. 4, p. 686–687.
Bibliography: leaves 181–185.
1. Attitude (Psychology) I. Title.
Microfilm AC-1 no. 11,311   Mic A 55–836

Michigan. Univ. Libr.
for Library of Congress   [1]†

NL 0346425   MiU DLC

LD3907   Lieberman, Solomon Sidney, 1917–
.E3   The relationship of eye-hand dominance
1954   and fantasies in boys.
.L5   132p. tables, forms.
Thesis (Ph.D.) - N.Y.U., School of
Education, 1954.
Bibliography: p.77–81.

NL 0346426   NNU-W

ND553   Lieberman, William Slattery, 1924–
.P5L535   FOR OTHER EDITIONS
Picasso, Pablo, 1881–   SEE MAIN ENTRY
Pablo Picasso: blue and rose periods. Text by William
S. Lieberman. New York, H. N. Abrams in association with
Pocket Books [1954]

FINE ARTS
ND
813
P58   Lieberman, William Slattery, 1924–
L62   Picasso and the ballet, by William S. Lieberman. [New York, 1946]
cover-title, [263]–[308] p. illus., port.
24cm. (Dance index, vol. V, no. 11, 12. Nov.-
Dec., 1946)

Bibliography: p. [308]

NL 0346428   NNC WaS OrP OCIMA NcGU

NE2210
.P5A57
Picasso, Pablo, 1881–
The sculptor's studio: etchings. With an introd. by Wil-
liam S. Lieberman. New York, Museum of Modern Art
[1952]

Lieberman, Zevi
see
Livne, Zvi, 1891–

Liebermann, Aaron Samuel, 1844–1880.
אהרן ליבערמאנס בריוו, מיט אן אריינפיר און דער
קלערונגען פון קלמן מרמר. ניוארק, ידישער וויס
שאפטליכער אינסטיטוט, New York, 1951.
252 p. 24 cm. (ייוא פון אשפאַ־בכעראל)
Added t. p.: Letters of Aaron Lieberman, with an introduction and
notes by Kalman Marmor.
In Yiddish, Hebrew, German, and Russian.
I. Marmor, Kalman, 1879– ed.
Title transliterated: Aron libermans briv.
HX312.L5   52–49502

NL 0346431   DLC

Liebermann, Aaron Samuel, 1844–1880, ed.
ha-Emet
see under title

PJJ
Hebraica
Liebermann, Aaron Samuel, 1844–1880.
HX312 כתבי א. ש. ליברמאן ... תל-אביב, הוצאת "דבר", תרפ"ח.
.L52   [Tel-Aviv, 1928–]
(Hebr.) v. port. 22½ cm.
copy in Edited by Michael Berkowicz.
volume Each section has special t.-p.
desired CONTENTS.—ספר א. ספר האוטפסיות, מכתבים ורשומות.
I. Berkowicz, Michael, 1865–1935, ed.
Title transliterated: Kithve A. Sh. Liberman.
44–35257

NL 0346433   DLC

4ND
759   Liebermann, Adolf von.
Die Gemälde-Galerie des verstorbenen Herrn Adolf von Liebermann, Berlin: Bilder moderner Meister, Aquarel-
le und Handzeichnungen moderner
Meister, Bilder älterer Meister.
Hrsg. von J. M. Heberle, H. Lemperts'
Söhne, Köln, a. Rh. Köln, Druck von
M. Dumont-Schauberg, 1894.
74 p.

NL 0346434   DLC-P4 ICU NN

Liebermann, Adolf von.
Die sammlung alter und moderner kunstsachen, möbel
und ausstattungs-gegenstände aus dem nachlasse des
herrn Adolf von Liebermann, Berlin. Hrsg. von J. M.
Heberle (H. Lempertz'söhne) Köln a. Rh. Köln, Druck
von M. Dumont-Schauberg, 1894.
2 p. l., 122 p. front., illus., 24 pl. 39cm.

1. Art—Private collections. 2. Art objects—Catalogs.
10–23078
Library of Congress   NK550.L5

NL 0346435   DLC MH-FA

LIEBERMANN, Arthur.
Das pronomen und das adverbium des babylonisch-
talmudischen dialektes. Inaug.-diss., Giessen.
Berlin, 1895.
pp.(4),63t.
"Vita", after p.63.

NL 0346436   MH ICRL OCH PU

Liebermann, Arthur.
Das pronomen und das adverbium des babylonisch-
talmudischen dialektes. [6],63,[1]p. Berlin,
Mayer & Müller, 1895.

NL 0346437   OC1 CU OCH DCU-H DSI PPDrop

Liebermann, Arthur.
Der Schulchan aruch. Von dr. A. Liebermann, rabbiner.
2. erweiterte aufl. Berlin, M. Poppelauer, 1912.
40 p. 23½cm.

1. Caro, Joseph, 1488–1575. Shulḥan 'arukh.
21–20894 Revised
Library of Congress   BM550.C35L5 1912

NL 0346438   DLC CU-L TNJ-R MH UU NN OCH PPDrop

Liebermann, Arthur.
Zur juedischen Moral; das Verhalten von Juden gegenüber
Nichtjuden nach dem jüdischen Religionsgesetze, quellenmässig
dargestellt von Dr. A. Liebermann.   Berlin: Philo-Verlag[,
1920]. 132 p. 8°.
Bibliography, p. 129.

1. Jews and Gentiles.   SCHIFF COLLECTION.
N. Y. P. L.   May 19, 1925

NL 0346439   NN UU MH OCH

Libermann, Benno, 1899–
Arthritis deformans. Beitrag zur ihrer Sufrogel-
Behandlung ... Leipzig, 1930.
Inaug.-Diss. - Leipzig,
Lebenslauf.
"Literatur-Verzeichnis": p. 83–86.

NL 0346440   CtY

Liebermann, Bernhard, 1858–
Der zweckbegriff bei Trendelenburg ... Meiningen,
Keyssner, 1889.
168 p. 21½cm.
Inaug.-diss.—Jena.

1. Trendelenburg, Friedrich Adolf, 1802–1872. 2. Teleology. I. Title.
1–16653
Library of Congress   B3158.T3L3

NL 0346441   DLC ICRL NjP PU

VOLUME 332

Liebermann, Bruno Franz Leopold
    see Liebermann, Franz Leopold Bruno,
    1759-1844.

QD319 Liebermann, Carl (Theodor) 1842-
.L71   De allyleno atque nonullis, ...
    Berolini [1865]
    Dissert.

NL 0346443   DLC DNLM

Liebermann (Elias). *Die Geburten bei
engem Becken in den Jahren 1896-1906 (eine
klinisch-statistische Studie). 36 pp. 8°.
Basel. Brin & Cie. 1908.

NL 0346444   DNLM MBCo CtY MiU

Liebermann, Elieser, b. ca. 1790.
אור נוגה, כולל דברי חכמה ומוסר בעמי עמודה ה'.
Dessau, Gedruckt bei C. Schlieder, 1818.
    2 v. in 1. 22 cm.
    A defense of the author's views on the reform of synagogue wor-
ship.

    1. Reform Judaism.   I. Title.   Title transliterated: Or nogah.
BM197.L54   52-48913

NL 0346445   DLC CU CtY CLU

Liebermann (Elka). *Ueber Orchitis und
Epididymitis typhosa. 31 pp. 8°. Zürich,
Gebr. Leemann & Co.. 1911.

NL 0346446   DNLM

Liebermann, Ernst, 1869-
    Allerlei Wetter. 10 Zeichnungen.   Berlin: Fischer und
Franke [1901]. 10 pl. f°. (Teuerdank. Fahrten und
Träume deutscher Maler. Folge 1.)
    Title from cover.

1. Drawings (German).   2. Seasons (The) in art.
N.Y.P.L.   February 27, 1911.

NL 0346447   NN

Liebermann, Ernst.
    Alt-Muenchen. 12 Zeichnungen. Berlin: Fischer u. Franke
[1901]. 12 pl. f°. (Teuerdank. Fahrten und Träume
deutscher Maler. Folge 5.)
    Title from cover.

1. Drawings (German).   2. Munich, in art.
N.Y.P.L.   February 27, 1911.

NL 0346448   NN

LIEBERMANN, Ernst.
    Aus deutscher Märchenwelt; 10 Zeichnungen.
Berlin, Fischer und Franke, [1901].

    4o. 10 plates.
    Cover serves as title-page.
    "Teuerdank. Fahrten und Träume deutscher
Maler. 10.Folge."

NL 0346449   MH

Liebermann, Ernst.
    Aus deutscher Märchenwelt. 10 Zeichnungen.   Berlin:
Fischer und Franke [1910]. 10 pl. f°. (Teuerdank. Fahrten
und Träume deutscher Maler. Folge 10.)
    Title from cover.

1. Drawings (German).   2. Fairy tales in art.
N.Y.P.L.   February 27, 1911.

NL 0346450   NN

Liebermann, Ernst.
    Deutsche landschaft; deutsche charak-
terlandschaften in farbigen bildern.
München [n.d.]
    pt. 1-2 sq. Q.

NL 0346451   RPB

Liebermann, Ernst.
    Die Poesie der Landstrasse. 10 Zeichnungen.   Berlin:
Fischer u. Franke [1902]. 10 pl. f°. (Teuerdank. Fahrten
und Träume deutscher Maler. Folge 18.)
    Title from cover.

1. Drawings (German).   2. Roads in art.
N.Y.P.L.   February 27, 1911.

NL 0346452   NN

Liebermann, Ernst, 1869-   illus.
    ... Der Froschkönig ...
        see under [Grimm, Jakob Ludwig Karl]
    1785-1863.

Liebermann, Ernst, 1869-
    Vier Originalsteinzeichnungen. Düsseldorf: Fischer &
Franke [1904]. 1 l., 4 pl. f°. (Steinzeichnungen deutscher
Maler. Nr. 4.)

1. Lithographs (German).
N.Y.P.L.   July 17, 1911.

NL 0346454   NN

LIEBERMANN, Felix, 1851-1925.
    Die angelsächsische verordnung über die
Dunsaete. [Berlin], n.d.)

NL 0346455   MH

LIEBERMANN, Felix.
    Anselm von Canterbury und Hugo von Lyon.
Hannover, Hahn, 1886.

    pp.iv,48.
    Separate-abdruck aus: Historische aufsätze
dem andenken an Georg Waitz gewidmet. "

NL 0346456   MH

LIEBERMANN, F[elix], 1851-1925.
    Beim frieden keine rücksicht auf opfer und
rache! n.p., [1916].

    Broadside, 17 x 12 in.
    "Aus 'Ethische kultur', oktober 1916."

NL 0346457   MH

Liebermann, Felix, 1851-1925, ed.
    Gt. Brit. *Laws, statutes, etc., 1014-1035 (Canute the Great)*
Consiliatio Cnuti, eine übertragung angelsächsischer gesetze,
aus dem zwölften jahrhundert. Zum ersten male hrsg. von F.
Liebermann. Halle a. S., M. Niemeyer, 1893.

Liebermann, Felix, 1851-1925.
    Drei nordhumbrische Urkunden um 1100.
Hrsg. von F. Liebermann. [Braunschweig,
1903]
    p. [275]-284. 2 plates (1 fold.) 22 cm.
    Caption title.
    Sonderabdruck aus dem Archiv für das
Studium der neueren Sprachen und Literaturen,
Bd. CXI, Hft. 3/4.

NL 0346459   CtY

Liebermann, Felix, 1851-1925.
    Einleitung in den Dialogus de scaccario ... Göttingen,
Druck von E. A. Huth, 1875.
    112 p., 1 l. 21½m.
    Inaug.-diss.—Göttingen.

    1. Fitzneale, Richard, bp. of London, d. 1198. Dialogus de scaccario.
    Library of Congress   HJ1028.F5   7—26714

NL 0346460   DLC CtY OC1 PBm MH NN

Liebermann, Felix, 1851-1925.
    Ex rerum Anglicarum scriptoribus
        see under [Ex rerum Anglicarum script-
oribus]

Liebermann, Felix, 1851-1925, ed.
    Die Gesetze der Angelsachsen
        see under Great Britain. Laws,
statutes, etc. 449-1066.

274.2 Liebermann, Felix, 1851-1925, ed.
L62h   Die heiligen Englands, angelsächsisch
    und lateinisch.   Hannover, Hahn, 1889.
    xix, 23 p. 24 cm.

    1. Gt. Brit.   --Church history.
    I. Title.

NL 0346463   LU NIC ICN MiU NjP MH

Pamph LIEBERMANN, Felix, 1851-1925.
v.448   Kesselfang bei den Westsachsen im sieben-
    ten Jahrhundert. [Berlin, 1896]
    7p 25.5cm. (Akademie der Wissenschaften
    zu Berlin. Sitzungsberichte. Philosophisch-
    historische Classe, 35)

NL 0346464   MH-AH MH-L

Liebermann, Felix, 1851-1925.
    The law of England at the Norman conquest ...
        see under Rightmire, George
Washington, 1868-1952.

[LIEBERMANN, Felix.] 1851-1925.
    Leet jurisdiction in the city of Norwich
during the thirteenth and fourteenth centuries.
Edited by William Hudson, [Review]. [London,
Spottiswoode and Co., 1894?]

    pp.5.
    Without title-page. Caption title.
    "Reprinted from the English Historical Re-
view, October 1894."

NL 0346466   MH

VOLUME 332

LIEBERMANN, Felix.
Matrosenstellung aus landgütern der kirche
London um 1000. n.p.,n.d.

NL 0346467   MH

Liebermann, Felix, 1851–1925.
The national assembly in the Anglo-Saxon period, by F.
Liebermann. Hale a. S., M. Niemeyer, 1913.
vii, 90 p. 23½ cm.

1. Witenagemot. 2. Anglo-Saxons—Pol. & govt. i. Title.

JN513.L5   13–22701

CU-AL
NL 0346468   DLC CtY PBm PHC MiU ICJ NN NjP WaU

LIEBERMANN, Felix.
Neuere literatur zur geschichte Englands im
mittelalter. [Freiburg,i.B.1889–92.]

From the "Berichte und besprechungen" of the
Deutsche zeitschrift für geschichtswissenschaft,
bd.I–VIII.
Imperfect:–lacks bd.I.463–476,VII.EI–E–?

NL 0346469   MH

Liebermann, Felix.
Neuere Literatur zur Geschichte Englands im Mittelalter.
n. t.-p. [Berlin, 1891.] 113–176 p. 8°.
Repr.: Deutsche Zeitschrift für Geschichtswissenschaft.

1. Great Britain.—History: Anglo-   Saxon period.
N. Y. P. L.   December 31, 1912.

NL 0346470   NN

LIEBERMANN, Felix.
Notes on the Textus roffensis. With a preliminary account by A.A.Arnold. London,1898.

Facsimile plates.
"Reprinted from "Archaeological cantiana".

NL 0346471   MH

Liebermann, Felix, 1851–1925.
On the Instituta Cnuti aliorumque regum Anglorum, by
F. Liebermann ...
(In Royal historical society, London. Transactions. London, 1893.
22ᶜᵐ. n. s., v. 7, p. 77–107)

1. Instituta Cnuti aliorumque regum Anglorum. 2. Law, Anglo-Saxon.

A C 36—323

Newberry library
for Library of Congress   [DA20.R9 n. s., vol. 7]
                            [a40c1]   (942.0062)

NL 0346472   ICN CLSU DLC MH MdBP

[LIEBERMANN,Felix.]
Peter's pence and the population of England
about 1164. Reprint. [London,1896?]

NL 0346473   MH

Liebermann, Felix, 1851–1925, ed.

Quadripartitus.
Quadripartitus, ein englisches rechtsbuch von 1114, nachge-
wiesen und, soweit bisher ungedruckt, herausgegeben von F.
Liebermann. Halle a. S., M. Niemeyer, 1892.

LIEBERMANN, Felix.
Raginald von Canterbury. [Hannover,1888.]

pp.(40).
Extract from Neues Archiv xiii,1888,pp.519–
556.

NL 0346475   MH

Liebermann, Felix, 1851–

Pauli, Elisabeth.
Reinhold Pauli. Lebenserinnerungen nach briefen und
tagebüchern zusammengestellt von Elisabeth Pauli. (Als
manuscript gedruckt für verwandte und freunde.) Halle
a. S., E. Karras, 1895.

Liebermann, Felix, 1851–
Shakespeares Anschauung von Staat, Gesellschaft und Kirche
in "Heinrich VIII," von Felix Liebermann. (In: Beitraege zur
Literatur- und Theatergeschichte. Ludwig Geiger zum 70. Geburtstage, 5. Juni 1918, als Festgabe dargebracht. Berlin, 1918.
8°. p. 13–41.)

226700A. 1. Shakespeare, William—   Single plays: Henry VIII.
N. Y. P. L.   March 24, 1926

NL 0346477   NN

Liebermann, Felix, 1851–1925, ed.
Gt. Brit. Sovereigns, etc., 1100–1135 (Henry I)
The text of Henry I.'s coronation charter. By F. Lieber-
mann ...
(In Royal historical society, London. Transactions. London, 1894.
22ᶜᵐ. n. s., v. 8, p. [21]–48)

Liebermann, Felix, 1851–
Über das englische rechtsbuch Leges Henrici; von
F. Liebermann. Halle a. S., M. Niemeyer, 1901.
vi, 59, [1] p. 23½ᶜᵐ.

1. Leges Henrici I.

                                        2–16492

NL 0346479   DLC CLU NIC InU NcD CtY NjP PBm

LIEBERMANN,Felix.
Über den quadripartitus,ein englisches rechtsbuch von 1114. Berlin,1891.

NL 0346480   MH-L

Liebermann, Felix, 1851–
Über die Leges Anglorum saeculo XIII. ineunte Lon-
doniis collectae. Von F. Liebermann. Halle a. S., M.
Niemeyer, 1894.
viii, 105, [1] p. 23ᶜᵐ.

                                        6–24542

NL 0346481   DLC NIC InU CtY PU-L OU MB NjP WaU-L

Liebermann, Felix, 1851–1925.
Über die Leges Edwardi Confessoris, von F. Liebermann.
Halle a. S., M. Niemeyer, 1896.
vii, 139, [1] p. 23½ᶜᵐ.

1. Law, Anglo-Saxon. 2. Gt. Brit. Laws, statutes, etc., 1042–1066
(Edward the Confessor) i. Title: Leges Edwardi Confessoris.

                                        6–24545

NL 0346482   DLC InU CU CtY OU OClW PBm NjP IaU

[LIEBERMANN,Felix.] 1851–1925
Über die Leis Willelme. (sonderabdruck).
[Braunschweig.] n.d.

NL 0346483   MH

---

ar W   Liebermann, Felix, 1851–1925.
8815   Ueber ostenglische Geschichtsquellen des
            12., 13., 14. Jahrhunderts, besonders den
            falschen Ingulf. [Frankfurt am Main, 1892]
            [225]–267 p. 23cm.

            Detached from Neues Archiv der Gesellschaft
            für ältere Deutsche Geschichtskunde, Bd. 18,
            Heft 1.

NL 0346484   NIC MH

Liebermann, Felix, 1851–
Über Pseudo-Cnuts Constitutiones de foresta. Von
F. Liebermann. Halle a. S., M. Niemeyer, 1894.
iv, 55, [1] p. 23ᶜᵐ.
Text: p. 49–55.

1. Constitutiones Canuti regis de foresta.

                                        6—24544

NL 0346485   DLC NIC CtY OClW PBm

Liebermann, Felix, 1851–1925, ed.
Ungedruckte anglo-normannische geschichtsquellen, hrsg.
von F. Liebermann. Strassburg, K. J. Trübner; [etc., etc.]
1879.
vi p., 1 l., 359, [1] p. 24ᶜᵐ.

1. Gt. Brit.—Hist.—Norman period, 1066–1154—Sources.

                                        1–G–796

Library of Congress   DA190.L71

        IU MH MB NjP PHC PU OCl
NL 0346486   DLC OrU CaBVaU ScU TU NcU IaU NN CtY

LIEBERMANN,Felix, 1851–1925.
Wulfstan und Cnut. Braunschweig,[n.d.]

NL 0346487   MH

---

47   Liebermann, Franz Leopold Bruno, 1759–1844.
L716   Institutiones theologicae. Moguntiae. In Seminario Episcopali,
in   1819–27.
1819   4 v. in 5.
Law
Library Vol. 3–4 published by Sim. Muller.
            Contents. - t. 1. Prolegomena in universam theologiam et
         demonstrationem religionis christianae. - t. 2. Demonstrationem
         catholicam. - t. 3–4. Theologiae specialis.

            1. Theology. 2. Christianity. 3. Catholic Church. I. Title.

NL 0346488   CU

                                        Bruno
Liebermann.   Franz Leopold, 1759–1844.
        Institutiones theologicae...ed. 2 emendata.
Moguntiae, Sim. Müller, 1827.

        4v. 21 cm.
        Vol. 1: Prologomena in universam theologiam
et demonstrationem Religionis Christianae.

        1. Dogmatic theology - Textbooks - 19th century.
        2. Theology - Introductions.

NL 0346489   PLatS

VOLUME 332

BT75
L5
1830

Liebermann, Franz Leopold Bruno, 1759-1844.
 Institutiones theologicae. Editio tertia emendata. Brixiae,
S. Barnabae, 1830-31.
 5 v.

 1. Theology, Doctrinal. 2. Christianity. 3. Catholic Church -
Doctrinal and controversial works.

NL   0346490   CU DCU

Liebermann, Franz Leopold Bruno, 1759-1844.
 Institutiones theologicae. Ed. 4 emendata.
Lovanii, Vanlinthout et Vandenzande, 1832-33.
 5 v. port.(front.,v.1) 20cm.

 1. Theology, doctrinal - 19th century.

NL   0346491   KAS InStme

Liebermann, Franz Leopold Bruno, 1759-1844.
 Institutiones theologicae. E. 6. emendatis-
sima. Moguntiae, Sumptibus Kirchhemi, Schotti
& Thielmanni, 1844.
 5v. port.(front.,v.1) 22cm.

NL   0346492   KAS

Liebermann,   Franz Leopold Bruno, 1759-1844.
 Institutiones theologicae. Ed. 7. emendatis-
sima. Moguntiae, sumptibus Kirchhemii et
Schotti, 1855.
 2 v. front.(v.1, port.) 22 cm.

NL   0346493   PLatS

Liebermann, Leop. Franz Bruno.
 Institiones theologicae. Moguntiae,
Kirchheimii, 1857.
 2 v.

NL   0346494   OCX

Liebermann,   Franz Leopold, 1759-1844.
 Institutiones theologicae ... ed. 8 emednatis-
sima. Moguntiae, Franciscus Kirchheim, 1857-1858.

 2 v. front. (port.) 24 cm.

 1. Theology - Introductions. 2. Dogmatic theology -
Textbooks - 19th century.

NL   0346495   PLatS KAS

Liebermann, Franz Leopold Bruno.
 Institutiones Theologicae.
Moguntiae, 1857-1861.
 2v.

NL   0346496   OClStM

Liebermann,   Franz Leopold Bruno, 1759-1844.
 Institutiones theologicae... ed. 10 cum
succincta vita auctoris. Moguntiae, Franciscus
Kirchheim, 1870.

 2 v. in 1, front. (port.) 23 cm.
 Contents; vol. 1: Prologomena necnon theologi-
am generalem; vol. 2: Theol. specialis. Cum appendice de Immaculata Conceptione B. Virginis Mariae.

 1. Theology - Introductions. 2. Dogmatic theology -
Textbooks - 19th century.

NL   0346497   PLatS PPWe DCU-H

BV4254
O4L5

Liebermann, Franz Leopold Bruno, 1759-1844.
 Predigten; hrsg. von Freunden und Verehrern
des Verewigten. Mainz, Kirchheim und Schott,
1851-53.
 5 v. in 1. 24 cm.

 1. Sermons, German. 2. Catholic Church--Ser-
mons. I. Title.

NL   0346498   IaDuU-S

Liebermann,   Franz Leopold, 1759-
1844. Schisma Graecorum; De Judaismo; De Mahu-
metismo; De Gentilismo. 11 pp. (Migne, J. P., Theol.
cur. compl. v. 6, p. 117f.)

NL   0346499   MdBP

LIEBERMANN Fritz VON.
 Über einen fall von gefässcheidensarcom bei
einem 1 1/2 jährigen kinde. Berl.,[1891.]

NL   0346500   MBCo DNLM

Liebermann, Hans: Über Luxationen des Radiusköpfchens, insbes.
in Verbind. m. Frakturen u. a. Deformitäten der Ulna. [Maschi-
nenschrift.] 19 S. m. Abb. 4°. — Auszug: Breslau 1924: 'Merkur'.
2 Bl. 8°
Breslau, Med. Diss. v. 15. Dez. 1924 [1925]   [U 25.960]

NL   0346501   ICRL

Liebermann, Hans.
 Über Succinylobernsteinsäureester und ihre Reaktionen
gegen Ammoniak und primäre Amine. Berlin, 1913.

 Habilitationsschrift - Berlin.

NL   0346502   MH-C

Liebermann, Hans, 1883-   : Die neueren Fortschritte
auf dem Gebiete der Beckenmessung. Freiburg i. B.:
Spéyer & Kaerner 1910. 54 S. 8°
Freiburg i. B., Med. Diss. v. 1911, Ref. Krönig
[Geb. 12. Jan. 83 Hamburg; Wohnort: Freiburg i. B.; Staatsangeh.: Ham-
burg; Vorbildung: Realgymn. d. Johanneums Hamburg Reife O. 03; Studium:
Heidelberg 2, Jena 2, Berlin 3, Greifswald 2, Freiburg i. B. 1, Berlin 1,
Freiburg i. B. 1 S.; Coll. 16. Dez. 10; Approb. 1. Okt. 11.]   [U 12.1157

NL   0346503   ICRL DNLM

Liebermann (Hans Heinrich) [1876-   ].
 Untersuchungen über den Farbstoff der Coche-
nille. 50 pp. 8°. Berlin, G. Schade, 1899.

NL   0346504   DNLM PU DLC

Liebermann, Isaac
  see Liebermann, Isaac.

D525
L716

Liebermann, Jakab.
 Lemberg visszavétele. Egyházi beszéd. A 77.
gyalogezred parancsnoksága által junius hó
29-ére elrendelt istentiszteleten a Leván
állomásozó galiciai izr. katonáknak elmon-
dotta Liebermann Jakab ... Léva, Hermes-
nyomda, 1915.

 14 p. 16ᵐ.

 1.European war, 1914-1918 - Addresses,
sermons, etc. I.Title.

NL   0346506   CSt-H CSt

Liebermann, Johanna, 1903-
 ... Erfahrungen mit der amerikanischen
Wurzelbehandlungsmethode ...   Trieste
[1926]
 23 cm.
 Inaug.-Diss. - Leipzig.
 Lebenslauf.
 Literaturverzeichnis: p. 30-31.

NL   0346507   CtY ICRL

Liebermann, Johannes Franz, 1871-   : Ueber neuere Me-
thoden der Empyem-Behandlung. Leipzig 1911: Lehmann.
39 S. 8°
Leipzig, Med. Diss. v. 25. Okt. 1911, Ref. v. Strümpell
[Geb. 16. Sept. 71 Filehne; Wohnort: Magdeburg; Staatsangeh.: Preußen;
Vorbildung: Päd. Züllichau Reife O. 92; Studium: Greifswald 6, Halle 5,
Breslau 2 S.; Coll. 25. Okt. 11; Approb. 20. Jan. 02.]   [U 12.3101

NL   0346508   ICRL CtY

SL5
+B86e
1(5

Liebermann, José, 1897-
 Los acridios de la zona subandina de Neuquen,
Rio Negro y Chubut (Orthop., Acrid) Buenos Aires,
Coni,1949.
 128-160p. illus. 28cm. (Buenos Aires. Insti-
tuto Nacional de Investigación de las Ciencias
Naturales. Revista; ciencias zoológicas, t.1,
no.5)
 Bibliography, p.160.

NL   0346509   CtY

429
L62

Liebermann, José.
 ...Los agrídios [!] sedentários y su relacion
con la produccion de forajes, por el dr. José
Liebermann... [Buenos Aires?] Tip. Gundlach,
1940.
 p. [365]-371. 27cm.

 At head of title: II Congresso Rio Grandese de
agronomia.
 Running title: Anais do II Congresso Rio
Grandense de agronomia.
 1. Locusts.

NL   0346510   DNAL

QH7
A6
no.12

Liebermann, José.
 Bioecologia y sistematica del grillo argen-
tino. Buenos Aires, 1955.
 [147]-156 p. illus. 27 cm. (Argentine
Republic. Administracion General de Parques
Nacionales. Publicación técnica no. 12)
 Cover title.
 "De Natura, tomo 1, ho. 2, (1955)."
 Bibliography; p. 153.

 1. Crickets.   I. Title. (Series)

NL   0346511   DI

QL
508
A2
L72

Liebermann, José,1897-
 Catálogo sistemático y biogeográfico de
acridoideos argentinos; trabajo efectuado en el
Instituto de Investigaciones sobre la Langosta.
Buenos Aires [1939?]
 14-118 p. 27 cm
 Pages also numbered 126-230.
 "Revista de la Sociedad Entomológica Argentina,
tomo X,no.2,1939,págs.125 a 230."
 Bibliography: p.118 (230)
 1.Orthoptera--   Argentine Republic.

NL   0346512   MiU

VOLUME 332

G595.727
L621c

Liebermann, José, 1897–
... Contribución a la zoogeografía, taxonomía y ecología de los Acridoideos de Entre Ríos, con datos obtenidos durante el viaje realizado en enero y febrero de 1940 a través de la provincia, bajo los auspicios del Instituto de investigaciones sobre la langosta de la Dirección de sanidad vegetal del Ministerio de agricultura de la nación y del gobierno de la provincia, por el dr. José Liebermann ... Paraná, 1941.
39p., 1l. II pl., maps. 27cm.

At head of title: Provincia de Entre Ríos.
Ministerio de hacienda, justicia e instrucción pública.
"Bibliografía": 1 leaf at end.

1. Acrididae. I. Argentine republic. Instituto de investigaciones sobre la langosta. II. Entre Ríos, Argentine republic. Ministerio de hacienda, justicia e instrucción.

NL 0346514   TxU NjP NN IaAS NNBG NIC

PQ 7797
.L498 E75

LIEBERMANN, JOSÉ, 1897–
La esfinge torturante; novela. Buenos Aires, Tor, 1924.
132 p.

NL 0346515   InU

G570.92
M814l

LIEBERMANN, JOSÉ, 1897–
Francisco P. Moreno, precursor argentino [conferencia pronunciada en la Sociedad Científica Argentina el 11 de setiembre de 1945. Buenos Aires] 1948.
35p. illus., port. 24cm.
Cover title.
"Edición especial de la Administración General de Parques Nacionales y Turismo."
"De los 'Anales de la Sociedad Científica Argentina', CXL (1945) 396-427."
I. Moreno, Francisco Josué Pascasio, 1852-1919. I. Argentine Republic. Administración General de Parques Nacionales y Turismo.

NL 0346516   TxU

Chi
QL
Pam

Liebermann, José, 1897–
... Generos y especies de nuevos acridoideos chilenos ... Buenos Aires, 1943.
cover-title, p. 400-410. plate. 27 cm.
"Revista de la Sociedad entomológica argentina. Tomo XI - N°. 5, 1943..."

NL 0346517   DPU

Liebermann, José, 1897–
... Monografía de las *Tinamiformes* argentinas y el problema de su domesticación; con siete mapas zoogeográficos y una lámina. Prólogo del dr. Roberto Dabbene. Buenos Aires, Edición del autor, 1936.
99, [14] p. incl. front., maps. 27ᶜᵐ.
"Bibliografía general de *Tinamiformes*": p. [100]-[102]
"Bibliografía del dr. José Liebermann": p. [108]-[113]

1. Tinamiformes. 2. Birds—Argentine republic.
38-32458

Library of Congress   QL696.T4L52
[2]   598.61

NL 0346518   DLC DSI DPU

591.982
L716p

Liebermann, José, 1897–
Problemas del campo. Buenos Aires, Editorial Bell [1946]
270 p. illus. 20 cm.

At head of title: Biblioteca de Pampa Argentina, revista mensual de agricultura, ganadería e interés general al servicio del país.

1. Zoology—Argentine Republic. 2. Zoology—Argentine Republic—Ecology. 3. Zoological specimens—Collection and preservation. I. Title.

NL 0346519   ICarbS DPU DNAL NjP

Liebermann, José, 1897–
Revisión bibliográfica sobre la generación estival de *Schistocerca cancellata* (Serville), la langosta migradora de América del Sur. Buenos Aires, 1948.
13 p. 23 cm.

At head of title: República Argentina. Ministerio de Agricultura de la Nación. Dirección General de Laboratorios e Investigaciones. Instituto de Sanidad Vegetal.
Bibliography : p. 13.

1. Schistocerca paranensis.

SB945.L7L45   57-23937

NL 0346520   DLC CU NIC

QD341
.A2L4

Liebermann, Josef.
Ueber die einwirkung von chlor auf para-oxybenzoesaeure.
Koenigsberg, 1904.
37p.
Inaug. diss. Koenigsberg.

NL 0346521   DNLM DLC MH-C CtY

DD491
S53L716

Liebermann, Kurt, 1902–
Die deutschen minderheitsschulen in Polnisch-Oberschlesien auf grund des deutsch-polnischen abkommens vom 15.mai 1922... Würzburg, Werkbund, 1928.
68 p., 1 l. 23cm.
Inaug.-diss. – Würzburg.
Lebenslauf.
"Literatur": p.[7-8]

1. Schools – Silesia. 2.Minorities. 3.Germany. Treaties, etc. 1919-1925(Ebert). La convention germano-   polonaise.

NL 0346522   CSt-H MH-Ed ICRL CtY

WA
25
L716a
1877

Liebermann, Leo, 1852-1926
Anleitung zu chemischen Untersuchungen auf dem Gebiete der Medicinalpolizei, Hygiene und forensischen Praxis für Ärzte, Medicinalbeamte und Physikats-Candidaten. Stuttgart, Enke, 1877.
xii, 274 p. illus.

Later ed. has title: Die chemische Praxis auf den Gebiete der Gesundheitspflege und gerichtlichen Medicin für Ärzte, Medicinalbeamte und Physikatscandidaten, sowie zum

Gebrauche in Laboratorien.
Bibliographical footnotes.

NL 0346524   DNLM NIC

Liebermann, Leo von, 1852-1926.
A blaskovics-féle tarsoplastika technikájához. Budapest, Pápai, 1919.
6 p. illus.

"Az Orvosi hetilap ... 1919. szemészet 1. szám."

1. Eyelids - Surgery.

NL 0346525   NNC

Liebermann, Leó von, 1852-1926.
Chemia; tankönyv egyetemi és főiskolai hallgatók számára. Irták Liebermann Leó és Bugarszky István. Budapest, Franklin-Társulat, 1913.
xviii, 856 p. diagrs.
1. Chemistry. I. Bugarszky, István jt. au.

NL 0346526   NNC

QD75
L5
1883
Biochem.
Library

Liebermann, Leo von, 1852-1926
Die chemische Praxis auf dem Gebiete der Gesundheitspflege und gerichtlichen Medicin für Ärzte, Medicinalbeamte und Physikatscandidaten, sowie zum Gebrauche in Laboratorien.
2., gänzlich umgearb. Aufl. Stuttgart, F. Enke, 1883.
xii, 291 p. illus.

"Zweite Auflage der 'Anleitung zu chemischen Untersuchungen auf dem Gebiete der Medicinalpolizei, Hygiene und forensischen Praxis.'"

1. Chemistry, Analytic - Laboratory manuals. 2. Chemistry, Forensic. 3. Chemistry, Medicinal and pharmaceutical.

NL 0346527   CU IU NRU MH IU DNLM

Liebermann von   Leo, 1852–
Gibt es in den höheren Lehranstalten eine Überbürdung? (In: Internat. Congress on School Hygiene, 4. Buffalo, 1913. Transac. Buffalo, 1914. 8°. v. 3, p. 382-383.)

1. Schools.—Overpressure.
N. Y. P. L.   June 25, 1917.

NL 0346528   NN

Liebermann, Leo von
Grundzüge der Chemie des Menschen für Ärzte und Studierende. Stuttgart, F. Enke, 1880.
238p.

NL 0346529   ICRL ICJ CtY-M

Liebermann, Leo, von, 1852-1926.
A szem enucleatiójáról kozmetikus szempontból s az azt helyettesítő mütétekről. Budapest, Pápai, 1918.
8 p.

"A Budapesti orvosi ujság ... 1918, 37. szám."

1. Eye - Surgery.

NL 0346530   NNC

QD121
.L5

Liebermann, Leo von
Tabellen zur reduction der gasvolumina auf 0 grad und 760, oder 1000 millimeter quecksilberdruck, zum gebrauche bei gasanalysen in chemischen und chemisch-technischen laboratorien. Stuttgart, Enke, 1882.
15l. tables. 26 cm.

1. Gases—Analysis.

NL 0346531   TU DP

LIEBERMANN, Leo, von, 1852-1926.
Untersuchungen über das chlorophyll, den blumenfarbstoff und deren beziehungen zum blutfarbstoff. [Wien, 1876].

pp.(20).
"Aus dem LXXII bde. der Sitzb.der K.Akad.der wissensch. II.abth. Oct.-heft.jahrg.1875".

NL 0346532   MH

Liebermann, Leonard Norman, 1915–
Reflection of sound from coastal sea bottoms. [n.p., n.d.]
p. 305-309. diagrs., tables. 25 cm.
(Woods Hole, Mass. Oceanographic Institution. Collected reprints, 1948. Contribution no.433)
"Reprinted from the Journal of the Acoustical Society of America, vol. 20, no. 3, 305-309, May, 1948."

NL 0346533   DI

VOLUME 332

Liebermann, Leonard Norman, 1915–
    Reflection of underwater sound from the sea surface. [n.p., n.d.]
    p. 498–503. diagrs., tables. 25 cm.
(Woods Hole, Mass. Oceanographic Institution. Collected reprints, 1948. Contribution no. 455)
    "Reprinted from the Journal of the Acoustical Society of America, vol. 20, no. 4, 498–503, July, 1948."

NL 0346534   DI

Liebermann, Leonard Norman, 1915–
    ... A rotational analysis of some CS_2 bands in the near ultraviolet system ... by L. N. Liebermann ... [Lancaster, Pa., Lancaster press, inc., 1941]
    1 p. l., [498–505 p. incl. tables, diagrs. 26½ x 20ᶜᵐ.
    Thesis (PH. D.)—University of Chicago, 1941.
    "Reprinted from the Physical review, vol. 60, October 1, 1941."
    Bibliographical foot-notes.

    1. Spectrum, Ultra-violet. 2. Carbon disulphide.

Chicago. Univ. Library   A 42–2974
for Library of Congress   QC437.L5
          [2,†

NL 0346535   ICU MH DLC

Liebermann, Leopold Bruno
    see   Liebermann, Franz Leopold Bruno, 1759–1844.

Liebermann, Lessia.
    Selbstmord in der Schweiz waehrend der jahre 1900–1904.
    Inaug. Diss. Freiburg, 1909
    Bibl.

NL 0346537   ICRL DNLM

Liebermann, Matvei.
    Im Namen der Sowjets; aus Moskauer Gerichtsakten, [by] Matwej Liebermann; autorisierte Übersetzung aus dem russischen Manuskript von Rudolf Selke. Berlin: Malik-Verlag[, cop. 1930]. 303 p. 12°.
    Contents: Das Duell im Njeskutschni-Park. Eine Dirne und ein Musiker. Die Schuhputzer von Moskau. Ein Mäzen von Heute. Der Mord an Galina Mrawina. Gefühle von Gestern. Die zerbrochene Glocke.

    1. Title. 2. Trials.
N. Y. P. L.   February 24, 1932

NL 0346538   NN NcD MH

Liebermann, Max, 1847–1935.
    ... A B C. Berlin, K. W. Mecklenburg [1908]
    45 l. incl. front., plates. 19 x 15¼ᶜᵐ.
    Cover-title: Ein A B C in bildern von Max Liebermann, mit begleitenden worten von Richard Graul.

    1. Alphabets.   I. Graul, Richard, 1862–   II. Title.
                        13–15324

Library of Congress   NC1145.L3

NL 0346539   DLC NN

Liebermann, Max, 1847–1935.

Menzel, Adolph Friedrich Erdmann von, 1815–1905.
    ... Adolph Menzel; fünfzig zeichnungen, pastelle und aquarelle aus dem besitz der Nationalgalerie; mit einer einleitung von Max Liebermann, und einem erläuternden verzeichnis von G. J. Kern. Berlin, J. Bard, 1921.

Liebermann, Max, 1847–1935.   על הדמיון בציור. [מתורגמים בידי מ. נרקיס ומעומרים בשרובמי האמן ירושלים [מוסד ביאליק] תש"ח.
    [Jerusalem, 1944/45]
    79 p. illus., port. 17 cm.   (["דברי אמנים", א])

    1. Painting.   I. Title.   (Series: Divre omanim, 1)
            Title transliterated: 'Al ha-dimyon ba-tsiyur.

ND1140.L516   A 52–268
New York. Public Libr.
for Library of Congress   [a58r52c]†

NL 0346541   NN DLC

Liebermann, Max, 1847–1935.
    Ausstellung Max Liebermann im Zürcher Kunsthaus ...
         see under   Zürich. Kunsthaus.

Liebermann, Max, 1847–1935.
    Ausstellung zum 70. Geburtstage des Künstlers
    see
    Akademie der Künste, Berlin.
    Max Liebermann. Ausstellung zum 70. Geburtstage
...

741.9
L716b
    Liebermann, Max, 1847–1935.
    Bilder ohne Worte; 17 Holzschnitt-Zeichnungen. Mit einer Einführung von Willy Kurth. Geschnitten von Reinhold Hoberg. Berlin-Zehlendorf, F. Heyder, 1922.
    24p. illus., port. 24cm.

    I. Kurth, Willi, 1881–   II. Title.

NL 0346544   IEN OCH

N8375
.L5A3
    Liebermann, Max, 1847–1935.

    Lichtwark, Alfred, 1852–1914.
    Briefe an Max Liebermann. Im Auftrage der Lichtwark-Stiftung hrsg. von Carl Schellenberg. Hamburg, J. Trautmann, 1947.

Liebermann, Max, 1847–1935, *illus*
    Das Buch Ruth... Berlin, 1924
        see under   Bible. O. T. Ruth.
    German. 1924.

Art
Library
J18
D33
899L
    Liebermann, Max, 1847–1935.
    Degas, von Max Liebermann. Berlin, B. u. P. Cassirer, 1899.
    23 p. illus. 25 cm.
    "Sonderdruck aus dem 'Pan' mit vermehrten Illustrationen."

    1. Degas, Hilaire Germain Edgar, 1834–1917.

NL 0346547   CtY MH-FA

Liebermann, Max, 1847–1935.
    Degas, von Max Liebermann; mit fünf tafeln und zwei abbildungen im text. 3. aufl. Berlin, B. Cassirer, 1902.
    23, [1] p. incl. illus., 5 pl. 25ᶜᵐ.

    1. Degas, Hilaire Germain Edgar, 1834–1917.   3–18547 Revised

Library of Congress   ND553.D3L7

NL 0346548   DLC MB

L759.4
D317Z/1.4 Liebermann, Max, 1847–1935.
    Degas. 4. Aufl. Berlin, B. Cassirer, 1909.
    28p. 13 plates. 24cm.

    1. Degas, Hilaire Germain Edgar, 1834–1917.

NL 0346549   IEN

Liebermann, Max, 1847–1935.
    Degas, von Max Liebermann ... 5. aufl. Berlin, Cassirer, 1912.
    28, [1] p. incl. illus., plates. 23½ᶜᵐ.

    1. Degas, Hilaire Germain Edgar, 1834–1917.

NL 0346550   NNC ViFreM

Liebermann, Max, 1847–1935.
    Degas. 6.Aufl. Berlin, Cassirer, 1917.
    28 p. plates, illus.

NL 0346551   MH

Liebermann, Max, 1847–1935.
    Degas ... ... Siebente Auflage. Berlin, Bruno Cassirer, 1918.
    29 p.

NL 0346552   OC1MA MH

Liebermann, Max, 1847–1935.
    Degas. Mit 13 Abbildungen. [8. Aufl.] Berlin, B. Cassirer, 1922.
    31 p. illus. 24 cm.

    1. Degas, Hilaire Germain Edgar, 1834–1917.

ND553.D3L7 1922   49–58234*

NL 0346553   DLC NjP OC1 NN

Liebermann, Max, 1847–
    Max Liebermann: Gedanken und Bilder, ausgewählt und eingeleitet von Alfred Kuhn ... München [c1923]
    22 p. illus. plates. 20 cm. (Kleine Delphin-kunstbücher. 27. bd.)
    "1. bis 5. tausend."

NL 0346554   RPB

Liebermann, Max, 1847–1935.
    ... Gedenkrede auf Max Liebermann, 1935
        see under   Goldschmidt, Adolph, 1863–1944.

ND588
.L7A2   Liebermann, Max, 1847–1935.
    Gesammelte Schriften. Berlin, B. Cassirer, 1922.
    296 p.
    Contents.—Autobiographisches.—Die Phantasie in der Malerei.—Persönlichkeiten.—Tagesfragen.—Sezession und Akademie.

    1. Art—Addresses, essays, lectures.

NL 0346556   ICU PSt MU MH NcU NjP InU NN CSt CLSU

VOLUME 332

Liebermann, Max, 1847-1935.
Graphische Kunst ...
see Friedländer, Max J., 1867-
Max Liebermanns graphische Kunst ...

Liebermann, Max, 1847-1935.
Die handzeichnungen Max Liebermanns, ausgewählt und
mit einer einleitung herausgegeben von Julius Elias. Berlin,
P. Cassirer, 1922.
21 p., 1 l. front. (port.) 94 pl. (part mounted) 42½ x 35½ᵐ.
"Dieses werk wurde in vierhundertachtzig in der presse numerierten
exemplaren hergestellt ... Nummer 471."

I. Elias, Julius, 1861-1927, ed.
44-28321
Library of Congress   NC1145.L32

NL 0346558   DLC CtY MB OCH

Liebermann, Max, 1847-1935.
Heinrich Heine: Der Rabbi von Bacherach.
Mit Originallitographien ...
see Heine, Heinrich, 1797-1856.
Der Rabbi von Bacherach. Mit Original-
litographien ...

Liebermann, Max, 1847-1935.
Liebermann, eine Auswahl aus dem Lebenswerk des Meisters in 101 Abbildungen, hrsg. von Gustav Pauli. Stuttgart, Deutsche Verlags-Anstalt, 1921.
xvi, 100 p. plates. 26 cm.

I. Pauli, Gustav, 1866-1938, ed.
ND588.L7P18   49-57545*

NL 0346560   DLC IEN RPB ICU MH PSt

*ND
588
L62P28
Liebermann, Max, 1847-1935.
Liebermann; eine Auswahl aus dem
Lebenswerk des Meisters in 101 Abbil-
dungen. Herausgegeben von Gustav Pauli.
Stuttgart, Deutsche Verlags-Anstalt,
1922.
xvi p. 101 plates. (Klassiker der
Kunst)

I. Pauli, Gustav, 1866-1938. II.
Series.

NL 0346561   CLU MtU PPDrop

Liebermann, Max, 1847-
Max Liebermann; acht farbige Wiedergaben seiner Werke,
mit einer Einführung von Hans Wolff. Leipzig: E. A. Seemann
[1917]. 4 l. illus., col'd mounted plates. f°. (E. A.
Seemanns Künstlermappen. [Nr.] 20.)

1. No subject. 2. Wolff, Hans.
N.Y.P.L.   May 19, 1924.

NL 0346562   NN RPB MdBP CtY NcD UU

20th
Cent
Ger
L716m
IN:
spec
Liebermann, Max, 1847-1935.
Max Liebermann, achtundvierzig Bilder.
Mit einem Text von Willy Kurth. Potsdam,
E. Stichnote, 1947.
16p., 49 plates (1 mounted col.) 21cm.
(Kunst der Gegenwart, 3)

I. Kurth, Willy, 1881-1963.

NL 0346563   IEN

ND588
L7KB
1949
Liebermann, Max, 1847-1935.
Max Liebermann, achtundvierzig Bilder, mit
einem Text von Willy Kurth. [2. Aufl.]
Potsdam, E. Stichnote, 1949.
16 p. 49 plates (1 mounted col., incl.
ports.) (Kunst der Gegenwart)

I. Kurth, Willi, 1881-

NL 0346564   CU

Liebermann, Max, 1847-1935.
Max Liebermann. Ausstellung, 1954
see under Hanover. Niedersächsische
Landesgalerie.

Liebermann, Max, 1847-1935.
Max Liebermann; des Meisters Gemälde in
304 Abbildungen
see under Pauli, Gustav, 1866-1938.

Liebermann, Max, 1847-
Bie, Oskar, 1864-
Max Liebermann, holländisches skizzenbuch, text von
Oscar Bie, mit 83 zeichnungen und einer originallitho-
graphie. Berlin, J. Bard, 1911.

Liebermann, Max, 1847-1935.
In memoriam Paul Cassirer
see under title

Liebermann, Max, 1847-1935.   4083.186
Jozef Israels. Kritische Studie. 2. Auflage.
— Berlin. Cassirer. 1902. 25 pp. Illus. Plates. 8°.

June 30   1903
E9567 — Israëls, Jozef.

NL 0346569   MB NN

J18
Is71
901Id
Liebermann, Max, 1847-1935.
Jozef Israels. 4. Aufl. Berlin, B. Cassirer,
1911.
32 p. illus. 23 cm.

1. Israëls, Jozef, 1824-1911.

NL 0346570   CtY CU OCH

ND
653
.I7
L5
1918
Liebermann, Max, 1847-1935
Jozef Israels. 5. Aufl. Berlin, B.
Cassirer, 1918.
32p. illus. 23cm.

1. Israels, Jozef, 1824-1911.

NL 0346571   TNJ MH OCH CSt

Liebermann, Max, 1847-1935.
Jozef Israels. Berlin, B. Cassirer, 1922.
26 p. illus., plates. 24 cm.
"Siebente und achte Auflage."

1. Israëls, Jozef, 1824-1911.

ND653.I 7L5   49-38719*

NL 0346572   DLC NcD OCH

ND
588
L7
A4
+
Liebermann, Max, 1847-1935.
Eine Kunstgabe von vierzehn
Bildern, mit einem Geleitwort von
Wilhelm F. Burr. Hrsg. von der
Freien Lehrervereinigung für
Kunstpflege. Mainz, J. Scholz, 1910.
35p. 29cm.

1. Liebermann, Max, 1847-1935 I.
Burr, Wilhelm F. II. Title.

NL 0346573   MU OCH

L759.3
L716Lk
Liebermann, Max, 1847-1935.
Liebermann Mappe. Hrsg. vom Kunst-
wart. Geleitwort von Wolfgang Schumann.
München, G. D. W. Callwey [1925]
[14]p. illus., 23 plates, port.
44x33cm.

I. Der Kunstwart. II. Schumann,
Wolfgang, 1887-

NL 0346574   IEN NN

Liebermann, Max, 1847-1935.
Max Liebermann ... 1921
see under Elias, Julius, 1861-1927.

Liebermann, Max, 1847-
... Max Liebermann, hrsg. von der Freien
lehrer-vereinigung für kunstpflege, Berlin.
Mit einem geleitwort von Wilhelm F. Burr.
Berlin [1925]
4 p. 12 plates. 29 cm. (Domkunstgaben
[15]
Caption title.

NL 0346576   RPB

Liebermann, Max, 1847-
Max Liebermann; hundert Werke des
Künstlers zu seinem 80. Geburtstage ...
see under Akademie der Künste, Berlin.

Liebermann, Max, 1847-1935.
Max Liebermann, memorial exhibition
see under Galerie St. Etienne, New York.

Liebermann, Max, 1847-1935.
... Max Liebermann, von Rudolf Klein
see under Klein Diepold, Rudolf, 1871-

Liebermann, Max, 1847-1935.
Max Liebermanns graphische Kunst
see under Friedländer, Max J
1867-

741.9
L695p
Liebermann, Max, 1847-1935.
Pencil sketches. [n.p., n.d.]
mounted plates. 14x20cm.

Cover title.

NL 0346580   IEN

VOLUME 332

N68
.L7
Liebermann, Max, 1847-1935.
Die Phantasie in der Malerei. Berlin, B. Cassirer, 1916.
xvi, 45 p.

1. Esthetics.

NL 0346581   ICU NcU FTaSU NcD MU CaBVaU TU

J25
916Ld
Liebermann, Max, 1847-1935.
Die Phantasie in der Malerei [4. Aufl.]
Berlin, B. Cassirer, 1916.
63 p. 23 cm.

1. Aesthetics (WPC) I. Title(1)
Art

NL 0346582   CtY OrCS DLC-P4 IEN OCH WU CLU

LIEBERMANN, Max, 1847-
Die phantasie in der malerei. [5e aufl.]
Berlin, B. Cassirer, 1917.

NL 0346583   MH NN

Liebermann, Max, 1847-1935.
Die Phantasie in der Malerei. Mit einem Nachwort von Erich Hancke. Leipzig, Volk und Buch Verlag [1948]
43 p. illus., port. 18 cm. (Die Humboldt-Bücherei, Bd. 9)
"Die vorliegende Ausgabe ist ein Neudruck des im Jahre 1916 in vierter Auflage bei Bruno Cassirer erschienenen Buches."
Contents.—Die Phantasie in der Malerei.—Empfindung und Erfindung in der Malerei.—Phantasie und Technik.

1. Painting. I. Title.

ND1140.L5   51-30815

NL 0346584   DLC MH

PT2309
.R2
1923
Rosen-
wald Coll
Liebermann, Max, 1847-1935, illus.
Heine, Heinrich, 1797-1856.
Der Rabbi von Bacherach, mit Originallithographien von Max Liebermann. Berlin, Propyläen-Verlag, 1923.

Liebermann, Max, 1847-
[The sewing school.]
— [Berlin? 190-?] Size, 19⅛ × 26⅞ inches. Colored.

M4107 — T.r. Painting.

NL 0346586   MB

Liebermann, Max, 1847-1935.
... Siebzig briefe, herausgegeben von Franz Landsberger. Berlin, Schocken verlag, 1937.
86, [1] p. illus., port., facsim. 19½ᶜᵐ. (Half-title: Bücherei des Schocken verlags. [84])

I. Landsberger, Franz, 1883- ed.
                     38-5593
Library of Congress   ND588.L7A4
        [2]   927.5

NL 0346587   DLC LU NcU UU NNC MoSW NN MH OCH

Typ
920
17.5222F
Liebermann, Max, 1847-1935, illus.
... 54 [i.e. Vierundfünfzig] Steindrucke zu kleinen Schriften von Heinrich von Kleist.
Im Verlag von Bruno Cassirer, Berlin [1917]
3p.ℓ.,11-76p.incl.front.,illus. 33.5cm.,in case 34.5cm.
Illus. on t.-p.
Includes the text of Kleist.
No.131 of 250 copies on Handbütten; there were also 20 copies on Japan; signed by the illustrator.
Original full   vellum, with illus. on
front cover; in   publisher's board
case.

NL 0346588   MH NN MB OCH

Liebermann, Max, 1847-1935.
Zeichnungen. Hrsg. von Hans Wolff. Dresden, E. Arnold, 1922.
29 p. illus., 101 plates. 28 cm. (Arnolds graphische Bücher, 2. Folge, Bd. 4)
"Druckfehler berichtigung" on slip inserted.

I. Wolff, Hans, writer on art, ed.

NC1145.L348   48-41496*

NL 0346589   DLC IEN CSt NRU MH KyLoS

Liebermann, Max, 1847-
Zeichnungen von Max Liebermann; fünfzig tafeln mit lichtdrucken nach des meisters originalen, mit einer einleitung von professor dr. Hans W. Singer. Leipzig, Baumgärtner [1912]
21 p. 50 pl. 30ᶜᵐ. (Added t.-p.: Meister der zeichnung ... 2. bd.)

I. Singer, Hans Wolfgang. 1867-

Library of Congress   NC1145.L45   13-5558

DLC
NL 0346590   CaBVaU NIC MH NNC CLSU OC1MA OU MB CLCM

Liebermann, Max, 1847-1935.
Die Zeichnungssammlung des Herrn L., Berlin. 316 Handzeichnungen von Max Liebermann. Mit einem Vorwort von Max J. Friedländer. Ausstellung 28. Februar-2 März, 1925, bei Paul Cassirer, Berlin. Versteigerung 3-4 März, 1925, bei Paul Cassirer, Berlin. Auktionsleitung: Paul Cassirer und Hugo Helbing. [Berlin, Gedruckt bei H. Klokow, 1925]

xii, 82 p. illus. 23 cm.

NL 0346591   MH-FA NN

WG
23687
Liebermann, Max, 1874-
Ueber einige neue Cyanurverbindungen.
[Berlin] 1904.
36 p.

Inaug.-Diss. - Berlin.

NL 0346592   CtY

Liebermann, Moissei, 1888-
... Die geburtsvorletzungen der kinder ...
Berlin, Blanke [1914]
34 p., 2 l.

Inaug.-diss., Berlin, 1914.
Lebenslauf.
"Literatur": p. [35]

1. Infants (New-born)

NL 0346593   NNC CtY DNLM

Liebermann, Oskar: Ueber kongenitale Anomalien der grossen Gallenausführungsgänge. [Maschinenschrift.] 42 S. 4°. — Auszug: (Breslau) 1922: (Wirtschaftsamt d. Studentenschaft.) 2 Bl. 8°
Breslau, Med. Diss. v. 1. Febr. 1923   [U 23. 1906

NL 0346594   ICRL

QD406
.L68
Liebermann, Paul.
Beitraege zur kenntnis einiger ghromonderivate.
Berlin, 1901.
34p.
Inaug. diss. Bern.

NL 0346595   DLC NN PU

---

ar W
54231
no.11
Liebermann, Paul von.
Beiträge zur Physiologie der Sekretionsvorgänge. Erlangen, Buchdr. von Junge & Sohn, 1911.
48 p. diagrs. 23cm.

Habilitationsschrift--Erlangen.

NL 0346596   NIC MiDW-M DNLM DLC NN

Liebermann, Paul von.
... Über orthosymphonie; beitrag zur kenntnis des falschhörens. Von Paul v. Liebermann und Géza Révész.
(In Stumpf, Karl, ed. Beiträge zur akustik und musikwissenschaft ... Leipzig, 1898-1924. 23½ᶜᵐ. 4. hft. [1909] p. 117-133 incl. tables)
At head of title: Institut für allgemeine und experimentelle pathologie der Universität Budapest.

1. Hearing. 2. Musical intervals and scales. I. Révész, Géza, 1878- joint author. II. Title: Orthosymphonie.

Stanford univ. Library   A C 37-397
for Library of Congress   [ML3805.S93   hft. 4]
           [2]   (781.082)

NL 0346597   CSt

Liebermann, Paul von, 1861-
Der Einfluss der Existenz des klägerischen Rechts zur Zeit der litis contestatio auf das Urtheil. Ein Beitrag zur Lehre von den Wirkungen der litis contestatio nebst einem Anhage betreffend die Fortentwicklung der Hauptfrage für das moderne Reichsrecht. (§§ 230 Nr. 2 und 235 Nr. 3 der R.C.Pr.O.) ... von ... Paul von Liebermann ... Berlin, G. Schade, 1886.

95 p. 22cm.

Inaug.-Diss. - Berlin.
With author's autograph.
"Lebenslauf": p. [4] of cover.
"Literatur-Angabe": p. [94]-95.

NL 0346599   MH-L ICRL

Liebermann, Richard, 1906-
Die sachenrechtliche nutzniessung ... Zürich, n.d.   74 p.
Inaug. Diss. - Zürich, [1933].
Lebenslauf.
Bibliography.

NL 0346600   ICRL

Liebermann, Rolf, 1910-
[Concerto, dance orchestra. Boogie woogie; arr.]
Boogie woogie, from the Concert for jazzband and symphony orchestra. Piano solo. Wien, Universal Edition, *1955.
6 p. 31 cm. (Universal Edition, 12373)

1. Piano music (Boogie woogie)

M35.L   M 57-1072

NL 0346601   DLC

VOLUME 332

Liebermann, Rolf, 1910–
₍Concerto, dance orchestra₎
  Concerto for jazz band and symphony orchestra. Wien,
Universal Edition ₍1954₎
  miniature score (127 p.) 19 cm. (Universal Edition, 12358)

  1. Concerti grossi—Scores.

M1040.L7C6   M 54–2743

AAP IaU FTaSU IU CSt CaBVaU NcD
NL 0346602   DLC FU LU MB ICU NN PP OC1 NBC NcU WaU

Liebermann, Rolf, 1910–
  Furioso, für Orchester. Partitur. Wien, Universal-Edition, ₍1948₎
  score (56 p.) 31 cm.
  Duration: 8½ minutes.

  1. Orchestral music—Scores.   I. Title.

M1045.L7197F8   49–23990*

NL 0346603   DLC ICU NcU ICN NN FTaSU

Liebermann, Rolf, 1910–
₍Leonore 40/45. Libretto. German₎
  Leonore 40/45; Opera semiseria in einem Vorspiel und
sieben Bildern (zwei Akte) von Heinrich Strobel. Musik
von Rolf Liebermann. Wien, Universal-Edition ₍1952₎
  42 p. 21 cm. (Universal-Edition, 12070)

  ₍1. Operas—Librettos₎   I. Strobel, Heinrich, 1898–   Leonore
40/45. II. Title.

ML50.L6902L36 1952   54–30418

NL 0346604   DLC

Liebermann, Rolf, 1910–
₍Leonore 40/45. Piano-vocal score. German₎
  Leonore 40/45; Opera semiseria in einem Vorspiel und
sieben Bildern (zwei Akte) von Heinrich Strobel; Musik
von Rolf Liebermann. Klavier-partitur von H. E. Apostel.
Wien, Universal-Edition, ₍1952₎
  238 p. 31 cm. (Universal-Edition, Nr. 12068)

  1. Operas—Vocal scores with piano.   I. Strobel, Heinrich, 1898–
Leonore 40/45. II. Title.

M1503.L7174L4 1952   M 54–2431

NL 0346605   DLC OrU NcU

Liebermann, Rolf, 1910–
₍Leonore 40/45. German₎
  Leonore 40/45; Opera semiseria in einem Vorspiel und
sieben Bildern (zwei Akte) von Heinrich Strobel; Musik
von Rolf Liebermann. Partitur. Wien, Universal-Edition,
*1952₎
  score (333 p.) 31 cm. (Universal-Edition, Nr. 12066)

  1. Operas—Scores.   I. Strobel, Heinrich, 1898–   Leonore 40/
45. II. Title.

M1500.L687L4   M 54–2430

NL 0346606   DLC NcU NN CU

qM782.15
L621ℓℓ Liebermann, Rolf, 1910–
          ₍Leonore 40/45. Lied der Yvette; arr.₎
          Lied der Yvette, aus der Oper, Leonore 40/45.
        Wien, Universal Edition, c1952.
          4p. 31cm. (Universal Edition, 12163)

          Acc. arr. for piano.
          French words; libretto by Heinrich Strobel.
          Stamp on cover: Sole agents: T. Presser Co.,
        Bryn Mawr, Pa.

NL 0346607   IU

VM   LIEBERMANN, ROLF, 1910–
1070   ₍Leonore 40/45. Suite₎ /Opernsuite. 6
L 71L   Stücke aus der Oper "Leonore 40/45". Partitur.
        Wien, c1952.
          score(68p.) 31cm.   (Universal-Edition
        Nr.12093)

          His opera "Leonore 40/45" was produced at
        Basel, March 25, 1952--cf. Grove.
          Duration: about 16 minutes.

NL 0346608   ICN MH-Mu

Liebermann, Rolf, 1910–
₍Penelope. Libretto. German₎
  Penelope, Opera semiseria, von Heinrich Strobel. Wien,
Universal Edition ₍1954₎
  35 p. 20 cm. (Universal Edition, 12236)

  ₍1. Operas—Librettos₎   I. Strobel, Heinrich, 1898–   Penelope.
II. Title.

ML50.L6902P4 1954   54–32392 ‡

NL 0346609   DLC IU NcU

Liebermann, Rolf, 1910–
₍Penelope. Piano-vocal score. German₎
  Penelope; Opera semiseria in 2 Teilen, von Heinrich
Strobel. Klavierauszug mit Singstimmen von H. E. Apostel.
Wien, Universal Edition *1954₎
  142 p. 31 cm. (Universal-Edition, Nr. 12235)

  1. Operas—Vocal scores with piano.   I. Strobel, Heinrich, 1898–
Penelope. II. Title.

M1503.L7174P4 1954   M 54–1834

NL 0346610   DLC ICU NIC NN CaBVa OrU CaBVaU

M
1503   Liebermann, Rolf, 1910–
.L717   ₍Penelope. Piano-vocal score. German₎
P4   Penelope; Opera semiseria in 2 Teilen, von Heinrich
1954   Strobel. Klavierauszug mit Singstimmen von H. E. Apostel.
        Wien, Universal Edition ₍1954₎
          142 p. 31 cm. (Universal-Edition, Nr. 12235)

          Label on cover: Sole agents Theodore Presser
        Co., Bryn Mawr, Penna.

NL 0346611   INS

Liebermann, Rolf, 1910–
₍Penelope. German₎
  Penelope; Opera semiseria, in 2 Teilen, von Heinrich
Strobel. Partitur. Wien, Universal Edition ₍*1954₎
  354 p. 31 cm. (Universal Edition, 12282)

  1. Operas—Scores.   I. Strobel, Heinrich, 1898–   Penelope.
II. Title.

M1500.L687P4 1954   M 57–414

NL 0346612   DLC MH-Mu PPiU NcU

M1500   Liebermann, Rolf, 1910–
L52P4   ₍Penelope. German₎
1955
          Penelope; Opera semiseria, in 2 Teilen, von Heinrich
        Strobel. Partitur. Wien, Universal Edition ₍c1955₎
          354 p. 31 cm. (Universal Edition, 12282)

NL 0346613   CU

Liebermann, Rolf, 1910–
₍School for wives. Piano-vocal score. English₎
  School for wives; rondo buffo after Molière's comedy
L'école des femmes. Libretto by Heinrich Strobel; English
adaptation by Elizabeth Montagu. Vocal score. Wien, Uni-
versal Edition ₍*1955₎
  190 p. 31 cm. (Universal Edition. Nr. 12423Z)
  "Commissioned and first performed by the Louisville (Kentucky)
Orchestra Society."

  1. Operas—Vocal scores with piano.   I. Strobel, Heinrich, 1898–
School for wives. II. Montagu, Elizabeth, 1917–   III. Title.

M1503.L7174S3 1955   M 56–1778 rev

            NcU ICN IEN NN FU CLU FTaSU
NL 0346614   DLC LU OU MB CtY OC1 CSt WaU MiU ICU

LIEBERMANN, ROLF, 1910–
[SYMPHONY, 1949]
  Sinfonie 1949 für Orchester.   Mainz, Ars Viva Verlag
(H. Scherchen) [c1957]   miniature score (59 p.) 23cm.
(Edition Ars Viva 53)

  Duration: about 20 min.

  1. Symphonies.

NL 0346615   NN

VM   LIEBERMANN, ROLF, 1910–
1001   ₍Symphony, no.1₎ Sinfonie Nr.1 für Or-
L 71s   chester. Komponiert 1949 in Zürich.   Zürich,
        Ars-viva Verlag₍1949₎
          score(79p.) 34cm.

          Duration: about 20 minutes.
          Biography and list of works preceding score.

NL 0346616   ICN MB

Liebermann, Rolf, 1910–
₍Sonata, piano (1951)₎
  Sonate, für Klavier. Wien, Universal Edition ₍*1951₎
  19 p. 31 cm. (Universal Edition, 12055)

  1. Sonatas (Piano)

M23.L714S6   M 57–500

NL 0346617   DLC IEN NN IU IaU MiU ICU

Liebermann, Rolf, 1910–
  Suite über sechs schweizerische Volkslieder. Partitur.
Wien, Universal-Edition, *1947.
  score (26 p.) 31 cm.
  For orchestra.
  Duration: 11 minutes.
  CONTENTS.—Es isch kei söllige Stamme.—Im Aargäu sind zwei
Liebi.—Schönster Abestärn.—Durs Oberland uf und durs Oberland
ab-S'isch äben e Mönsch uf Ärde.—Üsen Ätti.

  1. Suites (Orchestra)—Scores. 2. Folk-songs, Swiss (Instrumental
settings)

M1003.L64S8   48–20668*

NL 0346618   DLC ICU

Liebermann, Saul
  see
Lieberman, Saul, 1898–

Liebermann von Sonnenberg, Erich.
  Continental crimes, by E. Liebermann von Sonnenberg and
O. Trettin, with a foreword by George Dilnot. London,
G. Bles ₍1935₎
  xviii, 266, ₍1₎ p. front. (facsim.) ports. 22½ᵐ.
  "Translated by Winifred Ray from Kriminalfälle von E. Liebermann
v. Sonnenberg ... and O. Trettin."

  1. Crime and criminals—Germany. 2. Crime and criminals. 3. Mur-
der—Germany. 4. Murder.   I. Trettin, Otto, joint author. II. Ray,
Winifred, tr. III. Title.
                                                  36–2296
  Library of Congress   HV6975.L52
                        ₍5₎   364.943

NL 0346620   DLC WaU-L GU-L CU CtY NN

Liebermann von Sonnenberg, Erich.
  Kriminalfälle, von E. Liebermann v. Sonnenberg ... und
O. Trettin ... Mit 12 bildern und 1 faksimile. Berlin, Universitas, Deutsche verlags-aktiengesellschaft ₍1934₎
  3 p. l., 9–299, ₍1₎ p. plates, ports., facsim. 20½ᵐ.

  1. Crime and criminals—Germany. 2. Crime and criminals. 3. Mur-
der—Germany. 4. Murder.   I. Trettin, Otto, joint author. II. Title.
                                                  35–1994
  Library of Congress   HV6975.L5
  Copyright A—Foreign   25818
                        ₍2₎   364.943

NL 0346621   DLC

VOLUME 332

Liebermann von Sonnenberg, Erich.
Kriminalfälle, von E. Liebermann v. Sonnenberg ... und
O. Trettin ... Mit 12 bildern und 1 faksimile. Berlin, Universitas, deutsche verlags-aktiengesellschaft ₁1936₎
209, ₁1₎ p. plates, ports., facsim. 20¼ᶜᵐ.
"2. auflage. 5.–7. tausend."

1. Crime and criminals—Germany. 2. Crime and criminals. 3. Murder—Germany. 4. Murder. I. Trettin, Otto, joint author. II. Title.
38–38441

NL 0346622   DLC

Liebermann von Sonnenberg, Erich.
Kriminalistik im zahlungsverkehr, ein handbuch für behörden,
bankinstitute, handel und industrie zum schutze und zur abwehr gegen fälschungen, betrug und gewalttaten. Hrsg.
unter mitwirkung von ... Hubert Geissel ... regierungsrat
Liebermann von Sonnenberg ... Georg Opitz ... ₁u. a.₎ Mit
einem vorwort von ... Daluege ... Berlin, Rechts- und wirtschaftsliteratur aktiengesellschaft ₁1934₎

Liebermann von Sonnenberg, Erich.

Daluege, Kurt.
Nationalsozialistischer kampf gegen das verbrechertum, von
Kurt Daluege ... unter mitarbeit von regierungsdirektor Liebermann v. Sonnenberg ... München, Zentralverlag der
NSDAP, F. Cher, nachf., 1936.

Law
Liebermann von Sonnenberg, Erich, ed.
FOR OTHER EDITIONS
SEE MAIN ENTRY
Germany. *Laws, statutes, etc.*
Die Reichsmeldeordnung, Handausgabe mit Erläuterungen von Erich Liebermann von Sonnenberg und Artur Kääb.
5. Aufl., bearb. von Artur Kääb mit einem Geleitwort des
Chefs der Ordnungspolizei, Generaloberst der Polizei SS-Oberst-Gruppenführer Daluege. München, J. Jehle, 1942.

DD253
L52
1939
Liebermann von Sonnenberg, Erich.
Die Volkskartei, ein Handbuch von Liebermann von Sonnenberg und Artur Kääb.
1.–3. Aufl. München, J. Jehle, 1939.
vii,118 p.
Includes decrees by the Reichsministerium
des Innern.

NL 0346626   CU MH

Liebermann von Sonnenberg, Erich.
Die Volkskartei, ein Handbuch von Liebermann von Sonnenberg und Artur Kääb. Mit einem Geleitwort des Chefs
der Ordnungspolizei, General der Polizei, SS-Obergruppenführer Daluege. 19.–26. Aufl. München, J. Jehle, 1940.
xi, 158 p. 20 cm.
Includes decrees by the Reichsministerium des Innern.

1. Recording and registration—Germany. 2. Identification—Germany. I. Kääb, Arthur, joint author. II. Germany. Reichsministerium des Innern. III. Title.
50–49870

NL 0346627   DLC MH NN

Liebermann von Sonnenberg, Erich.
Die Volkskartei, ein Handbuch von Erich Liebermann von
Sonnenberg und Artur Kääb. 6. Aufl., bearb. von Artur
Kääb. Mit einem Geleitwort des Chefs der Ordnungspolizei,
Generaloberst der Polizei, SS-Oberst-Gruppenführer Daluege. München, J. Jehle, 1942.
xii, 179 p. 20 cm.
Includes decrees by the Reichsministerium des Innern.
1. Recording and registration—Germany. 2. Identification—Germany. I. Kääb, Arthur, joint author. II. Germany. Reichsministerium des Innern. III. Title.
49–30314*

NL 0346628   DLC MH

DD253
A1V87
v.45
Hoover
Library
Liebermann von Sonnenberg, Georg.
... Auslandsdeutschtum und vaterland, von
Georg Liebermann von Sonnenberg ... Der
"erhabene" jüdische hass in seiner auswirkung ₁
gegen das deutschtum im auslande, von Karl Nüse
... Leipzig, T. Weicher, 1925.
30 p., 1 l. 22½ᶜᵐ. (Der völkische
sprechabend ...45)
"Quellennachweis": p.₁31₎

1. Germans in foreign countries. 2. Jews. I.
Nüse, Karl Heinz. II. Title.

NL 0346629   CSt-H

B172
285kl
Liebermann von Sonnenberg, H
Die Seeschlacht vor dem Skagerrak am 31. Mai/I.
Juni 1916. Bearbeitet von Liebermann v. Sonnenberg
... Mit einem Beitrag von Marineoberpfarrer
Klein, sowie zahlreichen Illustrationsbeilagen
und Abbildungen im Text. Minden in Westfalen, W.
Köhler[1916]
104p. fold.front.,illus.(incl.ports.,map,
plans)2 fold.pl. 20cm.

NL 0346630   CtY DLC-P4 ICJ

DC
285
.L5
Liebermann von Sonnenberg, Max, 1848–1911
Aus der Glückszeit meines Lebens; Erinnerungen aus dem grossen deutschen Kriege 1870/71,
von Max Liebermann v. Sonnenberg. München,
J. F. Lehmann, 1911.
392 p. illus. 22 cm.

1. Franco-German War, 1870–1871 - Personal
narratives, German. I. Title.

NL 0346631   WU NN DLC-P4 MU

4DS
Jews-33
Liebermann von Sonnenberg, Max, 1848–1911.
Beiträge zur Geschichte der antisemitischen
Bewegung vom Jahre 1880–1885, bestehend in
Reden, Broschüren, Gedichten. Berlin,
Selbstverlag des Herausgebers, 1885.
331 p.

NL 0346632   DLC-P4

Liebermann von Sonnenberg, Max, 1848–
Der Blutmord in Konitz
see under title

Liebermann von Sonnenberg, Max, 1848–1911.
Neue Zeiten — Neue Parteien. Vortrag gehalten in der 1.
öffentlichen Versammlung des Deutschen Reform-Vereins zu
Leipzig, von Herrn Liebermann von Sonnenberg...am 23. Januar
1885 im grossen Saale der Centralhalle. Stenographische Niederschrift, aufgenommen von Herrn Referendar Dr. jur. A. Kaltschmidt, und Herrn B. Mühlig... Anhang: "Zur Charakteristik
der Leipziger Presse." Leipzig: Im Selbstverlag des Deutschen
Reform-Vereins, 1885. 31 p. 23½cm.

Cover-title.

732986A. 1. Jews in Germany—   Anti-Semitic writings.
N. Y. P. L.   April 30, 1935

NL 0346634   NN

LIEBERMANN VON SONNENBERG, MAX, 1848–1911.
Neue Zeiten—Neue Parteien; Vortrag gehalten in
der 1. öffentlichen Versammlung des Deutschen Reform-Vereins zu Leipzig, am 23. Januar 1885 im grossen
Saale der Centralhalle. Stenographische Niederschrift,
aufgenommen von A. Kaltschmidt, und B. Mühlig.
Anhang: Zur Charakteristik der Leipziger Presse.
Leipzig, Im Selbstverlag des Deutschen Reform-Vereins,
1885. 31 p. 24cm.

Film reproduction. Master   negative. Positive in *ZP-99.

NL 0346635   NN

Liebermann von Szentldurincz, Leo
SEE
Liebermann, Leo von, 1852–1926.

Liebermann von Wahlendorf, Hans Albrecht Schwarz-
see
Schwarz-Liebermann von Wahlendorf, Hans Albrecht.

Liebermann & Cie. firm, booksellers, Karlsruhe.
(1902? A. Bielefeld)
1000 Werke zur Goethe-Literatur. Eine
wertvolle und seltene Sammlung von Werken und
Schriften von und über Goethe... Hervorragende
Goethe-Sammlung. Erste und seltene Drucke
sowohl der Gesamtwerke als Einzel-Ausgaben.
Briefwechsel und Beziehungen zu andern Personen.
Biographien u. Charakteristiken. Uebersetzungen
u. Erläuterungsschriften. Porträts. Illustrationen
zu Goethes Werken. Autographen ... Karlsruhe
(Baden) A. Bielefeld (Liebermann & Cie.) [1902?]

cover-title, 50 p. 20 cm.
224 Katalog.
Back cover (p. 49-50) and inner front cover
contain text.
1023 entries.

NL 0346639   CtY

Liebermeister, Carl von, 1833–1901.
SEE
Liebermeister, Karl von, 1833–1901

Liebermeister, Gustav, 1879–
Beitrag zur casuistik des multiloculären *Echinococcus*
... Tübingen, F. Pietzcker, 1902.
39, ₁1₎ p. 23ᶜᵐ.
Inaug.-diss.—Tübingen.
Lebenslauf.
"Litteraturverzeichnis": p. 39.

1. Hydatids. 2. Liver, Hydatids of.

Library of Congress   RC242.L69   6-17131†

NL 0346641   DLC DNLM

Liebermeister, Gustav, 1879–
... Die bekämpfung der akuten kreislaufschwäche. Von
G. Liebermeister.
(*In* Beihefte zur Medizinischen klinik ... Berlin, 1909. 24½ᶜᵐ.
v. jahrg. p. ₁261₎–290)
At head of title: Aus der Cölner akademie für praktische medizin,
Abteilung professor Hochhaus.

1. Blood—Circulation. I. Title.   A C 34–2821

Title from Rochester   Univ. Printed by L. C.
₁2₎

NL 0346642   NRU

Liebermeister, Gustav, 1879–
Fortschritte unserer Kenntnisse von der Tuberkulose, von G.
Liebermeister ...
(*In* Neue deutsche Klinik. Berlin, 1935. 26ᶜᵐ. Bd. 13 (Erg. Bd. 3)
p. ₁566₎–616. illus., col. pl. 3)

NL 0346643   ICJ

VOLUME 332

Liebermeister, Gustav, 1879–
  Miliartuberkulose, von Dr. Gustav Liebermeister ...
  (*In* Neue deutsche Klinik. Berlin, 1931. 26ᵐᵐ. Bd. 7, p. 399–433. illus. (part col.))
  "Schrifttum": p. 433.

NL 0346644   ICJ

Liebermeister, Gustav, 1879–
  ... Die tuberkulose als allgemein-krankheit, von dr. G. Liebermeister ... Mit 23 abbildungen im text. Leipzig, J. A. Barth, 1939.
  iv, 106 p. illus., diagrs. 24½ᵐᵐ. (Tuberkulose-bibliothek; beihefte zur Zeitschrift für tuberkulose, hrsg. von dr. Franz Redeker ... ₍und₎ dr. Karl Diehl ... Nr. 72)
  1. Tuberculosis.
  Michigan. Univ. Library   A 42–2899
  for Library of Congress   ₍2₎

NL 0346645   MiU ICU

WF   **LIEBERMEISTER,** Gustav, 1879–
200   Tuberkulose; ihre verschiedenen
L716t   Erscheinungsformen und Stadien sowie
1921   ihre Bekämpfung. Berlin, Springer, 1921.
        vi, 456 p. illus.

NL 0346646   DNLM PPC

Liebermeister, Gustav.
  ... Über die Behandlung von Kriegsneurosen, von Dr. G. Liebermeister ... Halle a. S., C. Marhold, 1917.
  75 p. 23½ᵐᵐ. (*On verso of t.-p.:* Sammlung zwangloser Abhandlungen aus dem Gebiete der Nerven- und Geisteskrankheiten ... Bd. XI, Heft 7)
  At head of title: Aus dem Festungshilfslazarett II Ulm a. D.
  Bibliographical foot-notes.

NL 0346647   ICJ MiU

Liebermeister, Gustav, 1879–
  ... Ueber intravenöse strophanthintherapie. Von dr. G. Liebermeister.
  (*In* Beihefte zur Medizinischen klinik ... Berlin, 1908. 24½ᵐᵐ. IV. Jahrg., hft. 8, p. ₍209₎–240. tables, diagrs.)
  At head of title: Aus der Kölner akademie für praktische medizin, Innere abteilung.
  "Literatur": p. 240.
  1. Strophanthin.   A C 34–3466
  Title from Rochester   Univ. Printed by L. C.

NL 0346648   NRU

Liebermeister, Karl von, 1833–1901.
  Beiträge zur pathologischen Anatomie und Klinik der Leberkrankheiten, von Dr. C. Liebermeister ... Mit 3 Tafeln Abbildungen. Tübingen, H. Laupp (Laupp & Siebeck) 1864.
  ₍8, 3₎–378 p. III pl. (part fold.) 22½ᵐᵐ.
  Includes bibliographies.

NL 0346649   ICJ CtY-M DNLM PPC

WC   **LIEBERMEISTER,** Karl von, 1833–1901,
L716b   Beobachtungen und Versuche über die
1868   Anwendung des kalten Wassers bei fieber-
        haften Krankheiten, von C. Liebermeister
        und E. Hagenbach. Leipzig, Vogel, 1868.
        iv, 171 p. illus.
        Contents. —Therapeutische Resultate
        bei der Behandlung des Abdominal-
        typhus mit kühlen Bädern, von E.
        Hagenbach. —Experimentelle Studien über
        die Wirkungsweise der Wärmeentziehungen
        bei Fieberkranken, von C. Liebermeister.
  I. Hagenbach, Eduard, 1840–1916

NL 0346651   DNLM CtY-M

WB   **LIEBERMEISTER,** Karl von, 1833–1901
N912s   Cholera asiatica und Cholera nostras,
1894   von C. Liebermeister. Influenza und
Bd. 4   Dengue, von O. Leichtenstern. Der
Hälfte 1 Keuchhusten. Der Bostock'sche
        Sommerkatarrh, das sogenannte Heufieber,
        von Georg Sticker. Wien, Hölder, 1896.
        3 v. in 1. illus. (Specielle Pathologie
        und Therapie, hrsg. von Hermann Noth-
        nagel, 4. Bd., 1. Hälfte)
        I. Leichtenstern, O   Influenza
  und Dengue   II. Sticker, Georg,

  1860–   Der Keuchhusten. Der
  Bostock'sche Sommerkatarrh
  Series: Nothnagel, Hermann, 1841–1905,
  ed. Specielle Pathologie und Therapie,
  4. Bd., 1. Hälfte

NL 0346653   DNLM ICRL CtY IU-M ICJ IaU MB

Liebermeister (Karl) ₍1833– ₎. *De fluxione collaterale. 43 pp. 8°. *Gryphiswal-dia, F. G. Kunike, ₍1856₎.
  Dissertation

NL 0346654   DNLM

WA   **LIEBERMEISTER,** Karl von, 1833–1901,
9   Gesammelte Abhandlungen. Leipzig,
L716g   Vogel, 1889.
1889   vi. 454 p.

NL 0346655   DNLM ICJ MiU PPC

WB   **LIEBERMEISTER,** Karl von, 1833–1921.
L716g   Grundriss der inneren Medicin; für
1900   Aerzte und Studirende. Tübingen,
        Pietzcker, 1900.
        xii, 432 p.

NL 0346656   DNLM

WB   **LIEBERMEISTER,** Karl von, 1833–1921
L716g   Grundriss der inneren Medicin; für
1901   Studirende und Aerzte. 2. verm. Aufl.
        Tübingen, Pietzcker, 1901.
        xii, 448 p.

NL 0346657   DNLM ICJ MoSU PPC

Liebermeister, Karl von, 1833–1901.
  Handbuch der acuten Infectionskrankheiten, von...C. Liebermeister...H. Lebert...F. Haenisch...J. B. O. Heubner...J. Oertel... Theil   Leipzig: F. C. W. Vogel, 1874.   v.
  8°. (Handbuch der speciellen Pathologie und Therapie. Bd. 2.)
  1. Diseases (Infectious). 2. Series.
  N. Y. P. L.   February 24, 1921.

NL 0346658   NN MoSU

WC   **LIEBERMEISTER,** Karl von, 1833–1901
195   Handbuch der Pathologie und Therapie
L716h   des Fiebers. Leipzig, Vogel, 1875.
1875   x, 690 p. illus.

NL 0346659   DNLM WU-M CtY IU-M PPC ICJ MnU

Liebermeister, Karl von, 1833–1901.
  Handbuch der Pathologie und Therapie
  des Fiebers. Vogel. Leipzig, 1876.
  690 p.   8o.

NL 0346660   OClW-H

Liebermeister (K₍arl₎). ₍1833–1901₎.
Klinische Untersuchungen über das Fieber und
dessen Behandlung. 62 pp. 8°. *Prag, 1865.*
Repr. from: Vrtljschr. f. d. prakt. Heilk., Prag, 1865.
lxxxv.

NL 0346661   DNLM

WB   **LIEBERMEISTER,** Karl von, 1833–1901,
L716L   Leçons de pathologie interne et de
1887   thérapeutique (maladies infectieuses)
        Tr. et annotées par Guiraud. Paris,
        Steinheil ₍1887₎
        xxiv, 408 p. illus.
        Translation of Vorlesungen über
        specielle Pathologie und Therapie, v. 1.

NL 0346662   DNLM

Liebermeister, Karl von, 1833–1901.
  Pathology and treatment of the infectious diseases ... By Professor Karl Liebermeister ... Tr. by E. P. Hurd ... with notes and appendices. Detroit, Mich., G. S. Davis, 1888.
  2 v. diagrs. 19 x 14½ cm. ₍Physicians leisure library, no. 8₎
  Part 2 has title: Infectious diseases.
  Paged continuously; v. 1: vii, 141 p.; v. 2: 3 p. l., ₍143₎–200 p.
  Original German ed. published 1885 under title: Infectionskrankheiten, being v. 1 of the author's Vorlesungen über die specielle pathologie und therapie.
  1. Communicable diseases.   I. Hurd, Edward Payson, 1838–1899, tr.
  RC111.L72   7—22814

NL 0346663   DLC ICJ PPC MoSU

Liebermeister, Karl von, 1833–1901.
  Pest.
  (Ziemssen's Handb. der sp. Pathologie.
  Vol. 2, p. 457–476. Leipz., 1876)

NL 0346664   MB

Liebermeister, Karl von.
  The plague.
  (Cyclop. of practical medicine. Vol. 1,
  p. 463–483. N. Y. 1874)

NL 0346665   MB

Liebermeister, Karl von.
  Typhoid fever.
  (Cyclop. of practical medicine. Vol. 1,
  p. 35–233. N. Y. 1874)

NL 0346666   MB

Liebermeister, Karl von, 1833–1901.
  —— Ueber die Ursachen der Volkskrankheiten. Eine akademische Antrittsrede gehalten in der Aula des Museums zu Basel am 22. September 1865. 45 pp. 8°. *Basel, Schweighauser, 1865.*

NL 0346667   DNLM

Liebermeister, Karl von, 1833–1901.
  ——. Ueber Lungenschwindsucht und Höhenkurorte. 31 pp. 8°. *Leipzig, E. Keil, 1898.*

NL 0346668   DNLM

Liebermeister, Karl von, 1833–1901.
  Moore, Sir John William, 1845–   ed.
  ... Variola, vaccination, varicella, cholera, erysipelas, whooping cough, hay fever, by H. Immermann, Th. von Jürgensen, C. Liebermeister, H. Lenhartz, G. Sticker; ed., with additions, by John W. Moore ... Authorized translation from the German, under the editorial supervision of Alfred Stengel ... Philadelphia and London, W. B. Saunders & company, 1902.

VOLUME 332

Liebermeister, Karl von, 1833-1901.
Vorlesungen über die Krankheiten der Brustorgane (Respirations- und Circulationsorgane), von Dr. C. Liebermeister ... Mit 8 Abbildungen. Leipzig, F. C. W. Vogel, 1891.
vi, 516 p. 1 illus. diagrs. 23ᵐᵐ.
Added t.-p: Vorlesungen über specielle Pathologie und Therapie, von Dr. C. Liebermeister ... 4. Band.

NL 0346670   ICJ PPHPI

Liebermeister, Karl von, 1833-1901.
Vorlesungen über die Krankheiten der Unterleibsorgane, von Dr. C. Liebermeister ... Mit 15 Abbildungen im Text. Leipzig, F. C. W. Vogel, 1894.
xii, 481, [1] p. illus. 23ᵐᵐ. (*His* Vorlesungen über specielle Pathologie und Therapie ... Bd. 5)
Includes bibliographies.
Contents.—Krankheiten der Verdauungsorgane.—Krankheiten der Harn und Geschlechtsorgane.

NL 0346671   ICJ

Liebermeister, Karl von.
Vorlesungen über infectionskrankheiten. Lpz, 1885.

NL 0346672   Nh

LIEBERMEISTER, Karl.
Vorlesungen über Specielle Pathologie und Therapie. Leipzig, Vogel, 1885-1891.

4 v. 22 cm.

NL 0346673   MBCo

WB
L716v
1894
LIEBERMEISTER, Karl von, 1833-1901
Vorlesungen über specielle Pathologie und Therapie. Leipzig, Vogel, 1885-94.
5 v. illus.
Each vol. has also a special title-page.
Contents.—Bd. 1. Infektionskrankheiten.—Bd. 2. Krankheiten des Nervensystems. —Bd. 3. Allgemein-Krankheiten.—Bd. 4. Krankheiten der Brustorgane.—Bd. 5. Krankheiten der Unterleibsorgane.

NL 0346674   DNLM ICU

Liebernickel, Woldemar, 1887-   Die Rechtsverhältnisse beim Post-Zeitungsvertrieb. Borna-Leipzig: Noske in Komm. 1914. VIII, 129 S. 8° ¶Im Buchh. ebd. Leipzig, Jur. Diss. v. 5. März 1914
[Geb. 27. Juni 87 Aachen; Wohnort: Leipzig-Gohlis; Staatsangeh.: Sachsen u. Preußen; Vorbildung: G. Bromberg Reife 08; Studium: Leipzig 2, Tübingen 1, Leipzig 5 S.; Rig. 12. Jan. 12.]   [U 14-915

NL 0346675   ICRL

Lieberoth, Friedericus Carolus, respondent.
Casum de lienteria in puero observata et curata sistens
see under   Büchner, Andreas Elias, 1701-1769, praeses. [Supplement]

G1046
.G1W47
1928
Liebers, Adolf, 1887-   ed.
Westermann, Georg, *firm, publishers, Brunswick.*
Atlas der Weltwirtschaft; Teil III von Westermanns Weltatlas. Bearb. von Adolf Liebers unter Mitwirkung von R. Barmm [et al.] Ausgeführt in der Kartographischen Anstalt von Georg Westermann, Braunschweig. Braunschweig [1928]

Liebers, Adolf, 1887-
... Die finanzen der städte im königreich Sachsen, von dr. Adolf Liebers. Leipzig und Berlin, B. G. Teubner, 1914.
viii, 176 p. incl. tables, diagr. 24ᵐᵐ. (Ergänzungshefte zum Deutschen statistischen zentralblatt. hft. 5)
"Literaturverzeichnis": p. [vi]-viii.

1. Municipal finance—Saxony.

14-20183

Library of Congress   HJ9485.L5

NL 0346678   DLC NIC ICRL PU MH CtY

G1019
.W49
1928b
Map Div.
Liebers, Adolf, 1887-   ed.   FOR OTHER EDITIONS SEE MAIN ENTRY
Westermann, Georg, *firm, publishers, Brunswick.*
Weltatlas. 137 Haupt- und 118 Nebenkarten auf 109 Kartenblättern mit erläuterndem Text und einem alphabetischen Namenverzeichnis. Bearb. von Adolf Liebers unter Mitwirkung von R. Barmm [et al.] Ausgeführt in der Kartographischen Anstalt von Georg Westermann, Braunschweig. 28. Aufl. Braunschweig [1928]

Liebers, Adolf, 1887-   ed.
Westermanns atlas der weltwirtschaft; teil III von Westermanns weltatlas, bearb. von Adolf Liebers unter mitwirkung von R. Barmm, prof. dr. P. Groebe, dr. R. Müller, dr. H. Winter und anderen sachkundigen ... Braunschweig [etc.] G. Westermann [ᶜ1928]

Liebers, Adolf, 1887-   ed. FOR OTHER EDITIONS SEE MAIN ENTRY
Westermanns weltatlas. 137 haupt- und 118 nebenkarten auf 109 kartenblättern mit erläuterndem text und einem alphabetischen namenverzeichnis ... bearb. von Adolf Liebers unter mitwirkung von R. Barmm, professor dr. P. Groebe, dr. R. Müller, dr. H. Winter und anderen sachkundigen ... 26. neu bearb. aufl. Braunschweig [etc.] G. Westermann [ᶜ1928]

Liebers, Arthur, 1913-
American foreign service tests; complete preparation for the examinations which are given regularly for foreign service officer, U. S. State Department. New York, Arco Pub. Co., 1947.
1 v. (various pagings) illus. 27 cm. (Arco civil service series)
"Book list": 2 leaves at end.

1. U. S.—Diplomatic and consular service. 2. Civil service—U. S.—Examinations. I. Title.
JK851.L5   351.2   A 48—6361*
Illinois. Univ. Library
for Library of Congress   [a60f1]†

NL 0346682   IU MB TxU MiD DLC

Liebers, Arthur, 1913-
Careers in Federal service for the college-trained. Chicago, Wilcox & Follett Co. [1948]
v, 116 p. 26 cm.
"Study aids and practice for the JPA examination": p. 87-101.

1. Civil service—U. S. I. Title.
JK716.L66   351.1   48—2811*

NL 0346683   DLC MtBC OrPS DNAL Mi PPT PU NcGU

351.3
L62e
1950
Liebers, Arthur, 1913-
Civil engineer; a careful selection of civil service tests in civil engineering. Designed to show the candidate what he may expect on his examination and to provide practive in answering the questions, by the Arco Editorial Board. New York, 1950.
1 v. (various paging) illus. 27cm. (Arco civil service series)

Copyright 1947 under title Engineering Tests.
On cover: Arco courses for civil service jobs.

1. Civil service—U.S.—Examinations. 2. Civil engineering—Problems, exercises, etc. I. Title. II. Liebers, Arthur, 1913-   Engineering tests. III. Arco Publishing Company, New York.

NL 0346685   LU

Liebers, Arthur, 1913-
Civil engineer ...
see also   Arco Publishing Company, New York.

R
351.3
L71pp
Liebers, Arthur, 1913-
The civil service and promotional police manual ... Yonkers, N.Y., Alicat bookshop press, ᶜ1947.
36p. 21cm.

Bibliography:p.36.

1. Civil service. Examinations. 2. Police. U.S. I. Title: Police manual.

NL 0346687   N MiD

TK169
.I5
1953
Liebers, Arthur, 1913-
Electrician, a complete study guide for civil service and license examinations. Contains previous examinations: questions and answers. Latest 1953 ed. New York, Arco Pub. Co., 1953.
1 v. (various pagings) illus. 27cm. (Arco civil service jobs)
On cover: Arco courses for civil service jobs.
1. Electricians. 2. Electric engineering—Examinations, questions, etc. 3. Civil service—New York (City)—Examinations.

NL 0346688   MB

Liebers, Arthur, 1913-
Electrician, a study guide for civil service and license examinations. New York, ᶜ1947.
1 v. (various pagings) illus. 27 cm. (Arco civil service series)
On cover: Arco books for civil service jobs.

1. Electricians. 2. Electric engineering—Examinations, questions, etc. 3. Civil service—New York (City)—Examinations.
TK169.L5   351.3   47—7027*

NL 0346689   DLC OrP WaSp WaT MB Mi

Liebers, Arthur, 1913-
Electrician
see also under   Arco Publishing Company New York.

VOLUME 332

Liebers, Arthur, 1913–
Engineering tests, civil, mechanical and electrical; a careful selection of civil service engineering tests (with answers) Designed to help candidates pass high and receive appointments. New York, 1947.

1 v. (various pagings) 27 cm. (Arco civil service series)

On cover: Arco books for civil service jobs.

1. Engineers. 2. Electric engineering—Examinations, questions, etc. 3. Civil service—New York (City)—Examinations. I. Title. (Series)

A 48–6330*

San Francisco. Public   Library
for Library of Congress   [3]

NL 0346691   CSf WaT MB OCl Mi

Liebers, Arthur, 1913–
High school diploma equivalency tests; an Arco book for test success. New York, Arco Pub. Co., *1948.

1 v. (various pagings) 27 cm.

On cover: Arco books for civil service jobs.

1. Examinations—New York (State)—Questions. 2. Education, Secondary—Outlines, syllabi, etc. I. Title.

LB3052.N7L5   371.27   48–2246*

NL 0346692   DLC WaT PP MB Mi CoD

LB3052
.N7L5   **Liebers, Arthur,** 1913–
High school diploma equivalency tests; an Arco book for test success. New York, Arco Pub. Co., 1949.
1 v. (various pagings) 27cm.
On cover: Arco books for civil service jobs.
1955 ed. issued by Arco Publishing Company, New York.
1. Examinations—New York (State)—Questions. 2. Education, Secondary—Outlines, syllabi, etc. I. Title.

NL 0346693   MB PP

LB3052
.N7L5
1951   **Liebers, Arthur,** 1913–
High school diploma equivalency tests; designed for ambitious and intelligent students who avail themselves of the opportunity to receive a high school diploma by passing a test of their achievement in the prescribed high school curriculum. An Arco book for test success. Latest 1951 ed. New York, Arco Pub. Co., 1951.
1 v. (various pagings) 27cm.
On cover: Arco courses for civil service jobs.
1. Examinations—New York (State)—Questions. 2. Education, Secondary—Outlines, syllabi, etc. I. Title.

NL 0346694   MB

Liebers, Arthur, 1913–
High school diploma equivalency tests; designed for ambitious and intelligent students who avail themselves of the opportunity to receive a high school diploma by passing a test of their achievement in the prescribed high school curriculum. Latest 1952 ed. New York, Arco Pub. Co., 1952.
1 v. (various pagings)
At head of title: Arco book for test success.
On cover: Arco books for civil service jobs.
I. Arco Publishing Company, New York.

NL 0346695   MiD NBuG NN

Liebers, Arthur, 1913–
How to organize and run a club. New York, Oceana Publications [1953]
64 p. illus. 15 cm.

1. Clubs. I. Title.

HS2519.L5   367   53–5516 ‡

NL 0346696   DLC NN MB

Liebers, Arthur, 1913–   FOR OTHER EDITIONS
HG8538   SEE MAIN ENTRY
.N7A7   **Arco Publishing Company,** *New York.*
Insurance agent, broker; examination study book. Contains official N. Y. State Insurance Dep't instructions and data for license applicants. Questions, answers on all phases of your test ... by Arco Editorial Board and Arthur Liebers. New York, *1948.

Liebers, Arthur, 1913–
The investigator's handbook; a guide to opportunities in the vast field of commercial and civil investigation, and a manual of information for the investigator, by Arthur Liebers and Carl Vollmer. New York, Arco Pub. Co. [1954]
235 p. illus. 21 cm.

1. Investigations. I. Vollmer, Carl, 1900– joint author. II. Title.

H91.L5   *364.12 351.74   54–2966 ‡
Library of Congress   [5]

OOxM Wa WaS WaSp
NL 0346698   DLC CaBVa Or OrP MB PP PPT NcC NN TxU

Liebers, Arthur, 1913–
Librarian; a complete preparation guide for all grades of civil service librarian positions. New York, Arco Pub. Co., *1947.
1 v. (various pagings) 27 cm. (Arco civil service series)

1. Civil service—U. S.—Examinations. 2. Library science—Examinations, questions, etc. I. Arco Publishing Company, New York.

Z665.L74   351.3   47–11354 rev*

NL 0346699   DLC PP ICU TxU MB

Liebers, Arthur, 1913–
Librarian ... N.Y. Arco pub. co, 1950.
v. p. Q.

NL 0346700   PP

Liebers, Arthur, 1913–
Librarian; a complete preparation guide for all grades of civil service librarian positions. New York, 1952–
1 v. (various pagings) 26 cm. (Arco civil service series)

"Latest 1952 edition."

1. Civil service—U. S.—Examinations. 2. Library science—Examinations, questions, etc. I. Arco Publishing Company, New York.

NL 0346701   FMU

Z665
.A7   **Liebers, Arthur,** 1913–   Librarian.
Arco Publishing Company, *New York.*
Librarian, library assistant: Federal, State & city jobs. 1955 ed. New York [1955]

Liebers, Arthur, 1913–
Notary public; an examination study guide, to help candidates pass high on the test and receive appointments as notary public. New York, Arco Pub. Co., *1952.
35 p. 27 cm. (Arco career series)

1. Notaries—New York (State) I. Title.

347.96   52–3647 ‡

NL 0346703   DLC PP CoD NBuG MB WaSp OrP

RS98
.L4   **Liebers, Arthur,** 1913–   joint author.
Levine, Moses A
Pharmacist license tests; the Arco text for job and test training, by Moses A. Levine and Arthur Liebers. New York, Arco Pub. Co. [1955]

Liebers, Arthur, 1913–
Plumber, a complete study guide for civil service and license examinations. New York, *1947.
1 v. (various pagings) diagrs. 27 cm. (Arco civil service series)

On cover: Arco books for civil service jobs.

1. Plumbing. 2. Civil service—New York (City)—Examinations.

TH6128.L5   351.3   47–7028*

NL 0346705   DLC PP MB Mi Wa WaE WaT OrP

Liebers, Arthur, 1913–
Plumber ... latest 1949 ed. N.Y. Arco pub. co. 1949.
v. p. illus. map, diagr. Q.

NL 0346706   PP

Liebers, Arthur, 1913–
Plumber; a complete study guide for Civil service and License examinations by Arthur Liebers. Latest 1950 ed. N.Y., Arco pub. co. 1950.
v. p. diagrs. Q.

NL 0346707   PP

Liebers, Arthur, 1913–
Postmaster. New York, Arco Pub. Co. [194–]
1 v. (various pagings) illus. 27 cm. (Arco civil service series)

On cover: Arco books for civil service jobs.

1. Postal service—U. S.—Postmasters. 2. Civil service—U. S.—Examinations. I. Arco Publishing Company, New York. II. Title.

HE6499.L47   351.3   49–4688*

NL 0346708   DLC OrP MB Mi PP

Liebers, Arthur, 1913–
Stationary engineer and fireman; a complete preparation for civil service and license examinations. New York, *1947.
1 v. (various pagings) 28 cm. (Arco civil service series)

On cover: Arco books for civil service jobs.

1. Steam-boilers—Examinations, questions, etc. 2. Civil service—New York (City)—Examinations. I. Title.

TJ289.L6   351.3   47–30970*

NL 0346709   DLC WaT OrP

Liebers, Arthur, 1913–   4032H.39
Stationary engineer and fireman; a complete preparation for civil service and license examinations. Latest 1950 ed. New York, Arco Pub. Co., 1950.
1 v. (various pagings) 27cm. (Arco civil service series)
On cover: Arco courses for civil service jobs.
1. Steam-boilers—Examinations, questions, etc. 2. Civil service—New York (City)—Examinations. I. Title.

NL 0346710   MB

Liebers, Arthur, 1913–
Stationary engineer and fireman ...
see also under Arco Publishing Company, New York.

VOLUME 332

Liebers, Benno.
... Die Pfarrherren des Kreises Eckartsberga. Von Studienrat Dr. B. Liebers... Leipzig, 1931. 52 p. 23½cm. (Zentralstelle für deutsche Personen- und Familiengeschichte. Flugschriften. Heft 19.)

   Bibliographical footnotes.

1. Ecclesiastical biography—Germany   —Eckartsberga. I. Ser.
N. Y. P. L.   October 14, 1932

NL 0346712   NN

Liebers (Christianus Godofr.) *De aquis distillatis officinalibus. 39 pp. 4°. *Haia Magdeb., lit. Hilliart.* 1737.

NL 0346713   DNLM

Liebers (Fridericus Guilelmus). *De fracturis complicatis in crure. 24 pp. 8°. *Lipsia, typ. G. Staritzii.* [1846].

NL 0346714   DNLM

Liebers, Gerhard.
Virtus bei Cicero. Dresden, M. Dittert, 1942.
xi, 171 p. 21 cm.
Issued also as diss., Leipzig.
"Literaturverzeichnis": p. vii–ix.

1. Cicero, Marcus Tullius—Religion and ethics. 2. Virtue.
I. Title.
PA6319.L5 1942   50–45297

NL 0346715   DLC

Liebers, Johannes.
Was sagt der staatsanwalt zum verkehrsunfall von ... dr. Liebers ... Text der strassenverkehrsordnung in der fassung vom 24. 8. 1953 (GBGl. 1953, S. 1201) (Berl. Vo. Bl. 1953, S. 889) Essen, Ellinghaus, 1953.
80 p. illus. 21cm.
Includes legislation.

NL 0346716   MH-L

Liebers, Johannes, 1899-
Der wundverband in der antiseptischen aera und nach seinem uebergang zur Asepsis... 1931. 25 p.
Inaug. Diss. -Leipzig, 1931.
Lebenslauf.
Bibliography.

NL 0346717   CtY DNLM

Liebers, Max, 1879-
Zur kasuistik der ponserkrankungen.
Inaug. Diss. Leipzig, 1903
Bibl.

NL 0346718   ICRL DNLM CtY

... Lieber's international directory of the users of the Lieber code. New York, Lieber Code Co., °1891-[1922].
Library has no. 78, 140-223, Sept. 1891, 1900-July 1922. 24-18 x 25ᵐᵐ.

Cover-title.
Title and subtitle vary: no. 78-177, Lieber's manual. ...
Also called 8th-38th year.
No. 78-?, bimonthly; no. 140-213/14, quarterly; no. 215-223, semiannual.
No. 216 omitted in numbering?

NL 0346719   ICJ OrP OC1

Lieber's manual. Directory for the users of the Lieber standard code
   see   Lieber's International directory of the users of the Lieber code.

Lieber's standard telegraphic code
   see under   Lieber, Benjamin Franklin 1853-1915.

Liebersdorf, Johannes Evangelista Weis-

see

Weis-Liebersdorf, Johannes Evangelista, 1870-

ארן החיים. כולל ארבע מאות ארבעים ותשע מאמרי קדש מסאה ששים גאוני עולם. ירושלים, מסד להוצאת ספרי מסר וחסידות, ‎[Jerusalem, 1953].

40, 140 p. 25 cm.

1. Hasidism. I. Title. *Title transliterated: Erets ha-hayim.*

BM198.L5   56–52416

NL 0346723   DLC MH

Lieberson, Goddard, 1911- ed.
The Columbia book of musical masterworks; introd. by Edward Wallerstein. New York, Allen, Towne & Heath, 1947.
xiii, 546 p. 24 cm.
A collection of program notes first issued by Columbia Recording Corporation in Columbia masterworks albums.

1. Music—Analysis, appreciation. 2. Music—Discography. 3. Musicians. I. Columbia Recording Corporation. II. Title.
MT90.L5   780.072   47–11238*

    KyLx WaE WaS WaT Or OrP OrCS
    PSt MoU ICN IdU MtU CaBVa MtBC KEmT MoSW NcU MiU KyU
NL 0346724   DLC Wa PV OU TU TxU MH MB NcC NcD PBa

LIEBERSON, GODDARD, 1911- , ed.
The Columbia literary series. [New York, Columbia records, inc., c1953] 1v. (unpaged) ports. 22 x 30cm.

Preface signed: Goddard Lieberson.
Issued with The Columbia literary series [PHONODISC]. Includes an essay by Irwin Edman and biographies and portraits of the authors represented in the series.

I. The Columbia literary series   [PHONODISC]

NL 0346725   NN

Lieberson, Goddard, 1911-

Cradle song in a modern mining town. For medium voice and piano. New York, Associated music publishers, inc. [c1945]
5 p. 31 cm
First line: Before you sleep, my little son.
Words by Mildred E. Waterman.

        Printed for the Music Division.
1. Songs, U. S.   I. Waterman, Mildred
E. II. Song index (2).

NL 0346726   NN

Lieberson, Goddard, 1911-

...Love is a sickness. For medium voice and piano. New York, Associated music publishers inc. [c1945]

Words from Hymen's triumph, by Samuel Daniel.

      Printed for the Music Division.

1. Songs, U. S. I. Daniel, Samuel, 1562-1619.
II. Song index (1).

NL 0346727   NN

Lieberson, Goddard, 1911-
3 for bedroom C, by Goddard Lieberson. Garden City, N. Y., Doubleday & company, inc., 1947.
221 p. 19½ᵐ.
"First edition."

I. Title.
PZ3.L62206Th   47–629

NL 0346728   DLC Wa WaE WaS WaT Or OrP CaBVa PP

Lieberson, Samuel A.
...In a winter garden; suite for grand orchestra, by S. A. Lieberson. Boston: C. C. Birchard & co. [c1936] 107 p. 47½cm. (On cover: Birchard edition.)
Full score.
CONTENTS.—Backstage.—The musical clown.—The dancing prima ballerina.—The juggler.

                 HENRY HADLEY MEM. LIB.
5635B. 1. Suites—Orchestra—   1800-   I. Title.
N. Y. L.   August 9, 1939

NL 0346729   NN

Lieberson, Samuel A
Manual of functional harmony and key to 216 exercises, by Samuel A. Lieberson ... Los Angeles, W. F. Lewis [1946]
1 p. l., v-viii, 167 p. illus. (music) 23½ᵐ.

1. Harmony.
                46–21800
Library of Congress   MT50.L615
           [3]   781.3

NL 0346730   DLC WaS MtU MtBC FMU TxU IEN ICU PBm

NC1428
.T75

Lieberson, Will, ed.

True.
    Cartoon fun, from True, the man's magazine; the pick of the funniest, by Will Lieberson, cartoon editor. New York, Fawcett Publications [1954]

Lieberstein, Mel.
History of mathematics in cartoons. Lebanon, Illinois, n.d.
mimeographed.

NL 0346732   PWcS

Liebert, Major
  --see   Liebert, Eduard Wilhelm Hans von, 1850-1934.

Liebert [Adolf] Georg, 1874-
  see   Liebert, Georg, 1874-

Liebert (Æmilius Gustavus Richardus) [1839-]. *De atrophia hepatis acuta. 32 pp. 8°. *Berolini, G. Schade.* [1862].

NL 0346735   DNLM PPC

W 4   LIEBERT, Albertus Leonardus.
H25   Specimen medicum inaugurale, de moderamine caloris
1785   in variolis, diversisque medicorum de eo praeceptis ...
L. 1   Hardervici, Apud Joannem Moojen [1785]
        46 p. 24 cm.
        Diss. - Harderwijk.

NL 0346736   DNLM

VOLUME 332

LIÉBERT, Alphonse, 1826–
La photographie au charbon mise à la portée de tous; nouveau procédé d'impression inaltérable par les sels de chrome... Description pratique des operations. 1e ed. Paris, chez l'auteur, 1876.

19 cm.

NL 0346737   MH NN

Liébert, Alphonse, b. 1826.
La photographie en Amérique; ou, Traité complet de photographie pratique par les procédés américains...contenant les découvertes les plus récentes... Par A. Liébert... Illustré de figures sur bois intercalées dans le texte.   Paris: Leiber, 1864. xii, 422 p.   illus.   22cm.

——...traité complet de photographie pratique contenant les découvertes les plus récentes.   Par A. Liébert...Deuxième édition.   Paris: L'auteur A. Liébert, 1874.   xi, 536 p.   mounted front., illus., pl., mounted ports.   22cm.

NL 0346738   NN CtY

Liébert, Alphonse, b. 1826.   3976.59
La photographie en Amérique, traité complet de photographie pratique, contenant les découvertes les plus récentes. 2e édition. Paris. Liébert. 1874. xi, 536 pp. Illus. Portraits. Photographs. 8°.

H3304 — Photography.

NL 0346739   MB NN DLC OC1

Liébert, Alphonse, b. 1826.
La photographie en Amérique; traité complet de photographie pratique, contenant les découvertes les plus récentes, par A. Liébert ... 3. éd. Paris, Chez l'auteur, 1878.
x, 656, vi, [657]–679 p. front. (port.) illus., pl., photos. (part mounted) 22½cm.

1. Photography.   I. Title.

36–1948
Library of Congress   TR145.L5 1878   770

NL 0346740   DLC NN

Liébert, Alphonse, b. 1826.
La photographie en Amérique; traité complet de photographie pratique contenant les découvertes les plus récentes, par A. Liébert...   Quatrième édition, augmentée d'un appendice sur le gélatino-bromure.   Paris: B. Tignol, 1884.   x, 679 p. incl. tables.   mounted front. (port.), illus. (incl. plan), mounted plates.   22½cm.

The plates are mounted photographs.

42780B. 1. Photography.
N.Y.P.L.   May 10, 1940

NL 0346741   NN DSI ICJ

Liebert, Anna.
... Über die fundusdrüsen des magens beim rhesusaffen ... Wiesbaden, J. F. Bergmann, 1903.
46 p. illus., 2 pl. (1 double) 26cm.

Inaug.-diss.—Bern.
At head of title: Aus dem Anatomischen institut der Universität Bern.
"Litteraturverzeichnis": p. [43]–44.

1. Monkeys. 2. Stomach.

Library of Congress   QL862.L7

7–6300

NL 0346742   DLC

Liebert, Arnold, 1887–
Ueber die Ionisierungsstromkurven der a-strahlen. Inaug. diss.   Zuerich, 1920.

NL 0346743   ICRL

Liebert, Arthur, 1878–1946, ed.

Schulze, Gottlob Ernst, 1761–1833.
Aenesidemus; oder, Über die fundamente der von dem herrn professor Reinhold in Jena gelieferten elementar-philosophie, von Gottlob Ernst Schulze. Besorgt von dr. Arthur Liebert. Berlin, Reuther & Reichard, 1911.

Liebert, Arthur, 1878–1946.
August Strindberg, seine weltanschauung und seine kunst, von prof. dr. Arthur Liebert. Berlin, A. Collignon [1920].
155 p. front. (port.) 18½cm.   (Half-title: Sammlung Collignon, bd. 5)

1. *Strindberg, August, 1849–1912.
[Name originally: Arthur Levy]
Library of Congress   PT9816.L47   43–32749

NL 0346745   DLC CU CLSU CtY NcD NBC OCU OO MWelC

Liebert, Arthur, 1878–1946.
August Strindberg, seine weltanschauung und seine kunst, von prof. dr. Arthur Liebert. 3. aufl. Berlin-Charlottenburg, Pan-verlag R. Heise [1925]
155 p. incl. front. (port.) 19½cm.

1. Strindberg, August, 1849–1912.

NL 0346746   MiU OOxM MH IaU NcU

Liebert, Arthur, 1878–1946, ed. and tr.

Pico della Mirandola, Giovanni, 1463–1494.
... Ausgewählte schriften. Übersetzt und eingeleitet von Arthur Liebert. Jena und Leipzig, E. Diederichs, 1905.

Liebert, Arthur, 1878–1946.
...Die "Bestimmung" des philosophischen Unterrichts, von Arthur Liebert. Berlin: Pan-Verlagsgesellschaft m.b.H.[, 1931.]
32 p. 23cm.   (Pan-Bücherei. Gruppe: Philosophie. Nr. 5.)

1. Philosophy—Study and teaching.   I. Ser.
N.Y.P.L   March 6, 1934

NL 0346748   NN OCU

Liebert, Arthur, 1878–1946.
... Erkenntnistheorie, von dr. Arthur Liebert ... Unter förderung durch die Kant-gesellschaft. Berlin, E. S. Mittler & sohn, 1932.
2 v. 23cm. (Die philosophischen hauptgebiete in grundrissen; hrsg. von dr. Arthur Liebert)
"Literatur": v. 2, p. 161–164.
CONTENTS.—[I. bd.] Einführung.—[II. bd.] Systematischer teil.

1. Knowledge, Theory of.   I. Kant-gesellschaft.
[Name originally: Arthur Levy]
A C 34–1542
Title from Princeton   Univ. Printed by L. C.

NL 0346749   NjP LU CLSU

Liebert, Arthur, 1878–1946, (comp.)
... Ethik... Berlin, R. Heise, 1924.
288p. 19 1/2cm. (Quellen-handbücher der philosophie... 6 bd.)

1. Ethics.

NL 0346750   NNF

BJ21
.L7 LIEBERT, ARTHUR, 1878–1946, ed.
...Ethik... 2.aufl. Berlin, Pan verlag, R.Heise, 1925.
288 p. 19½cm. (Added t.-p.:Quellen-handbücher der philosophie... [6.bd.])
"Aus der literatur":p.287–288.

1.Ethics--Collections.

NL 0346751   ICU CLSU CU PBm NNU–W MH

Liebert, Arthur, 1878–1946.
... Der Fall Nietzsche zur Kritik der realistischen Lebensphilosophie ... Bukarest, 1938.
Pamphlet.
"Auszug aus 'Istoria filosofiei moderne' Band III. "

NL 0346752   CtY

Liebert, Arthur, 1878–1946.
... Geist und welt der dialektik ...
Berlin, Pan-verlag, K. Metzner g. m. b. h., 1929–
v. 24½cm.

1. Metaphysics. 2. Logic.   I. Title.
Library of Congress   BD113.L45   29–14654

NL 0346753   DLC CU–S OrU CLSU CU NIC IU

Liebert, Arthur, 1878–1946.
Die geistige krisis der gegenwart, von professor dr. Arthur Liebert. Berlin, R. Heise, 1923.
209, [1] p. 19½cm.
Bibliographical foot-notes.

1. History—Philosophy.   I. Title.
[Name originally: Arthur Levy]
Library of Congress   D16.8.L45   39–16172

NL 0346754   DLC OCU NIC CU MH ViU

Liebert, Arthur, 1878–1946.
Die geistige Krisis der Gegenwart, von Professor Dr. Arthur Liebert... Berlin: Pan-Verlag R. Heise, 1923. 209 p. 2. ed. 12°.
Bibliographical footnotes.

150728A. 1. History.—Philosophy   of.
N.Y.P.L.   September 24, 1924

NL 0346755   NN ICRL IU

LIEBERT, ARTHUR, 1878–1946.
Die geistige Krisis der Gegenwart. 2. Aufl. Berlin, Pan-Verlag R. Heise, 1923. 209 p. 20cm.

Microfiche (neg.) 5 sheet. 11 x 15cm. (NYPL FSN 12, 926)
Bibliographical footnotes.

1. History--Philosophy.

NL 0346756   NN

D16.8   Liebert, Arthur, 1878–1946.
L54   Die geistige Krisis der Gegenwart. 3. Aufl. Berlin, R. Heise, 1924.
209 p.

Includes bibliography.

1. History – Philosophy. I. Title.

NL 0346757   GEU

VOLUME 332

4BD
233
Liebert, Arthur, 1878-1946.
Der Geltungswert der Metaphysik.
Berlin, Reuther & Reichard, 1915.
65 p.

(Philosophische Vorträge, Veröffentlicht von der Kantgesellschaft, Nr. 10)

RPB NcD CU-S CU
NL   0346758   DLC-P4 OCU OO OU MoU CtY MH CLSU NN

Liebert, Arthur, 1878- 1946.
... Goethes platonismus zur metaphysik der morphologie, von
Arthur Liebert. Berlin, Pan-verlagsgesellschaft, m. b. h.,
1932.
1 p l., 48 p. 25ᶜᵐ. (Pan-bücherei. Gruppe: Philosophie. nr. 10)
"Diese abhandlung erschien zuerst in den Kant-studien, band xxxvii,
1/2."
Bibliographical foot-notes.

1. Goethe, Johann Wolfgang von—Philosophy. 2. Plato.   I. Title.
᷍Name originally: Arthur Levy᷍
A C 34-368

Title from Wellesley Col-   lege. Printed by L. C.

NL   0346759   MWelC NN

B
2799
L71k
Liebert, Arthur, 1878-1946.
Kants Ethik. Berlin, Pan-Verlags-
gesellschaft ᷍1931᷍
56p. 24cm. (Pan-Bücherei. Gruppe:
Philosophie, Nr.7)

1. Kant, Immanuel - Ethics.

NL   0346760   NRU MH NN OCU CU NNC

Liebert, Arthur, 1878- 1946, ed.
Kant-studien; philosophische zeitschrift. 1.–   bd.;
1897-19
Hamburg und Leipzig, L. Voss; ᷍etc., etc.᷍ 1897-99; Berlin,
Reuther & Reichard; ᷍etc., etc.᷍ 1899-19

Liebert, Arthur, 1878-1946.
... Die krise des idealismus. Zürich und Leipzig, Rascher,
1936.
238 p. 19ᶜᵐ. (Half-title: Bibliothek für idealistische philosophie, herausgegeben von Ernst Harms)

1. Idealism.
᷍Name originally: Arthur Levy᷍
A C 36-2223

Title from Yale Univ.   ᷍2᷍

NL   0346762   CtY ICU NIC NBC

Liebert, Arthur, 1878- 1946.
Der liberalismus als forderung, gesinnung und weltanschau-
ung; eine philosophische betrachtung, von dr. Arthur Liebert
... Zürich, Verlag: Rascher & cie a. g., 1938.
3 p. l., 9–207 p. 21ᶜᵐ.
Bibliographical foot-notes.

1. Liberalism.
᷍Name originally: Arthur Levy᷍
A C 39-1780
New York. Public library
for Library of Congress   ᷍2᷍

NL   0346763   NN CU CLSU NBuU

HOOSE
901.9
L716m
1925
Liebert, Arthur, 1878-1946.
Mythus und Kultur. Berlin, R.Heise,
1925.
87p. 20cm.

A revised version of the study first
published in Kant-Studien, Bd.27, Hft.
3-4, 1922.

√1.Civilization. √2.Mythology. √3.Ger-
many - Civilization. √I.Title.

NL   0346764   CLSU NIC

Liebert, Arthur, 1878- 1946.
Philosophie des unterrichtes, von dr. Arthur Liebert ...
Zürich ᷍etc.᷍, Verlag für recht und gesellschaft a.-g., 1935.
xix, 372 p. 23½ᶜᵐ.

1. Education—Philosophy. 2. Teaching.   I. Title.
᷍Name originally: Arthur Levy᷍
35-31454

Library of Congress   LB775.L45
᷍2᷍   370.1

NL   0346765   DLC CtY

Liebert, Arthur, 1878- 1946.
Die philosophie Giovanni Picos della Mirandola. Ein
beitrag zur philosophie der frührenaissance. (Einleitung.
Kapitel ɪ. Kapitel ɪɪ, abschnitt c.) ... Von Arthur Levy ...
᷍Berlin, Druck von E. Ebering, 1908᷍
49 p., 1 l. 23ᶜᵐ.
Inaug.-diss.—Berlin.
Lebenslauf.
"Mit genehmigung der hohen fakultät kommt hier nur ein teil der
ganzen arbeit zum abdruck."
"Verzeichnis der fertiggestellten werke Picos": p. ᷍7᷍

1. Pico della Mirandola, Giovanni, 1463-1494.
᷍Name originally: Arthur Levy᷍
34-3959

Library of Congress   B785.P54L5 1908   195

NL   0346766   DLC OU OCH CSt CU CtY MiU ICU NjP MH

Liebert, Arthur, 1878- 1946.
...Die Philosophie in der Schule, von Arthur Liebert.
Charlottenburg: R. Heise, 1927. 96 p. 8°. (Pan-Buecherei.
Gruppe: Philosophie. Nr. 1.)

1. Philosophy—Study and teaching.   2. Ser.
N.Y.P.L.   September 28, 1929

NL   0346767   NN MH

B2750
.K29
Liebert, Arthur, 1878-   ed.

Philosophische monatshefte der Kant-studien, im auftrage
der Kant-gesellschaft ... 1.–2. jahrg.; 1925-26. Berlin, R.
Heise ᷍1925-26᷍

Liebert, Arthur, 1878- 1946.
Das problem der geltung, von Arthur Liebert. Berlin,
Reuther & Reichard, 1914.
vi, 262 p., 1 l. 24ᶜᵐ. (On cover: "Kantstudien." Ergänzungshefte ...
no. 32)

1. Worth. 2. Philosophy, Modern.
᷍Name originally: Arthur Levy᷍
15-16212

Library of Congress   B2750.K28 no. 32

NcD MB NN NNUT CU-S ICarbS NIC
NL   0346769   DLC FU MoSU FTaSU OO OCU MiU OClW ICJ

BD
232
L71
1920
Liebert, Arthur, 1878- 1946.
Das Problem der Geltung. 2. Aufl.
Leipzig, F. Meiner, 1920.
viii, 262 p. 23cm.

1. Worth. 2. Philosophy, Modern.

NL   0346770   NIC MoU CtY OCU MH

Liebert, Arthur, 1878-1946, ed.
Quellenhandbuecher der Philosophie
see under title

Liebert, Arthur, 1878-1946.
Spinoza - brevier zusammengestellt und mit
einem nachwort versehen, von dr. Arthur Liebert.
Berlin, Reichl & co., 1912.
cover-title, 16 p. 18.5 cm.
1. Spinoza, Benedictus de, 1632-1677.

NL   0346772   ViU

Liebert, Arthur, 1878- 1946.
... Spinoza in den grundzügen seines systems; einleitung
zur 3. aufl. des Spinoza-breviers. Leipzig, Felix Meiner verlag
᷍1933᷍
cover-title, ix–xliv p. 19ᶜᵐ.

1. Spinoza, Benedictus de, 1632-1677.
A C 33-1735

Title from Columbia   Univ. Printed by L. C.

NL   0346773   NNC

Liebert + Arthur, 1878 - 1946.
Spinozas Bildnis. ᷍1910᷍
᷍117᷍-140 p. 23cm.

From Archiv für Geschichte der Philosophie,
Bd. XXIII, Neue Folge, XVI. Bd.

1. Spinoza, Benedictus de, 1632-1677 - Portraits.

NL   0346774   NNC

839.7267
L716S
Liebert, Arthur, 1878-1946.
Strindberg och nutidens andliga problem.
Till svenska och med förord av Alf Ahlberg.
᷍Stockholm᷍ Bokförlaget Natur och kultur ᷍1925᷍
136 p. 20 cm.

1. Strindberg, August, 1849-1912. I.
Ahlberg, Arthur, 1878- tr. II. Title

NL   0346775   NcD MnU MH CU IEN NN

Liebert, Arthur, 1878-1946.
Der universale humanismus; eine philosophie über das wesen
und den wert des lebens und der menschlich-geschichtlichen
kultur als philosophie der schöpferischen entwickelung ... Von
Arthur Liebert. Zürich, Rascher, 1946–
v. 21½ᶜᵐ.
Vol. 1: 1. bis 3. tausend.
CONTENTS.—4. Grundlegung, prinzipien und hauptgebiete des univer-
salen humanismus.
1. Humanism.   I. Title.
᷍Name originally: Arthur Levy᷍
B821.L5   144   47-17569

NL   0346776   DLC CU-S MH ICU CU MB NNC

JC
491
.L5
Liebert, Arthur, 1878-1946.
Vom Geist der Revolutionen.   Berlin, A.
Collignon [1919]
74 p. 22 cm.

1. Revolutions. I. Title.

NL   0346777   NBuU MH NN

JC491
.L68
Liebert, Arthur, 1878- 1946.
Vom geist der revolutionen, von prof. dr. Arthur Liebert.
3. aufl. Berlin, R. Heise ᷍1919᷍
᷍3᷍-74, ᷍1᷍ p. 21ᶜᵐ.

1. Revolutions.

NL   0346778   ICU DLC-P4

VOLUME 332

Liebert, Arthur, 1878–1946.
... Von der pflicht der philosophie in unserer zeit; ein aufruf und mahnruf an die philosophie und an die philosophen der gegenwart. Zürich und Leipzig, Rascher, 1938.
125 p. 21ᶜᵐ.

1. Philosophy, Modern.   ɪ. Title.
                                    ¡Name originally: Arthur Levy¡
Library of Congress   B804.L45   41–23
                                    ¡2¡   190

NL 0346779   DLC ICU

Liebert, Arthur, 1878–1946.   142 R900
.... Wie ist kritische Philosophie überhaupt möglich? Ein Beitrag zur systematischen Phaenomenologie der Philosophie, von Dr. Arthur Liebert, ... Leipzig, F. Meiner, 1919.
xvii, 228 p. 22½ᶜᵐ.   (Wissen und Forschen. Schriften zur Einführung in die Philosophie. Band 4.)
Bibliographical foot-notes.

NL 0346780   ICJ MH

Liebert, Arthur, 1878–1946.
... Wie ist kritische philosophie überhaupt möglich? Ein beitrag zur systematischen phaenomenologie der philosophie, von prof. dr. Arthur Liebert. 2. ergänzte aufl. Leipzig, F. Meiner, 1923.
xxii, 256 p. 19½ cm.   (Wissen und forschen; schriften zur einführung in die philosophie, bd. 4)

1. Phenomenalism. 2. Philosophy, Modern. 3. Reason. 4. Antinomy.   ɪ. Title; Kritische philosophie.
BD352.L5 1923   111.31   35—22131

NL 0346781   DLC OU MH NjP DAU CU NIC

Liebert, Arthur, 1878–1946.
Wilhelm Dilthey; eine würdigung seines werkes zum 100. geburtstage des philosophen, von Arthur Liebert. Berlin, E. S. Mittler & sohn, 1933.
viii, 77 p. 22ᶜᵐ.

1. Dilthey, Wilhelm, 1833–1911.   ¡Name originally: Arthur Levy¡
Title from Yale Univ.   Printed by L. C.   A C 34–3509

NL 0346782   CtY

Liebert, Arthur, 1878–1946.
Zur Kritik der Gegenwart. Von Prof. Dr. Arthur Liebert ... Langensalza: H. Beyer & Söhne, 1927. 84 p. (Paedagogisches Magazin. Heft 1173.)
On cover: 1928.
Bibliographical footnotes.

1. Civilization, Modern. 2. Ser.
N. Y. P. L.   June 30, 1928

NL 0346783   NN MH

Liebert (Benjamin-Gabriel). * Sur les maladies du sang-en-général, et sur la fièvre adynamique en particulier. 22 pp. 4º. Paris, 1836, No. 133, v. 301.

NL 0346784   DNLM PPC

Liebert (Carolus Eduardus). * De catarrho chronico. iv, 29 pp. 8º. Lipsia, ex off. O. Leiner, ¡1845¡.

NL 0346785   DNLM PPC

Liebert (Dagobertus) [1842–]. * De morbis ileotyphi decursum perturbantibus. 32 pp. 8º. Berolini, G. Lange, ¡1867¡.

NL 0346786   DNLM

355.0943
L716B1   Liebert, Eduard Wilhelm Hans von, 1850–1934.
          Aus einem bewegten Leben. Erinnerungen.
          München, J.F. Lehmann, 1925.
          226p. 23cm.

NL 0346787   ICarbS CaBVaU InU WU TNJ NN CSt-H NNC

Liebert, Eduard Wilhelm Hans von, 1850–1934.
Die Begründung des Deutschen Reiches. Berlin, Voss, 1910.
31 p. 20 cm. (Staats- und Bürgerkunde in Einzeldarstellungen, 1)

1. Germany—Hist.—1848–1870.   (Series)
DD210.L54   50–45128

NL 0346788   DLC

Liebert, Eduard Wilhelm Hans von, 1850–1934.   9325-343a6
Die deutschen Kolonien im Jahre 1904. Vortrag gehalten in Breslau am 16. Juni 1904.
— Leipzig. Weicher. 1904. 24 pp. 8º.

F7288 — Germany. Colo. — Colonization.

NL 0346789   MB

JV2027   Liebert, Eduard Wilhelm Hans von, 1850–1934.
L717   Die deutsche Kolonien und ihre Zukunft.
          Berlin, Voss, 1906.
          79 p. illus. 24cm.

1. Germany - Colonies. 2. Germany - Colonies - Africa   I. Title.

NL 0346790   CSt-H ICJ NN

Liebert, Eduard Wilhelm Hans von, 1850–1934.
... Das Deutsche Reich im jahre 1919, von general d. inf. z.d. von Liebert ... Leipzig, T. Weicher [1919]
8 p. 23 cm.
"Sonderdruck aus dem 'Deutschen volks wart', 6. heft, 4. jahrgang, juni, 1919.

NL 0346791   CSt-H

J
27   LIEBERT, EDUARD Wilhelm Hans   VON, 1850–1934.
335.0943 Die Entwickelung der Sozialdemokratie und
Q 603   ihr Einfluss auf das deutsche Heer.   Berlin,
          Vossische Buchhandlung, 1906.
          40p. 24cm.

NL 0346792   ICN ICJ

Liebert, Eduard Wilhelm Hans von, 1850–1934.
Friedrich der Grosse.   Neurode 1. Schles., etc., Verlagsanstalt E.Rose. [191–]
47 p. ports., illus. 20 cm.
"Illustrierte Helden-Bibliothek; Geistes- und Kriegshelden aller Völker und Zeiten, 1."
"Veröffentlichungen der 'Deutschen Gesellschaft zur Verbreitung guter Jugendschriften und Bücher', e.V., Berlin-Wilmersdorf."

NL 0346793   MH

4DD   Liebert, Eduard Wilhelm Hans von,
3036   1850–1934.
              Nationale Forderungen und Pflichten.
          München, J. F. Lehmann, 1905.
          22 p.
          (Flugschriften des Alldeutschen Verbandes, Heft 20)

NL 0346794   DLC-P4 NN

Liebert, (Eduard Wilhelm Hans Von) 1850–1934.
Neunzig tage in Zelt. Meine reise nach Uhehe. Juni bis September 1897. Berlin, E.S. Mittler und sohn, 1898.
48 p. fold. map. 23 1/2 cm.

NL 0346795   DNW CtY

UA 995   Liebert, Eduard Wilhelm Hans von, 1850–1934.
P6 L5   Der polnische Kriegsschauplatz; militär-geographische Studie, von Sarmaticus. Hannover, Helwing, 1880.
          2 v. in 1. 21 cm.

          Contents. - Heft 1. Der nordpolnische Kriegsschauplatz. - Heft 2. Der südpolnische Kriegsschauplatz. Operationsstudien.

          1. Military geography - Poland. I. Title.

NL 0346796   OU

[LIEBERT, Eduard Wilhelm Hans von, 1850–1934.
Der polnische kriegschauplatz militär-geographische studie von Sarmaticus [pseud.].
Hannover, Helwing, 1882.

2 pt.
Pt.I is "2ᵉ ausgabe."

NL 0346797   MH DLC-P4

Liebert, Eduard Wilhelm Hans von, 1850–1934.
Die rüstungen Napoleons für den feldzug 1812. Vom Liebert ... [Berlin, E.S. Mittler und sohn, 1888]
[355]–392 p. 24 cm. (Beiheft zum militär. wochenblatt. 1888, neuntes heft)
1. Napoléon I- Invasion of Russia, 1812.

NL 0346798   CU

LIEBERT, Eduard Wilhelm Hans von, 1850–1934.
Ueber Russlands volk und heer. [Neisse, 1888.

pp.(14).
"Vortrag, gehalten den 22. Dezember 1886."
With title-page, caption title.

NL 0346799   MH

DK 417   Liebert, Eduard Wilhelm Hans von, 1850–1934.
L5   Von der Weichsel zum Dnjepr; geographische, kriegsgeschichtliche und operative Studie. Von Sarmaticus. Hannover, Helwingsche Verlagsbuchhandlung, 1886.
          xi, 328 p. maps (1 fold.) 25 cm.

          1. Poland. 2. Poland - History. 3. Poland - History, Military.   I. Title.

NL 0346800   OU PPG

Liebert, Emmy.
... Frivolitäten, von Emmy Liebert. 2., verb. aufl. Leipzig, O. Beyer ¡1913¡
62 p. incl. front. (port.) illus. 26¼ᶜᵐ. (Handarbeitsbücher der "Deutschen moden-zeitung." bd. 36)   M. 1.50

1. Tatting.   ɪ. Title.
Library of Congress   TT840.L5   14–7240

NL 0346801   DLC

TT 840   Liebert, Emmy.
.L5   ...Schiffchenarbeit (frivolitaeten) ...
1915a   Leipzig [c1915]

NL 0346802   DLC

VOLUME 332

Liebert, Emmy.
... Schiffchenarbeit (frivolitäten) von Emmy Liebert. 5., verb. aufl. Leipzig, O. Beyer [*1916]

62 p. incl. front. (port.) illus. 27ᶜᵐ. (Beyers handarbeitsbücher der "Deutschen moden-zeitung," bd. 36)

Editions 1–3 pub. under title: Frivolitäten.

1. Tatting. I. Title.

Library of Congress   TT840.L5 1916   16–16711
                14046

NL 0346803   DLC

Liebert, Erich.
Aus dem nordalbanischen hochgebirge, von med. dr. Erich Liebert, mit 27 abbildungen und 1 kärtchen ... Sarajevo, D. A. Kajon, 1909.

2 p. l., v p. 1 l., 74 p. illus. map. 24ᶜᵐ. (Added t.-p.: Zur kunde der Balkanhalbinsel. Reisen und beobachtungen ... hft. 10)

1. Albania—Descr. & trav.

                           13–10463
Library of Congress   DR1.Z8 no. 10

NL 0346804   DLC CU NN

Liebert, Erich, 1901–
Statistisches zur encephalitis epidemica. Inaug. diss. Berlin, 1927.
Bibl.
23 p. 8°

NL 0346805   ICRL CtY DNLM

[**Liebert, Eugène**] 1839–
Le château de La Grange. Coulommiers, A. Brodard, 1866.

2 p. l., [vii]–viii, 228 p. 18½ᶜᵐ.

Dedicatory note signed: Eug. L. [i. e. Eugène Liebert]
An account of the owners of the castle from the 12th to the 19th century.

1. La Grange, Château de, France (Seine-et-Marne) I. Title.

                           35–21415
Library of Congress   DC801.L23L5   944.37

NL 0346806   DLC CtY

Liébert, G   A   L773.1 L625
67888   .... La photographie au charbon par transferts et ses applications, contenant la description détaillée de toutes les opérations, avec plusieurs illustrations dans le texte et une épreuve au charbon hors texte. Par G.-A. Liébert. Préface par A. Liébert. Paris, Gauthier-Villars, 1908.

viii, 283, [1] p. front. 26ᶜᵐ. (Bibliothèque photographique. La photographie par les procédés pigmentaires. [1.])

NL 0346807   ICJ CLU NN DP PHH

TR
440
L716   **Liébert, G   A**
       La photographie par les procédés pigmentaires. La photographie au charbon par transferts et ses applications. Par G.-A. Liébert. Paris, Gauthier-Villars, 1908.

2 p. l., [vii]–viii, 283, [1] p. front. illus. 25 cm. (Bibliothèque photographique)

1. Photography - Printing processes - Carbon.

NL 0346808   DSI

Liébert, Gaston Ernest, 1866–
Problems caused by the occupation of the Ruhr and the financial situation arising from it. Text of the address (slightly revised and completed) by Mr. Gaston Liébert ... at the annual meeting of the New York state bankers' association. Atlantic City, (New Jersey) June 11th, 1923. [New York? 1923?]

cover-title, 15 p. 22ᶜᵐ.

1. Germany—Hist.—Allied occupation, 1918–   I. New York state bankers' association.

Library of Congress   D650.R8L55   24–31894

NL 0346809   DLC

Liebert, Georg, 1874–
Ueber venenthrombose bei chlorose. Inaug. diss. Breslau, 1901.
Bibl.

NL 0346810   ICRL DNLM NN

Liébert (Georges). *De l'emploi des courants continus dans le traitement du rhumatisme chronique déformant. 72 pp. 8°. Paris, 1906. No. 163.

NL 0346811   DNLM

Liebert, Gösta.
Das Nominalsuffix -ti- im Altindischen; ein Beitrag zur altindischen und vergleichenden Wortbildungslehre. Lund, H. Ohlssons boktr., 1949.

xix, 240 p. 25 cm.

Akademische Abhandlung—Gothenburg.
Extra t. p., with thesis note, inserted.
"Literaturverzeichnis": p. [vii]–xvii.

1. Vedic language—Suffixes and prefixes. I. Title.

PK261.L47   491.2701   50–31222

NL 0346812   DLC ViU CtY TxU ICU PU NcD

AS284
L8
bd. 46,
nr. 3   **Liebert, Gösta.**
Über das enklit. Pronomen vaḥ als Subjektskasus im Rigveda. Lund, C. W. K. Gleerup [1950]

19 p. 26 cm. (Lunds universitets årsskrift. n. f., avd. 1, bd. 46, nr. 3)

1. Vedas. Rigveda. 2. Vedic language—Pronoun. 3. [Vaḥ (Word)] (Series: Lund. Universitet. Acta Universitatis Lundensis, n. s. Lunds universitets årsskrift, n. f., avd. 1, bd. 46, nr. 3)

[AS284.L8 bd. 46, nr. 3]   A 52–1153

Chicago. Univ. Libr.
for Library of Congress   [2]

NL 0346813   ICU PU TxU GU DLC

Liebert, Gösta.
Zum Gebrauch der w-Demonstrativa im ältesten Indoiranischen. Lund, Gleerup [1954]

96 p. 26 cm. (Lunds universitets årsskrift. n. f., avd. 1, bd. 50, nr. 9)

Bibliographical footnotes.

1. Indo-Iranian languages—Pronoun. (Series: Lund. Universitet. Acta Universitatis Lundensis, n. s. Lunds universitets årsskrift, n. f., avd. 1, bd. 50, nr. 9)

[AS284.L8 bd. 50, nr. 9]   A 55–2885

Chicago. Univ. Libr.
for Library of Congress   [2]

NL 0346814   ICU TxU PU CtY CU

LIEBERT, GÖSTA.
Zur Frage des auslautenden altslavischen -y. (IN: Lund, Sweden. Universitet. Slaviska institutionen. Årsbok. Lund. 30cm. 1953/54. p. 5–26)

Bibliography, p. 24–26.

1. Proto—Slavonic language.

NL 0346815   NN

PR3588
L47   **Liebert, Gustav.**
Milton; Studien zur Geschichte des englischen Geistes. Hamburg, O. Meissner, 1860.
396p. 20cm.

1. Milton, John - Criticism and interpretation.

NL 0346816   IaU IEN MiU ODW CSmH NN MH MB NjP

FILM
9160
PR   **Liebert, Gustav.**
Milton; Studien zur geschichte des englischen Geistes. Hamburg, O. Meissner, 1860.
vi,396 p. On film (Negative)

Microfilm. Original in Univ. of Michigan Library.

1. Milton, John, 1608–1674.

NL 0346817   CU

Liebert, Gustav, 1894–
Die audionröhre und ihre wirkung, von dr. Gustav Liebert ... mit 66 figuren. Berlin, H. Meusser, 1926.

xiv, 126 p. diagrs. 22½ᶜᵐ. (Half-title: Die hochfrequenztechnik, hrsg. von dr. C. Lübben, bd. v)

1. Vacuum-tubes. 2. Radio—Apparatus and supplies. 3. Electric waves. I. Title.

Library of Congress   TK5865.L5   29–11073

NL 0346818   DLC NN

Liebert, Herman W
An addition to the bibliography of Samuel Johnson.

(In Bibliographical Society of America. Papers. New York. 24 cm. v. 41 (3d quarter, 1947) p. 231–238. facsim.)

1. Johnson, Samuel, 1709–1784. 2. Lucas, Henry, fl. 1795. Poems to Her Majesty : to which is added a new tragedy, entitled the Earl of Somerset.

Z1008.B51P   vol. 41   51–3877

NL 0346819   DLC TxU MdBP MH

Liebert, Herman W   ed.
Dr. Johnson and the Misses Collier
   see under   Johnson, Samuel, 1709–1784.

Liebert, Herman W
Dr. Johnson's first book; an account of the variant issues of the first edition of A voyage to Abyssinia, with a facsimile of their title-pages, by Herman W. Liebert. [New Haven, The printing-office of the Yale university press, 1950] 7(1) p. illus. (facsims.) 25cm.

One of 150 copies printed.
Repr.: The Yale university library gazette. v. 25, no. 1. July 1950.
Author's presentation copy.

573723B. 1. Lobo, Jeronymo, 1596–   1678. A voyage to Abyssinia. 1735.
2. Johnson, Samuel, 1709–1784–Bibl.
N. Y. P. L.   April 6, 1951

NL 0346821   NN PBL

---

*EC75
J6371
T948ℓ   **Liebert, Herman W**
Johnson's last literary project: an account of the work which he contemplated on his deathbed but did not survive to execute; now newly related by H. Liebert on the occasion of a dinner given for a company of ladies and gentlemen to mark the anniversary of Dr. Johnson's birthday ...
New-Haven: Printed for the author and to be had only of him. XVIII September MCM.XLVIII.
14p., 1ℓ. 18cm., in folder 20cm.

Continued in next column

VOLUME 332

Continued from preceding column

"Of this pamphlet two hundred copies have
been printed by the printing-office of the
Yale university press."
"The literary project ... was the writing of
the life of John Scott, the Quaker poet of
Amwell ..."
Original printed blue wrappers; in cloth
folder.

NL 0346823   MH CtY CLU-C

Liebert, Herman W
   This harmless drudge.
   (*In* The New colophon. New York. 28 cm. v. 1, pt. 2 (1948)
p. 175–183)

1. Johnson, Samuel, 1709–1784.
[Z1007.C72 vol.1, pt.2]   A 52–4104

Grosvenor Library
for Library of Congress   [2]

NL 0346824   NBuG

Liebert, Hermann, tr.
   Die erneuerung der physiognomik durch
Gulielmus Gratarolus ...
   see under   Grataroli, Guglielmo,
1516?–1568?

Hist.
R499
865l

Liebert, Hermann, 1813–1878.
   Über den Einfluss der Wiener medizinischen
Schule des achtzehnten Jahrhunderts auf den
positiven Fortschritt in der Medizin. Berlin, A.
Hirschwald, 1865.
   2p. l., lxxxiiip. 29cm.

1. Medicine - Austria. 2. Vienna. Universität.
Medizinische Fakultät.

NL 0346826   CtY-M

Huk55
L62
A15

Liebert, Jerzy, 1905–1931.
   ... Pisma ... [Warszawa, F.Hoesick, 1934-]
   v. port., facsims. (t.1) 20½cm.
   Each volume has also special t.-p.
   In t.1, the inner form of the first gathering
has been struck off without ink, so that the
letterpress appears in blind impression on both
t.-ps. and on p.vi-vii.
   "Wydane z zasiłku Wydziału sztuki Min. w.r.
i o.p."
   Contents. - t.1 Poezje.

NL 0346827   CtY

X55Y
.L62
K

Liebert, Jerzy, 1905–1931.
   ... Kołysanka jodłowa. Warszawa, J.
Mortkowicz, 1932.
   3 p.l., 3–64 p. port. (Half-title;
Pod znakiem poetów, serja nowa)

NL 0346828   Wa

Liebert, Jerzy, 1905–1931.
   Poezje zebrane. Warszawa, Pax, 1951.
   190 p. 21 cm.

PG7158.L5P6   55–57847 ‡

NL 0346829   DLC IU CtY NcD CU MB ICU

Liebert, Johannes, 1866-
   Die metamorphose des froschmundes.
   Inaug. Diss. Leipzig, 1894.
   Bibl.

NL 0346830   ICRL

Liebert, Josef.
   ...Drei Fragen an die Februar-Schutzbundkämpfer, und eine
Antwort. [Basel] Prometheus-Verlag [1934] 16 p. 16cm.
(Schriftenreihe der proletarischen Einheit. 3.)

1. Bolshevism—Austria.
N.Y.P.L.   March 6, 1944

NL 0346831   NN MH CSt-H NcD

Liebert, Kurt, 1882-
   Die Rechtslage des Beklagten nach § 717
ZPO., wenn der Kläger die rechtschängige
Forderung abgetreten und der Zessionar aus
dem für vorläufig vollstreckbar erklärten
Urteil vollstreckt hat, unter besonderer
Berücksichtigung des Konkurses des Klägers
... von Kurt Liebert ... Borna-Leipzig,
R. Noske, 1908.
   xi, 61 p., 1 l. 21cm.
   Inaug.-Diss. - Heidelberg.
   "Lebenslauf":   leaf at end.
   "Literaturver-   zeichnis": p. [ix]-xi.

NL 0346832   MH-L ICRL

Liebert, Martin, 1866-
   Beiträge zur Kenntniss der sogenannten
Vanadin-Molybdänsäure ... Halle a.S.,
1891.
   53, [1] p., 1 l. 1 fold. tab. 21 cm.
   Inaug.-Diss.-Halle.
   Vita.

NL 0346833   CtY CU DLC

Liebert, Max, illus.
   Aladdin und die Wunderlampe
   see under   Aladdin.
German. 1912.

Liebert, Max, 1884-
   Begleichung von Abzahlungsraten durch den
pfändenden Gläubiger. Ein Beitrag zur Frage
der Pfändbarkeit sogenannter "Leihmöbel"
... von Max Liebert ... Borna-Leipzig, R.
Noske, 1907.
   xi, 54 p., 1 l. 22cm.
   Inaug.-Diss. - Heidelberg.
   "Lebenslauf": leaf at end.
   "Literaturverzeichnis": p. [ix]-xi.

NL 0346835   MH-L ICRL

PA6716
.L5

Liebert, Narcissus.
   De doctrina Taciti. Dissertatio inauguralis.
Wirceburgi, F.E. Thein, 1868.
   2 p.l., 122 p. 1 l. 8°.

NL 0346836   DLC NjP CU MH PU

AC831
A93
1876,
1880,
1887,
1898

Stack

Liebert, Narcissus.
   Lateinische Stilübungen. Augsburg, 1876-98.
   4 v.
   Programmschrift - Königl. kathol. Studien-
Anstalt St. Stephan, Augsburg.
   German and Latin on opposite pages.

1.Latin language - Style.

NL 0346837   CSt NjP

478.243
L62

Liebert, Narcissus.
   Lateinische Stilübungen... Mit dem Bildnis
des Verfassers. Augsburg, Kranzfelder, 1905.
   208p front (port) 23cm.

NL 0346838   MnCS

4PT
Ger.
559

Liebert, Paul.
   Den die Götter lieben; Episoden aus dem Leben
berühmter Männer und Frauen. Nürnberg, L.
Liebel [1948]
   152 p.

NL 0346839   DLC-P4

Liebert, Paul.
   ...Die Frage nach dem Sinn des Lebens. Baden-
Baden, W. Fehrholz & Co., 1949. 93 p. 21cm.

   Bibliography, p. [95]

1. Life. I. Title.

NL 0346840   NN

Liebert (Rudolphus). *De contractura genu.
28 pp., 2 l. 8°. Berolini, typ. fratrum Schlesinger,
[1841]

NL 0346841   DNLM

Liebert, Sarah L.
   Jewish history, by Sarah L. Liebert ... New York, Department of farm and rural work, National council of Jewish
women [1928,-
   v. plates, mounted map. 24½cm.

   Loose-leaf.
   A curriculum of Jewish education for the children of rural districts.

1. Bible. O. T.—History of Biblical events. 2. Jews—Hist.—To
A. D. 70. I. Title.

Library of Congress   BS551.L43

                 29–9526

NL 0346842   DLC

Liebert, Sarah L
מירעלע און אירע פריינד, און אנדערע מעשיות. אילוסטרירט
פון מאשע פישער. ניו-יארק, א. וו. בידערמאן.
[New York, 1952]
   79 p. illus. 22cm.

   Added t. p.: Mirele and her friends, and other stories. Illustrated
by Masha Fisher.

I. Title.   *Title transliterated:* Mirele un ire frayind.

PZ90.Y5L5   60–56491

NL 0346843   DLC

Liebert, Sarah L.
   Stories from Hebrew scriptures; a
collection of Biblical and Talmudic
tales. N.Y. Bloch pub. co. c1929, 1930.

   Part 1 - The Patriarchs
   Part 2 - Leaders and Judges.

NL 0346844   OClTem PPDrop

Liebert, Sarah L
ווארט און בילד. צייכענונגען פון נאטע קאזלאווסקי. ניו-יארק,
פארלאג מתנות.
[New York, 1933-
   v. illus. 27 cm.

1. Primera, Yiddish. I. Kozlowsky, Nota, 1906- illus. II.
Title.   *Title transliterated:* Vort un bild.

PJ5116.L5   52–59381

NL 0346845   DLC

VOLUME 332

Liebert, Siegfried, 1847-
Beiträge zur Lehre vom contractus
aestimatorius ... von Siegfried
Liebert. Opponenten: ... Aug. Mun-
ckel ... Paul Oertmann ... Hugo Sa-
linger. Berlin, H. S. Hermann [1890]
2 p.l., 118, [2] p. 22cm.
Inaug.-Diss. - Berlin
"Lebenslauf": p. [120]
"Litteratur": p. [117]-118.

NL 0346846   MH-L CU DLC

Liebert, Siegmund, 1822-1884.
see Lebert, Siegmund, 1822-1884.

Liebert, Stanisław.
Mechaniczne przenoszenie siły a bezpieczeństwo pracy.
Warszawa, 1934. 132 p. incl. diagrs., tables. illus. 20½cm.
(Instytut spraw społecznych, Warsaw. Sprawy bezpieczeństwa
i higjeny pracy. nr. 5.)
Added t.-p. in English: ... Safety precautions for transmission machinery ...
Summary in English.
"Literatura," preceding text.

1. Machinery—Safety appliances.   I. Ser.
N.Y.P.L.   June 20, 1940

NL 0346848   NN

Liebert, Vera.
"Far from the madding crowd" on the American stage.
(*In* The Colophon. New York, 1930-40. 24 cm. new ser., v. 3,
no. 3 (1938) p. 377-382. illus.)

1. Hardy, Thomas, 1840-1928. Far from the madding crowd.
[Z1007.C71 new ser., vol. 3, no. 3]   A 52-3170

Grosvenor Library
for Library of Congress   [2]

NL 0346849   NBuG

Liebert (Vincent). *Untersuchungen über die
physiologischen Wirkungen des Apomorphin.
67 pp. 8°. Dorpat, H. Laakmann, 1871.

NL 0346850   DNLM

Liebert, Walter, 1877-
Das Rechtsverhältnis des Schuldners zur
Hinterlegungsstelle bei der Hinterlegung
nach gemeinem Recht und dem Bürgerlichen
Gesetzbuche für das Deutsche Reich... von
Walter Liebert ... Greifswald, J. Abel,
1899.
61 p. 21cm.
Inaug.-Diss. - Greifswald.
"Lebenslauf": p. 61.
"Litteratur": p.[5]-[6]

NL 0346851   MH-L DLC

Liebert, Willibald.
Zur frage des peripheren wachstums der carcinome.
Inaug. diss. Heidelberg, 1900. (Tübingen)

NL 0346852   ICRL DNLM

Liebert, Willy Max, 1878-
... Chemische und toxikologische untersuchungen über
therosot ... Borna-Leipzig, Buchdr. R. Noske, 1909.
68 p., 1 l. 22½cm.
Inaug.-diss.—Bern.
Lebenslauf.
"Literaturverzeichnis": p.[67]-68.

Continued in next column

Continued from preceding column

1. Therosot.
                       Agr 10-567
Library, U. S. Dept. of   Agriculture 396L62

NL 0346853   DNAL DNLM ICJ PU

Microfilm
R 3094   Lieberth, Louise, 1925-
/2   Glossar und Reimwörterbuch zur Summa
theologiae. Wien, 1948.
230 p.
Diss. - Vienna.
Microfilm (negative) 1 reel. 35 mm.
1. Thomas Aquinas, Saint, 1225?-1274./
Summa theologica. I. Title.

NL 0346854   CaBVaU

Lieberthal, David.
A case of leprosy. Presented before the Chi-
cago Medical Society, April 13, 1898. n.p., n.d.
Repr. from the North American Practitioner.
July, 1898.

NL 0346855   NN

Lieberthal (David). Case of vitiligo presenting unusual features. 2 l. 8°. [St. Louis],
1897.
Repr. from: Am. J. Dermat. & Genito-Urin. Dis., St.
Louis, 1897, i.

NL 0346856   DNLM

Lieberthal, David.
[Collected papers.]   1897-.
Various paging. 18cm.-27cm.
Extracted or reprinted from various medical serials.

NL 0346857   ICJ

LIEBERTHAL, David.
Prevention of venereal diseases. Chicago,
1899.

NL 0346858   MBCo

Lieberthal, David.
Remarks on primary and secondary syphilis,
and a few remarks as to the application of mercury.
Read ... March 1, 1899. n.p., 1901.
2 l. 4°.
n.t.-p.
Repr.: American Journal of Dermatology,
January, 1901.

NL 0346859   NN

Lieberthal, Jules M
Snoopy, the nosey little puppy; illustrated by William
Neebe. Chicago, Rand McNally, *1955.
unpaged. illus. 21 cm. (A Rand McNally elf book, 509)

I. Title.
PZ10.3.L624Sn   55-10120 ‡

NL 0346860   DLC

Lieberthal, Robert H.
Advanced impression taking; scientific and correct
method based upon principles founded by Drs. Greene,
by Robert H. Lieberthal ... with forty-three half-tone
illustrations. New York, Professional publishing co.
[1918]
xi p., 1 l., 15-79, [2] p. illus. 21cm.

1. Teeth, Artificial.   I. Title.
Library of Congress   RK658.L5   18-6428

NL 0346861   DLC CtY-M ICRL OC1W-H OC1W OU ICJ

Lieberwirth, Roland.
Grenzströme bei anodischer polarisation von
metallen in wässrigen lösungen. ... Dresden, n.d.
48 p.
Inaug. Diss. - Techn. Hochsch. Dresden, [1934]

NL 0346862   ICRL

Lieberwirth, Rolf.
Christian Thomasius, sein wissenschaftliches Lebenswerk;
eine Bibliographie. Weimar, H. Böhlaus, Nachfolger, 1955.
213 p. 25 cm. (Thomasiana, Heft 2)

1. Thomasius, Christian, 1655-1728—Bibl.   (Series) ‡
Z8870.8.L5   56-33448

       CSt IU NN ScU MH-AH CBGTU IEN
NL 0346863   DLC MiU MH NNC NIC InU NjPT CU OU MiU

Lieberwirth, Rolf
Die kartell und konzessionsrechtliche gestaltung
der deutschen zuendholzindustrie.
Inaug. diss. Leipzig, 1929. (Rudolstadt.)
Bibl.

NL 0346864   DLC

Lieberz, Friedrich, 1910-
... Statistisches zur Schnittentbindung mit
besonderer Berücksichtigung der Mortalität und
Morbidität ... Köln, 1939.
Inaug.-Diss. - Köln.
Lebenslauf.
"Literatur-Verzeichnis": p. 27-29.

NL 0346865   CtY

Lieberz (Lorenz) [1891-] J. *Ueber den
Nutzen der künstlichen Höhensonne für die
Chirurgie. 32 pp. 8°. Bonn, E. Eisele, 1919.

NL 0346866   DNLM CtY ICRL

Liebes, Curt, 1890-
Der Ehemann als Verwalter des einge-
brachten Guts im Prozess. Ein Beitrag
zur Lehre von der prozessualen Wirkung
des gesetzlichen Güterstandes nach dem
deutschen bürgerlichen Gesetzbuche ...
von Curt Liebes ... Berlin, Frensdorf,
1913.
2 p.l., vi, 154 p. 22cm.
Inaug.-Diss. - Erlangen.
"Literatur": p.   iii-vi.

NL 0346867   MH-L NIC DLC

Liebes, Gerhard Joseph
see Liebes, Joseph Gerhard.

VOLUME 332

F869
S3
.7
L498
Liebes (H.) and Company, San Francisco.
Deed of trust to secure payment of six percent secured serial gold notes authorized to be issued to the amount of $750,000.00, interest payable February 1st and August 1st.   [San Francisco, Pernau-Walsh Print. Co., 1919]
51 p.   26cm.

At head of title: H. Liebes and Company to Anglo-California Trust Company, trustee.

I. Anglo-California Trust Company, inc., San Francisco.
II. Title.

NL 0346869   CU

F863
.6
L37
Liebes (H.) and Company, San Francisco, appellant-cross-appellee.
(C. Klengenberg, appellee-cross-appellant)
Libel.
No. 5200 in the United States Circuit Court of Appeals for the Ninth Circuit.
Contents.
[1-2] Apostles on appeal. San Francisco, 1927. (911 p.)

I. Trials (Libel) - San Francisco. I. Klengenberg, Christian, 1869- , appellee-cross-appellant. II. U.S. Circuit Court of Appeals. (9th Circuit)

NL 0346870   CU-B

PA6817
.2
.A5L5
Hebr
Liebes, Joseph Gerhard, tr.
(Ayne'is)
Vergilius Maro, Publius.
אינייאיס, פרקים נבחרים. ;תרגם יוסף ג. ליבס עם מבוא וביאורים מאת יוחנן לוי, הוצאת ספרי תרשיש.
;Jerusalem, 1945;

B363
.H4L5
Hebr
Liebes, Joseph Gerhard, tr.
(Kitve Aplaton)
Plato.
כתבי אפלטון. תירגם מיוונית. יוסף ג. ליבס. ירושלים, שוקן,
;1955-66;

PT2047
.O7S75
Hebr
Liebes, Joseph Gerhard, joint tr.
(ha-Kol medaber)
Wolfskehl, Karl, 1869-
הקול מדבר ;תרגמו פרנ;ק;ן ברנבור ונדהרד ליבס, תל-אביב,
;Tel-Aviv, 1942;

PT2359
.I2A6
1944
Hebraic
Sect.
Liebes, Joseph Gerhard, tr.
(shirim)
Hölderlin, Friedrich, 1770-1843.
שירים נבחרים. תרגם ג. ליבס ;Jerusalem, 1944/45;

PR2796
.H4J84
Hebraic
Sect.
Liebes, Joseph Gerhard, tr.
(Yulyus Kaisar)
Shakespeare, William, 1564-1616.
יוליוס קיסר. תרגם: יוסף ג. ליבס. תל-אביב, י. צ'צ'יק.
;Tel-Aviv, 1951;

;Liebes, Lloyd;
A wolume of worse; an intensive study of the characteristics of women, their care and prevention, by O. Helz-Belz ;pseud.;
Princeton: Privately printed for anyone who has the price, 1925.
45 p.   20½cm.

"A limited and numbered first edition...number 1."
"Printed at Princeton University Press..."

859243A.   1. Poetry, American.   2. Wit and humor, American.
I. Title.
N.Y.P.L.   February 25, 1937.

NL 0346876   NN

FILM
331.1973
L62l
Liebes, Richard Alan, 1914-
Longshore labor relationships on the Pacific coast, 1934-42. ;Berkeley, 1942;
ix, 391l. illus., map.

Thesis--University of California.
Vita.
Bibliography: leaves 387-391.
Microfilm. ;Berkeley; University of California, Library Photographic Service, 1969?
1. Longshoremen--Pacific States.   I. Title.

NL 0346877   IU CU

Liebe's first-   collection of quadrilles, with their proper figures, arr. for the piano forte. London, Preston ;181-
v. ; 32 cm.
Includes directions in English and French for the dances.

1. Quadrilles (Piano)

M31.L   75-204446

NL 0346878   DLC

PT2372
.K75Z8L7
Rare bk
room
LIEBES von der alten Karschin. ;Langensalza,Gedruckt bei J.Beltz,1926?;
29,;1;p. 2 facsim.(in pocket) 21cm.
"In 400 gezählten abzügen gedruckt... nr.17."
"Den teilnehmern an der 27.hauptversammlung der Gesellschaft der bibliophilen' zu Leipzig am 24.oktober 1926 gestiftet von M.B.,P.K.und F.v.Z.;i.e.Martin Breslauer,Paul Kressmann und Fedor von Zobeltitz;"

1.Karsch,Anna Louise,1722-1791.

NL 0346879   ICU

Die LIEBES-ARBEIT der evangelischen Kirche in der provinz Posen. Posen,n.d.

NL 0346880   MH

Liebes—Beschreibung Lysanders und Kalisten
see under   [Andiguier, Vital d'] 1569-1624.

PQ1288
L8L5
Liebesbriefe aus dem Rokoko. ;Auswahl, Übersetzung und Einleitung von Alfred Semerau.;
Berlin, Hyperionverlag ;1919;
214 p. 25ᵐ.

1.Love-letters. 2.French letters - Translations into German. I.Semerau, Alfred, 1879-   comp.

NL 0346882   CSt

Die liebesbriefe der Babet.
see under   [Boursault, Edme] 1638-1701.

Liebesbriefe einer Deutsch-Amerikanerin.
Dresden: E. Pierson, 1904.
viii, 142 p.   12°.

NL 0346884   NN

Liebesbriefe eines englischen Madchens.
Leipzig, 1904.

NL 0346885   NjP

Liebesbriefe grosser Musiker
see under   Jerger, Wilhelm, 1902-   ed.

Liebesbriefe historisch berühmter Personen. Ein Beitrag zur Kenntniss des menschlichen Herzens. Mit historischen Einleitungen versehen und nach den Nationen geordnet. [v.] 1.
Leipzig, J.J. Weber, 1851.
1 v.   16°.
v. 1. Frankreich.

NL 0346887   NN PPLT

Liebeschütz, Hans, 1893-
... Das allegorische weltbild der heiligen Hildegard von Bingen. Leipzig, Berlin, B. G. Teubner, 1930.
viii p., 2 L., 179 p. 1 illus., vi pl., fold. tab. 27 cm.   (Added t.-p.: Studien der Bibliothek Warburg ...

1. Hildegard, Saint, 1098?-1178.   I. Title.

BR65.H776L5   30—8080

PBm PU OC1W
NL 0346888   DLC OC1MA WaU MdBWA AU OO ICU MiU NN

Liebeschütz, Hans, 1893-   ed.

Ridevallus, Joannes, fl. 1330.
... Fulgentius Metaforalis, ein beitrag zur geschichte der antiken mythologie im mittelalter. Leipzig ;etc.; B. G. Teubner, 1926.

CB
3
W301
1923/24
Liebeschütz, Hans, 1893-
Kosmologische Motive in der Bildungswelt der Frühscholastik.
(In Warburg Institute. Vorträge der Bibliothek Warburg. Nendeln;Liechtenstein. 24 cm.
v.3 (1923-1924), p. ;83;-148)

(Series: Warburg Institute. Vorträge der Bibliothek Warburg, 1923/24)

NL 0346890   CU-S

Liebeschütz, Hans, 1893-
Mediaeval humanism in the life and writings of John of Salisbury. London, Warburg Institute, University of London, 1950.
126 p. 25 cm. (Studies of the Warburg Institute, v. 17)

1. John of Salisbury, Bp. of Chartres, d. 1180. (Series: London. University. Warburg Institute. Studies, v. 17)
B765.J44L5   189.4   A 51—5436
Brown Univ. Library
for Library of Congress   ;a60c;;†

DLC
NL 0346891   RPB TU TxU ViU MB CU IEN CtY NcGU NcD

Liebeschütz, Hans, 1893-
Mediaeval humanism in the life and writings of John of Salisbury. London, Warburg Institute, University of London, 1950.
126 p. 25 cm. (Studies of the Warburg Institute, v. 17)
Reprint by microfilm-xerox by University Microfilms, Ann Arbor, Mich., 1966.

NL 0346892   NBuU FTaSU IdPI

Liebeschütz, Hans, 1893-
Ranke. ;London; Published for the Historical Association by G. Philip, 1954.
20 p. 22 cm. (Historical Association publications, general series: G 26)

1. Ranke, Leopold von, 1795-1886.
D15.R3L5   54-27673 ‡

CaBVaU
NL 0346893   DLC TxU NIC NN IaU MB MH CaOTP OrU

VOLUME 332

CB 3 W301 1930/31
Liebeschütz, Hans, 1893-
Der Sinn des Wissens bei Roger Bacon.
(In Warburg Institute. Vorträge der Bibliothek Warburg. Nendeln/Liechtenstein. 24 cm.
v.9 (1930-1931), p. [28]-63)

(Series: Warburg Institute. Vorträge der Bibliothek Warburg, 1930/31)

NL 0346894   CU-S

Liebeschütz (John). *Beitrag zur Lehre der penetrirenden Gelenkwunden. 19 pp. 8°. Würzburg, A. Memminger. 1886.

NL 0346895   DNLM

Liebeschuetz, Julius.
Die locale verbreitung der throphoneurosen.
Inaug. Diss.   Strassburg, 1883.

NL 0346896   ICRL DNLM MH

Die Liebeschule der kleinen Japanerin
see Die Liebesschule der kleinen Japanerin.

Eine Liebes-Episode aus dem Leben ...
see under Lassalle, Ferdinand Johann Gottlieb, 1825-1864.

Liebesgedichte [1921]
see under [Schnellenbühel, Jenny von] comp.

831.08 L716
Liebesgedichte; eine kleine Anthologie.
Berlin, A. Juncker [1912]
62p. 14cm. (Orplidbücher, 2. Bd.)

1. German poetry. 20th cent. 2. Love poetry. Collections.

NL 0346900   IEN NjP

Liebesgeschichten des Orients
see under Blei, Franz.

Liebesgeschichten; Goethe, Kleist, Arnim, Stifter, Tieck, Hebbel, Grillparzer, Gotthelf, Mörike, Schiller
see under [Zeitler, Julius] 1874-   ed.

Liebeskind, A.   G.
Literarische Festgaben aus dem Verlag in Leipzig. Lnz., 1892.
S. 127+ J. P. il. 1 por.

NL 0346903   MiU

Law   Liebeskind, Adolf, ed.

Poland. *Laws, statutes, etc.*
Ustawy cywilne, obowiązujące w Małopolsce i na Śląsku cieszyńskim. Kodeks cywilny austriacki, Kodeks zobowiązań, Prawo ksiąg gruntowych, Ustawy związkowe. Zebrał i opracował Adolf Liebeskind; z przedm. Fryderyka Zolla. Kraków, Księgarnia Powszechna, 1937.

TA 7 S58 1954 no.1+
Liebeskind, Arthur S.
The "Porta-floor" loading system.
Ithaca, N.Y., 1954.
12 l. illus. 29cm. (Silent Hoist and Crane Company. Materials handling prize papers, 1954, no. 1)

"First prize."

1. Loading and unloading. I. Title. II. Series.

NL 0346905   NIC

TA 7 S58 1955 no.1+
Liebeskind, Arthur S.
The "protecto-foam" packing method.
Ithaca, N.Y., 1955.
12 l. illus. 29cm. (Silent Hoist and Crane Company. Materials handling prize papers, 1955, no.1)

1st prize.

1. Packing for shipment. I. Series.

NL 0346906   NIC

PT2563 .D8 1786
Liebeskind, August Jacob, d. 1793.
Wieland, Christoph Martin, 1733-1813.
Dschinnistan; oder, Auslesene Feen- und Geister-Märchen, theils neu erfunden, theils neu übers. und umgearb.
Winterthur, H. Steiner, 17

Liebeskind, August Jacob, *d.* 1793, *ed.*
Die Königin Zulikah, morgenländische Erzählungen. Heidelberg, H. Meister [193-]
62 p. 17 cm. (Die Kleinen Bücher, Nr. 10)
Selections from the author's Palmblätter.

1. Short stories, Oriental.   I. Title.

PZ34.1.L48   50-51675

NL 0346908   DLC CtY PU MH NN

[Liebeskind, August Jacob] d. 1793, ed.
Die Königin Zulikak; morgenländische Erzählungen. Heidelberg, H. Meister, 1946.
55 p. 17 cm. (Die kleinen bücher, 10)
" 'Palmblätter' nennt sich eine sammlung morgenländischer rezählungen, die A.J. Liebeskind zu ende des 18. jahrhundert hrsg. ... I [!] G. Herder eingeleitet hat." p. 54.

NL 0346909   PU

PZ 34 .1 L71 1913
Liebeskind, August Jacob, d. 1793, comp.
Morgenländische Erzählungen (Palmblätter)
Nach der von J. G. Herder und A. J. Liebeskind besorgten Ausg. neu hrsg. von Hermann Hesse. Leipzig, Insel-Verlag [1913]
xvi, 334 p. 17cm.
A collection originally done for Herder by his tutor, Liebeskind, and published by Herder, with an introduction, in 1786, under title: Palmblätter. Cf. R. Haym. Herder (Berlin, 1954)   v. 2, p. 358.

NL 0346910   NIC ICarbS LU ICU InU

PZ 34 .1 .L5 1786
Liebeskind, August Jacob, d. 1793
Palmblätter. Erlesene morgenländische Erzählungen für die Jugend. Jena, Akademischen Buchhandlung, 1786-1788.
2v. 17cm.

Introduction by Johann Gottfried Herder.

I. Herder, Johann Gottfried, 1744-1803. II. Title.

NL 0346911   TNJ

Liebeskind, August Jacob, d. 1793, ed.
Palmblätter, morgenländische Erzählungen; Umschlagzeichnung von Hans Fischer. Heidelberg, H. Meister, 1946.
204 p. 19 cm.
"Eine Sammlung ... die A. J. Liebeskind zu Ende des 18. Jahrhunderts herausgegeben und ... J. G. Herder eingeleitet hat."—Nachwort.

1. Short stories, Oriental.   I. Herder, Johann Gottfried von, 1744-1803.   II. Title.

PZ34.1.L5   A F 49-310 rev*
Chicago. Univ. Libr.
for Library of Congress   [r49b1]†

NL 0346912   ICU PU DLC

Liebeskind (Fr. Augustus) [1804-   ]. *De hiastoria. 20 pp., 2 l. 8°. Berolini, typ. Nietackianis, 1838. [Also in : P., v. 164.]

NL 0346913   DNLM

Liebeskind (Fr. Carol.) [1791-   ]. *De scarlatina. 43 pp. 8°. Berolini, formis Brüschkianis, [1841].

NL 0346914   DNLM PPC

Liebeskind, Friedrich.
Ueber das neue Strafverfahren in Bayern. Einzelne Desiderien zum Gesetze vom 10. Nov. 1848 von Friedrich Liebeskind ... Bamberg, F. Züberlein, 1849.
46 p. 20cm.
"Druckfehler": 1 leaf mounted on p. [3] of cover.
Author's autograph letters ([6] fold.p.) mounted on p. [2] of cover.

NL 0346915   MH-L

PT 2130 .I4 L72
LIEBESKIND, FRITZ.
Drei Ilmenauer Goethe-Erinnerungen. [Ilmenau, Im Eigenverlag des Verfassers [1928]
168 p. illus.

1. Goethe, Johann Wolfgang von--Homes and haunts--Ilm Valley. I. Title.

NL 0346916   InU

Liebeskind, Hermann.
Über die benutzung von quellen im geschichtsunterrichte der volksschule. Von Hermann Liebeskind ... Jena, F. Manke's verlag, 1891.
2 p. l., 35, [1] p. 22cm.

1. History—Teaching—Elementary schools.

                                      E 13-1020
Library, U. S. Bur. of   Education LB1582.G3L6

NL 0346917   DHEW

VOLUME 332

[Liebeskind, Johann Heinrich.]
Ruckerinnerungen von einer Reise durch einen Theil von Teutschland, Preussen, Kurland und Liefland, während des Aufenthalts der Franzosen in Mainz und der Unruhen in Polen, Strasburg, 1795. [Königsberg: Nicolovius, 1795.] 419 p. 16°.

161298A. 1. Germany—Descr. and trav., to 1800. 2. Baltic provinces—Social life, 18th cent.
N. Y. P. L. June 11, 1925

NL 0346918 NN

ML134
.G56W6

Liebeskind, Josef, 1866–1916.

Wotquenne, Alfred, 1867–1939.
Catalogue thématique des œuvres de Chr. W. v. Gluck. Leipzig, New York, Breitkopf & Härtel, 1904.

Liebeskind, Josef, 1866–1916.
Festmarsch für grosses Orchester, componirt von Josef Liebeskind. Op. 12. Partitur... Leipzig: Gebrüder Reinecke[, ca. 1899]. Publ. pl. no. G. 952. R. 27 p. 4°.

Full score.

1. Orchestra, Full—Marches. 2. Title.
N. Y. P. L. June 30, 1927

NL 0346920 NN

Liebeskind, Josef, 1866–1916, arr.
Ouverture zur Oper L'isola disabitata
(G moll)
see under Haydn, Joseph, 1732–1809.

Liebeskind, Josef, 1866–1916.
Symphonie (N°. 1 A moll) für Orchester, componirt von Josef Liebeskind. Op. 4. Partitur... Leipzig: Jost & Sander [1888]. Publ. pl. no. J. 23 S. 246 p. 4°.

Full score.

1. Orchestra, Full—Symphonies.
N. Y. P. L. January 12, 1925

NL 0346922 NN

ML134
.G56W614

Liebeskind, Josef, 1866–1916.

Wotquenne, Alfred, 1867–1939.
Thematisches Verzeichnis der Werke von Chr. W. v. Gluck (1714–1787) Deutsche Übersetzung von Josef Liebeskind. Leipzig, New York, Breitkopf & Härtel, 1904.

LIEBESKIND, PAUL.
Geschichte des Füsilier-Regiments Fürst Karl Anton von Hohenzollern (Hohenzollernschen) Nr. 40. Im Auftrage des Regiments bearb. und weitergeführt von Paul Liebeskind. 2. Aufl. Berlin, E. S. Mittler, 1909. xl, 556 p. ports., fold. maps (part col.) 26cm.

Unter Benutzung der Regimentsgeschichte von Major Kosch und Einfügung der Geschichte des Feldzuges 1870/71 von Oberst Gisevius."
1. Army, German—Regt. hist.

NL 0346924 NN

789.5
L716G

Liebeskind, Paul.
Die Glocken des Neustädter Kreises. Ein Beitrag zur Glockenkunde ... Mit 89 Abbildungen im Texte. Jena, G. Fischer, 1905. 140 p. illus. 22 cm. (Zeitschrift des Vereins für thüringische Geschichte und Altertumskunde. Neue Folge. 1. Supplementheft)

1. Bells. 2. Neustadt an der Orla. Antiquities. 3. Thuringia. Antiquities. I. Title.

NL 0346925 NcD CU MH MnU NN CBPac

4DD
3485

Liebeskind, Paul.
Die Trojaburgen in Thüringen. Zeitz, Sis-Verlag, 1922.
23 p.

NL 0346926 DLC-P4

Liebeskind, W.
Der Hühner- oder Geflügelhof, enthaltend praktische Anleitung zur rationellen Haltung und Zucht der Hühner... Gänse, Enten und Tauben, sowie des Ziergeflügels...mit ausführlicher Beschreibung der Rassenmerkmale... Hrsg. von W. Liebeskind ... Weimar: B. F. Voigt, 1895. viii, 197 p. incl. illus., tables. front. 8. ed., rev. 8°.

1. Poultry.—Breeding and raising.
N. Y. P. L. April 1, 1924.

NL 0346927 NN

Liebeskind, W., editor.
Die Nutz- und Sportgeflügelzucht; Beschreibung der Rassenmerkmale nebst Anleitung zur rationellen Haltung und Zucht der Hühner, Truthühner, Perlhühner, Gänse, Enten, des Ziergeflügels, der Pfauen, Fasanen, Schwäne, sowie der Tauben. Neunte verbesserte Auflage, hrsg. von W. Liebeskind... Leipzig: B. F. Voigt, 1911. viii, 196 p., 1 l. illus. 8°.

1. Poultry.—Breeding and raising.
N. Y. P. L. March 3, 1920.

NL 0346928 NN ICJ

Liebeskind, Wolfgang A.
Bischof Walters II. auf der Flüe Landrecht der Landschaft Wallis und Gerichtsordnung
see under Valais (Canton) Laws, statutes, etc.

Liebeskind, Wolfgang A.
La quatrième langue nationale suisse; en marge de la votation fédérale du 20 février 1938. [Geneva? 1938?]

[8] p. 25 cm.
Caption title.
"Extrait de la revue 'Voix des peuples', du 15 mars 1938."

NL 0346930 MH

Liebeskind, Wolfgang A.
... Das referendum der landschaft Wallis, von dr. iur. Wolfgang A. Liebeskind ... Mit 5 tafeln und 1 karte. Leipzig, T. Weicher, 1928.

viii, 95, [1] p. fold. map, 5 facsim. 26cm. (Leipziger rechtswissenschaftliche studien hrsg. von der Leipziger Juristen-fakultät, hft. 33)

"Verzeichnis der benutzten werke": p. [vii]-viii.

1. Valais (Canton)—Pol. & govt. 2. Referendum. 3. Valais (Canton)—Hist.—Sources. I. Title.

29–28902

NL 0346931 DLC CU-L MH

Liebeskind, Wolfgang A.
Die romanische Schweiz als nationales Problem. 2. Aufl. Glarus, R. Tschudy, 1936.

14 p. 23 cm.
Cover-title.

NL 0346932 MH

Das LIEBESLEBEN der Habsburger; Wahrheit statt Dichtung. Wien, L. Hübsch, 1922.

128 p. 23 cm.

1. Habsburg, House of.

NL 0346933 CaBVaU

Liebeslieder moderner frauen
see under Grabein, Paul, 1869– comp.

Liebesnovellen des französischen Mittelalters
see under Goyert, Georg, 1884– ed.

Liebesny, Herbert J 1911–
The government of French North Africa, by Herbert J. Liebesny. Philadelphia, University of Pennsylvania Press, the University Museum, 1943.
180 p. map. 22 cm. (African handbooks, 1)
"Guide to legal sources": p. 122–124.

1. Algeria—Politics and government. 2. Morocco—Politics and government. 3. Tunisia—Politics and government. I. Title. II. Series.
JQ3231.L5 354.61 43–16502

PPT PPD PU PBm DAU WaS OrU OrCS PB CaBViP CaBVaU
NL 0346936 DLC NN NcD ViU OU OClW OCl MiHM OO PU-L

PJ2195
.T5

Liebesny, Herbert J 1911–

Till, Walter Curt, 1894–
Koptische schutzbriefe, von Walter C. Till. Mit einem rechtsgeschichtlichen beitrag von Herbert Liebesny ... Berlin. Reichsverlagsamt, 1938.

Law

Liebesny, Herbert J. 1911– joint ed.

Khadduri, Majid, 1909– ed.
Law in the Middle East, edited by Majid Khadduri and Herbert J. Liebesny. With a foreword by Robert H. Jackson. Washington, Middle East Institute, 1955–

Liebesny, Herbert J. 1911– , joint ed.

Westermann, William Linn, 1873– ed.
Zenon papyri; business papers of the third century B. C. dealing with Palestine and Egypt, edited with introductions and notes by William Linn Westermann ... and Elizabeth Sayre Hasenoehrl ... New York, Columbia university press, 1934–

Liebesny, Paul, 1881–
Diathermie, heissluft und künstliche höhensonne, von privatdozent dr. Paul Liebesny ... mit 30 textabbildungen. Wien und Berlin, J. Springer, 1929.
3 p. l., 73 p. illus. 21cm. (On cover: Bücher der ärztlichen praxis, 15)

1. Thermotherapy. 2. Diathermy. 3. Phototherapy. 4. Spectrum, Ultra-violet.
Library of Congress RM865.L5
29–21528

NL 0346940 DLC PPC

WB
141
L716e
1923

LIEBESNY, Paul, 1881–
Einführung in die physiologisch-klinische Methodik, für Studierende der Medizin. Berlin, Urban & Schwarzenberg, 1923.
viii, 224 p. illus.

NL 0346941 DNLM

VOLUME 332

Liebesny, Paul, 1881–
Hydrotherapie im hause des kranken, von privatdozent dr. Paul Liebesny ... mit 16 textabbildungen. Wien und Berlin, J. Springer, 1932.
iv, 67, [1] p. illus. 20½ᶜᵐ. (*On cover:* Bücher der ärztlichen praxis, 33)

1. Hydrotherapy.
Library of Congress   RM811.L5   32–23740
Copyright A–Foreign   17395
                          [2]   615.853

NL 0346942   DLC CtY-M

Liebesny, Paul, 1881–
Kurz- und ultrakurzwellen; biologie und therapie. Von priv.-doz. dr. Paul Liebesny ... Mit 90 abbildungen. Berlin [etc.] Urban & Schwarzenberg, 1935.
xii, 208 p. illus., tables, diagrs. 25½ᶜᵐ. (*Added t.-p.:* Sonderbände zur Strahlentherapie ... bd. xix)
"Schrifttum": p. 201–202.

1. Electrophysiology. 2. Electrotherapeutics.   I. Title.
                                                A C 35–2941
Title from Rochester   Univ. Printed by L. C.

NL 0346943   NRU MiU OC1W-H CtY ICJ

Die Liebesschule der kleinen Japanerin. Sittengeschichte des fernen Ostens. Atzgersdorf bei Wien, Regina Verlag, 1930. 2 v. illus. 23cm.

1. Prostitution—Japan. 2. Zelle, Margaretha Geertruida, 1876–1917.

NL 0346944   NN MnU

Liebeszunder; oder: Das Mädchen und der jüngling, ein familien-gemälde in drey akten

See *under*

[Dyck, Johann Gottfried] 1750–1815.

Liebetanz (Arthur). *Ueber Gumma der Bindehaut.* 22 pp., 1 l. 8°. *Würzburg, P. Scheiner, 1896.*

NL 0346946   DNLM ICRL

Liebetanz, Erwin
Die parasitischen protozoen des wiederkäuermagens 1905.
Bern. Univ., Ph.D. Diss. 1905.

NL 0346947   PU

Liebetanz, Franz, 1866–
Calciumcarbid und Acetylen. Ihr Wesen, ihre Darstellung und Anwendung für die Bedürfnisse der Praxis. Leipzig, O. Leiner, 1898.
274p. illus.

NL 0346948   ICRL RPB ICJ

Liebetanz, Franz, 1866–
Die elektro-technik aus der praxis—für die praxis. In ihrem gesamten umfange auf grund der neuesten erfahrungen gemeinverständlich geschildert, von Franz Liebetanz. 3., wesentlich verm. aufl. Mit 290 abbildungen und den porträts mit biographischen notizen von Ohm, Ampère, Volta, Siemens, Schuckert, Edison, Reis, Morse und Franklin. Düsseldorf, Druck von J. B. Gerlach & co., 1898.
xv, [1], 352 p. illus., ports. 20½ᶜᵐ.

1. Electric engineering. 2. Electricity.
                                              33–7450
Library of Congress   TK146.L5 1898   621.3

NL 0346949   DLC

Liebetanz, Franz, 1866–   537.8 Q219
Die Elektrotechnik aus der Praxis — für die Praxis. In ihrem gesamten Umfange gemeinverständlich dargestellt von Fr. Liebetanz. Vierte, vollständig umgearbeitete und bedeutend erweiterte Auflage. Mit 373 Abbildungen, 13 Tabellen und den Porträts nebst biographischen Notizen von Ohm, Ampère, Volta, Faraday, Siemens, Schuckert, Edison, Reis, Morse und Franklin. Düsseldorf, J. B. Gerlach & Co., [1903].
x, [2], 416 p. illus. incl. diagrs., 10 ports. 21½ᶜᵐ.
Advertisements, p. 414–416.

NL 0346950   ICJ

Liebetanz, Franz, 1866–
Handbuch der Calciumcarbid- und Acetylentechnik. Nach den neuesten Fortschritten und Erfahrungen geschildert, von Fr. Liebetanz... 2. verm. und verb. Aufl.   Leipzig, O. Leiner, 1899. vii, 423 p. illus. 22cm.

270936B. 1. Calcium carbide.   2. Acetylene.
N. Y. P. L.   June 12, 1944

NL 0346951   NN CU NIC PSt OC1W

Liebetanz, Franz, 1866–
Hilfsbuch für Installationen von Acetylen-Beleuchtungsanlagen. Leipzig, O. Leiner, 1900.
104p. illus.

NL 0346952   ICRL ICJ MB

Liebetanz, Franz, 1866–   661.914 Q900
Die Kalziumcarbid-Fabrikation, von Fr. Liebetanz. Dritte Auflage des ersten Teiles des Handbuches der Kalziumcarbid-Fabrikation und Azetylenbeleuchtung. Leipzig, O. Leiner, 1909.
121, [2] p. illus. 23ᶜᵐ.

NL 0346953   ICJ

Liebetanz, Georg: Ueber einen Fall von Nebenhorn-Schwangerschaft. [Maschinenschrift.] 36 S. 4°. — Auszug: Kattowitz [1922]: Siwinna. 2 Bl. 8°
Breslau, Med. Diss. v. 10. Jan. 1922   [U 22.1474

NL 0346954   ICRL

Liebetanz, Gustav, 1896–
Die juristische konstruktion der annahme an erfüllungsstatt (§§ 364, 365 B. G. B.) ... von Gustav Liebetanz ... Berlin-Lichterfelde [Druck H. Büttner] 1926.
1 p. l., [1], iv, 58, [2] p. 23ᶜᵐ.
Inaug.-diss.—Breslau.
Lebenslauf.
"Literatur-verzeichnis": p. ii–vi.

1. Debtor and creditor—Germany. 2. Contracts—Germany. 3. Payment.
                    [Full name: Gustav Richard Erwin Max Liebetanz]
                                              30–2420 Revised

NL 0346955   DLC CtY

Liebetanz, Paul, 1875–
WG   Über die Verdampfungs- und die Mischungs-
34748   wärme von Aethylalkohol-Wasser-Gemischen
           bei 0° C. Breslau, 1892.
           40 p. 23 cm.

           Inaug.-Diss. - Breslau.

NL 0346956   CtY DNLM

Liebetrau (Conradus). *De visu.* 48 pp. 8°.
Jena, typ. Branii. [1836].

NL 0346957   DNLM PPC

Liebetrau, Edmund.
Beitraege sur kenntniss des unteren muschelkalks bei Jena.
Inaug. diss. Jena, 1890 (Berlin)

NL 0346958   ICRL MH OC1W CU PU

LIEBETRAU, Elisabeth.
Die testamentsform im deutschen internationalen privatrecht. Zeulenroda, 1936.
pp. 79.
Inaug.-diss. --- Hamburg.

NL 0346959   MH-L CtY

Liebetrau, Eugen 1901–
Das schweizerische bundesgesetz über die kautionen der deutschen lebensversicherungsgesellschaften vom 8. April 1924 und seine vorgeschichte ... Eisenach [1929?]
Göttingen diss. 1929
[Full name: Eugen Otto Paul Liebetrau]

NL 0346960   MiU ICRL

Liebetrau, Hans.
Macht und Geheimnis der Suggestion. Basel, Liebetrau [1951]
63 p.

NL 0346961   MH

Liebetrau, Hans.
Die Steigerung der Gedächtniskraft und Konzentration durch die zeitsparende Reaktivierungs-Methode. Avegno [1950]
56 p. 21 cm.
Pages [53]–[54] blank; pages 55–56 advertisements.
Based on the author's "Schule der Gedächtnismeisterschaft und Konzentration," but substantially a new work. Cf. p. [2]

1. Memory.   I. Title.
BF371.L5   154   50–57822

NL 0346962   DLC NN ICRL

W 4   LIEBETRAU, Hans Rudolf.
B29   Studien zum Problem der Pigment-
1951   bildung in der Haut. Basel, Karger,
          1951.
             p. [75]-89.
             Cover title.
             Inaug.-Diss. - Basel.
             Reprinted from Dermatologica,
          v. 103, no. 2, 1951.
             Contains errata slip.
             1. Pigmentation

NL 0346963   DNLM

Liebetrau, Heinrich, joint author.
TH7226
.L513
Lier, Heinrich.
Le chauffage et la ventilation, par Henri Lier [et] Henri Liebetrau. Lausanne, F. Rouge, 1943.

TK145   Liebetrau, Heinrich, joint author.
.S648
Spieser, Robert.
Elektrische Installationen, von R. Spieser [und] Hch. Liebetrau. Zürich, Polygraphischer Verlag [1943]

Liebetrau, Heinrich, joint author.
TH7226
.L5
Lier, Heinrich.
... Heizung und lüftung, von Hch. Lier ... [und] Hch. Liebetrau ... Zürich, Polygraphischer verlag a.-g. [1943]

VOLUME 332

TK145
.S65

Liebetrau, Heinrich, joint author.

Spieser, Robert.
Les installations électriques, par R. Spieser [et] H. Liebetrau. Lausanne, F. Rouge, 1944.

NL 0346969   DLC NN MdBJ

TH6291
.M413

Liebetrau, Heinrich, joint author.

Meier, Hermann, *engineer.*
Les installations sanitaires, par Hermann Meier [et] H. Liebetrau. Lausanne, F. Rouge, 1943.

Liebetrau, Heinrich.
Rheinfelden. Version française par Pierre Barrelet. Neuchâtel, Éditions du Griffon [1952]
48 p. illus. 25 cm. (Trésors de mon pays, 58)

1. Rheinfelden, Switzerland.

DQ851.R48L5   914.94   52-66766 ‡

NL 0346969   DLC NN MdBJ

Liebetrau, Heinrich.
Rheinfelden, die kleine Stadt mit den grossen Erinnerungen. Bern, P. Haupt [1952]
56 p. illus. 25 cm. (Schweizer Heimatbücher, Bd. 46. Aargauische Reihe, Bd. 3)

1. Rheinfelden, Switzerland.

DQ851.R48L53   53-29675 ‡

NL 0346970   DLC NIC MdBJ CU

TH6291
.M414

Liebetrau, Heinrich, joint author.

Meier, Hermann, *engineer.*
Sanitäre Installationen, von Hermann Meier [und] Hch. Liebetrau. Zürich, Polygraphischer Verlag [1943]

Liebetrau, Hermann, 1878-
Ueber primaere sarkome des calcaneus.
Inaug. diss. Jena, 1902.
Bibl.

NL 0346972   ICRL MBCo DNLM

B669
L62

Liebetrau, Leopold.
Gründliche Anweisung zur Bearbeitung des Kupfers, Zinkes, Zinnes und Bleies, um die bei diesen Metallen so häufig vorkommenden Schieferbrüche zu verhüten, sowie zur Anfertigung einer neu erfundenen Metall-Composition, und eines neuen haeten Schlaglothes. Für Kupferhütten und Kupferhämmer, sowie für Künstler, welche sich mit Anfertigung der Metall-Compositionen beschäftigen. Quedlinburg, G. Basse, 1841.
43, [1] p. 4 plates. 19 cm.

1. Metallurgy.

NL 0346973   NNC PPF

Liebetrau, Otto.
Die Massnahmen gegen den Alkoholismus im Verkehrswesen, von Direktor bei der Reichsbahn Liebetrau... Berlin-Dahlem: Verlag "Auf der Wacht," 1930. 19 p. 8°.

1. Alcoholism—Social and economic   effects.
N. Y. P. L.   June 17, 1931

NL 0346974   NN

Liebetrau, Otto, 1900-
Variationsstatistische untersuchungen ueber form und leistung an kuehen der schwarzbunten niederungsrasse der stammzuchtgenossenschaft eutin. Halle-Wittenberg, H. John, 1927.
Inaug.-diss. Halle-Wittenberg.
Bibl.
"Literatur", p. 125-126.
"Lebenslauf" at end.

NL 0346975   ICRL MiU CtY MH

Liebetrau, Otto, 1904-
... Untersuchungen über die Latenz der kalorischen Vestibularisprüfung bei verschiedenen pneumatisierten Schläfenbeinen ... Freiburg i. Br., 1936.
Inaug.-Diss. - Freiburg i. Br.
Lebenslauf.
"Schrifttum": p. 39-41.

NL 0346976   CtY MiU

RBS.
150756

Liebetraut, Johann Gottfried.
*Theses medico practicae...
Viennae: typis Joan. Thomae Trattnern, [1775],

NL 0346977   NNNAM

CS
2351
L71

Liebetrau, C   F
Specimen onomastici Romari. Berlin, gedruckt in der Nauk'schen Buchdruckerei, 1843.
24 p. 25 cm.

Accompanies "Programm"--Gymnasium zum grauen Kloster, Berlin.

1. Names, Personal--Roman.

NL 0346978   NIC PU NjP

BX8080   **Liebetrut, Friedrich.**
.S93L7   Arnold August Sybel ... nach seinem leben und wirken, und nach seinem schriftlichen nachlasse dargestellt, von dr. Friedrich Liebetrut ... Berlin, In kommission bei W. Thome, 1841.
xiv, 409, [1] p. front. (port.) 21 cm.

1. Sybel, Arnold August Eberhard Severus, 1804-1838.

NL 0346979   ICU NjPT

Liebetrut, Friedrich.
Dr. J.T. Beck, ordentlicher Professor der Theologie in Tübingen, und seine Stellung zur Kirche, insonderheit zu derjenigen seines Bekenntnisses. Berlin, G. Schlawitz, 1857-58.
2 v. in 1. 21 cm.

1 Beck, Johann Tobias, 1804-1878.

NL 0346980   NjPT

HQ
503
L5

Liebetrut, Friedrich.
Die Ehe nach ihrer Idee, und nach ihrer geschichtlichen Entwickelung; ein Beitrag zur richtigen Würdigung der Ehe...Nebst einem Vorwort von August Hahn. Berlin, F. Dümmler, 1834.
xxx, 382 p. 21 cm.

1. Marriage. I. Title.

NL 0346981   NRCR MH OCl

Liebetrut, Friedrich.
Reise nach dem Morgenlande, insonderheit nach Jerusalem und dem heiligen Lande ... Tl. 1-2. Hamburg: Rauh, [pref. 1853].
2 v.

NL 0346982   OCH

915.69   **Liebetrut, Friedrich.**
L62r   Reise nach dem Morgenlande, insonderheit nach Jerusalem und dem heiligen lande. Hamburg, 1854.
2 v. in 1, fronts., fold.map, fold.plan.

NL 0346983   IU CU

Liebetrut, Friedrich.
Reise nach dem Morgenlande, insonderheit nach Jerusalem und dem heiligen Lande ... Hamburg, 1858.
2 v. in 1. 17.5 cm.

NL 0346984   CtY

BV110   **Liebetrut, Friedrich.**
.L7   Der tag des Herrn und seine feier. In briefen. Mit biblischer, historischer und wissenschaftlicher begründung dargestellt...von dr. Friedrich Liebetrut ... Berlin, L. Oehmigke, 1837.
xx, 366, [2] p. 20 cm.

1. Sunday.

NL 0346985   ICU NRCR

4HQ   **Liebetrut, Friedrich.**
629   Ueber geordnete Entwicklung der Ehe; besonders über die kirchliche Leitung ihres Anfanges; zur Sicherung ihres Gedeihens und zur Verhütung der Scheidung. Eine Vorarbeit, vornämlich aus kirchlichem und pfarramtlichem Gesichtspunkt. Berlin, W. Hertz, 1856.
107 p.

NL 0346986   DLC-P4

Liebetruth, Christian, 1892-
... Zur behandlung der subcutanen nierenverletzungen ... Berlin, Blanke [1919]
34, [2] p.

Inaug.-diss., Berlin, 1919.
Lebenslauf.
"Literatur": p. [35]

1. Kidneys - Wounds and injuries.

NL 0346987   NNC CtY MiU

Liebetruth, Erich.
Die ergebnisse der altersstaroperationen an der universitätsaugenklinik zu Leipzig während der jahre 1925 bis 1930... Leipzig, 1932. 28 p.
Inaug. Diss. -Leipzig, 1932.
Lebenslauf.
Bibliography.

NL 0346988   DNLM

Liebetruth, Erich.

Trode, Eduard.
Die mutterschaftshilfe in Deutschland, herausgegeben von Eduard Trode ... in verbindung mit dr. E. Liebetruth ... Berlin-Lichterfelde, Langewort, 1937.

VOLUME 332

Liebetruth, Hugo, 1901-
Die haftung des beamten nach § 839 BGB.
Inaug. diss. Koenigsberg, 1928.
Bibl.

NL 0346990   DLC MH-L

Liebetruth, Johannes: Die Entzündungen der Speicheldrüsen bei
Typhus abdominalis an Hand der Typhusfälle der Leipziger Med.
Klinik von 1891 ab unt. bes. Berücks. d. Entstehungsmöglichk.
vom Munde aus. [Maschinenschrift.] 37 S. 4° [Lag nicht vor.] —
Auszug: (Zeulenroda in Thür. 1924: Oberreuter.) 4 S. 8°
Leipzig, Med. Diss. v. 7. Nov. 1924 [1925]   [U 25. 6801

NL 0346991   ICRL

Liebezeit, Georg, 1883-
Die rechte des eigentuemers und des frueheren
besitzers gegen den besitzdiener...
Inaug. Diss. Breslau, 1907
Bibl.

NL 0346992   ICRL

Liebezeit, Georg. Sigism.,   -1789.
——— * De abortus noxia et nefanda promotione.
46 pp. 4°. Hala Magdeb., lit. J. C. Hendelii,
1730. [Also. in P., v. 1386.]

NL 0346993   DNLM

Liebezeit (Georg. Sigism.) [-1789]. * De
tumore œdematoso podagrico. 30 pp., 1 l. sm.
4°. Hala Magdeb., typ. C. Henckelii, [1713].

NL 0346994   DNLM PPC

2530   Liebezeit, Gottfried, d.1711.
.584   [Novum dictionarium latino-sveco-germa-
nicum, sveco-latinum, et germanico-latinum]
Hamburg, In verlegung G.Liebezeits [etc.,
etc.] Gedruckt bey N.Spieringk, 1700.
3 pt.in 1 v. front. 17½ cm.

Added t.-p.in Swedish.
Parts 2 and 3 have each a special t.-p.

1.Latin language-Dict.-Swedish. 2.
Latin language-Dict.-German.

NL 0346995   NjP

Liebfrauenbruderschaft der Finsteren Kapelle,
Kye500   Würzburg.
C33   Das Seelbuch der Liebfrauenbruderschaft zu
Q33   Würzburg, 12.-15. Jahrhundert (Necrologia
7   episcopatus Herbipolensis II) Eingeleitet
und hrsg. von Wilhelm Engel. Würzburg,
F. Schöningh, 1953.
116 p. facsim. 24 cm. (Quellen und
Forschungen zur Geschichte des Bistums und
Hochstifts Würzburg, Bd. 7)
1. Clergy - Würzburg - Biog. 2. Würzburg -
Hist. - Sources. I. Engel, Wilhelm, 1905-
ed.   II. Title

NL 0346996   CtY NN IEN NIC MH NNC

Liebfrauengarten; geschichtliche beispiele,
legenden, sagen, parabeln und gleichnisse von der
macht und güte der Allerseligsten Jungfrau und
Gottesmutter Maria und ihrer verehrung, von einem
priester der diöcese Regensburg, mit vorwort von
Ludwig Mehler... viii,758p. Regensburg, A.
Coppenrath, 1864.

NL 0346997   OC1

Liebfrauenkirche, *Treves*
see Treves. Liebfrauenkirche.

Liebfreed, Edwin.
Lincoln. On seeing the George Grey Barnard head of
Lincoln that was donated to France to repose in the Lux-
embourg gallery in Paris. [n. p.] *1921.

leaf. 28ᶜᵐ.
Poem.

1. Lincoln, Abraham, pres. U. S.—Poetry.
Library of Congress   E457.9.L7   CA 21–277 Unrev'd

NL 0346999   DLC

Ayer
142   LIEBFRIEDT, CHRISTIAN, von Gross Seufftzen, pseud.
L71   An gantz Teutschlandt von dess Spanniers
1620   Tyranney welche er ohn unterscheid der Religion
auch an den aller Unschuldigsten verübt... Gedruckt zur Nachrichtung bey F. Smhcam, 1620.
[23]p. woodcut. 20cm.

NL 0347000   ICN InU

4K   Liebgott, L
Ger.   Repetitorium über das allgemeine
1889   Landrecht für die preussischen Staaten; ein Hand- und Hülfsbuch sowohl
für angehende Juristen beim Studium
dieses Gesetzbuches, als für Subaltern-
beamte, namentlich für diejenigen,
welche das Examen als Actuar 1. Klasse
bestehen wollen.   Schonebeck, E.
Berger, 1855.
380 p.

NL 0347001   DLC-P4

4K   Liebhaber, Erich Daniel von, d.1801.
9329   Beiträge zur Erörterung der
Staatsverfassung der Braunschweig
-Lüneburgischen Chur-Lande. Gotha,
Bey C. W. Ettinger, 1794.
240 p.
At head of title: Erich Daniel von
Liebhaber...
Bibliographical footnotes.

NL 0347002   DLC-P4 MH-L

4K   Liebhaber, Erich Daniel von, d.1801.
Ger.   Einleitung in das herzoglich
1610   Braunschweig-Lüneburgische Land
-Recht. Braunschweig, In der Schul-
buchhandlung, 1791.
2 v.

NL 0347003   DLC-P4

Liebhaber, Erich Daniel von, d.1801.
Vom Fürstenthum Blankenburg und dessen Staats-
Verfassung ... vom Ursprunge, Verfalle und
Reformation der Klöster... Wernigerode, Auf
Kosten des Verfassers gedruckt bey Struck, 1790

315 p. geneal. tables

NL 0347004   MH

OpaS5   Liebhaber, Ernest, baron de.
826l   Examen raisonné de l'état actuel de la
France, sous les différens rapports du système
de gouvernement adopté par ses ministres, de
l'application et des conséquences de ses lois
fondamentales, et de sa position dans l'ordre
politique de l'Europe ... Paris, Avril de
Gastel[etc.],1826.
180p. 21½cm.

NL 0347005   CtY

W 4   LIEBHABER, Henja, 1923-
M96   Flavone, Anthocyane und Catechine.
1950   München, 1950.
30 l.
Inaug.-Diss. - Munich.
Typewritten copy.
1. Flavones

NL 0347006   DNLM

Ein Liebhaber.
Cometa adumbratus
see under title

Ein Liebhaber christlicher Ubungen.
Neuer Helicon mit seinen neun Musen ...
see under   [Knorr von Rosenroth, Christian]
1636-1689.

Ein Liebhaber curieuser Sachen.
Die geöffnete Raritäten- und Naturalien-Kammer
see under title

Ein Liebhaber der christlichen Wahrheit.
Bau-fälliger Wachter-Thurn gegen dem unzer-
störlichen Felsen-Bau der Röm. Catholischen
Kirchen ausgeführet
see under title

Ein Liebhaber der Gerechtigkeit.
Einfältig Bedencken über die Frag, ob ...
see under title

Liebhaber der Gestirne.
Ein Gespräch zwischen einem Naturkündiger
see under title

Ein Liebhaber der Medicin.
Curieuse, neue, seltene, leichte ...
verwunderungswürdige Hausz-Apotheck...
see under title

Ein Liebhaber der rechten Kirchen.
Curioese Historie von einer Kirchen-Wallfarth...
see under title

VOLUME 332

Ein Liebhaber der reinen Wahrheit.
Königliche Hermetische Special-Concordanz ...
see under title

Ein Liebhaber der Sternwissenschaft.
Anzeige das der im Jahre 1682 erschienene und
von Halley nach der newtonianischen Theorie auf
gegenwärtige Zeit vorherverkündigte Comet wirklich
sichtbar sey...
see under title

Ein Liebhaber der teutschen Freyheit.
Das gedrückte und wieder erquickte
Deutschland ...
see under title [supplement]

Ein Liebhaber der teutschen Poeterey.
Strassburgische Chronick
see under [Kleinlawe, Michael] fl. 1625.

Ein Liebhaber der Vernunft und alles was
recht oder Vernünfftg [!] ist.
In der natur wohl gegründete, und
allen vernünfftigen menschen wohl begreiffliche
antwort...
see under title

Ein Liebhaber der wahren Weissheit.
Die güldene Hoffnung wie dieselbe von denen
sich selbstangebenden Alchymisten ...
see under title

Ein Liebhaber der Wahrheit.
Bedencken, ob den Reformierten Gemeinden
binnen Franckfurt am Mayn, ihr Religions Exerci-
tium zuverwaigern...
see under title

Ein Liebhaber der Wahrheit.
Critische Jesuiter-Geschichte
see under title

Ein Liebhaber der Wahrheit.
Freundliche antwort auff die 10 ersten von
den XL. fragen dess tit. Abraham Hinckelmanns ...
see under title

Ein Liebhaber der Wahrheit und Gerechtigkeit.
Bedencken ob Christliche Oberkeiten die im
heiligen Roemischen Reich gesessene Juedischeit
bey derohabenden Thorach und Thalmud...
see under title

Ein Liebhaber des friedens.
Gegründete ablehnung etlicher wieder den
pragischen frieden-schluss movirter *dubiorum*
see under title

Ein Liebhaber des oekonomischen Nutzens.
Der künstliche seiffen-sieder und kerzen-
oder liechter-zieher
see under title

Ein Liebhaber des Vatterlands.
Kursses einsehen und ohnmässgebliches
bedencken/die zur zeit im Heil. rom. reich
eingerissene silber-müntz-sorten besagend
see under title

Ein Liebhaber Jesu.
Der evangelische Gnaden-weg zur Seligkeit fuer
alle Religionen ...
see under title

Die Liebhaber nach der mode...
see under [Heufeld, Franz] 1731-1795.

Ein Liebhaber natürlicher geheimnisse, tr.

Philippi Aureoli Theophrasti Paracelsi Chymischer psalter, oder Philosophische grundsätze vom stein derer
weisen anno 1522 ... Aus dem höchst seltenen lateinischen grundtext übers. von einem liebhaber natürlicher
geheimnisse 1771. Berlin, J. F. Vieweg [1771]

Ein liebhaber oeconomischer wissenschafften.
Compendieuses und nutzbares Haushastungs-
Lexicon ...
see under title

Ein Liebhaber teutscher Freyheit.
Kön: Schwed: Victori Schlüssel
see under title

Liebhaber-Bibliothek. Bd. 1-
Berlin, O. Elsner, 1905-
v. illus. 31 cm.

"Alter und seltener Drucke in faksimile-
Nachbildung."

NL 0347033 NcD

NE1240 Liebhaber-bibliothek alter illustratoren in
.L5 facsimile-reproduction.
Muenchen, 1880-

NL 0347034 DLC NN MiU

M27
.C
Case
Eine Liebhaberin der Musik.

Canzonette fürs Klavier, von einer Liebhaberin der Musik,
mit verschiedenen Tonkünstlern. Gotha, C. W. Ettinger,
1781.

Die Liebhaberkünste in Einzelabhandlungen. Heft 1-[3]. ... .
Leipzig, W. Mösche, [1903].
3 nos. in 1 vol. 14½ cm.
Cover-title.
Contents. — Heft 1. Nordhausen, G. Die Malerei auf alle Arten von Stoff mit den
Heliosfarben (Helios-Malerei). 14 p. — Heft 2. Schütze, W. Die Plastin-Reliefmalerei.
24 p. 11 illus. — Heft 3. Buerge, M. Die Porzellanmalerei und Porzellanradierung.
20 p.

NL 0347036 ICJ

Liebhafsky, Erwin Eugene, 1922–
National science policy and technological progress. Ur-
bana, 1950.
11 p. 23 cm.
Abstract of thesis—University of Illinois.
Vita.

1. Science and state—U. S. 2. Patents—U. S. 3. Research—U. S.
Q180.U5L5   A 53–3022
Illinois. Univ. Library
for Library of Congress   [3]†

NL 0347037 IU NIC DLC

Liebhafsky, Herman Alfred, 1905–
The reduction of iodate ion by hydrogen
peroxide, by Herman Alfred Liebhafsky ...
[Berkeley, 1929]
2 p.l., 30 numb. l., 1 l. mounted plates.
29 cm.
Thesis (Ph. D.) – Univ. of California, Dec. 1929.
1. Iodates. 2. Hydrogen peroxide. I. Title.

NL 0347038 CU

Liebhard, Franz.
Schwäbische Chronik. Bukarest,
Staatsverlag für Kunst und Literatur
[1952] 85 p. 20cm.

Poems.

NL 0347039 NN

Liebhard, Joachim

see

Camerarius, Joachim, 1500-1574.

A30
A3
1668b
Liebhard, Ludwig, 1635-1687, *praeses.*
Apologia pro Friderico Primo imperatore
potentissimo quem a Romano Pontifice pedibus
conculcatum esse nonnulli scribunt. [Baruth?]
Recusa,172.
Diss. - Bayreuth,1668 (C.A. Bross, respondent)

NL 0347041 CtY

VOLUME 332

Liebhard, Ludwig, 1635-1687, praeses.
De serenissimi Electoralis Collegii
origine exercitatio historica ...
Cvriae Nariscorvm, Literis Mintzelia-
nis ₍1668₎

27, ₍1₎ p. 19½cm.

Diss. - Bayreuth (C.F. Pertsch, respondent)

NL 0347042   MH-L CtY

Liebhardt, Erich.
Riesenmyome des uterus. (Auszug).
Inaug. diss. (Nuernberg,)1919. Erlangen

NL 0347043   ICRL

RBS.   Liebhardt, Johann Heinrich.
1523h1   De generaliori catharticorum, notione et usu.
Erlangae; Typis Hilpertians, [1796].

NL 0347044   NNNAM

Liebhardt, *Mrs.* Louise (Dodge) 1897-
Love is a thistle, by Louise Liebhardt. Mill Valley, Calif.,
New York, N. Y., The Wings press, 1941.

57, ₍1₎ p. 22½ᵐ.

Poems.

I. Title.

Library of Congress   PS3523.I 275L8 1941
42-707
811.5

NL 0347045   DLC OrU

Liebhardt, Norbert, 1926-
Die Vorzugsaktie, ihre rechtliche und betriebswirtschaft-
liche Problematik. München, 1955.

v, 142 l. 29 cm.

Typescript (carbon copy)
Inaug.-Diss.—Munich.
Vita.
Bibliography : leaves 136-142.

1. Preferred stocks—Germany (Federal Republic, 1949-   )
I. Title.
58-35061

NL 0347046   DLC

₍Liebhart, Henry₎ 1832-1895.
A B C-buch und lese-uebungen für schule und haus.
Cincinnati, Walden und Stowe ₍1881₎

64 p. illus. 17ᶜᵐ.

"Vorbemerkungen" signed: H. Liebhart.

1. Primers, German.

Library of Congress   PF3115.L5
17-23226

NL 0347047   DLC OCU

H   [Liebhart, Henry   ] 1832-1875.
220.95   Biblische Geschichte, oder illustrirte
L62b   Kinderbibel. 126 Erzählungen des Alten und
c1882   Neuen Testaments. Mit 128 schönen Holzschnitten.
Berne, Ind., Welty & Sprunger [c1882]

[2] 319p. illus. 18cm.

NL 0347048   ViHarEM DLC

4BV   Liebhart, Henry, 1832-1895.
1077   Das Buch der Gleichnisse; nämlich:
Biblische Wahrheiten in Sinnbildern
und Beispielen; ein Handbuch für
Prediger, Lehrer und Eltern. Cincinnati, Hitchcock & Walden, 1876.
588 p.

NL 0347049   DLC-P4 PPLT

Liebhart, Henry, 1832-1895.
Drei Weihnachtsabende
see under title

Liebhart, Henry, 1832-1895, tr.

Stevens, Abel, 1815-1897.
Geschichte der Bischöflichen methodistenkirche in den Ver.
Staaten von Nordamerika. Von dr. Abel Stevens ... Frei aus
dem englischen übersetzt von H. Liebhart ... Cincinnati und
Chicago, Hitchcock & Walden ₍1867₎-72.

Liebhart, Henry, 1832-1895, ed.

Haus und herd. Ein familien-magazin für jung und alt ...
jahrg. 1-
jan. 1873-
Cincinnati, Hitchcock und Walden; New York, Nelson und
Phillips, 1873-

-VM   LIEBHART, HENRY, 1832-1895, comp.
1992   Jugend-Harfe. Eine Sammlung von 93 Melo-
L 7163   dien und 156 Liedern für Schule und Haus.
1867   Neueste, verb. Aufl.   Cincinnati,Hitchcock
& Walden,1867;
104p. 20cm.

NL 0347053   ICN PPPrHi InGO

M1994   Liebhart, Henry, 1832-1895, ed.
L68   Jugend-harfe. Eine sammlung von 93 mel-
odien und 156 liedern für schule und haus.
Bearbeitet von H. Liebhart ... Cincinnati,
Poe & Hitchcock; New York, Carlton & Porter
₍etc., etc.₎ 1868₌c1867₎

104p. 19½ cm.

Title vignette.
German words.

NL 0347054   NBuG

Liebhart, Henry, 1832-1895, ed.

Psalter und harfe. Lieder und melodien für
schule, haus und gottesdienstlichen gebrauch
bearb. von H. Liebhart. Cincinnati, Chicago
₍etc.₎ Cranston & Stowe: New York, Phillips &
Hunt ₍1876₎
276 p. 20cm.

MnU DLC-P4
NL 0347065   NcD CtY PPCS PP PPPrHi MiU OCl NNUT RPB

NM   Liebhart, Henry, 1832-1895.
L622l   Das Leben und Wirken in der Heidenwelt.
Charakterbilder aus der Mission, nebst Übersicht-
licher Darstellung der Missionsgeschichte und
einer vollständigen Missionsstatistik. Bearb.
von H. Liebhart. Cincinnati, Hitchcock & Walden,
1879.
344 p. 18 cm.

Contents.- Amerika.- Die Südsee.- Afrika.-
Asien.- Missions-Statistik.

1. Missions - Hist. - Modern. 2. Missions -
Statistics. I. Title.

NL 0347056   CtY-D

₍Liebhart, Henry₎ 1832-1895.
Lesebuch für die christliche jugend. Cincinnati, Walden & Stowe ₍1881₎

128 p. illus. 17ᵐᵐ.

"Vorbemerkungen" signed: H. Liebhart.

1. German language—Chrestomathics and readers.

Library of Congress   PF3115.L52
17-23225

NL 0347057   DLC NNU-W

RAM4.8   Liebhart, Henry, 1832-1895.
L71   Liederlust und Psalter. Cincinnati,
Cranston und Stowe ₌c1882₎
200, 276p.21cm.

Psalter und Harfe, bearbeitet von H.
Liebhart, 276p. at end.

1. Songs, German. I. Title. II. Cranston
and Stowe, Cincinnati.

NL 0347058   OC IU

Liebhart, Henry, 1832-1895, comp.

Liederlust und Psalter. Cincinnati,
Walden und Stowe ₍c1882₎
200 p. 21 cm.

With music.

1. Hymns, German. I. Title.

NL 0347059   RPB NcD

-VM   LIEBHART, HENRY, 1832-1895, comp.
2132.G3   Liederlust und Psalter, mit anhang.   Cin-
L 716L   cinnati,Cranston and Stowe₍c1884₎
1884   302p. 20½cm.

"Anhang. Lieder aus Psalter und harfe ohne
noten": p.₍197₎-289.

NL 0347060   ICN WaSp NNUT OCl

Liebhart, Henry, 1832-1895, comp.

Der neue kleine Psalter; Zionslieder
für den gebrauch in Erbauungsstunden und
Lagerversammlungen, redigirt von H. Liebhart.
Cincinnati ₍etc.₎ Curts & Jennings; New York
₍etc.₎ Eaton & Mains ₍c1889₎
202 p. 16 cm.

With music.

1. Hymns, German.   I. Title.

NL 0347061   RPB NNUT

VOLUME 332

H
783.9
L62p
Liebhart, Henry, 1832–1895.
Die Perle. Sang und Klang für Sonntagschulen
und Jugendvereine. Redigirt von H. Liebhart, D.D.
Berne, Mennonite Book Concern [c1894]

224p. 20cm.

NL 0347062   ViHarEM

Liebhart, Henry, 1832–1895.
Die Perle. Sang und Klang für Sonntagschulen und Jugend-
vereine. Redigirt von H. Liebhart ...   Cincinnati, Cranston
& Curts [etc., etc.] 1894.   224 p.   20cm.

Close score.

94811B. 1. Hymns, Sunday school.   2. Hymns, German. I. Title.
N. Y. P. L.   October 17, 1945

NL 0347063   NN NNUT IU MBU-T TxDaM

Liebhart, Henry, 1832–1895.
Das Pfarrhaus im Harz. Eine Erzählung
für die reifere Jugend und das Volk. Cincinnati, Hitchcock & Walden [pref.1869]
296 p. 18cm.

NL 0347064   FU

Liebhart, Henry, 1832–1895, ed.
Psalter und harfe. Lieder und melodien für
schule, haus und gottesdienstlichen gebrauch
bearb. von H. Liebhart. Cincinnati, Chicago
[etc.] Cranston & Stowe; New York, Phillips &
Hunt [1876]
276 p. 20cm.

MnU DLC-P4
NL 0347065   NcD CtY PPCS PP PPPrHi MiU OCl NNUT RPB

Liebhart, Henry, 1832–1895.

Cartwright, Peter, 1785–1872.
Die reformation im hinterwald. Ein charakterbild von
dr. Peter Cartwright und seiner zeit. Bearb. von H.
Liebhart, nach "Autobiography of Peter Cartwright"
und "Fifty years as a presiding elder." Cincinnati,
Hitchcock & Walden [1873]

Liebhart, Mathias.   L623.71 Q201
Lehrbuch der Terrainlehre, Terraindarstellung und Terrainauf-
nahme für die K. u. K. Militärakademie und Kadettenschulen
verfasst im Auftrage des K. u. K. Reichskriegsministeriums von
Mathias Liebhart, ... Erster–[zweiter] Teil. Wien, L. W.
Seidel & Sohn, 1902–1904.
2 vol. illus., maps in pocket, diagrs. 26½cm.
No more published.

NL 0347067   ICJ DNW

Liebhart, Otto, 1904–
Die Ortsnamen des Seklergebietes in Siebenbürgen.
96, 1 p
Inaug. diss. Leipzig. 1927.

Bibl.
Lebenslauf.

NL 0347068   ICRL IU

Liebheim, Ernst Karl Adolf August, 1870–
Beiträge zur kenntnis des lothringischen kohlengebir-
ges. Mit einem atlas von 7 tafeln ... Strassburg i/E.,
Strassburger druckerei und verlagsanstalt, vormals R.
Schultz u. comp., 1900.
1 p. l., 292 p., 1 l. illus., tables. 27cm. and atlas of VII pl. 38½ x 54cm.
Inaug.-diss.—Strassburg.
Biography.
Atlas has cover-title: Beiträge zur kenntniss des lothringischen kohlen-
gebirges ... Atlas.
Issued also as Abhandlungen zur geologischen specialkarte von Elsass-
Lothringen. Neue folge, hft. IV.
"Litteraturverzeichnis": p. 287–288.
1. Coal mines and mining—Lorraine.

Library of Congress   TN808.G4L69   7–1734

NL 0347069   DLC CU MH

Liebheim, Ernst Karl Adolf August, 1870–
Beiträge zur kenntnis des lothringischen kohlengebirges,
von E. Liebheim. Mit einem atlas von 7 tafeln. Strassburg,
Strassburger druckerei und verlagsanstalt, 1900.
3 p. l., 292 p. incl. 1 illus., tables, 2 diagr. 27½cm. and atlas of 4 fold.
pl., 2 fold. maps, fold. plan. 38 x 28cm. (Added t.-p.: Abhandlungen zur
geologischen specialkarte von Elsass-Lothringen. Neue folge, hft. IV)
"Litteraturverzeichnis": p. 287–288.
1. Geology—Lorraine.   2. Coal mines and mining—Lorraine.

Library of Congress   QE269.A19A   3–25264 Revised

NL 0347070   DLC ICJ

Liebheit, Edmund, 1862–
Ueber die Dupin'sche cyclide ... Halle a. S., 1886.
38 p., 1 l. diagrs. on fold. pl. 22cm.
Inaug.-dis.—Halle.
Vita.

1. Surfaces.

Library of Congress   QA573.L71   4–26739†

NL 0347071   DLC NjP RPB

Liebheit & Thiesen, firm, printers, Berlin.
Sechzig Jahre Liebheit & Thiesen Buch- und Kunstdruckerei,
1866–1926. Berlin [Liebheit & Thiesen] 1926. 22 p. front.,
illus. (plans), 24 pl. (part col'd, mounted.) 32cm.

892538A. 1. Printing—Germany—   Berlin.
N. Y. P. L.   June 23, 1937

NL 0347072   NN

HX276   Liebherr, Karl.
L711   Der bolschewismus in Russland und Deutschland
nach seinem wesen, wirken und werden volkstüm-
lich dargestellt von Karl Liebherr ... Berlin,
Kranz-verlag [1919]

51, [1] p. 22½cm.

1. Communism – Germany.   2. Communism –
Russia.   I. Title.

NL 0347073   CSt-H CU

Liebherr, Karl.
Bolschewistische Schlaglichter. Berlin, Kranz Verlag
[1919]

24 p.
"3. Ergänzungsheft zu 'Der Bolschewismus in Russland
und Deutschland'."

NL 0347074   MH

Liebhold, ——, 18th cent.   8044.312.9
Lo! to us is born an infant. For four-part chorus of mixed voices.
A cappella.
— New York. G. Schirmer (Inc.). 1931. 8 pp. [Westminster
choir series. No. 9.] 26½ cm.
There is a pianoforte accompaniment for rehearsal.

N9711 — T.r. Anthem. — S.r.c. — Church music. Anthems. etc. made.

NL 0347075   MB

Liebhold, ——, 18th cent.

Thüringische motetten der ersten hälfte des 18. jahrhunderts.
Nach ms. 13661 der Königsberger universitätsbibliothek
(Gottholdsche sammlung) herausgegeben von Max Seiffert.
Leipzig. Breitkopf & Härtel. 1915.

Liebhold (Augustus Ludovicus). * De ulceri-
bus. 30 pp. 4°. *Wittembergæ, lit. Tzschiedrichii,*
[1801].

NL 0347077   DNLM

Liebhold, K. J.
Die bedeutung des platonischen Gorgias, und
dessen Beziehungen. n. p., 1885.

NL 0347078   NjP

Liebhold, K. J.
Über den philosophischen zusammenhang der
drei Dialoge Phädrus. n. p., 1862.

NL 0347079   NjP

Liebhold, K. J.
Ueber die bedeutung d ... Phaedon für
die Platon. Erkenntnisstheorie. n. p., 1876.

NL 0347080   NjP

Liebhold, Trude, 1908–
Die reform der rechtsstellung des unehelichen
kindes...
Inaug. Diss. Heidelberg, 1931.
Contents only.

NL 0347081   ICRL

Liebhold, Trude, 1908–
... Die reform der rechtsstellung des unehelichen kindes als
problem der rechtsangleichung mit Österreich, von Trude
Liebhold. Heidelberg, C. Winter, 1930.
2 p. l., [3]–136 p. 23cm. (Heidelberger rechtswissenschaftliche abhandlungen, hrsg. von der Juristischen fakultät, 11)
"Literaturverzeichnis": p. [5]–7.

1. Illegitimacy—Germany. 2. Illegitimacy—Austria. 3. Children—
Law—Germany. 4. Children—Law—Austria.   I. Title.
34–24917

NL 0347082   DLC NIC MH-L

VOLUME 332

Liebhold, W
Die stellung des latein im lehrplan der höheren
Bürgerschule. n.p., 1881.

NL 0347083 NjP

Liebholdt, Christian.
Erheiterungen und Belehrungen aus dem Natur-, Kunst- und
Völkerleben. Für die reifere Jungend bearbeitet von Dr. Christian
Liebholdt. Philadelphia: J. Weik [1849?], 316 p. col'd
front., col'd plates. 18½cm.

106963B. 1. Juvenile literature,   German. I. Title.
N. Y. P. L.   May 29, 1941

NL 0347084 NN

Liebi, Alfred.
Das Bild der Schweiz in der deutschen Romantik. Bern,
P. Haupt, 1946.
xv, 191 p. 24 cm.
Inauguraldiss.—Bern.
Vita.
Published also as Sprache und Dichtung, Forschungen zur Sprach-
und Literaturwissenschaft, Heft 71.
Bibliography: p. [ix]–xv.
1. Romanticism—Germany. 2. Literature, Comparative—German
and Swiss (German) 3. Literature, Comparative—Swiss (German)
and German. 4. Germany—Relations (general) with Switzerland. 5.
Switzerland in literature.   I. Title.
PT363.S9L5 1946a   53–26166

NL 0347085 DLC CaBVaU CtY FTaSU

Liebi, Alfred.
Das Bild der Schweiz in der deutschen Romantik. Bern,
P. Haupt, 1946.
xv, 191 p. 24 cm. (Sprache und Dichtung, forschungen zur Sprach-
und Literaturwissenschaft, Heft 71)
Issued also as thesis, Bern.
"Quellen- und Literaturverzeichnis": p. [ix]–xv. Bibliographical
references included in "Anmerkungen" (p. [171]–191)
1. Romanticism—Germany. 2. Literature, Comparative—German
and Swiss (German) 3. Literature, Comparative—Swiss (German)
and German. 4. Germany—Relations (general) with Switzerland. 5.
Switzerland in literature.   I. Title.   (Series)
PT363.S9L5 1946   S30.9   A 48–9454*
Northwestern Univ.   Library
for Library of Congress   [2]†

PU IU GU UU NIC TxU CaBVaU
NL 0347086 IEN DLC MU TU MiU PU PPT OCU OU CtY MH

Liebi, Werner.
Ueber retrovesikale und retroprostatische
cysten.
Inaug. diss. Bern, 1908. (Leipzig)
Bibl.
33p. 8°

NL 0347087 ICRL DNLM

Liebich, [2.
Die Bilder des göttlichen Strafgerichtes
in Jesajah-Buche. Kapitel 1-39. Oels:
A. Ludwig, 1892.
38 p.

Beilage zum Janresbericht des Gymnasiums
u Oels für das Schuljahr 1891/92.

NL 0347088 OCH

Liebich, Andrzej.
WB   Na obcej ziemi; Polskie Siły Zbrojne
31691 1939-1945. Londyn, Wydawn. Światowego
Związku Polaków z Zagranicy, 1947.
160 p. illus., 10 maps (in pocket)
(Polska Historia Drugiej Wojny Światowej,
2)

Bibliography: p. 156-158.

1. World War, 1939-1945 - Poland.

NL 0347089 CtY CaBVaU MH NN MiD NjP

Liebich, Bruno, 1862-1939.
Analyse der Candra-vrtti. 38p. Heidelberg,
C. Winter, 1920. (His Zur einführung in die in-
dische einheimische sprachwissenschaft, v.4)

NL 0347090 OCl

Liebich, Bruno, 1862-1939, ed.

Candragomin.
Candra-vrtti, der original-kommentar Candragomin's zu
seinem grammatischen sûtra. Herausgegeben von dr. Bruno
Liebich ... Leipzig, In kommission bei F. A. Brockhaus,
1918.

Liebich, Bruno, 1862-1939.
Das Cāndra-vyākaraṇa. Von Bruno Liebich. [Göt-
tingen, 1895]
cover-title, 50 p. 24½ᶜᵐ.
Aus den Nachrichten der K. Gesellschaft der wissenschaften zu Göttingen. Philologisch-historische klasse. 1895. heft 3.

1. Chandra Gomi. Cāndra-vyākaraṇa. 2. Sanskrit language—Grammar.
                                                        11–23983
Library of Congress   PK541.C54L5

NL 0347092 DLC MB

Liebich, Bruno, 1862-1939, ed.

Candragomin.
Cāndra-vyākaraṇa; die grammatik des Candragomin. Sū-
tra, Uṇādi, Dhātupāṭha, herausgegeben von Bruno Liebich
... Leipzig, In commission bei F. A. Brockhaus, 1902.

Liebich, Bruno, 1862-1939.
Die Casuslehre der indischen Grammatiker
verglichen mit dem Gebrauch des Casus im
Aitareya-Brāhmana. Ein Beitrag zur Syntax der
Sanskrit-Sprache. I. Teil ... Göttingen, 1885.
Pamphlet.
Inaug.-Diss. - Göttingen.
Vita.
"Separatabdruck aus dem X. Bande [1886] der
Beiträge zur Kunde der indogermanischen
Sprachen."

NL 0347094 CtY

Liebich, Bruno, 1862-1939.
Der Dhatupatha...
see under Dhatupatha.

Liebich, Bruno, 1862-1939.
Historische einführung und Dhātupāṭha...
53,[1]p. Heidelberg, C. Winter, 1919. (His Zur
einführung in die indische einheimische sprachwissenschaft, v.2)

"Sitzungsberichte der Heidelberger akademie der
wissenschaften, stiftung Heinrich Lanz, philosophisch-historische klasse."

NL 0347096 OCl

Liebich, Bruno, 1862-1939, ed.

PK102
.I5   **Indische** Forschungen. Heft 1-10. Breslau, M. & H.
Marcus, 1906-35.

Liebich, Bruno, 1862-1939.
Konkordanz Panini-Candra von Dr. Bruno Liebich.   Bres-
lau: M. & H. Marcus, 1928.   52 p. incl. tables.   8°.   (Indische
Forschungen.   Heft 6.)

1. Pāṇini. 2. Chandra Gomi. 3. Ser.
N. Y. P. L.   November 16, 1928

NL 0347098 NN NjPT CtY OCl MH

Liebich, Bruno, 1862-1939, ed.
Ksiratarangini, Ksirasvamin's kommentar
zu Panini's Dhatupatha
see under Ksirasvamin.

AS   Liebich, Bruno, 1862-1939.
182   Materialien zum Dhātupāṭha. Heidelberg,
H456   C. Winter, 1921.
1921   60 p. 24cm. (Sitzungsberichte der
no.7   Heidelberger Akademie der Wissenschaften.
Philosophisch-historische Klasse, Jahrg.
1921, 7. Abhandlung)

1. Sanskrit language—Verb. 2. Sanskrit
language--Glossaries, vocabularies, etc.
I. Dhātupāth   a.

NL 0347100 NIC

Liebich, Bruno, 1862-1939.
... Materialien zum Dhātupāṭha, von Bruno Liebich ...
Heidelberg, C. Winter, 1922.
60 p. 24½ᶜᵐ. (Sitzungsberichte der Heidelberger akademie der wissenschaften ... Philosophisch-historische klasse. [bd. 12] jahrg. 1921.
7. abh.)

1. Sanskrit language—Verb. 2. Sanskrit language—Glossaries, vocab-
ularies, etc.   I. Dhātupāths.
                                              A C 36–4033
Title from Univ. of Chi-   cago AS182.H44 vol. 12
Library of Congress   [AS182.H44 bd. 12]
                              [2]   (063)

NL 0347101 OCU OCl OU NN

Liebich, Bruno, 1862-1939.
Panini. Ein beitrag zur kenntnis der indischen literatur
und grammatik. Von Bruno Liebich ... Leipzig, H. Haessel,
1891.
2 p. l., 161, [3] p. 23½ᶜᵐ.

1. Pāṇini. 2. Sanskrit language—Grammar.

Library of Congress   PK519.L5   11–23909

NL 0347102 DLC CtY ICU OCl MB NN NjP

VOLUME 332

Liebich, Bruno, 1862-1939, *ed.*
Sanskrit-lesebuch. Zur einführung in die altindische sprache
und literatur. Von Bruno Liebich ... Leipzig, Lesebuchver-
lag, in kommission bei O. Harrassowitz, 1905.

ix, ₁1₎, 650, ₂2₎ p. 28ᶜᵐ.

Each selection accompanied by German or English translation.
"Verzeichnis der texte und der (vorzugsweise) benützten quellen":
p. ₍III₎-iv.

1. Sanskrit language—Chrestomathies and readers. 2. Sanskrit literature—Translations. 3. Sanskrit language—Glossaries, vocabularies,
etc.   I. Title.

Library of Congress	PK669.L5	33—20164
	₍a44b1₎	891.20822

PU
NL 0347103   DLC NPurMC NIC ICU CtY MB NjP NN OC1 IU

LIEBICH, Bruno, 1862-*1939*.
Die vier indischen Āçrama's. Breslau, Preuss
& Jünger, 1936.

21 cm. pp. 40.
pp. 4-25: "Über die vier indischen Āçrama's
oder Lebensstufen", read at the University of
Breslau, June 30, 1892.

NL 0347104   MH

PF3585 Liebich, Bruno, 1862-*1939*.
.L7   Die wortfamilien der lebenden hochdeutschen sprache
als grundlage für ein system der bedeutungslehre. Nach
Heynes Deutschem wörterbuch bearbeitet von Bruno Liebich.
Breslau, Preuss & Jünger, 1899.

₁1₎, vi, ₁1₎, 520, ₂2₎ p. 28ᶜᵐ.

1. German language—Semantics.

CtY MdBJ MB CU
NL 0347105   ICU IaU NN PSC OrU CaBVaU OC1W OU DCU

PM 175   Liebich, Bruno, 1862-1939.
.L 5   Die Wortfamilien der lebenden hochdeutschen
1905 Q   Sprache als Grundlage für ein System der Bedeutungslehre. I. Die Wortfamilien in alphabetischer Ordnung. Nach Heynes deutschem Wörterbuch bearbeitet von Bruno Liebich ... 2.
unveränderte Ausg. Breslau, Preuss & Jünger,
1905.
1. p. 1., vi, [1], 520, [2] p. 26½cm.
No more published.
1. German   language – Word formation.   2. Ger-   man language – Semantics.   I. Heyne,
     I. Title.   Moriz, 1837-1906. II.

NL 0347106   MdBJ WaU OO

Liebich, Bruno, 1862-1939.
... Zur einführung in die indische einheimische sprachwissenschaft ... von Bruno Liebich ... Heidelberg, C. Winter, 1919-20.

4 v. 24½ cm. (Sitzungsberichte der Heidelberger akademie der
wissenschaften ... Philosophisch-historische klasse. ₁bd. 10₎ jahrg.
1919, 4., 15. abh.; ₁bd. 11₎ jahrg. 1920, 10., 13. abh.)
CONTENTS.—I. Das Kātantra.—II. Historische einführung und Dhātupātha.—III. Der Dhātupātha.—IV. Analyse der Candra-Vrtti.
1. Sanskrit language—Grammar.   I. Sarva-Varmā.   II. Dhātu.
III. Chāndra Gomī.

[AS182.H44 bd. 10, 11]   A C 36—2100

Chicago. Univ. Libr.
for Library of Congress   ₁a56c�2₁

NL 0347107   ICU PU NN OU NBuU NIC TxU

Liebich, Bruno, 1862-*1939*.
Zwei kapitel der Kāçikā
      see under   Jayāditya.

Liebich, Bruno Hermann, 1905-
Das problem der autarkie.
Inaug. Diss. Breslau, 1930.
Bibl.

NL 0347109   ICRL CtY

Liebich, Christa Margarete, 1912-
Über geschwülste von bau der parotismischtumoren
ausserhalb der speicheldrüsen. ... Breslau,
1935.
Inaug. Diss. - Breslau, 1935.
Lebenslauf.
Literatur-Verzeichnis.

NL 0347110   MiU

Liebich (Christianus Gottlieb.) *De neces-
saria consensus partium attentione practica. 20
pp. 4°. Francof. ad Viadr., ₁typ. M. Hubneri,
1741₎.

NL 0347111   DNLM

Liebich, Christoph, 1783-1874.
Compendium des Waldbaues. ... 2. verm.
Aufl. ... Wien, 1866.
23.5 cm.

NL 0347112   CtY

Liebich, Christoph, 1783-1874.
Die Forstwissenschaft nach der prager lehre.
Wien, Wilhelm Braumüller, 1859.
112 p. fold. diagr.   O.
1. Forest & forestry. Prague.

NL 0347113   NcD

HC   Liebich, Christoph, *1783-1874*.
263   Oesterreichs grösste Finanz-ausgabe. Prag,
L54   Druck der Vettel'schen Buchdruckerei, 1856.
1856   32 p.

1. Austria--Econ.condit.--19th cent. 2. Finance
Public--Austria. 3. Austria--Forest policy.
4. Forests and forestry--Econ.aspects--Austria.
I. Title.

NL 0347114   NSyU

Liebich, Christoph, 1783-1874.
Die Reformation des Waldbaues im Interesse
des Ackerbaues, der Industrie und des Handels.
Prag, Mallaschitz-Prager, 1844.
322 p.   O.
1. Silviculture.

NL 0347115   NcD

SF553   LIEBICH, CHRISTOPH, 1783-1874.
.B6L7   Der seidenbau in Böhmen, und seine grossen vorthei-
le, aus wirklicher erfahrung dargestellt von Christoph
Liebich... Prag, G.Haase söhne, 1837.
xii, [2], 127, [1]p. II pl. 22cm.

1. Sericulture.

NL 0347116   ICU

SD   Liebich, Christoph, 1783-1874.
401   Der waldbau nach neuen grundsätzen, als
.L72   die mutter des ackerbaues, von Christoph
Liebich ... Prag, J.G.Calve'sche buchhandlung, 1834.
xii, ₁13₎-80 p.   21ᶜᵐ.

1. Forests and forestry.

NL 0347117   MiU

Liebich, Constantin.
Obdachlos. Bilder aus dem sozialen und
sittlichen Elend der Arbeitlosen ... Berlin,
Wiegandt & Grieben, 1894.
xvi, 256 p.   8°.

NL 0347118   NN

Liebich, Constantin.   331.8 Q102
▀▀▀ Obdachlos. Bilder aus dem sozialen und sittlichen Elend der
Arbeitlosen. Mit einem Vorwort von Professor Dr. Adolph Wag-
ner. Zweite Auflage. xvi,269 p. D. Berlin: Wiegandt &
Grieben, 1901.

NL 0347119   ICJ DL

4CS   Liebich, Curt.
82   Zeichnerische Darstellungen
familiengeschichtlicher Forschungs-
ergebnisse. Leipzig, Degener, 1933.
48 p.

(Praktikum für Familienforscher; Sammlung
Sammlung gemeinverständlicher Ab-
handlungen über Art, Ziel und Zweck der
Familienforschung, Heft 26)

NL 0347120   DLC-P4 WU

PT2423   LIEBICH, EHRENFRIED, 1713-1780.
.L63G4   Geistliche lieder und oden, nebst einigen gedanken
1768   von den evangelischlutherischen kirchenliedern und denen damit vorgenommenen veränderungen, von Ehrenfried
Liebich... Hirschberg und Leipzig, I.Krahns, 1768.
₁32₁, 274, ₁32₁p. 17cm.
Imperfect; pages 209-242 wanting.

1. Hymns, German.

NL 0347121   ICU CU

Liebich, Ehrenfried, *1713-1780*.
Kurzes geistreiches gebetbuch...
Hirschberg, Krahn, 1751.
94 p.

NL 0347122   PPLT

1894-
Liebich, Elisabeth: Das kaufmännische Zurückbehaltungsrecht. [Ma-
schinenschrift.] v, 59 S. 4°. — Auszug: Greifswald 1921: Hartmann. 8 S. 8°
Greifswald, R.- u. staatswiss. Diss. v. 28. April 1922   ₁U 22. 5550₎

NL 0347123   ICRL

Liebich, Emanuel.
Die spiel-dose: The musical box; Op. 10
Ditson, n.d.
Piano.

NL 0347124   OrP

VOLUME 332

Liebich (Ernst) [1884–]. *Beckenendlagen, die an der Königlichen Universitäts-Frauenklinik zu Göttingen in den letzten 20 Jahren zur Beobachtung gekommen sind. [Göttingen.] 25 pp. 8°. Cassel, W. Fredenhagen [n. d.].

NL   0347125   DNLM

Liebich, Ernst, 1916–
Die Insel des Sebastian, Roman. Wien, Kremayr & Scheriau [1954]
279 p. 21 cm.

I. Title.

PT2623.I 33 I 6   54–39848 ‡

NL   0347126   DLC NN CtY

Liebich, Ernst, 1916–
Der Tanz um die Schüssel, Roman. Wien, Kremayr & Scheriau [1953]
454 p. 21 cm.

I. Title.

PT2623.I 33T3   833.91   53–38067 ‡

NL   0347127   DLC NN CtY

Liebich, Ferdinand Karl, 1909–
Die europäische Zollunion, ihre Möglichkeiten und Grenzen. Bonn, Deutscher Bundes-Verlag, 1951.
79 p. 21 cm.

On cover: Vom Zollverein zum Schumanplan.
Bibliography: p. 76–79.

1. Customs unions. 2. European federation. 3. Europe—Comm. I. Title.
HF2033.L5   51–33580

NL   0347128   DLC NN

Liebich, *Mrs.* Franz
    see
Liebich, Louise (Shirley)

Liebich (Fridericus Guilielmus). *Diss. sistens causas mortis submersorum, iisque succurrendi methodum. 40 pp., 1 l. 12°. *Vratislaviae, ex off. Kaupferiana,* [1822].

NL   0347130   DNLM

Liebich (Gustavus) [1812–]. *De febre phthisica. 30 pp. 8°. *Berolini, typ. Friedlænderiana,* [1837]

NL   0347131   DNLM

W 4   **LIEBICH, Hans Jörg,** 1921–
M961   Klinische Beiträge zum Fokalinfekt bei
1950   Polyarthritis unter besonderer Berücksichtigung odontogener Herdinfektion. [München], 1950.
56 ℓ.
Inaug.-Diss. - Munich.
1. Arthritis 2. Infection - Focal

NL   0347132   DNLM

Liebich, Heinrich August.
Dissertatio juridica utrum tortura penitus abroganda, an tantum limitanda videatur... Lipsiae, Langenhemia, 1772.
24 p.

NL   0347133   PU-L

Liebich (Henricus Christianus). *De morbis ex munditie intempestiva. 30 pp. sm. 4°. *Lipsia, ex off. Langenhemiana,* [1746].

NL   0347134   DNLM PPC

Liebich, Horst, 1913–
Quantitativ-chemische Untersuchungen über das Eisen in den Chloroplasten und übrigen Zellbestandteilen von Spinacia oleracea. Jena, 1941.
Inaug.-Diss. - Berlin.
Reprinted from "Zeitschrift für Botanik", 37. Bd, Heft 4.

NL   0347135   CtY

Liebich, Immanuel.
Alte hebräische Melodie. Transcription. [Leipzig: C. H. Friedlein, by Breitkopf & Härtel, 189–?]
p. 41–43.

Excerpt: Musikalische Gartenlaube.
Bd. 5. no. 6.

NL   0347136   OCH

Liebich (Joannes Ehrenfried.) [1795–]. *De deutitione difficili. 31 pp. 8°. *Berolini, T. Brüschcke,* [1819].

NL   0347137   DNLM PPC MH

Liebich, Kurt.
Der verantwortliche redakteur und seine haftung, aus §20 absatz 2 des Reichspressgesetzes ... Breslau, Koebner, 1905.
x, 125, [3] p. 22ᶜᵐ.
Inaug.-diss.—Würzburg.

1. Press law—Germany. 2. Liberty of the press.

                 6–4681
Library of Congress   7657.L65

NL   0347138   DLC ICJ

W 4   **Liebich, Lotte Lore,** 1913–
B51   Selbstversuche über die alkalisierende
1940   Wirkung verschiedener organischer Natriumverbindungen. Berlin, Pfau [1940]
14 p. illus.

Inaug.-Diss. - Friedrich Wilhelms Univ., Berlin.
Bibliography: p. 14.

NL   0347139   DNLM

Liebich, Louise (Shirley)
Claude-Achille Debussy, by Mrs. Franz Liebich. London, John Lane; New York, John Lane company, 1908.
6 p. l., 92 p. front. (port.) illus. (music) 2 pl. 19ᶜᵐ. (Half-title: Living masters of music)
"Claude Debussy's works": p. [91]–92.

I. *Debussy, Claude, 1862–1918.

              8–8847 Revised
Library of Congress   ML410.D28L7
              [r46c2]

       OO OC1 CU MB PHC PP PPT PBm NcC WaSp Or WaS OrCS
NL   0347140   DLC NIC MiU MB KMK OrP NN OU ODW OOxM

Liebich, Louise (Shirley)
Claude-Achille Debussy, by Mrs. Franz Liebich. London, John Lane; [1925]
6 p. l., 92 p. front. (port.) illus. (music) 2 pl. 19ᶜᵐ. (Half-title: Living masters of music)
"Claude Debussy's works": p. [91]–92.

NL   0347141   LU

Liebich, Louise (Shirley)   tr.

Laloy, Louis, 1874–
The future of music; coming changes outlined in regard to composer, conductor & orchestra, by Louis Laloy ... Tr. by Mrs. Franz Liebich. London, W. Reeves [1910]

ML410   **Liebich, Louise (Shirley)**
.N64A36
Nin, Joaquín, 1879–1949.
In the service of art; a plea for simplicity in music, by J.-Joachim Nin. Translated by Mrs. Franz Liebich. London, W. Reeves [1915]

Liebich, Louise (Shirley)   tr.

Wilder, Victor van, 1835–1892.
Mozart; the story of his life as man and artist according to authentic documents & other sources, by Victor Wilder. Translated by L. Liebich, with a comprehensive bibliography of Mozart literature, both English and foreign and a list of his compositions, 23 portraits, facsimiles, &c. now gathered from various sources ... New York, C. Scribner's sons; London, Reeves and Turner [1908]

Liebich, Richard.
Die zigeuner in ihrem wesen und in ihrer sprache. Nach eigenen beobachtungen dargestellt von dr. jur. Richard Liebich ... Leipzig, F. A. Brockhaus, 1863.
xii, 272 p. 21ᶜᵐ.

CONTENTS.—Herkunft der zigeuner. Ihre lebensanschauung und lebensweise.—Zigeunerisch-deutsches wörterbuch.—Deutsch-zigeunerisches wörterbuch.—Anhang: Einige sprachproben. Nachträge.

1. Gipsies. 2. Gipsies—Language. 3. Gipsies—Language — Dictionaries.
Library of Congress   DX115.L6   42–51905

NL   0347145   DLC NIC CtY NN MH ICN MdBP PU

VOLUME 332

Liebich, Rudolph.
Proletarian song book of lyrics from the operetta The last revolution. By Michael Gold & J. Ramirez. Music by Rudolph Leibich. [Chicago] Local Chicago workers party of America [193-?]

18 p. 16 cm.
Libretto. Words only.

NL 0347146   MH

Liebieg, Theodor.
Denkschrift über die Wirtschaftslage Nordböhmens
     see under Liberec, Czechoslovak Republic.
Handels- und Gewerbekammer.

Liebieg, Theodor.
Die Handels- und Gewerbekammer in Reichenberg; ein Überblick über ihren Wirkungskreis und ihre Einrichtungen. Reichenberg, Handels- und Gewerbekammer in Reichenberg, 1938.

80 p. illus.

1. Handels- und Gewerbekammer in Reichenberg

NL 0347148   MH

PA
6783
L71   Liebig, Adolf Ludwig Richard, b. 1825
     De genitivi usu Terentiano. Oels, 1853.
26 p. 23cm.

Accompanies "Programm"--Gymnasium, Oels.

1. Terentius Afer, Publius. Language--Grammar.

NL 0347149   NIC NjP CU PU

PA6784 Liebig, Adolf Ludwig Richard, b. 1825.
.L72   ... De hiatu in uersibus Terentianis ... Uratislauiae, typis E. Kleinii, 1848.
[3], 60 p. 21½cm.
Inaug.-diss.—Breslau.
Vita.

1. Terentius Afer, Publius.

NL 0347150   ICU NjP MH PBm

PA6769 Liebig, Adolf Ludwig Richard, b. 1825.
.L7   ... De prologis Terentianis et Plautinis ... [Görlitz, 1859]
50 p. 20½x17½cm.
Programm—Gymnasium, Görlitz.

1. Terentius Afer, Publius. 2. Plautus, Titus Maccius.

NL 0347151   ICU MH PU PBm CSt NjP MH CU

PA
6783
L71H9   Liebig, Adolf Ludwig Richard, b. 1825.
     Die hypothetischen Sätze bei Terenz [und] Zur grammatischen Erklärung der Alten, speciell des Caesar auf den Gymnasien. Görlitz, 1863.
36 p. 24cm.

"Programm"--Gymnasium, Görlitz.

NL 0347152   NIC NcD CU

Liebig, Adolf Ludwig Richard, b. 1825.
— Die innere Mission und die Schule. Görlitz, Druck von G.A. Remisch, 1867.
38 p., 23cm.

Accompanies program (Die Feier der vereinigten Aktus) - Gymnasium zu Görlitz

NL 0347153   NjPT

NA1088
L52D4
Arch.
Library   Liebig, Alfred, 1878-
     Neuere Arbeiten von Alfred Liebig. Mit einer Einleitung von Egbert Delpy. Berlin, F.E. Hübsch [1929]
59 p. (p. 15-59 plates, plans) illus., port. (Neue Werkkunst)

I. Delpy, Egbert, 1877-

NL 0347154   CU NN NNC NjP

Liebig, Bernhard, 1873—
Alte häuser & gassen in Frankfurt a. M. 12 original-radierungen, von Bernhard Liebig. Frankfurt a. M., M. Jacobs [n. d.]

cover-title, 12 pl. 22½cm.

1. Frankfurt am Main—Descr.—Views. I. Title.
[Full name: Georg Bernhard Liebig]
Library of Congress   NE2210.L5A4   40–36530
[2]   767

NL 0347155   DLC

TP612
L5
1870   Liebig, C
     Die Destillation auf kaltem Wege; oder, Praktische Anleitung die verschiedensten einfachen und doppelten Branntweine und Liqueure auf die billigste, bequemste und beste Weise zu bereiten ... sowie Mittheilung einer höchst einfachen Methode zur Fabrikation des Rums, Aracs ... und der Bereitung zahlreicher Extrakte und wohlriechender Essenzen ... mit über 400 Recepten und Anweisungen. 5. verm. Aufl. Berlin, S. Mode [1870?]
144 p.

Bound with Schedel, C.F.B. Praktische und bewährte Anweisung zur Destillirkunst. 7. verb. und verm. Aufl. Weimar, 1871.

1. Liquors. 2. Liqueurs. 3. Flavoring essences. I. Title. Bound with.

NL 0347157   CU-A

Liebig, Eugen Friedrich Wolfgang, Freiherr von, 1868–
Beiträge und Vorschläge zum Problem der Kreditversicherung, von Dr. E. von Liebig, ... Berlin, Puttkammer & Mühlbrecht, 1905.
[4], 110 p. 25cm.

NL 0347158   ICJ

Liebig, Eugen Friedrich Wolfgang, freiherr von, 1868–
Das deutsche feuerversicherungswesen, von dr. E. freiherr von Liebig ... Berlin, J. Guttentag, 1911.
211 p. 22cm.

1. Insurance, Fire—Germany. I. Title. 41–18668
Library of Congress   HG9809.L5
[2]   368.10043

NL 0347159   DLC NN ICJ CtY

Liebig, Eugen Friedrich Wolfgang, freiherr von, 1868–
Die Genossenschaft mit beschränkter Haftpflicht und ihre Behandlung in Konkurse ... von Eugen Freiherr von Liebig ... München [C.H. Beck], 1892.
63, [1] p. 22cm.
Inaug.-Diss. - Erlangen.
Bibliographical footnotes.

NL 0347160   MH-L CU DLC

Liebig, Eugen Friedrich Wolfgang, freiherr von, 1868–
Die transportversicherung. Von dr. Eugen freiherr von Liebig ... Berlin, J. Guttentag, 1914–
v. 23cm.

1. Insurance, Marine—Germany. I. Title. 16–15570
Library of Congress   HE965.L5

NL 0347161   DLC NN

Liebig, Friedrich]
Photographien aus dem ung. isr. Congresse. Treu gezeichnet. Wien, J. Schlossberg, 1869.
56 p. 8°.

NL 0347162   NN OCH PPDrop

Liebig, Fritz.
Ergebnisse der prostatektomie...(Auszug)
Inaug. Diss. Breslau, 1922.

NL 0347163   ICRL

Liebig, Fritz.
Sieben faelle von tetanus...
Inaug. Diss. Breslau, n.d.

NL 0347164   ICRL

Liebig, Georg, bacc. iur., Dresden: Eigentumserwerb am Wilde unter besonderer Berücksichtigung Sächsischen Landesrechts. Borna-Leipzig 1914: Noske. IX, 101 S. 8°
Leipzig, Jur. Diss. v. 1. Okt. 1914
[Geb. 27. März 84 Dresden-Plauen; Wohnort: Ölnitz i. V.; Staatsangeh.: Sachsen; Vorbildung: Kreuz-G. Dresden Reife 04; Studium: Freiburg 1, München 1, Leipzig 7 S.; Rig. 8. Febr. 09.] [U 14.916]

NL 0347165   ICRL

Liebig, Georg Bernhard
     see Liebig, Bernhard, 1873–

VOLUME 332

Liebig, Georg, Freiherr von, 1827–1903.
Arbeiten aus der pneumatischen Anstalt in
Reichenhall über die Wirkungen der verdichteten
Luft unter erhöhtem Luftdrucke [von Georg
Liebig]   [Wolf u. sohn, n. d.]
23 p.

NL   0347167   PPPCPh

Liebig, Georg, *Freiherr von*, 1827–1903.   S612.2
[Collected papers, chiefly on respiration and respiratory diseases   2
as affected by barometric pressure.]

NL   0347168   ICJ

Liebig, Georg, Freiherr von, 1827–1903.
Die geographische Vertheilung des Luftdruckes.   [Braun-
schweig, 1878.]   p. 313–318, 328–331.   col'd maps.   4°.

Author's name at head of title.
Excerpts: Globus. v. 34, no. 20–21.

1. Pressure (Atmospheric).
N. Y. P. L.   January 26, 1918.

NL   0347169   NN

WBI   LIEBIG, Georg von, 1827–1903.
L716r   Die Kurmittel von Reichenhall; ihre
1865   Wirkung und Anwendung, mit besonderer
Berücksichtigung des Klima's. [2. Aufl.]
München, Cotta, 1865.
viii, 141 p. illus.
1st and 3d eds. have title: Reichenhall,
sein Klima und seine Heilmittel.

NL   0347170   DNLM

WDA   LIEBIG, Georg von, 1827–1903.
L716L   Der Luftdruck in den pneumatischen
1898   Kammern und auf Höhen, vom ärztlichen
Standpunkt. Braunschweig, Vieweg,
1898.
x, 240 p. illus.

NL   0347171   DNLM PPC

RA866   Liebig, Georg von, 1827–1903.
R27   Reichenhall, sein Klima und seine Heilmittel
861ℓ   ... München, J. G. Cotta, 1861.
50p. 16cm.

1. Physical medicine - Hydrotherapy -
Reichenhall.

NL   0347172   CtY-M DNLM

WBI   LIEBIG, Georg von, 1827–1903.
L716r   Reichenhall, sein Klima und seine
1871   Heilmittel. [3. Aufl.] München, Riedel,
1871.
viii, 147 p. illus.
2d ed. has title: Die Kurmittel von
Reichenhall.

NL   0347173   DNLM ICJ

Liebig, Georg von, 1827–1903.
——. Ueber die Einflüsse der Temperatur und
Feuchtigkeit auf die Gesundheit. 25 pp. 8°.
Berlin, A. Hirschwald, 1870.

NL   0347174   DNLM

Liebig Georg, [1827–1903]. * Ueber die
Temperaturunterschiede des venösen und arte-
riellen Blutes. 1 p. l., 58 pp. 4°. *Giessen, W.
Keller, 1853.*

NL   0347175   DNLM

WAA   LIEBIG, Georg von, 1827–1903.
L716u   Untersuchungen über die Ventilation
1869   und Erwärmung der pneumatischen
Kammern vom ärztlichen Standpunkt,
angestellt am pneumatischen Apparate
der Gebrüder Mack in Reichenhall.
München, Oldenbourg, 1869.
35 p. illus.

NL   0347176   DNLM

RM787   Liebig, Georg, *freiherr* von, 1827–1903.
.L48   Zur beurtheilung der revaccination. Von
Toner   dr. G. v. Liebig ... [Berlin, Druck von G.
Coll.   Reimer, 1873]
12 p. 22cm.

Caption title.
"Separat-abdruck aus Goeschens 'Deutscher
klinik' no. 12, 1873."

1. Vaccination. I. Title.

NL   0347177   DLC

Liebig, George Frederick 1903–   joint
author.
Chapman, Homer Dwight, 1898–
Adaptation and use of automatically operated sand-culture
equipment. By H. D. Chapman ... and George F. Liebig,
jr. ...
(*In* U. S. Dept. of agriculture. Journal of agricultural research.
v. 56, no. 1, Jan. 1, 1938, p. 73–80. illus. 23½ᶜᵐ. Washington, 1938)

Liebig, George Frederick., 1903–   joint
author.
Chapman, Homer Dwight, 1898–
The production of citrus mottle-leaf in controlled nutrient
cultures. By H. D. Chapman and A. P. Vanselow ... and
George F. Liebig ...
(*In* U. S. Dept. of agriculture. Journal of agricultural research.
v. 55, no. 5, Sept. 1, 1937, p. 365–379. illus. 23½ᶜᵐ. Washington,
1937)

Liebig, George Frederick, 1903–   joint
author.
QK861
.V3   **Vanselow, Albert Percival,** 1897–
Spectrochemical methods for the determination of minor
elements in plants, waters, chemicals and culture media; a
detailed report of procedure developed in the Riverside Citrus Experiment Station of the University of California during a ten-year period, complete with description of equipment used, of particular interest to workers and especially
beginners, in the field of plant nutrition, by A. P. Vanselow
and George F. Liebig, Jr. Berkeley, University of California, College of Agriculture, Agricultural Experiment Station [1950?]

Liebig, Gunther Kurt Robert.
Ueber einen dicephalus bispinalis beim
kalbe. Berlin, 1925.
31 p. 23 cm.

NL   0347181   DNAL

Liebig, Gustav A.
Practical electricity in medicine and surgery. By G. A.
Liebig ... and George H. Rohé ... Profusely illustrated. Philadelphia and London, F. A. Davis, [1889]
viii, 383 p. illus. (incl. diagrs.) 2 pl. 25ᶜᵐ.

NL   0347182   DSI PPHa

Liebig, Gustav A.
Practical electricity in medicine and surgery. By G. A.
Liebig ... and George H. Rohé ... Profusely illustrated.
Philadelphia and London, F. A. Davis, 1890.
viii, 383 p. illus. (incl. diagrs.) 2 pl. 25ᶜᵐ.

1. Electrotherapeutics.   i. Rohé, George Henry, 1851–1899, joint
author.

Library of Congress   RM871.L7   7–14527

PPC ICJ ViU DNLM
NL   0347183   DLC NjP ICRL NcU-H NcD OClW-H OU MiU PU

W 4   Liebig, Gustav A   1913–
B51   Ueber histospectrographische Untersuchungen
1939   am Kayser-Fleischerschen Ring und Gerontoxon.
Charlottenburg, Hoffman [1939?]
13, [2] p. illus.

Inaug.-Diss. - Berlin.
Bibliography: p. [14]

NL   0347184   DNLM

Liebig, H   J   von.
Über den zuckergehalt der feinen weizenmehle, der
weizenmehlteige und der vergorenen mehlteige, sowie
über die diastatische kraft der weizenmehle.
Landw. jahrb. bd. 38, p. 251–271.   *Berlin, 1909.*

1. Wheat flour. Sugar content.

Library, U. S. Dept. of   Agriculture   Agr 9–1374
12

NL   0347185   DNAL

Liebig, Hans: Ein Beitrag zur Frage des Unterschiedes zwischen
vitalem und postmortalem Leberbefund bei der akuten gelben
Leberatrophie. [Maschinenschrift.] 43 S. 4°. — Auszug: Breslau
1923: Volkswacht-Buchdr. 2 Bl. 8°
Breslau, Med. Diss. v. 10. Dez. 1923 [1924]   [U 24. 1690

NL   0347186   ICRL

Liebig, Hans von. Studien in der Tritan-
reihe. [Giessen.] 3 pl. pp. 128–264.
Leipzig, J. Klinkhardt, 1908.

NL   0347187   DNLM MH PU ICRL

Liebig, Hans Wilhelm Hermann, *freiherr von*, 1874–1931.
... Bethmann-Hollweg—Erzberger—Scheidemann, von
Hans von Liebig. Berlin, G. Bath [1922]
109 p. 23½ᶜᵐ. (Reichsverderber, 1. t.)

1. European war, 1914–1918—Germany. 2. Bethmann-Hollweg, Theobald
von, 1856–1921. 3. Erzberger, Matthias, 1875–1921. 4. Scheidemann, Philipp, 1865–

Library of Congress   DD231.A2L5   25–23605

NL   0347188   DLC NN

VOLUME 332

LIEBIG, HANS Wilhelm Hermann, freiherr von, 1874–1931.
Bethmann - Hollweg —— Erzberger —— Scheidemann.
Berlin, G. Bath [1922] 109 p. 8° (Reichsverderber.
Teil 1.)

Film reproduction. Negative.
1. Bethmann-Hollweg, Theobald von, 1856-1921. 2. Erzberger, Matthias,
1875-1921. 3. Scheidemann   Philipp, 1865-1939.
4. Germany--Politics, 1888-   1918. I. Series.

NL 0347189   NN

Liebig, Hans Wilhelm Hermann, *freiherr von*, 1874– 1931.
Der betrug am deutschen volke, von prof. dr. Hans
freih. v. Liebig. Grosse ausg. München, J. F. Lehmann, 1919.
228 p. 23ᶜᵐ.

"Die vorliegende schrift ist ... aus den 'Politischen betrachtungen' entstanden, die ich während meiner schriftleitung der monatschrift 'Deutschlands erneuerung' allmonatlich veröffentlichte."—Vorwort.

1. Germany—Pol. & govt.—1918-   I. Title.

25-16166

Library of Congress   DD249.L53 1919

NL 0347190   DLC NBuU MH MU NN

Liebig, Hans Wilhelm Hermann, Freiherr von,
1874–1931, supposed author.
Das Deutsche Reich auf dem Wege zur
geschichtlichen Episode ...
see under   Sontag, Franz.

Liebig, Hans Wilhelm Hermann, Freiherr von, 1874–1931.
Erzberger als Staatsmann und Werkzeug, in seiner Rede vom
25. Juli, 1919, von Prof. Dr. H. Freih. von Liebig ...   München:
J. F. Lehmann [1919]. 44 p. 8°.

Sonderdruck aus der grossen Ausgabe von "Der Betrug am deutschen Volke."

1. Erzberger, Matthias, 1875-   2. European war, 1914-   .—Peace
agitation and mediation.   September 29, 1920.
N. Y. P. L.

NL 0347192   NN CU CSt-H NjP

Liebig, Hans Wilhelm Hermann, Freiherr von,
1874–1931, supposed author.
Nie wieder Krieg?! Ein Blick in Deutschlands
Zukunft
see under   [Sontag, Franz]

Liebig, Hans Wilhelm Hermann, *freiherr von*, 1874– 1931.
Die politik von Bethmann Hollwegs; eine studie von
professor dr. Hans freiherr von Liebig ...
München, J. F. Lehmann, 191
v. in   maps. 23ᶜᵐ.
CONTENTS.—1.-2. t. Das B-system vor dem kriege. 3., unveränderte
aufl. 1919.

1. Bethmann-Hollweg, Theobald von, 1856-1921. 2. Germany—For. rel.—
1871- 3. European war, 1914- 4. World politics. I. Title.

20-20612

Library of Congress   D515.L58

NL 0347194   DLC DNW CtY MnU WU NcD OClW MiU MH CaBVaU

Liebig, Hans Wilhelm Hermann, *Freiherr* von, 1874–1931.
Die Politik von Bethmann-Hollwegs, eine Studie. n. p.
[1915]
2 v. illus. 23 cm.
"Streng vertraulich."

1. Bethmann-Hollweg, Theobald von, 1856-1921. 2. Germany—For.
rel.—1871. 3. European War, 1914-1918. 4. World politics.   I. Title.

D515.L582   55-54458 ‡

NL 0347195   DLC

D515   Liebig, Hans Wilhelm Hermann, Freiherr von,
L58   1874-1931.
1919   Die Politik von Bethmann Hollwegs; eine Studie.   [2. Aufl.]
München, J. F. Lehmann, 1919.
3 v. in 2. (559 p.) maps.

Contents. - 1. -2. t. Das B-system vor dem Kriege. - 3. t. Das
B-System als Gieger.

1. Bethmann-Hollweg, Theobald von, 1856-1921. 2. Germany - For. rel. - 1871-1918. 3. European war, 1914-1918.
World politics.

NL 0347196   CU MH

D   Liebig, Hans Wilhelm Hermann, Freiherr
515   von, 1874-1931.
L71   Die Politik von Bethmann Hollwegs;
1919   eine Studie. 3. unveränderte Aufl.
München, J. F. Lehmann, 1919.
3 v. in 2(559p.) maps. 24cm.

1. Germany--Foreign relations--1871-
2. Bethmann--Hollweg, Theobald von, 1856-
1921. 3. European war, 1914-1918. I. Title.

NL 0347197   NIC

Liebig, Hans Wilhelm Hermann, Freiherr von, 1874–1931.
Die Politik von Bethmann Hollwegs. 3. Auflage.
— München. Lehmann. 1919. 2 parts in 1 v. Map. 22½ cm., in 8s.
On Germany's foreign relations before and during the European War.

M1381 — T.r. — European War, 19.   Germany. — Germany. For. rel. —
Bethmann-Hollweg, Theobald von, 1856—

NL 0347198   MB NjP

4DD   Liebig, Hans Wilhelm Hermann, **Freiherr**
3482   von, 1874-1931.
Das Versagen der Nationalen; ein
Warnruf. Leipzig, Hammer-Verlag,
1928.
34 p.

NL 0347199   DLC-P4

Liebig, Hans Wilhelm Hermann, *Freiherr von*, 1874–1931.
Die Verschweizerung des deutschen Volkes. Leipzig,
Hammer-Verlag, 1928.
129 p. 24 cm.

1. Germany—Pol. & govt.—1918-1933.   I. Title.

DD238.L5   53—55553 ‡

NL 0347200   DLC ICU NN

Liebig, Hans Wilhelm Hermann, *Freiherr* von, 1874–1931.
Wege zur politischen Macht. München, J. F. Lehmann,
1921.
132 p. 23 cm.

1. Germany—Pol. & govt.—1918-1933.   I. Title.

DD240.L45   53—55552 ‡

NL 0347201   DLC NN MH CSt-H CU CSt

WG   Liebig, Heinrich, Freiherr von, 1877-
25248   Überführung des Dibenzalacetons in Derivate des Diphenylcyklopentans. Halle a. d.
S., 1904.
54 p.

Inaug.-Diss. - Halle.

NL 0347202   CtY DLC PU MH ICRL

Liebig, Hermann von.
Durch welche säure lösen die pflanzenwurzeln die phos-
phate im boden?
Landw. jahrb. bd. 10, p. 603-612.   Berlin, 1881.

1. Phosphates. Solubility.

Library, U. S. Dept. of   Agriculture   Agr 4-1367

NL 0347203   DNAL

Liebig, Hermann von.
Die Ernährungsgesetze Liebig's in neuester
Fassung und das neue Nährmittel Malto-Leguminose
Ein Nachtrag zu den chemischen Briefen.
Kempten, T. Dannheimer, 1878.
26 p. , 1 l. 8°.

NL 0347204   DNLM

Liebig, Hermann von.
Mineraldünger und düngung.
Landw. jahrb. bd. 10, p. 29-42.   Berlin, 1881.

1. Fertilizers, Mineral.   Agr 4-1368

Library, U. S. Dept. of   Agriculture

NL 0347205   DNAL

Liebig, Hermann von.
Wird bei rationeller fütterung das fett der pflanzen-
fresser aus proteinstoffen gebildet oder aus kohlehydra-
ten?
Landw. vers. stat. bd. 8, p. 216-225.   Chemnitz, 1866.

1. Carbohydrates. 2. Fat formation in animals. 3. Protein.
Agr 4-2542

Library, U. S. Dept. of   Agriculture

NL 0347206   DNAL

Liebig, Hermann von.
Die zweckmassige anwendung der kunstlichen
dunger nabst einem anhang: uber versuchs-
worthschaften als erganzung der versuchs-
stationen, von Hermann von Liebig.
Braunschweig, F. Vieweg und sohn, 1867.
62p.

NL 0347207   OU

VOLUME 332

J
27
335.3
R 005
LIEBIG, HUGO.
Über die marxistisch-sozialdemokratische
Gedankenwelt und die Grenze des Sozialismus.
Mühlhausen i.Thür.,Heysche Buchhandlung,1910,
vi,186p. fold.pl. 20cm.

NL 0347208   ICN NN ICJ

Liebig, J. von, joint author.

,Ehgart, Hans Ludwig,
Frührot. Gedichte verfasst von drei Münchenern. Stuttgart, In kommissions-verlag von F. Krais. 1897.

Liebig (Joannes Gottlob.) * De salutari et noxio ,
antimonii crudi usu. 26 pp., 1 l. sm. 4°. *Er-
fordiæ, typ. J. C. Heringii,* [1739].

NL 0347210   DNLM

Liebig, Johann Justus, 1803-1873.
    see Liebig, Justus, freiherr von, 1803-
1873.

Liebig, Johanna, 1900-
Ergänzungen zur entwicklungsgeschichte von
Isoëtes Lacustre L. ... Marburg, 1931.
Inaug. Diss. -Marburg, 1931.
Lebenslauf.
Bibliography.

NL 0347212   ICRL MH CtY

Liebig, Johannes.
Über die ursachen des raschen gerinnens der milch bei
gewitter und die mittel, dasselbe zu verhindern ... Pirna,
Druck von F. J. Eberlein [1890]

1 p. l., 33, ,1, p., 1 l. 3 fold. diagr. 21½cm.

Inaug.-diss.—Heidelberg.

1. Milk.

Library of Congress   SF251.L5   7-17181

NL 0347213   DLC

Liebig, Justus, *freiherr* von, 1803-1873.
Abhandlung über die constitution der organischen
säuren, von Justus Liebig. (1838) Hrsg. von Hermann
Kopp. Leipzig, W. Engelmann, 1891.

86 p. 19½cm. (*On cover:* Ostwald's Klassiker der exakten wissenschaften, nr. 26)

First published in Annalen der pharmacie, bd. XXVI, 1838.

1. Acids, Organic.   I. Kopp, Hermann Franz Moritz, 1817-1892, ed.

Library of Congress   QD305.A2L7   4-31698

MH PBm PHC PU PPF
NL 0347214   DLC CU PBL OC1W CU-S ICJ OU OCU MiU PSt

Liebig, Justus, *freiherr* von, 1803-1873.
An address to the agriculturists of Great Britain, explaining the principles and use of his artificial manures.
By Professor Justus Liebig ... Liverpool, Muspratt and
co., 1845.

32 p. 21cm.

1. Fertilizers ,and manures,

Agr 26-148

Library, U. S. Dept. of   Agriculture 57L62

NL 0347215   DNAL CtY

633.3
M36c
Liebig, Justus, Freiherr von, 1803-1873.
Aforismos agricolas, vertidos al castellano
por Jose C. Seguro. México, Tip. de G. A.
Esteva, 1882.
13p. 22cm. (Biblioteca de la Sociedad
Agricola Mexicana)

Bound with Martínez del Río, Pablo. Curso
de agricultura. ¿México, 1882¿

NL 0347216   IU

Liebig, Justus, *freiherr* von, 1803-1873.
Animal chemistry; or, Organic chemistry in its application to physiology and pathology. By Justus Liebig
... Ed. from the author's manuscript by William Gregory ... With additions, notes, and corrections, by Dr.
Gregory, and others by John W. Webster. Cambridge
,Mass., J. Owen; New York, D. Appleton and company;
,etc., etc., 1842.
xl, 347, ,8, p. 20cm.
"Reply to a 'Notice' of Messrs. Wiley & Putnam, publishers of the un-
authorized reprint of the second part of Professor Liebig's report on
organic chemistry, published in the 'Boston daily advertiser,' of August 16,
and in other newspapers", signed: J. W. W. (8 p. at end)
1. Physiological chem-   istry.   I. Gregory, William, 1803-
1858. ed. and tr.   II.   Webster, John White, 1793-1850. ed.
III. Title.

Library of Congress   QP514.L72 1842   1-1383 Revised
,r21d2,

PPA PPL ICJ NjP NIC
NL 0347217   DLC CU DNLM NIC NcD-MC KyU NjR PPF PU

612.01
L62tEg
1842a
Liebig, Justus, Freiherr von, 1803-1873.
Animal chemistry or organic chemistry in its
applications to physiology and pathology.
Edited from the author's manuscript, by William
Gregory. London, Taylor and Walton, 1842.
xix, 354p. 23cm.

Translation of Die Thier-Chemie oder, Die
organische Chemie in ihrer Anwendung auf Physiologie und Pathologie.

NL 0347218   IU CaBVaU MB OC1W OU

---

*
QP514
.L72
1842
Liebig, Justus, Freiherr von, 1803-1873.
Animal chemistry, or Organic chemistry in
its application to physiology and pathology.
Ed. from the author's manuscript, by William
Gregory. New-York, Wiley and Putnam, 1842.
xxiv, 356 p. 20cm.

1. Physiological chemistry. I. Gregory, William,
1803-1858.

NL 0347219   ViU DNLM NN NcD-MC NNC DA MiU OU NcD OCU

Liebig, Justus, *freiherr* von, 1803-1873.
Animal chemistry, or Organic chemistry in its application
to physiology and pathology. By Justus Liebig ... Ed.
from the author's manuscript, by William Gregory ... New-
York, J. Winchester [1842]

cover-title, 48 p. incl. tables. 30 cm. (The New World. Extra
series. no. 25, 26)

1. Physiological chemistry.   I. Gregory, William, 1803-1858.
II. Webster, John White, 1793-1850.

QP514.L792   1—1384

NL 0347220   DLC NNC CtY-M MB

Liebig, Justus, *freiherr* von, 1803-1873.
Animal chemistry: or Organic chemistry in its
applications to physiology and pathology ed...
by William Gregory.
Phila., Peterson, pref. 1842.
111 p.

NL 0347221   PU ODW MB

Liebig, Justus, *freiherr* von, 1803-1873.
Animal chemistry, or Organic chemistry in its application to
physiology and pathology. By Justus Liebig ... Ed. from
the author's manuscript, by William Gregory ... With additions, notes, and corrections, by Dr. Gregory, and others by
John W. Webster ... 2d ed. Cambridge ,Mass., J. Owen;
New York, D. Appleton and company; ,etc., etc., 1843.

xl, 347 p. 20cm.

1. Physiological chemistry.   I. Gregory, William, 1803-1858.
II. Webster, John White, 1793-1850. III. Title.

Library of Congress   QP514.L724   1—1385

NL 0347222   DLC DNLM TU ICU PU-S

591.192
L622a
1843
Liebig, Justus, freiherr von, 1803-1873.
Animal chemistry, or chemistry in its
applications to physiology and pathology.
Ed. from the author's manuscript, by
William Gregory... 2d ed. London,
Printed for Taylor & Watson, 1843.
xxvi, 384p. 23cm.

1. Physiological chemistry. I. Gregory,
William, 1803- 1858, ed. II.
Title.

MnU OkU
NL 0347223   KU CaBVaU NN DNLM PBL NcD CtY NcD-MC

386.
L622A
1843
Liebig, Justus, freiherr von, 1803-1873.
Animal chemistry, Organic chemistry, in its
application to physiology and pathology.
,2d ed., New York, Winchester ,1843,
48 p.

Stereotype edition; reproduced from the
New world, Extra series, v.2, no. 1-2.

1. Biological chemistry. 2. Chemistry, Organic. I. Gregory, William, 1803-1858, ed.
II. Title.

NL 0347224   DNAL NNC

Liebig, Justus, *freiherr* von, 1803-1873.
Animal chemistry, or Organic chemistry in its applica-
tions to physiology and pathology. By Justus Liebig
... Ed. from the author's manuscript, by William Gregory
... Philadelphia, J. M. Campbell; New York, Saxton &
Miles, 1843.

x, 11-111 p. 25½cm.

1. Physiological chemistry.   I. Gregory, William, 1803-1858, ed.
II. Title.

Library of Congress   QP514.L72 1843a   3—27630
,a26d1,

IU MiU PBa PPC NcD ICJ
NL 0347225   DLC WaU NjR DNLM NN TU CtY ICRL OC1 OCU

Liebig, Justus, freiherr von, 1803-1873.
Animal chemistry, or organic chemistry in its
applications to physiology and pathology. By
Justus Liebig, ... Edited from the author's
manuscript, by William Gregory, ... Philadelphia and New York, James M. Campbell, 1845.
111, 16 p. 25 cm.

NL 0347226   PHi

VOLUME 332

Liebig, Justus, *freiherr* von, 1803–1873.
Animal chemistry, or Chemistry in its applications to physiology and pathology. By Baron Liebig ... Ed. from the author's manuscript, by William Gregory ... 3d ed., rev. and greatly enl. Pt. 1 ... London, Taylor and Walton, 1846.

xvii, 258 p. 21½cm.

No more published.

1. Physiological chemistry. 1. Gregory, William, 1803–1858, ed. and tr.

Library of Congress   QP514.L72 1846
1—1386

NL 0347227   DLC CaBVaU ICJ IaU MB MdBP PPC

Liebig, Justus, *freiherr* von, 1803–1873.
Animal chemistry, or Organic chemistry in its application to physiology and pathology. By Justus Liebig ... Ed. from the author's manuscript, by William Gregory ... Philadelphia, J. M. Campbell, 1847.

x, 11–111 p. 24cm.

1. Physiological chemistry. 1. Gregory, William, 1803–1858, ed. and tr.

Library of Congress   QP514.L72 1847
1—1387

NL 0347228   DLC DNLM MH NN

Liebig, Justus, *freiherr* von, 1803–1873.
Animal chemistry, or Organic chemistry in its application to physiology and pathology. By Justus Liebig ... Ed. from the author's manuscript, by William Gregory ... Philadelphia, J. M. Campbell, 1847.

x, 11–98 p. 24cm.

NL 0347229   NIC

Liebig, Justus, *freiherr* von, 1803–1873.
Animal chemistry, or Organic chemistry in its applications to physiology and pathology. By Justus Liebig ... Edited from the author's manuscript, by William Gregory ... Philadelphia, T. B. Peterson, 1847.

x, 11–111 p. 24cm.

1. Physiological chemistry. 1. Gregory, William, 1803–1858, ed.
36–34967

Library of Congress   QP514.L72 1847 a

NL 0347230   DLC PPC

Liebig, Justus, *Freiherr* von, 1803–1873.   547-9 K601
Animal chemistry, or, Chemistry in its applications to physiology and pathology. By Baron Liebig, ... Edited from the author's manuscript by William Gregory, ... From the third London edition, revised and greatly enlarged. New York, J. Wiley, 1848.

xiii, 173 p. 21cm.

NL 0347231   ICJ NN PPF PPC MiU MH

Liebig, Justus, *Freiherr von, 1803–1873.*
Animal chemistry: or Organic chemistry in its applications to physiology and pathology... ed. by William Gregory.
Phila., Peterson, pref. 1850.
111 p.

NL 0347232   PU

Liebig, Justus, Freiherr von, 1803–1873.
Animal chemistry; or, Chemistry in its application to physiology and pathology. Edited from the author's manuscript by William Gregory. From the 3d London ed., rev. and greatly enl. New York, Wiley, 1852.
xiii,173 p.

QP514
L56
1852

NL 0347233   CU OrU-M

Liebig, Justus, Freiherr von, 1803–1873.
Animal chemistry, or Organic chemistry in its applications to physiology and pathology, by ... ed. from the author's manuscript by William Gregory ... Philadelphia, T. B. Peterson, c1852.
x, 11–111 p.

(Liebig's complete works on chemistry c II)

NL 0347234   OCU PPWa PPHa

Liebig, Justus, Freiherr von, 1803–1873.
Animal chemistry, or Organic chemistry in its applications to physiology and pathology. Edited from the author's manuscript, by William Gregory. Philadelphia, T. B. Peterson c1856.
111 p. 24cm. (In his Complete works on chemistry. Philadelphia c1856)

NL 0347235   NNC

Liebig, Justus, *freiherr* von, 1803–1873.
Anleitung zur analyse organischer körper. Von dr. Justus Liebig ... Braunschweig, F. Vieweg und sohn, 1837.

2 p. l, 72, 2 p. diagrs. on 111 pl. (2 fold.) fold. tab. 21cm. With Naumann, K. F. A table of mineralogical species. Cambridge, 1833

Reprint of the article "Organische analyse" in the Handwörterbuch der chemie, with table added.

1. Chemistry, Analytic—Quantitative. 2. Chemistry, Organic.

Library of Congress   QD3.N31
3–22160

NL 0347236   DLC OCU CtNowaB

Liebig, Justus, *freiherr* von, 1803–1873.
Anleitung zur analyse organischer körper, von Justus Liebig. 2. umgearb. und verm. aufl. Mit 82 in den text eingedruckten holzschnitten. Braunschweig, F. Vieweg und sohn, 1853.

viii, 130 p. illus. 21½cm.

1. Chemistry, Analytic—Quantitative. 2. Chemistry, Organic.

Library of Congress   QD271.L71
3–22161

NL 0347237   ICJ NjR MB MH
DLC MU NNC ICRL MU MH OkU ScU PU OU

Liebig, Justus, freiherr von 1803–1878.
Annual report on the progress of chemistry
see under *title*

Liebig, Justus, Freiherr von, 1803–1873.
Atlas zum chemischen Laboratorium der Königlichen Akademie der Wissenschaften in München. Unter Mitwirkung von Justus von Liebig irbaut von A. von Voit _ Braunschweig,F.Vieweg und sohn,1859.
1p.l.,13 plates. 44 1/2 x 57cm.

NL 0347239   CtY-M

Liebig, Justus, *freiherr* von, 1803–1873.
Aus Justus Liebig's und Friedrich Wöhler's Briefwechsel in den Jahren 1829–1873; unter Mitwirkung von Emilie Wöhler hrsg. von A. W. Hofmann. Branuschweig, F. Vieweg, 1888.

QD39
L71w

2 v. fronts. 22½cm.

I. Wöhler, Friedrich, 1800–1882.

NNCoC NIC WaU CtY CU TNJ CoU MoU
NL 0347240   NCH IU OCU PSt MiU OClW ViU ICU ICJ

Liebig, Justus, *freiherr* von, 1803–1873.
Bemerkungen über das verhältniss der thier-chemie zur thier-physiologie. Von Justus Liebig. Heidelberg, C. F. Winter, 1844.

54 p. 21½ cm.

1. Physiological chemistry. 1. Chemistry, Physiological

QP514.L716
Agr 28–435

U. S. Dept. of Agr. Libr   386.2L622
for Library of Congress   a56b½ †

NL 0347241   DNAL MB DNLM DLC

Liebig, Justus, freiherr von, 1803–1873.

Berzelius, Jöns Jakob, *friherre,* 1779–1848.
Berzelius und Liebig, ihre briefe von 1831–1845 mit erläuternden einschaltungen aus gleichzeitigen briefen von Liebig und Wöhler sowie wissenschaftlichen nachweisen hrsg. mit unterstützung der Kgl. bayer. akademie der wissenschaften von Justus Carrière. München und Leipzig, J. F. Lehmann, 1893.

Liebig, Justus, Freiherr von, 1803–1873.
Ein bis jetzt unbekannter Brief von J. von Liebig an J. J. Berzelius aus dem Jahre 1836. Von Arne Holmberg, Stockholm. Leipzig, J. A. Barth, 1940
235 –238 p. 24cm.

QD
22
L71
A25

"Sonderabdruck aus: Mitteilungen zur Geschichte der Medizin, der Naturwissenschaften und der Technik, hrsg. von Rudolph Zaunick, Bd. 39 (Leipzig: J. A. Barth 1940) S. 235–238."

NL 0347243   NIC

Liebig, Justus, Freiherr von, 1803–1873.
Briefe von Justus Liebig, nach neuen Funden. Hrsg. von Ernst Berl im Auftrag der Gesellschaft Liebig-Museum in Giessen und der Liebighaus-Stiftung in Darmstadt. Giessen, Selbstverlag der Gesellschaft Liebig-Museum und der Liebighaus-Stiftung in Darmstadt, 1928.

88 p. port. 25 cm.

"Briefe des jungen Justus Liebig aus Heppenheim, Bonn, Erlangen und Paris an seine Eltern in Darmstadt."

1. Berl, Ernst, 1877– ed.

QD22.L7A4
50–52075

NL 0347244   DLC NN MiU MH PU-S

Liebig, Justus, *freiherr von,* 1803–1873.
Briefwechsel zwischen Justus v. Liebig und Theodor Reuning über landwirthschaftliche fragen aus den jahren 1854 bis 1873. Dresden, G. Schönfeld, 1884.

viii, 243 p. 21cm.

Edited by Reinhold Echtermeyer and Georg von Liebig. cf. Vorwort.
Book-plate: Ex libris A. Gutbier.

1. Agricultural chemistry. 1. Reuning, Theodor, 1807–1876. 11. Echtermeyer, Reinhold, ed. 111. Liebig, Georg, freiherr von, 1827–1903, jt. ed.

NL 0347245   MiU

VOLUME 332

S
405
L71
Liebig, Justus, Freiherr von, 1803-1873.
   Briefwechsel zwischen Justus v. Liebig und
Theodor Renning über landwirthschaftliche fragen
aus den Jahren 1854 bis 1873. Dresden, G.
Schönfeld, 1884.
   248 p. 22 cm.

   1. Agriculture - Germany. I. Reuning,
Theodor. II. Title.

NL   0347246   NIC

Liebig, Justus, Freiherr von, 1803-1873.
   Die Chemie in ihrer Anwendung auf Agricultur
und Physiologie. 5. umgearb. und sehr verm.
Aufl. Braunschweig, F. Vieweg, 1843.
   xiv, 506 p. 21 cm.
   Contents.- pt.1, Der chemische Process der
Ernährung der Vegetabilien.- pt.2. Der chemische
Process der Gährung, Fäulniss und Verwesung.

NL   0347247   OkU InU CtY PPG

Liebig, Justus, _freiherr_ von, 1803-1873.
   Die chemie in ihrer anwendung auf
agricultur und physiologie, von Justus
Liebig. 6. aufl. Braunschweig, F. Vieweg und sohn, 1846.
   xvi, 468(i.e.568)p. tables. 21cm.

   1.Agricultural chemistry. 2.Physiologi-
cal chemistry.

NL   0347248   OCU CtY MH PU

S585
L65
1862
Liebig, Justus, Freiherr von, 1803-1873.
   Die Chemie in ihrer Anwendung auf Agricultur und Physiologie ... 7.Aufl. Braunschweig, F. Vieweg, 1862.
   2 v.

   1. Agricultural chemistry.

NL   0347249   CU OkU NNU-W MH MiU OU

S
585
L716c
1865
Liebig, Justus, Freiherr von, 1803-1873.
   Die Chemie in ihrer Anwendung auf Agri-
cultur und Physiologie. 8. Aufl. Braun-
schweig, Vieweg, 1865.
   2 v.
   Earlier eds. have title: Die organische
Chemie in ihrer Anwendung auf Agricultur und
Physiologie.
   Contents.- Th. 1. Der chemische Process der
Ernährung der Vegetabilien.-- Th. 2. Die Natur
gesetze des Feldbaues.

NL   0347250   DNLM KMK IU MU

S585
L65
1875
Liebig, Justus, Freiherr von, 1803-1873.
   Die Chemie in ihrer Anwendung auf Agricultur und Physiologie.
9. Aufl., im Auftrage des Verfassers, hrsg. von Ph. Zöller. Braunschweig, F. Vieweg, 1875.
   320 p. diagrs.

   1. Agricultural chemistry.

NL   0347251   CU

S585 Liebig, Justus, _freiherr_ von, 1803-1873.
L68   Die chemie in ihrer anwendung auf agricultur und physiologie. Von Justus von Liebig. 9. aufl., im auftrage des verfassers hrsg. von dr. Ph. Zöller ... Braunschweig, F. Vieweg
und sohn, 1876.
   [iii]-xxxvi, 698 p. 22ᵐ.

   1. Agricultural chemistry. 2. Physiological chemistry.

NL   0347252   ICU PSt OkU OCU CtY NjR PBL OCU NN PU

Liebig, Justus, _freiherr_ von, 1803-1873.
   Chemische Analyse der Mineralquellen zu Kissingen.   Mün-
chen, 1856. 25 p. 8°.
   Repr.: Annalen der Chemie und Pharmacie. Bd. 98.

   1. Water (Mineral), Germany: Kissingen.
N. Y. P. L.   February 7, 1913.

NL   0347253   NN DNLM NNC PPC

540.4
L62c
Liebig, Justus, Freiherr von, 1803-1873.
   Chemische Briefe. Heidelberg, C. F.
Winter, 1844.
   xi, 342p. 20cm.

   English editions published in 1843 and
1844 under title: Familiar letters on
chemistry.

   1. Chemistry. I. Title.

NL   0347254   IU KU-M DNLM PPG NNC MiU CtY CU

Liebig, Justus, _Freiherr_ von, 1803-1873.   540.4 L62
   Chemische Briefe von Justus Liebig. Zweiter Abdruck. Heidelberg, C. F. Winter, 1845.
   xii, 342 p. 19ᶜᵐ.

NL   0347255   ICJ PPC PSC OrCS

QD 22
.L 7
LIEBIG, JUSTUS, Freiherr VON, 1803-1873
   Chemische Briefe. 3. umgearb. und verm.
Aufl. Heidelberg, C.F. Winter, 1851.
   668 p.

   1. Chemistry--Addresses, essays, lectures.
I. Title.

NL   0347256   InU

QD
39
L71
1851
Liebig, Justus, Freiherr von, 1803-1873.
   Chemische Briefe. 3. umgearb. und verm.
Aufl. Heidelberg, C. F. Winter, 1851.
   xxi, 725 p. 19cm.

   1. Chemistry. I. Title.

NL   0347257   NIC WU TNJ IU-M DNLM ICJ PPG CtY OU

Liebig, Justus, _Freiherr_ von, 1803-1873.
   Chemische Briefe, von Justus von Liebig. Vierte umgearbeitete und vermehrte Auflage. Erster-zweiter Band. Leipzig und Heidelberg, C. F. Winter, 1859.
   2 vol. in 1. 20½ᵐ.

NL   0347258   ICJ CU IaU CtY MiU OU NSyU OCU TxU DLC

Liebig, Justus, _freiherr_ von, 1803-1873.
   Chemische briefe, von Justus von Liebig. Wohlfeile
ausg. Leipzig und Heidelberg, C. F. Winter, 1865.
   xxviii, 532 p. 20ᵐ.

   1. Chemistry.

                             15-6294
Library of Congress   QD39.L6

       OCl ICJ DNLM UrCS
NL   0347259   DLC OkU OrCS LU NcD-MC CU KU CtY PPF

Liebig, Justus, _Freiherr_ von, 1803-1873.
   Chemische Briefe, von Justus von Liebig. 6. Aufl. Neuer
unveränderter Abdruck der Ausgabe letzter Hand. Leipzig,
C. F. Winter, 1878.
   xxiv, 479 p. 23ᵐ.

NL   0347260   ICJ CtY NjP

Liebig, Justus, freiherr von, 1803-1873.
   Chemische briefe. Hamburg, Tanssen, 1913.
   164 p. il. D.

NL   0347261   PPF

RA866
A14
85Lℓ
Liebig, Justus Freiherr von, 1803-1873.
   Chemische Untersuchung der Schwefel-Quellen
Aachen's. Aachen, Mayer, 1851.
   1p.ℓ., iii, 44p. 22cm.

   1. Physical medicine - Hydrotherapy - Aachen.

NL   0347262   CtY-M DNLM OCU

Liebig, Justus, _freiherr_ von, 1803-1873.
   Chemische untersuchung über das fleisch und seine zubereitung zum nahrungsmittel, von Justus Liebig. Heidelberg, C. F.
Winter, 1847.
   viii, 116 p. 20ᶜᵐ.

   1. Meat.   44-49573
Library of Congress   TX556.M4L5

NL   0347263   DLC WU MHi CtY MiU DNLM ICJ PU

Liebig, Justus, _freiherr_ von, 1803-1873.
   Chemistry, and its application to physiology, agricul-
ture, and commerce; by Justus Liebig ... Ed. by John
Gardner ... 2d thousand. New York, Fowlers and Wells,
1847.
   vi, [7]-54 p. 23ᶜᵐ.
   Contains sixteen letters.
   Other editions have title: Familiar letters on chemistry.

   1. Chemistry--Addresses, essays, lectures. I. Gardner, John, 1804-
1880, ed. II. Title.

                                  4-35929
Library of Congress   QD39.L7 1847

NL   0347264   DLC PSt NIC OU

VOLUME 332

QD39　Liebig,Justus,freiherr von,1803-1873.
.L693　　Chemistry,and its application to physiology,
　　　agriculture,and commerce, by Justus Liebig...
　　　Ed.by John Gardner... New York,Fowlers and
　　　Wells,1848.
　　　　vi,[7]-54 p.　22cm.

1.Chemistry.

NL　0347265　ICU PU NN MH

QD　　Liebig, Justus, Freiherr von, 1803-1873.
39　　　Chemistry, and its application to physiology,
L716f　agriculture, and commerce. Ed. by John
1850　Gardner. New York, Fowlers and Wells, 1850.
　　　　54 p.

　　　Contains 16 letters.
　　　Previous eds. have title: Familiar letters
　　　on chemistry.

　　　I. Gardner, John, 1804-1880, ed.　II. Title

NL　0347266　DNLM

QD3　Liebig, Justus, freiherr von, 1803-1873.
.L54
　　　Chemistry and physics in relation to
　　physiology and pathology, by baron Justus
　　Liebig ... from the 10th London ed., rev.
　　and cor.　Philadelphia, T.B. Peterson,
　　[1825?]
　　　48 p.　23½cm　(Liebig's complete
　　works on chemistry [V.])

　　　1.Physiological chemistry. I. Title.

NL　0347267　OCU OC1 PU

QU　LIEBIG, Justus, Freiherr von, 1803-1873.
L716c　　Chemistry and physics in relation to
1846　physiology and pathology.　London,
　　Baillière, 1846.
　　　116 p.　　　　QU L716c
　　　　Translation of Thier-Chemie, Abth. 1,
　　Th. 2.

NL　0347268　DNLM CaBVaU PPWa

LIEBIG,Justus,freiherr VON, 1803-1873.
　Chemistry and Physics in relation to physiology and pathology. 2d ed.　London,also Paris,
1847.

NL　0347269　MH-C

Liebig, Justus, freiherr von, 1803-1873.
　Chemistry in its application to agriculture
and physiology edited from the manuscript
of the author by Lyon Playfair. Philadelphia [pref. 1840.]

NL　0347270　ODW PU

Liebig, Justus, freiherr von, 1803-1873.　No. 2 in 7975-51
　Chemistry in its application to agriculture and physiology. Edited
from the manuscript of the author by Lyon Playfair. From the
last London edition.
　Philadelphia. Peterson. [1842?] 135 pp. 8°.
Two copies.
Published in Professor Liebig's Complete works on chemistry.
Translated from Die organische Chemie in ihrer Anwendung auf Agri-
cultur und Physiologie.

NL　0347271　MB

Liebig, Justus, freiherr von, 1803-1873.
　Chemistry in its application to agriculture and physiology.
By Justus Liebig ... Ed. from the manuscript of the author
by Lyon Playfair ... with very numerous additions, and a new
chapter on soils.　3d American, from the 2d English ed., with
notes, and appendix, by John W. Webster ...　Cambridge, J.
Owen; Boston, J. Munroe and company; [etc., etc.,] 1842.
　　xix, [21]-430 p. 20ᶜᵐ.

　　1. Agricultural chemistry.　I. Playfair, Lyon Playfair. 1st baron,
1818-1898, ed. II. Webster, John White, 1793-1850, ed.　　12—0828
　　Library of Congress　　　　S585.L72 1842 b

NL　0347272　DLC MB PHaT MiU MBH OU PPF

Liebig, Justus, freiherr von, 1803-1873.
　Chemistry in its application to agriculture and physiology.
By Justus Liebig ... Edited from the manuscript of the author.
By Lyon Playfair, PH. D. 2d ed., with very numerous addi-
tions. London, Taylor and Walton, 1842.
　　xii, 409, [1] p. 22¾ᶜᵐ.

　　1. Agricultural chemistry.　I. Playfair, Lyon Playfair, 1st baron,
1818-1898, ed.　　　　　　　　　　46-20662
　　Library of Congress　　　　S585.L72　1842 a

NL　0347273　DLC OrU-M TxU CaBVaU CtY-M PPF ICJ PPL

Liebig, Justus, Freiherr von, 1803-1873.
　... Chemistry, in its applications to
agriculture and physiology. By Justus Liebig ...
Edited from the manuscript of the author, by
Lyon Playfair.　New-York, J. Winchester,
Publisher, 1842.
　　64 p.　tables.　28 cm.　(The New world.
Extra series. no. 29, 30.　Vol. II.　No. 5, 6.
Oct. 1842)
　　Caption title.

NL　0347274　NNC CaBVaU

Liebig, Justus, freiherr von, 1803-1873.
　Chemistry in its application to agriculture and physiology ...　Edited from the manuscript of the author by
L. Playfair, with very numerous additions, and a new
chapter on soils.　4th American, from the 2d English ed.,
with notes, and app., by J. W. Webster ...　Cambridge,
J. Owen, 1843.
　　430 p.　8°.

Subject entries: Agricultural chemistry.
　　　　　　　　　　　　　　　　　1-3009

Library of Congress, no.　　S585.L719.

NL　0347275　DLC MH NcD KyU TU PPF ICJ Nh

Liebig, Justus, freiherr von, 1803-1873.
　Chemistry in its applications to agriculture and physiology.
By Justus Liebig ...　Edited from the manuscript of the au-
thor.　By Lyon Playfair.　3d ed., rev. and enl.　London,
Printed for Taylor and Walton, 1843.
　　x, 400 p. 23ᶜᵐ.

　　1. Agricultural chemistry.　I. Playfair, Lyon Playfair. 1st baron,
1818-1898, ed.　　　　　　　　　33-22311
　　Library of Congress　　　S585.L7　　　630.24

NL　0347276　DLC CaBVaU MNS PPAN CtY-M IU PSt PPF

Liebig, Justus, freiherr von, 1803-1873.
　Chemistry in its application to agriculture and physiology.　By Justus Liebig ... Edited from the manuscript
of the author, by Lyon Playfair ...　From the last London ed. much improved.　Philadelphia, J. M. Campbell
& co.; New York, Saxton & Miles, 1843.
　　iv, 5-135 p. 22ᶜᵐ.
　　[Agricultural pamphlets, v. 2, no. 1]

　　1. Agricultural chemistry.　2. Chemistry, Organic.　I. Playfair, Lyon
Playfair, 1st baron, 1818-1898, ed.

　　　　　　　　　　　　　　　　5-42941
　　Library of Congress　　　　S405.A27

DNLM OC1 MiU PU-S PBa PPL TU NN Nh
NL　0347277　DLC OO OCU WaU MdBP PPAN NcD CtY IU

Liebig, Justus, freiherr von, 1803-1873.
　Chemistry in its application to agriculture and
physiology.　Edited from the manuscript of the
author by L. Playfair ...　Philadelphia, J. M.
Campbell, 1845.
　　iv, 5-135 p.　8°.

NL　0347278　NN IdU

Liebig, Justus, Freiherr von, 1803-1873.
　Chemistry in its applications to agriculture and physiology. By
Justus Liebig ... Edited from the manuscript of the author, by
Lyon Playfair ... and William Gregory ... Fourth edition.
Revised and enlarged.　London, Taylor and Walton, 1847.
　　xii, 418 p. incl. tables. 23½ᶜᵐ.
　　Contents.—pt. 1. On the chemical processes in the nutrition of vegetables.—
pt. 2. On the chemical processes of fermentation, decay, and putrification.

NL　0347279　ICJ InU NNC OU ODW PU

S　Liebig, Justus, freiherr von, 1803-1873.
585　　Chemistry in its applications to agriculture
L71　and physiology, by Justus Liebig.　Edited from the
1847　manuscript of the author, by Lyon Playfair and
　　William Gregory.　From the 4th London ed., rev.
　　and enl.　New York, Wiley & Putnam, 1847.
　　　xiv, 401 p.　21 cm.

　　　1. Agricultural chemistry. 2. Chemistry,
　　Organic. I. Playfair, Lyon Playfair, 1st baron,
　　1818-1898. II. Gregory, William, 1803-
　　1858. III. Title.

NL　0347280　NIC CtHT-W MiD MH CtY NcAS OU

Liebig, Justus, freiherr von, 1803-1873.
　Chemistry in its application to agriculture and physiology.
By Justus Liebig ... Edited from the manuscript of the author by Lyon Playfair, PH. D.　From the last London ed.,
much improved.　Philadelphia, T. B. Peterson, 1847.
　　iv, 5-135 p. 24ᶜᵐ.
　　On cover: Agricultural chemistry.

　　1. Agricultural chemistry.　I. Playfair, Lyon Playfair, 1st baron,
1818-1898, ed.　　　　　　　　36-36355
　　Library of Congress　　　　S585.L72　1847

NL　0347281　DLC PHi NcU-H NN NcU ODW MiU PPC

Liebig, Justus, freiherr von, 1803-1873.

　Chemistry in its applications to agriculture and physiology; ed. from the manuscript of the author, by Lyon Playfair and
William Gregory.　From the 4th London ed.,
rev. and enl.　New York, Wiley & Putnam,
1848.
　　xiv, 401 p.　21ᶜᵐ.
　　1. Agricultural chemistry. I. Playfair, Lyon
Playfair, baron, 1818-1898, ed. II. Gregory,
William, 1803-　　1858, jt. ed.

NL　0347282　ViU OO

VOLUME 332

Liebig, Justus, *freiherr* von, 1803–1873.
Chemistry in its applications to agriculture and physiology. By Justus Liebig ... Ed. from the manuscript of the author, by Lyon Playfair ... and William Gregory ... from the 4th London ed., rev. and enl. New York, J. Wiley, 1849.
xiv, 401p.   21ᵐ.

NL 0347283   NcD-MC NcD

Liebig, Justus, *freiherr* von, 1803–1873.
Chemistry in its applications to agriculture and physiology. By Justus Liebig ... Ed. from the manuscript of the author, by Lyon Playfair ... and William Gregory ... from the 4th London ed., rev. and enl. New York, J. Wiley, 1852.
2 p. l., ₍vii₎-xiv. 401 p. 21ᶜᵐ.

NL 0347284   MiU OClW

631.41
L621c
1854
Liebig, Justus, freiherr von, 1803–1873.
Chemistry in its applications to agriculture and physiology. By Justus Liebig ... Ed. from the manuscript of the author, by Lyon Playfair ... and William Gregory ... from the 4th London ed., rev. and enl. New York, J. Wiley, 1854.
2 p.ℓ., ₍vii₎-xiv, 401p. 21cm.
1. Agricultural chemistry. I. Playfair, Lyon Playfair, 1st baron, 1818–1898, ed. II. Gregory, William, 1803–1858, ed. Sp.: Littlefield Fund.

NL 0347285   TxU NjP

8
585
L71
1856
Liebig, Justus, freiherr von, 1803–1873.
Chemistry in its applications to agriculture and physiology. Edited from the manuscript of the author by L. Playfair and W. Gregory. From the 4th London ed., rev. and enl. New York, Wiley & Halsted, 1856.
xiv, 401 p. 21cm.
I. Playfair, Lyon Playfair, 1st baron, 1818–1898, ed. II. Gregory, William, 1803–1858, ed.

NL 0347286   NIC

Liebig, Justus, Freiherr von, 1803–1873.
Chemistry in its application to agriculture and physiology. Edited from the manuscript of the author by Lyon Playfair. From the last London edition, much improved. Philadelphia, T. B. Peterson ₍1856₎
135 p. 24cm. (In his Complete works on chemistry. Philadelphia ₍1856₎)

NL 0347287   NNC

Liebig, Justus, *freiherr* von, 1803–1873.
Chemistry in its applications to agriculture and physiology. By Justus Liebig ... Ed. from the manuscript of the author, by Lyon Playfair ... and William Gregory ... from the 4th London ed., rev. and enl. New York, J. Wiley, 1861.
2 p. l., ₍viii₎-xiv, 401 p. 21ᶜᵐ.

1. Agricultural chemistry.   I. Playfair, Lyon Playfair, 1st baron, 1818–1898, ed. II. Gregory, William, 1803–1858, ed.

Library of Congress   S585.L724
12—9835

NL 0347288   DLC

Liebig, Justus, *freiherr* von, 1803–1873.
Chemistry in its applications to agriculture and physiology. By Justus Liebig ... Ed. from the manuscript of the author, by Lyon Playfair ... and William Gregory ... from the 4th London ed., rev. and enl. New York, J. Wiley, 1872.
2 p. l., ₍vii₎-xiv. 401 p. 21ᶜᵐ.

NL 0347289   ViU OCl OU

Liebig, Justus, *freiherr* von, 1803–1873.
Chimie appliquée à la physiologie végétale et à l'agriculture, par m. Justus Liebig ... Traduction faite sur les manuscrits de l'auteur, par m. Charles Gerhardt ... 2. éd., considérablement augm. Paris, Fortin, Masson et cⁱᵉ, 1844.
viii, 544 p. 21ᶜᵐ.

1. Agricultural chemistry.   I. Gerhardt, Charles Frédéric, 1816–1856, tr.

33–7316
Library of Congress   S585.L726   630.24

NL 0347290   DLC GU

S
585
L71a
Liebig, Justus, Freiherr von, 1803–1873.
Chimie organique appliquée a la physiologie végétale et a l'agriculture suivie d'un essai de toxicologie. Traduction faite sur les manuscrits de l'auteur par Charles Gerhardt. Paris, Fortin, Masson, 1841.
392 p. 23 cm.

Translation of Die Organische Chemie in ihrer Anwendung auf Agricultur und Physiologie.

NL 0347291   NIC NNC PU MH WU

QP514
L716c
1842
Liebig, Justus, Freiherr von, 1803–1873.
Chimie organique appliqués à la physiologie animale et à la pathologie. Traduction faite sur les manuscrits de l'auteur par Charles Gerhardt. Paris, Fortin, Masson, 1842.
xvi, 360 p. 22cm.

1. Physiological chemistry.

NL 0347292   GU MShM InU

Liebig, Justus, *Freiherr* von, 1803–1873.
Complete works on chemistry ... Philadelphia, T. B. Peterson ₍n. d.₎
1 v. (various pagings) illus. 24 cm.

1. Agricultural chemistry.

S585.L726a   49–39095*‡

OKentU
NL 0347293   DLC NcRS MiU OrCS IaU PU-S TU OCU MH

Liebig, Justus, freiherr von, 1803–1873.
Professor Liebig's Complete works on chemistry ... Philadelphia, Peterson ₍1850?₎
3 pts. in 1 v. illus.

Each part has individual t.-p.
Contents.--₍pt. 1₎ Researches on the motion of the juices in the animal body; and the effect of evaporation in plants; together with an account of the origin of the potato disease ... ed. from the manuscript of the author, by

Continued in next column

Continued from preceding column

William Gregory. ₍1850?₎--₍pt. 2₎ Chemistry in its application to agriculture and physiology ... ed. from the manuscript of the author, by Lyon Playfair ... From the last London ed., much improved. ₍1850?₎--₍pt.3₎ Animal chemistry; or, Organic chemistry in its applications to physiology and pathology ... ed. from the author's manu-   script, by William Gregory. ₍1850?₎

NL 0347295   NNC MH NcD CU Nh DSI OClW-n

Liebig, Justus, *Freiherr* von, 1803–1873.   547.04 L621
Liebig's complete works on chemistry. ... By Justus Liebig, ... Philadelphia, T. B. Peterson, [pref. 1852].
5 vol. in 1. 24ᶜᵐ.
Contents. — Chemistry in its application to agriculture and physiology. Edited by Lyon Playfair. iv, 7–135 p. — Animal chemistry, or Organic chemistry in its application to physiology and pathology. Edited by William Gregory. x, 11–111 p. — Familiar letters on chemistry, and its relation to commerce, physiology and agriculture. Edited by John Gardiner. 48 p. — Researches on the motion of the juices in the animal body; and the effect of evaporation in plants. Together with an account of the origin of the potato disease. Edited by William Gregory. iv, 5–47 p. 15 illus. — Chemistry and physics in relation to physiology and pathology. 48 p.

NL 0347296   ICJ NIC CtY NjP PBL ViU

Liebig, Justus, freiherr von, 1803–1873.   FOR OTHER EDITIONS SEE MAIN ENTRY
Youmans, Edward Livingston, 1821–1887.
The correlation and conservation of forces: a series of expositions, by Prof. Grove, Prof. Helmholtz, Dr. Mayer, Dr. Faraday, Prof. Liebig and Dr. Carpenter. With an introduction and brief biographical notices of the chief promoters of the new views, by Edward L. Youmans ... New York, D. Appleton and company, 1871.

Liebig, Justus, freiherr von, 1803–1873.   FOR OTHER EDITIONS SEE MAIN ENTRY
Youmans, Edward Livingston, 1821–1887, *ed.*
The culture demanded by modern life: a series of addresses and arguments on the claims of scientific education. By Professors Tyndall, Henfrey, Huxley ... etc. With an introduction on mental discipline in education, by E. L. Youmans ... New York, D. Appleton and company, 1870.

Liebig, Justus, *freiherr* von, 1803–1873.
Des engrais artificiels, par Justus Liebig. Tr. de l'allemand. Paris, Mᵐᵉ Vᵉ Bouchard-Huzard; ₍etc., etc.₎ 1846.
2 p. l., 38 p. 20ᶜᵐ.

1. Fertilizers ₍and manures₎

Agr 18–408
Library, U. S. Dept. of   Agriculture 57L625

NL 0347299   DNAL PU

Liebig, Justus von, 1803–1873.   507 M700
The development of ideas in physical science. ... [*In* YOUMANS, E. L., *editor*. The culture demanded by modern life, p. 345–370. New York 1867.]

NL 0347300   ICJ

Liebig,   Justus, Freiherr von, 1803–1873.   5599.130
The development of ideas in physical science.
(In Youmans. The culture demanded by modern life. Pp. 345–370. New York, 1875.)

NL 0347301   MB

VOLUME 332

Liebig (Justus), *freiherr von*, 1803-1873.
The development of science among nations. *Edinburgh:*
Edmonston & Douglas, 1867. 32 pp. 8°.
In : *C. p. v. 650.

NL 0347302   NN OU

Liebig, Justus, freiherr von, 1803-1873.
Le développement des idées dans les sciences
naturelles; études philosophiques par J. de Lie-
big ... Paris, G. Baillière, 1867.
2 p.l., 42 p.   22ᶜᵐ.
"Extrait de la Revue des cours scientifiques."
Translations of two papers, the first of which was
given at the Sitzung der K. Akademie der wissenschaften,
München, July 25, 1866.
"Induction et déduction dans les sciences": p. [25]-40.

1. Science—Philosophy.

NL 0347303   MiU

Liebig, Justus, freiherr von, 1803-1878, ed.

Turner, Edward, 1798-1837.
Elements of chemistry, including the actual state and
prevalent doctrines of the science. By the late Edward
Turner ... 8th ed. Ed. by Baron Liebig ... and William
Gregory ... London, Printed for Taylor and Walton,
1847.

Liebig, Justus, freiherr von, 1803-1873.
Die Entwicklung der Ideen in der
Naturwissenschaft. Rede in der öffentlichen
Sitzung der k. Akademie der Wissenschaften am
25. Juli 1866 zur Vorfeier des Geburts- und
Namensfestes Sr. Maj. des Königs gehalten von
Justus Freiherrn von Liebig ...
München 1866. Jm Verlage der königl. Akademie.
26p.   27cm., in case 28.5cm.
Original printed green wrappers; in cloth
case.

#fGC8
L6222
866e

NL 0347305   MH ICJ CtY NN MH NjP CU MdBP

Liebig, Justus, Freiherr von, 1803-1873.
Die Ernährung, Blut- und Fettbildung im
Thierkörper ... [Leipzig, etc.] 1841.
1 p.l., 45 p.   20.5 cm.   [Bound with his
Der Lebensprocess im Thiere und die Atmosphäre]
"Aus den Annalen der Chemie und Pharmacie
Band XLI. .3. besonders abgedruckt. "

NL 0347306   CtY

Liebig, Justus, Freiherr von, 1803-73.
Experimental Chemie; Vorlesungen von Prof. Dr. v.
Liebig, 1848. [Diese Wiedergabe des Kollegheftes
August Kekulés nach Vorlesungen Liebigs in Giessen -
das Original befindet sich im Besitze des Kekulé-Zimmers
der Technischen Hochschule Darmstadt - ist von der
AGFA J.G. Farben-Industrie A.G., Filmfabrik Wolfen.
Darmstadt, Ernst-Ludwig-Hochschulgesellschaft, n.d.]

298 [48] p.

NL 0347307   MH OCU InU WU

Liebig, Justus, *freiherr* von, 1803-1873.
.... Extract of meat. By Baron Liebig ... [London
1873]
cover-title, 3 p.   26ᶜᵐ.
Reprinted from the Pharmaceutical journal for January 18th, 1873.
At head of title: With the compliments of Liebig's extract of meat company, limited.

1. Meat extract.
8-13205

NL 0347308   DLC

Liebig, Justus, *freiherr* von, 1803-1873.
Familiar letters on chemistry, and its relation to commerce,
physiology, and agriculture. By Justus Liebig ... Ed. by
John Gardner ...   London, Printed for Taylor and
Walton, 1843.
xii, 179 p.   16½ᶜᵐ.
Contains 16 letters.

NL 0347309   OkU ICJ CtY ViU PU

Liebig, Justus, *freiherr* von, 1803-1873.
Familiar letters on chemistry, and its relation to commerce, physiology, and agriculture. By Justus Liebig ...
Ed. by John Gardner ...   New York, D. Appleton & co.;
[etc., etc.] 1843.
180 p.   15½ᶜᵐ.
Contains 16 letters.

1. Chemistry—Addresses, essays, lectures.   I. Gardner, John, 1804-
1880, ed.
1-23505

Library of Congress   QD39.L71

NL 0347310   DLC NWM MB CtY-M DNLM NcD IU OU MB MeB

Liebig, Justus, *freiherr* von, 1803-1873.
Familiar letters on chemistry, and its relation to com-
merce, physiology and agriculture. By Justus Liebig ...
Ed. by John Gardner ...   New York, J. Winchester, 1843.
iv, [5]-53 p.   24ᶜᵐ.
[Chemical pamphlets, v. 6, no. 16]
Contains 16 letters.

1. Chemistry—Addresses, essays, lectures.   I. Gardner, John, 1804-
1880, ed.
1-23506

Library of Congress   QD3.C5   vol. 6

NL 0347311   DLC DNLM CU PPL PPAN

Liebig, Justus, Freiherr von, 1803-1873.
Familiar letters on chemistry, and its relation to commerce, physiology, and agriculture. Ed. by John Gardner. Philadelphia,
Campbell, 1843.
55 p.   [With his Chemistry in its application to agriculture and physiology. Philadelphia, 1847]
Contains 16 letters.
Later ed. has title: Chemistry, and its
applications to physiology, agriculture, and

commerce.

S
585
L716c
1847

NL 0347313   DNLM MB WaU OClW

Liebig, Justus, *freiherr* von, 1803-1873.
Familiar letters on chemistry. Second series. The philo-
sophical principles and general laws of the science. By Justus
Liebig ... Ed. by John Gardner ... London, Printed for
Taylor and Walton, 1844.
xi, [1], 218 p.   16½ᶜᵐ.
Contains 11 letters.

1. Chemistry—Addresses, essays, lectures.   I. Gardner, John, 1804-
1880, ed.   II. Title.
1-23508

Library of Congress   QD39.L7   1844

NL 0347314   DLC CaBVaU MdBP PBa CtY ViU PPF PPL

Liebig, Justus, Freiherr von, 1803-1873.
Familiar letters on chemistry and its relation to commerce, physiology, and agriculture. Edited by John Gardner. 2d ed.
corr.   London, Printed for Taylor and
Walton, 1844.
x, 181p.   18cm.

German ed. published 1844 under title:
Chemische Briefe.
Contains 16 letters.

540.4
L62cE
1844

NL 0347315   IU

Liebig, Justus, Freiherr von, 1803-1873.
Familiar letters on chemistry. 1st-
2d series. Ed. by John Gardner. London,
Taylor and Walton, 1844-45.
2 v.

1st series, 3d ed., contains 16 letters;
2d series, 11 letters.
Title on spine: Chemical letters.

I. Gardner, John, 1804-1880, ed.   II. Title

QD
39
L716f
1844

NL 0347316   DNLM

Liebig, Justus, *freiherr* von, 1803-1873.
Familiar letters on chemistry, and its relation to commerce,
physiology, and agriculture. By Justus Liebig ... Ed. by
John Gardner ... 3d ed. London, Printed for Taylor and
Walton, 1845.
x, 181, [1] p.   16½ᶜᵐ.
Contains 16 letters.

1. Chemistry—Addresses, essays, lectures.   I. Gardner, John, 1804-
1880, ed.   II. Title.
1—23507

Library of Congress   QD39.L7   1845

NL 0347317   DLC CaBVaU PBa MH-BA DNLM MB PPAN

Liebig, Justus, freiherr von, 1803-1873.
Familiar letters on chemistry, and its
relation to commerce, physiology,   and
agriculture. By ... ed. by John Gardner
... New York, A. O. Moore & col, 1850.
180 1 p.

Contains 16 letters.

NL 0347318   MiU

Liebig, Justus, *freiherr* von, 1803-1873.
Familiar letters on chemistry, in its relations to physiology, dietetics, agriculture, commerce, and political
economy. By Justus von Liebig. 3d ed., rev. and much
enl. London, Taylor, Walton & Maberly, 1851.
xx, 536 p.   16½ᶜᵐ.
This edition contains 35 letters incorporating the subject matter of both
1st and 2d series.
Edited by William Gregory.

1. Chemistry—Addresses, essays, lectures.   I. Gregory, William, 1803-
858   II. Title.
1-23509

Library of Congress   QD39.L7   1851

PPAN PP NjP MB ICJ ViU
NL 0347319   DLC CaBVaU TxU NjN NIC CSt MB DNLM PPF

VOLUME 332

Liebig, Justus, freiherr von, 1803-1873.
Familiar letters on chemistry, and its
relation to commerce, physiology, and
agriculture, by baron ... ed. by John
Gardner ... from the last London ed.,
rev. and cor. Philadelphia, T. B.
Peterson [1852?]
48 p.

(Liebig's complete works on chemistry [III.])

NL 0347320   OCU PU PPWa

540.4
L62cE
1856
Liebig, Justus, Freiherr von, 1803-1873.
Familiar letters on chemistry and its relation
to commerce, physiology, and agriculture.
Edited by John Gardner. New York, C. M.
Saxton, 1856.
180p. 20cm.
German ed. published 1844 under title:
Chemische Briefe.
Contains 16 letters.

NL 0347321   IU MBH PBL MB

540.8
L62cE
1859a
Liebig, Justus, Freiherr von, 1803-1873.
Familiar letters on chemistry, in its relations to physiology, dietetics, agriculture,
commerce, and political economy. 4th ed.,
rev. and enl. Edited by John Blyth. London, Walton and Maberly, 1859.
xv, 536p. 19cm.

German ed. published in 1844 under title:
Chemische Briefe.

    IaU InU NjR
NL 0347322   IU NcRS NjP CU MiD OCU PBL MdBP PPWa MH

LIEBIG, Justus, freiherr von, 1803-1873.
Fleisch- oder pflanzenkost?/ Justus Liebig über nahrung, ernährung, zubereitung und zusammensetzung der speisen und getränke. Herausgegeben und mit erläuterungen versehen von Albert
Neuburger. Leipzig, R. Voigtländer, [1916?]

pp.137.
At head of title:-Voigtländers quellenbüch-
er, 85.

NL 0347323   MBCo

WS
100
L716s
1867
LIEBIG, Justus, Freiherr von, 1803-1873
    Food for infants; a complete substitute
for that provided by nature. 2d ed. Tr.
with Baron von Liebig's special permission by Elise von Lersner-Ebersburg.
London, Walton, 1867.
    30 p.
    Translation of Suppe fur Sauglinge.

NL 0347324   DNLM ICJ

Liebig, Justus, *freiherr* von, 1803-1873.
    Die grundsätze der agricultur-chemie, mit rücksicht
auf die in England angestellten untersuchungen. Von
Justus von Liebig. 2., durch einen nachtrag verm. aufl.
Braunschweig, F. Vieweg und sohn, 1855.
    4 p. l., 152 p. 21½ᵐ.

    1. Agricultural chemistry.

                       12-9829

Library of Congress   S585.L73

NL 0347325   DLC MH PPAN ICJ

LIEBIG, J[ustus], freiherr von, 1803-1873.
Guide pour l'introduction a l'étude de
chimie, contenant les principes généraux de
cette science, etc. Accompagné de considérations détaillées sur les acides, les bases et
les sels. Traduit de l'allemand par Ch. Gerhardt
Paris, E. Lacroix, [1838?]

    "Bibliothèque des professions industrielles
et agricoles   . Sér. G, No. 31."

NL 0347326   MH-C

Liebig, Justus, freiherr von, 1803-1873.
Hand-book of organic analysis; containing
a detailed account of the various methods
used in determining the elementary composition of organic substances. Edited by A. W.
Hofmann. London, Walton and Maberly, 1853.
135 p. illus. 20 cm.

1. Chemistry, Organic. I. Hofmann,
August Wilhelm von, 1818-1892, ed.

PU-S MBH PPC
NL 0347327   T CaBVaU NcRS N ICJ IU MdBP MH NN RPB OU

Liebig, Justus, *freiherr* **von, 1803-1873.**
Handbuch der chemie mit rücksicht auf pharmacie, von
d᷏. Justus Liebig ... Heidelberg, C. F. Winter; [etc.,
etc.] 1843.

    2 v. 22½ᶜᵐ. (*Added t.-p.:* Handbuch der pharmacie ... von **Philipp
Lorenz** Geiger. 1. bd., 5. aufl.)

    1. Chemistry.

Library, U. S. Dept. of   Agriculture 386L62   Agr 25-492

NL 0347328   DNAL DNLM PU MnU OGK OC1W

Liebig, Justus, Freiherr von, 1803-1873.
Handbuch der Pharmacie
    see under   Geiger, Philipp Lorenz,
1785-1836.

Liebig, Justus, frhr. von, 1803-73, & others.
Handwörterbuch der reinen and angewandten
chemie ... Braunschweig, Vieweg, 1837-1864.
9 v.

NL 0347330   OCU PU OC1

Liebig, Justus, freiherr von, 1803-1873.
Handwörterbuch der reinen und angewandten chemie. In verbindung mit mehren
gelehrten, hrsg. von J. Liebig, J. C. Pogg-
endorf und Dr. Fr. Wöhler. Braunschweig,
F. Vieweg und sohn, 1842-
    v. illus., fold. tables. 22cm.

--- ------ Supplementband,

    OrU-M
NL 0347331   PSt IaU NN DNLM CU OkU MH NjR WU ViU OCU

---

ar W
43875
Liebig, Justus, Freiherr von, 1803-1873.
Handwörterbuch der reinen und angewandten
Chemie; in Verbindung mit mehren Gelehrten,
hrsg. von J. Liebig, J. C. Poggendorff und
Fr. Wöhler. Braunschweig, F. Vieweg, 1848-
64 [v. 1, 1857]
9 v. 23cm.

    Vols. 1 & 2: 2d ed.
    Vols. 1, 2, & 9 edited by H. Von Fehling.
    Vols. 7 & 8 edited by H. von Fehling and H.
Kolbe.
    I. Poggendorff,   Johann Christian, 1796-
1877.   II. Wöhler,   Friedrich, 1800-1882.
III. Fehling, H   ohann von. IV. Kolbe,
Hermann, 1818-   1884.

NL 0347332   NIC NjR DLC-P4 NN

Liebig, Justus, freiherr von, 1803-1873.
Handworterbuch der reinen und angewandten
chemie. In verbindung mit mehren Gelehrten
herausgegeben von Dr. T. Liebig, Dr. T. C.
Poggendorff und Dr. Fr. Wohler. Redigirt von
Dr. Herman Kolbe. Supplementband.
Braunschweig: Verlag, Druck and Papier von
Friedrich vieweg und Sohn, 1850.
xii, 977 p., illus. 21.5 cm.

NL 0347333   LNT-M

Liebig, Justus, Freiherr von, 1803-1873.
HANDWÖRTERBUCH der reinen und angewandten
Chemie. . Begründet von J. Liebig, J. C. Poggendorff,,
und F. Fehling. Bearbeitet in Verbindung mit
mehren Gelehrten und redigirt von H. v. Fehling.
Band 6-9. Brunschweig. Vieweg. 1854-1365.

    4 v. 23 cm.

NL 0347334   MBCo

Liebig, Justus, Freiherr von, 1803-1873, and others.
    Handwörterbuch der reinen und angewandten Chemie. Be-
gründet von Dr. J. von Liebig, Dr. J. C. Poggendorff und Dr.
Fr. Wöhler... Zweite Auflage neu bearbeitet von Prof. Dr.
P. A. Bolley... Redigirt von Dr. Hermann v. Fehling...
Bd. 1-
Braunschweig: F. Vieweg und Sohn, 1856-   v. in
diagrs., illus., col'd pl., tables.   8°.

    Bibliographical footnotes.

    1. Chemistry.—Dictionaries, 1856-62.   2. Poggendorff, Johann Christian,
1796-1877, jt. au. 3. Woehler, Fried-   rich, 1800-82, jt. au. 4. Fehling,
Hermann Christian von, 1811-85,   editor. 5. Bolley, Pompejus Alexander, 1812-70, editor.   ander.
N. Y. P. L.   October 18, 1922.

NL 0347335   NN ViU

Liebig, Justus, *freiherr* **von, 1803-1873.**
    Handwörterbuch der reinen und angewandten che-
mie. Begründet von dr. J. von Liebig, dr. J. C.
Poggendorff und dr. Fr. Wöhler ... 2. aufl., neu
bearb. von mehren gelehrten und redigirt von dr.
Hermann v. Fehling ... Braunschweig, F. Vieweg
und sohn, 1857-
    v.   illus., col. pl. (v.2, pt.2) ta-
bles, diagrs.   22½ᶜᵐ.
    Vols. 1-2 edited by H. Fehling.
    Bibliographical foot-notes.

NL 0347336   ViU NN MB PBL CtY NjR OU

Liebig, Justus, freiherr von, 1803-1873.
HANDWÖRTERBUCH der reinen und angewandten
Chemie. . Begründ von J. von Liebig, J. C. Poggen-
dorff und Fr. Wöhler. 2 aufl. IIer bd. 1e-3e abth
[A-E.] 3 abth Braunschweig, 1359-62.

    Plates and woodcuts.
    IIes bd. 1e-3e abth. were edited by Hermann
r. Fehling.

NL 0347337   MH-C

VOLUME 332

5
585
.L73
Liebig, Justus, freiherr von, 1803–1873.
Herr dr. Emil Wolff in Hohenheim und die
agricultur-chemie. Nachtrag zu den "Grund-
sätzen der agricultur-chemie" von Justus von
Liebig. Braunschweig, F. Vieweg und sohn, 1855.
3 p.ℓ., 44 p. 22ᶜᵐ.
Written in answer to Wolff's reply to
Liebig's Grundsätze der agricultur-chemie.
cf. Vorwort.
With his Die moderne landwirthschaft. 1862.

1. Wolff, Emil Theodor von, 1818–1896.

NL 0347338   MiU OkU MH PU PPAN

Liebig, Justus, freiherr von, 1803–1873.
Induction und deduction. Von Justus von Liebig ... München, Im verlage der K. Akademie, 1865.
24 p. 21ᶜᵐ.

1. Science—Methodology.   I. Title.

                                                    P O 17—4
U. S. Patent office. Libr.   Q11.S66 1865
for Library of Congress   ₍a41b1₎

NL 0347339   DP NjP GEU CtY PPAmP NNBG

Liebig, Justus, freiherr von, 1803–1873.
Induction and deduction. A discourse by Justus baron von
Liebig. Delivered in the Royal academy of sciences, Munich.
(In Smithsonian institution. Annual report. 1870. Washington,
1871. 23½ᶜᵐ. p. ₍258,–267₎)

1. Science—Methodology.   I. Title.
                                                    S 15–284
Smithsonian inst. Library
for Library of Congress   ₍Q11.S66 1870₎
                                  ₍a38b1₎   (506)

NL 0347340   DSI MnHi I DLC

---

*fGC8
16222
8651
Liebig, Justus, freiherr von, 1803–1873.
Induction und Deduction. Rede in der
öffentlichen Sitzung der königl. Akademie der
Wissenschaften am 28. März 1865 zur Feier ihres
einhundert und sechsten Stiftungstages gehalten
von Justus Freiherrn von Liebig ...
München 1865. Jm Verlage der königl. Akademie.
19p. 27.5cm., in case 29cm.
Original printed green wrappers; in cloth
case.

NL 0347341   MH

Liebig, Justus, Freiherr von, 1803–1873.
Instructions for the chemical analysis
of organic bodies. Translated from the
German by William Gregory. Glasgow, R.
Griffin, 1839.
iv, 59 p. illus., tables. 23cm.
Bound with Hunt, Robert. A popular
treatise on the art of photography.
Glasgow, 1841.
1. Chemistry, Analytic—Quantitative.
2. Chemistry, Organic. I. Gregory,
William, 1803-   1858, tr.

CaBVaU
NL 0347342   MB MnU CtY DNLM NN MdBP CtY PPWa DSI MH

Liebig, Justus, Freiherr von, 1803–1873.
Introduction a l'etude de la chimie ...
Paris, 1837.
248 p.

NL 0347343   KyU

8306
.584
.1837
Liebig, Justus, Freiherr von, 1803–1873-
Introduction à l'étude de la chimie...,
par M.J. Liebig. Trad. de l'allemand par
Ch. Gerhardt. Paris, Mathias, 1837.
245 p. illus. 17 cm. (Bibliothèque
industrielle. Sciences)

NL 0347344   NjP

Liebig, Justus, freiherr von, 1803–1873.
Introduction to the first elements of chemistry, for the
use of students. By Dr. Justus Liebig ... Tr. from the
German, by Thomas Richardson. London, A. Schloss,
1837.
4 p. l., 110 p. 19ᶜᵐ.

1. Atomic theory.   I. Richardson, Thomas, 1816–1867, tr.
                                                    11–23468
Library of Congress   QD461.L71

NL 0347345   DLC KyU PPWa

Liebig, Justus, Freiherr von, 1803–1873.
Introduzione allo studio della chimica filoso-
fica. Traduzione dal Todesco di G.D.S. Verona,
1859.

NL 0347346   WU

Liebig, Justus, freiherr von, 1803–1873, ed.

Jahresbericht über die fortschritte der chemie und verwandter
teile anderer wissenschaften ... 1847/48–1910. Giessen, J.
Ricker, 1849–88; Braunschweig, F. Vieweg und sohn, 1888–
1913.

QD1
.L7
Liebig, Justus, Freiherr von, 1803–1873, ed.

Justus Liebigs Annalen der Chemie. Bd. 1–
1832–
Weinheim ₍etc.₎ Verlag Chemie.

Liebig, Justus, freiherr von, 1803–1873.
Justus von Liebig, an autobiographical sketch. Tr. from the
Germ. by Prof. J. Campbell Brown.
(In Smithsonian institution. Annual report. 1891. Washington,
1893. 23½ᶜᵐ. p. 257–268)
"From the Chemical news, June 5 & 12, 1891; vol. LXIII, pp. 265–267,
276–278."

I. Brown, James Campbell, 1843–1910, tr.
                                                    S 15–764
Smithsonian inst. Library
for Library of Congress   Q11.S66 1891

NL 0347349   DSI PBL PU-S OU OClMN OCl OO MiU

Liebig, Justus, Freiherr von, 1803–1873.
Justus von Liebig, in eigenen Zeugnissen und solchen
seiner Zeitgenossen ₍von₎ Hertha von Dechend. Mit einem
Geleitwort von Willy Hartner. Weinheim/Bergstrasse, Verlag Chemie, 1953.
141 p. illus. 23 cm.
Includes bibliography.

I. Dechend, Hertha von, 1915-   ed.

QD22.L7A3   925.4   53–34429 ‡

NL 0347350   DLC CtY NNC OCU ICJ NN NcD PPC CU

Liebig, Justus, freiherr von, 1803–1873.
Justus von Liebig nach dem leben gezeichnet.
Festrede gehalten in der öffentlichen sitzung der
K. b. Akademie der wissenschaften zu München
zur feier ihres 144. stiftungstages am 11. märz
1903
    see under Knapp, Georg Friedrich, 1842–
1926.

Liebig, Justus, freiherr von, 1803–1873.
Justus von Liebig und Christian Friedrich Schönbein.
Briefwechsel 1853–1868. Mit anmerkungen, hinweisen und erläuterungen versehen und hrsg. von Georg W. A. Kahlbaum
und Eduard Thon. Leipzig, J. A. Barth, 1900.
xxi, 278 p. 23ᶜᵐ. (Added t.-p.: Monographieen aus der geschichte der
chemie, hrsg. von dᴿ Georg W. A. Kahlbaum ... 5. hft.)

1. Chemistry—Collected works. I. Schönbein, Christian Friedrich,
1799–1868. II. Kahlbaum, Georg Wilhelm August, 1853–1905, ed. III.
Thon, Eduard, joint ed.
                                                    9—8020
Library of Congress   QD15.K2 hft. 5

NL 0347352   DLC OkU CU ICJ MH DSI

Liebig, Justus, freiherr von, 1803–1873.
Justus von Liebig und Emil Louis Ferdinand Güssefeld. Briefwechsel 1862–1866. 22 briefe Liebigs, zugleich ein beitrag zur geschichte der industrie künstlicher
dünger in Deutschland. Mit anmerkungen und erläuterungen versehen, hrsg. von dr. O. E. Güssefeld. Leipzig, J. A. Barth, 1907.
vii, ₍1₎, 72 p. 23½ᶜᵐ.

1. Fertilizers and manures. I. Güssefeld, Emil Louis Ferdinand, 1820–
1897, joint author. II. Güssefeld, O. E., ed.
                                                    22–15229
Library of Congress   S633.L58

NL 0347353   DLC ICJ

Liebig, Justus, freiherr von, 1803–1873.
Justus von Liebig und Friedrich Mohr in ihren briefen
von 1834–1870. Ein zeitbild. Hrsg. und mit glossen, hinweisen und erläuterungen versehen in gemeinschaft mit
Otto Merckens und W. I. Baragiola von Georg W. A.
Kahlbaum. Leipzig, J. A. Barth, 1904.
lviii, 274 p. double front. (ports.) 23ᶜᵐ. (Added t.-p.: Monographieen
aus der geschichte der chemie, hrsg. von dr. Georg W. A. Kahlbaum ...
8. hft.)

1. Chemistry—Collected works. I. Mohr, Friedrich, i. e. Karl Fried-
rich, 1806–1879. II. Kahlbaum, Georg Wilhelm August, 1853–1905, ed.
III. Merckens, Otto, joint ed. IV. Baragiola, Wilhelm Italio, joint ed.
                                                    9–8018
Library of Congress   QD15.K2 hft. 8

NL 0347354   DLC CU ICJ MH NN

S
585
L7216
1853
Liebig, Justus, freiherr von, 1803–1873.
Lettere prime e seconde di Giusto Liebig
sulla chimica e sue applicazioni all'
agricoltura, alla fisiologia, alla patologia,
all' igiene ed alle industrie. Nova
edizione condotta sull' originale tedesco
del Dott. Emilio Leone ed annotate dal
F. Selmi. Torino, Dalla Società Editrice
della Biblioteca dei Comuni Italiani, 1853.
519p. 19cm.

1. Agricultural chemistry.

NL 0347355   CLSU

Liebig, Justus, freiherr von, 1803–1873.
Letters on modern agriculture. By Baron von Liebig.
Ed. by John Blyth ... London, Walton and Maberly,
1859.
xxviii, 284 p. 20¼ᶜᵐ.

1. Agriculture. 2. Chemistry, Agricultural.
                                                    Agr 10–1042
Library, U. S. Dept. of   Agriculture 395L62L

NL 0347356   DNAL ICJ MiU OU CtY OkU CU-A CaBVaU PSt

VOLUME 332

Liebig, Justus, *freiherr* von, 1803–1873.
Letters on modern agriculture, by Baron von Liebig. Ed. by John Blyth ... With addenda, by a practical agriculturist. Embracing valuable suggestions, adapted to the wants of American farmers. New York, J. Wiley, 1859.
xxvi, 275 p. 20ᵐ.

1. Agricultural chemistry. 2. Agriculture.   I. Blyth, John, 1815–1892, ed.
12–9831

Library of Congress   S585.L742

NN MdBP
NL   0347357   DLC CtY PSt NjR NcD MBH PPL NcU OU MiU

Liebig,   Justus, Freiherr von, 1803–1873.   No. 3 in *8019.58
Letters on the subject of the utilization of the metropolitan sewage, addressed to the Lord Mayor of London, with the reports of the Coal and Corn and Finance Committee of the Court of Common Council.
London. Collingridge. [1864.] 44 pp. 21 cm., in 8s.

L1471 — Sewage disposal. — London. Sewerage.

NL   0347358   MB MH

Liebig,   Justus, Freiherr von, 1803–1873.   No. 2 in *8019.58
Letters on the subject of the utilization of the metropolitan sewage, addressed to the Lord Mayor.
[London. Taylor. 1865.] 15 pp. 33½ cm.

L1472 — Sewage disposal. — London. Sewerage.

NL   0347359   MB

S   Liebig, Justus, Freiherr von, 1803–1873.
585   Lettres sur l'agriculture moderne, par
L74a   Justus de Liebig, traduites par Théodore
        Swarts. Paris, Librairie agricole de la
        maison rustique [1862]
        xii, 244 p. 18 cm.

1. Agricultural chemistry. 2. Agriculture.
[I. Title]

NL   0347360   NIC IU

Liebig, Justus, *freiherr* von, 1803–1873.
Lettres sur la chimie considerée dans ses applications à l'industrie, à la physiologie et à l'agriculture, par M. Justus Liebig ... Nouv. éd. française pub. par M. Charles Gerhardt ... Paris, Charpentier [etc.] 1847.
2 p. l., iv, [5]–284 p. front. (port.) 18½ᵐ.

1. Chemistry—Addresses, essays, lectures.   I. Gerhardt, Charles Frédéric, 1816–1856.
14–22406

Library of Congress   QD39.L8

NL   0347361   DLC WU PU-S

Liebig, Justus, Freiherr von, 1803–1873.
Lettres sur la chimie; considerée dans ses applications a l'industrie, a la physiologie et a l'agriculture ... Nouvelle édition Française Publiee par M. Charles Gerhardt. Paris, Victor Masson, 1847.
284 p. D.

NL   0347362   PPF

Liebig, Justus, Freiherr von, 1803–1873.
Lettres sur la chimie; considérée dans ses rapports avec l'industrie, l'agriculture et la physiologie. Traduites de l'allemand sur la 2. éd. par F.Bertet-Dupiney et E.Dubreuil-Hélion. Paris, P.Masgana, J.-B.Baillière, 1845.
342 p.

I. Bertet-Dupiney, F., tr.

NL   0347363   ICJ MH CtY

Liebig, Justus, Freiherr von, 1803–1873.
Lettres sur la chimie et sur ses applications à l'industrie, à la physiologie et à l'agriculture, par Justus Liebig; traduites de l'Allemand par le Dr. G.-W. Bichon... Paris: Charpentier, 1845.
xi, 331 p.   front. (port.)   12°.

1. Chemistry. 2. Bichon, G. W., trans-   lator.
N. Y. P. L.   December 5, 1919.

NL   0347364   NN

Liebig, Justus, Freiherr von, 1803–1873.
Lettres sur la chimie et sur ses applications a l'industrie, a la physiologie et a l'agriculture. Traduites de l'allemand par G.-W. Bichon. Paris, Fortin, Masson, 1845.
xi,331p. port. 18cm.

NL   0347365   OkU

Liebig, Justus, Freiherr von, 1803–1873.
Liebig und die Bittersalz- und Salzsäurefabrik zu Salzhausen (1824–1831); nach neuen Funden herausgegeben von Prof. Dr. Ernst Berl im Auftrag der Vereinigung Liebighaus... Berlin: Verlag Chemie, G.m.b.H., 1931. 65 p. incl. tables. front. 8°.

585021A. 1. Acid, Hydrochloric—   Manufacture. 2. Magnesium sulphate.
I. Berl, Ernst, 1877–   , editor.
N. Y. P. L.   May 27, 1932.

NL   0347366   NN

Liebig, Justus, *freiherr* von, 1803–1873.
Lord Bacon, par Justus de Liebig; tr. de l'allemand par Pierre de Tchihatchef ... Paris, L. Guérin, 1866.
lix, 277 p. 18ᵐ.

1. Bacon, Francis, viscount St. Albans, 1561–1626.   I. Chikhachev, Petr Aleksandrovich, 1808–1890, tr.
11–10809

Library of Congress   B1197.L5

NL   0347367   DLC CaBVaU MiU

Liebig, Justus, *freiherr* von, 1803–1873.
Lord Bacon et les sciences d'observation au moyen age. 1877

NL   0347368   DI-GS

B   Liebig, Justus, freiherr von, 1803–1873.
1197   Lord Bacon et les sciences d'observation
L71   au Moyen Age. Traduit de l'allemand et
1877   annoté par P[] de Tchihatchef. 2. éd.
        Paris, J.-B. Baillière, 1877.
        lix, 207 p. 19cm.

1. Bacon, Francis, viscount St. Albans, 1561–1626. I. Chikhachev, Petr Aleksandrovich, 1808–1890, tr.

NL   0347369   NIC

Liebig, Justus, *freiherr* von, 1803–1873.
Manuel pour l'analyse des substances organiques, par J. Liebig ... Traduit de l'allemand par A.-J.-L. Jourdan; suivi de L'examen critique des procédés et des résultats de l'analyse des corps organisés, par F.-V. Raspail. Avec deux planches gravées. Paris, Londres, Chez J.-B. Baillière, 1838.
2 p. l., ii, 168 p. II fold. pl., fold. tab. 20ᵐ.

1. Chemistry, Analytic—Quantitative. 2. Chemistry, Organic.   I. Jourdan, Antoine Jacques Louis, 1788–1848, tr. II. Raspail, François Vincent, 1794–1878.
32–34957

Library of Congress   QD271.L73
[2]   543.8

NL   0347370   DLC MH NN CtY-M PPPH WU KyU

S   Liebig,Justus,freiherr von,1803–1873.
585   Die moderne landwirthschaft als beispiel
.L73   der gemeinnützigkeit der wissenschaften.
        Rede in der öffentlichen sitzung der k.
        Akademie der wissenschaften zu München am
        28.november 1861 gehalten von Justus freiherrn
        von Liebig ... Braunschweig, F.Vieweg und
        sohn, 1862.
        33 p.   22cm.
        With this is bound his Ueber theorie und
        praxis in der landwirthschaft. 1856; Die
        grundsätze der agricultur-chemie. 1855; and
        Herr dr.Emil Wolff   in Hohenheim und
        die agricultur-   chemie. 1855.
        1.Agricultural   chemistry.

NL   0347371   MiU CtY NNBG OU

Liebig, Justus, freiherr von, 1803–1873.

Moore's rural hand books. Fourth series ... New York, A. O. Moore, 1858.

Liebig, Justus, *freiherr* von, 1803–1873.
The natural laws of husbandry, by Justus von Liebig; ed. by John Blyth ... London, Walton & Maberly, 1863.
xx, 416 p. 22ᵐ.

1. Agricultural chemistry. 2. Agriculture. 3. Fertilizers and manures.
I. Blyth, John, 1815–1892, ed.
12–9833

Library of Congress   S585.L75

NL   0347373   DLC CaBVaU NjP NcD OU MiU MdBP

Liebig, Justus, *freiherr* von, 1803–1873.
The natural laws of husbandry. By Justus von Liebig. Ed. by John Blyth ... New York, D. Appleton and company, 1863.
387 p. 21ᵐ.

1. [Agricultural chemistry] 2. Agriculture. 3. [Fertilizers and manures] I. Blyth, John, 1815–1892, ed.
Agr 16–130

U. S. Dept. of agr. Library   30L62
for Library of Congress   S585.L75 1863 a

OClW OO ODW ICJ NN PPA PPAmP PPL PP CtY-M NcA-S
NL   0347374   DNAL MBH CaBVaU MtBC PSt   NcRS OCl

S   Liebig, Justus, Freiherr von, 1803–1873.
585   Die Naturgesetze des Feldbaues. [7. Aufl.]
L71N   Braunschweig [Ger.] F. Vieweg, 1862.
        xl, 467 p. 21 cm.

Vol. 2 of Die Chimie in ihrer Anwendung auf Agricultur und Physiologie.

NL   0347375   NIC

VOLUME 332

Liebig, Justus, Freiherr von, 1803-1873.
Naturvetenskapliga bref öfver vår tids
landtbruk. 1861.

NL 0347376 DNAL

Liebig, Justus, *Freiherr* von, 1803-1873.
Naturwissenschaftliche Briefe über die moderne Landwirthschaft, von Justus von Liebig.   Leipzig und Heidelberg,
C. F. Winter, 1859.
xviii, 254 p. 20½ᵐ.

NL 0347377 ICJ WU NN

S
633
.L725
Liebig, Justus, freiherr von, 1803-1873.
Der neu erfundene patent-dünger des
prof.dr.Justus Liebig in Giessen. Aus dem
Englischen übersetzt und mit erläuternden
zusatzen begleitet von dr.A.Petzholdt ...
Dresden und Leipzig, In der Arnoldischen
buchhandlung, 1846.
2 p.ℓ.,84 p.   18ᶜᵐ.
"Aus der von dem Landw.hauptverein o.für
das königreich Sachsen o.herausgegebenen
zeitschrift wieder abgedruckt aus veranlassung
der redaction derselben."
Trans.of An   address to the
agriculturists   of Great Britain.

NL 0347378 MiU

Liebig, Justus, Freiherr von, 1803-1873.
Neues Handwörterbuch der Chemie. ...
see under Fehling, Hermann von, 1812-
1885.

Liebig,   Justus, *Freiherr von,* 1803-1873.   7978.67
A new method of making bread. By Justus v. Liebig.
(*In* Horsford, Eben Norton. The theory and art of bread-mak-
ing. Pp. 35-47. [Providence. 1869.])
Translated from the January 1869, number of the "Annalen der Chemie
und Pharmacie."

M9727 — Bread. — Baking.

NL 0347380 MB

LIEBIG,Justus,Freiherr [von],1803-1873.
Nouvelles lettres sur la chimie considérée
dans ses applications à l'industrie,à la
physiologie et à l'agriculture. Éd.française
publiée par Charles Gerhardt. Paris,Charpen-
tier,1852.

18 cm.

NL 0347381 MH-C PU

Liebig, Justus, Freiherr von, 1803-1873.
Nouvelles lettres sur la chimie considérée
dans ses applications à l'industrie, à la
physiologie et à l'agriculture. Éd. française
pub. par Charles Gerhardt. Paris, V. Masson,
1852.
xii,330p. 19cm.

I. Gerhardt, Charles Frédéric, 1816-1856,
tr.

NL 0347382 OkU PPF

Liebig, Justus, *freiherr* **von,** 1803-1873.
On artificial manures.
(*In* U. S. Patent office. Report, 1845, p. 1039-1044. 23ᵐ. Washing-
ton, 1846)

1. Fertilizers [and manures]
                                                          Agr 14-714
Library, U. S. Dept. of   Agriculture 1Ag84 1845

NL 0347383 DNAL

Liebig, Justus,freiherr von, 1803-1873.
On the connection and equivalence of forces.
(In: The Correlation and conservation of
forces ... New York, 1865. 12°. p. 385-397)

NL 0347384 NN

S
L718e
LIEBIG, Justus, Freiherr von, 1803-1873.
Organic chemistry in its applications
to agriculture and physiology. Ed. from
the ms. of the author by Lyon Playfair.
[1st]- ed. London, Taylor and
Walton [etc.] 1840-
v.
Translation of Die organische Chemie
in ihrer Anwendung auf Agricultur und
Physiologie and Die Chemie in ihrer
Anwendung auf Agricultur und Physiologie.

Eds. of 1842- have title: Chemistry
in its application to agriculture and
physiology. 1847 ed. bound with his
Animal chemistry. Philadelphia, 1847,
and his Familiar letters on chemistry.
Philadelphia, 1843.
I. Liebig, Justus, Freiherr von,
1803-1873. Chemistry in its application to
agriculture and physiology II. Playfair,
Lyon Playfair, 1st baron, 1818-1898, ed.

NL 0347387 DNLM

Liebig, Justus, *freiherr* **von,** 1803-1873.
Organic chemistry in its applications to agriculture and
physiology. By Justus Liebig ... Edited from the manuscript of the author by Lyon Playfair, PH. D. London, Printed
for Taylor and Walton, 1840.
xiv p., 1 l., 387, [1] p. 23½ᵐ.

1. Agricultural chemistry. [1. Chemistry, Agricultural] 2. [Chemistry,
Organic] I. Playfair, Lyon Playfair, 1st baron, 1818-1898, ed.
                                                          Agr 10-1043
U. S. Dept. of agr. Library
for Library of Congress   S585.L72 1840

NL 0347388 DNAL PU CU NIC NN PSt PPC CtY DLC CaBVaU

Liebig, Justus, *freiherr* **von,** 1803-1873.
Organic chemistry in its applications to agriculture and
physiology. By Justus Liebig ... Ed. from the manuscript
of the author by Lyon Playfair ... 1st American ed., with
an introduction, notes, and appendix, by John W. Webster ...
Cambridge, J. Owen; Boston, J. Munroe and company; [etc.]
etc.] 1841.
xx, 435, [1] p. 19½ cm.

1. Agricultural chemistry. I. Playfair, Lyon Playfair, 1st baron,
1818-1898, ed. II. Webster, John White, 1793-1850, ed.

S585.L72 1841   12—9827

MWA MB NIC ViU PPL GU OkU TU
NL 0347389 DLC DNLM CtY NjP MB NN NIC NcU MiU ICJ

Liebig, Justus, *freiherr* von, 1803-1873.
Organic chemistry in its applications to agriculture and
physiology. By Justus Liebig ... Ed. from the manuscript of
the author by Lyon Playfair ... 2d American ed., with an
introduction, notes, and appendix, by John W. Webster ...
Cambridge, J. Owen; Boston, J. Munroe and company; [etc.,
etc.] 1841.
lxi, 424 p. 19½ᵐ.

NL 0347390 ViU DNLM

LIEBIG, JUSTUS, freiherr von, 1803-1873.
Die organische chemie in ihrer anwendung
auf agricultur und physiologie. Von Justus
Liebig ... Braunschweig, Verlag von F.
Vieweg und sohn, 1840.
xii, 352 p., 1ℓ. 8vo

First edition. Garrison-Morton: 677.
Bound in contemporary boards, with
calf spine; yellow edges; in cloth case.
From the library of J. K. Lilly, Jr.

NL 0347391 InU NcD-MC MHi CtY CU-M IaU NNC MiU IU

LIEBIG, Justus, freiherr von, 1803-1873.
Die organische chemie in ihrer anwendung
auf agricultur und physiologie. 2er unveränderter abdr. Braunschweig,F.Vieweg und sohn,1841.

NL 0347392 MH-C CU

Liebig, Justus *Freiherr* von, 1803-1873.   631.2 Koo2
Die organische Chemie in ihrer Anwendung auf Agricultur und
Physiologie. Von Justus Liebig, [....] Vierte Auflage. Braunschweig, F. Vieweg und Sohn, 1842.
xii, 351 p. 23½ᵐ.

NL 0347393 ICJ

Liebig, Justus, *freiherr* von, 1803-1873.
Die organische chemie in ihrer anwendung auf physiologie
und pathologie. Von Justus Liebig ... Braunschweig, F.
Vieweg und sohn, 1842.
xvi, p., 1 l., 342 p., 1 l. 22½ cm.

1. Physiological chemistry. I. Title.

QP514.L718   612.015   36—23673

                         NcD-MC ICU
NL 0347394 DLC CaBVaU DNLM WU ICJ KU-M OC1W NN NjP

Liebig, Justus, *freiherr* von, 1803-1873.
Principles of agricultural chemistry, with special reference to the late researches made in England. By Justus von Liebig. London, Walton & Maberly, 1855.
vii, 136 p. 20ᵐ.

1. Agricultural chemistry.

Library of Congress   S585.L732   12—9830
                                          [a19c1]

NL 0347395 DLC MiU OkU PSt PPC MdBP ViU

S
585
L53
Liebig, Justus, freiherr von, 1803-1873
Principles of agricultural chemistry, with
special reference to the late researches made in
England. By Justus von Liebig. New York,
John Wiley, 1855.
vii, [1], 105 p. 20 cm.

1. Agricultural chemistry.

NL 0347396 ICF MBH OU OC1 PU PHC CtY-M PPL NN MH CtY

VOLUME 332

Liebig, Justus, Freiherr von, 1803-1873.
Rede in der öffentlichen Sitzung der K. Academie der Wissenschaften am 28. November 1861 zur Feier des allerhöchsten Geburtsfestes Sr. Majestät des Königs Maximilian II., gehalten von Justus Freiherrn von Liebig ...   München, Auf Kosten der K. Akademie, 1861.
24 p.   26 cm.

NL   0347397   CtY PPAmP

Liebig, Justus, Freiherr von, 1803-1873.
Rede in der öffentlichen Sitzung der k. Akademie der Wissenschaften am 28. März 1863 zur Feier ihres einhundert und vierten Stiftungstages.   München, Auf Kosten der k. Akademie, 1863.
46 p.   28 cm.
Caption title: Francis Bacon von Verulam und die Geschichte der Naturwissenschaften.

NL   0347398   OkU CtY PPAmP PU-S ICN MH IU ICJ

---

*GC8
I6222
861r
Liebig, Justus, freiherr von, 1803-1873.
Rede zur Vorfeier des einhundert und zweiten Stiftungstages der k. Akademie der Wissenschaften am 26. März 1861 gehalten von Justus Freiherrn von Liebig ...
München, 1861. Auf Kosten der k. Akademie. Druck von J.G.Weiss, Universitätsbuchdrucker.
16p.   26cm.
Portion of original printed green front wrapper preserved, mounted on front cover; bound in marbled boards.

NL   0347399   MH

QD39   Liebig, Justus, freiherr von, 1803-1873.
.L7   Reden und abhandlungen, von Justus von Liebig.   Leipzig und Heidelberg, C. F. Winter, 1874.
viii, 334, [1] p.   23 cm.
"Vorwort" signed: M. Carriere.

1. Chemistry—Addresses, essays, lectures.

OrCS
NL   0347400   ICU CU MdBJ NNC NIC OCU MH NN NNU-W ICJ

Liebig, Justus, freiherr von, 1803-1873.
The relations of chemistry to agriculture, and the agricultural experiments of Mr. J. B. Lawes. By Justus v. Liebig. Tr. by Samuel W. Johnson, at the author's request. Albany, L. Tucker, 1855.
1 p. l., [7]-87 p.   18 cm.
[Rural economy pamphlets, v. 10, no. 1]

1. Agricultural chemistry. 2. Lawes, Sir John Bennet, bart., 1814-1900. I. Johnson, Samuel William, 1830-   tr.

Library of Congress   S405.R94   6-9168

NL   0347401   DLC MBH ICJ OU

Liebig, Justus, freiherr von, 1803-1873.
Researches on the chemistry of food. By Justus Liebig ... Edited from the manuscript of the author, by William Gregory ... London, Printed for Taylor and Walton, 1847.
xx, 156 p.   23 cm.

1. Food—Composition. [1. Food—Chemistry]   I. Gregory, William, 1803-1858, ed. and tr.

TX531.L48   Agr. 34-71

U. S. Nat'l Agr. Libr.   389L62
for Library of Congress   [462b½]

DNLM ICJ NcD-MC CU CaBVaU WU-M UU
NL   0347402   DNAL T ICU NcD CtY OU DP PPF PPL PPC IaU

QU
L716r
1848
LIEBIG, Justus, Freiherr von, 1803-1873
Researches on the chemistry of food, and the motion of juices in the animal body. Ed. from the ms. of the author by William Gregory. Ed. from the English ed. by Eben N. Horsford.   Lowell [Mass.] Bixby, 1848.
xxx, 219 p.   illus.

Translation of Chemische Untersuchung das Fleisch und seine Zubereitung zum Nahrungsmittel, and Untersuchung über einige Ursachen der Saftebewegung im Thierischen Organismus.

ViU NcD-MC
ODW OU OC1 MiU MH OO CtY NIC PPA PHC PU MiU KU-M
NL   0347404   DNLM PP NN MWA CaBVaU NjP OO ViU ICJ

Liebig, Justus, freiherr von, 1803-1873.
Researches on the motion of the juices in the animal body. By Justus Liebig. Ed. from the manuscript of the author, by William Gregory ... London, Taylor and Walton, 1848.
1 p. l., [v]-xiv, 109, [1] p.   illus.   22 cm.

1. Osmosis. 2. Fluids and humors, Animal. 3. Plants, Motion of fluids in.   I. Gregory, William, 1803-1858, ed.

Library of Congress   QH615.L68   11-5074

NL   0347405   DLC DNLM ICJ CU CaBVaU CtY

Liebig, Justus, freiherr von, 1803-1873.
Researches on the motion of the juices in the animal body; and the effect of evaporation in plants. Together with an account of the origin of the potato disease; with full and ingenious directions for the protection and entire prevention of the potato plant against all diseases. By Justus Liebig ... Illustrated with fifteen fine engravings. Edited from the manuscript of the author, by William Gregory ... Philadelphia, T. B. Peterson [1850]
iv, 5-47 p.   illus.   24½ cm.
"Method proposed by Dr. Klotzsch, for the protection of the potato plant against diseases [from the Journal of the Agricultural association of the grand duchy of Hesse, no. 7, 1848]": p. 45-47.
1. Osmosis. 2. Fluids and humors, Animal. 3. Plants, Motion of fluids in. 4. Potatoes—Diseases and pests. I. Gregory, William, 1803-1858, ed. II. Klotzsch, Johann Friedrich, 1805-1860.
Library of Congress   QH615.L68 1850   36-29143
—— Copy 2.   22 cm.   [2]   612.382

NL   0347406   DLC OCU PPC IU MB DNLM PU

Liebig, Justus, Freiherr von, 1803-1873.
Researches on the motion of the juices in the animal body; and the effect of evaporation in plants. Together with an account of the origin of the potato disease ... Edited from the manuscript of the author, by William Gregory. Philadelphia, T. B. Peterson [1856]
iv, 7-47 p.   illus.   24cm.   (In his Complete works on chemistry. Philadelphia [1856])

NL   0347407   NNC

Liebig, Justus, freiherr von, 1803-1873.
De scheikunde in hare toepassing op landbouw en physiologie. Door Justus von Liebig. Naar den 7. druk bewerkt, door E. C. Enklaar ... Zwolle, W. E. J. Tjeenk Willink, 1865-66.
2 v.   22½ cm.
On t-p. of v. 2: Naar de 7e en 8e drukken bewerkt.
Issued as supplements to "Vriend van den landman."
CONTENTS.—1. deel. Scheikundig proces van de voeding der planten.—2. deel. De natuurkundige wetten van den akkerbouw.

1. Agricultural chemistry.   I. Enklaar, Evert Cornelius, tr.

Library of Congress   S585.L727   12-9834

NL   0347408   DLC

QD
L716c
1850d
Liebig, Justus Freiherr von, 1803-1873.
Scheikundige brieven. [n.p., 185-?]
315 p.
Translation of Chemische Briefe.
Imperfect copy; title page wanting; title from cover.
I. Title

NL   0347409   DNLM

Liebig, Justus von, 1803-73.
—— Suppe für Säuglinge. Mit Nachträgen in Beziehung auf ihre Bereitung und Anwendung. 20 pp. 12°. Braunschweig, F. Vieweg & Sohn, 1866.

NL   0347410   DNLM

Liebig, Justus, freiherr von, 1803-1873.
Természettudományi értekezések
see under   Magyar természettudományi társulat, Budapest.

QP514   Liebig, Justus freiherr von, 1803-1873.
.L7   Die thier-chemie; oder, Die organische chemie in ihrer anwendung auf physiologie und pathologie. Von Justus Liebig ... 2. unveränderte aufl. Braunschweig, F. Vieweg und sohn, 1843.
xviii, 344, [1] p. tables   21 cm.
CONTENTS.—I. t. Der chemische process uer respiration und ernährung—2. t. Die metamorphosen der gebilde—3. t. Die bewegungserscheinungen im thierorganismus. Analytische belege zu dem chemischen process der respiration und ernährung so wie zu dem chemischen process der umsetzung der gebilde.

NL   0347412   ICU ICRL PPG MH MB ICJ CaBVaU NNC NIC

QU
L51
1843
Liebig, Justus, freiherr von, 1803-1873.
Die Thier-Chemie, oder, Die organische Chemie in ihrer Anwendung auf Physiologie und Pathologie. Von Justus Liebig. 2. unveränderte Aufl. Braunschweig, F. Vieweg, 1843.
382 p.   23 cm.
(1. Physiological chemistry.) [2. Biochemistry.] I. Title. II. Title: Die organische Chemie in ihrer Anwendung auf Physiologie   und Pathologie.

NL   0347413   CaBVaU

Liebig, Justus, freiherr von, 1803-1873.
Die thier-chemie; oder, Die organische chemie in ihrer anwendung auf physiologie und pathologie. Von Justus Liebig. 3. umgearb. und sehr verm. aufl. Braunschweig, F. Vieweg und sohn, 1846.
xvi, 231 p.   illus.   22½ cm.
[Chemical pamphlets, v. 3, no. 1]

1. Physical chemistry.   1-G-180

Library of Congress   QD3.C5

NL   0347414   DLC OkU CaBVaU ICRL CtY PBm ICJ

LIEBIG,   Justus, Freiherr von, 1803-1873.
Traité de chimie organique. Trad. par M. Ch. Gerhardt.   Paris: Fortin, M. & cie. 1840-44. 3 v. 8°.

NL   0347415   MB PU MeMacN

VOLUME 332

Liebig, Justus, *freiherr* von, 1803–1873.
Traité de chimie organique, par Justus Liebig. Édition française, rev. et considérablement augm. par l'auteur, et publiée par Ch. Gerhardt ... Paris, Fortin, Masson et cᵃ; ₍etc.,
etc.₎ 1841–44.
3 v. 21ᶜᵐ.

1. Chemistry, Organic.   ɪ. Gerhardt, Charles Frédéric, 1816–1856,
ed. and tr.
32–30155

Library of Congress   QD251.L5 1841   547

NL   0347416   DLC CaBVaU OkU PPC

Liebig, Justus, freiherr Von, 1803 - 1873.
Traite de chimie organique.
Bruxelles, Meline, 1843.
393 p.

NL   0347417   PPT

Liebig, Justus, freiherr von, 1803–1873.
Traité de chimie organique; tr. ...
par C. ₍F.₎ Gerhardt. Bruxelles, Meline,
1843.
111, 593 p.

NL   0347418   OCU

---

*GC8   Liebig, Justus, freiherr von, 1803–1873.
16222   Ueber das Studium der Naturwissenschaften.
852u   Eröffnungsrede zu seinen Vorlesungen über
Experimental-Chemie im Wintersemester 1852/53.
von Justus von Liebig.
München, 1852. Literarisch-artistische Anstalt
der J.G.Cotta' schen Buchhandlung.
23p. 22cm., in case 23.5cm.
Original printed buff wrappers; in cloth
case.

NL   0347419   MH PU–S IU

Liebig, Justus, *freiherr* von, 1803–1873.
Ueber das studium der naturwissenschaften und über den zustand der chemie in Preussen. Von Justus Liebig ... Braunschweig, F. Vieweg und sohn, 1840.
47 p. 22½ᵐ.
Running title: Der zustand der chemie in Preussen.

1. Science. 2. Science and state. 3. Chemistry. ɪ. Title: Der zustand der chemie in Preussen.
39–7803

Library of Congress   Q181.L6
₍2₎

NL   0347420   DLC MH ICJ CU

Liebig, Justus, *freiherr* von, 1803–1873.
Ueber Francis Bacon von Verulam und die methode der naturforschung. Von Justus von Liebig. München, Literarisch-artistische anstalt, 1863.
viii, 64 p. 24ᵐ.

1. Bacon, Francis, viscount St. Albans, 1561–1626. 2. Bacon, Francis,
viscount St. Albans. Sylva sylvarum. ɪ. Title.
3–25066

Library of Congress   B1198.L5

NL   0347421   DLC PPT CtY CLSU DNLM MdBJ MH

Liebig, Justus, Freiherr von, 1803–1873.
Ueber Gährung, üoer Quelle der Muskelkraft und Ernährung. Von Justus von Liebig. Leipzig, C.F. Winter, 1870.
xii,138p. 22cm.

"Aus den Annalen der Chemie und Pharmacie besonders abgedruckt."

1. Chemistry, Organic. 2. Alcohols. 3.
Vinegar. I. Title.

ICJ DP NjP
NL   0347422   PSt MH CaBVaU MnU CtY   IaU CU NIC

Liebig, Justus, *freiherr* von, 1803–1873.
Ueber theorie und praxis in der landwirthschaft. Von Justus von Liebig. Braunschweig, F. Vieweg und sohn, 1856.
viii, 134 p. 22½ᵐ.

1. Agricultural chemistry. ₍1. Chemistry, Agricultural₎
Agr 31–747

Library, U. S. Dept. of   Agriculture 395L62U

NL   0347423   DNAL WU CtY PSt OU MH IU PU

Liebig, Justus, freiherr von, 1803–1873.
Untersuchung der Mineralquellen zu Soden und Bemerkungen über die Wirkung der Salze auf den Organismus. Wiesbaden, E. Enders, 1839.
51 p. 8°.

NL   0347424   DNLM CtY–M

Liebig, Justus, freiherr von, 1803–1873, joint
author.
Untersuchungen über das radikal der benzoesäfre, von Woehler und Liebig
see under Wöhler ₍Friedrich₎ 1800–
1882.

Liebig, Justus, *freiherr* von, 1803–1873.
Untersuchungen über einige ursachen der säftebewegung im thierischen organismus, von Justus Liebig ... Braunschweig, F. Vieweg und sohn, 1848.
vi, 98 p. illus. 20 cm.

1. Osmosis. 2. Body fluids. 3. Plants, Motion of fluids in.
QH615.L66   11–5073
——— Copy 2.   ₍Chemical pamphlets, vol. 3, no. 2₎
QD8.C5   vol. 3, no. 2

NL   0347426   DLC MiEM CaBVaU CtY OCU ICJ DNLM

RA   Liebig, Justus, Freiherr von, 1803–1873.
1171   Zur Beurtheilung der Selbstverbrennungen
L71   des menschlichen Körpers. Heidelberg,
Vault C. F. Winter, 1850.
31 p. 23 cm.

ɪ. Combustion, Spontaneous human.
I. Title.

NL   0347427   NIC

612.0152 Liebig, Justus, Freiherr von, 1803–1873.
L62z   Zur Beurtheilung der Selbstverbrennungen
1850   des menschlichen Körpers. 2.Aufl. Heidelberg, C. F. Winter, 1850.
31, 8p. 20cm.

1. Physiological chemistry.

NL   0347428   IU NNC PU DNLM

TA408
.L5   Liebig, Karl.
Unsere Werkstoffe. Leipzig, Fachbuchverlag, 1953.
viii, 169 p. illus., tables. 24 cm.
Bibliography: p. 161–163.

1. Materials. 2. Metals. ɪ. Title.
A 54–2575

Illinois. . Univ. Library
for Library of Congress   ₍3₎

NL   0347429   IU DLC

Liebig, Karl.
... Werkstoffkunde im flugzeug- und motorenbau, von oberingenieur Karl Liebig ... 2. verm. und verb. aufl. Mit 15 abbildungen und einer mehrfarbigen tafel. Berlin, Dr. M. Matthiesen & co., 1940.
108 p. incl. illus., tables, diagrs. col. pl. 21ᵐ. (Luftfahrt-lehr-
bücherei, bd. 3)
Part 1 of Die praxis des metallflugzeugbauers, by Karl Liebig and
August Dresel (first published, Berlin, 1937).

1. Aeroplanes—Materials. ɪ. Title.
41–17522

Library of Congress   TL698.L5 1940
₍2₎   629.1342

NL   0347430   DLC

4TL   Liebig, Karl
351   Werkstoffkunde im Flugzeug- und
Motorenbau. 3. verm. und verb. Aufl.
Berlin, M. Matthiesen, 1941.
127 p.

(Luftfahrt-Lehrbücherei, Bd. 3)

NL   0347431   DLC–P4

Liebig, Kurt.
Sehkraft, Glaubenskraft, eines deutschen Christen Kampfbuch. Ludwigsburg, C. und A. Ulshöfer ₍Vorwort 1934₎
107 p. 19 cm.
Errata slip inserted.

1. Germany—Religion—1933–1945. ɪ. Title.
51–46547

BR856.L52

NL   0347432   DLC CtY PPG

Liebig, Margarete, 1907–
Beiträge zur frage des zusammenhangs zwischen persönlichkeitstypus und weltanschauung (mit besonderer berücksichtigung des kausalprinzips) ... von Margarete Liebig ... Marburg, 1937.
2 p. l., 83, ₍1₎ p. 22ᵐ.
Inaug.-diss.—Marburg.
Lebenslauf.
"Literatur-verzeichnis": p. 81–83.

1. Personality. 2. Philosophers. 3. Causation.
41–24904

Library of Congress   BF698.L47

NL   0347433   DLC CtY MH

VOLUME 332

Liebig, R   G   Max.
  Zink und cadmium und ihre gewinnung aus erzen und
nebenprodukten, von R. G. Max Liebig ... Mit 205 figuren
im text und auf 10 tafeln sowie einem titelbilde. Leipzig,
O. Spamer, 1913.

  xvi, 598 p. incl. front., illus. 10 pl. (9 fold.) 24½ cm. (*Half-title:* Chemische technologie in einzeldarstellungen. Herausgeber: prof. dr. Ferd. Fischer ... Spezielle chemische technologie)

  1. Zinc—Metallurgy.   2. Cadmium—Metallurgy.

TN796.L6   13—22367

NL 0347434   DLC MiU OCl OO NN CU ICJ NjP

4BJ   Liebig, Rudolf, 1920-
307   Vergleich der christlichen Ethik
      mit der formalen Ethik Kants und der
      materialen Ethik Schelers und Nicolai
      Hartmanns; Verträglichkeit und Unter-
      schied.   München, 1954.
          127 l.

NL 0347435   DLC-P4

Liebig, Walter: Die Preisentwicklung in der Klavierindustrie. [Ma-
schinenschrift.] 161 S. 4° [Lag nicht vor.] — Auszug (Rostock
1923: Winterberg). 1 Bl. 8°
Rostock, Phil. Diss. v. 1. März 1923   [U 23. 9066

NL 0347436   ICRL

Liebig, Werner, 1911-
  Verächtlichmachung der rechtspflege. Unlautere
einwirkung auf die rechtspflege. Beschimpfung
von amtsträgern. ... Würzburg, 1936.   48 p.
  Inaug. Diss. - Bonn, 1936.
  Lebenslauf.
  Verzeichnis der benutzten literatur.

NL 0347437   ICRL MH-L

---

ha
TX   Liebig Company.
719   Deux cent cinquante nouvelles recettes de
171 cuisine [par V.A. chef de cuisine à Paris.
     Paris, Liebig, 1889]
         72p.

  1. Cookery, French. 2. Meat extract. I. Title

NL 0347438   NIC

---

ha
TX   Liebig Company.
721   Geprüft und Bewährt 200 Kochrecepte.
171 [Antwerp, n.d.]
         100p.

  1. Cookery, German. 2. Meat extract. I. Title
       Kochrecepte

NL 0347439   NIC

Liebig Company's fleisch-extract.   [n. p.] [n. d.]
  1 v. (unpaged)   19 cm.   Bitting Collection

NL 0347440   DLC

Liebig Gold Mining and Mill Company.
  Prospectus of the Liebig Gold Mining & Mill Co. of Colorado
...   New York: Vinten, printer, 1864.   8 p.   front. (map.)
8°.

  1. Gold—Mines and mining: Com-   panies.
N. Y. P. L.   November 18, 1924

NL 0347441   NN

Liebig-Hochschule, Giessen, Germany
    see   Giessen, Universität.

Liebig's Annalen der chemie
    see
Justus Liebig's Annalen der chemie.

Das Liebig'sche gesetz vom minimum in
einer erweiterten form   [192-?]
Chart, 87 x 60cm.

NL 0347444   DNAL

Liebigt, Ruth, 1914-
  ... Histochemischer Nachweis von Zinn im
Kieferknochen des Meerschweinchens bei
experimenteller Zinnfütterung ...   Leipzig, 1937.
  Inaug.-Diss. - Leipzig.
  Lebenslauf.

NL 0347445   CtY

Liebing (Arno). Gesundheitsgemässes- und
  phonetisch richtiges Sprechen. Zur Aufklärung für Stimmleidende und Freunde
  einer rationellen Ausbildung der Stimme in
  Sprache und Gesang. port., 44 pp., 1 pl.,
  1 sheet in pocket. 8°. Dresden, Holze &
  Pahl. 1909.

NL 0347446   DNLM

4PN-281   Liebing, Arno.
      Lerne gesundheitsgemäss, klangschön und
    lautrichtig sprechen! Zur Aufklärung für
    Stimmleidende und Freunde einer vernunftgemässen
    Ausbildung der Stimmer in Sprache und Gesang.
    Im Auftrag des Deutsche Verein für Stimmbildung.
    3. Aufl.   Dresden, In Kommission bei E. Pahl,
    1926.
        60 p.

NL 0347447   DLC-P4

Liebing, B.
  Das säurebeständige Email und seine industrielle Anwendung
im Apparatebau; ein Handbuch für die chemische Industrie, Nah-
rungsmittelfabrikation und andere der Chemie verwandte Indus-
triezweige, von B. Liebing... Berlin: J. Springer, 1923.   iv,
99 p.   diagrs. 8°.

  1. Enamel ware.
N. Y. P. L.   April 25, 1924.

NL 0347448   NN IU

Liebing (C. A. W.) *Der schwarze Staar. 40
pp. 8° Würzburg, C. W. Becker. 1836.

NL 0347449   DNLM PPC

Liebing (Christianus). De amoliendis sanitatis
publice impedimentis. 32 pp. 4°. Lipsia, ex
off. Langenhemia. 1771.

NL 0347450   DNLM PPC

Liebing, Heinz, 1905-
  Die erzählungen H. Claurens (Carl Heuns) als
ausdruck der bürgerlichen welt- und lebensanschauung in der beginnenden Biedermeierzeit
... von Heinz Liebing ... Halle-Saale, E. Klinz
1931.

  4 p.l., 107, [1] p. front.(port.) 22½ cm.
  Inaug.-diss.—Halle-Wittenberg.
  Lebenslauf.
  Bibliographical foot-notes.

  1. Heun, Karl Gottlieb Samuel, 1771-1854.

NL 0347451   MiU PU PSt NcU RPB CtY

Liebing, Peter Paul.
  Miete und Pacht nach gemeinem Recht
und bürgerlichem Gesetzbuch ... von
Peter Paul Liebing ... [Mainz, H.
Prickarts] 1900.
  61 p.   22cm.
  Inaug.-Diss. - Giessen.
  Bibliographical footnotes.

NL 0347452   MH-L DLC MH

Liebing (R. H.). Hygiene des schulkindes im
Elternhause. 110 pp. 32°. Leipzig, O. Paul
[1906].

NL 0347453   DNLM

Liebinger, Julius , 1836-
  De rebus Pharaeis.
  Inaug. Diss. Halle, 1862.

NL 0347454   ICRL CtY PU NjP

Liebinger (Samuel) [1796-   ]. *De acidi
hydrocyanici usu interno. 40 pp. 8°. Berolini, typ. Schadii. 1827.

NL 0347455   DNLM

VOLUME 332

Liebisch, Arnold, 1896–
... Das wesen der unentgeltlichen zuwendungen unter lebendem im bürgerlichen recht und im reichssteuerrecht, von gerichtsassessor dr. jur. Arnold Liebisch ... Leipzig, T. Weicher, 1927.

ix, ₁1₎, 166 p. 26ᶜᵐ. (Leipziger rechtswissenschaftliche studien ... Hft. 27)

"Literaturverzeichnis" : p. ₁vii₎–ix.

1. Contracts, Gratuitous—Germany. 2. Inheritance and transfer tax—Germany.

28–17501

NL 0347456   DLC CU-L

Z7166 Liebisch, Bernhard, bookseller, Leipzig.
.Z9L7   Antiquariats-kataloge.   [Leipzig] 1898.

NL 0347457   DLC

Liebisch, Bernhard, *bookseller*, *Leipzig*.
Bibliotheca historica. Leipzig, 1923–27.

5 v. in 1. 22ᶜᵐ.

Title from publisher's lettering.
Antiquariats-katalog nos. 238–239, 258–259, and 262 issued in one volume.

Contents.— Geschichte des mittelalters. Katalog 262, 1926.—Geschichte der neuzeit, teil 1–4. Katalogs 238–239 and 258–259, 1923–27.

1. History — Bibl.— Catalogs. 2. Middle ages — Bibl. 3. History, Modern—Bibl.   I. Title.

Library of Congress   Z6209.Z9L7

cA 30–900 Unrev'd

NL 0347458   DLC OC1W ICU

Liebisch, Bernhard, bookseller, Leipzig.
... Geschichte Deutschlands ... [Leipzig, B. Liebisch] 1905.
22 cm.
At head of title: ... Antiquariatskatalog Nr. 145.
Enthält u. a. die Bibliotheken der verstorbenen ... Dr. von Gossler und ... Dr. G. Kirchhoff ...

NL 0347459   CtY

Liebisch, Bernhard, bookseller, Leipzig.
Katalog Nr. 5. Medicin. Vergleichende Anatomie, Physiologie und Entwickelungsgeschichte. Leipzig, 1885.
53 p.   8°.

NL 0347460   DNLM

Liebisch, Bernhard, bookseller, Leipzig.
Rechtsgeschichte. Leipzig, Bernh. Liebisch, [1924]
124 p.
Cover title.

NL 0347461   OC1

Liebisch, Bernhard, bookseller, Leipzig.
... Rechtswissenschaft ... Leipzig, B. Liebisch, 1927–31.
3 nos. in 1 v.
"Antiquariats-katalog Nr. 264". 1927; Nr. 292–293, 1931.

NL 0347462   WaU-L

AGA9 Liebisch, Bernhard, bookseller, Leipzig.
L622t   Theologischer bücherschatz. Leipzig, 1911–12.
8 v. in 1. 23 cm.

Antiquariatskatalog nos. 193–200 issued in one volume.
Contents.— 1. abt. Allgemeines. Zeitschriften. Encyklopädie. Geschichte der theologie. Bibelausgaben. Exegese im allgemeinen. Alttestamentliche exegese und theologie.— 2. abt. Neutestamentliche the-   ologie, exegese und

philologie.— 3. abt. Semitische geschichte und linguistik. Biblische archäologie. Aegyptologie.— 4. abt. Systematische theologie. Religionsgeschichte. Symbolik.— 5.–6. abt. Kirchengeschichte.— 7. abt. Praktische theologie.– ₈8. abt.₎ Kirchengeschichte. Drucke des XV.–XVII. jahrh.

NL 0347464   CtY-D OCH NcD

Liebisch, Gerhard.
Ueber augenverletzunge bei kindern. (Auszug)
Breslau, 1920.
Inaug.-diss.-Breslau.

NL 0347465   ICRL

Liebisch, Theodor, 1852–1922.
Cristallographie. Loi fondamentale et son application au calcul et à la représentation des cristaux; exposé, d'après l'article allemand de Th. Liebisch ... par F. Wallerant ... ₁1915–

(*In* Encyclopédie des sciences mathématiques. Paris ₁1915– ₎ 25ᶜᵐ. t. 5, v. 2, fasc. 1–   p. ₁72₎–   diagrs.)

1. Crystallography, Mathematical.   I. Wallerant, Frédéric Félix Auguste, 1858–

A 21—206

Brown univ.   Library
for Library of Congress   ₁a42c1₎

NL 0347466   RPB OCU

Liebisch, Theodor, 1852–1922.
Geometrische krystallographie, von dr. Th. Liebisch ... Mit 493 holzschnitten. Leipzig, W. Engelmann, 1881.
xii, 464 p. diagrs. 23½ᶜᵐ.

Crystallography, Mathematical.

NL 0347467   MH CtY MA PSt MiU PBL PPAN

Liebisch, Theodor, 1852–1922.
Grundriss der physikalischen krystallographie, von dr. Theodor Liebisch ... Mit 898 figuren im text. Leipzig, Verlag von Veit & comp., 1896.
viii, 506 p. illus., tables, diagrs.   23½ᶜᵐ.
Bibliographical foot-notes.

1. Crystallography.

PU PPAN
NL 0347468   ViU IU CU OCU OU MiU ICRL RPB DI-GS ICJ

Liebisch, Theodor, 1852–1922.
Krystallographie, von Th. Liebisch ... A. Schönflies ... und O. Mügge ...
(*In* Encyklopädie der mathematischen wissenschaften. Leipzig 1903–21. 25ᶜᵐ. bd. v–1, hft. 3, p. 391–492. illus., diagrs.)
"Litteratur" : p. 392–395.

1. Crystallography, Mathematical.   I. Schönflies, Arthur Moritz, 1853–1928. II. *Mügge, Otto, 1858–

A 13–114 Revised

Title from Brown Univ.
Library of Congress   QA36.E56

NL 0347469   RPB CU ODW OU MiU

Liebisch, Theodor, 1852–1922.
... Krystallographie. Von Th. Liebisch ... A. Schönflies ... und O. Mügge ... ₁Leipzig, Druck von B. G Teubner, 1906₎
₁391₎–492 p. diagrs. 24½ cm.
Caption title.
Sonderabdruck aus Encyklopädie d. mathematischen wissenschaften. v. 1. heft 3.
Litteratur: p. 392–395.

1. Crystallography.   I. Schönflies, Arthur Moritz, 1853– II. Mügge, Otto i. e. Johannes Otto Conrad, 1858–

G S 6—1196

U. S. Geol. Survey. Libr.
for Library of Congress   ₁a66b₎

NL 0347470   DI-GS ODW

Liebisch, Theodor, 1852–1922, ed.

QE1 Neues Jahrbuch für Mineralogie, Geologie und Paläontolo-
.C8   gie. Monatshefte. 1900–49. Stuttgart, E. Schweizerbart.

Liebisch, Th₁eodor₎ 1852–₁1922₎.
Physikalische krystallographie. Von Dr. Th. Liebisch ... Leipzig, Veit & comp., 1891.
viii, 614 p. illus., IX pl. (1 col.) diagrs. 24ᶜᵐ.

1. Crystallography.

Library, U. S. Geol.   survey

G S 5–523

ViU MH MB MiHM
NL 0347472   DI-GS CU ICRL CaBVaU NIC KU CU MiU PU

Liebisch, Theodor, 1852–1922.
Physikalische krystallographie. 1896.

NL 0347473   DI-GS

Liebisch, Theodor, 1852–1922.   552 Q103
Die Synthese der Mineralien und Gesteine. (Festrede im Namen der Georg-Augusts-Universität zur akademischen Preisverteilung am v. Juni MDCCCCI.) 28 p. O. Göttingen: Dieterich'sche Universitäts-Buchdruckerei, 1901.

NL 0347474   ICJ CtY MiU

Liebisch, Theodor, 1852–1922.
Ueber Absorptionsbüschel pleochroitischer Krystalle. Von Th. Liebisch. ₁Göttingen? 1888?₎
202–210 p. 33cm. ₁Lomb miscellaneous pamphlets, v. 18, no. 1₎
Caption title.
"Nachrichten von der Königlichen Gesellschaft der Wissenschaften und der Georg—Augusts—Universität zu Göttingen. 30. Mai. No. 8. 1888."
Original paper wrappers.

1. Optics, Geo   metrical. I. Title.

NL 0347475   ViU

Liebisch, Theodor, 1852–1922.
Ueber das Minimum der Ablenkung durch Prismen optisch zweiaxiger Krystalle. Von Th. Liebisch. ₁n. p., 1888?₎
197–201 p. 33cm. ₁Lomb miscellaneous pamphlets, v. 18, no. 2₎
Caption title.
"Nachrichten von der Königlichen Gesellschaft der Wissenschaften und der Georg—Augusts—Universität zu Göttingen. 30. Mai. No. 8. 1888."
Original paper wrappers.

1. Optics, Geo   metrical. I. Title.

NL 0347476   ViU

VOLUME 332

Liebisch, Theodor, 1852–1922.

Ueber die Bestimmung der Lichtbrechungs-
verhältnisse doppeltbrechender Krystalle durch
Prismenbeobachtungen. Von Th. Liebisch.
Stuttgart, E. Schweizerbart'sche
Verlagshandlung, 1886.
[14]–54 p. 33cm. [Lomb miscellaneous
pamphlets, v. 18, no. 3]
Cover title.
"Separat-Abdruck aus dem Neuen Jahrbuch für
Mineralogie, Geologie und Paläontologie, Jahrg.
1886, Bd. I."
Original paper wrappers.

NL 0347477   ViU

Liebisch, Theodor. 1852–1922.   *3334.2.1912.1
Über die Fluoreszenz der Sodalith- und Willemitgruppe im ultra-
violetten Licht. Illus.
(In Koeniglich preussische Akademie der Wissenschaften, Berlin.
Sitzungsberichte. Jahrgang 1912, Halbband I, pp. 229–240. Ber-
lin. 1912.)

K4164 — Fluorescence. — Silicates. — Ultraviolet light.

NL 0347478   MB

Liebisch, Theodor, 1852–1922.

Ueber die in form von diluvialgeschieben in Schlesien
vorkommenden massigen nordischen gesteine ... Breslau, Breslauer genossenschaftsbuchdr., 1874.

2 p. l., 40 p. 22cm.

Inaug.-diss.—Breslau.
Lebenslauf.

1. Geology—Silesia. 2. Geology, Stratigraphic—Quaternary.

12–6323

Library of Congress   QE696.L71

NL 0347479   DLC

Liebisch, Theodor. 1852–1922.   *3334.2.1910.1
Über die Rückbildung des kristallisierten Zustandes aus dem amor-
phen Zustande beim Erhitzen pyrognomischer Mineralien.
Charts.
(In Koeniglich-preussische Akademie der Wissenschaften, Ber-
lin. Sitzungsberichte. Jahrgang 1910, Halbband I, pp. 350–364.
Berlin. 1910.)

H6010 — Crystallization. — Minerals. Pyrognomic.

NL 0347480   MB

Liebisch, Theodor, 1852–1922.

Ueber die Totalreflexion an doppeltbrechenden
Krystallen. Von Th. Liebisch. Stuttgart,
E. Schweizerbart'sche Verlagshandlung, 1886.
[47]–66 p. plates. 33cm. [Lomb miscel-
laneous pamphlets, v. 18, no. 4]
Cover title.
"Separat-Abdruck aus dem Neuen Jahrbuch für
Mineralogie, Geologie und Palaeontologie. 1886.
Band II."
Original paper wrappers.

1. Optics, Phys   ical. I. Title.

NL 0347481   ViU

Liebisch, Theodor, 1852–1922.

Über die Totalreflexion an optisch einaxigen
Krystallen. [Von] Th. Liebisch. Königsberg [?]
1885 [?]
[248]–253 p. 33cm. [Lomb miscellaneous
pamphlets, v. 18, no. 5]
Caption title.
"Separat-Abdruck aus dem Neuen Jahrbuch für
Mineralogie etc. 1885. Bd. I."
Unbound.

1. Optics, Physical. I. Title.

NL 0347482   ViU

Liebisch, Theodor, 1852–1922.

Ueber eine besondere Art von homogenen
Deformationen krystallisirter Körper. Von Th.
Liebisch. [Göttingen? 1887?]
[435]–448 p. plate. 33cm. [Lomb miscel-
laneous pamphlets, v. 18, no. 6]
Cover title.
"Separat-Abdruck aus den Nachrichten von der
Königlichen Gesellschaft der Wissenschaften und
der Georg – Augusts – Universität zu Göttingen.
7. September. No. 15. 1887."
Original paper wrappers.

1. Optics, Phys   ical. I. Title.

NL 0347483   ViU

Liebisch, Theodor, 1852–1922.   *3334.2.1910.1
Über Silberantimonide. Illus.
(In Koeniglich-preussische Akademie der Wissenschaften, Ber-
lin. Sitzungsberichte. Jahrgang 1910, Halbband I, pp. 365–370.
Berlin. 1910.)

H6011 — Dyscrasite.

NL 0347484   MB

Liebisch, Theodor, 1852–1922.

Ueber thermoelektrische Ströme in Krystallen.
Göttingen, 1889
(5) p. 25cm.

Göttingen, Nachrichten,   1889, p. 531–535.

NL 0347485   DN-Ob

Liebisch, Willi: Der Anus anomalus vestibularis. [Maschinenschrift]
19 S. 4°. — Auszug: o. O. (1922). 2 Bl. 8°
Berlin, Med. Diss. v. 5. April 1922   [U 38. 397

NL 0347486   ICRL

Liebistorf, Nicolas Antoine Kirchberger, baron
de, 1739–1800.

Saint-Martin, Louis Claude de, 1743–1803.
Theosophic correspondence between Louis Claude de
Saint-Martin, the "unknown philosopher," and Kirchberger,
Baron de Liebistorf, member of the Grand Council of Berne.
Translated and edited by Edward Burton Penny. Covina,
Calif., Theosophical University Press [1949]

B2145
.Z7A4

RBS.
152243
Liebitsch, Georg Heinrich.
De apoplexia...
Erfordiae: Typis Groschianis, [1722],
16 p. 19.3 cm.
Thesis (M.D.) - Erfurt.

NL 0347487   NNNAM DNLM

Liebitsch (Rudolph Georg). *De hydrope.
22 pp. sm. 4°. Halæ Magdeb., lit. Hendelianis,
[1795].

NL 0347488   DNLM

Liebke, Carl Arthur Johannes, 1886–
see

Liebke, Joannes, 1886–

Liebke, Johannes, 1886–
Die historischen quellen zu dem roman "Wind-
sor castle" von W.H.Ainsworth ... Halle a.S.,
Buchdruckerei Hohmann, 1912.
128,[2] p.   22cm.
Inaug.-diss.—Halle-Wittenberg.
Lebenslauf.
"Literaturangabe": p.[7]–11.

1. Ainsworth,William Harrison,1805–1882. Windsor
castle. [Full name: Carl Arthur Johannes Liebke]

NL 0347490   MiU CtY ICarbS DLC MH NN ICRL TU IaU

Liebke, Max.
Revision der amerikanischen arten der unterfamilie *Col-
liurinae (Col. Carab.)* Von M. Liebke ...
(In Mitteilungen aus dem Zoologischen museum in Berlin. Berlin,
1930. 28cm. 15. bd. hft. 3/4, p. [647]–726. Illus.)

1. [Colliurinae] 2. Beetles—America.

A C 35–8340

Tit[e] from Ohio State   Univ.
Library of Congress   [QL1.B38 bd. 15, hft. 3/4]

NL 0347491   OU

Liebknecht (Curt) [1879–   ]. *Ueber die
akuten Aspirationstuberkulosen der Erwachsenen. 24 pp. 8°. Leipzig, E. Herrmann, 1907.

NL 0347492   DNLM CtY DLC

HD8388
.A8
Liebknecht, Gertrud, tr.

Aveling, Eleanor (Marx) 1855–1898.
Die Arbeiterclassen-bewegung in England. Von Elea-
nore Marx-Aveling. Uebers. von Gertrud Liebknecht. Mit
einem vorwort von W. Liebknecht ... Nürnberg, Wörlein
& comp., 1895.

Liebknecht, Guillaume
see   Liebknecht, Wilhelm Philipp Christian
Martin Ludwig, 1826–1900.

A31
L622
1729
Liebknecht, Johann Georg, 1679–1749, praeses.
Bina Sanctarvm Elisabetharvm velvti illvs-
trissimarvm sec. XII et XIII testivm veritatis
evangelicae in Hassia memoria. Giessae[1729]
Diss.-Giessen(J.P.J.Fabricius, respondent)

1.Elizabeth, of Hungary,Saint, 1294–1336
I.Fabricius, Johann Philipp Jacob, respondent

NL 0347495   CtY

238
C697

Theol.
Liebknecht, Johann Georg, 1679–1749, praeses.
De symbolorvm conceptv generalissimo epithemata
theologica qvae novatorvm maximam partem sentiendi
loqvendiqve prvrigini opponvntvr, svb praesidio
D[ni]. Io. Georg Liebknecht ... Respondens Henric.
And. Pilger ... Giessae Kassorvm, litteris
Ioannis Mvlleri [1723]
20 p. 19cm. [With other dissertations]
Imprint date given in manuscript on fly-leaf of
collected volume.

I. Pilger, Henri   k Andreae, respondent.

NL 0347496   TxDaM PPLT

VOLUME 332

Liebknecht, Johann Georg, 1679-1749.
Discursus de diluvio maximo etc. Giessae,
etc., 1714.

(22), 388 p. front., 2 plates.

NL 0347497 MH-Z

QB
42
L71
Liebknecht, Johann Georg, 1679-1749, Praeses.
Dissertatio cosmographica de harmonia cor-
porvm mvndi totalivm nova ratione in nvmeris
perfectis generatim definita, quam ... praeses
Io. Georgivs Liebknecht,.... respondente Friderico VVilhelmo Marqvard,.... anno MDCCXVIII
die Maii, eruditorum examini per modum
problematis exhibet. Giessae-Hassorvm,
Typis Iohannis Mvlleri [1718]
[6], 42 p. 20cm.

Diss.--Giessen (E. W. Marquard, respondent)

NL 0347498 NIC NN

Liebknecht, Johann Georg, 1679-1749.
D.Joh.Georg Liebknechts ... Grund-sätze der
gesammten mathematischen wissenschafften und
lehren ... auf eine leicht-und deutliche maniere vor lehrende und lernende besonders zur
praxi und gemeinen nutzen mit vernehmlichen
rissen vorstellet. Giessen und Franckfurt, Bey
E.H.Lammers, 1724-26.

2 v.in 1. front.(port.),plates (2 fold.; incl.plans,
diagrs.) 17°.

Vol.2, has title: Grund-sätze der heut su tag üblichen
und allen in krieg- und civil-bedienungen höchst-nöthi-
gen mathematischen wissenschaften und lehren.

Title vignettes (printer's device); head and tail
pieces.
CONTENTS.--l.th. Arithmetic,geometrie,trigonometrie,
mechanic,hydrostatic,aerometrie,hydravlic.--[2.th.]
Artillerie,architectvra militaris und civilis.
Autograph of Georg Louis comte d'Erbach on t.-p.of.
v.1.

1.Mathematics--Early works to 1800. 2.Military art
and science--Early works to 1800. 3.Architecture--Early
works to 1800.

NL 0347500 MiU

8220.93
L71h
Liebknecht, Johann Georg, 1679-1749.
Hassiae subterraneae specimen clarissima
testimonia diluvii universalis heic et in
locis vicinioribus occurrentia, ex triplici
regno, animali, vegetabili et minerali, peti-
quitatis exempla certissima exhibens. Occasione arboris in mineram ferri mutatae quae
variis observationibus, et nova ferrum ex
limo coquendi methodo illustratur. Guessae
et Francofurti, Apud Eberh. Henr. Lammers,
1730.
490p. 22cm.

1. Deluge. I. Title,

NL 0347501 TNJ DNLM CU MH IU

Liebknecht, Johann Georg, 1679-1749.
Hassiae subterraneae specimen clarissima
testimonia delivii universalis heic et in
locis vicinioribus occurrentia, ex triplici regno,
animali vegetaliti et minerali petita,
figurisque aeneis exposita.
Francefurti ad M., 1759.

NL 0347502 PPAN

Liebknecht, Johann Georg, 1679-1749, Praeses.
Pharvs; sive, De prodigiis ignis coelestibvs, vt vvlgo vocantvr,
ex omni aevo collectis, dissertatio...occasione corvscationvm
borealivm, nvper visarvm, vna cvm cavsis et praedictionibvs
istarvm, qvae moderante avctore I. G. Liebknecht...svbiicitvr...
respondente I. Webero. Giessae: typis I. Mülleri [1721]. 4 p.l.,
76 p., 1 l., 2 pl. 12° in fours.

Dissertation, Giessen.
In: OMW p. v. 8, no. 13.

1. Astronomy, 1721. 2. Aurora borealis, 1721. 3. Weber, Immanuel.
N.Y.P.L. January 30, 1913.

NL 0347503 NN CtY-M

Liebknecht, Karl Paul August Friedrich, 1871-1919.
Ausgewählte Reden, Briefe und Aufsätze. Mit einer Rede
von Wilhelm Pieck. Berlin, Dietz, 1952.

551 p. illus., ports. 21 cm.

Bibliographical references included in "Anmerkungen" (p. [581]-
546)

1. Communism--Germany. 2. Germany--Pol. & govt.--1888-1918.

HX273.L58 53-28466

NL 0347504 DLC OrU WU

Liebknecht, Karl Paul August Friedrich, 1871-1919.
... Briefe aus dem felde, aus der untersuchungshaft
und aus dem zuchthaus ... Berlin-Wilmersdorf, Verlag
"Die Aktion", 1919.

138 p., 1 l. front., plates, ports. facsim. 22½ cm.

At head of title: Karl Liebknecht.
"Dieses werk wurde unter mitarbeit der frau Karl Liebknechts heraus
gegeben von Franz Pfemfert."

NL 0347505 UU OkU IEN CaBVaU

HX273
L58A4
Liebknecht, Karl Paul August Friedrich,
1871-1919.
Briefe aus dem Felde, aus der Unter-
suchungshaft und aus dem Zuchthaus. Berlin-
Wilmersdorf, Verlag "Die Aktion", 1920.
138p. illus., ports., facsim. 23cm.

"Unter Mitarbeit der Frau Karl Liebknechts
hrsg. von Franz Pfemfert."

I. Pfemfert, Franz. 1877- ed.

NL 0347506 IaU MH INS CSt-H CtY

Liebknecht, Karl Paul August Friedrich, 1871-1919.
... Briefe aus dem felde, aus der untersuchungshaft
und aus dem zuchthaus ... Berlin-Wilmersdorf, Verlag
"Die Aktion", 1922.

138 p., 1 l. front., plates, ports. facsim. 22½ cm.

At head of title: Karl Liebknecht.
"Dieses werk wurde unter mitarbeit der frau Karl Liebknechts herausgegeben von Franz Pfemfert."

I. Pfemfert, Franz, 1877- ed. II. Liebknecht, Frau Sophie, joint ed.

26-24077

Library of Congress D640.L455

NL 0347507 DLC OU GU MB CtY NN

D 640
.L 72
1931
Liebknecht, Karl Paul August Friedrich,
1871-1919.
... Cartas del frente y de la prisión,
1916-1918; versión española de Luis Curiel ...
Madrid, Editorial Cenit, s.a. [1931]
254, [1] p., 1 l. 18cm. ("Documentos
vivos")

At head of title: Carlos Liebknecht.
"Primera edición."

NL 0347508 MdBJ

Liebknecht, Karl Paul August Friedrich, 1871-1919.
Compensationsvollzug und compensationsvorbringen...
Inaug. diss. Wuerzburg, 1897. (Paderborn)

NL 0347509 ICRL

LIEBKNECHT, Karl [Paul August Friedrich], 1871-1919.
Compensationsvollzug und compensationsvorbringen nach gemeinem rechte. Berlin,1898.

NL 0347510 MH-L CtY

Liebknecht, Karl Paul August Friedrich, 1871-1919.
The crisis in the German social-democracy
see under Luxemburg, Rosa, 1870-1919.

Liebknecht, Karl Paul August Friedrich, 1871-1919.
"The future belongs to the people", by Karl Liebknecht
(speeches made since the beginning of the war) ed. and tr. by
S. Zimand; with an introduction by Walter Weyl. New York,
The Macmillan company, 1918.

144 p. 19½ cm.

1. European war, 1914-1918--Addresses, sermons, etc. I. Zimand,
Savel, 1891- tr. II. Title.

18-23563

Library of Congress D639.S6L5

NcD NIC MU TNJ CoU WaU
OrP PU PP PBm NjP NN MH MB ICJ ICRL ViU OClW MiU OCl
NL 0347512 DLC IEN CaBVaU WaTC IdB WaSpG WaS WaT MtU

Liebknecht, Karl Paul August Friedrich, 1871-1919.
"The future belongs to the people," by Karl Liebknecht (speeches made since the beginning of the war)
ed. and tr. by S. Zimand; with an introduction by Walter
Weyl. New York, The Macmillan company, 1919 [c1918]
144 p. 19½ cm.

NL 0347513 OU

Liebknecht, Karl Paul August Friedrich,
1871-1919, defendant.
Der hochverratsprozess gegen Liebknecht vor dem Reichsgericht; verhandlungsbericht... Berlin, Buchhandlung Vorwärts, 1907.
87 p. 22½ cm.

NL 0347514 NjP CSt-H ICU NN MH

LIEBKNECHT, KARL PAUL AUGUST FRIEDRICH, 1871-
1919.
Der Hochverratsprozess gegen Liebknecht vor dem
Reichsgericht; Verhandlungsbericht nebst einem Nachwort. Berlin, Buchhandlung Vorwärts, 1907. 87 p.
21cm.

Film reproduction. Positive.

1. Treason--Trials--Germany.

NL 0347515 NN

VOLUME 332

HX273   Liebknecht, Karl Paul August Friedrich, 1871–
L5A3   1919, defendant.
(Film)   Der Hochverratsprozess gegen Karl Liebknecht
     1907 vor dem Reichsgericht; Verhandlungsbericht.
     Mit einem Anhang. Berlin, Dietz Verlag, 1917.
     222 p.
     "Neuauflage der 1907...erschienenen Broschüre
     'Der Hochverratsprozess gegen Liebknecht vor dem
     Reichsgericht.'"
     Microfilm (negative) of original in Library
     of Congress. 1 reel.
     I. Germany. Reichsgericht. II.T.

   NL   0347516   NjP

     Liebknecht, Karl Paul August Friedrich, 1871–1919.
     ... Karl Liebknecht; mit einleitung von Willi
     Münzenberg. Berlin, Neuer deutscher verlag,
     1926.
     98 [1] p.   20 cm.   (Redner der revolution, bd
     9)
     Portrait on cover.
     I. Münzenberg, Willi.

   NL   0347517   CU PU-E1

     Liebknecht, Karl Paul August Friedrich, 1871–
     1919.
     Karl Liebknecht; ein Gedenkbuch
       see under title

     Liebknecht, Karl Paul August Friedrich, 1871–
     1919.
     Karl Liebknecht, Lehrer und Freund der
     Jugend
       see under title

Liebknecht, Karl Paul August Friedrich, 1871–1919.
     Karl Liebknecht: politische aufzeichnungen aus seinem nach-
     lass, geschrieben in den jahren 1917–1918, unter mitarbeit von
     Sophie Liebknecht herausgegeben, mit einem vorwort und mit
     anmerkungen versehen von Franz Pfemfert. **Berlin-Wilmers-**
     dorf, Verlag der wochenschrift Die Aktion (F. Pfemfert) 1921.
     2 p. l., x p., 1 l., 5–162 p. 22ᶜᵐ. (*Half-title:* **Politische aktions-bib-**
     liothek, hrsg. von Franz Pfemfert)

     1. Socialism in Germany. 2. Germany—Pol. & govt.—1914–
     I. Liebknecht, Sophie, ed. II. Pfemfert, Franz, 1877–
                                 45–48528
     Library of Congress   HX276.L58

   NL   0347520   DLC MH IaU MiU NcD CSt-H CU NN

Liebknecht, Karl Paul August Friedrich, 1871–1919.
     Karl Liebknecht; politische Aufzeichnungen aus seinem Nach-
     lass, geschrieben in den Jahren 1917–1918, unter Mitarbeit von
     Sophie Liebknecht hrsg., mit einem Vorwort und mit Anmer-
     kungen versehen von Franz Pfemfert. Berlin-Wilmersdorf: Die
     Aktion, 1921. x, 5–162 p. 8°. (Politische Aktions-Biblio-
     thek. Bd. 10.)
     Film reproduction. Negative.

     1. European war, 1914–1918–-Social-   ism. 2. Bolshevism--Germany.
     3. Germany--Hist.--Revolution,   1918–1919. I. Series.

   NL   0347521   NN

     Liebknecht, Karl Paul August Friedrich, 1871–
     1919.
     Karl Liebknechts letzte Tage
       see under title

---

335   Liebknecht, Karl Paul August Friedrich,
L716m   1871–1919.
     Klassenkampf gegen den Krieg. Anhang: I.
     Betrachtungen und Erinnerungen aus "grosser
     Zeit." II. Karl Liebknecht zum Gedächtnis,
     von Karl Radek. Berlin, A.Hoffmann [1915]
     109p. illus. 22cm. [With his Militaris-
     mus und Antimilitarismus... Berlin, 1907]

     1. Class struggle. 2. Revolutions. 3.
     Communism. 4. War. I. Radek, Karl, 1885-
     jt.auth. II. Title.

   NL   0347523   IEN

Liebknecht, Karl Paul August, 1871–1919.
     Klassenkampf gegen den Krieg... Anhang: I. Betrach-
     tungen und Erinnerungen aus "grosser Zeit," geschrieben von
     Karl Liebknecht im Berliner Untersuchungsgefängnis (Moabit
     1916). II. Karl Liebknecht zum Gedächtnis von Karl Radek.
     Berlin: A. Hoffmanns Verlag, G.m.b.H. [1919.] 109 p. front.,
     port. 8°.

     1. European war, 1914–18.—Socialism.   2. European war, 1914–18, Germany.
     3. Radek, Karl, pseud. of Karl   Sobelson.
     N. Y. P. L.   May 13, 1924.

   NL   0347524   NN MnU IEN CU MH WU

940.9115   Liebknecht, Karl Paul August Friedrich, 1871–
L62k   1919.
1933   ... Klassenkampf gegen den krieg; mit vorwort,
     anmerkungen und fremdwörterverzeichnis hrsg. von
     Rudolf Arens. Wien [etc. Internationaler ar-
     beiter-verlag gmbh [c1933]
     147p. (Elementarbücher des kommunismus,
     bd.24)

     Includes his Betrachtungen und erinnerungen
     aus "grosser zeit" (p.105–119); Aus der parla-
     ments arbeit Karl Liebknechts (p.120–131)

   NL   0347525   IU

     Liebknecht, Karl Paul August Friedrich,
     1871–1919.
     Die Krise in der deutschen Sozial-
     demokratie
         see under   Luxemburg, Rosa,
     1870–1919.

     Liebknecht, Karl Paul August Friedrich, 1871–1919
     ... Lettres du front et de la geôle, 1916–1918.
     Tr. par Francis Treat et P. Vaillant-Couturier.
     Paris, l'Humanité, 1924.
     xxxvi, 203 p., 1 l. front., plates, ports.
     18.5 cm.

   NL   0347527   CSt-H CaBVaU

Liebknecht, Karl Paul August Friedrich, 1871–1919.
     Militarism, by Karl Liebknecht. New York, B. W.
     Huebsch, 1917.
     3 p. l., xviii, 178 p. 19 cm.
     "In September, 1906, Dr. Karl Liebknecht, the author, delivered a
     lecture on 'Militarism' at a conference of young people in Germany.
     The revised lecture was published in book form and the most impor-
     tant portions appear in the following pages."—p. l.

     1 Militarism.

     JX1952.L56   17—26892

     NN ICJ KEmT OrP WaTC WaT OrCS
     MU IU WaS NBuU GASC OrPR WaSp CaBVaU PPL PP PU MB
     OCIW PSC PHC DSI NcGU MtU WaSp OrPR NSyU ICRL CoU
   NL   0347528   DLC CtY NjP OU ODW OCU MiU OCl OOxM Or

LIEBKNECHT, Karl Paul August Friedrich, 1871–1919
     Militarism. Toronto, W.Briggs,[1917].

   NL   0347529   MH

JX   Liebknecht, Karl Paul August Friedrich, 1871–
1952   1919.
L613   Militarism and anti-militarism, with special
1917   regard to the International Young Socialist
     Movement. Glasgow, Socialist Labour Press
     [1917]
     176 p. 21cm.

     Bibliographical footnotes
     1. Militarism I. Title

   NL   0347530   WU IU NNC KyU CtY

     Liebknecht, Karl Paul August Friedrich, 1871–1919.
     Militarism and anti-militarism, with special
     regard to the international young socialist
     movement. [2d ed. trans. by A. Sirnis] Glas-
     gow, Socialist Labour Press [1917]
     xv, 176 p. port.

     Microfilm (negative) of copy at Columbia Uni-
     versity. N. Y., Columbia University Libraries,
     1963. 1 reel.

   NL   0347531   NNC

Liebknecht, Karl Paul August Friedrich, 1871–1919.
     Militarism och antimilitarism, med särskild hänsyn till den
     internationella ungdomsrörelsen, av dr. Karl Liebknecht. Auk-
     toriserad översättning. Malmö, "Fram" [1908] 212 p. 20cm.

     1. Militarism. 2. Youth move-   ment.
     N. Y. P. L.   July 20, 1949

   NL   0347532   NN

Liebknecht, Karl Paul August Friedrich, 1871–1919.
     Militarismus und Antimilitarismus unter besonderer Berück-
     sichtigung der internationalen Jugendbewegung, von Dr. Karl
     Liebknecht... Berlin: A. Hoffmann's Verlag, G.m.b.H. [1907].
     vii, 129 p. front. (port.) plates. 8°.

     197196A. 1. Militarism. 2. Youth   movement.
     N. Y. P. L.   October 21, 1925

   NL   0347533   NN MoU IEN

Liebknecht, Karl Paul August Friedrich, 1871–1919.
     Militarismus und antimilitarismus unter besonderer
     berücksichtigung der internationalen jugendbewegung, von
     dr. Karl Liebknecht. Leipzig, Leipziger buchdruckerei
     aktiengesellschaft, 1907.
     vii, 126 p. 22ᶜᵐ.

     1. Militarism.

   NL   0347534   ICU NRU MH DS

VOLUME 332

Liebknecht, Karl Paul August Friedrich, 1871–1919.
Militarismus und antimilitarismus unter besonderer berücksichtigung der internationalen jugendbewegung von dr. Karl Liebknecht. 3. aufl. Anhang: Referat des verfassers über den kampf gegen den militarismus gehalten am Stuttgarter kongress der jugendorganisationen. Zürich, Schweiz. Grütliverein, 1911.
vii, 140 p. 20½ cm.

1. Militarism.

13-14346

Library of Congress JX1952.L6

NL 0347535 DLC ICU ICJ

172.4 L62m Liebknecht, Karl Paul August Friedrich, 1871-
Militarismus und antimilitarismus unter besonderer berücksichtigung der internationalen jugendbewegung ... Berlin [1919]
129p. front.(port.) pl.

Bibliographical foot-notes.

NL 0347536 IU

Liebknecht, Karl Paul August Friedrich, 1871-
Militarizmas; vertė K.V. Kovietis. Philadelphia, Pa., Sapuda "Kovos", n.d.
[176 p.]

NL 0347537 OCl

Liebknecht, Karl Paul August Friedrich, 1871–1919.
Мой процесс по документам. Перевод с немецкого. Предисл. Г. Зиновьева. [Петроград] Изд. Петроградского Совета рабочих и красноармейских депутатов, 1918.
213 p. illus. 21 cm.
Cover title: Мой судебный процесс.

1. Socialism in Germany. 2. Germany—Pol. & govt.—20th cent. I. Title. II. Title: Moĭ sudebnyĭ protsess.
Title transliterated: Moĭ protsess po dokumentam.

HX276.L583 54-45906 rev

NL 0347538 DLC

Liebknecht, Karl Paul August Friedrich, 1871-1919.
Der mord an Karl Liebknecht und Rosa Luxemburg zusammenfassende darstellung des gesamten untersuchungsmaterials
see under title

4K 4980 Liebknecht, Karl Paul August Friedrich, 1871-1919.
Rechtsstaat und Klassenjustiz; Vortrag, gehalten zu Stuttgart am 23. August 1907. Stuttgart, Kommissionsverlag von P. Singer, 1907.
30 p.

NL 0347540 DLC-P4 WU

Liebknecht, Karl Paul August Friedrich, 1871–1919.
Reden und Aufsätze. Herausgeber: Julian Gumperz. Hamburg, Verlag der Kommunistischen Internationale, Auslieferungsstelle für Deutschland: C. Hoym Nachf., 1921.
vii, 374 p. 24 cm.
Bibliography: p. vi–vii.

1. Socialism in Germany. 2. Germany—Pol. & govt.—20th cent. 3. World War, 1914–1918—Germany. I. Title.

HX276.L585 51-53487

NL 0347541 DLC ICN INS NcD MiU NNU-W NN OU MU MB CLSU CU NNC

Liebknecht, Karl Paul August Friedrich, 1871-1919, ed.
Die Rote fahne; zentralorgan der Kommunistischen partei Deutschlands (Spartakusbund). 9. nov. 1918–
Berlin, A. Scherl g. m. b. h. [etc.] 1918–19; Leipzig, 1919–

DD235 .P3 no. 3 Rare Bk Coll Liebknecht, Karl Paul August Friedrich, 1871–1919.
Corey, Lewis.
The social revolution in Germany. Including two articles on socialism in Germany by Karl Liebknecht and Franz Mehring, of the Spartacus Group. Boston, The Revolutionary Age [n. d.]

Liebknecht, Karl Paul August Friedrich, 1871–1919.
... Speeches of Karl Liebknecht, with a biographical sketch. New York, International publishers [©1927]
93 p. 19 cm. (Voices of revolt. vol. IV)
Portrait on cover.
Biographical sketch by Willi Munzenberg.

I. Munzenberg, Willi.

27-20577

Library of Congress HX276.L6

NL 0347544 DLC IEN NBuU NIC CoU ICarbS CSt-H OKentU ViU

Liebknecht, Karl Paul August Friedrich, 1871–1919.
... Studien über die bewegungsgesetze der gesellschaftlichen entwicklung. München, K. Wolff [1922]
387, [1] p. 23 cm.
At head of title: Karl Liebknecht.
"Aus dem wissenschaftlichen nachlass ... hrsg. von dr. Morris."—p. [5]

1. Sociology. 2. Social psychology. I. Morris, Max, ed. II. Title. III. Title: Die bewegungsgesetze der gesellschaftlichen entwicklung.

24-25910

Library of Congress HM57.L5

NL 0347545 DLC OU CtY FU IU IEN MiU CaBVaU NcD NjP ICU CU

LIEBKNECHT, Karl [Paul August Friedrich], 1871-
Vorbehaltszahlung und eventualaufrechnung nach heute geltendem und künftigem reichsrecht Berlin, 1899.

NL 0347546 MH-L CtY

4K Ger. 1293 Liebknecht, Karl Paul August Friedrich, 1871-1919, defendant.
Das Zuchthausurteil gegen Karl Liebknecht; wörtliche Wiedergabe der Prozessakten, Urteile und Eingaben Liebknechts. Berlin, Hrsg. von der Kommunistischen Partei Deutschlands, 1919.
168 p.

NL 0347547 DLC-P4 CU WU OrU ICJ CSt-H MH NN

Liebknecht, Karl Paul August Friedrich, 1871-1919, defendant.
Das zuchthausurteil gegen Karl Liebknecht; wörtliche wiedergabe der prozessakten, urteile, und eingaben Liebknechts. Hrsg. von der Kommunistischen partei Deutschlands (Spartakusbund) Berlin, 1919.
164 p. 1 illus. 22 cm.

I. Title. II. Kommunistische partei Deutschlands.

NL 0347548 NjP

4K Ger. 1557 Liebknecht, Karl Paul August Friedrich, 1871-1919, defendant.
Das Zuchthausurteil gegen Karl Liebknecht; wörtliche Wiedergabe der Prozessakten, Urteile und Eingaben Liebknechts. Leipzig, Frankes Verlag, 1919.
168 p.

NL 0347549 DLC-P4 IEN

4K Ger. 1340 Liebknecht, Karl Paul August Friedrich, 1871-1919.
Das Zuchthausurteil; wörtliche Wiedergabe der Prozessakten, Urteile und der Eingaben Karl Liebknechts. Berlin-Wilmersdorf, Verlag der Wochenschrift "Die Aktion," 1919.
168 p.

(Politische Aktions-Bibliothek)

NL 0347550 DLC-P4 CU MnU NN IEN

LIEBKNECHT, KURT.
Deutsche Architektur. (IN: Deutsche Architektur. Berlin, 33cm. [Jahrg. 1, Heft]1(1952) p.6-12. illus., port.)

NL 0347551 NN

Liebknecht, Kurt.
Das grosse Vorbild und der sozialistische Realismus in der Architektur und in der Malerei. Vorträge von Kurt Liebknecht [und] Kurt Magritz. Zusammengestellt und hrsg. vom Haus der Kultur der Sowjetunion, Berlin. [Berlin, Verlag Kultur und Fortschritt] 1952.
47 p. 42 plates. 29 cm.
CONTENTS.—Die Erfahrungen der Sowjetunion bei der kritischen Verarbeitung und Entwicklung des kulturellen Erbes auf dem Gebiete der Architektur, von K. Liebknecht.—Die Sowjetmalerei und grundlegenden Aufgaben der neuen deutschen Malerei, von K. Magritz.
1. Architecture—Germany. 2. Painting, German. I. Magritz, Kurt. II. Title.
NA1068.L5 A 53-5004
Harvard Univ. Library for Library of Congress [a54b½]†

NL 0347552 MH DLC

Liebknecht, Kurt.
Die nationalen Aufgaben der deutschen Architektur. Berlin [Deutsche Bauakademie] 1954.
87 p. illus., plans. 24cm.

"Das Referat "Die nationalen Aufgaben ..." wurde von dem Präsidenten der Deutschen Bauakademie, Prof. Dr. Liebknecht, auf dem VIII (öffentlichen) Plenum der Deutschen Bauakademie gehalten."

NL 0347553 NNC

VOLUME 332

QD181 Liebknecht, Otto, 1876–
.I116   Ueber die sauerstoffsaeuren des jods.
          Berlin, 1899.
          65p.
          Inaug. diss. Berlin.

NL 0347554   DLC NN

NC1055 Liebknecht, Robert, tr.
.D63486 Dürer, Albrecht, 1471–1528.
          Quatre-vingts dessins. Adaptation française de Robert
          Liebknecht d'après F. Winkler. Paris, Braun ₍1950₎

Liebknecht, Frau Sophie, joint ed.

Liebknecht, Karl Paul August Friedrich, 1871–1919.
    ... Briefe aus dem felde, aus der untersuchungshaft
und aus dem zuchthaus ... Berlin-Wilmersdorf, Verlag
"Die Aktion", 1922.

Liebknecht, Sophie.

Luxemburg, Rosa, 1870–1919.
    ... Briefe aus dem gefängnis ... Basel, Mundus-verlag, a. g.
₍1945₎

HX276 Liebknecht, Sophie, ed.
.L58   Liebknecht, Karl Paul August Friedrich, 1871–1919.
          Karl Liebknecht: politische aufzeichnungen aus seinem nach-
          lass, geschrieben in den jahren 1917–1918, unter mitarbeit von
          Sophie Liebknecht herausgegeben, mit einem vorwort und mit
          anmerkungen versehen von Franz Pfemfert. Berlin-Wilmers-
          dorf, Verlag der wochenschrift Die Aktion (F. Pfemfert) 1921.

Liebknecht, Wilhelm, 1877–
    Zur geschichte der werttheorie in England ... Jena, G.
Fischer, 1902.
    2 p. l. 36 p. 2 l. 23½ᶜᵐ.
    Inaug.-diss.—Berlin.
    Lebenslauf.
    "Nur ein teil der eingereichten arbeit. Die ganze abhandlung erscheint
im verlage von Gustav Fischer."

    1. Value. 2. Economics—Hist.—Gt. Brit.
                                                        3—23351
    Library of Congress   HB205.G7L7

NL 0347559   DLC CU NSyU MiU

Liebknecht, Wilhelm, 1877–
    Zur geschichte der werttheorie in England. Von W. Lieb-
knecht ... Jena, G. Fischer, 1902.
    iv p., 1 l., 112 p. 24ᶜᵐ.
    Published in part as the author's inaugural dissertation, Berlin (36 p.)

    1. Value. 2. Economics—Hist.—Gt. Brit.
                                                        3—0452
    Library of Congress   HB205.G7L8

NL 0347560   DLC NcD CtY NN ICJ KU PU

HV1481 Liebknecht, Wilhelm Philipp Christian Martin
G38L71   Ludwig, 1826–1900.
          Das Alters- u. Invaliden- Versicherungsgesetz
          Vortrag gehalten von dem Reichstagsabgeordneten
          Wilhelm Liebknecht am 13. August d. Js. in
          einer öffentlichen Volksversammlung zu Wurzen.
          Nach stenographischen Aufzeichnungen. Wurzen,
          A. Schmidt, 1888.
          32 p. 18ᶜᵐ.

          1. Public welfare - Germany. 2. Old age.
          3. Insurance,   Social - Germany. I.Title

NL 0347561   CSt-H

335.08 Liebknecht, Wilhelm Philipp Christian
P191   Martin Ludwig, 1826–1900.
v.1   Angrepp och försvar; öfversättning från
no.2   fjärde tyska uppl. af Axel Danielsson.
          Stockholm, Socialdemokratiska Arbetarepartiets
          ₍1896₎
          64p. 19cm. (In Pamphlets on socialism.
          v.1, no.2)

NL 0347562   OrU

Liebknecht, Wilhelm Philipp Christian Martin
    Ludwig, 1826–1900.
    Attaque et défense, par Guillaume Liebknech-
... Traduit et remanié par le professeur Sander.
Gand, Imp. société coopérative "Volksdrukker-
ij", 1905.
    55 p. 17 cm.
    1. Labor and laboring classes. 2. Socialism.
3. Trade-unions. I. Sander,   tr. II. Title.

NL 0347563   CSt-H

Liebknecht, Wilhelm *Philipp Christian Martin Ludwig, 1826–1900*
    Ein blick in die Neue welt, von Wilhelm Liebknecht.
Stuttgart, J. H. W. Dietz, 1887.
    vii, 288 p. 16½ cm.

    1. U. S.—Descr. & trav.—1865–1900.   I. Title.

    E168.L71   2–4424

NL 0347564   DLC CtY NcD ICJ NN MdU MoU OrPR

Liebknecht, Wilhelm *Philipp Christian Martin Ludwig, 1826–*
    Ein blick in die Neue welt, von Wilhelm Liebknecht.
Stuttgart, J. H. W. Dietz, 1887.
    vii, 288 p. 16½ cm.

    Microfiche (negative). Louisville, Ky.,
Lost Cause Press, 1965. 8 sheets.
11 x 15 cm.

NL 0347565   GASC

Micro- Liebknecht, Wilhelm Philipp Christian Martin
card   Ludwig, 1826–1900.
94   Ein Blick in die Neue Welt, von Wilhelm
v.1   Liebknecht. Stuttgart, J.H.W. Dietz, 1887.
no.390   vii, 288p. 17cm.

          Micro-opaque. Louisville, Ky., Lost Cause
          Press, 1965. 4 cards. 8 x 13cm. (Travels
          in the new South, 1, 390)

          1. U.S. - Descr. & trav. - 1865–1900. I.
          Title. II. Series: Travels in the new South.
          1. 390.

NL 0347566   TxU

Liebknecht, Wilhelm Philipp Christian Martin
    Ludwig, 1826–1900.
    Das Brief-Geheimniss vor dem deutschen
Reichstag
        see under   Germany. Reichstag.

Liebknecht, Wilhelm *Philipp Christian Martin Ludwig, 1826–1900.*
    [Collected papers chiefly on socialism.]

NL 0347568   ICJ

Liebknecht, Wilhelm Philipp Christian Martin Ludwig, 1826–
    1900.
    Die Emser Depesche; oder, Wie Kriege gemacht werden. Von
W. Liebknecht... Nürnberg, Wörlein & Comp., 1891. 45 p.
19cm.

    1. Franco-German war, 1870–1871.
    N. Y. P. L.   November 6, 1944

NL 0347569   NN DLC OU NcD ICJ

Liebknecht, Wilhelm Phillipp Christian
    Martin Ludwig, 1826–1900.

    Die Emser Depesche, oder wie Kriege
gemacht werden. Mit einem Nachtrag:
Bismarck nackt. Nürnberg, Wörlein, 1899.

    102 p. 20 cm.
    U.B.C. copy lacks t.p.
    1. Franco-German War, 1870–1871.
2. France - For. rel. - Germany. 3. Germany
For. rel. - France. 4. Bismarck, Otto,
Fürst von,   1815–1898.
I. Title.

NL 0347570   CaBVaU

Liebknecht, Wilhelm Philipp Christian Martin
    Ludwig, 1826–1900.
Bebel, August i. e. Ferdinand August, 1840–1913.
    Gegen den militarismus und gegen die neuen steuern.
Zwei Reichstags-reden von A. Bebel und W. Liebknecht
gehalten bei der berathung des Reichshaushalts-etats am
27. und 30. november 1893. Berlin, Expedition des "Vorwärts" (T. Glocke) 1893.

Liebknecht, *Wilhelm Philipp Christian Martin Ludwig, 1826–1900.*
    Die Grund-und Bodenfrage. Vortrag gehalten im Saale
des Schützenhauses zu Meerane am 12. März 1870.
*Leipzig: Genossenschaftsbuchdruckerei, 1874. 128 pp.
12°.*
    Gift of F. A. Sorge.

NL 0347572   NN CtY

Liebknecht, Wilhelm Philipp Christian Martin Ludwig,
    1826–1900.
    ... Hochverrath und revolution. Von W. Liebknecht.
Hottingen-Zürich, Volksbuchhandlung, 1887.
    55 p. 20½ᵐ. (Sozialdemokratische bibliothek. XVII)
    "Nachstehendes ist ein abdruck meiner 'ungehaltenen rede' aus dem
Leipziger hochverrathsprozess ... Als anhang habe ich einen brief an die
'Morning post' und einen artikel des 'Volksstaat' beigefügt."—Vorwort.

    1. Socialism in Germany. 2. Revolutions. I. Title.
                                                        16–2360
    Library of Congress   HX276.L67

NL 0347573   DLC NcD CtY NN

VOLUME 332

335.0943
L716h
Liebknecht, Wilhelm Philipp Christian Martin
Ludwig, 1826-1900.
Hochverrath und Revolution. Neue Aufl.
Berlin, "Vorwärts", Berliner Volksblatt, 1892.
ix,51p. 21cm.

Cover title.
"Nachstehendes ist ein Abdruck meiner
'Ungehaltenen Rede' aus dem Leipziger
Hochverrathsprozess... Als Anhang habe ich
einen Brief an die 'Morning Post' und einen
Artikel des 'Volksstaat' beigefügt."

NL   0347574   IEN ICJ NcD

Liebknecht, Wilhelm Philipp Christian Martin Ludwig,
1826-1900, *defendant*.
Der hochverraths-prozess wider Liebknecht, Bebel,
Hepner, vor dem Schwurgericht zu Leipzig vom 11. bis
26. märz 1872. Mit einer einleitung von W. Liebknecht.
(Neu-auflage) Berlin, Expedition des "Vorwärts" (T.
Glocke) 1894.
944 p. 20cm.
The "anhang" (p. [741]-924) contains extracts from newspapers, addresses, programs, etc., illustrating the growth of the "Sozialdemokratische
partei Deutschlands."
1. Socialism in Germany.   1. Bebel, August *i. e.* Ferdinand August,
1840-1913. II. Hepner, Adolf, 1846-   III. Leipzig. Schwurgericht.
IV. Sozialdemokratische partei Deutschlands. V. Title.

CA 17-354 Unrev'd

Library of Congress   HX273.L6

NL   0347575   DLC CaBVaU IEN WU CU OU MiU MU ICU NcD NcU

Liebknecht, Wilhelm Philipp Christian Martin Ludwig,
1826-1900, *defendant*.
Der Hochverrats-Prozess wider Liebknecht, Bebel, Hepner vor dem Schwurgericht zu Leipzig vom 11. bis 26. März
1872. Mit einer Einleitung von W. Liebknecht und einem
Anhang. Nach der 2. Aufl. unveränderter Neudruck. Berlin, Buchhandlung Vorwärts P. Singer, 1911.
944 p. 20 cm.
I. Bebel, August, 1840-1913, defendant. II. Hepner, Adolf, 1846-
defendant. III. Sozialdemokratische Partei Deutschlands. IV. Saxony. Bezirksgericht, Leipzig. V. Title.

65-59422

NL   0347576   DLC InU MH FU KU CaBVaU

Liebknecht, Wilhelm Philipp Christian Martin
Ludwig, 1826-1900.
Der Hochverratsprozess gegen Liebknecht
vor dem Reichsgericht
see Liebknecht, Karl Paul August
Friedrich, 1871-1919.

Liebknecht, Wilhelm Philipp Christian Martin Ludwig,
1826-1900.
Karl Marx; biographical memoirs ... by Wilhelm Liebknecht; tr. by E. Untermann. Chicago, C. H. Kerr &
company, 1901.
181 p. front. (port.) 17½cm. (*On cover:* Standard socialist series)

1. Marx, Karl, 1818-1883.   I. Untermann, Ernest, tr.

Library of Congress   HB501.M5L6,   1—12899

TU ICJ
NNUN GU NSyU TNJ MiU OU ODW OCl OCH PSt MH OrU MU
NL   0347578   DLC DAU NIC CaQML FU OKentU WaU ICRL NjP

335
M39Yfx
1901
Liebknecht, Wilhelm Philipp Christian
Martin Ludwig, 1826-1900.
Karl Marx; biographical memoirs. Transla-
ted by Ernest Untermann. Chicago, Kerr;
Republished by Scholarly Press [c1901]
181p. 18cm.

1. Marx, Karl, 1818-1883.   I. Untermann,
Ernest, tr.

NL   0347579   IEN

Liebknecht, Wilhelm Philipp Christian Martin Ludwig, 1826-
1900.
Karl Marx; biographical memoirs ... by Wilhelm Liebknecht; tr. by E. Untermann. Chicago, C. H. Kerr & company,
1901. [Cleveland, Micro Photo Div., Bell &
Howell, 1969(?)]
181 p. front. (port.) 17½cm. (*On cover:* Standard socialist series)

NL   0347580   NBuC Wa OrP OrCS Or CaBVaU IU

335
M369B4Tu
Liebknecht, Wilhelm Philipp Christian Martin
Ludwig, 1826-1900.
Karl Marx; biographical memoirs ..., by Wilhelm
Liebknecht; tr. by E. Untermann. Chicago, C.H.
Kerr & company, 1904 [c1901]
181p. front. (port.) 17½cm. (On cover: Stand-
ard socialist series)

Frontispiece wanting in TxU copy.

1. Marx, Karl, 1818-1883.   I. Untermann, Ernest,
tr.

NL   0347581   TxU CU AU NcU

HB501
.M5L6
Liebknecht, Wilhelm Philipp Christian Martin
Ludwig, 1826-1900.
Karl Marx; biographical memoirs. Trans-
lated by Ernest Untermann. Chicago,
C. H. Kerr & company, 1906.[1901]
181 p.

Reprint by microfilm-xerox by Univ.
Microfilms, Ann Arbor, Mich., 1965.

I. Marx, Karl, 1818-1883.   I. Untermann,
Ernest, tr.

NL   0347582   NBuU

Liebknecht, Wilhelm, Philipp Christian Martin
Ludwig, 1826-1900.
Karl Marx; biographical memoirs.
Translated by Ernest Untermann. Chicago,
C. H. Kerr & Co., 1908.
181 p. 4th thous. 16°. (Standard
socialist series)

NL   0347583   NN MiU

LIEBKNECHT, WILHELM PHILIPP CHRISTIAN MARTIN
LUDWIG, 1826-1900.
Karl Marx; biographical memoirs. Translated by
Ernest Untermann. Chicago: C. H. Kerr & Co., 1908.
181 p. 16° (Standard socialist series)

Film reproduction. Master negative.

NL   0347584   NN OrU

Liebknecht, Wilhelm Philipp Christian Martin
Ludwig, 1826-1900.
Karl Marx, 1818-1883; extracts from reminiscences of Marx
by Wilhelm Liebknecht and Paul Lafargue; four letters of
Engels on the death of Marx; Engels' speech at the grave-
side of Marx; for the anniversary of Marx's death, 14 March,
1883. London, Lawrence and Wishart ltd. [1941?]

HX39
.5
L874
Liebknecht, Wilhelm Philipp Christian Martin
Ludwig, 1826-1900. Karl Marx, zum
gedächtniss.
Lafargue, Paul, 1842-1911.
Karl Marx, his life and work; reminiscences by Paul La-
fargue and Wilhelm Liebknecht. New York, International
publishers [1943]

HX39
.5
.L277
Liebknecht, Wilhelm Philipp Christian Martin
Ludwig, 1826-1900.
Lafargue, Paul, 1842-1911.
Karl Marx; recuerdos de su vida y su obra [por] Pablo La-
fargue [y] G. Liebknecht. La Habana, Ediciones sociales, 1943.

HX39
.5
L872
Liebknecht, Wilhelm Philipp Christian Martin
Ludwig, 1826-1900.
Lafargue, Paul, 1842-1911.
Karl Marx som menneske [af] Paul Lafargue og Wilhelm
Liebknecht. [Overs. af C. L. Skjoldbo] København, For-
laget Fremad, 1948.

Liebknecht, Wilhelm Philipp Christian Martin Ludwig,
1826-1900.
Karl Marx, zum gedächtniss. Ein lebensabriss und
erinnerungen. Von W. Liebknecht. Unter beigabe von
1 portrait von Marx, der abbildung seiner grabstätte und
2 facsimile-wiedergaben von briefen Marx' und Engels'.
Nürnberg, Wörlein & comp., 1896.
vii, 120 p., 1 l. front. (port.) pl., facsims. 20cm.
No. 4 in a vol. of pamphlets lettered: Karl Marx.

1. Marx, Karl, 1818-1883.

16-2351

Library of Congress   HB501.M5A15

NL   0347589   DLC OCH IEN NN

HX276
L751
Liebknecht, Wilhelm Philipp Christian Martin
Ludwig, 1826-1900.
Kein kompromiss, kein wahlbündniss. Von Wilhelm Liebknecht. Hrsg. im auftrage von genossen
Berlins und umgebung ... Berlin, Verlag Expedition der buchhandlung Vorwärts (T. Glocke)
1899.
cover-title, 32 p. 20cm. [With his Ueber die
politische stellung der Sozialdemokratie. Berlin, 1893]

1. Sozialdemokratische partei Deutschlands.
2. Suffrage - Ger many. 3. Germany - Pol. &
govt. - 1888-1918.   I. Title.

NL   0347590   CSt-H MH NcD

Liebknecht, Wilhelm Philipp Christian Martin Ludwig, 1826-
1900.
Kein Kompromiss, kein Wahlbündniss. Von Wilhelm Liebknecht. Hrsg. im Auftrage von Genossen Berlins und Umgebung... Berlin, Buchhandlung Vorwärts, 1899. 32 p.
22cm.
Film reproduction of the original. 35 mm. Reduction 12. Position III. Positive.
Cover-title.

F2947.   I. Socialism, Germany,   1891-
N. Y. P. L.   March 27, 1945

NL   0347591   NN CtY

J
27
335.0943
N401
LIEBKNECHT, WILHELM PHILIPP CHRISTIAN MARTIN
LUDWIG, 1826-1900, defendant.
Leipziger Hochverrathsprozess. Ausführlicher Bericht über die Verhandlungen des
Schwurgerichts zu Leipzig in dem Prozess gegen Liebknecht, Bebel und Hepner. Bearbeitet
von den Angeklagten. Leipzig, Druck und Verlag der Genossenschaftsbuchdruckerei, 1874.
600p. 18cm.

NL   0347592   ICN DLC KyU CSt-H NN PPT NcD MH

VOLUME 332

HD
5307
.B
Liebknecht, Wilhelm Philipp Christian Martin
Ludwig, 1826-1900.
Mit akar a szociáldemokrácia? ᵣIrtaᵧ Lieb-
knecht Vilmos. Ford. Suhogó B. 3. jav. kiad.
Budapest, Népszava, 1906.
48 p. 22 cm.

Translation of Was die Socialdemokraten sind
und was sie wollen.
Bound with Bresztóczy, Ernő. Általános sztrájk
és választói jog Magyarországon. 1907.

NL 0347593　　NNC

HX251
M966
v.5
Liebknecht, Wilhelm Philipp Christian Martin
Ludwig, 1826-1900.
... Mit akar a szociáldemokrácia? Forditotta
Somogyi Béla. Budapest, A Népszava-könyv-
kereskedés kiadása, ᵣ1919?ᵧ
64 p. 20½ᵐ. (On cover: Munkáskönyvtár, 5.
füzet)
At head of title: Liebknecht Vilmos.
Translation of the author's "Was die sozial-
demokraten sind und was sie wollen."
1.Sozialdemokr   atische partei Deutschlands
I.Somogyi, Béla,   tr. II.Title.

NL 0347594　　CSt-H

J
27
335.5
P 901
LIEBKNECHT, WILHELM PHILIPP CHRISTIAN MARTIN
LUDWIG, 1826-1900.
ᵣNo compromise: no political trading.
Translated by A.M.Simons and Marcus Hitch.
Chicago,C.H.Kerr,pref.1899ᵧ
64p. ᵣUnity library, no.102ᵧ

No title-page. Title taken from inside
cover.

NL 0347595　　ICN ICJ

Liebknecht, Wilhelm Philipp Christian Martin Ludwig,
1826-1900.
No compromise, no political trading, by Wilhelm Liebknecht, tr. by A. M. Simons and Marcus Hitch.
Chicago, C. H. Kerr & company (co-operative), 1900.
64 p. 14ᶜᵐ. (Unity library, no. 102)

Cover title.

NL 0347596　　OU MH

Liebknecht, Wilhelm Philipp Christian Martin Ludwig,
1826-1900.
No compromise, no political trading, by Wilhelm Liebknecht, tr. by A. M. Simons and Marcus Hitch. Rev. ed.
Chicago, C. H. Kerr & company (co-operative) 1903.
64 p. 14 cm.

1. Sozialdemokratische partei Deutschlands. 2. Political parties—
Germany. 3. Socialism. ɪ. Simons, Algie Martin. 1870—　　tr.
ɪɪ. Hitch, Marcus, joint tr. ɪɪɪ. Title.

HX279.L65　　　　　　　　　　CA 16—424 Unrev'd

NL 0347597　　DLC NN OU FU

335
M39m.E
1902
Liebknecht, Wilhelm Philipp Christian
Martin Ludwig, 1826-1900
No compromise; no political trading;
tr. by A.M. Simons and Marcus Hitch.
Rev. ed.　Chicago, Kerr, 1905.
64p. D.

Bound with Marx, Karl and Engels,
Frederick. Manifesto of the Communist party.

NL 0347598　　IaU NjP ODW

Liebknecht, Wilhelm Philipp Christian Martin Ludwig, 1826-
1900.
No compromise, no political trading. Translated
by A.M.Simons and Marcus Hitch. Rev.ed. Chicago,
Kerr, 1907.

64 p.
Bound as issued with Marx, K. & Engels, F.
Manifesto of the Communist party. Chicago, 1906

NL 0347599　　MH RPB PP

HX81
.S6
vol. 1,
no. 12
Liebknecht, Wilhelm Philipp Christian Martin
Ludwig, 1826-1900.
No compromise, no political trading ... tr.
by A. M. Simons and Marcus Hitch, rev. ed.
Chicago, C. H. Kerr & company (co-operative)
64 p. [Socialist party (U.S.) Collected
pamphlets, leaflets, etc., v. 1., no. 12]

NL 0347600　　DLC OrP WaS

335
M36amN
1913
Liebknecht, Wilhelm Philipp Christian Martin
Ludwig, 1826-1900.
No compromise, no political trading. Tr.
by A.M. Simons and Marcus Hitch. Rev. ed.
Chicago, Kerr, 1913.
64p. 17cm.

This is bound with Manifesto of the
Communist Party, by Karl Marx and Frederick
Engels.

1. Sozialdemokratische partei Deutschlands
2. Political   parties. Germany.
3. Socialism   I. Title. (Anal.)

NL 0347601　　KU PU CU

335
M39kX
1915
Liebknecht, Wilhelm Phillip Christian Martin
Ludwig, 1826-1900.
No compromise, no political trading. Trans-
lated by A.M.Simons and Marcus Hitch. Rev.ed.
Chicago, C.H.Kerr (co-operating) 1915.
64p. 17cm. [With Marx,K. Manifesto of the
Communist party. Chicago, 1915]

1. Sozialdemokratische Partei Deutschlands.
2. Political parties. Germany. I. Simons, Algie
Martin,1870- tr. II. Hitch, Marcus, jt. tr.
III. Title.

NL 0347602　　IEN PSC MiU OEac

Liebknecht, Wilhelm Philipp Christian Martin Ludwig,
1826-1900.
No compromise, no political trading, by Wilhelm Liebknecht, tr. by A. M. Simons and Marcus Hitch. Rev. ed.
Chicago, C. H. Kerr & company (co-operative) 1918.
64 p. 14ᶜᵐ.

NL 0347603　　NcD NjP MH

335.5
L26kEs
1919
Liebknecht, Wilhelm Philipp Christian Martin
Ludwig, 1826-1900.
No compromise, no political trading ... translat-
ed by A. M. Simons and Marcus Hitch. Rev.ed.
Chicago, C. H. Kerr & company, 1919.
72p.

1. Sozialdemokratische partei Deutschlands. 2
Suffrage--Germany. 3. Germany--Pol. & govt.--
1888-1918. I. Simons, Algie Martin, 1870- tr.
II. Hitch, Marcus, tr. III. Title.

NL 0347604　　IU MiU PSt PPT MH NcD ViU

Liebknecht, Wilhelm Philipp Martin Christian Ludwig, 1826-1900.
Odbudowanie Polski. (1868 rok. Z „Demokratisches Wochen-
blatt".)
(In Odbudowanie Polski. Pp. 110-145. Warzawa. 1910

3066.501

L3415 — Poland. Pol. hist. — Poland. Lang. Work. in Polish.

NL 0347605　　MB

Liebknecht, Wilhelm Philipp Christian Martin
Ludwig, 1826-1900.
Die Orientdebatte im Deutschen Reichstag
see under Germany. Reichstag.

Liebknecht, Wilhelm Philipp Christian Martin, 1826-1900
Over de politieke stelling der socialdemokratie.
in't bizonder met betrekking tot den Rijksdag.
Voordracht ... gehouden in ... 1869, met
voorwoord van F. Domela Nieuwenhuis.
Amsterdam, J. Hoekstra, 1894.
24 p. 8°.

NL 0347607　　NN

HX 276
.L 69
LIEBKNECHT, WILHELM PHILIPP CHRISTIAN MARTIN
Ludwig, 1826-1900.
ᵣPamphlets by or about W. Liebknecht,
1887-1900ᵧ
8 pamphlets in portfolio.

1. Socialism in Germany--Hist. 2. Liebknecht,
Wilhelm Philipp   Christian Martin Ludwig,1826-1900.

NL 0347608　　InU

Liebknecht, Wilhelm Philipp Christian Martin Ludwig,
1826-1900.
Пауки и мухи. ᵣПетроградъᵧ Социалистъ ᵣ1917ᵧ
8 p. 19 cm.
At head of title: Вильгельмъ Либкнехтъ.

1. Socialism.　I. Title.

Title romanized: Pauki i mukhi.

HX39.L485 1917　　　　　　　79-27913

NL 0347609　　DLC

Liebknecht, Wilhelm Philipp Christian Martin
Ludwig, 1826-1900, ed.
International socialist congress. 1st, Paris, 1889.
Protokoll des Internationalen arbeiter-congresses zu
Paris. Abgehalten vom 14. bis 20. juli 1889. Deutsche
uebersetzung. Mit einem vorwort von Wilhelm Lieb-
knecht. Nürnberg, Wörlein & comp., 1890.

HX276
L751
Liebknecht, Wilhelm Philipp Christian Martin
Ludwig, 1826-1900, defendant.
Der prozess Liebknecht. Verhandlung wegen
Majestäts-beleidigung vor dem Landgericht zu
Breslau am donnerstag, den 14. november 1895.
Mit einem vor- und nachwort von W. Liebknecht.
Berlin, Verlag der Expedition des "Vorwärts"
(T. Glocke) 1895.

31 p. 20ᵐ. ᵣWith his Ueber die politische
stellung der Sozialdemokratie. Berlin, 1895ᵧ

1.Political cri   mes and offenses - Germany.
2.Socialism in   Germany. 3.Sozialdemokrati-
sche partei Deutschlands. I.Title.

NL 0347611　　CSt-H NN IEN MH

VOLUME 332

LIEBKNECHT, WILHELM PHILIPP CHRISTIAN MARTIN
LUDWIG, 1826-1900.
Rede Liebknecht's über den Antrag auf Beurlaubung
der gefangenen soz.-demokr. Reichstagsabgeordneten.
(Reichstagssitzung vom 21. Nov. 1874.)
[Leipzig, Genossen schaftsbuchdr; 1874.]   40 p.
19cm.

Film reproduction. Positive.
Caption title.
1. Socialism--Germany,   to 1875.

NL 0347612   NN

DD [Liebknecht, Wilhelm Philipp Christian Martin
205   Ludwig] 1826-1900.
.B6   Robert Blum, eine biographische Skizze.
L5   [Leipzig, 1879]
        88 p.   illus.   19cm.

Includes bibliography.

NL 0347613   WU

Liebknecht, Wilhelm Philipp Christian
Martin Ludwig, 1826-1900.
Robert Blum und seine zeit ...   Nürn-
berg, Wörlein & comp., 1888.

vi, [7]-348 p.   21cm.

1. Blum, Robert, 1807-1848. 2. Germany
Politics and government. 1815-1866.

NL 0347614   MnU NBuU NcD

Liebknecht, Wilhelm Philipp Christian Martin
Ludwig, 1826-1900.
Robert Blum und seine zeit. Von W. Liebknecht.
2. aufl. Nürnberg, Wörlein & comp., 1889.
vi, [7]-422 p.   20½cm.

"Noch etwas vom tollen jahr und noch zwei reden
Robert Blum's": p.[349]-422.

1. Blum, Robert, 1807-1848.

NL 0347615   WU IaU CU DLC NRU MH ICJ CU

335.0943
B6582Yℓ.3 Liebknecht, Wilhelm Philipp Christian Martin
Ludwig, 1826-1900.
Robert Blum und seine Zeit. 3. erweiterte
und verb. Aufl. Nürnberg, Wörlein, 1896.
iv, 526p. 20cm.

1. Blum, Robert, 1807-1848. I. Title.

NL 0347616   IEN MH NcD

Liebknecht, Wilhelm Philipp Christian Martin
Ludwig, 1826-1900.
Robert Owen, sein Leben und sozialpolitisches
Wirken. Nürnberg, Verlag von Wörlein, 1892.
72 p. illus. 20cm.

NL 0347617   WU MB NcD

PT2423
.L55R9   Liebknecht, Wilhelm Philipp Christian Martin Ludwig,
1826-1900.
Рыцари труда; социальный роман. [Петроград] Изд.
Петроградского Совета рабоч. и красноармейск. депутатов, 1919.
132 p. 19cm.

I. Title.   *Title transliterated: Ryt͡sari truda.*

PT2423.L55R9   54-50050 ‡

NL 0347618   DLC

335.08
P191   Liebknecht, Wilhelm Philipp Christian
v.1   Martin Ludwig, 1826-1900.
no.3   Socialdemokratien och dess syften;
öfversättning fran tyskan af Fr. Sterky.
Stockholm, Socialdemokratiska Arbetarepartiets,
1890.
18p. 19cm. (In Pamphlets on socialism.
v.1, no.3)

1. Socialdemokratische Partei Deutschlands.

NL 0347619   OrU

HX15
.P3   Liebknecht, Wilhelm Philipp Christian Martin
vol. 3,   Ludwig, 1826-1900.
no. 12   Socialism; what it is and what it seeks to
accomplish ... Tr. by May Wood Simons.
Chicago, C. H. Kerr & company [n,d.]
64 p.   [Pamphlets on socialism,
communism, bolshevism, etc., v. 3, no. 12]

NL 0347620   DLC

Liebknecht, Wilhelm Philipp Christian Martin Ludwig,
1826-1900.
... Socialism, what it is and what it seeks to accomplish;
by Wilhelm Liebknecht. Tr. by May Wood Simons ...
Chicago, C. H. Kerr & company [1897]
cover-title, 64 p. 18¼ᶜᵐ. (Unity library, no. 71)

1. Socialism.   I. Simons, May Wood, tr.

Library of Congress   HX276.L7   9-15465

NL 0347621   DLC OU

LIEBKNECHT, Wilhelm Philip Christian Martin Ludwig, 1826-1900.
Socialism: what it is and what it seeks to
accomplish. Chicago, 1899.

NL 0347622   MH

Liebknecht, Wilhelm Philipp Christian Martin
Ludwig, 1826-1900.
Socialism: what it is and what it seeks
to accomplish, by Wilhelm Liebknecht. Translated by May Wood Simons. Chicago, C. H.
Kerr, 1900.
64p. port. 20cm. (Unity library, no.
110)

Cover title.

NL 0347623   IEN

Liebknecht, Wilhelm Philipp Christian Martin Ludwig,
1826-1900.
... Socialism, what it is and what it seeks to accomplish;
by Wilhelm Liebknecht. Tr. by May Wood Simons ...
Chicago, C. H. Kerr & company, 1901.
cover-title. 64 p. 20 cm. (Library of progress, no.
39)

NL 0347624   NcD

Liebknecht, Wilhelm, Philipp Christian Martin
Ludwig, 1826-1900.
Socialism: what it is, and what it seeks to
accomplish ... Translated by May Wood Simons.
Chicago, C. H. Kerr & Co., 1907.
64 p.   12 °.
Title fr. cover.

NL 0347625   NN

Liebknecht, Wilhelm Philipp Martin Christian Ludwig, 1826-1900.
Souvenirs. Traduits en français pour la première fois par J. G.
Prod'homme & Ch. A. Bertrand.
— Paris. Bellais. 1901. xiv, (1), 188, (2) pp. Portraits. 16°.
Contents. — Souvenirs d'exil en Suisse (anno 1849). — Souvenirs de
jeunesse. — Premier discours quand j'étais maître d'école.

April 11,   1902.
E2436 — Bertrand, Charles A., tr. — Prod'homme, J. G., tr.

NL 0347626   MB RPB CtY CSt-H CaBVaU

Liebknecht, Wilhelm Philipp Christian Martin
Ludwig, 1826-1900.
Sozialdemokratische partei Deutschlands.
Die sozialdemokratie im deutschen Reichstag; tätig-
keitsberichte und wahlaufrufe aus den jahren 1871 bis
1893. Berlin, Buchhandlung Vorwärts (H. Weber) 1909.

Liebknecht, Wilhelm Philipp Christian Martin Ludwig,
1826-1900.
... Speeches of Wilhelm Liebknecht, with a critical introduction. New York, International publishers [1928]
96 p. 19ᶜᵐ.
Portrait on cover.

1. Socialism in Germany.
Library of Congress   HX276.L72   28-9670

NL 0347628   DLC CaQML NBuU WU MH OKentU CoU NcD OCIW

MICROFORMS
CENTER
Film   Liebknecht, Wilhelm Philipp Christian Martin
4006   Ludwig, 1826-1900
Speeches of Wilhelm Liebknecht, with a
critical introduction. New York, International
Publishers [c1928]
96p. (Voices of revolt, v. 7)
Microfilm (negative) Washington, Library of
Congress, 1972. 1 reel.

1. Socialism in Germany I. Title

NL 0347629   WU

Liebknecht, Wilhelm Philipp Christian Martin Ludwig, 1826-1900
Totaanvalen verdediging. Eene voordracht
van Willem Liebknecht ... uit het Hoogduitsch
vertaalddoor E. V. B. Gent, F. van Gyseghem,
1886.
48 p.   8°.
4 ed.

NL 0347630   NN

VOLUME 332

Liebknecht, Wilhelm Philipp Christian **Martin Ludwig,**
1826-1900.
　　Trutz-Eisenstirn. Erzieherisches aus Puttkamerun; ein
vierblättriges Broschüren-Kleeblatt nebst einem Anhang,
vom Vetter Niemand.　London, German **Cooperative Print.**
and Pub. Co., 1889-90.
　　2 v.　20 cm.　(Sozialdemokratische Bibliothek, 29-30)

　　1. Socialism.　2. Socialism in Germany.　ɪ. Title.　(Series)

HX276.L722　　　　　　　　　　　　　　　57-52741

NL　0347631　　　DLC NcD CtY MiU ICJ

HX251
M966
v.3
　　Liebknecht, Wilhelm Philipp Christian **Martın**
　　Ludwig, 1826-1900.
　　　A tudás: hatalom! A hatalom: tudás! Unnepi
beszéd tartotta 1872 február hó 5-én, a drez-
dai munkásképző-egyesület alapitó ünnepén
Liebknecht Vilmos; forditotta Bresztovszky
Erno.　Budapest, Népszava-könyvkereskedés
kiadása, 1914.
　　98 p., 1 l.　20ᵐ.　(On cover: Munkáskönyvtár,
3. szám)
　　Translation of the author's "Wissen ist macht
- macht ist wissen.
　　1. Education -　　　　Germany.　2. Socialism in
Germany.　I. Bre　　　　sztovszky, Erno, tr.
II. Title.

NL　0347632　　　CSt-H

Liebknecht, ([Wilhelm]) Philipp Christian, Martin Ludwig, 1826-1900.
Ueber die politische Stellung der Sozial-Demokratie,
insbesondere mit Bezug auf den norddeutschen " Reichs-
tag." Vortrag.. in der am 31. Mai abgehaltenen Ver-
sammlung des Berliner demokratischen Arbeiter-Vereins.
[*Leipzig : F. Thiele*, 186-] 16 pp. nar. 12° (8°.)
In: 8F. p. v. 5.
Gift of F. A. Sorge.

NL　0347633　　　NN

JN3946
.S83L54
　　Liebknecht, Wilhelm Philipp Christian Martin
　　Ludwig, 1826-1900.
　　　Ueber die politische Stellung der Sozial-
Demokratie, insbesondere mit Bezug auf den
Reichstag. Ein Vortrag, gehalten zu Berlin am
31. Mai 1869, in einer öffentlichen Versamm-
lung des demokratischen Arbeitervereins. Mit
einem Vorwort und einem tragikomischen
Nachspiel. 2. Aufl.　Leipzig, Expedition des
"Volksstaat", 1872.
　　24 p.　18 cm.

　　1. Sozialdemok　　　ratische partei Deutschlands.　I. Title.

NL　0347634　　　NjR PU

4-JN
Ger.
213
　　Liebknecht, Wilhelm Philipp **Christian**
　　Martin Ludwig, 1826-1900.
　　　Ueber die politische Stellung der
Sozialdemokratie insbesondere mit Be-
zug auf den Reichstag; ein Vortrag,
gehalten in einer öffentlichen Ver-
sammlung des demokratischen Arbeiter-
vereins zu Berlin am 31. Mai 1869.
Mit einem Vorwort und einem tragi-
komischen Nachspiel. 3. unveränderte
Aufl.

　　Leipzig, Druck und Verlag der Genossenschaftsbuchdr., 1874.
　　　24 p.

NL　0347636　　　DLC-P4 CtY NN MH

HX271
.S751
v.25
　　Liebknecht, Wilhelm Philipp Christian **Martin**
　　Ludwig, 1826-1900.
　　　Ueber die politische stellung der Sozialdemo
kratie, insbesondere mit besug auf den **Reichstag**
ein vortrag, gehalten in einer öffentlichen ver-
sammlung des Demokratischen arbeitervereins zu
Berlin am 31. mai 1869. Von W. Liebknecht. Mit
vorwort und tragikomischem nachspiel.　London,
German cooperative publishing, 1889.
　　30 p.　20ᵐ　(Sozialdemokratische bibliothek
XXV)

　　1. Sozialdemokra　　　tische partei Deutschlands.

NL　0347637　　　CSt-H NN CtY MH NcD

HX276
L751
　　Liebknecht, Wilhelm Philipp Christian **Martin**
　　Ludwig, 1826-1900.
　　　Ueber die politische stellung der Sozialdemokratie, insbesondere mit bezug auf den
Reichstag. Ein vortrag gehalten in der öffentlichen versammlung des Demokratischen arbeiter-
vereins zu Berlin am 31. mai 1869, von W. Liebknecht. Mit vorwort und tragikomischen nachspiel.　Neue unveränderte aufl.　Berlin,
Verlag der Expedition des "Vorwärts", Berliner
volksblatt (T.Glocke) 1893.
　　32 p.　20ᵐ.
On spine: Lieb　　　knecht: Diverse reden und
abhandlungen.
　　1. Sozialdemokratische partei Deutschlands.

NL　0347638　　　CSt-H MB

Liebknecht, Wilhelm Philipp Christian Martin Ludwig,
1826-1900.
דיא וואהרהייט איבער דעם סאציאליזמוס. ;איבערז. פון מ.
מילמאן; לאנדאן, פיילישע סאציאלימטישע פארטיי.
[London], 1902.
54 p.　illus.　18 cm.

　　1. Socialism.　*Title transliterated:* Di vahrhayt iber dem sotsializmus.

HX276.L7224　　　　　　　　　　　57-56270 ‡

NL　0347639　　　DLC

Liebknecht, Wilhelm Philipp Christian Martin Ludwig,
1826-1900, ed.
　　Volks-Bibliothek des gesammten menschlichen
Wissens. Dresden, Kommissions-Verlag von R.
Schnabel.　1888-1889.
　　　Abt.　　　　　illus.
　　Library has: Abt. I. Band 17, Abt. II Band 17-
18, Abt. III Band 22 and 25, all in one.

NL　0347640　　　ICRL

Liebknecht, Wilhelm Philipp Christian **Martin Ludwig,**
1826-1900.
　　Volks-Fremdwörterbuch. 7. Aufl., neu bearb., berichtigt
und verm. Stuttgart, J. H. W. Dietz [1894]
　　viii, 616 p.　20 cm.

　　1. German language—Foreign words and phrases—Dictionaries.
ɪ. Title.

PF3670.L5　1894　　　　　　　　　　55-53009

NL　0347641　　　DLC

LIEBKNECHT, Wilhelm Philipp Christian Martin Ludwig, 1826-1900.
　Volks-Fremdwörterbuch. 9ᵉ Aufl.　Stuttgart,
J.H.W.Dietz Nachf., 1907.

　　20 cm.　pp. viii, 616

NL　0347642　　　MH

Himl2
428
　　Liebknecht, Wilhelm Philipp Christian Martin
　　Ludwig, 1826-1900.
　　　... Volksfremdwörterbuch, völlig neu bear-
beitet, berichtigt und vermehrt. 20. Aufl.
Berlin, Neuer deutscher Verlag, 1929.
　　xviii, 600p.　19cm.

　　1. German language - Foreign words and
phrases - Dictionaries.

NL　0347643　　　CtY MH

433
L62v22
　　Liebknecht, Wilhelm Philipp Christian Martin Ludwig, 1826-
　　　... Volksfremdwörterbuch. Neue [22.]...
gekürzte Aufl.　Berlin, Dietz [1948]
　　288 p. 21cm.

　　1. German language—Foreign words
and phrases—Dictionaries.

NL　0347644　　　LU

Liebknecht, Wilhelm Philipp Christian Martin Ludwig, 1826-
　Volksfremdwörterbuch. Neu bearbeitete,
berichtigte und erweiterte aufl.　Berlin,
Dietz [c1948]
　　xvi, 562 p.

　　1. German language - Foreign words and
phrases - Dictionaries.

NL　0347645　　　NNC

PF3670
.L52
1953
　　Liebknecht, Wilhelm Philipp Christian Martin Ludwig,
　　1826-1900.
　　　Volksfremdwörterbuch. [22.] neue, umgearb. und gekürzte Aufl. Berlin, Dietz, 1953.
　　288 p.　18 cm.

　　1. German language—Foreign words and phrases—Dictionaries.
ɪ. Title.

Wisconsin. Univ. Libr.
for Library of Congress　　　　　　ᵃ.
　　　　　　　　　　　　　　　　　　　A 55-566

NL　0347646　　　WU DLC CtY

944.08
L26w
　　Liebknecht, Wilhelm Philipp Christian Martin
　　Ludwig, 1826-1900.
　　　W. Liebknecht et l'affaire Dreyfus.　[Paris,
Bureaux de l'Action française, 1899]
　　40p.　18cm.　(L'Action française, 1.année,
no 10.　Supplément)

　　Caption title.

　　1. Dreyfus, Alfred, 1849-1935.

NL　0347647　　　IU MH

Liebknecht, Wilhelm Philipp Christian Martin Ludwig, 1826-1900.
　Was die Sozialdemokraten sind und was sie wollen.
Neue berichtigte und vervollständigte Aufl., die 2. in
Deutschland.　Berlin, 1891.

NL　0347648　　　MH

VOLUME 332

Liebknecht, Wilhelm Philipp Christian Martin Ludwig,
1826–1900.
Was die sozialdemokraten sind und was sie wollen.
Von W. Liebknecht. Chemnitz, A. Langer, 1894.
52 p. 21½ᶜᵐ.
"Das nachstehende schriftchen ist aus zwei, um die mitte der 70er jahre
von mir geschriebenen agitations-nummern des 'Volksstaat' zusammengestellt, also jetzt ungefähr 20 jahre alt."—Vorwort.

1. Sozialdemokratische partei Deutschlands.   I. Title.

16-2987

Library of Congress   HX279.L7

NL 0347649   DLC NN IaU CtY

Liebknecht, Wilhelm Philipp Christian Martin Ludwig, 1826-1900.
Was die Sozialdemokraten sind und was sie wollen.
Chemnitz, A.Langer [1894]

47 p.

NL 0347650   MH

Liebknecht (W[ILHELM]) Philipp Christian Martin Ludwig, 1826-
Was ich im Berliner "Reichstag" sagte. *Leipzig: C.
W. Vollrath*, [1867]. iv, 5-23 pp. 2. ed. 12°.
In: SF. p. v. 4.

NL 0347651   NN

HF
5564
.S5
Liebknecht, Wilhelm Philipp Christian Martin
Ludwig, 1826-1900.
Weltpolitik, Chinawirren, Transvaalkrieg;
eine Rede gehalten zu Dresden im "Trianon"
am 28. Juli 1900.   Dresden, Kaden, 1900.
23 p. 22 cm.

Bound with Schaefer, W. Der Handel in der Volkswirtschaft.
Berlin, 1900.

1. World politics. 2. Imperialism. 3. Socialism.
I. Title.

NL 0347652   WU DLC IEN NN

LIEBKNECHT, WILHELM PHILIPP CHRISTIAN MARTIN
LUDWIG, 1826-1900.
Weltpolitik, Chinawirren, Transvaalkrieg; eine
Rede gehalten zu Dresden im "Trianon" am 28. Juli
1900. Dresden, Kaden, 1900. 23 p. 23cm.

Film reproduction. Positive.

1. Territorial expansion.

NL 0347653   NN

Liebknecht, Wilhelm Philipp Christian Martin Ludwig, 1826–
1900.
...Wilhelm Liebknecht (1826–1900); mit einem Vorwort von
Kurt Kersten.   Berlin: Neuer Deutscher Verlag [, cop. 1925].
93 p.   12°.   (Redner der Revolution. Bd. 5.)

262519A. 1. Socialism. Pro.   2. Ser.
N.Y.P.L.   October 6, 1926

NL 0347654   NN IEN CU MH NcU

RARE BOOK
DEPT.
HWS47
L62
CUTTER
Liebknecht, Wilhelm Philipp Christian
Martin Ludwig, 1826-1900.
Wissen ist Macht - Macht ist Wissen. Vor-
trag gehalten zum Stiftungsfelt des
Dresdener Arbeiterbildungs-Vereins am 5.
Februar 1872, und zum Stiftungsfelt des
Leipziger Arbeitsbildungs-Vereins am 24.
Februar 1872. Nach dem in Dresden aufgenom-
menen stenographischen Bericht bearbeit.
Leipzig, Verlag der Genossenschafts-
buchdruckerei, 1872.
48p. 18cm.
Bound with the   author's Zu Trutz und

Schutz. Leipzig [187-]

1. Socialism in Germany 2. Communism
and education I. Title

NL 0347656   WU

4-L
74
Liebknecht, Wilhelm Philipp Christian
Martin Ludwig, 1826-1900.
Wissen ist Macht - Macht ist
Wissen; Vortrag gehalten zum Stiftungsfest des Dresdener Arbeiter-
bildungs-Vereins am 5. Februar 1872,
und zum Stiftungsfest des Leipziger
Arbeiterbildungs-Vereins am 24. Februar 1872.   Leipzig, Verlag der
Genossenschaftsbuchdr., 1873.
48 p.

NL 0347657   DLC-P4 CtY IEN CU

Liebknecht, Wilhelm Philipp Christian Martin Ludwig, 1826-1900.
Wissen ist nacht, macht ist wissen, vortrag
gehalten zum stiftungsfest des Dresdener am 5.
Februar 1872 und zum stiftungsfest des Leipziger
arbeiterbildungs vereins am 24. Februar 1872.
ed. 2.
Lpz., Genossenschaltsbuchdruckiris, 1874.
63 p.

NL 0347658   PU

Liebknecht (Whilhelm) Philipp Christian Martin
Ludwig, 1826-1900.
Wissen ist Macht-Macht ist Wissen. Vortrag, gehalten zum Stiftungsfest des Dresdener
Arbeiterbilaungs-Vereins am 5. Februar 1812 und
zum Stiftungsfest des Leipziger Arbeiter-
bildungs-Vereins am 24. Febr. 1872.   Leipzig,
Genossenschaftsbuchdruckerei, 1875.
63, (1) p.   16°.
2. ed.
In: SFC p. v. 35, nᵒ. 4.

NL 0347659   NN

Liebknecht, Wilhelm Philipp Christian Martin
Ludwig, 1826-1900.
335.5
8731
Wissen ist Macht--Macht ist Wissen. Festrede gehalten zum Stiftungsfest des Dresdener
Arbeiter-Bildungs-Vereins am 5. Februar 1872.
Hft.
22
Gottingen-Zürich, Volksbuchhandlung, 1888.
63 p. 20 cm. (Sozialdemokratische Bibliothek, 22)
1. Socialism and education 2. Socialism
in Germany   I. Title

NL 0347660   NcD NN MH CSt OU CSt-H CtY

Liebknecht, Wilhelm Philipp Christian Martin Ludwig, 1826-1900.
Wissen ist Macht— Macht ist Wissen. Festrede gehalten zum
Stiftungsfest des Dresdener Bildungs-Vereins am 5. Februar 1872,
von Wilhelm Liebknecht. Neue Auflage. Berlin, T. Glocke,
1891.
72 p. 21½ᶜᵐ.

NL 0347661   ICJ

4-L
63
Liebknecht, Wilhelm Philipp Christian
Martin Ludwig, 1826-1900.
Wissen ist Macht - Macht ist
Wissen; Festrede gehalten zum Stif-
tungsfest des Dresdener Bildungs-
Vereins am 5. Februar 1872.   Neue
Aufl.   Berlin, Verlag der Expedition
des "Vorwärts", Berliner Volksblatt,
1894.
72 p.

NL 0347662   DLC-P4 MnU

Liebknecht, Wilhelm Philipp Christian
Martin Ludwig, 1826-1900.
Wissen ist Macht - Macht ist Wissen.
Festrede gehalten zum Stiftungsfest des
Dresdener Bildungs-Vereins am 5. Februar
1872 ... Neue Aufl. Berlin, Verlag:
Buchhandlung Vorwärts, 1908.
72 p. 20cm.

NL 0347663   NcD

Liebknecht, Wilhelm Philipp Christian Martin Ludwig, 1826-1900.
Wissen ist Macht - Macht ist Wissen; Festrede gehalten
zum Stiftungsfest des Dresdener Bildungsvereins am
5. Februar 1872. Neue Aufl. Berlin, Buchhandlung Vorwärts, 1920.

72 p.

NL 0347664   MH

Pam.
Coll.
3155
Liebknecht, Wilhelm Philipp Christian
Martin Ludwig, 1826-1900.
Zu Trutz und Schutz. Festrede, ge-
halten zum Stiftungsfest des Crimmit-
schauer Volksvereins am 22. Oktober 1871
... Nach der stenographischen Niederschrift.
Leipzig, Verlag der Expedition des Volks-
staat, 1871?
37 p. 16½cm.
1. Socialism. Addresses, essays, lectures.
I. Title

NL 0347665   NcD

Liebknecht (WILHELM) Philipp Christian Martin Ludwig, 1826-
Zu Trutz and Schutz. Festrede gehalten zum Stiftungsfest des Crimmitschauer Volksverins am 22 Oktober.
1871. *Leipzig: Expedition des Volkstaat*, [1871] 45
pp. 3. ed. 12°.
Gift of F. A. Sorge.

NL 0347666   NN

LIEBKNECHT, WILHELM PHILIPP CHRISTIAN MARTIN
LUDWIG, 1826-1900.
Zu Trutz and Schutz. Festrede gehalten zum
Stiftungsfest des Crimmitschauer Volksvereins am 22
Oktober. 1871. Leipzig, Expedition des Volkstaat
[1871]   45 p. 3. ed. 19cm.

Film reproduction. Negative.

1. Socialism, 1848-1876.

NL 0347667   NN

VOLUME 332

Liebknecht, Wilhelm Philipp
Christian Martin Ludwig, 1826-1900.
Zu Trutz und Schutz. Festrede
gehalten zum Stiftungsfest des
Crimmitschauer Volksvereins am
22. Oktober 1871. 4. verm. Aufl.
Leipzig, Genossenschaftsbuchdruckerei
1874.
48 p. 18cm.
With this is bound Eulenburg, F.A.
Die Regierung des Deutschen Reichs und
der Deutsche Reichstag in ihrer
Stellung zur Sozialdemokratie.
Leipzig, 1876.

NL 0347668   MnU PU

Liebknecht, Wilhelm Philipp Christian Martin Ludwig, 1826-1900.
Zu Trutz und Schutz. Festrede, gehalten zum Stiftungsfest des
Crimmitschauer Volksvereins am 22. Oktober 1871. Nach der
stenographischen Niederschrift. 4. verm. Aufl. Leipzig, Genossenschaftsbuchdr., 1874.   48 p.   19cm.

Film reproduction. Positive.

1. Socialism—Hist., 1848-

NL 0347669   NN

LIEBKNECHT, Wilhelm Philipp Christian Martin Ludwig, 1826-1900.
Zu trutz und Schutz. Festrede gehalten
am 22. okt. 1871. 5e aufl. Hottingen-Zürich.
1883.

sm.8°.

NL 0347670   MH CtY

4-HX   Liebknecht, Wilhelm Philipp Christian
606   Martin Ludwig, 1826-1900.
Zu Trutz und Schutz; Festrede gehalten zum Stiftungsfest des Crimmitschauer Volksvereins am 22. Oktober
1871. Nach der stenographischen
Niederschrift. 6. Aufl.   Berlin,
Verlag der Expedition des "Vorwärts"
Berliner Volksblatt, 1891.
55 p.

NL 0347671   DLC-P4 CSt-H

943.07   Liebknecht, Wilhelm Philipp Christian Martin
L716z   Ludwig, 1826-1900.
Zum 18. März und Verwandtes; den Hamburger
Sozialdemokraten gewidmet. Hamburg, Auer,
1891.
47p. 20cm.

1. Germany. Hist. Revolution, 1848-1849.
2. Paris. Hist. Commune, 1871.

NL 0347672   IEN

Liebknecht, Wilhelm Philipp Christian Martin Ludwig, 1826-1900.
Zum 18. März und Verwandtes. Nürnberg, 1893.

NL 0347673   MH

Liebknecht, Wilhelm Philipp Christian Martin Ludwig,
1826-1900.
Zum 18. märz und verwandtes. Von W. Liebknecht.
Neue unveränderte ausg. Nürnberg, Wörlein & comp.,
1895.
46 p. 19½cm.
CONTENTS.—Märzfeier des Hamburger arbeiter-sängerbundes. 17. märz
1891.—Die Pariser junischlacht. (1873 geschrieben)—Eine geschichte der
Commune. (Histoire de la Commune de 1871, par Lissagaray)—Die Pariser blutwoche. 21.-28. mai 1871. ("Volksstaat" vom 31. mai 1873)—Zur
erinnerung an die letzten maitage 1871. (Poem, signed: H. H. "Volksstaat" vom 29. mai 1872)

1. Germany—Hist.—Revolution, 1848-1849. 2. Paris—Hist.—Commune.
1871. 3. Lissagaray, Prosper Olivier, 1838-   Histoire de la commune.

16-18875

Library of Congress   DC318.L7

NL 0347674   DLC

Liebknecht, Wilhelm Philipp Christian Martin Ludwig,
1826-1900.
Zum jubeljahr der märzrevolution. Von Wilhelm Liebknecht. Berlin, Expedition der buchhandlung Vorwärts
(T. Glocke) 1898.
96 p. 19½cm.

1. Germany—Hist.—Revolution, 1848-1849. 2. Socialism.

15-21699

Library of Congress   DD207.5.L5

NL 0347675   DLC NN

4HN   Liebknecht, Wilhelm Philipp Christian Martin
-66   Ludwig, 1826-1900.
Zur Grund- und Bodenfrage. 2. vervollständigte Aufl. Leipzig, Druck und Verlag
der Genossenschaftsbuchdr., 1876.
200 p.

NL 0347676   DLC-P4 PU NN NIC IEN CtY MH

LIEBKNECHT, WILHELM PHILIPP CHRISTIAN MARTIN
LUDWIG, 1826-1900.
Zur Grund- und Bodenfrage. 2. vervollständigte
Aufl. I. Leipzig, Genossenschaftsbuchdr., 1876.
200 p. 19cm.

Film reproduction. Positive.
Published also with title: Vortrag gehalten im Saale des
Schützenhauses zu Meerane am 12. März 1870.
1. Land—Germany.

NL 0347677   NN

Liebknecht, Wilhelm Philipp Christian Martin Ludwig,
1826-1900.
Zur orientalischen frage, oder Soll Europa kosackisch
werden? Ein mahnwort an das deutsche volk, von Wilhelm Liebknecht. Leipzig, R. E. Höhme [1878]
46 p., 1 l. 19½cm.
Articles previously published in "Vorwärts," "Neue welt," and "Sozialdemokratische correspondenz." cf. p. 6.

1. Eastern question. 2. Europe—Politics—1871-

11-2379

Library of Congress   D376.G4L7

NL 0347678   DLC NcD CtY

Liebl (Franz). *Action de l'acide sulfurique
sur les nitramines secondaires. 66 pp. 8°
Genève. A. Kündig. 1912.

NL 0347679   DNLM

Liebl (Fritz) [1880-   ] *Weitere Untersuchungen über die Wirkung photodynamischer
Stoffe und Diastase. 18 pp. 8°. München. C. Wolf & Sohn, 1905.

NL 0347680   DNLM

LIEBL, Hans.
Beitrage zu den Persius-Scholien. Progr.
Straubing. Druck der A.Lechner'schen Buchdruck-
erei,1883.

pp.54.

NL 0347681   MH NIC NjP CU MiU

Liebl, Hans, ed.
Die disticha Cornuti, auch Cornutus oder
Distigium
see under Joannes de Garlandia,
ca. 1195-ca. 1272.

517.4   Liebl, Hans, 1901-
L622u   Über positiv-definite variationsprobleme auf
flächen vom zusammenhang der kugel … Zürich,
Diss.-druckerei a.-g. Gebr. Leemann & co., 1929.
43p.

Inaug.-diss.--Zürich.
Lebenslauf.

1. Calculus of variations.

NL 0347683   IU DLC CtY RPB

W 4   LIEBL, Herbert, 1926-
M96   Sind Spätfolgen von Seiten der Leber
1952   nach einem Ikterus verschiedener
Genese, der während einer Schwangerschaft
sich abgespielt hatte, schwerer und
häufiger als nach einem Ikterus ausserhalb
einer Schwangerschaft? München, 1952.
126 ℓ.
Inaug.-Diss. - Munich.
Typewritten copy.
1. Jaundice

NL 0347684   DNLM

Liebl, Jella.
Ta3   Das Feuerzeug. Ein Schattenspiel nach Andersen
Z91   von Jella Liebl. Mit Bildern und einem Bilder-
^Z22t bogen von Erwin Tintner. Wien[etc.]Rikola Verlag[c1922]
20,[1]p. illus. 22½cm. and sheet of
silhouettes. 43x56cm.
The sheet of silhouettes has been cut up and
is in pocket inside back cover. The following
pieces are missing (cf.p.16-19): A-D, H-M, O-Q,
S-V, W, X, Y, Cc.

1.Puppet-plays.

NL 0347685   CtY

Liebl, Josef.
Kapitalerhaltung und Bilanzrechnung;
mit einer Einführung von prof. dr. Hasenack,
Göttingen. Wolfenbüttel, Heckners Verlag,
1954.
88 p. (Veröffentlichungen zur Betriebswirt-
schaft, Hft.6)

Bibliographical footnotes.

NL 0347686   MH-BA

VOLUME 332

Liebl, Ludwig   1874-
Ueber traumatische lungengangraene infolge von
oesophagusruptur.
Inaug. Diss. Leipzig, B. Georgi, 1907.
Bibl.
45p.

NL 0347687   ICRL DNLM CtY

W 4   LIEBL, Ludwig, 1912-
M96   Die habituelle Schulterluxation; ihre
1949   Behandlung, mit einer kritischen Würdigung. München, 1949.
43 ℓ. illus.
Inaug.-Diss. - Munich.
Typewritten copy.
1. Shoulder - Dislocation

NL 0347688   DNLM

Liebl, Therese, 1908-
... Kraurosis vulvae und Carzinom ... [n.p.]
1937.
Inaug.-Diss. - München.
Lebenslauf.

NL 0347689   CtY

Liebl, W   , tr.
Der Student zu Padua
see under   Fusinato, Arnaldo.

Liebl, Zeno von.
The sorely tried maiden; a comedy in three acts.   Vienna, G.
Marton, c1936.   133 p.   21cm.
Film reproduction. Positive.

1. Drama, German—Translations   into English. I. Title.

NL 0347691   NN

Lieblang, Adalbert, 1901-
*Erythema exsudativum multiforme (Hebrae)
[Freiburg]   Saarbrücken, 1929.
31 p.   8°.

NL 0347692   DNLM MiU CtY

Lieblang, Alice Scherer.
see under   Scherer, Alice, 1904-

---

240   Lieblang, Franz.
005   Grundfragen der mystischen Theologie nach
P87   Gregors des Grossen Moralia und Ezechielhomilien.
v.37   Freiburg i.B., Herder, 1934.
x, 184p 24cm   (Freiburger theologische
Studien. 37. Heft.)

Literatur: p.179-184.

NL 0347694   MnCS DDO IMunS NNG CBPac

Lieble, Philippe Louis. 1734-1813.   Mémoire
sur les limites de l'empire de Charlemagne.   45 pp.
(Leber, J. M. C., Dissert. rel. Hist. de France, v. 2. p. 314.)

NL 0347695   MdBP

940.15
C47z   Lieble, Philippe Louis, 1734-1813.
L7   Mémoire sur les limites de l'Empire
de Charlemagne, qui a remporté le Prix
proposed par l'Académie Royale des Inscriptions et Belles-Lettres, par D. Philippe-
Louis Lieble, Bénédictin de la Congregation
de S. Maur, à l'Abbaye de S. Germain-des-Prés.
Paris, H. L. Guerin & L. F. Delatour, 1764.
73p.   18cm.

1. Charlemagne, 742-814. I. Title.

NL 0347696   TNJ

Lieble, Philippe Louis, 1734-1813.
Mémoire sur les limites de l'empire de Charlemagne.
(In Collection des meilleurs dissertations ... relatifs à l'histoire
de France .. Vol. 2, pp. 316-357. Paris, 1826.) **G.3516.1.2

NL 0347697   MB

LIEBLEIN, Franz Kaspar.
Flora Fuldensis. Frankfurts/M.1784.

pp.482.

NL 0347698   MH-P

LIEBLEIN, Jakob.
Kegelbahnen. Illus. Plans.
(In Handbuch der Architektur. Th. 4. Entwerfen, Anlage und
Einrichtung der Gebäude. Halb-Bd. 4, pp. 384-392. Darmstadt, 1885.)
Literatur, p. 392.

NL 0347699   MB

LIEBLEIN, Jakob, and Heinrich Wagner, architect.   *8092.52.4
Panoramen. Illus. Plans.
(In Handbuch der Architektur. Th. 4. Entwerfen, Anlage und
Einrichtung der Gebäude. Halb-Band 4, pp. 410-425. Darm-
stadt. 1885.)
Literatur, p. 425.

K8686 — It. auth. — Panoramas. Buildings for.

NL 0347700   MB

LIEBLEIN, Jakob.   *8092.52.4
Schiessstätten und Schützenhäuser. Plans.
(In Handbuch der Architektur. Th. 4. Entwerfen, Anlage und
Einrichtung der Gebäude. Halb-Bd. 4, pp. 363-384. Darmstadt, 1885.)

NL 0347701   MB

Lieblein, Jens Daniel Carolus, 1827-1911.
Aegyptische chronologie. Ein kritischer versuch von
J. Lieblein ... hrsg. von der Gesellschaft der wissenschaf-
ten zu Christiania. Christiania, Druck von Brögger &
Christie, 1863.
2 p. l., 143, [1] p. 23cm.

1. Egypt—Hist.—Chronology.   I. Videnskabs-selskabet i Christiania.

Library of Congress   DT83.L71
5-9463

NL 0347702   DLC NIC CtY

Lieblein, Jens Daniel Carolus, 1827-1911.
Die aegyptischen denkmäler in St. Petersburg, Helsingfors,
Upsala und Copenhagen. Von J. Lieblein ... Mit 35 auto-
graphirten tafeln. Christiania, Gedruckt von A. W. Brøgger,
1873.
3 p. l., 3-82 p. xxxv pl. (part col.) 24cm.
Title vignette.
"Universitäts-programm für das 1ste semester 1874."

1. Egypt—Antiq.   I. Oslo. Universitet.
5-9492
Library of Congress   DT61.L71

CtY NNUT
NL 0347703   DLC NIC OC1 NjP PPAmP PU ICJ NN MH NBB

Lieblein, Jens Daniel Carolus, 1827-1911.
Les ancien Egyptiens connaissaient-ils le mouvement de la Terre? St. Etienne, 1878.

(Mem. du Congres des Orientalistes-St-Etienne)

NL 0347704   DCU-H

Lieblein, Jens Daniel Carolus, 1827-1911.
Deux papyrus hiératiques du musée de
Turin
see under   Turin. Museo di antichità.

Lieblein, Jens Daniel Carolus, 1827-1911.
Dictionnaire de noms hiéroglyphiques en ordre généalogique
et alphabétique. Pub. d'après les monuments égyptiens, par
J. Lieblein ... Christiania, Brögger & Christie; [etc., etc.]
1871.
2 p. l., iv p., 1 l., [2], 555 p. 23cm.
Added t.-p. in German.
Autographed; t.-p. and preliminary matter printed.
Issued in 2 parts.
En partie aux frais de la Société des sciences à Christiania.
Bibliography; p. iii-iv.

1. Egyptian language—Dictionaries. 2. Names, Egyptian.
11—15471
Library of Congress   PJ1435.L5

PU-Mu
NL 0347706   DLC KyLoS CtY   NN MdBP CtY NBB OC1 PU

Fw189   Lieblein, Jens Daniel Carolus, 1827-1911.
L62   Dictionnaire de noms hiéroglyphiques en ordre
généalogique et alphabétique. Publié d'après
les monuments égyptiens, par J. Lieblein ...
Christiania, Brögger & Christie[etc.,etc.]
1871-92.
2v.   23cm.
Added t.-p. in German.
Autographed text.
Paged continuously.
Issued in 4 parts; vol.2: Supplement.
Bibliography:[v.1],p.iii-iv; [v.2],p.iii-iv.

NL 0347707   CtY CU

DT60   Lieblein, Jens Daniel Carolus, 1827-1911.
.L75   Egypten i dess minnesmärken och i dess för-
(Or)   hållande till Palestina och Grekland. Stockholm, Klemmings antiqvariat, 1877.
120 p. illus. (Ur vår tids forskning, 19)

1. Egypt--Antiq. 2. Monuments--Egypt.

NL 0347708   ICU MH MB

VOLUME 332

BL2441 Lieblein, Jens Daniel Carolus, 1827-1911.
.R43L7   Egyptian religion, by J. Lieblein ... Leipzig, I. C. Hinrichs, 1884.
    46 p. 24ᵐ.
    Mainly a criticism of P. Le Page Renoufs Lectures on the origin and growth of religion as illustrated by the religion of ancient Egypt.

    1. Renouf, Sir Peter Le Page, 1822-1897. Lectures on the origin and growth of religion as illustrated by the religion of ancient Egypt. 2. Egypt—Religion.

NL   0347709   ICU NNUT NRCR NN

Lieblein, Jens Daniel Carolus, 1827-1911.
    Etude sur la chronologie egyptienne.

    (Congres (xie International) des Orientalistes Actes, 5-7, p. 1-32)

NL   0347710   DCU-H

Lieblein, Jens Daniel Carolus, 1827-1911.
    Etude sur le nom et le culte primitif du Dieu hebrew: Jahvhe.

    (Congres provincial des orientalistes, Lyon. I. 265-275)

NL   0347711   DCU-H

DS 66   Lieblein, Jens Daniel Carolus, 1827-1911.
L5   Études sur les Xétas, par J. Lieblein. Leide, E. J. Brill, 1878.
    22 p. 25 cm.

    Cover title.
    "Tiré du vol. II des Travaux de la 3e session du Congrès international des orientalistes."
    Bibliographical footnotes.

    1. Hittites. 2. Ethnology - Egypt. 3. Egyptology.   I.   Title.

NL   0347712   OU

Lieblein, Jens Daniel Carolus, 1827-1911.
Christiania. Universitet.
    Festskrift til Hs. Maj. kong Oscar II. ved regjeringsjubilæet den 18ᵈᵉ september, 1897, fra det K Norske Frederiks universitet. Christiania, H. Aschehoug & co., 1897.

PJ1051   Lieblein, Jens Daniel Carolus, 1827-1911.
L5   Det gamla Egypten i dess skrift. Stockholm, Klemmings Antiqvariat, 1877.
    86 p. illus., ports. 22 cm.   (Ur vår tids forskning, populära skildringar, 18)

    1. Egyptology.   (Series)

NL   0347714   RPB NN MH

299.31   Lieblein, Jens Daniel Carolus, 1827-1911.
L62g   Gammelægyptisk religion; populært fremstillet, af J. Lieblein ... Kristiana, Aschehoug & co.; [etc., etc.] 1883-85.
    3v. illus.

    Bibliographical foot-notes.
    Contents.- 1.del. Gudsbegrebets udvikling.- 2.del. Folkereligionen.- 3.del. Udødelighedslæren.

    1. Egypt--Religion.

NL   0347715   IU MH

Lieblein, Jens Daniel Carolus, 1827-1911.
    Handel und schiffahrt auf dem Rothen meere in alten zeiten. Nach ägyptischen quellen, von J. Lieblein ... hrsg. von der Gesellschaft der wissenschaften zu Christiania. Christiania, A.W. Broggers buchdruck. , 1886.
    150 p. , 1 l.   23.5 cm.
    On cover: Leipzig, I.C. Hinrichs.
    1. Red Sea--Commerce--Hist. 2. Phenicians. 3. Egypt--Commerce--Hist. I. Norske videnskaps akademi i Oslo.

NL   0347716   CU PPDrop

Lieblein, Jens Daniel Carolus, 1827-1911.
    Handel und schiffahrt auf dem Rothen meere in alten zeiten. Nach ägyptischen quellen, von J. Lieblein ... hrsg. von der Gesellschaft der wissenschaften zu Christiania. Christiania, In commission bei J. Dybwad, 1886.
    150 p., 1 l.   23½ᵐ.

    1. Red sea—Comm.—Hist. 2. Phenicians. 3. Egypt—Comm.—Hist. I. Norske videnskaps; Oslo. II. Title.

                    24—12094

Library of Congress   HF385.L5

NL   0347717   DLC MH NBB ViU ICU OC1

PJ   Lieblein, Jens Daniel Carolus, 1827-1911.
1095   Hieroglyphisches Namen-Wörterbuch;
L71   genealogisch und alphabetisch geordnet, nach den aegyptischen Denkmaelern hrsg. Christiania, Brögger & Christie, 1871.
    iv, 555 p. 23cm.

    1. Egyptian language--Writing, Hieroglyphic. 2. Names, Egyptian.

NL   0347718   NIC NjP MdBP MB

Lieblein, Jens Daniel Carolus, 1827-1911.

Illustrerad verldshistoria.

    Illustreret verdenshistorie. Efter den svenske af Ernst Wallis redigerede originaludgave ved L. Daae og A. C. Drolsum ... Kristiania, A. Cammermeyer, 1876-80.

PJ1557   LIEBLEIN, JENS DANIEL CAROLUS, 1827-1911.
.Z8   Index alphabétique de tous les mots contenus dans
1875   le Livre des morts pub. par R.Lepsius, d'après le papyrus de Turin, par J.Lieblein ... Paris, F.Vieweg, librairie A.Franck, 1875.
    [8], 186 p.   18½ cm.
    Text autographed.

    1. Book of the dead.

    NIC
NL   0347720   ICU ICN OC1 TxDaM NjP   NBB CtY RPB

Lieblein, Jens Daniel Carolus, 1827-1911.

Oslo. Universitet.
    ... J. Lieblein, Om Io-mythen; M. J. Monrad, Den menneskelige viljefrihed og det onde; Gustav Storm, Afgifter fra den norske kirkeprovins til det Apostoliske kammer og Kardinalkollegiet 1311-1523 efter optegnelser i de pavelige arkiver; Alf Torp, Bemerkungen zu den venetischen inschriften; Sophus Bugge og Moltke Moe, Torsvisen i sin norske form, udg. med en afhandling om dens oprindelse og forhold til de andre nordiske former ... Christiania, I kommission hos H. Aschehoug & co., 1897.

Lieblein, Jens Daniel Carolus, 1827-1911.
    Lettre à M. Ernest de Saulcy. [Christiania 1878]

    4p.   23cm. (Running title: Christiania vidensk.-selsk. forhandl. 1878. no. 5)

    Caption title.
    Article signed: J. Lieblein.

NL   0347722   NBB

Lieblein, Jens Daniel Carolus, 1827-1911, ed. & tr.
    Le livre égyptien que mon nom fleurisse
    see under   Book of the dead.

Lieblein, Jens Daniel Carolus, 1827-1911.
    Le mot Anti n'indique pas myrrhe, mais encens, oliban. Christiania: J. Dybwad, 1910. 9 p. illus. 8°. (Videnskabs-Selskabet i Christiania. Forhandlinger. Aar 1910, no. 1.)

    I. Egyptian language.
    N.Y.P.L   March 22. 1912.

NL   0347724   NN

Lieblein, Jens Daniel Carolus, 1827-1911, ed.
    Norden. Et maandeskrift
    see under title

Lieblein, Jens Daniel Carolus, 1827-1911.
    Notice sur les monuments égyptiens trouvés en Sardaigne, par J. Lieblein. [Christiania, 1879]

    58p.   illus. fold. plate.   24cm. (Running title: Christiania vidensk.-selsk. forhandl. 1879. no. 8)
    Caption title.
    "Les objets d'antiquité égyptiens et phénico-égyptiens, sont la matière spéciale de ce travail ...La plus grande partie se trouve recueillie et exposée dans le musée de Cagliari..."; p. 4.
    Bibliographical foot-notes.

NL   0347726   NBB OC1

Lieblein, Jens Daniel Carolus, 1827-1911.
    Nutidens opdagelser om de gamle ægypter. Ved J. Lieblein. Med flere større og mindre træsnit ... Christiania, P. T. Mallings bogtrykkeri, 1865.

    2 p. l., 186 p. illus. 19ᶜᵐ.
    Udg. af Selskabet for folkeoplysningens fremme.
    2. tillægshefte til "Folkevennen," 14. aarg. 1865.

    1. Egypt—History, Ancient. 2. Egypt—Civilization.   I. Selskabet for folkeoplysningens fremme, Christiania. II. Folkevennen.

                     14-3825

Library of Congress   DT83.L715

NL   0347727   DLC

Lieblein, Jens Daniel Carolus, 1827-1911, ed.
    Nyt norsk tidsskrift. Udg. af proff. J. E. Sars og J. Lieblein. 1.-4. bd.; 1877-78. Kristiania, H. Aschehoug & co., 1877-78.

Lieblein, Jens Daniel Carolus, 1827-1911.
    Om en af H. M. Kongen til det Ethnografiske musaeum skjaenket aegyptisk mumie, af J. Lieblein... Christiania, J. Dybwad, 1890.

    17p.   22½cm. (Christiania videnskabsselskabs forhandlinger 1890. no. 5)

    "Foredrag i Faellesmode 28 marts 1890."

NL   0347729   NBB

VOLUME 332

Lieblein, Jens Daniel Carolus, 1827-1911.
On et indfald i Aegypten af Middelhavsfolk ved
Trojanerkrigens tider. n.p. 1869.
30 p. illus. 23 cm.
Saerskilt aftyrkt of Vidensk.-Selsk.
Forhandlinger for 1869.
Cover title.

NL 0347730 RPB

Lieblein, Jens Daniel Carolus, 1827-1911.
Opraab til gaardbrugerne. Af J. Lieblein ... Kristiania, C. Schibsteds bogtrykkeri, 1893.
16 p. 22ᵐᵐ.
Særaftryk af "Aftenposten."

1. Norway—Pol. & govt.—1814-1905.

17-12091

Library of Congress DL506.L5

NL 0347731 DLC

Lieblein, J[ens Daniel Carolus], 1827-1911.
Pistis Sophia; l'antimimon gnostique est-il le Ka égyptien?
Christiania: J. Dybwad, 1908. 10 p. 8°. (Videnskabs-Sel-
skabet i Christiania. Forhandlinger. Aar 1908, no. 2.)

1. Pistis Sophia. 2. Gnosticism.
N. Y. P. L. March 26, 1912.

NL 0347732 NN

Lieblein, J[ens Daniel Carolus], 1827-1911.
Pistis Sophia; les conceptions égyptiennes dans le gnosti-
cisme. Christiania: J. Dybwad, 1909. 13 p. 8°. (Videnskabs-Selskabet i Christiania. Forhandlinger. Aar 1909, no. 2.)

1. Pistis Sophia. 2. Gnosticism.
N. Y. P. L. March 26, 1912.

NL 0347733 NN

Lieblein, Jens Daniel Carolus, 1827-1911.
Recherches sur l'histoire et la civilisation de l'ancienne
Egypte, par J. Lieblein ... Leipzig, J. C. Hinrichs;
[etc., etc.] 1910–
v. fold. tab. 24ᵐᵐ.

1. Egypt—History, Ancient. 2. Egypt—Civilization.

12-14724

Library of Congress DT83.L73

CtY NN
NL 0347734 DLC MiU OCl OCU KyLoS NjP IEG CU NcD

Lieblein, J[ens Daniel Carolus] 1827-1911.
Recherches sur la chronologie égyptienne d'après les
listes généalogiques, par J. Lieblein. (Avec neuf tables
autographiées.) Christiania, Impr. de A. W. Brögger,
1873.
2 p. l., 147, [1] p. 11 pl., facsims. (partly fold.) 24½ᵐᵐ.
Title in red and black, with vignette.
"Programme de l'université pour le 1er sémestre, 1872."

1. Egypt—Hist.—Chronology. I. Christiania. Universitet.

5-9465

Library of Congress DT83.L72

PPWa PPWe OCU PU ICU CtY OCU NN ICJ DCU-H NjP MH
NL 0347735 DLC MnHi CtY NIC NBB WU IEG MdBP PPAmP

Lieblein, Johan Nicolai Severin
see
Lieblein, Severin, 1866–

Lieblein, Johann, 1834-1881.
Sammlung von aufgaben aus der algebraischen
analysis. Bearb. von Johann Lieblein ...
Prag, H. C. J. Satow, 1867.
iv p., 2 l., 192 p. 22 cm.

NL 0347737 ViU MWelC MH

Lieblein, Johann, 1834-1881.
J. Lieblein's Sammlung von aufgaben
aus der algebraischen analysis zum
selbstunterricht. 2., verbesserte und
vermehrte aufl., hrsg. von dr. W. Láska...
Prag, G. Neugebauer, 1889.
180 p.

NL 0347738 MiU

QA
276
.L72   Lieblein, Julius.
A new method of analyzing extreme-value data.
Washington, National Advisory Committee for
Aeronautics, 1954.
88 p. diagrs., tables. 27 cm. (U.S.
National Advisory Committee for Aeronautics.
Technical note 3053)
Cover title.
Bibliography: p.68-69.
1. Mathematical statistics. 2. Aerodynamic
load. I. Title: Extreme-value data.

NL 0347739 MiU NcU

Lieblein, Julius.
... Wartime changes in family income, by
Julius Lieblein and Albert Gailord Hart ...
Washington, D. C., 1944.
1 p. l., 5, xii p. tables. 27ᵐᵐ.

Reproduced from type-written copy.
1. Income - U. S. I. Title. II. Hart, Albert
Gailord jt au.

NL 0347740 NNC

Film
DD-1   Lieblein, Jupp, ed.
reel 15,   Deutsch-amerikanische berufsgemeinschaft.
no. 4.   Wir; erlebnisse deutscher jugend in U. S. A. New York,
DAB-jugendschaft, 1939.

Lieblein, Robert.
... Provisorische resultate aus den fort-
laufenden polhöhen-messungen an der K. K.
Sternwarte zu Prag vom 26. februar 1889 bis
29. mai 1892, abgeleitet von Robert Lieblein
... hrsg. von professor dr. L. Weinek... Prag,
A. Haase, 1897.
18 p. tables. fold. col. diagr. 31-24½ cm.
(Appendix zu: Astronomische beobachtungen an
der k.k. Sternwarte zu Prag in den jahren 1888,
1889, 1890 und 1891. Prag 1893)
Bibliographical foot-notes.

NL 0347742 DN-Ob NjP MiU

Lieblein, Robert.   525.41
Q400
MRFI4 ... Die verschiedenen Bestimmungen der geographischen
Breite von Prag seit 1751. Von Prof. Dr. Robert Lieblein ...
Kgl. Weinberge, Verlag des K. K. Staatsgymnasiums, 1904.
p. 1-27. 25ᵐᵐ.
Programm—Staatsgymnasium, Königliche Weinberge.
"Literaturnachweis," p. [25]-27.

NL 0347743 ICJ

Lieblein, Severin i. e. Johan Nicolai Severin, 1866-1933.
... Abdallahs gurbi. Kristiania og København, Gyldendal, Nordisk forlag, 1916.
175 p. 20ᵐᵐ. kr. 3.25

I. Title.

Library of Congress PT8950.L6A65 1916   17-9723

NL 0347744 DLC

Lieblein, Severin, 1866-1933.
Bedre mands barn. Kristiania, J.
Dybwad [1902]
252 p. 18cm.

NL 0347745 MnU NdU NN

Lieblein, Severin i. e. Johan Nicolai Severin, 1866-1933.
... Blaamænd. Kristiania og København, Gyldendalske boghandel, Nordisk forlag, 1912.
162 p. 20ᵐᵐ. kr. 2.50

I. Title.

12-27234

NL 0347746 DLC

Lieblein, Severin i. e. Johan Nicolai Severin, 1866-1933.
... I baldakinens skygge. Kristiania og København,
Gyldendal, Nordisk forlag, 1917.
136 p. 20ᵐᵐ. kr. 3
At head of title: Severin Lieblein.
Contents.—Der var engang. — Smugleren. — Onkel Indigo. — Nytaars-
nat. —Den fremmede fra Syden. — Cholera morbus.—Akerhønsene.—In-
schaallah.—Farvel storkerede.

I. Title.

Library of Congress PT8950.L6I2 1917   18-11457

NL 0347747 DLC

Lieblein, Severin, 1866-1933.
... Kismet; roman fra Marokko. Kristiania og Kjøbenhavn, Gyldendalske boghandel, Nordisk forlag, 1909.
2 p. l., 230 p. 20ᵐᵐ. Kr. 3.80

9-30156

NL 0347748 DLC WaS NN

VOLUME 332

Lieblein, Severin, 1866- 1933.
... Der letzte seines geschlechts; die geschichte einer jugend.
Leipzig, G. Merseburger, 1913.
253 p. 19½ᶜᵐ. (*Half-title:* Nordische bücherei)
"Einzig autorisierte übersetzung von Pauline Klaiber."

I. Klaiber, Pauline, tr. II. Title.   *Translation of Den sidste av*
sin slegt.
                            ₍Full name: Johan Nicolai Severin Lieblein₎
                                         14-14549 Revised
Library of Congress   PT8950.L6S53 1913

NL 0347749   DLC

Lieblein, Severin i. e. Johan Nicolai Severin, 1866- 1933.
... Peter Plytts hændelser; en borgerlig historie. Kristiania og Kjøbenhavn, Gyldendal, Nordisk forlag, 1913.
209 p. 20ᶜᵐ. kr. 3

I. Title.

                                                   14-904

NL 0347750   DLC

Lieblein, Severin, 1866- 1933.
Den sidste av sin slegt, et blad av Jonas Værns ungdomskrønike. Kristiania og Kjøbenhavn, Gyldendalske boghandel, Nordisk forlag, 1910.
3 p. l., 206 p. 20ᶜᵐ. kr. 3.40

                                                   10-29123

NL 0347751   DLC

Lieblein, Severin i. e. Johan Nicolai Severin, 1866- 1933.
... Det unge blod. Kristiania og København, Gyldendal, Nordisk forlag, 1915.
134 p. 19ᶜᵐ. $3.75
CONTENTS. — Indledning—Bjørken.—Fredens engel—Minervas næse.—Den avskyelige dreng.— Sunt pueri, pueri.— Collegium politicum. — Den fregnede Isidor, eller Løgnens fader.—Naar vaaren kalder.

I. Title.

Library of Congress   PT8950.L6U5 1915   16-17738

NL 0347752   DLC

Lieblein, Viktor, 1869-
Die Geschwüre und die erworbenen Fisteln des Magen-Darmkanals. Von Viktor Lieblein und Heinrich Hilgenreiner. Stuttgart, F. Enke, 1905.
623p. illus., plates. 25cm. (Deutsche Chirurgie. Lfg.46c)

"Literaturverzeichnis": p.1-66.

1. Peptic ulcer. I. Hilgenreiner, Heinrich, joint author.

NL 0347753   IU-M MiDW-M CtY ICJ ViU ICRL

LIEBLEIN, Viktor, 1869-
Ueber die wichtigsten fehlerquellen bei der deutung von Röntgenbefunden.

In HANDBUCH der ärztlichen sachverständigentätigkeit, v.3, 1906.

NL 0347754   MH

Liebleitner, Karl, ed.
Das **Deutsche** volkslied. Zeitschrift für seine kenntnis und pflege ... Hrsg. von dem Deutschen volksgesang-vereine in Wien.
Wien,

LIEBLEITNER, Karl.
Dreissig echte Kägntnerlieder gesammelt und für vierstimmigen manner-chor gesetzt. Wien, verlag des Deutschen volksgesang-vereines, 1903.

pp. 54.
(Zur kenntnis und pflege des deutschen volksliedes, 8.)

NL 0347756   MH

AC851   Liebleitner, Karl.
E68   Die Entwicklung der Stadt Horn vom Ausgange
1920   des Mittelalters bis zum Weltkriege. Horn,
           1920.
Stack   14 p.
           Programmschrift - NiederÖsterr. Landes-Real-
           und Obergymnasium, Horn.
           Accompanies Schulnachrichten.

           1. Horn, Austria - Hist.

NL 0347757   CSt

ML5   Liebleitner, Karl, ed.
.D5
       Volkslied, Volkstanz, Volksmusik. Zeitschrift **für deren**
       Kenntnis und Pflege.

       Wien.

GR159   LIEBLEITNER, KARL.
.C2L5   Wulfenia-Blüten, einige fünfzig Lieder
          und Jodler aus Kärnten, im Volke gesammelt.
          Wien, Universal-Edition ₍1931₎
          48 p. scores. (Österreichisches
          Volkslied-Unternehmen, Kleine Quellenausgabe, Bd. 6)

          Arbeitsausschuss für Kärnten, Bd. 1.

          1. Folk-songs—Austria—Carinthia. I. tc.
          Folk-lore cd.

NL 0347759   InU

Liebleitner, Karl.
...Wulfenia-Blüten; einige fünfzig Lieder und Jodler aus Kärnten im Volke gesammelt von Karl Liebleitner. Wien ₍etc.₎ Universal-Edition A. G. und Österr. Bundesverlag f. Unterr., Wissensch. u. Kunst, 1932. Publ. pl. no. U. E. 9999. 51 p. 8cm. (Österreichisches Volksliedunternehmen. Kleine Quellenausgabe. Bd. 6.)

German dialect words; songs for 1 or 2 voices unacc.
Publisher's plate number on verso of t.-p. only.

1. Folk songs, German. I. Title.   II. Ser.
N. Y. P. L.   April 10, 1936

NL 0347760   NN

Liebler, E   G
    Il primo libro dei bambini; metodo fonico. Lettura e scrittura simultanea ad uso degli asili infantili, dei giardini d'infanzia e della prima classe elementare inferiore, per E. G. Liebler ... 7. ed. Napoli, Presso G. Regina, 1886.

    105 p. illus. 19ᶜᵐ

NL 0347761   CSt

PA3902   Liebler, Georg, 1524-1600.
.L7   Epitome philosophiae naturalis, ex Aristotelis summi philosophi libris ita excerpta, ut
Rare bk   eorum capita breuiter & dilucide explicet, & ad
           eosdem cum fructu legendos praeparare studiosos
           possit: per Georgium Lieblerum, professorem
           physices in schola Tubigensi ... Basileae, per
           I. Oporinum ₍1566₎
           ₍24₎, 302, ₍24₎ p. diagrs. 15cm.
           Colophon: Basileae, ex officina Ioannis Opori
           ni, anno salutis humanae M.D.LXVI ...
           Device of Oporinus on t.-p.; initials.

NL 0347762   ICU IU

W 4   LIEBLER, Georg, 1524-1600, praeses.
T91   Theses de anima vegetante, seu naturali ... Tubingae, Apud
1586   Georgium Gruppenbachium, 1586.
L 1   ₍2₎, 11 p. 20 cm.
         Diss. - Tübingen (J. H. Beyer, respondent)
         Respondent's presentation copy.

       L Beyer, Johann Hartmann, 1563-1625, respondent

NL 0347763   DNLM

Liebler, Harold Baxter.
    Anima Christi, practical meditations on the prayer of
St. Ignatius. By H. Baxter Liebler. New York, The
Catholic churchman press, 1925.
3 p. l., 9–39, ₍1₎ p. 23½ᶜᵐ.

1. Loyola, Ignacio de, Saint, 1491-1556. I. Title.

Library of Congress   BX2182.L5   25-17612

NL 0347764   DLC

Liebler, Harold Baxter.
    Moccasin tracks ₍by₎ H. Baxter Liebler; illustrated with original linoleum cuts. New York: The Blackshaw press, inc.
₍1939₎ 96 p. incl. pl. illus. 14cm.

1. Indians, N. A.—Culture.   I. Title.
N. Y. P. L.   September 23, 1941

NL 0347765   NN NjP MH

Liebler, Josef.
Die anerkennung der ausserehelichen vaterschaft
Inaug. Diss. Würzburg, 19
Bibl.

NL 0347766   ICRL MH-L

Liebler, P. A.
Abriss der geschichte des alterthums. 4te auflage.
Mannheim, 1842.
12mo.

NL 0347767   NN

Liebler, P   A.
Die badische geschichte. Mannheim, Schwan und Götz, 1829.
nar. 16°. pp. (2), ii, 76.

Baden (Grand Duchy)-Hist.||

NL 0347768   MH

VOLUME 332

Liebler, P   A
Die badische geschichte. Für den ersten unterricht bearbeitet von P. A. Liebler ... 2. verb. und stark verm. aufl. Mannheim, Schwan und Götz, 1830.
1 p. l., 11, 92 p. 17ᶜᵐ.

1. Baden—Hist.
43–42597
Library of Congress   DD801.B15L5 1830

NL 0347769   DLC PLatS

Liebler, P. A.   2819.05
Die deutsche Geschichte. Für den ersten Unterricht. 10. Auflage. Mannheim. Götz. 1845. (1), iv, 128 pp. 16°.

F4621 — Germany. Hist.

NL 0347770   MB

Liebler, Theodore A.   jr.
... "God's pal." A play in a prologue and three acts, by Theodore A. Liebler, jr. ¡Riverside? Conn.; c1921.   v, 7, 22, 28, 25 f.   27cm.
Prompt-book, typewritten; playbill with cast of characters of first production at Stamford, Conn., June 29, 1923, included.
Produced under title "The earthquake."

257685B. 1. Drama, American.   2. Prompt-books. I. Title.
II. Title: The earthquake.
N.Y.P.L.   December 15, 1943

NL 0347771   NN

Liebler, Theodore A   jr.
Q. E. D.; or, Never count your chickens: a dramatization of Wentworth's Elementary arithmetic, by Theodore A. Liebler, jr. ... New York, N. Y., Los Angeles, Calif., S. French; London, S. French, ltd.; ¡etc., etc.; °1936.
24 p. diagr. 18½ᶜᵐ.

I. Title.
36–16679
Library of Congress   PN6120.A5L47
——— Copy 2.
Copyright D pub. 43192   ¡2;   812.5

NL 0347772   DLC OU OC1

Liebler, Theodore A.   jr.
..."The tongue of Adam." (Suggested by an idea by David Joseph — asst. city editor, N. Y. Times.) By Theodore A. Liebler, jr... Riverside, Conn. ¡192–;   79 l.   34½cm.
Scenario; typewritten, with description of settings, stage directions, and ms. notes.

96Z782A. 1. Moving picture plays—   Texts and outlines. I. Title.
N.Y.P.L.   September 17, 1940

NL 0347773   NN

Liebler, Thomas

see

Erastus, Thomas, 1524–1583

Liebler & Co., *New York.*
[Disraeli.] Souvenir of the play. George Arliss in Disraeli. The great English statesman of Parker's play, his life, his wit, and his achievements.
New York. 1912. (32) pp. Illus. Portraits. Plates. Map. Ornamental borders. 23½ cm.
The play, Disraeli, may be found on shelf-number 4579a.300.

L8510 — Arliss, George, 1868– . — Disraeli, Benjamin, Earl of Beaconsfield, 1805–1881.

NL 0347775   MB

Liebler & Company, New York.
A single presentation of Robert Browning's poetic drama, In a balcony, with Otis Skinner as Norbert... Eleanor Robson as Constance, Sarah Cowell LeMoyne as the queen. Preceded by The land of heart's desire. a symbolic fantasy by W. B. Yeats... Liebler & Co., managers. ¡New York, 1901.;   6 l.   illus. (part mounted.)   ob. 8°.

1. Stage.—Playbills and pro-   grammes, U. S.: N. Y.: New
gramme. 2. Browning, Robert,   York City.
N.Y.P.L.   1812–89: In a balcony.
                                  October 30, 1920.

NL 0347776   NN NBuG

Liebler & company, New York.
Viola Allen as Julia in The hunchback,
see under   Glover, Lyman, Beecher, 1846–1915.

Lieblich, Berta, 1903–
Untersuchungen über allergische Hautreaktionen bei rheumatischen Erkrankungen ... Steele-Ruhr; 1928.
Inaug.-Diss. - Freiburg.
Lebenslauf.
"Literaturangabe": p. 19.

NL 0347778   CtY

LIEBLICH, E. *Influence des maladies sur les caractères.* 43p. 8°   Par., 1935.

NL 0347779   DNLM

Lieblich, Karl, 1895–
... Das proletarische brautpaar, ein volkslied in prosa. 1. bis 3. tausend. Jena, E. Diederichs, 1926.
2 p. l., 3–147, ¡1; p. 20½ᶜᵐ.

I. Title.
27–15536
Library of Congress   PT2623.I 35P7 1926

NL 0347780   DLC

Lieblich, Karl, 1895–
... Die traumfahrer, zwei erzählungen. Jena, E. Diederichs, 1923.
3 p. l., 5–129, ¡1; p., 1 l. front. 20ᶜᵐ.
CONTENTS.—Thomas Münzer und sein krieg.—Der kinderkreuzzug.

I. Title.
25–30
Library of Congress   PT2623.I 35T7 1923

NL 0347781   DLC PPG

Lieblich, Karl, 1895–
Was geschieht mit den Juden? Öffentliche Frage an Adolf Hitler. Stuttgart, Im Zonen-Verlag, 1932.
96 p. 20 cm.

1. Jewish question.   I. Title.
52–53997
DS141.L69

NL 0347782   DLC MH OCH CtY MoSW WU CtY NN

Lieblich, Karl, 1895–
... Die welt erbraust; sechs schilderungen. 1. bis 3. tausend. Jena, E. Diederichs, 1924.
3 p. l., 5–133, ¡1; p., 1 l. 20ᶜᵐ.

I. Title.
25–11467
Library of Congress   PT2623.I 35W4 1924

NL 0347783   DLC PPG

Lieblich, Karl, 1895–
... Wir jungen Juden; drei untersuchungen zur jüdischen frage. Stuttgart, Zonen-verlag, 1931.
160 p. 21ᶜᵐ.
"Diese drei vorträge wurden je im herbst 1928, 1929 und 1930 auf einladung des Berthold-Auerbach-vereins in Stuttgart gehalten."—p. 156.
CONTENTS.—Judenhass als Judenschicksal (Über das problem jüdischer vergangenheit)—Wozu (über das problem jüdischer gegenwart)—Wir jungen Juden (über das problem jüdischer zukunft)

1. Jewish question.   I. Title.
31–19294
Library of Congress   DS141.L7

NL 0347784   DLC MiU ICU NN OCH

LIEBLICH, KARL, 1895–
Wir jungen Juden; drei Untersuchungen zur jüdischen Frage.   Stuttgart, Zonen-Verlag. 1931.
160 p. 21cm.

Film reproduction. Negative.

I. Jewish question.

NL 0347785   NN

Ein lieblich und nützbarlich spil ...
see   Greff, Joachim, 16th century.

Zg17
L615
696
Der liebliche und anmuhtige historische Lust-Garten, das ist: Ein sehr lust-und lehrreiches Tractätlein von allerhand feinen Historien, Geschichten und Begebenheiten ... dem Leser zum Zeitvertreib und Gemühts-Ergötzung herfür gegeben. Hamburg, In Verlegung Hieronymus Fried. Hoffmann, Buchh. in Zell, 1696.
552p. 13½cm.
Added t.p., engr.

NL 0347787   CtY

Liebliche und erbauliche Lieder ...
This work is available in this library in the Readex Microprint edition of Early American Imprints published by the American Antiquarian Society.
This collection is arranged according to the numbers in Charles Evans' American Bibliography.

NL 0347788   DLC

VOLUME 332

PT1358
.L7
Rare bk
room

Lieblicher sommer-klee und anmuthiges winter-grün das ist:Allerhand lächerliche/iedoch höfliche schwänk, üd kurzweilige schnaken/bestehend in mancherley artigen fragen/possierlichen beantwortungen/gutgemeinten ernst- und lustigen schimpf- und scherz-reden... Also zusammen gelesen und gebunden durch Ernst Immerlustig [pseud.] [n.p.]1670.
[4],256 p. plates. 13cm.
1.German wit and humor.

NL   0347789   ICU

Liebling, Abbott Joseph, 1904-*1963*.
Back where I came from, by A. J. Liebling. New York, Sheridan house [*1938*]
303 p. 21cm.

1. New York (City)—Soc. life & cust.   I. Title.
Library of Congress   F128.5.L66   38-39406
— — —— Copy 2.
Copyright A 125112   917.471

NL   0347790   DLC NIC CU CoU OC1 NN MtU   WaTC WaS OrP

Liebling, Abbott Joseph, 1904–
Chicago, the second city. Drawings by Steinberg. [1st ed.] New York, Knopf, 1952.
143 p. illus. 21 cm.

1. Chicago—Descr.

F548.5.L5   917.7311   52-8506 †

NSyU OWorP PBm PP NcD OU WaU NcRS CU NN MiU
NL   0347791   DLC WaTC OrCS IdPI OrU OrP Or WaT MeB PU

Liebling, Abbott Joseph, 1904–
The honest rainmaker; the life and times of Colonel John R. Stingo. [1st ed.] Garden City, N. Y., Doubleday, 1953.
317 p. 22 cm.

1. Macdonald, James A., 1874–   I. Title.

CT275.M432L5   818.5   52-13568 ‡

WaE WaT Or
NL   0347792   DLC PU NN ViU PPL GU IdB OrU OrP Wa

Liebling, Abbott Joseph, 1904–
Mink and red herring, the wayward pressman's casebook. [1st ed.] Garden City, N. Y., Doubleday, 1949.
251 p. 21 cm.
Articles which first appeared in the New Yorker.

1. Press—U. S.   I. Title.

PN4867.L46   071   49-9550 †

ICU OC1W WaE WaT Or OrU OrP IdPI CaBVa Wa
NL   0347793   DLC IEN WU OKentU KEmT PPL PP PPT OU TxU

E99
P2L7

Liebling, Abbott Joseph, 1904-1963.
A reporter at large; the lake of the cui-ui eaters. [New York, 1955]
1v. (various pagings)
Photocopy. Originally appeared in the New Yorker, Jan. 1-22, 1955.

NL   0347794   DI

Liebling, Abbott Joseph, 1904–   ed.
The republic of silence, compiled and edited by A. J. Liebling ... New York, Harcourt, Brace and company [1947]
viii, 522 p. 21 cm.
Maps on lining-papers.
"Selections ... written by Frenchmen between May 10, 1940 ... and early September, 1944."—p. 5.
"The excerpts were translated by Ramon Guthrie."—Dust jacket.
"First edition."
1. World war, 1939-1945—Underground movements—France.
I. Guthrie, Ramon, 1896–   tr. II. Title.
D802.F8L53   940.5344   47—30277

OrSaW OrU
TxU NcD NcGU WaS MtBC WaTC CaBVa WaWW CaBVaU Or OrP
NL   0347795   DLC KU OU NBuU PPG1 NN MH ICU MiHM MB ViU

D802
F8L53   Liebling, Abbott Joseph, 1904-   ed.
The republic of silence. New York, Harcourt, Brace [1947]
viii, 522 p. maps. 21cm.

Xeroxed copy, Ann Arbor, University Microfilms, 1970.

1. World War, 1939-1945 - Underground movements - France. I. Guthrie, Ramon, tr. II. Title.

NL   0347796   GU

Liebling, Abbott Joseph, 1904–   ed.
La république du silence, the story of French resistance, edited by A. J. Liebling ... and Eugene Jay Sheffer ... New York, Harcourt, Brace and company, 1946.
x, 534 p. illus. 20½ cm.
Maps on lining-papers.
"Selections ... written by Frenchmen between May 10, 1940 ... and early September, 1944."—p. 3.

1. French language—Chrestomathies and readers (Hist.) 2. World war, 1939-1945—Underground movements—France.   I. Sheffer, Eugene Jay, joint ed. II. Title.

PC2127.H8L5   448.6   46—4216

NL   0347797   DLC OrCS WaU KEmT PCM MiU PIm

Liebling, Abbott Joseph, 1904–
... The road back to Paris. Garden City, New York, Doubleday, Doran and co., inc., 1944.
x, 300 p. 22cm.
At head of title: A. J. Liebling.
"First edition."

1. World war, 1939-   —Personal narratives, American.   I. Title.

Library of Congress   44-40016
                   D811.5.L53
                   [20]   940.548173

WaE IdPI WaSp CaBVa OrU WaT WaTC WaSpG Or OrP IdB
OU OEac OLak OC1 ViU NcC Mi PPLas CoU WaU AAP FTaSU
NL   0347798   DLC PPG1 PPT PPFr PHC PP PPL LU OOxM OC1

Liebling, Abbott Joseph, 1904–
... The road back to Paris. London, M. Joseph ltd [1944]
260 p. 21cm.
At head of title: A. J. Liebling.
"First published 1944."

1. World war, 1939-   —Personal narratives, American.   I. Title.

Library of Congress   44-46488
                   D811.5.L53 1944 a
                   [2]   940.548173

NL   0347799   DLC

Liebling, Abbott Joseph, 1904-
Sur la piste de Mollie, nouvelle inédite.
(In France Illustration littéraire et théâtrale Paris, 1948. no. 23, 23-32 p. 28 cm.)
"Tr. de l'américain par George Adam."

NL   0347800   OU

Liebling, Abbott Joseph, 1904–
The telephone booth Indian [by] A. J. Liebling. Garden City, N. Y., Doubleday, Doran and company, inc., 1942.
3 p. l., v-ix p, 1 l., 266 p. 20ᵐ.
Title on two leaves.

1. New York (City)   I. Title.
                                                  42-11082
Library of Congress   F128.5.L67
                   [12]   917.471

OC1 OOxM OCU OU ViU PBm PP
NL   0347801   DLC WaT WaTC NcU CoU NcC CU OEac OLak

Liebling, Abbott Joseph, 1904–   ed.

Marks, Edward Bennet, 1865–
They all sang, from Tony Pastor to Rudy Vallée, as told to Abbott J. Liebling by Edward B. Marks. New York, The Viking press, 1934.

Liebling, Abbott Joseph, 1904–
The wayward pressman. [1st ed.] Garden City, N. Y., Doubleday, 1947.
284 p. 21 cm.
Most of the articles appeared in the New Yorker under title: The wayward press.
Erratum slip inserted.
"Reading list": p. [277]-284.

1. Press—U. S.   I. Title.

PN4867.L5   071   47-11624*

IdPI Wa Or OrP OrU TxU ScU ICU NcC MiU MH MB
NL   0347803   DLC WaWW MtBC IdU WaE WaS WaSp WaT MtU

*PN4867
.L5
1948   Liebling, Abbott Joseph, 1904–
The wayward pressman. Garden City, N. Y., Doubleday, 1948.
284 p. 21 cm.
Most of the articles appeared in the New Yorker under the title: The wayward press.
"Reading list": p. [277]-284.

1. Press—U.S. I. Title

NL   0347804   MB KEmT

Liebling, Alice.
Die Liebesschule. Lustspiel in einem Akt. Leipzig, G. Richter, [1907].
31 p. 8°. (Lustspiele, no. 6).

NL   0347805   NN

Liebling, *Mrs.* Alice (Goldberger)
An emperor's great love (Barbara Blomberg); historic drama in three acts with a prologue, by Alice Liebling. San Bruno, Calif., W. Webster [1934]
141, [2] p. front. (port.) 23ᵐ.
"First printing."

1. Karl v, emperor of Germany, 1500-1558—Drama. 2. Blomberg, Barbara, 1527ca.-1597—Drama.   I. Title.

Library of Congress   PS3523.I 28E6 1934   34-19842
Copyright D pub. 30011   [2]   812.5

NL   0347806   DLC ClSU NBuU

VOLUME 332

M
786.4
L72a

Liebling, Emil, 1851-1914

    Album Blatt (Album leaf) op.18. Chicago
Music Co., °1881.
    5 p.

    For piano.

NL 0347807   OrP

ML160
.H85

Liebling, Emil, 1851-*1914*, ed.

    Hubbard, William Lines, 1867-   *ed.*
    The American history and encyclopedia of music ... W. L.
Hubbard, editor ... Toledo, New York [etc.] I. Squire
[°1908-10]

Liebling, Emil   ed.
    Anthology of classical and modern piano
compositions; edited, critically revised
and fully annotated by ... N.Y. Irving
Squire.

    Contents: J.S. Bach.-Georges Bachmann.-
Ludwig van Beethoven.- Franz Bendel.- F.F.
Chopin.- Muzio Clementi.- A. F. Durand.-
John Field.-G. F. Handel.- Theodore Lack.-
Franz Liszt.- Albert Loeschorn.- et.c

NL 0347809   OC1W

V
29
.495

LIEBLING, EMIL, 1851-1914.
    ...As others see us. A faithful record of
Mr. Emil Liebling's experiences during the concert season of 1893-94. [Chicago?]Printed for
private distribution[1894?]
    cover-title,xliiip.

NL 0347810   ICN

M786.4
L72c

Liebling, Emil, 1851-1914

    Caprice in C major, for the piano, op.32,
no.2. Summy [°1896]
    7 p.

NL 0347811   OrP

Liebling, Emil
    ... Complete scales for the piano, with
explanatory notes ... Chicago, the Chicago
music co., c1880.
    17 p.

NL 0347812   OC1

Liebling, Emil, 1851-1914.
    The complete scales for the piano with explanatory notes, by
Emil Liebling. Op. 13. Newly revised by the author... New
York: G. Schirmer[, cop. 1908]. Publ. pl. no. 20753. 15 p.
f°.

1. Piano—Exercises. 2. Scales.
N. Y. P. L.   June 30, 1927

NL 0347813   NN

VM
22
L 71c

LIEBLING, EMIL, 1851-1914.
    ...Compositions for pianoforte...   New York,G.
Schirmer[c1907]
    3 no.in 1v.   36cm.

    Plate nos.: 19228-19230.
    Contents.—Op.39. Lolita, souvenir.—Op.40.
Scherzo in E♭.—Op.41. Concert polonaise in G
minor.

NL 0347814   ICN

M786.4
L716c

Liebling, Emil, 1851-1914.
    [Concert polonaise, op.41, G minor]
Concert polonaise. [New York] Schirmer,
1907.
    11p.   31cm.

    Caption title.
    For piano.

NL 0347815   IEN

BVM
221
L 71c

LIEBLING, EMIL, 1851-1914.
    Cradle song. Op.23. Violin & piano.   Chi-
cago,S.Brainard's sons co.,c1891.
    5p.   35½cm.

    Violin part (3p.) laid in.
    Plate no.: 16663-6.

NL 0347816   ICN OrP

Liebling, Emil, 1851-1914.
    [Elfentanz, op. 34, no.]]
Elfentanz.   [New York], Schirmer, 1899.
    7 p.   31 cm.
    Caption title.
    For piano.
    I. Title.

NL 0347817   IEN OrP

Liebling, Emil, 1851-1914
    Feu follet (Will-o-the-wisp) scherzo for the
piano, op.17. Chicago Music Co., °1881.
    7 p.

    I.Title xLiebling, Emil, 1851-1914. Will-o'-the-wisp

NL 0347818   OrP

M786.4
L72g1

Liebling, Emil, 1851-1914

    Gavotte moderne, for the piano, op.11. Rev.
ed. Boston, Schmidt, °1889.
    7 p.

NL 0347819   OrP

M786.4
L716ℓ

Liebling, Emil, 1851-1914.
    [Lolita]
Lolita, souvenir for the piano. Op.39.
[New York] Schirmer, 1907.
    7p.   31cm.

    Caption title.

NL 0347820   IEN

SCORE

M781.5
L716m

Liebling, Emil, 1851-1914.

    Manuela. Air de ballet. Op.29.   [Cincinnati,
The John Church Company] c1896.
    7p.   35cm.

    Caption title.
    On cover: Piano music selected by Ignace
Jan Paderewski.

    I.Title. √LC

NL 0347821   CLSU OrU

Liebling, Emil, 1851-1914.

    Mathews, William Smythe Babcock, 1837-1912.
    Mathews and Liebling pronouncing and defining dic-
tionary of music, compiled and edited by W. S. B. Mathews and Emil Liebling; with a supplement containing
an English-Italian vocabulary, a list of prominent composers and artists ... Cincinnati, New York [etc.] The
John Church company, 1925.

M786.4
L72m

Liebling, Emil, 1851-1914

    Mazurka de concert, for the piano, op.30.
Church [°1896]
    11 p.

NL 0347823   OrP

Liebling, Emil, 1851-1914.   No. 4 in **M.451.24
    Momento appassionato for piano. Opus 24.
= *Autograph manuscript.* [189-?] 3 pp. 34½ cm.

    K8010 — T.r. Pianoforte music. — Pianoforte. Music. — Manuscripts in this
Library. Music.

NL 0347824   MB

Liebling, Emil, 1851-1914.   No. 5 in **M.451.24
    Momento scherzando for the piano. Op. 25.
= *Autograph manuscript.* [189-?] 5 pp. 34? cm.

    K8008 — T.r. Pianoforte music. — Pianoforte. Music. — Manuscripts in this
Library. Music.

NL 0347825   MB

Liebling, Emil, *1851-*
    Piano compositions. vp. Cincinnati,
The John Church company [c1895-1896].

    Contents: menuetto scherzoso; Op. 28.-
Manuela, air de ballet; Op. 29.- Maxurka de
concert; Op. 30. V 1se poetique; Op. 31.

NL 0347826   OC1

Liebling, Emil, 1851-1914.

    Mathews, William Smythe Babcock, 1837-1912.
    Pronouncing and defining dictionary of music, by W. S. B.
Mathews and Emil Liebling. Cincinnati, New York [etc.] The
J. Church co., °1896.

VOLUME 332

Liebling, Emil, 1851-1914, ed.
  Selected Czerny studies...1906
    see under Czerny, Carl, 1791-1857.
[Supplement]

WM
21   LIEBLING, EMIL, 1851-1914, ed.
L 71t   Twelve piano lessons on classical and modern
      masters... Chicago,S.Brainard's sons co.,c1897.
      64p. 32cm.
        Contents.--Andante from Sonata, op.14, no.2
      [by] L.van Beethoven.--Au matin [by] B.Godard.--
      Bird as prophet [by] R.Schumann.--Caprice, op.16,
      no.1 [by] F.Mendelssohn.--Eighth two-voiced inven-
      tion [by] J.S.Bach.--Invitation à la valse [by]
      C.M.von Weber.--Nocturne in F-minor [by] F.Chopin.
      --Passacaille [by] G.F.Handel.--Second humoresque
      [by] E.Grieg.--Sere-   nata [by] M.Moszkowski.--
      Slumber song [by] L.   Schytte.--Turkish march
      [by] W.A.Mozart.

NL 0347829   ICN

M1508   Liebling, Estelle, 1884-   ed.

Verdi, Giuseppe, 1813-1901.
  [La traviata. Ah, fors' è lui che l'anima, arranged]
    ... Ah, fors' è lui che l'anima (Is he the one), recitative and
  aria from the opera "La traviata." F min. ... New York, G.
  Schirmer, inc. [*1942]

M1508   Liebling, Estelle, 1884-

Bellini, Vincenzo, 1801-1835.
  [La sonnambula. Ah! non credea mirarti; arr.]
    Ah! non credea mirarti. Ah, non giunge (Who thought
  to see thee languish. Add no thought from the world of
  mortals) Aria, from La sonnambula. [Rev. by and sup-
  plied] with cadenzas [written by Estelle Liebling] New
  York, G. Schirmer [*1942]

Liebling, Estelle, 1884-
  Carnival of Venice (after a popular Italian
  tune)
    see under   Benedict, Sir Julius, 1804-
  1885.

MT825   Liebling, Estelle, 1884-
.P6
Pierce, Anne Elise, 1892-
  Class lessons in singing [by] Anne E. Pierce ... with addi-
  tional suggestions by Estelle Liebling ... New York, Boston
  [etc.] Silver Burdett company [*1937]

Liebling, Estelle, 1884-   ed. and arr.
  The Estelle Liebling coloratura digest, containing traditional
  and new cadenzas, cuts, technical exercises, and suggested con-
  cert programs. Compiled, arranged, and edited by Estelle
  Liebling. New York, G. Schirmer, inc. [*1943]
    112 p. 30cm.
  Publisher's plate no.: 40627.

    1. Vocal music--Cadenzas.   I. Title: Coloratura digest.
                                                45-14160
    Library of Congress   M1497.L54E8
                                  [3]   784.08121

OrP MtU
NL 0347834   DLC PP MB LU FTaSU OO CoU IEN INS CLU

Liebling, Estelle, 1884-   ed. and arr.
  The Estelle Liebling coloratura digest...
  [c1948]

NL 0347835   FU

Liebling, Estelle, 1884-   ed.
  Fifteen arias for coloratura soprano. New York, G.
  Schirmer [1944]
    142 p. 30 cm.
  For voice and piano.
  Words in original language, with English translation ; a few arias
  include words in a third language.

    1. Operas — Excerpts — Vocal scores with piano. 2. Songs (High
  voice) with piano.
    M1507.L67A7   44-49910 rev*

    OU OOxM
NL 0347836   DLC NN MB IEN KEmT CtY-Mus CaBVa WaT NcU

Liebling, Estelle, 1884-   , arr.
  Music, art, music and literature keep memory
  alive
    see under   Thompson, John Sylvanus, 1889-

M1508   Liebling, Estelle, 1884-   ed.

Donizetti, Gaetano, 1797-1848.
  [Linda di Chamounix. O luce di quest' anima, arranged]
    ... O luce di quest' anima (O light divine that shines from
  love), recitative and cavatina from the opera "Linda di Chamounix" ... New York, G. Schirmer, inc. [*1942]

M1508   Liebling, Estelle, 1884-   ed.

Meyerbeer, Giacomo, 1791-1864.
  [Le pardon de Ploërmel. Ombre légère, arranged]
    ... Ombre légère (Shadow song), from "Dinorah" (with
  cadenzas) ... New York, G. Schirmer, inc. [*1942]

MT885   Liebling, Estelle, 1884-   ed.
.M316
ap. 32   Marchesi, Mathilde (Graumann) 1822-1913.
  Thirty vocalises for high or medium voice, with piano acc.
  Op. 32. Rev. and ed. by Estelle Liebling. New York, G
  Schirmer, *1941.

M1621   Liebling, Estelle, 1884-   ed.
.D
Defesch, Willem, fl. 1733-1758.
  [Canzonette, 1st set. Tu fai la superbetta, arr.]
    Tu fai la superbetta. Dorilla, you are haughty. Canzo-
  netta [by] Wilhelm Fesch, ed. by Estelle Liebling. English
  version by Theodore Baker. [New York] G. Schirmer, *1945.

MT885   Liebling, Estelle, 1884-   ed.
.L26
Lamperti, Francesco, 1813-1892.
  [Studi di bravura]
    Vocal studies in bravura, provided with explanatory
  text of a pedagogical nature by Estelle Liebling. New
  York, G. Schirmer, *1942.

Liebling, George, 1865-1946.
  ...American toccata; impressions of Hollywood in modern
  rhythm for piano, composed by George Liebling... Op. 140...
  San Bruno, Calif., W. Webster [c1935] 7 p. 30cm.

    1. Piano. I. Title.
  N.Y.P.L.   July 5, 1949

NL 0347843   NN

MUSIC   Liebling, Georg, 1865-1946.
M
2013   Concert mass, op.100 [for] 4 solos,
L5   soprano, contralto, tenor, bass, orches-
      tra, organ. Los Angeles, G.Liebling
      [c1931]
        miniature score (96p.) 25cm.
      Cover title.
      Choral score with piano acc.

      √1.Choruses, Sacred (Mixed voices, 4 pts.) with or-
      chestra - Vocal scores with piano. √2.Masses - Vocal
      scores with pi-   ano.

NL 0347844   CLSU

M   Liebling, Georg, 1865-1946.
1011   [Concerto, piano, op.22, A major; arr.]
L622c   Concerto Eroico; A-dur [A-major] Op.22.
1900   2. Aufl. 2d ed. München, Odeon-Verlag,
      c1900.
        score (55 p.)

        1. Concertos (Piano) - 2-piano scores.
      I. Title.

NL 0347845   CLU

M787.1   Liebling, Georg, 1865-
L71f
      Fairy dance (Elfentanz) Op.80, no.2.
      Schmidt [c1926]
      score (9 p.) & part.

      Violin and piano.

NL 0347846   OrP

Liebling, Georg, 1865-1946.
  ...Impromptu on black keys. Op. 60...   Boston [etc.] A. P.
  Schmidt co. [c1925]   Publ. pl. no. A.P.S.13571. 7 p. 31cm.
  Composer's autographed presentation copy to Ossip Gabrilowitsch.

    1. Piano. 2. Autographs—Signa-   tures, etc.—Liebling, G. I. Title.
  N.Y.P.L.   May 14, 1946

NL 0347847   NN

Liebling, Georg, 1865-1946.
  [Katharina von Cicilien.] Musik zur Katharina von Cicilien. Dra-
  matische Legende in 4 Akten und einem Nachspiel von Jan
  Michailowicz [Pseud. für Alice Liebling]. Mit 12 musikalischen
  Illustrationen von André Myrot [Pseud. für Georg Liebling].
  Klavierauszug mit Text. Op. 56].
  [Berlin.] Im Selbstverlag des Autors. 1904. 63 pp. 34 cm.
                                          No. 2 in **M.416.14
  Same. 1906.   No. 1 in **M.416.14
  This edition has the composer's name on the title-page.

  K4141 — Double main card. — Liebling, Georg. (M1) — Liebling, Alice. (M2)
  — Music. Incidental. (1) — T.r. (1)

NL 0347848   MB

VOLUME 332

Liebling, Georg, 1865-1946.
... Octaven-etude für das pianoforte, componirt von Georg Liebling. Op. 8... Berlin, Schlesinger; [etc., etc., c1894].
7 p. 34 cm.
Publisher's no.: S. 8521.

NL 0347849   CU

Liebling, Georg, 1865-1946.
[Préludes d'après Heine, piano, op. 29; arr.]
Trois préludes d'après Heine, op. 29. For violin and piano. Arr. by the composer and Louis H. Hillier. London, Forsyth Bros.; New York, E. Schuberth [*1898]
score (3 v.) and part. 36 cm.
L. C. copy incomplete: v. 1-2 wanting.
Contents.—no. 1. Wenn ich in deine Augen seh' (C major)—no. 2. Die Lotosblume (A minor)—no. 3. Du bist wie eine Blume (D major)
1. Violin and piano music, Arranged. I. Title: Préludes d'après Heine.
M223.L   51-47557

NL 0347850   DLC

Liebling, Georg Lothar
     see Liebling, Georg, 1865-1946.

Liebling, Hyman Sanford, 1908-
... Die Erstgeburt im höheren Alter ... Zürich, 1937.
Inaug.-Diss. - Zürich.
Lebenslauf.
"Literaturverzeichnis": p. 18-19.

NL 0347852   CtY

Liebling, Joseph Martin.
In memoriam, for Marc Tarlow, died March 31, 1945; words from a poem by Elinor Marcus, music by Joseph Liebling. New York, 1945.
[1], 66 (i. e. 68) p. 36 x 28^{cm}.
Includes extra numbered pages 8a-8b.
Black-line print, from manuscript copy, on double leaves folded Chinese style.
Score: solo voices, chorus (SSAATTBB) and orchestra.
1. Choruses, Secular (Mixed voices, 8 pts.) with orchestra—Scores.
2. Tarlow, Marc, d. 1945. I. Marcus, Elinor. II. Title.
     45-10392
Library of Congress   M1530.L72 I 6

NL 0347853   DLC

Liebling, Karl, 1873-
Ueber das Verhältnis zwischen Raub und Erpressung. XX. Abschnitt des St.-G.-B.'s für das Deutsche Reich ... von Karl Liebling ... Berlin, G. Pintus, 1897.
55 p. 22cm.
Inaug.-Diss. - Erlangen.
"Lebenslauf": p. 55.
"Litteratur-Verzeichnis": p. 51-54.

NL 0347854   MH-L ICRL NIC

Liebling, Leonard, 1874-1945.
The girl and the Kaiser. Operetta in three acts
     see under Jarno, Georg, 1868-1920.

Liebling, Leonard, 1874-1945.
Lacrimosa. [New York? 19—] 12 l. 29cm.
Typescript.

1. Drama, American. 2. Mozart, Drama. 3. Drama—Promptbooks and —Hist. characters—Mozart, Wolfgang
Wolfgang Amadeus, 1756-1791— Typescripts—One-act. 4. Drama Amadeus, 1756-1791. I Title.

NL 0347856   NN

Liebling, Leonard, 1874-
... Rêverie poétique ... [Op. 2] New York: G. Schirmer, c1895. Publ. pl. no. 12010. 5 p. 34½cm.
At head of title: Three pieces for piano solo by Leonard Liebling ... No. 2.
Composer's autographed presentation copy to Rafael Joseffy.

1. Piano—1800- 2. Auto- graphs—Signatures, etc.—Liebling, L.
N. Y. P. L.   November 30, 1942

NL 0347857   NN

Liebling, Leonard, 1874-1945.
Wagner, Richard, 1813-1883.
Richard Wagner and the seamstress; first publication in the English language of a collection of letters by Richard Wagner. Accompanied by Daniel Spitzer's comments, with an introduction and epilogue by Leonard Liebling. New York, F. Ungar [1941]

Liebling, Sabine.
*Zur Genese der Retractio bulbi [Basel] 24p. 8° Mülhausen, 1934.

NL 0347859   DNLM CtY MiU

641.5943 R201
Die Lieblingsgerichte der deutschen Familie. 276 preisgekrönte Rezepte hervorgegangen aus einem gemeinschaftlichen Preis-Ausschreiben der Deutschen Moden-Zeitung und der Deutschen Frauen-Zeitung. Leipzig, O. Beyer, [1913].
112 p. 21½cm.
1 page at end for notes.

NL 0347860   ICJ

Lieblings-märchen, den lieben kleinen erzählt. Mit farbendruck-bildern. Cincinnati und Leipzig, M. & R. Burgheim [*1880]
93 p., 1 l. 5 col. pl. (incl. front.) 23½cm.
1. Fairy tales.
Library of Congress   PZ34.L5   19-12534

NL 0347861   DLC

Edc 1
Die Lieblingsschlösser König Ludwigs II von Bayern. [n.p.,188-?]
photog.views (fold.strip of 18 l.) 10½x16cm.
Title from cover.
Descriptive letterpress in German, English and French.
1.Castles - Bavaria. 2.Ludwig II, king of Bavaria, 1845- 1886.

NL 0347862   CtY

M922 no.3
... Lieblingswalzer der Königin Luise... Leipzig [etc.] Breitkopf & Härtel [191-?] Publ. pl. no. 21806. 4 p. 34cm.
[Musik am preussischen Hofe... Nr. 3]
Arranged for piano by Waldemar Waege.
First published as no. 3 of this series in 1896 with plate number 21415. Republished 1897 in no. 14 of the series, and now reprinted from the plates of that edition.
Title stamped on cover. Caption-title reads: Luisen-Walzer. Lieblingsstück der Königin Luise.
At head of title: Breitkopf & Härtel's Klavier-Bibliothek.
     Carnegie Corp. of New York.
1. Waltzes—Piano. I. Waege, Waldemar, arr. II. Title: Luisen-Walzer. III. Ser.
N. Y. L.   November 17, 1944

NL 0347863   NN

Liebman (Carl) [1839-97]. Della medicazione entro-uterina. 28 pp. 8°. *Milano, frat. Rechiedei,* 1876.
Repr. from: Ann. univ. di med., Milano, 1876, ccxxxv.

NL 0347864   DNLM

Liebman, Carl, 1839-97.
Intorno alla perforazione delle pareti dell' utero con l' interometro. Osservazioni, esperienze, considerazioni. 48 pp., 1 l. 8°. *Trieste,* 1878.

NL 0347865   DNLM

Liebman, Carl, 1839-1897.
Über die Perforation der Uteruswände mittelst der Sonde. Casuistik, Experimente und Beobachtungen. Aus dem Italienisches von Siegfried Hahn. Berlin, Demicke, 1879.
39 p. 8°.

NL 0347866   DNLM

Liebman, Charles, 1890-
Fireman civil service examination instruction
     see under Civil service chronicle, New York.

Liebman, Charles, 1890-
Hecht, Solomon.
Police patrolman examination instruction, a complete course of instruction for entrance examinations. In addition to the text matter there are 750 ques. and ans. for patrolman, police matron and policewoman candidates ... By Solomon Hecht ... assisted by Charles Liebman ... 4th ed. 160,000 words (illustrated) New York, Civil service chronicle, *1919.

Liebman, Charles, 1890-
Postal clerk and letter carrier; how to enter the service of the Post office department, by Charles Liebman .. [New York] The N. Y. civil service employees' pub. co., inc. [*1922]
130 p. 17^{cm}. $1.00
1. Postal service—U. S. 2. Civil service—U. S.—Examinations.
Library of Congress   HE6499.L5   22-21404

NL 0347869   DLC OCl

VOLUME 332

Liebman, Charles, *1890-*
Postal clerk and letter carrier; how to enter the service of the Post office department (2d ed.) by Charles Liebman ... ₁New York₁ The N. Y. civil service employees' pub. co., inc. ₁°1924₁
136 p. 17ᶜᵐ.

1. Postal service—U. S. 2. Civil service—U. S.—Examinations.

Library of Congress   HE6499.L5 1924   24–12429

NL 0347870   DLC

Liebman, Charles, *1890-*
Probation officer, comp. and ed. by Charles Liebman, associate editor, "The Chief". ₁New York₁ The N. Y. civil service employees' pub. co., inc. ₁°1923₁
192 p. diagr. 17ᶜᵐ.

1. Probation system—New York (City) 2. Civil service—New York (City)—Examinations.   I. The Chief.

Library of Congress   HV9278.L5   23–4718

NL 0347871   DLC MH

₁**Liebman, Charles**₁ 1890-
Supreme court attendant; previous questions and answers covering subjects of examinations—courts and their jurisdiction and government. New York, N. Y.. Civil service home studies, inc. ₁1935₁
1 p. l., 35 numb. l., 1 l. 28ᶜᵐ.
Mimeographed.

1. Courts—New York (State) 2. New York (State) Supreme court. 3. Civil service—New York (State)—Examinations.   I. Title. II. Title: Court attendant.

CA 35–191 Unrev'd

NL 0347872   DLC

Liebman, Charles, 1908- *ed.*
Directory of American judges; with a table of the Federal and State courts. Compiled and edited by Charles Liebman; Merrie Anne Newman, administrative editor. Foreword by Roscoe Pound. Chicago, American Directories, 1955.
1 v. (unpaged) 27 cm.

1. Judges—U. S.—Direct.   I. Title.

55—3160

PPT-L FU
KU-L WHi MeB OCIW NN IaU OU PBL TU NcD TxU PU-L PP
NL 0347873   DLC WaU-L PV PSt Or OrP Wa WaS NBuU-L

Liebman, Charles Joseph, *jr.*
Étude sur la vie en prose de saint Denis, par Charles J. Liebman ... Geneva, N. Y., The W. F. Humphrey press inc., 1942.
4 p. l., cxxvii p., 1 l., 246 p. 24ᶜᵐ.
Includes manuscript texts.

1. Denis, Saint, abp. of Paris, 3d cent.

44–2159
Library of Congress   BX4700.D4L5
₁3₁   922.244

NL 0347874   DLC NcU NIC IxU NN PU

Liebman, Dorothy Bachman.
The Christmas spirit. An operetta for children, composed by Dorothy S. Liebman. Newark, N. J., Franklin school, 1943.
14 l. 35½ᶜᵐ.
Reproduced from type-written and manuscript copy.
With piano accompaniment.

1. Operas, Juvenile. 2. Christmas music.   I. Newark, N. J. Franklin school. II. Title.
45–18604

Library of Congress   M1995.L695C5
₁2₁   782.8

NL 0347875   DLC

QH91
.L43
(Hebr.)   **Liebman, Emil,** 1900-
חים. ספר מדעי פופולרי. תל-אביב. הוצאת "המבע והארץ"
₁1935₁
76 p. 7 plates. 24 cm.   (סמרית המבע והארץ, א/2)

1. Marine biology. 2. Ocean.   (Series: Sifriyat ha-Teva' veha-arets, 1/2)
Title transliterated: ha-Yam.

QH91.L43   53–53216 rev

NL 0347876   DLC

Liebman, Enrico Tullio.
Corso di diritto processuale civile; nozioni introduttive, parte generale, il processo di cognizione. Milano, Giuffrè, 1952.
250 p. 25 cm.

1. Civil procedure—Italy.

52–42095 ‡

NL 0347877   DLC NcD ICU

Liebman, Enrico Tullio.
... La cosa juzgada en las cuestiones de estado. Buenos Aires, Antología jurídica, 1939.
17 p. 21ᶜᵐ. ₁Antología jurídica; cuadernos mensuales ... año XXI, nᵒ 260 (2. época, t. x, nᵒ 10) octubre de 1939₁
"De 'La Ley,' nᵒ del 20 de octubre de 1939."—p. ₁3₁

1. Res judicata.

44–52855

NL 0347878   DLC

4K-366   **Liebman, Enrico Tullio.**
Efficacia ed autorità della sentenza. Milano, A. Giuffrè, 1925.
133 p.

NL 0347879   DLC-P4

Liebman, Enrico Tullio.
Eficácia e autoridade da sentença e outros escritos sôbre a coisa julgada (com aditamentos relativos ao direito brasileiro) Tradução de Alfredo Buzaid e Benvindo Aires. Rio de Janeiro, Revista Forense, 1945.
211 p. 25 cm.

1. Res judicata.   I. Title.

51–36169

NL 0347880   DLC MH-L NNC

Liebman, Enrico Tullio.
Embargos do executado. Tradução da 2. ed. italiana por J. Guimarães Menegale. São Paulo, Saraiva, 1952.
286 p. 24 cm.
Translation of Le opposizioni di merito nel processo d'esecuzione.

1. Executions (Law)   I. Title.

53–34664 ‡

NL 0347881   DLC MH-L FU

Liebman, Enrico Tullio.
Estudos sôbre o processo civil brasileiro. S. Paulo, Saraiva, 1947.
212 p. 24 cm.

1. Civil procedure—Brazil.

51–21876

NL 0347882   DLC NNC

Law   **Liebman, Enrico Tullio.**

Chiovenda, Giuseppe, 1872–1937.
... Instituições de direito processual civil ... Tradução da 2. edição italiana por J. Guimarães Menegale, acompanhada de notas pelo prof. Enrico Tullio Liebman ... São Paulo, Livraria acadêmica, Saraiva & cia., 1942–45.

Liebman, Enrico Tullio.
Lezioni di diritto processuale civile. Milano, Giuffrè, 1951.
2 v. 26 cm.

1. Civil procedure—Italy.

52–31266 ‡

NL 0347884   DLC NNC

Liebman, Enrico Tullio.
Manuale di diritto processuale civile. Milano, A. Giuffrè, 1955–
v. 25 cm.

1. Civil procedure—Italy.

58–26655 ‡

NL 0347885   DLC MH-L

4K Ital.   **Liebman, Enrico Tullio.**
-412   Le opposizioni di merito nel processo d'esecuzione. Roma, "Foro Italiano," 1931.
263 p.   (Biblioteca del "Foro italiano.")

NL 0347886   DLC-P4

Liebman, Enrico Tullio.
... Processo de execução. S. Paulo, Saraiva & cia ₁1946₁
345 p., 2 l. 23½ᶜᵐ.

1. Executions (Law)—Brazil.

47–18125

NL 0347887   DLC

VOLUME 332

KD1794 Liebman, Enrico Tullio.
.I389   Sul riconoscimento della domanda. Padova, C.E.-
1927   D. A. M., 1927.
       47 p.
       "Estratto dagli Studi di diritto processuale in
       onore di Giuseppe Chiovenda nel XXV anno del suo
       insegnamento."
       1. Confession (Law)--Italy. 2. Civil procedure
       --Italy. 3. Confession (Law) I. Studi di diritto
       processuale in onore di Giuseppe Chiovenda nel
       XXV anno del suo insegnamento. II. Title.

NL 0347888   ICU

Liebman, Ernst
    Labor lawyers in the Boston community with
special emphasis on the role strain

    Honors thesis - Harvard, 1952

1. Labor - Boston, Mass. 2. Lawyers - Boston, Mass.

NL 0347889   MH

Liebman, Isaac, 1899–
ביער און שאפער פון מיין דור. נוי-יארק, פארלאג וואכנבלאם.
נוי-יארק, 1953–
    v. ports. 24 cm.
    Added t. p.: Builders and creators of my generation.

1. Jews—Biog. I. Title.
            Title transliterated: Boyer un shafer fun mayn dor.

DS115.I47   62-55784

NL 0347890   DLC IEN CoU CtY CLSU

PJ5129
.G547   Liebman, Isaac, 1899–
Z66   ... דער 14-טער, הערמאן גאלד ... נוי-יארק, פארלאג
(Hebraic   וואכנבלאם.* נוי-יארק, 1944.
Sect.)   31 p. port. 20¼ᵐ.
       "פון דער סעריע: פארשוינען אידישע שרייבער."

1. Gold, Herman, 1888–   *Title transliterated:* Der fernter.
                                         46-20033
Library of Congress   PJ5129.G547Z66

NL 0347891   DLC

PJ5129   Liebman, Isaac, 1899–
L533 I 5   אין געזאנג צום פאלק. נוי-יארק, פארלאג "וואכנבלאם."
       נוי-יארק, 1953.
       126 p. 24 cm.
       I. Title.
             Title transliterated: In gezang tsum folk.
       PJ5129.L533 I 5   59-58044

NL 0347892   DLC CoU

DS102.5   Liebman, Isaac, 1899–
L48   אין ליכט פון צייט. נוי-יארק, פארלאג וואכנבלאם.
       נוי-יארק, 1953.
       222 p. 24 cm.
       Essays.
       1. Jews—Addresses, essays, lectures. I. Title.
             Title transliterated: In likht fun tsayt.
       DS102.5.I48   59-55807

NL 0347893   DLC CoU

DS126
.I47   Liebman, Isaac, 1899–
Hebraic   אימן שיידוועג, פון יצחק ליבמאן.
Sect.   נוי-יארק, 1945.
           15 p. 21½ᵐ.

1. Jewish question. I. Title. *Title transliterated:* Oifn scheidweg.
                                         46-20022
Library of Congress   DS126.I47

NL 0347894   DLC

HD8073
H5L5   Liebman, Isaac, 1899–
Hebraic   סידני הילמאן, 1887–1946. נוי-יארק, פארלאג "וואכנ-
Sect.   בלאם.* נוי-יארק, 1946.
           32 p. port., facsim. 22 cm.

1. Hillman, Sidney, 1887–1946. *Title transliterated:* Sidni Hilman.
HD8073.H5L5   48-17324*
Library of Congress   [1]

NL 0347895   DLC

PJ5129
.L533A17   Liebman, Isaac, 1899–
1944   וואריאציעס, געקליבענע לידער. נוי-יארק, פארלאג
(Hebr)   וואכנבלאם. נוי-יארק, 1944.
           32 p. port. 33 cm.
           Added t. p.: Variations, selected poems.

I. Title   *Title transliterated:* Varyatsyes.
PJ5129.L533A17 1944   61-55940

NL 0347896   DLC NNU-W MH MB

DS149
.L53   Liebman, Isaac, 1899–
Hebraic   צום געוויסן פון דער וועלט.
Sect.   To the conscience of the world.
           נוי-יארק, פארלאג "וואכנבלאם.* New York, 1946
           16 p. 21 cm.

1. Zionism. I. Title.
             Title transliterated: Zum gewisn fun der welt.
DS149.L53   50-46950

NL 0347897   DLC

HN43
.J4L5   Liebman, Joshua Loth, 1907–1948.
    The American Jewish adventure, an address at
the 1948 annual meeting of the National
Jewish Welfare Board, May 9, 1948. Chicago.
[New York, National Jewish Welfare Board,
1948]
    22 p. 22cm.

1. Community centers. I. National
Jewish Welfare Board. II. Title.

NL 0347898   MB

Liebman, Joshua Loth, 1907–1948.
    Livsvisdom och levnadskonst. Översättning och inledning
av Erik Berggren. [Stockholm] Forum [1947]
    271 p. 20 cm.
    "Amerikanska originalets titel: Peace of mind."

1. Psychology, Applied. I. Title.
BF636.L478   150.13   51-32998

NL 0347899   DLC

4BM-   Liebman, Joshua Loth, 1907–1948.
271   Mach Frieden mit dir. Aus dem Amerikanischen
    übertragen von Sophie Angermann. Berlin, H.
Ullstein, H. Kindler [1948]
    197 p.

NL 0347900   DLC-P4

Liebman, Joshua Loth, 1907–1948.
    The meaning of life. Cincinnati, Hebrew Union College
Jewish Institute of Religion [1950]
    15 p. 21 cm. (Hebrew Union College-Jewish Institute of Religion.
Joshua Loth Liebman Dept. of Human Relations. [Publications]
Ser. A, no. 4)

1. Life. I. Title. (Series)
BD431.L415   128   51-339

NL 0347901   DLC NNJ NN

SPECIAL COLLECTIONS
SPINOZA

Liebman, Joshua Loth, 1907–1948.
Mendelssohn shocked. [1929]
10-13 p. 26cm.

From the Hebrew Union College monthly, vol.
XVII, no. 1, Oct. 15, 1929.
Includes references to Spinoza.

NL 0347902   NNC

Liebman, Joshua Loth, 1907–1948.
    Morality and immorality; the problem of conscience.
Cincinnati, Hebrew Union College-Jewish Institute of Re-
ligion [1950]
    15 p. 21 cm. (Hebrew Union College-Jewish Institute of Religion.
Joshua Loth Liebman Dept. of Human Relations. [Publications]
Ser. A, no. 5)

I. Title. (Series)
BJ1471.L5   171.6   51-338

NL 0347903   DLC MB NcU NIC

Liebman, Joshua Loth.
    Pace dello spirito. [Trad.dall
'inglese di B.M.Oddera. Milano,
Bompiani,1948. 241p. (Avventure
del pensiero, v.61)

    Titolo originale: Peace of mind.

NL 0347904   CaBVa

4BF-   Liebman, Joshua Loth, 1907–1948.
238   La paix de l'esprit. Pref. de Jacques Madaule.
Traduction de Jacques Laury. Paris, Payot,
1950.
    188 p.

NL 0347905   DLC-P4

159.1
L622   Liebman, Joshua Loth, 1907–1948.
    Paz de espírito. Tradução de Hylario
Corrêa. Curitiba, Guaíra [194-?]
    217 p. (Estante americana. 8)

I. Corrêa, Hylario,   tr.

NL 0347906   NNC

VOLUME 332

Liebman, Joshua Loth, 1907–
    Peace of mind, by Joshua Loth Liebman. New York, Simon
and Schuster ₁1946₎
    xiv, 203 p., 1 l. 21ᶜᵐ. ₁Jewish institute of religion, New York. Charles
W. Eliot lectures₎

1. Psychology, Applied.   I. Title.
                                                    46–25090
    Library of Congress   BF636.L47
                    ₁20₎   150.13

NcC NcD NcRS PPA PP PU PBm PPL WaSpG WaWW ICJ
OrSaW Wa WaE WaOB WaS WaSp WaT OrU–M IdB NcGW
KyMdC MdBJ MiHM MB ViU OClW ODW OCl OCU OOxM OrP
    IdU Or OrCS OrU OrP MtBC KyWA KyU AU MB KEmT
    NL 0347907   DLC CaBVa NSyU CaBViP CaBVaU MiU IdB

BF636
.L47   Liebman, Joshua Loth, 1907–1948.
1947   Peace of mind. New York, Simon and
            Schuster [1947]
                xiv, 203 p. 21cm.

                1. Psychology, Applied. I. Title.

    NL 0347908   MB

BF636
.L47   Liebman, Joshua Loth, 1907–1948.
1948   Peace of mind. New York, Simon and
            Schuster [1948]
                xiv, 203 p. 21cm. (Jewish Institute
            of Religion, New York. Charles W. Eliot
            lectures)

                1. Psychology, Applied. I. Title.
            II. Series: Charles W. Eliot lectures.

    NL 0347909   MB ViU

JUDAICA
BF636
.L47   Liebman, Joshua Loth, 1907–1948.
1949   Peace of mind. New York, Simon and
            Schuster [1949]
                xiv, 203 p. 21cm.

                1. Psychology, Applied.   I. Title.

    NL 0347910   MB PU

BF636
.L47   Liebman, Joshua Loth, 1907–1948.
1950   Peace of mind. New York, Simon and Schuster
            [1950, c1946]
                xiv, 203 p. 21cm. (Jewish Institute of
            Religion, New York. Charles W. Eliot lectures)

                1. Psychology, Applied. I. Title.
            II. Series: Charles W. Eliot lectures.

    NL 0347911   MB

BF636
L47   Liebman, Joshua Loth, 1907–1948.
1951   Peace of mind. New York, Simon and Schuster
            [1951? c1946]
                xiv, 203 p. 21cm.

                1. Psychology, Applied. I. Title.

    NL 0347912   MB

BM652
.5   Liebman, Joshua Loth, 1907–1948, ed.
.I6
1947a   **Institute on Religion and Psychiatry,** *Congregation Adath
        Israel, Boston, 1947.*
            Psychiatry and religion, ed. by Joshua Loth Liebman.
        Introd. by Albert A. Goldman. Boston, Beacon Press, 1948.

Liebman, Joshua Loth, 1907–
    The road to inner serenity, by Dr. Joshua Loth Liebman,
rabbi of Temple Israel, Boston. ₁Boston, Old corner book
store, 194–₎
    ₁16₎ p. 15½ x 11½ᶜᵐ. ₁Greater Boston church addresses₎

1. Sermons, Jewish—U. S.   I. Title.
                                                    45–46366
    Library of Congress   BM740.L55
                    ₁2₎   296

    NL 0347914   DLC

Liebman, Joshua Loth, 1907–1948.
    Si ja til livet. ₁Overs. av Aadel Tschudi. Bergen₎ J.
Grieg ₁1947₎
    220 p. 23 cm.
    "Originalens titel: Peace of mind."

1. Psychology, Applied.   I. Title.

    BF636.L476   50–21679

    NL 0347915   DLC

Liebman, Mac.
    Vot is kemp life? and a couple odder tings, by Mac Lieb-
man. New York, Lobel-Young, inc., 1927.
    62 p. illus. 21ᶜᵐ.

I. Title.
    Library of Congress   PN6161.L48   27–13369
        Copy 2

    NL 0347916   DLC

ND553
.C33R42   Liebman, Margaret H., tr.
            Rewald, John, 1912–
                Paul Cézanne, a biography. ₁Translation by Margaret H.
            Liebman₎ New York, Simon and Schuster ₁1948₎

Liebman, Max.
    Off to Buffalo; a comedy in three acts, by Max Liebman and
Allen Boretz. ₁New York, c1938. 51, 68, 40 f. 29cm.

    Original title: Big time.
    Produced at the Plymouth theatre, Boston, Nov. 10, 1938 as Flying Ginzburgs;
first New York production at the Ethel Barrymore theatre, Feb. 21, 1939.

194130B. 1. Drama, American.   I. Boretz, Allen, 1900– , jt. au.
II. Title. III. Title: Flying Ginz-   burgs. IV. Title: Big time.
N. Y. P. L.   March 25, 1943

    NL 0347918   NN

Liebman, Rebekah Rutledge, 1907–
    Herbartianism as a factor in American
education, by Rebekah R. Liebman ...
Baltimore, 1948.
    v, 173 (i.e. 175) numb. l., 1 l. 28½cm.

    Thesis (Ed.D.) – Johns Hopkins university,
1948.
    Required type-written copy.
    Vita.
    Bibliography: l. [164]–173; "Representative
articles on Herbartianism in selected periodicals": l. 152–163.

    NL 0347919   MdBJ

Liebman, Samuel, *ed.*
    Stress situations. Philadelphia, Lippincott ₁1955₎
    144 p. 19 cm.
    "Published in American practitioner and digest of treatment, for
November, 1954."

1. Emotions.   I. Title.

    BF531.L5   157   55–7098 ‡

    CaBVaU
    NL 0347920   DLC PPJ NcC PPT NcD PPC MiU DNLM NNC CU

Liebman, Solomon.
    אידישע פארמערײ אין אמעריקא. אדר פראגע און ליזונג
... פון דלמן ליבמאן. ניו היווען, קאנ., 1930.
    98 p. 19½ᵐ.

1. Jews in the U. S. 2. Jews as farmers.   I. Title (transliterated):
Yidishe farmerei in Amerika.
                                                    30–31406

    NL 0347921   DLC

Liebman, Turo, *respondent.*
    ... Specimen academicum, de similitude
vitae physicae in animalibus et plantis ...
    see under Harmens, Gustav, 1699–1774,
praeses.

Liebman (Vittorio). L' actinomicosi con speciale riguardo alla forma polmonare. pp. 413–
460, 2 pl. 8°. *Milano, F. Vallardi,* [n. d.]
    In: TRATT. ital. di patol. e terap. med. *Milano,* [n. d.]
1, pt. 2.

    NL 0347923   DNLM

Liebman, Walter Henry, 1874–
    National conference of Jewish social service. *Committee on
transportation.*
    Transportation rules and digest of decisions of Transporta-
tion committee. New York, N. Y., The National conference
of Jewish social service, 1929.

Liebmann, *Adolf, 1863–*
    ... Die klein- und strassenbahnen, von A. Liebmann ...
mit 82 abbildungen. Leipzig, B. G. Teubner, 1910.
    viii, 126 p. illus. (incl. maps, tables) 18½ᵐ. (Aus natur und geistes-
welt; sammlung wissenschaftlich-gemeinverständlicher darstellungen. 322.
bdchen.) M. 1.25

1. Railroads, Local and light. 2. Street-railroads.
                                                    10–17332
    Library of Congress   TF670.L7

    NL 0347925   DLC ICJ

VOLUME 332

Liebmann, Adolf, 1863–
... Der landstrassenbau, von A. Liebmann ... mit 44 abbildungen. Berlin und Leipzig, G. J. Göschen, 1912.
147 p. illus., diagrs. 16ᵐᵐ. (Sammlung Göschen. [598])
Literatur: p. [2]

1. Roads.
13–7389

Library of Congress   TE145.L6

NL 0347926   DLC MiD MB

Liebmann, Adolf, 1863–
Der landstrassenbau; ein hilfsbuch für den selbstunterricht und die praxis, von ingenieur A. Liebmann. 3. unveränderte aufl. mit 85 abbildungen. Leipzig, H. A. L. Degener [1926?]
3 p. l., 112 p.   illus., diagrs.   23½ᶜᵐ.
"Benutzte werke": p. 112.

1. Roads.

NL 0347927   MiU

Liebmann (Adolph). *Ueber Querulantenwahn. Ein primärer geistiger Schwächezustand. 41 pp. 8°. Jena, A. Neuenhahn, 1876.

NL 0347928   DNLM ICRL

WG
22420

Liebmann, Adolph, 1852–
Ueber die Einwirkung von Alkoholen und Phenolen auf Säureamid- und -imidchloride. Bonn, 1879.
46 p. illus.

Inaug.-Diss. - Bonn.

NL 0347929   CtY DLC

RC
469
L71

Liebmann, Albert, 1865–
Die Sprache der Geisteskranken nach stenographischen Aufzeichnungen von Alb. Liebmann und Max Edel, mit einem Vorwort von E. Mendel. Halle a. S., C. Marhold, 1903.
182 p. 23cm.

1. Mental illness—Diagnosis. 2. Speech, Disorder of.

NL 0347930   NIC CU IaU ICJ PPC MH DNLM MiU NNNPsI

WM
475
L718S
1901

Liebmann, Albert, 1865–
Die Sprachstörungen geistig zurückgebliebener Kinder. Berlin, Reuther & Reichard, 1901.
78 p. 23 cm. (Sammlung von Abhandlungen aus dem Gebiete der pädagogischen Psychologie und Physiologie, Bd. IV, Heft 3)

1. Mental Retardation. 2. Speech Disorders - in infancy and childhood. I. Title. II. Series.

NL 0347931   WU-M NIC NjP PU MB MWelC MnU

Liebmann, Albert, 1865–
Stottern und stammeln, ihre ursachen, verhütung und heilung.
Berlin, Steinitz, 1895.
87 p.

NL 0347932   PU

Liebmann, Alb[ert], 1865–   Educ 2050.6.2
Stotternde kinder. Berlin, Reuther & Reichard, 1903.
pp. 96. (Sammlung von abhandlungen aus dem gebiete der pädagogischen psychologie und physiologie, vi. 2.)

NL 0347933   MH OU MWelC MB PU DNLM

Liebmann (Albert) [1865–   ]. Ueber Diabetes insipidus bei Kindern. 30 pp., 1 l. 8° Berlin, G. Francke, 1888.

NL 0347934   DNLM

Liebmann, Albert, 1865–
Die untersuchung und behandlung geistig zurückgebliebener kinder, von dr. med. Alb. Liebmann ... Berlin, Berlinische verlagsanstalt, 1898.
36 p. 23½ᶜᵐ.

1. Backward children. 2. Feeble-minded.
E 13–282

Library, U. S. Bur. of   Education LC4601.L6

NL 0347935   DHEW KyHi ViU ICJ MiU OU ICU CtY DNLM PU

Liebmann, Albert, 1865–
Vorlesungen über Sprachstörungen. Berlin, O. Coblentz, 1898-1909.
8 v.
Contents. -1-2. Heft. Die Pathologie und Therapie des Stotters und Stammelns. -3. Heft. Hörstummheit. - 4. Heft. Poltern (Paraphrasia praeceps) - 5. Heft. Übungstafeln für Stammler sowie für hörstumme und geistig zurückgebliebene Kinder. - 6. Heft. Kinder, die schwer lesen,

schreiben und rechnen lernen.- 7. Heft. Sprachstörungen bei Schwerhörigkeit, mit Übungstafeln zur Erlernung des Absehens der Sprache vom Munde.- 8. Heft. Lispeln; mit deutschen, französischen, englischen und italienischen Übungstafeln.

NL 0347937   DNLM

Liebmann, Albert, 1865–
Vorlesungen über sprachstörungen. vol. 1.
2. völlig umgearb. aufl. Berlin, O. Coblentz, 1924.
v.

NL 0347938   OU

Liebmann, Albert, 1869–
Spectrophotometrische untersuchungen ... Köln, P. Gehly'sche buchdruckerei, 1893.
53 p. 22½ᶜᵐ.
Inaug.-diss.—Giessen.
Lebenslauf.

1. Spectrum analysis.

Library of Congress   QD95.L71   6–6396†

NL 0347939   DLC

Liebmann, Alfred
Zur kenntnis der oberflaechenspannungen geschmolzener metalle und salze.
Inaug. Diss. Zürich, 1909

NL 0347940   ICRL

Liebmann (Arthur). *Ueber die Nebennieren und den Sympathicus bei Herniocephalen. 27 pp. 8°. Bonn, C. Georgi, 1886.

NL 0347941   DNLM

Liebmann, Arthur, 1900–
Acht Jahrzehnte im Dienste der Wirtschaft; ein Lebensbild der Allgemeine deutsche Credit-Anstalt, von Dr. Arthur Liebmann. Leipzig: Bibliographisches Institut AG., 1938.   236 p. incl. diagrs.   charts, facsims., col'd front., plates, ports., tables. 25cm.
Map in pocket.
Bibliography included in "Anmerkungen" (p. 233-236).

980591A. 1. Banks and banking—   Germany. I. Allgemeine deutsche Credit-Anstalt, Leipzig.
N. Y. P. L.   January 24, 1939

NL 0347942   NN

LIEBMANN, Arthur, 1900–
Eine kritische betrachtung der wirtschaftswissenschaftlichen theorie des bankkredits von Dr. Albert Hahn auf dogmengeschichtlicher grundlage. Inaug.-diss. Leipzig, druckerei der werkgemeinschaft, 1928.
pp. 93†.
"Lebenslauf", at end.   Econ 5100.2

NL 0347943   MH CtY PU

[LIEBMANN, AUGUST GEORGE] 1881–
Documentary relics of finance. Washington, D.C.: A. G. Liebmann, c1932. 48 p. incl. tables. illus. 13cm.

Mostly tables.

1. Railways—Securities. 2. Bonds, Government.

NL 0347944   NN

Liebmann, August George, 1881–
... The McAfee-Skiles-Liebmann memorial; the history of the lives and times of three American soldiers and their families and connections ... Chicago, Ill., A. G. Liebmann, °1929.
3 p. l., 93, [7] p., 1 l.   front. (port.) illus. (incl. maps, facsim.)   23½ᶜᵐ.
At head of title: [For private circulation only]
"First edition limited to five hundred copies."
"Compiled by the private research of August George Liebmann."
Bibliography: p. 91–92.

1. McAfee, John, 1784–1867. 2. Skiles, George Baker, 1831–1863. 3. Liebmann, August, 1828–1910. 4. McAfee family (James McAfee, 1707–1785) 5. Skiles family. 6. Liebmann family (August Liebmann, 1828–1910) I. Title.
29–18089

Library of Congress   C871.M12 1929

NL 0347945   DLC

[Liebmann, August George] 1881–
Moribund securities and corporations, 1933. (Rev. ed.) ... [Boise, Id., Printed by Syms-York company] °1933.
209, [2] p. 23ᶜᵐ.
Introduction signed: August George Liebmann.

1. Securities—U. S. 2. Corporations—U. S.   I. Title.
Library of Congress   HG4927.L5 1933   33–31701
—— Copy 2.
Copyright A 60698   [3]   332.670973

NL 0347946   DLC ICJ

VOLUME 332

[Liebmann, August George] 1881–
    Railway track economics ... [Butte, Mont., Printed by the Bessette Stork co.] °1915.
    46 p., 1 l. 23½ᶜᵐ.
    Introduction signed: August G. Liebmann.

    1. Railroads—Track.   I. Title.

    Library of Congress   TF240.L5   16–1328

NL   0347947   DLC

Liebmann, August George, 1881–
    Railway track economics. Rev. ed. A tabloid treatise upon railroad problems. [Butte, Mont., Printed by the Bessette Stork co.] °1916.
    66 p. 16½ᶜᵐ.
    Preface signed: August G. Liebmann.

    1. Railroads—Track.   I. Title.

                         A 18–711
    Title from Bureau of   Railway Economics. Printed by L. C

NL   0347948   DBRE ICJ

Liebmann, Bruno.
    Christian Traumann und die erste meteorologische station der Oberlausitz... Loebua, Kessner, 1889.
    32p.

AC901 [Haverford-Bauer pamphlets, v. 175, no. 5]
.H3
v.175

NL   0347949   DLC

Law   Liebmann, Carl, plaintiff.

    Garber, Thornton and Bishop, *lawyers, San Francisco.*
    ... Carl Liebmann, *vs.* city and county of San Francisco. Addenda. Garber, Thornton & Bishop, attorneys for defendant ... San Francisco, Bacon & company, printers, 1885.

    Liebmann, Carl Julius

              see

    Liebmann, Julius i. e. Carl Julius, 1880–1914

R135
L623
    Liebmann, Chr   Ludovico Eduardo
    Quos medicina progressus fecerit, per Herophilum, Erasistratumque et asseclas. Dissertatio inauguralis ... Wirceburgi, Thein, 1845.
    32 p.

    1. Medicine, Greek and Roman. 2. Herophilus. 3. Erisistratus.

NL   0347952   NNC

B
1878
L8
L539
1902
    Liebmann, Curt, 1879–
    Die logik von Port-Royal im Verhältnis zu Descartes. Leipzig, 1902.
    46 p. 24 cm.
    Inaug. Diss. - Leipzig.
    Vita.
    Bibliographical footnotes.

    1. Port-Royal des Champs (abbey of Cistercian nuns) 2. Descartes, René, 1596–1650. 3.   Logic. I. Title.

NL   0347953   CaBVaU ICRL NjP CtY

Liebmann, David.
    Ueber baryumphosphorvanadinmolybdate.
    Inaug. diss. Bern, 1910.

NL   0347954   ICRL PU

1881–
Liebmann, David, Neuere Methoden in der Behandlung des Nabelschnurrestes. Freiburg i. B: Hammerschlag & Kahl 1910. 32 S. 8°.
Freiburg i. B., Med. Diss. v. 1910. Ref. Krönig
[Geb. 23. Febr. 81 Riga; Wohnort: Freiburg i. B.; Staatsangeh.: Rußland; Vorbildung: Oberrealsch. Riga Reife O. 04; Studium: Bonn 5, Freiburg i. B. 5 S.; Rig. 25. Nov. 10.]   [U 11. 1091

NL   0347955   ICRL DNLM

    Liebmann, Eduard Rudolf Harry
        see   Liebmann, Harry, 1877–

    Liebmann, Emil
        see
    Liebman, Emil, 1900–

Liebmann, Erich: Das Wesen und die Behandlung des großen Carbruckels m. bes. Berücks. d. Locopans. [Maschinenschrift.] 88 S. 4° [Lag nicht vor.] — Auszug: o. O. u. J. 2 Bl. 8° [Ersch. auch im Buchh.
Leipzig, Med. Diss. v. 7. Aug. 1922 [1923]   [U 22. 8015

NL   0347958   ICRL

1887–
Liebmann (Erich). *Experimentelle Untersuchungen über den Einfluss des Kamphers auf den kleinen Kreislauf.* [Zürich.] 26 pp. 8°. Leipzig, F. C. W. Vogel, 1912.

NL   0347959   DNLM

RC76   Liebmann, Erich, *1887–*
.3   ... Stethographische studien ... Berlin, Druck von L.
.L7   Schumacher, 1917.
    73 p. illus., diagrs. 24½ᶜᵐ.
    Habilitationsschrift—Zürich.

    1. Respiratory organs—Diseases.

NL   0347960   ICU DNLM

Liebmann, Ernö
    A saját ténybe ütköző kifogás és bírói gyakorlatunk. Írta Dᴿ Liebmann Ernö ... Budapest [Franklin Társulat nyomdaja] 1907.
    21 p. 23cm.
    "Különlenyomat a Jogtudományi Közlöny 1907. évi 27. és 28. számaiból."

NL   0347961   MH-L

Liebmann, Ernö
    ... A záloglevél mint értékpapír. Írta Dᴿ Liebmann Ernö ... Budapest, Franklin-Társulat [1930?]
    16 p. 23cm. (A Jogtudományi közlöny könyvtára, 18.)
    Bibliographical footnotes.

NL   0347962   MH-L

Liebmann, Ernst.
    Dardanellenflieger, von kapitänleutnant z. d. Liebmann. Berlin, Voll u. Pickardt, 1918.
    128 p. illus. (map) plates. 17½ᶜᵐ.

    1. European war, 1914–1918—Aerial operations. 2. European war, 1914–1918—Personal narratives, German.   I. Title.

                       34–4328
    Library of Congress   D604.L5   940.44943

NL   0347963   DLC MH   CSt-H DNW

DN34
L622t
    Liebmann, Ernst, 1875–
    Der text zu Jesaia 24–27. Leipzig, W. Drugulin, 1901.
    35 p. 22 cm.

    Inaug.-diss. - Halle-Wittenberg.
    Curriculum vitae.
    "Vorliegende dissertation ist der erste teil eines grösseren ganzen, das vollständig in der Zeitschrift für die alttestamentliche wissenschaft erscheinen   wird."

NL   0347964   CtY-D MH-AH DCU-H ICRL CtY ViRUT PGratz

Liebmann (Ewald). *Ueber die Behandlung einiger Magenkrankheiten mittelst der Magenpumpe und Magendouche.* 24 pp. 8°. *Leipzig, O. Leiner. 1870.* [P., v. 281.]

NL   0347965   DNLM

Liebmann (Felix) [1830–]. *De venaesectionibus in pneumonia adhibenda.* 29 pp., 1 l. 4°. *Berolini, B. Schlesinger.* [1853].

NL   0347966   DNLM

Liebmann (Felix) [1830–]. *De venaesectionibus in pneumonia adhibenda.* 29 pp., 1 l. 4°. *Berolini, B. Schlesinger.* [1853].

NL   0347966   DNLM

VOLUME 332

1890—
Liebmann, Franz Artur, Referendar: Die Geschäftsführung gegen den Willen des Geschäftsherrn. Bonn 1914: **Eisele.** 73 S. 8°
Breslau, Jur. Diss. v. 20. April 1914, Ref. Leonhard, Schott
[Geb. 7. März 90 Cöln; Wohnort: Cöln; Staatsangeh.: Preußen; Vorbildung: G. in d. Kreuzgasse Cöln Reife o8; Studium: Freiburg 3, München 1, Bonn 5 S.; Rig. 16. Dez. 13.] [U 14. 231

NL 0347967 ICRL MH-L

1813-1856.)
Liebmann, Frederik Michael, The Begoniæ of Mexico and Central America. Communicated to the Association of natural-history at Copenhagen, 1852. Translated by Dr. Wallich. [London. 1853.] 8°. pp. 3.
From 'Hooker's journal of botany and Kew garden miscellany, 1853, v 84-86.

NL 0347968 MH-A

Liebmann, Frederik (Michael). Bidrag til meliosmeernea familie. [Kjøbenhavn. 1850.] 8°.
"*Videnskabelige meddelelser fra den Naturhistoriske forening i Kjøbenhavn*," 1850, ii, 65-73.

NL 0347969 MH-A

Liebmann, Frederik Michael, 1813–1856.
Chênes de l'Amérique tropicale. Iconographie des espèces nouvelles ou peu connues. Ouvrage posthume de F. M. Liebmann. Achevé et augm. d'un Aperçu sur la classification des chênes en général par A. S. Ørsted. Ouvrage subventionné par la Société royale des sciences de Copenhague. Leipzig, L. Voss, 1869.
x, 29 p., 1 l. illus., 57 pl. 45 x 35cm.
Plates numbered A–I, K, I–XLVII.
CONTENTS.— Notice sur la vie de Liebmann et spécialement sur son voyage au Mexique.—Aperçu sur la classification des chênes en général (publié d'abord en danois dans "den Nat. forenings Vidensk. meddelelser" pour 1867, avec deux planches et des analyses des genres Pasania et Cyclobalanus)—Diagnoses de 52 espèces de chênes décrites par Liebmann.—Explication des planches.
I. Oak. 1. Ørsted, Anders Sandøe, 1816–1872. II. K. Danske videnskabernes selskab, Copenhagen.
Library of Congress   QK495.Q4L7   5—38650

NL 0347970 DLC NIC PPAN MBH MiU MH-A CtY CU MH

QK98
.F63
Liebmann, Frederik Michael, 1813–1856, ed.

Flora danica.
Icones plantarum sponte nascentium in regnis Daniæ et Norvegiæ, in ducatibus Slesvici et Holsatiæ et in comitatibus Oldenburgi et Delmenhorstiæ: ad illustrandum opus de iisdem plantis, regio jussu exarandum, Floræ danicæ nomine inscriptum; editæ ab ejus operis auctore, Georgio Christiano Oeder ... Hafniæ, typis [fratrum] C. [& A.] Philiberti, 1766 [i. e. 1761]–1883.

Liebmann, [Frederik Michael]. De islandske varme Kilders Vegetation. *Extr. fr.*
Forhandlinger ved de skandinaviske Naturforskeres andet Møde i Kjøbenhavn. 1840.
Kjøbenhavn, 1841. 8°. pp. 336–40.
IcC19L716

NL 0347972 NIC

Liebmann, Frederik Michael, 1813–1856.

Wainio, Edvard August, 1853–1929.
... Lichenes mexicani a F. M. Liebmann annis 1841–1843 collecti, in Museo hauniensi asservati, enumeravit Edv. A. Vainio. København, H. Hagerup, 1926.

Liebmann, F[rederik Michael].
Mexicos Bregner, en systematisk, critisk, plantegeographisk Undersögelse... (Kongeligt Dansk Videnskabernes Selskab. Skrifter. Kjøbenhavn, 1849. 4°. Række 5. Naturvidenskabelig og mathematisk Afdeling. Bind 1, p. 151-322.)

1. Ferns, Mexico.
N. Y. P. L.   December 21, 1911.

NL 0347974 NN MiU MH-A IaU NNBG

584.84
L716
Liebmann, Frederik Michael, 1813–1856.
Mexicos Halvgraes bearbeidede efter forgaengernes og egne materialier med tillæg af de i Nicaragua og Costa Rica af Mag. A.S.Ørsted samlede samt nogle faa ubeskrevne vestindiske former. Kjøbenhavn, B.Luno, 1850.
92 p. 25x20cm.
"Saerskilt aftrykt af det Kgl. Danske Videnskabernes selskabs Skrifter, 5te række, naturvidenskabelig og mathematisk afdeling, 2det bind."

1.Cyperaceae.   2.Botany - Mexico. 3.
Botany - Central   America.

NL 0347975 CSt NNC

Liebmann, F[rederik Michael].
Mexicos Halvgræs, bearbeidede efter Forgængernes og egne Materialier med Tillæg af de i Nicaragua og Costa rica af A. S. Örsted samlede, samt nogle faa ubeskrevne vestindiske Former. (Kongeligt Dansk Videnskabernes Selskab. Skrifter. Kjøbenhavn, 1851. 4°. Række 5. Naturvidenskabelig og mathematisk Afdeling. Bind 2, p. 189-277.)

1. Cyperaceæ, Mexico. 2. Cypera-   ceæ, Central America.
N. Y. P. L.   December 26, 1911.

NL 0347976 NN MH-A CU

Liebmann, Frederik Michael.
13. — Mexicos juncaceer. [Kjøbenhavn. 1850.] 8°. pp.
Reprinted from *Videnskabelige meddelelser fra den Naturhistoriske forening i Kjøbenhavn,* 1850, ii, 36-48.

NL 0347977 MH-A

Liebmann, Frederik Michael, 1813–1856.
Mexicos og Central-Americas neldeagtige planter (Ordo: *Urticaceæ*) indbefattende familierne: *Urticeæ, Moreæ, Artocarpeæ* og *Ulmaceæ*. Af F. Liebmann ... Kjøbenhavn, Trykt hos Kgl. hofbogtrykker B. Luno, 1851.
59, 2 p. 26cm.
Særskilt aftrykt af det Kgl. danske videnskabernes selskabs Skrifter, 5. række, naturvidenskabelig og mathematisk afdeling, 2. bind.

1. Central America. Botany. 2. Mexico. Botany. 3. Urticales.
Agr 13—457

U. S. Dept. of agr. Library   452.3L62
for Library of Congress   [a41b1]

NL 0347978 DNAL NN MH-A

Liebmann, Frederik Michael.
— Mexicos og central-americas Rubi. [Kjøbenhavn 1852.] 8°.
Videnskabelige meddelelser fra den Naturhistoriske forening i Kjøbenhavn 1852, iv, 150-164.
— The same, reprinted.

NL 0347979 MH-A

Liebmann, Frederik Michael.
— Novorum plantarum mexicanarum generum decas. [Kjøbenhavn. 1853.] 8°.
Videnskabelige meddelelser fra den Naturhistoriske forening i Kjøbenhavn, 1853, v. 90-107.
— The same, reprinted.

NL 0347980 MH-A

Liebmann, [Frederik Michael]. En ny islandsk Carex. *Extr. fr.* Forhandlinger ved de skandinaviske Naturforskeres andet Møde i Kjøbenhavn. 1840. Kjøbenhavn, 1841. 8°. pp. 320–321. IcC19L716

NL 0347981 NIC

LIEBMANN, Frederik [Michael].
Philetaeria; en ny anomal slaegt af Polemoniac. Mit Tafel. (Kjøbenh.),1850.
4°.

NL 0347982 MH

Liebmann, F[rederik Michael], 1813–1856.
Philetæria; en ny anomal Slægt af Polemoniaceernes Familie. (Kongeligt Dansk Videnskabernes Selskab. Skrifter. Kjøbenhavn, 1851. 4°. Række 5. Naturvidenskabelig og mathematisk Afdeling. Bind 2, p. 279-284, 1 pl.)

1. Polemoniaceæ.
N. Y. P. L.   December 26, 1911.

NL 0347983 NN

Liebmann, Frederik Michael, 1813–1856.
— To nye arter af slægten Castelia Turp. [Kjøbenhavn. 1853.] 8°.
Videnskabelige meddelelser fra den Naturhistoriske forening i Kjøbenhavn, 1853, v, 108-111.

NL 0347984 MH-A

457—
Liebmann, Fritz, Referendar: Eigenschaftsirrtum und Sachmängelhaftung beim Kauf. Borna-Leipzig 1912: **Noske.** XI, 117 S. 8°
Marburg, Jur. Diss. v. 20. Juni 1912, Ref. Enneccerus
[Geb. 29. April 87 Wiesbaden; Wohnort: Wiesbaden; Staatsangeh.: Preußen; Vorbildung: Gymn. Wiesbaden Reife O. 05; Studium: München 3, Berlin 1, Bonn 1, Marburg 2 S.; Rig. 4. Mai 12.]   [U 12. 3454

NL 0347985 ICRL

Liebmann, Gerhard, 1906–
Die temperaturstrahlung der ungefaerbten Oxyde im sichtbaren.
Inaug. Diss., Berlin, 1930
404 - 436 p.
From Zeitschrift für Physik, Bd. 63.

NL 0347986 ICRL CtY OU

ar V
2395
Liebmann, Gerhard, 1910–
Erstergebnisse einer Reihe von Gaumenspalt-Operation nach Axhausen. Sarstedt, Meyer, 1938.
45 p. 21 cm.
Diss.—Göttingen, 1938.

NL 0347987 NIC

QP121
L62
Liebmann, Gustav
Versuche über die rhythmik der athembewegungen ... Tübingen, Laupp, 1856.
28 p. fold. table.
Thesis, Tübingen.

1. Respiration.

NL 0347988 NNC DNLM

VOLUME 332

Bf3 101 81   Liebmann, Hans, 1886–
Deutsches Land und Volk nach italienischen Berichterstattern der Reformationszeit, von Dr. Hans Liebmann. Berlin, E. Ebering, 1910.
4 p. ℓ., 241 p., 1 ℓ. 23 cm. (Historische Studien, veröffentlicht von E. Ebering ... Heft LXXXI)
"Bücherverzeichnis": p. [1]-12.
Published in part as the author's inaugural dissertation, Jena, 1910.

NL   0347989   CtY MH ICRL OU MH NN

Liebmann, Hans, 1910–
Handbuch der Frischwasser- und Abwasserbiologie; Biologie des Trinkwassers, Badewassers, Fischwassers, Vorfluters und Abwassers. München, R. Oldenbourg, 1951–
v. illus. (part col.) 24 cm.
Bibliography: v. 1, p. [510]-524.

1. Fresh-water biology.

QH96.L5   574.929   51–32490

ICU PU MH-GM MtBC PPAN OrCS CaBVaU IdU
NL   0347990   DLC IU CU NcRS NN OU PU-Z CtY DNLM NIC

QH96 .M8   Liebmann, Hans, 1910–
Münchner Beiträge zur Abwasser-, Fischerei- und Flussbiologie. Heft 1–
München, R. Oldenbourg, 1953–

Liebmann, Hans, 1910–
Zooparasiten und fischpathogene Keime im Abwasser und Fischwasser
see under title

Liebmann   , Harry) [1877–
Das Rhinophyma und seine chirurgische Behandlung. 32 pp., 1 pl. 8°.
Leipzig, B. Georgi, 1906.
[Full name: Eduard Rudolf Harry Liebmann]

NL   0347993   DNLM ICRL CtY

Liebmann, Heinrich, of Chemnitz.
Beitraege zur kenntnis der salpetrigen saeure. Inaug. diss. Dresden, techn. hochs., 1914 (Leipzig).
72 p.

NL   0348001   ICRL

Liebmann, Heinrich, 1874–
Die Aufschliessung von Differentialinvarianten. Von Heinrich Liebmann... Berlin: W. de Gruyter & Co., 1925. 16 p. 8°. (Heidelberger Akad. der Wissenschaften. Mathematisch-naturwissenschaftliche Klasse. Abt. A, Jahrg. 1924–25, Abhandl. 11.)

1. Invariants, Differential.
N.Y.P.L.   September 30, 1925

NL   0348002   NN

Liebmann, Heinrich, 1874–
Berührungstransformationen, von Heinrich Liebmann ...
(In Encyklopädie der mathematischen wissenschaften. Leipzig, 1902–27. 25ᶜᵐ. bd. III—3, hft. 4, p. [441]–502)
"Abgeschlossen im oktober 1914."
Published May 14, 1915.
"Literatur": p. [441]–442.

1. Transformations, Tangential. 2. Differential equations.
3. Invariants.
[Full name: Karl Otto Heinrich Liebmann]
Brown univ. Library   A 21–1382
for Library of Congress   [QA36.E56 bd. III–3]

NL   0348003   RPB CU OU ODW OC1W DLC

Liebmann, Heinrich, 1874–
Die berührungstransformationen. Geschichte und invariantentheorie. Zwei referate der Deutschen mathematiker-vereinigung, erstattet von H. Liebmann und F. Engel. Leipzig, B. G. Teubner, 1914.
3 p. l., 79 p. 25½ᶜᵐ. (Added t.-p.: Jahresbericht der Deutschen mathematiker-vereinigung. Der ergänzungsbände v. bd.)

1. Transformations, Tangential. 2. Invariants. I. Engel, Friedrich, 1861–
[Full name: Karl Otto Heinrich Liebmann]
Library of Congress   QA385.L75   14–13230 Revised
Copyright A—Foreign   10876

NL   0348004   DLC OCU NjP OU NcU NcD PBm ICJ PU-Math

LIEBMANN, Heinrich, 1874–
Die construction des geradlinigen dreiecks der nichteuklidischen geometrie. n. p., n. d.
Math 5030.3.5

NL   0348005   MH

Liebmann, Heinrich, 1874–   ed.
Die darstellung ganz willkürlicher functionen durch sinus- und cosinusreihen, von Lejeune Dirichlet (1837), und Note über eine eigenschaft der reihen, welche discontinuirliche functionen darstellen, von Philipp Ludwig Seidel (1847) Hrsg. von Heinrich Liebmann. Leipzig, W. Engelmann, 1900.
58 p. 19½ cm. (On cover: Ostwald's Klassiker der exakten wissenschaften, nr. 116)
Dirichlet's treatise first published in Repertorium der physik, von H. W. Dove und L. Moser, bd. 1, 1837; Seidel's treatise in Abhandl. der Math.-phys. klasse der K. Bayerischen akademie der wissenschaften, bd. 5, 1847.
1. Fourier series.   I. Lejeune-Dirichlet, Peter Gustav, 1805–1859. II. Seidel, Philipp Ludwig von, 1821–1896.
[Full name: Karl Otto Heinrich Liebmann]
QA404.L7   3–20437
Library of Congress

NL   TU 0348006   DLC CU-S CU ICJ CLSU PPF PBL MiU OCU OU

Liebmann, Heinrich, 1874–
Die einzweideutigen projektiven punktverwandtschaften der ebene ... Jena, Druck von A. Kämpfe, 1895.
52 p. diagr. 21½ᶜᵐ.
Inaug.-diss.—Jena.

1. Transformations (Mathematics)
[Full name: Karl Otto Heinrich Liebmann]
4–28724
Library of Congress   QA601.L71

NL   0348007   DLC NjP

Liebmann, Heinrich, 1874–
Geometrische theorie der differentialgleichungen, von H. Liebmann ...
(In Encyklopädie der mathematischen wissenschaften. Leipzig, 1902–27. 25ᶜᵐ. bd. III—3, hft. 4, p. [503]–539. diagrs.)
"Abgeschlossen im oktober 1914."
Published May 14, 1915.
"Literatur": p. [503]

1. Differential equations. 2. Geometry, Differential.
[Full name: Karl Otto Heinrich Liebmann]
Brown univ. Library   A 21–1383 Revised
for Library of Congress   [QA36.E56 bd. III–3]

NL   0348008   RPB DLC CU

Liebmann, Heinrich, 1874–   ed. and tr.
Lobachevskiĭ, Nikolaĭ Ivanovich, 1793–1856.
... N. J. Lobatschefskijs Imaginäre geometrie und Anwendung der imaginären geometrie auf einige integrale. Aus dem russischen übers. und mit anmerkungen hrsg. von Heinrich Liebmann. Mit 39 figuren im text und auf einer tafel. Leipzig, B. G. Teubner, 1904.

LIEBMANN, Heinrich, 1874–
Die kegelschnitte und die planetenbewegung im nichteuklidischen raum. Leipzig, [1902.]

NL   0348010   MH

Liebmann, Heinrich, 1874–   517.38 Q001
Lehrbuch der Differentialgleichungen. vi,226 p. 31 il. O. Leipzig: Veit & Co., 1901.

MH DBS NNU-W
NL   0348011   ICJ NjP MA OCU MiU OC1W OO ODW PSt CtY

[EB] (Heidelberger)
Liebmann, Heinrich, 1874–
Die Lie'sche Cyklide und die Inversionskrümmung, von Heinrich Liebmann... Berlin: W. de Gruyter & Co., 1923. 20 p. 8°. (Heidelberger Akad. der Wissenschaften. Sitzungsb. Mathematisch-naturwissenschaftliche Klasse. Abt. A, Jahrg. 1923, Abhandl. 2.)

1. Cyclide. 2. Inversion (Mathematical).
N.Y.P.L.   October 8, 1923.

NL   0348012   NN

Liebmann, Heinrich, 1874–
... Nichteuklidische geometrie, von Heinrich Liebmann ... Mit 22 figuren. Leipzig, G. J. Göschen, 1905.
viii, 248 p. diagrs. 19½ᵐᵐ. (Sammlung Schubert XLIX)
Series title also at head of t.-p.

1. Geometry, Non-Euclidean.
[Full name: Karl Otto Heinrich Liebmann]
Library of Congress   QA685.L7   5–12150 Revised
r25d2r

NL   0348013   DLC NjP PPL CU OU OOxM MiU ICJ NjR

LIEBMANN, Heinrich, 1874–
Nichteuklidische geometrie. 2e, neubearbeitete aufl. Berlin, etc., G. J. Göschen, 1912.
(Sammlung Schubert, 49.)   Math 5039.12.5

NL   0348014   MH PU-Math

QA685 L7 1923   Liebmann, Heinrich, 1874–
Nichteuklidische Geometrie. 3., neubearbeitete Aufl. Berlin, W. de Gruyter, 1923.
150 p. illus. 24 cm.

1. Geometry, Non-Euclidean. I. Title.

OrCS
NL   0348015   GU MH CU OCU MiU ODW NjP CtY PSC NcD

*Liebmann, Heinrich, 1874–   ed.
Bonola, Roberto, 1874–1911.
... Die nichteuklidische geometrie, historisch-kritische darstellung ihrer entwicklung. Autorisierte deutsche ausg. besorgt von prof. dr. Heinrich Liebmann. Mit 76 figuren im text. Leipzig und Berlin, B. G. Teubner, 1908.

VOLUME 332

510 ₍Liebmann,₎ Heinrich₎ *1874-*
L62n ₍Notwendigkeit und freiheit in der mathematik.₎ Leipzig, 1905₎
231-248 p.
Akademische antrittsvorlesung, gehalten in Leipzig am 25. februar, 1905.

1. Mathematics.

NL 0348017 IU

---

*Liebmann, Heinrich, 1874-

Lobachevskiĭ, Nikolaĭ Ïvanovich, 1793-1856.
Pangeometrie, von N. J. Lobatschefskij. Kasan 1856.
Uebers. und hrsg. von Heinrich Liebmann. Mit 30 figuren
im text. Leipzig, W. Engelmann, 1902.

Liebmann, Heinrich, 1874-   ed.

Mitzscherling, Arthur, 1879-1912.
Das problem der kreisteilung, ein beitrag zur geschichte
seiner entwicklung, von dr. Arthur Mitzscherling ... mit
einem vorwort von dr. Heinrich Liebmann ... Mit 210
figuren im text. Leipzig und Berlin, B. G. Teubner, 1913.

Liebmann, Heinrich, 1874-
... Synthetische geometrie, von Heinrich Liebmann ... Mit
45 figuren. Leipzig und Berlin, B. G. Teubner, 1934.

viii, 119 p. diagrs. 20½ᶜᵐ. (Teubners mathematische leitfäden, bd.
40)

1. Geometry, Projective.   I. Title.
₍Full name: Karl Otto Heinrich Liebmann₎
35-3530
Library of Congress   QA471.L4S

₍2₎   516.57

NL 0348020 DLC CU MiU ODW PSC ICU OrU

Liebmann, Heinrich, 1874-
Über die verbiegung der geschlossenen flächen positiver
krümmung ... ₍von₎ dr. Heinrich Liebmann ... Leipzig,
Druck von B. G. Teubner, 1899.

1 p. l., 32 p. diagrs. 24½ᶜᵐ.
Habilitationsschrift—Leipzig.
"Sonderabdruck aus den 'Mathematischen annalen', bd. LIII."

1. Surfaces, Deformation of.
₍Full name: Karl Otto Heinrich Liebmann₎
4-23618 Revised
Library of Congress   QA648.I.71

NL 0348021 DLC NjP MiU

---

* EE
Liebmann, Heinrich, 1874-
Umkehrung des Variationsproblems der ebenen Affingeo-
metrie, von Heinrich Liebmann ... Berlin: W. de Gruyter &
Co., 1924.   8 p.   8°. (Heidelberger Akad. der Wissen-
schaften.   Sitzungsb.   Mathematisch - naturwissenschaftliche
Klasse. Abt. A, Jahrg. 1924, Abhandl. 2.)

1. Calculus of variations.
N. Y. P. L.   August 22, 1924

NL 0348022 NN

Liebmann, Heinrich i.e. Karl Otto Heinrich,
1874-   tr.

Markov, Andreĭ Andreevich, 1856-
Wahrscheinlichkeitsrechnung, von A. A. Markoff; nach
der 2. aufl. des russischen werkes übersetzt von Heinrich
Liebmann. Mit 7 figuren im text. Leipzig und Berlin,
B. G. Teubner, 1912.

Liebmann, Helene (Riese), b. 1796.
Lied von Göthe aus Wilhelm Meister, komponirt ... von
Helene Riese. Op. 4.   Berlin: Kunst- und Industrie-Comptoir₍,
1811₎. 3 p.   22 x 31cm.

German words; music for 1 voice with piano acc.
First line: Kennst du das Land? Wo die Citronen blühn.

1. Songs, German. I. Goethe, Johann
N. Y. P. L.   Wolfgang von.
CARNEGIE CORPORATION OF NEW YORK.
Wilhelm Meister.
November 9, 1933

NL 0348024 NN

---

box
Liebmann, Helene (Riese), b. 1796.
Variations de la romance favourite de la petite Cendrillon (ôu
Aschenbrödel) pour le piano-forte. Composées ... par E. Lieb-
mann. Vienne, L. Maisch ₍ca. 1815₎ Publ. pl. no. 455.   5 p.
23 x 33cm.

For piano.

1. Piano.
N. Y. P. L.   November 15, 1946

NL 0348025 NN

HD 8443 LIEBMANN, HERMANN
.A57 L7   Die Politik der Generalkommission; ein
Sündenregister der Zentralvorstände der
freien Gewerkschaften Deutschlands un die
Wegweiser für die Zukunft.   Leipzig, Leipziger
Buchdruckerei, 1919.
72 p.

1. Generalkommission der Gewerkschaften Deutschlands. I. Tc.

NL 0348026 InU DLC-P4 MH

Liebmann, Hermann, 1907-
Zur bestimmung der teilchengrösse in
zinnsäuresolen. ... Köln, 1934.
Inaug. Diss. - Köln, 1934.
Lebenslauf.

NL 0348027 ICRL CtY

Liebmann, Irmgard, 1909-
*Praktische Erfahrungen mit
Wiga-Schmelzmetall ₍Leipzig₎ 28p. 8°. Zeu-
lenroda, 1934.

NL 0348028 DNLM CtY

Liebmann, J
Bibliothek des verstorbenen Herrn Justizrat
Dr. J. Liebmann
see under   Baer (Joseph) & Co., Frankfurt
am Main.

LIEBMANN, Jacob, *d. 1926.*
Kommentar zum gesetz betreffend die gesellschaften mit beschränkter haftung in der fassung vom 20 mai 1898.   4te, vollständig umgearbeitete auflage auf grundlage des Hergenhahn'schen
kommentars.   Berlin, 1899.

NL 0348030 MH-L CtY

Liebmann, Jacob, d. 1926.
Kommentar zum gesetz betreffend die
gesellschaften mit beschränkter haftung.
5., gänzlich neubearb. und verm. aufl.
nebst einem anhange: Die einkommenbe-
steuerung der gesellschaften mit beschränkter haftung in Preussen und die
reichsstempelabgabe auf den tantiemen,
von dr. J. Liebmann ... Berlin, O.
Liebmann, 1906.
x, 260 p.   20⅔cm.
"Abkürzungen"   (bibliographical):
p. viii-x.

NL 0348031 MH-L

Liebmann, Jacob, d. 1926.
Kommentar zum gesetz betreffend die gesellschaften
mit beschränkter haftung.   Nebst einem anhange: Das
österreichische gesetz über die gesellschaften mit beschränkter haftung.   Von dr. J. Liebmann ...   6. gänzlich neu bearb. und verm. aufl.   Berlin, O. Liebmann,
1921.
x, 374 p.   22½ᶜᵐ.
1. Corporation law—Germany. 2. Corporation law—Austria. 3. Stock
companies—Austria. ₍3. Joint-stock companies—Germany₎ 4. Stock companies—Austria. ₍4. Joint-stock companies—Austria₎ 5. Limited liability.
I. Germany.   Laws, statutes, etc., 1888-1918 (William II) Gesetz, betreffend
die gesellschaften mit beschränkter haftung. II. Austria. Laws, statutes,
etc., 1848-1916 (Francis   Joseph I) Das gesetz vom 6. märz
1906. III. Title.
26-8174
Library of Congress   ₍2₎

NL 0348032 DLC MH

Liebmann, Jacob, d. 1926.
Kommentar zum Gesetz betreffend die gesellschaften mit beschränkter haftung.   Nebst mustern für gesellschaftsverträge,
für anmeldungen und gesellschafterbeschlüsse und dem österreichischen Gesetz über die gesellschaften mit beschränkter
haftung. Von dr. J. Liebmann ... und dr. A. Saenger ...   7.,
neubearb. und stark verm. aufl.   Berlin, O. Liebmann, 1927.
x, 465 p.   22ᶜᵐ.
"Abkürzungsverzeichnis" (bibliography): p. ₍viii₎-x.
1. Private companies—Germany. 2. Private companies—Austria.   I.
Saenger, August, 1884-   joint author. II. Germany. Laws, statutes,
etc. III. Austria. Laws, statutes, etc.

Bibliography: p. ₍viii₎-x.

1. Corporation law—Germany. ₍1. Corporations—Germany₎ 2. Corporation law—Austria. ₍2. Corporations—Austria₎ 3. Stock companies—
Germany. ₍3. Joint-stock companies—Germany₎ 4. Stock companies—
Austria. ₍4. Joint-stock companies—Austria₎ 5. Limited liability.
I. Saenger, August, 1884-   joint author. II. Germany. Laws, statutes, etc. III. Austria. Laws, statutes, etc.
30-20740

NL 0348034 DLC

Liebmann, Jacob, ed., *d. 1926.*
Das Reichsgesetz betreffend die Gesellschaften
mit beschränkter Haftung vom 20. April 1892 ...
Berlin ... 1895
see under   Germany. Laws, statutes, etc.

PN511 Liebmann, James Alexander.
L5   Essays in ancient & modern literature.   Cape Town, Printed
at the Cape Times Printing Works, 1893.
79 p.

Contents. - On the Oresteia of Aeschylus. - Racine's Phèdre and
its relation to the Hippolytus of Euripides. - Goethe's Faust. -
Molière, a study of the rise and progress of French comedy. -
Lessing's Minna von Barnheim, a study on the rise and progress of
German comedy.

1. Literature - Addresses, essays, lectures.

NL 0348036 CU

VOLUME 332

Liebmann, James Alexander.
   Goethe's 'Faust': an essay compiled from various sources and authorities. By Professor James Alex. Liebmann ...
   (*In* Royal society of literature of the United Kingdom, London. Essays by divers hands, being the transactions. London, 1898. 22ᶜᵐ. 2d ser., vol. XIX, p. ₍107₎–150)
   "Read November 8th, 1897."
   "Works consulted": p. 150.

   1. Goethe, Johann Wolfgang von. Faust.
                   A 44–5588
Illinois. Univ. Library
  for Library of Congress   PN22.R6   2d ser., vol. 19
                  ₍3₎†

  NL 0348037   IU DLC

Liebmann, James Alexander.
   Racine's Phèdre, and its relation to the Hippolytus of Euripides. By Professor James Alex. Liebmann ...
   (*In* Royal society of literature of the United Kingdom, London. Essays by divers hands, being the transactions. London, 1899. 22ᶜᵐ. 2d ser., vol. XX, p. ₍133₎–158)
   "Read December 14th, 1898."

   1. Racine, Jean Baptiste, 1639–1699. Phèdre. 2. Euripides. Hippolytus.
Illinois. Univ. Library   A 44–5597
  for Library of Congress   PN22.R6   2d ser., vol. 20
                  ₍3₎†

  NL 0348038   IU DLC

Liebmann, James Alexander.
   Vocabulary of technical military terms, English-German, German-English, for the use of military students, by Prof. James Alex. Liebmann ... With a preface by Gen Sir William Gordon Cameron ... London and Aldershot, Gale & Polden, ltd. ₍1896₎
   215 p. 19ᶜᵐ. (*Lettered on cover:* Gale & Polden's military series)

   1. Military art and science—Dictionaries. 2. English language—Dictionaries—German. 3. German language—Dictionaries—English.
                   18–2997
Library of Congress   U25.L6

  NL 0348039   DLC DNW DN DAL MB NjP ICJ ViU

Liebmann (Joannes Augustus). *De furore uterino. 31 pp. sm. 4°. Halæ ad Salam, prelo Gurtiano, ₍1700₎.

  NL 0348040   DNLM PPC NNAM

                           NAC p.v.390
Liebmann, Johannes Aenotheus.
   De Isaei vita et scriptis commentatio. Scripsit Jo. Aenoth. Liebmann ... Addita est Annalium Scholae Latinae Halensis particula sexta. Auctore J. G. Diek ... Halis Saxonum: In Libraria orphanotrophei, 1831. 30 p. 22ᶜᵐ.
   "Historische Nachrichten von der lateinischen Schule im Waisenhause," p. 19–30.

781637A. 1. Isæus. 2. Schools,   Private—Germany—Halle. I. Diek, Johann Gottlieb.
N. Y. P. L.   September 3, 1936

  NL 0348041   NN MH PU

Liebmann, Julius i. e. Carl Julius, 1880–1914.
   Beiträge zu einer universelleren anwendung der querlibelle für die controlle der fundamentalen sternörter ... ₍Berlin, Mayer & Müller₎ 1905.
   1 p. l., 26 p., 1 l. fold. tables, diagrs. 27½ x 22ᶜᵐ.
   Inaug.-diss.—Berlin.
   Vita.

   1. Astronomy, Spherical and practical.

Library of Congress   QB154.L7   7–17149

  NL 0348042   DLC CtY ICRL

Liebmann, Karl, 1890–
   Die grenzen der haftung des gattungsschuldners auf die erfuellung.
   Inaug. diss. Marburg, 1919. (Leipzig)
   Bibl.

  NL 0348043   ICRL

Liebmann, Karl Otto Heinrich
   see
Liebmann, Heinrich, 1874–

DD491
S5L716
Liebmann, Karl Theodor.
   Eine brennende gefahr für die deutsche arbeiterschaft. Von Karl Theodor Liebmann. ₍n.p., 1920?₎
   ₍4₎ p. 21ᶜᵐ.
   A comparison of the German and Polish laboring classes for the consideration of the Silesians before the plebiscite.
   1.European war, 1914–1918 – Territorial questions – Silesia. I.Title.

  NL 0348045   CSt-H CSt

Liebmann, Kurt, 1897–
   Adolph Menzel als Graphiker. Dresden, VEB Verlag der Kunst, 1955
   25 p. 17 illus. (Das kleine Kunstheft, 14)

  NL 0348046   MH MH-FA

                           51538.2.80
Liebmann, Kurt, 1897–
   Das dichterische Lebenswerk von Friedrich Kurt Benndorf; eine Betrachtung. Dresden, Jess, 1936
   24 p. music

  NL 0348047   MH

831.9
L716e
Liebmann, Kurt, 1897–
   Entwerden; Dichtung. [n.p.] Privatdruck, 1921.
   95p. 24cm.

  NL 0348048   IEN InU MH

PT 2623 LIEBMANN,KURT,1897–
.I197 F45   Feststellungen I. Dessau, Liebmann & 1926   Mette, 1926.
        15 p.

  NL 0348049   InU

Liebmann, Kurt, 1897–
   Friedrich Boettger, ein lebensbild, von Kurt Liebmann. Berlin-Steglitz, Dion-verlag ₍1938₎
   20 p. front. (port.) 21ᶜᵐ.
   "Die nachstehende ansprache wurde zur Friedrich Boettger-gedächtnisfeier am 14. dezember 1936 in Dessau gehalten."
   "Der nachlass dr. Friedrich Boettgers": p. 16–20.

   1. Boettger, Friedrich, 1895–1936.
                   41–13176
Library of Congress   ML410.B685L5
          ₍2₎   927.8

  NL 0348050   DLC

193
N67Z Lieb **Liebmann, Kurt,** 1897–
   Friedrich Nietzsche, die Deutung eines Schicksals. München, E. Reinhardt, 1943.
   145p. 20cm.

   1. Nietzsche, Friedrich Wilhelm, 1844–1900.

  NL 0348051   IEN DLC-P4 ICU NcD MH NNC

Liebmann, Kurt, 1897–
   Kleist, eine dramatische vision. Dresden, W. Jess [c1932]
   88 p. 24 cm.
   "Geschrieben 1927 am fusse des Brockens."

  NL 0348052   PU

PT 2623 LIEBMANN,KURT,1897–
.I197 K95   Kreuzigung; Dichtung. Dessau, K. Rauch, 1924   1924.
        31 p. (Die Drucke der Schau, no. 2)

  NL 0348053   InU

                           MCK
                         (Nebel)
LIEBMANN, KURT, 1897–
   Der Malerdichter Otto Nebel; ein Beitrag zur Philosophie der modernen Kunst, von Kurt Liebmann... Zürich [etc.] Orell Füssli [1935] 37 p. col'd front., plates. 22½cm.

825546A. 1. Nebel, Otto, 1892–

  NL 0348054   NN CLU

Liebmann, Kurt, 1897–
   Nietzsches Kampf und Untergang in Turin, Nietzsche und Mussolini. Leipzig, M. Möhring ₍19—₎
   85 p. 25 cm. (Italien in Vergangenheit und Gegenwart, Heft 8)

   1. Nietzsche, Friedrich Wilhelm, 1844–1900. 2. Mussolini, Benito, 1883–1945. (Series)
B3317.L53   50–20094

  NL 0348055   DLC

PT 2623 LIEBMANN,KURT,1897–
.I197 S37   Schräg geöffnet; Kreis Gedichte. Dessau, 1924   K. Rauch, 1924.
        40 p. illus.

  NL 0348056   InU

3009
.587   **Liebmann, Kurt,**   ed.
   Vom Ursprung zur Vollendung. Ein Lebensbuch kosmisch-religiöser Bindung. Hrsg. und eingeleitet von Kurt Liebmann. Jena, Diederichs, 1929.
   210 p. illus. 22 cm.

   1. Religion and literature. I. Title.

  NL 0348057   NjP

VOLUME 332

Liebmann, Kurt, *1897-*
Wassili Iwanowitsch Surikow. Dresden, VEB Verlag der Kunst, 1954

21 p. 16 illus. (Das kleine Kunstheft, 12)

NL 0348058   MH MH-FA

Liebmann, ⌐Leopold.⌐
Die 50 jährige Jubelfeier des Ober-lehrers ⌐L.⌐ Liebmann in Esslingen am 26. August 1872. ⌐Ed. by A. Elsaesser.⌐ Esslingen: L. Harburger, 1872.
23 p.   8.

NL 0348059   OCH

Liebmann (Leopold) [1882-   ]. *Bericht über die Wirksamkeit der Universitätsaugen-klinik zu Giessen. 44 pp. 8°. Emmendingen, Dölter, 1908.

NL 0348060   DNLM ICRL MBCo

3431   Liebmann, Louis.
.4   Bettina von Arnim und Freiherr von Drais.
.787   ⌐Frankfurt a.M., Würsten, 1920⌐
28 p. illus. 23 cm.

Limited ed.
"Sonderdruck aus der Festgabe für Friedrich Clemens Ebrard."

1.Arnim, Bettina (Brentano)von, 1785-1859.

NL 0348061   NjP TU ICN

Liebmann, Louis.
Frankfurt am Main. Internationale luftschiffahrts-aus-stellung, 1909.
Führer durch die historische abteilung der Internationalen luftschiffahrts-ausstellung, Frankfurt a. M., 1909. Mit 10 ab-bildungen ... Frankfurt a. M., Druck der Kunstanstalt Wüsten & co. ⌐1909⌐

Liebmann, Louis.
Berlin. Internationale luftfahrt-ausstellung, 1928.
Internationale luftfahrt-ausstellung, Berlin 1928, 7.-28.okto-ber, ausstellungshallen am Kaiserdamm, unter dem protektorat des herrn reichspräsidenten von Hindenburg, veranstaltet von der deutschen luftfahrt-industrie unter mitwirkung des Aus-stellungs-, messe- u. fremdenverkehrs-amtes der stadt Berlin. Offizieller katalog. Berlin, Verlag G. Braunbeck g. m. b. h. und Union deutsche verlagsgesellschaft, zweigniederlassung Berlin ⌐1928⌐

Liebmann, Louis.
Frankfurt am Main. Internationale luftschiffahrts-aus-stellung, 1909.
Katalog der historischen abteilung der ersten Inter-nationalen luftschiffahrts-ausstellung (I L A) zu Frank-furt a. M. 1909, von dr Louis Liebmann ... und dr Gustav Wahl ... mit 2 tafeln und 80 abbildungen. Frankfurt a. M., Wüsten & co., 1912.

Liebmann, Louis, *Chemist.*
Condensation von Benzaldehyd mit Brens-weinsäure. Tübingen, 1888.
42 p. illus.

Inaug.-Diss. - Basel

WO 25028

NL 0348065   CtY CU

Liebmann, Manfred
Die verwaltungsrechtliche stellung der filmprüfstellen und der filmoberprüfstelle ... Aschaffenburg, 1933.   69 p.
Inaug. Diss. -Würzburg, 1933.
Bibliography.

NL 0348066   ICRL

Liebmann, Margarete, 1908-
Der sterische verlauf einiger additions-reaktionen. ... 1936.   34 p.
Inaug. Diss. - Kiel, 1936.
Lebenslauf.

NL 0348067   ICRL CtY

Liebmann (Michael). *De influenza quæ a. 1833, verno tempore Gryphiam tenuit. 32 pp. 8°. *Gryphiæ, Kunike, 1834.*

NL 0348068   DNLM

Liebmann, N⌐   ⌐.
Hebräische Lesefibel für die zwei ersten Schuljahre. 7. Auflage. Vermehrt und vollständig neu bearbeitet von S. Dingfelder. Frankfurt a.M.: J. Kauffmann, 1907.
49, 7 p.

NL 0348069   OCH

Liebmann, O.
Das staatsrecht des fürstenthums Reuss älterer linie. Von O. Liebmann ...
(*In* Meyer, G.   Das staatsrecht der Thüringischen staaten ... Frei-burg i. B. ⌐etc.⌐ 1884. p. ⌐175⌐-185)
Handbuch des oeffentlichen rechts. 3. bd., 2 halbbd., 2. abt.

1. Reuss (Elder line)—Constitutional law. 2. Reuss (Elder line)—Pol. & govt.

Library of Congress   JF13.H4   vol.3   G-250

NL 0348070   DLC NIC

Liebmann, Otto, 1840-1912.
Divina commedia. (*In*: Zeitschrift für Philosophie und philosophische Kritik. [1897] Bd. cx. p. 165).

NL 0348071   NIC

Liebmann, Otto, 1840-1912.
Gedanken und thatsachen. Philosophische abhandlun-gen, aphorismen und studien von Otto Liebmann. ... Strassburg, K. J. Trübner, 1882-1904.
2 v. 22½ᶜᵐ.

Vol. 1 is without general t.-p., but each of the three parts has special t.-p., dated 1882-89; v. 2 has general t.-p. only, but was issued in four parts, 1901-1904. Each volume is paged continuously.

1. Philosophy, German.

NL 0348072   MiU MH NcD

Liebmann, Otto, 1840-1912.
Gedanken und Thatsachen. Philosophische Abhandlungen, Aphorismen und Studien. Strassburg, K. J. Trübner, 1899-1904.
2 v. illus. 23cm.

1. Philosophy—Addresses, essays, lectures.
2. Psychology—Addresses, essays, lectures.
I. Title.

B 3286 L71 G2

NL 0348073   NIC CU

Liebmann, Otto, *1840-1912.*
Gedanken und thatsachen. Philosophische abhand-lungen, aphorismen und studien, von Otto Liebmann. Strassburg, Karl J. Trübner, 1901.

v.   21.5cm.

1. Philosophy. 2. Metaphysics. 3. Knowledge, Theory of. I. Title.

NL 0348074   NNF

Liebmann, Otto, 1840-1912.
Gedanken und thatsachen. Philosophische abhandlungen, aphorismen und studien von Otto Liebmann ... Strassburg, K. J. Trübner, 1904-28.
2 v. 1 illus. (music) 22½ᶜᵐ.
Vol. 1 issued in 3 parts, v. 2 in 4 parts, each with special t.-p. Vol. 2, pts. 3 and 4 have imprint: Berlin und Leipzig, Vereinigung wissenschaft-licher verleger, W. de Gruyter & co.
CONTENTS.—t. bd. ⌐1. hft.⌐ Die arten der nothwendigkeit. Die mecha-nische naturerklärung. Idee und entelechie. 2. aufl. 1904. 2. hft. Gedanken über natur und naturkenntnis. 1899, neudruck 1925.

3. hft. Die bilder der phantasie. Das zeitbewusstsein. Die sprachfähig-keit. Psychologische aphorismen. 1899, neudruck 1925.—II. bd. ⌐1. hft.⌐ Geist der transcendentalphilosophie. 1904, neudruck 1928. 2. hft. Grundriss der kritischen metaphysik. 1901, neudruck 1925. 3. hft. Trilogie des pessimismus. Gedanken über schönheit und kunst. Anasta-tischer neudruck 1920. 4. hft. Der ursprung der werthe. Episoden; eine gedankensymphonie. Gedanken über das wesen der moralität. Gang der geschichte. Anastatischer neudruck 1920.

1. Philosophy—Addresses, essays, lectures. 2. Psychology—Addresses, essays, lectures. I. Title.

Library of Congress   B3286.L53G4 1904   40-2144
⌐2⌐   104

NL 0348076   DLC

Liebmann, Otto, 1840-1912.
Immanuel Kant; eine Gedächtnissrede ge-halten am hundertjährigen Todestage-Kants, den 12.Febr.1904, vor versammelter Universität in der Collegienkirche zu Jena. Strassburg, K.J.Trübner, 1904.
vii,18p. 23cm.

1. Kant, Immanuel, 1724-1804.   I. Title.

B 2797 L711

NL 0348077   NRU ICRL ICJ GEU CaBVaU

Liebmann, Otto, 1840-1912.
Kant und die epigonen. Eine kritische abhandlung von dr. Otto Liebmann ... Stuttgart, C. Schober, 1865.
218, ⌐2⌐ p. 21½ᶜᵐ.

1. Kant, Immanuel, 1724-1804. 2. Philosophy, German.

           36-12597
Library of Congress   B2743.L5   193

NL 0348078   DLC ScU NIC NjP OClW MH PU PBm WaTC

VOLUME 332

Liebmann, Otto, 1840–1912.
   Kant und die epigonen.   Eine kritische abhandlung von
Otto Liebmann ...   Besorgt von Bruno Bauch.   Berlin,
Reuther & Reichard, 1912.
   xii, ᵢ4ᵣ, 239, ᵢ1ᵣ p. 22ᶜᵐ.   (*Added t.-p.:* Neudrucke seltener philosophischer
werke, bd. II)
   With facsim. reproduction of original t.-p., 1865.
   "Otto Liebmann": p. ᵢ223ᵣ–239.

   1. Kant, Immanuel, 1724–1804. 2. Transcendentalism.   I. Bauch, Bruno,
1877–   ed.

              MoU CU ICRL CaBVaU
NL   0348079   IU NN OCU ViU CU ICJ CLSU NRU OCU ViU

---

193   Liebmann, Otto, 1840–1912.
L716k   Die Klimax der Theorieen; eine Unter-
         suchung aus dem Bereich der allgemeinen
         Wissenschaftslehre.   Strassburg, K.J.
         Trübner, 1884.
            iv,113p. 22cm.

            1:Knowledge, Theory of. I.Title.
         LC.

NL   0348080   CLSU ICJ PU MH CaBVaU

Q
175
.L54   Liebmann, Otto, 1840–1912.
1914   Die Klimax der Theorieen; eine Untersuchung
         aus dem Bereich der allgemeinen Wissenschafts-
         lehre. Strassburg, Karl J. Trübner, 1884.
         Anastatischer Neudruck, 1914.
            v, 113 p.

NL   0348081   NNC GEU

---

193   Liebmann, Otto, 1840–1912.
L716p   Psychologische Aphorismen. Leip-
         zig, C.E.M. Pfeffer, 1892.
            54p. 21cm.

            "Separat-Abdruck aus der Zeitschrift
         für Philosophie. Band 101."

NL   0348082   CLSU

---

123   Liebmann, Otto, 1840–1912.
L716u   Ueber den individuellen Beweis für die
         Freiheit des Willens. Ein kritischer
         Beitrag zur Selbsterkenntniss. Stuttgart,
         C. Schober, 1866.
            vi,145p. 22cm.

            Errata slip mounted on p.145.

            1.Free will and determinism. LC

NL   0348083   CLSU MBU NNUT OC1W MH

BF241 Liebmann, Otto, 1840–1912.
 .L7   Ueber den objectiven anblick. Eine kritische abhandlung
         von dr. Otto Liebmann ... Stuttgart, C. Schober, 1869.
            xi, ᵢ3ᵣ, 182 p. fold. tab., diagrs. 22ᶜᵐ.

            1. Sight. 2. Perception.

NL   0348084   ICU MH CLSU RPB OC1W NN

---

193   Liebmann, Otto, 1840–1912.
L716ue   Ueber philosophische Tradition; eine
         akademische Antrittsrede gehalten in der
         Aula der Universität Jena am 9.December
         1882. Strassburg, K.J.Trübner, 1883.
            32p. 20cm.

            1.Philosophy - Addresses, essays, lec-
         tures. I.Title; Die philosophische Tra-
         dition. ✓LC.

NL   0348085   CLSU MH

4DC-   Liebmann, Otto, 1840–1912.
411   Vier Monate von Paris, 1870–1871; Belager-
         ungstagebuch eines Kriegsfreiwilligen im Garde-
         füsilierregiment. 2. Aufl., zur 25. Gedenk-
         feier der Einnahme von Paris hrsg. und mit einer
         Vorrede eingeleitet. München, C.H. Beck,
         1896.
            288 p.

NL   0348086   DLC-P4

B   Liebmann, Otto, 1840–1912
3283   Zur Analysis der Wirklichkeit; philosophische
L573   Untersuchungen. Strassburg, K. J. Trübner,
Z8   1876.
            619p. 24cm.

            1. Philosophy I. Title

NL   0348087   WU MH RPB OC1W MdBP

B   Liebmann, Otto, 1840–1912.
3283   Zur Analysis der Wirklichkeit; eine
L73   Erörterung der Grundprobleme der
Z9   Philosophie. 2. beträchtlich verm. Aufl.
1880   Strassburg, Karl T. Trübner, 1880.
            viii, 680 p. 22cm.

            1. Philosophy.

NL   0348088   NIC ICU CtY CU MB PU PBm

Liebmann, Otto, 1840–1912.   Philos. Lib.
   Zur analysis der wirklichkeit; eine erörterung der grundprobleme der philosophie. 3ᵉ verbesserte und vermehrte aufl. Strassburg, K. G. Trübner, 1900.
   pp. (1), x, 722.

NL   0348089   MH OCU CtY NcD NBuU

Liebmann, Otto, 1840–1912.
   Zur analysis der wirklichkeit. Eine erörterung der grundprobleme der philosophie, von Otto Liebmann ... 4., verb.
aufl. Strassburg, K. J. Trübner, 1911.
   2 p. l., ᵢIIIᵣ–x, 722 p. diagrs. 22½ᶜᵐ.

   1. Philosophy.   39–33805

   Library of Congress   B3283.L573Z8 1911
                                          ᵢ2ᵣ   100

NL   0348090   DLC MdBJ ICN UU CU ICJ OU CaBVaU

Liebmann, Otto, 1865–
Deutsche juristen-zeitung.
   Aus anlass des zehnjährigen bestehens der Deutschen juristen-zeitung, 1896–1906, gewidmet von Otto Liebmann.
ᵢBerlin, O. Liebmann, 1906ᵣ

Liebmann, Otto, 1865–   ed.

Deutsche juristen-zeitung.
   Festgabe der Deutschen juristen-zeitung zum 31. Deutschen
juristentage in Wien. Herausgegeben von dr. jur. h. c. Otto
Liebmann ... Berlin, O. Liebmann, 1912.

Liebmann, Otto, 1865–   ed.

Deutsche juristen-zeitung.
   Festgabe der Deutschen juristen-zeitung zum 500jährigen
jubiläum der Universität Leipzig, herausgegeben von dr. jur.
Otto Liebmann. Berlin, O. Liebmann, 1909.

Liebmann, Otto, 1865–
   Festgabe für dr. jur. h. c. Otto Liebmann
see under title

Liebmann, Otto, 1865–

Fünfzigjahr-feier des Reichsgerichts. Berlin, O. Liebmann,
1929.

Liebmann, Otto, 1865–
   Die Juristische fakultät der Universität Berlin von
ihrer gründung bis zur gegenwart in wort u. bild, in urkunden u. briefen. Mit 450 handschriftlichen widmungen.
Hrsg. von dr. jur. Otto Liebmann. Berlin, O. Liebmann,
1910.
   xxii, ᵢ1ᵣ, 526, ᵢ2ᵣ p. 39 pl. (incl. ports., 3 col.) facsims. (partly fold.)
23 x 27ᶜᵐ.
   "1810. Festgabe der Deutschen juristen-zeitung zur jahrhundertfeier
der Friedrich-Wilhelms-universität zu Berlin. 1910."
   Illustrated t.-p.
   1. Berlin. Universität. Juristische fakultät.   I. Deutsche juristen-
zeitung.

   Library of Congress   LF2413.L7   11–8471

NL   0348096   DLC NjP ICU PU-L ICJ CtY-L NN WaU-L

                                              1886–
Liebmann, Paul, Referendar: Die Bedeutung des § 93 Z.P.O.
   Marburg 1912: (Knauer, Frankfurt a. M.). VIII, 75 S. 8°
Marburg, Jur. Diss. v. 20. Aug. 1912, Ref. Traeger
   [Geb. 27. Aug. 86 Frankfurt a. M.; Wohnort: Frankfurt; Staatsangeh.: Preußen;
Vorbildung: Goethe-Gymn. Frankfurt Reife O. 04; Studium: Heidelberg 2,
München 1, Berlin 1, Marburg 2 S.; Rig. 11. Mai 12.]   [U 12. 6269]

NL   0348097   ICRL MH-L

Liebmann, Robert.
   Caravan, French version, from the novel
Gypsy melody, by Melchior Lengyel
      see under   Caravan (Motion picture script)
[Supplement]

Liebmann, Siegfried, 1904–
   Verbrauchsveränderungen in Deutschland nach
der stabilisierung gegenüber der vorkriegszeit...
Frankfurt a. M., 1931.

   Inaug.-diss.—Frankfurt am Main.

NL   0348099   MiU

VOLUME 332

Liebmann, Susanne, 1897-
Ueber das verhalten farbiger formen bei helligkeits-gleichheit von figur und grund. Berlin, 1927
In. Diss.

NL 0348099-1   ICRL CtY

6179   Liebmann, Walter.
.67   Nietzsche für und gegen Vaihinger. Die Rolle
.789   der Fiktionen in der Erkenntnistheorie Friedrich
       Nietzsches. München, Rösl, 1923.
       194 p. 17 cm. (Philosophische Reihe, 60)

       Bibliography: p. 189-[192]

       1. Nietzsche, Friedrich Wilhelm, 1844-1900.
       2. Vaihinger, Hans, 1852-

NL 0348100   NjP NNC IEN NcD CLSU DLC-P4 MH

Liebmann, Walter.
...Wahn; Drama in vier Aufzügen.   Dortmund: F. W.
Ruhfus, 1927. 111 p. 8°.

1. Drama, German. 2. Title.
N. Y. P. L.   October 11, 1928

NL 0348101   NN

Liebmann, Walter H.
Social service in The family court. A paper read
before the National conference of Jewish social workers
Atlantic City, May 29, 1919, by Walter H. Liebmann...
Atlantic City 1929
8 p. 23½ cm.

NL 0348102   DL

LIEBMANN, Walther.
Der widerruf eines testamentes nach §2256
B.G.B.,etc. Inaug.-diss. Tübingen. Stuttgart,
1906.

NL 0348103   MH ICRL

Liebmann, Willy.
Die Schutzeinrichtungen der Samen und Früchte gegen unbefugten Vogelfrass.   Jena: G. Fischer, 1910. iii, 64 p., 1 l.
8°.

Dissertation, Jena.
Repr.: Jenaische Zeitschrift für Naturwissenschaft. Bd. 46 (N. F. 39). Heft 2.
Teil 2 and Anhang appear in later nos.

1. Seeds. 2. Fruit. 3. Birds.—Food.
N. Y. P. L.   March 4, 1913.

NL 0348104   NN CtY ICRL PPAmP

1889-
Liebner, Adolf. Beiträge zur Kenntnis der Akonitalkaloide.
Halle a. d. S. 1914: Waisenhaus. 54 S. 8°
Halle, Phil. Diss. v. 15. Aug. 1914, Ref. Schulze
[Geb. 30. Juli 89 Magdeburg-S.; Wohnort: Halle a. S.; Staatsangeh.: Preußen;
Vorbildung: G. Eisleben Reife 10; Studium: Halle 9 S.; Rig. 22. Juli 14.]
[U 14. 3787]

NL 0348105   ICRL CtY MH PU OO MiU

Liebner, Albert, 1803-
   see   Liebner, Theodor Albert, 1803-1871.

Liebner, Hans, 1905-
...Untersuchungen über plötzliche todesfälle
bei schweinen und ihre beziehungen zu veränderungen des herz-muskels... Leipzig, 1932.
22 p.

NL 0348107   DNAL

Liebner, Karl Theodor Albert
   see   Liebner, Theodor Albert, 1803-1871.

Liebner, Theodor Albert, 1803-1871.
Ein blick in das evangelische urbild der synode...
Dresden, Kaufmann, 1871.
22p.

AC931 [Haverford-Bauer pamphlets, v. 68, no. 1]
.H3
v.68

NL 0348109   ICRL

Liebner, Theodor Albert, 1803-1871.
Christologie oder die christologische
einheit des dogmatischen systems.
Göttingen, 1849.
8°

NL 0348110   NNUT MH-AH

---

ar W   Liebner, ___ Theodor Albert, 1803-1871.
35195   Hugo von St. Victor und die theologischen
         Richtungen seiner Zeit.   Leipzig, A.
         Lehnhold, 1832.
         vi,509 p. 22cm.

         1. Hugo of Saint Victor, 1096 or 7-1141.

NL 0348111   NIC NN MH IU CU NNUT NjPT

BV   Liebner, Theodore Albert, 1803-1871.
4254   Predigten, gehalten in der
G4L54   Universitätskirche zu Göttingen.
         Göttingen, Vandenhoeck und Ruprecht,
         1841.
         viii, 269 p. 21 cm.

         1. Sermons, German - Collections.
         I. Title.

NL 0348112   NRCR MH-AH CtY

LIEBNER, Theodor Albert, 1803-1871.
Richardi a S.Victore de contemplatione
doctrina. Gott.,1837-39.

2 pt.in 1.

NL 0348113   MH-AH

Liebner, Thomas respondent.
... Fundamenti legis naturalis brevi evolutio...
see under   Alert, Gottlieb, praeses.
[Supplement]

Lieboeth-Joffe, Isaac.
See
Joffe, Isaac Lieboeth-.

PT2623 Liebold,Albert,1891-
.I19E5   Der engel von Augsburg,roman von Albert Liebold. Leipzig,F.W.Grunow c1936
1936   288 p. 19cm.

NL 0348116   ICU

4PT Ger. Liebold, Albert, 1891-
-2505   Der Held im Labyrinth.   Berlin, W. Limpert
           [c1939]
           432 p.

NL 0348117   DLC-P4

Liebold, Albert, 1891-
... Silva, weg einer liebe. Leipzig, A. Bergmann [1940]
359 p. 19ᵐ.

                                      41-3216
Library of Congress   PT2623.I 353S5 1940
                           [2]   833.91

NL 0348118   DLC

Liebold, Albert, 1891-
Versuchung, Roman. Leipzig, A. Bergmann [1941]
534 p. 19 cm.

PT2623.I 353V4   50-41176

NL 0348119   DLC

Liebold, Alexander, 1909-
... Zahntüber- und Unterzahl ...   Leipzig,
1935.
Inaug.-Diss. - Leipzig.
Lebenslauf.
"Literaturverzeichnis": p. 29-37.
Full name: Alexander Gerhard Leibold.

NL 0348120   CtY

Liebold, Alexander Gerhard
   see   Liebold, Alexander, 1909-

Liebold, Arno Friedhelm, 1906-
   see   Liebold, Friedhelm, 1906-

VOLUME 332

Liebold (Carolus Theodorus) [1831–   ]. *De resectione articuli manus. 32 pp. 8°. Berolini. G. Lange. 1862.*

NL 0348123   DNLM PPC

Liebold, Erich, 1907–
... Zur Kasuistik der traumatischen Intoxikation mit metallischem Quecksilber ... Bln.-Charlottenburg,[n. d.].
Inaug.-Diss. - Berlin.
Lebenslauf.
Published also in "Deutsche Zeitschrift für Chirurgie", 239. Bd.
Bibliography: p. 526.

NL 0348124   CtY

Liebold, Friedhelm, 1906–
... Monocytenangina und Drüsenfieber von Pfeiffer als einheitliche Infektionskrankheit ... [Zeulenroda i. Thür., 1931?]
Lebenslauf.
"Literatur-Verzeichnis": p. 46–47.

NL 0348125   CtY

Liebold, B.
Braunschweig und Wolfenbüttel. [Eine Sammlung von Gegenständen der Architektur, Decoration und Kunstgewerbe in Original-Aufnahmen.]
(In Ortwein, A. Deutsche Renaissance. Abtheilung 29. Heft 1–3. (4) pp. 30 plates. Leipzig. 1871–88.) No. 9 in *8070.103.3
Same. (In Same. Heft 4–6. Schluss. Plates 31–60.)   No. 3 in *8070.103.5
Plates 51–60 relate to Wolfenbüttel.
By B. Liebold and G. Heuser.

L769 — Brunswick, Germany. F.a. — Wolfenbuettel, Germany. F.a. — Jt. auth.

NL 0348126   MB

Liebold, B.
Höxter. [Eine Sammlung von Gegenständen der Architektur, Decoration und Kunstgewerbe in Original-Aufnahmen.]
(In Ortwein, A. Deutsche Renaissance. Abtheilung 5. (4) pp. 10 plates. Leipzig. 1871–88.)

K9174 — Hoexter, Prussia.

NL 0348127   MB

Liebold, B.
Holzarchitectur. Sammlung von Façadenausbildungen... Hrsg. von B. Liebold... Enthaltend ca. 500 Figuren. Holzminden: C. C. Müller, 1885. 4 p.l., 175 p. 2. ed. 12°. (Taschenbuch für Bauhandwerker. Theil 2.)

1. Building construction (Wood). 2.   Façades.
N. Y. P. L.   August 25, 1913.

NL 0348128   NN

Liebold, B.
Holzarchitektur. (Holzbau.) ... Hrsg. von B. Liebold ... 4. aufl., enthaltend ca. 550 figuren. Holzminden, C. C. Müller, 1903.
2 p. l, 183 p. of illus. 19ᵐᵐ. (*His* Taschenbuch für bauhandwerker. II. t.)

8-8314

NL 0348129   DLC

LIEBOLD, B.
Münden. (Eine Sammlung von Gegenständen der Architektur, Decoration, und Kunstgewerbe in Original-Aufnahmen.) 20 Tafeln.
(*In* Ortwein, A. Deutsche Renaissance. Abth. 13. Leip 1871–88.)   No. 3 in *.*8070.10

NL 0348130   MB

Liebold, B.
Schloss Bevern. [Eine Sammlung von Gegenständen der Architektur, Decoration und Kunstgewerbe in Original-Aufnahmen.]
(In Ortwein, A. Deutsche Renaissance. Abtheilung 4. Lieferung 1–2. (4) pp. 20 plates. Leipzig. 1871–88.)

K9173 — Bevern, Brunswick, Germany.

NL 0348131   MB

Liebold, B.
Der Zement in seiner Verwendung im Hochbau und der Bau mit Zement-Béton zur Herstellung feuersicherer, gesunder und billiger Gebäude aller Art. Nach eigenen und fremden Erfahrungen bearbeitet. Neue Ausgabe. xvi,143 p. 50 il. 4 pl. 1 table. O. Leipzig: J. J. Arnd, [1875].

NL 0348132   ICJ

Liebold B.
Ziegelrohbau. Sammlung von Façaden- und Giebelausbildungen...zusammengestellt von B. Liebold... Enthaltend 440 Figuren. Holzminden: C. C. Müller, 1883. 4 p.l., 160 p. 2. ed. 12°. (Taschenbuch für Bauhandwerker. 1.)

1. Brick construction. 2. Façades.
N. Y. P. L.   August 25, 1913.

NL 0348133   NN ICarbS

Liebold, B.
Ziegelrohbau. Taschenbuch für bauhandwerker. (1. th.) Zusammengestellt von B. Liebold ... 4. aufl. Holzminden, C. C. Müller, 1901.
3 p. l., 162 (i. e. 193) p. of illus. 20ᵐᵐ.

2-7466

NL 0348134   DLC MH

TG 157 L71+
Liebold (B.) and Co.
30 i.e. Dreissig, jähriges Geschäfts-Jubiläum. Unternehmung für Bruchstein-Brücken und Betonbauten, Röhren- und Kunststein-Fabrik...Holzminden, 1903.
1 v. (unpaged) of illus. 21 x 30cm.

On cover: Bauausführungen 1903.

1. Bridges--Catalogs. 2. Bridge construction.

NL 0348135   NIC

Liebold, Herbert, 1908–
... Ein einfaches Verfahren zur Eiweissbestimmung im Liquor cerebrospinalis ... [Zeulenroda, 1934]
Inaug.-Diss. - Leipzig.
Lebenslauf.
"Literaturverzeichnis": p. 22–24.

NL 0348136   CtY

Liebold, Ilse, 1910–
... Cholesterin und Karotinoidstoffwechsel bei Hypo- und Hyperthyreose ... Heidelberg, 1935.
Inaug.-Diss. - Heidelberg.
Lebenslauf.
"Literatur": p. [10].
[Full name: Ilse Margarete Liebold].

NL 0348137   CtY

Liebold, Ilse Margarete
see Liebold, Ilse, 1910–

Liebold, Johannes
Fahrlässige transportgefährdung durch den kraftfahrer... 1932. 74 p.
Inaug. Diss. -Leipzig, 1932.
Bibliography.

NL 0348139   ICRL

Liebold Johannes [1877–   ].
Ueber Melanosarkome des harten Gaumens nebst Beobachtungen über das Schwanken der Pigmentbildung in Recidivtumoren und Metastasen. 30 pp., 1 l. 8°. Leipzig, W. Wigand, 1901.
[Full name: Wilhelm Paul Johannes Liebold]

NL 0348140   DNLM CtY ICRL

1884–
Liebold, Max; Über den Einfluß der Nitrogruppe auf die Sulfurierbarkeit von Diphenylmethan, Triphenylmethan und Fluoren. Jena 1912: Neuenhahn. 40 S. 8°
Tübingen, Naturwiss. Diss. v. 2. Aug. 1911, Ref. Wislicenus
[Geb. 19. Nov. 84 Eineborn; Wohnort: Eineborn; Staatsangeh.: Sachsen-Altenburg; Vorbildung: Gymn. Eisenberg Reife O. 05; Studium: Berlin 2, Tübingen 11 S.; Rig. 2. Aug. 11.]   [U 12. 6858]

NL 0348141   DLC

Liebold, Rudolf
Das potentialfeld eines drehstromkabels
Inaug. Diss. Dresden, 1931

NL 0348141-1   ICRL

Liebold, Rudolf, 1904–
Die stellung Englands in der russisch-türkischen krise von 1875/78 ... Wilkau Sa., Buchdruckerei F. K. Zschiesche, 1930.
4 p.l.,220 p.,1 l. 22ᶜᵐ.
Inaug.-diss.—Leipzig.
Lebenslauf.
"Literaturverzeichnis": 2d-3d prelim.leaf.

1.Eastern question (Balkan) 2.Gt.Brit.—For.rel. 3.Russo-Turkish war,1877-1878.
[Full name: Rudolf Gerhard Liebold]

NL 0348142   MiU PU CtY IU MH InU NNC ICRL MiU

Liebold, Rudolf Gerhard
see Liebold, Rudolf, 1904–

VOLUME 332

Liebold, Werner, 1911–
Untersuchungen über den Einfluss des Trägerwerkstoffes auf die thermische Elektronenemission von Oxydkathoden. ₍Berlin, 1941₎
30 p. illus. 21 cm.
Inaug.-Diss.—Berlin.
Vita.
Bibliography : p. 19–20.

1. Electrodes, Oxide. 2. Vacuum-tubes. I. Title.
TK7872.V3L5   57–56105

NL 0348144   DLC MH NIC

Liebold, Wilhelm Paul Johannes.
see   Liebold, Johannes, 1877–

Lieboldt ₍Paul... Friderich Arnold..₎. ₍De usu tubæ Eustachianæ ex anatome tam humana quam comparata et phænomenis pathologicis illustrato. Certamen literarium. 28 pp. 4°. Gottingae, typ. Dieterichianis, ₍1829₎.

NL 0348146   DNLM

WBF LIEBOLDT, Paul Friedrich Arnold
L717h   Die Heilkräfte des Meerwassers;
1837   zur Belehrung für Gebildete, mit
         besonderer Berücksichtigung der
         Seebade-Anstalt bey Travemünde.
         Lübeck, Rohden, 1837.
         vi, 136 p.

NL 0348147   DNLM

Lieboldt, Wilhelm Alexander
Hamburg von seinem Ursprunge bis zum Jahre 1842; ein Gedenkbuch. Nürnberg, Expedition der Nürnberger Zeitung (W.Tümmel) 1843
142 p. front.

NL 0348148   MH

PN2658 Lieboldt, Wilhelm Alexander.
K95L54   Wilhelm Kunst und seine bisherigen
         Beziehungen zur deutschen Schaubühne.
         Königsberg, Hartungsche Hofbuchdruckerei,
         1841.
         58 p. 23cm.

1. Kunst, Wilhelm, 1799–1859. 2. Theater - Germany.

NL 0348149   CoU CLSU

Liebolt, Frederick Lee.
Illustrated review of fracture treatment. 1st ed. Los Altos, Calif., Lange Medical Publications, 1954.
229 p. illus. 26 cm.

1. Fractures. I. Title.
RD101.L6   617.15   53–11060 ‡

CtY-M TxU-M OrU-M
NL 0348150   DLC FU-HC OU NcD PPT-M PPJ DNLM WU-M

Lieboner, Heinrich.
Wertgleichheit und konjunktur nach vorkriegsbilanzen ... Mannheim, 1926.
Inaug. -diss. Frankfurt a.M., 1926.

NL 0348151   MiU

Liebovitz, David, 1892–
The canvas sky, by David Liebovitz. New York, Harcourt, Brace and company ₍1946₎
3 p. l., 3–489 p. 21ᶜᵐ.
"First edition."

I. Title.
Library of Congress   PZ3.L62213Can   46–25102

NL 0348152   DLC CoU PSt PP WaS WaE

Liebovitz, David, 1892–
Chronicle of an infamous woman, by David Liebovitz ... New York, The Macaulay company ₍ᶜ1933₎
336 p. 19½ᶜᵐ.

I. Title.
Library of Congress   PZ3.L62213Ch   33–34145
———— Copy 2.

NL 0348153   DLC ViU

PS3523 Liebovits, David, 1892–
.I34   Jerry Green, by David Leibovits.
1922   (In Clay. Brooklyn,1922. vol.1,no.1,p.22–33)
Atkinson
Coll   Caption title.
            A detached copy.

NL 0348154   ICU

₍Liebovitz, David₎ 1892–
· Youth dares all, anonymous. New York, The Macaulay company, 1930.
3 p. l., 11–299 p. 19½ᶜᵐ.

I. Title.
                                          30–21950 Revised
Library of Congress   ₍PZ3.L62213Yo₎

NL 0348155   DLC OC1

Liebovitz, H   A
A Clevelandi magyarok története; adatok és elbeszélések nyomán összeállították és szerkesztették: D₋. H. A. Liebovitz és Parlagh Mihály. Cleveland, Liebovitz, n.d.
₍185 p.₎

Contains an abbreviated English version by Frederic Gonda.

NL 0348156   OC1

WN   LIEBOW, Averill A
610   Pathology of atomic bomb casualties
qL717p   ₍by₎ Averill A. Liebow ₍and others₎
1949   Ann Arbor ₍1949₎
         p. 853–1027. illus.
         Reprinted from the American journal of pathology, 1949, v. 25.
         1. Atomic bomb 2. Radiation - Effects

NL 0348157   DNLM

RD536 Liebow, Averill A., joint author.
.L55
       Lindskog, Gustaf E
         Thoracic surgery and related pathology, by Gustaf E. Lindskog and Averill A. Liebow. New York, Appleton-Century-Crofts ₍1953₎

QZ
200
N277a Liebow, Averill A
Sec.5   Tumors of the lower respiratory tract.
Fasc.17 Washington, Armed Forces Institute of
1952   Pathology, 1952.
         189p. illus. (National Research Council
         Committee on Pathology. Atlas of tumor
         pathology, sec.5, fasc.17)

         1. Respiratory tract neoplasms I. Title
         II. Series III. Series: Atlas of tumor
         pathology, sec.5, fasc.17

NL 0348159   DNLM NcU PHeM CtY-M ICJ OC1W-H TxDaS

Liebow, Bessie Rebecca (Silver) 1887–
Keepsake, an autobiography. ₍New York? ᶜ1951₎
110 p. illus. 24 cm.

I. Title.
CT275.L434A3   920.7   52–30523 ‡

NL 0348160   DLC

Liebowitz, Benjamin, 1890–
Electrical oscillations from mercury vapor tubes, by Benjamin Liebowitz ... Lancaster, Pa., Press of the New era printing company, 1915.
1 p. l., ₍1₎, ₍450₎–477, ₍1₎ p. diagrs. 25½ᶜᵐ.
Thesis (PH. D.)—Columbia university, 1915.
Vita.
"Reprinted from the Physical review, n. s., vol. VI, no. 6, December, 1915."

1. Electric waves. I. Title. II. Title: Mercury vapor tubes.
                                          16–8598
Library of Congress   QC665.L7
Columbia Univ. Libr.

NL 0348161   NNC NIC DLC

4HQ-   Liebrandt, M   P
120   Jugendfürsorge und Jugendpflege. Ein Hilfsbuch
         für Jugendleiter und Jugendpfleger. Mit Anhängen.
         Berlin, Verlagsgesellschaft des Allgemeinen Deutschen Gewerkschaftsbundes, 1929.
         175 p.

NL 0348162   DLC-P4 MH-L

La liebre y la rabia, ó La venta. Saynete nuevo.
136. Para nueve personas. Valencia, José Ferrer de Orga, 1814.
₍1₎–11 p. ₍B₎ 23 cm.
- Oyes Juanillo has limpiado.
- perdon de defectos tantos.

NL 0348163   NcU MB

Liebrecht, Dr.
Reichshülfe für Errichtung kleiner Wohnungen. Von Landesrat Dr. Liebrecht... Göttingen: Vandenhoeck & Ruprecht, 1900. 16 p. 8°. (Deutscher Verein für Wohnungsreform. Die Wohnungsfrage und das Reich. Heft 2.)

I. Habitations for the working classes.   Germany.
N. Y. P. L.   November 19, 1914.

NL 0348164   NN ICJ

VOLUME 332

1882–
Liebrecht, Albert, appr. Arzt: Über multiple primäre Dick-darmkarzinome. Borna-Leipzig 1914: Noske. 52 S. 8°
Leipzig, Med. Diss. v. 28. März 1914, Ref. Payr
[Geb. 16. Dez. 82 Raguhn; Wohnort: Dessau; Staatsangeh.: Anhalt; Vor-bildung: G. Dessau Reife 03; Studium: Freiburg 1, Berlin 1, Halle 10 S.; Coll. 28. März 14; Approb. 17. Jan. 11.]   [U 14.2327]

NL 0348165   ICRL CtY

Liebrecht, Arthur, ed.
   Gesetz betreffend die Unterstützung von
Familien in den Dienst eingetretener Mannschaften.
Vom 28. Februar 1888 in seiner Neufassung vom
4. August 1914
      see under   Germany. Laws, statutes, etc.

Liebrecht, Arthur,   ed.
   Gesetz über die Kriegsleistungen vom 13. Juni
1873.   Berlin, 1915
      see under   Germany. Laws, statutes, etc.

Liebrecht, Arthur
   Die Kriegsfursorge, von A. Liebrecht...Leipzig
und Berlin, G. B. Teubner, 1916
   2 p.l., 37 l p. plates 18 cm. (Deutsche Feld-
und Heimatbücherei, 3. Bd., 14. [i.e. 15] Bändchen)

NL 0348168   DNW

Liebrecht, Arthur.
Invalidenversicherung und arbeiterwohlfahrt; eine fest-schrift aus anlass des 25jährigen jubiläums der deut-schen reichsversicherung; im auftrage der deutschen versicherungsanstalten. Hrsg. von Elle ... dr. Freund ... dr. Liebrecht ... von Schmid ... Berlin, E. Was-muth a. g., 1910.

Liebrecht, Arthur
   Preussisches tumultschadengesetz. Gesetz betreffend
die verpflichtung der gemeinden zum ersatz des bei öf-fentlichen aufläufen verursachten schadens, vom 11. märz
1850. Mit erläuterungen von dr. Arthur Liebrecht ...
Berlin, F. Vahlen, 1919.
   55 p. 16ᵐᵐ.
   I. Prussia. Laws, statutes, etc., 1840–1861 (Frederick William IV)
   II. Title.
                                              21–12343

NL 0348170   DLC CtY

Liebrecht, Arthur, 1862–   joint author.
Heinz, Robert, 1865–
   ... Alumnol, ein neues adstringo-antisepticum. Von Dr.
med. R. Heinz und Dr. phil. A. Liebrecht. [Berlin, 1892]

Liebrecht (Arthur) [1892–   ]. *Ueber Nicotin. 32 pp., 1 l. 8°. Kiel, Schmidt & Klaunig,
1886.*

NL 0348172   DNLM OU

WG   Liebrecht, Arthur, 1862–
33654   Ueber Nicotin. Kiel, 1886.
         38 p.

      Inaug.-Diss. - Kiel.

NL 0348173   CtY ICRL MH

949.4   Liebrecht, Carl.
L38aY.Ei   Replik zu gut teutsch: Widerlegung des
         Schreibens des Pfarrer Lavaters in Zürich
         an das Directorium der französischen Re-
         publik. Hrsg. von einem echten Teutschen.
         Rastadt, 1798.
         16p. 16cm.

NL 0348174   IU

Liebrecht (Curt). *Untersuchungen über den
Fettgehalt der Leberzellen und der Epithe-
lien der intrahepatischen Gallengänge unter
normalen und pathologischen Bedingungen.
Zugleich ein Beitrag zur Kenntnis der Leber-
zirrhose des Hundes. [Zürich.] 46 pp., 1 l.,
3 pl. 8°. Dresden, O. Franke, 1910.*

NL 0348175   DNLM

Liebrecht, *Frau Elfriede.*
   ... Das buch der frau. [Berlin, Modern paedagogischer
und psychologischer verlag, ᶜ1909]
   2 p. l., [7]–123 p. 21ᶜᵐ.
   Cover-title: Das buch der frau; frauenberufe.

   1. Woman—Employment. 2. Women in Germany.

   Library of Congress   HD6149.L7   9–23763

NL 0348176   DLC ICJ MB

Liebrecht, Elfriede.
   Muhme Strehlen: Märchen in Versen.   Berlin,
C. Wigand, 1909.
   47 (1) p. 12°.

NL 0348177   NN

LIEBRECHT, ELFRIEDE.
   Muhme Strehlen, Märchen in Versen. Berlin,
C. Wigand, 1909. 47 p. 20cm.

   Film reproduction. Positive.

   I. Title.

NL 0348178   NN

Liebrecht, Ernst, 1890–
   Die Grundlagen der polnischen Staatsorganisa-
tion in ihrer historischen Entwicklung und Gestal-
tung nach den Staatsgrundgesetzen von 1791/92.
Eine staatsrechtliche Studie als Beitrag zur Vor-
bereitung der künftigen Polenfrage ...   Greifs-
wald, 1916.
   Inaug.-Diss. - Greifswald.
   Lebenslauf.
   "Schriftennachweis": p. [96]–98.

NL 0348179   CtY

Liebrecht, Fe   , Jc   .
   Hebräische Gebetstellen mit Wortübersetzung
für den Jugend-Unterricht versehen und
durchgehends accentuirt, von F. J. Liebrecht.
Breslau: H. Sulzbach, 1844.
   91 p.

NL 0348180   OCH

LIEBRECHT, Felix. 1812–*1890.*
   Arabische Sagen über Aegypten.
   (*In* Benfey, Theodor, editor. Orient und Occident. Vol.
358–363. Göttingen, 1864.)   *3, 1/2 p.*

NL 0348181   MB

LIEBRECHT, Felix. 1812–*1890.*
   Eine alte Todesstrafe.
   (*In* Benfey, T., ed. Orient und Occident. Vol. 2, pp. 269-
Göttingen, 1864.)   *–278.*

NL 0348182   MB

Liebrecht, Felix, 1812–1890, tr.
   Des heiligen Johannes von Damascus Barlaam
und Josaphat
      see under   Barlaam and Joasaph. German.

Liebrecht, Felix, 1812–1890, tr.
Dunlop, John Colin, 1785–1842.
   John Dunlop's Geschichte der prosadichtungen oder
geschichte der romane, novellen, märchen u. s. w. Aus
dem englischen übertragen und vielfach verm. und berichtigt, so wie mit einleitender vorrede, ausführlichen anmerkungen und einem vollständigen register versehen
von Felix Liebrecht ... Berlin, G. W. F. Müller, 1851.

Liebrecht, Felix. Isländisches. *Extr. fr.
his* Zur Volkskunde. 1879. 8°. pp. 362–
873.   IcD11L718

NL 0348184   NIC

LIEBRECHT, Felix, 1812–1890.
   [Miscellaneous collection of articles and
book reviews relating to folk-lore, from periodicals.] 29 pam.in 1 vol. [1865–79.]

NL 0348185   MH

Liebrecht, Felix, *1812–*
   —— Die Quellen des "Barlaam und
Josaphat." *Extr. fr.* Jahrbuch für romanische und englische Literatur. II. Berlin,
1860. 8°. pp. 314–334.   IcF78Ba712

NL 0348186   NIC

Liebrecht, Felix, *1812–*
   —— Die Ragnar Lodbroksage in Per-
sien. *Extr. fr.* (Benfey's) Orient und Occident. I. Jahrg. Göttingen, 1861. 8°. pp.
561–567.   IcF74R713

NL 0348187   NIC

VOLUME 332

LIEBRECHT, Felix. 1812–
Rose und Cypresse.
(*In* Benfey, T., *ed.* Orient und Occident. Vol. 2, pp.
97. Göttingen, 1864.)
" Dies ist der Titel einer Erzählung, welche Garcin de Tassy aus dem Hindustani über-
gen und in der Revue orientale et américaine. 4e année. pp. 1-130 mitgetheilt hat."

NL 0348188   MB

Liebrecht, Felix, 1812-1890
Ueber die deutsche kriegsdichtung des gegen-
wärtigen jahrhunderts. [1],68-95p. Elberfeld,
Gedruckt bei R. L. Friderichs u. comp., 1874.

Programm - Städtische höhere töchterschule und
lehrerinnen-bildungsanstalt zu Elberfeld.

NL 0348189   OC1

Liebrecht, Felix, 1812-1890.
Der Wind in der Dichtung und auch anderswo.
n.p., n.p., n.d.
c.p. O.   (In, Collected monographs. V. 9)

NL 0348190   NcD

Liebrecht, Felix, *1812–*   (Leipzig, 1867).
Zu Petrarca's Trionfi.

NL 0348191   NIC

Liebrecht, Felix, 1812–1890.
Zur volkskunde. Alte und neue aufsätze, von Felix Liebrecht. Heilbronn, Gebr. Henninger, 1879.
xvi, 522 p. 22½cm.
CONTENTS. — Vorwort.—Verzeichniss der hier meist mit abge-
kürztem titel angeführten schriften.—Sagenkunde.—Märchen und fabeln.
—Novellistik und schwänke.—Volkslieder.—Mythologie, religions-
gesch., volksglauben, sitten u. gebräuche etc.—Allgemeine literaturgeschichte.—Sprachliches, redensarten u. s. w.

1. Folk-lore—Addresses, essays, lectures. 2. Folk-literature. 3. Manners and customs.

Library of Congress   GR71.L5
3–8152

ViU MH NN NIC MdBP NjP ICN NcU PHC PBm
NL 0348192   DLC NBuU ICarbS CU CtY ODW OCH OC1 MiU

Film
GR
10   Liebrecht, Felix, 1812-1890.
L5   Zur Volkskunde. Alte und neue Aufsätze.
reel   Heilbronn, Henninger, 1879.
244   xvi, 522p.
            Microfilm (positive. Literature of
        folklore, reel 244)

            1. Folk-lore. 2. Legends. 3. Folk
        songs. 4. Proverbs. I. Title.

NL 0348193   UU

BS
1645   Liebrecht, Ferdinand.
L5   Spicilegium in Zephaniam Prophetam
        Minorem. Vratislaviae, 1828.
            20 p.   21 cm.

            1. Bible. O.T. Zephaniah--Criticism,
        interpretation, etc. I. Title

NL 0348194   OCH

1882 –
Liebrecht, Franz; Beiträge zur Geologie und Paläontologie
des Gebietes um den Dreiherrnstein am Zusammenstoß
von Wittgenstein, Siegerland und Nassau. Marburg 1911:
(A. W. Schade, Berlin). 77 S. 8°   ¶ (Aus: Jahrbuch der
Kgl. Preuß. Geol. Landesanst. Bd 32, T. 1.)
Marburg, Phil. Diss. v. 19. Dez. 1911, Ref. Kayser
[Geb. 20. Mai 82 Lippstadt; Wohnort: Marburg; Staatsangeh.: Preußen; Vor-
bildung: Realgymn. Lippstadt Reife O. 02; Studium: Marburg 4, Freiburg
i. B. 3, Marburg 3 S.; Rig. 21. Dez. 10.]   [U 12. 3546]

NL 0348195   ICRL MH PU CtY

Liebrecht, Géo.
    see Libbrecht, Géo, 1891-

Liebrecht, Georg *Friedrich Konrad, 1891-*
... Arteriomesentorialer duodenalverschluss
... [Berlin, Feilchenfeld, 1919]
71 p.

Inaug.-diss., Berlin, 1919.
Lebenslauf.
"Literatur": p. 68-70.

1. Duodenum - Diseases.

NL 0348197   NNC CtY DNLM

DD
801   Liebrecht, H
B395   Bayern's Unglück; der bayerische
P5   Premierminister Freiherr van der Pforten
        in seinem planmässigen Wirken für Preussen,
        von H. Liebrecht. Brixen, A. Weger, 1870.
            95p. 21cm.

            1. Pfordten, Ludwig, Freiherr von der
        2. Bavaria - Pol. & govt. I. Title

NL 0348198   WU

LIEBRECHT, Hans.
    Das verhältnig des schatzes zur fundsache nach
römischem und burgerlichem recht. Borna-
Leipzig,1903.

    9+(1)+70 p.
    Inaug.-diss. - Leipzig.

NL 0348199   MH-L ICRL

Liebrecht, Heinrich: Allgemein verbindlich erklärte Tarifverträge und
ihre Abänderung. [Maschinenschrift.] viii, 111 S. 4°.—Auszug:
Luckenwalde (1923): Mechel. 2 Bl. 8°
Göttingen, R- u. staatswiss. Diss. v. 4. Dez. 1923   [U 23. 3982]
0

NL 0348200   ICRL

PQ3857
.L6A2   Liebrecht, Henri, 1884-
        ...A l'ombre du minaret; cinq petits
        contes orientaux. Imagés par Paul Collet.
        Bruxelles, Aux éditions Vanderlinden,
        1936.
            2p.l.,[7]-121p.,2 l. illus. 20cm.
            Illustrated t.-p.

        I.Title. II. Bibliotheca Belgica.

NL 0348201   NNU-W

Liebrecht, Henri, 1884–
    Albert Giraud. Bruxelles, Office de publicité, 1946.
    86 p. ports. 20 cm. (Collection nationale, 6. sér., no 72)
    Bibliography : p. [83]–86.

    1. Giraud, Albert, 1860–1929.

    PQ2260.G73Z76   74–242333

NL 0348202   DLC NN OrPR MiU

[Liebrecht, Henri] 1884–
    ... Albert 1er, le roi-soldat. [Paris] Hachette [*1934]
    64 p. incl. front., illus. (incl. ports.) 24cm. (Encyclopédie par l'image.
    [Histoire])
    Illustrated t-p.
    Signed : Henri Liebrecht.

    1. Albert I, king of the Belgians, 1875–1934.   I. Title.
    Library of Congress   DH681.L5   35–4561

NL 0348203   DLC OU NBC

PQ
2392   Liebrecht, Henri, 1884-
S9Z8   Albert Samain. Bruxelles, Collection
        de la Revue d'art: Le Thyrse, 1905.
            36 p. port. 20 cm.

            Edition limited to 50 numbered copies.
        This is copy no. 31.

            1. Samain, Albert Victor, 1858-1900.

NL 0348204   LU

Liebrecht, Henri, 1884-
    L'autre moyen. Comédie en un acte. Bruxelles,
La Belgique Artistique et Littéraire, 1908.
    43 p. , 1 l. 12°.

NL 0348205   NN

Liebrecht, Henri, 1884-
    Les chambres de rhétorique. Bruxelles, Renaissance du
livre [1948]
    139 p. plate. 19 cm. (Collection "Notre passé", 5. sér., 2)
    "Bibliographie" : p. [125]–139.

    1. Chambers of rhetoric.   I. Title.   (Series)

    PT5145.C5L5   839.3112   49–18647*

NL 0348206   DLC NcU PU CU DS

Liebrecht, Henri, 1884–
    ... Comédiens français d'autrefois à Bruxelles. Nombreuses
illustrations. Préface de mme Dussane ... Paris, Maison du
livre français; [etc., etc., 1932]
    [257] p. illus. (facsims.) plates (1 double) ports., plan. 18¼cm.
    Various pagings.
    "Imprimé en Belgique."
    "Le présent exemplaire appartient à l'édition originale."
    Bibliographical foot-notes.

    1. Actors, French. 2. Theater—Brussels.
                                        A 35–1063
    Title from N. Y. Pub.   Libr. Printed by L. C.

NL 0348207   NN MdBJ MoU GU CtY

VOLUME 332

PQ
2623
I44
E29
1905
Liebrecht, Henri, 1884–
L'école des valets; comédie fiabesque
en un acte. Bruxelles, Éditions "Le
Thyrse", 1905.
51 p. 18 cm.

Main/
Ja73jg

NL 0348208   CaBVaU

PN149
.A2
Liebrecht, Henri, 1884–

Académie royale de langue et de littérature françaises,
Brussels.
L'écrivain et son public, discours prononcés à la séance
publique annuelle du 24 octobre 1953 (par) Henri Liebrecht
(et al.) Bruxelles, 1953.

Z998S
.A75
Liebrecht, Henri, 1884–

**Association belge des collectionneurs et dessinateurs d'ex-
libris.**
Ex-libris. Bruxelles, Éditions A. B. C. D. E. (1929)

Liebrecht, Henri, 1884–   ed.

Grande encyclopédie de la Belgique et du Congo ... Bruxelles,
Editorial-office, H. Wauthoz-Legrand (°1938–

Liebrecht, Henri, 1884–
La guirlande en roses der papier; quelques traditions et
coutumes de folklore belge. Bruxelles, Côte d'or (1948)
120 p. illus., col. plates. 30 cm.

1. Folk-lore—Belgium. I. Title.
A 50–5197
Indiana. Univ. Libr.   GR185.L7
for Library of Congress   (8)

NL 0348212   InU

LIEBRECHT, HENRI, 1884–   ed.
Histoire de la guerre des nations
unies, 1939–1945, publiée par un groupe
de collaborateurs. Bruxelles, Éditions
"Le Sphinx" (cl947)
534 p. illus., col. plates, ports.,
maps. 32 cm.

NL 0348213   VtMiM

D443.4
L717
Liebrecht, Henri, 1884–   ed.
Histoire de la guerre des Nations Unies,
1939–1945; publiée par un groupe de collaborateurs. Bruxelles, Éditions "Le Sphinx"
(1948–49)
2 v. illus.,col.plates,ports.,maps (part
col.) facsims. 33cm.

1. World War, 1939–1945. 2.World politics.
3. United Nations.   I.Title.

NL 0348214   CSt-H PU

PQ3814
L54
Liebrecht, Henri, 1884–
Histoire de la littérature belge d'expression française. Préf.
d'Edmond Picard. Bruxelles, Vanderlinden, 1909.
ix, 472 p. illus., ports., facsims.

On cover: 1910.
Bibliography: p.[445]-453.

1. Belgian literature (French) - Hist. & crit. 2. French
literature - Belgian authors - Hist. & crit.

NL 0348215   CU OC1 WaU MiU NcU

PQ3814
.L7
LIEBRECHT,HENRI,1884–
Histoire de la littérature belge
d'expression française. Préface d'Edmond Picard.
2. ed. rev. et corr. Bruxelles, Vanderlinden,
1913.
9+472 p. plates, ports., facsims.

1. Belgian literature (French)--Hist. & crit.
2. French literature--Belgian authors.

NL 0348216   InU

Liebrecht, Henri, 1884–

... Histoire du livre et de l'imprimerie en Belgique des origines à nos jours ... Bruxelles, Musée du livre, 1923–(34)

Liebrecht, Henri, 1884–
Histoire du théâtre français à Bruxelles au XVIIe et au
XVIIIe siècle, par Henri Liebrecht; préface de Maurice
Wilmotte ... (Bruxelles) Société des bibliophiles et iconophiles de Belgique, 1923.
viii, 373 p., 3 l. col. front., illus., plates, ports., plans, facsims. 30[cm].
155 copies printed. "131 exemplaires sur papier d'Arches, numérotés de
1 à 131 ... Exemplaire n° 131, imprimé pour le Congressional library de
Washington."
Each plate accompanied by guard sheet with descriptive letterpress.
"Bibliographie": p. 365–373.
1. Theater—Brussels—Hist. 2. Actors, French. I. Société des bibliophiles et iconophiles de Belgique, Brussels.
26–17235
Library of Congress   PN2706.B7L5

NL 0348218   DLC InU IU NIC TxU

Liebrecht, Henri, 1884–
... Histoire du théâtre français à Bruxelles au XVIIe et au
XVIIIe siècle. Préface de Maurice Wilmotte ... Paris, E.
Champion, 1923.
viii, 377 p. front., illus., plates, ports., plans, facsims. 29[cm]. (Half-
title: Bibliothèque de la Revue de littérature comparée, tome XI)
Bibliographical foot-notes.
"Bibliographie": p. 365–373.

1. Theater—Brussels—Hist. 2. Actors, French. I. Title.
27–11991
Library of Congress   PN2706.B7L5 1923 a

ICU NjP OrU CaBVaU
NL 0348219   DLC CU OC1 OCU MiU OU NcD PU PBm NN IU

PQ3814
.L7
Liebrecht, Henri, 1884–
... Histoire illustrée de la littérature belge de langue fran-
çaise (des origines à 1925) Bruxelles, Vanderlinden, 1926.
(4), 454 p. illus. (incl. ports., facsims.) 22½[cm].
At head of title: Henri Liebrecht et Georges Rency.
Contains bibliographies.

1. Belgian literature (French)—Hist. & crit. 2. French literature—Belgian
authors—Hist. & crit.

NL 0348220   ICU NNU-W NN InU CU CaBVaU OrPR

Y
7621
.51
Liebrecht, Henri,   1884–
...Histoire illustrée de la littérature
belge de langue française (des origines
à 1930) 2.éd., rev. et aug....   Bruxelles,1931.

At head of title: Henri Liebrecht
et Georges Rency.
Contains bibliographies.

NL 0348221   ICN NNU-W OC1 MH CtY

Liebrecht, Henri, 1884–
Iwan Gilkin. Bruxelles, Off. de publicité, 1941.
80 p. port. 20 cm. (Collection nationale (1. sér.) no 5)
"Bibliographie sommaire": p. 78–80.

1. Gilkin, Iwan, 1858–1924.   (Series)
PQ2260.G44Z7
A F 48–4012*
Chicago. Univ. Libr.
for Library of Congress   (1)†

NL 0348222   ICU OrPR CU ICRL NN DLC

PQ3857
.L60M2
Liebrecht, Henri, 1884–
...Le masque tombe; roman de moeurs
théâtrales.   Paris, Nilsson (19– ?)
4p.l.,224p. 19cm.

Bibliotheca Belgica.

I. Title.

NL 0348223   NNU-W

Liebrecht, Henri, 1884–
... Miss Lili; comédie en trois actes, en prose ...
Paris, Liége, L'Édition artistique, 1905.
155, (1) p. 18[cm].
At head of title: Henri Liebrecht et F.-Charles Morisseaux.
"Représentée pour la première fois à Bruxelles sur la scène du Théâtre royal
du Parc le 12 avril 1905".

I. Morisseaux, François Charles, 1880–1912, joint author. II. Title.

NL 0348224   MiU

PN
2706
.B71
T4
L72
(Liebrecht,Henri) 1884–
Théâtre royale de la Monnaie; deux cent cinquan-
tième anniversaire. (Paris, Éditions-Publicité,
1949)
90 p.(p.(1)-22,71-90 advertisements) illus.,
col.plates,ports.,5 facsims.(in envelope) 32 cm.
Signed (p.58): Henri Liebrecht.

1.Brussels. Théâtre royal de la Monnaie.

NL 0348225   MiU

Liebrecht, Henri, 1884–
... L'Université de Bruxelles et la guerre. Bruxelles, La Renaissance du livre (1944)
2 p. l., 7–109 p., 1 l. 19[cm].

1. Brussels. Université libre. 2. Belgium—Hist.—German occupation,
1940–1945. I. Title.
A 45–4220
Yale univ. Library
for Library of Congress   (2)

NL 0348226   CtY CSt-H NSyU MH

VOLUME 332

Liebrecht, Henri, 1884-
La vie et le rêve de Charles de Coster. Bruxelles, Éditions du Hibou, 1927

70 p. illus.

NL 0348227   MH

Liebrecht, Johann Matthias, d. 1776
Predigten, nach dessen tode hrsg. von O. C. Schuchmacher.
Hamburg, Harmsen, 1777-80.
2 v. in 1.

NL 0348228   PPLT

LIEBRECHT, Julius.
Über die Beziehungen der Bettruhe nach gynäkologischen Operationen zur Frage der Thrombose und Embolie. Kiel, 1905. 19 S.

Kiel, Med. Diss.

NL 0348229   MBCo ICRL DNLM CtY

Liebrecht (Karl [Wilhelm H.]) [1862-].
*Ueber die tuberkulöse Form der Mastdarmfisteln. 47 pp. 11. 8°. Halle a. S., E. Karras, 1886.

NL 0348230   DNLM

Liebrecht, Kurt: Die Zulässigkeit der Verschiedenheit der getäuschten und geschädigten Person beim Betrug (§ 263 St. G. B.) und die Abgrenzung des Betruges bei Verschiedenheit der bezeichneten Personen vom Diebstahl in mittelbarer Täterschaft (§ 242 St. G. B.). [Maschinenschrift.] IV, 52 S. 4°. — Auszug: Breslau 1922: Schles. Volkszeitung. 2 Bl. 8°
Breslau, R.- u. staatswiss. Diss. v. 20. Mai 1922   [U 22. 1188]

NL 0348231   ICRL

PT   Liebrecht, L
2496   Schillers Verhältnis zu Kants ethischer
B9L5   Weltansicht.   Hamburg, Verlagsanstalt
        und Druckerei A-G, 1889.
        36p. 20cm.

        Cover title.
        Reprint of Sammlung gemeinverständlicher
        wissenschaftlicher Vorträge, n., IV, 79.
        Pages also numbered 271-304.

        1. Schiller, Johann Christoph Friedrich
        von, 1759-   1805. I. Title.

NL 0348232   CLSU PU MWelC IU MB NIC MH NN CtY

LIEBRECHT, Lioba, Sister, 1893-
Über die folge der ableitungen einer reellen funktion von 1,2 und mehr argumenten. Göttingen, druck der Dieterichschen Universitäts-buchdruckerei (W. Fr. Kaestner), 1930.

pp. 19.
Inaugural-dissertation - Münster in Westfalen
"Lebenslauf", at end.

NL 0348233   MH

1841-
Liebrecht (Paul), De l'administration de l'ergotine par la voie rectale. Quatre observations de fibroides de l'utérus traités par l'ergotine. 7 pp. 8°. [Bruxelles, H. Manceaux, 1880.]
Repr. from: J. de méd., chir. et pharm., Brux., 1880. lxx.

NL 0348234   DNLM

Liebrecht, Paul, 1841-
Sur la fièvre après les transfusions, par le docteur Paul Liebrecht ... [Bruxelles, Impr. de H. Manceaux, 1874]
8 p. 24½ᵐ.

Caption title.
"Extrait du Journal de méd., chir. et pharmacol. publié par la Société royale des sciences méd. et nat. de Bruxelles" (vol. LIX, p. 293-300)

1. Blood—Transfusion.

Library of Congress   RM171.L71   7-18647†

NL 0348235   DLC

W1   Liebrecht, Suzanne.
PR619   Le malade: soins, par S. Liebrecht. Alimentation,
no.15   par H. Gounelle et S. Liebrecht. Paris, Foucher [1953]
1953   106 p. illus. (Professions médicales et sociales, 15)
            1. Nursing Care I. Gounelle, Huges.   Alimentation
        II. Title III. Series

NL 0348236   DNLM

Liebrecht, Wilhelm, 1850-

Invalidenversicherung und arbeiterwohlfahrt; eine festschrift aus anlass des 25jährigen jubiläums der deutschen reichsversicherung; im auftrage der deutschen versicherungsanstalten. Hrsg. von Elle ... dr. Freund ... dr. Liebrecht ... von Schmid ... Berlin, E. Wasmuth a. g., 1910.

LIEBRECHT und Hörwald, oder so gehts zuweilen auf dem lande; ein schauspiel in drey aufzügen. Bearbeitet nach Shakespear. 1789.

(In DEUTSCHE schaubühne, 1789, iv, [137]-254.)

NL 0348238   MH

DT   Liebrechts, Charles
351   Cinquantième anniversaire de l'arrivée de
S9   Stanley à Boma, le 9 Août 1877. Conférence
P27   donnée par le colonel Charles Liebrechts ...
        [Bruxelles, Etoile Belge] 1927?
        47 p. illus., port.

        1. Stanley, Sir Henry Morton, 1841-1904.

NL 0348239   MBU NNC IEN

DT   Liebrechts, Charles
646   Congo: Léopoldville, Bolobo, Équateur
L5   (1883-1889) Bruxelles, J. Lebègue [1909?]
        266p. illus. 23cm. (Souvenirs d'Afrique)

        1. Zaire - Description & travel - 1881-
        1950 I. Title

NL 0348240   WU CSt NcD

MY76   Liebrechts, Charles
L622c   Congo, suite à mes souvenirs d'Afrique.
        Vingt années à l'administration centrale de
        l'État indépendant du Congo (1889-1908)
        Bruxelles, J. Lebègue, 1920.
        336 p. 24 cm.

        1. Congo - Missions.   I. Title.

MiEM
NL 0348241   CtY-D DLC-P4 CtY WU NjP MBU ICU NNC MH

Liebrechts, Charles.
Guide de la section de l'État indépendant du Congo à l'Exposition de Bruxelles-Tervueren en 1897
        see under Brussels. Exposition internationale, 1897.

Liebrechts, Charles.
... Léopold II, fondateur d'empire. Bruxelles, Office de publicité, 1932.
360 p. plates, ports., facsims. (part fold.) 25½ᵐ.
At head of title: Lieutenant-colonel Liebrechts.

1. Kongo, Belgian—Hist. 2. Belgium—Colonies—Kongo. 3. Léopold II, king of the Belgians, 1835-1909.   32-21155
Library of Congress   DT652.L4
Copyright A—Foreign   17489
                             [2]   967.5

NL 0348243   DLC NSyU ICU CU-S

DT652   Liebrechts, Charles
L54   Notre colonie. Préf. d'Albert Giraud.   Bruxelles, Office
        de Publicité, 1922.
        viii, 246 p.

        "Recueil des articles publiés dans l'Étoile belge, sous le
        pseudonyme Un vieux Congolais."

        1. Congo, Belgian - Pol. & govt.

NL 0348244   CU NBuU WU MBU IEN CtY CSt-H MH NNC

967.5   Liebrechts, Charles.
L717r   Rapport sur Léopoldville.   Bruxelles,
        Impr. Ch. Vanderauwera [189?]
        40p. plan.   (Publications deu l'État
        indépendant du Congo, no. 2)

        1. Léopoldville, Congo.

NL 0348245   IEN

916.75 Liebrechts, Charles.
L717a   Souvenirs d'Afrique: Congo, Léopoldville,
        Bolobo, Equateur (1883-1889)   Bruxelles,
        J. Lebègue [1909]
        266p. illus. 23cm.

        1. Congo, Belgian. Descr. & trav. I. Title.

NL 0348246   IEN MBU ICU CtY MH

Liebrechts, Charles Adolphe Marie.
        see Liebrechts, Charles.

VOLUME 332

Liebreich (Adolf) [1879-   ]. *Ein Fall von Ureteritis cistica. 24 pp. 8°. Tübingen, F. Pietzcker. 1906.

NL 0348248   DNLM ICRL

Liebreich, Aenne, 1899–
Claus Sluter, par Aenne Liebreich ... Bruxelles, Dietrich & cie, 1936.
246 p., 1 l. illus., 40 pl. 27½ cm.
"Bibliographie critique": p. 213–237.

1. Sluter, Claus, d. 1406?

A C 36—3315

Vassar College. Library
for Library of Congress   [n60c½]

PSC MWiW-C GEU TNJ PPiU
PU-FA MdBWA NIC ICU CtY NcU NNU-W DAU PSt NjP KU
NL 0348249   NPV NcD MiU IU FU OOxM TU FTaSU IEN GU

---

q759.3 Liebreich, Aenne, 1899–
L623k   Kostümgeschichtliche studien zur kölnischen malerei des 14.jahrhunderts ... Leipzig, Klinkhardt & Biermann, 1929.
68p.
Inaug.-diss.--Bonn.
Lebenslauf.
"Separatdruck aus dem Jahrbuch für kunstwissenschaft."
Without the plates.
Bibliographical foot-notes.
1. Painting--Cologne--Hist.   2. Costume--Germany.

NL 0348250   IU ICU MH

Liebreich, Aenne, 1899–
Recherches sur Claus Sluter ... par Aenne Liebreich ... Bruxelles, Dietrich & cᵉ, 1936.
247 p. illus., xl pl. 26¾ cm.
Thèse--Univ. de Paris.
"Bibliographie critique": p. 213–237.

1. Sluter, Claus, d. 1406?

42–13238

Library of Congress   NB553.S6L5

NL 0348251   DLC OU CtY NNC

Liebreich, Émile.
... Le sang in vitro; éosinophilie, fibrinogenèse, phagocytose des hématies; deux planches hors texte. Paris, Masson et cᵉ, 1921.
128 p. 3 pl. on 2 l. 21½ cm.   fr. 10
"Index bibliographique": p. [117]–125.

1, Blood.   I. Title.

22–5546

Library of Congress   QP91.L7
Copyright A—Foreign   19067
[2]

NL 0348252   DNLM CU ICRL OClW-H MiU PPC CtY DLC

[1884–]
Liebreich, E[rik] Änderung der Brechungsexponenten mit der Temperatur im Ultrarot bei Steinsalz, Sylvin und Fluorit. Leipzig: J. A. Barth 1910. 38 S. 8°
Berlin, Phil. Diss. v. 1. Aug. 1910. Ref. Rubens
[Geb. 28. Sept. 84 Charlottenburg; Wohnort: Charlottenburg; Staatsangeh.: Preußen; Vorbildung: Französ. Gymn. Berlin Reife O. 05; Studium: Berlin 1, Straßburg 1, München 1, Berlin 6 S.; Rig. 23. Juni 10.]   [U 10. 206

NL 0348253   DLC CtY ICRL MH PU

Liebreich, Erik, 1884–
Mangan und Chrom, von Dr. E. Liebreich ...
(*In* Handbuch der technischen Elektrochemie. Leipzig, 1931. 24½ cm.
1. Bd., 1. Teil, p. [277]–287)
Bibliographical foot-notes.

NL 0348254   ICJ

Liebreich, Erik, 1884–
Rost und rostschutz, von dr. Erik Liebreich ... Mit 22 abbildungen ... Braunschweig, F. Vieweg & sohn, 1914.
2 p. l., 112 p. illus., diagrs. 22¾ cm. (*On cover:* Sammlung Vieweg; tagesfragen aus den gebieten der naturwissenschaften und der technik, hft. 20) M. 3.20

1. Corrosion and anti-corrosives.

15–5479

Library of Congress   TA467.L7

NL 0348255   DLC OCU ICJ NN NjP

Liebreich (Fridericus Richardus). *De ichthyosi intra-uterina. 12 pp., 1 l., 1 pl. 4°. Halis Sax., form. express. Gebauerio-Schwetschkiana. [1863 ;

NL 0348256   DNLM

Liebreich, Joachim: Die Entwicklung der Arbeitnehmerorganisationen im Gastwirtsgewerbe. [Maschinenschrift.] VII, 114 S. 4°. — Auszug: o. O. (1924.) 1 Bl. 8°
Kiel, R.- u. staatswiss. Diss. v. 6. Jan. 1925   [U 25. 5127

NL 0348257   ICRL

LIEBREICH, Leon J.
The Compilation of the "Pesuke De-Zimra". Reprinted from Proceedings of the American Academy for Jewish Research, vol.18,1949, p.255-267.

1.Genizah. 2.Liturgy-Psalms. 3.Benedictions. 4.Pesuke De-Zimra.

NL 0348258   NNJ

LIEBREICH, Leon J
The Intermediate Benedictions of the "Amidah". Reprinted from Jewish Quarterly Review, New Series, vol.42, no.4,p.423-426, 1952.

1.Liturgy-Shemoneh Esrah.2.Benedictions.

NL 0348259   NNJ

LIEBREICH, Leon J.
The "Pesuke De-Zimra" Benedictions. Reprinted from the Jewish Quarterly Review, New Series, vol.41, no.2,p.195-206. 1950.

1.Genizah. 2. Lit.-Psalms. 3.Benedictions. 4.Pesuke De-Zimra.

NL 0348260   NNJ

Liebreich, Leon J   .
Silverstone's Aquila and Onkelos. Philadelphia: Dropsie College for Hebrew and Cognate Learning, 1937. p. 287-291.

Title taken from paper-cover.
Repr.: J.Q.R. n. s. v. 27, no. 3.

NL 0348261   OCH

Liebreich, Mathias Eugen Oscar
see
Liebreich, Oscar, 1839–1908.

Liebreich, Oscar, 1839–1908.
RD86   Das Chloralhydrat; ein neues Hypnoticum und
C4   Anaestheticum und dessen Anwendung in der
869L   Medicin, eine Arzneymittel-Untersuchung.
2. unveränderte Aufl. Berlin, G. F. O. Müller, 1869.
2 p. l., 60 p. 24 cm.

1. Anesthetics.   2. Chloral.

NL 0348263   CtY-M KU-M MnU MB DNLM WU CaBVaU

RM666 Liebreich, Oscar *i. e.* Mathias Eugen Oscar, 1839–1908.
.C5L7   Das chloralhydrat, ein neues hypnoticum und anaestheticum und dessen anwendung in der medicin. Eine arzneimittel-untersuchung von dr. Oscar Liebreich ... 3., umgearb. und mit therapeutischen erfahrungen verm. aufl. Berlin, O. Müller, 1871.
[3], 122, [2] p. 22 cm.
"Literatur": p. [109]–122.

1. Chloral.

NL 0348264   ICU ICJ PPC MiU IU-M DNLM

QV   LIEBREICH, Oscar, 1839-1908
L717c   Compendium der Arzneiverordnung, von Oscar Liebreich und Alexander Langgaard. [1.]-   Aufl. Berlin, Fischer, 1884-
v.
1st ed. has title: Medicinisches Recept-Taschenbuch.

I. Langgaard, Alexander II. Liebreich,

Oscar, 1839-1908. Medicinisches Recept-Taschenbuch

LIEBREICH, Oscar, 1839-1908

NL 0348266   DNLM

Liebreich, Oscar, 1839–1908.
[Compendium der Arzneiverordnung. 2. Aufl. 3 p. l., 847 pp. 8°. Berlin, Fischer, 1887.

NL 0348267   DNLM

Liebreich, Oscar, 1839–1908.
Compendium der Arzneiverordnung, von Dr. Oscar Liebreich und Dr. Alex. Langgaard. Nach dem Arzneibuch für das Deutsche Reich und den neuesten fremden Pharmacopoeen. 3. vollständig umgearb. Aufl. Berlin N. W., Fischer (H. Kornfeld) 1891.
777 p. 21 cm.

NL 0348268   ICJ DNLM CaBVaU

VOLUME 332

RS125
L62
1896
Liebreich, Oscar, 1839-1908.
Compendium der arzneiverordnung, von dr.
Oscar Liebreich und dr. Alexander Langgaard.
Nach der pharmakopoe für das deutsche reich
und den neuesten fremden pharmakopoeen. 4.
vollständig umgearb. aufl. Berlin, Fischer,
1896.
3 p. l., 762 p.

1. Medicine - Formulae, receipts, prescriptions.
I. Langgaard, Alexander, 1847-1917, jt au.

NL 0348269 NNC

615.1
L717c5
Liebreich, Oscar, 1839-1908.
Compendium der Arzneiverordnung, von Oscar Lie-
breich und Alexander Langgaard. Nach der Pharma-
copoea germanica ed. IV und den neuesten fremden
Pharmakopoeen. 5., vollständig umgearb. Aufl.
Berlin, H. Kornfeld, 1902.
827p. 22cm.

1. Materia medica. I. Langgaard, Alexander,
1847-1917, joint author.

NL 0348270 IU-M ICRL N

Liebreich, Oscar, 1839-1908.
_____ Compendium
der Arzneiverordnung. Nach der Pharma-
copoea germanica ed IV. und den neuesten
fremden Pharmacopoeen. 6. ed. 2 p. l.,
809 pp. 8°. Berlin, H. Kornfeld, 1907.

NL 0348271 DNLM PPC

Liebreich ¡Oscar.) [1839-
]. *Duo describuntur specimina embolis
arteriæ femoralis. 32 pp. 8°. _Berolini, G.
Schade,_ 1865.

NL 0348272 DNLM

615.503
L747e
Liebreich, Oscar, 1839-1908, ed.
Encyklopaedie der therapie. Hrsg. von Oscar
Liebreich ... unter mitwirkung von Martin Mendel-
sohn ... und Arthur Würzburg ... Berlin, A.
Hirschwald, 1896-1900.
3v.

1. Therapeutics--Dictionaries. I. Mendelsohn,
Martin Alfred, 1860-1930, joint ed. II. Würzburg, Arthur, 1853- joint ed.

NL 0348273 IU-M PPC CtY DNLM

Liebreich, Oscar, 1839-1908.
Effects of borax and boracic acid on the human system. By
Dr. Oscar Liebreich ... (Tr. from the German.) London,
J. & A. Churchill, 1899.
1 p. l., iv, 44 p. II col. pl. 27cm.
"Literature": p. 41-43.

1. Boric acid, Physiological effect of. 2. Borax, Physiological effect of.
¡Full name: Mathias Eugen Oscar Liebreich¡
7-38375
Library of Congress QP913.B1L7

NL 0348274 DLC ICJ

WBC
qL717e
1904
LIEBREICH, Oscar, 1839-1908
Encyclopedie der therapie, door Oscar
Liebreich en anderen. Te 's-Hertogen-
bosch, Heusden ¡1901-04¡
5 v.
Translation of Encyklopaedie der
Therapie.

NL 0348275 DNLM

Liebreich, Oscar, 1839-
... Gutachten über die wirkung der borsäure und des borax.
Von dr. Oscar Liebreich ... Berlin ¡Buchdruckerei von G.
Schade (O. Francke)¡ 1899.
51, ¡1¡ p. II col. pl. 26¼cm.
"Litteratur": p. ¡50¡-51.

1. Boric acid—Physiological effect. 2. Borax—Physiological effect.
¡Full name: Mathias Eugen Oscar Liebreich¡
Library of Congress QP913.B1L6 7-38376

NL 0348276 DLC MiU

Liebreich, Oscar _i.e._ Matthias Eugen
Oskar, 1839-
.... Gutachten über die Wirkung der Borsäure und des Borax.
Von Dr. Oscar Liebreich, ...
(_In_ Vierteljahrsschrift für gerichtliche Medicin und öffentliches Sanitätswesen. Ber-
lin, A. Hirschwald, 1900. 24cm. Dritte Folge, xix. Band, p. [83]-125. II col. pl.)
"Literatur," p. 123-125.

NL 0348277 ICJ

Liebreich, Oscar, 1839-1908.
Die historische Entwickelung der Heilmittellehre. Rede,
gehalten zur Feier des Stiftungstages der militärärztlichen
Bildungsanstalten am 2. August 1887, von Dr. Oscar Liebreich
... Berlin, Buchdruckerei von G. Lange, jetzt O. Lange [1887]
34 p. 23¼cm.
Bibliographical foot-notes.

NL 0348278 ICJ CtY-M NcU NNC DNLM MiU

Liebreich ¡Oscar)¡ [1839-
]. L'hydrate de chloral. Traduit de l'allemand sur la 2. éd. par Is. Levaillant. 1 p. l.,
66 pp. 8°. _Paris, Germer-Baillière,_ 1870. [F., v.
1459.]

NL 0348279 DNLM

Liebreich, Oscar, 1839-1908.
_____. Kritische Bemerkungen über die Mate-
rialien zur technischen Begründung eines Ge-
setz-Entwurfs gegen die Verfälschung der Nah-
rungs- und Genussmittel, etc., vom 12. Februar
1879. 14 pp. 8°. _Berlin,_ [1879].

NL 0348280 DNLM

615.14
L622m
1884
197474
Liebreich, Oscar, 1839-1908.
Medicinisches recept-taschenbuch, von dr.
Oscar Liebreich und dr. Alex. Langgaard.
Berlin, T. Fischer, 1884.
967 p. 18. cm.

1. Prescription writing. I. Langgaard,
Alexander, 1847-   joint author. II. Title.

NL 0348281 MoSU DNLM

616.5
L717p
Liebreich, Oscar, 1839-1908.
Phaneroskopie und Glasdruck für die Diagnose
des Lupus vulgaris. Berlin, A. Hirschwald,
1894.
46p. illus., col.plates. 25cm.

1. Skin--Diseases.

NL 0348282 DNLM PPC IU-M

Liebreich, _Oscar, 1839-_
The relation of therapeutics to other sciences in the nineteenth century.
(In Congress of Arts and Science ... St. Louis, 1904. Vol. 6, pp.
153-169. Boston. 1906.)

G3103 — Therapeutics. — Nineteenth century. Science.

NL 0348283 MB

QV
qL717u
1902
LIEBREICH, Oscar, 1839-1908
Second treatise on the effects of borax
and boric acid on the human system, with
two supplements. Tr. from the German.
London, Churchill, 1902.
87 p. illus.
Traslation of Über die Wirkung der
Borsäure und des Borax; ein zweites
Gutachten.

NL 0348284 DNLM ICJ MH CtY

Liebreich, Oscar, 1839-1908.
Third treatise on the effects of borax and boric acid on the
human system ... Being a critical review of the report of
Dr. H. W. Wiley, chief of the Bureau of chemistry of the U. S.
Department of agriculture, to the secretary of agriculture.
By Dr. Oscar Liebreich ... (Tr. from the German.) London,
J. & A. Churchill, 1906.
vii, 70 p. incl. diagrs. (1 fold.) 27cm.

1. Borax. 2. Boric acid. ¡2. Boracic acid¡
¡Full name: Mathias Eugen Oscar Liebreich¡
Agr 7-1395 Revised
Library, U. S. Dept. of Agriculture 389.3L62A

NL 0348285 DNLM PU ICJ PPC DNAL

Liebreich, Oscar _i.e._ Matthias Eugen Oscar, 1839-
Ueber Beziehungen der pharmakodynamischen Therapie zu anderen Wissenschaften im 19. Jahrhundert. Vortrag, gehalten in
der Sektion für Therapie und Pharmakologie auf dem International Congress of Arts and Science zu St. Louis, 24. September
1904 von Oscar Liebreich, ... Berlin, A. Hirschwald, 1905.
39, [1] p. 24cm.

NL 0348286 ICJ DNLM

Liebreich, Oscar _i.e._ Matthias Eugen Oscar,
1839-
Ueber die Wirkung der Borsäure und des Borax. (Ein zweites
Gutachten.) Von Dr. Oscar Liebreich, ... Mit 5 Tafeln.
Berlin, A. Hirschwald, 1903.
iv, 80 p. v pl. (1 fold.) 26cm.
"Das erste Gutachten ist in der Vierteljahrsschrift f. gerichtl. Medicin und öffentl.
Sanitätswesen 3. Folge, xix. 1, veröffentlicht worden."

NL 0348287 ICJ DNLM PPC

543.1
L717z
Liebreich, Oscar, 1839-1908.
Zur frage der bor-wirkungen. Eine kritik des
dr. Wileyschen berichtes an des amerikanische
ackerbau-ministerium ... Berlin, A. Hirschwald,
1906.
51p. 4 fold.tables.

1. Borax--Physiological effect. 2. Boric acid
--Physiological effect. I. Wiley, Harvey Washington, 1844-1930. Influence of food preservatives
and artificial colors on digestion and health.
I. Boric acid and borax. 1904.

NL 0348288 IU-M PPC ICRL ICJ

VOLUME 332

Liebreich, Ralph H   1883–
Wie ist die L. 11 D. 46, 3 mit L. 15
D. 46, 3 zu vereinigen? Gelten die in
beiden Stellen enthaltenen Grundsätze
auch heute? ... von Ralph H. Liebreich ...
Borna-Leipzig, R. Noske, 1908.
viii, 42 p., 1 l. 21cm.
Inaug.-Diss. - Heidelberg.
"Lebenslauf": leaf at end.
"Literaturverzeichnis": p. ₍vii₎-viii.

NL   0348289   MH-L ICRL

---

138   Liebreich, Richard, 1830–1917.
L717a   Die Asymmetrie des Gesichtes und ihre
Entstehung. Wiesbaden, J.F.Bergmann, 1908.
26p. illus. 28cm.

1.Face. 2.Physiognomy. I.Title. LC

NL   0348290   CLSU DNLM NjP ICJ

Liebreich, Richard, 1830–1917.
Atlas d'ophthalmoscopie, représentant l'état normal et les modifications pathologiques du fond de l'œil visibles à l'ophtalmoscope,
composé de 12 planches contenant 57 figures tirées en chromolithographie. Accompagnées d'un texte explicatif et dessinées
d'après nature par le docteur Richard Liebreich. Berlin, A.
Hirschwald; Paris, G. Baillière, 1863.
x, 42 p. xII col. pl. (1 fold.) 39⁴ᶜᵐ.
Added t.-p. in German; text in French and German.

NL   0348291   ICJ RPB DNLM NN KU-M T CtY-M MiU PPC

RE 78   LIEBREICH, RICHARD, 1830–
.L 72   Atlas d'ophthalmoscopie, représentant l'état
normal et les modifications pathologiques du
fond de l'œil visibles a l'ophthalmoscope;
tirées en chromolithographie accompagnées d'un
texte explicatif et dessinées d'après nature.
2.éd. Paris, G. Baillière, 1870.
4+36 p. illus.

1. Opthalmoscope and opthalmoscopy. 2. Eye--
Diseases and defects. I. Title.

NL   0348292   InU MB

Liebreich, Richard, 1830-1917.
Atlas der Ophthalmoscopie
see his   Atlas d'ophthalmoscopie.

WW   LIEBREICH, Richard, 1830-1917
fL717a   Atlas of ophthalmoscopy, representing
1885   the normal and pathological conditions of
the fundus oculi as seen with the ophthalmoscope. The text tr. by H. Rosborough
Swanzy. 3d ed. London, Churchill,
1885.
viii, 31 p. illus.

Translation of Atlas der Opthal-
moscopie.

NL   0348294   DNLM ICJ KU-M PPHa PPC NNNAM MiDW-M

Liebreich, Richard, 1830–
Atlas of ophthalmoscopy. Representing the normal and
pathological conditions of the fundus oculi as seen with
the ophthalmoscope. Composed of 12 chromolithographic
plates, containing 59 figures, drawn from nature and accompanied by an explanatory text, by Dr. R. Liebreich, the
text translated by H. Rosborough Swanzy. 2d ed. (enl. and
rev.) London, J. Churchill and sons; ₍etc., etc.₎ 1870.
viii, 31 p. xII col. pl. (1 fold.) 36 cm.

1. Ophthalmoscope and ophthalmoscopy. 2. Eye—Diseases and
defects. I. Swanzy, Sir Henry Rosborough, 1843-1913. II. Title.

RE86.L7   17–30991

ICJ NNC
NL   0348295   DLC KU-M N DNLM NcD-MC PPC CtY NcD WaU

---

ar W   Liebreich, Richard, 1830–
26316   A contribution to school hygiene. A
paper read at a meeting of the National
Health Society on June 12th, 1873. London,
J. & A. Churchill, 1873.
12 p. 21cm.

"Reprinted from Public Health for July,
1873."
No. 7 in a vol. lettered: Pamphlets, 3.

NL   0348296   NIC MB

Liebreich (Richard) [1830–]. De l'examen
de l'œil au moyen de l'ophthalmoscope. (Extrait de la traduction française du traité pratique
des maladies de l'œil, par W. Mackenzie, faite
sur la 4. édition par MM. Warlomont et Testelin).
62 pp., 1 l. 8°. Bruxelles, J. Van Buggenhoudt,
1857.

NL   0348297   DNLM PPC

Liebreich, Richard, 1830–
——. De la rétinite leucémique et de l'embolie
de l'artère centrale de la rétine. Traduit par le
Prof. Van Kempen. 12 pp. 8°. Bruxelles, Fre.
J. Van Buggenhoudt, [1861]. [P., v. 1439.]

NL   0348298   DNLM

WW   LIEBREICH, Richard, 1830-1917
L717h   Handleiding tot het onderzoek van
1859   het oog met den oogspiegel. Toegevoegd
aan de Fransche vertaling van Mackenzie's
Handboek der oogheelkunde. Ten dienste
van het onderwijs aan 's Rijks Militaire
Geneeskundige School in het Nederduitsch
bewerkt door A. F. Bauduin. Utrecht,
Dekema, 1859.
128 p. illus.
I. Mackenzie, William, 1791-1868.

A practical treatise on the diseases
of the eye
WW L717h   59-15008

NL   0348300   DNLM

WW   LIEBREICH, Richard, 1830-1917
L717n   Nouveau procédé d'extraction de
1872   cataracte. Paris, Baillière, 1872.
16 p. illus.

NL   0348301   DNLM

Liebreich, Richard, 1830–
——. Instrument destiné à empêcher l'empoi-
sonnement par l'atropine. 1 l. 8°. [n. p., n. d.]
[P., v. 1404.]

NL   0348302   DNLM

WW   LIEBREICH, Richard, 1830-1917
L717o   Eine neue Methode der Cataract-
1872   Extraction. Berlin, Hirschwald, 1872.
20 p. illus.
Translation of On a new method for
extraction of cataract.

NL   0348303   DNLM MB NcD-MC

Liebreich, Richard, 1830-1917.
Nouveau procédé d'extraction de cataracte...
Paris, 1872.
16 p. illus. 22.5 cm. [Pamphlets on
diseases and defects of the eye, v. 8. Miscellaneous on cataract].

NL   0348304   CtY

Liebreich, Richard, 1830– ed.
Verein deutscher aerzte in Paris.
Recueil des travaux de la Société médicale allemande
de Paris ... Paris ₍etc.₎ Au siège de la Société, 1855-65.

---

ar W   Liebreich, Richard, 1830–
26316   School life in its influence on sight.
A lecture delivered before the College of
Preceptors at the house of the Society of
Arts, July 13, 1872. London, J. & A.
Churchill, 1872.
16 p. 21cm.

No. 3 in a vol. lettered: Pamphlets, 3.

1. School hy   giene. 2. Eye--Diseases
and defects.   I. Title.

NL   0348306   NIC MH DNLM MB

Liebreich, Richard, 1830–1917.
School life in its influence on sight and figure. Two
lectures. By R. Liebreich ... London, J. & A. Churchill,
1878.
36 p. illus. 20⁴ᶜᵐ.

1. School hygiene. 2. Eye—Diseases and defects. 3. Spine—Abnor-
malities and deformities. I. Title.

E 15-1431

Library, U. S. Bur. of   Education LB3415.L6

NL   0348307   DNLM CtY MiU DHEW

Liebreich, Richard, 1830–
——. Turner and Mulready; the effect of certain faults of vision on painting, with especial
reference to their works. The real and ideal in
portraiture; the deterioration of oil paintings.
Three lectures (delivered in 1872, 1875, and 1878,
respectively). 45 pp. 8°. London, J. & A.
Churchill, 1888.

NL   0348308   DNLM CtY NjP

Liebreich, Richard, 1830–1917.
A vida na escola, considerada em relação á sua influencia sobre a vista. Conferencia, perante o Collegio de
preceptores, de Londres, pelo Dr. R. Liebreich ... Tr. e
offerecida ao director geral de instrucção publica, para
bem da conveniente organisação das novas escolas em
Portugal, por Julio Roberto Dunlop. Londres, Typ.
Waterlow and sons, limited, 1877.
27 p. 21½ᶜᵐ.

1. School hygiene. 2. Eye—Diseases and defects. 3. Spine—Abnormi-
ties and deformities. I. Dunlop, Julio Roberto, tr.

18-6755

Library of Congress   LB3408.L55

NL   0348309   DLC

VOLUME 332

Liebrich, Adolf,
Beitrag zur kenntniss des Bauxit's vom Vogelsberge.
Inaug. diss.   Zurich, 1891.

NL 0348310   ICRL

Liebrich (August). *Beiträge zur Kenntnis
des papillären Kystoms der Ovarien.* 26 pp., 1 l.
8°. *Würzburg.* 1895.

NL 0348311   DNLM

BR
350
.G36
L7

Liebrich, Auguste Fréderic.
Nicolas Gerbel, jurisconsulte-théologien du
temps de la Réformation. Strasbourg, Imprimerie de veuve Berger-Levrault, 1857.
35 p. 20 cm.

Thèse—Faculté de théologie protestante de
Strasbourg.
"Sources consultées": p. 2.

1. Gerbel, Nikolaus, 1485-1560.

NL 0348312   DCU

Liebrich, Em.
... Essai sur le mysticisme spiritualiste de
Sébastien Franck de Woerd...   Strasbourg, J. H.
E. Heitz, 1872.
2 p.l., 60 p. 20½cm.

NL 0348313   PHC

Liebrich, Friedrich Mattmueller-

see

Mattmueller-Liebrich, Friedrich

Liebrich, Fritz, *writer on foreign exchange.*
Elemente des Devisenrechts. Basel, Helbing und Lichtenhahn, 1955.
123 p. 23 cm. (Basler Studien zur Rechtswissenschaft, Heft 43)

1. Foreign exchange—Law.   I. Title.

55-43594 ‡

NL 0348315   DLC CU-AL MnU-L NNC MH-L

836.7B2
L52

Liebrich, Fritz, 1879-
Baseldytsch; mundartgedichte aus dem nachlass von Fritz Liebrich. Hrsg. von der Kommission zur förderung des heimischen schrifttums. Basel, B. Schwabe, 1938.
68 p.

1. German language - Dialects - Basel.
I. Switzerland. Staatliche kommission zur
förderung des heimischen schrifttums.
II. Title.

NL 0348316   NNC ScU PU

Hin13
37oh

Liebrich, Fritz, *1879-*
Baseldytsch; die Basler Mundart-Gedichte von
Fritz Liebrich, hrsg. von der Staatlichen Litera-
turkredit-Kommission, Basel-Stadt. Basel, B.
Schwabe, 1951.
134p. 22cm.

1. German language - Dialects - Basel - Texts.

NL 0348317   CtY

Liebrich, Fritz, *1879-*
Die "befreier" Elsass-Lothringens nach erlebnissen der
"befreiten". Hrsg. nach urkundlichem material von Liebrich,
ev. pfarrer aus Masmünster i. Els., und Gapp, kath. vicar aus
Lutterbach, O.-Els. Freiburg im Breisgau, J. Bielefeld,
1918.
74 p. 1 illus. 22°.

1. European war, 1914-1918—Alsace-Lorraine.   I. Gapp, Josef,
joint author. II. Title.

27-25675

Library of Congress   DD801.A57L4

NL 0348318   DLC NN

LIEBRICH, Fritz, *1879-*
Johann Peter Hebel. Basel, E. Finckh, 1918.

pp.16. Port.on cover.
"Volks-bücher des Deutschschweizerischen
sprachvereins, 3."

NL 0348319   MH CU

PT2298
.H326

Liebrich, Fritz, *1879-*
Johann Peters Hebel und Basel, von
Fritz Liebrich. Basel, Verlag Helbing &
Lichtenhahn, 1926.
131 p. illus., port. 20 cm.

"Auf den 100. Todestag J.P. Hebels
(22. September 1926)"

1. Hebel, Johann Peter, 1760-1826.

NL 0348320   TU MH OrU NjP

NGB p.v.217, no.4

Liebrich, Fritz, 1879–
Masken; ein Aufzug, von Fritz Liebrich. Der Stellvertreter,
Basler Totentanz; ein Akt, von Carl Albrecht Bernoulli. Basel:
Verein Quodlibet, 1920. 90 p. 16°. (Theaterstuecke
des Verbandes Schweizerischer Dialekt-Buehnen. Serie Basel,
Heft 1.)

1. Drama, Swiss-German. 2. Ger-   man language—Dialects, Swiss—
Basel.   3. Bernoulli, Carl Albrecht,   1868–   4. Title.   5. Title:
Der Stellvertreter.   6. Ser.   March 6, 1928
N. Y. P. L.

NL 0348321   NN

Liebrich, Georges.
Contribution à l'etude de quelques complications
de la dysenterie bacillaire et leur traitement
par le serotherapie.
Inaug. diss. Strasbourg, 1928.
Bibl.

NL 0348322   ICRL CtY

Liebrich, Hans, 1912–
Die historische wahrheit bei Ernst Troeltsch. ...
Giessen, 1937.   71 p.
Inaug. Diss. - Giessen, 1937.
Lebenslauf.
Literaturverzeichnis.

NL 0348323   ICRL NjP RPB CtY

Liebrich, Peter. *Erfolge der intranasalen
Stirnhöhlenoperation nach Halle mit besonderer
Berücksichtigung der Röntgenbefunde [Frei-
burg] 23p. 8°. Schopfheim (Baden) 1935.

NL 0348324   DNLM CtY

Liebrucks, Bruno, 1911–
Platons Entwicklung zur Dialektik; Untersuchungen zum
Problem des Eleatismus. Frankfurt am Main, V. Kloster-
mann [1949]
255 p. 24 cm.
Bibliographical footnotes.

1. Plato. 2. Dialectic. 3. Eleatics.

B395.L5   184.1   A 51-7006
Harvard Univ. Library
for Library of Congress   [2]†

CtY OCU PBm NcD DLC
NL 0348325   MH TxU CSt NBuU NN OOxM CU NIC ICU NBC

Liebrucks, Bruno, 1911–
Probleme der subjekt- objektrelation. ...
Königsberg Pr., 1934.
Inaug. Diss. - Königsberg Pr., 1934.
Lebenslauf.

NL 0348326   ICRL CtY

Liebs, Richard Wilhelm
see Liebs, Wilhelm, 1903–

Liebs, Wilhelm, 1903–
Die Nachbildung von Flüssen mit beweglicher Sohle im
Modell; Grundlagen, Durchführung der Modellversuche,
Übertragbarkeit der Ergebnisse. Würzburg, 1942.
55 p. illus., diagrs. 30 cm.
Diss.—Technische Hochschule, Hanover.
Vita.
"Vorliegende Arbeit erscheint gleichzeitig als Heft 43 der 'Mit-
teilungen der Preussischen Versuchsanstalt für Wasser-, Erd- und
Schiffbau, Berlin.'"
Bibliography: p. 49.
1. Hydraulic models.   I. Title.

Full name: Richard Wilhelm Liebs.

TC163.L5   62-57094

NL 0348328   DLC

Liebsch, Albert,
Die mit der rechtlichen bedeutung des kreuz-
verhörs in zusammenhang stehenden rechtsein-
richtungen, insbesondere deren beurteilung nach
englischem und deutschem rechtsempfinden. ...
Dresden, 1937.   102 p.
Inaug. Diss. - Leipzig, 1937.
Literaturnachweis.

NL 0348329   ICRL

Liebsch, Artur.
Bruno Héroux
see under Héroux, Bruno, 1868–

VOLUME 332

Liebsch, Georg.
Syntax der wendischen sprache in der Oberlausitz, von Georg Liebsch. Bautzen, M. Hórnik, in commission bei Schmaler & Pech in Leipzig, 1884.
xv, ₍1₎, 240 p.   22ᶜᵐ.
Bibliography: p. 239-240.

6-31693

NL   0348331   DLC ICU

Liebsch, Karl.
Praktikum der Weberei. Handbuch für alle Weberei-Betriebsangehörigen. Anleitung zur Auffindungen von Fehlerquellen. München, Eder ₍1952₎
188 p. illus., diagrs. 17 cm.

1. Weaving.   ɪ. Title.
A 53-3612

Georgia Inst. of Tech.   Library
for Library of Congress   ₍3₎

NL   0348332   GAT

Liebsch, Willi, 1897-
Über die Atmung einiger Heliciden. Eine Untersuchung zum Oberflächengesetz... ₍Jena₎, 1928.
Inaug.-Diss. - Berlin.
Lebenslauf.
"Abdruck aus den Zoologischen Jahrbüchern, Bd. 46, Abt. f. allg. Zool. und Physiol."
"Literaturverzeichnis": p. 206-208.

NL   0348333   CtY ICRL OU

Liebsch, Willi Albert, 1897-
see   Liebsch, Willi, 1897-

Liebschaften und galanterien der regenten und aristokraten Frankreichs, älterer und neuerer zeiten Leipzig, Weygand, 1791.
190 p.

NL   0348335   PPLT

Liebscher,
D443   Die politischen und wirtschaftlichen trieb-
L717   kräfte im weltkriege; eine übersicht für mann-
schaften, die nicht regelmässig zeitungen lesen können, zusammengestellt von Liebscher... Berlin, "Concordia", 1916.
88 p. 22ᵐ.

1. Europe - Politics - 1871-   2. European war, 1914-1918 -   Causes. 3. Triple alliance, 1882. 4. Triple   entente, 1907-   ɪ.Title.

NL   0348336   CSt-H

Liebscher.
Vierhundert Millionen Auslandsgelder für Kriegsverletzte. Ein Vorschlag zur wirtschaftlichen Sicherung unserer Verletzten, von Oberleutnant Liebscher...   Ilmenau in Thüringen: A. Schroeter, 1916. 40 p. 12°.

1. Poultry.—Breeding and raising,   Germany. 2. Disabled.—Rehabilitation, etc., Germany.
N. Y. P. L.   December 13, 1920.

NL   0348337   NN NjP IU

Liebscher, A., illus.
DB201   Kronika českého národa v obrazech. Od českých malířů-
.1   umělců: A. Liebschera ₍et al.₎ Slovem doprovází Josef
.K7   Hais Týnecky. ₍V Bohušovicích n. O., Nakl. V. Kováříka, 1946₎

Liebscher ₍A.H.W.₎ H.
see   Liebscher, Hellmuth, 1900-

LIEBSCHER, Adolf
Národní kroje slovanské.   Praza, F.Topic, ₍1898.
f°. pp.(4). Colored plates (mounted.)
On cover: Vijstava architektury a inzenýrstvi v Praze roku 1898.

NL   0348340   MH

Liebscher, Adolf.
Národní kroje slovanské.
— V Praze. Topič. ₍1913.₎ (1) p. (27) colored plates. Size, 10 × 6½ inches, mounted on cards 15¼ × 11⅜ inches.

K442 — T.r. — Slavic nations. Costume.

NL   0348341   MB

Liebscher, Art.
TV sweep alignment techniques; introducing the new Supermark method. ₍1st ed.₎ New York, J. F. Rider ₍1953₎
123 p. illus. 22 cm.

1. Television—Receivers and reception.   ɪ. Title.
TK6653.L5   621.38836   53-7283 ‡

NL   0348342   DLC NN MB CaBVa OrP WaS

LIEBSCHER, August Hugo.
Charron und sein Werk : „De la sagesse." Inaugural-Dissertat₎
Leipz. Bär. 1890. (3), 65, (1) pp. 8°.

NL   0348343   MB

Liebscher, Bruno, 1870-
Das Oberlausitzer tiefland ... Mit einer übersichts-
karte. ₍Görlitz, Druck von H. Gretsel, 1904?₎
4 p. l., 106 p., 1 l. map. 24ᶜᵐ.
Inaug.-diss.—Leipzig.
Vita.
Bibliographical foot-notes.

1. Geology—Saxony—Lusatia.
G S 12-721

Library, U. S. Geol.   survey

NL   0348344   DI-GS ICRL CU CtY PU ICJ

Liebscher, C. Oswald, *firm, Chemnitz.*
Handbuch für die flachs- und wergspinnerei, herausgegeben von C. Oswald Liebscher ... ₍Chemnitz i. Sa., C. Oswald Lieb-scher, 19—₎
156 p. illus. 14½ x 11½ᶜᵐ.

1. Spinning.   ɪ. Title : Flachs- und wergspinnerei.
45-32561

Library of Congress   TS1705.L5

NL   0348345   DLC

Liebscher, C. Oswald, firm, Chemnitz.
Handbuch für die Hanfspinnerei und Bindfaden-Fabrikation. Chemnitz i. Sa.: C. O. Liebscher ₍19—₎ 157 p. illus. 14cm.

239256B. 1. Hemp—Spinning.
N. Y. P. L.   July 19, 1943

NL   0348346   NN

Liebscher ₍Daniel₎. *De morbis intestini coli ex anatomia dijudicandis. 25 pp. 4°. Erfor-
dia, typ. Groschiania, 1728.*

NL   0348347   DNLM

Liebscher ₍Felix₎ ₍1880-   ₎. *Askaridiasis der Gallenwege mit Beschreibung eines eigenen Falles. 20 pp. 8°. Leipzig, A. Edel-
mann, 1919.*

NL   0348348   DNLM CtY ICRL

Liebscher, Franz, ed.
Oesterreichischer Liederkranz für allgemeine Volksschulen. Herausgegeben von F. Liebscher. Heft 1.   Komotau, Brüder Butter, 1892.
48 p. 16°.

NL   0348349   NN

Liebscher, Georg, 1853-1895.
Anbau-versuche mit verschiedenen roggensorten. (Schlussbericht.) Auf veranlassung der Deutschen land-wirtschaftsgesellschaft, Saatgut-abteilung, in verbindung mit praktischen landwirten ausgeführt von prof. dr. Lieb-scher ... Berlin, Druck von Gebr. Unger, 1896.
2 p. l., 85 p., 1 l. 24ᶜᵐ. (Added t.-p.: Arbeiten der Deutschen landwirt-schafts-gesellschaft ... hft. 13)

1. Rye.
Agr 11-941

Library, U. S. Dept. of   Agriculture 18D48 no. 13

NL   0348350   DNAL MoU

Liebscher, Georg, 1853-1895.
Edler, Wilhelm, 1855-
Anbau-versuche mit verschiedenen sommer- und winter-weizen-sorten. Auf veranlassung der Deutschen land-wirtschafts-gesellschaft, Saatgut-abteilung, in verbindung mit praktischen landwirten, begonnen von weil. prof. dr. Liebscher ... weitergeführt von prof. dr. Edler ... Bearb. von prof. dr. Edler ... Berlin, Druck von Gebr. Unger, 1898.

VOLUME 332

LIEBSCHER, Georg.
Die erscheimungen der Vererbung bei einem
Kreuzungsprodukte zweier varietäten von hordeum
sativum. [Jena], Mrs. J. E. Humphrey, [1890.]

NL 0348352   MH

Liebscher, Georg, 1853–1895.
Gedächtnisrede gehalten bei der feier der aufstellung der
büsten von Gustav Drechsler und Wilhelm Henneberg im auditorium des Landwirtschaftlichen instituts der Universität Göttingen, am 23. mai 1894; von dr. Liebscher ... Mit einer licht-
drucktafel. Berlin, P. Parey, 1894.

29, [1] p. front. 21½ᶜᵐ.
Added t.-p.: Journal für landwirtschaft ... 42. Jahrgang. Ergänzungsheft.

1. Drechsler, Gustav, 1833–1890. 2. Henneberg, Wilhelm, 1825–1800.
I. Journal für landwirtschaft.

30–23117

Library of Congress   S415.L7

NL 0348353   DLC

Liebster, Georg.
Kirche und Sozialdemokratie. Giessen,
A. Töpelmann, 1908.

128 p. 23 cm. (Studien zur praktischen
Theologie, Bd. 2, Heft 1)

1. Socialism, Christian. 2. Socialism and
religion. I. Title. (Series)

NL 0348354   CaBVaU

Liebscher, Georg, 1853–1895.
Japan's landwirthschaftliche und allgemeinwirthschaftliche
verhältnisse. Nach eignen beobachtungen dargestellt von dr.
Georg Liebscher. Mit einer terraindarstellung und fünf statistischen karten. Jena. G. Fischer, 1882.

viii, 176, [8] p. fold. map, 5 fold. charts. 23ᶜᵐ.

1. Japan—Econ. condit. 2. Agriculture—Japan.

3–26108

Library of Congress   HC462.L7

NL 0348355   DLC ICU MH-A MH

Liebscher, [Georg] 1853–1895.
Das landwirtschaftliche studium an der Universität
Göttingen. Von Dr. Liebscher ... Mit 4 lichtdruckta-
feln. Berlin, P. Parey, 1893.

52 p. 4 pl. 27ᶜᵐ.

1. Agricultural education. 2. Göttingen. Universität.

4–21226

Library of Congress   S539.G5L7

NL 0348356   DLC

Liebscher, Georg, 1853–1895.
La marche de l'absorption des principes nutritifs par les
plantes et son importance pour la théorie des engrais. 10 pl.

Ann. sci. agron. 1888, tome 1, p. 25–120, 213–296.   Paris, 1888.
Translation of article in Journal für landwirtschaft. bd. xxxv, 1887,
p. 335–518.

1. Fertilizers. 2. Plant nutrition.

Agr 4—674

U. S. Dept. of agr. Library
for Library of Congress

NL 0348357   DNAL

Liebscher, Georg.
Der nährwerth der steinnussspähne nach versuchen von
Dr. Schuster und Prof. Dr. Liebscher.

Landw. jahrb. bd. 19, p. 143–148.   Berlin, 1890.

1. Ivory-nut as a feeding stuff.

Agr 4–1369

Library, U. S. Dept. of   Agriculture

NL 0348358   DNAL

Liebscher, Georg, 1853–1895, ed.
Referate über die im Vorlesungskursus für ältere praktische
Landwirte vom 1. bis 6. Februar 1892 gehaltenen Vorträge.
Unter Mitwirkung der Königlichen Landwirtschafts-Gesellschaft,
Centralverein für die Provinz Hannover, herausgegeben von Dr.
G. Liebscher, ... Hannover, Göhmannsche Buchdruckerei,
1892.

[6], 126 p. incl. tables. 3 fold. charts. 22½ᶜᵐ.
"Das landwirtschaftliche Studium an der Universität Göttingen. Von Prof. Dr.
Liebscher," p. [105]–126.

NL 0348359   ICJ

Liebscher, Georg.
Ueber den einfluss, welchen die beschaffenheit der rü-
benschnitzel auf deren haltbarkeit in den mieten ausübt.

Landw. vers. stat. bd. 31, p. 186–189.   Berlin, 1885.

1. Beet silage.

Agr 4–2543

Library, U. S. Dept. of   Agriculture

NL 0348360   DNAL

Liebscher, Georg, 1853–1895.
Über die beziehungen von *Heterodera sehachtii* zur
rübenmüdigkeit ... Halle a. S., 1879.

2 p. l., 41 p. 24½ᶜᵐ.
Inaug.-diss.—Halle.
Vita.

1. Heterodera schachtii.

12–27052

Library of Congress   SB608.B4L7

NL 0348361   DLC

Liebscher, Georg.
Ueber die ursachen der rübenmüdigkeit.   5 tables.

Landw. jahrb. bd. 7, p. 313–339.   Berlin, 1878.

1. Beet sickness. 2. Rotation of crops.

Agr 4–1370

Library, U. S. Dept. of   Agriculture

NL 0348362   DLC DNAL

Liebscher, Georg, 1853–1895. ed.
Vorträge für praktische landwirte... 1895.
46 p.

NL 0348363   DNAL

LIEBSCHER, H.
Anlage, besatz und ausnützung von fischteichen
Vortrag, gehalten in der Okonomischen gesell-
schaft im königreiche Sachsen zu Dresden, am
4. Dezember 1908, von ... H. Liebscher... Leipzig,
Verlagsbuchhandlung Fritzsche & Schmidt, 1908.

Cover-title, 22 p. 23 cm.   F 6209.08.60

NL 0348364   MH

RC389
L62   Liebscher, Hellmuth, 1900–
... Ein kartographischer beitrag zur geschichte
der tanzwut; inaugural-dissertation zur erlangung der doktorwürde in der zahnheilkunde
einer hohen Medizinischen fakultät der Universität Leipzig, vorgelegt von Hellmuth Liebscher
... [Zeulenroda i. Thür., Oberreuter, 1931]
22 p. incl. maps.   23ᶜᵐ.

At head of title: Aus dem Institut für
geschichte der medizin an der Universität
Leipzig, Direktor: professor dr. Henry E.
Sigerist.

NL 0348365   NNC CtY DNLM

4D 127   Liebscher, Hermann.
Der Aufstieg des Abendlandes, die Zukunft
Europas als religiöses Problem.   [Strehla
25 p.

NL 0348366   DLC-P4

---

ar W
21046   Liebscher, Hugo, 1864–
Charron und sein Werk: "De la sagesse".
Leipzig, 1890.
65 p. 22cm.
Diss.—Leipzig.

1. Charron, Pierre, 1541–1603.

NL 0348367   NIC ICRL MH

Liebscher, Imfried.
Technologie der Keramik, von Imfried Liebscher und
Franz Willert. [Dresden] Verlag der Kunst, 1955.

410 p. illus., map. 25 cm. (Keramisches Schaffen, Bd. 1)
Bibliography: p. [391]–394.

1. Ceramics.   I. Willert, Franz, joint author. II. Title.
(Series)

TP807.K37 Bd. 1   56–26061

NL 0348368   DLC DP ICJ IU NN MiDW

DB975 Liebscher, Karl.
.B6L7   Der politische amtsbezirk Bischofteinitz.   Von Karl
Liebscher ... Bischofteinitz, E. Bayand, 1913.

512, [8] p. 23½ᶜᵐ.
3. aufl.
Bibliography: p. [6–7]

1. Bischofteinitz (District) Bohemia.

NL 0348369   ICU

Liebscher, Kurt.
Gärfutterwirtschaft; kurze anleitung zur gewinnung und
verfütterung von eingesäuertem futter, von oberregierungs-
und oberlandwirtschaftsrat dr. Kurt Liebscher. 3. aufl. [Wien]
Reichsnährstand verlags-ges. m. b. h., zweigniederlassung Do-
nauland, 1941.

85, [1] p. illus. 23ᶜᵐ.

1. Ensilage. 2. Feeding and feeding stuffs. I. Title.

45–22731

Library of Congress   SB195.L5 1941

NL 0348370   DLC DNAL CU IU

VOLUME 332

60.1
L622

Liebscher, Kurt.
Heu- und Gärfutterbereitung.   Wien,
Fromme, 1951.
83 p.

Also
in
33.29
Sch52
Ed. 9

1. Hay. Fermentation. 2. Feeding stuffs.
Preparation.

NL 0348371   DNAL

830
D584
eL

Liebscher, Otto, 1883-
Franz Dingelstedt; seine dramaturgische
Entwicklung und Tätigkeit bis 1857 und
seine Bühnenleitung in München.   Halle
a.S., Druck von Paalzow, 1909.
152p. 23cm.

Inaug.-Diss. - München.
Vita.

1.Dingelstedt, Franz, Freiherr von,
1814-1881.

NL 0348372   CLSU PU MH NjP

Liebscher, Otto, 1883-
Verskunst auf der Bühne; ein Weg zur Leistungssteigerung
in der Schauspielerkunst. Tübingen, M. Niemeyer, 1953. 93 p.
21cm.

1. Actors and acting, German.   2. Expression. 3. Prosody.
I. Title.

NL 0348373   NN OCU MH PU PSt

HC54
I5
1941

Liebscher, Roland
Die Staatliche und wirtschaftliche Gestaltung
der Erde, von Roland Liebscher und Paul Wagner.
2. verb. Aufl.   Bamberg, C.C. Buchners Verlag,
1941.
203 p. maps, tables, diagrs. (Fischer-
Geistbeck Erdkunde. 7.T.)

1. Commercial policy. 2. Economic policy.
I. Wagner, Paul, writer of geography.

NL 0348374   CU MH

Liebscher, Roland
... Die staatliche und wirtschaftliche
gestaltung der erde, von Roland Liebscher
zusammen mit Richard Bitterling und Theodor
Otto, mit 42 karten und bildern, 15 diagram-
men, 114 tabellen und 8 tafelbildern. 3.
aufl. München und Berlin, R. Oldenbourg,
1942 etc.
7. teil   197p.

Fischer-Geistbeck - Erdkunde, hrsg. von
Richard Bitterling   und Theodore Otto.)

NL 0348375   MH NjR MoU

Liebscher, Roland.
Die staatliche und wirtschaftliche Gestaltung
der Erde. Von Roland Liebscher zusammen mit
Richard Bitterling und Theodor Otto. 4.Aufl.
München, R.Oldenbourg, etc., etc., 1943.

vi, 197 p. (Fischer-Geistbeck, Erdkunde,
7.Teil)

NL 0348376   MH NcU

Liebscher, Rudi, ed.

Germany (*Democratic Republic, 1949-*   *Laws, stat-
utes, etc.*
Versicherungsrecht der Deutschen Demokratischen Re-
publik; eine Zusammenstellung der wichtigsten gesetzlichen
Vorschriften und allgemeinen Versicherungsbedingungen.
Stand: 31 März 1954. Zusammengestellt und bearb. von
Rudi Liebscher. Berlin, Deutscher Zentralverlag ₁1954₎

Liebscher, Wilhelm, joint author.

Hönigschmid, R.
Der einfluss von hartem wasser auf den stoffwechsel nach
versuchen am wiederkäuer. Von R. Hönigschmid und W.
Liebscher.

Landw. vers. stat. bd. 124, p. 329-344.   Berlin, 1936.

Liebscher, Wilhelm.
Über den einfluss des zusatzes einer mineralsalzmischung
zum futter auf menge und einige bestandteile der milch.

Landw. vers. stat. bd. 109, p. 347-362.   Berlin, 1929.

1. Milk—₁Effect of mineral salts₎

[87.L293 bd. 109]   Agr 30-833

Library, U. S. Dept. of   Agriculture 105.8L23 bd. 109

NL 0348379   DNAL OU

Liebscher, firm, machinery manufacturers, Chemnitz, Germany

see   Liebscher, C. Oswald, firm,
Chemnitz.

LIEBSCHÜTZ, HANS, 1893-
Das allegorische Weltbild der heiligen Hildegard von Bingen.   Leipzig, Berlin, B.G. Teubner,
1930.

viii, 179 p.   (Added t.-p.: Studien der
Bibliothek Warburg, xvi).

NL 0348381   DDO

909
R 167.yL

LIEBSCHÜTZ, HANS, 1893-
Ranke.   ₁London₎Published for the
Historical association by G.Philip,1954.
20p. 22cm.   (Historical association publications₁general series₁G26)

"Bibliographical note": p.18.

NL 0348382   PU

Liebschutz, Joseph Henry
Investigation of the catalytic effect
of the killing of staphylococcus aureus by
mercuric chloride through addition of
sodium oleate. ... ₁Cincinnati, 1935₎.
23 l.

NL 0348383   OCU

PN
6120
J4L5.3

Liebson, Jacob J
Too much Haman. A Purim comedy. New
York, Bloch ₍c1903₎
13 p.   23 cm.

1. Purim (Feast of Esther)--Drama.
I. Title

NL 0348384   OCU

Liebson, Sarah Gertrude
see Millin, Sarah Gertrude (Liebson)
1889-1968.

Liebson, Sidney H   1920-
The discharge mechanism of self-quenching Geiger-
Mueller counters. ₁College Park, Md.₎ 1947.
iv, 21 l. diagrs., tables. 32 cm.

Thesis—University of Maryland.
Typewritten (carbon copy)
"Selected bibliography": leaf 16.

1. Geiger-Müller counters.

QC787.G4L5   A 50-6591
Maryland. Univ. Libr.
for Library of Congress   ₍3₎†

NL 0348386   MdU DLC

BT 800
.L717

LIEBS-REU UNERSCHÖPFLICHER SCHATZ ZU TÄGLICHEM
Gebrauch und unbeschreiblichen Nutzen. Zusamm.
getragen von einem Priester der Gesellschaft
Jesu. Regenspurg, J. B. Lang, 1719.
176 p.

√1. Repentance. *I. von Priester der
Gesellschaft Jesu*

NL 0348387   InU

Liebst, Aage.
Frigjort. Skuespil i fire Akter.   Kjøbenhavn: S. Bern-
steen, 1910. 3 p.l., 96 p.   8°.

1. Drama (Danish). 2. Title.
N. Y. P. L.   February 6, 1911.

NL 0348388   NN

BX
2234
L5

Liebst, Leo, Father.
Gelobtes heiliges Messopfer. Frankfurt a. Main, Verlag
der Weissen Väter, 1952.
211 p. 17cm.

Errata slip inserted.

1. Mass. I. Title.

NL 0348389   CLgA

Liebstaedter (Hermann). Zur Würdigung
der Behandlung des Morbus Brightii acutus mit
Methylenblau. 23 pp. 8°. Würzburg, 1894.

NL 0348390   DNAL

HD9490
L717

Liebstaedter, Otto, 1900-
Die konzentration in der deutschen margarine-
industrie ... Berlin, Druck von P. Funk, 1927.

80 p. incl. tables. 22½ᶜᵐ.

Inaug.-diss. - Giessen.
Lebenslauf.
"Literaturverzeichnis": p.79-80.

1.Oleomargarine. 2.Trusts, Industrial -
Germany.

NL 0348391   CSt-H PU MiU ICRL DNAL MH NNC

VOLUME 332

Das **Liebste** Lied; eine Sammlung von volkstümlichen Liedern für Klavier mit Singstimme und vollständigen Texten. Mainz, B. Schott's Söhne ¡19—¡ Pl. no. B. S. S. 36281.

45 p. 31 cm. (Edition Schott 3799)

For voice and piano.

1. Songs with piano.

M1619.L4284   51–36715

NL 0348392   DLC NRU NN

Das **liebste** Lied; eine Sammlung von volkstümlichen Liedern für Klavier mit Singstimme und vollständigen Texten. Mainz, B. Schott's Söhne [n.d.] 2 v. (Edition Schott 3799, 4000)

NL 0348393   CSf

Liebstein, Abraham Morris, 1889–
Commentary on the Ten Commandments...by A. M. Liebstein ... ¡New York¡ Maimonides hygienic assoc., 1945.   22 p. 16cm.

1. Ten Commandments. I. Mai-   monides hygienic association, inc.,
New York.   June 28, 1948
N. Y. P. L.

NL 0348394   NN

Liebster, Arno, ed.

Hincke, August.
Alphabetische sportel- und stempeltaxe für das königreich Sachsen. Für gerichts- und verwaltungsbehörden, ephoren, advocaten, notarien, gerichtsärzte, etc. mit auszügen aus dem sportelregulative vom 3. december 1827, sowie mit erläuterungen und entscheidungen hoher behörden versehen, nebst einem anhange, die allgemeine sporteltaxe für das Ober-appellationsgericht, die bezirks-appellationsgerichte und einige andere mittelbehörden enthaltend, von August Hincke. 3., verm. und verb. aufl. hrsg. von Arno Liebster ... Leipzig, B. Tauchnitz, 1854.

BR   **Liebster, Georg,** *1863–1926.*
856   Kirche und Sozialdemokratie. Giessen,
L524   A. Töpelmann, 1908.
        128p. 23cm. (Studien zur praktischen Theologie, Bd. 2, Heft 1)

1. Church and state in Germany   I. Title

NL 0348396   WU CU-L OU NN MH ICU MH-AH

627.75   LIEBSTER, Georg, 1863–1926.
L717s   Der soziale Pfarrer; aus Georg Liebsters Lebensarbeit. In Verbindung mit Pfarrer Urban Hager und Pfarrer Hans Vogel herausgegeben von Johannes Herz. Mit einem Bildnis. Goettingen, Vandenhoeck & Ruprecht, 1928.
        168p. front.(port.) 23cm.

NL 0348397   MH-AH

Liebster, Irmgard.
... Frauentypen und frauenbildung; eine pädagogische plauderei. Leipzig, H. Haessel, 1927.

95, ¡1¡ p. 16¼ᵐ.

1. Education of women. 2. Woman—Biog.   I. Title.

Library of Congress   LC1483.L5   28–29913

NL 0348398   DLC

Liebstoeckl, Hans.
Die Geheimwissenschaften im Lichte unserer Zeit. Zürich, Amalthea-Verlag ¡*1932¡

432 p. 23 cm.

1. Anthroposophy.   I. Title.

BP595.L5   51–51100

NL 0348399   DLC CLSU OkU

---

837   **Liebstoeckl, Hans**
L717v   Von Sonntag auf Montag, ausgewählte Theaterfeuilletons. Wien, "Renaissance," 1923.
        296 p. 27 cm.

NL 0348400   NcU MH

BR817   Das **liebthätige** Gera gegen die saltzburgischen
.S3S3   emigranten. Das ist:Kurtze und wahrhafte erzehlung, wie dieselben in der...stadt Gera angekommen,aufgenommen und versorget...worden... Leipzig,S.B.Walther,1732.
       56,8 p. 17cm. ¡With Schelhorn,J.G. Historische nachricht vom ursprunge...der evangelischen religion in den salzburgischen landen. Leipzig,1732¡

Appended: "Bericht eines christlichen freundes in Gera von denen...saltzburgischen emigranten; so als eine fortsetzung dem tractätlein,Liebthätig Gera genannt" signed:Hanss Hager . (8 p.)

1.Salzburgers--Emigration,1731-1735.

NL 0348402   ICU

Liebus, Adalbert, 1876–
... Bibliographia foraminiferum recentium et fossilium. Berlin, W. Junk, 1931–33.

3 v. 25¼ᵐ. (Fossilium catalogus. I: Animalia. Editus a W. Quenstedt. Pars 49, 59 et 60)
At head of title: ... A. Liebus et H. E. Thalmann.
Issued in three parts, each with special t-p. Vol. 2 by A. Liebus, published 1931.
Contents.—I. 1910.—II. 1911–1930.—III. 1911–1930, supplementum.

1. Foraminifera—Bibl. 2. Foraminifera, Fossil—Bibl.   I. Thalmann, Hans Ernst, joint author. II. Title.
                                35–29822 Revised

Library of Congress   Z7996.F72L7

         ¡r43c2¡   016.59612

NL 0348403   DLC FTaSU CSt TxU

Liebus, Adalbert, 1876–   ed.

Botanisch-phaenologische beobachtungen in Böhmen ... hrsg. von der Gesellschaft für physiokratie in Böhmen, bearb. von deren Botanisch-phaenologischen sektion. ¡1.¡– hft.; 1907–
Prag, Gesellschaft für physiokratie in Böhmen, 1909–

Prussia. *Geologische landesanstalt.*
Die fauna des deutschen Unterkarbons ... Hrsg. von der Preussischen geologischen landesanstalt. Berlin, Im vertrieb bei der Preussischen geologischen landesanstalt, 1930–

Liebus, Adalbert, 1876–
... Die fossilen foraminiferen; eine einführung in die kenntnis ihrer gattungen; vorgelegt am 20. jänner 1931, von dr. Adalbert Liebus ... V Praze, Nákladem Stát. geologického ústavu Československé republiky s podporou Ministerstva školství a nár. osvěty, Tiskem Státní tiskárny, 1931.

158, ¡1¡ p. illus. 23ᵐ. (Czechoslovak republic. Státny geologicky ústav. Knohovna, svazek 14B)
"Verzeichnis der wichtigsten grundlegenden arbeiten ... mit besonderer berücksichtigung der Mitteleuropäischen vorkommnisse": p. 149–153.

1. Foraminifera, Fossil.
                       G S 32–58
Library, U. S. Geo'ogical   Survey (532) K no.14b

NL 0348406   DI-GS TxU

Liebus, Adalbert, 1876–
Neue Schildkrötenreste aus den Tertiären Süsswassertonen von Preschen bei Bilin in Böhmen. Nové nálezy želv v Terciерních jílech Břešťanských u Biliny v Čechách. Mit 4 Tafeln und 1 Textfigur. Praha, Nákl. Státního geologického ústavu, 1930.

57 p. 4 plates (in pocket) 30 cm. (Rozpravy Státního geologického ústavu Československé republiky, sv. 4)
Czech and German.
Bibliography: p. 29–30.
1. Turtles, Fossil. ¡1. Reptilia (Fossil)¡ 2. Paleontology—Czechoslovak Republic. 3. Paleontology—Tertiary. I. Title. II. Title: Nové nalezy želv v Terciерních jílech Břešťanských u Biliny v Čechách. (Series: Prague. Státní geologický ústav. Rozpravy, sv. 9)
   QE862.C5L5   G S 31–63 rev*
U. S. Geol. Survey. Libr.
for Library of Congress   ¡a52d1¡†

NL 0348407   DI-GS DLC TxU

Liebus, Adalbert, *1876–*
Die Tertiärformation in Albanien. Die Foraminiferen. (*In* Palaeontographica. Band 70, pp. 41–114. Illus. Plate. Map. Tables. Stuttgart, 1928.)
Verzeichnis der benützten Literatur, pp. 110–114.

D4933 — Tertiary fossils. — Foraminifera. Fossil. — Albania. Geol. & paleon.

NL 0348408   MB

Liebusch, Georg.
Büttner, Johann Carl, *b.* 1754.
Büttner der Amerikaner. Eine selbstbiographie Johann Carl Büttners, jetzigen amts-chirurgus in Senftenberg und ehemaligen nordamerikanischen kriegers ... 2. aufl., nebst einem anhange, welcher einen theil der erweiterten chronik der stadt und des amts Senftenberg enthält. Camenz, Gedruckt bei C. S. Krausche, 1828.

Liebusch, Georg.
Chronik der Stadt und des Amts Senftenberg, umgearbeitet und vervollständigt bis zum Jahre 1539 von Georg Liebusch... ¡Camenz: C. S. Krausche,¡ 1827. 1 p.l., (i)vi–vi, 126 p. 17cm. (In: Büttner, J. C. Büttner, der Amerikaner. Camenz, 1828.)

633516A. 1. Senftenberg, Germany   —Hist.
N. Y. P. L.   August 31, 1933

NL 0348410   NN PU

Liebusch, Georg.
Elisabeth von Dänemark, kurfürstin von Brandenburg; ein lebensbild. Berlin, Heinersdorff, n.d. 95 p.

NL 0348411   PPLT

VOLUME 332

PT
919
K9
L71

Liebusch, Georg.
Sagen und Bilder aus Muskau und dem
Parke. ₍Muskau, 1860₎
96 p. 19cm.

1. Folk-lore--Germany--Muskau.
2. Tales, German--Muskau. I. Title.

NL 0348412   NIC

Liebusch, Georg
Sagen und bilder aus Muskau und dem Park.
2. aufl. unverändert hrsg. von C. Petzold.
[4],82p. Dresden, Von Zahn & Jaensch, 1885.

Title-page, illus.

NL 0348413   OC1

PG303
.L7

Liebusch, Georg.
Skythika, oder etymologische und kritische Be-
merkungen über alte Bergreligion und späteren
Fetischismus, mit besonderer Berücksichtigung der
slavischen Völker- und Götter-Namen. Mit einem
Vorwort von Carl Ritter. Camenz, Gedruckt bei
C. S. Krausche, 1833.
xlv, 321 p.

1. Slavic languages--Etymology--Names. 2.
Names, Personal--Slavic. 3. Mythology, Slavic.
I. Title.

NL 0348414   ICU MH OC1 CtY NcD

PT
2381
A7L71+

Liebusch, Georg.
Ueber das Vaterländische in Klopstocks
Oden. Quedlinburg, G. Basse, 1874.
13 p. 28cm.

1. Klopstock, Friedrich Gottlieb, 1724-
1803. Oden.

NL 0348415   NIC

848
C80
L72

Lieby, Adolphe, 1865-1907.
Corneille; études sur le théâtre classique
... Paris, Lecène, Oudin, 1892.
ix,440 p. 19 cm.
Bibliography: p. ₍421₎-424.
CONTENTS.--Le Cid.--Horace.--Cinna.--
Polyeucte.--Nicomède.--Le menteur.

1.Corneille,Pierre,1606-1684.

MiU OCU PSt PBm ICU MH InU CaBVaU
NL 0348416   MiU CU-S CU ViLxW NIC NBuU NjP MB OO

PQ1965 **Lieby, Adolphe,** 1865-1907.
.Z8L7   Étude sur le théâtre de Marie-Joseph Chénier ... Paris,
Société française d'imprimerie et de librairie, 1901.
514 p. 25ᶜᵐ.
Thèse--Univ. de Paris.
"Notice bibliographique": p. ₍507₎-509.

1. Chénier, Marie Joseph Blaise, 1764-1811.

InU MB OCU MiU CaBVaU IaU NjP NRU IaU WU CU MiDW
NL 0348417   ICU NNU-W MH PU OCU CtY CoU NcD TU NNC

Lieby, Adolphe, 1865-1907.
Incertitudes. [Poems.]   Paris, A. Lemerre,
1905.
2 p.l., 98 p., 1 l. 12°.

NL 0348418   NN

Lieby, Adolphe, *1865-1907.*
Quantum philosophiae studio ad augendam dicendi
facultatem Cicero tribuerit ... Parisiis, edebat Societas
gallica libraria, 1901.
2 p. l., 124 p. 25ᶜᵐ.
Thèse--Univ. de Paris.
CONTENTS.--Procemium.--pars I. Quid de philosophia ad oratorium
usum cognoscenda M. Tullius sensisse videatur.--pars II. Quomodo
M. Tullius suum philosophiae studium ad forensem eloquentiam exercen-
dam adhibuerit.

6-908

NL 0348419   DLC NcD OCU CU CtY MiU PU

Lieby, Adolphe, 1865-1907.
Rêves et caresses. Paris, A. Lemerre, 1905.
2 p.l., 123 p. 1 l. 12°.

NL 0348420   NN

Lieby, Gustav.
Gestaltung von Druckgussteilen (Spritz- und Pressguss)
Stuttgart, Franckh ₍1949₎
157 p. Illus. 24 cm.
Bibliography: p. 155.

1. Die-casting.

TS239.L5   50-36679

NL 0348421   DLC NN ICJ

LIECHE, Otto, 1878-
I. Über die akroleïndarstellung, etc.
II. Beiträge zur kenntnis der phenylhy-
drazone, etc. Weida i. Thür. Inaug.diss.
Leipzig. 1904.

NL 0348422   MH

Liechevitch (Sophie) [1887-   ]. *Les formes
mortelles de la scarlatine. 42 pp. 8°. Lille,
1909. No. 23.

NL 0348423   DNLM

Liechtblitzer, Erasinus, pseud., praeses
... Discursus theoreticopracticus ad
§. Non avtem omnes Inst. de perpet. &
temporal. action continens naturam et
proprietatem actionum pennalium ...
Fuchstehudae, excudebat Tarqvinius
Superbus, impensis Petri Tenacis, 1627.

1 p.l., 29 p. 20cm.

Diss. (T. I. Spuelwurm, pseud., respondent)
In satyrical vein.

NL 0348424   MH-L

Liechte, Heinrich Gottfried, respondent.
De fluxu ventris dysenterico
see under Richter, Georg Gottlieb,
1694-1773, praeses.

Liechte, Heinrich Gottfried.
Viri doctissimi Henrici Godofredi Liechten
Disputationem inavgvralem indicit ad diem
XV. Sept. MDCCXLII. et De valvula coli
observationes uberiores praemittit
see under Haller, Albrecht von, 1708-1777.

Liechte, Henricus Gothofridus
see Liechte, Heinrich Gottfried.

Liechte, Paul.
Versuche über die wirkung der phosphorsäure
im knochenmehl und valser inephosphate im
vergleich zur superphosphat- und
Thomasmehlphosphorsäure.
1897

NL 0348428   DNAL

BF1600
.L7
Rare bk

Liechtenberg, Jacob, Freiherr von.
Goêtia, vel Theurgia, sive Praestigiarum magi-
carum descriptio, revelatio, resolutio, inquisitio, & executio. Das ist/ wahre vnd eigentliche
Entdeckung/ Deklaration oder Erklärunge führneh-
mer Articul der Zauberey, und was von Zauberern/
Unholden/ Hexen/ derer Händel ... Artzneyen/
woher sie erwachsen/ vnd jhrer Machination ...
zu halten sey ... Etwan durch ... Jacob Freyherrn von Liechtenberg/ etc. vor vielen Jahren
aus jhren Urgichten erfahren/ durch ... Jacob
Weckern M.D. etwas weitleuffiger beschrieben.
Nun aber an   jetzo mit allem Fleisse

revidiret vbersehen/ mit Artzneyen wider die
Zauberey schaden ... Weit mehr vber zweymal so
viel augirt, vermehrt/ vnd in den Druck geferti-
get durch Wolfgangum Hildebrandum ... Leipzig,
In Verlegung Joh. Francken S. Erben vnd Samuel
Scheiben Buchh., 1631.
₍16₎, 342, ₍17₎ p. 20cm.
Title in red and black.
Published in 1575 under title: Hexen Büchlin ...
durch J. Wecker an   tag geben. cf. Brit. Mus.
cat.

NL 0348430   ICU PPPM CtY MH

LIECHTENBERG, Jacob, freiherr von.
Hexen büchlein das ist ware entdeckung und
erklärung oder Declaration fürnämlicher artick-
el der zauberey, und was von zauberern unholden,
hengsten, nachtschadin, schützen, etc. Ettwan
durch Jacob, freyherrn von Liechtenberg auss
ihrer gefengknuss erfaren, und jetz durch ein
gelerten doctor (Wecker) züsamen bracht und
weitleüffiger beschriben &c. [Cologne? 1544?]

NL 0348431   MH OC1

Liechtenberger, Johann.
See
Lichtenberger, Johann, 15th cent.

Liechtenecker, Arthur.
Die Krisensteuer. Erläutert von Hofrat Dr. Arthur Liechtenecker. ₍Wien: Im Selbstverlage des Verfassers, 1932.₎ 1 l.
26cm.
Caption-title.

735816A. 1. Taxation--Austria,   1932.
N. Y. P. L.   November 13, 1934

NL 0348433   NN

VOLUME 332

HJ
4342
L543
1909

Liechtenecker, Arthur.
Die neue österreichische Gebäudesteuer.
Kurze systematische Darstellung des Gesetzent-
wurfes mit praktischen Beispielen. Wien,
Manz, 1909.
56 p.

1. Real property tax--Austria. I. Title.

NL 0348434   NSyU

LIECHTENECKER, Arthur.
Die personalsteuernovelle. 3e aufl.,7.-9.
tausend. Wien, A. Hölder, 1914.

NL 0348435   MH

Liechtenecker, Arthur
Personalsteuernovelle vom jahre 1924
samt durchführungsverordnung. Erwerb-,
einkommen- und vermögenssteuer, von hofrat
dr. Arthur Liechtenecker. Wien, M. Perles,
1924.
64 p.

NL 0348436   OU

Liechtenhan, Eduard, 1891-
    see Liechtenhan, Eduard August, 1891-

Liechtenhan, Eduard August, 1891-1965 ed.

Anthimus, *physician.*
... Anthimi De observatione ciborvm ad Theodoricvm, re-
gem Francorvm epistvla, recensvit Edvardvs Liechtenhan.
Lipsiae et Berolini, in aedibvs B. G. Tevbneri, 1928.

Liechtenhan, Eduard August, 1891-
    Sprachliche bemerkungen zu Marcellus Empiricus.
viii,118,[1]p.   Basel, Buchdruckerei Werner-
Riehm, 1917.

    Inaug.-diss. - Basel.
    Vita.
    Literatur: p.v-viii.

NL 0348439   NjP IU OCl MiU ICRL PU MH CtY-M

Liechtenhan, Felix.
    Die Elektrizitätsversorgung des Kantons Solothurn...von
Felix Liechtenhan...   Solothurn: Vogt-Schild A.-G., 1939.
98 p.   charts, illus., table.   23cm.

    Inaugural-Dissertation — Bern, 1938.
    "Literaturangaben," p. 5-6.

1. Electric power industries—   Switzerland—Solothurn.
N. Y. P. L.   December 31, 1940

NL 0348440   NN CtY NNC

WG
22717

Liechtenhan, Karl, 1883-
Über Cinensäure. Basel, 1907.
48 p. illus.

    Inaug.-Diss. - Basel.

NL 0348441   CtY PU ICRL

W 4
B29
1945

LIECHTENHAN, Katharina
    Über Gewicht und Volumen von Rinde
und Mark im menschlichen Kleinhirn.
Basel, Karger, 1945.
16 p. illus.
Cover title.
Inaug.-Diss. - Basel.
Reprinted from Acta anatomica, v. 1,
1945/46.
    Summary in German, English, and
French.
    1. Cerebellum

NL 0348442   DNLM CtY

Liechtenhan, Rudolf, 1875-
    Die göttliche vorherbestimmung bei Paulus und in der
posidonianischen philosophie, von lic. theol. R. Liechtenhan
... Göttingen, Vandenhoeck & Ruprecht, 1922.
    vi, 132 p. 24½ cm. (Forschungen zur religion und literatur des
Alten und Neuen Testaments ... n. f., 18. hft. Der ganzen reihe
35. hft.)
    "Literatur über Posidonius und posidonianische philosophie": p. v.

    1. Predestination. 2. Bible. N. T. Epistles of Paul—Theology.
3. Posidonius, of Apamea.

                                              A C 35—798

Chicago. Univ. Libr.
for Library of Congress   [a54c1]

        DDO NjNbS PPT TNJ-R IEG
NL 0348443   ICU CU CtY-D OU OCU MiU NcD PU MH ICU

BS2525
.L7

Liechtenhan, Rudolf, 1875-
    Gottes gebot im Neuen Testament; sein ursprüng-
licher sinn und seine bleibende bedeutung ...
Basel, Helbing & Lichtenhahn, 1942.
    x, 165 p.

    1. Bible. N. T.--Theology.

NL 0348444   ICU CtY-D NjPT MH TxDaM

Liechtenhan, Rudolf, 1875-
Jeremia. Tübingen, J. C. B. Mohr, 1909.
    48 p. 21 cm. (Religionsgeschichtliche Volksbücher für die deutsche
christliche Gegenwart. 2. Reihe, 11. Heft)

    1. Jeremiah, the prophet.   (Series)
    BL25.R4 Reihe 2, Heft 11   9–28779 rev*

NL 0348445   DLC MiU OCH OO CtY

JC62
L623o

Liechtenhan, Rudolf, 1875-
    Die offenbarung im Gnosticismus. Göttingen,
Vandenhoeck & Ruprecht, 1901.
    vi, 168 p. 24 cm.

    Bibliographical footnotes.

NL 0348446   CtY-D MH OO PU

BS2505
.L67

LIECHTENHAN, RUDOLF, 1875-
    Paulus. Seine welt und sein werk. Von lic. Rudolf
Liechtenhan... Basel, F. Reinhardt [1928]
    251 p. 21cm.

    1. Paul, Saint, apostle.

NL 0348447   ICU NjPT

Liechtenhan, Rudolf, 1875-
    Paulus, seine welt und sein werk, von lic. Rudolf Liechten-
han... 2. aufl. Basel, F. Reinhardt [193-?]
    251 p. 21½ᵐ.

    1. Paul, Saint, apostle.

                                              46–42583
Library of Congress   BS2505.L48

        [2]   [922.1] 225.92

NL 0348448   DLC NcD

BR
125
L5.35

Liechtenhan, Rudolf, 1875-
    Soziale Religion. Drei Vorträge.
Basel, Helbing & Lichtenhahn, 1908.
    66 p. 22 cm.

    1. Christianity--Addresses, essays,
lectures. I. Title

NL 0348449   OCH

BR165
.L68

Liechtenhan, Rudolf, 1875-
    Die urchristliche Mission: Voraussetzungen,
Motive und Methoden. Zürich, Zwingli-Verlag,
1946.
    98 p. (Abhandlungen zur Theologie des Alten
und Neuen Testaments, 9)
    Bibliographical foot-notes.

    1. Church history--Early church. 2. Missions.

        NjPT RPB OSW
NL 0348450   ICU MoSCS CLSU IEG NcD TxFTC NIC MH NNUT

LIECHTENSTEIN, Alois, prince.
    Die bodenfrage, beleuchtet durch die ver-
hältnisse Russlands und der länder der ehemaligen österreichischen-ungarischen monarchie.
2e aufl. Innsbruck, etc., verlagsanstalt
Tyrolia, [1920?]

NL 0348451   MH

309.37
L62r

Liechtenstein, Alois, Prince.
    Das reich der Römer. Socialpolitische
studie. Wien [1899]
    63p.   (On cover: Allgemeine bücherei,
22)

NL 0348452   IU NjP

LIECHTENSTEIN, Alois, Prince.
    Ueber interessenvertretung im staate, mit
besonderer beziehung auf Oesterreich. 2e
vermehrte aufl. Wien, Mayer & comp., 1877.

NL 0348452-1   MH

Liechtenstein, Eduard Victor Maria, prinz von und zu,
    1872-
    Hinterbliebenen- und Jugendfürsorge. Vortrag vom Mini-
sterialrat Dr. Eduard Prinz von und zu Liechtenstein... gehalten am 11. Mai, 1918. Wien: Verlag F. A. St., 1918. 14 p.
diagr. 8°.

1. Pensions, Military and naval—   Austria-Hungary, 1914-
N. Y. P. L.   September 10, 1925

NL 0348453   NN

VOLUME 332

Liechtenstein, Eduard Viktor Maria, *prinz* von und zu, 1872–
    Liechtensteins weg von Österreich zur Schweiz; eine rückschau auf meine arbeit in der nachkriegszeit, 1918–1921 ⟨von⟩ dr. Eduard prinz von und zu Liechtenstein ... ⟨Vaduz, Selbstverlag des verfassers, 1946⟩
    1 p. l., v, ⟨1⟩, 600 p. incl. illus. (facsims.) III geneal. tab. 23ᶜᵐ.

    1. Liechtenstein—Pol. & govt. 2. Liechtenstein, House of.
    DB540.5.L5   A 47–3117
    Harvard univ. Library
    for Library of Congress   ⟨2⟩†

NL 0348454   MH ICU CU MiU DLC

Liechtenstein, Eleonora Maria Rosalia, *fürstin* von
    see
Troppau und Jägerndorf, Eleonora Maria Rosalia, *herzogin* zu, 1647–1704.

Liechtenstein, Franz von Paula Maria Karl August fuerst von und zu, 1853–
    see
Franz, prince of Liechtenstein, 1853–

Liechtenstein, Marie Henriette Norberte, *prinzessin* von, 1843–
    Holland house. By Princess Marie Liechtenstein ... London, Macmillan and co., 1874.
    2 v. fronts., illus., ports., facsims. (part fold.) 22½ᶜᵐ.

    1. Holland house. 2. Gt. Brit.—Pol. & govt.—1800–1837. 3. London—Intellectual life.
                                    4–34337 Revised
    Library of Congress   DA687.H7L7

TU CtY PP PPL PBm NcD NjP WaU ViU NN MB NNC TNJ
NL 0348457   DLC CSt TxHU DAU GU CSmH MiU CLU CU–A PU

AC–L   **Liechtenstein, Marie Henriette Norberte,** *prinzessin* von,
qW357L   1843–
L623h   Holland house. By Princess Marie Liechtenstein ... London, Macmillan and co., 1874.
    2 v. fronts., illus., ports., facsims. ~~(part fold.)~~ ~~22½ᵐ~~. 31cm.

    Armorial bookplates of Dartrey.
    Bookplates of Evelyn Waugh.

NL 0348458   TxU

Liechtenstein, Marie Henriette Norberte, *prinzessin* von, 1843–
    Holland house. By Princess Marie Liechtenstein ... 2d ed. London, Macmillan and co., 1874.
    2 v. fronts., illus., ports., facsims. (part fold.) 22½ᵐ.

    1. Holland house. 2. Gt. Brit.—Pol. & govt.—1800–1837. 3. London—Intellectual life.
                                    17–20688 Revised
    Library of Congress   DA687.H7L7   1874 a

NL 0348459   DLC NcD PPLas OU MiU MB MdBP PPSteph

DA   **Liechtenstein, Marie Henriette Norberte,** prinzessin von, 1843–
687   Holland house. By Princess Marie Liechtenstein. 3d ed. London, Macmillan, 1875.
.H7   xx, 370 p. illus., ports., facsims. 23 cm.
L7
1875

    1. Holland house. 2. Gt. Brit.—Pol. & govt. 1800–1837. 3. London—Intellectual life.

    WaS NcGU NcU OKentU
NL 0348460   AU CU OC1W ViU PP PU–F CtY OC1 OC1WHi

Liechtenstein, O   Franc von.
    Ueber Chondrome der Lunge...   Göttingen, 1868.
    Inaug.–Diss. – Göttingen.

NL 0348461   CtY

Liechtenstein, Ulrich von
    see
Lichtenstein, Ulrich von, *fl.* 1255.

---

*GC5   **Liechtenstein, Wolfgang von,** 16th cent.
A100   Poemata ad amicos. Avctoribvs VVolfgango a
B584p   Liechtenstain. Ioanne Iacobo Söll ab Aichberg. Christophoro Ammano abenspergensi.
    Monachii excudebat Adamus Berg.M.D.LXXXI.
    4°. [31]p. 21,5cm.
    Signatures: A–D⁴.
    Title & each page of text within border of type ornaments.
    No.7 in a volume of poetical miscellanies.

NL 0348463   MH

Z999   **Liechtenstein, House of.**
.K88
Rosenwald   **Kraus, H. P.,** *firm, booksellers, New York.*
Coll.   Choice manuscripts, books, maps and globes, important for the history of European civilization and the discovery of America. Illuminated codices, early drawings, incunabula and illustrated books, remarkable maps from the Prince Liechtenstein Collection and globes from a private library. Offered for sale. New York ⟨1951⟩

NL 0348465   DLC IU MiD NN

Liechtenstein, House of.
    Katalog der in den bibliotheken der regierenden linie des fürstlichen hauses von und zu Liechtenstein befindlichen bücher aus dem XVI.–XX. jahrhundert, im auftrage Seiner Durchlaucht des regierenden fürsten Franz von und zu Liechtenstein bearbeitet von dr. Hanns Bohatta ... Wien, Fürstlich liechtensteinische gemälde-galerie, 1931.
    3 v. 48 pl. (incl. facsims.) on 24 l. 24ᶜᵐ.
    Catalog of collections in Eisgrub, Feldsberg, Vaduz, Wartenstein, and the Fidelkommiss-bibliothek in Vienna.
    I. Franz, prince of Liechtenstein, 1853–   II. Bohatta, Hanns, 1864–   III. Fürstlich liechtenstein'sche fideikommiss-bibliothek, Vienna.

    Library of Congress   Z997.L718   35–21190
    ⟨2⟩   018.2

NL 0348465   DLC IU MiD NN

Z999   **Liechtenstein, House of.**
.K88
no. 66   **Kraus, H. P.,** *firm, booksellers, New York.*
        A myrrour of four centuries; the growth of Western civilization reflected in illustrated books from the 15th to the 18th century, originating from the most part from the Prince Liechtenstein library. Offered for sale by H. P. Kraus. New York ⟨1954?⟩

Liechtenstein, House of
    see also
Fürstlich Liechtenstein'sche fideikommiss-bibliothek, *Vienna.*

Liechtenstein.
    Demande d'admission du Liechtenstein dans la Société des Nations. Memorandum
    see under   League of Nations. Secretary-General, 1919–1933 (Earl of Perth)

Liechtenstein.
    Fürstentum Liechtenstein. München, Artis-verlag (dr. Fleischmann) ⟨1929?⟩
    68 p. illus. (incl. ports.) diagr. 31½ᶜᵐ.
    "Zum geleit !" signed: Dr. Josef Hoop, fürstlicher regierungschef.
    Advertising matter: p. 49–68.

    1. Liechtenstein.   I. Hoop, Josef.   II. Title.
                                    31–3649
    Library of Congress   DB540.5.A5   1929   914.3648

NL 0348469   WaU DLC

Liechtenstein.
    Kurzer Bericht zum Personen- und Gesellschaftsrecht.   ⟨n. p., 192–⟩   58 p.   12°.

    538125A.   1. No subject.
    N. Y. P. L.   August 26, 1931

NL 0348470   NN

Liechtenstein.
    Liechtensteinisches landes-gesetzblatt. Jahrgang 1863–
    Feldkirch, Druck von J. Graff's wittwe; ⟨etc., etc.⟩, 1863–
    v. 21ᶜᵐ.
    Issued irregularly.
    —— Inhalts-register der in den jahren 1862–1878 durch das Liechtenstein'sche landesgesetzblatt kundgemachten gesetze und verordnungen. ⟨Feldkirch, Druck von H. Graff, 1878?⟩
    6 p. 21ᶜᵐ.
    Caption title.

    —— Alphabetisches inhalts-register der in den jahren 1863 bis einschliesslich 1892 durch das Landesgesetzblatt des fürstenthums Liechtenstein kundgemachten gesetze und verordnungen. Buchs, Buchdr. J. Kuhn, 1892.
    20 p. 21ᶜᵐ.

                                    15–16550–2
NL 0348472   DLC NN CU

LIECHTENSTEIN.
    Liechtensteinisches Landes-Gesetzblatt.1912-date (incomplete)
    Vaduz.   v.   21cm.

    Film reproduction. Positive.

NL 0348473   NN

Liechtenstein. Liechtensteinisches landes-gesetzblatt.

Liechtenstein. *Laws, statutes, etc.*
    Zivilprozessgesetze für das fürstentum Liechtenstein ... ⟨Wien, Druck von A. Holzhausen, 1912⟩

VOLUME 332

Liechtenstein.
Rechenschafts-bericht der fürstlichen regierung an den hohen Landtag ... 1922–
Vaduz ₍etc.₎, 1923–
v.   tables. 26–31ᶜᵐ.
The 1922 report (2 v.) covers the period Jan. 1919 to July 1922.
1928 has title: Jahres-bericht und landes-rechnung.

1. Liechtenstein—Pol. & govt.

35–30134

Library of Congress   J340.R12   336.43648

NL 0348475   DLC NNC-L ICU CU NNC NN

Liechtenstein.
Recueil des arrêts

see under

Hague. International Court of Justice.

Liechtenstein.
Revidirter und erweiterter lehrplan für die elementarschulen des fürstenthums Liechtenstein. **Feldkirch** ₍Graff'sche buchdr., 185–?₎
35 p.   21ᶜᵐ.

1. Education—Liechtenstein.

15–1571

Library of Congress   LB1564.L5A3

NL 0348477   DLC

Liechtenstein. Amt für Statistik.
Ausländerstatistik.

₍Vaduz₎
v. 30 cm. 2 no. a year.

1. Liechtenstein—Foreign population—Statistics. 2. Alien labor—Liechtenstein—Statistics.

DB540.5.A3   312'.93'0943648   73–641338

NL 0348478   DLC

Liechtenstein. Amt für Statistik.
Krankenkassenstatistik.
Vaduz.
v. 21 cm.
Began in 1946.

1. Insurance, Health—Liechtenstein.   I. Title.

HD7102.L5A25   70–613138

NL 0348479   DLC

Liechtenstein. Amt für Statistik
Liechtensteinische Volkszählung, 1. Dezember 1950.
Vaduz, Fürstliche Regierung, 1953
xii, 51 p.

1. Liechtenstein – Census, 1950. X ref.: Liechtenstein, Statistisches Amt (to main entry)

NL 0348480   MH FU

Liechtenstein. Amt für Statistik.
Obstbaumzählung.
₍Vaduz₎
v. 30 cm.

1. Fruit-culture — Liechtenstein — Statistics — Collected works. 2. Fruit trees—Liechtenstein—Statistics—Collected works.   I. Title.

SB354.6.L54A25   73–641009
MARC-S

NL 0348481   DLC

312.43648
L623z   **Liechtenstein. Amt für Statistik.**
Zivilstands-Statistik und Wohnbevölkerung.

Vaduz,
v. tables. 28cm.

At head of title, 19 –   : Fürstentum Liechtenstein.
Title varies slightly. Cf. New serial titles, 1950–60, v.2.

1. Liechtenstein   – Population.

NL 0348482   TxU

Law

Liechtenstein. *Constitution.*
Constitution de la principauté de Liechtenstein du 5 octobre 1921. Traduite et mise à jour par Pierre Raton.
₍Paris, 195–?₎
38 p. 24 cm.

58–48706

NL 0348483   DLC NNUN

Law

Liechtenstein. Constitution.

Liechtenstein. *Laws, statutes, etc.*
Liechtensteinisches Landes-Gesetzblatt. 1863–
₍Vaduz₎

Liechtenstein. *Constitution.*
Die Verfassung und die amtsinstruktion der staatsbehörden des fürstenthums Liechtenstein, nebst dem Liechtensteinischen landesgesetzblatte von 1863 und 1864.
₍Feldkirch, Druck von J. Graff's wittwe, 1864₎
1 p. l., 19, 15 p., 1 l. 21ᶜᵐ.

15–16553

NL 0348485   DLC

Liechtenstein. *Constitution.*
Verfassung des fürstentums Liechtenstein vom 5. oktober 1924 ₍i. e. 1921₎ ₍Feldsberg, 1921₎
cover-title, 30, ₍2₎ p. 20¼ᶜᵐ.   JN2273.1921.A5

—— Alphabetisches sachregister zur Verfassung des fürstentums Liechtenstein vom 5. oktober 1921. ₍Feldsberg, 1921₎
cover-title, 8 p. 20¼ᵐ.

I. Title.

33–35225

Library of Congress   JN2273.1921.A5 Index 342.4364801

NL 0348486   DLC WaU NN MiU-L

FL8   Liechtenstein. Courts.
L5.68   Entscheidungen des fürstlich liechtensteinischen Staatsgerichtshofes und Auszug aus dem Urteil
E611   des Obersten Gerichtshofes und Auszüge aus Entscheidungen der Verwaltungsbeschwerdeinstanz. 19 –   Beilage zum Rechenschaftsbericht der fürstlichen Regierung. ₍Schaan, 19

v. 26ᵐ.

1. Reports, digests. etc. - Liechtenstein.

NL 0348487   MiU-L

KE2079   Liechtenstein. Courts.
.2   Entscheidungen der Liechtensteinischen Gerichtshöfe von 1947/54–
Vaduz,
v. For additional items see Official catalog.
Hrsg. von der Fürstlichen Regierung als Beilage zum Rechenschaftsbericht im Auftrage des Liechtensteinischen Landestages.
1. Law reports, digests, etc. - Liechtenstein. I. Liechtenstein./ Rechenschaftsbericht der Fürstlichen Regierung
bericht der Für-   an den hohen   Landtag.

NL 0348488   CLL

Liechtenstein. Handelskammer

see

Liechtensteinische handelskammer.

4K   **Liechtenstein.** *Laws, statutes, etc.*
10995   Gesetzentwürfe zur Reform des Zivilprozesses im Fürstentume Liechtenstein.
₍19 ₎
255 p.

NL 0348490   DLC-P4

4K   **Liechtenstein.** *Laws, statutes, etc.*
8039   Hochfürstlich Johann Liechtensteinische Normalien-Sammlung   Wien,
Im Selbstverlage der Hochfürstlich Liechtensteinischen Hofkanzlei, 1865.
1019 p.

NL 0348491   DLC-P4

Liechtenstein. *Laws, statutes, etc.*
(Laws translated by International labor office) (Basle, 1922–31)
3 v. 24½ cm. (I.L.O. Legislative series, 1922, Liecht. 1.

NL 0348492   DL

Liechtenstein. *Laws, statutes, etc.*
Liechtensteinisches Landes-Gesetzblatt. 1863–
₍Vaduz₎
v. in   22 cm. irregular.
Issues for 1863–64 combined in 1 v. with title: Die Verfassung und die Amtsinstruktion der Staatsbehörden des Fürstenthums Liechtenstein nebst dem Liechtensteinischen Landesgesetzblatte von 1863 und 1864.
INDEXES:
1863–78, with 1878.
1863–92, with 1892.
1. Liechtenstein. Constitution.

15–16550 rev*

NL 0348493   DLC

VOLUME 332

Liechtenstein. *Laws, statutes, etc.*
Liechtensteinisches Zivilgesetzbuch. ₍Vaduz, 1923–

v. 21 cm. (Liechtensteinisches Landesgesetzblatt, 1923, Nr.
4; 1926. Nr. 4

CONTENTS.—₍1₎ Sachenrecht.—₍2₎ Das Personen- und Gesellschafts-
recht.

1. Civil law—Liechtenstein.
                                               40–20139 rev*
—— Copy 2. With v. 2 is bound: Beck, Wilhelm. Unterneh-
mungen und selbständige Vermögensverwaltungen im Fürstentum
Liechtenstein. 3. Aufl. Vaduz, 1931.

NL 0348494   DLC CtY MH-L

Law

Liechtenstein. *Laws, statutes, etc.*
Liechtensteinisches Zivilgesetzbuch. Vaduz, Verlag der
Regierungskanzlei ₍19

v. 21 cm. (Liechtensteinisches Landesgesetzblatt 1926 Nr. 4,
1928 Nr. 6;

"Liechtensteinisches Landes-Gesetzblatt 1926 Nr. 5, 1938 Nr. 12,
1942 Nr. 1, 1950 Nr. 28, 1951 Nr. 6, 1955, Nr. 2" (6 pieces) inserted.

CONTENTS.—

3. T. Das Personen- und Gesellschaftsrecht vom 20. Jänner 1926 und
das Treuunternehmen (die Geschäftstreuhand) vom 10. April 1928.-

1. Civil law—Liechtenstein.   I. Title.   (Series)

                                               57–55796₍₎

NL 0348495   DLC

Liechtenstein. *Laws, statutes, etc.*
... Das personen- und gesellschafts-recht (Pgr) Vaduz,
Regierungskanzlei ₍1926₎

xxxviii, 651, 5 p. 20¼ᶜᵐ. (Liechtensteinisches Zivil-gesetzbuch.
L. g. b. nr. 4)

"Verordnung vom 20. februar 1926 zum personen- und gesellschafts-
recht": 5 p at end.
With this is bound: Beck, W. Unternehmungen und selbständige
vermögensverwaltungen im fürstentum Liechtenstein. Von dr. W. Beck
und dr. A. Ritter ... 3. aufl. Vaduz, 1931.

1. Persons (Law)—Liechtenstein. 2. Stock companies—Liechtenstein.
3. Corporation law—Liechtenstein.   I. Title.

                                               36–2782

NL 0348496   DLC

Liechtenstein. Laws, statutes, etc.

... Das Personen- und Gesellschafts-
recht (Pgr) vom 20. Jänner 1926 und
das Treuunternehmen (Die Geschäftstreuhand) (Tr. U;) vom 10. April 1928 (Art.
932a) Vaduz, Regierungskanzlei ₍1928₎

xliv, 777 p. 21cm. (Liechtensteinisches Zivil-gesetzbuch. L. g. b. nr.
4 ₍und₎ 6)

"Verordnung vom 20. Februar 1926 zum

Personen- und Gesellschaftsrecht" (5 p.);
"Gesetz vom 28. Jänner 1942 betreffend
die Abänderung des Personen- und Gesell-
schaftsrechtes" (₍2₎ p.); "Gesetz vom 7.
November 1950 betreffend die Änderung
des Gesetzes vom 20. Jänner 1926 und des
Gesetzes vom 10. April 1928" (₍1₎ p.):
inserted at end.

NL 0348498   MH-L

Liechtenstein. *Laws, statutes, etc.* Personen- und gesellschafts-
                                               recht (Index)
Index zum liechtensteinischen personen- und gesellschafts-
recht. Anhang: Index zu den übergangs- und schlussbestim-
mungen des P. G. R. ₍Liechtenstein, 1931₎

82 p. 20¼ᶜᵐ.

1. Persons (Law)—Liechtenstein. 2. Corporation law—Liechtenstein.   I. Title.

                                               32–17906

NL 0348499   DLC

Liechtenstein. Laws, statutes, etc.

Beck, Wilhelm.
Das recht des fürstentums Liechtenstein (systematisch dargestellt, nebst literaturangabe) ein grundriss von dr. jur. Wilh.
Beck ... Zürich, Aktien-buchdruckerei Zürich rv, selbstverlag
des verfassers, 1912.

Liechtenstein. *Laws, statutes, etc.*
... Sachenrecht (s.r.)
see its   Liechtensteinisches Zivilgesetzbuch.

Liechtenstein. *Laws, statutes, etc.*
Strafprozessordnung für das fürstentum Liechtenstein.
(Liechtensteinisches landesgesetzblatt nr. 3, jahrgang 1914).
₍Buchs, Buchdruckerei J. Kuhn, 1914₎

1 p. l, 104 p. 20¼ᶜᵐ.

Caption: Liechtensteinisches landes-gesetzblatt. Jahrgang 1914. Nr.
3. Ausgegeben am 25. mai. Inhalt: Gesetz betreffend einführung einer
Strafprozessordnung.—Strafprozessordnung.—Inhaltsverzeichnis.

1. Criminal procedure—Liechtenstein.   I. Title.

                                               38–13800

NL 0348502   DLC

Liechtenstein. *Laws, statutes, etc.*
Strafprozessordnung für das fürstentum Liechtenstein... ₍Buchs, J. Kuhn, 1922₎
cover-title, 104 p., 1 l., 15 p.   19.5 cm.
Extracts from Liechtensteinisches landes-
gesetzblatt: p. 1–104, from Jahrg. 1914, nr. 3;
p. [105], from Jahrg. 1916, nr. 9; p. 1–15 at
end, from Jahrg. 1922, nr. 17.

NL 0348503   CtY-L

Liechtenstein. Laws, statutes, etc.

Beck, W   *ed.*
Unternehmungen und selbständige vermögensverwaltungen
im fürstentum Liechtenstein. Von dr. W. Beck und dr. A.
Ritter ... 3. aufl. Vaduz, Cura treuinstitut, 1931.

Liechtenstein. *Laws, statutes, etc.*
Zivilprozessgesetze für das fürstentum Liechtenstein
... ₍Wien, Druck von A. Holzhausen, 1912₎
cover-title, 200 p. 21ᶜᵐ.
Liechtensteinisches landesgesetzblatt nr. 9, jahrgang 1912.

I. Liechtenstein. Liechtensteinisches landes-gesetzblatt.

                                               15–16554

NL 0348505   DLC

Liechtenstein.   Offizieller verkehrs-
            verein Schaan

see

Schaan, Liechtenstein.   Offizieller verke-
hrsverein.

Liechtenstein.   Treaties, etc., 1929–
     (Francis I)
U. S. *Treaties, etc., 1933–*   *(Franklin D. Roosevelt)*
... Extradition. Treaty between the United States of Amer-
ica and Liechtenstein ... Signed at Bern, May 20, 1936 ...
Washington, U. S. Govt. print. off., 1937.

Liechtensteinsche gemäldegalerie,
     Vienna

see

Vienna.   Fürstlich Liechtensteinsche
gemäldegalerie.

Liechtensteinische handelskammer.
     Das wirtschaftsjahr.

₍Vaduz₎ 19

v. 24ᶜᵐ. (*Its* Mitteilungen)

1. Liechtenstein—Econ. condit.

                                               43–16357
Library of Congress   HC267.L5L5
                          ₍2₎   330.9436

NL 0348509   DLC NN

Kress   **Liechtenstern, Joseph Marx, freiherr von,**
Room   **1765–1828.**
Allgemeine bemerkungen über den zustand der
landwirthschaft in den ländern der oestreichischen erbmonarchie. Mit einer summarischen übersicht der wesentlichsten geschäftsgegenstände
bey der verwaltung der landgüter nach der
abhandlung über diesen gegenstand, in der skizze
einer statitischen schilderung des östreichischen
staats ... Wien, 1802.

2 p.l., 132 p. 20.5 cm.

1.Agriculture - Austria. I.Title.

NL 0348510   MH-FA

Liechtenstern, Joseph Marx, *Freiherr von,*
     1765–1828.
Allgemeine Karte der Oestreichischen Monarchie. Mit Benü-
zung der sichersten und neuesten Beobachtungen und Nachrichten
der richtigsten geographischen Specialkarten und einer Menge
verlcslicher Handzeichnungen entworfen und gezeichnet von
Joseph Marx, Freiherr von Lichtenstern, ... Wien, Die
Kosmographische Gesellschaft, 1795.

1 map.   47 x 69¼ᶜᵐ.
Scale, 8.1ᶜᵐ. = 30ᵍᵉᵒᵍʳ. Meilen.
"Gestochen von Anton Amon."
Hand-tinted boundary lines.

NL 0348511   ICJ

Liechtenstern, Joseph Marx, Freiherr von, 1765–
1828, ed.
Allgemeines deutsches Sach-Wörterbuch
see under   Allgemeines deutsches Sach-
Wörterbuch.

Liechtenstern, Joseph Marx, freiherr von,
1765–1828.
Aphorismen und notizen über wichtige
zweige des finanzwesens ... Altenburg, C.
Hahn, 1821.
76 p.

With his: Ueber Oesterreich's seeküste,
seeschiffahrt und seehandel. 1821.

NL 0348513   MiU

[Liechtenstern, Joseph Marx, Freiherr von, 1765–1828]
Atlas des österreichischen Kaiserthums. Atlas de
l'Empire Autrichie... Wien, Im Verlage des Kunst- und
Industrie-Comptoirs, 1805 [i.e. 1802–06]

1 v.   40 maps
"Carte des Bouches de Cattaro et du Montenegro par
Max. de Traux" (1808) inserted at end

NL 0348514   MH

VOLUME 332

Kress
Room
Liechtenstern, Joseph Marx, freiherr von,
1765-1828.
Grundlinien einer statistik des österreichischen kaiserthums, nach dessen gegenwärtigen verhältnissen ... Neue ausg.
Wien, C.Gerold, 1817.
236 p. 18 cm.

1.Austria - Statistics.

NL 0348515 MH-BA CSt

GB201
L5
Liechtenstern, Joseph Marx, Freiherr von,
1756-1828.
Handbuch der neuesten Geographie des
österreichischen Kaiserstaates. Wien, B.
P.Bauer, 1817-
v. 20cm.

1.Physical geography - Austria.
SC

NL 0348516 CSt

Liechtenstern, Joseph Marx von
Das herzogthum Venedig, auf befehl Sr. öster.
Kais. Maj. 1801-5...n.p., n.d.
f°

NL 0348517 NN

Liechtenstern, Joseph Marx, freiherr von,
1765-1828.
Lehrbuch der statistik aller gegenwärtig
bestehenden europaischen staaten; nach dem
plane des verstorgenen hofraths Johann
Georg Meusel ... Wien und Dresden, Beck'schen
und Arnoldischen buchhandlung, 1821.
256 p.

"Erste abtheilung". No more published.

NL 0348518 MiU

[LIECHTENSTERN, Joseph Marx, freiherr von.]
Reisen durch das österreichische Illyrien,
Dalmatien und Albanien im jahr 1818. Von R.
von H....g. Meissen, F.W.Goedsche, 1822.

2 vol. Front.

NL 0348519 MH

638.2
L623s
1828
Liechtenstern, Joseph Marx, Freiherr von,
1765-1828.
Seidenbau in den preussischen Staaten und
dem nördlichen Teutschland, so wie über die
Bedingungen seines sichern und reichlichen
Gelingens. Mit einer Tabelle der täglichen
Verrichtungen der Seidenzüchter. 2. Aufl.
Berlin, A. Hirschwald, 1828.
xiv, 114p. fold. table. 20cm.

1. Sericulture - Germany. I. Title.

NL 0348520 TxU

Liechtenstern, Joseph Marx, Freiherr von
Skizze einer statistischen Schilderung des österreichischen Staats; in Rücksicht auf seine geographisch und
phisikalische Landesbeschaffenheit... Wien, Auf Kosten
des Verfassers, 1800

202 p.

1. Austria - Descr. - 1740-1848

NL 0348521 MH

HA1187
L5
1805
Liechtenstern, Joseph Marx Freiherr von,
1765-1828.
Skizze einer statistischen Schilderung
des östreichischen Staats; in Rücksicht auf
seine geographische und physikalische Landesbeschaffenheit...und mit Bemerkungen über
das Staatsinteresse dieser Monarchie, in
Hinsicht auf jene Gegenstände. 3.Aufl.
Wien, Im Verlage des Kunst und Industrie
Comptoirs, 1805.
133 p. 21cm.

1.Austria - Statistics. I.Title.

NL 0348522 CSt

LIECHTENSTERN, Joseph Marx, freiherr von, 1765-1828.
Statistisch-topographischer landesschematis-
mus des herzogthums Steyermark. Wien, Heubner
und Volke, 1818.

NL 0348523 MH

LIECHTENSTERN, Joseph Marx, freiherr von.
Ueber die lage, grosse, bestandtheile und
bevölkerung der oestreichischen erbmonarchie.
Wien, 1802.

NL 0348524 MH

Kress
Room
Liechtenstern, Joseph Marx, freiherr von,
1765-1828.
Ueber Oesterreich's seeküste, seeschifffahrt
und seehandel nach ihren gegenwärtigen verhältnissen und daraus abgeleiteten ansichten ...
4.neubearb. ausg. Altenburg, C.Hahn, 1821.
iv, [5]-84 p. 19.5 cm.

1.Austria - Commerce. 2.Shipping - Austria.

NL 0348525 MH-BA MiU

314.36
162v
Liechtenstern, Joseph Marx, Freiherr von,
1765-1828.
Vollständiger Umriss der Statistik des
österreichischen Kaiserstaats, mit Rücksicht
auf dessen neuesten Zustande. Brünn, J. G.
Trassler, 1820.
viii, 519p. 20cm.

1. Austria--Stat. I. Title.

NL 0348526 IU MH

Liechtenstern, Joseph Marx, *freiherr von*, 1765-1828.
Was hat die diplomatie als wissenschaft zu umfassen und
der diplomat zu leisten? Ein umriss der hauptmomente der
erstern und der pflichten des letzteren, von Joseph Marx freiherrn v. Liechtenstern. Altenburg, C. Hahn, 1820.
68 p., 1 l. fold. tab. 20cm.
"Diplomatische bibliothek": p. [60]-68.

1. Diplomacy. I. Title.
44-18802
Library of Congress JX1659.L5

NL 0348527 DLC

Liechtenstern, Theodor, Freiherr von, 1799-
Die neusten Ansichten von der Erdkunde in
ihrer Anwendung auf den Schulunterricht.
Braunschweig, 1846.

ix, 227 p. 8°.

NL 0348528 MH-Z MWC

G1019
.L491
1855
Map
Liechtenstern, Theodor, Freiherr von, b. 1799.
Neuster Schul-Atlas zum Unterrichte in der
Erdkunde.
Liechtenstern, Theodor, *Freiherr von*, b. 1799.
Schul-Atlas, von Theodor Frhrn. v. Liechtenstern und
Henry Lange. [Erstes und] zweites Ergänzungsheft[e] für
die Besitzer des Schul-Atlas in 29 Karten. Braunschweig,
F. Vieweg, 1855-57.

LIECHTENSTERN, THEODOR, Freiherr VON, b. 1799.
Neuester Schul-Atlas zum Unterrichte in der
Erdkunde; nach den neusten wissenschaftlichen
Forschungen in 29 Karten. Entworfen und bearb. von
Theodor Freiherrn von Liechtenstern und Henry
Lange. 11. Aufl. Braunschweig, F. Vieweg und
G. Westermann [Vorwort 1861] [8] p. 29 col. maps
29cm.

1. Geography--Atlases, 1861. I. Lange, Henry, 1821-
1893, joint author.

NL 0348530 NN

Liechtenstern, Theodor, *Freiherr von*, b. 1799.
Schul-Atlas, von Theodor Frhrn. v. Liechtenstern und
Henry Lange. [Erstes und, zweites Ergänzungsheft[e] für
die Besitzer des Schul-Atlas in 29 Karten. Braunschweig,
F. Vieweg, 1855-57.
2 v. col. maps. 30 x 35 cm.
"[Erstes] Ergänzungsheft" and "zweites Ergänzungsheft" also called
"zweite Section" and "dritte Section" of "Schul-Atlas in 29 Karten."

1. Atlases, German. I. Lange, Henry, 1821-1893, joint author.
II. Liechtenstern, Theodor, Freiherr von, b. 1799. Neuester Schul-
Atlas zum Unterrichte in der Erdkunde.
G1019.L491 1855 Map 56-351

NL 0348531 DLC

Liechtenstern, Theodor, Freiherr von, b. 1799.
Th. von Liechtenstern's und Henry Lange's Schul-Atlas zum
Unterricht in der Erdkunde. Für den Gebrau h der oberen Klassen der Lehranstalten... Vierzehnte Auflage. Neu bearbeitet
von Dr. Henry Lange. Braunschweig: G. Westermann, 1869.
2 p.l., 44 maps. 28½cm.
"Zur Karte über die Meeresströmungen," and "Literatur," verso of map [2]

11277B. 1. Geography--Atlases, 1869. I. Lange, Henry, 1821-1893,
jt. au.
N. Y. P. L. March 4, 1940

NL 0348532 NN

VOLUME 332

q912
L61t
1871
Liechtenstern, Theodor von, baron.
Th. von Liechtenstern's und Henry Lange's
Schul-Atlas zum Unterricht in der Erdkunde.
Für den Gebrauch der oberen Klassen der
Lehranstalten. In 44 karten. 20.Aufl. (14.
Aufl. 7 Abdruck) Neu bearb. von Henry Lange.
Braunschweig, G. Westermann, 1871.
2p., 44 double, col.maps. 29cm.

NL   0348533   IU CU

Liechtenstern, Theodor, *Freiherr von*, b. 1799.
Th. von Liechtenstern's und Henry Lange's Schul-
Atlas zum Unterricht in der Erdkunde; für den Gebrauch
der oberen Klassen der Lehranstalten. 21. Aufl. (14. Aufl.
8. Abdruck) neu bearb. von Henry Lange. Braunschweig,
G. Westermann, 1872.
r4₁ p. 44 col. maps. 29 cm.

1. Atlases, German.   I. Lange, Henry, 1821–1893, joint author.

Map 50–39

NL   0348534   DLC

Liechtenster, Theodor, Freiherr von, 1799–
Schul-Atlas zum Unterricht in der Erdkunde, für den
Gebrauch der oberen Klassen der Lehranstalten. [By] T.
von Liechtenstern und H.Lange. 26.Aufl., neueste Revision
von 1874. Neu bearb.von H.Lange. Braunschweig, Westermann, 1875

NL   0348535   MH

LIECHTENSTERN, THEODORE von.

...Schul-atlas zum unterricht in der erdkunde. Für den gebrauch der unteren klassen
der lehranstalten. In 29 karten. 45.aufl.
Neueste revision. Neu bearb.von dr.Henry
Lange. Braunschweig,G.Westermann,1877.
ₗiv₁p. 29 double maps. 29cm.

At head of title: Th.von Liechtenstern
und Henry Lange.

NL   0348536   PU

G1020
.L7
1878
Liechtenstern, Theodor von.

... Schul-atlas zum unterricht in der
erdkunde. Für den gebrauch der oberen
klassen der lehranstalten. In 45 karten.
45. auflage. Neuste redaction. Neu bearbeitet von dr.Henry Lange.   Braunschweig, G. Westermann, 1878.
2p.ₗ,₂p. 45 double maps. 29cm.

1. Atlases. I. Lange, Henry, 1821–
1893.II.Title. 2. Geography – Text-books
– 1870.–

NL   0348537   OCU MiU

Liechtenstern, *Theodor, Freiherr von, 1799–*
Th. von Liechtenstern und Henry Lange's Schul-atlas zum unterricht in der erdkunde. Für den gebrauch der oberen klassen der
lehranstalten. In 45 karten. 50. aufl. neueste redaction. Neu
bearb. von Henry Lange. 2 p. l., 44 (i. e. 45) maps. fol. Braunschweig, G. Westermann, 1880.   4198

NL   0348538   OCU

Lxe
+853ℓp
Liechtenstern, Theodor von, freiherr.
Th. von Liechtenstern und Henry Lange's
Schul-Atlas zum Unterricht in der Erdkunde.
Für den Gebrauch der oberen Klassen der
Lehranstalten. In 45 Karten. 55. Aufl. Neueste
Redaction. Neu bearb. von Dr. Henry Lange.
Braunschweig,G.Westermann,1882.
2p.ℓ.,45 double col.maps. 29cm.

NL   0348539   CtY

Lxe2
+853ℓs
Liechtenstern, Theodor von, Freiherr
Th. von Liechtenstern und Henry Lange's
Schul-Atlas zum Unterricht in der Erdkunde.
Für den Gebrauch der unteren Klassen der
Lehranstalten. In 29 Karten. 60. Aufl. Neueste
Redaction. Neu bearb. von Dr. Henry Lange.
Braunschweig,G.Westermann,1884.
2p.ℓ.,29double.col.maps. 29cm.

NL   0348540   CtY

RC78
.H27
1943
Liechti, Adolf, 1898–1946.

Haenisch, George Fedor, 1874–
Einführung in die röntgenologie, ein lehrbuch für ärzte und
studierende, von G. F. Haenisch ... und H. Holthusen ... mit
einem physikalisch-technischen beitrag von A. Liechti ... 3.,
verm. und verb. aufl. Mit 378 abbildungen und skizzen.
Leipzig, G. Thieme, 1943.

WD
1041
L718r
1944
Liechti, Adolf, 1898–1946
Die Röntgendiagnostik der Wirbelsäule und ihre Grundlagen.
Wien, Springer, 1944.
x, 352 p. illus. (part col.)

Bibliography: p. ₂254₋₋345.

1. Spine – Radiography

NL   0348542   DNLM IaU MdBJ CtY NNC-M ViU MnU

Liechti, Adolf, 1898–1946.
Die Röntgendiagnostik der Wirbelsäule und ihre Grund-
lagen. 2., neubearb. und ergänzte Aufl., durchgesehen von
A. Eggli. Wien, Springer-Verlag, 1948.
xi, 364 p. illus. 26 cm.
"Literaturverzeichnis": p. ₂261₁–357.

1. Spine–Diseases–Diagnosis.   2. Diagnosis, Radioscopic.
I. Eggli, Alfred, ed.   II. Title.

RC78.L5   1948   616.730757   48–20394*

NL   0348543   DLC MiU OU ICU DNLM MiEM

Liechti, Adolf, 1898–
Röntgenphysik, von dr. med. Adolf Liechti ... mit beiträgen
von dr. phil. Walter Minder ... mit 227 textabbildungen. Wien,
J. Springer, 1939.
ix, 308 p. incl. illus., tables, diagrs. 25¼ᶜᵐ.
"Literaturverzeichnis": p. ₂301₁–303.

1. X-rays.   I. Minder, Walter.   II. Title.
Library of Congress   QC481.L54   40–3267

NL   0348544   DLC OCU CtY OU PPC

Liechti, Adolf, 1898–
Röntgenphysik, von dr. med. Adolf Liechti ... mit beiträgen
von dr. phil. Walter Minder ... mit 227 textabbildungen. Wien,
J. Springer, 1939 ₁Ann Arbor,J.W. Edwards,1944₁

NL   0348545   ICJ CU NcD

Liechti, Adolf, 1898–1946.
Röntgenphysik. 2., vollständig neubearb. Aufl. von Walter
Minder. Wien, Springer, 1955.
306 p. illus. 25 cm.

1. X-rays.   I. Minder, Walter.   II. Title.

QC481.L54   1955   56–25538 ‡

NL   0348546   DLC PPF DNLM ICJ CU FTaSU

Liechti, Adolf, 1904–
Probleme des berufs, der berufswahl und der
berufsberatung... Zürich, 1932.   223 p.
Inaug. Diss. Zürich, 1932.
Vitae.
Bibliography.

NL   0348547   ICRL CtY

Liechti, Albert, 1908–
Etude de la polymérisation du styrolène dans
le champ électrique à 50 périodes, et de la
polymérisation de l'huile dans les
condensateurs électriques. ... Bâle, 1938.
Inaug. Diss. - Techn. Hochschule Zürich, 1938.
Lebenslauf.

NL   0348548   ICRL CtY

HV5080 Liechti, Anna, 1896–
.S9L7   Die sichernde massnahme der trinkerheilanstalt in den
entwürfen zu einem schweizerischen strafgesetzbuche. Eine
kriminalpolitische untersuchung ... Zürich, 1921.
53, ₂3₁ p. 22ᶜᵐ.
Inaug.-diss.–Zürich.
Curriculum vitae.
Bibliographical foot-notes.

1. Liquor laws–Switzerland.   2. Alcoholism and crime.

NL   0348549   ICU ICRL

Liechti, Eugen.
Die verrufserklärungen im modernen erwerbsleben
speciell boykott und arbeitersperre ... Zürich, Art. institut O. Füssli, 1897.
149, ₂1₁ p. 22ᶜᵐ.
Inaug.-diss.–Zürich.
"Verzeichnis der speciallitteratur": 1 p. at end.

1. Boycott.   2. Strikes and lockouts.

1–G–2766

Library of Congress   HD5461.L5

NL   0348550   DLC

Ozq93
934ℓ
Liechti, Eugen, 1908–
Das Abkommen der Schweiz mit Italien über die
Anerkennung und Vollstreckung gerichtlicher
Entscheidungen vom 3.Januar 1933 ... [Innsbruck,
₁agner'sche Universitäts-Buchdruckerei,1934]
62p.,ℓ. 21cm.
Diss. - Zürich.
Curriculum vitae.
"Literaturverzeichnis": p.61–62.

NL   0348551   CtY ICRL

Liechti, Hans, 1915–
Beitrag zum erneuerungsproblem ... von Hans Liechti ...
Bern, Gedruckt bei Stämpfli & cie., 1942.
24 p. diagrs. 23ᶜᵐ.
Inaug.-diss.–Bern.
Lebenslauf.
"Literaturnachweiss": p. 23.

1. Mathematical statistics.   2. Population.   I. Title.

Library of Congress   QA276.L53   46–40939

NL   0348552   DLC CtY

VOLUME 332

Liechti, Hans Rudolf, 1917–
Der Storno in der Krankenversicherung; Beitrag zur Theorie der Krankengeldversicherung. Biel, 1949.

75 p. 6 diagrs., tables. 21 cm.

Inaug.-Diss.—Bern.
Vita.
Bibliography: p. 73.

1. Insurance, Health. I. Title.

HD7101.L5   50–34743

NL 0348553   DLC CtY-M

Liechti, Hans Wilhelm, 1917–
Polydispersitätsbestimmungen an hochmolekularen Stoffen. Biel, 1946.

124, ₍6₎ p. diagrs. 24 cm.

Inaug.-Diss.—Bern.
Vita.
Bibliography: p. ₍125₎–₍129₎

1. Chemistry, Physical and theoretical. I. Title.

QD471.L63   50–32011

NL 0348554   DLC CtY NN

Liechti, Henri, 1906–
Recherches petrographiques et tectoniques dans la vallée de Göschenen ... Zürich, 1933.
Inaug. Diss. -Bern, 1933.
Vitae
Bibliography.

NL 0348555   ICRL CtY

Liechti, Johanna.
Untersuchungen zur Konstitution des Lycopodiumsporonins. Zürich, 1941.

56, ₍1₎ p. 23 cm.

Inaug.-Diss.—Bern.
Bibliography: p. ₍57₎

1. Spores (Botany) 2. Pollen. 3. Botanical chemistry.

QK662.L5   57–50611

NL 0348556   DLC ICRL CtY

Liechti, Karl.
Rechts-gewaehrleistung und entwehrung im schweizerischen obligationenrecht.
Inaug. diss. Bern, 1927.
Bibl.

NL 0348557   ICRL

W 4
B52
1955
LIECHTI, Markus
Blutgruppenbestimmungen aus bündnerischen Walsersiedlungen. Zürich, 1955.
20 p. illus.
Inaug.-Diss. - Bern.
Summary in German and English.
1. Blood groups

NL 0348558   DNLM

Liechti (Paul). *Studien über die Fruchtschalen der Garcinia mangostana. [Bern.] 16 pp. 8°.
Berlin, Norddeutsch. Buchdr. 1891.

NL 0348559   DNLM ICRL MH-A

Liechti, Paul.
Untersuchungen über das kalkbedürfnis schweizerischer kulturböden. Von Dr. Paul Liechti und Dr. Werner Mooser ... Bern, Buchdr. K. J. Wyss, 1904.

cover-title, 35 p. illus., tables. 25ᶜᵐ.

Separatabdruck aus dem Landwirtschaftlichen jahrbuch der Schweiz. 1904.

1. Switzerland. Soils. 2. Soil, Lime in. I. Mooser, Werner, joint author.

Agr 8–595

Library, U. S. Dept. of   Agriculture 57L.622U

NL 0348560   DNAL

Liechti, Paul.
Zur frage der wiesendüngung. Von Dr. Paul Liechti ... Bern, Buchdr. K. J. Wyss, 1904.

cover-title, 40 p. pl. 24½ᶜᵐ.

Separatabdruck aus dem "Landwirtschaftlichen jahrbuch der Schweiz."

1. Fertilizers for pastures.

Agr 8–596

Library, U. S. Dept. of   Agriculture 57L.622Z

NL 0348561   DNAL

Liechti, Paul, 1906–
Geologische Untersuchung der Dreispitz-Standfluhgruppe und der Flyschregion südlich des Thunersees .. von Paul Liechti ... Bern: P. Haupt, 1931.   78–206 p. incl. tables. illus., plates. 22½ cm.

Repr.: Naturforschende Gesellschaft in Bern. Mitteil. 1930.
Inaugural-Dissertation — Bern, 1931.
Vita.
"Literaturverzeichnis," p. 195–204.

647102A. 1. Geology—Alps.
N. Y. P. L.   July 8, 1933

NL 0348562   NN ICRL

PR6045
.A34B53
Liechti, Rudolf, tr.

Walpole, *Sir* Hugh, 1884–1941.
Ein Leben ohne Licht, Roman. ₍Übertragung von Rudolf Liechti₎ Zürich, Humanitas Verlag ₍1943, *1944₎

PR6045
.A34B73
Liechti, Rudolf, tr.

Walpole, *Sir* Hugh, 1884–1941.
... Die lustgärten Gottes, roman. Zürich, Humanitas verlag ₍*1943₎

PR6045
.A34K53
Liechti, Rudolf, tr.

Walpole, Hugh, 1884–1941.
... Der mörder und sein opfer, eine seltsame geschichte. Zürich, Humanitas verlag ₍1945₎

LIECHTI, S.
Zwölf Schweizer-Märchen. Frauenfeld, 1865.

NL 0348566   MH

Liechti, Urs, *pseud.*
see
Hoegner, Wilhelm, 1887–

Liechti, Werner.
... Geologische untersuchungen der Molassenagelfluhregion zwischen Emme und Ilfis (kanton Bern) Mit 1 textfigur und 6 tafeln. Von Werner Liechti. (Ausgegeben im dezember, 1928) Bern, In kommission bei A. Francke a.-g. ₍Gedruckt bei Stämpfli & cie., 1928.

xii, 83 p. incl. tables. vi fold. pl. (part col.; incl. map, tab., 2 profiles, 2 diagr.) 32ᶜᵐ. (Schweizerische geologische kommission. Beiträge zur geologischen karte der Schweiz, n. f., 61. lfg. (gangen werkes 91. lfg.))
"Literaturverzeichnis": p. vi–xii.

1. Geology—Switzerland—Bern. 2. Geology—Alps. I. Title. II. Title: Molassenagelfluhregion zwischen Emme und Ilfis.

G S 29–19

Library, U. S. Geological   Survey (535) qB2 n.f., 61.lfg.

NL 0348568   DI-GS GU CoU ICRL CtY CU ICJ

Liechti-von Brasch, Dagmar, 1911–
... Frühdiagnose des Portiokarzinoms (kolposkopische, histologische und klinische Befunde) ... Zürich, 1938.
Inaug. -Diss. - Zürich.
Curriculum vitae.
"Literaturverzeichnis": p. [95]–99.

NL 0348569   CtY

WQ
175
L718g
1954
LIECHTI-VON BRASCH, Dagmar, 1911–
Gesunde Schwangerschaft, glückliche Geburt. ₍9., vollständig umgearb. und erweiterte Aufl.₎ Zürich, Wendepunkt-Verlag, 1954.
251 p. illus.
— Körperschulung der werdenden Mutter und Übungen für Wochenbett und Rückbildung; Übungsbuch. Zürich, Wendepunkt-Verlag, 1954.
56 p. illus.
1. Exercise 2. Pregnancy - Hygiene
WQ175 L718g   59–13237

NL 0348570   DNAL

Liechti-von Brasch, Dagmar, 1911–
Kopfschmerzen und Migräne: Ursachen, Linderung und Heilung. ₍1. Aufl.₎ Zürich, Bircher-Benner ₍1953₎
18 p. 21 cm.

1. Headache. I. Title.

RB128.L5   54–21669 ‡

NL 0348571   DLC DNLM

Liechty, Hermann.
Die Lokomotive für grosse Fahrgeschwindigkeiten, von H. Liechty, und ihre Vorgeschichte. Deutsche Ausgabe bearbeitet von Hermann Liechty... Bern: A. Francke A. G., 1939.
59 p. illus. 29½cm.

Cover-title: Liechty's Lokomotivsystem...

1. Locomotives, 1939.
N. Y. P. L.   May 23, 1940

NL 0348572   NN MH-BA

Liechty, Hermann.
Die Umgestaltung des Berner Bahnhofgebäudes; eine Studie in wirtschaftlicher Beziehung, von Hermann Liechty. Bern: A. Francke, A.-G.₍, 1925.₎   8 p. illus. f°.

Repr.: Schweizerische Techniker-Zeitung. Jahrg. 1925, Nr. 46.

1. Railways—Stations—Switzerland —Bern. 2. Cities—Plans—Switzerland—Bern.
N. Y. P. L.   June 22, 1927

NL 0348573   NN

VOLUME 332

Liechty, John A   1864-1947
Brief outline, containing list of names of
families connected with the Ramseyer-Rich
reunion. Louisville, Ohio, 1907.
96p.   10x13½cm.

Includes blank pages for additions.
On cover: Ramseyer-Rich decendants [!].

1. Ramseyer family (John Ramseyer, 1776-1853).
2. Rich family (Joseph Rich, 1800-1853).

NL   0348574   InGo

Liechty, Philippe Reinhard de
        see
Reinhard de Liechty, Philippe, 1829-1883.

WG   Lieck, Albert, 1880-
24096   Ueber einige Derivate des Phtalazins.
        [Berlin] 1905.
        43 p.

        Inaug.-Diss. - Berlin.

NL   0348576   CtY PU ICRL

Lieck, Albert Henry, supposed author.
Alice in Police Court land
see under title

Lieck, Albert Henry, ed.
    Betting and lotteries, by Albert Lieck ... London,
Butterworth & co. (publishers), ltd.; Toronto, Butterworth &
co. (Canada), ltd.; [etc., etc.], 1935.
    xxiv, 172 p. 22 cm.
    "This book is devoted to the subjects of the new act ... [It] begins
by setting out and annotating the older acts."—Introd.

    1. Wagers—Gt. Brit. 2. Lotteries—Law and legislation—Gt. Brit.
I. Gt. Brit. Laws, statutes, etc. II. Title.

                    [174.6] 351.762   35—21317

NL   0348578   DLC NcD

Lieck, Albert Henry.
    Bow street world, by Albert Lieck ... London, R. Hale lim-
ited, 1938.
    xiii, [15]-284, [1] p. front., plates, ports. 22ᶜᵐ.

    1. London. Metropolitan police courts. 2. Crime and criminals—
England—London. I. Title.

                    39—1809

NL   0348579   DLC ICU PU NNC

Lieck, Albert Henry, ed.
    The Criminal justice act, 1925, with explanatory notes. By
Albert Lieck ... and A. C. L. Morrison ... foreword by Sir
A. H. Bodkin ... London, Stevens and sons, limited, 1926.
    xxxi, 136 p. 21½ᶜᵐ.

    1. Criminal law—Gt. Brit. 2. Criminal procedure—Gt. Brit. I.
Morrison, Arthur Cecil Lockwood, joint ed. II. Gt. Brit. Laws, statutes, etc. III. Title.

                    27—20335

NL   0348580   DLC MH

Lieck, Albert Henry, ed.
    The Criminal justice acts; being the Criminal justice ad-
ministration act, 1914, and the Criminal justice acts, 1925 and
1926, with portions of other acts concerned with the same
matters, with explanatory notes by Albert Lieck ... and
A. C. L. Morrison ... 2d ed. Foreword to the first edition
by Sir A. H. Bodkin ... London, Stevens and sons, limited,
1927.
    xxxix, 344 p. 22ᶜᵐ.

    1. Criminal law—Gt. Brit. 2. Criminal procedure—Gt. Brit. I.
Morrison, Arthur Cecil Lockwood, joint ed. II. Gt. Brit. Laws, statutes, etc. III. Title.

                    28—20430

NL   0348581   DLC CtY OU PU-L MH

Lieck, Albert Henry, ed.

Disney, Henry William, 1858-1925.
    The criminal law. A sketch of its principles and practice.
By Henry W. Disney ... 2d ed. London, Stevens and sons,
limited, 1926.

Lieck, Albert Henry, ed.

Knowles, Vincent Devereux.
    Knowles's Evidence in brief; a clear and concise statement
of the principles of evidence, by Albert Lieck ... and Sophie
Lieck ... 4th ed. London, Sir I. Pitman & sons, ltd., 1933.

Lieck, Albert Henry.
    Justice and police in England, by Albert Lieck ... foreword
by Sir Chartres Biron ... London, Toronto, Butterworth &
co., ltd.; [etc., etc.] 1929.
    xii, 152, [1] p. 19ᶜᵐ.
    "Bibliographical note": p. 146-147.

    1. Justice, Administration of—Gt. Brit. 2. Police—Gt. Brit. 3. Crimi-
nal law—Gt. Brit. I. Title.

                    29—16470

NL   0348584   DLC NIC NcD CU OU CtY PU-L IU OrPR

Lieck, Albert Henry.
    The justice at work, by Albert Lieck ... London, But-
terworth & co. [etc.] 1922.
    2 p. l., 28 p. 18½ᶜᵐ.

    1. Justices of the peace—Gt. Brit. I. Title.

                    23—12459

NL   0348585   DLC CtY ViU-L

Lieck, Albert Henry, ed.   FOR OTHER EDITIONS
                                  SEE MAIN ENTRY
Lushington, Guy, 1861-1916.
    Lushington's Law of affiliation and bastardy, with statutes,
notes, forms, &c. 6th ed., by Albert Lieck ... London, Butterworth & co. (publishers) ltd. [etc.] 1936.

Lieck, Albert Henry.
    Lieck and Morrison on domestic proceedings, by A. C. L.
Morrison. London, Butterworth, 1949.
    xiii, 291 p. 23 cm.
    "This book might almost be regarded as a new edition of ... Lieck
and Morrison's 'Matrimonial and family jurisdiction of justices.' "
    ———— Supplement, by A. C. L. Morrison. London,
Butterworth, 1951.
    xvi, A65 p. 22 cm.
    1. Divorce—Gt. Brit. 2. Marriage law—Gt. Brit. 3. Justices of
the peace—Gt. Brit. 4. Jurisdiction—Gt. Brit. 5. Children—Law—
Gt. Brit. I. Morrison, Arthur Cecil Lockwood, 1881- II. Gt.
Brit. Laws, statutes, etc. III. Title. IV. Title: Domestic proceedings.

                    49—4398 rev*

NL   0348587   DLC CaBVa

Lieck, Albert Henry, ed.
Magisterial law, 1932-   being the statutes and
    parts of statutes of 1932-   affecting the work of
    courts of summary jurisdiction, together with statutory
    orders and notes of decided cases ... London, Sir I. Pitman
    & sons, ltd., 1933-

Lieck, Albert Henry.
    Matrimonial and family jurisdiction of justices, by Albert
Lieck ... and A. C. L. Morrison ... 2d ed. London, The
Solicitors' law stationery society, limited, 1932.
    xxxi, 323, [1] p. 22ᶜᵐ.
    First edition, 1926, has title: Matrimonial jurisdiction of justices.
    Appendices (p. [281]-304): 1. Statutes.—2. Statutory rules and
orders.—3. Note on the local jurisdiction of the metropolitan magistrates.—4. Navy, army and air force special provisions.

    1. Divorce—Gt. Brit. 2. Marriage law—Gt. Brit. 3. Justices of the
peace—Gt. Brit. 4. Jurisdiction—Gt. Brit. 5. Children—Law—Gt. Brit.
I. Morrison, Arthur Cecil Lockwood, joint author. II. Gt. Brit. Laws,
statutes, etc. III. Title.

                    41—32508

NL   0348589   DLC CtY

Lieck, Albert Henry.
    Matrimonial jurisdiction of justices, by Albert Lieck ... and
A. C. L. Morrison ... London [etc.] The Solicitors' law stationery society, limited, 1926.
    xxviii, 262 p., 1 l. 22½ᶜᵐ.
    Appendices: 1. Statutes and statutory orders.—2. Notes on the local
jurisdiction of the metropolitan magistrates.—3. Navy, army and air
force special provisions.—4. The Adoption of children act 1926.

    1. Divorce—Gt. Brit. [1. Separation—Gt. Brit.] 2. Marriage law—
Gt. Brit. 3. Justices of the peace—Gt. Brit. 4. Jurisdiction. I. Morrison, Arthur Cecil Lockwood, joint author. II. Gt. Brit. Laws, statutes, etc. III. Title.

                    29—21444

NL   0348590   DLC CtY CU MH

920   [Lieck, Albert Henry]
L623ℓ   Narrow waters; the first volume of the
        life and thoughts of a common man. Lon-
        don, W. Hodge, 1935.
        305p. 23cm.

        1. Lieck, Albert Henry. I. Title.
        II. common man.

NL   0348591   OrU PU NN

Lieck, Albert Henry, ed.

Knowles, Benjamin, defendant.
    Trial of Benjamin Knowles, edited by Albert Lieck ...
Edinburgh and London, W. Hodge & company, limited [1933]

Lieck, Antonius, 1836-
    De refractione luminis in crystallis biaxinus.
    Inaug. Diss. Bonn, 1859

NL   0348593   ICRL

Lieck, Charles Joseph, 1902-
    Legal trial aid. [San Antonio? 1951]
    398 p. 30 cm.

    1. Trial practice—Texas. 2. Employers' liability—Texas.
I. Title.

                    347.9   51—31463

NL   0348594   DLC

VOLUME 332

Lieck, Charles Joseph, 1902–
Legal trial aid. Rev. San Antonio ₁1951₎
288 p. 29 cm.

1. Trial practice—Texas. 2. Employers' liability—Texas.
I. Title.
347.9   52–16045 ‡

NL 0348595   DLC TxU

Lieck, Franz.
... Der flugzeugmotor und seine behandlung, von dipl.-ing.
Franz Lieck. 5. aufl., 7.–10. tausend. Berlin, Klasing & co.,
g. m. b. h., 1918.
131, ₁1₎ p. illus., diagrs. 17½ᶜᵐ. (Klasings flugtechnische bücher.
Die fliegerschule. bd. 1)
On cover: Klasings flugtechnische sammlung. bd. 1.
Advertising matter: p. ₁1–2₎, 120–₁132₎

1. Aeroplanes—Motors.   I. Title.
33–25410
Library of Congress   TL701.L47 1918   629.13435

NL 0348596   DLC NN

Lieck, Franz.
Frankfurt – wie es war. 28 Meisteraufnahmen.
Heidelberg, Brausdruck [1945].

NL 0348597   MH IU

Lieck, Fritz, 1901–
Ein beitrag zur frage der haematogenen
pulpitis ...
Inaug. Diss. –Berlin, [1933]
Lebenslauf.
(Deutschen Monatsschrift für zahnheilkunde 1933,
Heft 18.)

NL 0348598   ICRL CtY

Lieck, Hans.
Ueber einige derivate des mesityloxyds. Basel, 1900
In. Diss.

NL 0348598-1   ICRL PU

Lieck, Heinrich.
... Die Anstaltsbuchführung, von Heinrich Lieck ... Berlin: Wohlfahrtshaus, 1927. 86 p. illus., table. 8°. (Deutsche Liga der freien Wohlfahrtspflege. Schriften. Heft 4.)

1. Bookkeeping for institutions.   2. Ser.
N. Y. P. L.   June 6, 1928

NL 0348599   NN

₁881   **Lieck, Karl von der,** 1909–
X2.Y1ie   Die Xenophontische schrift von den
          einkünften ...   Würzburg, K. Triltsch,
          1933.
          58p.
          Inaug.-diss.--Köln.
          Lebenslauf.
          Bibliographical foot-notes.

NL 0348600   IU CtY OCU

Lieck, Sophie, joint ed.

Knowles, Vincent Devereux.
Knowles's Evidence in brief; a clear and concise statement
of the principles of evidence, by Albert Lieck ... and Sophie
Lieck ... 4th ed. London, Sir I. Pitman & sons, ltd., 1933.

Lieck, Sophie, joint ed.
Magisterial law, 1932–   being the statutes and
    parts of statutes of 1932–   affecting the work of
courts of summary jurisdiction, together with statutory
orders and notes of decided cases ... London, Sir I. Pitman
& sons, ltd., 1933–

Lieck, Walter.
Annelie, die geschichte eines lebens in 12 bildern, von Walter
Lieck; mit musik von Walter Lieck und Heinz Hoffmann.
Klavierauszug mit text. Berlin-Wilmersdorf, Felix Bloch
erben, ᶜ1940.
60 p. 33 x 26¼ᶜᵐ.

1. Operas—Vocal scores—Pianoforte accompaniment.   I. Hoffmann,
Heinz, joint composer.   II. Title.
42–1522
Library of Congress   M1508.L718A7

NL 0348603   DLC

M1508   **Lieck, Walter.   Schwarzer Peter.**

Schultze, Norbert, 1911–
          ₁Schwarzer Peter. Selections; arranged₎
Schwarzer Peter, eine oper für kleine und grosse leute; musik
von Norbert Schultze, text von Walter Lieck; ein querschnitt
für klavier und gesang. Berlin, Neuer theaterverlag g. m. b. h.
₁ᶜ1937₎

ML50   **Lieck, Walter.   Schwarzer Peter.**
.S399
S35   **Schultze, Norbert,** 1911–
1940   ₁Schwarzer Peter. Libretto. Italian₎
L'uomo nero (Schwarzer Peter) opera per grandi e piccoli;
testo di Walter Lieck, tratto dalla fiaba nordico-germanica
"Erica" di Heinrich Traulsen, rielaborata da Wilhelm Wisser.
Musica di Norberto Schultze. Versione ritmica dal tedesco di
Rinaldo Küfferle. Milano, Sonzogno ₁1940₎

Liecker (Heinrich). *Beiträge zur Diagnose
des Unterleibstyphus. 20 pp. 8°. Göttingen,
W. F. Kaestner, 1900.*

NL 0348606   DNLM

·Lieckfeld, Albert
Autogene leuchtgas-schweissmethoden.
Inaug. Diss. Freiburg, 1909

NL 0348607   ICRL

621.43   **Lieckfeld, Georg,** d. 1918.
L718   Aus der Gasmotoren-Praxis. Auswahl,
          Prüfung und Wartung der Gasmotoren. 2. Aufl.
          München, R. Oldenbourg, 1906.
          121 p. diagrs. 22 cm.

1. Gas and oil engines. I. Title.

NL 0348608   N NIC MiU

Lieckfeld, Georg, d. 1918.
Oil motors: their development, construction, and management. A handbook for engineers, owners, attendants, and all
interested in engines using liquid fuel. By G. Lieckfeld ...
Sole authorised English ed. With 306 illustrations. London,
C. Griffin & company, limited, 1908.
xv, 272 p. incl. illus., tables. fold. pl. 23ᶜᵐ.
"A translation of the third edition of Die petroleum- und benzinmotoren."—Pref.

1. Gas and oil engines.
9–27951 Revised
Library of Congress   TJ785.L5

NL 0348609   DLC CU MB NN OU OCl MiU ICJ WaS

Lieckfeld, Georg, d. 1918.
Die Petroleum- und Benzinmotoren, ihre
Entwicklung, Konstruktion und Verwendung. Ein
Handbuch für Ingenieure, Studierende des Maschinenbaues, Landwirte und Gewerbetreibende aller
Art, [aus der Praxis für die Praxis.] Bearbeitet
von G. Lieckfeld, ... Mit 147 in den Text gedruckten Abbildungen. München und Leipzig, R.
Oldenbourg, 1894.
xii, 230 p. 147 illus. incl. diagrs. 24 cm.
1. Gas and oil engines.

NL 0348610   CU

Lieckfeld, Georg, d. 1918.
Die Petroleum- und Benzinmotoren, ihre Entwicklung, Konstruktion und Verwendung. Ein Handbuch für Ingenieure, Studierende des Maschinenbaues, Landwirte und Gewerbetreibende aller
Art, aus der Praxis für die Praxis. Bearbeitet von G. Lieckfeld,
... . Zweite umgearbeitete und vermehrte Auflage. Mit 188
in den Text gedruckten Abbildungen. München und Berlin, R.
Oldenbourg, 1901.
x, 297 p. 188 illus. incl. diagrs. 24ᶜᵐ.

NL 0348611   ICJ MH MiU

TJ   **Lieckfeld, Georg, d. 1918.**
785   Die petroleum- und benzinmotoren, ihre entwick-
.L72   lung, konstruktion, verwendung und behandlung. Ein
1908   handbuch für ingenieure, motorenbesitzer und wär-
          ter; aus der praxis für die praxis, bearb. von G.
          Lieckfeld ... 3. aufl. ... München und Berlin, R.
          Oldenbourg, 1908.
          4 p.l.,304 p. illus.,fold.pl.,diagrs. 24ᶜᵐ.
          1. Gas and oil engines.

NL 0348612   MiU

Lieckfeld, Georg, d. 1918.
Die Petroleum- und Benzin-Motoren, mit besonderer Berücksichtigung der Treiböl-Motoren; ein Handbuch für Ingenieure, Motorenbesitzer und Wärter — aus der Praxis für die
Praxis. München: R. Oldenbourg, 1913.   4 p.l., 320 p., 1 pl.
illus. 4. ed. 8°.

1. Engines (Gas and oil), 1913.
N. Y. P. L.   February 6, 1914.

NL 0348613   NN

Lieckfeld, Georg, d. 1918.
A practical handbook on the care and management of gas
engines, by G. Lieckfeld, C. E. Authorized translation by
G. Richmond ... New York, Spon & Chamberlain; ₁etc., etc.₎
1896.
xiv, 103 p. front., illus. 16½ᶜᵐ. (On cover: Spon & Chamberlain's
series of practical handbooks)

1. Gas and oil engines.   I. Richmond, George, tr.
6–33907 Revised
Library of Congress   TJ755.L7

NL 0348614   DLC NIC MB ICJ OClW MiU MB NN MiHM

VOLUME 332

Lieckfeld, Georg, d. 1918.
A practical handbook on the care and management of gas engines, by G. Lieckfeld ... authorized translation by G. Richmond ... with instructions for running oil engines. 3d ed. New York, Spon & Chamberlain, 1901.
xiv, 103 p. front., diagrs. 17cm. (On cover: Spon & Chamberlain's series of practical handbooks)

1. Gas and oil engines. I. Richmond, George, tr.

NL 0348615   NNC

ar W Lieckfeld, Georg, d. 1918.
51038   Die Sauggasanlagen; ihre Entwicklung Bauart, Wartung und Prüfung; aus der Praxis für die Praxis. München, R. Oldenbourg, 1909.
131 p. illus. 21cm.

NL 0348616   NIC ICJ

Lieckher, Friedrich Jacob, fl. 1677.
Vitae tripartitae ivrisconsvltorvm vetervm a Bernardino Rvtilio, Ioanne Bertrando et Gvilielmo Grotio conscriptae
see under   Franck, Johannes Christophorus, fl. 1717, ed.

Liečnički viestnik. ... Vlastnik i izdavatelj Sbor liečnika kraljevina Hrvatske i Slavonije. ... U Zagrebu, Donička tiskara, 122028 1899-1900.
Library has vol. 21, no. 2-vol. 22, no. 8, Feb. 1899-Sept. 1900, incomplete; vol. 25, no. 7, July, 1903. illus. 26cm.
Editor: M. pl. Čačkovič.
Monthly.
From v.1-27, 1879-1904 called Liečnički viestnik, 1905-1909: Liječnički viestnik u Zagrebu, 1909- Liječnički vjesnik.

NL 0348618   ICJ DNLM

Lied, Jonas, 1881-
Over de høye fjelle. Oslo, J. Dybwad, 1946.
319p. illus.,ports.,fold.map. 21cm.

Autobiography.

NL 0348619   IEN OC1

Lied, Jonas, 1881-
Pionnier en Sibérie et dans la mer de Kara; histoire d'une vie. Préf. et traduction de R. Jouan. Paris, Payot, 1951.
292 p. illus. 23 cm. (Collection de documents et de témoignages pour servir à l'histoire de notre temps)

I. Title.
CT1308.L5A314   52-32359 ‡

NL 0348620   DLC

Lied, Jonas, 1881-
Prospector in Siberia: the autobiography of Jonas Lied. New York, Oxford university press, 1945.
7 p. l., 317, [1] p. front., plates, ports., maps (1 fold.) 22¼cm.
London edition (Macmillan & co. ltd, 1943) has title: Return to happiness.

I. Title.
                                    45-8723
Library of Congress *   CT1308.L5A3 1945
                              [5]   923.8481

PU NcGU OrCS OrU OrP WaSpG
KyLx TU CSt-H MB CU OC1W OC1 OEac PPL PP PPD PSC PHC
NL 0348621   DLC CaBVa WaS IdB CaBVaU Or NIC KEmT KU

Lied, Jonas, 1881-
Return to happiness, by Jonas Lied. London, Macmillan & co. ltd, 1943.
xi, 317, [1] p., 1 l. front., plates, ports., maps (1 fold.) 22¼cm.
Autobiography.

I. Title.
                                    A 43-3779
Harvard univ. Library
for Library of Congress   CT1308.L5A3
                            [3]†   923.8481

NL 0348622   MH KU OC1 DLC Or CaBVa

Lied, Jonas, 1881-
Return to happiness, by Jonas Lied. London, Macmillan & co. ltd, 1944.
xi, 317, [1] p., 1 l. front., plates, ports., maps (1 fold.) 22.5 cm.
Autobiography.
"First edition 1943; reprinted 1944."
Published in New York, 1945, under title: Prospector in Siberia.

NL 0348623   CtY

Lied, Jonas, 1881-
Sidelights on the economic situation in Russia, by Jonas Lied, F. R. G. S. Moscow [Printed at the Kushnerev printing works] 1922.
viii, 148 p., 2 l., 59 p. 2 fold. maps. 22cm.
Appendices: Soviet Russia's constitution (Soviet domestic relations law). Soviet Russia's code of labour law.

1. Russia—Econ. condit.—1918-   2. Russia—Pol. & govt.—1917-
I. Title.
Library of Congress   HC335.L5   23-17695

NL 0348624   DLC

Lied, Paulino, *pseud.*
see
García Gómez Caminero, Juan.

Lied, an des Königs Geburtstag zu singen
see under   [Fischer, Gottlob Nathanael] 1748-1800, ascribed author.

*GC7   Lied der deutschen Fürsten im August 1785.
G4824 [Berlin? 1785?]
B787k 8°. [4]p. 17.5cm.,in case 19cm.
Begins: Gott ist mit uns! Wir sehen ihn ...
No.2 in a volume of verse by Gleim & others.

NL 0348627   MH

*GB8   Lied der Freiwilligen bei ihrem Ausmarsche
V6755R nach Italien. (Nach der Melodie: Fridolin.)
4.31.48 [Wien]Gedruckt bei M.Lell.[1848]
broadside. 22.5x14cm.
Not recorded in Helfert (Wiener Parnass).
Without the music.

NL 0348628   MH

Das Lied der Front; Liedersammlung des Grossdeutschen Rundfunks...
see under   Berndt, Alfred Ingemar,
1905-   ed.

Das Lied der Lieder
see   Bible. O.T. Song of Solomon.
(German) [date. e.g. 1756]

Das Lied der Lieder. Aus dem hebräischen urtext in neue deutsche Reime gebracht von Hermann Rosenthal...
see under   Bible. O.T. Song of Solomon. German. Paraphrases. 1893. Rosenthal.

PT 5488 HET LIED DER MINNE, VAN VROEGER EN NU. Bij-
.L8 L72 eengelesen door A. Nonymus. [Wassenaar] In
den Bloemhof, 1944.
25 p.

1. Love poetry--Dutch--Collections.

NL 0348632   InU

Lied der welt, eine auswahl neuer deutscher gedichte
see under   [Weidner, Walther] 1901-1959.

611./Lied einer Amerikanerin. (In: H. P. Gallinger. Die Haltung der deutschen Publizistik zu dem amerikanischen Unabhängigkeitskriege 1775-1783. Leipzig, 1900. 8°. p. 65-66.) IG

NL 0348634   NN

*GC7   Lied eines Bürgers zu Minden an die
G4824 Alliirte Armee nach der Schlacht bey Todten-
758p hausen am 2ten August 1759.
[Berlin,Voss]1759.
8°. 16p. 12.5cm.
No.3 in a volume lettered on spine:
Kriegslieder.

NL 0348635   MH

551./Lied eines Deutschen in fremden Kriegsdiensten. (Musenalmanach für 1777. Herausgegeben von Joh. Heinr. Voss. Hamburg: Bey L. E. Bohn [17771 24°. p. 108-111.) NFA

NL 0348636   NN

. Lied eines jungen Engländers in Amerika. (Der Teutsche Merkur. Weimar [1775]. 8° Jahr 1775, Vierteljahr 4 [Bd. 12], p. 105.)

NL 0348637   NN

DB40 Lied eines kaiserl. königl. Grenadiers, als
1767 Ihro Kaiserl. Königl. Majestät Ihre öffent-
L5 liche Danksagung bey St.Stephan abstattet.
Wien, Gedruckt bey J.T.Trattner, 1767.
6 ℓ. 20cm.
Title and text within decorative borders; title vignette, headpieces.

1.Maria Theresia, Empress, of Austria, 1717-1780 - Poetry.

NL 0348638   CSt

VOLUME 332

Lied eines lehrers, an seine confirmanten; oder, Denkringlein
... Reading, Gedruckt bey J. Ritter und comp., 1821.
12 p. 16⅓ᵐ.

Library of Congress   PT3919.A1L5   25-13049 Revised

NL 0348639   DLC CtY PSt PHi

---

792. LIED eines Negersklaven in Amerika.
(Musen Almanach. A. MDCCLXXXIV. Göttingen:
Bey J. C. Dietrich [1784]. 32°. p. 88-89.) NFA

NL 0348640   NN

Lied eines Schustergesellen
see under   [Irmscher, Carl Gottlieb]

Lied for life, 1892
see under   Turner, Henry Gaines.

B936
D71
Ein lied für die landsknecht gemacht. Inn
diesen kriegsleufften nützlich zu singen. Im
Dennmarcker/oder im Schweitzer thon. Mense
Augusto. An. M. D. XLVI.
[8] p. 20ᶜᵐ.

Bound with Donati, Geronimo. Hieronymi Donati ... Oratio ... [1510?]

NL 0348643   NNC OC1 IEN

---

*GB8
V6755R
8.32.48
Ein Lied ganz neu, von der alten Polizei!
Von einem bussfertigen und reuevollen Spitzel,
nach der beliebten Melodie des Fuchsliedes.
[Wien] Gedruckt bei M. Lell. [1848]
[2] p. 21.5x13.5cm.
Helfert (Wiener Parnass) 1560.
Caption title; imprint on p. [2].
Without the music.

NL 0348644   MH

LIED, Gesungen in der Synagoge zu Kassel
am Hohen Geburtsfeste Sr. Majestät des
Königs von Westphalen, den 15ten November 1810. Kassel. Gedruckt in der Waisen-
haus-Buchdruckerey. (4)p 20.5cm
7 stanzas, the last two in Hebrew
(Schlusschor).
1. Liturgy- Special. 2. History-
Germany-Cassel.

NL 0348645   NNJ

Lied gewidmet den freunden zu ihrem fröhlichen
mahle in weisen Schwanen zu Alzey, am abend des
12. Novembers 1833. Kirchheimbolanden, Gedruckt
... Zhieme. [1833]
[4] p.

NL 0348646   OC1WHi

Het lied Heer Halewijn
see Heer Halewijn (Ballad)

Das Lied im Volke (Liederschatz) ...
see under   Kremser, Eduard, 1838-1914,
editor.

4PN
1069
Ein Lied lasst uns singen; internationale Kampflieder. Halle, Mittel-
deutscher Verlag [   ]
144 p.

NL 0348649   DLC-P4

Lied und Kampf. Wien, 1926
see under   [Jalkotzy, Alois]

Lied und Volk; eine Streitschrift wider das
falsche deutsche Lied ...

See

[Janiczek, Julius] 1887-

Lied van Hare Majesteit Koningin Wilhelmina en
het prinselijk gezin na een vijfjarige ballings-
chap
see under   [Keuken, Gerrit Jan van der]
1903-

Lied, volgens ordre van zyne Majesteit den koning van
Pruissen gezongen, op den uittogt uit Berlin. Uit het
Hoogduyts vertaald. n. p., [17-?] 2l. 4°.

NL 0348653   NN

---

*GB8
V6755R
3.19.48
Das Lied vom Bürgermeister.
[Wien, 1848]
folder([4]p.) 20x13.5cm.
Helfert (Wiener Parnass) 486.
Printer's imprint on p. [4]: Druck von U.
Klopf sen. und A. Eurich, Wollzeile Nr. 782.
On the resignation & flight of Metternich.

NL 0348654   MH

... Das **lied** vom Hürnen Sewfrid; Nürnberg, Kunegund Hergotin c. 1530. Zwickau, F. Ullmann, 1911.

4 p. l., facsim.: [79] p. illus. 14½ᵐ. (Zwickauer facsimiledrucke,
no. 6)

"Ein exemplar des drucks der Hergotin ... besitzt die Zwickauer ratsschulbibliothek."—Pref., signed: O. Clemen.

1. Siegfried. 2. Illustrated books—15th and 16th cent.—Facsimiles.
I. Clemen, Otto Constantin, 1871-   II. Zwickau. Ratsschulbibliothek.

Library of Congress   NE1255.85L5

12—5241

NL 0348655   DLC OC1 OU TxU CaBVaU

Lied vom hürnen Seyfrid.
Hörnen Siegfried; aus dem ältesten drucke.
16 p.   25.5 x 21.5 cm.   (In Hagen, F. H.
von der, and others, eds. Deutsche gedichte des
mittelalters. 1808-[25] v. 2, pt. 2 [no. 2])

NL 0348656   PHC

Das **lied** vom hürnen Seyfrid nach der druckredaction des
16. jahrhunderts. Mit einem anhange: Das volksbuch vom
gehörnten Siegfried nach der ältesten ausgabe (1726) hrsg.
von Wolfgang Golther. Halle a. S., M. Niemeyer, 1889.

xxxvi p., 1 l., 95 p. 18½ᵐ. (On cover: Neudrucke deutscher litterar-
werke des XVI. und XVII. Jahrhunderts. No. 81-82)

With reproductions of original title-pages.

I. Golther, Wolfgang, 1863-   ed. II. Title: Volksbuch vom gehörnten Siegfried. III. Title: Siegfried.

1—7334 Revised

Library of Congress   PT1126.N4   no. 81-82

PSt PPT

NL 0348657   DLC PU FTaSU MiU CtY RPB OU OCU OC1W NcD

830.82
N393
Nr.81-82
Das Lied vom hürnen Seyfrid, nach der Druck-
redaction des 16. Jahrhunderts. Mit einem
Anhange: Das Volksbuch vom gehörnten Sieg-
fried nach der ältesten Ausgabe (1726) hrsg.
von Wolfgang Golther. 2. Aufl. Halle a.
S., M. Niemeyer, 1911.
1v, 99 p. 19cm. (Neudrucke deutscher
Literaturwerke des XVI. und XVII. Jahrhun-
derts, Nr. 81-82)
With reproduction of original title-pages.

NN PSC OOxM NcU

NL 0348658   MiDW IEN PHC ICU ViU IU PU CU WaU CaBVaU

[1913]

831.28
N57.p
Germ.
Das Lied vom hürnen Seyfrid.
Der hürnene Siegfried; ein helden-
gedicht nach dem ältesten drucke bearb.
von Karl Pannier. Leipzig, Reclam
[1913]
67p. T. (On cover: Universal-
bibliothek, 5553)

NL 0348659   IaU MB

Das Lied vom Kinde
see under Herold, Theodor, 1871-   ed.

Das Lied vom Magdalener Wein
see under Scherer, Georg, 1828-1909.

Das Lied vom Prinzen Friedrich Karl...
see under Schneider, Emil.

Das Lied vom Troste
see under Gillet, Grete, ed.

VOLUME 332

Das **lied** vom wiegendruck. ₍Berlin, M. Breslauer, 1927₎
₍7₎ p. 19ᶜᵐ.
"Zum 29. oktober 1927 für Konrad Haebler in 125 abzügen in druck gegeben."
Colophon: Dieses gegenwirtig auserlesene edel und fruchtbringet geticht hat getruckt vnnd säliglich vollendet meister Eduardus Tieffenbach zu Berlin gesessen in der Martinsgassen hinder stegelitzn in seinem haus zur officina serpentis am Dornstag vor sanct konrads tag auf anregung vnnd begern des erbern vnnd weysen Martini Vratislaviensis (nit on vrsach) da man von der halligen hallsamen hönigflüssigen vnd allerseligsten geburdt vnnsers lieben herren Jhesu cristi gezelt hat ᴍᴅᴄᴄᴄ vnnd xxvii iar.
1. Breslauer, Martin, 1871–

                                    29–23140

Library of Congress   Z720.H15L

NL 0348664   DLC

Wing
ZP-
fac.
5471
.52
   Ein **LIED** von Belagerung der Stadt Frankfurt im Jahre 1552. Namens der Stadtbibliothek den Teilnehmern an den bibliophilen Veranstaltungen am 10. Oktober 1920 überreicht von Friedrich Clemens Ebrard.   Frankfurt am Main, 1920.
₍6₎l., facsim.: ₍4₎l. 20cm.

   Title of original: Vonn Belegerunge der Statt Franckfurt, ein Lied, im Thon: Frisch auff inn Gottes Namen. M. D. LII.

   "... der Druck in der Hausdruckerei von Gebr. Klingspor in Offenbach am Main hergestellt. Auflage 400 Stück. Nr.163."

NL 0348666   ICN

Das **LIED** von Charon.

   (In SZCZEPÁNSKI, Georg von. Der romantische schwindel in der deutschen mythologie, etc. Elberfeld, ₍1885?₎. pp.₍23₎–37.)

NL 0348667   MH

Das **lied** von dem alten Hildebrand.
     Nürnberg, Kunegund Hergotin, 1530.
     Microfilm

NL 0348668   CU

... Das **lied** von dem alten Hildebrand; Nürnberg, Kunegund Hergotin, c. 1530. Zwickau, F. Ullmann, 1912.
7 p., facsim.: ₍7₎ p. 14½ᶜᵐ. (Zwickauer facsimiledrucke, no. 7)
Reproduced from the copy in the Ratsschulbibliotek, Zwickau. cf. Pref., signed: O. Clemen.
Original title, with vignette: Das Liede von dem alten· Hiltebrand. (First line: Ich wil zů land auss reite)

1. Hildebrand.   I. Clemen, Otto Constantin, 1871–   II. Zwickau. Ratsschulbibliothek.
                                     15–21331

Library of Congress   PT1121.Z8 no.7

NL 0348668–1   DLC

... Das **lied** von dem edlen Tannhäuser. Nürnberg, Kunegund Hergotin, c. 1530. Zwickau, F. Ullmann, 1912.
2 p. l., facsim.: 1 p. l., ₍5₎ p. 14½ᶜᵐ. (Zwickauer facsimiledrucke, no. 8)
"Der hier facsimiliierte druck ... ist wahrscheinlich ein nachdruck der ausgabe des Jobst Gutknecht von c. 1515."—Pref., signed : O. Clemen.
Original title, with vignette: Das Liede von dem edlen Danheuser. (First line: Nvn wil ich aber heben an)

1. Tannhäuser.   I. Clemen, Otto Constantin, 1871–
                                       15–21332

Library of Congress   PT1121.Z8 no. 8

NL 0348669   DLC OCl NN CU

... Das **lied** von dem grafen von Rom. Nürnberg, Georg Wachter, c. 1530. Zwickau, F. Ullmann, 1912.
2 p. l., facsim.: ₍8₎ p. 14½ᶜᵐ. (Zwickauer facsimiledrucke, no. 9)
Preface signed : O. Clemen.
Original title, with vignette: Eyn lied von dem Grafen von Rom. (First line: Ich verkünd euch newe mere)

1. Clemen, Otto Constantin, 1871–
                                       15–21333

Library of Congress   PT1121.Z8 no. 9

NL 0348670   DLC CU NN

Das lied von dem schachspiele
     see under   ₍Güttle, J   ₎

... Das **lied** von dem Schlaraffenland im roten zwingerton. Nürnberg, Kunegund Hergotin, c. 1530. Zwickau, F. Ullmann, 1912.
2 p. l., facsim.: 1 p. l., ₍5₎ p. 14½ᶜᵐ. (Zwickauer facsimiledrucke, no. 14)
Introduction signed : O. Clemen.
Original title, with vignette: Ein abentheürisch Lied in dem Roten Zwinger thon / von dem Schlawraffen lande / seltzam schwenck / lüstig zu hören. (First line: In disem land kan ich nymmer bleyben)

1. Clemen, Otto Constantin, 1871–   II. Title: Schlaraffenland.
                                     15–21329

Library of Congress   PT1121.Z8 no. 14

NL 0348672   DLC CU NN IU

Y
952
.M 2913
   Das **lied** von dem wurstmarkte. (Travestie nach Schiller's Lied von der glocke) Allen fröhlichen wurstmarktsgästen, wackern·zechern und holden tänzerinnen zur erinnerung an den Dürkheimer wurstmarkt gewidmet. (Mit erklärenden bemerkungen für fremde leser)... Neustadt a.d.H., 1839.   (with ₍Malss, Karl₎ Die entführung; oder, Der alte bürger-capitain. 1833)

NL 0348673   ICN

Das Lied von der Glocke; Cantata
     see under   Bruch, Max, 1828–1920.

Das Lied von der Majestät... Für eine Singstimme mit Piano...
     see under
₍Hartkäs, Johann Friedrich Wilhelm₎ 1805–

"Ein **Lied** Von der Taufe," being a hymn of nine stanzas.
Lancaster, H. W. Villee, 1828?
1 p.

NL 0348676   PHuJ

Ein **lied** von doktor Favstˢ hoellenfahrt. Fliegendes blatt.   Dresden, Privatdruck ₍Flössel₎ 1908.
7 p. 20ᶜᵐ.
Illustrated t.–p.and cover.
Cover title: Doktor Favstˢ hoellenfahrt.

NL 0348677   MiU OCl CtY

... Ein **lied** von einer wirtin und einem pfaffen. Nürnberg, Georg Wachter, c. 1530. Zwickau, F. Ullmann, 1913.
3 p. l., facsim.: ₍7₎ p. 14ᶜᵐ. (Zwickauer facsimiledrucke, no. 20)
Introduction signed : Johannes Bolte.
Original title, with vignette: Ein hübsch new Lied / von eyner wirtin vnd eim Pfaffen. (First line: Ein wirtin vnd ein Pfaffe)

1. Bolte, Johannes, 1858–
                                     15–21330

Library of Congress   PT1121.Z8 no.20

NL 0348678   DLC CU OCl IU

Das Lied von Herzog Ernst (89 stanzas)
     see
Herzog Ernst (Version G, 89 stanzas)

Das lied von King Horn
     see under   King Horn (Metrical romance)

Das **LIED** von ursprung der eidgenossenschaft. n.p., 1889.
pp.7.
Edited by Wolfgang Golther.
"Separat-abdruck aus dem Anzeiger für schweiz Geschichte', 1889, nr.4 and 5, s. 387–392."

NL 0348681   MH

                 Swi 74.12(Abt.3, Bd.2, T.1)
Das Lied von Ursprung der Eidgenossenschaft
Das Lied von der Entstehung der Eidgenossenschaft. Das Urner Tellenspiel. Hrsg.von M.Wehrli Aarau, Sauerländer, 1952.
99 p. (Quellenwerk zur Entstehung der Schweizerischen Eidgenossenschaft, Abt.3, Bd.2, T.1)

   I. Wehrli, Max, 1909–   ,ed. X ref.: Das Lied von der Entstehung der Eidgenossenschaft. (to main entry)   genossenschaft. (to main entry)

NL 0348682   MH

Das Lied vum Lockschen
     see under   Worscht, Mausche, pseud.

---

*GC7
A100
B798l
   Lied was hat auf di Nujahrstag di bekannti ungarischi Heubauer zu di allererstimal in di Birthshaus bey di Goldspinna naher am Saumarkt z'Wien sungen.
     Wien, 1798. Auf Kosten des vormahligen Buchdruckers Weimar, und in Commission in der Rehm'schen Buchhandlung am Kohlmarkt.
     8°. 8p. 20cm., in case 21cm.
     No.9 in a volume of anonymous verse in the Viennese dialect.

NL 0348684   MH

---

*GC7
A100
B798l
   Lied was hot auf di allerhöchste Burtstag Koyser Franziskus an di zwölfti February 1798 di bekannti ungarischi Heubauer z'Wien sungen. Wien, 1798. Auf Kosten des vormahligen Buchdruckers Weimar, und in Commission in der Rehm'schen Buchhandlung am Kohlmarkt.
     8°. 8p. 20cm., in case 21cm.
     No.10 in a volume of anonymous verse in the Viennese dialect.

NL 0348685   MH

VOLUME 332

Lied was hot auf di Burstag von di Held Erzherzeg Karli an di vierte September 1797. di bekannti ungarischi Heubauer in di Birtshaus bey di Schwanni uf der Landstrasse z'Wien sungen.
Wien,1797.Auf Kosten des vormahligen Buchdruckers Weimar,und in Kommission bey Peter Rehm, Buchhändler am Kohlmarkt.
8°. 8p. 20cm.,in case 21cm.
No.3 in a volume of anonymous verse in the Viennese dialect.

*GC7
A100
B798l

NL 0348686 MH

Lied was hot auf di Karoli=Tag ein ungarischi Heubauer zu Wien sungen.
Wien,1796.Auf Kosten des vormahligen Buchdruckers Weimar.
8°. 8p. 20cm.,in case 21cm.
No.1 in a volume of anonymous verse in the Viennese dialect.

*GC7
A100
B798l

NL 0348687 MH

Lied was hot auf di Präliminari-Frid di bekannti ungarischi Heubauer in di Birthshaus bei di Tauben noher am Heumarkt zu Wien sungen.
Wien,1797.Auf Kosten des vormahligen Buchdruckers Weimar,und in Kommission in der Rehm'schen Buchhandlung am Kohlmarkt.
8°. 8p. 20cm.,in case 21cm.
No.2 in a volume of anonymous verse in the Viennese dialect.

*GC7
A100
B798l

NL 0348688 MH

Lied was hot auf di Sterbtog von di Fasching, di bekannti ungarischi Heubauer z'Wien sungen
...
Wien,1798.Auf Kosten des vormahligen Buchdruckers Weimar,und in Commission in der Rehm'schen Buchhandlung am Kohlmarkt.
8°. 8p. 20cm.,in case 21cm.
No.11 in a volume of anonymous verse in the Viennese dialect.

*GC7
A100
B798l

NL 0348689 MH

Lied was hot auf di wieder gewordne Sundheit unsrer guiten und lieben Muitter der durchleuchtigsten Erzherzeginn Christina di bekannti ungarischi Heubauer z'Wien sungen.
Wien,1798.Auf Kosten des vormahligen Buchdruckers Weimar,und in Commission in der Rehm'schen Buchhandlung am Kohlmarkt.
8°. 8p. 20cm.,in case 21cm.
No.12 in a volume of anonymous verse in the Viennese dialect.

*GC7
A100
B798l

NL 0348690 MH

Lied wos hot auf di wirklichi Frid di bekannti ungarischi Heubauer z'Wien sungen.
Wien,1797.Auf Kosten des vormahligen Buchdruckers Weimar,und in Commission in der Rehm'schen Buchhandlung am Kohlmarkt.
8°. 8p. 20cm.,in case 21cm.
No.8 in a volume of anonymous verse in the Viennese dialect.

*GC7
A100
B798l

NL 0348691 MH

WBG LIEDBECK, C H
L718d   A description of the vibrator (Amer.
1891   pat. n:o 433011) and directions for use.
Stockholm, Norstedt, 1891.
vi, 64 p. illus.

NL 0348692 DNLM

Liedbeck (C. H.) Gymnastiska dagöfningar valda bland dem som begagnats vid Stockholms stads folkskolor under åren 1870-80. [Gymnastics chosen from methods used in the Stockholm folk schools from 1870-80.] 2 p. l., 80 pp. sm. 4°. Stockholm, P. A. Norstedt & Söner, [1881].

NL 0348693 DNLM PBa

Liedbeck, C H.
Manuel de gymnastique suédoise à l'usage des écoles primaires, par C. H. Liedbeck. Traduit sur la seconde édition suédoise, par M. le dr Jentzer...et Mlle Stina Béronius... Deuxième édition revue et augmentée. Adopté pour les écoles primaires du canton de Genève. Genève: Stapelmohr [etc., etc., 1901] 199 p. illus., plates. 27cm.

171691B. 1. Gymnastics, Swedish. I. Jentzer, Alcide, 1849-1907, tr. II. Béronius, Stina, tr.
N. Y. P. L. August 19, 1942

NL 0348694 NN DNLM

839.71 [Liedbeck, Henrika Sofia Karolina] 1810-
L62d   Dikter, af J. L. Med förord af professor
Atterbom. Upsala, Tryckt hos P. Hanselli, 1849.
168p. 17cm.

I. Atterbom, Per Daniel Amadeus, 1790-1855.

NL 0348695 IU

B521.8 Liedbeck, Lars, praeses
L62   ... Dissertatio astronomica de eclipsibus in genere, qvam ... praeside ... Lars Liedbeck ... publicae ... submittit ... Håkan Berthelius ... ad diem VII Sept. anni MDCCLI. ... Londini, Gothorum, Ex officina directoris Caroli Gustavi Berling [1751]
[4], 14 p. 19cm.

1. Eclipses. I. Berthelius, Håkan

NL 0348696 NNC

B529 Liedbeck, Lars, praeses.
Z   ... Dissertatio gradualis, de divisione temporis, quam ... in alma Gothorum Carolina ... praesidio ... Lars Liedbeck ... dei [!] XXI August. A. O. R. MDCCLI ... modeste submittit Olavus Austrin ... Londini Gothorum, Officina Directoris Caroli Gustavi Berling [1751]
[6], 13, [1] p. 20cm. in 24cm.

Volume of pamphlets.

NL 0348697 NNC

B523.7 Liedbeck, Lars, praeses.
Z1   ... Dissertatio mathematica de altitudine solis horaria, qvam ... in Regia Academia Goth. Carolina, sub praesidio ... D. Lars Liedbeck ... publico bonorum examini ... subjicit Jonas Godtfr. Callman ... ad diem VIII Septembr. anni MDCCLIII. Londini Gothorum, Ex Officina director. Caroli Gustavi Berling [1753]
[6], 14 p. tables. 21cm.

Volume of pamphlets.

NL 0348698 NNC

B523.7 Liedbeck, Lars, praeses.
Z1   ... Dissertatio mathematica, de amplitudine solis, quam ... praeside ... Lars Liedbeck ... publico bonorum examini ... subjicit, Joan Hagelquist ... ad diem XXVIII Julii MDCCLII ... Londini Gothorum, Ex Officina director. Caroli Gustavi Berling [1753]
[2], 8 p. tables. 21cm.

Volume of pamphlets.

NL 0348699 NNC

B522 Liedbeck, Lars, praeses.
Z2   ... Dissertatio mathematica, de clepsammis, quam ... praeside ... Lars Liedbeck ... publico examini submittit ... Johan Sandahl ... die XIII Julii anni MDCCLVI ... Londini Gothorum, Ex Officina directoris Caroli Gustavi Berling [1756]
[2], 13, [1] p. 21cm.

Volume of pamphlets.

NL 0348700 NNC

B525.14 Liedbeck, Lars, praeses.
Z   Dissertatio mathematica, de dimensione graduum longitudinum telluris, quam ... sub moderamine ... Dni: Lars Liedbeck ... ad publicum bonorum examen ... defert Sven P. Lilljenroth ... die XXIII. Septembr. MDCCXLIX. .... Londini Gothorum, Typis Caroli Gustavi Berling [1749]
[4], 14 p. 21cm.

Volume of pamphlets.

NL 0348701 NNC

B510 Liedbeck, Lars, 1707-1762, praeses.
L62   ... Dissertatio mathematica de lamellis Neperianis, qvam ... praeside ... Lars Liedbeck ... submittit ... Johan Bergman Håkansson ... Londini Gothorum, Ex officina directoris Caroli Gustavi Berling [1755]
[8], 18 p. 20cm.

Thesis, Lund.

NL 0348702 NNC

B526.62 Liedbeck, Lars, praeses.
Z2   ... Dissertatio mathematica de longitudine loci, ex tempore invenienda, quam ... sub praesidio ... Lars Liedbeck ... publicae disquisitioni committit ... Jonas Lindahl ... die XXX. Junii a. MDCCLVI ... Londini Gothorum, Ex Officina directoris Caroli Gustavi Berling [1756]
1 p. l., 13 p. 19cm. in 23cm.

Volume of pamphlets.

NL 0348703 NNC

VOLUME 332

B525.74
Z

Liedbeck, Lars, praeses.
... Dissertatio mathematica, de maculis
solaribus, quam ... in Regia Academic Goth.
Carolina, sub praesidio ... Lars Liedbeck ...
submittit ... Lars Ralin ... ad diem XXIV.
Decembr. anni MDCCLIII ... Londini Gothorum,
Ex Officina director. Caroli Gustavi Berling
₁1753₎
1 p. l., 2-13 p. 21cm.

Volume of pamphlets.

NL   0348704   NNC

521
32

Liedbeck, Lars
...₁Dissertatio mathematica de motu et mag-
nitudine apparente, spectatore in quiete po-
sito, quam ... in Regia Academia Goth. Carolina sub praesidio ... Lars Liedbeck ... submittit Carolus Iohannes Kempff ... ad diem
XIII. Mart. anni MDCCLIV ... Londini, Ex Officina Directoris Caroli Gustavi Berling
₁1754₎
₁8₎, 12 p. 20cm.

NL   0348705   NNC

B510
L623

Liedbeck, Lars, 1707-1762, praeses.
... Dissertatio mathematica de numeris
pronicis qvam ... sub praesidio ... Lars
Liedbeck ... submittit ... Daniel Ekelund ...
Londini Gothorum, Ex officina director Caroli
Gustavi Berling ₁1753₎
₁4₎, 13, ₁1₎ p. 19ᶜᵐ.

Thesis, Lund, 1753.

NL   0348706   NNC

B523.7
Z1

Liedbeck, Lars, praeses.
... Dissertatio mathematica, de ortu & oc-
casu solis, quam ... praeside ... Lars Liedbeck ... publico bonorum examini ... submittit Carl Gustav Lange ... die XI Aug. anni
MDCCLIII ... Londini Gothorum, Ex Officina
director. Caroli Gustavi Berling ₁1753₎
₁2₎, 15 p. tables. 21cm.

Volume of pamphlets.

NL   0348707   NNC

B523.31
Ek6

Liedbeck, Lars, praeses.
... ₁Dissertatio mathematica, de parallaxi
lunae, qvam ... sub moderamine ... Lars Liedbeck ... publico examini modeste submittit
Peter Ekmark ... die XX Junii anno MDCCL ...
Londini Gothorum, Typis Caroli Gustavi Berling
₁1750₎
₁4₎, 13, ₁4₎, 14-15, ₁1₎ p. tables. 21cm.

NL   0348708   NNC

523.3
22

Liedbeck, Lars, praeses.
... Dissertatio mathematica de phasibus
lunae, quam ... sub ... Domini Lars Liedbeck
... publice examinandam exhibet Olaus Hageman
die XXIX. Maji anno MDCCLIV ... Londini
Gothorum, Ex Officina Caroli Gustavi Berling
₁1754₎
15 p.

Volume of pamphlets.

NL   0348709   NNC

B529.7
L82

Liedbeck, Lars, 1707-1762, praeses.
₁Dissertatio mathematica de reductione
temporis et mensurae graduum, quam ...
praeside ... Lars Liedbeck ... publice
censurae committit ... Jonas Holmsten ...
Londini Gothorum, Ex officina directoris
Caroli Gustavi Berling ₁1754₎
16 p. tables. 20ᵐ.

Thesis, Lund.

NL   0348710   NNC

B526.73
Z1

Liedbeck, Lars, praeses.
... Dissertatio mathematica de VI centripeta,
qvam ... sub praesidio ... Lars Liedbeck ...
submittit Johannes V. Söderberg ... Jun. anni
MDCCLIX ... Londini Gothorum, Ex officina
directoris Caroli Gustavi Berling ₁1759₎
20 p. 19cm. in 25cm.

Volume of pamphlets.

NL   0348711   NNC

B514
L82

Liedbeck, Lars, 1707-1762, praeses.
... Dissertatio mathematica de trigonometria
plana, qvam ... sub praesidio ... Lars Liedbeck ... subjicit Jonas Lindahl ... Londini
Gothorum, Ex officina director Caroli Gustavi
Berling ₁1753₎
₁2₎, 13, ₁1₎ p. 19ᵐ.

Thesis, Lund, 1753.

NL   0348712   NNC

B529
Z

Liedbeck, Lars, praeses.
... Dissertatio mathematica epochas sive
aeras sistens, qvam ... praeside ... Lars
Liedbeck ... pro gradu magisterii ... modeste
submittit Conrad Runell ... die XII Septembr.
an. MDCCLII ... Londini Gothorum, Ex Officina Direct. Caroli Gustavi Berling ₁1752₎
₁4₎, 16 p. 19cm. in 24cm.

Volume of pamphlets.

NL   0348713   NNC

B532.3
Sol

Liedbeck, Lars, 1707-1762, praeses.
... Dissertatio physico-mathematica de cor-
poribus natantibus, qvam ... praeside ...
Lars Liedbeck ... subjicit Johannes v. Söderberg ... Londini Gothorum, Ex officina Directoris Caroli Gustavi Berling ₁1760₎
18, ₁2₎ p. 20cm.

1. Floating bodies. I. Söderberg, Johannes
von

NL   0348714   NNC

B526.73
Z1

Liedbeck, Lars, praeses.
... Dissertatio physico-mathematica de gra-
vitate corporum, qvam ... praeside ... Lars
Liedbeck ... publico eruditorum examini submittit Johan Sandahl ... die xix. Martii
MDCCLX ... Londini Gothorum, Ex officina
directoris Caroli Gustavi Berling ₁1760₎
16 p. 19cm. in 25cm.

Volume of pamphlets.

NL   0348715   NNC

B526.73
Z1

Liedbeck, Lars, praeses.
... Dissertatio physico-mathematica de gra-
vitate telluris quam ... praeside ... Lars
Liedbeck ... submittit ... Conrad Runell ...
die xiii. Jan. anni MDCCL ... Londini Gothorum, Typis Caroli Gustavi Berling ₁1750₎
₁6₎, 17, ₁1₎ p. 19cm. in 25cm.

Volume of pamphlets.

NL   0348716   NNC

B525.14
Z

Liedbeck, Lars, praeses.
Dissertatio physico-mathematica de inaequalitate superficiei telluris, quam ... sub
praesidio D:ni Lars Liedbeck ... ad publicum
eruditorum examen defert Caspar Liefertz ...
anni MDCCLX ... Londini Gothorum, Ex officina Caroli Gustavi Berling ₁1760₎
15, ₁1₎ p. 19cm. in 21cm.

Volume of pamphlets.

NL   0348717   NNC

B543.7
A84

Liedbeck, Lars, 1707-1762, praeses.
... Dissertatio physico-mathematica de pro-
prietate aeris, qvam ... sub moderamine ...
Lars Liedbeck ... submittit, pro gradu magisterii, Nicolaus Alin, junior ... Londini
Gothorum, Ex officina directoris Caroli Gustavi Berling ₁1760₎
₁8₎, 2-10, ₁1₎ p. 19cm.

NL   0348718   NNC

Liedbeck, Per Jakob, 1802-76.
——. Anvisning att bota torfrysning och köld-
skador, samt läka bränskador. [On the use of
remedies for congelation and frost-bitten parts,
also to heal burns.] 42 pp. 12°. Stockholm,
R. Wall, 1850.

NL   0348719   DNLM

Liedbeck, Per ⸺ Jacob ⸺. 1802-76.
——. * De cerebello humano observata et com-
mentata. Respondente Amdrea Georg. Berglind.
1 p. l., 32 pp. 8°. Upsaliæ, G. Torselll, [1845].

NL   0348720   DNLM

QH9
.T6
no. 256
Rare bk.

Liedbeck, Per Jakob, 1802-1876, respondent.
Thunberg, Karl Peter, 1743-1828, praeses.
De pipere cubeba ... Upsaliæ, excudebant Palmblad & c.
₁1827₎

H615.53
L72
L4

Liedbeck, Per ⸺ Jakob ⸺, 1802-1876.
Homöopathiens närvarande ställning i
främmande länder, af dr. P. J. Liedbeck. Andra
upplagan. Stockholm, J. Beckman, 1854.
1 p. l., 114, [2] p. front. 20½ cm.

NL   0348722   MiU PPHa

VOLUME 332

Liedbeck, Per Jakob, 1802-1876, respondent.

QH9
.T6
no. 242-
250
Rare bk.
coll.

Thunberg, Karl Peter, 1743-1828, praeses.
Horti upsaliensis plantæ cultæ ab initio sæculi ... Upsaliæ, excudebant Palmblad &c. ₍1826₎

W 6
P3

LIEDBECK, Per Jakob, 1802-1876
Kort anvisning til några homöopathiska läkemedels användande mot koleran, af P. J. Liedbeck ₍och₎ Frans Th. Noréus. ₍Stockholm, Norstedt, 1854₎
14 p.   W6 P3
Caption title.
I. Noréus, Frans Theodor

NL 0348724   DNLM

WBK
L718k
1846

LIEDBECK, Per Jakob, 1802-1876
Kort framställning af homeopathiens närvarande ställning i främmande länder. Stockholm, Elmén & Granberg, 1846.
31 p.   WBK L718k

NL 0348725   DNLM

Liedbeck, Per Jakob, 1802-76.
——. 'Om den akuta fosforförgiftningen. 24 pp. 8°. Stockholm, L. J. Hjerta, 1845.

NL 0348726   DNLM

Liedbeck (P₍er₎ J₍akob₎) ₍1802-76₎. Om kräkning och de vanliga kräkmedlen, i förhållande till naturläkningen, vid inammätenae, serdeles hjernans, blodöfverfylnad och inflammation. ₍Vomiting and emetics, with reference to cure by nature in diseases of the brain, hyperæmia, and inflammation.₎ 22 pp. 8°. Upsala, Wahlström & Lästbom, 1843.

NL 0348727   DNLM

Liedbeck, Per Jakob, 1802-76.
——. Om lilla hjernans function. Medicinskfysiologisk afhandling. 30 pp., 2 l., 1 pl. 8°. Upsala, G. Torssell, 1845.

NL 0348728   DNLM

WQ
L718o
1848

LIEDBECK, Per Jakob, 1802-1876
Om qwinnans förhallande wid förlossning och barnsäng, samt det nyfödda barnets skötsel och behandling ... Stockholm, Oberg [1848]
57 p.   WQ L718o

NL 0348729   DNLM

Liedbeck, Petrus Jacobus
see Liedbeck, Per Jakob, 1802-1876.

PT
9995
.L4P5

Liedberg, C   Emil.
The Pioneer Limited och Norrlands kolonister. ₍Chicago, Tryckt af North Chicago Print. Co., 1913₎
32 p. illus. 15 cm.

Cover title.

1. Norrland, Sweden. 2. Svenska krigareförbundet. I. Title.

NL 0348731   MnHi

Liedberg, Nils, 1900-
Avel och produktion, hur några gjort som lyckats. ₍Stockholm₎ Lantbruksförbundets Tidskrifts AB ₍1951₎
78p.

NL 0348732   InLP

Liedberg, Nils, 1900-
... Klinische studien über die akute cholecystitis, von Nils Liedberg. Lund, H. Ohlssons buchdruckerei, 1937.

247, 182* p. incl. tables, diagrs. 24ᵐᵐ. (On cover: Acta chirurgica scandinavica ... Supplementum XLVII)

At head of title: Aus der Chirurgischen universitätsklinik in Lund.
Translated by E. Blauert. cf. Vorwort.
Summary also in English and French.
"Literatur": p. ₍169*₎-182*.

1. Gall-bladder—Diseases.   I. Blauert, Ernst, tr.
                          ₍Full name: Nils Karl Bertil Liedberg₎
                                              A C 37-3298
John Crerar library
for Library of Congress   ₍4₎

NL 0348733   ICJ ViU ICRL

Liedberg, Wilhelm, 1813-1891, respondent.

Fries, Elias Magnus, 1794-1878, praeses.
Anteckningar öfver de i Sverige växande ätliga svampar ... Upsala, Palmblad, Sebell & c., 1836.

Liedecker, Charles, pseud.
see Kaser, Arthur LeRoy, 1890-

DS509
G490
L71

Liedekerke, Guy de, comte.
Sous le sourire des Bouddhas: Ceylan, Java, Bali, Sumatra, Siam, Cambodge. Paris, Editions Albert, 1933.
285 p. illus. 22cm.

1. Southeast Asia--Descr. & trav.
I. Title.

NL 0348736   NIC InU

DH687
L5L71

Liedekerke, Raoul de, Comte.
Examinons l'affaire du roi; trois études. Bruxelles, Chez l'auteur ₍1946₎
76 p. 21ᶜᵐ.
Contents.- Un grand roi méconnu.- L'affaire royale du point de vue constitutionnel et légal.- L'entrevue de Berchtesgaden.

1. Léopold III, King of the Belgians, 1901-
2. Belgium - Pol.   & govt. - 1940-1945. 3.
Belgium - Const   itutional law. I. Title.

NL 0348737   CSt-H CaBVaU NN

Liedekerke-Beaufort, Auguste de, comte, 1792-1856.
... Rapporti delle cose di Roma (1848-1849). A cura di Alberto M. Ghisalberti. Roma, Vittoriano, 1949. xviii, 212 p. 25cm. (Regio istituto per la storia del risorgimento italiano. Biblioteca scientifica. Fonti. v. 35)

Bibliographical footnotes.

1. Rome (City)—Hist.—Revolu-   tion of 1848-1849. I. Ghisalberti,
Mario, 1902-   , ed.
N. Y. P. L.   December 13, 1951

MWelC MH
NL 0348738   NN NNC MH NcD LU MH CtY NIC ICU CSt TU

DC146
.L3A2
1951

Liedekerke-Beaufort, Aymar Marie Ferdinand de, comte, 1846- ed.   FOR OTHER EDITIONS
                                        SEE MAIN ENTRY
La Tour du Pin Gouvernet, Henriette Lucie (Dillon) marquise de, 1770-1853.
Journal d'une femme de 50 ans, 1778-1815. Recueilli par son arrière petit-fils, le colonel comte Aymar de Liedekerke-Beaufort. Paris, Berger-Levrault, 1951.

Liedekerke de Beaufort, Florent Charles Auguste de, 1792-

SEE

Liedekerke-Beaufort, Auguste de, comte, 1792-1856.

Liedel, Fritz: Die Versorgung Erlangens mit Brotgetreide, Brot und Mehl im Weltkrieg. [Maschinenschrift.] 72 S. m. Tab. 4° [Lag nicht vor.] — Auszug [Autogr.]: 1 Bl. 4°
Erlangen, Phil. Diss. v. 23. Mai 1923   [U 23. 1912

NL 0348741   ICRL

Liedel, Oscar.
La guerre et l'occupation. ₍Bruxelles, J. Rozez, 1947₎
₍34₎ l. illus., 30 col. plates. 40 cm.
Issued in portfolio.

1. World War, 1939-1945—Pictorial works. I. Title.

ND1974.L5   759.9493   49-53300*

NL 0348742   DLC

AS
262
T19A2
ser.A
v.19

Liedemann, Helene.
Über die Sonnenscheindauer und Bevölkerung in Eesti. Tartu, 1930.
29 p. illus. 24cm. ₍Tartu. Ülikool.
Acta et commentationes Universitatis tartuensis (dorpatensis) A: Mathematica, physica, medica. XIX³₎

NL 0348743   NIC

Kress
Room

[Liedemann, János Sámuel] 1755-1834.
Beschwerden und ohnmassgeblicher vorschlag, wie dem handel in Ungarn aufzuhelfen wäre. Von P**. H**. St**.[i.e., Pester handels stand]. [n.p., 1790]
80 p. 16.5 cm.

1. Hungary - Economic conditions. 2. Hungary - Economic policy. 3. Hungary - Commerce.
I. Title. II. St   , P   H
III. Pester handels stand.

NL 0348744   MH-BA

VOLUME 332

HE
4779
.B6
G85
L7
     Liedemann, Kurt.
     Die Grosse Berliner strassenbahn, eine
studie zur privatwirtschaft der verkehrs-
unternehmungen ... Zürich, F.Lohbauer,
1918.
     viii,105 p. illus. 23cm.
     Inaug.-diss.--Bern.
     "Literatur": p.vii-viii.
     1.Grosse Berliner strassenbahn.

NL   0348745   MiU ICRL PU CtY IU

Liedén, Elizabeth
     see
     Liedén, Lizzie, 1873–

Liedén, Lizzie, 1873–
     Ledd av Guds hand; en missionärs självbiografi. Jönkö-
ping, Svenska alliansmissionens förlag ₁1954₎
     70 p. illus. 20 cm.

     I. Title.

     BV3269.L48A3   56–45111 ‡

NL   0348747   DLC CtY-D

Lieder, Benno [Ludwig].
     Die rechtliche natur des erbschaftsanspruchs
und sein verhältnis zu den singular-ansprüchen.
Königsberg Pr., 1926.
     (2)+56+(1) p.
     Inaug.-diss. --- Königsberg Pr.

NL   0348748   MH-L ICRL

Lieder, Francis.
     Miscellaneous writings. v. 1–2.   Philadel-
phia, J. B. Lippincott & Co., 1881.
     2 v.   1 portr.   8°.
     v. 1: Reminiscences, addresses and essays.
     v. 2: Contributions to political science.

NL   0348749   NN

Lieder, Franciszek, 1791–1867.
     Grammatyka niemiecka układu Franciszka Lieder ...
Wydanie 5. poprawne ... Warszawa, W drukarni J. Ja-
worskiego, 1862.
     2 p. l., 275, ₁1₎ p. 18¼ᶜᵐ.

     1. German language—Grammar—1800–1870.

                      10–27553†

     Library of Congress   PF3129.S6L5

NL   0348750   DLC

Lieder, Frans, pseud.
     see Cuypers, Firmin.

150
L718p
     Lieder, Franz.
     **Die psychische Energie und ihr Umsatz;
eine Philosophie des Seelenlebens.** Berlin,
E.Hofmann, 1910.
     vii,411p. 22cm.

     CONTENTS.-1.T.Das Gefühlsleben als ener-
getischer Prozess. Das Willensleben als
energetischer Prozess. Das Denken als energetischer Prozess. Gesamtseelische Erscheinungen.-2.T.Der Erkenntnisvorgang als energetischer Prozess.

     1.Psychology.   I.Title.

NL   0348752   CLSU CtY NjP MB MH ICJ ICRL

[LIEDER, Frederick William Charles.] 1881–
     Bayard Taylor's adaptation of Schiller's
Don Carlos. [Urbana,Ill.,University of Illinois
1917.]

     pp.26.
     "Reprinted from the Journal of English and
Germanic philology,vol.xvi,no.1,Jan.1917."
             AL 3621.030

NL   0348753   MH

Lieder, Frederick William Charles 1881– ed.
                  FOR OTHER EDITIONS
                  SEE MAIN ENTRY
Moser, Gustav von, 1825–1903.
     ... Der bibliothekar, schwank in vier akten. Edited with
exercises, notes and vocabulary by Frederick W. C. Lieder ...
₁Boston₎ Ginn and company ₁ᶜ1941₎

Lieder, Frederick William Charles, ed. ₁1881–₎

Schiller, Johann Christoph Friedrich von, 1759–1805.
     ... Schillers Don Carlos, infant von Spanien, ein dra-
matisches gedicht; ed. with introduction, bibliography,
appendices, notes, and index, by Frederick W. C. Lieder
... New York, Oxford university press, American branch;
₁etc., etc.₎ 1912.

Lieder, Frederick William Charles, 1881–
     ... The Don Carlos theme, by Frederick W. C. Lieder. The
Russian primary chronicle, by Samuel H. Cross. Cambridge,
Harvard university press, 1930.
     5 p. l., ₁3₎–320 p. fold. map. 23ᶜᵐ.   (Harvard studies and notes in
philology and literature, vol. xii)
     "The Don Carlos theme" gives a review of the Don Carlos litera-
ture. the books listed in chronological arrangement.
     The translation of the "Russian primary chronicle" is based upon the
text edited by E. F. Karski, published in 1926.   cf. p. 80.
     "Studies in which two or more treatments of the ₁Don Carlos₎ theme
are listed": p. 4; "Translations": p. 72–73.
     1. Carlos, prince of Asturias, 1545–1568—Bibl.   2. Russia—Hist.—
To 1533—Sources.   i. Nestor, annalist, d. 1115?   ii. Cross, Samuel
Hazzard, 1891–   tr. iii. Title.   iv. Title : The Russian primary chronicle.
     Library of Congress   PN35.H4   vol. xii   30—27837
                                          Provisional
     ——— Copy 2.   PN57.C3L5
     Copyright A 23742   ₁a37h1₎   (406.2)   809

     NcD IaU OU MiU OCU DDO MB MH NN ViU PBm
NL   0348756   DLC IdU OrPR CaBVaU MtU NIC WU MU PPEB

PT
2468
D9L71
     Lieder, Frederick William Charles, 1881–
     The Don Carlos theme in literature.
₁Urbana, Ill.₎ 1910.
     483-498 p. 23cm.

     Reprinted from the Journal of English and
Germanic philology, vol. IX, no. 4.

     1. Schiller, Johann Christoph Friedrich von,
1759–1805. Don Carlos.

NL   0348757   NIC

Lieder, Frederick William Charles, joint author

Howe, George Maxwell, 1873–
     ... First German reader, with notes, exercises, and vocabu-
lary, by G. M. Howe ... and F. W. C. Lieder ... Boston, New
York ₁etc.₎ D. C. Heath and company ₁ᶜ1930₎

---

arW
35389
     Lieder, Frederick William Charles, 1881–
     Friedrich Spe and the Théodicée of Leib-
niz. ₁Urbana, Ill., 1912₎
     50 p. 23cm.

     "Reprinted from the Journal of English
and Germanic Philology. v. 9, no. 3, 1912."

     1. Spee, Friedrich von, 1591–1635. 2.
Leibniz, Gottfried Wilhelm, Freiherr von,
1646–1716.

NL   0348759   NIC MH

LIEDER Frederick William Charles.
     Fridrich Spe: studies on the Trutz Nachtigal,
and on the relation between the Güldenes Tugend-
buch and Leibniz's Théodicée. Extracts pub.as
"Friedrich Spe and the Théodicée of Leibniz,"in
Journ.Eng.and Germ.Philol.,1912. 11:149–172,329–
354; and a small part as a review of Weinrich's
edition of Trutznachtigall,ibid.,1909,8:129–
134.
     Official copy of the thesis presented for a
doctor's degree at H.   U.

NL   0348760   MH

Lieder, Frederick William Charles, 1881–   *ed.*
     ... German poems and songs, edited with musical settings,
notes, vocabulary, table of authors and composers, and index
of titles and of first lines, by Frederick W. C. Lieder ... New
York ₁etc.₎ Oxford university press, 1929.
     xii, 300 p. 18¼ᶜᵐ.   (Oxford German series)

     1. German poetry (Collections)   2. Songs, German.   I. Title.

                                   29—21797

     Library of Congress   PT1155.L5

NL   0348761   DLC MtU CLU NIC FTaSU ViU

Z
8350
L71
     Lieder, Frederick William Charles, 1881–
     Goethe in England and America. ₁Urbana,
Ill., 1911₎
     ₁535₎-556 p. 24cm.

     Reprinted from the Journal of English and
Germanic philology, v. 10, no. 4, 1911.

     1. Goethe, Johann Wolfgang von--Bibl.

NL   0348762   NIC

Lieder, Frederick William Charles, ed.

Goethe, Johann Wolfgang von, 1749–1832.
     ... Goethe's Hermann und Dorothea, ed., with introduction,
appendices, notes, and vocabulary, by Frederick W. C. Lieder
... New York, Oxford university press, American branch;
₁etc., etc.₎ 1917.

VOLUME 332

Lieder, Frederick William Charles, 1881–
Manual of military German, by Frederick W. C. Lieder ... and Ray Waldron Pettengill ... Cambridge, Harvard university press; [etc., etc.] 1918.
vii, 364 p., 1 l. 19½ cm.
1. German language—Conversation and phrase books (for soldiers, etc.) 2. German language—Chrestomathies and readers (Military science) I. Pettengill, Ray Waldron, 1885– joint author. II. Title: Military German.
PF3120.S7L5 19—1270
NL 0348764 DLC NjP CU ViU MB OO MiU OU IdU

Lieder, Frederick William Charles, 1881– *ed.*
Popular German stories ... edited with notes and vocabulary by Frederick W. C. Lieder ... New York, F. S. Crofts & co., 1931.
vii, 221 p. 19½cm.
CONTENTS.—Hauff: Die geschichte von Kalif Storch.—Storm: Immensee.—Gerstäcker: Germelshausen.—Heyse: L'Arrabbiata.
I. Hauff, Wilhelm, 1802–1827. Die geschichte von Kalif Storch. II. Storm, Theodor, 1817–1888. Immensee. III. Gerstäcker, Friedrich Wilhelm Christian, 1816–1872. Germelshausen. IV. Heyse, Paul Johann Ludwig von, 1830–1914. L'Arrabbiata. V. Title.
Library of Congress PT1338.L5 31—5870
Copyright A 34359 [a37g1] 833.08
NL 0348765 DLC NN PPT NcD

Lieder, Frederick William Charles, ed.
Popular German stories. Edited with notes and vocabulary by Frederick W.C.Lieder. New York, F.S. Crofts, 1932.
NL 0348766 MH

Lieder, Frederick William Charles, 1881– *ed.*
Popular German stories ... edited, with notes, vocabulary, German questions, and composition exercises, by Frederick W. C. Lieder ... New York, F. S. Crofts & co., 1933.
vii, 259 p. 19½ cm.
"First printing, January, 1931 ... Fourth printing, February, 1933."
CONTENTS.—Hauff: Die geschichte von Kalif Storch.—Storm: Immensee.—Gerstäcker: Germelshausen.—Heyse: L'Arrabbiata.
I. Hauff, Wilhelm, 1802–1827. Die geschichte von Kalif Storch. II. Storm, Theodor, 1817–1888. Immensee. III. Gerstäcker, Friedrich Wilhelm Christian, 1816–1872. Germelshausen. IV. Heyse, Paul Johann Ludwig von, 1830–1914. L'Arrabbiata. V. Title.
PT1338.L5 1933 833.082 33—13630
NL 0348767 DLC IdB TxU AAP NcD

Lieder, Frederick William Charles, 1881– ed.
Popular German stories ... edited with notes, vocabulary, German questions and composition exercises, by .... New York, F.S. Crofts & Co.,
1944.
259 p.
"First printing Jan., 1931. Eleventh printing May, 1944.
NL 0348768 PU

Lieder, Frederick William Charles, 1881– ed.
Popular German stories ... edited with notes, vocabulary ... by Frederick W.C. Lieder ... New York, F.S. Crofts & co., 1947.
221 p.
NL 0348769 PPEB

Lieder, Frederick William Charles, 1881– tr.
Germany. *Reichsbank.*
... The Reichsbank, 1876–1900. Washington, Govt. print. off., 1910 [*i. e.* 1911]

Lieder, Paul Robert, 1889– *ed.*
The art of literary criticism [edited by] Paul Robert Lieder ... and Robert Withington ... New York, London, D. Appleton-Century company, incorporated [©1941]
xii, 689 p. 23cm.
"Some of the significant critical writing from Plato to our own day—excluding the work of living authors."—Pref.
Bibliography: p. 679–683.
1. Criticism. 2. Poetry. 3. Literature—Hist. & crit. I. Withington, Robert, 1884– joint ed. II. Title.
Library of Congress PN86.L5 41—9668
[10] 801
NL 0348771 OrSaW IdPI OrStbM NcRS NBuC OClMA WaSpG OrU OrP OrPR WaWW OrLgE CaBVaU WaT DLC PU PSC ViU PPD PSt OClW PPT MiU CU

Lieder, Paul Robert, 1889– *ed.*
The art of literary criticism [edited by] Paul Robert Lieder ... and Robert Withington ... New York, Appleton-Century-Crofts [195-?]
xii, 689 p. 23 cm.
"Some of the significant critical writing from Plato to our own
NL 0348772 ViU MB

Lieder, Paul Robert, 1889– *ed.*
British drama; ten plays, from the middle of the fourteenth century to the end of the nineteenth, edited by Paul Robert Lieder ... Robert Morss Lovett ... [and] Robert Kilburn Root ... Boston, New York [etc.] Houghton Mifflin company [©1929]
iv p., 2 l., [3]–374 p. 22½cm.
"A companion volume to the editors' British poetry and prose."—Pref.
CONTENTS.—The Brome Abraham and Isaac.—The second shepherds' play.—Everyman.—The tragical history of Dr. Faustus, by Christopher Marlowe.—The alchemist, by Ben Jonson.—Philaster; or Love lies a-bleeding, by Beaumont and Fletcher.—All for love; or, The world well lost, by John Dryden.—The way of the world, by William Congreve.—The school for scandal, by R. B. Sheridan.—Lady Windermere's fan, by Oscar Wilde.
1. English drama (Collections) I. Lovett, Robert Morss, 1870– joint ed. II. Root, Robert Kilburn, 1877– joint ed. III. Title.
PR1245.L45 29—19007
NL 0348774 WaS MtU OrLgE CaBVaU WaSpG DLC IdU WaU IU NcD NN MH NcC ViU TU GU

Lieder, Paul Robert, 1889– *ed.*
British poetry and prose; a book of readings ... edited by Paul Robert Lieder ... Robert Morss Lovett ... Robert Kilburn Root ... Boston, New York [etc.] Houghton Mifflin company [©1928–
v. 23 cm.
1. English literature (Collections) I. Lovett, Robert Morss, 1870– joint ed. II. Root, Robert Kilburn, 1877– joint ed.
PR1109.L5 28—25872
NL 0348775 OCX ViU NcD CoU LU IU KU AAP WaU MB NcRS NBC DLC MtBC OrU OrLgE OrMonO OrCS IdU ViU

Lieder, Paul Robert, 1889– *ed.*
British poetry and prose. Rev. ed. Edited by Paul Robert Lieder ... Robert Morss Lovett ... [and] Robert Kilburn Root ... Boston, New York [etc.] Houghton Mifflin company [©1938]
2 v. double front., maps. 25 cm.
CONTENTS.—v. 1. From Beowulf to Blake.—v. 2. From Wadsworth to Yeats.
1. English literature (Collections) I. Lovett, Robert Morss, 1870–1956, joint ed. II. Root, Robert Kilburn, 1877– joint ed. III. Title.
PR1109.L5 1938 820.822 38—13386
NL 0348776 WaS WaWW CaBVa Wa DLC GU OClU AAP TU FMU FU OrU OrP IdU

Lieder, Paul Robert, 1889– *ed.*
British poetry and prose, edited by Paul Robert Lieder, Robert Morss Lovett [and] Robert Kilburn Root. 3d ed. Boston, Houghton Mifflin [1950]
2 v. illus., ports., maps, facsims. 25 cm.
CONTENTS.—v. 1. From Beowulf to Blake.—v. 2. From Wordsworth to Spender.
1. English literature (Collections) I. Title.
PR1109.L5 1950 820.82 50—7020 rev
NL 0348777 WaT PRosC GU FTaSU OrP Or OrCS OrAshS MtBC WaSpG WaS DLC NcU IU FU LU UU NBuU NcD TU CU OCl

Lieder, Paul Robert, joint ed.
Matthews, Brander, 1852–1929, *ed.*
The chief British dramatists, excluding Shakespeare; twenty-five plays from the middle of the fifteenth century to the end of the nineteenth, edited by Brander Matthews ... and Paul Robert Lieder ... Boston, New York [etc.] Houghton Mifflin company [©1924]

Lieder, Paul Robert, 1889– *ed.*
Eminent British poets of the nineteenth century. Complete ed.: Wordsworth to Housman. Edited by Paul Robert Lieder ... New York and London, Harper & brothers, 1938.
xxviii, 655, lv, 759 p. 24cm.
"First edition."
Includes biographies and bibliographies of the poets.
CONTENTS.—The early nineteenth century.—The later nineteenth century.
1. English poetry—19th cent. I. Title.
Library of Congress PR1221.L47 38—13385
Copyright A 117777 [5] 821.70822
NL 0348779 WaS CaBVa CLSU MB NIC FMU ICarbS OU ViU IU MH PU PP DLC NcD TNJ TxU NcRS WaU WaSpG WaSp OrP

Lieder, Paul Robert, ed.
Tegnér, Esaias, 1782–1846.
Poems by Tegnér: The children of the Lord's supper, tr. from the Swedish by Henry Wadsworth Longfellow; and Frithiof's saga, tr. by Rev. W. Lewery Blackley; with an introduction by Paul Robert Lieder ... New York, The American-Scandinavian foundation, 1914.

LIEDER, Paul Robert.
Scandinavian influences on English literature, 1815-1850.
Official copy of a thesis presented for the doctor's degree at Harvard University.
NL 0348781 MH

Lieder, Paul Robert, 1889–
... Scott and Scandinavian literature, by Paul Robert Lieder ...
(*In* Smith college studies in modern languages ... Northampton, Mass. [1920] 22½cm. vol. II, no. 1, p. [8]–57)
1. Scott, Sir Walter, bart., 1771–1832. 2. Literature, Comparative—English and Scandinavian. 3. Literature, Comparative—Scandinavian and English.
Library of Congress PB13.S6 vol. II, no. 1 22—6951
——— Copy 2. PR5340.L5
NL 0348782 DLC NIC MU NcD ViU MH OrU OrPR

VOLUME 332

Lieder, Walter, 1909–
　　Lutheran dictionary. St. Louis, Concordia Pub. House
　　₍1952₎
　　　47 p. 21 cm.

　1. Lutheran Church—Dictionaries.　ɪ. Title.

BX8007.L5　　　　203　　　　53–222

NL　0348783　　DLC

W 4　　**LIEDER-MRAZEK, Michael,** 1923–
M96　　　Die Häufigkeit der Tubenendometriose
1950　　bei der Tubargravidität. München, 1950.
　　　35 *l*.
　　　Inaug.-Diss. - Munich.
　　　　1. Endometriosis　2. Fallopian tubes
　　　3. Pregnancy - Ectopic

NL　0348784　　DNLM

W 4　　**LIEDER-MRAZEK, Sara,** 1923–
M96　　　Der plötzliche Tod bei Kindern und
1950　　Jugendlichen. München, 1950.
　　　50 *l*. illus.
　　　Inaug.-Diss. - Munich.
　　　　1. Death - Sudden

NL　0348785　　DNLM

דער ליעדער אלבום. א זאמלונג פון אלע אידישע מעהראסטער ליעדער.
The song-album.
קאמצערם ליעדער. קופלעטען און פאלקס ליעדער.
New York ₍n. d.₎ ניו יארק, ראזענבוים און זיורבעלאוומסקי.
　　v. 19 cm.
In Yiddish.
Without the music.
Contents.—　　　　　　1. בוך. אלע מעהראסטער ליעדער.

　1. Songs, Jewish.　　*Title transliterated:* Der lieder album.

M1852.L5　　　　　　　　M 55–632

NL　0348786　　DLC OCl

Lieder aus dem Gesangbuch fur die evangelisch-
protestantische Kirche in Baden
　　see under　Evangelische Landeskirche in
Baden.

Lieder aus dem Metzer lande
　　see under　Erbrich, Emil, tr.

Lieder aus dem rinnstein
　　see under　Ostwald, Hans Otto August,
1873–1940, ed.

Lieder aus dem Tagebuch eines dänischen Soldaten ...
　　see under　Lobedanz, Edmund Adolph
Johannes.

LIEDER aus der Fremde. In Beiträgen von
Friedrich Bodenstedt, Adolf Ellissen, Ferdinand
Freiligrath, [and others]. Hannover, C. Rümpler,
1857.
　　18.5 cm.

NL　0348791　　MH

Lieder aus der Mimik, Judith und Holofernes;
oder, die Jungfrau von Judäa von Fusel, zur
Feier des 25. Stiftungs-Festes des A.J.G.V.
₍Berlin: E.Baruch₎1908.
　　15 p.

　Bd. with: Akademischer Verein fuer juedische
Geschichte und Litteratur, Berlin. Lieder fuer
den Festkommers ...Berlin,1908.

NL　0348792　　OCH

Lieder bei der Gutenbergs-foier in Königsberg.
Den 5. december 1840. ₍Königsberg₎ Dalkowski
₍1840₎
　　cover-title, ₍8₎ p. 20½ cm.

　1. Printing - History - Celebrations of invention.

NL　0348793　　NNC

Lieder bey einem Hochamte.
　　16 p.　18.5 cm.
　　Lacks title page.

NL　0348794　　NNUT

Lieder Buch. ₍Gedruckt im Internierungslager₎ Baviaans-
poort, Süd-Afrika ₍1940₎
　　53 l. illus. 18 x 23 cm.
　　Without the music.

　1. Nationalsozialistische Deutsche Arbeiter-Partei — Songs and
music.

M1734.L692　　　　　　　M 55–625 ‡

NL　0348795　　DLC

830.81　Lieder büchlein/ darin begriffen sind zwey hundert
L6232　　vnd sechtzig/ allerhandt schöner weltlichen lie-
1580f　　der/ allen jungen gesellen vnd züchtigen jung
　　frauwen zum newen jar/ in druck verfertiget.
　　Auffs neuw gemehret mit vil schönen liedern/ die
　　in den andern zuvor aussgegangenen drücken/
　　nicht gefunden werden　　　Gedruckt zu Franck
　　furt am Mayn, 1580.
　　facsim.: 117 mounted l.

　Colophon: Gedruckt zu Franckfurt am Mayn/ durch
Nicolaum Basseum/ Jm iar/ 1580.

　Photographic reproduction of the copy, Pal.V.
468, no.2, in the Biblioteca vaticana.
　Collation of original as reproduced: 116 l.;
signatures: A-O⁸, P⁴.
　Compiled for the printer, Nikolaus Basse.

　1. German ballads and songs.　2. Folk-songs,
German.　3. German poetry--Early modern (to 1700)
I. Basse, Nikolaus, fl.1580-1600.

NL　0348797　　IU

830.81　Lieder büchlein/ darinn begriffen sind zwey hun-
L6233　　dert vnd sechtzig/ allerhand schöner weltlichen
1582f　　lieder/ allen jungen gesellen vnd züchtigen
　　jungfrawen/ zum newen jar/ in druck verferti-
　　get. Auffs newe gemehret mit viel schönen lie-
　　dern/ die in den andern zuvor aussgegangenen
　　drücken/ die nicht gefunden werden　　n.p., 1582.
　　facsim.: 127 sheets on 64 l.
　Photographic reproduction of the copy preserved
in a volume designated "Vexierbuch" in the Kunst-
historisches museum, Vienna.

　Collation of original as reproduced: 127 l.;
signatures: A-P⁸, Q⁷.
　Designated "Ambraser liederbuch" by Joseph
Bergmann, and "Liederbuch 1582A" by Arthur Kopp.

　1. German ballads and songs.　2. Folk-songs,
German.　3. German poetry--Early modern (to 1700)
I. Ambraser liederbuch.

NL　0348799　　IU

830.81　Lieder büchlein/ darin begriffen sind/ zwey hun-
L6232　　dertzwey vnd sechtzig/ allerhand schöner welt-
1584f　　licher lieder/ allen jungen gesellen vnd züchti-
　　gen jungfrauwen zum neuwen jar/ in druck verfer-
　　tiget. Auffs neuw gemehret mit viel schönen lie-
　　dern/ die in den andern zuvor aussgegangenen
　　drücken/ nicht gefunden werden　　Gedruckt zu
　　Franckfurt am Mayn/ 1584.
　　facsim.: 117 sheets on 59 l.
　Colophon: Gedruckt zu Franckfurt am Mayn/ durch
Nicolaum Basseum/ Jm jar/ 1584.
　Composite photographic reproduction from two

copies, namely sig.A-O from the copy, 8° P. germ.
1034 (Cm.62) in the Universitätsbibliothek, Munich, and sig. P from the only known complete
copy, Auct. Germ. Coll. 412, in the Stadtbibliothek, Frankfurt am Main.
　Collation of the composite copy as reproduced:
116 l.; signatures: A-O⁸, P⁴. Reproduction shows
also, from the Munich copy, page with manuscript
notes facing sig.O⁵ verso.
　Compiled for the　　　　　printer, Nikolaus Basse.

NL　0348801　　IU OCl

830.81　Lieder büchlin/ zwey hundert vnd LVII. aller-
L6235　　handt schöner ausserlesener/ weltlicher lieder/
　　allen jungen gesellen vnd züchtigen jungfrawen
　　zum newen jar in truck verfertigt. Auffs newe
　　gemehrt/ mit vilen schönen liedern/ die in an-
　　dern liederbüchern nit gefunden werden.　Zu
　　Cöllen/ in der Margardengassen/ Bey Henrich
　　Nettessem ₍1580?₎
　　facsim.: 98 mounted l.
　Photographic reproduction of copy, Pal.V.468,
no.1, in the Biblioteca vaticana.
　Collation of original as reproduced: 96 l.; sig-

natures: A-M⁸. Reproduction shows also ₍5₎p. preceding first leaf, of these the 1st, 4th and 5th
are blank and the 2d and 3d have manuscript verse.

　1. German ballads and songs.　2. Folk-songs,
German.　3. German poetry--Early modern (to 1700)

NL　0348803　　IU

830.81　Lieder büchlin/ zwey hundert/ ausserlesene newe
L6235　　lieder/ allen jungen gesellen vnd züchtigen
1582f　　jungfrawen/ zum newen jar getruckt/ mit jhren
　　melodeyen/ sampt einem register. Vormals nie
　　inn truck aussgangen. ₍n.p.₎ 1582.
　　facsim.: 81 sheets on 42 l.

　Photographic reproduction of the unique copy,
Yd 5041, in the Preussische staatsbibliothek,
Berlin.
　Collation of original as reproduced: 80 l.;
signatures: A-K⁸. Reproduction shows also ₍3₎p.

Continued in next column

VOLUME 332

Continued from preceding column

preceding first leaf, the 1st and 3d of these are
blank, the 2d has a manuscript note.
Known as "Liederbuchlein 1582B".

1. German ballads and songs. 2. Folk-songs,
German. 3. German poetry--Early modern (to 1700)

NL 0348805   IU

Lieder der Deutschen
see under   [Ramler, Karl Wilhelm] 1725-
1798, ed.

Lieder der Deutschen.   Zürich, Orell,
Gessner, Füssli und comp. 1784
see under   [Füssli, Johann
Heinrich] 1745-1832.

Lieder der deutschen Mystik
see under   Bernhart, Joseph, 1881-
ed.

PT
1229   Lieder der Deutschen zu Erbauung. Hamburg,
.L54   Buchenröder und Ritter, 1774.
520p. 17cm.

1. German poetry - Collections. 2. Religious
poetry, German - Collections.

NL 0348809   TNJ

Lieder der Florinesen...
see under   Heerkens, Petrus Martinus,
1897-1944, comp.

Lieder der Freiheitskriege
see under   Glässer, Paul, ed.

Lieder der Freunde. Bad Pyrmont, Quäkerverlag,
[193-?]

NL 0348812   PHC

Lieder der Freunde der geselligen Freude, mit
Begleitung des Forte-Piano, den hiesigen
sämmtlichen Herrn Bürger-Capitains zugeeignet
... Hamburg, J.A.Böhme[179-?]
42p. 22cm.
Contents on inside back cover.

NL 0348813   CtY

841.6
L718   *Lieder der Freyheit gewidmet; Beytrag zur
Unterhaltung für gebildetere Stände. Altona, Verlagsgesellschaft, 1795.*
· 96p. 17cm.

French and German.

1. Revolutionary poetry, French. I. Title.

NL 0348814   IEN

Lieder der Gegenwart
see under   [Gottschall, Rudolf von] 1823-
1909.

LIEDER der grossen Carnevals-Gesellschaft
bei Harff auf'm Domhofe,1845. n.p.,F.X.
Schlösser,[1845].

19 cm. pp.65-152.
Paper cover serves as title-page.
Inserted at end are 12 pages entitled "1842.
Neue Lieder",and 4 pages "Kölnisches Quodlibet".

NL 0348816   MH

Die Lieder der Heidelberger Handschrift Pal. 343
see   Volks- und Gesellschaftslieder des
XV. und XVI. Jahrhunderts. I. Die Lieder der
Heidelberger Handschrift Pal. 343.

Lieder der Heimat.   Berlin, P. Schaeffer [194-]
15 p. 30 cm.
Principally for voice and piano.

1. Music, Popular (Songs, etc.)—Germany.

M1735.18.L5   52-27607

NL 0348818   DLC NN MB IaU

Lieder der Hudhailiten ...
see under   [al-Sukkarī, Abu Saʿīd
al-Ḥasan ibn al-Husayn, 827 or 8-888 or 9.

Die lieder der Hutterischen brüder, gesangbuch ...
see under   Hutterite brethren.

Lieder der Landsknechte.   Leipzig: Insel-Verlag[, 1915].   83 p.   **NFK**
illus. 12°. (Insel-Bücherei. Nr. 158.)
Compiled by F. A. Hünich.

194519A. 1. Poetry, German—Col-   lections. 2. Huenich, Fritz Adolf,
1885-   , compiler.
N. Y. P. L.   June 8, 1926

NL 0348821   NN WaU CoFS

PT1231
L6L5   Lieder der Liebe; der Freude; und des ge-
1810   selligen Vergnügens.   Pest, J. Leyrer, 1810.
4 v. in 1.

Without music.

1. Love poetry. 2. German ballads and
songs.

NL 0348822   CU

Die lieder der mönche und nonnen Gotamo
Buddhos
see under   Theragāthā.

SPECIAL
COLLECTIONS
HX
8641   Die lieder der Mormonin. 2. Aufl.   Leip-
L54   zig, H. Dürselen, 1887.
1887   97 p.

Printed on single sheets pasted end-to-end
and carried on two spindles of turned wood,
each of which bears labels giving the title
of the work and the imprint. The "pages" are
numbered.
Pages 53-55 and 94-96 are wanting.

NL 0348824   CU-I

Lieder der Sowjet-Heimat. [Moskau] Deutsche Zentral-Zeitung [19—]
7 p. 28 cm.
Unacc. melodies.

1. National songs, Russian. 2. Communism—Songs and music.

M1756.L714   52-25347

NL 0348825   DLC

Lieder der spanischen Revolution. [Moskau] Verlag Deutsche-
Zentral-Zeitung [1937]
7 p. 21 cm.
Unacc. melodies.

1. Spain—Hist.—Civil War, 1936-1939—Songs and music.

M1779.L7   50-52799

NL 0348826   DLC

4PT   Lieder der Steingrube. [
Ger.-   56 p.
2181

NL 0348827   DLC-P4

Lieder der UdSSR. Lieder um Stalin
see under   [Busch, Ernst] 1900-   ed.

Lieder der Wehmuth und der Trauer. Eine Anthologie für Geist
und Gemüth. Zweite wohlfeilere Ausgabe.   Leipzig: I. Müller,
1819.   1 p.l., x p., 1 l., 216 p.   16°.

1. Poetry (German).—Collections.
N. Y. P. L.   September 23, 1919.

NL 0348829   NN

VOLUME 332

PT1217   Lieder der Zeit. Stuttgart, A. Krabbe, 1841.
.L7   v, 208 p.

    1. Political ballads and songs, German.
2. Germany--Hist.--1815-1866--Poetry.

NL   0348830   ICU CU

4M-132   Lieder des Bundes. [Plauen i. V., G. Wolff,
     1933]

NL   0348831   DLC-P4

Die lieder des Mirza-Schaffy, ⟨pseud.⟩

  See *under*

⟨Bodenstedt, Friedrich Martin von⟩

Lieder des Trostes. Oelzweige auf Soldatengräber...   Stuttgart: W. Nitzschke ₍186-?₎   112 p.   16cm.

176441B. 1. Poetry, German—   Collections. 2. Death—Consolation.
N.Y.P.L.   April 30, 1943

NL   0348833   NN

Lieder des Volkes; Erbe und Aussaat
     see under   Jung, Theo, 1897-   ed.

Lieder die wir sangen
     see under   Germany. Heer. 2. Garde
Fussartillerie Regiment. 1. Bataillon.

... Lieder die zur christlichen Glaubens-Lehre
gehören ... No pub., n. d.
952 ₍71₎ p.

T.-p. lacking.
Includes music.
Pt. 2 has title: Lieder die zur christlichen
Sittenlehre gehören.
Bound with this; Evangelien und Episteln auf
alle Sonn- und Festtage durch ganze Jahr. Incom-
plete.

NL   0348836   MiD

Lieder einer früh vollendeten
     see under   [Karbe, Anna] 1852-1875.

Lieder einer Verborgenen
     see under   [Heusser, Meta (Schweizer)]
1797-1876.

Lieder eines deutschen Barden
     see   Heggelbacher, Maximilian Anton,
comp.
       Den Freund- und Freundinen des Gesanges.

PT1231
.S6L7   Lieder eines freiwilligen. Gedichte von August S. ...
     Freiw. im v. d. Tann'schen corps. Hamburg, Druck von J.
     C. M. Köhler, 1848.
       105, ₍4₎ p. 13x11ᶜᵐ.

NL   0348840   ICU

Lieder eines kosmopolitischen nachtwächters
     see under   [Dingelstedt, Franz, freiherr
von] 1814-1881.

Lieder eines malers, mit randzeichnungen seiner
freunde
     see under   [Reinick, Robert] 1805-1852.

Lieder eines norddeutschen Poeten
     see under   [Glassbrenner, Adolf] 1810-
1876.

Lieder, Fabeln und Romanzen, Leipzig, 1758
     see under   [Gleim, Johann Wilhelm Ludwig]
1719-1803.

Lieder für Bergleute; gesammelt und hrsg. von
der Gesellschaft "Glück auf, Arschleder" zu
Berlin, W. Moeser, 1859.
120 p.

NL   0348845   MiD

... Lieder für Christen
     see under   Meister, Christoph Georg Lude-
wig, 1738-1811.

Lieder für das Volk.

  See *under*

⟨Gleim, Johann Wilhelm Ludwig⟩ 1719-1803.

LIEDER für den festcommers der studentenschaft zu der feier des neunzigsten geburt-
stages des kaisers, am 21. märz 1887. Berlin,
[1887].

NL   0348848   MH

Lieder für den Militär-Gottesdienst in Lodz ... 5./4, 9./5, 1915.
— [Lodz. 1915.] 2 v. in 1. 25 cm.

L9851 — European War, 1914- . Poetry and song. German.

NL   0348849   MB

Lieder für den öffentlichen Gottesdienst...
     see under   Dietrich, Johann Samuel.

Y   LIEDER für die Deutschen Amerika's.   Detroit,
9584   1916.
.4998   cover-title, 23p. 18cm.

     Contains advertising.
     German and English.

NL   0348851   ICN

Lieder für die freiwillige Schaar des Herzogs von
Weimar. Von F.M. ... Weimar, 1814.
16 p.   20.5 cm.
     Der Ertrag ist zum Besten der freiwilligen
Schaar im Felde bestimmt.

NL   0348852   CtY

Lieder für die Jugend der Evangelischen Gemeinden in
Frankfurt a. M. Frankfurt am Main, 1946.
112 p. 15 cm.
Without the music.

1. Hymns, German.

BV482.L5   51-37237

NL   0348853   DLC CtY NN

Lieder für die Versammlungen der Evangelischen
Allianz in Basel
     see under   Evangelical alliance.

Lieder für eidsgenössische krieger...
[6],64p. Bern, C. A. Jenni, 1822.

     Title-page, engr.
     Contains music.
     Contains the Joliet book-plate.

NL   0348855   OCl

Lieder für Frauengruppen; herausgegeben von der Reichsfrauenführung.
Nr.

Potsdam ₍193   nos.   illus.   19cm.
Nos. 6—   dated Sept. 1937 –

1. Choral music, Secular—Women   —Collections. 2. Political music—
Germany.   I. Deutsche Arbeitsfront.   Frauenamt. II. Nationalsozia-
listische deutsche Arbeitspartei.   Reichsfrauenführung. III. Lieder für
Werk-Frauengruppen.   Frauengruppen.
N.Y.P.L.   November 15, 1945

Melodies, in part accompanied.
Occasional issues have also special titles.
Title varies: Nr.   Lieder für Werk-Frauengruppen; herausgegeben vom Frau-
enamt der Deutschen Arbeitsfront.
Nr.   Lieder für Frauengruppen; herausgegeben von der Reichsfrauen-
führung.

NL   0348857   NN

VOLUME 332

HS   Lieder für die Freimäurer-Logen in
454   Deutschland.   Hamburg, 1776.
L71   66 p. 15cm.

1. Freemasons--Songs.

NL   0348858   NIC

Lieder für Freunde der geselligen Freude,
mit Begleitung des Forte-Piano, den hiesigen
sämmtlichen Herrn Bürger-Capitains zugeeignet ... Hamburg,J.A.Böhm[179-?]
42p. 22cm.
Contents on inside back cover.
[reprint of Friedländer 449]
School of Music Library, Yale University

NL   0348859   CtY-Mus

Lieder für Kinder
     see under   [Weisse, Christian Felix]
1726-1804.

Lieder für Kleinkinderschulen ...
     see under   Svoboda, Jan, 1803-1844.

-sVM   [LIEDER für vier stimmen]   n.p.,n.d.
1579.4   4 pts.
L 71
     For soprano, alto, tenor, and bass, unaccom-
panied.
     Contents.—Jägerchor a. d. drama Rosamunde.
Schubert.—Lebenslust. Schubert.—Schon gut!
Oelschlaeger.—Die nixen. Oelschlaeger.—Mai-
königin. Billeter.—Romanze. Bruch.—Sturm und
frieden. Taubert.
     Imperfect: all after first portion of Die
nixen missing from   alto part.

NL   0348862   ICN

Lieder für Werk-Frauengruppen
     see   Lieder für Frauengruppen;

Lieder für Werktätige
     see under   Freier Deutscher Gewerkschafts-
bund.

Lieder geselliger Freude.

     See *under*

[Reichardt, Johan Friedrich] 1752-1814, comp.

Lieder gesungen bei der Feier des 15 Jährigen
     Stiftungsfestes ... Mittwock den 29. November
     1899
         see under   Gabelsberger Shorthand Society,
New York.

Lieder gesungen bei der Gabelsberger-Feier ...
     Sonnabend, den 12. Februar 1898
         see under   Gabelsberger Shorthand Society,
New York.

Lieder gesungen bei der Gabelsberger-Feier ...
     Sonnabend, den 25. Februar 1899
         see under   Gabelsberger Shorthand Society,
New York.

Lieder im höheren Chor,.. 1871.
     see under
     Krummacher, Friedrich Wilhelm, 1796-1868.

Lieder in der mundart des Salzburger-flach-
     landes.   1845
         see under   Pichler, Georg Abdon,
1806-1864.

... Lieder in Kranckheiten wie auch vom Tode,
     jüngsten Gericht, Himmel, Hölle und der
     Ewigkeit.   1765
         see under   Moser, Johann Jakob, 1701-1785.

Lieder in schwäbischer volksprache
     see under   [Hoser, H.]

Lieder mit melodien. Anspach, Posch, 1758.
The title is within engraved border.

Folk-songs–German||AcS 185761

NL   0348873   MH

Lieder, mit neuen Melodien.   Anspach: J. C. Posch, 1756.
25 p.   obl. 8°.
     German words; music on 2 staves, voice and bass, unfigured.
     Title of first song is: Lob der Tonkunst, beginning: "Beym Schall der freudigen
Schallmeyen."

476350A.   1. Songs, German.
N.Y.P.L.   May 21, 1930

NL   0348874   NN

Die Lieder Sineds [anagr.] des Barden...
     Wien, 1772.

     see

[Denis, Michael,] 1729-1800.

830.81
M5691   Lieder teutscher jugend.   Stuttgart,
     I. B. Metzler, 1822.
     127p.

NL   0348876   IU

Lieder teutscher Jugend.   Zweite umgearbeitete
     Auflage.   Stuttgart, In der J. B. Metzler'schen
     Buchhandlung, 1833.
     viii, 124 p.   12.5 cm.
     Gustav Benjamin Schwab's copy, with his
name inscribed on t.-p.
     Interleaved with ms. music, in a hand-
writing unidentified, but possibly by G. B.
Schwab.
     "Anhang," 32 p. in ms. in the same hand-
writing, bound at end.

NL   0348877   CtY

VS45   **Lieder über die Berg-Predigt Jesu, Matthäi 5.6.**
H14   **und 7. Kapitel. Aus Veranlassung geschrieben von**
1819   **Johann Michael Hahn...** 1819.
         see under
     Hahn, Johann Michael, 1758-1819.

PT1204.5   [Lieder und Arien.   v.p., 1813?-1850?]
R9   40 nos. in 1v. 17cm.
     Collections of 3-7 songs and arias each,
from various places and publishers, bound
together and variously entitled "Sechs schöne
Lieder und Arien," "Neue Arien und Lieder,"
"Fünf neue schöne Lieder," etc.

     1.Folk-songs, German.

NL   0348879   CSt

Lieder und Bilder aus der Schweiz
     see under   Reinick, Robert.

Lieder und bilder für jung und alt
     see under   Cologne. Jugendschriftenaus-
schuss.

Lieder und Chöre zur Feiergestaltung. Berlin, Volk und
Wissen Verlag, 1949.
     64 p. 23 cm.
     Communist songs for voices and instruments.
     Errata slip inserted.

     1. Songs, German.   2. Communism—Songs and music.

     M1734.L69   M 53-226

NL   0348882   DLC

Lieder und erzählungen
     see under   Patzke, Johann Samuel.

Lieder und Gedichte zum gebrauch für
     Versammlung ...
         see under   Schünemann-Pott, Friedrich.

VOLUME 332

Lieder und gesänge für freimaurer
    see under   Freemasons. Germany.
Grosse National-Mutterloge zu den Drei Welt-
kugeln.

Lieder-und Kommersbuch fürs deutsche Haus
    see under   Aus der Jugend-Zeit.

ML184
.R94
1969

Die Lieder und Melodien der Geissler des Jahres
1349.

Runge, Paul, 1848–1911.
    Die Lieder und Melodien der Geiseler des Jahres 1349.
Nach der Aufzeichnung Hugo's von Reutlingen. Nebst
einer Abhandlung über die italienischen Geisslerlieder von
Heinrich Schneegans und einem Beitrage zur Geschichte
der deutschen und niederländischen Geissler von Heino
Pfannenschmid. Hrsg. von Paul Runge. (Reprografischer
Nachdruck der Ausg. Leipzig, Breitkopf und Härtel, 1900.)
Hildesheim, G. Olms; Wiesbaden, Breitkopf u. Härtel, 1969.

Lieder und Reime in fliegenden Blättern des 16. und 17. Jahrhunderts.
Teil 1

Strassburg: I. H. E. Heitz (Heitz u. Mündel), 1911   23½cm.
v. facsims.
DLC: PT1201.B5

1. Songs, German—Collections.   2. Poetry, German—Collections.
N.Y.P.L.   October 9, 1936

NL 0348888   NN DLC

Lieder und scherzgedichte... *Altona, 1757*
    see under   [Leyding, Johann Dieterich]
1721-1781.

Lieder und schwänke aus der deutschen vergangenheit,
    mit bildern von Bernhard Wenig, Georg Barlösius und
    Franz Stassen ... Berlin, Fischer und Franke [1900]
    4 pt. in 1 v. illus. 19½ x 16½ᶜᵐ. (*Added t.-p.:* Jungbrunnen, ein schatz
    bey alter deutscher kunst und dichtung. (2. bd.))
    CONTENTS.—[pt. 1] Lieder der minnesänger ins hochdeutsche übertragen
    von E. Escherich, in bildern von Bernhard Wenig.—[pt. 2] Des weyland
    Nürnberger handwerksmeisters Hans Sachsens lustige schwänke, mit bil-
    dern verziert von Georg Barlösius.—[pt. 3] Allerlei teufelsschwänte, mit
    bildern verziert von Georg Barlösius.—[pt. 4] Romanzen, balladen, legen-
    den, in bildern von Franz Stassen.
    1. German poetry—Middle High German—Translations into German
    (Modern) 2. German poetry—Translations from Middle High German.
    3. German poetry—Early modern (to 1700) 4. German wit and humor.
    I. Escherich, Frau Emilie, 1856–   tr.   II. Wenig, Bernhard, illus.
    III. Sachs, Hans, 1494–   1576.   IV. Barlösius, Georg, illus.
    v. Stassen, Franz, 1869–   illus.
                                                          G-2010 Revised
    Library of Congress   PT1394.L5

NL 0348890   DLC OC1

PT
1155
L5

Lieder- und Spruchbuch für die Thurgauischen
Primarschulen. Frauenfeld, J. Huber[18--?]
92p. illus. 17cm.

    1. German poetry (Collections).
    2. Children's poetry, German.

NL 0348891   MU

Lieder und Tänze auf die Lauten...
        see under   Bischoff, Heinz, ed.

LIEDER und Weisen des alten und neuen
Vaterlands, den Deutsch - Amerikanern gewidmet.
New York,etc.,C.Fischer,1914.

23 cm. pp.(2),40.
Paper cover serves as title-page.

NL 0348893   MH

Lieder unserer Soldaten.   Berlin: A. Juncker, 1914.   62(1) p.
illus. (partly col'd) 24°. (Orplid-Bücher. Bd. 11.)
On cover: Soldaten-Lieder neu gedruckt im Kriegsjahr 1914.

1. War songs (German). 2.   Songs (National): German. 3.
Series.
N.Y.P.L.   August 26, 1915.

NL 0348894   NN NjP IEN

Lieder unserer Zeit. Berlin, A. Bennefeld [194–] Pl. no.
E. M. 700.
39 p. 31 cm.
Principally for voice and piano.

1. Music, Popular (Songs, etc.)—Germany.

M1735.18.L55   M 55–496

NL 0348895   DLC

M1734
G34L5

Lieder unseres Volkes.   Berlin, Deutscher
Schul-Verlag [n.d.]
184p. illus. 19cm.

Principally for 1-2 voices.
"Herausgegeben von Hermann Peter Gericke,
Hugo Moser [und] Alfred Quellmalz."
"Die zweite Stimme schrieb Fritz Dietrich."-
p.179.

NL 0348896   IaU

M
784.4943
G315L

Lieder unseres Volkes. Ausg. für das
Ausland. Kassel, Bärenreiter, 1938.
176 p. illus. (Bärenreiter Ausgabe 1370)

Principally for 1-2 voices.
"Herausgegeben von Hermann Peter Gericke,
Hugo Moser [und] Alfred Quellmalz."
"Die zweite Stimme schrieb Fritz
Dietrich." - p.171.

Includes music manuscript paper.
"Aus der Geschichte der Volksliedsammlung
und -forschung": p.167-170.

NL 0348898   WaU FTaSU

Lieder unseres Volkes. [Hrsg. von Hermann Peter Gericke,
Hugo Moser, und Alfred Quellmalz] Reichsdeutsche Ausg.
Kassel, Bärenreiter-Verlag, 1941.
184 p. 19 cm. (B[ärenreiter]–A[usgabe] 1250)
For 1-2 voices.

1. Folk-songs, German.   I. Gericke, Hermann Peter, 1902–   ed.
II. Moser, Hugo, ed. III. Quellmalz, Alfred, ed.

M1734.L689 1941   45–34244 rev/M

      NjP NN NRU NcD
NL 0348899   DLC MB IEN NNC MH IU TxHR NNM LU CoDU

Lieder unseres volkes. Reichsdeutsche ausg.
... Kassel, Bärenreiter-verlag, 1943.
184 p. illus. 18 cm. (B[ärenreiter]–
a[usgabe] 1250)
Principally for 1 - 2 voices.
"Hrsg. von Hermann Peter Gericke, Hugo
Moser [und] Alfred Quellmalz."
"Die zweite stimme schrieb Fritz Deitrich."
p. 179.

NL 0348900   OCU

Lieder vom Tod und Sterben, 1757.

NL 0348901   PPeSchw

Lieder vom Tod und Sterben, cpd., 1758.

NL 0348902   PPeSchw

Lieder vom Tod und Sterben, cpd, 1760.

NL 0348903   PPeSchw

Lieder vom Tod und Sterben, cpd., 1761.

NL 0348904   PPeSchw

VM50
L71

Lieder zu drey Seelenämtern und III. Libera.
Samt einem Anhange von mehrern Liedern bey
Begräbnissen. Mit gnädigster Erlaubniss der
churfürstl. Büchercensur Spezialkommission.
Landshut, Joseph Attenkofer, 1803.
79, [1] p.   18 x 23.5 cm.

Pieces not numbered.
With music.

NL 0348905   NNUT

Lieder zu Schutz und Trutz; Gaben deutschen
Dichter an der Zeit des Krieges in den Jahren 1870–
1871. Berlin, Lipperheide, 1879.
211 p.

NL 0348906   PPG

VOLUME 332

ar W
38678
Lieder zum Commerse zu Ehren des Herrn
Professor Dr. von Treitschke, am 14.
Februar, 1874. Heidelberg, A. H. Avena-
rius, 1874.
16 p. 20cm.

1. Treitschke, Heinrich Gotthard von,
1834-1896.

NL 0348907   NIC

---

*GC8
F7350
A852l
Lieder zum 25. Stiftungsfeste des Sonntags-
Vereins zum Tunnel über der Spree. Am 3.
December 1852.
[Berlin] Verlag der Quästur.[1852]

35,[1]p. 20.5cm.
Title vignette.
Contains 2 contributions (signed
"Lafontaine") by Theodor Fontane.
Original printed wrappers preserved,
mounted on modern boards.

NL 0348908   MH

Lieder zum Gebrauch der Freimaurer-Loge
in Koeln am Rhein
see under   Freemasons. Cologne. Loge
Minerva zum Vaterlandischen Verein un Rhenana
zur Humanitat.

HS
454
F81
Lieder zum Gebrauch der Freymäurer-
Loge zur Einigkeit in Frankfurt am Mayn.
Frankfurt am Mayn, Heinrich Ludwig
Brönner, 1782.
48 p. 17cm.

1. Free   masons--Songs and
music.   I. Title.

NL 0348910   NIC

Lieder zum gebrauch der Freymäurer-loge Zur einigkeit
in Frankfurt am Mayn. Frankfurt am Mayn, H. L.
Brönner, 1784.
64 p. 18ᵐᵐ.
Without music.

1. Freemasons — Songs and music.   I. Freemasons. Frankfurt-am-
Main. Loge Zur einigkeit.

24-27857

NL 0348911   DLC

Lieder zum Gebrauch der unter Constitution der
Grossen Loge zu Hamburg vereinigten Logen
see under   Freemasons. Hamburg.
Vereinigte Fünf Logen.

H
245
L62G
1896
Lieder zum Gebrauch für Missionsgottesdienste.
Heubuden, 1896. Marienburg, O. Halb.

37p. 18cm.

NL 0348913   ViHarEM NjPT

LIEDER zum Julfest. [n.p., 1940?] [11]p. 21cm.

Words only.

1. Christmas--Poetry, songs,   hymns, etc., German.
2. Christmas music--Songs,   German.

NL 0348914   NN

LIEDER zum musikalischen frühschoppen zur
feier des 90.geburtstages des kaisers,in
Kroll's Établissement. [Berlin,1887].

NL 0348915   MH

Yb
H3
764
Lieder zum unschuldigen Vergnügen ...
[Hamburg?] 1764. 86[2]pp. 17½cm.
[Bound with Hagedorn, Friedrich von, 1708-
1754 ... Sämmtliche poetische Werke ... Hamburg,
J.C.Bohn,1764]
Vorrede signed E.

NL 0348916   CtY

4PT
Ger.
8691
Lieder zur Erbauung und Ermunterung
für Schulkinder und Erwachsene. Gesammelt von Verfasser der Indersdorfer
-Schulgeschichten. München, Im
Königlichen Central-Schulbücher-Verlage,
1834.
239 p.

NL 0348917   DLC

Lieder zur geselligen feier des dritten ju-
belfestes der uebergabe der augsburgischen
confession, 25 ⁓sten juni 1830. [Bonn.].[1830].
And. H.

NL 0348918   MH-AH

Lieder zur Laute. [Für Laute oder Klavier.] Berlin: Ullstein &
Co., cop. 1913.   183-204 p.   sq. f°.   (Music für Alle. Nr.
106.)

German words.
Marsch-und Soldatenlieder: Jetzt kommt die Zeit, wo ich wandern muss; Wenn
wir marschieren; Le joli tambour; Kapitän und Leutenant; Morgen muss mein
Schatz abreisen; Der Nachtwandler; Berennung von Breslau. Liebeslieder: Feins-
liebchen du sollst nicht barfuss gehn. Mädle ruck, ruck, ruck. Alle Tage ist
kein Sonntag. Also eng verbunden. Scherzlieder: Der Tod von Basel; 's Bettel-
weibel wollt' wallfahrten gehn; Ach Modr, ich well en Ding han; Burlala; Vetter
Michel; Frühlingssymphonei; Die Liebe ist ein Galgen.

1. Germany--Music. 2. Songs (with   CENTRAL CIRCULATION.
N.Y.P.L.   music).
December 17, 1919.

NL 0348919   NN

LIEDER zur Weihnachtszeit. Instrumental-Ausgabe.
Neuauflage von "Hohe Nacht der klaren Sterne."
Wolfenbüttel, G. Kallmeyer, 1943. score [49 p.]
illus. 17 x 25cm.

For various combinations of voices and instruments.

1. Christmas music--Choral music--Collections. 2. Christmas music--
Songs, German. I. Title: Hohe   Nacht der klaren Sterne.

NL 0348920   NN

Lieder-Album; a collection of German Songs
(with English and german words) for a medium
voice with pianoforte accompaniment. Lond.,
Augener,n.d.
8 pts.

NL 0348921   OOxM OO

Lieder-album aus Tyrol, Kärnten und Steiermark; 30 beliebte volks- und nationallieder für
pianoforte mit unterlegtem text. Leipzig [etc.]
Gebrueder Hug [19-?]
2v. in 1.

Bound with Schweizer-lieder-album. Zuerich
[19-?]

NL 0348922   OCl

784.061M
L 623 P Lieder-Album für eine Singstimme mit Pianoforte und Violin Begleitung. Leipzig,
C.F. Peters, n.d. Pl. no. 5912.
score (29 p.) 31cm.

For voice; with piano and violin acc.
Contents.--Hauptmann, M. Op. 31, no. 1-3:
Meerfahrt; Nachtgesang; Der Fischer.--Reinecke,
C. Op. 26, no. 1-2: Waldesgruss; Frühlings-
blumen.--Kalliwoda, J.W. In die Ferne.

NL 0348923   OU

Lieder-Album lettischer Komponisten. Album de chansons
de compositeurs lettons. Für eine Singstimme und Klavier.
Pour une voix et piano. Wien, Universal-Edition, °1940.
40 p. 31 cm.

1. Songs with piano.

M1619.L429   48-39118*

NL 0348924   DLC NcU NN CoU

Liederavonden voor het volk
see under   Algemeen Nederlandsch Verbond.
Antwerpshe tak.

Liederbach, A. A.

North Dakota. Killdeer Mountain park commission.
Report of the Killdeer Mountain park commission.
1919. [n. p., 1919]

Liederbach, Clarence A., 1910-   ed. and tr.
BX2266
.M3K512
Kiefer, Charles, 1866-
Instructio pro confessariis. Translation arranged and
edited by Clarence A. Liederbach. Milwaukee, Bruce [1950]

Liederbach, Clarence A   1910-
When a Catholic marries. Milwaukee, Bruce Pub. Co.
[1949]
77] 19 cm.
Bibliography: p. 77.

1. Marriage—Catholic Church.   I. Title.

BX2250.L5   265.5   49-3303*

NL 0348928   DLC OEac OU WaS

VOLUME 332

Liederblatt der Hitler-Jugend. 1.–   Jahresband (Folge
1–   ; 1935–
Wolfenbüttel, G. Kallmeyer.
    v. in   22 cm.
Includes unacc. melodies.
Vols. 1–5 issued together in 1941 as 2d ed. and called "Gesamt-
band"
"Herausgegeben von der Reichsjugendführung."

1. Song-books, German. 2. National songs, German. 3. Folk-
songs, German. I. Nationalsozialistische Deutsche Arbeiter-Partei.
Hitlerjugend. II. Nationalsozialistische Deutsche Arbeiter-Partei.
Reichsjugendführung.

M1734.L69   784.8   51–36705

NL 0348929   DLC IEN MB

LIEDERBLATT der Hitler-Jugend; Sonderausgabe für
Jungmädel. Wolfenbüttel, G. Kallmeyer [194–?]
8 v. 13 x 19cm.

Film reproduction. Negative.
Blatt 1–4, 6, 8–10.
For 1–3 girls' voices, principally with instrumental accompaniment.
"Verantwortlich für die Herausgabe: Bannmädelführerin Waltraute
Standfuss, Musikreferentin im   Kulturamt der Reichsjugend-
führung. "

CONTENTS. --Blatt 1, Im Frühjahr. --Blatt 2. Wir können spielen.
--Blatt 3. Tierlieder. --Blatt 4. Fahrtenlieder. --Blatt 6. Zur Kirmes. --
Blatt 8. Abendlieder. --Blatt 9. Ständelieder. --Blatt 10. Dreh dich, dreh
dich, Mädchen.

1. School songbooks, German. 2. Children's music--Choral music.
I. Nationalsozialistische deutsche Arbeiterpartei. Reichsjugendführung.
Kulturamt./ II. Standfuss, Waltraute   , ed. III. Standfuss, Waltraute.

NL 0348931   NN

Liederbuch. Eine Sammlung Volkslieder
    see under Gerhard,   comp.
[Supplement]

M   Liederbuch der Anna von Köln (um 1500). Ein-
2   geleitet und hrsg. von Walter Salmen und
D397   Johannes Koepp. Düsseldorf, L. Schwann,
v.4++   1954.
          66 p. music. 31cm. (Denkmäler rheini-
        scher Musik, Bd.4)

          1. Sacred songs--Collections. 2. Hymns,
        German. I. Anna, of Cologne, fl. 1500. II.
        Salmen, Walter, 1926-   ed. III. Koepp,
        Johannes, ed.   IV. Series.

NL 0348933   NIC NN NjPT MH NcU MiU CoU CLSU

Liederbuch der Cincinnati freie presse
    see under Cincinnati freie presse. [Sup-
plement]

Liederbuch der Clara Hätzlerin.
    Liederbuch der Clara Hätzlerin. Aus der Handschrift
des Böhmischen Museums zu Prag hrsg. und mit Einleitung
und Wörterbuch versehen von Carl Haltaus. Quedlinburg,
G. Basse, 1840.
    lxxviii, 370 p. (p. 367-370 advertisement) 22 cm. (Bibliothek der
gesammten deutschen National-Literatur von der ältesten bis auf die
neuere Zeit, 1. Abth., 8. Bd.)
    Original compiler of the collection copied in 1471 by Clara Hätz-
lerin is unknown. Cf. Stammler. Verfasserlexikon.
    Errata: leaf inserted.
    1. German poetry--Middle High German. I. Hätzlerin, Clara,
ca. 1430-1476 or 7. II. Haltaus, Karl Ferdinand, 1811-1848, ed. III.
Prague. Národni muzeum. Knihovna. MSS. (MS. X A 12) (Series: Bibliothek der ge-   sammten deutschen National-Literatur, 1. Abth., 8. Bd.)

PT1371.B6 1.   Abth., 8. Bd.   G-687

NL 0348935   DLC CtY ICU MH

Liederbuch der Kriegsmarine
    see under Germany. Kriegsmarine.
Oberkommando.

Liederbuch der Siebenbürger Deutschen ...
    see under Geltch, Johann Friedrich,
ed.

Liederbuch der Tübinger Hochschule.   Tübingen,
E. T. Eifert [184–?]
    1 p.l., 442 p. nar. 16°.
    13 ms. leaves bound in, 3 ms. leaves
pasted in.
    2. ed.
    I. Tübingen. Universität.

NL 0348938   NN

Das Liederbuch des Arnt von Aich
    see under Aich, Arnt von.

Liederbuch des deutschen Volkes.   2879a.46
    Leipzig., Breitkopf & Härtel. 1843. iv, 380 pp. 15 cm., in 8s.

L29 — Folk-songs. — Songs. Without music. Colls. — Germany. Lit. Poetry.
Colls.

NL 0348940   MB

Das liederbuch des jungbrunnen, mit bildern von
Hans von Volkmann, Hans Heise, Georg A. Stroedel,
Franz Stassen. [188]p. il. Berlin, Fischer und
Franke [1903] (Jungbrunnen, 9)

    Covers of the original parts bound in.
    Contents.--Wald- und waidmannslieder.--Das fest-
liche jahr.--Winterreise, von Wilhelm Mueller.-
Lieder der romantischen lyrik.

NL 0348941   OC1

Liederbuch des Logenbundes im Königreiche
Hannover
    see under [Blumenhagen, Wilhelm] 1781-1839

Liederbuch dreier freunde
    see under Mommsen, Theodor, 1817-1903.

Liederbuch für den Deutschen Krieger-Bund
    see under Müller, R.

Liederbuch für deutsch-amerikanische schulen
    see under New York turnverein.

Liederbuch für deutsche Aerzte und Naturforscher
    see under Korb, Hermann, 1836-   comp.
[Supplement]

Liederbuch für deutsche Ärzte und Naturforscher.
    1. Abschnitt. Vivat Bacchus, enthaltend Fest-,
    Tafel- und Commers-Lieder ernsten und
    heiteren Inhalts für naturwissenschaftliche,
    allgemein- und spezialärztliche sowie auch
    Doctor-, Jubilar-, etc., Versammlungen.
    Neue Ausgabe. Hamburg, Gebr. Lüdeking,
    1893.
        292 p. 12°.

NL 0348947   DNLM

Liederbuch für deutsche Ärzte und Naturforscher.
    2. Abschnitt. Ambrosia und Nektar, enthaltend:
    200 ernste und heitere Fest- und Tafellieder,
    Reden, Aufsätze, etc., medicinischen und
    naturwissenschaftlichen Inhalts, mit mancherlei
    Illustrationen. Hamburg, Gebr. Lüdeking,
    1892.
        viii, 510, viii p. 12°.

NL 0348948   DNLM

Liederbuch für deutsche Ärzte und Naturforscher.
    2. Abschnitt. Ambrosia und Nektar, enthaltend:
    200 ernste und heitere Fest- und Tafellieder,
    Reden, Aufsätze, etc., medicinischen und
    naturwissenschaftlichen Inhalts, mit mancherlei
    Illustrationen. Hamburg, Gebr. Lüdeking,
    1892.
        viii, (1 l.), 513-744 p. 12°.
        Supplement Bändchen zu dem zweiten
    Abschnitte "Ambrosia und Nektar" No. 201-287.

NL 0348949   DNLM

Liederbuch für deutsche Gesellen. Berlin,
Oemigke's Buchhandlung (Julius Bülow), 1844.
149 p. music. 14cm.

NL 0348950   OrPR

Liederbuch für deutsche künstler
    see under [Kugler, Franz Theodor]
1808-1858, ed.

M1961   Liederbuch für deutsche Studenten.
.L5   Mit grösstentheils mehrstimmigen Sangweisen.
        2. Aufl. Halle, H. Schmidt, 1852.
        555 p. 13 x 11 cm.

        1. Students' songs, German.

NL 0348952   NjR

Liederbuch für deutsche Studenten. Mit
ein- und mehrstimmigen Sangweisen. 4., neu
bearb. Aufl. Erlangen, Deichert, 1881.
397p.

NL 0348953   OC1W

VOLUME 332

Liederbuch fuer deutsche studenten 6. verb.
und verm. aufl. Heidelberg, "inter,[1900]
208p.

p.201-208 blank.

NL 0348954   MiU

Liederbuch für deutsche Turner. In letzter
Redaktion vom Berliner Turnrath. 22. Aufl.
Braunschweig, G. Westermann, 1863.
240 p. port. 11 cm.
1. Gymnastics.

NL 0348955   IEN

34292 Liederbuch für deutsche turner, begründet
.5825 1849 vom Braunschweiger männer-turnverein; hrsg. seit der 6.aufl.1858 vom
Berliner turnrath.. Braunschweig, Westermann ₍187-?₎
16,225 p.incl.front.(port.) 13 cm.

1.German ballads and songs.

NL 0348956   NjP

Liederbuch für Deutsche Turner. Begründet 1849
vom Braunschweiger Männer-Turnverein.
Hrsg. seit 1858 vom Berliner Turnrath.
112. Aufl. Braunschweig, Georg Westermann,
[18--]
13 cm.
Without music, tunes indicated by title.

NL 0348957   CtY

Liederbuch für deutsche turner, begründet 1849
vom Braunschweiger männer-turnverein; hrsg. seit
1858 vom Berliner Turnrat. 167.aufl.
Braunschweig,George Westermann,₍1907₎

NL 0348958   InU

830.81 Liederbuch für deutsche turner ...
L6251 Hrsg. seit 1858 vom Berliner Turnrath.
200. aufl.   Braunschweig [1923]
222p. port.

NL 0348959   IU

[Liederbuch fuer die israelitischen Volkschu-
len. By various authors.] n.p., n.d. [187-?]
5-194p.

NL 0348960   OCH

Liederbuch für die Jugend
see under   American tract society.

Liederbuch für Front und Heimat; ₎Textbuch mit Singstimme. Leipzig, W. Gebauer ₍194-₎
62 p. 15 cm. (Deutsche Wacht in Ost und West, Heft 1)
Cover title.
Unacc. melodies.

1. Song-books, German.

M1734.L693   52-41589

NL 0348962   DLC

Ein Liederbuch für Naturforscher und Aerzte
see under   Hoffmann-Donner, Heinrich,
1809-1894, comp. [Supplement]

Liederbuch für Niedersachsen
see under   Koldewey, Friedrich, 1866-

Coll Liederbuch für S. Adler. [n.p.] 1846
LI185 ₍67₎p. 17 cm.
Harris
Collection Without the music.
Mss Words in German and in English.

NL 0348965   RPB

Liederbuch für Schleswig-Holstein
see under   Schleswig-Holsteiner-Bund.

Liederbuch für Sonntag-Schule und Haus₍Altaburg₎1900
see under   German Evangelical Protestant
Ministers' Association.

Liederbuch für Sonntagschulen
... Gettysburg ... 1832
see under   Evangelical Lutheran Synod of
West Pennsylvania.

TS K65.16
Liederbuch für Volksschulen Moselland./ Trier, J.Lintz
[1941]

Contents:-1. Erstes bis viertes Schuljahr.

NL 0348969   MH

Liederbuch fürs jahr 1787. Freunden und freun-
dinnen des klaviers und gesanges zum neujahrs-
geschenk übergeben...
see under   [Burmann, Gottlob Wilhelm] 1737-
1805.

Das liederbuch Ludwig Iselins ...
see under   Iselin, Ludwig, 1559-1612.

Liederchronik der Antiquarischen Gesellschaft in
Zürich
see under   Antiquarische Gesellschaft in
Zürich.

Lieder-Concordanz über die gebräuchlichsten
evangelischen Kirchenlieder...
see under   Bollert, G.

Liederen-bundel voor janmaat en soldaat
see under   Clockener Brousson, Henri
Constant Claude, 1871-   comp. [Supplement]

HS ₍Liederer, Karl Leopold₎
607 Rede zum Gedächtniss des Bruders G.
L71 P. Laugner,₎ gehalten an seinem Grabe von
Br. v. Liederskron am 17. Dec. 1821. Auf
Verlangen der Freunde des Verstorbenen
für sie abgedruckt. Erlangen, 1821.
7 p. 17cm.

1. Laugner. G P
2. Freemas ons--Addresses, essays,
lectures.

NL 0348975   NIC

Liederer von Liederscron, Fr. Adolf.
Statistik der von 1855-1875 in der Klinik der
August Rothmind, behandelten Verletzungen und Fremd-
körper des Auges nebst einigen Krankheitsgeschichten
... München, 1876.
26 p.
Inaug. Diss.

NL 0348976   PPC

Liederfibel; Kinderlieder in Bildernoten
see under   Grüger, Heribert, 1900-   ed.

Ein Liederfreund.
Ist es recht die alten Kirchengesänge zu
verändern?
see under title

Liedergarten ... Sammlung älterer und neuerer
Lieder ...
see under   Koehler, Wilh., comp.
[Supplement]

VR80 Liedergave geofferd op het altaar der zending.
L623 Ten voordeele van het Ned. Zend. Gen. Rotterdam, J.C. Neurdenburg; Hallum,S.J. Rutgers,
1869.
vi, 88 p. 20 cm.

"Niet in den handel."
"Voorbericht" signed: A.J. Rutgers ₍en₎ J.F.
Rutgers.

1. Missionary hymns. I. Nederlandsch
Zendelinggenootschap.

NL 0348980   CtY-D

VOLUME 332

Liedergeschichten. Segenspuren der Kernlieder unserer Kirche
    see under   Wackernagel, William, 1838-1926.

M1736   **Liederhandschrift aus Halle, vom Jahr 1799.**
.H2   An unpaged mss. collection of German
Case   folk-songs (text and music). 4°.

NL   0348982   DLC

... **Die Liederhandschrift des cardinals de Rohan** (xv. jahrh.)
Nach der Berliner hs. Hamilton 674, hrsg. von Martin
Löpelmann. Göttingen, Gedruckt für die Gesellschaft für
romanische literatur, 1923.
   xxii, 428 p. facsim. 24½ cm. *(Half-title:* Gesellschaft für romanische literatur. 19. jahrg. 1920, einziger bd.; der ganzen reihe bd. 44)
   Copy no. "254, Library of Congress, Washington."
   Manuscript of the 15th century (ca. 1470) probably written for
Louis Malet de Graville, whose arms it bears at the foot of the 1st
page; later in possession of Cardinal Rohan (1674-1749), afterward
in the Hamilton palace collection (no. 674 of the sale catalogue 1882);
now at Berlin, originally acquired for the Königliche (now Staats)
bibliothek, it was later transferred to the Staatliche kupferstichkabinett (no. 78B17) There it was discovered in 1913 by Siegfried Lemm,
who undertook its publication, but did not live to accomplish it.

   1. French poetry—Old French.   I. Löpelmann, Martin, 1891-
ed.   II. Rohan, Armand Gaston Maximilien de, cardinal, 1674-
1749.   III. Malet, Louis, seigneur de Graville, 1441?-1516.   IV. Hamilton, Alexander Hamilton Douglas, 10th duke of, 1767-1852. v. Berlin.
Preussische staatsbibliothek. Mss. Hamilton 674.   VI. Berlin. Staatliche museen. Kupferstichkabinett. Mss. 78B17.   VII. Lemm, Siegfried, d. 1915.

PC3.G5 bd. 44   24—5344

   NBuU CU NcD
NL   0348984   DLC OCU MiU MH ViU PBm NcU OU NcD CU

Liederheft. 174 kirchliche und weltliche
Gesänge ...
    see under   Beck, C.A., comp. [Supplement]

Liederheft für Margot und H. H. S. ₍initials represented by
musical notes₎; sieben Lieder nach Gedichten von Carl Sand-
burg. Berlin, Bote & Bock ₍1952₎
   16 p. 31 cm.
   Cover title.
   For voice and piano.
   CONTENTS.— Nebel, von B. Blacher.— Büffel-Dämmerung, von G.
Klebe.—Hütte, von F. Burt.—Brandung, von M. Sheinkman.—Splitter,
von H. Erbse.— Fünf-Cent-Ballons, von H. Nowoweljski.— Sterne-
Lieder-Gesichter, von R. Wagner-Régeny.
   1. Songs (High voice) with piano.   I. Blacher, Boris, 1903-
II. Sandburg, Carl, 1878-

M1619.5.S2L5   M 54—2233

NL   0348986   DLC TxU

Liederik, pseud.
     see   Fassotte, Joris.

327.492   **Liederkerke de Beaufort, Florent Charles**
L621r   **Auguste de, comte,** 1792-1855.
      Rapporti delle cose di Roma (1848-1849), a
cura di Alberto M. Ghisalberti.   Roma,
Vittoriano, 1949.
     xviii, 212p. 26cm. (Istituto per la storia
del Risorgimento italiano. Biblioteca scientifica. Ser.2: Fonti, v.35)

     Diplomatic dispatches.

NL   0348988   IU

Liederkranz.   Sammlung der berühmtesten
Lieder ...
     see under   Dörffel, Alfred, 1821-1905.

Liederkranz Bruchsal.
     ...Festbuch zum goldenen Jubiläum 11.-13. Juni, 1904...
Bruchsal: Druck von M. J. Stoll, 1904.   63 p.   front.(port.),
illus.   19½cm.

   1. Music—Assoc. and org.—Germany   —Bruchsal.
N. Y. P. L.   August 23, 1933

NL   0348990   NN

Liederkranz-Frohsinn, Bern.
     ... Denkschrift zur feier des 75jährigen be-
standes 1849-1924, herausgegeben auf den 16. märz
1924. Bern, Pochon-Jent, 1924.
     viii, 281 p. plate, ports. 23½ cm.

     At head of title: Liederkranz-Frohsinn, Bern.

     1. Choral societies - Bern.

NL   0348991   NNC

Liederkranz für bergleute ... Frankfurt,
Trowitzsch, 1857.
142 p.

NL   0348992   PU

**Liederkranz fuer sonntags-schulen und jugend
vereine**
     see under   Evangelical synod of North
America. [Supplement]

Liederkranz Gaildorf.
     100 jahre Liederkranz Gaildorf (e. v.) 1834-1934. ₍Gail-
dorf, Druck von H. Schwend, 1934₎
     40 p. incl. 1 illus., group ports. 22ᶜᵐ.
     Verse and prose.

   1. Music—Germany—Gaildorf.

   Library of Congress   ML37.G25H98   39—34087
                                            ₍2₎   784.60624347

NL   0348994   DLC

Liederkranz of the City of New York.
     Charter und Statuten des Gesangvereins Deutscher Lie-
derkranz der Stadt New York, gegründet am 9. Jan. 1847,
inkorporiert am 24. März 1860. 1905. ₍New York, 1905₎
     88 p. 16 cm.

     ML28.N3L45   10—18282 rev*

NL   0348995   DLC

Liederkranz of the city of New York.
     Dem Wiener Männergesang Verein zur Erinnerung an seinen
Aufenthalt in der Stadt New York im Wonnemonat des Jahres
1907 gewidmet vom Gesangverein deutscher Liederkranz der Stadt
New York.   ₍New York, 1907₎   16, viii, 112 p.   illus.
 ³8½cm.

     Added t.-p.: King's views New York. Four hundred plates.

   208312B. 1. New York (City)—   Views.
N. Y. P. L.   March 10, 1943

NL   0348996   NN

Liederkranz of the City of New York.
     ₍1847 — 1922. Liederkranz, New York. 21. Januar 1922.
₍New York, 1922.₎   4 l.   ports.   28cm.
       Seventy-fifth anniversary dinner, with menu, list of officers, poem by Albert
Leisel, etc.

   1. New York (city)—Societies,   Musical, etc. 2. Germans in the
U. S.—N. Y.—New York.   N. Y. P. L.
                                              February 6, 1924

NL   0348997   NN

Liederkranz of the City of New York.
     History of the Liederkranz of the City of New York,
1847 to 1947, and of the Arion, New York. Comp. during
the centennial year of the Liederkranz, 1947, by the History
Committee. New York, Drechsel Print. Co., 1948.
     xiv, 161 p. illus., ports. 27 cm.
     Bibliography: p. 159.

     1. Arion, New York.

     ML200.8.N52L55   784.6062747   49—26426*

NL   0348998   DLC NN

Liederkranz of the City of New York.
     Jahres-bericht und mitglieder-liste.
New York, 18
     v. tables. 16½ᶜᵐ.
     Report year irregular.
     Full title of report for 1898/99: Jahres-bericht und mitglieder-liste des
gesang-vereins Deutscher liederkranz der stadt New York.

                                   CA 10-1764 Unrev'd
   Library of Congress   ML28.N3D35

NL   0348999   DLC

q917.471   **Liederkranz of the City of New York.**
D48s   **Souvenir ausgabe. King's views.
New York. 400 Illustrations.
cover-title, 112p. ports.**

NL   0349000   IU

Liederkranz of the City of New York. Damen Verein.
     Stiftungsfest.
₍Nr.₎
     ₍New York, 18   8°.
     no.

   1. Music—Assoc., etc.—U. S.—New   York (state).
N. Y. P. L.   November 16, 1928

NL   0349001   NN

Liederkranz of the City of New York.
     61stes Stiftungsfest, Sonnabend, den 11. Januar, 1908. ₍Pro-
gramm.₎ New York, 1908. 3 l. 8°.

NL   0349002   NN

Liederkranz of the City of New York
     see also Arion, *New York.*

VOLUME 332

Liederkranz, *Ratisbon.*
Regensburger Liederkranz. Neueste, sehr verm. Stereotypaufl. Regensburg, A. Coppenrath, 1904.
parts (v.) 9 x 15 cm.
CONTENTS.—₁₁ Sammlung ausgewählter vierstimmiger Lieder mit Nachtrag.

1. Song-books, German.

M1734.L712R4   M 58–782

NL 0349004   DLC

Liederkranz Schweinfurt.
Blüthen und Blätter gesammelt zur Erinnerung
see under title

Liederkranz Zürich
see also Sängerverein Helvetia Zürich.

Liederkreis; 100-vorzuegliche lieder₁ und gesaenge fuer eine stimme, mit begleitung des pianoforte. Neue ausgabe. Leipzig, Breitkopf & Haertel, n. d.
223p.

German words.

NL 0349007   OC1

Liederleben der evangelischen Kirche
see under Wendebourg, Hermann.

Liederlust der Zionspilger
see under ₁Böttcher, Carl Julius₁ ed.

Liederman, Earle Edwin, 1888–
Behind the mask, by Earle Liederman. New York, Priv. print., 1929.
3 p. l., 9–79 p. 18ᵐᵐ.
Poems.

I. Title.

Library of Congress   PS3523.I3B4 1929   29–11041

NL 0349010   DLC WaS OC1 OC1JC PP MB

Liederman, Earle E.
Endurance; author and publisher, Earle E. Liederman ... New York ₁°1926₁
176 p. incl. front. (port.) 18½ᵐᵐ.

1. Physical education and training. I. Title.

Library of Congress   GV341.L47   26–15047

NL 0349011   DLC NN MH NNU PP IEN WaU

Liederman, Earle E.
Here's health, by Earle E. Liederman. New York, E. E. Liederman ₁°1924₁
7 p. l., 185 p. incl. front., port. 18½ᵐᵐ.

1. Hygiene. I. Title.

Library of Congress   RA776.L71   25–2981

NL 0349012   DLC DNLM PP PPC

Liederman, Earle E.
The hidden truth about sex; author and publisher, Earle E. Liederman. New York ₁°1926₁
1 p. l., ₁7₁–179 p. 18½ᵐᵐ.

1. Sex. 2. Hygiene, Sexual. I. Title.

Library of Congress   HQ31.L5   26–23865

NL 0349013   DLC

Liederman, Earle Edwin, 1888–
The maelstrom ₁by₁ Earle Liederman. ₁Buffalo, °1930₁
1 p. l., ₁5₁–74 p. 21ᵐᵐ.
Title from cover.
Poems.

I. Title.

Library of Congress   PS3523.I3M3 1930   30–14217
—— Copy 2.
Copyright A 22908   ₁2₁   811.5

NL 0349014   DLC

Liederman, Earle Edwin, 1888–
Muscle building, by Earle Liederman ... New York, E. Liederman ₁°1924₁
4 p. l., 7–217 p. front., illus. (incl. ports.) 23½ cm.

1. Physical education and training. I. Title.

GV341.L5   24–23132 rev

NL 0349015   DLC OLak DNLM PP OKentU

Liederman, Earle Edwin, 1888–
Muscular development, ... [9th ed.]
New York City [c1922]

GV343
.L5
1922

NL 0349016   DLC

Liederman, Earle E.
Muscular development, by Earle E. Liederman... New York₁, cop. 1924₁. 64 p. illus. 12. ed. 12°.

1. Gymnastics.
N. Y. P. L.   December 29, 1925

NL 0349017   NN DLC

Liederman, Earle E.
Philosophy of a cynic, by Earle Liederman. New York, Priv. print., 1928.
85 p. 19ᵐ.
Poems.

I. Title.

Library of Congress   PS3523.I3P5 1928   28–13022

NL 0349018   DLC

Liederman, Earle Edwin, 1888–
The science of wrestling and the art of jiu-jitsu, by Earle Liederman. New York, E. Liederman ₁°1923₁
223 p. incl. front., illus., ports. 23½ᵐ.

1. Wrestling. 2. Jiu-Jitsu.
Library of Congress   GV1195.L6   23–16063 Revised

NL 0349019   DLC

Liederman, Earle E
The science of wrestling and the art of jiu-jitsu, by Earle Liederman. New York, E. Liederman ₁°1924₁
223 p. incl. front., illus., ports. 23½ cm.
Second edition.

1. Wrestling. 2. Jiu-Jitsu.

GV1195.L6 1924   24—6741

NL 0349020   DLC OC1 OrU

Liederman, Earle Edwin, 1888–
The science of wrestling and the art of jiu-jitsu, by Earle Liederman. New York, E. Liederman ₁°1925₁
223 p. incl. front., illus., ports. 23½ᵐ.
"Third edition."

1. Wrestling. 2. Jiu-Jitsu.
Library of Congress   GV1195.L6 1925   25–2909 Revised

NL 0349021   DLC CaBVa PPGi

796
L71a   **Liederman, Earle E**
The science of wrestling and the art of jiu-jitsu. ₁4th ed.₁ New York, E. Liederman ₁°1926₁
223 p. illus., ports. 23 cm.

1. Wrestling. 2. Jiu-Jitsu. I. Title.

NL 0349022   N

Liederman, Earle Edwin, *1888–*   4008.565
The science of wrestling and the art of jiu-jitsu. [5th edition.]
— New York. Liederman. [1927.] 3–223 pp. Portraits. Plates. Autograph facsimile. 23 cm.

N7261 — Jiu-jitsu. — Wrestling.

NL 0349023   MB WaS PPC

Liederman, Earle Edwin, 1888–
The science of wrestling and the art of jiu-jitsu. New York, E. Liederman, 1930.
223 p. incl. front., illus., ports. 24 cm.

NL 0349024   TU

VOLUME 332

Liederman, Earle E.
Secrets of strength, by Earle Liederman ... New York, E. Liederman [1925]
2 p. l., [9]-218 p. front. illus. (ports.) 23½ᶜᵐ.

1. Physical education and training. ɪ. Title.

Library of Congress   GV341.L55   25-11131

NL 0349025   DLC ViU

Liederman, Earle E.
Sexual guidance; author and publisher, Earl E. Liederman ... New York [1926]
2 p. l., 172 p. front. (port.) 18½ᶜᵐ.

1. Hygiene, Sexual. 2. Sexual ethics. ɪ. Title.

Library of Congress   HQ31.L55   27-1045

NL 0349026   DLC DNLM

Liederman, Earle Edwin, 1888–
The unfinished song of Achmed Mohammed. Black and white illus. by Keye Luke. Hollywood [Calif.] House-Warven, 1951.
unpaged. illus. 28 cm.

ɪ. Title.

PS3523.I 3U5   811.5   51-37322 ‡

NL 0349027   DLC CLU

Lieder-perlen
see under [Concordia publishing house, St. Louis]

Lieder-Sammlung für Jünglinge, zusammengetragen von einem Freunde der Jugend.
6. unveränderte Aufl. Regensburg, New York, F. Pustet, 1867.
205 p. 14 cm.
With music, for two voices.

NL 0349029   PLatS

Lieder-Sammlung für Jünglinge, zusammengetragen von einem Freunde der Jugend. 8., verb. Aufl. Regensburg, New York, F. Pustet, 1874.
206 p. 15 cm.
First published in 1854 by Andreas Thorwart.
"Vorwort" signed: Joh. de Matha Jaeggle.
Contents.--Geistliche Lieder.--Lieder vermischten Inhalts.

NL 0349030   PLatS

Lieder-Sammlung für Jungfrauen, zusammengetragen von einem Freunde der Jugend.
7., unveränderte Aufl. Regensburg, New York, F. Pustet, 1870.
174 p. 14 cm.
With music, for two voices.

NL 0349031   PLatS

Lieder-Schatz. Eine Auswahl der beliebsten Volks-, Vaterlands-, Soldaten-, Jäger-, Studenten-, und Liebes-Lieder für eine Singstimme mit Pianoforte-Begleitung. Leipzig & Berlin, C. F. Peters [n.d.]
2(?)v. in 1. 27cm.

1. Songs, German. 2. Songs with piano.
M1734.L7

NL 0349032   MH CtY PU KAS

JMF
72-491
Lieder-Schatz; eine Auswahl der beliebtesten Volks- , Vaterlands- , Soldaten- , Jäger-, Studenten- und Liebes-Lieder, für eine Singstimme mit Pianoforte-Begleitung. Leipzig, C. F. Peters [ca. 1870] Pl. no. 4868. 216 p. 27 cm.

1. Folk-songs, German. 2. Songs, German.

NL 0349033   NN

Liederwald, Anna-Elisabeth.
Glass vessels in Netherlands paintings of the 17th century. [London] 6 p. 32 cm.
NK5100 (Circle of Glass Collectors. Notes. no. 125)
C57
no.125

1. Glass in painting. I. Title.

NL 0349034   NCoeniC

PT2047   **Liederwald, Carl Gotthelf Traugott,** 1887–
C6L718   Der Begriff "edel" bei Goethe. Schleiz, Druck von F. Weber, 1913.
171 p. 22cm.
Cover title.
Inaug.-Diss. - Greifswald.
Vita.

1.Goethe, Johann Wolfgang von, 1749-1832 - Language. I.Title.

NL 0349035   CSt InU

023.2   **Lieders, Arthur**
L718ℓ   ...Librarian, a complete preparation
1950   guide for all grades of civil service librarian positions. Latest 1950 ed. New York, Arco Publishing Co., 1950.
v.p. Q. (Arco civil service series)

Reproduced from typewritten copy.

1.Librarians. U.S. 2.Civil service examinations.

NL 0349036   IaU

Lieder-Saal
see under [Lassberg, Joseph Maria Christoph, Freiherr von] 1770-1885.

---

32   Lieder-sammlung fuer die schuljugend. 2. heft.
10060   In den schulen des kantons Schwyz obligatorisch eingefuehrt. Einsiedeln, New York und Cincinnati, gebr. K. & N. Benziger, 1867.
1 p. l., 32 p., 1 l. 18°.

NL 0349038   DLC

Liedersammlung für Kinder und Kinderfreunde am Clavier
see under   Partsch, Placidus, comp.

Lieder-Sammlung zum gottesdienstlichen gebrauch
see under   Evangelical Lutheran ministerium of Pennsylvania and adjacent states. [Supplement]

Liederschatz. 200 der beliebtesten volks-vaterlands-, -soldaten-, -jäger - studenten- und liebes-lieder; für eine singstimme mit pianoforte-begleitung. Die begleitung zu sämmtlichen liedern, sowie ein theil der lieder selbst, ist eigenthum des verlegers. Leipzig u. Berlin, C. F. Peters [1870?]
2 p. l., 216 p. 27½ᶜᵐ.
Publisher's plate no.: 4868.

1. Songs, German. 2. Folk-songs, German. 3. Ballads, German. 4. German ballads and songs.

NL 0349041   ViU OCl OrSaW MB

Liederschatz gewidmet dem N. A. Turnerbunde zum 30. Bundesturnfest. Cincinnati, Juni, 1909
see under   Baldwin Company, Cincinnati.

Liederscron, Fr. Adolf Liederer von
see   Liederer von Liederscron, Fr. Adolf.

Liederscron, Mathilde von
Der freiheit traum; deutsch-amerikanische filmmotive in 3 abschnitten. Nürnberg, Spindler [1927]
48 p. (Deutsche filmbücherei)

Manuscript letter from the author inserted.

NL 0349044   NNC

---

von Liederskron (F. Leopold). *Die Verkrümmungen des Rückgrats.* 35 pp. 8°. *Erlangen. Junge.* 1838.

NL 0349045   DNLM

Liedert, Jacob Heinrich.
... De exceptione non sum heres
see under   Amsel, Johann, 1665-1732, praeses.

Liedertafel, Berlin
see   Berliner Liedertafel.

Liedertafel, *Bern*
see   **Berner Liedertafel.**

VOLUME 332

Liedertafel, *Mühlhausen, Ger. (Thuringia)*
... Festschrift zum 100 jährigen jubelfeste der Liedertafel Mühlhausen i. Thür., am 19. januar 1938. Zusammengestellt nach den vereinsakten von sangeskamerad Erich Kleeberg. ₍Mühlhausen i. Thür., Druck von R. Sayle, 1938₎

32 p. 23¹ᵐ.

At head of title: 1838–1938.
Cover-title: 100 jahre Liedertafel Mühlhausen (Thüringen)

1. Music—Germany—Mühlhausen (Thuringia)   I. Kleeberg, Erich.
II. Title.   44-33728

Library of Congress   ML279.8.M9L5

NL 0349049   DLC

Liedertafel, Stralsund.
Liederbuch für frohe stunden.   Zusammengestellt von der Stralsunder liedertafel.   Stralsund, E. Berndt, 1886.
56 p. 14 cm.

NL 0349050   CU

Liedertafel, *Treves.*
... Festschrift zur hundertjährigen jubel-feier der Trierischen liedertafel ... ₍Trier, Volksfreund-druckerei₎ 1935.
1 p. L, 5–118 p. illus. (incl. ports.) 23ᵐ.
At head of title: 1835.
Cover-title: 100 jahre ... Trierische liedertafel.
"Verantwortlich für den gesamtinhalt: Josef Bins."—p. 108.
Advertising matter interspersed.
CONTENTS.—Entstehung und frühzeit der Liedertafel (1835–1850) von P. F. Schmidt.—1848–1912.—Die letzten 25 jahre. Die ehrung der jubilare, von ₍Josef₎ Bins₎—Mitgliederverzeichnis.—Festfolge, 20.–22. Juni 1935.
1. Music—Germany—Treves.   I. Bins, Josef. II. Schmidt, Peter Franz. III. Title.
                                          39-34088
Library of Congress   ML36.T81
                           ₍2₎   780.794342

NL 0349051   DLC

Liedertafel der deutschen Studenten, Prague.   No. 7 in **M.373.60
Jahres-Bericht des Universitäts-Gesangvereines „Liedertafel der deutschen Studenten" in Prag. Vereinsjahr 1891–1892. Prag. [1892.] 66 pp. 8°.

NL 0349052   MB

Liedertafel Harmonia, *Bernburg.*
... Festschrift und vereinsgeschichte zur hundert-jahrfeier. Bernburg an der Saale, "Liedertafel Harmonia", 1938.
cover-title, 32 p. 21ᵐ.
At head of title: Hundert jahre deutscher männergesang in Bernburg.
Advertising matter interspersed.
CONTENTS.—Veranstaltungsplan.—Texte zu den gesängen.—Geschichte der "Liedertafel Harmonia", zusammengetragen und dargestellt von ihrem chormeister Erich Litte.
1. Music—Germany—Bernburg.   I. Litte, Erich.
                                          40-37864
Library of Congress   ML28.B52L5
                           ₍2₎   784.60624319

NL 0349053   DLC

---

784   **Liedertafel Society of the City of Buffalo.**
L718   Constitution und Nebengesetze des Gesangvereins Buffalo Liedertafel zu Buffalo, N.Y. Amendirt und verbessert den 12. Dec. 1879. [Buffalo?] Grant Bros., printers, 1880.
            19 p. 15 cm.

NL 0349054   N

---

784   **Liedertafel Society of the City of Buffalo.**
L718h   History of the Buffalo Liedertafel and a roster of its members. Published on the occasion of the fair, held February 13–18, 1882. [Buffalo, Gies, lithographers and printers, 1882?]
            16 p. 15 cm.

NL 0349055   N

Lieder-Texte, für die Gesang-Aufführungen am 28. Februar 7., 14. und 21. März 1915 im Zirkus Sarasani (Zirkus-Busch-Gebäude) zum Besten der Kriegshilfe. n.p. [1915?]

[12] p. 24 cm.

NL 0349056   MH

Liedertexte zum feste der Wandervögel...
15p. Strassburg, 1911.

Autographed.

NL 0349057   OC1

Liederwald, Carl Gotthelf Traugott, 1887–
Der begriff "edel" bei Goethe ... Schleiz, F. Weber, 1913.
2 p. l., 171, ₍1₎, p. 21½ᶜᵐ.
Inaug.—diss.—Universität Greifswald.
Lebenslauf.

1. Goethe, Johann Wolfgang von—Language.

NL 0349058   MiU NNU CtY NNU-W

Liederwald, Hans.
Auf einem deutschen Kreuzer in die Welt. Mit einem Geleitwort von Vizeadmiral a. D. Engel. Stuttgart-S., P. Mähler ₍1936₎
104 p. plates, ports. 21 cm.

1. Leipzig (Light cruiser, 1st of the name)   I. Title.
DD106.L5   50-50449

NL 0349059   DLC

Liederwald. 276 der beliebtesten Volks-, Vaterlands-, Soldaten-, Studenten-, Gesellschafts-, Wander- und andere Lieder ...
see under Tonger, Peter Josef, 1845–1917.

SH   **Liedes, Matti.**
293   Suomen kalansaalistilasto vuodelta, 1953.
F5   Otantaan perustuva kokeilu. Helsinki, 1955.
L4   145, [68] ℓ. illus., tables.

           Typewritten.
           At head of title: Maataloushallituksen kalataloudellinen tutkimustoimisto₎

NL 0349061   WaU

Liédet, Loyset, *fl.* 1445–1475.
Histoire de Charles Martel, reproduction des 102 miniatures de Loyset Liédet (1470) ; par J. van den Gheyn ... Bruxelles, Vromant & cᵉ, 1910.
23 p. 102 pl. 21ᵐ.
Reproduction of the miniatures in the prose romance "Histoire de Charles Martel et ses successeurs," compiled by David Aubert (mss. 6, 7, 8 and 9 of the Bibliothèque royale de Belgique)
"Relevé complet des travaux d'enluminure de Loyset Liédet": p. 11–12.
Bibliographical foot-notes.
1. Illumination of books and manuscripts — Specimens, reproductions, etc. 2. Aubert, David, 15th cent.   I. Brussels. Bibliothèque royale de Belgique. Mss. (no. 6-9) II. Gheyn, Joseph van den, 1854–   III. Histoire de Charles Martel et ses successeurs.
                                          10-27282
Library of Congress   ND3399.C4L5

PU-FA NN
NL 0349061-1   DLC CLSU NjP MH OC1MA NcD MiU OC1 OCU

Liédet, Loyset, *fl.* 1445–1475.
... Les histoires romaines de Jean Mansel, illustrées par Loyset Lyedet; 55 planches reproduisant les miniatures et les encadrements des manuscrits 5087 et 5088 de la Bibliothèque de l'Arsenal. Paris, Impr. Berthaud frères, Catala frères, succ. ₍19—₎
1 p. l., 24 p. LV pl. 20½ᵐ.   (Les joyaux de l'Arsenal, III)
In portfolio in case.
At head of title: Henry Martin, administrateur de la Bibliothèque de l'Arsenal.
"Les ... miniatures ... forment l'illustration de deux grands volumes manuscrits exécutés en 1454 pour Philippe le Bon, duc de Bourgogne."—p. ₍1₎

"Naguère encore on ne pouvait nommer ni l'auteur du texte, ni celui des peintures. L'un et l'autre sont maintenant connus ... Le texte ... ne constitue ... qu'une partie de l'ouvrage intitulé 'La fleur des histoires.'"—p. 2.
"Jean Mansel ... fut chargé de passer un marché avec l'enlumineur pour l'illustration de l'ouvrage. Cet enlumineur ... c'est Loyset Lyedet, l'un des miniaturistes les plus féconds de toute l'équipe d'illustrateurs engagés au service de Philippe le Bon. Le document qui nous révèle et le nom de Loyset Lyedet et le rôle de surveillance joué par Jean Mansel au moment de l'exécution matérielle du manuscrit se trouve actuellement aux Archives du Département du Nord."—p. 4.
1. Rome—Hist. 2. Illumination of books and manuscripts—Specimens, reproductions, etc. 3. Philippe le Bon, duke of Burgundy, 1396-1467.   I. Mansel, Jean, 15th cent., comp. II. Martin, Henry, 1852–   ed. III. Paris. Bibliothèque de l'Arsenal. Mss. (5087-88) IV. Title.
                                          CA 19–442 Unrev'd
Library of Congress   ND3399.M25L5

NL 0349063   DLC OC1 CtY ViW FTaSU NN

Liedgens, Alfons: Von der freien Vereinbarung in der Rheinschifffahrt zum Tarifvertrag. [Maschinenschrift.] 69, m S. 4° [Lag nicht vor.] — Auszug: [Maschinenschrift]: 2 Bl. 8°
Gießen, Phil. Diss. v. 21. Juli 1924   [U 24. 3336

NL 0349064   ICRL

Liedgens, Josef
Ueber den einfluss des areens auf die eigenschaften des flusseisens
Inaug. Diss. Berlin, Techn. Hoch, 1912

NL 0349065   ICRL PU

Liedgren, Emil, 1879–
Den andliga sången på anglosaxisk mark; en historisk översikt med hänsyn till svenska förhållanden, av Emil Liedgren... Stockholm: Sveriges kristliga studentrörelses förlag₍, 1927₎.
175 p. 12°.

1. Poetry, Religious—Hist. and   crit.
N. Y. P. L.   November 28, 1928

NL 0349066   NN MH-AH PPAmSwM

Liedgren, Emil, 1879–   comp.
Communio in adorando et serviendo oecumenica
see under title

Liedgren, Emil, 1879–
Johan Olof Wallin i yngre år (1779–1810) Stockholm, Svenska kyrkans diakonistyrelses bokförlag ₍1929₎

268 p. illus., ports. 22cm.

1. Wallin, Johan Olof, 1779–1839.

NL 0349068   MnU CtY-D

VOLUME 332

Liedgren, Emil, 1879–
274.85   Neologien, romantiken uppvaknandet,
S968   1809–1823. Stockholm, Svenska Kyrkans Dia-
bd.6   konistyrelses Bokförlag ₍1946₎
     383 p. illus. 23 cm. (Svenska kyrkans
     historia, VI, 2. delen)

     "Källor och litteratur": p. 337–376.
     1. Religious thought. Sweden. 19th century.
   2. Sweden. Church history. I. Title
            ₍Full name: Karl Gustaf
            Emil Liedgren₎

NL   0349069   NcD CtY-D

Liedgren, Emil, 1879–
WB   Präster och poeter. Uppsala, J. A.
34762   Lindblad ₍1933₎
     191 p. illus.

     1. Authors, Swedish.
     cdu

NL   0349070   CtY

245.397 Liedgren, Emil, 1879–
L623s   Svensk psalm och andlig visa. Olaus Petri-före-
     läsningar i Uppsala mars 1924, av Emil Liedgren.
     Stockholm, Svenska kyrkans diakonistyrelses bok-
     förlag ₍1926₎
     577, ₍1₎p.
     "Register över omnämnda psalmförfattare": p.
     ₍560₎–575.

     1. Hymns, Swedish--Hist. & crit. 2. Svenska
     kyrkan--Hymns--Hist.& crit. I. Olaus Petri-före-
     läsningar.

NL   0349071   IU

Liedgren, Emil, 1879–   comp.
     Svensk psalmdiktning i urval för skolor
     och självstudium. Lund, Gleerup ₍1929₎
     44 p. (Skrifter utgivna av Moders-
     målslärarnas förening ₍nr.33₎)

NL   0349072   CU

BV500   LIEDGREN,EMIL,1879–
.L7   ...Den svenska psalmboken;en historisk överblick
     av Emil Liedgren. 5.genomsedda upplagan. Stock-
     holm,Sveriges kristliga studentrörelses förlag₍1929₎
     113,₍1₎p. 19cm. (Sveriges kristliga studentrö-
     relses skriftserie. N:r 8)

     1.Svenska psalmboken. 2.Hymns,Swedish--Hist.&
     crit.

NL   0349073   ICU

BV501
.L8L5
1952   Liedgren, Emil, 1879–
     Den svenska psalmboken; en historisk överblick.
     7. uppl. Stockholm, Sveriges kristliga studentrörelses förlag ₍1952₎
     126, ₍2₎ p. 19 cm.
     "Litteratur": p. 126–₍127₎

     1. Svenska kyrkan. Psalmbok.

                A 53–3499
     Harvard Univ. Library
     for Library of Congress   ₍1₎

NL   0349074   MH DLC

F-44.7 Liedgren, Emil, 1879–
L6235   Vox angelica; hymnologiska skisser
     och studier... Stockholm, Svenska
     kyrkans diakonistyrelses bokförlag
     ₍1917₎
     196 p. 23ᶜᵐ.

NL   0349075   NjPT

Liedgren, Emil, 1879–
     Wallins läroår som psalmdiktare 1806–1812. Med en
     inledning om religionens plats i sjuttonhundratalspoesien
     och den estetisk motiverade psalmboksreformen ... Upp-
     sala, Almqvist & Wiksells boktryckeri-a.-b., 1916.
     xv, 246 p., 1 l. 24ᶜᵐ.
     Akademisk afhandling—Upsala.
     "Särtryck ur Kyrkohistorisk årsskrift 1915–1917."
     "Källor och litteratur": p. ₍v₎–xii.

     1. Wallin, Johan Olof, 1779–1839.
           ₍Full name: Karl Gustaf Emil Liedgren₎

                   20–6251

     Library of Congress   BV330.W3L5

NL   0349076   DLC CtY MH ICU

Liedgren, Jan, 1909–
     Inrättandet av stiftsstyrelse i Karlstad. Ett trehundraårs-
     minne. Karlstad, Nya Wermlands-Tidningens boktr., 1947.
     24 p. facsims. 25 cm.
     Cover title.
     Includes bibliography.

     1. Karlstad, Sweden (Diocese)
                Full name: Lars Jan Liedgren.
     BX8040.K3L5   60–43096*

NL   0349077   DLC

Liedgren, Karl Gustaf Emil

          see

Liedgren, Emil, 1879–

Liedgren, Lars Jan
   see Liedgren, Jan, 1909–

Liedhegener ₍Augustus₎. "De noma. 29 pp.
   8°. Bonna, C. Krüger, 1856.

NL   0349080   DNLM

Liedhegener, Clemens
Lng2   Das Würzburger Universitätsgut Mariaburg-
W9   hausen von 1582–1880. Lucka S.–A.,1915.
+1   Pamphlet
     Inaug.–Diss. – Würzburg.
     Issued also as Wirtschafts- und Verwaltungs-
     studien mit besonderer Berücksichtigung Bay-
     erns,52.

NL   0349081   CtY MiU ICRL MH

HB41   Liedhegener, Clemens.
.W77   Das Würzburger Universitätsgut Mariaburghau-
no.52   sen von 1582–1880. Leipzig, W. Scholl, 1915.
     xii, 82 p. tables. (Wirtschafts- und Ver-
     waltungsstudien mit besonderer Berücksichti-
     gung ₍Bayerns, 52)
     Includes bibliography.

     1. Würzburg. Universität. I. Title: Maria-
     burghausen von 1582–1880.

NL   0349082   ICU NN PU ICJ

Liedholm, Alf Anton Fredrik B:son, 1898–
     Auguste Rodin. ₍Stockholm₎ Lindfors bokförlag ₍1947₎
     263 p. plates. 22 cm.
     Bibliography: p. 256–258.

     1. Rodin, Auguste, 1840–1917.

     NB553.R7L58   48–18574*

NL   0349083   DLC NN

LIEDHOLM, ALF ANTON FREDRIK B:SON,
     1898–
     Einar Palme, en generations-
     förmedlare. ₍Stockholm₎ Medéns
     ₍1951₎
     104p. illus.,plates(4 col.) 18cm.

NL   0349084   NhD

Liedholm, Alf Anton Fredrik B:son, 1898–
     Gustave Courbet, den moderna realismens fader. ₍Stock-
     holm₎ Lindfors ₍1945₎
     187 p. illus., ports., map. 21 cm.
     Bibliography: p. 186.

     1. Courbet, Gustave, 1819–1877.

     ND553.C9L5   50–29507

NL   0349085   DLC

Liedholm, Alf Anton Fredrik B:son, 1898–
     Konstnärens värld; en studie i konstnärspsykologi. Lund,
     H. Ohlssons boktr., 1932–
     v. 25 cm.
     Cover of v. 1 has imprint: Lund, Gleerupska univ.-bokhandeln.
     Vol. 1 is the author's thesis, Uppsala.
     Extra t.-p., with thesis note, inserted in v. 1.
     "Litteraturförteckning": v. 1, p. ₍230₎–237.

     1. Art—Psychology. I. Title.

     N71.L5 1932   701   34–41752 rev*

NL   0349086   DLC NjP ICRL CtY NNC PU

Liedholm, Astri, 1903–   tr.

Ehnmark, Ernst, 1897–
     ... The gall stone disease, a clinical-statistical study, by Ernst
     Ehnmark. Göteborg, Elanders boktryckeri aktiebolag, 1939.

Liedholm, Astri, 1903–
     A phonological study of the Middle English romance
     Arthour and Merlin (ms. Auchinleck) Uppsala, Almqvist
     & Wiksells boktr., 1941.
     xxiii, 192 p. facsim. 25 cm.
     Inaug. diss.—Uppsala.
     Bibliography: p. ₍ix₎–xvi.

     1. Arthour and Merlin. 2. English language — Middle English
     (1100–1500)—Phonology.
          Full name: Astri Sofia Mathilda Liedholm.

     PR2065.A41L5   821.1   49–39232*

     NcU NcGU
NL   0349088   DLC PU CtY NNC MH CU ICU NjP OU TxU IU

Liedholm, Astri, 1903–   tr.

RC316
.S8B4   Berg, Gunnar, 1906–
1939   The prognosis of open pulmonary tuberculosis; a clinical-
     statistical analysis. ₍Translator, A. Liedholm₎ Lund,
     Printed by H. Ohlsson, 1939.

VOLUME 332

Liedholm, Astri, 1903–   tr.

Lunding, Karl, 1896–
... The symptomatology of diverticulum formations of the colon, especially with regard to the catalase action in faeces, by Karl Lunding. Lund, Printed by H. Ohlsson, 1935.

Liedholm, John Gustav Hernfrid, 1895–
Genum le't, dikter av Jönn (John Liedholm) Med teckningar av författaren. ₍Falköping, 1945₎
82 p. illus. 32 cm.

1. Swedish language—Dialects—Skaraborg—Texts.   I. Title.

PD5828.L5   56–38059 ‡

NL 0349091   DLC

Liedholm, Knut Alvar, 1905–
Studien über das Verhalten des Venendruckes beim Valsalvaschen Versuch. Lund, H. Ohlssons Buchdr., 1939.
₍2₎ 1, ₍3₎–213 p. illus., diagrs., 2 fold. tables. 24 cm.
Akademische Abhandlung—Lund.
Added t.-p., with thesis note, inserted.
"Diese Arbeit erscheint auch in Acta medica Scandinavica als Supplementum cvi."
Tr. by E. Blauert; summary in English by Christina Hedström.
"Literaturverzeichnis": p. ₍204₎–213.

1. Blood—Pressure. 2. Respiration.   I. Blauert, Ernst, tr.
II. Hedström, Christina, 1916–

QP101.L53 1939   Med 47–3457*

NL 0349092   DLC ViU ICJ

Liedig (Anton). "Zur Anatomie der Uterusschleimhaut beim Menschen: Das Flimmerepithel und die dadurch erzeugte Strömungsrichtung. 25 pp. 8°. *Würzburg, A. Göb & Co.,* 1893.

NL 0349093   DNLM

Liedjesboek of verzameling van Vlaamsche volksliederen. 23 pp. *Gent: Snoeck-Ducaju & Zoon,* [189–?] 24°.

NL 0349094   NN

Liedke, Alfred, 1867–
Die verbreitungsweise der diphtherie.
Inaug. diss. Koenigsberg, 1901.
Bibl.

NL 0349095   ICRL DNLM MH CtY

Liedke, Erwin, 1910–
Das Dienststrafrecht der Ruhestandsbeamten ... Würzburg, 1935.
Inaug.-Diss. – Frankfurt am Main.
Lebenslauf.
"Literaturverzeichnis": 4th–6th prelim. ℓ.

NL 0349096   CtY

Liedke, Fritz, 1904–
Die Elbinger Industrie von 1772 bis zur Gründung der Schichauwerft im Jahre 1837 ... von Fritz Liedke ...   Elbing: E. Wernich, 1932. 68 p. incl. tables. 22½ cm.

Inaugural-Dissertation — Königsberg, 1931.
Lebenslauf.
Bibliography, p. ₍3₎–₍5₎

1. Industries—Germany—Elbing.
N.Y.P.L.   September 30, 1938

NL 0349097   NN MH PU CtY

Kress Room
Liedke, Gottlieb Samuel, 1803–1852
Rechnungs-abschluss und verwaltungs-bericht der Spargesellschaft des Hamburger thor-bezirks zu Berlin (Erste sparperiode v. 1. April–1. Octbr. 1845) ... Berlin, In commission der Enslinschen buchhandlung (F. Seelhaar.), 1846.
30, [1] p. 19.5 cm.

1. Spargesellschaft des Hamburger thor-bezirks, Berlin. 2. Berlin - Poor. 3. Benefit societies - Berlin.

NL 0349098   MH-BA

Kress Room
Liedke, Gottlieb Samuel, 1803–1852.
Die schlacht- und mahlsteuer und die armen; oder: kann die im interesse der armuth beantragte aufhebung der schlacht- und mahlsteuer den armen wirklich zu gute kommen? und wenn nicht: wie wird den armen ein wünschenswerther ersatz für diese steuerlast gewährt ... Berlin, In commission der Enslin'schen buchhandlung (F. Geelhaar.), 1847.
24 p. 20.5 cm.

Bound with Ueber die nothwendigkeit der umwandelung der mahl- und schlachtsteuer von einem bürger, 1847.

1. Bread - Taxation. 2. Consumption (Economics - Taxation. 3. Meat - Taxation. 4. Taxation - Prussia. 5. Poor - Prussia. I. Title.

NL 0349100   MH-BA

Liedke, Gustav Adolf
Der Regress mangels Annahme. Ein Beitrag zu Artikel 25 und 26 der deutschen Wechselordnung ... von Gustav Adolf Liedke ... Greifswald, J. Abel, 1899.
45 p. 22½ cm.
Inaug.-Diss. - Greifswald.
"Litteratur": p. ₍6₎–6.

NL 0349101   MH-L ICRL

Liedke, Hans, 1882–
Sind einzelne Gemeindemitglieder zur Klage aus Gemeindeservituten aktiv legitimiert? ... von Hans Liedke ... Greifswald, J. Abel, 1904.
39 p. 21½ cm.
Inaug.-Diss. - Greifswald.
"Benutzte Literatur": p. ₍7₎

NL 0349102   MH-L ICRL NN

Liedke, Herbert R   1905–
Literary criticism and romantic theory in the work of Achim von Arnim, by Herbert R. Liedke ... New York, Columbia university press, 1937.
x p., 1 l. 187 p., 1 l. 22¼ᶜᵐ. (*Half-title:* Columbia university Germanic studies, ed. by R. H. Fife. New ser., no. 6)
Thesis (PH. D.)—Columbia university, 1937.
Vita.
Published also without thesis note.
Bibliography: p. 179–182.

1. *Arnim, Ludwig Achim, freiherr von, 1781–1835.   I. Title.
                                                38–6461
Library of Congress   PT1809.Z5L5 1937
Columbia Univ. Libr.   ₍2₎   [833.66] 830 81

NL 0349103   NNC CaBVaU OrU NBuU CU UU ViU DLC

Liedke, Herbert R   1905–
Literary criticism and romantic theory in the work of Achim von Arnim, by Herbert R. Liedke ... New York, Columbia university press, 1937.
x p., 1 l., 187 p. 22½ cm. (*Half-title:* Columbia university Germanic studies, ed. by R. H. Fife. New ser., no. 6)
Issued also as thesis (PH. D.) Columbia university.
Bibliography: p. 179–182.

I. *Arnim, Ludwig Achim, freiherr von, 1781–1831.   I. Title.
PT1809.Z5L5 1937a   38–6460
———Copy 2.   PD25.C6 n. s., no. 6
                  (430.82) [833.66] 830.81
                  PU AAP

NL 0349104   DLC FMU ScU OrCS GU NSyU OU NcU OO MB

Liedke, Kathe Beyer, 1902–
Lens competence in *Rana pipiens* ₍by₎ Kathe Beyer Liedke ... ₍Philadelphia, Press of the Wistar institute of anatomy and biology, 1942₎
1 p. l., 331–351 p., 1 l. incl. 2 pl. 25½ᵐ.
Revision of thesis (PH. D.)—Columbia university, 1942.
"Reprint from the Journal of experimental zoology, vol. 90, no. 3, August, 1942."
Vita.
"Literature cited": p. 345–347.

1. Eye. 2. Frogs. 3. Embryology—Batrachia.   I. Title.
                                          A 43–2645
Columbia univ. Libraries
for Library of Congress   QL949.L5
                  ₍3₎†

NL 0349105   NNC DLC

Liedke (Otto Gottlieb). "Kritische Betrachtungen der herrschende Ansichten über die Ursachen der Eintritts der Geburt. 55 pp. 12°. *Berlin, G. Schade,* [1883].

NL 0349106   DNLM

Liedke, Otto Karl, 1906–
Aktivismus und Passivismus in der erzählenden Prosa der modernen deutschen Literatur. ₍Ithaca, N. Y.₎ 1937.
182 l. 28 cm.
Thesis (Ph. D.)—Cornell University, September, 1937.

1. German literature—Hist. & crit.

NL 0349107   NIC

Liedkowna, Charlotte.
Sylvia, ein kammerspiel in drei akten ... Berlin, Drei masken verlag, *1938.
99 p. 20ᵐ.
Reproduced from type-written copy.

I. Title.
                                    42–28641
                                    Brief cataloging
Library of Congress   PT2623.I 355S9

NL 0349108   DLC

Liedl, Charles, joint author.

Calder, Alexander.
Animal sketching, by Alexander Calder and Charles Liedl. 5th ed. rev. Pelham, N. Y., Bridgman publishers, inc. ₍1936₎

Liedl, Charles.
How to draw animals. New York, Greenberg ₍1953₎
68 p. (chiefly illus.) 25 cm.

1. Animal painting and illustration.   I. Title.

NC780.L47   743.6   53–9333 ‡

NL 0349110   DLC CaBVa WaS WaT TxU MB OCl

VOLUME 332

799.2971
L623h   **Liedl, Charles**
     Hunting with rifle and pencil.   Fredericton, N.B., Brunswick Press ₍c1955₎
     186p.   illus.

     Pencil sketches by the author.

     1. Hunting - Canada.   I. Title.

NL   0349111   PP CaBViP CaBViPA MB MH CaBVa

FILM
83N361   **Liedl, Erich.**
DL62   Heinzes Italienerleben verglichen mit dem
     Goethes.   Wien, 1947.
     112, ₍3₎l.

     Diss.--Vienna.
     Bibliography: leaf ₍114₎
     Microfilm (negative) of typescript in the
     Universitätsbibliothek, Wien. Wien, 1969.
     1 reel.   35mm.

NL   0349112   IU

Liedl, Eugen, 1926-
     Die Zulässigkeit oder Unzulässigkeit des ordentlichen
Rechtsweges nach § 22, der in der Amerikanischen Zone
erlassenen Gesetze über die Verwaltungsgerichtsbarkeit und
der Verordnung Nr. 165 der britischen Militärregierung über
die Verwaltungsgerichtsbarkeit. München, 1951.
     ii, 84 l.   31 cm.
     Typescript (carbon)
     Inaug.-Diss.--Munich.
     Vita.
     Bibliography: leaves 79-81.
     1. Jurisdiction—Germany (Federal Republic, 1949-　) 2. Administrative courts—Germany (Federal Republic, 1949-　) I. Title.

                                     55-17342

NL   0349113   DLC

Liedl, Kurt, 1890-
     Der strafrechtliche Inhalt des bayerischen Gesetzes über das Lotteriespiel
vom 11. Oktober 1912 ... von Kurt Liedl
... München, Heindl & Co., 1914.
     67 p.   22cm.

     Inaug.-Diss. - Erlangen.
     "Literatur und Abkürzungen": p.5-6.

NL   0349114   MH-L MH NIC ICRL

Liedl, Michael.
     Der katholische Priester im Gebete und in
seinen gewöhnlichen Verrichtungen; ein bequemes
Vademecum für katholische Seelsorger. 5. verb.
u. verm. Aufl.   Lindau, Johann Th. Stettner,
1854.
     xii, 384p 13cm

NL   0349115   MnCS

Liedl, Michael
     Der Katholische Priester im Gebete und in seinen gewöhnlichen Verrichtungen. Ein bequemes
Vademecum für katholische Seelsorger. Mit benützung des kleinen Rituals für die Diözese Passau
herausgegeben von Michael Liedl ... Passau, Fr.
Winkler, 1857.

     145 p. 13 cm.

     1. Pastoral theology. 2. Priests - Prayerbooks
and devotions. 3. Priests - Spiritual life.
4. Rites and cerem　onies. I. Title.

NL   0349116   PLatS

Liedl, Michael.
     Lehr- und Mahnworte, der christlichen Jungfrau an's Herz gelegt. 2. Ausgabe.   Passau,
A. Deiters, 1878.
     viii, 285 p. 21 cm.

NL   0349117   PLatS

1882-
Liedloff, August. Über die Vie Saint Franchois. (Erlangen 1910:
Junge.) 59 S. 8° ¶ (Aus: Romanische Forschungen. Bd 29.)
Berlin, Phil. Diss. v. 16. Febr. 1910, Ref. Tobler
    [Geb. 4. Febr. 82 Goslar; Wohnort: Charlottenburg; Staatsangeh.: Braunschweig; Vorbildung: Gymn. Wolfenbüttel Reife O. 01; Studium: Berlin 2,
Zürich 1, Berlin 7 S.; Rig. 18. Nov. 09.]   [U 10. 207

NL   0349118   ICRL DHN CtY PU

Liedloff, August, 1882-   *4682.6.29
     Über die Vie Saint Franchois.
     (In Romanische Forschungen. Band 29, pp. 72-130. Erlangen.
1911.)

L174 — Vie Saint Franchois. — Francis of Assisi, Saint, 1182-1226.

NL   0349119   MB MiU

Liedloff, Curt Clemens, 1860-
     De tempestatis, necyomanteae, inferorum
descriptionibus, quae apud poetas romanos primi
p. Ch. saeculi leguntur ... Scripsit Curtius
Liedloff.   Lipsiae, Leopold & Baer, 1884.
     28 p., 1 l.   23 cm.
     Inaug.-Diss. - Leipzig.
     Vita.

NL   0349120   CU ICRL NjP PU PHC

Liedloff, Ernst.
     Teaching English; ein Buch für Lehrer.
Braunschweig, G. Westermann, 1951.
     302 p.   illus.
     1. English language - Study and
teaching - German students.   I. Title.

NL   0349121   CLU NN NNC-T

LIEDLOFF, Kurt.
     Die nachbildung griechischer und römischer
muster in Seneca's Troades und Agamemmon.
[Progr.] Grimma, 1902.

     4°.   pp.(2),18.

NL   0349122   MH

Liedloff, Kurt Werner
     see   Liedloff, Werner, 1895-

            Liedloff, Werner, 1895-
Lbb89   Beiträge zur Psychologie der mathematischen
N9   Schulbegabung ... [Langensalza] 1927.
1   Pamphlet
     Inaug.-Diss. - Jena.
     Lebenslauf.
     "Diese Arbeit erscheint gleichzeitig in erweiterter Form als Heft 6 der Jenaer Beiträge
zur Jugend- und Erziehungspsychologie.
Langensalza 1927."

NL   0349124   CtY ICRL MiU MH

Liedloff, Werner, 1875 -
     Beiträge zur psychologie der mathematischen schulbegabung, von Werner Liedloff.   ₍Langensalza, J. Beltz,
1928₎
    94 p. diagrs.   23ᶜᵐ.   *(On cover:* Jenaer beiträge zur jugend- u. erziehungspsychologie, hrsg. von A. Argelander, W. Peters, O Scheibner. ₍hft.₎ 6)
    Half-title.
    "Aus der Psychologischen anstalt der Universität Jena."
    Bibliographical foot-notes.

     1. Mathematics—Study and teaching.   2. Educational psychology.

NL   0349125   MiU MH CtY

Liedloff, Werner, 1895-
     Die entwicklung des höheren schulwesens in Thüringen von
der marxistischen revolution 1918 bis zur nationalsozialistischen erhebung 1933, von dr. dr. Werner Liedloff ... Borna,
Verlag Robert Roske, 1936.
    vii, 86 p. tables (2 fold.) diagr.   21ᶜᵐ.
    "Literatur": p. v-vii.

     1. Education—Thuringia.   2. Education, Secondary.
                                         A C 37-982
    Teachers college library,   Columbia univ.
      for Library of Congress   ₍2₎

NL   0349126   NNC-T

W 4
B51   **Liedmann, August Heinrich,** 1903-
1940   Über die Aufhebung der gerinnungshemmenden Wirkung von Algenpräparaten durch
Thionin, und Prüfung dieser Algenpräparate auf hämolytische Wirkung in vivo
und vitro.   Borna, Noske, 1940.
     15, ₍4₎ p.

     Inaug.-Diss. - Berlin
     Bibliography: p. ₍15₎

NL   0349127   DNLM

PA
4369   **Liedmeier, Christiana.**
A38   Plutarchus' Biographie van Aemilius
L71   Paullus; historische commentaar.   Utrecht,
     Dekker & Van de Vegt, 1935.
     312 p.   25cm.

     Inserted at end is "Plutarchus Vita
Aemilii Paulli tekst." in Greek.
     "Résumé de la thèse et des principaux
problèmes envisagés." ₍290₎-299 p.

NL   0349128   NIC IU NjP MiU

₍**Liedmeier, J**   M   ₎ 1915-
     De kinderkruistocht, door Agnes van der Marke ₍pseud.₎
Tilburg, Nederland's Boekhuis ₍1947₎
    189 p. illus. 21 cm.

     1. Children's crusade, 1212—Fiction.   I. Title.
    PZ15.L5   49-12601*

NL   0349129   DLC

264.025
C286l   **Liedsman van den deugdzamen Christen.**
1914   Geestelijk handboek bevattende litanieën,
gebeden en oefeningen. Nieuwe uitgave.
₍Turnhout, Brepols, 1914.
     124p. front. 11cm.

     1. Catholic   Church. Prayer
books & devotions.   Dutch. 2. Catholic
Church. Liturgy & ri　al. Dutch. I. Title.

NL   0349130   KU

VOLUME 332

Liedstrand, Emil.
Social insurance in Sweden, by Dr. Emil Liedstrand ...
(*In* International labour review, Geneva. Feb. 1924, v. 9, p. 177–195)

1. Insurance, State and compulsory—Sweden. 2. ¡Insurance, Social—Sweden¡ I. Title.

Library, U. S. Dept. of   Labor   L 27–117
                               ¡2¡

NL   0349131   DL MiU

---

823   **Liedstrand, Frithjof,** 1897–
N17uY1   ... Metapher und vergleich in "The unfortunate
        traveller" von Thomas Nashe und bei seinen vorbildern François Rabelais und Pietro Aretino. Weimar, G. Uschmann, 1929.
        ix, 138, ¡1¡p.

        Inaug.-diss.--Münster.
        Vita.
        "Literatur": p.¡vii¡-ix.

NL   0349132   IU NcD MH PU-F

Liedtke, Antoni.
...Biblja gutenberga w Pelplinie.   Toruń: Towarzystwo
bibljofilów im. Lelewela, 1936. 11 p. illus. (facsims.) 35cm.

Bibliography included in "Przypisy," 1 p. at end.

892539A. 1. Bible. Latin. 1455.   Vulgate. 2. Gutenberg, Johann,
¡1397?–1468¡ I. Towarzystwo   bibljofilów imienia Lelewela, Thorn,
Poland.   Poland.
N. Y. P. L.   July 1, 1937

NL   0349133   NN WU MH CtY

DK425   **Liedtke, Antoni.**
L5   Walka księcia Jana Opolskiego "Kropidły" z
        krzyżakami w obronie majątkowych praw diecezji
Stack   włocławskiej.   Toruń, Nakł. Towarzystwa Naukowego, 1932.
        xv,138 p. 25cm. (Roczniki Towarzystwa Naukowego w Toruniu, 38)
        Summary in French.
        Bibliography p.¡vii¡-xv.

        1.Poland - Hist. - Jagellons, 1386–1572.
        2.Opolsky, Jan, Bishop. I.Title. II.Ser.¡ Towarzystwo Naukowe w Toruniu. Roczniki, 38.
        NUC ' SC

NL   0349134   CSt NcD CtY NNC

Liedtke (Eduard) [1843-]. *Die physiologische Wirkung des Brucin. 02 pp., 1 l. 8°.
Königsberg, E. J. Dalkowski, 1876.

NL   0349135   DNLM

Liedtke, Ernst, 1902–
Die uebernahme von hypothekenschulden bei grundstücksverwässerungsverträgen durch den erwerber unter besonderer berücksichtigung der rechtsprechung.
Inaug. Diss.   Breslau, 1930?

NL   0349136   ICRL

820.5   **Liedtke, Ernst Artur,** 1886–
L72   Die numerale auffassung der kollektiva im
        verlaufe der englischen sprachgeschichte ...
        von Ernst Liedtke ...   Königsberg i.Pr., Karg
        & Mannock, 1910.
        212 p.,1 ł.   21cm.
        Inaug.-diss.--Königsberg.
        Lebenslauf.

        1. English language--Noun.

NL   0349137   MiU IU PU CtY MH NN NcD ICRL

Liedtke, F   **W.**
Tax calculator. This work comprises the most complete system of tables ever published, and is designed especially for the use of clerks, auditors, treasurers and others, to facilitate the work of computing and balancing tax lists ... Comp. by F. W. Liedtke and Lee Love. Des Moines, Ia., Mills & company, 1877.

1 p. l., 61 p. 29 x 25cm.

1. Taxation—Rates and tables.   I. Love, Lee, joint author.

Library of Congress   H J9993.L4   8–23488†

NL   0349138   DLC

Liedtke, Franz, 1888–
... Zur Säuglingssterblichkeit in Königsberg
i. Pr. ...   Leipzig, 1913.
        Inaug.-Diss. - Königsberg.
        Lebenslauf.
        "Sonderabdruck aus der 'Zeitschrift für
Hygiene und Infektionskrankheiten'. Bd. LXXIV.
1913."
        "Literatur-Verzeichnis": p. 53–54.

NL   0349139   CtY MH

Liedtke, Friedrich Wilhelm, 1861–
A B C des skat in deutsch und englisch von F. W.
Liedtke ... Philadelphia, Pa., Schaefer & Koradi ¡1909¡
51 p. 15cm.

English part has special t-p.

1. Skat (Game)

Library of Congress   GV1257.L6   9–6869

NL   0349140   DLC PPGi

Liedtke, Friedrich Wilhelm, 1861–
Nordöstlicher sängerbund.
Sängerfest-almanach des Nordöstlichen sängerbundes
von Amerika, nebst preis-tabellen nach vereinen und
städten klassifizirt; zusammengestellt von F. W. Liedtke.
¡Philadelphia, J. M. Kaupp, printer, °1912¡–

NL   0349141

Liedtke, Friedrich Wilhelm, 1908–
Über hydrops des foetus und der Placenta...
Greifswald, 1931.   77 p.
        Inaug. Diss. Königsberg, 1931.
        Lebenslauf.
        Bibliography.

NL   0349142   CtY

Liedtke, Friedrich Wilhelm, 1913–
... Spätergebnisse nach Schädelbasisfrakturen unter besonderer Berücksichtigung
der Unfallbegutachtung ... Lengerich i.W.,
1938.
        Inaug.-Diss. - Greifswald.
        Lebenslauf.
        "Literaturnachweis": p. 25–26.

NL   0349143   CtY

Liedtke, Gerhard Pommeranz-
see
Pommeranz-Liedtke, Gerhard.

Liedtke, Günter, illus.

Klaffke, Bernhard, comp.
Seht, das ist Deutschland! Ein buntes kartenbilderbuch,
zusammengestellt und herausgegeben von Bernhard Klaffke
und gezeichnet von Günter Liedtke und Wilhelm Plünnecke.
Leipzig, Bibliographisches institut ag. ¡°1936¡

Liedtke, Hans, 1909–
...Shelley — durch Berkeley und Drummond beeinflusst?
... Von Hans Liedtke...   Greifswald: H. Adler, 1933.   40 p.
23cm.

At head of title: Englische philologie.
Inaugural-Dissertation — Greifswald, 1933.
Lebenslauf.
"Bibliographie," p. 39–40.

752959A. 1. Shelley, Percy Bysshe,   1792–1822. 2. Berkeley, George,
bp. of Cloyne, 1685–1753. 3. Drum-   mond, Sir William, 1770?–1828.
N. Y. P. L.   May 16, 1935

NL   0349146   NN IU MiU PU CtY CSmH

Liedtke, Harry, 1888–1945.
Das Harry Liedtke - Buch
see under title   [Supplement]

Div.S.   **Liedtke, Heinrich Viktor Theodor,** 1870–
Pem.   Die Beweise für das Dasein Gottes bei
Coll.   Anselm von Canterbury und Renatus Cartesius.
1745   Heidelberg, J. Hörning, 1893.
        37 p.   22 cm.

        Inaug.-Diss. - Heidelberg.
        Lebenslauf.
        Bibliography: p. 1.
        1. Anselm, Saint, Abp. of Canterbury, 1033–
1109. 2. Descartes, René, 1596–1650. I. Title.

NL   0349148   NcD CU MH ICRL PU

Liedtke, Heinz, 1910–
Kellogg-Pakt und völkischer Staat ...
Würzburg, 1936.
        Inaug.-Diss. - Köln.
        Lebenslauf.
        "Literaturübersicht": 4th-5th prelim l.

NL   0349149   CtY

Liedtke, Irmgard
*Diabetes in der Schwangerschaft und Geburt [Berlin] 43p. 8° Charlottenb., 1937.

NL   0349150   DNLM CtY

Liedtke, Karl Heinz, 1904–
Biologisch-chemische reinigung Königsberger
abwässer einschliesslich der sulfitzellstoffschlempen nach dem belebtschlammverfahren. ...
140 p.
        Inaug. Diss. - Königsberg i. Pr., 1936.
        Lebenslauf.

NL   0349151   ICRL CtY

Liedtke, Kurt: Das Hotelgewerbe und seine Stellung im deutschen
Wirtschaftsleben. [Maschinenschrift.] 136 S. m. Tab. 4°. —
Auszug: Königsberg i. P. 1924. S. 202–207. 8°
Königsberg, R.- u. staatswiss. Diss. v. 26. Juli 1924   [U 24. 6907

NL   0349152   ICRL

VOLUME 332

Liedtke, Leo.
Das Füsilier-regiment Graf Roon (Ostpreussisches) nr. 33 im weltkriege 1914/1918. Nach amtlichen unterlagen, berichten von mitkämpfern und eigenen erinnerungen verfasst und herausgegeben von prof. Liedtke ... Mit zahlreichen bildern, skizzen und übersichtskarten. Berlin, Bernard & Graefe, 1935.

4 p. l., 5–486 p. front., illus. (incl. coat of arms) plates, ports. 6 fold. maps (in pocket) 24½ᶜᵐ. (*Added t.-p.:* Deutsche tat im weltkrieg 1914/1918; geschichten der kämpfe deutscher truppen ... bd. 26)

"Zum geleit" signed: v. Falk.
Blank pages for "Meine dienstzeit" (₂) following half-title)
1. European war, 1914–1918—Regimental histories—Germany—Infantry—Füsilier-regiment Graf Roon.

A C 35–2705

Title from N.Y. Pub.   Libr. Printed by L.C.

NL 0349153   NN

Liedtke, Max
Ueber o-a dimethyl-chinaldin.
Inaug. diss. Freiburg, 1902.
29p.

NL 0349154   ICRL PU

Liedtke, Paul.   610.6322
                                5   v.3
... Zur Geschichte der Wurzelbehandlung, von Dr. Paul Liedtke ... Greifswald, L. Bamberg, 1927.

44 p. 24ᶜᵐ. (Arbeiten der deutsch-nordischen Gesellschaft für Geschichte der Medizin, der Zahnheilkunde und der Naturwissenschaften ... 3)

Anmerkungen: p. 39–41; Literatur-Angaben: p. 42–44.

NL 0349155   ICJ PPWI

Liedtke, Rudolph Henry von, 1891–
The superheterodyne, by Dr. R. H. von Liedtke ... chief engineer, Radio research laboratories, Fort Wayne, Indiana. Fort Wayne, Ind., Radio research publications, *1935.

2 p. l., 35 (i. e. 44) numb. l., 3 l. tables, diagrs. 28¼ x 23ᶜᵐ.

Cover-title: The superheterodyne receiver ...
Mimeographed.

1. Radio—Apparatus and supplies.   I. Radio research laboratories, Fort Wayne, Ind.   II. Title.

Cincinnati. Univ. Library   TK6565.S8L5
for Library of Congress   (2)

A 38–1166

NL 0349156   OCU IdU CU

281.12
V
Liedtke, Rudolph Henry von, 1891–
A brief of the agricultural plan... by R.H. von Liedtke... (n.p., 1936)
67 l. port. 30cm.

Mimeographed.
Caption title used.

NL 0349157   DNAL

(Liedtke, Rudolph Henry von, 1891–
The plan for agriculture. n.p.
(Radio research laboratories, c1936.
67 l. front.(port.) 29½cm.
Mimeographed.
Caption title.
Various pagings.

NL 0349158   DL

Liedtke, Rudolf Max Willi, 1889–
... Beiträge zur frage von alterserscheinungen am rehgehörn ... Neudamm, Druck: J. Neumann, 1920.

4 p., 1 l. 24½ᶜᵐ.

Inaug.-diss.—Tierärztl. hochschule, Berlin. Auszug.
Lebenslauf.

1. Deer. 2. Horns.

Agr 26–149

Library, U. S. Dept. of   Agriculture 412.7L622

NL 0349159   DNAL

Liedtke, Traute, 1911–
Die Magenkrebs-Kranken der Ludolf-Krehl-Klinik zu Heidelberg (die Jahrgänge 1931–1935) Würzburg, Mayr, 1938.
19, (2) p. illus.

Inaug.-Diss. - Heidelberg.
Bibliography: p. (20)

NL 0349160   DNLM

Liedtki,
Andeutungen über die inneren Zustände des röm. Reiches ... der 2 letzten jahrhunderte.
n.p., 1867.

NL 0349161   NjP

Liedtki,
Der delphische Apollontempel seiner weltgeschichtlichen Bedeutung nach.   n.p., 1861.

NL 0349162   NjP

Liedts, Augusta (Godin) baronne, 1850–1885.

Bruges. Musée de dentelles.
Anciennes dentelles belges, formant la collection de feue Madame Augusta Bᵐᵉ Liedts, et donnée au Musée de Gruuthuus à Bruges. Anvers, Phototypies J. Maes, 1889.

Liedts, Augusta Marie Gerardine Lambertine (Godin) baronne

see

Liedts, Augusta (Godin) baronne, 1850–1885

Liedvogel, Johann Theodor, respondent.
... Procvs divinitatis Ivlivs Procvlvs
see under   Arnold, Johann Konrad, 1658–1735, praeses.

Liedzén (Sveno Magnus)
Loca Taciti, Svethice tradita. Upsaliæ, 1809. 1 p.l., 10 pp. 4°.

NL 0349166   NN

Lief, Alfred, 1901–
Brandeis; the personal history of an American ideal, by Alfred Lief. New York, Harrisburg, Pa., Stackpole sons, 1936.

508 p. front., plates, ports. 22 cm.

Bibliography: p. 489–497.

1. Brandeis, Louis Dembitz, 1856–1941.   I. Title: The personal history of an American ideal.

E664.B819L5   923.473   36—20433

Library of Congress   (a57d²)

NL 0349167   DLC PV PPT PPL PSC OO OCl OU PPD ViU-L

OKentU NcD MeB ScU WaS TU NBuU-L KEmT MtU CaBVaU WaUPBm NN MB OrP MtU IdU IdB OrPR Or OrCS OrU WaU-L

Lief, Alfred, 1901–
Brandeis; the personal history of an American ideal, by Alfred Lief. New York, Harrisburg, Pa., Stackpole sons, 1936 (i. e. 1937)

508 p. front., plates, ports. 22 cm.

"First printing, September, 1936 ... fourth printing, March, 1937." Bibliography: p. 489–497.

1. Brandeis, Louis Dembitz, 1856–1941.   I. Title: The personal history of an American ideal.

E664.B819L55   923.473   40—37633

NL 0349168   DLC FU GU MB WaTC MsSM WaT Or

Lief, Alfred, ed.

Brandeis, Louis Dembitz, 1856–1941.
The Brandeis guide to the modern world, edited by Alfred Lief. Boston, Little, Brown and company, 1941.

Lief, Alfred.
... Camillus, the story of an American small business, by Alfred Lief ... New York, Printed by Columbia university press, 1944.

88 p. incl. plates, ports. front. 24ᶜᵐ. (Business life in America series)

1. Camillus cutlery company.   I. Title.
44–5189

Library of Congress   HD9745.U5C32
                            (10)   671

NL 0349170   DLC OrCS PPT OrU MtU OU OCl CU PP

Lief, Alfred, 1901–   ed.
Camillus digest, 1876–1951
see under   Camillus Cutlery Company.

RC60½
.M48

Meyer, Adolf, 1866–
The commonsense psychiatry of Dr. Adolf Meyer; fifty-two selected papers ed. with biographical narrative, by Alfred Lief. 1st ed. New York, McGraw-Hill Book Co., 1948.

Lief, Alfred, ed.

Lief, Alfred.
Democracy's Norris; the biography of a lonely crusade, by Alfred Lief. New York, Stackpole sons (*1939)

546 p. plates, ports. 22¼ᶜᵐ.

"Notes on sources": p. 529–538.

1. Norris, George William, 1861–   2. U. S.—Pol. & govt.—20th cent.   I. Title.

                                                39–27867

Library of Congress   E748.N65L5

———— Copy 2.
Copyright A 132370   (20)   923.273

OrSaW OrMonO Or WaS OrU OrCS
TU PPT Ok MH NcD MeB NIC MU KEmT CU-I OrP IdU WaSp
NL 0349173   DLC TxU MiU ViU PP PU OO OCIh OU PPD

VOLUME 332

**E
748
N65
L5
1939**
Lief, Alfred.
Democracy's Norris; the biography of a lonely crusade, by Alfred Lief. New York, Stackpole sons [°1939]
546 p. plates, ports. 21 cm.
"Notes on sources": p. 529–538.
Photocopy (Positive) Ann Arbor, Mich., University Microfilms, 1970.

NL 0349174 NBuC

Lief, Alfred, ed.   FOR OTHER EDITIONS
SEE MAIN ENTRY

Holmes, Oliver Wendell, 1841–1935.
The dissenting opinions of Mr. Justice Holmes; arranged, with introductory notes, by Alfred Lief, with a foreword by Dr. George W. Kirchwey ... New York, The Vanguard press [°1929]

Lief, Alfred, ed.

Einstein, Albert, 1879–
... The fight against war, edited by Alfred Lief. New York, The John Day company [°1933]

Lief, Alfred, 1901–
The Firestone story; a history of the Firestone Tire & Rubber Company. New York, Whittlesey House [1951]
437 p. illus. 24 cm.

1. Firestone Tire and Rubber Company. 2. Firestone, Harvey Samuel, 1868–1938. I. Title.
HD9161.U54F53   678.065   51–12664 ‡

OrCS IdPI OrPR OrP MtBC OrStbM MtU OrSaW
CaBVa CaBVaU DNAL CoU CaBViP IdB CU MU Or IdU MiU
NN MdBP Wa WaE WaS WaSp WaSpG WaTC PPAtR WaT WaWW
NL 0349177   DLC MB TU MiHM TxU ViU ICJ NIC OFH

Lief, Alfred, 1901–
Happy the helping hand; the first quarter-century of the Fur Trade Foundation, 1923–1948. [1st ed.] New York, Priv. print. [1948]
85 p. ports. 24 cm.

1. Chest and Foundation of the Fur Industry of the City of New York, inc. 2. Fur workers—New York (City) I. Title.
HV3174.F82L4   362.8   49–13209*

NL 0349178   DLC DNAL NN

Lief, Alfred, 1901–
Harvey Firestone, free man of enterprise; foreword by Allan Nevins. New York, McGraw-Hill [1951]
xi, 324 p. illus., ports. 21 cm.

1. Firestone, Harvey Samuel, 1868–1938. 2. Firestone Tire and Rubber Company.
HD9161.U54F55   926.78   51–11692

ViU WaS CaBVa CSt OrP OrU CaBViP IdB WaT Or MtBuM
NL 0349179   DLC OKentU Wa TU ICU TxU NN CU MB FU

Lief, Alfred, 1901–
The Mennen story. New York, McGraw-Hill, 1954.
89 p. illus. 21 cm.

1. Mennen Company.   I. Title.
HD9999.T64M45   668.5   54–6726 ‡

PP TU OU NcG NjR FTaSU MtU WaSpG
NL 0349180   DLC CaBVaU OrU MB ViU NN NcD TxU OC1

Lief, Alfred, joint author.

**Z654
.G6**
Gotshal, Sylvan, 1897–
... The pirates will get you; a story of the fight for design protection [by] Sylvan Gotshal ... [and] Alfred Lief ... New York, Printed by Columbia university press, 1945.

Lief, Alfred, ed.

Stone, Harlan Fiske, 1872–
Public control of business, selected opinions by Harlan Fiske Stone ... edited by Alfred Lief. New York, Howell, Soskin & company [°1940]

Lief, Alfred, ed.

Holmes, Oliver Wendell, 1841–1935.
Representative opinions of Mr. Justice Holmes, arranged, with introductory notes, by Alfred Lief, with a foreword by Harold J. Laski ... New York, The Vanguard press [°1931]

Lief, Alfred, 1901– ed.   FOR OTHER EDITIONS
SEE MAIN ENTRY

Brandeis, Louis Dembitz, 1856–
The social and economic views of Mr. Justice Brandeis, collected, with introductory notes, by Alfred Lief, with a foreword by Charles A. Beard. New York, The Vanguard press [°1930]

Lief, Arthur.
He's gone away; folk song from the southern Appalachians, arr. by Arthur Lief [for] SSATBB. N[ew] Y[ork] Music Press [1947]
score (11 p.) 27 cm.
With piano reduction.

1. Choruses, Secular (Mixed voices, 6 pts.), Unaccompanied. 2. Folk-songs, American—Southern States. I. He's gone away (Folk song)
M1586.L   48–15587*

NL 0349185   DLC PU

Lief, Arthur.
Sourwood Mountain, folk song from the Appalachians; SSATBB, arr. by Arthur Lief. N[ew] Y[ork] Music Press [1947]
score (11 p.) 27 cm.
With piano reduction.

1. Choruses, Secular (Mixed voices, 6 pts.), Unaccompanied. 2. Folk-songs, American—Appalachian Mountains. I. Sourwood Mountain (American folk song)
M1586.L   48–15992*

NL 0349186   DLC PU

Lief, Arthur.
The wee cooper of Fife, folk songs [!] from North Carolina, SATBB. N[ew] Y[ork] Music Press [1947]
score (10 p.) 27 cm.
With piano reduction.
"Also known as The wife wrapped in the wether's skin."

1. Choruses, Secular (Mixed voices, 5 pts.), Unaccompanied. 2. Folk-songs, American—North Carolina. I. Title.
M1585.L   48–15993*

NL 0349187   DLC PU

LIEF, FLORENCE S
Studies on the soluble complement-fixing antigen of influenza virus. [Philadelphia] 1955.
84 numb. l. mounted illus., tables. 29cm.
Thesis (Ph.D.) - University of Pennsylvania, 1955.
Typewritten.
Includes bibliographies.

NL 0349188   PU-Med

Lief, Jacob Oscar, 1888–
Temptation in spades, a comedy with music, by J. O. Lief. New York, city, °1944.
112 l. 29ᵐ.
Type-written; leaves variously numbered.
Without music.

I. Title.
Library of Congress   PS3523.L814T4
[9]
46–16870

NL 0349189   DLC

**Film
300**
Lief, Leonard, 1924–
The fortunes of King Lear, 1605–1838. [Syracuse, N.Y.] 1953.
291 l.
Thesis--Syracuse University.
Vita.
Bibliography: l. 278–291.
For full information, see Dissertation abstracts
Microfilm (negative) of typescript. Syracuse, N.Y., Hall & McChesney, 1969. 1 reel.

NL 0349190   NSyU

Lief, Max.
Hangover, by Max Lief. New York, H. Liveright, 1929.
318 p. 19½ᵐ.

I. Title.
Library of Congress   PZ3.L6222Han
29–22806

NL 0349191   DLC PBm

Lief, Max, 1899–
A musical comedy in three acts [based on Object: matrimony]
see under Levey, Harold, 1898–

Lief, Max.
Sextacy; cartoon humor from all over the world, plus limericks, miscellanea. Selected verse by Max Lief. New York, Shepsel Books [1955]
160 p. illus. 23 cm.

1. American wit and humor. I. Title.
PN6231.S54L5   55–59144 ‡

NL 0349192   DLC

VOLUME 332

QT
235
L719d
1950
LIEF, Stanley
How to eat for health; diet reform
simplified. [Enl. and completely rev.]
London, Health for All Pub. Co. [1950]
104 p.
First published under title: Diet reform
simplified.
1. Diet - Popular works

NL 0349193   DNLM

Lief hebber
see also Liefhebber.

Een Lief-hebber des vaderlandts
Adoni-Beseeck of lex talionis...
see under title

Een lief-hebber des vaderlants.
Extract wt-ghegheven by een lief-hebber des
vaderlants
see under title

Een lief hebber van de vrede.
Copye van eeen brief aen N.N.
see under title

Een lief hebber van't Vaderlant.
Kort verhael, van den oorspronck en onderganck
der loevesteynsche factie
see under title

Liefde, Carel Lodewijk de.
Le Saint-Simonisme dans la poésie française entre 1825 et
1865 ... [Haarlem, Drukkerij "Amicitia," 1927]
4 p. l., 192 p. 24 cm.
Proefschrift—Amsterdam.
Bibliography: p. [185]–190.

1. French poetry—19th cent.—Hist. & crit. 2. Saint-Simonianism.
I. Title.
PQ433.L5   28—2643

NL 0349199   DLC CaBVaU NcD CtY ICU WU IU

Liefde, Jacob B de, 1847–1878.   495-63
Agnes and Karel: a story of the founders of the Dutch Republic.
New York. Randolph & Co. 1869. 16°.
Another edition, with the title The beggars, may be found on shelf-number
484.25. This story was also published under the title, "Galama," which may
be found on shelf-number 4871.137.

F8671 — T.r. — Netherlands. Hist. Fict.

NL 0349200   MB

KD 9215
Liefde, Jacob B   de, 1847–1878.
The beggars (Les gueux) or The founders of
the Dutch republic; a tale. London, Hodder and
Stoughton, 1868.

NL 0349201   MH

LIEFDE, JACOB B   DE, 1847–1878.
The Beggars (Les Gueux); or, The founders of the Dutch
republic. By J. B. de Liefde. Second edition. London:
Hodder and Stoughton, 1869. vii, 376 p. 17½cm.

116248B. 1. Fiction, Dutch 2. Gueux—Fiction. I. Title.

NL 0349202   NN

LIEFDE, JACOB B   DE, 1847–1878.
The beggars (Les gueux); or, The founders of the Dutch
republic. By J.B.de Liefde. Third edition. London: Hodder and Stoughton, 1873. vii, 376 p. 17½cm.

Issued also under title: Galama; or, The beggars.

885063A. 1. Fiction, Dutch. 2. Gueux—Fiction. I. Title.

NL 0349203   NN MB

PZ3
.L6223
Br
Liefde, Jacob B   de, 1847–1878.
A brave resolve; or, The siege of Stralsund.
A story of heroism and adventure, by J. B. de
Liefde ... with eight illustrations. 2d ed.
London, Hodder and Stoughton, 1883.
iv, 363 p. front., plates. 17cm.

1. Thirty year's war, 1618–1648—Fiction.
2. Stralsund—Siege, 1628—Fiction. I. Title.
II. Title: The siege of Stralsund.

NL 0349204   MB

PZ3
.L6223
GaL
Liefde, Jacob B. de, 1847–1878.
Galama; or, The beggars. (The founders of
the Dutch Republic) By J. B. de Liefde. New
York, Scribner, Armstrong & co. [1873]
3 p. l., [5]–166, [1] p. 24 1/2cm. [Library
of choice fiction]
Printed in double columns.
"Originally published in England, under the
name of 'The beggars' ..."—Pref.

1. Netherlands—History—Wars of independence, 1556–1648—Fiction. I. Title.
II. Title: The beggars. III. Series.

NL 0349206   MB PPL NN MH ICU

KC 19483
Liefde, Jacob B   de, 1847–78.
Geusit (kerjälkiset) eli Alankomaiden tasavallan
perustajat. Englannin kielestä suomentanut Kaarlo
Forsman. Helsingissä, Suomalaisen kirjallisuuden
seuran kirjapainossa, 1876

292 p.

NL 0349207   MH

Liefde, Jacob B   de, 1847–1878.
De geuzen; een verhaal uit den tachtigjar-
igen oorlog... uit het Engelsch vertaald, 2. druk
opnieuw herzien en bewerkt door L. Penning,...
Kampen, Kok, 1909.

NL 0349208   OCl

Liefde, Jacob B   de, 1847–1878.
The great Dutch admirals, by Jacob de Liefde. With
illustrations by Townley Green and others. London,
H. S. King & co., 1873.
4 p. l., 351 p. 11 pl. (incl. front.) 19cm.
Reprinted from "Good words for the young."

1. Admirals—Netherlands. 2. Netherlands—History, Naval.
5-23410 Revised

Library of Congress   DJ131.L7

NL 0349209   DLC NjP MdBP MB

Liefde, Jacob B. de
Great Dutch admirals, 1884.
(4th and 5th eds.)

NL 0349210   DN

Liefde, Jacob B   de, 1847–1878
The great Dutch admirals, by Jacob de Liefde.
6th ed. With illustrations by Townley Green and
others. London, Sonnenschein, 1886.
4 p. l., 351 p. 11 pl. (incl. front.)
Reprinted from "Good words for the young."

NL 0349211   MiD NN

Liefde, Jacob B   de, 1847–1878.
The maid of Stralsund. A story of the thirty years'
war. By J. B. de Liefde ... New York, Lovell, Adam,
Wesson & co., 1876.
333 p. 19cm.

1. Thirty years' war, 1618–1648 — Fiction. 2. Stralsund — Siege, 1628—
Fiction.   I. Title.
7–15849 Revised

Library of Congress   PZ3.L6224M

NL 0349212   DLC MB PP PPL

PZ3
.L6223
WaL
Liefde, Jacob B   de, 1847–1878.
Walter's escape; or, The capture of Breda,
by Jacob de Liefde ... London, F. Marne and
co. [1870]
viii, 197 p. incl. front. plates. 17 1/2cm.

I. Title. II. Title: The capture of Breda.

NL 0349213   MB

889
L719a
LIEFDE, Jan de, 1814–1869
Achttal Leerredenen over verschillende
onderwerpen. Amsterdam, Hamel, 1852
24p. 23cm.

NL 0349214   MH-AH

VOLUME 332

Liefde, J[an] de, 1814-1869.
Een blik op den christelijken waterdoop,
bij het licht van schrift en historie. Een
woord ten gunste van den kinderdoop.
Amsterdam, H. de Hoogh, 1854.
22 p. 12°.
Repr.: Volksmagazijn voor burger en boer.

NL 0349215   NN

Liefde, Jan de, 1814-1869.
Charities of Europe.   London, Strahan, 1866.

NL 0349216   PPGi

Liefde, Jan de. 1814-1869.   3579.48
The charities of Europe.
London. Strahan & Co. 1872. (6), 480 pp. Illus. Portraits.
Plates. 18 cm., in 8s.
Contains the substance of the larger work, Six months among the charities
of Europe [3570.30].

K1736 — T.r. — Europe. Charities.

NL 0349217   MB NN MH

Liefde, Jan de, 1814-
[Des Christen einnahme und ausgabe; einige seiten
aus dem tagebuche eines geistlichen; aus dem
Holländischen übersetzt von J.Molenaar. Stuttgart,
Rümelin,1851.
50p.   (Verlag des Vereins für religiös-
sittliche hebung des volkes.)

Bound 3rd with nine other pamphlets with
binder's title "Ethics and religion"

NL 0349218   OC1W

[Liefde, Jan de] 1814-1869.
A Dutchman's difficulties with the English language.
London, New York, A. Strahan, 1865.
30 p. 18 cm.
"Reprinted from 'Good words.'"

I. Title.

PZ3.L6223Du   66-81764

NL 0349219   DLC OC1 PPL ICN MH

---

889   LIEFDE, Jan de, 1814-1869.
1731   De eerste ontmoeting tusschen God en den
1848   mensch na den val. Leerrede over Gen.III,
no.4   vs.9, 10. Amsterdam, Hamel, 1852.
24p. 22.5cm.

No.4 in a bound volume lettered on spine:
Leerredenen.

NL 0349220   MH-AH

Liefde (Rev. JAN DE) 1814-
Gevaar! Gevaar! en geen vrede! Een woord tot
de slapenden en in slaap gewiegden. *Zutphen: de
Schrijver,* 1844. 2 p.l., 110 pp. nar. 8°.

NL 0349221   NN

LIEFDE, Jan de, 1814-
A glance at the Dutch Reformed church.
Edinburgh, 1854.
pp.16. 17.5cm.

NL 0349222   MH

Liefde, Jan de, 1814-1869.
The inheritance and the journey to obtain it.
[By Rev. J. De Liefde] (In his: The signet-ring,
and its heavenly motto ... Boston, [18-] 16°.
p. 99-240)

NL 0349223   NN

Y88   LIEFDE, Jan de, 1814-1869.
L719k   Keur van proza en poëzie uit de geschriften van J. de Liebde door S. Coolsma.
Nijkerk, Callenbach, 1919-1922.
2v. in 1. 20cm.

NL 0349224   MH-AH ViHarEM

---

889   LIEFDE, Jan de, 1814-1869
L719k   De koningin van het zuiden, een getuige
tegen het geslacht der ongeloovigen.
Amsterdam, De Hoogh [n.d.]
142p. 20cm.

NL 0349225   MH-AH

---

686   LIEFDE, Jan de, 1814-1869.
Menn.   Niet de kinderdoop, maar de doop der
Box 1   bejaarden is het bondszegel des Nieuwen
Verbonds. Een leerstellig vertoog ...
Zutphen, Wansleven, 1844.
2p.l., 52p. 23.5cm.

NL 0349226   MH-AH

Liefde, Jan de, 1814-1869.
The postman's bag and other stories. By the Rev. J. de Liefde
... Illustrated by John Pettie, Alfred W. Cooper, W. Mac-
Taggart...R. T. Ross...W. P. Burton, and others. Edin-
burgh, A. Strahan and co. [etc., etc.] 1862. iv, 194 p. front.,
plates. 17½cm.
Gleeson White, p. 116.   Reid, p. 204.
Illustrations: 16 lithographs (including frontispiece) by A. Ritchie, 1 after R.
Bell, 1 after W. P. Burton, 3 after A. W. Cooper, 2 after W. MacTaggart, 6 after
J. Pettie, 1 after R. T. Ross and 2 after W. F. Vallance.

NL 0349227   NN

Epsteen   Liefde, Jan de, 1814-1869.
Coll.   The postman's bag and other stories. Illus.
            by John Pettie [and others] London, A. Stra-
in   han, 1863.
RareBooks   iv, 194 p. illus. 17cm.
Room

NL 0349228   CoU

Liefde, Jan de.
The postman's bag, and other stories. New edition.
London. Strahan. 1866. Illus. 16°.

A1068 — T.r.

NL 0349229   MB

Liefde, Jan de, 1814-1869.
The postman's bag, and other stories. London,
A. Strahan, 1867.

NL 0349230   MH

PZ8   Liefde, Jan de, 1814-1869.
.L6224 The postman's bag and other stories, by
Po   John de Liefde ... London, Strahan and co.,
1870.
iv, 194 p. front. plates. 16cm.
CONTENTS.—The postman's bag.—New-Year's
day.—The clouds.—The hedge of thorns.—

Herman the hypocrite.—The open door.—The
fox, the goat, and the carrots.—David and his
little dog.—First love.—The gluttonous
bear.—Charles cologne-pot.—The praying
children.—Three boys.—The golden cap.

I. Title.

NL 0349232   MB

Liefde, Jan de, 1814-1869.
The romance of charity, by John de Liefde. London, A.
Strahan, 1867.
3 p. l., 480 p. incl. illus., plates, ports. front. 18½cm.
"This book will be found to contain the substance of the large work,
'Six months among the charities of Europe', by the same author."—2d
prelim. leaf.

1. Charities—Europe. I. Title.
                                                34-3224
Library of Congress   HV238.L68   362.94

NL 0349233   DLC CtY MB PHC PU PP NjP

Liefde, J[an] de, 1814-1869.
The signet-ring, and its heavenly motto.
From the Dutch ...   Boston, D. Lothrop,
[18-]
xii, 1 l., 15-362 p. pl. 16°.

NL 0349234   NN

[Liefde, Jan de] 1814-1869.   No. 6 in *4490b.52
The signet-ring and its heavenly motto.   Translated
from the German [sic].
Boston. Gould & Lincoln. 1856. 66 pp. Plate. 16 cm., in 6s.

NL 0349235   MB MH CtY

Liefde, Jan de, 1814-1869.
The signet-ring, and other gems. From the Dutch of
the Rev. J. de Liefde. Boston, Gould and Lincoln; New
York, Sheldon and company; [etc.] 1860.
xii p., 1 l., [15]-362 p. incl. front. 17½cm.
CONTENTS.—The signet-ring.—The inheritance.—The shipwrecked traveller.

Library of Congress   PZ3.L6223S   7-15842†

NL 0349236   DLC MB

Liefde, Jan de, 1814-1869.
Six months among the charities of Europe, by John de
Liefde ... London, A. Strahan, 1865.
2 v. fronts., illus., plates, ports., plan. 19½cm.

1. Charities—Europe.
                                                9-13490†
Library of Congress   HV238.L7

IEN MiU PHC ICJ MdBP
NL 0349237   DLC DNLM OrU CtY T OCU NcU CU PU NN OrU

VOLUME 332

Liefde, Jan de, 1814–1869.
Six months among the charities of Europe, by John de Liefde ... London and New York, A. Strahan, 1866.
2 v. fronts., illus., plates, ports., plan. 20½ᶜᵐ.

1. Charities—Europe.
33-9813

Library of Congress   HV238.L7 1866   360.94

NL   0349238   DLC PPFr OC1 ODW FMU

---

889   **LIEFDE,** Jan de, 1814-1869.
L719t   Twintig leerredenen. Met een woord vooraf van C. C. Callenbach. Nijkerk, Callenbach, 1870.
2pts. in 1v. 23cm.

NL   0349239   MH-AH

H
230   **Liefde,** Jan de, 1814-1869
L62w   Waarschijnlijkheid of zekerheid? Een woord naar aanleiding der jongste openbaring op het gebied der moderne theologie.... Utrecht, 1864.

79p. 22cm.

NL   0349240   ViHarEM

Liefde, John de
see Liefde, Jan de, 1814-1869.

Liefde, Willem Cornelis de.
De invloed van intensieve droging op innerlijke omzettingen.
Inaug. diss.   Amsterdam, 1927.

NL   0349242   ICRL MH MiU CtY

Liefde boven all. Liedjes, uitgereikt bij gelegenheid der maskerade, ter viering van het 215 jarig bestaan der Utrechtsche hoogeschool . . . . 25. Junij 1851.
44 pp., 1l. *Utrecht: Dannenfelser en Doorman*, 1851. 8°.

NL   0349243   MH

De **LIEFDE** op de proef; eene schets door een neefje van Jan de Rymer. 's Hertogenbosch, A. H. Kante, 1858.

pp. 48.

NL   0349244   MH

De **liefde** tot zijn land is ieder aangeboren
see under Leeuwen, Willem Lion Marinus Ernest van, 1895-   ed.

De **Liefde** van Psiche en Kupido
see under Apuleius Madaurensis. Metamorphoses. Selections. (Amor et Psyche) Dutch. [Supplement]

Liefdezusters van den H.Carolus Borromeus
Gedenkboek bij het honderd-jarig bestaan der Liefdezusters van den H.Carolus Borromeus. [1837-1937]
Maastricht, 1937

xx, 448 p. illus.

NL   0349247   MH

---

080   **Liefeld,** Elsa Thusnelda, 1890-
T4132   Application of Heinrich Wölfflin's
v.23   Principles of art history to the
no.4   German drama... [Boston], 1941.
cover-title [4]p. O.

Translation of abstract of thesis (Ph.D.) - Boston university, 1941.

NL   0349248   IaU

L[iefeld], Friedrich Wilhelm Albert
Erinnerungen aus der südafrikanischen mission. Von F. W. A. L. Columbus, O., Druck des Lutherischen verlags, 1891.
2 p. l., 94 p. 16½ᶜᵐ.

1. Missions—Africa, South. 2. Africa, South—Descr. & trav.

Library of Congress   DT763.L71   5-15648†

NL   0349249   DLC PPLT

L[iefeld], F[riedrich] W[ilhelm] A[lbert]
Erntekranz. Gewunden aus den Evangelien-Perikopen des Kirchenjahres. von F. W. A. L.
[i. e. F.W.A. Liefeld] Theil 1-   Milwaukee, Wis., G. Brumder, 1881.
2 v. in 1. 8°.
v. 2. Imprint. Columbus, Ohio: Lutherische Verlagshandlung.

NL   0349250   NN ICN

Liefeld, F[riedrich] W[ilhelm] A[lbert]
Gespräche über die heiligen Sakramente.
Columbus, O., Lutherische Verlagshandlung, 1895.
31 p. 12°.

NL   0349251   NN

L[iefeld], F[riedrich] W[ilhelm] A[lbert]
Reminiscences of the South African Mission.
By F.W.A.L. [i. e. F.W.A. Liefeld]   Columbus, Ohio, Lutheran Book Concern, 1895.
4 p.l., 102 p. 7 pl., 2 plans, 3 port. 8°.

NL   0349252   NN PPLT

DD
67   **Liefeld, Theophilus.**
.L5   Faces and phases of German life. By Theophilus Liefeld ... New York, Fowler & Wells co.; [etc., etc., ᶜ1910]
5 p. l., [9]-315 p. 20ᶜᵐ.

"In connection with each character sketch I shall study also some phase of German life, giving a description of the country, its inhabitants, its government, the habits and customs."—Pref.

1. Germany—Soc. condit. 2. Germany—Soc. life & cust. 3. Americans in Germany.
10—15207

Library of Congress   DD67.L5

NL   0349253   DLC OC1 ICJ NN MB IdU DAU

Liefeldt, Joachim, 1907-
Untersuchungen über das wahlgeheimnis...
Berlin, 1931.   70 p.
Inaug. Diss. -Heidelberg, 1931.
Lebenslauf.
Bibliography.

NL   0349254   ICRL MH-L

Eenen **liefelijcken** || Christelijcken troostbrief / waermede alle vrome Christenen / met Cruys || ende Lijden beladen zijnde / in dese || sorchelycke benaude tijden || hun troosten connen: door M. L. J. . . . . T'Hantvverpen, by Aernout s'Coninex, 1581.
1 p. l., [60] p. 16ᶜᵐ.
Title vignette.

1. Theology, Practical and devotional.

NL   0349255   MiU

Liefer, Fred
see
Leifer, Fred.

Lieferant, Henry, 1892-
... Charity patient. New York, E. P. Dutton & co., inc., 1939.
247 p. 19½ᶜᵐ.
At head of title: By Henry and Sylvia Lieferant.
"First edition."

I. Lieferant, Mrs. Sylvia (Saltzberg) 1896-   joint author. II. Title.
39-8476
Library of Congress   PZ3.L6225Ch

NL   0349257   DLC MB

Lieferant, Henry, 1892-
Doctors' wives [by] Henry and Sylvia Lieferant. Boston, Little, Brown, and company, 1936.
5 p. l., [3]-322 p. 20ᶜᵐ.

I. Lieferant, Mrs. Sylvia (Saltzberg) 1896-   joint author. II. Title.
30-12741
Library of Congress   PZ3.L6225Do

NL   0349258   DLC WaSp

Lieferant, Henry, 1892-
Grass on the mountain, by Henry and Sylvia Lieferant. New York, E. P. Dutton & company, inc., 1938.
443 p. 21½ᶜᵐ.
Illustrated t.-p.
"First edition."

I. Lieferant, Mrs. Sylvia (Saltzberg) 1896-   joint author. II. Title.
38-5293
Library of Congress   PZ3.L6225Gr

NL   0349259   DLC NcD

VOLUME 332

Lieferant, Henry, 1892–
Heavenly harmony, by Henry and Sylvia Lieferant. New York, The Dial press ₁1942₎
281 p. 21ᵐ.

I. Lieferant, Sylvia (Saltzberg) 1896–   joint author. II. Title.

Library of Congress   PZ3.L6225He
42–21518

NL 0349260   DLC

Lieferant, Henry, 1892–
Hilda Cassidy; a play, by Henry and Sylvia Lieferant. New York, I. S. Richter [n.d.]
45,23,19 f.   28cm.

Typescript.

1. Drama, American. I. Lieferant, Sylvia (Saltzberg), 1896–   jt. au. II. Title.

NL 0349261   NN

Lieferant, Henry, 1892–
Hospital—quiet please! By Henry and Sylvia Lieferant. New York, E. P. Dutton & co., inc., 1941.
278 p. 19½ cm.
"First edition."

I. Lieferant, Sylvia (Saltzberg) 1896–   joint author. II. Title.

PZ3.L6225Ho
41—11498

NL 0349262   DLC

Lieferant, Henry, 1892–
One enduring purpose, by Henry and Sylvia Lieferant. New York, E. P. Dutton & co., inc., 1941.
275 p. 19½ᵐ.
"First edition."

I. Lieferant, Mrs. Sylvia (Saltzberg) 1896– joint author. II. Title.
41–1830
Library of Congress   PZ3.L6225On

NL 0349263   DLC OrP

Lieferant, Henry, 1892–
Seven daughters, by Henry and Sylvia Lieferant; drawings by Allen Pope. New York, Coward-McCann, inc. ₁1947₎
127 p. illus., plates.   21ᵐ.

I. Lieferant, Sylvia (Saltzberg) 1896– joint author. II. Title.
PZ3.L6225Se
47–30222

NL 0349264   DLC CaBVa WaE PP

Lieferant, Henry, 1892–
Teacher's husband, by Henry and Sylvia Lieferant. New York, The Dial press ₁ᶜ1941₎
4 p. L, 3–327 p. 21ᵐ.

I. Lieferant, Mrs. Sylvia (Saltzberg) 1896–   joint author.
II. Title.
41–24065
Library of Congress   PZ3.L6225Te

NL 0349265   DLC OrP OLak PP

Lieferant, Henry, 1892–
They always come home, by Henry and Sylvia Lieferant. New York, E. P. Dutton & co., inc., 1942.
320 p. 20½ᵐ.
"First edition."

I. Lieferant, Mrs. Sylvia (Saltzberg) 1896–   joint author. II. Title.

Library of Congress   PZ3.L6225Th
42–570

NL 0349266   DLC Or OrP OOxM OClh OLak PP

Lieferant, Henry, 1892–
United they stand, by Henry and Sylvia Lieferant. New York, E. P. Dutton & co., inc., 1940.
256 p. 19½ᵐ.
"First edition."

I. Lieferant, Mrs. Sylvia (Saltzberg) 1896–   joint author. II. Title.
40–4095
Library of Congress   PZ3.L6225Un

NL 0349267   DLC WaSp WaS Or

Lieferant, Mrs. Sylvia (Salzberg) 1896–
joint author.

Lieferant, Henry, 1892–
... Charity patient. New York, E. P. Dutton & co., inc., 1939.

Lieferant, Mrs. Sylvia (Saltzberg) 1896–
joint author."

Lieferant, Henry, 1892–
Doctors' wives ₁by₎ Henry and Sylvia Lieferant. Boston, Little, Brown, and company, 1930.

Lieferant, Mrs. Sylvia (Saltzberg) 1896–
joint author.

Lieferant, Henry, 1892–
Grass on the mountain, by Henry and Sylvia Lieferant. New York, E. P. Dutton & company, inc., 1938.

Lieferant, Sylvia (Saltzberg) 1896–   joint author.

Lieferant, Henry, 1892–
Heavenly harmony, by Henry and Sylvia Lieferant. New York, The Dial press ₁1942₎

Lieferant, Mrs. Sylvia (Saltzberg) 1896–
joint author.

Lieferant, Henry, 1892–
Hospital—quiet please! By Henry and Sylvia Lieferant. New York, E. P. Dutton & co., inc., 1941.

Lieferant, Mrs. Sylvia (Saltzberg) 1896–
joint author.

Lieferant, Henry, 1892–
One enduring purpose, by Henry and Sylvia Lieferant. New York, E. P. Dutton & co., inc., 1941.

PZ3
.L6225
Se
Lieferant, Sylvia (Saltzberg) 1896–   joint author.

Lieferant, Henry, 1892–
Seven daughters, by Henry and Sylvia Lieferant; drawings by Allen Pope. New York, Coward-McCann, inc. ₁1947₎

Lieferant, Mrs. Sylvia (Saltzberg) 1896–
joint author.

Lieferant, Henry, 1892–
Teacher's husband, by Henry and Sylvia Lieferant. New York, The Dial press ₁ᶜ1941₎

Lieferant, Mrs. Sylvia (Saltzberg) 1896–
joint author.

Lieferant, Henry, 1892–
They always come home, by Henry and Sylvia Lieferant. New York, E. P. Dutton & co., inc., 1942.

Lieferant, Mrs. Sylvia (Saltzberg) 1896–
joint author.

Lieferant, Henry, 1892–
United they stand, by Henry and Sylvia Lieferant. New York, E. P. Dutton & co., inc., 1940.

Der Lieferant

see

Handels- und export jahrbuch "Der Lieferant."

Lieferanten-Verzeichnis der Elektrizitätswerke...
Auflage

Stuttgart ₁19
v.

Issued as a suppl. to Elektrizitätswirtschaft.

1. Engineering, Electrical—Directo-   ries.
N. Y. P. L.   February 19, 1936

NL 0349279   NN

Lieferbedingungs-Gemeinschaft
see
Verein Deutscher Werkzeugmaschinenfabriken.

1881–
Liefering, Max: ₁Das Rheinisch-Westfälische Kohlensyndikat und sein Einfluß auf die Kohlenpreise und die Lage der Bergarbeiter. Dortmund 1910: Ruhfus. '85 S. 8°
Tübingen, Staatswiss. Diss. v. ⁴⁄₂. Jan. 1911, Ref. Fuchs
[Geb. 7. Juni 81 Krefeld; Wohnort: Mainz; Staatsangeh.: Preußen; Vorbildung: Lehrersem. Mörs; Studium: Berlin Handelshochsch. 5, Straßburg 2, Tübingen 2 S.; Rig. 30. Juni 10.]   [U 11. 4430

(Nur in beschränkter Anzahl für den Austausch)

NL 0349281   ICRL

VOLUME 332

Liefering, Max, 1881–
Das Rheinisch-westfälische Kohlensyndikat und sein Einfluss auf die Kohlenpreise und die Lage der Bergarbeiter. Dortmund, 1910 ¡i. e. 1911¡
Microfilm copy. Negative.
Collation of the original : 85 p.
Imperfect : pages 73–85 not filmed.

1. Rheinisch-westfälisches Kohlen-Syndikat, Essen. 2. Coal trade—Rhine River and Valley. 3. Coal trade—Westphalia. 4. Coal-miners—Rhine River and Valley. 5. Coal-miners—Westphalia.

Microfilm HD–2359   Mic 54–292

NL 0349282   DLC

Liefertz, Caspar, respondent.
Dissertatio physico-mathematica de inaequalitate superficiei telluris, quam ...
see under   Liedbeck, Lars, praeses.

Lieff (Alfred). *Einfluss von Flüssigkeitsentziehung und Flüssigkeitszufuhr auf die Sekretionskurve des Magens. [Leipzig.] 32 pp. 8°.
Halle a. S.. R. P. Metzchmann 1904.

NL 0349284   DNLM CtY ICRL

Lieffland; so den Namen von den alten Heydnischen Völckern den Lieven hat
see   Ceumern, Caspar von, 1613–1692.
Theatridium Livonicum.

WH   **LIEFFRING, Émile**
L719d   De l'ectopie de la rate.   Paris, Stein-
1894   heil, 1894.
              131 p. illus.

NL 0349286   DNLM PPC

Lieffring, Robert
L'étude du profil en orthodontie. Paris,
A. Legrand, 1934.
                                    65 p

Thèse.

NL 0349287   DNLM NNC CtY

Lieffroy, Aimé   Fr 1597.02.15
Le général Radet à Besançon. Besançon, 1894.

36 p.

NL 0349288   MH

Lieffroy, Aimé.
Le maréchal Ney en Franche-Comté, d'après les
ouvrages de MM. Welschinger et Henri Houssaye.
Besançon, Imprimerie Dodivers, 1896.
¡163¡–199p. 23cm. (Mémoires de la Société
d'émulation du Doubs, sér. 6, v.10)

1. Welschinger, Henri, 1846–1919. Le maréchal
Ney, 1815. 2. Houssaye, Henry, 1848–1911. 1815,
la première restauration. 3. Ney, Michel, duc
d'Elchingen, prince de la Moskowa, 1769–1815.

NL 0349289   NcU

Liefhebber
see also   Lief hebber.

Een liefhebber der astrologische wetenschap.
De astrologische geheimschryver...
see under title

Liefhebber der geschiedenissen.
Verzamelde mengelstoffen ...
see under title

Een Liefhebber der vrouwen.
Corpus juris foeminini: of Wetboek der vrouwen
see under title

Een liefhebber der waarheid.
Kort-bondig verhaal van den op en ondergang,
van d'heer Constantyn Faulkon ...
see under title

Een liefhebber des vaderlandts.
Extract, uyt-ghegheven by een liefhebber des
vaderlandts
see under title

Een liefhebber en voorstander der zuivere
evangelie wahrheit.
Het Geopenbaarde geheim
see under title

Een liefhebber van de nederduytsche tael.

Mast, Dirck Heymansz van der.
Practique des notarischaps, seer nut, profijtelick ende noodigh
alle jonckheyt die haer willen offenen in dese konst. Midtsgaders voor alle andere persoonen. Beschreven door Dirck Heymansz vander Mast ... Den derden druck, van nieuws oversien, gecorrigeert en veel vermeerdert, by den autheur selfs. Tot Delf, By J. Pietersz Waelpot, 1649.
8 p. l., 336, ¡4¡ p. 16°.

Liefhebber van de Reuse-compagnie.
De Goden vervoegt in cavalcade
see under title

Een Liefhebber van de Waerheydt, ende van
Vaderlandt.
Ontdeckinghe van de valsche Spaensche
Iesuijtsche Practijcke
see under title

Een Liefhebber van eenigheyd en liefde.
Boetbazuyn voor de lasteraars
see under title

Een liefhebber van Hollandsch. Oorspronkelijk blijspel ... Zutphen: Thiems,
[188–?]   27 pp.   16°.
By G.L.B.

NL 0349301   NN

Een Liefhebber van Zion.
Exempel van de vrye genade gods
see under title

LIEFHELM, Stephanus Josephus.
Dissertatio inauguralis medica de remediorum
domesticorum abusu, etc. Berolini, 1817.

NL 0349303   MBCo PPC

Liefländische gemeinnützige und ökonomische societät
see
Livländische gemeinnützige und ökonomische sozietät.

Der Liefländische Tischler
see under   Duval, Alexandre, 1767–1842.

FILM   Liefländisches Magazin der Lektüre. 1. Jahrg. , 1.–4. Quartel–
3457
PH   1782–

Mitau, J. F. Steffanhagen.
v.on   reel. On film (Positive)

Microfilm. Original in Latvijas PSR. Zinātnu Akademijas
Fundamentālā biblioteka.
Text in German and French.

NL 0349306   CU

Liefland, Juliette Decreus-
see   Decreus, Juliette.

Liefland, W   A   van.
Inleiding tot de orthopaedagogiek van het zwakzinnige
kind. 's-Gravenhage, Haga, 1952.
224 p. 25 cm. (Afwijkende kinderen, 11)
Bibliography : p. 212–219.

1. Mentally handicapped children—Education. (Series)

LC4661.L5   65–42434

NL 0349308   DLC

VOLUME 332

Liefland, W. A. van.
Over de opvoeding van de "Wilde van Aveyron," bewerkt naar de oorspronkelijke rapporten. Batavia, 1949.
85p.

NL 0349309   ICRL

Liefmann, Else, 1881-   joint author.

Bonte, Theodor.
Untersuchungen über die eidetische veranlagung von kindern and jugendlichen, von Theodor Bonte ... Else Liefmann ... und Fritz Roessler, mit 22 abbildungen im text. Leipzig, J. A. Barth, 1928.

Liefmann, Else, 1881-
Volksschülerinnen, ihre geistigen und körperlichen leistungen und die beziehung zur konstitution; eine psychologisch-medizinische untersuchung, zugleich ein beitrag zur frage nach dem geist-körperzusammenhang, von dr. med. et phil. Else Liefmann ... mit 10 abbildungen im text. Leipzig, J. A. Barth, 1932.
2 p. l., 124 p. illus., diagrs. 24½ᶜᵐ.
"Erweiterte sonderausgabe aus 'Zeitschrift für angewandte psychologie', band 42, heft 1 bis 3 (1932)"
"Literaturverzeichnis": p. 121-124.
1. Child study. 2. Mental tests. 3. Psychology, Physiological. I. Title.
Library of Congress   LB1121.L5   33-13785
Copyright A—Foreign   17274
[2]   [159.9227]   136 7

NL 0349311   DLC

Liefmann (Else) [1881-]. *Zur Klinik der Tubenturberkulose. 52 pp., 1 l. 8°.
Freiburg i. B., C. A. Wagner [1908]

NL 0349312   DNLM ICRL

Liefmann, Emil, 1878-
Ein fall von asthenischer bulbaerparalyse... Inaug. diss. Freiburg, 1902. (Leipzig)
Bibl.

NL 0349313   ICRL DNLM

Liefmann (Fridericus). *De febri ephemera. 36 pp. 4°. *Jenae, lit. Nisiani,* 1696.

NL 0349314   DNLM

Liefmann, Gottlieb.
Dissertatio historica de fanaticis silesiorum, et speciatim Quirino Kuhlmanno ...
Vitembergae, 1698.
[58] p.   19 cm.
Bibliography: Foot-notes.

NL 0349315   CU

Liefmann, Harry, 1877-
Aus dem staatlichen hygienischen Institut in Hamburg. Ein Beitrag zur Frage nach der ätiologischen Bedeutung gewisser Pflanzenpollenkörner für das Heufieber.   Leipzig, Veit & Co., 1904.
153-178 p.   2 tab.   8°.
Repr.: Zeitschrift für Hygiene und Infectionskrankheiten. Band 47.
Title from cover.

NL 0349316   NN

Liefmann, Harry, 1877-
Der einfluss der hitze auf die sterblichkeit der säuglinge in Berlin und einigen anderen grossstädten (New York, München, Essen Ruhr) von H. Liefmann ... und Alfred Lindemann ... mit 33 kurventafeln. Braunschweig, F. Vieweg & sohn, 1911.
vi p., 1 l., 74 p. diagrs. (partly fold.) 24½ᶜᵐ.   M. 5
"Literatur": p. 69.
1. Infants—Mortality.   I. Lindemann, Alfred, joint author.
11-23780
Library of Congress   HB1323.I 4L6

NL 0349317   DLC OC1W OC1W-H PPC DL

Liefmann, Harry, 1877-   628.53 Q703
Über den Nachweis von Russ in der Luft. ... von Dr. H. Liefmann. Halle a. S., C. A. Kaemmerer & Co., 1907.
31 p. illus., 1 fold. table. 24ᶜᵐ.
Habilitationsschrift—Halle-Wittenberg.

NL 0349318   ICJ ICRL CtY DAS

Liefmann, Harry, 1877-   4018.275
Über die Rauch- und Russfrage, insbesondere vom gesundheitlichen Standpunkte und eine Methode des Russnachweises in der Luft. — Braunschweig. Vieweg. 1908. vii, (1), 90 pp. Illus. Diagrams. Table.   8°.
Literatur, pp. 74-90.
Sonder-Abdruck aus der „Deutschen Vierteljahrsschrift für öffentliche Gesundheitspflege," Band 40, Heft 2.

G955t — Smoke.

NL 0349319   MB OC1 NN

Liefmann, Harry, 1877-
Untersuchungen ueber die Wirkung einiger Saeuren auf gesundheitsschädliches Trinkwasser.
Freiburg, 1902.
Inaug. -Diss. - Freiburg.

NL 0349320   ICRL DNLM

Liefmann, M.
... Kunst und heilige; ein ikonographisches handbuch zur erklärung der werke der italienischen und deutschen kunst. Jena, E. Diederichs, 1912.
2 p. l., 3-319 p. 20½ᶜᵐ.
1. Saints—Art. 2. Christian art and symbolism.   I. Title.
13-6950
Library of Congress   N8080.L5

NL 0349321   DLC OrU NcGU NN CtY NcD

Liefmann (Michael. Frieder.) *De adynamia artis medicae in sensibus. 1 p. l., 30 pp., 1 l. 4°. *Erfordiae, typ. Heringii,* [1737].

NL 0349322   DNLM PPC

330.943
L623a
Liefmann, Robert, 1874-1941.
Der Abbau der Preise nach dem Kriege und die einmalige Vermögensabgabe. Berlin, D. Reimer, 1918.
36p. 22cm. (Veröffentlichungen des Deutsch-Argentinischen Centralverbandes zur Förderung Wirtschaftlicher Interessen. Heft 12)
"Vortrag, gehalten am 11. September 1918 ... Berlin."
1. Germany - Econ. condit. - 1918-1945.   I. Title. II. Series: Deutsch-Argentinischer Zentralverband zur Förderung Wirtschaftlicher Veröffentlichungen. Interessen, Berlin. gen, 12.

NL 0349323   TxU NN

Liefmann, Robert, 1874-
Allgemeine volkswirtschaftslehre, von Robert Liefmann. Leipzig und Berlin, B. G. Teubner, 1924.
2 p. l., 95 p. 24ᶜᵐ.
"Die vorliegende schrift ist entstanden aus der abhandlung: Theoretische grundlegung des Teubnerschen Handbuch zur staatsbürgerkunde und volkswirtschaftslehre."—Vorwort.
"Literatur": p. 95.
1. Economics.
Library of Congress   HB175.L65   24-22558

NL 0349324   DLC NN OrU

Liefmann, Robert, 1874-
Allgemeine volkswirtschaftslehre, von dr. Robert Liefmann ... 2., erweiterte aufl. 4. bis 6. tausend. Leipzig und Berlin, B. G. Teubner, 1927.
2 p. l., 119 p. 24ᶜᵐ.
"Literatur": p. 119.
1. Economics.
Library of Congress   HB175.L65 1927   27-24762

NL 0349325   DLC NcD CU

1874-
Econ 3853. **Liefmann, Robert,** Die allianzen, gemeinsame monopolistische vereinigungen der unternehmer und arbeiter in England.   Jena, 1900. 8°. pp. (4), 45.
Habilitationsschrift — Giessen.

NL 0349326   MH PU ICRL

LIEFMANN, ROBERT, 1874-
Die Allianzen, gemeinsame monopolistische Vereinigungen der Unternehmer und Arbeiter in England...von Dr. Robert Liefmann. Jena, 1900. 45 p. 23cm.

Film reproduction. Positive.

Habilitationsschrift—Giessen, 1900.

1. Industrial combination—Gt. Br. 2. Trade and open price associations—Gt. Br.

NL 0349327   NN

HD4945   Liefmann, Robert, 1874-
.L7   ... Arbeitslöhne und unternehmergewinne nach
Rare bk   dem kriege ... Stuttgart, J. Hess, 1919.
room   cover-title, 24 p. (Flugschriften zur schaffung sozialen rechtes, hft. 8)

1. Wages.

NL 0349328   ICU MH DL

Liefmann, Robert, 1874-
Beteiligungs- und finanzierungsgesellschaften; eine studie über den modernen kapitalismus und das effektenwesen (in Deutschland, den Vereinigten Staaten, England, Frankreich, Belgien und der Schweiz) von prof. dr. Robert Liefmann ... Jena, G. Fischer, 1909.
x, 495, [1] p. fold. diagrs. 24½ᶜᵐ.
"Quellen und literatur": p. [ix]-x.
1. Corporations. 2. Stock companies. 3. Trust companies.
[Full name: Walter Robert Liefmann]
Library of Congress   HG4011.L6   9-31052

NL 0349329   DLC MtU NcD CtY MiU ICJ NN CU

VOLUME 332

Liefmann, Robert, 1874–
Beteiligungs- und finanzierungsgesellschaften; eine studie über den modernen kapitalismus und das effektenwesen in Deutschland, den Vereinigten Staaten, der Schweiz, England, Frankreich und Belgien, von Robert Liefmann. 2., verm. aufl. Jena, G. Fischer, 1913.
     xiv, 626 p. fold. diagrs. 24½ᵐ.
     "Quellen und literatur" : p. ₍xiii₎–xiv.
     1. Corporations. 2. Holding companies. 3. Stock companies. 4. Trust companies.
                        ₍Full name: Walter Robert Liefmann₎
     Library of Congress   HG4011.L6 1913   14–9442

NL   0349330   DLC OrU NcD CtY NN NjP

HG
4497
.L46
1921
Liefmann, Robert, 1874–
    Beteiligungs- und finanzierungsgesellschaften;
eine studie über den modernen effektenkapitalis-
mus in Deutschland, den Vereinigten Staaten,
der Schweiz, England, Frankreich und Belgien.
3. neu bearb. Aufl.   Jena, G. Fisher, 1921.
    viii, 582 p. 26 cm.

    Includes bibliographies.
    1. Investment trusts. 2. Holding companies.
3. Securities. I. Title.

NL   0349331   OkU MH PU-L

Liefmann, Robert, 1874–
    Beteiligungs- und Finanzierungsgesellschaften. Eine Studie über den modernen Effektenkapitalismus in Deutschland, den Vereinigten Staaten, der Schweiz, England, Frankreich und Belgien, von Robert Liefmann...   Jena: G. Fischer, 1923.   x, 625 p. tables. 4. ed., rev.   4°.
    Bibliography, p. ₍ix₎–x.

105047A. 1. Corporations. 2. Cor-   porations.—Finance.   October 24, 1923.
N. Y. P. L.

NL   0349332   NN IEN CU MH OrPR

Liefmann, Robert, 1874–
    Beteiligungs- und finanzierungsgesellschaften; eine studie über den effektenkapitalismus, von Robert Liefmann. 5. neubearb. aufl. Mit 2 graphischen darstellungen. Jena, G. Fischer, 1931.
    x, 642 p. 2 fold. tab. 25ᵐ.
    "Quellen und literatur" : p. ₍ix₎–x.

    1. Investment trusts. 2. Holding companies. 3. Securities. I. Title.
                               A 32–830
Columbia univ. Libraries
for Library of Congress   HG4497.L46
                       ₍a44c1₎†   658.114

NL   0349333   NNC CaQMM MU IU NN DLC

Liefmann, Robert, 1874–
    Bringt uns der krieg dem sozialismus näher† Von prof. dr. Robert Liefmann ... Stuttgart und Berlin, Deutsche verlags-anstalt, 1915.
    44 p. 23ᵐ. (*Added t.-p.:* Der deutsche krieg; politische flugschriften, hrsg. von E. Jäckh. 56. hft.)

    1. Socialism in Germany.
                             A 20–1217
Title from Carnegie   Endow. Int. Peace.   Printed by L. C.

NL   0349334   NNCE NjP CU NcD OU MiU CtY NN

Liefmann, Robert, 1874–1941.
    Cartels, concerns and trusts, by Dr. Robert Liefmann ... with an introduction by D. H. Macgregor ... London, Methuen & co. ltd. ₍1932₎
    xxix, 379, ₍1₎ p. fold. tab. 23 cm.
    Translated by D. H. Macgregor.

    1. Trusts, Industrial.   I. Macgregor, David Hutchinson, 1877–
tr.   II. Title.
                             33—3849
Library of Congress   HD2734.L82
                    ₍a48e1₎   338.8

     MH-L WaU ICU INS IdU
NL   0349335   DLC CaBVaU CU ICU CtY OOxM PU PU-W NN IU

HD
2734
L8213
Liefmann, Robert, 1874–1941.
    Cartels, concerns and trusts, by Dr. Robert Liefmann ... with an introduction by D. H. Macgregor. New York, E. P. Dutton ₍1932₎
Translated by D. H. Macgregor.
    379p.

    1. Trusts, Industrial. I. Macgregor, David Hutchinson, 1877–   tr. II. Title.

    OrCS
NL   0349336   CU-AL OrPR WaS MB ViU OCU MiU OC1W WaSp

Liefmann, Robert, 1874–
    Cartells et trusts; évolution de l'organisation économique par Robert Liefmann... Traduit d'après la deuxième édition allemande par Savinien Bouyssy... Paris: M. Giard & É. Brière, 1914. vi, 264 p., 1 l. 8°. (Bibliothèque internat. d'économie politique.)
    Bibliography, p. 263-264.

1. Cartels. 2. Trusts. 3. Bouyssy,   Savinien, 1861-   , translator.
3. Series.
N. Y. P. L.   May 20, 1915.

NL   0349337   NN CLSU ICU

HB201
.L71
Liefmann, Robert, 1874–1941.
    Ertrag und Einkommen auf der Grundlage einer rein subjektiven Wertlehre, ein wirtschafts-theoretischer Versuch. Jena, G. Fischer; 1907.
    viii, 72 p.

    1. Value.

NL   0349338   ICU CtY PBm NjP MH

Liefmann, Robert, 1874–
    ... Les formes d'entreprises, par Robert Liefmann ... traduit d'après la 2. éd. allemande, par H. Stelz † et J. Loussert ... Paris, M. Giard, 1924.
    viii, 287 p. 22ᵐ. (Bibliothèque internationale d'économie politique, pub. sous la direction de Alfred Bonnet)

    1. Industry.   I. Stelz, H., d. 1914. tr.   II. Loussert, J., joint tr.
                     Full name: Walter Robert Liefmann₎
                            43–22641
Library of Congress   HD33.L5

NL   0349339   DLC ICU RPB MH NjP MnU CU

HD35
.L557
Liefmann, Robert, 1874–1941.
    Формы предприятий; кооперация и социализация. Пер. с 3. немецкого изд. Е. А. Яновского. Берлин, Обелиск, 1924.
    268 p. 24 cm.

    1. Corporations. 2. Cooperative societies. 3. Corporations, Government.   *Title transliterated:* Formy predpriiatii.
                     Full name: Walter Robert Liefmann.
    HD35.L557   48–37482

NL   0349340   DLC

Liefmann, Robert, 1874–
    Geld und gold, ökonomische theorie des geldes, von Robert Liefmann. Stuttgart und Berlin, Deutsche verlags-anstalt, 1916.
    241 p. 23½ᵐ.

    1. Money. 2. Gold. 3. Currency question.   I. Title.
                       ₍*Full name:* Walter Robert Liefmann₎
                            29–9251
    Library of Congress   HG221.L5

NL   0349341   DLC OrU ICJ NN MU

HG186
.G3L53
Liefmann, Robert, 1874–1941.
    Die Geldvermehrung im Weltkriege und die Beseitigung ihrer Folgen; eine Untersuchung zu den Problemen der Übergangswirtschaft. Stuttgart und Berlin, Deutsche Verlags-Anstalt, 1918.
    199p. tables. 24cm.

    1. Capital. 2. Finance - Germany. 3. European War, 1914-1918 - Finance - Germany. 1. Title.

NL   0349342   FMU MH ICJ CIU NN

335
L623g
1922
Liefmann, Robert, 1874–1941.
    Geschichte und Kritik des Sozialismus. Leipzig, Quelle & Meyer, 1922.
    191p. 22cm.

    Bibliography: p.₍189₎-191.

    1. Socialism. History. 2. Socialism. I. Title.

NL   0349343   KU CaBVaU CtY IaU CSt-H MH NN

Liefmann, Robert, 1874–1941.
    Geschichte und Kritik des Sozialismus. 2., verb. Aufl. Leipzig, Quelle & Meyer, 1923.
    xii, 182 p. 21 cm.

    1. Socialism—Hist. 2. Socialism. I. Title.
    HX21.L5 1923   49–33095*

NL   0349344   DLC ICU OO OU

Liefmann, Robert, 1874–
    Grundsätze der volkswirtschaftslehre, von Robert Liefmann ... Stuttgart und Berlin, Deutsche verlags-anstalt, 1917–19.
    2 v. 25½ᵐ.
    Contents.—1. bd. Grundlagen der wirtschaft.—2. bd. Grundlagen des tauschverkehrs.

    1. Economics. 2. Exchange.   I. Title.
                     ₍*Full name:* Walter Robert Liefmann₎
                           21–17406 Revised
    Library of Congress   HB155.L5

NL   0349345   DLC CLSU ICJ

HB175
L719
ed.2
Liefmann, Robert, 1874–
    Grundsätze der Volkswirtschaftslehre. 2. neu bearb. Aufl. Stuttgart, Deutsche Verlags Anstalt, 1920-22.
    2 v. 25ᶜᵃ.
    Contents.- 1. Bd. Grundlagen der Wirtschaft. 2. Bd. Grundlagen des Tauschverkehrs.

    1.Economics. 2.Exchange. I.Title.

NL   0349346   CSt-H MH PSt

Liefmann, Robert, 1874–
    Grundsätze der Volkswirtschaftslehre ...
Stuttgart [etc.] 1922-23.
    2 v. 24.5 cm.
    Contents. - v. 1. Grundlagen der Wirtschaft. 3. neu bearb. Aufl. , 1923. - v. 2. Grundlagen des Tauschverkehrs, 2. neu bearb. Aufl. , 1922.

NL   0349347   CtY

VOLUME 332

Liefmann, Robert, 1874 – *9330.436.8.*
 Die Hausweberei im Elsass.
 (In Verein fuer Socialpolitik. Schriften. 84. Pp. 191–247. Leipzig, 1899.)

E6766 — Alsace. Manuf.

NL 0349348   MB

Liefmann, Robert, 1874–
 Inlandskapital, auslandskapital, kriegstribute; untersuchungen über die probleme der kapitalbildung, von Robert Liefmann. Leipzig, Deutsche wissenschaftliche buchhandlung g. m. b. h., 1930.
 180 p. 18¼ᶜᵐ. (Added t.-p.: Weltwirtschaftliche vorträge und abhandlungen ... hft.)

 1. Capital. 2. Finance—Germany.   I. Title.
 [Full name: Walter Robert Liefmann]
                                31–8137
 Library of Congress   HG186.G3L5
                        [2]   332.0943

NL 0349349   DLC CU NN

Liefmann, Robert, 1874–
 ... International cartels, combines and trusts, by Prof. Dr. Robert Liefmann, with an introduction by Charles T. Hallinan; a record of discussion on cartels at the International economic conference and a summary of legislation on cartels. London, Europa publishing co. ltd. [etc., 1927]
 152 p. 19ᶜᵐ. (Europa handbooks)

 1. [Cartels] 2. [Commerce] 3. Trusts, Industrial.   I. International economic conference, Geneva, 1927. II. Title.
 [Full name: Walter Robert Liefmann]
 U. S. Dept. of agr.   Library   286L62   Agr 28—314
 for Library of Congress   HD272.L5
                           [a41f1]

 PU-W ICJ
NL 0349350   DNAL NIC MH-L CU CtY OU MiU OCU MB PU NN

Liefmann, Robert, 1874–
 ... Die kartelle in und nach dem kriege, von univ.-prof. dr. Robert Liefmann. Berlin, D. Reimer (E. Vohsen) 1918.
 40 p. 23ᶜᵐ. (Veröffentlichungen des Deutschen wirtschaftsverbandes für Süd- und Mittelamerika, hft. 2)

 1. Trusts, Industrial. 2. European war, 1914—   —Economic aspects—Germany.   I. Title.
 Title from Stanford Univ.   Printed by L. C.   A 21–1204

NL 0349351   CSt CU MH OrPR

Liefmann, Robert, 1874–
 Kartelle, Konzerne und Trusts. 7.umgearbeitete Aufl. Stuttgart,E.H.Moritz,1927.
 xiv,423p. 17cm. ([His Die Unternehmungen und ihre Zusammenschlüsse, Bd.2)

NL 0349352   CtY MH

Liefmann, Robert, 1874–
 Kartelle, konzerne und trusts ...
 8. umgearb. und erweiterte aufl. (29.–33. tausend) Stuttgart, 1930.
 428 p. 20 cm. (Added t. -p. : Die unternehmungen und ihre zusammenschlüsse, 2)
 This work is a continuation of the author's Die unternehmungsformen.

NL 0349353   RPB

Liefmann, Robert, 1874–   338.8 Q5o1
 49974 Kartelle und Trusts. Von Prof. Dr. Robert Liefmann ... . Stuttgart, E. H. Moritz, 1905.
 143 p. 17¼ᶜᵐ.
 "Literatur," p. [8].

NL 0349354   ICJ MH

Liefmann, Robert, 1874–
 Kartelle und trusts und die weiterbildung der volkswirtschaftlichen organisation, von prof. dr. Robert Liefmann ... 2., stark erweiterte aufl. (6.–10. tausend) Stuttgart, E. H. Moritz, 1910.
 210 p. fold. diagr. 18ᶜᵐ. (On cover: Bücherei der rechts- und staatskunde)
 "Literatur": p. [7]–8.

 1. Trusts, Industrial.
                                12–1552;
 Library of Congress   HD2734.L8

NL 0349355   DLC OrU NIC MH-L NjP TxU ICJ NN PV-L ICU

338.8
L719k.3 Liefmann, Robert, 1874–
 Kartelle und Trusts und die Weiterbildung der Volkswirtschaftlichen Organisation. 3., stark erweiterte Aufl. (11.–14.Tausend) Stuttgart, E. H. Moritz, 1918.
 315p. 18cm. (Bücherei der Rechts- u. Staatskunde, 12)

 Includes bibliography.

 1. Trusts, Industrial.   I. Title.

NL 0349356   IEN

Liefmann, Robert, 1874–1941.
 Kartelle und Trusts und die Weiterbildung der volkswirtschaftlichen Organisation. 4., erweiterte und verb. Aufl. Stuttgart, E. H. Moritz, 1920.
 xi, 310 p. 18 cm. (Bücherei der Rechts- und Staatskunde, Bd. 12)

 1. Trusts, Industrial.   I. Title.   (Series)
                        Full name: Walter Robert Liefmann.
 HD2734.L8 1920   55–54803

NL 0349357   DLC GU MiEM FU

HD2734   Liefmann, Robert, 1874–
L719   Kartelle und trusts und die weiterbildung der
ed.5   volkswirtschaftlichen organisation, von prof. dr. Robert Liefmann ... 5., erweiterte und verb. aufl. (18–22. tausend) Stuttgart, E.H. Moritz, 1922.
 vii,[1],311 p. 17½ᶜᵐ.
 "Literatur": p.[308]–311.

 1.Trusts, Industrial. I.Title.

NL 0349358   CSt-H InU NIC CU MH

Liefmann, Robert, 1874–
 Kartelle und trusts und die weiterbildung der volkswirtschaftlichen organisation, von prof. dr. Robert Liefmann ... 6., erweiterte und verb. aufl. (23.–25. tausend) Stuttgart, E. H. Moritz, 1924.
 4 p. l, 173 p. 25½ᶜᵐ.

 1. Trusts, Industrial.   I. Title.
 Library of Congress   HD2734.L8 1924   24–22906

NL 0349359   DLC NN OU

Liefmann, Robert, 1874–
 Die kommunistischen gemeinden in Nordamerika, von Robert Liefmann. Jena, G.Fischer, 1922.
 2 p.l., 95 p. 22ᶜᵐ.
 A revised and enlarged edition of an article published in the Jahrbücher für nationalökonomie und statistik v. 91,1908. cf.Vorwort.
 "Eine ergänzung dieser schritt in bezug auf die probleme des sozialismus und kommunismus bildet meine ... Geschichte und kritik des sozialismus."—Vorwort.

 1.Communism—U.S.—Hist.

NL 0349360   MiU InU FU ICU IU NN MiU UCL MH CtY CU

Liefmann, Robert, 1874–
 ... Mineralölwirtschaft. Breslau, F. Hirt, 1927.
 128 p. 1 l. incl. illus. (maps) plates. 19½ᶜᵐ. (Added t.-p.: Jedermanns bücherei ... abt.: Sozialwissenschaft und wirtschaftswissenschaft)
 At head of title: Robert Liefmann und Franz Angelberger.
 "Literatur": p. [106]

 1. Petroleum.   I. Angelberger, Franz, joint author. II. Title.
                                28–303
 Library of Congress   HD9565.L5

NL 0349361   DLC NN

LIEFMANN, Robert, 1874–
 Monopoly or competition as the basis of a government trust policy. [Cambridge,Harvard university press,etc.,etc.,1915.]

 Quarterly Journal of Economics, vol. XXIX , no12, Feb. 1915, pp. 308–325.

NL 0349362   MH

Liefmann, Robert, 1874–
 Petroleum. (Handwörterbuch der Staatswissenschaften. Jena, 1925. 4. ed. 4°. Bd. 6, p. 837–859. tables.)
 Signed: Robert Liefmann.
 Bibliography, p. 858–859.

 1. Petroleum.
 N. Y. P. L.   September 13, 1927

NL 0349363   NN

Liefmann, Robert, 1874–
 Schutzzoll und kartelle. Von dr. Robert Liefmann ... . Jena, G. Fischer, 1903.
 iv, 74 p. 24ᶜᵐ.

 1. Trusts, Industrial. 2. Tariff.   I. Title.
                                3–26127
 Library of Congress   HF2591.L7

NL 0349364   DLC NIC PU ICJ

HB175
.L65 Liefmann, Robert, 1874–
 ...Ueber objekt, wesen und aufgabe der wirtschaftswissenschaft. 1.t. Heutige richtungen und objekt der wirtschaftswissenschaft. Von Robert Liefmann...
 [Jena, G. Fischer, 1916]
 p.1–63. 25cm.
 Caption title.
 "Der zweite teil dieses aufsatzes folgt im februar-heft."
 "Jahrbücher für nationalökonomie und statistik... 106. band - III. folge. 51. band. Erstes   heft."
 1.Economics.

NL 0349365   NNU-W

VOLUME 332

Liefmann, Robert, 1874–
  ... Über wesen und formen des verlags (der hausindustrie). Ein beitrag zur kenntnis der volkswirtschaftlichen organisationsformen, von dr. Robert Liefmann. Freiburg i. B. ₁etc.₎ J. C. B. Mohr (P. Siebeck) 1899.
  viii, 132 p. 24ᶜᵐ. (Volkswirtschaftliche abhandlungen der badischen hochschulen ... 3. bd. 1. hft.)

  1. Home labor. 2. Industry.

                                 10–11421
Library of Congress   HD2331.L6

    NL 0349366   DLC ICJ

Liefmann, Robert, 1874–
  Unser Geldwesen nach dem Weltkriege. Von Professor Dr. Liefmann... Leipzig: Reichenbach₁, 1918?₎. 19 p. 8°. (Oekonomische Gesellschaft im Königreich Sachsen. Schriften.)

  1. Money—Germany, 1918.   2. European war, 1914–1918—
Economic aspects—Germany.   3. Oekonomische Gesellschaft im
Koenigreich Sachsen, Dresden.   Koenigreich Sachsen, Dresden.
N. Y. P. L.   January 10, 1925

    NL 0349367   NN

Liefmann, Robert, 1874–
  Die unternehmerverbände (konventionen, kartelle) ihr wesen und ihre bedeutung; von Robert Liefmann. Freiburg i B. ₁etc.₎ J. C. B. Mohr (Paul Siebeck) 1897.
  xii, 199 p. 24ᶜᵐ. (*Added t.-p.:* Volkswirtschaftliche abhandlungen der badischen hochschulen. 1. hft.)
  "Litteraturübersicht": p. 7–9.

  1. Trusts, Industial.   I. Title.
                      ₁*Full name:* Walter Robert Liefmann₎
                            3—11908
Library of Congress   HF2501.L7

    NL 0349368   DLC NIC NjP ICJ

Liefmann, Robert, 1874–
  Die unternehmungen und ihre zusammenschlüsse, von prof. dr. Robert Liefmann ... Stuttgart, E. H. Moritz, 1928, '27.
  2 v. 18ᶜᵐ.
  Each volume has special t.-p., and was previously issued separately.
  Contents.—I. Die unternehmungsformen mit einschluss der genossenschaften und der sozialisierung. 4. aufl.—II. Kartelle, konzerne und trusts. 7. aufl.
  1. Corporations. 2. Cooperative societies. 3. Trusts, Industrial. 4. Government ownership. 5. Business enterprises.
                     ₁*Full name:* Walter Robert Liefmann₎
                        28–19160 Revised 2
Library of Congress   HD35.L55 1927

    NL 0349369   DLC IEdS NjP OKentU MH NN

Liefmann, Robert, 1874–
  Die Unternehmungen und ihre Zusammenschlusse, von Prof. Dr. Robert Liefmann... 8., umgearb. und erweit. Aufl. Bd. 2 Stuttgart, E. H. Moritz, 19–.   v. 20cm.
  Each volume has also special t.-p.
  Contents.—
  Bd. 2. Kartelle, Konzerne und Trusts.

  1. Cartels. 2. Trusts.
N. Y. P. L.   August 23, 1944

    NL 0349370   NN

HD35
.L55
1927   **Liefmann, Robert,** 1874–
  Die unternehmungen und ihre zusammenschlüsses, von prof. dr. Robert Liefmann ... Stuttgart, E. H. Moritz, 1930.
  2 v. 18ᶜᵐ.
  Each volume has special t.-p., and was previously issued separately.
  Contents.—I. Die unternehmungsformen mit einschluss der genossenschaften und der sozialisierung. 4. aufl.—II. Kartelle, konzerne und trusts. 7. aufl.

    NL 0349371   O

Liefmann, Robert, 1874–
  Die unternehmungsformen, von prof. dr. R. Liefmann. Stuttgart, E. H. Moritz ₁1912₎
  viii, 216 p. 18½ᶜᵐ.

  1. Corporations. 2. Cooperative societies. 3. Corporations, Government. I. Title.

                     ₁*Full name:* Walter Robert Liefmann₎
    HD35.L5   1912   12–16096

    NL 0349372   DLC NjP ICU NN ICJ

HD35
L5
1921   **Liefmann, Robert,** 1874–1941.
  Die Unternehmungsformen, mit Einschluss der Genossenschaften und der Sozialisierung. 2. umgearb. Aufl. Stuttgart, E.H. Moritz, 1921. 259 p. 18cm.

  Literatur: p. ₁258₎-259.

  1. Business. 2. Stock companies. 3. Corporations. I. Title.

    NL 0349373   GU KU IU CLSU NN NNC

Liefmann, Robert, 1874–
  Die unternehmungsformen, mit einschluss der genossenschaften und der sozialisierung; von prof. dr. Robert Liefmann. 3. umgearb. aufl. (10. bis 14. tausend) Stuttgart, E. H. Moritz, 1923.
  viii, 152 p. 24ᶜᵐ.

  1. Corporations—Germany. 2. Cooperative societies—Germany. 3. Government ownership—Germany. 4. Entrepreneur. I. Title.
                     ₁*Full name:* Walter Robert Liefmann₎
Library of Congress   HD35.L5 1923   23–17275

    NL 0349374   DLC NN

FILM
8252
HD   **Liefmann, Robert,** 1874–
  Die Unternehmungsformen, mit Einschluss der Genossenschaften und der Sozialisierung. 4. umgearb. und erweitere Aufl. ... Stuttgart, E.H. Moritz, 1928.
  xii,327 p. On film (Negative) (His Unternehmungen und ihre Zusammenschlüsses, Bd.I)

  Microfilm. Original in Harvard Univ. Library.

    NL 0349375   CU

Liefmann, Robert, 1874–
  Vom reichtum der nationen; untersuchungen über die sogenannten reparationsfragen und die internationalen verschuldungs- und währungsprobleme, von dr. Robert Liefmann ... Karlsruhe, G. Braun, 1925.
  vii, ₁1₎, 143 p. 22½ᶜᵐ.

  1. European war, 1914–1918—Reparations. 2. Debts, Public. 3. Currency question. 4. Europe—Econ. condit.—1918—
                     ₁*Full name:* Walter Robert Liefmann₎
                       25—20724
Library of Congress   D648.L5

    NL 0349376   DLC GU ICJ NjP PU

Liefmann, Robert, 1874–1941
  ... Wirtschaftstheorie und wirtschaftsbeschreibung, von Robert Liefmann. Tübingen, Mohr, 1929.
  48 p. 23ᶜᵐ. (Recht und staat in geschichte und gegenwart ... 61)

  1. Economics—Addresses, essays, lectures.   I. Title.
                     ₁*Full name:* Walter Robert Liefmann₎
Library of Congress   HB175.L66   29–12643

    NL 0349377   DLC MiU

Liefmann, Walter Robert
  see
Liefmann, Robert, 1874– 1941.

Liefmann-Keil, Elisabeth.
  Organisierte konkurrenz-preisbildung, grosshandelsversteigerung und warenbörse, von dr. rer. pol. Elisabeth Liefmann-Keil. Leipzig, Hans Buske verlag, 1936.
  160 p. incl. tables, diagrs. 23ᶜᵐ.
  Pages 158–160, advertising matter.
  Also issued as the author's thesis, Freiburg i. Breisgau.
  Bibliographical foot-notes.

  1. Prices. 2. Competition. 3. Auctions. 4. Produce trade.

                         A 40–543
New York. Public library
  for Library of Congress   ₁2₎

    NL 0349379   NN CtY

PA111
I54   **Liefooghe, A**
  Notions élémentaires de grammaire comparée du grec et du latin. Paris, A. Hatier, 1949.
  120 p. (Bibliothèque des humanités)

  Bibliography: p. ₁108₎

  1. Latin language - Grammar, Comparative - Greek. 2. Greek language - Grammar, Comparative - Latin.

    NL 0349380   CU

₁**Liefooghe, Michiel**₎ 1891–
  De mensch is alleen ₁door₎ Roel de Ridder ₁pseud.₎ Omslag door Moritz van Reeth. Diest, Pro Arte ₁1945₎
  370 p. 19 cm.

  I. Title.

  PT6436.L48M4   A F 48–4955*
California. Univ. Libr.
  for Library of Congress   ₁1₎†

    NL 0349381   CU NN PU DLC

GB1105
.K7   **Liefrinck, F. A.,** joint author.

Krul, Wilhelmus Franciscus Johannes Marie, 1893–
  Recent groundwater investigations in the Netherlands, by W. F. J. M. Krul and F. A. Liefrinck. New York, Elsevier Pub. Co., 1946.

Liefrinck, Frederik Albert, 1853–1927.
  Bali en Lombok. Geschriften van F. A. Liefrinck; met een inleiding van Prof. J. C. van Eerde. Amsterdam, J. H. de Bussy, 1927;
  3 p.l., 542 p. front. (port.) 22 cm. [Uitgave van het Bali-instituut]
  1. Bali (Island) 2. Lombok (Island) I. Bali instituut, Amsterdam.

    NL 0349383   CU MnU NIC CtY NN

Liefrinck, Frederik Albert
  Bijdrage tot de kennis van het eiland Bali. [Batavia? 1889?] 463 p. 24cm.

  1. Bali (Island)—Descr. and trav.

    NL 0349384   NN

VOLUME 332

Liefrinck, Frederik Albert, 1853-1927.
P70   De landsverordeningen der Balische vorsten
L623   van Lombok. Uitg. door het Koninklijk Insti-
915   tuut voor de Taal-, Land- en Volkenkunde van
       Ned.-Indië. 's-Gravenhage, M. Nijhoff, 1915.
       2 v. 25 cm.

       Balinese and Dutch.

       1. Law - Lombok (Island)

NL 0349385   CtY TxFTC WaU CLU ICU CU MiU-L NIC

DS 647 LIEFRINCK, FREDERIK ALBERT,   ed.
.B2 L7   Landsverordeningen van de inlandsche vor-
        sten op Bali. Uitgeg. door het K. Instituut
        voor de Taal-, Land- en Volkenkunde van Ned.-
        Indië. 's-Gravenhage, M. Nijhoff, 1917-21.
        2 v. in 1. illus., ports.

        Vol. 2 has title: Nog eenige verordeningen
        en overeenkomsten van Balische vorsten.
        Balinese and Dutch on opposite pages.

        1. Law--Bali. 2. Balinese language--Texts.
        I. K. Instituut   voor Taal-, Land- en
        Volkenkunde, The   Hague. II. Tc.

NL 0349386   InU MiU-L WU NIC NNC MH WaU CSt-H

Asia
DS647   Liefrinck, Frederik Albert, 1853-1927.
.B2L54   Nog eenige verordeningen en
        overeenkomsten van Balische vorsten.
        's-Gravenhage, M. Nijhoff, 1921.
        541 p. illus.
        Forms vol. 2 of his Landsverordeningen
        van de inlandsche vorsten of Bali.
        "Uitgegeven door het Koninklijk
        Instituut voor de taal -, land- en
        volkenkunde van Ned. -Indië."

        1. Bali   (island) -- Hist. --
        Sources.   I. Title.

NL 0349387   HU MH NIC WaU MiU-L CtY-L

Liefs, Jacob.
    Lof-dicht, over de wijt-vermaerde noyt-gehoorde
leser landen vreughden-rijke victorie, by het
veroveren vande schatrijcke silver-vloot der
konings van Spangien, door het manhaftelijk be-
leydt vande seer kloecke ende onvertsaeghde zee-
helden Pieter Pietersz Heyn, den heere generael:
ende Henderick Cornelisz Lonq, admirael over de
uytgesonden vloot der VVest-Indische compagnie
... Geschiet anno M.DC.XXVIII. ₍In's Graven-
Haghe?₎ Gedruct int Jaer ons Heeren 1629.
    ₍8₎ p. 19 x 15½ cm.
    Signed: I.Liefs.

    Written to celebrate the battle in Matanzas Bay,
September 8, 1628.

    1. Netherlands--Hist.--Wars of independence, 1556-1648--
Poetry. 2. Heyn, Pieter Pieterszoon, 1578-1629. I. Title.

NL 0349389   MiU

LIEFSON, Einar.
    Bacterial spores and the development of
flagella on newly germinated spores. Chicago,
₍1931₎.

    Dissertation - University of Chicago.
    "Reprinted from Journal of Bacteriology,
vol. XXI, no. 5, May, 1931."

NL 0349390   MH-C

Liefsting, Fokko Bernadus Coninck
    see Coninck Liefsting, Fokko Bernadus.

Liefstingh, G.
SB183
.W24   Graszaadteeltproeven. Wageningen, 19 -
nr. 149,
etc.

Lieftinck, Ferd.
    Japanese colour prints together with some books;
the collection a.o. of F. Lieftinck, Haren. To
be sold at auction 22-23 November. Amsterdam,
Internationaal antiquariaat, Menno Hertzberger,
n.v. ₍1938₎
    72 p.

NL 0349393   PPPM

Lieftinck, Ferd.
    Summary catalogue of drawings by Utagawa
Kuniyoshi in the collection of Ferd. Lieftinck,
by B. W. Robinson. Groningen, Verenigde druk-
kerijen Hoitsema, 1953. 96 p. illus. 27cm.

    Bibliography, p. 8.
                                Basil William.
    I. Kuniyoshi, 1797?-1861. ₍II. Robinson,

NL 0349394   NN

Lieftinck, Ferd.
    Tentoonstelling tekeningen van Utagawa
Kuniyoshi uit de versameling van Ferd Lieftinck
    see under   Hague. Gemeentemuseum.

Lieftinck, Gerard Isaäc, 1902-
    Bisschop Bernold (1027-1054) en zijn geschenken aan de
Utrechtse kerken. Openingscollege gegeven bij de aanvaar-
ding van het ambt van lector in de middeleeuwse hand-
schriftenkunde aan de Rijksuniversiteit te Leiden op Vrijdag
19 Maart 1948. Groningen, J. B. Wolters, 1948.
    22 p. facsim. 24 cm.
    Bibliographical references included in "Noten" (p. 20-22)

    1. Bernulphus, Saint, Bp. of Utrecht, d. 1054. 2. Manuscripts--
Netherlands.
    BX4700.B56L5   49-26211*

NL 0349396   DLC NN

LIEFTINCK, GERARD ISAÄC, 1902-
    De librijen in scriptoria der Westvlaamse cister-ciënser-
abdijen Ter Duinen en Ter Doest in de 12ᵈᵉ en 13ᵉ eeuw en de
betrekkingen tot het atelier van de kapittelschool van
Sint Donatiaan te Brugge. Brussel, 1953. 96 p. plates.
27cm. (Koninklijke Vlaamse academie voor wetenschappen, letteren en
schone Kunsten van Belgie. Letteren, Klasse der. Mededelinge. Jaarg.
15, nr. 2)

    French summary.
    Bibliographical footnotes.

    1. Manuscripts--Collections--Belgium--Bruge. 2. Notre Dame des Dunes
Bruges (Cistercian abbey). 3. Ter Doest, Lissenweghe, Belgium (Cistercian
abbey) I. Series.

NL 0349398   NN NcU

Lieftinck, Gerard Isaäc, 1902-
PF776
.V3   Verwijs, Eelco, 1830-1880.
        Middelnederlandsch woordenboek, van E. Verwijs en J.
    Verdam. 's-Gravenhage, M. Nijhoff, 1885-19

Lieftinck, Gerard Isaäc, 1902-
    De Middelnederlandsche Tauler-handschriften. Gronin-
gen, J. B. Wolters, 1936.
    xxxiiij, 443 p. illus. facsims. 24 cm.
    The author's thesis, Amsterdam.
    "Literatuur": p. ₍ix₎-xv.
    "Tekstgedeelte": p. ₍209₎-366.

    1. Tauler, Johannes, 1300 (ca.)-1361. 2. Manuscripts, Dutch.
I. Title.
    BV5080.T5L5   149.3   38-23769 rev*

NL 0349400   DLC OrU CtY IU

LIEFTINCK, J. H., & Zoon.
    Tabak; overzicht van den import-handel in
Nederland. Amsterdam 1908.

    pp. (2), 37.

NL 0349401   MH

Lieftinck (Jan)
    Copie, van . . . missive . . . aen d' . . . Staten 's landts
van Utreecht ₍sic₎ . . . om te betoonen dat indien hij het
ongeluk gehad heeft haer ed. mog. eenighsins te injuri-
ieren, 't selve niet geschiet is uijt een boos . . . opset,
maer wel eer door een over-moet &c . . . 4 Jany. 168₂.
₍Utrecht, 168₂.₎ 3ℓ. 4°.

NL 0349402   NN

BS2535 Lieftinck, Jan Wolter.
.M3L7   Anthropologische grondbeginselen van Jezus, naar de
        synoptische evangeliën ... Groningen, Gebroeders Hoitse-
        ma ₍1873₎
        ₍13₎, 125, ₍7₎ p. 22½ᶜᵐ.
        Proefschrift--Groningen.

        1. Jesus Christ--Teachings. 2. Sin.

NL 0349403   ICU NjPT

QL
513   Lieftinck, Maurits Anne
.02   The dragonflies (Odonata) of New Guinea and
L72   neighbouring islands. ₍Leide, E.J.Brill, 1932-
       49₎
       7 pts. illus., plates, map. 32 cm. (pt.6:
28 cm.)
       Caption title.
       Pt.6 has imprint: Buitenzorg, Archipel
Druckkerij.

       Pts.1-5 and 7 originally published in Nova
Guinea, Zoologie, v.15, livr.5, 1932; v.17, livr.1-2,
1933-35; new ser., v.1-2, 1937-38; and v.5, 1949;
pt.6 in Treubia, v.18, pt.3, 1949.
       Univ. of Mich. copies of pts.1-5 are offprints
from Nova Guinea, with cover titles in French
(pts.4-5 in English)
       1. Odonata--   New Guinea.

NL 0349405   MiU NIC

Lieftinck, Maurits Anne
    Further studies on southeast Asiatic species
of Macromia Rambur, with notes on their ecology,
habits and life history, and with descriptions
of larvae and two new species (Odon., Epophthalmi-
inae). 1950.

    (In Treubia, v. 20, pt. 3, p. 657-716)

NL 0349406   PPAN

VOLUME 332

QL 513 02 L52
Lieftinck, Maurits A
Handlist of Malaysian Odonata; a catalogue of the dragonflies of the Malay Peninsula, Sumatra, Java and Borneo, including the adjacent small islands. Bogor, Java, Archipel, 1954.
202 p. map. 24½cm. (Treubia. Supplement, v.22)

1. Dragonflies - Malay Peninsula.
2. Dragonflies - Indonesia. I. Title.
(Series)

NL 0349407   IdU PPAN

Lieftinck, Maurits A
On some Odonata collected in Ceylon, with descriptions of new species and larvae. [Ceylon, 1940]
[79]-117 p. illus. 25cm.

"Reprinted from the Ceylon journal of science, section B, Zoology and geology. Vol. 22, part 1. June 12, 1940."

1. Dragon-flies.

NL 0349408   NIC

QH1 A14 no.1488
Lieftinck, Maurits Anne
Results of the Archbold expeditions, no. 64. Odonata of the 1948 Archbold Cape York expedition, with a list of the dragonflies from the peninsula. New York, 1951.
46 p. illus., map. 24 cm. (American Museum of Natural History, New York. American museum novitates, no. 1488)
"References": p. 44-45.

1. Dragon-flies. I. Title. II. Title: Odonata of the 1948 Archbold Cape York expedition. (Series)

NL 0349409   DI

Lieftinck, Maurits Anne
Studies on oriental Gomphidae (Odon.) with descriptions of new or interesting larvae. Buitenzorg, Java, Archipel drukkerij [1941]
233-253 p. plates. 28cm.

"Separate from: Treubia. Vol. 18, part 2, December 1941."

1. Gomphidae.

NL 0349410   NIC

Lieftinck, Pieter, 1902–
Inleiding tot de geldtheorie. Leiden, H. E. Stenfert Kroese, 1946.
[6] l., [5]-295 p. 24 cm. (Capita selecta der economie, 3)
"Geraadpleegde litteratuur": p. [294]-295.

1. Gold. 2. Gold standard. I. Series.

HG289.L54   332.422   47-26141*

NL 0349411   DLC OU CLU OrU

Lieftinck, Pieter, 1902–
Moderne struktuurveranderingen der industrie in de Verenigde Staten van Amerika ... door mr. Pieter Lieftinck ... Groningen [etc.], J. B. Wolters, 1931.
x, 392 p. incl. tables. 24½cm.
Proefschrift—Utrecht.
"Stellingen": 2 p. laid in.

1. U. S.—Indus. 2. U. S.—Econ. condit. I. Title.

                                         33-23707
Library of Congress   HC106.3.L45 1931   330.973

NL 0349412   DLC MiU CU NSyU ICU MH CtY

Lieftinck, Pieter, 1902–
De overheid neemt en geeft. De financiële politiek van de regering en de sociale achtergrond daarvan. Amsterdam, Arbeiderspers, 1951.
36 p. 20 cm.

1. Finance—Netherlands.

Chicago. Univ. Libr.   A 52–64
for Library of Congress   [1]

NL 0349413   ICU NN

Lieftinck, Pieter, 1902–
...Overzicht van de ontwikkeling der handelspolitiek van het koninkrijk der Nederlanden van 1923 tot en met 1938, samengesteld onder leiding van Prof. Mr. P. Lieftinck, met medewerking van G. Brouwers...W. Glastra...Mr. D. J. Hulshoff Pol [en] Mr. W. Veenstra. Haarlem: De Erven F. Bohn n. v., 1939.
xv, 176 p. incl. tables. illus. (charts.) 24½cm. (Nederlandsch economisch instituut, Rotterdam. [Publicatie] no. 28.)

1. Commerce—Netherlands.   1923-1938. I. Brouwers, G.
II. Glastra, W. III. Hulshoff Pol,   D. J. IV. Veenstra, W. V. Ser.
N. Y. P. L.   April 10, 1940

NL 0349414   NN CtY ICU

Lieftinck, Pieter, 1902–
De toekomst onzer monetaire politiek; rede uitgesproken op de Christelijk-historische Zomerconferentie te Lunteren op Vrijdag 19 Juli 1935, door Prof. Mr. P. Lieftinck... Groningen [etc.], J. B. Wolters' Uitgevers-Maatschappij N. V., 1935. 27 p. 24cm.

871585A. 1. Money—Netherlands.
N. Y. P. L.   March 18, 1937

NL 0349415   NN

LIEFWENDAL, KÅGE, ed.
Svenskt konstnärsgalleri: nittonhundratalet. Målare, skulptörer, grafiker. Redaktion: Kåge Liefwendal [och] Carl-Erik Ohlén. Stockholm, Lindqvist [1948] 2 v. (855 p.) illus. (part col.),ports. 31cm.

1. Art, Swedish, 20th cent. 2. Artists, Swedish—Dictionaries. I. Ohlén, Carl Erik, joint ed. II. Title. III. Liefwendal, Kåge. IV. Ohlén, Carl Erik.

NL 0349416   NN

Liefwendal, Maj Sandmark-
see Sandmark-Liefwendal, Maj.

Liégard, Aimé Adrien Léon.
...Considérations pratiques sur la nature et le traitement de la fièvre cérébrale ou encéphalo-méningite. 50 pp. 4°. Paris, 1854.

NL 0349418   DNLM

Liégard, Aimé Adrien Léon.
—, Deux problèmes de physiologie. 28 pp. 8°. Caen, F. Le Blanc-Hardel. 1865. [P., v. 788.]

NL 0349419   DNLM

581.9441 L623b Biol Lib'y
Liégard, Alfred Pierre Auguste.
Bleuniou-Breiz. Flore de Bretagne. Paris, F. Savy, 1879.
3 p.t., xlviii, 405p. 19cm.

French text.

1. Botany - Brittany. I. Title.

NL 0349420   TxU MH-A MBH

WB L718m 1837
LIÉGARD, Alfred Pierre Auguste
Mélange de médecine et de chirurgie pratiques. Caen, Pagny, 1837.
401 p.

NL 0349421   DNLM

WB L718q 1856
LIÉGARD, Alfred Pierre Auguste.
Quelques sujets de médecine et de chirurgie pratiques. Caen, Hardel, 1856.
214 p.
Reprinted from the Mémoires de la Société de médecine, Caen, 1856.
Bound with his Réflexion sur le mémoire de M. Roulland, intitulé, De la diathèse purulente. [Caen, 1856]
Author's autograph presentation copy. Signed.

NL 0349422   DNLM

WB L718q 1856
LIÉGARD, Alfred Pierre Auguste
Réflexion sur le mémoire de M. Roulland, intitulé, De la diathèse purulente. [Caen, 1856]
20 p.
Bound with his Quelques sujets de médecine et de chirurgie pratiques. Caen, 1856.
Caption title.
Reprinted from the Mémoires de la Société de médecine, Caen, 1856.

1. Roulland, François Gabriel Victor, 1817-1874

NL 0349424   DNLM

Liégard, Auguste
see Liégard, Alfred Pierre Auguste.

Liégard (Georges). *Emploi du collyre huileux à l'éserine dans le traitement adjuvant des ulcères infectieux à hypopion. 70 pp. 8°. Paris, 1908.

NL 0349426   DNLM

Liégard (Henri). *Les saints guérisseurs de la Basse-Bretagne. 91 pp. 8°. Paris, 1903.

NL 0349427   DNLM

VOLUME 332

Liegau, Friedrich Wilhelm.
Welches Verfahren bietet bei der Pulpa-
abtötung in der Praxis die besten Aussichten?
Auszug... Greifswald, 1921.
12 p. 22.5 cm.
Inaug.-Diss. - Greifswald.

NL 0349428 CtY

LIÉGAULT, Gustave.
Du diagnostic de l'appendicite chronique sim-
ulant la tuberculose pulmonaire. Paris, 1911.

8° [91 p.].

Official copy of a thesis presented for the
doctor's degree at Harvard University.

NL 0349429 MH DNLM

Liége, Henri de Gueldre, bishop of.
See
Henri de Gueldre, bishop of Liége, d. 1284.

French Rev.
DC
141
F87+
v.151

Liége, Jacques Louis, 1745-1811.
Exposé de la vie politique de
Jacques Louis Liége, juge de paix de
la division de Brutus. ₍n.p.₎, 1796?₎
4 p. 20cm.

NL 0349431 NIC

Liege (Petrus). *De apoplexia. 10 l. 4°.
Francof. ad Vladr., typ. Zeitleri, 1600.

NL 0349432 DNLM

LIÉGE, Pierre.
...Commentaires sur la coustume du comté et pays
de Poitou, anciens ressorts et enclaves d'ice-
luy, avec le procès verbal de messieurs les
commissaires de la reformation de la coûtume.
Poitiers, 1695.

I) Poitou. Laws, statutes, etc.

NL 0349433 MH-L

WA
1254.F8
L719p
1948

Liége, Robert, 1900-
Pratique médicale scolaire. Paris,
Doin, 1948.
171 p. illus.

Bibliographical footnotes.

1. School hygiene - France I. France.
Laws, statutes, etc.

NL 0349434 DNLM

WB
356
L528t
1934

LIÉGE, Robert, 1900-
Transfusion du sang et immuno-
transfusion en pratique médicale;
indications, résultats, accidents. Paris,
Masson, 1934.
174 p. illus. (Médecine et chirurgie
pratiques, 66)
1. Blood transfusion

NL 0349435 DNLM

Liége, Robert, 1900-
Tuberculose du nourrisson et vaccin B.C.G. ...
Paris, 1930.
Thèse - Univ. de Paris.
"Index bibliographique": p.[145]-151.

NL 0349436 CtY

WS
200
L719v
1939

LIÉGE, Robert, 1900-
Vingt études pratiques de médecine
infantile. Paris, Doin, 1939.
210 p. illus.
1. Children - Diseases

NL 0349437 DNLM ICJ

Liége, Sedulius de
see
Sedulius Scotus, 9th cent.

X
758703
.5

LIÉGE D'IRAY,
...Vocabulaire du jargon local et de quelques
particularités du langage populaire dans le département de la Vienne. Châtellerault, Dupuy
et Bousquet, 1923.
83p.

Preface signed: J.D.

NL 0349439 ICN

Liége
Les administrateurs et officiers municipaux de Liége,
aux Français. n.p. [1795?]

4 p.

NL 0349440 MH

Liége
... Budget pour
Liége,
v. 27ᵐ

1. Budget—Liége (City)

31-11978

Library of Congress HJ9053.L5B2 352.109493

NL 0349441 DLC NN

Liége.
Budget
see also its Bulletin administratif de la
ville de Liége.

Liége.
Bulletin administratif de la ville de Liége.

Liége, Éditions Biblio ₍etc.₎
v. in illus. 22-24 cm. annual.

Each vol. 18 -19 accompanied by a vol. of "annexes."
Contains proceedings of the Conseil communal; annexes consist
usually of Rapport sur l'administration et la situation des affaires
de la ville, Budget, Compte d'administration, Rapport sur le compte
d'administration, and various other municipal reports.

1. Liége—Pol. & govt. I. Title.

JS81.L5 58-48953 ‡

NL 0349443 DLC

Liége.
——. Bulletins hebdomadaires de statistique
démographique et médicale, dressée sur les documents officiels. Oct. 20, 1884; Feb. 21 to March
7, March 21 to April 11, April 25 to May 16,
June 6 to July 11, Aug. 1 to Oct. 31, 1885; Jan.
2, 16, to March 6, March 27 to May 15, May 29,
June 12, July 10, 17, Aug. 21, Sept. 13, 20, Oct.
4, 16, Nov. 6, 1896; May 17, June 21, Aug. 23,
1890. sm. 4°. Liége, 1884-90.

NL 0349444 DNLM

Liége.
Flamand-Grétry, Louis Victor, 1764-1843.
Cause célèbre relative à la consécration du cœur de Grétry, ou précis historique des faits énoncés dans le procès intenté à son neveu Flamand-Grétry par la ville de
Liége, auquel sont jointes toutes les pièces justificatives.
Déposé aux pieds de Sa Majesté Charles x, et présenté
à la famille royale. Ce précis est orné de différentes vues
par des artistes distingués, d'un beau portrait de Grétry
d'après Isabey, de fac simile, etc. ... Paris ₍Impr. de
Chaignieau fils aîné₎ 1825.

Liége Neth 1470.2
Chartres et privileges [des bons métiers] de la ville, cité, & ban-
lieue de Liége. [Liége? 1730.]
2 vol. f°. Plates.
Without title-pages, caption titles.

NL 0349446 MH NNC

Liége
Français républicains! Des administrateurs et officiers
municipaux liégeois se sont affichés une seconde fois
dans Paris... [np, 1793]

16 p.
Includes extracts from memoirs of P. Chaussard.

NL 0349447 MH

Liége
Mémorial de la ville de Liége.

see under

₍Ancion, J. D.₎ comp.

Liége.

N6971
.L4M8

Musées de la ville de Liége. Photos de A. C. L., J. Cayet
et Ch. Dessart. Ouvrage publié sous les auspices de la ville
de Liége. Bruxelles, C. Dessart ₍1952₎

Liége
Note sur le projet de budget pour

Liége, 8°.

1. Municipal finance, Belgium: Liége.
N. Y. P. L. August 9, 1924

NL 0349450 NN

VOLUME 332

Liège
...Notices relatives à l'organisation des services communaux
[Liège? 19-

JS6047
.4
.A4

NL 0349451 DLC

Liège.

D542
.L5P45 Philippe, Joseph, 1919–
Le 40ᵐᵉ ¡i. e.¡quarantième¡ anniversaire de la bataille de Liège; catalogue de l'exposition ¡par Joseph Philippe¡. Introd. historique par le lieutenant-général e. r. Mozin¡ Salle des pas-perdus de l'Hôtel de Ville du 18 septembre au 17 octobre 1954. ¡Liège, Association intercommunale de mécanographie, 1954¡

Liège.
Rapport sur la situation de l'industrie minérale et métal-lurgique dans la province de Liége pendant l'année 1879–

Liège, 18
v. fold. tables, diagrs. (part fold.) 21ᶜᵐ.

1. Mines and mineral resources—Liége.
U. S. Geol. survey. Library   G S 15–700 Revised
for Library of Congress   TN68.L5A4

NL 0349453 DI-GS DLC

Liège.
La Région liegeoise
see under title

Q 1029
Liège,
¡ La révolution liégeoise, 1789–1795; catalogue de l'ex-position, l'Hotel de Ville du 27 septembre au 11 octobre 1953¡ [Liège, 1953?]

NL 0349455 MH

Liège. Academia leodiensis
see
Liège. Université

Liège. Academie des beaux-arts.
...Nouveau reglement.
Bruxelles, 1859.

N332
.L6

NL 0349457 DLC

Liège. Administration communale.
La Région liégeoise; démographie; logement, industrie et commerce: l'évolution depuis 1846 et les données du recense-ment général de 1947. Publié avec la collaboration des com-munes de la région liégeoise par l'Administration communale de Liège (Échevinat de la prévoyance sociale) Liège, 1951.

Liège. Archives communales.
Memorial de la ville de Liége
see under Ancion, J.D., comp.

Liège. Archives de l'État
see
Belgium. *Archives de l'État, Liège.*

Liège. Association des ingénieurs sortis de l'Ecole de
see Association des ingénieurs sortis de l'Ecole de Liège.

Liège. Association des licenciés sortis de l'Université de Liège
see Société d'etudes et d'expansion.

Liège. Barreau. *Bibliothèque.*
... Catalogue de la bibliothèque. Liège, Impr. H. Vail-lant-Carmanne, 1896.
228 p. 24ᶜᵐ.
At head of title: Barreau du Liége.
Blank spaces for additions.

1. Law—Belgium—Bibl.
Library of Congress   Z6459.L55 '96   5–11446

NL 0349463 DLC

Liège. Barreau. *Bibliothèque.*
... Catalogue de la bibliothèque. Liège, Imprimerie H. Vail-lant-Carmanne (s. a.) 1907.
xv, 264 p. 24ᶜᵐ.
At head of title: Barreau de Liége.
Blank spaces for additions.

1. Law—Belgium—Bibl. 2. Law—Bibl.—Catalog.
Library of Congress   Z6459.L72 1907   42–41843

NL 0349464 DLC

Liège. *Bureau de l'État-Civil*
see
Liège. *Service de l'État-Civil.*

Liège. *Bureau de la population*
see
Liège. *Service de la population*

Liège. Centre belge d'étude et de documentation des eaux
see
Centre belge d'étude et de documentation des eaux.

Liège. Centre de documentation économique et sociale africaine
see
Centre de documentation économique et sociale africaine.

Liège. Centre médical du Beauregard.
Entretiens cliniques
see under title

Liège. Chambre de commerce
see
Liège. Chambre de commerce et d'industrie.

Liège. Chambre de commerce de Liege, Huy & Waremme.
Rapport sur la situation du commerce & de l'industrie dans les arrondissements de Liége,... Liège, 1901

HF314
.L75

NL 0349471 DLC

Liège. Chambre de commerce et d'industrie.
Bulletin mensuel.
Liège.
v. illus. 22–28 cm.
Irregular,
Title varies: monthly,
Vols. for   Bulletin.
                            published by the chamber under
its earlier name: Chambre de commerce.

HF314.L68   8–26155 rev*

NL 0349472 DLC

Liège. Chambre de commerce *et d'industrie*
...Composition de la Chambre de commerce pour 1902. ...
Liège, 1902

HF314
.L7

NL 0349473 DLC

HF314
L75
Liège. Chambre de commerce et d'industrie.
Rapport sur les travaux.
Liége, G. Thiriart ¡etc.¡
v. 23 cm. annual.
Title varies:¡   Rapport sur la situation du com-merce & de l'industrie.
Other slight variations in title.
Vols. for¡1867–1901¡ published by the chamber under its earlier name: Chambre de commerce.

HF314.L75   62–57338

NL 0349474 DLC

LIÈGE. Collège des bourgmestre et échevins
Rapport sur l'administration et la situation des affaires de la ville présenté en séance du Conseil communal, le 5 octobre, 1903.¡ Liège, G. Thiriart, 1903.
Charts.

NL 0349475 MH

VOLUME 332

Liége. Collégiale de Saint-Jean l'Évangeliste
see Liége. Saint Jean l'Évangéliste (Collegiate church)

Liége. Collegium Anglorum Societatis Jesu, etc.
Florus anglo-bavaricvs serenissimo principi Maximi-
liano Emmanveli, duci Bavariæ, etc., et Mariæ Antoniæ,
Leopoldi cæsaris filiæ, auspicato nuptiarum fœdere conjunctis inscriptus. Leodii, ex officinâ typographicâ Gui-
lielmi H. Streel, 1685.
8 p. l., 205, ⟨1⟩ p., 1 l. 26½ᶜᵐ.
John Keynes, s. j., is the principal author of the work.
The first part contains an account of the foundation and the history of
the English Jesuit college at Liége, the second a history of Oates' plot
with biographies of the English Jesuits alleged to be implicated in it.
1. Popish plot, 1678. 2. Jesuits in England. I. Keynes, John, 1625?-
1697. II. Title.
12-11802
Library of Congress DA448.L6
NL 0349477 DLC DFO

Bt71l
3
Liége. Commission communale de l'histoire de
l'ancien pays de Liége.
Annuaire d'histoire liégeoise. t.1-
1929-30-
Liége,H.Vaillant-Carmanne.
25cm.
At head of title: Annuaire de la Commission
communale de l'histoire de l'ancien pays de
Liége.
NL 0349478 CtY MiU OU NN

Neth 12.4.18
Liége. Commission communale de l'histoire de l'ancien
pays de Liége
Documents et mémoires.
fasc.1 (1946) and later numbers
Title varies 1-3: Documents et mémoires sur le
pays de Liége.
NL 0349479 MH MiU NN

Liége. *Commission communale de l'histoire de l'ancien pays
de Liége.*
... Régestes de la cité de Liége; édités par Ém. Fairon ...
avec glossaire philologique par Jean Haust ... Liége, Éditions
de la Commission communale de l'histoire de l'ancien pays de
Liége, 1933-
v. 30½ᶜᵐ.
Contains bibliographical references.
1. Liége—History—Sources. I. Fairon, Émile, ed. II. Haust, Jean.
III. Title.
A C 34-4015
Title from Princeton Univ. Printed by L. C.
NL 0349480 NjP CaBVaU CU MH CU-S CtY PU

Ndq40
N3
L623R
Liége. Commission Communale de l'Histoire de
l'Ancien Pays de Liége.
Règlements et privilèges des XXXII métiers
de la cité de Liége. fasc.1-
Liége, 1943- [fasc. 1, 1950]
25 cm.
Running title: Métiers de la cité de Liége.
NL 0349481 CtY NN MiU

Liége. — *Commission d'agriculture.* Rapport adressé à la députation permanente du conseil provincial
sur le défrichement des landes et bruyères. [Liége. 1844.]
sm. 8°. pp. 14.
NL 0349482 MH-A

Liége. Commission spéciale d'hygiène publique
chargée de l'enquête sur l'épidémie de fièvre
typhoïde de 1882-3.
Rapport adressé au collége des bourgmestre
et échevins. Liége, G. Thiriart, 1885.
110, 20, 56 p., 2 l. 1 map, 1 ch., 11 tab.
8°.
NL 0349483 DNLM

Liége. Commission spéciale instituée pour
l'examen des plans d'agrandissement et
d'amélioration de l'hôpital de Bavière.
Hospices civils de Liége. Rapport ...
21 juin 1867. Liége, L. De Thier & F. Lovin-
fosse, 1867.
46 p., 1 l. 2 plans. 8°.
NL 0349484 DNLM

Liége. Concours international de quatuor à cordes
see Concours international de quatuor à
cordes, Liége, 1954.

Liége. Conférence lainière internationale. 6th, 1930
see International Wool Conference.

Liége. Conférence libre du jeune barreau
see
Conférence libre du jeune barreau de Liége.

Liége. Congrès international d'éducation
et de protection de l'enfance dans la
famille, 1st, 1905
see
International congress on home education. 1st,
Liége, 1905

Liége. Congrès international d'horticulture de
see International horticultural Congres,
Liége.

Liége. Congrès international de génie
rural, 1930
see
Congrès international de génie rural, Liége,
1930.

Liége. Congrès international des chambres
de commerce et des associations commerciales et industrielles, 1st, 1905
see
International congress of chambers of commerce,
1st, Liége, 1905

Liége. Congrès international des mines, de la
métallurgie, de la mécanique et de la géologie
appliquées. 4th, 1905
see Congrès international des mines, de la
métallurgie et de la géologie appliquée. 4th, Liége,
1905.

Liége. Congrès international des oeuvres de
patronage, 1905
see Congrès international des oeuvres de
patronage, 4th, Liége, 1905.

Liége. Congrès international pour la reproduction
des manuscrits, des monnaies et des sceaux, 1905
see Congrès international pour la reproduction des manuscrits, des monnaies et des sceaux,
Liége, 1905.

Liége. Congrès international pour l'étude de la
radiologie et de l'ionisation, 1905
see Congrès international pour l'étude de la
radiologie et de l'ionisation. 1st, Liége, 1905.

Liége. Conseil.
[Chartres et privilèges des trente-deux
métiers de Liége. Liége? 1730]
see Liége.
Chartres et privilèges [des bons métiers] de la
ville.

Liége. Conseil communal.
Rapport sur l'administration et la situation
des affaires de la ville présenté en séance du
Conseil communal, le 5 octobre, 1903
see under Liége. Collége des bourgmestre
et échevins.

Liége. Conseil municipal pro-
visoire.
Extrait du procès verbal
see under Cochelet, Adrien Pierre
Barthélémy, 1733-1804.

Liége. Conseil provincial
see Liége (Province) Conseil provincial.

ML410
.F8L5
Liége. Conservatoire royal de musique.
...Célébration du centenaire de César
Franck, 1822-1922. ⟨Liége? 1922?⟩
1p.l.,45,⟨1⟩p. front.(port.)illus.
(music) 24cm.
1.Franck, César Auguste, 1822-1890.
I.Dupuis, Sylvain, 1856-
NL 0349500 NNU-W CU

VOLUME 332

MT5
.L5C6   Liége. Conservatoire Royal de Musique.
Centième anniversaire de sa fondation
1826-1926. ₍Liége? 1926?₎
4p.l.,XXXII,104p₎,1 l. illus.,ports.
25cm.
"Commission de surveillance" ₍as of
1946.₎ typed sheet tipped in following
2nd. p.l.
"Principaux ouvrages consultés:
p. XXXII.

NL 0349501   NNU-W NcU

Liége. Conservatoire Royal de Musique.
Notice sur le Conservatoire Royal de
Musique de Liége et sur ses directeurs
see under   Ledent, Richard, 1867-

ML136 LIÉGE. CONSERVATOIRE ROYAL DE MUSIQUE. Biblio-
.L72C76   thèque.
Catalogue de la Bibliothèque du Conservatoire
royal de musique de Liége. Fonds Terry: Musique instrumentale.₎ ₍Liége, n. d.₎
51 p.
At head of title: Eugène Monseur.

1. Music—Bibl.—Catalogs. 2. Instrumental
music—Bibl. I. Terry, Leonard, 1816-1882.
II. Monseur,   Eugène, ed.

NL 0349503   ICU NIC

Music
781.97   Liége. Conservatoire royal de musique. Biblio-
L623   thèque.
Catalogue de la Bibliothèque du Conservatoire royal de musique de Liége. Fonds Terry:
Musique vocale profane. ₍n.p., n.d.₎
39 p.   24 cm.

At head of title: Eugène Monseur.

NL 0349504   KyU

Liége.   *Cour d'appel*
see   **Belgium.** *Cour d'appel (Liége)*

Liége. *Cour supérieure (1815–1830)*
see
Netherlands *(Kingdom, 1815–) Hoog geregtshof (Liége)*

Liége. Direction des travaux communaux.
...Rapport sur les locomotives pour tramway, système Vaessen. Liége: L. de Thier, 1878. 12 p. 1 pl.₎ 4°.
Cover-title.
"Traction mécanique des tramways. Machine Vaessen. Rapport adressé, le
23 septembre 1878, à l'Administration communale de Liége, par M. Mahiels," ₍4₎ p. at
end.

912424. 1. Locomotives—Belgium,   1878. 2. Railways, Street—
Belgium—Liége. I. Mahiels, Armand.   *Revised*
N.Y.P.L.   August 29, 1931

NL 0349507   NN

Liége. ₎ispensaire du mineur.
Lutte contre l'ankylostomasie dans le bassin
de Liége. 1903-1912. Liége,Thone,1913.

pp.18. Tables,charts. 21 cm.

NL 0349508   MBCo

LIBRARY SERVICE
D028.5
A162   Liége. Échevinat de l'instruction publique.
Catalogue collectif des bibliothèques pu-
bliques pour la jeunesse et l'adolescence.
₍Liége₎ 1955.
296 p.

Date on cover: 1956.
Maurice Destenay, échevin.

NL 0349509   NNC

Liége. Échevinat de l'instruction publique.
Exposition le romantisme au pays de Liége
see under   Liége. Musée des beaux-arts.

Liége. École des arts et manufactures et
des mines. Association des ingénieurs
sortis de l'École de Liége.

see

Association des ingénieurs sortis de l'École
de Liége

Liége. Église Sainte-Croix
see
Liége. Sainte-Croix *(Collegiate church)*

Liége. Exposition d'ameublement du foyer de
l'ouvrier, 1923.
(Catalogue et programme des fêtes) Liége, 1923.
43 p. 21 cm.

NL 0349513   DL

Liége   Exposition de l'art ancien au
pays de Liége, 1881.
Catalogue officiel. Liége, L.Grandmont-
Donders, 1881.

21 cm.
Various pagings.
At head of title: Cinquantième anniversaire
de l'indépendance nationale.

NL 0349514   MH-FA NN OCIMA CtY

Fine Arts
NK
2360   Liége. Exposition de l'art ancien au pays
L71   de Liége, 1881.
Meisterstücke der Kunst-Tischlerei, zu-
meist aus dem XVII. und XVIII. Jahrhundert.
Berlin, C. Claesen [188-?]
2 v. 60 plates. 46cm.

In portfolio.
At head of title: L'exposition de l'art
ancien au pays de Liége.
Contents.—1. Ser. Barock- und Rococo-
Möbel.—2. Ser.   Barock- und Rococo-
Möbel. Louis   XVI.-Möbel.
1. Furnitu   re. I. Title.

NL 0349515   NIC

Liége. Exposition de l'art de l'ancien pays
de Liége et des anciens arts wallons
see   Liége. Exposition internationale, 1930.

Liége. Exposition internationale, 1930.
... Architecture internationale moderne
see under   Antwerp. Exposition
internationale, 1930.

Liége. Exposition internationale, 1930.
... Catalogue de l'Exposition de l'art de l'ancien pays de
Liége et des anciens arts wallons. Liége, Imprimerie G. Thone,
1930.
2 p. L, 7–452 p. 21½ᶜᵐ.
At head of title: Exposition internationale de Liége.
"Catalogue publié par les soins de Joseph Brassinne."

1. Art—Liége. 2. Art—Exhibitions.   I. Brassinne, Joseph, 1877-
    33–22050 Revised
Library of Congress   N6969.L5L5
——— Copy 2.   ₍r38c2₎   708.9493

NL 0349518   DLC NIC CU MiU PU WaU CtY DSI

Liége. Exposition internationale, 1930.
...Catalogue général officiel... Partie ... Officieele alge-
meene catalogus... Deel ₍Bruxelles: Imp. Puvrez,
v. illus. (ports.) 21½cm.
At head of title: Exposition internationale de la grande industrie sciences et applications et d'art wallon ancien, Liége, 1930. Internationale tentoonstelling van nijverheid,
wetenschappen en hare toepassingen oud Waalsche kunst, Luik, 1930.
CONTENTS.—
Partie 2. Sections étrangères.

1. Exhibitions—Liége, 1930.
N.Y.P.L.   December 4, 1940

NL 0349519   NN

V
2
.504   LIÉGE. EXPOSITION INTERNATIONALE, 1930.
Catalogus samengesteld door S.Bottenheim.
Catalogue rédigé per S.Bottenheim. ₍Liége?
1930.₎
50p. illus.,plan. 25cm.

NL 0349520   ICN KU NN

Liége. Exposition internationale, 1930.
... Comptes rendus des assemblées générales
et des séances des sections; publiés sous la
direction de Jean Gessler ...
see under   International Congress on Home
Education, 4th, Liége, 1930.

S401
.C57   Liége. Exposition internationale, 1930.
1930a   Congrès international de génie rural, *1st Liége*, 1930.
Comptes-rendus, vœux. Liége: 1ᵉʳ au 15 août 1930.
Gembloux, Impr. J. Duculot, 1931.

Liége. Exposition internationale, 1930.

Belgium. *Commissariat général, Exposition internationale,
Liége, 1930.*
... Congrès et concours organisés à l'occasion de l'Exposition
internationale de Liége, 1930. Léon Michel ... secrétaire général du Commissariat général du gouvernement près l'Exposition internationale de Liége, 1930. Liége (Belgique) ₍Impr.
A. Larock, 1930₎

NL 0349515   NIC

Liége. Exposition internationale, 1930.
L'économie sociale à l'Exposition internationale
de Liége, 1930
see under   Warnotte, Daniel.

VOLUME 332

Liège. Exposition internationale, 1930.

S401
.C57
1930

Congrès international de génie rural, *1st, Liège,* 1930.
Organisation & rapports, Liége: 1ᵉʳ au 15 août 1930.
Gembloux, Impr. J. Duculot, 1930.

Liége. Exposition internationale, 1930.
... Rapports présentés à la 1ᵉ [-5ᵉ] section ...
see under International Congress on
Home Education. 4th, Liége, 1930.

Liége. Exposition internationale, 1930.
Les vieilles chansons wallonnes.
[Liege, Senard, 1930]
unp. illus. obl. D.

NL 0349527 PP

Liége 4045-334
1930. Exposition internationale,
Catalogue. Section de la musicologie.
= [Liége. 1930.] 59 pp. Plates. 23.5 cm.
Held under the auspices of the Commission spéciale pour la musicologie
of the Netherlands.
The text is in French and Dutch.
Includes bibliographies.

D9870 — Netherlands. Bijzondere c issee voor de muziek. Pubs. — Musicology. — Netherlands. F.a. Music.

NL 0349528 MB NNMM

VM5
.C73
1939c

Liège. Exposition internationale, 1939.

Congrès international des ingénieurs navals, *Liège,* 1939.
Congrès international des ingénieurs navals, 18, 19, 20
août 1939; [compte rendu] Liège, G. Thone [1939]

Liége. Exposition internationale, 1939.
... Quinzaine internationale rurale
see under Giele, J.

Liège. Exposition internationale, 1939.
Rétrospective d'art; peinture, sculpture, tapisserie, gravure, art japonais. Liège, 1939.
224 p. (p. 115-224 illus.) 29 cm.

1. Art—Exhibitions. I. Title.

N4672.A5 707.4 49-55221*

NL 0349531 DLC

N
6961
1624

Liège. Exposition internationale, 1951.
Art mosan et arts anciens du pays de Liège;
exposition internationale [1ᵉʳ sept. - 31 oct.
1951. Liège, Éditions de l'A. S. B. L. le
Grand Liège, 1951.
327 p. 92 plates on 46 l. 24cm.

"Réalisée ... avec le concours du Ministère
de l'instruction publique de Belgique, de la
province de Liège et de la ville de Liège."
Includes bib- liography.

NL 0349532 NNC MdBWA KyU NN OC1MA

Liège. Exposition internationale de l'eau, 1939
see Liège. Exposition internationale, 1939.

Liège. Exposition Universelle et Internationale,
1905.
Album illustré de l'Exposition Universelle.
Weltaustellungs Album. Exhibition album. Publication officielle parue sous les auspices
de l'Exposition Universelle. Souvenir de
Liège...1905. Bruxelles, [1905].
26p. illus.

NL 0349534 ICRL ICJ

NK
975
.L574

Liége. Exposition Universelle et Internationale, 1905,
L'art ancien au pays de Liége. Album publié
sous le patronage du comité exécutif... par
m.G.Terme. [Liége, ?1905]
3 portfolios. plates. 26 cm.
Contents: Art religieux. - Orfèvrerie. Dinan-
derie. Ivoiries. - Mobilier et sculpture.

NL 0349535 PPPM

Liège. Exposition universelle et internationale,
1905.
Catalogue de la section italienne
see under Italy. R. Commissione,
Esposizione Universale, Liége, 1905.

Liège. Exposition universelle et internationale, 1905. 070.227 2
.... Catalogue général officiel. .... Liége, C. Desoer;
Bruxelles, imp. Vᵉ A. Mertens et fils, [1905].
3 vol. in 1. front. (port.), 2 col. fold. plans. 22½ᶜᵐ.
At head of title: Exposition universelle et internationale Liége 1905.

NL 0349537 ICJ ICRL NN

Liège. Exposition Universelle et Internationale,
1905.
Catalogue officiel de la section japonaise
see under Japan. Commission
Impériale à l'Exposition Universelle de Liége,
1905.

Liège. Exposition universelle et internationale, 1905.
...Catalogue spécial officiel de la Section française. Paris:
M. Vermot[, 1905]. xxviii, 872 p. front., plans. 12°.

1. Exhibitions—Liége, 1905—French exhibit.
N. Y. P. L. December 31, 1926

NL 0349539 NN

Liège. Exposition Universelle et Internationale,
1905.
[Circulars, blanks and broadsides. 1901.-.]
Illus.

NL 0349540 ICRL ICJ

JV 1827 LIEGE--Exposition universelle et internationale,
.L719 1905
1905 Les colonies françaises. [Paris, Les
actualités diplomatiques et coloniales, 1905?]
399 p. illus., ports.

1. France--Colonies. I. Title.

NL 0349541 InU

Liége. Exposition Universelle et Internationale,
1905.
Commune de Schaerbeek. Délégation
ouvrière à l'Exposition Universelle de Liége de
1905
see Schaerbeek, Belgium. Délégation
ouvrière à l'Exposition universelle de Liége, 1905.
Rapport au Conseil.

Liége. Exposition universelle et internationale,
1905.
... Compte-rendu officiel
see under Congrès wallon, Liége, 1905.

Liége. Exposition Universelle, 1905.
... Compte rendu, procès-verbaux, rapports,
notes & documents
see under International Congress of
Photography. 4th, Liége, 1905.

Liége. Exposition Universelle et Internationale,
1905.
Les dentelles de Belgique au Palais de la
Femme. Paris, C. Schmid [190-?]
2 l. 32 pl. in portfolio. f°.

NL 0349545 NN

Liége. Exposition universelle et internationale
1905.
Congrès international des mines, de la métallurgie, de la
mécanique et de la géologie appliquées, *Liége,* 1905.
... Documents généraux et liste des adhérents. Bruxelles, Imp. L. Narcisse, 1905.

Liége. Exposition universelle et internationale, 1905. 070.2277 1
Exposition de l'art ancien au pays de Liége./ Catalogue général.
1905. Liége, A. Bénard, [1905].
[826] p. illus., plates, 1 plan. 23ᶜᵐ.
Various pagings.
Caption title: 75ᵐᵉ anniversaire de l'indépendance nationale. Exposition universelle
et internationale de Liége.

NL 0349547 ICJ CU MH

Liége. Exposition universelle et internationale, 1905.
Exposition internationale de Liége,
1905 [France]
see under Comité français des
expositions.

Liége. Exposition universelle et internationale,
1905.
Exposition universelle de Liége 1905. Suéde.
Catalogue see under Ekstrand, Åke Gerhard,
1846-

VOLUME 332

Liège.   Exposition universelle et internationale,
        1905.
    La fonderie Deberny & cie à l'exposition de
Liège.
        see under   Deberny et cie, typefounders,
Paris.

**T679
A1
1905** Liège   Exposition universelle et
        internationale, 1905.
    Guide remboursable illustré.\ 2. éd.
    Partie littéraire par L. Souguenet.   Liège,
    C. Desoer ₍1905₎
    516 p. illus.,ports.,2 fold.col.maps.

NL 0349551   CU

Liège.   Exposition universelle et internationale, 1905.
    ... L'instruction publique en Russie
        see under   Kovalevskiĭ, Evgraf Petrovich,
1865-

Liège.   Exposition universelle et internationale,
    1905.
        La nation belga 1830-1905; conférences
    jubilaires faites à l'Exposition ...   Liège,
    Desaer; ₍etc., etc., 1906₎
        xxi, 486 p., 2 l.   27 cm.

NL 0349553   CU

**Bk18
022** Liège. Exposition universelle et internationale.
    1905.
        Notice sur l'État indépendant du Congo,
    publiée par les soins du Comité exécutif de
    l'Exposition universelle et internationale de
    Liège.   Bruxelles,Imprimerie veuve Monnom,1905.
    203p. front.(port.)illus.,plates,fold.map.
    28cm.

    1. Kongo, Belgian.

NL 0349554   CtY MBU NcD IEN

Liège. Exposition universelle et internationale, 1905.
    ... Notice sur les charbonnages du Horloz à Tilleur lez-Liège.
    ₍Liége?₎ 1905.   28 p.   diagrs.   8°.
    At head of title: Exposition universelle de Liège.

1. Coal.—Mines and mining, Bel-   gium.
N. Y. P. L.   November 10, 1921.

NL 0349555   NN

Liège. Exposition universelle et internationale, 1905.
    ... Notice sur la Société des mines de houille de Lens, France
    (Pas-de-Calais).   Lille: L. Danel, 1905.   41 p. incl. tables.
    diagrs., illus., maps, plates.   f°.

1. Coal.—Mines and mining, France: Lens.
N. Y. P. L.   April 10, 1923.

NL 0349556   NN DL

Liège. Exposition universelle et internationale, 1905.   070.227 4
    .... Plan général.   [Paris, L. Braun, 1905.]
    cover-title, fold. plan.   46 x 62½ᶜᵐ., bound 12½ x 16¼ᶜᵐ.
    At head of title: Liège.   Exposition universelle 1905.

NL 0349557   ICJ ICRL

Liège. Exposition Universelle et Internationale,
    1905.
        ... Quatrième Congrès international de
    l'acétylène, tenue à Liège les 17,18,19 juillet,
    1905...
            see under   International Congress of
    Acetylen, Oxy-acetylene Welding and Allied In-
    dustries.   4th, Liège, 1905.

Liège. Exposition universelle et internationale, 1905.
    ... Section belge, groupe XVI.   Catalogue des classes 101 à
    110.   Économie sociale.   Bruxelles, Impr. des Grands annuaires,
    1905.   124 p.   21cm.

    1. Labor—Bibl. 2. Social   sciences—Exhibitions and museums—
Belgium—Liège, 1905.
N. Y. P. L.   May 29, 1944

NL 0349559   NN

Liège. Exposition universelle et internationale, 1905.   070.22762 X
                                                      Bureau commercial.
    .... Monographie du Hall des machines.   Liège, imprimerie
    liégeoise H. Poncelet, 1905.
    219, [1] p. illus., 5 fold. pl., 3 fold. diagr. 24ᶜᵐ.
    At head of title: Exposition universelle et internationale de Liège.   Publications du
Bureau commercial.

NL 0349560   ICJ ICRL

Liège. Exposition universelle et internationale, 1905. 609.493 Q500
                                                      Bureau commercial.
    .... Monographies des industries du bassin de Liège. ... .
    Liège, imprimerie liégeoise H. Poncelet, 1905.
    12 vol. in 2. Illus., 18 pl. (partly fold.), 1 fold. map, 1 fold. table, 3 fold. diagr.
24ᶜᵐ.
    At head of title: Exposition universelle et internationale de Liège.   Publications du
Bureau commercial.

NL 0349561   ICJ

Liège.   Fédération des associations commerciales
    et industrielles liégeoises.
        ...Rapport sur les travaux du Comité de la
    Fédération pendant l'exercise 1900-1901...
    Liège, 1901

**HF314
.L8**

NL 0349562   DLC

Liège. Foire internationale.
    Catalogue officiel.
    ₍Liège₎
        v. 21 cm. annual.

    HF5474.B3L53   52-33000 ‡

NL 0349563   DLC IEN

Liège.   Foire internationale.
    Journées d'études internationales sur les
    applications industrielles de l'énergie
    nucléaire

    see under title

LIÉGE. Fonds intercommunal d'assurance
    contre le chomage involontaire de l'ag-
    glomération liégeoise.
    Mémoire présenté à MM. les Membres de la
conférence international de Paris,1910,par le
comité administratif de l'institution.   Liége,
Imprimerie La Meuse, 1910.

    Pamphlet.

NL 0349565   MH

Liège. Grande saison internationale de l'eau
    see   Liège. Exposition internationale, 1939.

Liège. *Hoog geregtshof*
        see
Netherlands (*Kingdom, 1815-) Hoog geregtshof (Liège)*

Liège. Imprimeries nationales des in-
    valides
    Vade-mecum à l'usage des candidats
aux fonctions de garde champêtre ou de
brigadier champêtre; édité par les
Imprimeries nationales des invalides
avec la collaboration de fonctionnaires
communaux.   Liège, Imprimeries nationales des invalides ₍n.d.₎
    ix, ₍11₎-66, ₍1₎ p. 25cm.

    Includes legislation.
    Erratum slip inserted.

NL 0349569   MH-L

Liège. Institut archéologique
    see   Institut archeologique liégeois.

Liège. Institut électrotechnique Montefiore
    see   Liège. Université. Institut
    électrotechnique Montefiore.

Liège. Institut national de l'Industrie Charbonnière
    see   Belgium. Institut national de l'Industrie
    Charbonnière, Liège.

Liège. Institut provincial de coopération agricole
    see
    Institut provincial de coopération agricole, Liège.

Liège. Institut royal des sourds-muets et des
    aveugles.
        ... Rapport sur les travaux de la commission
    administrative, depuis l'année 1830 jusques inclus
    1838, et sur l'état actuel de l'instruction dans
    l'Institut; lu à l'Assemblée générale des
    fondateurs et protecteurs de cet établissement,
    du 13 mai 1839.   Liège, 1839.
        52 p.   24.5 cm.

NL 0349574   CtY

VOLUME 332

Liége. International conference on complete
gasification of mined coal
see International conference on complete
Gasification of Mined Coal, Liége, 1954.

Liége. International Congress for General Mechanics. *1st,
1930*
see
International Congress for General Mechanics. *1st, Liége,
1930.*

Liége. International Office for Documentation of Military
Medicine
see
Liége. Office international de documentation de médecine
militaire.

Liége. International Water and Waterways Fair
see Liége. Exposition internationale, 1939.

Liége. Internationale tentoonstelling, 1930
see Liége. Exposition internationale, 1930.

Liége. Jeune Chambre Economique de Liége.
  Liége en l'an 2000. Liége, Belgium,
Editions desoer, 1965.
  259 p. illus. charts 22 cm.
  Cover title: Demain nos villes.

NL 0349580   MH

Liége. Maison de la Motte (Williamite
  Benedictine priory)
  see Ferrières, Belgium. Bernardfague
(Williamite Benedictine priory)

ML410   Liége   Maison Grétry.
G83L5   Catalogue illustré, rédigé par l'Oeuvre des artistes et précédé
Music   d'une étude par M. Fierens-Gevaert. Liége, Bénard, 1913.
Library   94 p. illus., ports., facsim.

  I. Grétry, André Ernest Modeste, 1741-1813. I.
Fierens-Gevaert, Hippolyte, 1870-1926.

NL 0349582   CU NN

ML410   Liége. Maison Grétry
G83M6   Catalogue illustré
rédigé par l'Oeuvre des Artistes et précédé
d'une étude par M.Fierens-Gevaert. Liége,
Chez Bénard, 1913 [1930]
  94,40p. illus. 19cm.

  "Suppléments au Catalogue du Musée, 1914
à Mai 1930": 40p. at end.

  1. Grétry, André Ernest Modeste, 1741-1813.
I. Fierens-Gevaert, Hippolyte, 1870-1926.

NL 0349583   IaU

Liége. Musée archéologique.
  Founded 1857 by the Institut archéologique liégeois.

Liége. Musée archéologique.
  Catalogue descriptif du Musée provincial de
Liége fondée par l'Institut archéologique
liégeois (Première suite). Liége, Grandmont-
Donders [n. d.]
    p. 61-116.]

NL 0349585   DDO

Liége. Musée archéologique.
  Catalogue descriptif du Musée provincial de Liége.
Fondé par l'Institut archéologique liégeois. [Liége Typ.
de J. G. Carmanne, 1857]
  1 p. l. [5]-86 p. 22ᶜᵐ. (*In* Institut archéologique liégeois. Bulletin.
Liége, 1857. t. III)

Library of Congress   DH801.L5I5   5-30487

NL 0349586   DLC

Liége. Musée archéologique.
  Catalogue descriptif du Musée provincial
de Liége fondé par l'Institut archéologique
liégeois. Liége, Grandmont-Donders, 1864.
  60 p., plates.

NL 0349587   DDO

4CC   Liége. Musée archéologique.
90   Catalogue sommaire [de la] Section
préhistorique par Jean Servais, conservateur en chef et Joseph Hamal-Nandrin,
chargé de cours a l'université.
[Liége, G. Thone] 1929.
    147 p. illus.

NL 0349588   DLC-P4 MH-P MoU

708.39   Liége. Musée Archaeologique
L623H4   Guide sommaire, par H. van Heule. [Liége,
1930]
    87p. illus.

  "La maison Curtius -affectée au Musée
Archéologique Liégeois ... le 1 er Avril
1909."

  I. Heule, H van II. Maison Curtius,
Liége.

NL 0349589   MiDA

KF 16142
Liége. Musée communal.
  Catalogue de l'exposition de gravures des anciens
maitres liégeois, organisée en 1869, par l'Union des artistes, au Musée communal de Liége, avec un avant-propos
par M. Emile Tasset. Liége, Impr. et litographie de Daxhelet [1869?]

  "Extrait des Annales de la Société de l'union des artistes."

NL 0349590   MH

Liége. Musée Curtius
see
Liége. Musée archéologique.

399   Liége.   Musée d'Armes.
L623g   Guide sommaire du Musée d'Armes de Liège,
par D. Techy. Liège, 1954.
    51 [1]p. illus.

  Bibliography: p. [52]
  Introduction in English, inserted.

  1. Arms and armor.   I. Techy, D.

NL 0349592   MiDA

NK6604   Liège. Musée d'armes
L62   Musée d'armes, fondé en 1885. [Liège, 1930?]
535 p. 21 cm.

  Errata sheet inserted.

  1. Arms and armor - Catalogs. I. Title.

NL 0349593   NjP

Liège. Musée de la vie wallonne.
  Enquêtes du Musée de la vie wallonne...
Tome 1–

Liège, 1924–   22½cm.
  v. illus., plates.

  Quarterly (irregular; 1929-30 in 1 no., published 1931).
  Numbering continuous; tome 1, individual nos. lack tome numbering; tome
1–   also called année 1–

  1. Walloons—Per. and soc. publ.   I. Title.
N. Y. P. L.   February 10, 1934

NL 0349594   NN InU NIC NcD

LIÈGE. MUSÉE DES ARTS DÉCORATIFS
  Trésors d'art de la vallée de la Meuse; art
mosan et arts anciens du pays de Liège [Expos-
ition] décembre 1951 - fevrier 1952, Musée des
arts décoratifs. Paris, Les presses artistiques
[1951]

  1 v. (unpaged) 71 plates 21 cm.
  Text by Jean Lejeune and J. de Borchgrave d'
Altena.
  Includes bibliographical notes

NL 0349595   MH-FA

ND   Liège. Musée des beaux-arts.
1265   L'apport wallon au surréalisme: peinture,
.L72   poésie. [Exposition, Musée des beaux-arts, Liège,
13 oct.-12 nov. 1955.] [Liège, 1955?]
    22 p. plates. 24 cm.
  Pref. signed: Léon Koenig.
  "Cette exposition est organisée par la
Commission des beaux-arts de l'Association pour
le progrès intellectuel et artistique de la
Wallonie."
  Includes bibliographies.
    1. Surrealism. 2. Paintings, Walloon--Exhibitions.
3. Walloon poetry--   Bibl.--Catalogs.
I. Association pour   le progrès intellectuel
et artistique de la   Wallonie. II. Title.

NL 0349596   MiU NNC

Ger. Mus.
Liege. Musée des beaux-arts.
  Catalogue. Liége, Imp. Bénard, 1926.

    xix, 137 p. 19 cm.

NL 0349597   MH

VOLUME 332

N
1850   Liège. Musée des Beaux-Arts.
L5A6   Catalogue des peintures.   [Liège] 1954.
1954   77 p., 23 p. of plates.

           Includes bibliography.

           1. Paintings - Liège - Catalogs.

NL 0349598   CLU

Liège. Musée des Beaux-Arts.
   Catalogue des peintures françaises. Bruxelles, Éditions de la connaissance, 1950.

   24 p. 32 plates.

NL 0349599   MH-FA MiDA PU MdBWA

N
6969   Liège. Musée des beaux-arts.
.L7   Exposition le romantisme au pays de Liège.
L72   Musée des beaux-arts, 10 sept.--31 oct. 1955, Liège.
           [Liège, 1955?]
              243 p. 53 plates.   24 cm.
              At head of title: Ville de Liège. Échevinat de
           l'instruction publique.
              Introd. signed: Rita Lejeune, Jacques Stiennon
           [et] Jean Lejeune.
              1. Art--Liège. 2. Belgian literature (French)--
           Bibl.--Catalogs. 3. Romanticism--Belgium--Liège.
           I. Lejeune-Dehousse,   Rita. II. Title. III. Ti-
           tle: Le romantisme   au pays de Liège.

NL 0349600   MiU MH CtY NNC NjP

Liège. Musée des beaux-arts.

Rotterdam. Museum Boymans-van Beuningen.
   19e i. e. Negentiende, eeuwse en moderne schilderkunst uit
het Museum van Schone Kunsten te Luik. [Rotterdam?]
1951.

Liège. Musée des beaux-arts.

   Ville de Liège; collections communales.
   Catalogue des oeuvres exposées au Musée
   des beaux-arts...et au Palais des beaux-
   arts...Mai--Août, 1935

   Liège, Société des beaux-arts, 1935

   83p., 21cm.

NL 0349602   MdBWA

Liège. Musée provincial
          see
Liège. Musée archéologique.

ND
671   Liège. Musées Curtius et d'Ansembourg.
.L7   Catalogue des peintures de l'école liégeoise,
L72   XVe-XIXe siècle, par Joseph Philippe. Préf.
           d'Olympe Gilbart. Liège, 1955.
              53 illus. (Inventaire des collections
           des Musées Curtius et d'Ansembourg, 1)
           Includes bibliography.

              1. Painting--Liège. 2. Paintings, Belgian.
           3. Paintings--Liège--Catalogs. I. Philippe,
           Joseph, 1919-   II. Title.

NL 0349604   MiU MH NNMM

Liège. Museum van Schone Kunsten
   see Liège. Musée des beaux-arts.

RC970   Liège. Office international de documentation
.B77   de médecine militaire.
           Bulletin international des services de santé des armées de
           terre, de mer et de l'air.

           Bruxelles, Imprim. J. Vroman [19

Liège. Office international de documentation de médecine
militaire.
   [Comptes rendus de la] session.

Liège.
      v. illus. 26 cm. annual.
      At head of title, 19   : Comité permanent des Congrès inter-
   nationaux de médecine et de pharmacie militaires.
      Began publication with report for the 1st session, 1931.

      1. Medicine, Military—Congresses. 2. Pharmacy, Military—Con-
   gresses.   I. International Congress of Military Medicine and
   Pharmacy.

      RC970.L5   48-43413*

NL 0349607   DLC DNLM

Liège. Office International de Documentation
   de Médecine Mititaire.
      Liste des chefs des services de santé
   des armée, janvier 1937 . . .
              see under   International Comit-
   tee of Military Medicine and Pharmacy.

RC970   Liège. Office international de documentation de
.B77   médecine militaire.
           Revue internationale des services de santé des armées de
           terre, de mer, et de l'air.   International review of the army,
           navy, and air force medical services.

           [Liège, etc., Office international de documentation de méde-
           cine militaire, etc.]

NL (no number visible)

Liège. Office International de Documentation
   de Médecine Militaire.
      Sessions de conférences [de l'Office
   international de documentation de médecine
   militaire]
              see under   International Comit-
   tee of Military Medicine and Pharmacy.

Liège. Ordre des avocats à la Cour d'appel
          see
   Ordre des avocats à la Cour d'appel de Liége.

C   LIÈGE. ST. JACQUES (Benedictine abbey)
.505   Catalogue des livres de la bibliothèque de
         la célèbre ex-abbaye de St. Jacques à Liege,
         dont la vente se tiendra publiquement au plus of-
         frant, sur les cloîtres de ladite ex-abbaye,
         le 3 mars 1788, & jours suivans.   [Liège, 1788]
            285p. 22cm.

NL 0349612   ICN

Liège. Saint Jacques (Benedictine abbey)
   Die jahrbücher von Sanct Jacob in Lüttich
      see under   Annales Sancti Jacobileodiensis.

Liège. Saint-Jacques (Benedictine abbey)
   Der Liber ordinarius des Lütticher St. Jakobs-
   Klosters...
      see under   Catholic Church. Liturgy and
   ritual. Ordines. [Liège. Saint-Jacques (Benedictine abbey)]

Liège. Saint Jean l'Évangéliste (*Collegiate church*)
   ... Inventaire analytique des chartes de la Collégiale de
Saint-Jean l'Évangéliste à Liége, par L. Lahaye ... Bruxelles,
Kiessling et cie, P. Imbreghts succ., 1921-31.

   2 v. 22¼.
   At head of title: Commission royale d'histoire.
   Vol. II has imprint: Bruxelles, M. Lamertin, 1931.

   I. Lahaye, Léon Henri Pierre Joseph, 1857-   ed. II. Académie
royale des sciences, des lettres et des beaux arts de Belgique, Brussels.
Commission royale d'histoire.

                                              24-3425 Revised
   Library of Congress   DH811.L5A25
                                    [r33b2]   949.3

NL 0349615   DLC IEN CU MoU GU NcRS IaU MB CtY OC1 NN

BX2612   Liège. Saint-Lambert (*Abbey*)
f.L7A3   Documents relating to St. Lambert's abbey, 1479-
1673   1673. Ms. copies in French or Latin. 17th century[
Mss room   [155] p. 33½.
         Preceded by 32 blank leaves for index; followed by 31 blank leaves.
         Binder's title: Curia feudalis S. Lamberti.
         Presented by Miss Shirley Farr.

           1. Manuscripts, French. 2. Manuscripts, Latin.

NL 0349616   ICU

Liège. Saint Lambert (*Cathedral*)
   Cartulaire de l'église Saint-Lambert de Liége; publié par
S. Bormans et E. Schoolmeesters. Bruxelles, F. Hayez,
1893-1933.

   6 v. 31 cm. (Académie royale des sciences, des lettres et des
beaux-arts de Belgique. Commission royale d'histoire. Collection de
chroniques belges inédites, 28)

   Imprint varies: v. 4-5, Kiessling; v. 6, M. Lamertin.
   Vols. 5-6 "publié par Édouard Poncelet."
   Vols. 1-4 have Latin text; v. 5-6, French.

   CONTENTS.—t. 1, no. 1-482, 26. avril, 826-23. déc., 1250.—t. 2, no.
484-890, 15. mars, 1251-[vers 1300).—t. 3, no. 891-1279, 20. mai, 1301-
23. oct., 1342.—t. 4, no. 1280-1813, 4. jan., 1343-6. avril, 1389.—t. 5,
no. 1814-5301, 1. jan., 1390-27. juillet, 1797.—t. 6. Supplément.

   1. Liége—Hist.—Sources. I. Bormans, Stanislas, 1835-1912, ed.
II. Schoolmeesters, Émile, 1842-1914, ed. III. Poncelet, Édouard,
1865-   ed. IV. Title. (Series: Académie royale des sciences,
des lettres et des beaux-arts de Belgique, Brussels. Commission royale
d'histoire. Publications in-quarto, 28)

   DH403.A2   vol. 28   34-8785 rev*
   Library of Congress   [r52c1]

             NN Mi ICU ICN PP
NL 0349618   DLC OC1W MiU NcU NcD GU NIC CU MoU OU

Liège. Saint Lambert (*Cathedral*) Chapitre
   Inventaire analytique et chronologique des chartes
du chapitre de Saint-Lambert, à Liége, publié par J. G.
Schoonbroodt ... Liége, J. Desoer, 1863.

   1 p. l., xii, 446 p., 1 l. 29cm.
   "Arrêté du roi, qui ordonne la publication des Archives du royaume": p.
[iii]

   1. Belgium—Hist.—To 1555—Sources. 2. Belgium—Hist.—1555-1765—
Sources. I. Schoonbroodt, Jean Guillaume, 1804-1884, ed. II. Belgium.
Archives générale du royaume.

NL 0349619   MiU CtY NNC

Liège. Saint Martin (*Collegiate church*)
   Inventaire analytique et chronologique des chartes du
chapitre de Saint-Martin, à Liége, publié par J. G. Schoonbroodt ... Liége, J. Desoer, 1871.

   viii, 303, [1] p. 28½cm.
   "Arrêté du roi, qui ordonne la publication des Archives du royaume": p.
[v]

   1. Belgium—Hist.—To 1555—Sources. 2. Belgium—Hist.—1555-1765—
Sources. I. Schoonbroodt, Jean Guillaume, 1804-1884, ed. II. Belgium.
Archives générale du royaume.

NL 0349620   MiU NNC CtY

VOLUME 332

DH
811
.L5L54
Liége. Saint Paul (Collegiate church)
Cartulaire; ou, Recueil de chartes et
documents inédits de l'Église collégiale
de Saint Paul, actuellement cathédrale de
Liége, par O. J. Thimister. Liége, L.
Grandmont-Donders, 1878.
704 p. illus.

#Liége.--Hist.--Sources.
#Cartularies.
Thimister, Olivier Joseph.

NL 0349622   MoU NcD PU CtY

Liége. Saint-Pierre (*Collegiate church*)
... Inventaire analytique des chartes de la Collégiale
de Saint-Pierre à Liége, par Édouard Poncelet ... Bruxelles, Kiessling et cⁱᵉ, P. Imbreghts, successeur, 1906.
xciii p., 1 l., 539, ₍1₎ p. 22¼ᶜᵐ. ₍Académie royale de Belgique. Commission royale d'histoire₎

At head of title: Commission royale d'histoire.
"Le présent ouvrage avait été commencé par M. S. Bormans."—p. xxi.
"Liste des dignitaires & des chanoines de Saint-Pierre" : p. ₍xxii₎–xciii.

I. Poncelet, Édouard, ed. II. Bormans, Stanislas, 1835–

Library of Congress   8–10132

NL 0349623   DLC CU IaU GU OU MoU NIC MB MiU MH

Liége. Sainte-Croix (*Collegiate church*)
... Inventaire analytique des chartes de la collégiale de
Sainte-Croix à Liége, par Édouard Poncelet, conservateur des archives de l'état, à Mons ...   Bruxelles, M. Weissenbruch, imprimeur du roi, 1911.
v. 22ᶜᵐ.

At head of title : Commission royale d'histoire.
On cover : Académie royale de Belgique. Commission royale d'histoire.

I. Poncelet, Édouard. II. Title.

                                  12–16424

Library of Congress

NL 0349624   DLC IaU CU MiU NN MH

---

*DH403
.A15
v.31
Liége, Sainte-Croix (Collegiate church)
Inventaire analytique des chartes de
la collégiale de Sainte-Croix à Liége,
par Édouard Poncelet, conservateur des
archives de l'état, à Mons. Bruxelles,
M. Weissenbruch, imprimeur du roi,
1911 [1922]
2 v. 23cm. [Académie royale des
sciences, des lettres et des beaux-arts
de Belgique, Brussels. Commission
royale d'histoire. Publications in
octavo. 31]
I. Poncelet,   Édouard, 1865–
II. Series.

NL 0349625   MB MoU GU

Liège. Sansculottes.

—— Réponse des sans-culottes liégeois et
autres aux Brissotins et Girondins de leur pays.
[1793.]

NL 0349626   NIC

Liége. Séminaire de géographie
see Liége. Université. *Séminaire de géographie.*

Liége. Service de l'État-Civil.
Rapport.
Liége.
v. tables. 23 cm. annual.
At head of title,   : Ville de Liége. Services de l'État-
Civil et de la population (varies slightly)

1. Liége—Population. I. Liége. Service de la population.

HA1409.L5A32   56–49604

NL 0349628   DLC

HA1409
.L5A32
Liége. Service de la population.

Liége. Service de l'État-Civil.
Rapport.
Liége.

Liége. Société belge d'études et d'expansion
see Société d'études et d'expansion.

Liége. Société d'art et d'histoire du
diocèse de

see

Société d'art et d'histoire du diocèse de
Liége.

Liége. Société des bibliophiles liégeois
see Société des bibliophiles liégeois.

Liége. Société géologique de Belgique
see
Société géologique de Belgique.

Liége. Société libre d'émulation.

see

Société libre d'émulation de Liege

Liége. Société liégeoise de litterature wallonne
see Société de litterature wallonne.

Liége. Société royale agricole de l'Est
de la Belgique

see

Société royale agricole de l'Est de la Belgique,
Liege

LIÉGE. Société royale d'horticulture.

See SOCIÉTÉ ROYALE D'HORTICULTURE
DE LIÉGE.

Liége. Société royale des sciences
see Société royale des sciences de Liége.

Liége. Tribunal civil
see Belgium. Tribunal civil, Liège.

Liége. Université.
Annales Academiæ leodiensis ...   1817/18–1826/27.
Leodii, apud P. J. Collardin, 1819–29.
10 v. in 7. pl., plan, diagr. 26ᶜᵐ.
Each paper is separately paged, except in volumes for 1824/25–1825/26.

                                  7–29804
Library of Congress   AS242.L3

NL 0349640   DLC PPAN

Liège. Université.
Cahiers de pédagogie de l'Université de Liège
see under title

W
19.5
GB4
L7L7
LIÉGE. Université
Catalogs, announcements of courses,
requirements for admission and other
publications relating to the academic
program will be found under the above
call number. Included also are similar
publications of individual schools or
departments of instruction of the
institution.

NL 0349642   DNLM

Liége. Université.
Catalogue général des périodiques de l'Université de Liège.
Liège, Imprimerie Saint-Jean, 1929.
3 p. l., ₍9₎–106, ₍4₎ p., 1 l. 18½ᶜᵐ.

"La première édition ... 1923, signalait uniquement les publications
déposées au cabinet des périodiques de la bibliothèque de l'Université.
Ce nouveau catalogue mentionne les titres de tous les périodiques reçus
tant par la bibliothèque que par les différents services de l'Université."

CONTENTS.—Liste alphabétique des périodiques.—Catalogue systématique.—Table des rubriques.

1. Periodicals — Bibl. — Catalogs.   I. Liége. Université. Bibliothèque. –
Library of Congress   Z6945.L72   29–20409
                       ₍9₎.

NL 0349643   DLC PU ICJ DSI WaU

Liége. Université.
Centenaire d'Alexandre de Winiwarter, 1848–1948. Université de Liège, séance académique; discours. ₍Liège, 1948₎
42 p. port. 21 cm.

1. Winiwarter, Alexander, Ritter von, 1848–   I. Title.

R524.W5L5   65–48418

NL 0349644   DLC IEN NIC DNLM IaU WaU TxU

C44
L623J
Liége. Université.
Les congrès et colloques.
₍Liège₎
v. illus. 25cm.

NL 0349645   IU

VOLUME 332

Liége. Université.
    Cours de geometrie projective
      see under   Godeaux, Lucien, 1887-
[Supplement]

Liége. Université.
    ... Cours d'astronomie et de géodésie.
    Publié par M. Dehalu ...
      see under   Le Paige, C[onstantin Marie
Michel Jérôme] 1852-

Liége. Université.
    ... Dispositions réglementaires. Liége, Impr. De Thier, 1890.
    46 p., 1 l. 25½ᶜᵐ. S
    At head of title: Université de Liége.

                                CA 7-6791 Unrev'd
    Library of Congress   LF4001.A7 1890

  NL   0349648   DLC

Liége. Université.
    ... Esquisse historique sur les bâtiments universitaires. Liége, A. Bénard [1892]
    55, [8] p. incl. front., illus. 21ᶜᵐ.
    At head of title: Université de Liége.
    On cover: Publiée par l'Association générale des étudiants.

                                30-33071
    Library of Congress   LF4004.A5 1892
    ———— Copy 2.   378.493

  NL   0349649   DLC ICJ MiU DSI PPT DHEW WaU

.F4001
A7
892

Liége. Université.
    ... Extraits des dispositions législatives & réglementaires sur l'enseignement supérieur et la collation des grades académiques. Liége, Impr. H. Vaillant-Carmanne, 1892.
    85 p., 1 l. 22½ᶜᵐ. S
    At head of title: Université de Liége.

                                CA 7-6792 Unrev'd
    Library of Congress   LF4001.A7 1892

  NL   0349650   DLC

Liége. Université.
    ... Extraits des dispositions législatives & réglementaires sur l'enseignement supérieur et la collation des grades académiques. Liége, Impr. liégeoise, H. Poncelet, s. a., 1908.
    147 p. 22ᶜᵐ.

    I. Title.

                                  CA 12-911 Unrev'd
    Library of Congress   LF4001.A7 1908

  NL   0349651   DLC PU

Liége. Université.
    Honneurs funèbres, rendus par l'Université de Liége aux professeurs décédés pendant les années 1914 à 1918. Séance solennelle du 28 juillet 1919. [Liège, 1919]

  NL   0349652   MH

Liége. Université.
    ... Leçons de chimie analytique...
      see under   Chandelle, R

Liége. Université.
    Liber memorialis. L'Université de Liége de 1867 à 1935; Notices biographiques publiées par les soins de Léon Halkin ... avec une introduction par Paul Harsin ... Liége, Rectorat de l'Université [Gembloux, J. Duculot] 1936.
    3 v. front., plates. 27cm.
    Contents. - t.I. Faculté de philosophie et lettres. Faculté de droit. - t.II. Faculté des sciences. Écoles spéciales. Faculté technique. - t.III. Faculté de médecine.

  NL   0349654   CtY WU

Liége. Université.
    Liber memorialis. L'Université de Liége depuis sa fondation
      see under   Le Roy, Alphonse, 1822-1896.

Liége. Université.
    Liège et son université
      see under   Duesberg, Jules, 1881-   comp.

Liége. Université.
    ... Les locaux de la faculté de médecine. Liége, C. Desoer [1902]
    44, [3] p. illus., fold. pl. 32¼ᶜᵐ.

    1. Clinics—Belgium—Liége.

    Library of Congress   R781.23.L4   5-29843

  NL   0349657   DLC

Liége. Université.
    ... Manifestation Émile Witmeur, jeudi 27 avril 1939. [Liège? 1939]
    2 p. l., 7–48 p. incl. front. (port.) illus., facsim. 24¼ᶜᵐ.
    At head of title: Université de Liége.

    1. Witmeur, Émile, 1874-   41–1874
    Library of Congress   HB111.W5L5
                            [2]   923.3493

  NL   0349658   DLC CtY

[Liége. Université]
    Manifestation en l'honneur de m. G. Cesàro, professeur à l'Université de Liége, 16 juillet 1929. [Liége, H. Vaillant-Carmanne, imprimeur de l'Académie, 1930]
    184 p., 1 l. 25½ᶜᵐ.
    "Bibliographie de m. G. Cesàro": p. [101]–117.

    1. *Cesàro, Giuseppe, 1849-   2. Mineralogy—Collected works.
    I. Title.
                                 31–4997
    Library of Congress   QE361.C4L5
                            [2]   925.49

  NL   0349659   DLC

Liége. Université.
    Mélanges offerts à Ernest Mahaim, professeur émérite de l'Université de Liège, ancien directeur de l'Institut de sociologie Solvay, par ses collègues, ses amis, ses élèves, Liège, 5 novembre 1935 ... Paris, Librairie du Recueil Sirey, société anonyme, 1935.

Liége. Université.
                                3597.285
    Note on the teaching of art and archeology in the Belgian universities.
    — [Bruxelles. Polleunis & Ceuterick. 1904.] 9, (1) pp. [Saint Louis, Missouri. Exhibitions. Louisiana Purchase Exposition, 1904. Belgium.] 8°.

F9267 — S.r.

  NL   0349661   MB

Liége. Université.
    ... Ouverture solennelle des cours ... Discours de M. le recteur ... Rapport sur la situation de l'Université ... Liége,
    v. 21–23ᶜᵐ.
    Title varies: 18   Université de Liége. Réouverture solennelle des cours ... Rapport ... Programme des cours. Dispositions réglementaires.
    18   Université de Liége. Ouverture solennelle des cours ... Discours inaugural & rapport ... Programme des cours. Dispositions réglementaires.
    18   Université de Liége. Ouverture solennelle des cours ... Discours de M. le recteur ... Rapport sur la situation de l'Université.

                              5-1551 Additions
    Library of Congress   LF4001.B3

  NL   0349662   DLC ICRL NcU TxLT ICJ MiU PU PPT

Liége. Université.
    ... Programme des cours.
    Liége, 18
    v. 22–26ᶜᵐ.
    At head of title: Université de Liége.
    Title varies slightly.

                              CA 7-5907 Unrev'd
    Library of Congress   LF4001.C7
                              [s20511]

  NL   0349663   DLC PPC ICJ PU PPT

Liége. Université.
    Recueil de quelques travaux d'anatomie végétale, exécutés à Liége de 1929 à 1935. Bruxelles, M. Hayez, imprimeur de l'Académie royale de Belgique, 1936.
    [385] p. illus., plates, diagr. 25¼ᶜᵐ.
    Various pagings.
    Articles by A. Gravis, J. [1] Joyeux, E. Fritsché, A. Monoyer and D. Rousseau, reprints from the Mémoires publiés par l'Académie royale de Belgique (Classe des sciences) and other periodicals.
    "Ces travaux font suite à d'autres qui ont été publiés dans les premiers volumes des Archives de l'Institut botanique (1897 à 1925)"—Préface.

    1. Botany — Anatomy.   I. Gravis, Auguste, 1857-   II. Joyeux, Laurent.   III. Title.
    Library, U. S. Dept. of   Agriculture   463.4L62   Agr 36–000
                                     [QK671   ]
                                     [8]

  NL   0349664   DNAL CU PPAN DSI

Liége. Université.
    ————. Réouverture solennelle des cours. Discours inaugural [et rapport du recteur, M. A.- Spring. Programme des cours. Dispositions réglementaires. Année 1862–3. 54 pp. 8°. Liége, J. Desoir, 1862.

  NL   0349665   DNLM

Liége. Université.
    Laport, George, 1898-
    ... Sainte-Beuve à Liége. Liége, Imprimerie centrale [1933]

VOLUME 332

Liège. Université. Association des amis
see Association des amis de l'Université de Liège.

LIÉGE. Université. Association des classiques.
Bulletin semestriel. 1. - année; mars, 1953-
Heusy-Verviers. v. 24cm.

1. Classical education-- Belgium. 2. Classical
studies--Per. and soc. publ.

NL 0349668 NN

Liège. Université. Association des licenciés sortis de
l'Université
see
Société d'études et d'expansion.

PC2
.M33

Liège. Université. Association des romanistes.

Marche romane.
[Liège] Association des romanistes de l'Université de Liège.

Liège. Université. *Bibliothèque.*
Accroissement.
Liège,
v. 22½cm.
"Extrait du Catalogue d'entrée."

CA 9-6300 Unrev'd

Library of Congress Z927.L695

NL 0349671 DLC ICJ PPT

Liège. Université. *Bibliothèque.*
Annexes au Catalogue des manuscrits de la Bibliothèque de l'Université de Liége, par Joseph Brassinne ...
Liége, D. Cormaux, 1904.
72 p. 23½cm.

1. Manuscrits--Catalogs. 2. Manuscrits. Belgique. I. Brassinne, Joseph.

Library of Congress Z6621.L715

5-37524†

NL 0349672 DLC MiU

Liège. Université. Bibliothèque.
Bibliotheca leodiensis
see under title

Liège. Université. Bibliothèque.
La bibliothèque de l'Université de Liège
see under Gobeaux-Thonet, Jeanne.

Z
935
Iq L719c

LIÉGE. Université. Bibliothèque
Catalogue des livres de la biblio-
thèque de l'Université de Liége ...
Liége, Collardin, 1844-
v.
Contents. -

t. 4. Medécine.
1. Medicine - Bibl. - Catalogs

NL 0349675 DNLM NN

Liège. Université. *Bibliothèque.*
... Catalogue des manuscrits. Liége, Impr. H. Vaillant-
Carmanne, 1875.
vii p., 1 l., 589 p. 3 fold. facsim. 23cm.
At head of title: Bibliothèque de l'Université de Liège.
Published after the death of the librarian, M. Fiess, by M. Grandjean.

1. Manuscripts. Belgium--Catalogs. 2. Liège - Hist. — Sources — Bibl.
I. Fiess, Mathieu Georges Joseph, 1802-1875. II. Grandjean, Mathieu Lambert, b. 1815.

Library of Congress Z6621.L715 1875

10-21085

NL 0349676 DLC PU NjP DNLM MH

MICROFILM
F
7594

Liège. Université. *Bibliothèque.*
...Catalogue des manuscrits. Liége, Impr. H. Vaillant-
Carmanne, 1875.
vii p., 1 l., 589 p. 3 fold. facsim. 23cm.
At head of title: Bibliothèque de l'Université de Liège.
Published after the death of the librarian, M. Fiess, by M. Grandjean.
Microfilm (negativo) of copy at Princeton.
New York, Columbia University Libraries, 1971.
1 reel.

NL 0349677 NNC

Liège. Université. *Bibliothèque.*
... Catalogue des manuscrits légués à la bibliothèque de
l'Université de Liège par le baron Adrien Wittert. Liège,
D. Cormaux, 1910.
xv, 242 p., 1 l. front. 25½cm.
Compiler's name, Joseph Brassinne, at head of title.
"Il a été tiré de cet ouvrage dix exemplaires sur papier de Hollande Van
Gelder, et deux cents exemplaires sur papier de Hollande, dont cent ex-
emplaires, numérotés de 1 à 100, en souscription."
117 manuscripts.

1. Manuscripts. Belgium--Catalogs. I. Wittert, Adrien i. e. Évrard
Adrien François Joseph, baron, 1823-1903. II. Brassinne, Joseph.

Library of Congress Z6621.L715 1910

11-4648

NL 0349678 DLC CLSU NcD MiU CtY PU

Liège. Université. *Bibliothèque.*
Catalogue des périodiques de la bibliothèque de l'Université de Liége. Liége, Printing co., 1923.
90, [4] p. 17cm.
CONTENTS.--I. Liste alphabétique des périodiques.--II. Catalogue systématique.--III. Table des rubriques.

1. Periodicals--Bibl--Catalogs.

Library of Congress Z6945.L71

25-8202

NL 0349679 DLC CU PU PPC

Liège. Université. Bibliothèque.

Liège. Université.
Catalogue général des périodiques de l'Université de Liège.
Liège, Imprimerie Saint-Jean, 1929.

Liège. Université. Bibliothèque.

Z6611
.S8C3

Catalogus codicum hagiographicorum Latinorum in biblio-
thecis publicis Namurci, Gandae, Leodii et Montibus asser-
vatorum, ampla documentorum appendice instructum. Bruxelles, Société des Bollandistes, 1948.

Liège. Université. Bibliothèque.
Catalogus codicum hagiographicorum
Bibliothecae publicae civitatis et academiae
Leodiensis
see under title [Supplement]

Z
935
.L725
no.6

Liège. Université. Bibliothèque.
Les délices du païs de Liège. Exposition
Saumer et son temps, 8-23 mai 1953. Catalogue
[par Madeleine Lavoye et Jacques Stiennon] Liège,
Maison Desoer, 1953.
35 p. front. 26 cm. (Bibliotheca
Universitatis Leodiensis. Publications, no 6)

1. Saumer, Pierre Lambert De, ca.1690-ca.1767--
Bibl. 2. Saumery, Pierre Lambert de, ca.1690-ca.1767.
Les délices du païs de Liège. I. Lavoye, Madeleine.
II. Stiennon, Jacques. III. Title.

NL 0349683 MiU NcU

Liège. Université. Bibliothèque.
Journées d'étude organisées par la Bibliothèque
de l'Université de Liège (24-27 octobre 1949) Les
problèmes de la documentation dans les bibliothèques
universitaires
see its Les problèmes de la documentation ...

LIÉGE. Université. Bibliothèque.
Le livre illustré à travers les siècles. Le XVe siècle
[Exposition] Catalogue [avec une introduction de
Madeleine Lavoye. Liège, Maison Desoer [1950]
24 p. 3 plates (2 col.) 25cm. (ITS: Publications. no. 3)

1. Incunabula--Bibl. 2. Illustration of books--Hist., 15th cent.
I. Series.

NL 0349685 NN NNC NjP MiU NIC

Z7402
955l

Liège. Université. Bibliothèque.
Maîtres liégeois de l'illustration scientifique;
catalogue de l'exposition organisée à la bibliothèque
de l'université du 13 octobre au 6 novembre 1955.
Liège, Maison Desoer, 1955.
25, [1] p. facsims. 26cm. (Bibliotheca
universitatis leodiensis. Publications: no. 7)

1. Science - Early works to 1800 - Bibl. -
Catalogs. 2. Illustrations of books -
Exhibitions.

NL 0349686 CtY-M CLU MH MiU RPB

Z7840
C7L5

Liège. Université. Bibliothèque.
Les manuscrits des croisiers de Huy,
Liège et Cuyk au XVe siècle. Exposition,
24 février-15 mars 1951; catalogue.
[Liège, Desoer, 1951.
8 p. illus. (part col.) 26cm. (Bibliotheca universitatis Leodiensis. Publications,
no. 5)

1. Crosiers - Bibl. 2. Manuscripts -
Exhibitions. I. Title. II. Series: Liège.
Université. Bibliothèque. Publications.

NL 0349687 IaU MiU NNC NIC NjP ICN

378.493
L6231m

Liège. Université. Bibliothèque.
Mélanges de bibliothéconomie et de bibliographie. no.1- 1949-
Liège, G. Michiels [etc.]
v. 25cm. irregular.

At head of title: Bibliotheca Universitatis Leodiensis.

1. Library science. Collections.
2. Bibliography. Collections. I. Title.

NL 0349688 KU CaOTU

VOLUME 332

Z
935
.L725
no.2
Liège. Université. Bibliothèque.
Les peintures anciennes de la collection Wittert. Catalogue précédé d'une notice sur le baron Adrien Wittert par Léon Dewez. Préface de Jeanne Gobeaux-Thonet. Liège, Maison Desoer ₍1949₎
59 p. illus.(2 col.),port. 26 cm.
(Liège. Université. Bibliothèque. Publications no.2)

I.Dewez,Léon. II.Wittert,Adrien,baron,1823-1903.

NL 0349689   MiU NjP NN

Z675
.U5L5
Liège. Université. Bibliothèque.
Les problèmes de la documentation dans les bibliothèques universitaires. Liège, Association des Amis de l'Université de Liège, 1950.
170 p. 25cm. (Bibliotheca Universitatis Leodiensis. Mélanges de bibliothéconomie et de bibliographie, no. 2)
"Journées d'étude organisées par la Bibliothèque de l'Université de Liège (24-27 octobre 1949)"
1. Libraries, University and college. I. Title.   II. Series.

NL 0349690   MB NNC NIC

Liège. Université. *Bibliothèque.*
Publications. no. 1-
Liège ₍etc.₎ 1948-
no. in   v. illus. 27 cm.

N1850.L5A5   56-26114 ‡

NL 0349691   DLC NN CaOTU KyU KU MdBJ WaU TxLT IaU

DH
801
.M5
L72
Liège. Université. Bibliothèque.
Quelques sites et monuments du pays mosan; ensemble de gravures et de dessins anciens entourant les plans en relief et les maquettes de Gustave Ruhl appartenant à la Bibliothèque de l'Université de Liège,exposés ... de la Bibliothèque de l'Université ... du 3 nov.au 31 déc.1949. Notes liminaires,de Madeleine Lavoye ₍et₎ Léon Dewez. ₍Liège? Maison Desoer₎ 1949₎
13 p. 26 cm.
1.Meuse River and Valley--Descr.& trav.---Views-Cat-elogs. I.Ruhl,Gustave,d.1929. II. Lavoye,Madeleine.

NL 0349692   MiU

378.493
L6231r
Liège. Université. Bibliothèque.
Recueil de documents de la bibliothèque de l'Université de Liège. no.1-
1926-   Liège.
v. 25cm.   irregular.

At head of title: Bibliotheca Universitatis Leodiensis.

1. Liège. Université. Bibliothèque.
History. Collections. I. Title.

NL 0349693   KU

Z
11465
.513
Liège. Université-Bibliothèque.
Tables analytiques de 425 pièces tant manuscrites qu'imprimées portant les numéros 1015-1035 annexées aux six volumes in-folio manuscrits intitulés: Mémoires pour servir à l'histoire ecclésiastique du pays et du diocèse de Liège, par François-Nicolas-Jean-Baptiste Delvaulx... [Liège?187-?]

Caption ti-   tle.

Continued in next column

Continued from preceding column

"Supplément au catalogue des manuscrits de la Bibliothèque de l'Université de Liège publié en 1875" preceded by "...Renseignements sur les manuscrits..." p.[48]-96.

NL 0349695   ICN MiU

Liège. Université. Bibliothèque. MSS. (343)
Ms. 343 de Liège [Actus quidam ...]
see under   Francesco d'Assisi, Saint. Legend. Actus beati Francisci et sociorum eius. MSS.

Liège. Université. Bibliothèque. *MSS. 431 (Cat. 1875, no. 10)*
Psautier liégeois du XIII° siècle; reproduction de 42 pages enluminées du manuscrit 431 de la Bibliothèque de l'Université de Liège, publiées avec une introduction par Joseph Brassinne ... Bruxelles, Vromant & c°. ₍1923₎
17 p., facsim.: 42 pl. 21 x 16 cm.
"Notre manuscrit et ceux de la même famille dérivent ... d'un psautier composé dans la seconde moitié du XII° siècle, par Lambert le Bègue."—Introd.
In portfolio.
1. Illumination of books and manuscripts—Specimens, reproductions, etc. I. Catholic church. Liturgy and ritual. Psalter. II. Brassinne, Joseph, 1877- ed.

ND3357.L5 1923   27—6957

PU-FA CLU ScClcU
NL 0349697   DLC DDO IaU NSyU MiU CtY ICN OCl NIC CU

Microfilm
2144
in
music
Liège. Université. Bibliothèque. Mss. 888.
₍Virginal music. n.p., n.d.₎
microfilm. negative. reel. 35mm.

1. Harpsichord music - To 1800.

NL 0349698   CoU

Liège. Université. Bibliothèque. *Mss. (Wittert 13)*
Livre d'heures de Gysbrecht de Brederode, évêque élu d'Utrecht; reproduction de 38 pages enluminées du manuscrit Wittert 13 de la Bibliothèque de l'Université de Liège, publiées avec une introduction par Joseph Brassinne ... Bruxelles, Vromant & c° ₍1924₎
19 p., facsim.: 38 pl. 21 x 16ᵐᵐ.
In portfolio.
1. Hours, Books of. 2. Illumination of books and manuscripts—Specimens, reproductions, etc. 3. Brederode, Gysbrecht van, bp. of Utrecht, 1416 (ca.)-1475. I. Catholic church. Liturgy and ritual. Hours. II. Brassinne, Joseph, 1877- ed.

27—6954
Library of Congress   ND3363.B63

NL 0349699   DLC MH WU PPC NIC MiU OCl CtY PU CU MiU

Liège. Université. Bibliothèque. *Mss. (Wittert 33)*
Deux livres d'heures néerlandais; reproduction des 25 miniatures du manuscrit Wittert 33 et des 12 miniatures du manuscrit Wittert 34 de la Bibliothèque de l'Université de Liège, par Joseph Brassinne ... Bruxelles, Vromant & c° ₍1923₎
10 p., facsim.: 37 pl. 21 x 16ᵐᵐ.
In portfolio.
1. Hours, Books of. 2. Illumination of books and manuscripts—Specimens, reproductions, etc. I. Catholic church. Liturgy and ritual. Hours. II. Liège. Université. Bibliothèque. Mss. (Wittert 34) III. Brassinne, Joseph, 1877- ed.

27—6955
Library of Congress   ND3363.W5

CU PPC
NL 0349700   DLC CLU MH ICN NN NIC OCl MiU CtY PU ICU

Liège. Université. Bibliothèque. Mss. (Wittert 34)

Liège. Université. Bibliothèque. *Mss. (Wittert 33)*
Deux livres d'heures néerlandais; reproduction des 25 miniatures du manuscrit Wittert 33 et des 12 miniatures du manuscrit Wittert 34 de la Bibliothèque de l'Université de Liège, par Joseph Brassinne ... Bruxelles, Vromant & c° ₍1923₎

Liège. Université. *Centre d'étude des eaux*
see Liège. Université. *Institut de chimie et de métallurgie. Centre d'étude des eaux.*

620.74
L53
Liège. Université. Centre d'études de recherches et d'essais scientifiques des constructions du génie civil et d'hydraulique fluviale.
Bulletin. t.1-   Louvain ₍etc.₎
1940-
Publication suspended between 1941 and 1947. 19 -1948, pub. in Liège.

NL 0349703   ICJ PU-Sc FU NNC NN MH-GM CSt

Liège. Université. *Clinique chirurgicale.*   S617.07450 N800
Rapport de la Clinique chirurgicale de l'Université de Liège, ₁₉₀₇₈₅ (1ᵉʳ mars 1876 au 1ᵉʳ mars 1878). Ch. Gussenbauer, professeur. Th. Pincker, assistant. Liège, Impr. H. Vaillant-Carmanne, 1878.
₂₀₆, ₍₂₎ p. incl. tables. VIII pl. (part fold.) 25ᶜᵐ.

NL 0349704   ICJ

WB
L7185a
1886
LIÈGE. Université. Clinique interne
Annales de la Clinique interne₍ mars 1877-juin 1882, par Masius [et al.] Liége, Vaillant-Carmanne, 1886.
xi, 340 p. illus.

I. Masius, Jean Baptiste Nicholas Voltaire, 1836-1912

NL 0349705   DNLM

W
L721r
1877
LIÈGE. Université. Commission chargée d'élaborer un project de réorganisation de l'enseignement médical
Rapport presenté à la Faculté de médecine de l'Université de Liége dans la séance du 27 juillet 1877. Liége, Vaillant-Carmanne, 1877.
27 p.

NL 0349706   DNLM

LIÈGE - Université - École des arts et manufactures et des mines.
Recueil des dispositions organiques et réglementaires et des programmes. Liège, C.A.Desoer,1884.
23 cm.

NL 0349707   MH

Liège. Université. *École spéciale de commerce*
see Liège. Université. *École supérieure de sciences commerciales et économiques.*

Liège. Université. École supérieure de sciences commerciales et économiques.
Bibliothèque
see Bibliothèque de l'École supérieure de sciences commerciales et économiques. [Supplement]

VOLUME 332

Liège. Université. Faculté de droit.
  Collection sceintifique. 1-
  Liège, 1953-
    v. 24 cm.

NL 0349710   DCU

Law

Liège. Université. Faculté de droit.

Del Marmol, Charley.
  ... Les origines et les principes de la réglementation de la
  faillite dans les pays de common law; étude de législation et de
  jurisprudence faite dans le cadre de la loi anglaise de 1914,
  thèse pour l'agrégation de l'enseignement supérieur par Charley
  del Marmol ... Paris, Librairie générale de droit et de jurisprudence; ₁etc., etc., 1936.

Liège. Université. *Faculté de droit.*
  Problèmes économiques contemporains: colloquia de la
  chaire Francqui, 1951–1952. ₁Liège, 1953.
  viii, 150 p. 24 cm. *(Its Collection scientifique, 1)*
  Contents.—Crises, cycles et croissance.—Monnaie, inflation, sa-
  laire.—Sécurité sociale et redistribution du revenu national.—L'objet
  de l'économie politique.

  1. Economics—Collections. I. Title. (Series)

      HB39.L5   55–59522

NL 0349713   DLC NNU

LIÈGE. Université. Faculté de droit.
  Problèmes économiques contemporains: colloquia de
  la chaire Francqui, 1951–1952. [Liège] 1953.
  viii, 150 p. 24cm. (ITS: Collection scientifique. 1)

  Film reproduction. Positive.

  1. Economics--Congresses--Belgium, 1951-1952. I. Series.

NL 0349714   NN

Liège. Université. *Faculté de droit. École supérieure de
  sciences commerciales et économiques*
  see Liège. Université. *École supérieure de sciences
  commerciales et économiques.*

Liège. Université. *Faculté de droit. Institut de sociologie*
  see
  Liège. Université. *Institut de sociologie.*

Liège. Université. *Faculté de droit. Séminaire de sociologie*
    see
  Liège. Université. *Institut de sociologie.*

AS   Liège. Université. Faculté de Philosophie et
242   Lettres.
L5   Bibliothèque.
         Liège, 1897–
           v.

         Vols. after 1959 cataloged separately.

      CU OU OCU NN CtNIC
NL 0349718   KMK NcU KU AzU KyU NcD NhD TxLT IaU ICN

Liège. Université. *Faculté de philosophie et lettres.*
  Mélanges Godefroid Kurth; recueil de mémoires relatifs à l'histoire, à la philologie et à l'archéologie, publié
  par la Faculté de philosophie et lettres de l'Université de
  Liège ... Liège, Impr. Vaillant-Carmanne; Paris, H.
  Champion, 1908.
    2 v. illus., 3 pl. (1 fold.) 2 port. 27½ᶜᵐ. (*Half-title:* Bibliothèque de la
  Faculté de philosophie et lettres de l'Université de Liège. Sér. grand in-8°
  (jésus) fasc. I–II)
    The two volumes contain same preliminary matter (p. ₁VI₁-lxxxix) and
  duplicate portraits.

      "Godefroid Kurth ₁par Karl Hanquet₁": p. ₁xxi₁-xxxvii.
      "Bibliographie des travaux de M. Godefroid Kurth, 1863–1908": p.
  ₁xxxix₁-lxxxix.
      Contents.—I. Mémoires historiques.—II Mémoires littéraires, philo-
  logiques et archéologiques.

      I. Kurth, Godefroid Joseph François, 1847–1916. 2. History—Collections.
  3. Philology—Collections. 4. Belgium—Hist—Addresses, essays, lectures.
  I. Title.

      Library of Congress   D7.L5   19–16348

NL 0349720   DLC NIC LU

Liège. Université. Faculté des sciences.

QA845   **Bureau, Florent.**
.B87   Leçons de dynamique. Liège, Sciences et lettres, 1946–

TA7   Liège. Université. *Faculté des sciences appliquées.*
.L5   Hommage à l'Association des ingénieurs sortis de l'École
        de Liège à l'occasion de son centenaire. ₁Liège, G. Thone,
        1947.
          296 p. illus. 31 cm.
          Includes bibliographies.

          1. Association des ingénieurs sortis de l'École de Liège. 2. Engi-
        neering—Collected works.

          TA7.L5   51–23084

NL 0349722   DLC CU IU TxU NN PV PBL GAT LU NIC

Liège. Université. Faculté des Sciences
  appliquées.
    Notes du cours de machines hydrauliques

    see under

  Schlag, Albert.

Liège. Université. *Faculté des sciences appliquées. Institut de chimie et de métallurgie*
    see Liège. Université. *Institut de chimie et de métal-
  lurgie.*

Liège. Université. Faculté technique. Association
  des ingénieurs sortis de l'École de Liège
    see Association des ingénieurs sortis de
  l'École de Liège.

Liège. Université. *Institut astronomique*
    see
  Liège. Université. *Institut d'astronomie et de géodésie.*

Liège. Université. Institut botanique.
  Archives. v.1-
  Bruxelles, 1897-
    v. illus. 26cm.

    1. Botany—Societies.

      PPT NySL TxLT KyU
NL 0349726   NIC PPC PU MiU DSI OU NcD GU NcRS IaAS

Liège. Université. *Institut botanique.*
  Catalogue des broméliacées cultivées au Jardin botani-
  que de l'Université de Liège. Janvier 1873. Gand, Impr.
  C. Annoot-Braeckman, 1873.
    17 p. 22½ᶜᵐ.
    Éd. Morren, directeur; E. Rodembourg, jardinier-chef.

    1. Bromeliaceae. I. Morren, Édouard i. e. Charles Jacques Édouard,
  1833–1886. II. Rodembourg, E.

      Library of Congress   QK73.L5A6   5–34995†

NL 0349727   DLC

Liège. Université. Institut botanique.
  Recueil de quelques travaux d'anatomie
  végétale exécutés à Liège de 1929 à 1935
    see under Liège. Université.

Liège. Université. Institut d'astronomie et de
  géodésie.
    Collection de mémoires in 8°
      see under Liège. Université. Institut
  d'astrophysique.

---

q526.6 Liège. Université--Institut d'astronomie et de
L62g   géodésie.
          ... Géodésie n°1₁-2₁ ...   Bruxelles, M. Hayez,
        imprimeur de l'Académie royale de Belgique, 1926.
          2 no.   illus., V fold.pl. on 3 l., tables,
        diagrs.

          No.2 has cover-title only.
          No more published.

          1. Geodesy. 2. Astronomy. I. Title.

NL 0349730   IU CU CtY PU

Liège. Université. *Institut d'astronomie et de géodésie.*
  Physique du globe. no. 1-
  Liège ₁etc.₁ 1931-
    v. maps. 23–30 x 24 cm.

      QB1.L5   55–54084

NL 0349731   DLC OCIW CU IU NN

Liège. Université. Institut d'astrophysique.
  Collection de mémoires in 8°. v.₁1₁-
  (no.1-   )
  ₁Liège₁ 1924-

    Nos.1-180 issued without series title.
    Nos.1- issued by the university's Institut
  d'astronomie et de géodésie.

NL 0349732   MiU TxU ViU MBdAF OCU LU CtY OU

VOLUME 332

QB1
.L53
Liége. Université. Institut d'astrophysique.
    Collection in 4°. no.1-   1936-
Liége, 1936-
    v. illus. 28 cm.

    No.1-   numbered also v.1-
Largely reprints.
Some issued without series title.

    1. Astronomy--Collected works.

NL 0349733   LU OClW OU IEN CtY MiU OCU

523.4
L625e
Engin
Lib'y
Liége. Université. Institut d'astrophysique.
    L'étude optique de l'atmosphère terrestre;
communications présentées au colloque international tenu à l'Institut d'astrophysique
de l'Université de Liège les 3 et 4 septembre 1951. Louvain, Impr. Ceuterick, 1952.
    2p.l.,[7]-319p. diagrs. 23cm.
    Includes bibliographies.
    "Extrait des Mémoires in-8° de la Société
royale des sciences de Liège, quatrième
série, tome XII, fasc. I-II."
    1. Planets.   2. Atmosphere. I.
Title.

NL 0349734   TxU DAS CU

Liége. Université. *Institut de chimie et de métallurgie.
   Centre d'étude des eaux.*
    Travaux. [1]-
Liége, 1941-
    v. in illus. 23 cm.
    Vols. 1- pub. by the institute under a variant name: Institut
de chimie industrielle minérale et de biochimie appliquée. Centre
d'étude des eaux.

    1. Water--Collected works.

    TD7.L5   50-30710

NL 0349735   DLC CtY CLSU IU

Liége. Université. *Institut de chimie industrielle minérale
et de biochimie appliquée*
   see Liége. Université. *Institut de chimie et de métallurgie.*

614.2
L719t
Liége. Université. Institut de médecine légale.
   Travaux de l'Institut de médecine légale de
l'Université de Liège. 1898-1903. [Liège, 1904]
    1 v. (various pagings) illus.,2 plates (1 fold)
24 cm.
    At head of title: Gabriel Corin; introductory
note signed: G.Corin.
    "Travaux de médecine légale publiés par l'In-
stitut de Liège": 3d prelim.leaf.
    CONTENTS.--I. Corin,G. Sur la présence dans les
tissus des cadavres de volumineux cristaux de
phosphate ammoniaco magnésien.--II. Anten,H.
Recherches sur l'action diurétique de la caféine
et de la théobro-   mine.--III. Corin,G.
Recherches sur la   mort par subersion.--IV.
Corbey,V. Sur la   valeur médico-légale de
la docimasie hepati   V. Duquenne,L. Sur

la valeur médico-légale des cristaux de Florence.
--VI. Corin,G. Le séro-diagnostic du sang en
médecine légale.--VII. Corbey,V. Recherches sur
la nature intime du sang et de la toxicité de l'acide oxa-
lique et des oxalates.--VIII. Corin,G. Recherches
sur certaines causes de rupture de l'utérus au
cours de l'avortement.--IX. Stockis,E. Recherches
sur la pathogénie de la mort par brûlure.--X.
Corin,G. De la cryoscopie comme moyen de déter-
miner la date de la mort.--XI. Corin,G. Cristaux d'hématoïdine comme preuve de l'ancienneté
des lésions traumatiques.
    1. Medical juris-   prudence--Collected works.
I.Corin,Gabriel.

NL 0349738   MiU

Liége. Université. Institut de pharmacie A.
   Gilkinet. Cercle scientifique des anciens
   élèves.
Tall
L6
934
    ... Congrès de pharmacie à l'occasion du cin-
quantenaire de cet Institut, novembre 1934.
Liége. Paris,Masson & cie.,1935.
    4p.l.,[11]-315p.incl.front. illus.(incl.
diagrs.) 25cm.
    Includes bibliographies.

NL 0349739   CtY

Liége. Université. Institut de physiologie.

Colson, Ch.
    Recherches physiologiques sur l'occlusion de l'aorte tho-
racique, par le dᵉ Colson...

    (*In* Académie royale des sciences, des lettres et des beaux-arts de
Belgique, Brussels. Mémoires couronnés et autres mémoires ... Collection in-8°. Bruxelles, 1891. 21½ᶜᵐ. t. XLIV [Sciences. no. 6] 57,
[1] p. diagrs.)

Liége. Université. *Institut de physiologie.*
    ... Travaux du laboratoire de Léon Fredericq.
7   -[1904]
Liége, Impr. H. Vaillant-Carmanne; [etc., etc.] 18
1904.
    v. illus., plates, diagrs. 25ᶜᵐ.
    At head of title: Université de Liège. Institut de physiologie.
    Vol. -5 have imprint Paris, Liège.
    Discontinued after v. 7, owing to the publication of a new periodical en-
titled: "Archives internationales de physiologie, pub. par Léon Fredericq
[et] Paul Heger."

    1. Physiology—Collected works.   I. Fredericq, Léon, 1851-

                           12-11468

    Library of Congress   QP6.F85

NL 0349741   DLC ICJ CU DNLM MiU PU-M

LIÈGE, Belgium - Univ-Institut de physique.
   Bulletin. Liége. 1904. fasc.I; 1905,III;
1906,II.

NL 0349742   MH-C OU

RA 410.8
.B3 L7
LIÈGE--Université--Institut de Sociologie
   Médecins, dentistes et pharmaciens dans
la Province de Liège; contribution à l'étude
des débouchés professionnels. Liège, Imprimerie,H. Vaillant-Carmanne, 1954.
    97 p. illus. (Its Travaux, 4)

    1. Physicians--Liège. 2. Dentists--Liège.
3. Pharmacists--Liège. I. Title. Ser.

NL 0349743   InU RPB TU NcD CoU

HF5549
.L71
LIÉGE. UNIVERSITE. Institut de sociologie.
   Problèmes de la fonction de personnel [par]
Robert Toubeau [et al. Liège, n.d.]
    201 p. (Its Sciences sociales et administra-
tion des affaires, 3)

    1. Personnel management. I. Toubeau, Robert.
II. Title. Series.

NL 0349744   ICU

Liége. Université. *Institut de sociologie.*
    Travaux du Séminaire de sociologie de la Faculté de droit
de Liège, effectués sous la direction de René Clémens. Liège,
1949.
    xiv, 119 p. 25 cm.
    CONTENTS.—L'évolution démographique dans une commune du Con-
droz liégeois, par H. Hourant.—Immigration et assimilation, par J.
Libert.—L'instabilité de la main-d'œuvre italienne, par L. Degeer.—
L'orientation des jeunes gens au sortir des humanités anciennes, par
P. Minon.

    1. Social sciences—Societies, etc.   I. Clémens, René. II. Title.

    H13.L522   52-17620 rev

NL 0349745   DLC KU NNC NN NcD NIC MiU TxU KU

Liége. Université. Institut Ed. van Beneden.
   Travaux. Liége. 1, 1929 -
    53 - 75.

NL 0349746   ICF

Liége. Université. *Institut électrotechnique Montefiore.*
    ... Les installations et les programmes de l'Institut
électrotechnique Montefiore. [Liége? 1903?]
    1 p. l., 53 p. illus., diagrs. 30½ᶜᵐ.
    At head of title: Université de Liège.
    "Association des ingénieurs électriciens sortis de l'Institut électrotechni-
que Montefiore ... liste des membres en l'année 1903": p. 34-53.

                      E 10-1296

    Library, U. S. Bur. of   Education T173.L62

NL 0349747   DHEW

Liége. Université. Institut electrotechnique
   Montefiore. Association des ingénieurs
électriciens sortis de l'Institut
    see Association des ingénieurs électriciens
sortis de l'Institut électrotechnique Montefiore.

Liége. Université. *Institut supérieur d'histoire et de littératures orientales.*
    Mélanges de philologie orientale publiés à l'occasion du xᵉ
anniversaire de la création de l'Institut supérieur d'histoire et
de littératures orientales de l'Université de Liège [Liège, Institut supérieur d'histoire et de littératures orientales de l'Uni-
versité] Louvain, M. Istas, 1932.
    3 p. l., [v]-xvi, 283 p., 2 l. plates, tab. 26ᶜᵐ.
    Includes Persian, Syriac and transliterated Sumerian texts.
    CONTENTS.
    Bricteux, A. Pacquinade sur la ville de Tébriz par maître Lissâni de
Chiraz.—Capart, J. L'usurpation des monuments dans l'antiquité égyptienne.—Cotton, G. La revanche du Brahman.—Dossin, G. Une nouvelle
valeur du signe

    Dossin, G., et Fohalle, R. Sur un passage d'un traité hittite (Bo 2027,
col. I, l. 11-18)—Gilbert, P. Le créateur de la pyramide funéraire.—
Gobeaux-Thonet, J. Agt Rizâ ou Rizâ Abbâsi?—Generet, R. H. de. Une
élégie inédite de Mouhtacham de Kachan.—Janssens, H. F. Les dix
vertus du chien. Texte inédit extrait du manuscrit syriaque no. 9 de
l'India office.—Mansion, J. Le sanscrit védique, langue morte.—
Prickartz, J. Le début du premier cylindre de Goudéa (cyl. A. I-VI 14)—
Straeten, Ol. van der. La métrique des Lamentations.—Walle, B. van de.
Les soi-disants "signes déterminatifs" du système hiéroglyphique égyptien.—Fohalle, R. Note sur un passage de "Çakuntalā" (I 4)
    1. Oriental philology—Collections. I. Title.

                    A C 33-1473 Revised

    Yale univ. Library
    for Library of Congress   [r38c2]

NL 0349750   CtY WaU UU MiU CU NjP NNC OC1

Liége. Université. *Journées d'étude, 1949*
   see Journées d'étude, *Université de Liège, 1949.*

W 1
LI292
LIÈGE. Université. Laboratoire
   d'embryogénie et d'anatomie comparée
    Recherches faites au Laboratoire.
    v. 1; 1875/76. Bruxelles.
    1 v. (various pagings) illus.
    No more published?
    1. Embryology - Collected works

NL 0349752   DNLM

Liége. Université. Laboratoires d'essais
   des constructions du génie civil et
   d'hydraulique fluviale.

    See

Liége. Université. Centre d'études de
   recherches et d'essais scientifiques des
   constructions du génie civil et d'hydraulique fluviale.

VOLUME 332

Liège. Université. *Séminaire de géographie.*
Cinquantième anniversaire du Séminaire de géographie (1903-1953) et vingt-cinquième anniversaire du Cercle des géographes liégeois (1928-1953) volume commémoratif. Liège, Impr. H. Vaillant-Carmanne, 1953.
102 p. port., maps. 30 cm.
Bibliography: p. 10-19.

I. Cercle des géographes liégeois.

G19.C45   55-29500

NL 0349754   DLC IU ICU IEN

Liège. Université. Séminaire de géographie.
Treveux...fasc. I-VIII.
Liège, 1905-07.

NL 0349755   DI-GS IU CU

Liège. Université. *Séminaire de sociologie*
see
Liège. Université. *Institut de sociologie.*

Liège. Williamite convent
see
Ferrières, Belgium. Bernardfagne
(Williamite Benedictine priory).

Liège (Bishopric)
see
Liège (Diocese)

LIÉGE, Belgium (Diocese).
Mandements, lettres pastorales, circulaires et autres documents, publiés dans le diocèse de Liège depuis le Concordat de 1801 jusqu'à 1830. Liège, H. Dessain, 1851.
2 vol.
Contents: I.1801-1814.-II.1814-1830.

NL 0349759   MH

Liège *(Diocese)*
Statvta consistorialia, ac reformatio judiciorum spiritualium, ciuitatis & diœcesis Leodiensis. Per Reuerendiss. in Christo patrem, ac Illustriss. D. Dominum Georgivm ab Avstria, Dei & Apostolicœ sedis gratia episcopum Leodiensem ... Iam recens œdita, & in iustum ordinem digesta. Atque per Sanctissimum in Christo patrem ac dominum, Dominum Iulium III. pontificem max. approbata & confirmata. Traiecti, ex mandato Reuerend. & Illustriss. principis episcopi Leodiens. Iacobus Bathenius excudebat, 1553.
1 p. l., 74 numb. l. 20ᵐᵐ.

Colophon (surmounted by printer's device): Traiecti ad Mosam ex officina Iacobi Bathenij, anno 1553.
Title vignette (coat of arms) Initials.
Manuscript notes.

1. Liège—Hist. 2. Ecclesiastical law—Netherlands. I. Georg von Österreich, d. 1557, ed. II. Title.

27-8054

NL 0349761   DLC MiU

Liège *(Diocese)*
Statuta synodalia leodiensia. ₁Louanii, Johannes de Westfalia, 1486₁
116 l. 4° (194ᵐᵐ)
Not in Hain, Proctor, or Reichling; Cop. 5616; Campbell 1601*; Holtrop, p. 49 (pl. 87d) Goff, S—743.
Signature: a-π⁸, o-p⁶. (First and last leaves blank)
Capitals, paragraph marks and initial strokes in red. Marginal notes.
Folio 12 signed b⁶ (for b⁷); f. 26, d for dˢ.
Campbell refers to f. 52 as siᵒ g⁴ (for g⁵)
Imperfect: first and last leaves (blank) wanting.

I. Title.

CA 18-763 Unrev'd

Library of Congress   Incun.X.L65

NL 0349762   DLC

Beinecke Library 1972 241
Liège (Diocese)
Statuta synodalia ecclesiae Leodiensis.
[Cologne, Ludwig von Renchen, April 6, 1492]
76 ff. 1 illus. 20 cm. 4°.
Copinger 5617; Polain 3603; Proctor 1267; British Museum, XV cent., vol. 1, p. 267; Goff, Census S—744.
For fuller description see collation slip in volume.
1. Incunabula in Yale Library. 2. Cologne. Ludwig von Renchen. 1492. I. Title.

Zi.1267

NL 0349763   CtY

Beinecke Library 1972 275
Liège (Diocese)
Statuta synodalia ecclesiae Leodiensis.
[Louvain, Thierry Martens, July 31, 1500]
110 ff. 20 cm. 4°.
Imperfect: fol. 110, blank, wanting.
Hain-Copinger 8418; Campbell 1602; Proctor 9315; British Museum, XV cent., vol. 9, p. 169; Goff, Census S—745.
For fuller description see collation slip in volume.

1. Incunabula in Yale Library. 2. Louvain. Martens, Thierry. 1500.

NL 0349765   CtY

BX 1937 .N2 L73 1501
Liège (Diocese)
Statuta synodalia Leodien₁sia. Lovanii, Per Theodoricum Martini, 1501₁
226₁ p. 20 cm.
Signatures: A-B⁸,C⁴,D-E⁸,F⁶G⁴,H⁶,I-K⁸,L-R⁶ (last leaf blank); 4 l. unsigned.
Imperfect: A1 (t.p.) wanting.
Colophon: Confirmatio & approbatio statuoᵣᵧ synodalium & curiæ Leodieñ.& illorum modificationum ... expliciunt per Theodoricum Martini Alosteñ.poᵍˢᵗ exactam reuisionem diligēter exarata ... ₁15 Ianuarii 1501₁
A reissue of the edition of July 31,1500 with the Con-   firmatio & approbatio statutorum   appended on 4 leaves
added at the end. Cf.the colophon of the 1500 ed. (sig.R5ᴿ) and Brit.Museum. Cat. (XV cent.) v.9 (1962) p.169 (from which the t.and the description of a complete copy of the 1500 ed. are taken)
Additions in manuscript bound at end.:
₁1₁ Reformatio curiarum spiritualium Leodien. facta per R.P.D.Cornelium (ad 1544) de Bergis episcopum Leodien.anno Dni.1538. 65 p.—De consilio Leodien. 6 p.
₁2₁ Sequuntur quedam extracta ex statutis consistorialibus   et reformatione iudiciorum spiritualium   civitatis Leodien.iussu ...
D.Ernesti (ab 1581 ad 1612) editis. 1582. De processu fulminando. 16 p.
₁3₁ Extracta ex statutis iussu ... D.Ferdinandi (ab 1612 ad 1650) electi et confirmati episcopi Leod. ... editis. 1613. Caput septimum. De processu ordinario. 15 p.—Salarium notariorum. 3 p.

1.Ecclesias-   tical law—Netherlands.
I.Title.   II.Title: Confirmatio et
approbatio   statutorum synodalium &
curiæ Leodien.

NL 0349768   MiU

Liège *(Diocese)*
Statuta synodalia Leodiens.
Lovanii, apud P. Phalesium & M. Rotarium 1549. sm.8vo.

NL 0349769   MWiW-C

Liège (Diocese) Bishop, 785?-809 (Ghaerbaldus)
see also Gerbaldus, Bp. of Liège, d. 809.

Liège *(Diocese) Bishop, 1200-1229 (Hugues de Pierrepont)*
Actes des princes-évêques de Liège: Hugues de Pierrepont, 1200-1229, par Édouard Poncelet. Bruxelles, 1941.
xcvii, 314 p. illus., facsims. 31 cm. (Commission royale d'histoire. Recueil des actes des princes belges. ₍3₎)
Bibliographical footnotes.

1. Belgium—Church history—Sources. I. Poncelet, Édouard, 1865-   ed. II. Title. (Series: Académie royale des sciences, des lettres et des beaux-arts de Belgique, Brussels. Commission royale d'histoire. Recueil des actes des princes belges)

DH403.A23 vol. 3   50-45527

NL 0349771 MiU MoU OU GU CU   DLC CaBVaU PU NN MH MdBP CtY OClW NcD

LIÉGE (Diocese). Bishop, 1581-1612? (Ernest of Bavaria)₁
Copie Uan het Placcaet van d'Jnquisitie ghemaeckt ende ghepubliceert byden nieuwen Bisschop van Luyck. Midtsgaders een Christelijcke Waerschouwinghe aende Jnwoonders des Landts van Luyck, ende alle andere goedthertighen... Hantwerpen, Ten huyse van Jasper Troyens, 1582. 4 l. 21cm.(4°.)

Knuttel 609. Cockx-Indestege: Belgica typographica, I, 3048.
Edict of the prince-bishop dated at Liège 20 April 1582.

1. Church and state—Belgium—Liège. 2. Inquisition—Belgium—Liège.

NL 0349773   NN

Liège (Diocese) *Cathedral Chapter*
see **Liège. Saint Lambert** *(Cathedral) Chapitre.*

Liège (Principality)
Catalogue des actes de Jean de Bavière
see under Bacha, Eugène.

DC 141 F674 v.261
Liège (*Principality* **)**
Seconde lotterie dans la principauté de Liège. ₁Liège, 1763₁
₁2₁ p. 24cm.

1. Lotteries—Liège.

NL 0349776   NIC

Liège *(Principality). Laws, statutes, etc.*   332-49493 E₁
Edicts et pvblications des monnoyes forgées & lesquelles ont eu cours par les pays & principauté de Liège, dez l'an 1477, iusques à l'an 1623, courant. Liège, C. Oswerx, imprimeur, [1623?]
[176] p. 18½ x 14ᵐᵐ.
Has four pages of inserted manuscript and marginal notes; mutilated by trimming.

NL 0349777   ICJ

VOLUME 332

HG1060 **Liége** (*Principality*)   *Laws, statutes, etc.*
.L7A3   Edits et pvblications des monnoyes, lesquelles ont eu
1675   cours par les pays & principauté de Liege, depuis l'an 1477.
jusques à present. Ausquels sont adjouté es les reductions
de toutes sortes de grains, en muids, stiers, quartes, poug-
noux, mesurettes; & en argent ... Liege, Chez G. H. Streel,
imprimeur, 1675.

   [1], 222 p. 18ᵐ.

   Title vignette.

   1. Money—Liége (Principality)

NL   0349778   ICU NNC

Liége (*Principality*)
Les feudataires de la principauté de Liège sous Englebert
de la Marck. Bruxelles, Palais des académies, 1948–49.

   2 v. (922 p.) 22 cm. (Académie royale de Belgique. Commission
royale d'histoire. Publications in-octavo)

   CONTENTS.—[1], Introduction, par É. Poncelet. Livre original des
fiefs du 13 avril au 26 décembre 1845. Actes féodaux de 1846 à
1861.—[2], Table onomastique, par J. Vannérus.

   1. Liége (Diocese)—Hist.—Sources. 2. Feudalism—Belgium. 3.
La Marck, Engelbert de, Abp., d. 1368. I. Poncelet, Édouard, 1865-
ed. II. Title. (Series: Académie royale des sciences, des lettres et
des beaux-arts de Belgique, Brussels. Commission royale d'histoire.
Publications in-octavo)

   DH801.L5L48   51–37204 rev

NL   0349779   DLC CU GU MoU ICU IaU NIC NN

Liége (*Principality*)
Genart, Charles.
  ... L'industrie cloutière en pays wallon, par Charles
Genart, avocat. [Bruxelles, J. Lebègue et cⁱᵉ, 1900]

Liége (*Principality*)
Le livre des fiefs de l'église de Liége sous Adolphe de La
Marck, par Édouard Poncelet ... Bruxelles, Hayez, 1898.

   2 p. l., lxviii, 745 p. 21½ᵐ. (Académie royale des sciences, des lettres et des beaux-arts de Belgique, Brussels. Commission royale d'histoire. Publications in octavo)

   1. Liége—Hist.—Sources. 2. Marck, Adolphe de La, prince, bp. of
Liége, d. 1344. I. Poncelet, Édouard, 1865- ed. II. Title.

   Library of Congress   DH801.L5L5   4–33654 Revised
                              [r28d2]

NL   0349781   DLC GU CU MB PU MiU IaU MoU

Liége (*Principality*)
Le livre des fiefs du comté de Looz sous
Jean d'Arckel
     see under   Looz (Comté)

Liége (*Principality*)   Laws, statutes, etc.
Sohet, Dominique, 1728–1811.
Instituts de droit, ou Sommaire de jurisprudence cano-
nique, civile, féodale et criminelle, pour les pays de Liege,
de Luxembourg, Namur & autres. Par Mr. Sohet ...
A Bouillon, Chez A. Foissy, imprimeur & se vend à Liege
[etc.] 1770–81 [v. 1, '72]

                      Neth 12.4.18(1)
Liège (*Principality*) Laws, statutes, etc.
La Paweilhar Giffou; édition critique par Albert
Baguette. Préf. de Maurice Yans. Liège, Éditions de
la Commission communale de l'histoire de l'ancien
Pays de Liège, 1946

   lxvii, 122 p. (Commission communale de l'histoire
de l'ancien Pays de Liège. Documents et mémoires
sur le Pays de Liège, 1)

NL   0349784   MH CtY

Liége (Principality) Laws, statutes, etc.
Recueil contenant les edits et reglemens faits
pour le país de Liège & comté de Looz, par les
evêques & princes, tant en matiere de police
que de justice; les privileges accordez par les
empereurs au même país & aux terres dépendantes
de l'eglise de Liege; les concordats et traitez faits
avec les puissances voisines, & ceux faits entre
l'evêque & prince, & les etats ou autres membres
dudit país; le tout accompagné de notes. Par
Mr. M. G. de Louvrex ... Nouvelle ed. continuée,
augm., cor. & remise en meilleur ordre avec des

notes ulterieures, par Bauduin Hodin ... Liege,
E. Kints, 1750–51.
   3 v.   fold. plates.   33 cm.
   Vol. 2 dated 1750.

NL   0349786   DLC

Liége (*Principality*)   *Laws, statutes, etc.*
Recueil contenant les edjts et reglemens faits pour le país de
Liège & comté de Looz, par les evêques & princes, tant en
matiere de police que de justice; les privileges accordez par
les empereurs au même país & autres terres dépendantes de
l'eglise de Liege; les concordats et traitez faits avec les puissances voisines, & ceux faits entre l'evêque & prince, & les etats
ou autres membres dudit país; le tout accompagne de notes.
Par mr. M. G. de Louvrex ... Nouv. ed. continuée, augm.,
cor. & remise en meilleur ordre, avec des notes ulterieures,

par Bauduin Hodin ... A Liege, Chez E. Kints, 1750–52
[v. 1, '51]
   4 v. fold. plates. 33ᵐ.
   "Mandement publié ... le 30 avril 1779 ..." ([10] p.) and "Mandement
publié ... le 26 août 1772 ..." ([16] p.) inserted in v. 2; ordinance of
September 2, 1780 (3 p.) inserted in v. 4; many pages of manuscript
notes inserted.

   [I. Holy Roman empire. Laws, statutes, etc. II. Liége (Principality)
Treaties, etc. III. Louvrex, Mathias Guillaume de, 1665–1734, ed. IV.
Hodin, Bauduin, ed. V. Title.

                         30–21574

NL   0349788   DLC WU MH ICN

Liége (Principality) Laws, statutes, etc.
Recueil des ordonnances ...
     see under   Belgium. Commission royale
pour la publication des anciennes lois et
ordonnances de la Belgium.

Lilly
Library
DH 811
.L5 L53   **LIEGE** (*Principality*) . Laws, statutes, etc.
Reglement van Ferdinandvs by der Gratie
Gods ghekooren Bisschop van Ceulen, ende Prince
van Luyck, In dewelcke vervat wert, waer
na hun de Gilden sullen hebben te reguleeren
... Amsterdam, Jan van Hilten, 1649.
   1 p.l., [6] p.   4to

   Knuttel: 5816
   Translated from the French
   Reorganization of munccipal government
at Liege.

NL   0349790   InU

Liége (**Principality**) Laws, statutes, etc. (*Index*)
Liste chronologique des édits et ordonnances de
la principauté de Liège
     see under
Belgium. Commission royale pour la publication
des anciennes lois et ordonnances de la Belgium.

Liége (Principality) Treaties, etc.
Recueil contenant les edits et reglemens faits
pour le país de Liege & comté de Looz
     see under   Liége (Principality) Laws,
statutes, etc.

Liége (province),
  ... L'organisation judicieuse des loisirs nouveaux de la classe
ouvrière.   Liége: L. Renier-Gillon, 1920.   53 p.   8°.

   CONTENTS: Préface. LIÉGE (PROVINCE), BELGIUM. LOISIRS, COMMISSION
SPÉCIALE DES. Rapport de la Commission spéciale chargée, par le Conseil provincial
de Liége, de rechercher les meilleurs moyens d'utiliser judicieusement les loisirs nouveaux procurés à la classe ouvrière par la limitation des heures de travail. LIÉGE
(PROVINCE), BELGIUM. CONSEIL PROVINCIAL. Délibération votée par le Conseil provincial de Liége après discussion du rapport de la commission spéciale. PECQUEUR, O.
Les loisirs de la classe ouvrière; conférence faite le 25 avril 1920, au théâtre de Huy.

   1. Leisure.   2. Working classes—   Education.   3. Liège (province),
Belgium.   Loisirs, Commission spéciale   des.
N. Y. P. L.   February 17, 1926

NL   0349793   NN DL

Liége,   (Province).
  ... Verwaltungsblatt für die Provinz Lüttich.   Memorial administratif de la province de Liége.   Nr. 1–79; Dec. 1915 – Oct.
1918.   [Lüttich, 1915–18]   79 nos. in 5 v.   23½cm.

   Caption-title.
   German and French.
   Issued during the German occupation in place of the Memorial administratif de la
province de Liége.
   Includes semiannual indexes to issues of Dec. 1915 – June, 1918.

   1. European war, 1914–1917—   Campaigns—Belgium—German occupation.   2. European war,   1914–1918—Belgium—Liége.
N. Y. P. L.   March 24, 1938

NL   0349794   NN

Liege (Province) Commission speciale des loisirs.
  ... Loisirs de la classe ouvriers. Rapport.
1922–26
Liege, 1922–26
   5 v.   22 cm.

NL   0349795   DL NN

Liége (Province) Commission spéciale des
Loisirs.
  ... L'organisation judicieuse des loisirs
nouveaux de la classe ouvrière
     see under   Liége (Province)

10
4182   **Liège** (Province) Conseil de salubrité publique.
Annales du conseil de salubrité publique de la
province de Liege.   Liège, imprimerie de J. G.
Lardinois, and L. Severyns, 18[ ]
   v.   8°.

NL   0349797   DLC DNLM

10
4182   **Liège** (Province) Conseil de salubrite publique.
Compte-rendu des travaux, pendant l'année
1849–50, 1853–59, 1860–64, 1867, 1868. Par A.
Spring, president du conseil.   Liège, A. Denoel
[&] J. -G. Carmanne, 1850–69.
   16 p.   8°.

NL   0349798   DLC

Liége(Province) Conseil de salubrité
publique ..
   ——. Rapport sur les travaux de l'année 1900.
   8 m.   8°.   Liége, H. Vaillant-Carmanne, [1901].

NL   0349799   DNLM

Liege (Province) Conseil provincial.
Procès-verbaux non officiels des seances ...
1913.

NL   0349800   PP

VOLUME 332

(Province)
Liége₍ Conseil provincial. Députation
permanente.
Exposé de la situation administrative de la
province de Liège, fait par la Députation
permanente au Conseil provincial, en 1841 ...
₍Liège? 1842?₎
1 p.ℓ.,175 p.   tables (part fold.) 21ᶜᵐ.   (Half-
title: Supplément au n°.569 du Mémorial administratif
de la province de Liège)

Caption title.

1.Liège—Pol.& govt.

NL 0349801   MiU

Liége (Province) Société de salubrité publique
see   Liége (Province) Conseil de salubrité
publique.

Liége. Photographies de J. Cayet ₍et al.₎ Introd. historique de Carlo Bronne. Bruxelles, C. Dessart ₍°1949₎
₍70₎ p. ₍p. ₍13₎–70₎ illus., map) 27 cm. (Images de Belgique)
French and English.

1. Liège—Descr.—Views.   I. Cayet, J.   II. Bronne, Carlo, 1901–

DH811.L5L5   914.93   50–24179

NL 0349803   DLC

Liege chess congress, Aug. 19th–Aug. 30th,
1930
see under   International Chess Tournament,
Liège, 1930.

... Liège & ses affiches de guerre; affiches placardées à
Liège & environs du 4 août 1914 au 1ᵉʳ mars 1915. Documents des plus curieux concernant l'occupation des
villes fortifiées. Ixelles-Bruxelles, Les Éditions Brian
Hill ₍1915?₎
2 p. l., ₍7₎–108 p., 1 l. 22ᶜᵐ.
At head of title: Souvenirs historiques.

1. Liège—Hist.—Sources. 2. European war, 1914–   —Documents,
etc., sources.

Library of Congress   D623.B4L7   17–29763

NL 0349805   DLC DNW CtY

... Liège & ses affiches de guerre ... documents des plus cu-
rieux concernant l'occupation des villes fortifiées ... Ixelles-
Bruxelles, B. Hill ₍1915–16₎
2 v. 22ᶜᵐ (v. 2: 20ᶜᵐ)
At head of title: Souvenirs historiques.
Vol. 2 has cover-title only.
On cover: Il a été tiré 50 exemplaires sur papier de choix pour la
librairie Deman à Bruxelles. no. 32.
CONTENTS.—₍1₎ Affiches belges & allemandes placardées à Liège &
environs du 4 août 1914 au 1ᵉʳ mars 1915.—II. Affiches placardées à
Liège du 1ᵉʳ mars 1915 au 31 mars 1916.
1. Liège—Hist.—Sources. 2. European war, 1914–1918—Documents,
etc., sources.   I. Title: Souvenirs historiques.

Library of Congress   D623.B4L7 1915 a   30–6924

NL 0349806   DLC

Liège et son université
see under   ₍Duesberg, Jules₎ 1881–   comp.

KF 30783
Liège: histoire, arts, lettres, sciences,
industrie, travaux publics. Texte par Eugene
M.O.Dognée ₍et al.₎ Illustrations par d'Heur,
L.Salme ₍et al.₎ Liège, Impr. Daxhelet, 1881

526 p. illus.

NL 0349808   MH

L610.54 L62
... Liège médical, ... Journal de médecine et de chirurgie
pratiques et des intérêts professionels. Liège, ₍1920–₎.

Library has 1920 to date. illus. 27ᶜᵐ.

Caption title.
Editor: M. Brocha.
Weekly.
Liège médical was established in 1907. In 1908 it united with Le Scalpel under the
title, Le Scalpel et Liège médical, which suspended publication 1914?–1919. It resumed
separate publication, Jan. 4, 1920, under the original title.
1920–   called 13ᵉ année.
Jan. 22, 1921; Aug. 20, Nov. 26, 1922; March 25, April 22, 1923; index to 1920,
1921, 1923, wanting.

NL 0349809   ICJ ICRL DNLM

Liégeard (Charles). *Étude de la mécanique
animale appliquée à l'extérieur du cheval, suivant les divers services auxquels il est employé.
30 pp. 4°. Paris, 1843.

NL 0349810   DNLM

Liégeard, Edme François Charles Joseph, b.
1821.
Watrigant, Jean François Théodore Arthur Henri de, 1866–
Manuel de l'étalonnier et de l'éleveur, par H. de Watrigant,
d'après l'ouvrage de Charles Liégeard ... Libourne, Paris,
G. Maleville ₍etc.₎ 1908.

Liégeard, François Émile Stéphen.
See
Liégeard, Stéphen, 1830–1925.

Liégeard (Gustave). *De la phlegmatia alba
dolens. 30 pp. 4°. Paris, 1870.

NL 0349813   DNLM

₍Liégeard, Stéphen,₎ 1830–1925.
À Guillaume de Hohenzollern.   ₍Dijon: Jobard, 1914.₎
2. ed. 8°.
Cover-title.
Signed: Stéphen Liégeard.

1. European war, 1914–   —Poetry.   2. William II., German emperor,
1859–   —Poetry. 3. Poetry   (French). 4. Title.
N.Y.P.L.   February 18, 1916.

NL 0349814   NN NjP

Liégeard, Stéphen i. e. François Émile Stéphen, 1830–
... A travers l'Engadine, la Valteline, le Tyrol du sud,
et les lacs de l'Italie supérieure. Paris, Hachette et cⁱᵉ,
1877.
2 p. l., vi, 491 p. 18½ᶜᵐ.

Subject entries: Europe—Descr. & trav.

Library of Congress, no.   D919.L71.

NL 0349815   DLC

Liégeard, Stéphen, 1830–1925.
Les abeilles d'or; chants impériaux...
Paris, E.Dentu, 1859.
xx, 264 p. 23½ᶜᵐ.

NL 0349816   NjP MH

Liégeard, Stéphen, 1830–   Dn 532.16
All' ombra di Dante Alighieri; canto. Traduzione libera di
Luigi Silva. Parma, P. Grazioli, 1878.
pp. 63.
French and Italian texts.

Dante—Poems on||AcS 183766

NL 0349817   MH NIC

L944.9
L719c   Liégeard, Stephen, 1830–1925.
La Côte d'Azur.   Paris, Maison Quantin
₍1887₎
430p. illus. 35cm.

1. Riviera. Hist. 2. Riviera. Descr. &
trav. I. Title.

NL 0349818   IEN

Liégeard, Stéphen, 1830–
La côte d'azur...   Paris: Quantin, 1894.   2 p.l., iii, 628 p.
illus. New ed. 8°.
Author's name at head of title.

1. Riviera (The). 2. Title.
N.Y.P.L.   November 21, 1916.

NL 0349819   NN OCU

Liégeard, Stéphen, 1830–   Ger 2300.10.14
Le crime du 4 septembre. Bruxelles, J. Rozez, 1871.
pp. 67.

France—Hist. 1870–71||AcS

NL 0349820   MH CU

Liégeard, Stéphen, 1830–1925.
De l'origine, de l'esprit et des cas d'application de la maxime
Le partage est déclaratif de propriété ... par Stéphen Liégeard
... 2. éd. Paris, A. Durand ₍etc., etc.,₎ 1855.
x, 168 p. 23ᶜᵐ.
"Mémoire couronné par la Faculté de droit de Dijon, le 15 novembre
1854 dans la séance solennelle de rentrée."

1. Partition—France. I. Title.
₍Full name: François Émile Stéphen Liégeard₎
                                       39–23371

NL 0349821   DLC

8451623 Liégeard, Stéphen, 1830–1925.
Or   Rêves et combats.   Paris, Hachette, 1892.
242p. 21cm.

Poems.

NL 0349822   IU

VOLUME 332

Liégeard, Stéphen, 1830-1925.
Rimes vengeresses. 1916.
In French.

NL 0349823   RP

DC
280.5 Liégeard,Stéphen,1830-1925.
L72   Trois ans à la Chambre. Paris, E.Dentu, 1873.
A35   396 p.

1.France--Pol.& govt.--1852-1870. 2.France.
Corps législatif,1852-1870. I.Title.

Full name: François Émile
Stéphen Liégeard.

NL 0349824   MiU MB

Liégeard, Stéphen, 1830-1925.
Vingt journées d'un
touriste au pays de Luchon.   Paris, Hachette
et cie, 1874.

NL 0349825   NNH

Liégeart, A   684.1 R600
.... Petit guide de l'ajusteur-tourneur et du mécanicien à
l'usage des élèves des écoles pratiques d'industrie et des candidats
aux écoles nationales d'arts et métiers, par A. Liégeart, ...
Quatrième édition. Dijon, F. Rey, 1916.
222 p. incl. illus., tables, diagrs. 22ᶜᵐ.
At head of title: Technologie.

NL 0349826   ICJ

Liégeart, Albert.
... Manuel du cordonnier, technologie à l'usage des élèves des
écoles pratiques, des cours professionnels et des apprentis, par
A. Liégeart ... 3. éd. Avec 246 figures dans le texte. Paris,
J.-B. Baillière et fils, 1943.
298 p. illus. diagrs. 18ᶜᵐ. (Bibliothèque professionnelle, pub. sous la
direction de m. René Dhommée)

1. Boots and shoes—Trade and manufacture.
45–18610
Library of Congress   TS990.L5   1943
⟨2⟩   685.31

NL 0349827   DLC NN

Liégeas, Marie Thérèse.
Z927
.P18
Paris. Bibliothèque historique de la ville.
Inauguration de la Bibliothèque George Sand (Donation
Aurore Sand) 15 juin 1954. ⟨Catalogue rédigé avec le con-
cours de Patrice Boussel, conservateur adjoint, et Marie-
Thérèse Liégeas, bibliothécaire. Paris, 1954⟩

Liegel, Armin, 1909-
Kiefernekrosen und Zahnschädigungen nach
Röntgenbestrahlungen ... Meissen, 1933.
Inaug. -Diss. - München.
Lebenslauf.

NL 0349829   CtY

Liegel, Georg
Anweisung, mit welchen sorten verschiedene obstbaum-anlagen besetzt werden sollen. Nebst angabe der
individuellen eigenheiten dieser bäume, sammt einer kurzen charakteristischen beschreibung ihrer früchte. Für
liebhaber von obst-anpflanzungen. Zugleich systematisches, räsonnirendes verzeichniss der in den gärten und
in der baumschule gezogenen obstsorten, von G. Liegel ...
Salzburg, F. X. Duple, 1822.
xv, 88 p. front. (port.) 19½ᶜᵐ.
1. Pomology.
Agr 10-1322

Library, U. S. Dept. of   Agriculture 93L62

NL 0349830   DNAL

Liegel, Georg
Anweisung mit welchen sorten verschiedene
obstbaum-anlagen besetzt werden sollen. 2.,
neu bearb. aufl.   Salzburg, F.X. Duyle, 1842.
192 p.

NL 0349831   CU-A

Liegel, Georg.
Beschreibung neuer obstsorten, von dr. G. Liegel ... Regensburg, G. J. Manz, 1851.
2 v. 22ᶜᵐ.

1. Fruit-culture. ⟨1. Pomology⟩
Agr 30-222

Library, U. S. Dept. of   Agriculture 93L62B

NL 0349832   DNAL

Liegel, Georg. Beschreibung neuer obstsorten. 3 hefte
(in 1 vol.). Regensburg. 1851-56. 8°.
i. Die pflaumen. 1851. pp. 182+.—ii. Früchte von allen obstgat-
tungen nebst pomologischen notizen. 1851. pp. 179 +.—iii. Die
pflaumen, nebst pflaumen-notizen. 1856. pp. viii, 78 +.

NL 0349833   MH-A

Liegel, Georg
Lehrbuch der pomologie, mit neuen kirschen-
charakteren. Zugleich als pomologisches wörterbuch zu gebrauchen. 2. aufl.   Regensburg,
F. Pustet, 1830.
141 p.

NL 0349834   CU-A

Liegel, Georg.
Die pomologische kunstsprache systematisch bearbeitet.
Oder Lehre der charakteristik der obstfrüchte und der obst-
tragenden gewächse, von Georg Liegel ... Passau, F. Pustet,
1896.
x, 133, xxiv p. vii pl. 20½ᶜᵐ.

1. Gardening—Dictionaries. ⟨1. Horticulture—Dictionaries⟩ 2. Fruit-
culture. ⟨2. Pomology⟩
Agr 30-946

Library, U. S. Dept. of   Agriculture 93L62K

NL 0349835   DNAL

Liegel, Georg
Systematische anleitung zur kenntniss der vorzüglichsten sorten des kern-, stein-, schalen-
und beerenobstes, mit angabe der eigenthümlichen
vegetation seiner bäume und sträucher, etc.
Passau, F. Pustet, 1825.
224 p. front. (port.)

NL 0349836   CU-A

Liegel, Georg.
Systematische anleitung zur kenntniss der pflaumen. Oder:
Das geschlecht der pflaumen in seinen arten und abarten.
Von G. Liegel ... Passau, F. Winkler; ⟨etc., etc.⟩ 1838-41.
2 v. in 1. 2 fold. pl., port., fold. tab. 20ᶜᵐ.
Vol. 2 has imprint: Linz, F. Eurich und sohn.

1. Plum.
Agr 30-47

Library, U. S. Dept. of   Agriculture 94L62

NL 0349837   DNAL MH-A

SB357
L6
Liegel, Georg
Systematische Anleitung zur Kenntniss
der vorzüglichsten Sorten des Kern-Stein-
Schalen- und Beerenobstes mit Angabe der
eigenthümlichen Vegetation seiner Bäume
und Sträucher ... Enthält zugleich das
3. Verzeichniss der angepflanzten Obstsorten ... Wien, Mörschner und Jasper,
1825.
xxiv,224 p. port.

NL 0349838   CU

Liegel, Georg
Uebersicht der pflaumen. Nach dem jetzigen
standpunkte. Passau, Pustet, 1847.
55 p.

NL 0349839   CU-A

Liegel, Georg.
Vollständige uebersicht aller von dem verfasser kulti-
virten und in verschiedenen werken beschriebenen pflaumen mit ihren charakteren. Von dr. G. Liegel ... Regensburg, G. J. Manz, 1861.
viii, ⟨4⟩, 84 p. 22ᶜᵐ.

1. Plum.
Agr 12-1411

Library, U. S. Dept. of   Agriculture 93L62P

NL 0349840   DNAL

Liegel, Hermann.
Über den ausstülpungs-apparat von *Malachius* und
verwandten formen ... Hannover, Druck von C. L. Schrader ⟨1875⟩
31 p. pl. 21ᶜᵐ.
Inaug.-diss.—Göttingen.

1. Malachius.
8–22988†

Library of Congress   QL596.M2L7

NL 0349841   DLC NIC DNLM

Liegel, Theodor, 1922-
Reichsstadt Regensburg und Klerus im Kampf um ihre
Rechte. München, 1950.
155 l. 30 cm.
Typescript (carbon copy)
Inaug.-Diss.—Munich.
Vita.
Bibliography: leaves 150-154.

1. Ratisbon—Pol. & govt. 2. Justice, Administration of—Ratisbon.
56–46557

NL 0349842   DLC

VOLUME 332

Liegel, Tuisco Achilles.
Die Jesuiten, ihre geschichte, ihre moral und ihre politische wirksamkeit, aus den quellen beleuchtet, von T.A. Liegel ... Hamburg, J.F. Richter, 1872.

132 p. 19½cm.

NL 0349843 MH-L

Liegel, Tuisco Achilles
Kaiser Maximilian I von Mexiko. Erinnerungen aus dem leben eines unglücklichen fürsten. Von T. A. Liegel. Mit den portraits des kaisers Maximilian I und der kaiserin Charlotte. Hamburg, W. Oncken, 1868.

3 p. l., 178 p. double front. (ports.) 18cm.

1. Maximilian, emperor of Mexico, 1832–1867. 2. Mexico—Hist.—European intervention, 1861–1867. 3. Charlotte, empress consort of Maximilian, emperor of Mexico, 1840–1927.

9—10373

Library of Congress   F1233.M458

NL 0349844 DLC CU

Liegelsteiner, Georg.
Wohl fundirter zwerg-baum; oder, Courieuser unterricht wie die zwerg-bäume alle jahr beschnitten, wodurch solche in kurtzer zeit nicht nur in zierlich wachsthum gebracht, sondern auch die früchte vermehret, vergrössert und zu annehmlichem geschmack verbessert werden können ... hrsg. durch Georg Liegelsteiner ... Franckfurt am Mayn, J. M. Bencard, 1702.

7 p. l., 124 p. front., 8 pl. (6 fold.) 16cm.

1. Plant dwarfing.

Agr 13–1390

Library, U. S. Dept. of   Agriculture 90L621

NL 0349845 DNAL

Liegelsteiner, Georg.
Georg Liegelsteiners ... wohl-fundirter zwerg-baum / oder, Curieuser unterricht / wie die zwerg-bäume alle jahr beschnitten / wodurch solche in kurtzer zeit nicht nur in zierlich wachsthum gebracht / sondern auch die früchte vermehret / vergrössert und zu annehmlichen geschmack verbessert werden können ... Regenspurg, J. M. Hagen, 1716.

7 p. l., 120 p. front., 8 pl. (6 fold.) 17cm.

1. Fruit-culture. ₁1. Dwarf fruit trees₁ 2. Pruning.

Agr 28–1143

Library, U. S. Dept. of   Agriculture 93L622

NL 0349846 DNAL CU

Liegelsteiner, Georg.
Wohlerfahrner zwerg-baum-meister / in sich haltend / wie die zwerg-bäume auf neue vortheilhaffte art jährlich künstlich zu beschneiden / wodurch solche in kurtzen zu schönen wachsthum gelangen / nicht weniger die früchte vermehret / vergrossert / und zu lieblich-annehmlichen geschmack gebracht werden können. Imgleichen wie alle wurtzeln und aeste / welche gut oder bös / reifflich zu beobachten / wie ein jeglicher ast genennet / und an dem baum erkennet werde / wie einem verdorbenen ruinirten baum wieder aufzuhelffen /

und in die früchte zu bringen sey / und dann was nutzen von solchen gegen hochwachsenden zu hoffen ... Durch B. ₁L. ₁n. p.₁ 1708.

8 p. l., 111 p. plates (part fold.) 16¼cm.

Reprinted with only slight verbal changes from Liegelsteiner, Georg. Wohl fundirter zwergbaum ... Franckfurt am Mayn, J. M. Bencard, 1702.

1. ₁Dwarf fruit trees₁ 2. Pruning.

Agr 28–1667

Library, U. S. Dept. of   Agriculture 93L622 1703

NL 0349848 DNAL CU

Liegelsteiner, Georg.
... Wohlgezogener zwerg-baum; oder Gründlicher unterricht wie die frantz-bäume gewartet werden müssen, dass selbige bald und gute früchte bringen, und damit grösserer nutzen, als mit hohen bäumen zu schaffen, wobey um der deutlichkeit willen die aeste und deren benennung in kupfern und saubern figuren beygefüget sind, nebst einer besondern vorrede eines erfahrnen gartenliebhabers der selbst dergleichen anweisung vor nöthig und sehr nützlich befunden, ingleichen einem anhang von verbesserung des erdreichs und waldung. Leipzig, W. Deer, 1747.

12 p. l., 15–148, 9 p.   Illus., 2 pl. (1 fold.) 17cm.
1. ₁Plant dwarfing₁   2. Fruit-culture. ₁2. Pomology₁
                                                        Agr 16—976
U. S. Dept. of agr. Library   93L622
for Library of Congress   ₁a41b1₁

NL 0349849 DNAL CU

Liegelsteiner, Georg.
Wohl-untersuchter zwerg-baum.   Frankfurt, 1725.
110 p.

NL 0349850 OCLloyd

Liegener (Albert) [1845–]. * Ueber Hydraunics. 36 pp., 8°. Berlin, G. Lange, [1869].

NL 0349851 DNLM

Liégeois, Auguste Theodore, d. 1871.
——"Anatomie et physiologie des glandes vasculaires sanguines. 72 pp., 2 l., 3 pl. 8°. Paris, A. Delahaye, 1860. Concours.

NL 0349852 DNLM

Liégeois (Auguste-Théodore) [–1871]. De l'emploi des courants électriques continus contre la syncope et les accidents causés par le chloroforme. 19 pp. 8°. Paris. Jannin, 1869.

NL 0349853 DNLM

Liégeois (Auguste-Théodore). * Physiologie du nerf facial. 64 pp. 4°. Paris, 1858, No. 225, v. 621.

NL 0349854 DNLM

QT
L719t
1870
LIÉGEOIS, Auguste Théodore, d. 1871
Traité de physiologie appliquée à la médecine et à la chirurgie. Paris, Masson, 1869-70.
2 v. in 1. illus.

NL 0349855 DNLM PPC PU

Liégeois, Camille.
Gilles de Chin, l'histoire et la légende, par Camille Liégeois. Avec trois tableaux lithographiés. Louvain, Typ. C. Peeters; ₁etc., etc.₁ 1903.

xxiv, 169 p. 3 tab. (2 fold.) 24cm. (On cover: Université de Louvain. Recueil de travaux, pub. par les membres des Conférences d'histoire et de philologie ... 11. fasc.)

"Dissertation doctorale."—Univ. de Louvain. Annuaire. 1904 (p. 246)
"Liste alphabétique des ouvrages cités": p. ₁xiii₁–xxiv.

1. Gilles de Chin, seigneur de Berlaymont, d. 1137.

9—6748

Library of Congress   PQ1463.G6L5

NL 0349856 DLC OC1 PU

Liégeois, Camille.
Le théâtre et éloquence en France et en Belgique. Chrestomathie à l'usage de la classe de première par C. Liégeois ₁et₁ L. Mallinger. Namur, Ad. Wesmael Charlier, 1908.
842 p. O.

NL 0349857 NcD

Liégeois (Charles-Auguste). * Essai critique sur le rôle généralement attribué à l'excès de température dans la pathogénie des symptômes de la fièvre typhoïde. [Nancy.] 95 pp., 1 l. 4°. Paris. 1877.

NL 0349858 DNLM

LIÉGEOIS, CONSTANCE.
Calvaire de femmes [Saint-Gilles, Waldeheim, Cottbus, Ravensbrück, Mauthausen] Ciney, Éditions Marsia [1945] 124 p. 20cm.

1. Concentration camps—Germany. 2. World War, 1939-1945—Prisoners and prisons, German.

NL 0349859 NN CSt-H

Liégeois, Cornélis, 1860-1921? arr.
Plainte ...
see under   Caix d'Hervelois, Louis de, ca. 1670-ca. 1760.

Liégeois, Cornélis, d. 1921?
₁Duos. 2 violoncellos. Op. 9, no. 1–6₁
Six grands duos pour deux violoncelles ... par Cornélis Liégeois. Op. 9 ... Leipzig: J. Rieter-Biedermann, 1895. Publ. pl. no. 2001-2003. 3 v. in 1. 34cm.

Parts only.
CONTENTS.—Cahier 1. No. 1 en ut mineur. No. 2 en la mineur.—Cahier 2. No. 3 en fa majeur. No. 4 en sol mineur.—Cahier 3. No. 5 en la majeur. No. 6 en ré mineur.

1. Violoncello—2 violoncellos—   1800–
N. Y. P. L.   October 13, 1939

NL 0349861 NN

ML
910
.L72
Liégeois, Cornélis, 1860-1921?
Le violoncelle: son histoire, ses virtuoses ₁par₁ C.Liégeois et E.Nogué. Paris, Costallat ₁1913?₁
315 p. illus.
Includes bibliography.

1.Violoncello—Hist. 2.Violinists, violoncellists, etc. I. Nogué, Édouard. Joint author.

NL 0349862 MiU CU ViU NcU

Liégeois, Danielle, 1913–
... Hérédo-syphilis de seconde génération ... ₁Lille, 1939₁
86 p. 24 cm. (Lille. ₁Université₁ Faculté de médecine et de pharmacie. Thèse. 1938/39. no. 31)

1. Syphilis, Congenital₁, hereditary, and infantile₁ I. ₁Series₁
                                                        Med 47–2767
U. S. Army Medical Library   [W4LT2]
for Library of Congress   ₁1₁

NL 0349863 DNLM

VOLUME 332

Liégeois, F
    ... Traité de pathologie médicale des animaux domestiques, par F. Liégeois ... Gembloux, J. Duculot; Paris, Librairie agricole de la maison rustique, 1933.
    725 p. illus., diagrs.   24 cm.

    At head of title: Encyclopédie agronomique & vétérinaire.

    1. Veterinary pathology.

NL   0349864   IaAS

SF   LIÉGEOIS, F
761   Traité de pathologie médicale des
L719t   animaux domestiques. 3. éd., remaniée
1949   et mise à jour. Gembloux, Duculot, 1949.
    xxv, 926 p.   illus. (Encyclopédie
    agronomique et vétérinaire)
    "Ouvrage couronné par l'Académie
    royale de médecine de Belgique. Prix
    Hamoir 1933-1937."
        1. Veterinary medicine

NL   0349865   DNLM PU—V CU MdBP IaAS

Liégeois, F
    Traité de pathologie médicale des animaux domestiques.
    4. éd. Remaniée et mise à jour. Gembloux, J. Duculot, 1955.
    1004 p. illus. 26 cm. (Encyclopédie agronomique et vétérinaire)

    1. Veterinary pathology.   A 56-5997

    Iowa. State Coll. Libr.
    for Library of Congress   (8)

NL   0349866   IaAS IU ICJ

Liégeois, Jean.
    Mort du Frère Liégeois
        see under title

Liégeois, Jules, 1833-1908.
    De l'organisation départementale; ou, Commentaire de la loi du 10 août 1871 sur l'organisation et les attributions des conseils généraux et des commissions départementales, par Jules Liégeois ... Paris, Marescq aîné, 1873.
    160 p. 24½ᵐ.

    "La présente étude ... est extraite textuellement des Répétitions écrites sur le droit administratif, de M. Cabantous."—Avertissement.

    1. Local government—France. 2. Administrative law—France.
    I. Title: Conseils généraux, L'organisation et les attributions des.

    Library of Congress   J84903.L5

                        29-27872

NL   0349868   DLC MiU IU

Liégeois, Jules,   1833-1908.
    De la suggestion et du somnambulisme dans leurs rapports avec la jurisprudence et la médicine légale, par Jules Liégeois ... Paris, O. Doin, 1889.
    3 p. l., vii, 758 p. 18½ᵐ. (Half-title: Bibliothèque des actualités médicales et scientifique, ix (i. e. x))

    1. Hypnotism. 2. Mental suggestion. 3. Medical jurisprudence.

NL   0349869   MiU NIC DNLM MH MdBP PPC CU CtY-M NNC

RA1171
884t   LIÉGEOIS, Jules, 1833-
    De la suggestion hypnotique dans ses rapports avec le droit civil et le droit criminel; mémoire lu à l'Académie des sciences morales & politiques (séances des 5, 19, 26 avril, 3 et 10 mai 1884. Paris, A. Picard, 1884.
    70p. 21cm.
    "Extrait du Compte-rendu de l'Académie des sciences morales et politiques."
    1. Hypnosis. 2. Medical laws and legislation - France.
    I. Title.

NL   0349870   CtY-M DNLM

Liégeois, Jules, 1833-1908.
    Du prêt a intérêt en droit Romain et en droit Français. ... Par Jules Liégeois. ...   Nancy, A. Lepage, 1863.
    251 p.   22 cm.
    Thesis (Ph.D.) - University of Strasburg.

NL   0349871   NcD

Liégeois, Jules, 1833-1908.
    Essai sur l'histoire et la législation de l'usure, par Jules Liégeois ... Paris, A. Durand, 1863.
    3 p. l., 5, 248 p. 22ᵐ.

    1. Interest and usury—Hist. 2. Usury laws—France. 3. Law, Comparative. (3. Comparative law) I. Title.

                        29-23683

NL   0349872   DLC NIC MH-BA MH-L MdBP NN

Liégeois, Jules Joseph
        see   Liégeois, Jules, 1833-1908.

Liégeois, Louis.
    ...Le bavard et l'inconnue, comédie en un acte...
    [Liège, 1941] 16 p.   21cm. (Éditions Pro arte no. 154)

    1. Drama, Belgian-French. I. Title.

NL   0349874   NN

Liégeois, Louis
    On demande une dame de compagnie; comédie en 1 acte, par L. Liégeois...   Paris [etc.] Édition Pro arte, [1937] 12 p. 27cm.

    1. Drama, Belgian-French.   I. Title.
    N.Y.P.L.   February 17, 1941

NL   0349875   NN

Liégeois, Louis.
    ...Petite ficelle! Comédie-vaudeville... [Bruxelles, Remacle & cie, c1948] 99 p. 22cm.

    1. Drama, Belgian-French.   November 15, 1951
    N.Y.P.L.

NL   0349876   NN

Liégeois (Marcel) [1886-   ]. *De l'origine intestinale du poison éclamptique. 107 pp. 8°. Lyon. 1911.

NL   0349877   DNLM

Liégeois, René, 1892-
    ... Les épanchements pleureux puriformes, aseptiques parapneumoniques chez l'enfant ... Lyon, 1920.
    25.5 cm.
    Thèse - Univ. de Lyon.

NL   0349878   CtY

Liégeois, Robert, 1914-
    ... Les formes anormales de contagion de la syphilis ...   Lille, 1938.
    Thèse - Univ. de Lille.

NL   0349879   CtY

PA4409 Lieger, Paulus, 1865-1944.
.L7   ... De epistula Sapphus ... Wien, 1902.
    28 p. 23ᵐ.
    Programm—Ober-gymnasium zu den Schotten, Vienna.

    1. Sappho.

NL   0349879-1   ICU NjP

PA2329 Lieger, Paulus, 1865-1944.
.C8L7   ... J. Cornus beiträge zur lateinischen metrik. Eine kritik und würdigung mit ergänzungen aus dem nachlasse. Wien, Hölder-Pichler-Tempsky, 1927.
    71, (1) p. incl. tables. 22ᵐ.
    Musical illustrations.

    1. Cornu, Jules, 1849-1919. 2. Latin language—Metrics and rhythmics.

NL   0349880   ICU InU OCU NjP

Lieger, Paulus, 1865-1944.
    Quaestiones Sibyllinae; II. Sibylla hebraea. Wien, 1906.

NL   0349881   NjP PU

Lieger, Paulus, 1865-1944.
    Streifzüge ins Gebiet der griechischen Metrik. Mit einem Anhange: Die Cantica in Sophokles' Antigone metrisch analysiert. Wien, The author, 1914.
    110 p.
    Includes musical illustrations.

    1. Greek language—Metrics and rhythmics.
    I. Sophocles. Cantica.

NL   0349882   ICU CU

Lieger, Paulus, 1865-1944.

    Symbolae scotenses. Wissenschaftliche beilage zum Jahresberichte des K. K. Obergymnasiums zu den Schotten in Wien über das schuljahr 1913/1914 ... Wien und Leipzig, C. Fromme, 1914.

Liegey, F
    The fishes of Olean Creek, Cattaraugus Co., New York, by F. Liegey, E. H. Donahue & S. W. Eaton. St. Bonaventure, N. Y., The university, 1955.
    p. 5-25. maps, diagr. 23 cm.

    Extract from Science studies, St. Bonaventure University, v. 17.

NL   0349884   PPAN

VOLUME 332

Liegey, Gabriel Michael, 1904–   joint ed.

Loomis, Roger Sherman, 1887–   ed.
The fight for freedom; college readings in wartime, edited by Roger Sherman Loomis ... and Gabriel M. Liegey ... New York, Farrar & Rinehart, inc., 1943.

Liegey, Gabriel Michael, 1904–

Cicero, Marcus Tullius.
... Cicero's Pro Archia; Latin text and commentary by James F. Brady, jr. ... Gabriel M. Liegey ... ₁and₎ Joseph S. Murphy ... New York, Fordham university press ₁°1940₎

Liegey, Gabriel Michael
The rhetorical aspects of Richard Rolle's Melos contemplativorum. New York ₁c1954₎
vii, 143 l. 29cm.

Thesis, Columbia university.
Typescript.
Bibliography: l. 138–143.

NL 0349887   NNC

Liegey, Gabriel Michael, 1904–
The rhetorical aspects of Richard Rolle's Melos contemplativorum. Ann Arbor, University Microfilms ₁1954₎
(₁University Microfilms, Ann Arbor, Mich.₎ Publication no. 8716)
Microfilm copy of typescript. Positive.
Collation of the original: vii, 143 l.
Thesis—Columbia University.
Abstracted in Dissertation abstracts, v. 14 (1954) no. 9, p. 1396.
Bibliography: leaves 138–143.

1. Rolle, Richard, of Hampole, 1290?–1349. Melos contemplativorum.

Microfilm AC–1   no. 8716   Mic A 54–2048

Columbia Univ.   Libraries
for Library of Congress   ₁1₎†

NL 0349888   NNC LU CtY MiEM DLC

Liégey, N. F.
—— A propos d'un travail intitulé: Note sur les abcès critiques, par J. Ossieur. ₁4 pp., 8°. ₁Rambervillers, M.Grat, 1859.₎

NL 0349889   DNLM

Liégey (N.-F.) Quelques aperçus sur les fièvres pernicieuses. 21 pp. 8°. Épinal, Gley, 1849.
₁F., v. 1348.₎ *Repr. from: Ann. méd. de la Flandre occid., Roulers, 1849, iv.*

NL 0349890   DNLM

Liégey (N.-F.) Singulier cas de mort par strangulation chez un jeune enfant. 4 pp. 8°. ₁Bruxelles, 1864.₎ *Repr. from: J. de méd., chir. et pharmacol., Brux., 1864.*

NL 0349891   DNLM

Liégey (Nicolas). De l'hydropisie ascite. 24 pp. 4°. Paris, 1836, No. 357, v. 305.

NL 0349892   DNLM

LIEGGE, Clayton M.
Thelma; a dramatization of Marie Corelli's novel, ₁in five acts₎.

Typewritten. 4°.

NL 0349893   MH

Lieggi, Vincent.
Study of the pineal gland.
13 p.
Thesis.

NL 0349894   PV

D810
.J4L5
Hebr)

Liegiec, Władysław.
די זעלנער פֿון דער יידישער קאמפס-ארגאניזאציע און זײערע פֿריינד. ₁Warszawa₎ 1953."
31 p. 21 cm.

1. Żydowska Organizacja Bojowa. 2. World War, 1939-1945—Underground movements—Jews. 3. World War, 1939-1945—Underground movements—Poland.
Title transliterated: Di zeiner fun der Yidisher kamfs-organizatsye un zeyere fraynd.

D810.J4L5   58-51129 ‡

NL 0349895   DLC

M459
.G

Liegl, Leopold Joseph, 1899–   arr.

Grieg, Edvard Hagerup, 1843–1907.
₁Peer Gynt (suite no. 1) Aases død, arranged₎

... Ase's death, from "Peer Gynt suite no. 1"; quartet for B ₁i. e., B♭₎ clarinets. ₁By₎ Edvard Grieg, transcribed by Leopold Liegl ... New York, C. Fischer, inc., °1940.

788.6   Liegl, Leopold Joseph
L62b
The Carl Fischer basic method for the clarinet (Albert and Boehm systems)... New York, C. Fischer, °1937.
48p. illus. 31cm.

Publisher's Plate no. 27723-47.

M.1. Clarinet—Instruction and study. M.1.
Title: Basic method   for the clarinet.

NL 0349897   LU

J788.620.7M
L 625 M   Liegl, Leopold Joseph, 1899–
The music educator's basic method for the clarinet (Albert and Boehm systems). New York, C. Fischer ₁°1937₎
48 p. illus. 30ᶜᵐ. (The Music educator)

NL 0349898   OO

Liegl, Leopold Joseph, 1899–   arr.
Sarabande; quartet for B♭ clarinets
see under   Händel, Georg Friedrich, 1685-1759.

Liegle, Josef, 1893–1945.
Euainetos, eine Werkfolge nach Originalen des Staatlichen Münzkabinetts zu Berlin. Berlin, W. de Gruyter, 1941.
64 p. illus., 14 plates. 30 cm. (Winckelmannsprogramm der Archäologischen Gesellschaft zu Berlin, 101)
Includes "Jahresbericht für 1941" (p. 55–56) and "Mitglieder-Verzeichnis (November 1941)" p. 57–64) "Anmerkungen" (bibliographical) : p. 52–53.

1. Coins, Greek. 2. Numismatics—Sicily. 3. Euainetos, fl. 412 B.C. I. Berlin. K. Museen. Münzkabinett.   (Series: Archäologische Gesellschaft zu Berlin. Winckelmannsprogramm, 101)

N5325.A8   Bd. 101   737.4   A 48-4435*
California. Univ. Libr.
for Library of Congress   ₁2₎†

NL 0349900   CU OCU NN MdBP PBm MoU DLC

Liegle, Josef, 1893-1945.
Die Münzprägung Octavians, nach dem Siege von Actium und die augusteische Kunst.
(*In* Deutsches Archäologisches Institut. Jahrbuch. Berlin ₁1943₎ 28 cm. Bd. 56 (1941) p. ₁91₎-119. illus.)

1. Coinage—Rome. 2. Art, Roman.

DE52.D5   Bd. 56   A 54-357
Cincinnati. Univ. Libr.
for Library of Congress   ₁2₎†

NL 0349901   OCU DLC

Liegle, Josef, 1893-1945.
Der Zeus des Phidias. Berlin, Weidmann ₁1952₎
580 p. 85 plates. 22 cm.

1. Phidias, ca. 500-ca. 430 B.C. 2. Zeus. I. Title.

NB100.L53   53-18122 rev

NcD OCU DDO MdBWA PU TxU PBm NcU CSt MiU MU MiDA
NL 0349902   DLC CaBVaU ICU IaU NjP IEN NN NIC CtY NNC

SPEC. COLL.
PT   ₁Liegler, Leopold₎ 1882–
2621   In memoriam Karl Kraus. Wien, Richard
R27Z62   Lányi, 1936.
1936   1 p. l., ₁5₎-13, ₁1₎ p., 1 l. front. (port.) 22cm.

"Diese Arbeit von Leopold Liegler geht zurück auf seinen Nachruf in der Basler National Zeitung von 16. Juni 1936 ..."
"In einer einmaligen numerierten Auflage von 1000 Exemplaren gedruckt von Jahoda & Siegel, Wien. Dieses Exemplar trägt die Nummer 0247."
1.₎ Kraus, Karl,   874-193 . I. Title.

NL 0349903   MU NNC NjP

Liegler, Leopold, 1882–
Karl Kraus und die sprache, von Leopold Liegler. Wien, R. Lányi, 1918.
19, ₁1₎ p. 24ᶜᵐ.

1. Kraus, Karl, 1874-1936.   43-48017

Library of Congress   PT2621.R27Z59

NL 0349904   DLC ICU CU WU ViU CU-AL TxU CLSU

Liegler, Leopold, 1882–
Karl Kraus und sein werk, von Leopold Liegler. Wien, R. Lányi, 1920.
427 p., 4 l. pl., ports., fold. facsim. 28½ᶜᵐ.
"Bibliographie": 3d leaf at end.

1. Kraus, Karl, 1874-1936.   43-39528

Library of Congress   PT2621.R27Z6
₁2₎

TxU NcD IEN
NL 0349905   DLC CaBVaU OrCS ICU CtY MH CU NN MU WaU

VOLUME 332

838   Liegler, Leopold, 1882-
K912Fℓ   Karl Kraus und sein werk. 2.,
        unveränderte aufl.   Wien, Lányi,
Germ.   1933.
        427p. front.,illus.,plate, ports.,facsims.
        0.
        "Die schriften von Karl Kraus": 3d leaf
        at end.

NL   0349906   IaU CU-I IEN MiU

---

*GC9   Liegler, Leopold, 1882-
R4574   Rainer Maria Rilkes xv. Orpheus-Sonett, eine
LSi322   Gedichtanalyse.
        (In Das Silberboot. Salzburg,1946. 23.5
        cm.,in case 25cm. 2.Jahrg.,7.Hft.,p.97-101)
        Ritzer K1559.

NL   0349907   MH

PT1906   Liegler, Leopold, 1882-
.L53   Zwei Aufsätze über Goethes Lyrik. Wien,
        R. Lányi, 1932.
        30p. 21cm.

        1. Goethe, Johann Wolfgang von - Addresses,
        essays, lectures. I. Title: Goethes Lyrik.

NL   0349908   NcU

                    1889-
Liegner, Benno, Aus d. Univ.-Frauenkl. zu Breslau. Zur
Histologie des Carcinoma cervicis uteri. Breslau 1913:
Breslauer Genossensch.-Buchdr. S. 329—363, 1 Taf. 8°
¶ Aus: Beiträge z. Geburtsh. u. Gynäkol. Bd 18.
Breslau, Med. Diss. v. 14. Jan. 1914, Ref. Küstner
[Geb. 26. Febr. 89 Steinau a. O.; Wohnort: Breslau; Staatsangeh.: Preußen;
Vorbildung: Johannes-G. Breslau Reife 07; Studium: Breslau 1, Freiburg 1,
München 1, Breslau 2, München 1, Berlin 1, Breslau 3 S.; Coll. 3. Mai 13;
Approb. 9. Jan. 14.]   [U 14·1570

NL   0349909   ICRL DNLM

Liegnitz, Ger.
    Chronik von Liegnitz
        see under Kraffert, Hermann, b. 1828.

Liegnitz, Ger. Evangelische Gemeinde.
    Privilegirtes allgemeines u. vollständiges
    Gesang-Buch
        see under [Krause, Johathan] comp.

Liegnitz, Germany. Evangelische Gemeinde.
    Die Reformation in Liegnitz
        see under Bahlow, Ferdinand, 1865-

Liegnitz, Ger. Geschichts- und Altertumsverein
    see Geschichts- und Altertumsverein zu Liegnitz.

Liegnitz, Ger.   Handels-kammer.
    Jahres-bericht der Handels-kammer zu Liegnitz
    umfassend die kreise Liegnitz (stadt-und landkreis)
    Bunslau,...
    Liegnitz, 18-

HF308
.L7

NL   0349914   DLC CtY

Liegnitz, Germany. Haupt-Kasse.
    Haupt-Etat.

(Liegnitz,   8°.

1. Municipal finance—Germany—   Liegnitz.
N.Y.P.L.   October 1, 1926

NL   0349915   NN

Liegnitz, Ger. Peter-Paul-Kirchenbibliothek.
    Die Handschriften der Petro-Paulinischen
    Kirchen-Bibliothek ...
        see under Gemoll, Wilhelm, 1850-1934.

Liegnitz, Ger. Peter-Paul-Kirchenbibliothek.
    Katalog der Leichenpredigten-Sammlungen der
    Peter-Paul-Kirchenbibliothek und anderer
    Bibliotheken in Liegnitz. Marktschellenberg,
    Verlag Degener & Co., Inhaber O. Spohr, 1938-
    40.
        viii, 755 p. (Bibliothek familiengeschicht-
    licher Quellen. Bd. 9)

    "Vorwort" signed: Richard Mende.
    Issued in parts.

NL   0349917   NNC DLC-P4 NN TxU MH

Liegnitz, Ger. Ritter-akademie.
    Die musik-handschriften der königl. ritter-akademie zu
    Liegnitz. Verzeichnet von dr. Ernst Pfudel ... (Leipzig,
    Breitkopf & Haertel, 1886-89,
    (8,–74 p. 24½ᶜᵐ. (Musik-handschriften auf öffentlichen bibliotheken.
    Verzeichnet von verschiedenen. Herausgegeben von Robert Eitner. 1.
    bd.)
        Caption title.
    "Beilage zu den Monatsheften für musikgeschichte (1886, 1889,"
        1. Music—Bibl.—Manuscripts. 2. Manuscripts—Germany—Catalogs.
    I. Pfudel, Ernst. II. Monatshefte für musikgeschichte. Supplement.

Library of Congress   ML135.L5R5
                                            5-19876

NL   0349918   DLC NcD MiU

Liegnitz, Ger. Ritter-akademie.
    Quaestionum Tullianarum specimen
        see under Keil, Oswald Theodor.

Liegnitz, Ger. (Regierungsbezirk)
    Amtsblatt der Regierung zu Liegnitz.
    Jahrg.

18

Liegnitz(, 18   sq. 8° and sq. 4°.
    Weekly.
    Title varies slightly.
    Some of the volumes include its: Oeffentlicher Anzeiger and other Beilagen.

NL   0349920   NN

                                            K=10
                                            1070
                                            No. 1
LIEGNITZ, Ger. (Regierungsbezirk)
    De-population of the Legnica regency. Memorial of
    the German president of regency of September 15th,
    1938, IC9 no.4278. Pref. and commentaries by
    Józef Kobot. Revealed and translated from the original,
    copy no. 1256 by Józef Zaremba and Irene Kubat.
    Poznań) Zahodnia agencja prasowa, 1947.   27 p.
    diagrs. 25cm. (German testimonies. no. 1.)

        Caption title.

    1. Liegnitz, Germany—Population. I. Series. II. Kokot, Józef, ed.
    t. 1947.

NL   0349922   NN

Liegnitz, Ger. (Regierungsbezirk) Ordinances, etc.
    Die baupolizeilichen Vorschriften im Regierungs-Bezirk Liegnitz.
    Zusammengestellt von Otto Kotze, ... Zweite vermehrte
    Auflage. Berlin, A. W. Hayn's Erben, 1905.
        viii, 326 p. illus. 22½ᶜᵐ.

NL   0349923   ICJ NN

Liegnitz (Germany) (Regierungsbezirk) Ordinances, etc.
    Baupolizeiverordnung für das platte Land des Regierungsbe-
    zirk Liegnitz.   Berlin: A. W. Hayn's Erben, 1910.   43(1) p.
    Half clo. 8°.

    1. Building construction.—Juris-   prudence, Germany: Liegnitz.
    N.Y.P.L.   August 28, 1916.

NL   0349924   NN

Liegnitz (Germany)(Regierungsbezirk) Ordinances, etc
    Die Polizeigesetze und Verordnungen des Regierungsbezirks
    Liegnitz.) Bearbeitet von Otto Kotze... (Hayn'sche Samm-
    lung der Polizei-Verordnungen und polizeilichen Vorschriften der
    Regierungsbezirke der östlichen Provinzen der preussischen Mo-
    narchie.)

        Bd. 1.

    Bd. 2. Teil I. Enthaltend die Verordnungen über I. Die Organisation, Ge-
    schäfte und Zuständigkeit der Polizei. II. Sicherheitspolizei. III. Sitten- und Ord-
    nungspolizei. IV. Baupolizei. V. Feuerpolizei. VI. Gewerbepolizei. VII. Ge-
    sindepolizei. Berlin: A. W. Hayn's Erben, 1906. xv(i), 232 p. clo. 8°.
    Bd. 2, Teil 2. Enthaltend die Verordnungen über VIII. Gesundheitspolizei.
    IX. Veterinär- (Viehseuchen-) Polizei. X. Verkehrspolizei. XI. Deich und Wasser-
    polizei. XII. Landwirtschafts- (Feld-), Forst- und Jagdpolizei. XIII. Fischerei-
    polizei. id. 1906. xviii p., 1 l., 287 p. clo. 8°.
    Bd. 2, Teil 3. Enthaltend die Verordnungen über Bergwerkspolizei. id.
    (1906?) vi p., 1 l., 96 p. clo. 8°.

    1. Municipal charters and ordinances,   Germany: Liegnitz. 2. Kotze, Otto.
    3. Series.
    N.Y.P.L.   September 26, 1916.

NL   0349926   NN

Liegnitz, Ger (Regierungsbezirk) Ordinances, etc.   379·1443 R101
    Verordnungen betreffend das Schulwesen des Regierungsbezirks
    Liegnitz./ Aus amtlichen Quellen zusammengestellt und herausge-
    geben von C. Altenburg, ... Dritte Bearbeitung. Breslau, F.
    Hirt, 1911.
        xxxi, 892 p. incl. tables, diagrs. 22ᶜᵐ.

NL   0349927   ICJ

Liegnitzer Gesangbuch. 1752.
    see [Krause, Johathan] comp.
    Privilegirtes allgemeines u. vollständiges
    Gesang-Buch.

VOLUME 332

941.5942
Q001

Liegnitzer Koch-Buch; die besten Recepte für den bürgerlichen Mittagstisch nebst einer gediegenen Auswahl von Recepten und Anleitungen über die Bereitung von Backwerk, über das Einmachen der Früchte und die Herstellung kalter und warmer Getränke, nebst einem Anhang, eine Anzahl praktischer Winke enthaltend. Liegnitz, H. Preiser [1900]

viii, 247 p. 21ᶜᵐ.

Page 247 printed on lining-paper.

NL 0349929   ICJ

Liegnitzer tageblatt.
Kriegs-tagebuch, geschichte des weltkrieges 1914, zusammengestellt aus den berichten des Liegnitzer tageblattes ... Liegnitz, H. Krumbhaar ₁1914–17₎

1482 p. illus. (incl. ports., maps) pl. 23½ᶜᵐ.

Issued in 29 parts.
Cover-title, pt. 1, 3–4: Kriegs-tagebuch, geschichte des weltkrieges 1914; pt. 2, 5–16: Kriegs-tagebuch, geschichte des weltkrieges 1914/15; pt. 17–27: Kriegs-tagebuch, geschichte des weltkrieges 1914/16; pt. 28–29: Kriegs-tagebuch, geschichte des weltkrieges 1914/17.

1. European war, 1914–1918.   I. Title.

29–8894

Library of Congress   D521.L5

NL 0349930   DLC

DS777
.53
.M2542F35
1970

Fang, Yao.
(Hsin min chu chu i ti ko ming) 新民主義的革命与前途 ₁方耀 丁宗恩 列熙寇著 n. p. 北社 1940₎

Lieh, Yü-k'ou, joint author.

Lieh, Yü-k'ou, *4th cent. B. C.*
see
Lieh-tzŭ, *4th cent. B. C.*

Lieh-Tsze
see Lao Tsŭ.
[Not to be confused with Lieh-tzu, 4th cent., B. C.]

Lieh-tsze, *4th cent. B.C.*
see
Lieh-tzŭ, *4th cent. B. C.*

Lieh-tzŭ, *4th cent. B. C.*
列子 選註者唐敬杲 ₁上海₎ 商務印書館 ₁1926₎

2, 10, 1, 1, 101 p. 19 cm. (學生國學叢書 Student's Chinese classics series)

Added colophon title: Selections from Lieh Tse, with introduction and notes by Tang Ching Kao.
本書以上海涵芬樓景印寉氏鐵琴銅劍樓藏北宋刊本為底本

1. Philosophy, Chinese.   I. T'ang, Ching-kao, ed.
Title romanized: Lieh-tzŭ.

B128.L5A3   C 67–3159

NL 0349935   DLC CaBVaU

BL1940
.L5A24
1884b
Orien
China

Lieh-tzŭ, *4th cent. B. C.*
列子冲虛至德眞經 ₁8 卷 張湛注 臺北 藝文印書館 195–₎

126 p. 19 cm.

Photo-offset from 光緒甲申 (1884) 翻刻清黃丕烈藏宋本

₁I. Chang, Chan, 4th cent., ed.   II. Title.   III. Title: Ch'ung hsū chih tē chēn ching.
Title romanized: Lieh-tzŭ.

BL1940.L5A24   1884b   C 67–632

NL 0349936   DLC

Lieh-tzŭ, *4th cent. B. C.*
Der naturalismus bei den alten Chinesen, sowohl nach der seite des pantheismus als des sensualismus; oder, Die sämmtlichen werke des philosophen Licius, zum ersten male vollständig übersetzt und erklärt von Ernst Faber ... Elberfeld, R. L. Friderichs; ₁etc., etc.₎ 1877.

xxvii, 228 p. 24ᶜᵐ.

1. Philosophy, Chinese.   I. Faber, Ernst, 1839–1899, ed. and tr.
II. Title.

Library of Congress   B128.L52G43   39–21955

NL 0349937   DLC ICU OC1 ICU NcD NIC NjP MSaE MdBP

Lieh-tzŭ, *4th cent., B. C.*
... Taoist teachings from the book of Lieh Tzŭ; tr. from the Chinese, with introduction and notes, by Lionel Giles ... London, J. Murray, 1912.

121, ₁1₎ p. 17 cm. (*Half-title:* The wisdom of the East series ed. by L. Cranmer-Byng ₁and₎ Dr. S. A. Kapadia)
At head of title: Wisdom of the East.

I. Giles, Lionel, 1875–   tr.   II. Title.

BL1900.L5G5   CA 14—275 D

NL 0349938   DNW V1U NN DLC MH-AH PP ICJ MSaE OCU ScU OO ODW PSC

Lieh-Tzŭ, 4th cent. B.C.
...Taoist teachings from the book of Lieh Tzŭ, tr. from the Chinese, with introduction and notes, by Lionel Giles... London, Murray, 1925.
121 p. 17ᶜᵐ. (Wisdom of the East...)

1. Taosim.   I. Giles, Lionel, 1875– tr.

NL 0349939   NjP OrP HU WaPS PU PHC MH NN

Lieh Tzu 4th cent. B.C.
...Taoist teachings from the book of Lieh Tzu; tr. from the Chinese....London, Murray[1939]
121 p. 17cm. (Half-title: The wisdom of the East series, ed. by L. Cranmer-Byng [and] Dr. S.A. Kapadia)

NL 0349940   OU TNJ-R

B
923
.506

Lieh-Tzŭ, 4th cent., B.C.
Taoist teachings from the book of Lieh tzŭ, translated from the Chinese, with introduction and notes by Lionel Giles. ₁2d ed.₎ London, J. Murray₁1947₎
121p. 17cm. (The Wisdom of the East series)

NL 0349941   CaQMM NBC AAP CaBVaU ICN NNC IEN IaU MiU ICU KU WaU AU IdU OU

BL
1900
.L5
W5

Lieh-tsu, 4th cent. B. C.
Das wahre Buch vom quellenden Urgrund 'Tschung hū dschen ging'; die Lehren der Philosophen Liä Yū kou und Yang Dschu. Aus dem chinesischen verdeutscht und erläutert von Richard Wilhelm. Jena, E. Diederichs, 1911.
174 p. illus. 22cm. (Die Religion und Philosophie Chinas, 3: Taoismus und Sekten, Bd. 8, 1. Halbband)
Added t. p. in Chinese

I. Wilhelm, Richard, 1873–1930; ed. and tr.
II. Title.

NL 0349942   WU CLU OC1 NIC MH NN CaBVaU

B
1021
.L 627

LIEH-TZŬ, 4th cent., B.C.
Liä dsi, das wahre Buch vom quellenden Urgrund, Tschung hū dschen ging. Die Lehren der philosophen Liä yū kou und Yang dschu. Aus dem Chinesischen verdeutscht und erläutert von Richard Wilhelm. Jena, E. Diederichs₁c1921₎
xxxiii,174p. fold.pl.,port. 21cm.

NL 0349943   ICN MH NcGU ArU TNJ-R ICU

181.1
L623c03

LIEH-TZŬ, 4th century B.C.
Das wahre buch vom quellenden urgrund (Tschung hū dschen ging) Die lehren der philosophen Liä Yu Kou und Yang Dschu. Aus dem chinesischen verdeutscht und erläutert von Richard Wilhelm. ₁3. aufl.₎ Jena, E. Diederichs ₁c1921₎
xxxiii, 174 p. illus., plates (1 fold.) ports., facsims.

Added title-page in Chinese (facsimile)

Published also as v.8, pt.1 of Religion und philosophie Chinas.
Translation of Ch'ung hsū chen ching.

1. Philosophy, Chinese.   I. Yang, Chu, 4th century B.C.   II. Wilhelm, Richard, 1873–1930.   III. Title.   IV. Title: Tschung hū dschen ging.

NL 0349945   WaU PU NIC IEN

299.51
L623G

Lieh-Tzu, 4th cent., B.C.
Liä Dsi. Das wahre buch vom quellenden urgrund Tschung Hü Dschen Ging, die lehren der philosophen Liä Yü Kou und Yang Dschu. Aus dem chinesischen verdeutscht und erläutert von Richard Wilhelm. ₁3. aufl.₎ Jena, E. Diederich ₁pref. 1936₎
xxxiii, 174 p. pl., port. 22cm.

I. Wilhelm, Richard, 1873–1930, tr. II.   Title.

NL 0349946   MnU InU

₁Lieh-tzu₎ 4th cent. B. C.

Liä Dsi. Das wahre buch vom quellenden urgrund Tschung Hü Dschen Ging. Die lehren der philosophen Liä Yü Kou und Yang Dschu. Aus dem chinesischen verdeutscht und erläutert von Richard Wilhelm. Jena, Eugen Diederichs ₁1937₎
xxxiii p., 1 l., 175 p. fold. illus., 21cm. ₁Die religion und philosophie Chines, bd. 8, heft. 1₎

Title in ornamental border.
Added title-page in Chinese.
First edition 1911.
Dritten aufl., 1936. cf. Verword.

NL 0349948   NcD CtY

VOLUME 332

Lieh-wei
  see
  Lévi, Sylvain, 1863-1935.

(Lieh-ning ch'ing nien)
列寧青年 第1- 卷 (第1- 期) 1928 年
10月22日1—
[上海]
  v. 19 cm.
  Frequency varies.
  Supersedes 無産青年
  Title varies: May 1, 1929— 青年雜誌—
青年 半月刊— 青年
旬刊
  Superseded by 青年實話 1932.
  1. Communism—China—Periodicals.   I. Title: Ch'ing nien tsa
chih. II. Title: Ch'ing   nien pan yüeh k'an. III. Title:
Ch'ing nien hsün k'an.
HX9.C5L5   70-842267
                                                    Õ

NL 0349950   DLC

Liehburg, Max Eduard, 1899-
  ...Bachs Passionen; zwei sakrale Dramen, nebst einer Be-
trachtung: Von der Dramatik des Dramas und vom Drama der
Dramatik. Zürich: Orell Füssli[, 1930]. 118 p. illus. (plan.)
8°.
  Includes libretto, in German, of the St. John and St. Matthew Passions.

489398A. 1. Bach, Johann Sebastian,   JUILLIARD FOUNDATION FUND.
music. I. Title.   1685-1750—Passions. 2. Passion
N. Y. P. L.   September 11, 1930

NL 0349951   NN

Liehburg, Max Eduard.
  ...Christus, ein sakrales Spiel.   Zürich: Orell Füssli Verlag[, cop. 1928].   64 p.   8°.

409617A. 1. Drama, German.   2. Jesus Christ—Drama. 3. Title.
N. Y. P. L.   May 9, 1929

NL 0349952   NN OC1W

Liehburg, Max Eduard, 1899-
  ... Frauen. Zürich und Leipzig, Rascher & cie. [1934]
186 p. 22½cm.
  Poems.

1. Women in poetry.   I. Title.
                                            A C 35-868
Title from N. Y. Pub.   Libr. Printed by L. C.

NL 0349953   NN

Liehburg, Max Eduard, 1899-
  ...Hüter der Mitte.   Zürich [etc.] Rascher & Cie. A.-G./Ver-
lag [1934] 117 p. 22cm.

813167A. 1. Drama, Swiss-German.   I. Title.
N. Y. P. L.   July 15, 1936

NL 0349954   NN

Liehburg, Max Eduard, 1899-
  ... Das neue Weltbild. Zürich und Leipzig,
O. Füssli[c1932]
  63,[1]p. 22½cm.

NL 0349955   CtY

LIEHBURG, MAX EDUARD, 1899-
  ...Rolf... [Bd.] 1—   Zürich [etc.] Orell Füssli
[1932]—   v. 22½cm.
  Poems.

1. Poetry, German. I. Title.

NL 0349956   NN

LIEHBURG, MAX EDUARD, 1899-
  Schach um Europa; europäisches Drama.   Zürich,
Orell Füssli [c1930] 180 p. 23cm.

1. Drama, Swiss-German.   I. Title.

NL 0349957   NN

Liehenie, Gotthard
  see Lihnie, Gotthard, 1738-1789.

LIEHL, Otto.
  Der umfang der zeugenpflicht der presse und
der zeugniszwang gegen die presse im straf-
und disziplinarverfahren.   Freiburg i. Br.,
1908.
  Inaug.-diss.—Freiburg.

NL 0349959   MH-L NN

LIEHL, OTTO.
  Der Umfang der Zeugenpflicht der Presse und der
Zeugniszwang gegen die Presse im Straf- und Diszplin-
arverfahren. Freiburg i. Br., 1908. v, 108 p. 23cm.

  Film reproduction. Positive.
  Inaug.-Diss.—Freiburg i. Br.
  Bibliography. p. [iii]-v.

1. Press—Jurisp.—Germany,   1908. 2. Press, Liberty of—
Germany.

NL 0349960   NN

PF 3853 LIEHL, ROBERT, 1890-
  .L719   Mittelvokale und Mittelvokallosigkeit vor
          m, n, l und r in den ältesten altsächsischen
          und althochdeutschen Sprachdenkmälern. Frei-
          burg i. B., 1913.
            87 p.
            Inaug.-Diss.—Freiburg i. B.
            Lebenslauf.
          1. German language—Old High German—Vowels.
          2. Old Saxon langu age—Vowels. I. Tc.

NL 0349961   InU MH TxU PU ICRL

---

*
M1
.8444 Liehmann, Jos
v.27
no.11   Die Unermüdlichen. Drei Polka für das
         Pianoforte. Prag, Joh. Hoffmann [18—?]
           Pl. no. 466, 475, 476.
           7 p. 34cm. [Sheet music collection, v. 27,
           no. 11]
           CONTENTS.—Budweiser Polka.—Pilsner Polka.—
         Prachimer Polka.
           Polka titles given also in Czech, on cover.
           1. Polkas (Piano). I. Title. II. Title:
         Budweiser Polka. III. Title: Pilsner Polka.
         IV. Title: Prachimer Polka.

NL 0349962   ViU

---

*
.8444 Liehmann, Jos
v.27
no.19   Veilchen-Kränze. Drei Polka für das
         Pianoforte 24tes Werk. Prag, Berra &
         Hoffmann [18—?] Pl. no. 1773, 1774, 1775.
           7 p. 34cm. [Sheet music collection, v. 27,
           no. 19]
           CONTENTS.—Graciosa Polka.—Giganten Polka.—
         Milostenka Polka.
           1. Polkas (Piano) I. Title. II. Title:
         Graciosa Polka. III. Title: Giganten Polka.
         IV. Title: Milost   enka Polka.

NL 0349963   ViU

Liehmann (Josephus Guil.) *Diss. sistens no-
sographiam pimelotici, adjecta simul epicrisi de
pimelosi in genere, et methodo secundum Le Roy
Gallum drastica. 37 pp., 1 l. 8°. Praga, J. vid.
Vetteri, [1836].

NL 0349964   DNLM

Liehr, Alfons, 1908-
  Dauerschäden und sportliche leistungsfähigkeit
nach infektionskrankheiten. ... Breslau, 1936.
  21 p.
    Inaug. Diss. - Breslau, 1936.
    Lebenslauf.
    Literaturverzeichnis.

NL 0349965   CtY

                                        HU 90.6798.5
Liehr, Andrew David
  The interaction of vibrational and electronic motions
in some simple conjugated hydrocarbons

  Thesis - Harvard, 1955

NL 0349966   MH

Liehr (Ernst Wilhelm Albert) [1876-
  *Ueber einen Fall von sympathischer Oph-
thalmie. 33 pp. 8°. Kiel, H. Fiencke, 1905.

NL 0349967   DNLM ICRL CtY MH

Liehr, Gerda, 1899-
  Die struma congenita und ihr einfluss auf die
koerperlaenge der neugeborenen.
    Inaug. diss. - Freiburg, 1927. (Neisse)
    Bibl.

NL 0349968   ICRL CtY

Liehr, Hans Günther, 1903-
  Konkurrierendes und kollidierendes handeln des
vertreters und des vertretenen oder mehrerer
vertreter
    Inaug. Diss. Breslau, 19-
    Bibl.

NL 0349968-1   ICRL

Liehr, Heinrich, 1902-
  Die arbeitsproduktivitaet.
    Inaug. diss. Jena [1929]

NL 0349969   ICRL PU MH CtY MiU

VOLUME 332

Liehr (Hugo). "Kasuistischer Beitrag zur Kenntniss der Sclerodermie. 24 pp. 8°. Erlangen, Junge & Sohn, 1886.

NL 0349970 DNLM

Liehr, Oskar, joint author.

Haselhoff, Emil, 1862–
Der gehalt der bodenluft an kohlensäure. Von E. Haselhoff und O. Liehr.
Landw. vers. stat. bd. 102, p. 60–72.   Berlin, 1924.

LIEHR, Oskar, 1889–
Ist die angenommene verwandtschaft der Helobiae und Polycarpicae auch in ihrer cytologie zu erkennen? Inaug.-Diss. Breslau, R. Nischkowsky, 1916.
86 p. 4 plates.

"Lebenslauf", at end.

NL 0349972 MH ICRL

Liehr, Oskar, joint author.

Haselhoff, Emil, 1862–
Untersuchungen über die biochemische beschaffenheit eines bodens bei verschiedener organischer düngung. Von E. Haselhoff und O. Liehr.
Landw. vers. stat. bd. 102, p. 43–59.   Berlin, 1924.

Liehr, Oskar, 1889– joint author

Haselhoff, Emil.
Versuche mit rhenaniaphosphat. Von E. Hasselhoff und O. Liehr.
Landw. vers. stat. bd. 100, p. 21–30.   Berlin, 1922.

Liehr, Oskar, 1889– joint author.
Versuche mit stickstoffdüngern
see under Haselhoff, Emil.

Liehr, Walter, 1900–
... Über eine Fieberbehandlung der progressiven Paralyse mit einem unspezifischen Reizmittel. ... Neisse, 1925.
Inaug.-Diss. - Freiburg.
Lebenslauf.
"Literatur-Verzeichnis": p. 33–35.

NL 0349976 CtY ICRL

Liehr, Willibald, ed.

Law

Austria. *Laws, statutes, etc.*
Das österreichische Polizeirecht, mit einschlägigen Vorschriften und erläuternden Bemerkungen, sowie einem Sachverzeichnis; hrsg. von Willibald Liehr [und] Albert Markovics. Wien, Manz, 1949–

Liehr, Willibald.
Das österreichische und ausländische Staatsbürgerschaftsrecht. Wien, O. Höfels [1950]
v. 21 cm. (Fachbücherei des Standesbeamten, Bd. 1
Includes legislation.
Bibliography: v. 1, p. 8.
CONTENTS.—1. T. Das österreichische Staatsbürgerschaftsrecht.

1. Citizenship—Austria.   I. Austria. Laws, statutes, etc.
II. Title.
Library of Congress   [1]   52–27104

NL 0349978 ICU DLC

Liehrmann, *née* Colson (Joséphine-Victorine) [1858–]. "Contribution à l'étude de la pathogénie et du traitement de la phlegmatia alba dolens puerpérale. 103 pp. 4°. Paris, 1896.

NL 0349979 DNLM

W
L722b
1842
LIEHRSCH, Bernhard
Bilder des ärztlichen Lebens; oder, Die wahre Lebenspolitik des Arztes für alle Verhältnisse vom Beginn seiner Vorbildung bis zu Ende seines Wirkens. Berlin, Liebmann, 1842.
viii, 216 p.

NL 0349980 DNLM

Liek, Frau Anna, ed.

Liek, Erwin Gustav, 1878–1935.
Am kamin; Aus der sandgrube und andere erinnerungen, von Erwin Liek. München, J. F. Lehmann [*1935]

R117
.L48
1942
Liek, Erwin Gustav, 1878–1935.
... Gedanken eines arztes, eine auswahl aus den beiden werken Die welt des arztes und Im bannkreis des arztes; aus 30 jahren praxis. 3. aufl. Berlin, O. Arnold, 1942.

Liek, Edna B., joint author.

Whitford, William Garrison, 1886–
... Art stories ... by William G. Whitford, Edna B. Liek and William S. Gray.
Chicago, Atlanta [etc.] Scott, Foresman and company [*1933–

Liek, Edna B., joint author.

Gray, William Scott, 1885–
... Teacher's guidebook for the Elson basic readers ...
by William S. Gray and Edna B. Liek. Chicago, Atlanta [etc.] Scott, Foresman and company [*19

Liek, Edna B., joint author.

Gray, William Scott, 1885–
... Teacher's guidebook for the Elson-Gray basic readers ...
by William S. Gray and Edna B. Liek ... Chicago, Atlanta [etc.] Scott, Foresman and company [*1937–

Liek, Erwin Gustav, 1878–1935.

Klussmann, Walther, 1889–   *comp.*
Das ärztebüchlein; eine sammlung besinnlicher worte für die feierstunde des arztes, zugleich ein ratgeber für die tägliche praxis, unter mitbenutzung hinterlassener aufzeichnungen Erwin Lieks, von Walther Klussmann ... Mit einem geleitwort von prof. dr. Klare ... Leipzig, Georg Thieme, 1937.

WZ
310
L719a
1933
LIEK, Erwin Gustav, 1878–1935
Ἡ ἀγυρτεία ἐν τῇ Ἰατρικῇ, ἐκ τοῦ συγγράμματος "Ὁ ἰατρὸς καὶ ἡ ἀποστολή του," μετάφρασις Κων. Α. Ἀλεξανδροπούλου. Ἀθῆναι, 1933.
46. p. (Βιβλιοθήκη "Ἰατρικῶν χρονικῶν," ἀρ. 1)   WZ310 L719a
Title transliterated: Hē agyrteia en tē iatrikē.

NL 0350002 DNLM

Liek, Erwin Gustav, 1878–1935.
Am kamin; Aus der sandgrube und andere erinnerungen, von Erwin Liek. München, J. F. Lehmann [*1935]
128 p. front. (port.) plates. 19cm.
Vorwort signed: Anna Liek.
Anhang: Erwin Liek; aus seinem leben und wirken, von Hugo Holthöfer.—Erwin Liek; ein deutscher arzt und sein lebenswerk, von Heinz Bottenberg.—Nachruf auf Erwin Liek, von Walter Ziesemer.

I. Liek, Frau Anna, ed.   II. Title.
Library of Congress   35–35706
Copyright A—Foreign   29298
                                               926.1

NL 0350003 DLC ICU NN ViU NNC DNLM

Liek, Erwin Gustav, 1878– 1935.
... Arzt und bodenreform, von dr. med. Erwin Liek ... Berlin, Bodenreform g. m. b. h., 1927.
14 p. 22cm. (Soziale zeitfragen ... hrsg. von A. Damaschke, hft. 86)

1. Housing—Germany. 2. Physicians—Germany. 3. Hygiene, Public.
I. Title.
Library of Congress   HD655.S6 hft. 86   30–8752

NL 0350004 DLC

Liek, Erwin Gustav
Der arzt und seine sendung; gedanken eines ketzers, von Erwin Liek ... München, J. F. Lehmann [1926]
132 p. 22½cm.
"Schrifttum": p. 130–132.

1. Physicians. 2. Medicine—Practice.   I. Title.
Library of Congress   R707.L5   27–1460

NL 0350005 DLC CtY NNC

R707
.L7
Liek, Erwin Gustav, 1878–1935.
Der arzt und seine sendung; gedanken eines ketzers, von Erwin Liek... 2. aufl. ... München, J. F. Lehmann, 1926.
140 p. 23cm.
"Schrifttum": p.137–140.

1. Physicians. 2. Medicine—Practice.

NL 0350006 ICU

Liek, Erwin Gustav, 1878–
Der arzt und seine sendung; gedanken eines ketzers, von Erwin Liek ... 4. aufl. (10.–15. tausend) München, J. F. Lehmann, 1927.
174 p. 23cm.
"Schrifttum": p. 171–174.

1. Physicians. 2. Medicine—Practice.   I. Title.
Library of Congress   R707.L5 1927   27–22316

NL 0350007 DLC ICRL

VOLUME 332

Liek, Erwin Gustav, 1878–   **610.4 L624**
  Der Arzt und seine Sendung, von Erwin Liek ... Fünfte Auflage (16.–21. Tausend). München, J. F. Lehmann, 1927.
  182 p. 23ᶜᵐ.
  Cover-title: Der Arzt und seine Sendung. Gedanken eines Ketzers.
  "Schrifttum," p. 179–182.
  Contents.—1. Die ersten Zweifel.—2. Die klinischen Semester.—3. Die erste Praxis.—4. Die Assistentenjahre.—5. Arzt und Kranker.—6. Ärzte und sociale Versicherungen.—7. Arzt und Rassenhygiene.—8. Arzt, Technik und Wissenschaft.—9. Der heutige Wissenschaftsbetrieb.—10. Fachärzte und Krankenhäuser.—11. Kurpfuscherei.—Schlussbetrachtung.

NL 0350008   ICJ ICRL OC1W

W 9   LIEK, Erwin Gustav, 1878–1935
L719a   Der Arzt und seine Sendung. 6. Aufl.
1927   München, Lehmann, 1927.
    195 p.
    1. Medicine - Addresses, essays, lectures

NL 0350009   DNLM NBuU

W 9   LIEK, Erwin Gustav, 1878–1935
L719a   Der Arzt und seine Sendung. 10. Aufl.
1928a München, Lehmann [c1928]
    254 p.

NL 0350010   DNLM

LIEK, ERWIN GUSTAV, 1878–
  Der Arzt und seine Sendung, von Erwin Liek... Achte Auflage... München: J. F. Lehmann, 1931. 214 p. 23cm.

  "Schrifttum," p. [207]–214.

772705A. 1. Medicine—Practice.

NL 0350011   NN MH

W9   Liek, Erwin Gustav, 1878–1935
L719a   Der Arzt und seine Sendung. 9. Aufl.
1934   München, Lehmann, 1934.
    254 p.

    Bibliography: p. [245]–254.
    Mutilated copy.

    1. Medicine - Addresses, essays, lectures

NL 0350012   DNLM

    B–20846
    Cat. A
Liek, Erwin Gustav, 1878–1935.
  Die Basedowsche Krankheit. München, O. Gmelin, 1929.
  38p. (Sammlung diagnostisch-therapeutischer Abhandlungen für den praktischen Arzt, Hft.31)

NL 0350013   ICRL MiDW

W 1   LIEK, Erwin Gustav, 1878–1935
SA456   Chirurgisch wichtige Erkrankungen der
Heft 45 Niere. München, Gmelin, 1933.
    44 p. (Sammlung diagnostisch-therapeutischer Abhandlungen für den praktischen Arzt, Heft 45)
    1. Kidneys - Diseases 2. Kidneys - Surgery   Series

NL 0350014   DNLM

Liek, Erwin Gustav, 1878– 1935.
  The doctor's mission; reflections, reminiscences and revelations of a medical man, by Dr. Erwin Liek ... translated and introduced by J. Ellis Barker. London, J. Murray [1930]
  xxxix, 276 p. 19ᶜᵐ.

  1. Physicians. 2. Medicine—Practice. ɪ. Barker, J. Ellis, 1870– tr. ɪɪ. Title.

  Library of Congress   R707.L53   31–4165
                                  926.1

  CaBVaU
NL 0350015   DLC ICJ ICRL DNLM OC1 OC1W PPC CtY-M

R710 Liek, Erwin, 1878–1935.
L62   ... Gedanken eines arztes; eine auswahl aus den beiden werken: Die welt des arztes und Im bannkreis des arztes. Aus 30 jahren praxis. Dresden, Reissner, 1937.
    254 p. 21ᶜᵐ.

    Vorwort signed: Anna Liek.
    "Erwin Liek zum gedächtnis, von dr. Werner Zabel": p. 242–254.

NL 0350016   NNC

Liek, Erwin Gustav, 1878–1935.
  ... Gedanken eines arztes, eine auswahl aus den beiden werken Die welt des arztes und Im bannkreis des arztes; aus 30 jahren praxis. 3. aufl. Berlin, O. Arnold, 1942.
  254 p. 20ᶜᵐ.
  At head of title: Erwin Liek.
  "Vorwort der herausgeberin" signed: Anna Liek.
  "Erwin Liek zum gedächtnis, von dr. Werner Zabel": p. 242–254.

  1. Medicine—Addresses, essays, lectures. ɪ. Zabel, Werner. ɪɪ. Liek, Anna, ed. ɪɪɪ. Title.

  Library of Congress   R117.L48 1942   46–38156
                                  610.4

NL 0350017   DLC

W 9   LIEK, Erwin Gustav, 1878–1935
L719g   Gedanken eines Arztes; aus 30 Jahren
1949   Praxis. 4. Aufl. Berlin, Arnold, 1949.
    254 p.
    A selection from the author's Die Welt des Arztes and Im Bannkreis des Arztes.
    1. Medicine - Addresses, essays, lectures

NL 0350018   DNLM

Liek, Erwin Gustav, 1878–1935.
  Im bannkreis des arztes, aus dem nachlass von Erwin Liek. Dresden, Carl Reissner verlag, 1935.
  166 p. 21ᶜᵐ.

  1. Medicine—Addresses, essays, lectures. ɪ. Title.

                                  8 G 37–63
  U. S. Surg.-gen. off. Library
  for Library of Congress   [R117]

NL 0350019   DI-GS NN

Liek, Erwin Gustav, 1878–
  Irrwege der chirurgie; kritische streifzüge von Erwin Liek ... München, J. F. Lehmann, 1929.
  235 p. illus. 22½ᶜᵐ.
  "Schrifttum": p. 71–73.
  Contents.—Ueber pseudoappendizitis, insbesondere über das krankheitsbild des nervösen darmspasmus.—Ueber die chronischreidivierende appendizitis.—Misserfolge nach gallensteinoperationen.—Irrwege der chirurgie.—Sollen wir den senkmagen operieren?—Zur Basedowfrage.—Die entstehung der heilkunde.—Kritische bemerkungen zur heutigen sympathikuschirurgie.—Mechanisches und funktionelles denken in der chirurgie.—Anatomische abweichungen im bereich der unteren wirbelsäule.—Schlussbetrachtung.
  1. Surgery—Addresses, essays, lectures. 2. Appendicitis. ɪ. Title.
  Library of Congress   RD14.L6   29–17558
                            3367

NL 0350020   DLC CtY-M ICJ DNLM OkU

Liek, Erwin Gustav, 1878–
  Der kampf gegen den krebs, von Erwin Liek ... München, J. F. Lehmann, 1934.
  222 p. 23ᶜᵐ.

  1. Cancer.

  Library of Congress   RC261.L7   34–29723
                                616.994

NL 0350021   DLC DNLM ICJ

Liek, Erwin Gustav, 1878–
  Krebsverbreitung, krebsbekämpfung, krebsverhütung, von Erwin Liek ... München, J. F. Lehmann, 1932.
  252 p. 22½ᶜᵐ.

  1. Cancer.

                                  33–18009
  Library of Congress   RC261.L73   616.994

NL 0350022   DLC ICRL DNLM MnU PPC

Liek, Erwin Gustav
  ... Das Kropfrätsel. München, O. Gmelin, 1929.
  53 p. (At head of t.-p: Sammlung diagnostischtherapeutischer Abhandlungen für den praktischen Arzt, hft. 30.)

NL 0350023   MiDW ICRL

W 9   LIEK, Erwin Gustav, 1878–1935
L719a   Lékař a jeho poslání. Přel. Marie
1928   Dolejší. V Praze, Kočí, 1928.
    168 p.
    Translation of Der Arzt und seine Sendung.

NL 0350024   DNLM

Liek, Erwin Gustav, 1878–1935.
  ... Les méfaits des assurances sociales en Allemagne et les moyens d'y remédier. Préface de M. le professeur Georges Weiss ... Traduction française par Raoul Lantzenberg ... Edgard Lantzenberg ... Paris, Payot, 1929.
  2 p. l., [7]–219, [1] p. 22½ᶜᵐ. (Bibliothèque politique et économique)
  "Bibliographie": p. [209]–212.
  "Bibliographie française": p. [213]–217.

  1. Insurance, Health—Germany. 2. [Insurance, Social—Germany] ɪ. Lantzenberg, Raoul, tr. ɪɪ. Lantzenberg, Edgard, joint tr. ɪɪɪ. Title.
                                 L 29—80
  U. S. Dept. of labor. Libr   HD7179.L6
    —Copy 2. for Library of Congress [a42c1]

NL 0350025   DL CU

R708 Liek, Erwin Gustav, 1878–1935.
933L   Il Miracolo in Medicina. Tr. di T. Oliaro.
    1.ed. italiana sulla 2. tedesca. Torino, Minerva Medica, 1933.
    200p. 19cm.

    1. Medicine - Addresses, essays, lectures.

NL 0350026   CtY-M

Liek, Erwin Gustav, 1878–
  Rakbetegseg, rakgyogyitas, rakmegelozes. [Budapest] Cserepfalvi kiadas, [c1936]
  177 [2]p.

  Forditotta es atdolgozta: Dr. Totis Bela.
  Hungarian.

NL 0350027   OC1

VOLUME 332

LIEK, ERWIN GUSTAV, 1878–
Die Schäden der sozialen Versicherungen und Wege
zur Besserung. München, J.F. Lehmann, 1927.
84 p. 23cm.

1. Insurance, Workmen's — Germany.

NL 0350028 NN

Liek, Erwin Gustav, 1878–1935.
Die Schäden der sozialen Versicherungen und Wege zur
Besserung. 2., stark verm. Aufl. München, J. F. Lehmann,
1928.
118 p. 23 cm.
"Schrifttum": p. [117]–118.

1. Insurance, Social—Germany. I. Title.

HD7179.L54 1928 49–40149*

NL 0350029 DLC

Liek, Erwin Gustav, 1878–1935.
Soziale Versicherungen und Volksgesundheit. Langensalza, H. Beyer, 1929.
66 p. 21 cm. (Schriften zur politischen Bildung. 7. Reihe: Volkstum, Heft 9)
Pädagogisches Magazin, Heft 1278.

1. Insurance, Social. I. Series. II. Series: Pädagogisches Magazin, Heft 1278.

HD7091.L55 331.2544 48–31041*

NL 0350030 DLC PU-W MH

RD47
L62   Liek, Erwin, 1878–1935.
1912   Studienreise eines deutschen chirurgen nach
den Vereinigten Staaten. Nach einem vortrag im
Aerztlichen verein zu Danzig am 18. april 1912.
[Berlin, Urban & Schwarzenberg, 1912]
15 p.

"Sonderabdruck aus Medizinische klinik, 1912
nr. 32, 34, 36."

1. Surgery – Addresses, essays, lectures.
2. Surgery – History United States.

NL 0350031 NNC-M

Liek, Erwin, 1878–
Ueber den einfluss der arteriellen hyperaemie auf die
regeneration.
Inaug. diss. Koenigsberg, 1902. (Berlin)

NL 0350032 ICRL DNLM MH CtY

Liek, Erwin Gustav.
Die Welt des Arztes; aus 30 Jahren Praxis, by Erwin Liek.
Dresden: Carl Reissner [cop. 1933] 242 p. 12°.

1. Medical profession. 2. Title.
July 1, 1936

NL 0350033 NN DNLM OLak

RM921
.L47   Liek, Erwin Gustav, 1878–1935.
1930
Das Wunder in der Heilkunde. München,
J. F. Lehmann, 1930.
208 p. diagrs. 20 cm.

1. Medicine. 2. Therapeutics, Suggestive.
3. Miracles. I. Title.

NL 0350034 ViU CLU

Liek, Erwin Gustav.
Das Wunder in der Heilkunde. [by] Erwin Liek-Danzig.
München: J. F. Lehmanns, 1931[, cop. 1930]. 208 p. illus.
2. ed. 12°.

1. Medical profession. 2. Title.
December 28, 1932

NL 0350035 NN NNUT MH NBC DNLM CSt NBuU PPC

Liek, Erwin Gustav, 1878–1935.
Das wunder in der heilkunde, von Erwin Liek ... 3. aufl.,
21.–24. tausend. München, J. F. Lehmann, 1936.
247 p. 19½ᵐ.
"Vorwort des herausgebers" signed: Dr. Hugo Holthöfer.

1. Medicine. 2. Therapeutics, Suggestive. 3. Miracles. I. Holthöfer,
Hugo, 1883– ed. II. Title.
38–25037

Library of Congress RM921.L47 1936
615.851

NL 0350036 DLC

WB
885   LIEK, Erwin Gustav, 1878–1935
L719w   Das Wunder in der Heilkunde. 4. Aufl.
1951   Stuttgart, Marquardt, 1951.
196 p.
1. Mental healing

NL 0350037 DNLM NN

Liek, Erwin Gustav, 1878– 1935.
... Die zukünftige entwicklung der heilkunde, von Erwin
Liek ... Stuttgart, F. Frommann (H. Kurtz) [1931]
31 p. 20ᵐ. (Zeichen der zeit, heft 3)

1. Medicine—[Condition and progress of] I. Title.
8 G 32–66

[Li]brary, U. S. Surgeon- General's Office

NL 0350038 DI-GS DNLM

Liek, Gerhard, 1908–
... Ein Beitrag zur Erforschung angeborener
Sarkome ... Göttingen, 1936.
Inaug. -Diss. - Göttingen.
Lebenslauf.
"Schrifttum": p. 10–11.

NL 0350039 CtY

Halle, 55   Liek, Gustav,   ed.
Festwünsche für Schule und Haus. Mit
Original-Beiträgen von H.Frischbier,Hedwig
Gaede,G.Hilde,Marie Jhering,Charlotte Krug
geb. Schnorr von Carolsfeld,Auguste Kurs,
Marie Mindermann,H.J.Rättig und K.L.Stein.
Gesammelt und hrsg. von Gustav Liek. Leipzig,
A.Krüger,1876.
2p.ℓ.,92p. 18cm

1. German poetry - Collections. I. Title.

NL 0350040 CtY

Liek, Gustav.   Ger 39.8 (25–29)
Die stadt Löbau in Westpreussen mit berücksichtigung des
landes Löbau. Marienwerder, R. Kanter, 1892 [1890–92].
pp. viii, 640. Plans, and seal.
"25.–29. heft der *Zeitschrift des Hist. ver. für den reg.-bes. Marienwerder.*" Published in 5 pts. Title-pages of pt.[1–4 retained.

NL 0350041 MH

Liek, Walter.
Der Anteil des Judentums am Zusammenbruche Deutsch-
lands, von Dr. Walter Liek... Jubiläums-Ausgabe... Mün-
chen: J. F. Lehmann [1919]. 16 p. 8°.
Cover-title.
"Flugblatt aus 'Deutschlands Erneuerung'..."

1. European war, 1914– , Jews.   2. European war, 1914– , Germany.
3. Jews in Germany.
December 11, 1919.

NL 0350042 NN OCH CSt-H MH

Liek, Walter.
Der deutsche Arbeiter und das Judentum, von Dr. Walter
Liek... München: J. F. Lehmann, 1920. 32 p. 22½cm.
Cover-title.
"Flugblatt aus 'Deutschlands Erneuerung.'"

678430A. 1. Labor—Germany.   2. Jews in Germany—Anti-
Semitic writings. I. Deutschlands   Erneuerung.
Erneuerung.   November 16, 1933.

NL 0350043 NN NcD IEdS CSt-H NNJ

Liek-Danzig, Erwin.
See
Liek, Erwin Gustav, 1878–1935

[Rare Bk.
Coll.]   Лѣкарство отъ праздности и скуки; или, Забавное пре-
провожденіе празднаго времяни угадывать накартахъ все,
что мы ни пожелаемъ. 1. тисненіемъ. Въ Москвѣ, Въ
Тип. А. Рѣшетникова, 1790.
vi, 52 p. illus. 17 cm.

1. Fortune-telling by cards. *Title transliterated:* Lěkarstvo ot prazdnosti i skuki.

BF1876.L5   55–51160

NL 0350045 DLC

Liekefett, Heinrich.
Eigenschaften und integraldarstellungen
der Bessel'schen U(x) und ihre beziehungen zu
den Bessel'schen funktionen nach Nielsen.
Zürich, 1915.
54 p. diagrs.
Inaug-Diss. - Bern.

NL 0350046 IU ICRL RPB CtY

BQV110
L719   [Liekefett, Samuel Gottfried] 1750–1827,
1791   supposed author.
Geschichte des römischen, canonischen und
teutschen Rechts zu Vorlesungen] Leipzig,
Adam Friedrich Böhme, 1791.
[12] 324 [14] p.

Robbins   Attribution of author by dealer; unverified.
Coll.

1. Canon law - History. 2. Roman law -
History. 3. Germany - History of law. I. Title.

NL 0350047 CU-L

4K   [Liekefett, Samuel Gottfried] 1750
Roman   -1827.
216   Kurze theoretisch- praktische
Erläuterung der Pandekten, nach dem
Hellfeldischen Lehrbuch mit Rücksicht
auf die Abweichungen der Königl.
Preussischen und Chursächsischen Gesetze zum Gebrauch bey den Vorlesungen über die Pandekten und auf Gymnasien vom Verfasser des Handbuchs
des bürgerlichen Rechts in Teutschland.

Continued in next column

VOLUME 332

Continued from preceding column

Leipzig, C. G. Rabenhorst, 1797
-1800.
      7 v.

    Vol 1 has added t. p.:Geschichte
des Römischen Rechts als Einleitung
zu den Vorlesungen
über die Pandekten.

NL 0350049   DLC-P4

Liekefett, Samuel Gottfried, 1750-1827.
    Praktischer commentar über die Pandekten nach dem lehrbuch des herrn grr. Hellfeld ... Leipzig, A. F. Böhme, 1796-1804.
    15 v. 20ᵐ.

    1. Roman law. 2. Civil law.   I. Corpus juris civilis. Digesta. II. Hellfeld, Johann August, 1717-1782. III. Title.

40-30902

NL 0350050   DLC

HX8
.I9

Liekens, Enrique, ed.

Izquierdas.   Periódico de acción.

México, 1934-

Liekens, Enrique.
    Los zapotecas no son zapotecas sino zâes; ensayo etimológico y semántico de la voz zâ.   Villahermosa, 1952.
    34 p. 20 cm.   (Publicaciones del Gobierno del Estado, 79)

    "Conferencia sustentada por el autor en la Agrupación Cultural de Acción Social el día 7 de diciembre de 1947 y en la Sociedad Mexicana de Geografía y Estadística el 17 de febrero de 1948."

    1. Zapotec Indians.   I. Title.   (Series: Tabasco, Mexico. Publicaciones del Gobierno del Estado, 79)

F1221.Z3L5   75-210216

NL 0350052   DLC MH

Liekens, Lodewijk, 1867-
    Hoe de stedemaagd Arscota hare plaats vond onder de zon. Eene historische fantasie over het ontstaan van de stad en het land van Aarschot. Heist-op-den-Berg, Gedrukt bij L. Liekens-van Steen, 1942.
    104 p. maps. 18 cm.

    1. Aarschot, Belgium—Hist. 2. Aarschot, Belgium—Antiq. I. Title.
DH811.A2L5   A F 48-3460*
Stanford Univ. Library
for Library of Congress

NL 0350053   CSt NN DLC

Liekens Gaxiola, César L
    La empresa de participación estatal, sociedades de economía mixta. México, 1955.
    110 p. 24 cm.

    Tesis profesional—Universidad Nacional Autónoma de México.

    1. Corporations, Government—Mexico. 2. Corporations, Government. I. Title.
                                57-21742 ‡

Library of Congress

NL 0350054   DLC MH-L

Liekens Gaxiola, Enrique.
    El estudio de las relaciones internacionales. México, 1954.
    85 p. 23 cm.

    Tesis profesional—Universidad Nacional Autónoma de México. Includes bibliography.

    1. International relations.

JX1395.L48   59-46755 rev ‡

NL 0350055   DLC MH-L

Lieker-Wentzlau, Hanna.
    Elsa Brandstrom-dank; ein deutsches frauenbuch, hrsg. von Hanna Lieker-Wentzlau.   Leipzig, M. Koch, 1932.

    70 p. illus. 21cm.

    1. Brändström, Elsa, 1888-

NL 0350056   MnU

Hitler
coll.

Lieker-Wentzlau, Hanna, ed.
    Elsa Brändström-Dank. Neue erweiterte Ausgabe. Eilenburg, Kommissionsverlag Bruno Beckers Buchhandlung, 1935.

    142 p. illus. fold. map.

    Special binding and dedication page.

NL 0350057   DLC

Lieker-Wentzlau, Hanna, ed.
    Elsa Brändström-dank, herausgegeben von Hanna Lieker-Wentzlau. Berlin, Säemann-verlag [1938]
    151, [1] p. front., illus. (facsims.) plates, ports., fold. map. 24½ᵐ.
    "5. erweiterte auflage 1938."
    By various authors.

    1. Brändström, Elsa, 1888-   2. European war, 1914-1918—Hospitals, charities, etc. 3. Red cross.   I. Title.
Library of Congress   D630.B7L5 1938   39-18720
Copyright A—Foreign   42584
                                   923.643

NL 0350058   DLC

Lieker-Wentzlau, Hanna, ed.
    Elsa Brändström dank. [7. aufl.] Berlin, Heliand-verlag [1942]
    151 p. illus., ports., fold. map.

    By various authors.

    1. Brändström, Elsa, 1888-   2. European war, 1914-1918 - Hospitals, charities, etc. 3. Red cross.

NL 0350059   NNC

Liekker, Carl Heinz, 1904-
    ... Ein Beitrag zur Frage der Erblichkeit der Luxatio coxae congenita und der Subluxation der Hüfte ... Springe, 1932.
    Inaug.-Diss. - Berlin.
    Lebenslauf.
    "Literatur": p. [18]

NL 0350060   CtY

Lieknis, Edvarts, 1883-1940
    ...Bikeris; dsejoli ar W. Eglischa preekschwahrdu. [Rigā: J. Kruhmiņis, pref. 1907.] 91 p. 16°.
    Author's pseud., Wirsa, at head of title.

    1. Poetry (Lettish). 2. Title.
                             September 30, 1924

NL 0350061   NN

LIEKNIS, EDVARTS, 1883-1940.
    Biķeris. Dsejoļi ar W. Eglischa preekschwahrdu. [Rigā] Imanta apgands [pref. 1907] 91 p. 17cm.

    Film reproduction. Positive.
    At head of title: Wirsa [pseud.]

    1. Poetry, Lettish. I. Title.

NL 0350062   NN

Hvd48
1
L623

Lieknis, Edvarts, 1883-1940
    Dievi un zemnieki; poema. [Osnabrück] Daile [1947] 46p. port. 13cm.
    Author's pseud., Edvarts Virza, at head of title.

NL 0350063   CtY

Lieknis, Edvarts, 1883-1940.
    ...Dieviškigās rotaļas; dzejoļi.   Rigā: A. Gulbis, 1936. 243 p. 20½cm.
    Author's pseud., Ed. Virza, at head of title.

    925112A. 1. Poetry, Lettish.   I. Title.   April 20, 1938

NL 0350064   NN

Lieknis, Edvarts, 1883-
    ...Dzejas; dzejoļu izlase. [Rigā] Izdevnieciba p./s. "Zemnieka domas," 1935. 301 p. 20½cm.
    Author's pseud., Ed. Virza, at head of title.

    925111A. 1. Poetry, Lettish.   June 9, 1938

NL 0350065   NN

Lieknis, Edvarts, 1883-
    ...Dzejas un poēmas.   Rigā: A. Gulbis, 1933. 156 p. 19½cm.
    Author's pseud., Ed. Virza, at head of title.

    785152A. 1. Poetry, Lettish. I. Title.
                         January 31, 1936

NL 0350066   NN

Lieknis, Edvarts, 1883-
    Frančanu renesanses lirika. Atdzejojis Edvarts Virza [pseud.]. Rigā: A. Gulbis, 1930. 319 p. ports. 8°.
    Added t.-p. in French.

    555519A. 1. Poetry, French—   Collections. I. Title.
                               February 10, 1932

NL 0350067   NN

PG9048
L48H4
1922

Lieknis, Edvarts, 1883-1940.
    Hercogs Jēkabs [Edvarta Virzas poema. Rigā?] Daile [1922]
    58 p. illus. 14 cm.

    1. Jēkabs, Duke of Courland, 1610-1682 - Poetry. I. Title.

NL 0350068   OU

VOLUME 332

₍Lieknis, Edvarts₎ 1883–1940.
Hercogs Jēkabs; Edvarta Virzas ₍pseud.₎ poema. ₍Rīgā₎
Zelta ābele, 1937. 58 p. incl. plates. illus. 17cm.

1. Poetry, Lettish. I. Title.

September 25, 1940

NL 0350069 NN

Lieknis, Edvarts, 1883–

Die Himmelsleiter ₍von₎ Fduard Virza ₍einzig berechtigte Uber-
tragung aus dem Lettischen von Willi Stöppler₎ Leipzig: Paul
List ₍cop. 1935₎ 320 p. 12°.

NL 0350070 NN

₍Lieknis, Edvarts₎ 1883–
...Jaunā junda. Rīgā: Valtera un Rapas akc. sab. apgāds,
1936. 216 p. 19½cm.

Author's pseud., Ed. Virza, at head of title.

1. Latvia, 20th cent. 2. Youth—		Latvia.

December 5, 1938

NL 0350071 NN

Lieknis, Edvarts, 1883–1940.
Karalis Nameitis; poēma. ₍n. p.₎ Jaunā vārda apgāds,
1946.
74 p. 21 cm.
Author's pseud., Edvarts Virza, at head of title.

ɪ. Title.

PG9048.L5K3						56–56871 ‡

NL 0350072 DLC CtY NIC

PG9048   Lieknis, Edvarts, 1883–1940.
L5K3   Karals Nameitis un citas poemas. [Stockholm] Z. Abele,
1947   1947.
         95 p. (Universalā biblioteka. Nr. 6)
         Author's pseud., Edvarts Virza, at head of title.

NL 0350073 CU OCl

Lieknis, Edvarts, 1883–1940.
Kārlis Ulmanis. Rīgā, Zemnieka domas, 1935.
276 p. illus., ports. 20 cm.
At head of title: Ed. Virza.

1. Ulmanis, Kārlis, Pres. Latvia, 1877–1940?

DK511.L168U46					68–47974

NL 0350074 DLC

DK   Lieknis, Edvarts, 1883–1940.
511   Karlis Ulmanis; monografija. Kopenhagena,
L168U43 Imanta, 1955.
         208 p. illus., ports.
         At head of title: Edvards Vizra.

1.Ulmanis, Karlis, Pres. Latvia, 1877–1940.

NL 0350075 CLU OCl CtY NN CU

₍Lieknis, Edvarts₎ 1883–
...Laikmeta dokumenti.   Rīgā: Paju sab. "Zemnieka
domas" apgādienā, 1930.   376 p.   8°.

Author's pseud., Ed. Virza, at head of title.

556977A. 1. Essays, Lettish.

February 2, 1932

NL 0350076 NN

Lieknis, Edvarts, 1883–1940.
Laikmets un lira; dzejoļu izlase. ₍Sakārtojis Jānis
Rudzītis. Vesterozā, Ziemeļblāzma, 1949.
190 p. illus. 17 cm.
Author's pseud., Ed. Virza, at head of title.

ɪ. Title.

PG9048.L5A6 1949					58–40431 ‡

NL 0350077 DLC MiD NN NNC TCle

₍Lieknis, Edvarts₎ 1883–1940.
... La littérature lettone depuis l'époque du réveil national.
₍Braine-l'Alleud, Impr. R. Berger, 1926₎
1 p. L, 53 p. 23ᶜᵐ.
Author's pseud., Ed. Virza, at head of title.
"Edité par la Section de la presse du Ministère des affaires étran-
gères, Riga, (Lettonie)"

1. Lettish literature—Hist. & crit. 2. Latvia—Bio-bibl.   ɪ. Latvia.
Ārlietu ministrija. Preses nodaļa. ɪɪ. Title.

Library of Congress		PG9005.L5		28–8406 Revised

NL 0350078 DLC MB NN CtY

Lieknis, Edvarts, 1883–1940.
Pirmais Latvijas nacionalo karaspēku virspavēlnieks
pulkvedis Oskars Kalpaks. Meiranos, Pulkveža Kalpaka
pieminekļa komiteja ₍1927₎
69 p. illus. 23 cm.
Author's pseud., Ed. Virza, at head of title.

1. Kalpaks, Oskars, 1882–1919.

U55.K3L5						63–56666 ‡

NL 0350079 DLC

LIEKNIS, EDVARTS, 1883–1940.
Sarakstīšanās ar Edvartu Virzu [pseud.] un Viktoru
Eglīti; vēstules.   Kopenhagenā, Imanta, 1954.
131 p. ports. 23cm.

At head of title: Valdemārs Dambergs.

1. Letters, Lettish. I. Eglītis, Viktors, 1877–1945. II. Dambergs, Valdemārs, 1886–   , ed.

NL 0350080 NN CtY OCl MH

Lieknis, Edvarts, 1883–1940.
Straumehni; eines alten semgallischen Gehöftes Jahreslauf
₍von₎ Ed. Virza ₍pseud. Übertragung aus dem Lettischen
von Willi Stöppler₎ Riga, Verlag "Zemnieka Domas," 1934.
329 p. illus. 21 cm.

ɪ. Title.

PG9048.L5S85					52–45587 ‡

NL 0350081 DLC

LIEKNIS, EDVARTS, 1883–1940.
Straumeni; la vie d'une antique ferme lettone à
travers les saisons. Poème [par] Edvarts Virza [pseud.]
Préf. et traduction de Aia Bertrand. Paris, Édition
de l'Akademia R. Duncan [1938, c1939] 287 p. 22cm.

1. Fiction, Lettish. I. Title.

NL 0350082 NN ICU

₍Lieknis, Edvarts₎ 1883–
...Straumēni; vecā Zemgales māja gada gaitās. Poēma.
₍Trešais iespiedums.   Rīgā: Valtera un Rapas akc. sab., 1936.
357 p.   19½cm.

Author's pseud., Ed. Virza, at head of title.

25083A. 1. Zemgale, Latvia.

April 22, 1938

NL 0350083 NN OCl

Lieknis, Edvarts, 1883–1940.
Straumēni; vecā Zemgales māja gada gaitās;
poēma. Augsburgā, Pūrs, 1946.
253 ₍1₎ p. illus.

NL 0350084 MiD

Lieknis, Edvarts, 1883–1940.
Straumēni; veca Zemgales māja gada gaitās, poēma.
₍Stockholm₎ Z. Abele, 1946.
354 p. 13 cm.
Author's pseud., Edvarta Virza, at head of title.

ɪ. Title.

PG9048.L5S8						55–22625

NL 0350085 DLC

Hvd48   Lieknis, Edvarts, 1883–1940
L62   Straumēni. Vecā Zemgales māja gada gaitās.
S6   Poēma. (Hamburg) Ausma [195–?]
        253p. 15cm.
        Author's pseud.,Ed.Virza, at head of title.

NL 0350086 CtY

Lieknis, Edvarts, 1883–1940.
Straumēni; vecā Zemgales māja gada gaitās, poēma.
[New York] Grāmatu Draugs [195–?]
282 p.

Author's pseud., Ed. Virza, at head of title.

NL 0350087 CU

Lieknis, Edvarts, 1883–1940.
Страумен; жизнь стараго латышскаго хутора. Переводъ В. Т. Рīгā, М. Didkovska izdevnieciba, 1939.
279 p. 21 cm.
Author's pseud., Эд. Вирза, at head of title.

ɪ. Title.			*Title transliterated: Straumeni.*

PG9048.L5S88					56–52940 ‡

NL 0350088 DLC

₍Lieknis, Edvarts₎ 1883–   *comp.*
Z. A. Meierovics, Latvijas pirmā ārlietu ministra darbības
atcerei veltīts rakstu krājums. Sakopojis Ed. Virza ₍pseud.₎
Rīgā, Z. A. Meierovica piemiņas fonda izdevums, 1935.
479 p. front., plates, ports. 24½ᵐ.

1. Meierovics, Zigfrīds Anna, 1887–1925.			38–24065

Library of Congress		DK511.L168M45

								923.2474

NL 0350089 DLC

₍Lieknis, Edvarts₎ 1883–
...Zaļā Zemgale; tēlojumi.   Rīgā: Lapsenes izdevums ₍192–₎
120 p.   17½cm.

Author's pseud., Edvarts Virza, at head of title.

789296A. 1. Latvia—Descr. and			trav.

November 25, 1936

NL 0350090 NN

VOLUME 332

⌐Lieknis, Edvarts⌐ 1883– 1940
...Zem karoga. ⌐Rīgā⌐ "Pagalms," 1935. 511 p. 20cm.
Author's pseud., Ed. Virza, at head of title.

925072A. 1. Latvia.

June 9, 1938

NL 0350091 NN

KD1334 Liekweg, Friedrich Wilhelm, 1907–
.I2H3 Handelsgebräuche, Einheitsbedingungen und
1954 Schiedsgerichte. 2. verb., ergänzte und erweiter
te Aufl. Hannover, A. Strothe ⌐1954⌐
48 p. ("ED"-Schriftenreihe zur Nachwuchsschu-
lung, Heft 1)

1. Law merchant--Germany.

NL 0350092 ICU

Liekweg, Friedrich Wilhelm, 1907–
Die rückwirkungsmöglichkeiten von
tarifverträgen ... Göttingen, 1931. 46 p.
Inaug. Diss. -Göttingen, 1931.
Lebenslauf.
Bibliography.

NL 0350093 ICRL MiU

W 4 LIEL, Elisabeth von, 1913–
M96 Die "hellen Zellen" im menschlichen
1951 Endometrium. ⌐München⌐ 1951.
30 ℓ. illus.
Inaug.-Diss. - Munich.
Typewritten copy.
1. Endometrium

NL 0350094 DNLM

Liel, Wilhelmine.
Gegen eine voluntaristische Begründung der Werttheorie. 3605.293
(In Untersuchungen zur Gegenstandstheorie und Psychologie . . .
Pp. 527–578. Leipzig. 1904.)

G7168 — Utilitarianism. — Will. — Value.

NL 0350095 MB

Liel, Wilhelmine, joint author.
Die verschobene schachbrettfigur
see under Benussi, Vittorio.

Lieżczewska, Maria.
O podstawy geograficzne polski z 16 mapkami.
Poznan, Wydawnictwo Instytutu Zachodniego, 1946.
146 p.

NL 0350097 OC1

Lielegg, Andreas, 1830–
Die spektralanalyse. Erklärung der spektralerschei-
nungen und deren anwendung für wissenschaftliche und
praktische zwecke, mit berücksichtigung der zu ihrem
verständnisse wichtigen physikalischen lehren in leicht
fasslicher weise dargestellt von Andreas Lielegg ... Weimar, B. F. Voigt, 1867.
viii, 99 p. illus., double col. pl., diagrs. 22cm.

1. Spectrum analysis.

Library of Congress   QC451.L71   4-31242†

NL 0350099 DLC MCM ViU

⌐Lomb
*
Q311 Lielegg, Andreas, 1830–
.L65
v.5,
no.1   Über das Spectrum der Bessemerflamme.
⌐n. p., 1867?⌐
153–161 p. 38cm. ⌐With Brücke, Ernst. Über
asymmetrische Strahlenbrechung im menschlichen
Auge. ⌐n. p., 1868⌐⌐
⌐Lomb miscellaneous pamphlets, v. 5, no. 1⌐
Caption title.
Detached from Sitzungsb. d. k. Akad. d. w. math.
naturw. cl. LV. Bd. II. Abth.
1. Optics, Physical. I. Title.

NL 0350100 ViU

Lielegg, Andreas, 1830–
Ueber die anwendung der spectralanalyse für den
Bessemerprocess; von Andreas Lielegg ... ⌐Augsburg,
Buchdr. der J. G. Cotta'schen buchhandlung, 1868⌐
12 p. fold. diagr. 21½cm.
Besonderer abdruck aus Dingler's polytechn. journal, bd. CLXXXVII
s. 390, erstes märzheft 1868.

1. Spectrum analysis. 2. Bessemer process.

9-4697†

Library of Congress   QD133.L72

NL 0350101 DLC

WBI LIELENIEWSKI, Michal
L718w Wody lekarskie szczawnickie. Kraków,
1852 1852.
vii, 127 p. illus.

NL 0350102 DNLM

Lielens, Georgette.
Marie-Louise Henin, héroïne de la résistance... ⌐Bruxelles,
n. d.⌐ 31 p. illus. 19cm.

1. Henin, Marie Louise, 1898–   1944. 2. World war, 1939–1945—
Free and resistance movements,   Belgian.

NL 0350103 NN

Lielgalvis, K
Siernieciba. Rīgā, Lauksaimniecïbas pārvaldes izdevums,
1930.
480 p. illus. 23 cm.

1. Cheese. I. Title.

SF271.L5   59-57748 ‡

NL 0350104 DLC NN

RC182
.P8L5
1930 Lielie, Ralph Dougall
...Psithacoisis: rickettsia-like inclusions
in man and in experimental animals...
Washington, 1930
1 pam. 8°

NL 0350105 DLC

W 4 LIELL, Anton, 1913–
B71 Zur Ätiologie des postoperativen
1941 paralytischen Ileus. Bonn, Brand,
1941.
28 p.
Cover title.
Inaug.-Diss. - Bonn.
1. Intestines - Obstruction

NL 0350106 DNLM

Liell (Edward Nicholas). Double pyosalpinx
evacuating through the uterus; curettage, followed by pregnancy and delivery of a living
child at term. 6 pp. 8°. New York, 1896.
Repr. from: Am. Gynec. & Obst. J., N. Y., 1896, vi.

NL 0350107 DNLM

NB9070 Liell, H f Jos.
.L7   Die darstellungen der allerseligsten Jungfrau und Gottes-
gebärerin Maria auf den kunstdenkmälern der katakomben.
Dogmen- und kunstgeschichtlich bearb. von H. F. Jos. Liell ...
Freiburg i. B., Herder, 1887.
xix, 410 p. front., illus., plates (part col.) 23cm.
"Titel der gebrauchten archäologischen werke": p. ⌐xiii⌐-xv.

1. Mary, Virgin—Art. 2. Catacombs.

NRCR InU InStme IU IEG
NL 0350108 ICU CU ICN IMunS CtY DDO MH MB NjP CLU

Lielland, Else Christie.
The human figure: the development from the
Egyptian to the Greek way of presenting it in
paintings, drawings, and relief. ... ⌐Oslo⌐
Aschehoug ⌐1947⌐
29 p.

NL 0350109 OCU

Lielmanis, Jānis.
...Kā nodrošināt mūsu laukaugu ražas? Rīgā: Lauksaim-
niecïbas pārvaldes izdevums, 1934. 84 p. 22½cm.
"Pielikums. Priv. doc. P. Konrāds. Zāļāju izveidošana tirumu zemēs", p. 75–84.

856704A. 1. Insurance, Crop—Latvia.   I. Konrads, Pēteris. II. Latvia.
Lauksaimniecïbas pārvalde.   November 6, 1936

NL 0350110 NN

Lielmanis, Jānis.
... Sēlekcijas un izmēģinājumu darbi valsts Stendes sēlekcijas stacijā 1923.–1928. Travaux de sélection et essais entre-
pris par la Station de sélection d'état à Stende. Rīgā ⌐Grāmatu
spiestuves kooper. "Grāmatrūpnieks"⌐ 1931.
289 p., 2 l. incl. illus., tables. 26cm.
At head of title: Agr. J. Lielmanis, agr. E. Bērziņš, agr. J. Garbars.
"Lauksaimniecïbas pārvaldes izdevums."
Caption titles and table headings in Latvian and French; résumés
in French.
1. Agricultural experiment stations—Latvia. 2. Agriculture—Latvia.
I. Stende, Latvia. Valsts sēlekcijas stacijā. II. Bērziņš, Emils, joint
author. III. Garbars, Juris, joint author. IV. Latvia. Lauksaimniecïbas
pārvalde. V. Title.

Library of Congress   S242.L3L5   33-38413
630.72

NL 0350111 DLC NN

Lielmetius, Livius.
Extremvm ivdicivm D. Livii Lielmetii ... In
algam. Monostichon ... Vincentiae [Apud Perinum
bibliopolam] 1585.
[22] p. 21.5 cm.

NL 0350112 CtY

---

*IC5 Lielmetius, Livius.
L6237 Sacra idyllia d. Iduij Lielmetij patauini
593s ...
Vincentiae, apud Georgium Grecum. CIↃ. IↃ. XCIII.
4°. 12 numb. ℓ. 23cm.
Papal arms (Clement VIII) on t.-p.

NL 0350113 MH

VOLUME 332

Liem, Bun Hwat
Recept-batik. Pekalongan, Fortuna, 19
v. illus. 25 cm.
CONTENTS.—
djilid 3. Babaran roepa-roepa kleur jang paling baroe laen dari pada jang laen.

1. Dyes and dyeing. I. Title.

TP910.L45   55-39698 ‡

NL 0350114   DLC

Liem, Channing.
America's finest gift to Korea : the life of Philip Jaisohn.
New York, William-Frederick Press, 1952.
89 p. illus. 23 cm.

1. Jaisohn, Philip, 1868-1951. I. Title.

DS916.5.J3L5   923.2519   52-7537 ‡

NL 0350115   DLC CaBVaU OrU HU NN OU PPAmP PSt

Liem, Channing.
The influence of Western political thought upon China.
Ann Arbor, University Microfilms [1952]
([University Microfilms, Ann Arbor, Mich.] Publication no. 2997)
Microfilm copy of typescript. Positive.
Collation of the original, as determined from the film: 229, 9 l.
Thesis—Princeton University.
Bibliography : leaves 218-229.

1. China—Pol. & govt. 2. Political science—Hist.—China.
I. Title.
Microfilm AC-1 no. 2997   Mic 56-4169

NL 0350116   DLC CSt NIC

Liem, Han T., 1890
Ueber die reinheitsprüfung offizineller alkaloide.
Inaug. Diss. Zürich, 1929

NL 0350117   ICRL CtY

Wason   **Liem, Khiam Soen.**
DS632   Kedoedoekan bangsa Tionghoa di Indonesia;
C5168+   De positie der Chineezen in Indonesië.   Soerabaia, Sawahan Chung Hua Hui [1947]
23 p. 21cm.
At head of title: Bangsa Tionghoa dan perdjoeangannja.
In Indonesian and Dutch.
Photocopy. Ithaca, N.Y., Cornell University Libraries, 1964. 23 p. (on double leaves) 26cm.

NL 0350118   NIC

Liem, Khouw Keng
see Khouw, Keng Liem.

---

ar W   **Liem, Lie Pok, 1921-**
8875   Enkele aspecten van de persoonlijkheidsdiagnostiek en de toepassing van de mozaïektest.   Leiden [1954]
140 p. illus. 25cm.
Diss.--Leiden.
Summary in English.

1. Personality tests.

NL 0350120   NIC

Liem, Soei Diong.
Onderzoekingen over triatoma infestans als overbrenger van enkele pathogene organismen en over de complementbindingreactie bij de ziekte van Chagas ... Utrecht [1938]
Academisch proefschrift - Leiden.
"Literatuurlijst": p. [141]-145.

NL 0350121   CtY

DS   **Liem, Thian Joe, d. 1963.**
646.29   Riwajat Semarang, dari djamannja Sam Poo
S4   sampe terhapoesnja Kongkoan. Tjit. 1. Semarang, Boekhandel Ho Kim Yoe [1933]
L54   324, viii p. illus. 25 cm.

1. Semarang, Indonesia (City) 2. Chinese in Indonesia. I. Title (1)
NUC SA

NL 0350122   CtY

Liem, Thian Ju, d. 1963.
Pusaka Tionghoa. Semarang, Ho Kim Yoe; pusat pendjual Hoe Sien [1951]
118 p. 20 cm.

I. Title.

PL5089.L5   55-56626 ‡

NL 0350123   DLC HU

Wason   **Liem, Thian Ju, d. 1963**
Film   Riwajat Semarang (dari djamannja Sam
3160   Poo sampe terhapoesnja Kongkoan)   Semarang,
no.7   Ho Kim Yoe [permoela'an kata 1933]
324, viii p. illus.
Advertising matter interspersed.
Microfilm. 1 reel. 35mm.
Filmed with: Hogendorp, D. van. Brief van Dirk van Hogendorp aan alle vryheid en vaderland lievende Bataven in Nederlandsch Oost-Indien. Bombay, 1799.
1. Semarang, Indonesia (City)--Hist. 2. Chinese in Indonesia.
I. Title.

NL 0350124   NIC

Liem, Tjay Tie.
Tentang angka kematian baji Indonesia di kota Semarang dalam tahun 1952 & 1953. Jogjakarta, Jajasan Fonds Universitit Negeri Gadjah Mada [1955]
22 p. 24 cm.
Summary in English.
Includes bibliographical references.

1. Infants—Mortality. 2. Semarang, Indonesia (City)—Statistics, Vital. I. Title.

HB1323.I 4L63   74-276711

NL 0350125   DLC NIC

Liem, Twan Djie.
De distribueerende tusschenhandel der Chineezen op Java.
's-Gravenhage, M. Nijhoff, 1947.
viii, 104 p. 25 cm.
Bibliography : p. [102]-104.

1. Java—Comm. 2. Chinese in Java. I. Title.

HF5349.I 6L5   59-53914

NL 0350126   DLC NN NSyU CLU NNC IU WaU MH-BA NIC

DS   **Liem, Twan Djie.**
632   De distribueerende tusschenhandel der
C5L71   Chineezen op Java. 2. ongewijzigde druk.
1952   s'Gravenhage, Nijhoff, 1952 [c1947]
viii,104 p. 24cm.

1. Chinese in Java. 2. Java--Commerce.
I. Title.

NL 0350127   NIC PU CSt-H CU CtY

Liem Boen Hwat
see
Liem, Bun Hwat.

Liem Soei Diong
see Liem, Soei Diong.

Liem Thian Joe
see
Liem, Thian Ju.

Liem Twan Djie
see Liem, Twan Djie.

Lieman, Otto
see
Lehmann, Otto, *retired major.*

Lieme, H   **de.**
Israel's historie. [2. druk. n. p., voorbericht 1941]
139 p. 22 cm.

1. Jews—Hist.—To A. D. 70. I. Title.

DS118.L63 1941   49-36506*

NL 0350133   DLC OCH

Lieme, Nehemia de, 1882-1940.
בשבילי יחיד. לזכר נחמיה דה־לימה עשר שנים לפטירתו.
בעריכת נתן ביספוריצקי. ירושלים, הקרן הקיימת לישראל, תש״י. [Jerusalem, 1950]
211 p. ports. 20 cm.
Material by and about the author.

I. Title.   *Title transliterated: Bi-shevile yaḥid.*

DS151.L49A3   62-55273

NL 0350134   DLC

Liemke, H   **H.**
... Equitable co-operation. The methods of the American co-operative society, by H. H. Liemke ... [St. Louis, 1896]
47 p. 20ᶜᵐ.

1. Cooperation—U. S. 2. American co-operative society.

Library of Congress   HD3445.L4   7-27665†
                  (Copyright 1896: 33322)

NL 0350135   DLC

Liemke, Otto.
Das kloster Haina im mittelalter. Ein beitrag zur baugeschichte der Cistercienser Deutschlands Lüdenscheid, Gedruckt: Spannagel & Caesar [1911]
72 p. illus. 27ᶜᵐ.
Zur erlangung der würde eines doktor-ingenieurs — Tech. hochschule, Berlin.
"Quellennachweis": p. 71-72.

1. Haina, Ger. Cistercienserkloster.

                  12-8299

Library of Congress   NA5586.H15L5

NL 0350136   DLC PU

VOLUME 332

W
4
B72   Liemny, Mohammed Es-Salah, 1909–
1938/39   L'absence de régénération osseuse après
    diaphysectomie pour ostéomyélite. Bordeaux,
    Bière, 1939.
    67 p. (Bordeaux. Université. Faculté
    de médecine et de pharmacie. Thèse. 1938/39.
    no. 169)

NL 0350137   DNLM

Liemohn, Edwin.
    The chorale through four hundred years of musical
development as a congregational hymn. Philadelphia,
Muhlenberg Press [1953]
    xii, 170 p. music. 21 cm.
    Bibliography: p. 160–166.

    1. Chorale.

    ML3184.L5   783.6   53—10130

WaWW WaTC CaBVaU OrU OrSaW IdPI
NBuG OOxM OU NcD OrP ViU NN MB PU TxU MsSM PSt CoU
NL 0350138   DLC OrCS WaS PPP OCl OO OC1W TU PSt PP

Liemohn, Edwin, *comp. and arr.*
    Chorales for concert and church. Arr. for 4-part women's
voices. Minneapolis, Augsburg Pub. House [1935]
    score (36 p.) 27 cm.
    For chorus (SSAA) in part with piano reduction.

    1. Choruses, Sacred (Women's voices, 4 pts.), Unaccompanied.
    2. Chorales.   I. Title.

    M2084.4.L5C5   M 54—230

NL 0350139   DLC

Liemohn, Edwin.
    Essentials in modern harmony; copyright ... by E. Liemohn.
[Fargo, N. D.] ©1934.
    3 p. l., 2–12, 12a, 13–54 numb. l. illus. (music) 28cm.
    Mimeographed.

    1. Harmony.   I. Title.
                CA 34—1010 Unrev'd
    Library of Congress   MT50.L62E8
    Copyright AA 156857   781.2

NL 0350140   DLC

Liempt, Johannes Antonius Maria van, 1896–
    De afscheiding van wolfraam uit gasvormige verbindingen
en hare toepassing ... door Johannes Antonius Maria van
Liempt ... Purmerend, J. Muusses, 1931.
    4 p. l., 117, [2] p. incl. illus, tables, diagrs. 4 pl. 23½cm.
    Proefschrift—Delft.
    "Summary": p. 114–117.
    "Stellingen": [5] p. laid in.

    1. Tungsten.   2. Molybdenum.   3. Electroplating.
                34—39172
    Library of Congress   TS692.T8L5 1931   671

NL 0350141   DLC MH NN PPF

Liempt, Johannes Antonius Maria van, 1896–
    Kunstlicht in de fotografie, met 125 afbeeldingen en 55
kunsfoto's. Amsterdam, Meulenhoff, 1942.
    225 p. illus., diagrs. 28 cm. (Philips technische bibliotheek)
    "Aanbevolen literatuur": p. 232–233.

    1. Photography—Artificial light.   2. Photography, Artistic.
    I. Title.   (Series)

    TR600.L5   771.443   48—40295*

NL 0350142   DLC

Liempt, Johannes Antonius Maria van, 1896–
    ... The production of metallic single crystals, by J. A. M.
van Liempt ... New York, American institute of mining and
metallurgical engineers, inc., ©1927.
    1 p. l., 8 p. illus., diagrs. 23cm. (American institute of mining and
metallurgical engineers. Technical publication no. 15. Class E, Institute of metals, no. 2)
    Bibliographical foot-notes.

    1. Crystallization.

                P O 29–119
    Library, U. S. Patent   Office TN1.A49
    Library of Congress   TN1.A525 no. 15

NL 0350143   DP

Liempt, Johannes Antonius Maria van, 1896–
    ... Das trocknen von gasen, von J. A. M. van
Liempt. Gepubliceerd in: Recueil des travaux
chimiques des Pays-Bas 61, 341–347, Avril 1942.
            [341]–347 p.
    Laboratoria n. v. Philips' gloeilampenfabrieken,
Eindhoven (Holland) – separaat 1609).

NL 0350144   NN

PA4260   Liempt, Leonard van.
L5   De vocabulario hymnorum orphicorum
    atque aetate... submittet Leonardus van
    Liempt... Purmerend, J. Muusses, 1930.
        4 p. l., 72, [5] p.   22 cm.
        Proefschrift – Utrecht.
        Bibliography: p. [74]–[77]

        1. Orpheus. Hymni. 2. Hymns, Greek.
    I. Title.

NL 0350145   OCU ICRL CtY PU IU ViU MH CU NRU

Lien, *Frau A.*
    Das märchen von der französischen kultur, von A. Lien;
hrsg. von dr. Franz Oppenheimer. Berlin, K. Curtius,
1915.
    3 p. l., [3]–224 p. 19½cm.

    1. France—Soc. life & cust.   2. France—Civilization.   I. Oppenheimer,
Franz, 1864–   ed. II. Title.

                21–5007

NL 0350146   DLC MH NN NjP CtY

Lien, Abel Edvard, 1863–
    A brief history of the Lien family, Norwegian pioneers of
East Koshkonong, Dane county, Wisconsin. By Abel E. Lien.
Portland, N. D., 1930.
    71 p. illus. (incl. ports.) 23cm.

    1. Lien family.

    Library of Congress   CS71.L716 1930   33—6838

NL 0350147   DLC WaS

Lien (Alfred-Ernest-Félicien-Alois-Marie-Jo-
seph). *De l'inspection otologique à l'école.
62 pp. 8°. Lille. 1911. No. 14.

NL 0350148   DNLM

Lien, Arnold Johnson, 1882–
    The acquisition of citizenship by the native American Indians,
by Arnold J. Lien... [Concord, N. H., 1925.]   121–179 p.
4°.
    Cover-title.
    Bibliographical footnotes.
    Repr.: Washington Univ. studies. v. 13. Humanistic ser. no. 1, 1925.

    1. Indians, N. A.—Citizenship.
                July 1, 1927

NL 0350149   NN WaSp MH ODW

Lien, Arnold Johnson, 1882–
    The American people and their government; a textbook for
students in introductory college courses and for the active
electorate, by Arnold J. Lien ... and Merle Fainsod ... New
York, London, D. Appleton-Century company, incorporated
[©1934]
    xiv, 629 p. 23cm.
    "For further reading" at end of each chapter, except XII; Bibliog-
raphy: p. 511–514.

    1. U. S.—Pol. & govt.   I. Fainsod, Merle, joint author.   II. Title.

    Library of Congress   JK274.L57   34–7819

    Copyright A 70900   342.73

NL 0350150   DLC WaWW WaSp OrU ViU OU OC1 PU PJB

Lien, Arnold Johnson, 1882–
    Privileges and immunities of citizens of the United
States, by Arnold Johnson Lien ... New York, 1913.
    1 p. l., 5–95 p. 25cm.
    Thesis (PH. D.)—Columbia university, 1913.
    Vita.
    Published also as Studies in history, economics and public law, vol. LIV,
no. 1.
    "A few select references": p. 94.

    1. Citizenship—U. S.
                13–17478
    Library of Congress   JK1756.L6 1913 a
    Columbia Univ. Libr.   320.4

NL 0350151   NNC DLC

Lien, Arnold Johnson, 1882–
    ... Privileges and immunities of citizens of the United
States, by Arnold Johnson Lien ... New York, Columbia
university; [etc., etc.], 1913.
    94 p. 24 cm. (Studies in history, economics and public law, ed. by
the Faculty of political science of Columbia university. vol. LIV, no. 1.
Whole no. 132)
    Published also as author's thesis (PH. D.) Columbia university, 1913.
    "A few select references": p. 94.

    1. Citizenship—U. S.

    H31.C7 vol. 54, no. 1   13—15025
                JK1756.L6

CoU KEmT MU
ViU PU ODW MiU OO PP PU-L PSC PBm ICJ NN MB TxU
NL 0350152   DLC WaTC DAU CaBVaU WaU-L WaS OrU OrP Or

Lien, Arthur Philip, 1914–
    Methods of synthesis of di- and trialkyl-
benzenes ... [Columbus] The Ohio state univ.
1941.
    4 p. l., 107 numb. l.
    Thesis (PH.D.) Ohio state univ.

NL 0350153   OU

Lien, Ch'en.
    隨軍西征記 廉臣著 [n. p.] 生活書店經售 民
    國 27 [1938]
    74 p. 17 cm.

    1. Long March, 1934–1935.   I. Title.
                Title romanized: Sui chün hsi chêng chi.

    DS777.47.L47   C 67–756

NL 0350154   DLC

Lien Chi, *pseud.*
*fBC75   An answer from Lien Chi, in Pekin, to Xo Ho
A100   [i.e. Horace Walpole], the Chinese philosopher
757a   in London, to which is annexed a letter from
    Philo-Briton [pseud.] to Lien-Chi.
        London: Printed for M. Cooper, in Pater-noster-
    row. [1757] <Price sixpence.>
        f°. 10p. 30cm.

NL 0350155   MH

VOLUME 332

Lien, Chieh-ch'ün.
現代新藥集　連潔羣編　杭州　新醫書局　1953.
170 p.　21 cm.

1. Pharmacopoeias.　I. Title.
Title romanised: Hsien tai hsin yao chi.

RS139.L5　　　　　　　　　　C 62–2194 ‡

NL　0350156　　DLC

Lien, Chieh-ch'ün.
現代內科治療技術　連潔羣編　杭州　新醫書局
1953.
102 p.　illus.　20 cm.

1. Medicine—Practice.　I. Title.
Title romanised: Hsien tai nei k'o chih liao chi shu.

RC46.L64　　　　　　　　　　C 62–1810 ‡

NL　0350157　　DLC

Lien, Chieh-ch'ün.
磺胺類之臨床應用　連潔羣編　修訂　杭州
新醫書局　1952.
44 p.　illus.　21 cm.

1. Sulphonamides.　I. Title.
Title romanised: Huang an lei chih lin ch'uang ying yung.

RM666.S88L46　　　　　　　　C 62–1790 ‡

NL　0350158　　DLC ICU–FE DNLM MH

Lien, Chieh-ch'ün.
實用急救學　連潔羣編著　杭州　新醫書局
1951.
8, 127 p.　illus.　18 cm.
Cover title.

1. First aid in illness and injury.　I. Title.
Title romanised: Shih yung chi chiu hsüeh.

RC87.L59　　　　　　　　　　C 66–1538

NL　0350159　　DLC

Lien, Chieh-ch'ün.
最新藥物治療學　臨床必備　連潔羣編著　上海
新醫書局　1951.
218 p.　illus.　19 cm.

1. Materia medica.　2. Therapeutics.　I. Title.
Title romanised: Tsui hsin yao wu chih liao hsüeh.

RM126.L5　　　　　　　　　　C 60–1189 ‡

NL　0350160　　DLC

Lien, Chieh-ch'ün.
眼科護病學　連潔群編著　上海　新醫書局
1951.
113 p.　illus.　19 cm.
At head of title: 高級醫事職業學校適用

1. Eye—Diseases and defects.　I. Title.
Title romanised: Yen k'o hu ping hsüeh.

RE46.L7　　　　　　　　　　C 59–581 ‡

NL　0350161　　DLC

Wason
PL2718
I63N2+
Lien, Ch'üan, d. 1932.
南湖集　錢　庚泉著　孫道毅編　上海
中華書局　民國 13 [1924]
2 v. in 1 (double leaves)　port.　26 cm.

I. Title.
Title romanised: Nan hu chi.
C 58–7042

Hoover Library
for Library of Congress

NL　0350162　　CSt–H OU NIC

Lien, Chün.
東三省經濟實況攬要　連濤著　上海　民國20
[1931]
2, 2, 2, 458 p.　illus., ports., maps (part fold.)　26 cm.

1. Manchuria—Econ. condit.　I. Title.
Title romanised: Tung san shêng ching chi shih k'uang lan yao.

C 60–5387

Harvard Univ. Chinese-
for Library of Congress
Japanese Library 4357.11

NL　0350163　　MH–HY

Lien, Claude de Saint, 16th cent.
see Sainliens, Claude de, 16th cent.

LF4535
.N3A66
Lien, Ejnar.
Namdals høgskulelag.
Namdals folkehøgskule, 1884–1954. [Skriftstyrar: Ejnar Lien. Namsos, 1955]

Lien, Elias Johnson, 1868–　　　ed.
Simmons, John Bell, 1851–
A digest of the decisions of the Supreme court of Wisconsin, new, rev. and complete, from the earliest period to the beginning of the August term, 1908, including all the official reports down to vol. 136 and the Northwestern reporter to and including vol. 116 ... by John B. Simmons ... Chicago, Callaghan and company, 1909–10.

Lien, Hêng, 1878–1936.
臺灣通史　連雅堂[連橫]著　臺北　臺灣通史社
大正 9–10 [1920–21]
3 v. (8, 1154 p.)　illus., maps (2 fold.) ports.　23 cm.

1. Formosa—Hist.　I. Title.
Title romanised: T'ai-wan t'ung shih.

DS895.F72L499　　　　　　　C 65–1633

NL　0350167　　DLC

Lien, Hêng, 1878–1936.
臺灣通史　連橫著　臺北　中華叢書委員會　民
國 44 [1955]
13, 15, 792 p.　fold. maps, tables.　21 cm.　(雅堂全書第 1 種)
中華叢書

1. Formosa—Hist.　I. Title.
Title romanised: T'ai-wan t'ung shih.

DS895.F72L5　　　　　　　　C 59–427

NL　0350168　　DLC

Lien, Hêng, 1878–1936.
臺灣通史　[連橫著　臺北　中華叢書委員會
臺灣書店總經銷 1955]
2 v. (12, 11, 792 p.)　21 cm.　(中華叢書)

1. Formosa—History.　I. Title.
Title romanised: T'ai-wan t'ung shih.

DS895.F72L5　1955b　　　　79–836687

NL　0350169　　DLC

Lien, Herbert Abraham, 1904–
Labor law and relations; the law and statutes involved in dealings and relations with labor as interpreted by the courts and administrative agencies, by Herbert A. Lien ... Albany, N. Y., New York, N. Y., M. Bender & company, incorporated, 1938.
xv, 747 p.　26 cm.
Supplement inserted in pocket on inside of back cover.

—— Supplement to Labor law and relations, by Herbert A. Lien. Wages and hours guide (Fair labor standards act of 1938) Albany, N. Y., New York, N. Y., M. Bender & company, incorporated, 1938.
72 p.　26 cm.
HD7833.L5　Suppl.

1. Labor laws and legislation—U. S.　2. U. S. National labor relations board.　3. Labor contract.　4. Hours of labor—U. S.　5. Wages—U. S.　I. U. S. Laws, statutes, etc.　II. U. S. Courts.　III. Title.

HD7833.L5　　　　331.0973　　　38–38000

WaU–L IdU OrP
NL　0350171　　DLC PU–W OU PPT–L ViU–L OClW PU–L NcD

Lien, Huan, ed.
先鋒　連環編　[南京？ (1931?–　)]
4, 132 p.　19 cm.
Cover title.

1. Sino-Japanese Conflict, 1937–1945—Addresses, essays, lectures.　I. Title.
Title romanised: Hsien fêng.

DS777.53.L4845　　　　　　C 67–1320

NL　0350172　　DLC

Lien-keng Kho
see Kho, Lien-keng.

Lien, Liu Chai-

see

Chai-Lien, Liu

Lien, Marie Elizabeth, 1911–
Norwegian national organization for the promotion of home arts and crafts 〈husflid〉 [by] Marie Elizabeth Lien ... [Oslo] Fabritius & sønner [1946]
135, [1] p.　col. front., illus. (map) plates.　24 cm.
Thesis (PH. D.)—Columbia university, 1941.
Thesis note on label mounted on t.-p.
Vita on label mounted on p. [136]
Bibliography: p. 131–[136]

1. Art industries and trade—Norway.　2. Arts and crafts movement.　3. Handicraft.　4. Art—Norway.　I. Title.

NK991.L5　　　　745.3　　　A 47–3967
Columbia univ.　Libraries
for Library of Congress　　　　†

NL　0350175　　NNC ICU NN DLC

Lien, Martin.
Nomografi. [Stockholm, Maskinaktiebolaget Karlebo, 1945]
152 p. (p. 149–152 advertisements)　illus., diagrs. (1 fold. in pocket)　22 cm.　(Karleboserien, 3)
"Litteraturförteckning": p. 148.

1. Nomography (Mathematics)

QA90.L48　　　　　　　　　48–18384*

NL　0350176　　DLC

VOLUME 332

QP551
L5
Lien, Oliver Gordon, 1918-
Chromatographic and isotopic tracer studies
of amino acid metabolism. ₍Berkeley, 1951₎
11,76 *l.* diagrs.,tables.

Thesis (Ph.D.) - Univ. of California,
Sept. 1951.
Bibliography: p.42-43.

NL 0350177 CU

Lien, Petra M
...Coming to America in 1868 to Hanska...
see under Broste, Ole K

W 4A
qL719d
1942
LIEN, Richard Joseph, 1910-
The decline in the incidence of con-
genital syphilis. ₍Minneapolis₎ 1942.
27 *l.*
Thesis (M. S. in Pediatrics) - Univ.
of Minnesota.
Typewritten copy.

NL 0350179 DNLM

Lien, Shih-shêng, 1907-
回首四十年 連士升著 新加坡 南洋商報社
1952.
2,160 p. 18 cm. (南洋商報叢書第21種)

I. Title.   *Title romanized:* Hui shou ssŭ shih nien.
                                          C 61-4045
Harvard Univ. Chinese-   Japanese Library 9159
for Library of Congress

NL 0350180 MH-HY

Lien, Shih-shêng, 1907-
祖國紀行 連士升著 ₍新加坡 南洋報社有限公
司 1948₎
130 p. 19 cm. (南洋商報叢書第1種)

1. Chinese in foreign countries.   I. Title.
                          Title romanized: Tsu kuo chi hsing.
DS732.L52   75-840285

NL 0350181 DLC CaBVaU

31
L5
Le Lien; revue mensuelle grecque-catholique.

Le Caire, Collège patriarcal grec-catholique.
v. illus., ports. 25 cm.

1. Catholic Church. Byzantine rite (Melchite)—Period.
I. Cairo. Collège patriarcal grec-catholique.
BX4711.31.L5   61-48106

NL 0350182 DLC

HQ744
.T725
Orien
China
Lien ai, chieh hun, chia t'ing.
Tsung, Lu.
戀愛結婚家庭 宗魯 宗誠 陳遊著 ₍桂林₎
科學書店 民國32 ₍1943₎

戀愛·婚姻與夫婦生活 張帆等著 ₍上海₎ 展望周刊
社 ₍1952₎
4, 92 p. 17 cm. (生活小叢書)

1. Marriage—Addresses, essays, lectures.   I. Chang, Fan.
                     Title romanized: Lien ai, hun yin yü fu fu shêng huo.
HQ743.L44   C 67-1857

NL 0350184 DLC

(Lien ch'in yüeh k'an)
聯勤月刊

₍臺北₎
no. illus. 27 cm.
Began with Jan. 1952 issue.   CSF monthly.
Title also in English.
Some articles also in English.
Continued by 中國聯勤

1. China. Lu chin—Supplies and stores—Periodicals.   I. Title:
CSF monthly.
UC265.F6L5   72-835239

NL 0350185 DLC

Lien d'Israel.   Journal populaire pour
favoriser les interets religieux et moraux des
Israelites francais. Publication mensuelle non
politique. ₍Ann. 1-3, 1855-58, fortnightly. Ed.
by S.Dreyfus. Annee 5-7. Strasbourg,1859-1861₎
3v.

Ann. 1-3 pub. in Mulhausen.

NL 0350186 OCH

(Lien ho kuo chi ko chuan mên chi kuan chu Hua pan
shih ch'u hsien ming lu)
聯合國暨各專門機關駐華辦事處銜名錄 Offices of
United Nations and specialized agencies in the Republic
of China.
₍臺北₎ 中華民國外交部禮賓司 Protocol Dept.,
Ministry of Foreign Affairs, Republic of China.
v. 19 cm.
Chinese and English.
1. United Nations—China—Directories.   I. China. Wai chiao
pu. Li pin ssŭ. II. Title: Offices of United Nations and specialized
agencies in the Republic of China.
JX1977.2.C5A3   70-838522

NL 0350187 DLC

Lien-ho-kuo chiao yü k'o hsüeh wên hua tsu chih
see
United Nations Educational, Scientific and Cultural Organization.

HB3638
F7C53
Lien ho kuo Chung-kuo t'ung chih hui.
The balance between population and production.
₍Taipeh, Taiwan₎ 1951.
21 p. 21cm. (Unachina publications. Ser. I,
4)
Contents.- Introduction by Chu Chia-hua. Dr.
₍John B.₎ Baker's address. Free discussion.

1. Formosa - Population. 2. Food supply -
Formosa. I. Baker, John B. II. Title.

NL 0350189 CSt-H NIC

Lien ho kuo Chung-kuo t'ung chih hui.
Can Mao Tse-tung become a Tito? ₍Taipeh₎ Chinese
Association for the United Nations, 1950.
36 p. 21 cm. (*Its* Unachina publications, ser. I, 3)

1. Mao, Tsê-tung, 1893-   2. China—Pol. & govt.—1949-
I. Title.   (Series)
DS778.M3L52 1950   951.042   51-8702 rev

NL 0350190 DLC NNC CSt-H OrCS OrU

Lien ho kuo Chung-kuo t'ung chih hui.
Can Mao Tse-tung become a Tito? 2d & enl. ed. Taipei,
Taiwan, Chinese Association for the United Nations, 1952.
70 p. 22 cm. (*Its* Unachina publications, ser. I, 10)

1. Mao, Tsê-tung, 1893-   2. China—Pol. & govt.—1949-
I. Title.
DS778.M3C5 1952   951.05   60-31357 ‡

NL 0350191 DLC PBm MH-L NIC NNC MH IaU OrU

Lien ho kuo Chung-kuo t'ung chih hui.
The Economic Cooperation Administration Program in Taiwan. ₍Taipeh₎
1951.
34p. 21cm. (*Its* Unachina publications.
Series 1, 5)

1. Economic assistance, American.
Formosa.

NL 0350192 IEN NIC MH CtY

Lien ho kuo Chung-kuo t'ung chih hui.
Freedom from FCAL
see under   P'u, Hsüeh-fêng, 1901

DS721
C52
Lien ho kuo Chung-kuo t'ung chih hui.
An interpretation of the ancient Chinese
civilization. Taipei, Taiwan, China, 1592
₍i.e. 1952₎
34p. 22cm. (*Its* Unachina publications.
Ser. 1. 9)

1. China. Civilization. I. Series.
II. Title.

NL 0350194 IaU PBm PPD

Lien ho kuo Chung-kuo t'ung chih hui.
News letter.

Taipei, Chinese Association for the United Nations.
v. in   26 cm. monthly.
Began publication with June 1951 issue. Cf. New serial titles,
1964.

1. United Nations—Period. 2. United Nations—China. 3. China—
For. rel.—1949-
JX1977.A1L5   66-51797

NL 0350195 DLC OrCS OrU NN

Lien ho kuo Chung-kuo t'ung chih hui.
A report on Russian destruction of our industries in the
North-eastern Provinces. ₍Taipei₎ Chinese Association for
the United Nations, 1952.
27 p. 22 cm. (*Its* Unachina publications, ser. I, 7)

1. Manchuria—Indus.
HC428.M3L48   55-40133 rev ‡

OrU OrCS
NL 0350196 DLC PPD NIC CSt-H CtY NcD MH NNC PBm IEN

Lien ho kuo Chung-kuo t'ung chih hui.
The Sino-American treaty of mutual defense. Taipei,
Taiwan, Chinese Association for the United Nations, 1955.
40 p. 22 cm. (*Its* Unachina publications series, I, 13)

1. Military assistance, American—China. 2. China—Defenses.
I. Title.
JX1428.C6L5   61-26915 ‡

ViU NBronSL ViU
NL 0350197 DLC MiU CSt-H ViU FU NIC NNC NNC-L MH-L

CE73
N596
Lien ho kuo Chung-kuo t'ung chih hui.
A symposium on the world calendar ₍Two lec-
tures₎ by Tung Tso-pin and Kao Ping-tze, and
discussions. Taipei, Taiwan, Hsin Sheng
Printing Works₎ 1951.
36 p. illus. 21ᵐ. (Unachina publications, ser.I, 6)

1.Calendar. 2.Calendar, Chinese. I.Tung,
Tso-pin. II.Kao, Ping-tze. III.Title.

NL 0350198 CSt-H OrCS TxU NIC MH NNC IEN

VOLUME 332

DS 777.53 C541
Lien ho kuo Chung-kuo t'ung chih hui.
Unachina publications. Series 1
[no.]1–
[Taipei, Taiwan, 19–]
no. illus. 21cm.

1.China. 2.United Nations – China.
I.Title. II.

NL 0350199 CLSU

Lien ho shê.
新民主主義的政治 聯合社編輯部編 北京 新潮書店 1950.
5, 147 p. 17 cm. (新民主主義論學習資料)

1. Mao, Tsê-tung, 1898– Hsin min chu chu i lun.
I. Title.
Title romanised: Hsin min chu chu i ti chêng chih.

DS778.M3L53   C 66–8051

NL 0350200 DLC MH-HY

Lien ho shê.
人民大憲章學習資料 聯合社編輯部編 第 8 版 增訂本 [天津] 聯合圖書出版社 1950.
150 p. 18 cm.

1. China (People's Republic of China, 1949–)—Constitutional law. I. Title.
Title romanised: Jên min ta hsien chang hsüeh hsi tsü liao.

G 63–1397 ‡

NL 0350201 DLC WaU-FE FTaSU CaBVaU

Lien ho shê.
人民大憲章學習資料 聯合社編輯部編 第 10 版 修訂本 天津 聯合圖書出版社 1950.
188 p. 17 cm.

1. China (People's Republic of China, 1949–)—Constitutional law. I. Title.
Title romanised: Jên min ta hsien chang hsüeh hsi tsü liao.

G 63–1295 ‡

NL 0350202 DLC

Lien ho shê.
歷史唯物論—社會發展史學習資料 聯合社編輯部編 修正本 北京 新潮書店 1950.
154 p. 17 cm.

1. Dialectical materialism. 2. Social classes. I. Title.
Title romanised: Li shih wei wu lun.

B809.8.L55 1950   C 61–4553

Harvard Univ. Chinese-Japanese Library for Library of Congress 4290.3
                               †

NL 0350203 MH-HY DLC

Lien ho shê.
歷史唯物論—社會發展史學習資料 聯合社編輯部編 修正本 天津 聯合圖書出版社 1950.
154 p. 17 cm.

1. Dialectical materialism. 2. Social classes—China. I. Title.
Title romanised: Li shih wei wu lun.

B809.8.L55 1950a   C 61–2619 ‡

NL 0350204 DLC

Lien ho shê.
論共產主義的勞動態度 聯合社編 天津 聯合圖書出版社 1950.
30 p. 18 cm.

1. Labor and laboring classes—Russia. I. Title.
Title romanised: Lun kung ch'an chu i ti lao tung t'ai tu.

HD8526.L57   C 61–2341

NL 0350205 DLC

The lien law applying to the City of New York ... Kings and Queens Counties
see under New York (State) Laws, statutes, etc.

J7 L624
Liénard,
Pochette Jeanne d'Arc en 10 tableaux par le commandant Liénard ... Paris, Librairie P. Lethielleux [18--?]
10 colored post cards.

1. Jeanne d'Arc, 1412–1431.

NL 0350207 NNC

Liénard [1861–]. *Contributions à l'étude de la dilatation du cœur droit chez les tuberculeux.* 65 pp. 4°. *Paris,* 1886, No. 10.

NL 0350208 DNLM

LIÉNARD, A.
Le Marseillais et leurs titres historiques depuis la fondation de la colonie phocéennee jusqu'à nos jours. Marseille, Bellue, 1862.

f°. pp. 848. Front.
On cover:- Publication populaire. Paris, Bourselet, etc., etc., 1864.

NL 0350209 MH

Lienard, A.P. and Higgins, E.S.
Twenty years of revival effort. 1899
see under Howard, G[reenberg] B., 1837–

Liénard, Mme. Aglae' Emma Chuppin de Germigny.

SEE

Chuppin de Germigny, Emma.

Liénard, Albert, 1875–
Anthologie des matinées poétiques de la Comédie française. Année 1. Paris, Delagrave, 1923–
v. 16°.
Editor : 1920/1921. Louis Payen (pseud. of Albert Liénard).
1. Poetry, French-Collections.

NL 0350212 NN RPB OO IU CtY WU

PQ1184 .L5
Liénard, Albert, 1875–
Anthologie des matinées poétiques de la comédie française, publiée par Louis Payen [pseud.] Paris, Librairie Delagrave, 1927–
v. 16cm. (Collection Pallas)

1. French poetry (Collections)
I. Title.

NL 0350213 NcU PPT NN MtU

[Liénard, Albert,] 1875–
...Cleopatra; an opera in four acts, the book by Louis Payen [pseud.]. The music by Jules Massenet. English translation by Martia Leonard. New York: G. Schirmer [cop. 1915]. vii, 2–85 p. 8°. (G. Schirmer's collection of opera-librettos.)

Cover-title reads: The Chicago Opera Association libretto...Cleopatre. Published by Fred Rullman, Inc...
French and English.
Libretto.

1. Drama (French). 2. Massenet, Jules Émile Frédéric, 1842–1912.
3. Leonard, Martia, translator. 4. Title.
                               May 2, 1919.

NL 0350214 NN Or IaU IEN MiD CSt

PQ2623 .I 45 C6
Lienard, Albert, 1875–
La coupe d'ombre; poèmes [par] Louis Payen [pseud.] Amiens, E. Malfère, 1925 [c1924]
222p. (Bibliothèque du Hérisson)

NL 0350215 NcU

Hfr ℓ175
[Liénard, Albert] 1875–
... Les esclaves, tragédie lyrique en trois actes, musique de Aymé Kunc. Représentée pour la première fois à Béziers, sur le Théâtre des Arènes, le 27 août 1911. Paris, Mercvre de France, 1911.
78p., 1ℓ. 18½cm. [Binder's title: Liénard]
Author's pseud., Louis Payen, at head of title.
Without the music.

NL 0350216 CtY

M1500 .F43G6 Case
Liénard, Albert, 1875–
Février, Henry, 1875–1957.
[Gismonda]
Gismonda; drame lyrique en 4 actes d'après Victorien Sardou. Poème de H. Cain et L. Payen. Paris, Heugel, *1920.

[Liénard, Albert,] 1875–
... L'imperia, pièce en 5 actes, en vers. Paris, Librairie théâtrale, *1929.
3 p. l., [9]–113 p. 19cm.
Author's pseud., Louis Payen, at head of title.

1. Title.

Library of Congress   PQ2623.I 45 I 6 1929   29–25832
Copyright D pub. 2241

NL 0350218 DLC

Liénard, Albert, 1875–
Le roi d'Yvetot
see under Boucoiran, Camille.

PQ2623 .I 45 S2
Liénard, Albert, 1875–
Les saisons rouges; poèmes. [Par] Louis Payen [pseud.] Paris, E. Figuière [19–]
189p. (Collection de petit livres de chevet)

NL 0350220 NcU

VOLUME 332

₍Liénard, Albert₎ 1875–
... Siséra, tragédie en deux actes, en vers ... préface de l'auteur. Paris, Mercure de France, 1911.
62 p., 1 l. 18¼ᶜᵐ.
Author's pseudonym, Louis Payen, at head of title.

1. Sisera (Biblical character)—Drama.   I. Title.
11–17691
Library of Congress   PQ2623.I 4S85 1911

NL 0350221   DLC

₍Liénard, Albert₎ 1875–
La tentation de l'abbé Jean; pièce en trois actes, en prose; préface de Catulle Mendès. Paris: Librairie Molière, 1907.
87 p.   12°.
Author's pseudonym, Louis Payen, at head of title.

1. Drama (French). 2. Mendès,   Catulle, 1841–1909. 3. Title.
November 4, 1915.

NL 0350222   NN CtY

Hfr
ℓ175
[Liénard, Albert] 1875–
... La victoire, pièce en trois actes, en vers. Représentée pour la première fois au Théâtre antique d'Orange, le 7 août 1909. Paris, B.Grasset, 1909.
4 p.l.,86p., 1 l.   19½ cm.   [Binder's title: Liénard]
Author's pseud, Louis Payen, at head of title.

NL 0350223   CtY

Liénard, Alfred.
Entre la larve et moi; journal de guerre d'un potager. Paris, Stock (Delamain et Boutelleau) 1947.
222 p. 19 cm. (Les Livres de nature, 70)

1. Gardening—Addresses, essays, lectures.   I. Title.   (Series)
SB103.L5   52–15215

NL 0350224   DLC

Liénard, Alfred Marie, 1869–
... Application de la thermodynamique aux théories électrodynamiques de Hertz et de H. Lorentz pour les corps en mouvement, par m. Alfred Liénard.
(In Annales de la Faculté des sciences de l'Université de Toulouse pour les sciences mathématiques et les sciences physiques ... Paris, 1941. 28ᶜᵐ. (55° v.) 4. sér., t. v, p. 1–48₎)
Bibliographical foot-notes.

1. Electrodynamics. 2. Thermodynamics.
A 46–803
Ohio state univ. Library
for Library of Congress   [Q46.T75 ser. 4, vol. 5]
(508)

NL 0350225   OU

Liénard, Alfred Marie, 1869–
... Cours d'électricité industrielle. ₍Théorie et mesures₎ Par m. Liénard. Saint-Etienne, Société de l'imprimerie Théolier, J. Thomas et cⁱᵉ, 1904.
163 p. illus. diagrs. 28¼ᶜᵐ. (École des mines de Saint-Étienne)

1. Electricity. 2. Electric measurements
6–46808
Library of Congress   QC518.L7

NL 0350226   DLC MB NN DSI

Q46
.T75
4. sér.,
t. 7
Liénard, Alfred Marie, 1869–
Électrodynamiques de Lorentz et de Hertz et principe de la moindre action, par A. Liénard.
(In Annales de la Faculté des sciences de l'Université de Toulouse pour les sciences mathématiques et les sciences physiques ... Paris, 1945. 28ᶜᵐ. (57° v.) 4. sér., t. VII, p. ₍71₎–98. tab.)
Bibliographical foot-notes.

1. Electrodynamics. 2. Least action.
(508)   A 47–306
Ohio state univ. Library
for Library of Congress

NL 0350227   OU

Q46
.T75
4. sér.,
t. 8
Liénard, Alfred Marie, 1869–
Thermodynamique. Quelques particularités des déplacements de l'équilibre et stabilité.
(In Toulouse. Université. Faculté des sciences. Annales. Toulouse, 1947. 29ᶜᵐ. (58. v.) 4. sér., t. 8, p. ₍1₎–57)

1. Phase rule and equilibrium. 2. Thermodynamics.
(508)   A 48–6507*
Ohio State Univ. Libr.
for Library of Congress

NL 0350228   OU DLC

Liénard (C.-H.-N.) * Considérations générales sur la vaccine, et quelques modifications dans le traitement de la variole. 16 pp. 4°. Paris, 1833. No. 254. v. 263.

NL 0350229   DNLM

Liénard, Charles, 1897–
... Dix filles dans un pré, roman. Grenoble, Paris, B. Arthaud ₍1946₎
256 p., 2 l. 18¼ᶜᵐ.

I. Title.
PQ2623.I 453D5   47–21569

NL 0350230   DLC

PQ1184
.L4
Liénard, Charles, 1897–   ed.
L'offrande au Rhône; hommage à Valence aux mémoires romaines. ₍Édité par₎ Charles Liénard ₍et₎ Pierre Pontiès. Préf. de Marcel Guinand, avec un bois gravé d'Henri Arnoux. Textes et poèmes de Louis Le Cardonnel ₍et al.₎ Valence-sur-Rhône, Impr. Passas et Deloche, 1952.
59 p. illus. 25 cm.
On verso of t. p.: XVIᵉᵐᵉˢ congrès et fêtes du Rhône du 13 au 16 juin 1952. Valence-sur-Rhône.

1. Poetry of places—France—Valence (Drôme) 2. Valence, France (Drôme)—Descr.—Poetry.   I. Le Cardonnel, Louis, 1862–1936.   II. Pontiès, Pierre, joint ed.   III. Title.
A 54–447
Illinois. Univ. Library
for Library of Congress

NL 0350231   IU OU DLC

PA6235
.L5
1943
Caesar, C. Julius.
... La campagne de Belgique, par Edm. Liénard ... 2. éd. rev. et corr. Bruxelles, Office de publicité, 1943.

PA6235
.L52
Caesar, C. Julius.
... Finis Galliae, par Edm. Liénard ... Bruxelles, Office de publicité, 1942.

Liénard, Élizé.
Catalogue de la faune malacologique de l'île Maurice et de ses dépendances comprenant les îles Seychelles, le groupe de Chagos composé de Diego-Garcia, Six-iles, Peros-Banhos, Salomon, etc., l'île Rodrigues, l'île de Cargados ou Saint-Brandon, par Élize liénard. Paris, Impr. de J. Tremblay, 1877.
2 p.l., iv, 115 p.   22 cm.
1. Mollusks – Mauritius   2. Mollusks – Seychelles.

NL 0350234   CU MH-Z

Liénard (Ernest). *Influence de l'alimentation azotée sur le coefficient d'assimilation des hydrates de carbone des diabétiques. 200 pp. 8°. Paris. 1913. No. 113.

NL 0350235   DNLM CtY

Liénard, Ernest Henri.
... . Étude des hydrates de carbone de réserve de quelques graines de Palmiers. ... Par Liénard (Ernest-Henri), ... Lons-le-Saunier, impr. L. Declume, 1903.
90 p. 24½ᶜᵐ.
Thèse—Univ. de Paris.

NL 0350236   ICJ DNLM DLC

Liénard, Félix, 1812–
... Archéologie de la Meuse; description des voies anciennes et des monuments aux époques celtique et gallo-romaine, par M. Félix Liénard ... Verdun, Impr. de C. Laurent, 1881–85.
3 v. pl., maps, plans. 36ᶜᵐ.
At head of title: Publication de la Société philomathique de Verdun.
Contents.—t. I. Partie sud du département.—t. II. Partie centrale du département.—t. III. Partie nord du département.

Subject entries: Meuse, Département de la—Antiq.

Library of Congress, no.   DC611.M599L7.

NL 0350237   DLC MH MB

Liénard, Félix, 1812–
Dictionnaire topographique du département de la Meuse comprenant les noms de lieu anciens et modernes, rédigé sous les auspices de la Société philomathique de Verdun par M. Félix Liénard ... Paris, Imprimerie nationale, 1872.
2 p. l., xliv, 297 p. 28ᶜᵐ. (France. Comité des travaux historiques et scientifiques. Dictionnaire topographique de la France ... 1861–)
Half-title: Dictionnaire topographique de la France comprenant les noms de lieu anciens et modernes, publié par ordre du ministre de l'instruction publique et sous la direction du Comité des travaux historiques et des sociétés savantes.
1. Meuse, France (Dept.)—Descr. & trav.—Gazetteers. 2. Names, Geographical—France.   I. Société philomathique de Verdun (Meuse)   II. Title.
Library of Congress   DC611.M598L6   26–14710

MiU
NL 0350238   DLC MU CU GEU GU NcU ViU OCl PU NN MH

[Liénard, Fortune]
Great Siege, The, of Paris: 1870–71. [By Philippoteaux.] Also, the assassination of the Archbishop of Paris [Darboy] at the hands of the Commune of 1871. [By Desbrosses. Description of the pictures.]
[Boston. 187–?] 23 pp. 17 cm.
"On exhibition cor. Columbus Ave. and Ferdinand Street, Boston."

K8576 — Boston. Gall. — Darboy,   Georges, Archevêque de Paris 1813–1871. — Debrosses, Jean Alfred, 1835—.—Panoramas.—Paris Hist. Franco-German War and Commune, 1870, 1871. — Philippoteaux, Félix Emmanuel Henri, 1815–1884.

NL 0350239   MB

VOLUME 332

[Liénard, Fortuné]
The great siege of Paris, 1870–71. From authentic historical data. New York and Philadelphia, A. G. Torrey, 1875–76.

24 p. 14¼ x 11¼ᶜᵐ.

Description of a panorama, painted by Col. Fortuné Liénard, and exhibited at the Colosseum, New York.

1. Paris—Siege, 1870-1871. 2. Panoramas.

Library of Congress   DC315.5.L5

CA 17–550 Unrev'd

NL 0350240   DLC NN

LIÉNARD, FORTUNÉ.
The great siege of Paris, 1870-71. From authentic historical data. New York, A.G. Torrey [c1875]
24 p. 15cm.

Film reproduction. Positive.
"1875-76. "
Description of a panorama, by Liénard, exhibited at the Colosseum, New York.
1. Paris- -Hist., 1870 -1871.   2. Panoramas. I. Title.

NL 0350241   NN

Liénard (Gustave-Émile). *De l'asystolie du cœur. 2 p. l., 44 pp. 4º. Strasbourg, 1865, 2. s., No. 886.

NL 0350242   DNLM

Liénard, J
Sur le calcul des variations d'eclat d'une petite planete en rotation, par J. Lienard et J. F. Cox.
(In Academie royale de Belgique. Classe des sciences. Bulletin. Bruxelles. 1931. 25 cm. 5. ser., t. XVII. p. 914-920)
-- --- Copy 2. (In Brussels. Université libre. Institut d'astronomie. (Publications) Bruxelles. 1931. 25½ cm. 2. ser., no. 17)

NL 0350243   DN-Ob

Lienard, J
Sur les variations d'éclat de la petite planète 433 Éros, par J. Liénard et J. F. Cox.
(In Academie royale de Belgique. Classe des sciences. Bulletin. Bruxelles. 1931. 25 cm. 5. sér., t. XVII. p. 793-796)
Bibliographical foot-notes.
-- --- Copy 2. (In Brussels. Université libre. Institut d'astronomie. (Publications) Bruxelles. 1931. 25½ cm. 2. sér., no. 17)

NL 0350244   DN-Ob

Liénard (J.-B.-M.-N.). *Sur la structure de l'oreille et l'ouie. 37 pp. 4º. Paris, an XII [1804]. No. 229, v. 48.

NL 0350245   DNLM

Liénard, Jacques L   1875-1901.
... Lettres et fragments, précédés d'une notice biographique par Daniel Benoit... Cahors, A. Coueslant, 1902.
303 p. port., plan. 19ᶜᵐ.

I Benoit, Daniel, 1944-

NL 0350246   NjPT CtY-D CtY

MZ14   Liénard, Jacques L   1875-1901.
L624n   Notre voyage au Zambèze. Notes et impressions par Jacques-L. Liénard, de la Société des Missions Évangéliques de Paris. Préf. de François Coillard. Paris, En vente: À la Maison des Missions [1900]
xxiii, 226 p. illus., maps (1 fold.) ports. 20 cm.

At head of title: Souvenir de l'expédition de M. Coillard au   Zambèze en 1899

NL 0350247   CtY-D CtY

Liénard, Jean.
... Recherches sur le venin d'abeilles, deductions pratiques ...   Paris, Librairie Le François, 1940.
31 p.
These.

NL 0350248   DNLM MwU

DD76   Liénard, Jean, 1936-1944, tr.
L82   Ludwig, Emil, 1881-
... Comment traiter les Allemands ... Traduit par Jean Liénard. New York, N. Y., Éditions de la Maison française inc., ^1944.

Liénard, Jean, 1936-1944, tr.   [KOT IN LC.]

Frank, Philipp, 1884-
... La fin de la physique mécaniste, par Philipp Frank ... Traduction de Jean Liénard, revue et mise à jour par l'auteur. Introduction de m. Marcel Boll. Paris, Hermann & cⁱᵉ, 1936.

A940.9181 Liénard, Julien.
L621   ... La littérature inspirée par Verdun. Essai de bibliographie des oeuvres littéraires, artistiques, musicales, publiées depuis 1914 et tirant leur substance de la grande bataille de Verdun, 1914-1918. Verdun, 1929.
39p.

At head of title: Julien Liénard & Louis Frémont.

NL 0350251   IU PU MH

---

ar W   Liénard, Louis.
53593   Du sort dans les faillites des créanciers
no.3   armés d'un droit de rétention; résolution et compensation. Droit français et étranger. Toulouse, Impr. Saint-Cyprien, 1904.
119 p. 24cm.

Thèse--Toulouse.

NL 0350252   NIC ICRL

Liénard, Michel.
Livre d'ornements...   Paris, Guérinet, [19--]
3 pt. in 1 v. 126 pl. (part. col.) 45.5 cm.
Three special title-pages, lettered A, B, C, "Spécimens de la décoration et de l'ornementation au XIXme siècle par Liénard", all with ornamental borders, included in number of plates.
No text.

NL 0350253   NjP OC1W

Liénard, Michel.
Das Ornamenten-Buch von Liénard. Hrsg. von C. Claesen in Lüttich. [Lüttich, etc.] 1866.
1 p.l., 37 pl. 43 cm.
Two special title-pages: Specimen der Decoration und Ornamentik im XIXth Jahrhundert von Liénard ..." with ornamental borders, included in number of plates.
Incomplete.

NL 0350254   CtY

Lienard, Michel.
L'ornementation au 19e siecle, ouvrage dedie a l'industrie artistique, contenant des compositions de L. Gsell, Rambert, etc. Paris, [1853†]
f°

NL 0350255   NN

Liénard, Michel.
Portefeuille de Liénard; motifs inédits applicables aux arts industriels et somptuaires, choisis et mis en ordre par MM. P. Liénard et A. Doussamy...   Paris [etc.] C. Claesen [186-?]
4 p.,   44cm.

In portfolio.
Imperfect: 62 plates wanting.

311403B. 1. Decorative art, French.   I. Doussamy, A.   December 17, 1945

NL 0350256   NN

NK   Liénard, Michel.
1535   Spécimens de la décoration et de l'orne-
L71   mentation au XIXe. siècle... Liège, C. Claesen [1866]
4 p., 125 plates. 43cm.

1. Decoration and ornament. 2. Architecture--Details. I. Title.

NL 0350257   NIC CU RPB NN

NK1535 Liénard, Michel.
.L7   Specimens de la decoration et de l'ornementa-
1868   tion au XIX me siecle par Lienard...
fol.   Liege, [1868]

NL 0350258   DLC CU

Liénard, Michel.
Spécimens de la décoration et de l'ornementation au XIXe siècle. Approuvé par le Conseil de perfectionnement de l'enseignement des arts du dessin en Belgique et inscrit sur la liste officielle de modèles susceptibles d'être recommandés aux académies et écoles de dessin. Partie 1-3.
Liège. Claesen. 1872. 3 parts in 1 v. 125 plates. 44 cm.
Has also an engraved title-page which reads, "Livre d'ornements par Liénard."
There is a heliotype reproduction of this work on shelf-number *Cab.80.-39.3.

L327I — Decoration.

NL 0350259   MB CLU ICU OC1MA NN

Liénard, Michel.
Liénard's specimens of decoration and ornamentation ... New-York, J. O'Kane [18-]
1 p.l., 6 p. 127 pl. 40½ᵐ.

Another edition published at Boston, by J. R. Osgood and company, in 1875.
Added t.-p.: "Book of ornaments, by Liénard," and three special title-pages, lettered A, B, C, "Spécimens de la décoration et de l'ornementation au XIXᵐᵉ siècle par Liénard," all with ornamental borders, included in number of plates.

1. Decoration and ornament. 2. Architecture—Details.

15–12955

Library of Congress   NK1535.L68

NL 0350260   DLC NIC CLSU PPD

VOLUME 332

Liénard, Michel.
Specimens of the decoration and ornamentation of the xixth century, by Liénard ... 127 plates arranged in 3 parts. Boston, J. R. Osgood and company, 1875.
3 v. in 1. 127 pl. (incl. port.) 40ᶜᵐ.

1. Decoration and ornament. 2. Architecture—Details.

12–15110

Library of Congress   NK1535.L7

NL 0350261   DLC OU CtY MB

Lienard, P.
L'ameublement
see under   Prignot, Eugene

Liénard, P
Éléments d'acoustique aéronautique, par P. Liénard, M. Kobrynski [et] P. Antzenberger. Paris, Office national d'études et de recherches aéronautiques [1950]
84 p. diagrs. 27 cm. (Office national d'études et de recherches aéronautiques. Publication no 40)
Cover title.
"Références et bibliographie": p. 81–82.

1. Soundproofing. 2. Aeroplanes—Design and construction. (Series: Office national d'études et de recherches aéronautiques, Paris. Publication no 40)

TL507.O4   no. 40   Library   A 52–3660
Mass. Inst. of Tech.   Library
for Library of Congress   †

NL 0350263   MCM DLC OC1CS NN

Liénard (Paul). *De l'influence de l'hypertrophie prostatique sur les rétrécissements de l'urètre. 60 pp., 1 l. 4°. *Lyon, A. Pastel*, 1884, 1. s., No. 234.

NL 0350264   DNLM

Liénard, Paul.
... Droit romain, le préteur pérégrin; droit français de la compétence des tribunaux français à l'égard des étrangers...par M. Paul Liénard...   Paris: L. Larose, 1893.   lxxx, 145 p.   8°.
Dissertation, Paris.

114208A. 1. Officials (Public),   Rome. 2. Aliens.—Jurisprudence,
Rome. 3. Aliens.—Jurisprudence,   France.
                           April 24, 1924.

NL 0350265   NN CtY

Liénard, Paul.
... Le préteur pérégrin ... De la compétence des tribunaux français à l'égard des étrangers ... par m. Paul Liénard ... Paris, L. Larose, 1893.
4 p. l., [ii]-lxxx, 145 p.   24½ᶜᵐ.
Thèse—Faculté de droit de Paris.
Bibliographical foot-notes.

1. Aliens—France. 2. Courts—France.   I. Title.

                        24–18416
Library of Congress   JX4270.F8L5

NL 0350266   DLC

Liénard, Pierre.
Étude d'une méthode de résonance pour la mesure de la transmission des vibrations sonores à travers une cloison et de leur réflexion. Clermont-Ferrand,1948.
Thèse - Univ. De Paris.

NL 0350267   CtY

Liénard, Pierre.
Étude d'une Méthode de Résonance pour la mesure de la transmission des vibrations sonores àtravers une cloison et de leur réflexion.   Paris, 1948.
167p.   (Publications du Groupement francais pour le développement des Recherches Aéronautiques. Éditées par l'Office National d'Études et de Recherches Aéronautiques. Rapport technique, no.33)

NL 0350268   InLP

QA55
I5   Lienard, R
Tables fondamentales à 50 décimales des sommes S_n, u_n, Σ_n. Paris, 1948.
14,[40] p.

Includes "Notes et references."

1. Mathematics - Tables, etc. 2. Numbers, Theory of - Tables, etc.

NL 0350269   CU RPB NNC

Liénard, René Albert, 1907-
... Paracelse (Theophrast Bombast von Hohenheim) 1493-1541; sa vie, son oeuvre; étude historique et critique ...   Lyon, 1932.
Thèse - Univ. de Lyon.
"Bibliographie": p. [127]-139.
1. Paracelsus, 1493-1541.

NL 0350270   CtY

WZ
100   LIENARD, René Albert, 1907-
P221LJ   Paracelse, Theophrast Bombast von
1932   Hohenheim, 1493-1541; sa vie, son oeuvre; étude historique et critique. Lyon, Bosc et Riou, 1932.
139 p. port.
Issued also as thesis, Univ. de Lyon.
1. Paracelsus, 1493-1541

NL 0350271   DNLM NcD-MC MoSMed

Liénard (Victor-Anthime-Louis-Joseph) [1879-]. *De l'éventration médiane post-opératoire et de son traitement chirurgical. 128 pp. 8°. *Lille*, 1904. No. 9

NL 0350272   DNLM

Liénard-Fiévet, Ch
... Manuel de blanchiment-teinture; chimie tinctoriale, par Ch. Liénard-Fiévet ... Avec 36 figures intercalées dans le texte. Paris, J.-B. Baillière et fils, 1926.
460 p. illus. 16ᶜᵐ.   (*Half-title:* Bibliothèque professionnelle.)
Series title also at head of t.-p.

NL 0350273   ICJ NN

Liénart, jurisconsulte.
Charles, ou Mémoires historiques de M. De La Bussière, ex-employé au Comité de salut public... Paris, 1803.
4 v.   18 cm.

NL 0350274   CtY

BX4705
T5L71   Liénart, A
L'âme d'un régiment: l'Abbé Thibaut, aumônier du 1er R.I... Préf. du Lt.-Colonel Frère du 1er R.I.   Cambrai, O. Masson, 1922.
xii, 109 p. ports. 20cm.

1. Thibaut, Philippe, 1885-1916. 2. European War, 1914-1918 - Religious aspects. I. Title.

NL 0350275   CSt-H NN

DS108
.5   Liénart, Achille, Cardinal, 1884-
.D8   Duran, Frédérique, 1921-
Dans les pas de Jésus. Présentation de S. É. le Cardinal Liénart. Introduction historique et archéologique de René Leconte. Photos de Frédérique Duran. [Paris] Hachette [1953]

NL 0350277   DCU

Lienart, Achille, Cardinal, 1884-
Hommage à Francois de Salignac de la Mothe-Fénelon. Lille, S.I.L.I.C., 1951.
8 p.

NL 0350277   DCU

Liénart, Achille, cardinal, 1884-
La Sainte Bible...publiée sous... la direction de Cardinal Liénart... Paris, 1951.
see under   Bible. French. 1951.
(also 1955)

BX1526
.L57A5   Liénart, Achille, Cardinal, 1884-
Lille (*Diocese*)
Statuts synodaux du diocèse de Lille, promulgués par Son Éminence le cardinal Liénart à la suite du synode du 16 avril 1953. Lille, Société d'impressions littéraires, industrielles et commerciales, 1954.

NL 0350280   DNLM CtY

Liénart (Mme. Marie) [1884-]. *Traitement de la péritonite tuberculeuse par la recalcification. 74 pp. 8°. *Paris*, 1916. No. 7.

NL 0350280   DNLM CtY

Liénart (O.) [1889-]. *Des hémorragies secondaires par blessures de guerre et de leur traitement. 107 pp. 8°. *Paris*, 1917. No. 51.

NL 0350281   DNLM CtY

Lienart-Odevaere.
L'anglomanie; comédie en trois actes et en vers, par M.ʳ Lienart-Odevaere, représentée pour la première fois sur le théâtre de Bruges, le 22 janvier 1823...   Bruges: De l'impr. de Bogaert-Dumortier [1823?]   86 p.   22cm.

1. Drama, Belgian-French.   I. Title.
                          July 9, 1940

NL 0350282   NN

LIENAU, A. *Psychosen als Initialsymptom der Encephalitis epidemica [Rostock]. 36p. 8°. Bergdorf, 1929.

NL 0350283   DNLM

Lienau (Arnold [Robert Matthias]) [1870-]. *Ueber die Häufigkeit von Ascaris lumbricoides und Trichocefalus dispar in Kiel, und ihre Beziehung zur Wasserversorgung. 13 pp. 8°. *Kiel, H. Fiencke*, 1896.

NL 0350284   DNLM MH CtY

Lienau, Cai, 1910-
... Trauma und Parkinsonismus ... Rostock, 1936.
Inaug.-Diss. - Rostock.
Lebenslauf.
"Literatur-Verzeichnis": p. 37-39.

NL 0350285   CtY

VOLUME 332

Lenau, Detlev
   see   Lenau, Michael Detlev, 1874–

LIENAU, Heinrich.
  Heidlüchen; niederdeutsches Drama in fünf Aufzugen. Vollstandige Regiebearbeitung. Neumünster, F. Reussner, [1917].

  18 cm. pp.76.

NL 0350287   MH

Lienau, Hermann.
  Nemo, ein Mann, das Meer und tausend Abenteuer. Berlin, Vorhut-Verlag [1935]
  210 p. 20 cm.

I. Title.

PZ33.L47   54–48256 ‡

NL 0350288   DLC

Lienau, Hermann, 1874–
  Beiträge zur Kenntnis der Uranylsalze. Leipzig: O. Brandstetter, 1898. 68 p. 8°.

Dissertation, Berlin.

1. Uranium.—Salts.

February 2, 1911.

NL 0350289   NN ICRL PU

Lienau, J Henry
  Detlef Lienau, architect, 1818–1887; biography, memorabilia, prepared by J. Henry Lienau. [New York? 1942?]
  cover-title, 28 l. incl. mount. ports., mount. facsims. 39ᵐ.

  Contains typewritten articles and letters by various persons, photostats of newspaper clippings, letters, and certificates issued to Detlef Lienau.
  Presentation copy to Avery with author's inscription and   signature.

NL 0350290   NNC

Avery

Lienau, L Henry   comp.
  [Architectural details, arranged by subject by L. Henry Lienau; taken from "Matériaux et documents d'architecture et de sculpture", under the direction of A. Raguenet. 19—]
  2 v. of plates. 31cm.

No title-page.

NL 0350291   NNC

LIENAU, M.
  Catalog der Orchideen-Sammlung, von M. Lienau in Jersey-City. n.p., C. Wäser, 1867.

  pp.37. 20 cm.

NL 0350292   MH

Lienau, Michael Detlev, 1874–
  Die entstehung der ackerböden erläutert an den geologisch-agronomischen verhältnissen in der provinz Sachsen, im herzogtum Anhalt und in den Thüringischen Staaten. Von dr. Detlev Lienau ... Halle a. S., L. Hofstetters verlag, 1912.

  ix, 223, [1] p. illus., III fold. maps in pocket, fold. tab. 23ᶜᵐ.

1. Germany. Soils. 2. Soil.

Agr 12–2190

Library, U. S. Dept. of   Agriculture 57L623

NL 0350293   DNAL ICJ NjR

Lienau, Michael Detlev, 1874–
  Über den einfluss der in den unteren teilen der halme von cerealien enthaltenen mineralstoffe auf die lagerung des getreides ... Königsberg i. Pr., Buch- und steindruckerei von H. Herrmann, 1903.

  84 p., 2 l., [2] p., 1 l. plates, tables, fold. diagr. 22ᶜᵐ.
  Inaug.-diss.—Königsberg.
  "Literaturübersicht" : p. [5–6]

1. Cereals.

Agr 4–119

Library, U. S. Dept. of   Agriculture 59L621

NL 0350294   DNAL DNLM CU PU

Lienau, Michael Martin, 1857–
  Die grabungen des Museumsvereins. Von Michael Martin Lienau. Lüneburg, V. Stern'sche buchdr., 1910.
  cover-title, 32 p. illus., 2 pl. 22ᶜᵐ.

  "Sonderabdruck aus dem 7. hft. der 'Lüneburger museumsblätter'."

1. Lüneburg—Antiq.

21–22297

DD491.H34L6

NL 0350295   DLC

Lienau, Michael Martin, 1857–
  ... Über megalithgräber und sonstige grabformen der Lüneburger gegend, von M. M. Lienau. Mit 1 karte, 30 tafeln und 5 text-abbildungen. Würzburg, C. Kabitzsch, 1914.

  2 p. l., 42 p. illus., xxx pl., fold. map, diagrs. 29ᶜᵐ. (Mannusbibliothek, hrsg. von professor dr. Gustaf Kossinna. nr. 13)

1. Megalithic monuments—Germany. 2. Lüneburg—Tombs.

32–30724

Library of Congress   GN705.M3 no.13
             (571.08) 571.9094353

NL 0350296   DLC ICJ NN CtY PU-M PPAmP PBm

Lienau, Michael Martin, 1857–
  Über stelenartige grabsteine, sonnenkult und opferstätten, anzeichen von menschenopfern, sowie über mehrfache bestattungen in stein- und bronzezeitlichen grabhügeln der Lüneburger gegend ... Von Michael Martin Lienau. [Würzburg, C. Kabitzsch, 1913]
  p. [195]–234. illus., pl. XII–XVI. 25½ᶜᵐ.
  Caption title.
  From Mannus, v. 5.

1. Hanover—Antiq.

23–1965

Library of Congress   CN814.H3L5

NL 0350297   DLC

Lienau, Michael Martin, 1857–
  ... Vor- und frühgeschichte der stadt Frankfurt a. d. Oder von den ältesten anfängen bis zum jahre 1253, von Michael Martin Lienau ... Mit einer seite abbildungen im text und einem stadtplan. Leipzig, C. Kabitzsch, 1921.

  1 p. l., 32 p. illus., fold. plan. 26ᶜᵐ. (Mannus-bibliothek, hrsg. von professor dr. Gustaf Kossinna. nr. 25)

1. Frankfurt-an-der-Oder.

32–30733

Library of Congress   GN705.M3 no. 25
             (571.08) 943.15

NL 0350298   DLC NN MH CtY ICJ PPAmP PBm PU-M

4V   Lienau, Otto, 1877–
78   Die Bootsfunde von Danzig-Ohra aus der Wikingerzeit. Danzig, Danziger Verlags-Gesellschaft, 1934.
     52 p.

NL 0350299   DLC-P4 CtY NN

Lienau, Otto, 1877–
  ...Festrede gehalten bei der Übergabe des Rektorates am 29. Juni 1930, von Prof. Dr.-Ing. E.h. O. Lienau. [Danzig: Druck von W. F. Burau, 1930?] 15 p. 7 pl. 24cm.

  At head of title: Technische Hochschule, Danzig.
  Caption-title: Danziger Schiffahrt und Schiffbau in der zweiten Hälfte des 15. Jahrhunderts.
  "Literatur", p. 15.

824623A. 1. Shipping—Danzig.   2. Shipbuilding—Danzig.   June 10, 1936

NL 0350300   NN

Lienau, Otto, 1877–
  Wasserbau und verwandte anwendungen ... Uferbefestigungen, schleusen, wehre, talsperren, leuchttürme und leuchtbaken, hellinge, schiffe und schwimmkörper, bearbeitet von O. Lienau, E. Marquardt, F. W. Otto Schulze und B. Kressner. Mit 1200 textabbildungen. Berlin, W. Ernst & sohn, 1926.
  xvi, 489 p. illus., tables, diagrs. 27ᶜᵐ. (Added t.-p.: Handbuch für eisenbetonbau. 3. neubearb. aufl. ... hrsg. von ... F. Emperger ... 4. bd.)
  Bibliographical foot-notes.
  1. Concrete, Reinforced. 2. Hydraulic engineering. 3. Retaining walls. 4. Locks (Hydraulic engineering) 5. Weirs. 6. Dams. 7. Lighthouses. 8. Buoys. 9. Ships. Concrete. I. Marquardt, Erwin, 1889– joint author. II. Schulze, F. W. Otto, 1868– joint author. III. Kressner, Bernhard, joint author.
  Library, U. S. Patent   Office   TA683.H236   P O 28–11

NL 0350301   DP

Lienau, Robert, vormals Schlesinger'sche Buch- und Musikhandlung, Berlin.
  ...Musikalien-Verlags-Catalog derjenigen Artikels welche für 8 Pfennige pro Bogen und in 7/6 Exemplaren baar aus unserem Verlage geliefert werden... Berlin, Schlesinger; Wien, C. Haslinger qd. Tobias [etc., etc.] 1895. 35 p. 21cm.

  Excerpt: Verband der deutschen Musikalienhändler. Musik-Katalog. Gesammelte Verlags-Kataloge... Leipzig, 1895–97.
  At head of title: Nicht für das Publikum!

1. Music—Bibl.

November 20, 1946

NL 0350302   NN

Lienau, Robert, vormals Schlesinger'sche Buch- und Musikhandlung, Berlin.
  Musik-Verlag der Schlesingerschen Buch- und Musikhandlung (Rob. Lienau) Berlin, und des Carl Haslinger qdm. Tobias (Rob. Lienau) Wien... [Berlin] 1890. 3 v. in 1. 25cm.

  Excerpt: Verband der deutschen Musikalienhändler. Musik-Katalog. Gesammelte Verlags-Kataloge... Leipzig, 1895–97. Ergänzungsbd. 2.

——— ——— Nachtrag 1– 1890/92–1893/94   nos.

  Supplements 1–2, excerpts: Verband der deutschen Musikalienhändler. Musik-Katalog. Gesammelte Verlags-Kataloge... Leipzig, 1895–97. Ergänzungsbd. 2.
  Supplements 1–2 bound with the above.

324666B. 1. Music—Bibl.   November 22, 1946

NL 0350304   NN

VOLUME 332

Lienau, Robert, vormals Schlesinger'sche Buch- und Musikhandlung, Berlin.
Neues Musikalien-Verlags-Verzeichnis, Schlesingersche Buch-und Musik-Handlung...und Carl Haslinger qdm. Tobias in Wien... 1891–1902. ₍Leipzig, 1903?₎ 20 l. 26cm.

———— ———— Nachtrag. 1903–08. 8 p.

1. Music—Bibl.

November 20, 1946

NL 0350305   NN

Lienau, Robert, vormals Schlesinger'sche Buch-
und Musikhandlung, Berlin.
Verzeichnis des musik-verlags der
Schlesingerschen buch- und musikhandlung
(Rob Lienau) Berlin und des Carl Haslinger
q^am Tobias (Rob Lienau) Wien. [Berlin und
Wien] 1890–1902.
2 v. in 1.   26 cm.
The issue for 1890 is vol. 2 of a three
volume edition and has the contents: Für clavier,
orgel, harmonium, harfe, zither, guitarre.
The issue for 1902 has a cover title: Carl

Haslinger, q^dm Tobias. Musikalien-verlags-
verzeichnis, Wien I, 1902 (1891-1901).
Binder's title: Catalog-Haslinger pt. 2. 1.
1. Music - Bibl. - Catalogs, Publishers'.
2. Catalogs, Publishers' - Germany. I. Lienau
Rob. II. Haslinger, Carl.

NL 0350307   MB

Lienau, Robert, 1866–
Erinnerung an Johannes Brahms ... von Robert Lienau.
Berlin-Lichterfelde, 1934.
1 p. l., 5–48 p. diagr. 19½ᵐ.

1. Brahms, Johannes, 1833–1897.
38–4914

Library of Congress   ML410.B8L72

927.8

NL 0350308   DLC NN

Lienau, Robert, 1866–   ed.
Schwert und Leier; 303 ernste und fröhliche
deutsche Vaterlands-, Soldaten- und Volkslieder
in der grossen Kriegszeit. 3.Aufl. Berlin,
R.Lienau, etc., etc. [1916]

"Vollständiges Liederbuch zum Mitsingen für
die grosse Klavierausgabe... (3. Bd.)"

NL 0350309   MH MB MiD CtY DLC-P4 NN

Lienau, Robert Albrecht, 1905–
Stellung und befugnisse des präsidenten des
ständigen internationalen gerichtshofes. ...
Kiel, 1938. 147 p.
Inaug. Diss. - Kiel, 1938.
Lebenslauf.
Literatur und quellen verzeichnis.

NL 0350310   ICRL MH CtY

Lienau (Rudy). * Ueber Lagerung der Kreis-
senden. 27 pp. 8°. *Würzburg, F. E. Thein,
1875.*

NL 0350311   DNLM

Lienau, Walter, 1906–
Ueber freimaurer und logen, von Walter Lienau. Leipzig,
T. H. Fritsch (jun.) ₍1936₎
77 p. 15ᵐ.

"Literaturnachweis": p. 77.

1. Freemasons. 2. Secret societies.
45–53568

Library of Congress   HS405.L55

366.1

NL 0350312   DLC NN MH CoFS CtY IaU

Lienau, Walter, 1906–
Ueber freimaurer und logen, von Walter Lienau. Leipzig,
T. H. Fritsch (jun.) ₍1936₎
Film copy made in 1943 by the Library of Congress. Negative.
Collation of the original, as determined from the film: 77 p.
"Literaturnachweis": p. 77.

1. Freemasons. 2. Secret societies.
44–17536

Library of Congress   Film DD–1 reel 33, no. 7

NL 0350313   DLC

HS395   Lienau, Walter, 1906-
L45   Über Freimaurer und Logen. ₍2. Aufl.₎
1939   Berlin, Fritsch ₍1939₎
78 p.

"Literaturnachweis": p.78.

1. Freemasons. 2. Secret societies.

NL 0350314   CU

Lienau, Wolfgang, 1900–
Der stand der versorgung Lübecks mit einigen
der wichtigsten lebensmittel in den jahren 1927
und 1928... Göttingen, 1930. 112 p.
Inaug. Diss. -Göttingen, 1930.
Lebenslauf.
Bibliography.

NL 0350315   ICRL MH MiU CtY

QR49   Liénaux, E., joint author.
.M9
Mosselman, Gustave.
Manual of veterinary microbiology. By Professors Mos-
selman and Liénaux ... Tr. and ed. by R. R. Dinwiddie
... Cincinnati, The R. Clarke company, 1894.

Liénaux, Fd.
...Croquis d'animaux et commentaires biologiques... Méthode nouvelle, créée par Fd. Liénaux...   La Louvière (Belgique): Les Éditions Studio ₍1938₎ 116 p.   illus., 16 pl.
29½cm.   (Collection pédagogique de l'enseignement du dessin.
Cours 5.)

"Table bibliographique," p. 116.

1. Drawing, Animal. 2. Anatomy   for artists.
February 10, 1942

NL 0350317   NN

Liénaux, Fd.
...La pratique du croquis au pinceau et de la linogravure;
méthode nouvelle, créée par Fd. Liénaux.   La Louvière (Belgique): Les Éditions Studio ₍1938₎ 19 p.   illus. (incl. ports.),
plates.   30cm.   (Collection pédagogique de l'enseignement
du dessin. Cours 6.)

1. Drawing—Handbooks.
February 10, 1942

NL 0350318   NN

Liénaux, Ferdinand.
O desenho racional na escola. Traduzido por Flora
Marques d'Elia. Pôrto Alegre, Livraria do Globo ₍1943₎
106 p. illus. 24 cm.

1. Drawing—Instruction. 2. Art—Study and teaching. I. Title.

NC615.L516
51–46848

NL 0350319   DLC

Lienbacher, Georg, 1822–1896.
Das österreichische polizei-strafrecht. Von Georg Lienbacher ... 4., verm. und verb. aufl. Wien, Manz, 1880.
1 p. l., 295 p. 24ᵐ.

1. Police—Austria. 2. Criminal law—Austria.   I. Austria. Laws,
statutes, etc. II. Title.
37–35704

NL 0350320   DLC MH-L NcD PU-L

Lienbacher, Georg, 1822–1896, ed.
Austria. *Laws, statutes, etc.*
Die österreichische pressgesetzgebung. Von Georg
Lienbacher... Wien, W. Braumüller, 1863–68.

Lienbacher, Georg, 1822-1896.
Sollen in Oesterreich schwurgerichte
eingeführt werden? Die antwort widmet
den österreichischen landtagen und den
geschworenen der jahre 1850 und 1851 ein
praktischer justizmann. Wien, Manz,
1861.
38 p. 22½cm.

NL 0350322   MH-L

LIENBACHER, V   , ed.
Glockner-Gruppe; ein Führer für Täler Hütten, Berge.
Ein Gemeinschaftswerk der Kenner und Freunde der
Glockner-Gruppe. [1.-3. Aufl.] München, Bergverlag
R. Rother [1953] 176 p. (p. 172-176 advertisements) illus., fold.
map. 17cm. (Alpenvereinsführer. Bd. 6. Reihe: Zentralalpen)

Bibliography, p. 22-23.

1. Grossglockner, Austria--   Guidebooks, 1953.
2. Mountaineering--Alps.   I. Lienbacher, Vera.

NL 0350323   NN

Lienbacher, V
Kleiner Führer durch die Ötztaler Alpen und die angrenzenden Stubaier Alpen; Ötztal, Pitztal, Kaunertal und
Oberinntal mit ihren Orten, Wegen, Hütten, Übergängen
und Gipfeln. ₍1.-3. Aufl.₎ München, R. Rother ₍1952₎
167 p. illus. 17 cm.

1. Ötztaler Alpen—Descr. & trav.—Guide-books. 2. Stubai Alps.
I. Title.

DB765.L55 1952
58–43815 ‡

NL 0350324   DLC MH

Lienores, Antonio Losada Y Frenandez

see

Losada y Fernandez de Lienores, Antonio.

Liencres, Manuel Fernández de
see **Fernández de Liencres, Manuel.**

VOLUME 332

PN2061 **Lienden, Herman Johan Hendrik van.**
.L7   Psychologische beschouwing over tooneelspel en tooneel-
speler ... Groningen, Gebroeders Hoitsema, 1924.
  ⟨8⟩, 91, ⟨2⟩ p. diagrs. 23½ᶜᵐ.
  Proefschrift–Groningen.

    1. Acting. 2. Actors.

NL 0350327   ICU NN

Liendo, Arturo.
Lat.Amer.   Alburas, versos. ⟨Prologo del Dr. René
LI225a   Capistrán Garza. Habana⟩ Imprenta la Milagrosa
Harris   Amargura y Compostela, 1935.
Collection   159p. 21 cm.

    1. Cuban poetry. I. Capistrán Garza, René.
II. Title.

NL 0350328   RPB FU NN

Liendo, José.
Pamphlet   Discurso laudatorio que pronunció el presi-
Peru   dente del acto academico doctor don Jose Liendo,
1812   vice rector del Colegio Real de San Juan Bau-
L62   tista de la Plata en 22 de julio de 1812. en
honor del señor mariscal de campo don Jose
Manuel de Goyeneche, general en xefe del Exér-
cito Real del Alto Perú. [Lima,1812]

    1. Goyeneche, José Manuel de, 1775-1846.

NL 0350329   CtY NcD

---

4 K-584   **Liendo, Hilario.**
  Notas al Código de enjuiciamiento civil con un
indice analitico por orden alfabético. Lima,
B. Gil, 1886.
  122 p.

NL 0350330   DLC-P4 NNC

Liendo, José Florentino Conejo y
  see   Conejo, Florentino.

Liendo, Rosa Dominga Pérez
see
Pérez Liendo, Rosa Dominga.

LIENDO LAZARTE, MANUEL.
  Breve introduccion etnografica sobre
el origen y evolucion del hombre.
La Paz,Bolivia⟨Editorial Fenix,1948⟩
71p. illus. 20cm.

  "Publicaciones de divulgacion cientifica popular del Museo nacional Tihuanacu."

NL 0350333   PU-Mu

Liendo Lazarte, Manuel.
  ... Nota preliminar sobre un pequeño toxodonte del Altiplano:
Poonanskytherium desaguaderoi gen. nov. sp. nov. Por:
Manuel Liendo Lazarte ... La Paz, Bolivia, Editorial del
estado, 1943.
  12 p. pl. 21½ᶜᵐ.
  At head of title: Museo nacional Tihuanacu. Sección Paleontología.

    1. Posnanskytherium desaguaderol. I. La Paz, Bolivia. Museo
nacional.
                           44-9272
Library of Congress   QE882.N6L5
                                  569.643

NL 0350334   DLC

⟨**Lieneman, Catharine⟩** 1899–
  ... Observations on *Thyronectria denigrata.* ⟨New York,
1938⟩
  ⟨1⟩, 494-511 p. illus. 23ᶜᵐ.

  Thesis (PH. D.)—University of Nebraska, 1934.
  Thesis note on label mounted on p. ⟨1⟩
  "Contributions from the Department of botany, University of Ne-
braska, n. s. no. 107."
  "⟨By⟩ Catharine Lieneman."
  "Reprinted from Mycologia, vol. xxx, no. 5 ... Sept.-Oct. 1938."
  "Literature cited" : p. 509.

    1. Thyronectria denigrata. 2. Honey locust—Diseases and pests.
                        Full name: Catharine Mary Lieneman⟩
                                   39-10775
Library of Congress   QK623.P9L5 1934
Univ. of Nebraska Libr.   632.4354

NL 0350335   NbU PPT DLC

Lieneman, Catharine Mary

see

Lieneman, Catharine, 1899-

QC367   **LIENEMAN, Jan Ernst.**
L54   Over de helderheid der kleuren.
1914   Amsterdam, M.J. Portielje, 1914.
  198, [3]p. illus. 24cm.
  Academisch proefschrift - Amsterdam.
  "Stellingen": [3]p. at end.
  acc. no. 7762. LC° cat. ° SG°°°

    1. Optical measurements 2. Photometry
3. Color 4. Color-blindness I. Title
Prov. Dusser de Barenne, Joannes Gregorius, 1885-19   40

NL 0350337   CtY-M MH DNLM

W 4   **LIENEMANN, Elfriede, 1925-**
W95   Über eine Methode, die Messung der
1954   Funktion der Seitenwender des Auges zur
Beurteilung des Heilverlaufes schielo-
perierter Muskeln heranzuziehen.
Würzburg, 1954.
  23 p. illus.
  Inaug.-Diss. - Würzburg.
  1. Eye - Muscles

NL 0350338   DNLM

LIENEMANN, KURT, 1881-
  Die Belesenheit von William Wordsworth.
Kapitel I: Englische Litteratur bis Dryden.
⟨Weimar, R. Wagner Sohn⟩ 1908.
  1 p.ℓ., 55, ⟨1⟩ p. 8vo

  Inaug.-Diss.—Berlin.
  Lebenslauf.
  Consists of the first 51 pages of a
259 p. book published in 1908, in Berlin,
by Mayer & Müller, without thesis note.

NL 0350339   InU CtY

Wor   **Lienemann, Kurt, 1881-**
PR   Die Belesenheit von William Wordsworth ...
5873   Berlin, Mayer & Müller, 1908.
L71   259 p. 23cm.

    1. Wordsworth, William, 1770-1850.

  IaU InU IU MA NjP OrPR
NL 0350340   NIC OOxM MH PU OC1 InU ICRL ScU NcU NcD

Lienemann, Louise Joanne, 1900–
  A botany laboratory manual. Copyright ... ⟨by⟩ Louise
Joanne Lienemann ... Denver, Col., °1941.
  1 p. l., 103 p. 28 x 22ᶜᵐ.

  Reproduced from type-written copy.
  Blank versos not included in paging.

    1. Botany—Laboratory manuals.
                              41-20718
Library of Congress   QK53.L5
                               580.72

NL 0350341   DLC

Thesis   **Lienemann, Louise Joanne, 1900-**
1937   A study of the blood and urine of Cambarus
L720   clarkii (Girard). ⟨Ithaca, N. Y.⟩ 1937.
  vi, 244 l. illus. 28 cm.

  Thesis (Ph. D.) - Cornell Univ., June 1937.

    1. Blood. 2. Urine. 3. Osmosis. 4. Cray-
fish. 5. Cambarus clarkii. ⟨I. Title⟩

NL 0350342   NIC

Lienemann, Oskar.
  Eigentümlichkeiten des Englischen der Vereinigten Staaten nebst
wenig bekannten Americanismen.
  Leipzig. Fock. 1886. 32 pp. 25 cm., in 4s.

  K9310 — English language. Dialects. United States.

NL 0350343   MB NcD CtY

LIENEMANN, Oskar.
  Eigentümlichkeiten des englischen der vereinigten Staaten, nebst wenig bekannten americanismen. Zittau, 1886.

  4°. pp. (2), 32.
  "Wissensch.beilage zum progr. des königl.
realgym. 1886,nr.507 [513]."

NL 0350344   MH NjP

Ph.D.   **Liener, Irvin Ernest.**
Bio   The mechanism of growth inhibition of the
'49   soybean trypsin inhibitor. June 1949.
L719   vii,140 ℓ. mounted diagrs. 29cm.

  Thesis - Univ. of Southern California.
  Typewritten.

    1. Soy-bean. 2. Trypsin.   IC

NL 0350345   CLSU

Liener, Josef.
  Der neue Christ. 2.Aufl. Innsbruck, Tyrolia-Verlag,
1937
  340 p. (His Die Zukunft der Religion, 2)

NL 0350346   MH

Liener, Josef.
  Psychologie des Unglaubens. Innsbruck, Tyrolia-
Verlag, 1935.
  258 p. (His Die Zukunft der Religion, 1)

NL 0350347   MH DGU

Liener, Josef.
  Die Zukunft der Religion. Innsbruck, Tyrolia-Verlag
[1935-37]
  2 v.
  Vol.2: 2.Aufl.

NL 0350348   MH

Lienert, Emil.
  Die Dasselplage; Bericht über eine ECA-Studienreise
(technical assistance) nach Deutschland. Wien, Österreichisches Produktivitäts-Zentrum, 1952.
  47, ⟨1⟩ p. illus. 21 cm. (Die Studienreise, Schriftenreihe des
Österreichischen Produktivitäts-Zentrums)
  Bibliography: p. 47-⟨48⟩

    1. Warble-flies. I. Title.
  SF967.W3L5   56-47245

NL 0350349   DLC DNAL RU

VOLUME 332

BF 431 L468
Lienert, Gustav Adolf.
Belastung und Regression; Versuch einer Theorie der systematischen Beeinträchtigung der intellektuellen Leistungsfähigkeit, von Gustav A. Lienert. Meisenheim am Glan, A. Hein, 1864.
117p. illus. 23cm. (Psychologia universalis, Bd. 7)
Thesis - Marburg.
Includes bibliography.
1. Intellect I. Title

NL 0350350   WU

---

4 PT Ger. -4138
Lienert, Hans.
Im heiligen Ring; ein Bauernroman aus Siebenbürgen. Hermannstadt, Heimatverlag, 1925.
194 p.

NL 0350351   DLC-P4

---

4 Music -865
Lienert, Hans.
Hochzeit; ein sächsisches Lustspiel in drei Aufzügen. Mediasch, G.A. Reissenberger, 1913.
94 p.

NL 0350352   DLC-P4

Lienert, Hans.
Wahrheit; ein Bauerndrama in drei Aufzügen. Leipzig: M. Hesse [1912]. 75 p. 12°.

1. Drama (German). 2. Title.
June 9, 1913.

NL 0350353   NN MH

Lienert, Hermann.
Über Derivate des 1-Methyl-, des 3-Methyl- und des 1, 6-Dimethyl-Fluorenons. [Einsiedeln, Benziger, 1948]

Inaug.-Diss. - Freiburg (Switzerland)

NL 0350354   MH CtY

LIENERT, JOSEF, 1898-
Umstellung der Wirtschaft auf heimische Energiequellen. Wien, 1947. 24 p. graphs. 30cm.
(Österreichisches Institut für Wirtschaftsforschung. Sonderheft. 4)

Film reproduction. Negative. Original discarded.
Cover title.
1. Electric power industries--Austria. 2. Electric power--Costs--Austria.

NL 0350355   NN

Lienert, Josef, 1898-
Führer durch die elektrizitätswirtschaft, von dipl.-ing. Josef Lienert ... Mit 38 abbildungen. Wien, Springer, 1943.
vii, 138 p. illus., diagrs. 21ᶜᵐ.

1. Electric industries. 2. Electric power—Rates. I. Title.
45-21232
Library of Congress   HD9685.A3A94
621.3

NL 0350356   DLC

Lienert, Konrad, 1868-
Gedenket der gefallenen krieger! Trostworte und gebete von p. Konrad Lienert ... 3. aufl. Einsiedeln, New York [etc.] Benziger & co. [1915]
63, [1] p. incl. front. 12¼ᶜᵐ.

Continued in next column

Continued from preceding column

I. Title.
21-19567
Library of Congress   BX2170.W2L5

NL 0350357   DLC

Lienert, Konrad, 1868-
Der moderne Redner. Eine Einführung in die Redekunst, nebst einer kurzen Geschichte der Beredsamkeit und einer Sammlung vollständiger Reden aus neuester Zeit zum Gebrauche in Schulen und zum Selbstunterricht. Von P. Konrad Lienert... Einsiedeln: Benziger & Co., A.-G., 1907. 444 p. 8°.

1. Oratory.
March 28, 1927

NL 0350358   NN PPCCH PLatS

Lienert, Lina Schips-
see Schips, Lina (Lienert) 1892-

Lienert, Meinrad, 1865-1933.
La belle histoire des premiers Suisses, par Meinrad Lienert; traduction francaise de J. Bohy. Avec six gravures en couleurs. Lausanne, Spes [19--?]
31 p. incl. 6mounted col. pl. 23.5cm.

NL 0350360   OO

Lienert, Meinrad, 1865-1933.
... Bergdorfgeschichten. Frauenfeld, Huber & co., 1914.
2 p. l., 439 p. 19½ᶜᵐ.   M. 5.60
CONTENTS.—Das blaue wasser.— Der kalte brand.— Das klauslaufen.— Die schmiedjungfer. — Die raucher. — Das altarbild.— Das hustende Seppeli.—Lützelweisschen.—Der jungfernraub.—Die landstrasse.

I. Title.
14-642
Library of Congress   PT2623.I 38B4 1914

NL 0350361   DLC

Lienert, Meinard, 1865-1933.
Dr. Schällechingg; es vaterländisches Spiel... vom Meinrad Lienert. [Luzern, 1939] 85 f. 21cm. (Spielbuch der Luzerner Spielleute. Nr. 3)

Caption-title.

1. Drama, Swiss-German. 2. German language—Dialects—Switzerland—Lucerne. I. Title.

NL 0350362   NN

Lienert, Meinrad, 1865-1933.
Der doppelte Matthias und seine töchter, roman von Meinrad Lienert. Berlin, G. Grote, 1929.
2 p. l., 403 p. 19ᶜᵐ. (Half-title: Grote'sche sammlung von werken zeitgenössischer schriftsteller. bd. 178)

I. Title.
30-18467
Library of Congress   PT2623.I 38D6 1929

NL 0350363   DLC OC1 CtY PPGi

Hxy L623 D6
Lienert, Meinrad, 1865-1933.
Drei altmodische Liebesgeschichten. Frauenfeld, Huber [c1916]
79 p. 16 cm. (Schweizerische Erzähler, Bd. 2)

NL 0350364   CtY ICarbS

Lienert, Meinrad, 1865-1933.
Drei altmodische Liebesgeschichten, von Meinrad Lienert. Frauenfeld [etc.] Huber & Co., 1917. 79 p. 15½cm. (Halftitle: Schweizerische Erzähler. Bd. 2.)

1. Fiction, Swiss-German.   I. Title.
February 17, 1941

NL 0350365   NN

Lienert, Meinrad, 1865-1933.
... Drei altmodische liebesgeschichten. Zürich, Rascher, 1946 [i. e. 1945]
3 p. l., 3-80 p. 18½ᶜᵐ. (Half-title: Schweizerische bibliothek)
"Copyright 1946."
"12. bis 15. tausend."
CONTENTS.—Das bauernkätzchen.—Die schlosshütte.—Die stier von Uri.

I. Title.
PT2623.I 38D7 1945   833.91   47-19436

NL 0350366   DLC

PT 2623 I38 E7
Lienert, Meinrad, 1865-1933.
Erzählungen aus der Schweizergeschichte. Zeichnungen von Aug. Aeppli. Aarau, H. R. Sauerländer [1930?]
351p. illus. 21cm.

1. Tales, Swiss I. Title

NL 0350367   WU

Lienert, Meinrad, 1865-1933.
Fünfzig Lieder aus dem Schwäbelpfyffli, von Meinrad Lienert. Zur Erinnerung an den Dichter... ihren Mitgliedern dargebracht von der Schweizerischen Schillerstiftung. Aarau, H. R. Sauerländer & Co., 1934. 80 p. illus. 18cm.

1. Poetry, Swiss-German. 2. German language—Dialects—Switzerland—Aarau. I. Schweizerische Schillerstiftung.

NL 0350368   NN

Lienert, Meinrad, 1865-1933.
Gedenkschrift zum 75. Geburtstage von Meinrad Lienert
see under Schmid, Gotthold Otto, ed.

Lienert, Meinrad, 1865-1933.
Das Glöcklein auf Rain. [Roman.]
— Frauenfeld. Huber & Co. [1933.] 367 pp. 18.5 cm., in 8s.

E117 — T.r.

NL 0350370   MB PPGi

PT 2623 I38 H3
Lienert, Meinrad, 1865-1933.
Hansjörlis Fahrt nach dem Zauberwort. Frauenfeld, Huber, 1922.
310p. 19cm.

NL 0350371   WU

Lienert, Meinrad, 1865-1933.
Die Kunst zu Illendorf, eine Erzählung. Berlin, Grote, 1931.
319 p.

NL 0350372   PPG

PT 2623 I38 L4
Lienert, Meinrad, 1865-1933.
Der letzte Schwanauritter; ein fröhlicher Sang aus der Urschweiz. Mit Zeichnungen von Peter Schnorr. Frauenfeld, J. Huber, 1896.
115p. illus. 19cm.

NL 0350373   WU TNJ IEN

VOLUME 332

Lienert, Meinrad, 1865-1933.
Meinrad Lienart zu seinem 50. Geburtstag,
21. May 1915
see under Eschmann, Ernst, 1886-

Leinert, Meinrad, 1865-1933.
Meiredli; die schönsten Geschichten aus den
Bänden, Das war eine goldene Zeit, und, Berg-
spieglein. Frauenfeld, Huber [1951]
222 p. illus.

NL 0350375 OCl

PT
2623
I38
P4
Lienert, Meinrad, 1865-1933.
Der Pfeiferkönig; eine Spielmannsges-
chichte. 2., bearb. Aufl. Aarau, H. R.
Sauerländer, 1919.
266p. 19cm.
Cover title: Der Pfeiferkönig; eine
Zürchergeschichte.

NL 0350376 WU PPG

Lienert, Meinrad, 1865-1933.
Der Schellenkönig. Erzählung aus dem Schwyzer Bergland.
(In Deutsche Roman-Bibliothek. Jahrgang 29, Band 2. Stutt-
gart, 1901.)

NL 0350377 MB

Lienert, Meinrad, 1865-1933.
Die Schmiedjungfer; eine Geschichte. 3. Aufl
Frauenfeld, Huber, 1923.
184 p. 21 cm.

NL 0350378 WU

Lienert, Meinrad, 1865-1933.
Die schöne Geschichte der alten Schweizer. Zürich,
Schweizer Spiegel Verlag [1941]
39 p. plates. 25 cm.

1. Switzerland—History, Juvenile. 2. Tell, Wilhelm. I. Title.

PZ35.L5   50-50178 rev

NL 0350379 DLC

831.91
L719s
1913
Lienert, Meinrad, 1865-1933.
's Schwäbelpfyffli. 3. sehr verm. Aufl.
Aarau, H. R. Sauerländer, 1913.
2v. music.

NL 0350380 ICarbS

Lienert, Meinrad, 1865-1933.
Schweizer Sagen und Heldengeschichten der
Jugend erzählt. Mit sechs bunten Vollbildern
und zahlreichen Textillustrationen von Wilh.
Roegge. 2 Aufl. Stuttgart, Olten Levy &
Müller, [1914]
viii, 294 p., col. front., il., 5col. pl.

NL 0350381 OCl

LIENERT, Meinrad, compiler.
Schweizer sagen und heldengeschichten der
jugend erzählt. Mit 6 bunten vollbildern und
zahlreichen textillustrationen von Wilh, Roegge
Stuttgart-Otten, Levy u. Müller, [1917].

Plates (partly colored) and other illustr.

NL 0350382 MH

Hkl8
153
Lienert, Meinrad, 1865-1933.
... Schweizer Sagen und Heldengeschichten.
Mit sechs farbigen Vollbildern und 40 Text-
bildern von Wilh. Roegge. 22.Auflage.
Stuttgart, Levy & Müller [1935?]
366p. col.front., illus., col.plates. 22cm.
(Die Heroldbücher)

1.Legends - Switzerland. 2.Folk-lore -
Switzerland. 3.Heldensage. x.ser.^

NL 0350383 CtY

LIENERT, Meinrad, 1865-1933.
Die stimme der heimat. Basel, E.Finckh,
1918.

pp.19. Illustr.(on cover).
"Volks-bücher des Deutschschweizerischen
sprachvereins, 6."

NL 0350384 MH

Lienert, Meinrad, 1865-1933.
Der Überfall, und andere Erzählungen, von Meinrad Lienert.
Hrsg. von der Lehrervereinigung für Kunstpflege zu Berlin, e. D.
Mit Bildern von Eduard Stiefel. Reutlingen, Ensslin & Laiblin
[1924] 51 p. illus. 21cm. (Bunte Jugendbücher. Heft
50.)
Contents.—Der Überfall.—Der Verräter.—Die Entdeckung Amerikas.—Der Gang
zur Post.

I. Title.
January 23, 1948

NL 0350385 NN

Lienert, Meinrad, 1865-1933.
... Von lieb und leid; schwyzer geschichten; ausgewählt und
eingeleitet von Gottfried Bohnenblust. Frauenfeld und Leipzig, Huber & co. aktiengesellschaft [1943]
xx, 291 p. 18½ᵐ.
Contents.—Vorwort.—Aus der jugendzeit: Zum blauen see. Das
gespenst. Meine erste liebe.—Aus alten zeiten: Die getreuen. Das
fähnlein. Der kreuzgärtner von Goldau.—Von lieb und leid: Das berg-
spieglein. Tönis brautfahrt. Das ruhebänklein.

I. Bohnenblust, Gottfried, 1883-   ed. II. Title.

A 44-5740

Harvard univ. Library
for Library of Congress

NL 0350386 MH

Hky
L623
Z68
Lienert, Meinrad, 1865-1933.
Ziumarstalden; eine Erzählung aus der
Urschweiz. Zürich, Gute Schriften, 1940.
111p. 20cm. (Gute Schriften, Nr.197)

NL 0350387 CtY

LPT
Ger
4945
Lienert, Otto Hellmut.
Die alte Schmiede; Gedichte.
Affoltern a. A., Aehren Verlag,
1952.
67 p.

NL 0350388 DLC-P4 CtY NN

Lienert, Otto Hellmut.
...'s Ampeli; schwyzerdütschi Gidicht. Frauenfeld [etc.]
Huber & Co. [1934] 59 p. 21cm.

A26037B. 1. Poetry, Swiss-Ger-
lects—Switzerland.   man. 2. German language—Dia-
September 21, 1951

NL 0350389 NN

WB
16345
Lienert, Otto Hellmut.
Das Bild der Madonna; ein Roman. Olten,
O.Walter [cl953]

NL 0350390 CtY

Lienert, Otto Hellmut.
's Gültetrükli; nü Värs. Einsiedeln/Köln,
Benziger, 1937.

NL 0350391 MH

Lienert, Otto Hellmut.
Die heilige Kümmernis; Erzählung. Einsiedeln,
Benziger[1949]
271p.

NL 0350392 CtY

Lienert, Otto Hellmut.
Nu nued, aber gly; aes Lustspili mit dry Aekte, vom Otto Hellmut Lienert. Aarau: H. R. Sauerländer & Co.[, 1927.] 88 p.
12°.

1. Drama, Swiss-German. 2. German   language—Dialects, Swiss—Aarau.
3. Title.
N. Y. P. L.   April 2, 1928

NL 0350393 NN

Lienert, Otto Hellmut.
Tobias und die goldvögel, ein frölicher
roman. Benziger, 1936.

NL 0350394 OrP

Lienert, Xaver.
Die Schuld bei der Ehescheidung nach schweizerischem
Recht. Aarau, H. R. Sauerländer, 1950.
134 p. 23 cm. (Zürcher Beiträge zur Rechtswissenschaft, n. f.,
Heft 167)
Diss.—Zürich.
Without thesis statement.
Bibliography: p. 7-8.

1. Divorce—Switzerland.   I. Title.   (Series)

51-27601

NL 0350395 DLC MH-L IU

Lieneweg, Fritz, 1900-
Temperaturmessung. Leipzig, Geest & Portig, 1950.
vii, 219 p. illus. 25 cm.
Errata slip inserted.
Bibliographical footnotes.

1. Thermometers and thermometry.   I. Title.
Full name: Hermann Fritz Lieneweg.

QC271.L5   536.5   51-18813

NL 0350396 DLC ICU

Lieneweg, Hermann Fritz
see Lieneweg, Fritz, 1900-

LIENEWEG, Wilhelm.
Die bedeutung der erbschafteteuer für letzt-
willigen und andere verfügungen des bürgerlich
rechts. Gütersloh, 1927.

5 + (1) + 87 p.
Inaug.-diss.----Münster i.W.

NL 0350398 MH-L

VOLUME 332

Liengme, André.
  Les quatre règles fondamentales de la vie; essai de psychologie pratique. Préf. de Arnold Reymond. ₍2. éd.₎ Lausanne, F. Rouge ₍1944₎
  191 p. 18 cm.

1. Psychology, Applied.

New York. Public Libr.   A 50-4123
for Library of Congress

NL 0350399   NN

Liengme, André.
  Le quattro regole fondamentali della vita; saggio di psicologia pratica. Traduzione di Luigi Simonazzi. Milano, G. Bolla, 1949.
  172 p. 20 cm. (I Libri della salute, 49)

1. Conduct of life.   i. Title.

BJ1582.L515   50-32380

NL 0350400   DLC NN ICRL

Liengme, André.
  Die vier Grundregeln des Lebens, ein Stück praktischer Seelenkunde ₍übersetzt von Dora Spörri₎ Zürich, Gotthelf-Verlag ₍1947₎
  107 p. 20 cm.

1. Conduct of life.   i. Title.

BF1582.L52   50-28255

NL 0350401   DLC

Liengme (André). *Y a-t-il relation de cause à effet entre la présence des oxyures dans l'appendice et l'appendicite. 35 pp., 5 pl. 8°. Genève ₍n. d.₎

NL 0350402   DNLM

RC494
890l   **LIENGME, Georges.**
    Contribution à l'étude de l'hypnotisme et de la suggestion thérapeutique. Neuchâtel, Attinger, 1890.
    99 p. 22 cm.
    Thèse - Genève.
    1. Hypnotism - Therapeutic use. 2. Therapeutics, Suggestive.

NL 0350403   CtY-M DNLM CU

Liengme, Georges L   1859-1936.
  Pour apprendre à mieux vivre. Conseils pratiques aux "nerveux." Neuchâtel ₍etc.₎ Attinger ₍1936₎
  211 p. port. 22 cm.
  2d ed.
  Bibliography : p. 211.

1. Neuroses. 2. Psychotherapy.

U. S. Army Medical Libr.   [WM170L719p 1936]   Med 48-1076
for Library of Congress

NL 0350404   DNLM

Liengme, Jean François, illus.

NE2210
.P53L5   **Piguet, Jean François.**
Rare Bk.   Chevaux et canons; xvii eaux fortes originales de J.-F.
Coll.   Liengme. Texte de J.-F. Piguet. Préf. du colonel commandant de corps Louis de Montmollin. Carra-Genève, Chez le graveur ₍1949₎

Lienhard, A
  Was jedermann vom eidg. Fabrikgesetz wissen muss; kleiner Leitfaden. Zusammenfassende Darstellung mit Erläuterungen der hauptsächlichsten Bestimmungen von Gesetz und Verordnung. 2. verb. Aufl. Zürich, Kommissionsverlag der Genossenschaftsbuchhandlung, 1951.
  46 p. 22 cm. (Gewerkschaftliche Schriften, Heft 8)

1. Factory laws and legislation—Switzerland. 2. Labor laws and legislation—Switzerland. i. Title.

52-29201 ‡

NL 0350406   DLC MH-IR NN

W 4
296   **Lienhard, Alfred,** 1920-
1945   Ein Beitrag zur Untersuchung des Kontusionssaums. Winterthur, Jäggli-Meyle, 1945.
    35 p.

    Inaug.-Diss. - Zürich.
    Bibliography: p. 31-33.

NL 0350407   DNLM

W 1
MO543   **LIENHARD, Carlos Pedro.**
no. 61   Cáncer y virus filtrables, probable
1954   acción de los virus en la génesis del cáncer. ₍Buenos Aires₎ 1954.
    24 p. (Monografías médicas argentinas, no. 61)
    Cover title.
    Summary in Spanish, English, French, and German.
    1. Neoplasms - Etiology & pathogenesis
    2. Viruses

NL 0350408   DNLM

W 1
MO543   **LIENHARD, Carlos Pedro.**
no. 56   Tromboflebitis y flebotrombosis.
1952   ₍Buenos Aires₎ 1952.
    27 p. (Monografías médicas argentinas, no. 56)
    Cover title.
    Summary in Spanish, English, French, and German.
    1. Thrombophlebitis   Series

NL 0350409   DNLM

PC315   **Lienhard, Dorothea Ruth,** 1918-
I5   Die Bezeichnungen für den Begriff "schweigen" in Frankreich, Italien und der romanischen Schweiz. ₍Biel, 1947₎
    ix, 122 p.

    Abhandlung - Zürich.
    Lebenslauf.
    "Bibliographie": p. ii-vii.

    1. Romance languages - Synonyms.

NL 0350410   CU DLC-P4 PU CtY CU IU ICU NjP

Lienhard, Emil.
  Allgemeine Einführung in die Biorhythmenlehre nach Dr. Med. Wilhelm Fliess. Verfasser: Emil Lienhard und Hans Früh. ₍Zürich, ˢ1948₎
  47 p. diagrs. 20 cm.
  On cover: Ebbe und Flut im Menschenblut? Vorausberechenbar auch für "unberechenbare" Tatsachen, die sich bezahlt machen.

1. Blood—Circulation.   i. Fliess, Wilhelm, 1858-1928. Biorhythmenlehre. ii. Früh, Hans R., joint author. iii. Title. iv. Title: Ebbe und Flut im Menschenblut? v. Title: Biorhythmenlehre.

Temple Univ. Library   QP111.L5   A 53-1165
for Library of Congress

NL 0350411   PPT DNLM

Lienhard, Emil.
  Beitrag zur Kenntnis der thermischen Zersetzung von Harnstoff. Zürich, 1954.
  98 p. diagrs. 21 cm.
  Promotionsarbeit—Eidgenössische Technische Hochschule, Zürich.
  Vita.
  Bibliography : p. 94-98.

1. Urea.

QD315.L6   56-46102

NL 0350412   DLC CtY NN

There are no cards for numbers
NL 0350413 to NL 0352000

833.91
L719   **Lienhard, Friedrich,** 1865-1929.
    Gesammelte Werke in drei Reihen.   Stuttgart, Greiner & Pfeiffer, 1924-26.
    15 v. front port. (v.1)

    Contents.—1. Reihe.—1.-4. Bd. Erzählende Werke. 2. Reihe.—1.-5. Bd. Lyrik und Dramatik. 3. Reihe.—1.-6. Bd. Gedankliche Werke.

NL 0352001   ICarbS CtY IU NBuU

₍Lienhard, Friedrich,₎ 1865-1929, editor.
  L'Alsace-Lorraine.   Zurich: Rascher & Cⁱᵉ., 1916.   94 p. incl. map.   8°.
  "Aux lecteurs" signed : Frédéric Lienhard.
  On cover : "Par quelques Alsaciens."

1. Alsace-Lorraine.—History.   2. European war, 1914- .—Peace terms.
N. Y. P. L.   August 12, 1919.

NL 0352002   NN DLC-P4

Lienhard, Friedrich, 1865-1929.
  Ahasver; tragödie von Fritz Lienhard. Stuttgart, Greiner & Pfeiffer, 1903.
  63 p. 20ᶜᵐ.
  "Den bühnen gegenüber manuskript."
  Contents.—i. Ahasver in Jerusalem.—ii. Ahasver am Rhein.

  i. Title.

Library of Congress   PT2623.I 41A7 1903   4-9208 Revised

NL 0352003   DLC

Lienhard, Friedrich, 1865-1929.
  Ahasver; trauerspiel in rei aufzügen mit einem vorspiel "Ahasver in Jersalem." 3. dunchgearbeitete aufl. Stuttgart, Greiner & Pfeiffer, 1925.
  88 p.

NL 0352004   OC1

PT 2623   **LIENHARD, FRIEDRICH,** 1865-1929.
.I2 A73   Ahasver am Rhein; Trauerspiel aus der Gegenwart in drei Aufzügen. Stuttgart, Greiner & Pfeiffer, 1914.
    86 p.

NL 0352005   InU RPB

Lienhard, Friedrich, 1865-1929.
  Auf Goethes Pfaden in Weimar
  see under   Tornquist, Ellen.

VOLUME 332

DC
610
L71a
Lienhard, Friedrich , 1865-1929.
   Aus dem Elsass des XVIII. jahrhunderts
... Strassburg i.E., F.Bull, 1910.
   vii,[1],39p. 22cm. (Added t.-p.: Aus schule
und leben; beiträge zur pädagogik und allgemeinen
bildung ... 2.hft (1.abt.))

NL 0352007 NRU

Lienhard, Friedrich,1865-1929.
   ... Ausgewaehlte werke... Stuttgart, Tuermer...&
Pfeiffer [193-?]
   4 v. front., v.1 (port.) D

NL 0352008 OO

Lienhard, Friedrich, 1865-1929.
   Die Bäckerin von Winstein; ein Scherz für die Laienbühne.
Von Friedrich Lienhard... (Der Türmer. Stuttgart, 1923.
8°. Jahrg. 25, p. 808–814.)

1. Drama (German). 2. Title.
N. Y. P. L.   November 1, 1923.

NL 0352009 NN

Lienhard, Friedrich, 1865-1929.
   ...Die Baeckerin von Winstein; Schills Offiziere, zwei Spiele
für die Laienbühne, von Friedrich Lienhard. Leipzig: A.
Strauch[, 1924?]. 24 p. illus. (music.) 12°. (Neue Volksstücke. [Nr.] 6.)

1. Drama, German. 2. Title.   3. Title: Schills Offiziere. 4. Ser.
N. Y. P. L.   November 27, 1928

NL 0352010 NN

Lienhard, Friedrich, 1865-1929.
   ...Baer und Elfe; die Schwätzerin, zwei Scherze, von Friedrich Lienhard. Leipzig: A. Strauch[, 1926?] 36 p. illus.
(music.) 12°. (Neue Volksstücke. [Nr.] 9.)

Incidental music for Baer und Else, by Hans Ernst, p. [13-]22.

1. Drama, German. 2. Title. 3. Title: Die Schwätzerin. 3. Ser.
N. Y. P. L.   November 20, 1928

NL 0352011 NN

Lienhard,Friedrich, 1865-1929.
   Burenlieder. Leipzig, G.H.Meyer, 1900.

   39 p. (Flugschriften der Heimat, 2)

NL 0352012 MH

PT
501
L5
Lienhard, Friedrich, 1865-1929.
   Deutsche Dichtung in ihren geschichtlichen
Grundzügen. Leipzig, Quelle & Meyer, 1917.
   141p. 19cm. (Wissenschaft und Bildung,
150)
   Includes bibliography.

   1. German poetry - Hist. I. Title

NL 0352013 WU

Lienhard, Friedrich, 1865-1929.
   ... Deutsche dichtung in ihren geschichtlichen grundzügen, dargestellt von prof. dr. Friedrich Lienhard. 2.
aufl. Leipzig, Quelle & Meyer, 1919.
   142 p. 18½ᶜᵐ. (Wissenschaft und bildung ... 150)
   "Literatur-angaben" p. [138]

   1. German poetry—Hist. & crit.

NL 0352014 MiU OO NcU MH CU PBm

Liennard, Friedrich, 1865-
   Das deutsche Elsass, von Friedrich Lienhard. Stuttgart und Berlin, Deutsche verlags-anstalt, 1914.
   32 p. 23ᶜᵐ. (Added t.-p.: Der deutsche krieg; politische flugschriften,
hrsg. von E. Jäckh. 17. hft.)

   1. Alsace. 2. Alsace-Lorraine question.   ɪ. Title.
                                                     A 20-839
Title from Carnegie   Endow. Int. Peace.   Printed by L. C.

NL 0352015 NNCE CU OU NcD CtY NN

Lienhard, Friedrich, 1865-1929.
   Deutscher Aufstieg, Worte für Neudeutschlands Jugend.
Ausgewählt und eingeleitet von Paul Bülow. 5. Aufl. Stuttgart, Greiner & Pfeiffer [194-?]
   78 p. 20 cm.

   ɪ. Title.
   PT2623.I 41A6   838.91   51–22546

NL 0352016 DLC NBuU N

Lienhard, Friedrich, 1865-
   Deutsches Krippenspiel. Von Friedr. Lienhard. (Der
Türmer. Stuttgart, 1923. 8°. Jahrg. 26, p. 160–171.)

1. Drama (German). 2. Christmas.   —Drama.
N. Y. P. L.   January 29, 1924.

NL 0352017 NN

Lienhard, Friedrich, 1865-
   ...Ein deutsches Krippenspiel, von Friedrich Lienhard;
Music von Hans Ernst... Leipzig: A. Strauch[, 1924]. 32,
17 p. illus. (music.) 2. ed. 12°. (Neue Volksstücke.
[Nr.] 7.)

Incidental music, p. 1–17.

1. Drama, German. 2. Christmas—   Drama. 3. Title. 4. Ser.
N. Y. P. L.   November 20, 1928

NL 0352018 NN

Lienhard, Friedrich, 1865-1929.
   Deutschlands europäische sendung, von Friedrich Lienhard.
Stuttgart, Greiner & Pfeiffer, 1914.
   30 p. 21ᶜᵐ.

   1. European war, 1914–1918—Addresses, sermons, etc.   ɪ. Title.
                                                     33–37323
Library of Congress   D525.L485   940.343

NL 0352019 DLC NN CtY

PT
1925
L523
Lienhard, Friedrich, 1865-1929.
   Einführung in Goethes Faust. Leipzig,
Quelle & Meyer, 1913.
   170 p. 19cm. (Wissenschaft und
Bildung, 116)

   1. Goethe, Johann Wolfgang von.
Faust.

NL 0352020 CoFS CtY MiU PPT MH OCU RPB CU

PT
1925
.L5
1916
Lienhard, Friedrich, 1865-1929.
   Einführung in Goethes Faust. 2. Aufl.
Leipzig, Quelle & Meyer, 1916.
   123 p. (Wissenschaft und Bildung)

   1. Goethe, Johann Wolfgang von. Faust.
I. Title.

NL 0352021 NBuU TU

PT1925
L5
1919
Lienhard, Friedrich, 1865-1929
   Einführung in Goethes Faust. 4. Aufl.
Leipzig, Quelle & Meyer, 1919.
   118 p. 19 cm. (Wissenschaft und Bildung,
116)

   1. Goethe, Johann Wolfgang von, 1749-1832.
Faust. (Series)

NL 0352022 MeB

PT
1925
.L5
1920
Lienhard, Friedrich, 1865-1929.
   Einführung in Goethes Faust. 5. Aufl.
Leipzig, Quelle & Meyer, 1920.
   118p. 19cm. (Wissenschaft und Bildung,
130)

   1. Goethe, Johann Wolfgang von, 1749-1832.
Faust.

NL 0352023 OrU OU

4PT
Ger.
8129
Lienhard, Friedrich, 1865-1929.
   Einführung in Goethes Faust. 6.
Aufl. Leipzig, Quelle & Meyer, 1922.
   118 p.

   (Wissenschaft und Bildung; Einzeldarstellungen aus allen Gebieten des
Wissens, 116)

NL 0352024 DLC-P4 IU CaBVaU GU OCU OO NjP NcU

PT1925
.L7
Lienhard, Friedrich, 1865-1929.
   ... Einführung in Goethes Faust, von prof. dr. Friedrich
Lienhardt [!] 7. aufl. ... Leipzig, Quelle & Meyer, 1923.
   118 p. 18½ᶜᵐ. (Wissenschaft und bildung ... 116)

   1. Goethe, Johann Wolfgang von, 1749-1832. Faust. 2. Faust.

NL 0352025 ICU OrPR GEU ICU CtY OCU

Lienhard, Friedrich, 1865-1929.
   ...Einführung in Goethes Faust, von prof. dr.
Friedrich Lienhardt. 8. aufl. 36-40 tausend.
Leipzig, Quelle and Meyer, 1924.
   118 p.

NL 0352026 PSC CLSU MoSU

VOLUME 332

PT
2623
.I41E4
  Lienhard, Friedrich, 1865-1929.
    Der Einsiedler und sein Volk; Erzählungen.
  25. Aufl. Stuttgart, Greiner & Pfeiffer
  [n.d.]
    180 p.

NL 0352027 NBuU N

LIENHARD, Friedrich, 1865-1929.
Der einsiedler und sein volk; erzählungen.
6e aufl. Stuttgart, Greiner & Pfeiffer, [191-

NL 0352028 MH

PT
2623
I41
E3
  Lienhard, Friedrich, 1865-1929.
    Der Einsiedler und sein Volk; Erzählungen.
  Stuttgart, Greiner & Pfeiffer [1914]
    190p. 20cm.

NL 0352029 WU NjP CtY PPGi NN

    Lienhard, Friedrich,1865-1929.
     Der einsedler und sein volk; erzaehlungen.
   Stuttgart, Greiner & Pfeiffer,1923.

NL 0352030 OCl

LIENHARD, Friedrich.
Eulenspiegels ausfahrt; schelmenspiel in
drei aufzügen. 4e umgearbeitete aufl.
Stuttgart, Greiner & Pfeiffer, 1910.

  pp. (4), 62.
  (In his Till Eulenspiegel,1911,teil 1.)

NL 0352031 MH RPB

LIENHARD, Friedrich.
Eulenspiegels heimkehr; schauspiel in drei
aufzügen. 4e aufl. Stuttgart, Greiner &
Pfeiffer, 1911.

  pp. (4), 44.
  (In his Till Eulenspiegel,teil 3.)

NL 0352032 MH

834L619 Lienhard, Friedrich, 1865-1929.
Of   Der Fremde, Schelmenspiel im einem Aufzug [von]
    Fritz Lienhard. Leipzig, G. H. Meyer, 1900.
    39p. 18cm.

NL 0352033 IU IaU KyU OCU

    Lienhard, Friedrich, 1865-1929.
     Der Fremde. Schelmenspiel in einem Aufzug
   [von] Fritz Lienhard. Leipzig und Berlin,
   Georg Heinrich Meyer, 1900.
    39p.

    Microcard edition.

NL 0352034 ICRL

LIENHARD, Friedrich.
Der fremde; schelmenspiel in einem augzug.
3e aufl. Stuttgart, Greiner & Pfeiffer, 1910.

  sm. 4°, pp. (4), 27.   50558.33.6

  The same. (In his Till Eulenspiegel,1911,
teil 2.)

NL 0352035 MH

    Lienhard, Friedrich, 1865-1929.
     Der fremde, schelmenspiel in einem aufzug...
   4. aufl. Stuttgart, 1914.
   27 p.   20 cm.
   With his König Arthur...1908.

NL 0352036 RPB

PT2623 Lienhard, Friedrich, 1865-1929.
I23F8   Der fremde; schelmenspiel in einem aufzug von Friedrich
1921 Lienhard. 6. aufl. Stuttgart, Greiner und Pfeiffer, 1921.
    31 p. 20cm.

NL 0352037 ICU

  Lienhard, Friedrich, 1865-1929.
   Friedrich Lienhard, eingeführt von Reinhold Braun ...
 Chemnitz [etc.] M. Müller [1924?]
   1 p. l., 5-50 p., 1 l. 19 cm.
   Verse and prose.

   I. Braun, Reinhold, 1879-   ed.

 PT2623.I41A6 1924   47-40497

NL 0352038 DLC

  Lienhard, Friedrich, 1865-1929.
   Friedrich Lienhard und wir
     see under title

PT
2623
.I41A17
1902
  Lienhard, Friedrich, 1865-1929.
    Gedichte [von] Fritz Lienhard. Leipzig,
  G. H. Meyer, 1902.
    283 p.

NL 0352040 NBuU TNJ InU WU

PT
2623
.I41A17
1906
  Lienhard, Friedrich, 1865-1929.
    Gedichte [von] Fritz Lienhard. 2. Aufl.
  Stuttgart, Greiner & Pfeiffer, 1906.
    217 p. illus.

NL 0352041 NBuU

    Lienhard, Friedrich, 1865-1929.
     Gedichte. Buchschmuck von Herm. Hirzel.
   3e. aufl. Stuttgart, Greiner und Pfeiffer,
   1906.
    sm. 4°.

NL 0352042 MH OU CU PPLT

PT
96
L71g
1927
  Lienhard, Friedrich , 1865-1929.
    ... Geschichte der deutschen dichtung;
  eine kurze deutsche literaturgeschichte
  ... 3.durchgesehene aufl. ... Leipzig,
  Quelle & Meyer, 1927.
    143p. 19cm. (Wissenschaft und bildung; ein-
  zeldarstellungen aus allen gebieten des wissens.
  150)

NL 0352043 NRU OCU NcD

PT
2623.
.I41G6
1902
  Lienhard, Friedrich, 1865-1929.
    Gottfried von Strassburg; dramatische
  Dichtung in fünf Aufzügen [von] Fritz
  Lienhard. 2. Aufl. Leipzig, G. H. Meyer,
  1902.
    128 p.

NL 0352044 NBuU MH PU N

 Lienhard, Friedrich, 1865-1929.
   Gottfried von Strassburg; dramatische Dichtung in fünf Aufzügen, von Friedrich Lienhard... Stuttgart: Greiner & Pfeiffer, 1925. 104 p. 4. ed., rev. 12°.

 283085A. 1. Drama, German.   2. Gottfried von Strassburg, 13th
 N. Y. P. L.   cent.—Drama.   February 8, 1927

NL 0352045 NN

    Lienhard, Friedrich, 1865-1929.
     Das harzer Bergtheater. Stuttgart, 1907.

NL 0352046 NjP

Lienhard, Friedrich, 1865-1929.
  Die heilige Elisabeth; Trauerspiel in
fünf Aufzügen von Friedrich Lienhard. 5.
Aufl. Stuttgart, Greiner und Pfeiffer,
1920.
   2 p.f.,110 p.

NL 0352047 DHN

832
L6243h
  Lienhard, Friedrich, 1865-1929.
    Die heilige Elisabeth: Trauerspiel
  in fünf Aufzügen. 4. Aufl. Stuttgart,
  Greiner & Pfeiffer, 1918.
    110 p. , music. 20cm.

NL 0352048 KyU

PT2623
.I6H3
1925
 Lienhard, Friedrich, 1865-1929.
   Die heilige Elisabeth; Trauerspiel in fünf
 aufzügen. 8. aufl. Stuttgart, Greiner & Pfeiffer,
 1925.
   104 p. music. 20cm. (His Wartburg [2])

   1. Elizabeth, of Hungary, Saint, 1207-1231 -
 Drama. 2. Walther von der Vogelweide, 12th cent. -
 Drama. I. Title.

NL 0352049 OCU

PT
2623
L72h
  Lienhard, Friedrich, 1865-1929.
    Die heilige Elisabeth; trauerspiel in
  fünf aufzügen ... 9.aufl. Stuttgart,
  Greiner & Pfeiffer [19-?]
    104p. 19½cm.
    Part two of the dramatic trilogy: Wartburg.

    1. Elizabeth, of Hungary, Saint - Drama
  I. Title.

NL 0352050 NRU

VOLUME 332

830　Lienhard, Friedrich, 1865-1929.
L719　　Heinrich von Osterdingen; Drama in
tH　　fünf Aufzügen.　Stuttgart, Greiner &
　　Pfeiffer, 1903.
　　　121p. 20cm. (His Wartburg; drama-
　　tische Dichtung in drei Teilen, 1)

　　　I.Title. (Series: Lienhard, Fried-
　　rich, 1865-1929. Wartburg)

NL　0352051　CLSU

PT2623 Lienhard, Friedrich, 1865-1929.
.I23H4　Heinrich von Ofterdingen; dramatische dichtung in fünf
1919　aufzügen, von Friedrich Lienhard. 5. aufl. Stuttgart,
　　Greiner und Pfeiffer, 1919.
　　　[4], 126 p. 19ᶜᵐ.

NL　0352052　ICU CtY

PT　Lienhard, Friedrich, 1865-1929.
2623　　Heinrich von Ofterdingen; dramatische
L72he　　dichtung in fünf aufzügen ... 9.aufl.
　　Stuttgart, Greiner & Pfeiffer [19-?]
　　　119p. 19½cm.
　　　Part one of the dramatic trilogy: Wartburg.

NL　0352053　NRU

PT2623 LIENHARD, FRIEDRICH, 1865-1929.
.I41H3　HEINRICH VON OFTERDINGEN; DRAMATISCHE DICHTUNG
1923　IN FÜNF AUFZÜGEN. 8.AUFL. STUTTGART, GREINER &
　　PFEIFFER, 1923.
　　　119 P. 20CM. (HIS WARTBURG [1])

　　　1. HEINRICH VON OFTERDINGEN, 13TH CENT. - DRAMA.
　　2. WOLFRAM VON ESCHENBACH, 12TH CENT. - DRAMA. 3.
　　WALTHER VON DER VOGELWEIDE, 12TH CENT. - DRAMA. I.
　　TITLE.

NL　0352054　OCU

4PT　Lienhard, Friedrich, 1865-1929.
Ger.　　Helden; Bilder und Gestalten.
8348　　Leipzig, G. H. Meyer Heimatverlag,
　　1900.
　　　102 p.

NL　0352055　DLC-P4 NBuU

Lienhard, Friedrich, 1865-1929.
　　Helden; bilder und gestalten ... 2.,
verm.aufl. Stuttgart, Greiner & Pfeif-
fer, 1908.
　　3 p.l., [5]-190p. illus. 20cm.
　　Contents. - Der dichter. - Tatamatvira. - Pro-
metheus. - Die sintflut. - Moses auf dem Nebo. -
Die kreuzigung. - Das wilde heer. - Brunhilds
todesfahrt. - Merlin der königsbarde. - Das trau-
lied. - Widukind. - Tauler und der einsiedler. -
Der pandurenstein. - Tafelgespräch un Sanssouci. -
Königin Luise. - Shakespeare und Byron. - Gordon.
Ein schottischer sommertag. - Der dorfschmied.
　　I. Title.

NL　0352056　NRU IEN RPB OCl

PT　Lienhard, Friedrich, 1865-1929.
2623　　Helden; Bilder und Gestalten. 4. Aufl.
.I41H4　Stuttgart, Greiner & Pfeiffer [19-]
　　204 p.

　　　"Die Erstausg. des Buches erschien 1900."

NL　0352057　NBuU N

PT　Lienhard, Friedrich, 1865-1929
2623　　Helden; Bilder und Gestalten. 5. Aufl
I41　Stuttgart, Greiner & Pfeiffer [1900]
H4　　204p. illus. 20cm.

NL　0352058　WU

Lienhard, Friedrich, 1865-1929.
　　Helden. 17. Aufl. Berlin, Singer [1900]
　　153 p. 20 cm.

　　Bound with his Thüringer Tagebuch [1903]

NL　0352059　NjP

Lienhard, Friedrich, 1865-1929.
　　Hochzeit in Schilda; eine Frühlingsdichtung
in zehn Gesängen. Stuttgart, Greiner & Pfeiffer
[1905]
　　103 p.

NL　0352060　WaU

PT　Lienhard, Friedrich, 1865-1929.
2623　　Hochzeit in Schilda; eine frühlings-
L72ho　　dichtung in zehn gesängen ... Mit buch-
　　schmuck von Hermann Hirzel. 3.aufl. der
　　"Schildbürger". Stuttgart, Greiner und
　　Pfeiffer, 1919.
　　　130p. 19½cm.
　　　Illustrated half-title precedes t.-p. and
　　each song.

NL　0352061　NRU

PT2623 Lienhard, Friedrich, 1865-1929.
.I23H6　Hochzeit in Schilda; eine frühlingsdichtung in zehn ge-
1923　sängen von Friedrich Lienhard. Mit buchschmuck von
　　Hermann Hirzel. 5. aufl. der "Schildbürger." Stuttgart,
　　Greiner und Pfeiffer [1923?]
　　　130 p. 19½x15½ᶜᵐ.
　　　Each part has ornamental half-title; head and tail pieces; initials.

NL　0352062　ICU

LIENHARD, Friedrich, 1865-1929.
　　Jugendjahre; erinnerungen. 10.aufl.
Stuttgart, Greiner & Pfeiffer, 1918.

　　Ports.and plates.

NL　0352063　MH

Lienhard, Friedrich, 1865-
　　Jugendjahre. Errinerungen von Friedrich
Lienhard. 11 aufl. Stuttgart, 1920.
　　198 p. illus. ports. 20 cm.

NL　0352064　RPB

Lienhard, Friedrich, 1865-1929.
　　Jugendjahre. 12te Aufl. Stuttgart, Greiner &
Pfeiffer, pref. 1917-1919.
　　198 p. illus. ports.

NL　0352065　MiD

PT　Lienhard, Friedrich, 1865-1929.
2623　Jugendjahre; erinnerungen ... 16.aufl.
L72ju　Stuttgart, Greiner & Pfeiffer, 1923.
1923　　185p. plates,ports. 19½cm.

　　　1. Lienhard, Friedrich.　I. Title.

NL　0352066　NRU

Lienhard, Friedrich, 1865-1929.
　　Das klassische Weimar, von Fritz Lienhard. Leipzig, Quelle &
Meyer, 1909.
　　pp. 161. (Wissenschaft und bildung, 35.)

　　German lit.-Weimar　　|Weimar,

NL　0352067　MH NjR IaU MWelC CU

DD　Lienhard, Friedrich, 1865-1929.
901　　... Das klassische Weimar, von professor dr. Friedrich
W4　Lienhard. Zweite auflage. Leipzig, Verlag von Quelle &
L71　Meyer, 1914.
1914　　147 p. 18½ᶜᵐ. (Wissenschaft und bildung; einzeldarstellungen au-
　　allen gebieten des wissens. 35)
　　　Contents.—Deutschlands geistige sendung.—Das revolutionäre und
　　philosophische jahrhundert.—Friedrich der Grosse.—Rousseau, Klopstock
　　und die gefühlsbewegung.—Lessing und die aufklärung.—Herder und
　　die volkspoesie.—Von Kant zu Schiller.—Schiller.—Weimar aus der
　　vogelschau.—Schiller und Goethe.—Goethe.—Das klassische ideal der
　　zukunft.

NL　0352068　NIC CU

DD901　Lienhard, Friedrich, 1865-1929.
.W4L7　　Das klassische Weimar. Dritte auflage.
1918　Leipzig, Verlag von Quelle & Meyer, 1918.
　　　148p. 19cm. (Wissenschaft und bildung;
　　einzeldarstellungen aus allen gebieten des
　　wissens, 35)
　　　Contents.—Deutschlands geistige sendung.—Das revolutionäre und
　　philosophische jahrhundert.—Friedrich der Grosse.—Rousseau, Klopstock
　　und die gefühlsbewegung.—Lessing und die aufklärung.—Herder und
　　die volkspoesie.—Von Kant zu Schiller.—Schiller.—Weimar aus der
　　vogelschau.—Schiller und Goethe.—Goethe.—Das klassische ideal der
　　zukunft.

NL　0352069　NBC TU

DD　Lienhard, Friedrich, 1865-1929.
901　　Das Klassische Weimar. 4. Aufl. Leipzig,
.W4L7　Verlag von Quelle & Meyer, 1920.
1920　　147 p. 19 cm. (Wissenschaft und
　　Bildung, 35)

　　　1. Weimar - Intellectual life. I. Title.
　　(Series)

NL　0352070　NBuU CU

Lienhard, Friedrich, 1865-1929.
　　... Das klassische Weimar, von professor dr. Friedrich
Lienhard. Fünfte auflage. Leipzig, Verlag von Quelle &
Meyer, 1926.
　　147 p. 18½ᶜᵐ. (Wissenschaft und bildung; einzeldarstellungen aus
allen gebieten des wissens. 35)
　　Contents.—Deutschlands geistige sendung.—Das revolutionäre und
philosophische jahrhundert.—Friedrich der Grosse.—Rousseau, Klopstock
und die gefühlsbewegung.—Lessing und die aufklärung.—Herder und
die volkspoesie.—Von Kant zu Schiller.—Schiller.—Weimar aus der
vogelschau.—Schiller und Goethe.—Goethe.—Das klassische ideal der
zukunft.

　　　1. Weimar—Intellectual life.　I. Title.

　　　　　　　　　　　　　　　A 40-3291

Rochester. Univ. Library　　DD901.W4L7
　for Library of Congress　　　[2]

　　MiU OrPR P
NL　0352071　NRU CLU NcD ICU PSC CtY PPT CU NcU

VOLUME 332

Lienhard, Friedrich, 1865-1929.
Koehler's Zeppelin-kalender. 1.-2. jahrg.; 1909-[10] ... Illustrierte chronik der luftschiffahrt ... Gera-Untermhaus und Leipzig, Koehler [1908-09]

834L619   Lienhard, Friedrich, 1865-1929.
Ok   König Arthur, Trauerspiel in einem Vorspiel un fünf Aufzügen.   Leipzig, G. H. Meyer, 1900.
112p. 19cm.

1. Arthur, King--Drama. I. Title.

NL   0352073   IU ViU ICN NBuU N

PT2623 Lienhard, Friedrich, 1865-1929.
.I23K8   König Arthur.   Trauerspiel in fünf aufzügen von Friedrich Lienhard. 3. aufl. Stuttgart, Greiner & Pfeiffer, 1908.
114 p.   20cm.

NL   0352074   ICU RPB CtY PU MH NN

Lienhard, Friedrich, 1865-1929.
König Arthur; Trauerspiel in fünf Aufzügen.
4. Aufl. Stuttgart, Greiner & Pfeiffer, 1925.
103p. 21cm.

NL   0352075   PSt

Lienhard, Friedrich, 1865-1929.
Das Landhaus bei Eisenach; ein Burschenschaftsroman aus dem 19. Jahrhundert. 1.-6. Tausend. Leipzig, A. Deichert, 1928.
189p. front., pl., ports. 19cm. (Bilder aus Thüringens Vergangenheit ... X)

NL   0352076   IEN ICarbS TNJ

832.91   Lienhard, Friedrich, 1865-1929.
L71Le   Lebensfrucht, Gesamtausgabe der Gedichte
1916   von Friedrich Lienhar. 4. Aufl. Stuttgart, Greiner und Pfeiffer, 1916.
287p. illus. 20cm.

Each section has engraved special t.p.

Contents.- Heimat.- Weltstadt.- Nordland.-
Burenlieder (1900).- Drei Erzählungen.-
Kriegsgedichte (1914).- Hochlang.- Das Kinderland.
I. Title.

NL   0352077   TNJ

4PT   Lienhard, Friedrich, 1865-1929.
Germ   Lebensfrucht. Gesamtausg. der
8342   Gedichte von Friedrich Lienhard.
9. Aufl. Stuttgart, Greiner & Pfeiffer [191]
291 p.

NL   0352078   DLC-P4

PT   Lienhard, Friedrich, 1865-1929.
2623   Lebensfrucht; Gesamtausg. der Gedichte.
.I41L4   10. Aufl. Stuttgart, Greiner & Pfeiffer,
1915   1915.
291 p.

NL   0352079   NBuU PPGi OOxM InU N

PT   Lienhard, Friedrich, 1865-1929.
2623   Lebensfrucht; gesamtausgabe der gedichte von Friedrich Lienhard. 14.aufl.
L72€e   Stuttgart, Greiner & Pfeiffer [1926]
viii,347p. 20cm.

NL   0352080   NRU CU OCl

PT   Lienhard, Friedrich, 1865-1929.
2623   Lichtland; neue Gedichte.   Stuttgart,
.I41L5   Greiner & Pfeiffer, 1912.
1912   105 p.

NL   0352081   NBuU NcD N

Lienhard, Friedrich, 1865-1929.
Litteratur-Jugend von heute; eine Fastenpredigt von Fritz Lienhard.   Leipzig [etc.], G. H. Meyer, 1901.   28 p.   19cm.
(Grüne Blätter für Kunst und Volkstum. Heft 1.)
"Ein Separat-Abdruck aus dem grösseren Buch des Verfassers 'Neue Ideale'."

1. German literature—Hist. and   crit., 1870-
N.Y.P.L.   July 10, 1947

NL   0352082   NN CU

PT2623   Lienhard, Friedrich, 1865-1929.
.I23L8   ...Luther auf der Wartburg, schauspiel in fünf aufzügen...   Stuttgart, Greine & Pfeiffer [1906].
102p. 20cm. (His Wartburg. bd.3)

I.Title. II.Wartburg. bd.3.

NL   0352083   NNU-W

Lienhard, Friedrich, 1865-1929.
Luther auf der Wartburg; schauspiel in 5 aufzügen, von Friedrich Lienhard. 2., durchgearb.aufl. Stuttgart, Greiner & Pfeiffer, 1909.
vi,120 p. 19½ cm.   (Wartburg;dramatische dichtung...3)
Music.

NL   0352084   MiU

Div.S.   Lienhard, Friedrich, 1865-1929.
832.91
L719L   Luther auf der Wartburg; Schauspiel in fünf Aufzügen. 3. Aufl. Stuttgart, Greiner & Pfeiffer, 1914.
120 p. 20 cm. (His Wartburg; dramatische Dichtung in drei Teilen, 3)

1. Luther, Martin. Drama. I. Title.

NL   0352085   NcD

4BX-513   Lienhard, Friedrich, 1865-1929.
Luther auf der Wartburg. Schauspiel in fünf Aufzügen. 4. bearb. Aufl. Stuttgart, Greiner & Pfeiffer, 1917.
112 p.

NL   0352086   DLC-P4

PT   Lienhard, Friedrich, 1865-1929.
2623   Luther auf der Wartburg; Schauspiel in
I41   fünf Aufzügen. 5. Aufl. Stuttgart,
L8   Greiner & Pfeiffer [1916?]
112p. music. 20cm. (Wartburg Trilogie, 3)
1. Luther, Martin, 1483-1546 - Drama
I. Title

NL   0352087   WU

---

832   Lienhard, Friedrich, 1865-1929.
L624€6   Luther auf der Wartburg. [6. bearb. Aufl.] Schauspiel in fünf Aufzügen (1906) Stuttgart, Greiner und Pfeiffer [1917]
102 p.

1. Luther, Martin, 1483-1546 - Drama.
I. Title.

NL   0352088   WaU

---

832   Lienhard, Friedrich, 1865-1929.
L6243£   Luther auf der Wartburg: Schauspiel in fünf Aufzügen. 7. Aufl.   Stuttgart, Greiner & Pfeiffer [1918?]
111 p.   20 cm.

NL   0352089   KyU

PT2623   Lienhard, Friedrich, 1865-1929.
.I41W5   Luther auf der Wartburg; Schauspiel in fünf
1923   Aufzügen. 11.Aufl. Stuttgart, Greiner & Pfeiffer, 1923.
102 p. music. 20cm. (His Wartburg [3])

1. Luther, Martin - Drama. I. Title.

NL   0352090   OCU

PT   Lienhard, Friedrich, 1865-1929.
107   Der Meister der Menschheit; Beiträge
L71m   zur Beseelung der Gegenwart. 2.,neugeord-
1923   nete Aufl. Stuttgart, Greiner & Pfeiffer [1923]
3v. plates,ports. 20cm.
Contents. - 1.Bd. Die Abstammung aus dem Licht. -- 2.Bd. Akropolis, Golgatha, Wartburg. - 3.Bd. Reichsbeseelung.

NL   0352091   NRU PBm PPT OCl ICU DLC

PT   Lienhard, Friedrich, 1865-1929.
2623   Meisters Vermächtnis; ein Roman vom
.I41M4   heimlichen König. 5. Aufl. Stuttgart,
Greiner & Pfeiffer [n.d.]
300 p.

NL   0352092   NBuU N

834L619   Lienhard, Friedrich, 1865-1929.
Om   ... Münchhausen; ein lustspiel in drei aufzügen. Leipzig und Berlin, G. H. Meyer, Heimatverlag, 1900.
106p.

At head of title: Fritz Lienhard.
"Den bühnen und vereinen gegenüber als manuskript gedruckt."

NL   0352093   IU NBuU KyU InU NRU

VOLUME 332

Lienhard, Friedrich, 1865-1929.
Münchhausen. Ein Lustspiel in drei Aufzügen ‹von› Fritz Lienhard. Leipzig und Berlin, Georg Heinrich Meyer, 1900.
106p.

Microcard edition.

NL 0352094 ICRL

LIENHARD, Friedrich, 1865-1929.
Münchhausen; komödie in drei aufzügen. 2e, durchgearbeitete aufl. Leipzig, etc., G.H. Meyer, 1901.

pp. (4), 88.
(DEUTSCHE heimat. Probenummern.)

NL 0352095 MH

PT2623 Lienhard, Friedrich, 1865-1929.
.I23M8 Münchhausen; lustspiel in vier aufzügen von Friedrich
1914 Lienhard. 3., bearb. aufl. Stuttgart, Greiner & Pfeiffer, 1914.
⸢7⸣, 86 p. 20ᶜᵐ.

NL 0352096 ICU

Lienhard, Friedrich, 1865-1929.
Muenchhausen; Lustspiel in vier Aufzügen, von Friedrich Lienhard... Stuttgart: Greiner & Pfeiffer, 1925. 87 p. 4. ed. 12°.

283087A. 1. Drama, German. 2. Muenchhausen, Hieronymus
Karl Friedrich, Freiherr von, 1720- 1797—Drama.
N.Y.P.L. February 8, 1927

NL 0352097 NN

PT Lienhard, Friedrich, 1865-1929.
772 Neue Ideale; gesammelte Aufsätze von
.I5 Fritz Lienhard. Leipzig, G. H. Meyer,
1901 1901.
271 p.

Add t.p.

1. German literature - 20th cent. - Addresses, essays, lectures. I. Title.

NL 0352098 NBuU N

Lienhard, Friedrich, 1865-1929.
PT772 Neue Ideale nebst Vorherrschaft Berlins;
L5 gesammelte Aufsätze. 2, neugestaltete Aufl.
1913 Stuttgart, Greiner und Pfeiffer, 1913.
202 p. 20ᵐ.

1.German literature - 20th cent. -
Addresses, essays, lectures. I.Title.

NL 0352099 CSt RPB MH

Lienhard, Friedrich, 1865-1929.
Neue Ideale nebst Vorherrschaft Berlins; gesammelte Aufsätze. 3. verm. Aufl. Stuttgart, Greiner und Pfeiffer, 1920.
229 p. 20 cm.

1. German literature—20th cent.—Addresses, essays, lectures.

PT772.L5 1920 52-47333

NL 0352100 DLC

PT Lienhard, Friedrich, 1865-1929.
772 Neue Ideale nebst Vorherrschaft Berlins;
.L5 gesammelte Aufsätze. 5. Aufl. Stuttgart,
1920 Greiner und Pfeiffer, 1920.
229 p. 20 cm.

1. German literature - 20th cent. -
Addresses, essays, lectures.
PT772.L5 1920 60z 52-47333

NL 0352101 NBuU MiU OCU NjP N

Lienhard, Friedrich, 1865-1929.
Neue ideale nebst vorherrschaft Berlins; gesammelte aufsaetze. 7 aufl. Stuttgart, Greiner & Pfeiffer, n.d.

NL 0352102 OC1

Lienhard, Friedrich, 1865-1929.
Oberflächen-kultur. Stuttgart, Greiner, ⸢1904⸣.
63p.

NL 0352103 ICRL InU OCU

PT Lienhard, Friedrich, 1865-1929.
2623 Oberlin. Roman aus der Revolutionszeit im
.I41 O2 Elsass. 157. Aufl. Berlin, J. Singer
⸢n.d.⸣
447 p.

1. Oberlin, Johann Friedrich, 1740-1826 -
Fiction. 2. France - Hist. - Revolution -
Fiction. 3. Alsace - Hist. - Fiction.

PT2623.I41O2 1911 25-16833
60z

NL 0352104 NBuU OO N

Lienhard, Friedrich, 1865-
Oberlin. Roman aus der Revolutionszeit im Elsass. 5. Auflage.
— Stuttgart. Greiner & Pfeiffer. [1911.] vi, (1), 480 pp. Vignettes.
19 cm., in 8s.
A story connected with the life of Johann Friedrich Oberlin (1740-1826).

H7233 — T.r. — Oberlin, Jean Frédér.. 1740-1826. — France. Hist. Fict. Rev.,
1789-1795. — Alsace. Hist. Fict.

NL 0352105 MB

Lienhard, Friedrich, 1865-1929.
Oberlin. Roman aus der revolutionszeit im Elsass, von Friedrich Lienhard. 7. aufl. Stuttgart, Greiner & Pfeiffer ⸢1911⸣
vi p., 1 l., 480 p. illus. (incl. ports.) 20ᵐᵐ.
First published in "Der Türmer", 1909-10.

1. Oberlin, Johann Friedrich, 1740-1826-Fiction. 2. France—Hist.—
Revolution—Fiction. 3. Alsace—Hist.—Fiction.

25-16833

Library of Congress PT2623.I41O2 1911

NL 0352106 DLC ICU OO OC1W NcD

Lienhard, Friedrich, 1865-1929.
Oberlin: Roman aus der Revolutionszeit im Elsass. 13 aufl. Stuttgart, Greiner,&Pfeiffer n.d.
478p.

NL 0352107 OC1 CtY

LIENHARD, Friedrich, 1865-1929.
Oberlin; roman aus der revolutions-zeit im Elsass. 15e aufl. Stuttgart, Greiner & Pfeiffer, [1913?].

NL 0352108 MH

Lienhard, Friedrich, 1865-1929
Oberlin, Roman aus der Revolutionszeit im Elsass. 16th ed. Stuttgart, Greiner ⸢1911⸣
478 p. illus., ports.

1.Oberlin, Johann Friedrich, 1740-1826 -
Fiction. 2.France - Hist. - Revolution -
Fiction. 3.Alsace - Hist. - Fiction.
I.Title.

NL 0352109 OrP

Lienhard, Friedrich, 1865-1929.
Oberlin. Roman aus der revolutionszeit im Elsass, von Friedrich Lienhard. 35 aufl. Stuttgart, Greiner & Pfeiffer ⸢1917?⸣
vi, 478. 20cm.
First published in "Der Türmer," 1900-10.

NL 0352110 PPT

PT Lienhard, Friedrich, 1865-1929.
2623 Oberlin. Roman aus der revolutionszeit im Elsass,
I21 von Friedrich Lienhard. 57. aufl. Stuttgart, Greiner &
O2 Pfeiffer, 1919.
1919 478 p. illus. (incl. ports.) 20ᶜᵐ.
First published in "Der Türmer", 1909-10.

NL 0352111 NIC

PT Lienhard, Friedrich, 1865-1929
2623 Oberlin. Roman aus der Revolutionszeit im
I41 Elsass. 78. Aufl. Stuttgart, Greiner &
O2 Pfeiffer [192-?]
478p. illus. 20cm.

1. Oberlin, Johann Friedrich, 1740-1826 -
Fiction 2. France - Hist. - Revolution -
Fiction 3. Alsace - Hist. - Fiction I. Title

NL 0352112 WU

Lienhard, Friedrich, 1865-1929.
Oberlin; roman aus der Revolutions-zeit im Elsass... Stuttgart, Greiner & Pfeiffer, 1922
444 p. 20 cm.

This copy inscribed to Dr. Schiedt by the author.

NL 0352113 PLF

VOLUME 332

833
L7183o   Lienhard, Friedrich, 1865-1929.
Oberlin; Roman aus der Revolutionszeit im
Elsass.   Hamburg, Agentur des Rauhen Hauses
»1933»
318p.   22cm.

1. Oberlin, Johann Friedrich, 1740-1826 -
Fiction. 2. Alsace - Hist. - Fiction.
I. Title.

NL 0352114 NcU

PT2623
.I 41 O2 Lienhard, Friedrich, 1865-1929.
1933   Oberlin; Roman aus der Revolutionszeit
im Elsass. Hamburg, Agentur des Rauhen
Hauses ,1933,
viii, 446 p. 20cm.

1. Oberlin, Johann Friedrich, 1740-1826—
Fiction. 2. France—Hist.—Revolution—Fiction.
3. Alsace—Hist.—Fiction.

NL 0352115 ViU

PT
2623   Lienhard, Friedrich, 1865-1929.
.I41 O5   Odilia; Legende in drei Aufzügen von
1898   Fritz Lienhard. Strassburg, Schlesier &
Schweikhardt, 1898.
86 p.

NL 0352116 NBuU KyU N

Lienhard, Friedrich, 1865-1929.
Odilia. Legende in drei Aufzügen von Fritz
Lienhard. Strassburg i.E., Schlesier &
Schweikhardt, 1898.
86p.

Microcard edition.

NL 0352117 ICRL

LIENHARD, Friedrich, 1865-1911.
Odilia, legende in drei aufzügen. 2e., durch
gesehene aufl. Stuttgart, Greiner & Pfeiffer,
1911.
pp. (4), 77.

NL 0352118 MH

LIENHARD, Friedrich, 1865-1929.
Odysseus; [poesie. Berlin, 1901.]

4°. pp. (2).
Blätter für deutsche erziehung,1901,3.27-28.

NL 0352119 MH

Lienhard, Friedrich, 1865-1929.
Odysseus; dramatische Dichtung in drei Aufzügen.   Stuttgart: Greiner & Pfeiffer, 1911. 2 p.l., 70 p. 12°.

NL 0352120 NN RPB MH

Lienhard, Friedrich, 1865-1929.
Odysseus auf Ithaka. Geleitwort zur zweiten Auflage.
(Bühne und Welt.   Hamburg, 1914.   4°.   Jahrg. 16.
p. 438-453.)

1. Drama (German). 2. Title.
N.Y.P.L.   April 14, 1914.

NL 0352121 NN

LIENHARD, Friedrich, 1865-1929.
Odysseus auf Ithaka; dramatische dichtung in
drei aufzügen. 2e, bearbeitete aufl. Stuttgart,
Greiner & Pfeiffer, 1914.

pp. (8), 93.

NL 0352122 MH DLC-P4 NjP

Lienhard, Friedrich, 1865-1929.
Odysseus auf Ithaka; dramatische Dichtung in drei Aufzügen,
von Friedrich Lienhard...   Stuttgart: Greiner & Pfeiffer, 1920.
94 p. illus. (music.) 3. ed., rev. 12°.

491333A. 1. Drama, German.   I. Title.
N.Y.P.L.   January 5, 1931

NL 0352123 NN OC1

PT
2623   Lienhard, Friedrich, 1865-1929.
L62404   Odysseus auf Ithaka; dramatische
dichtung in drei aufzügen, von Friedrich Lienhard. Nach der dritten
auflage für den schulgebrauch hrsg.
von Ludwig Buck.   Stuttgart, Greiner
& Pfeiffer, 1921.
x, 101 p. incl. map.

Contains music.
"Literaturnachweis": p. 97.

I. Buck, Ludwig,   ed.
II. Title.

NL 0352124 CLU

4PT   Lienhard, Friedrich, 1865-1929.
Ger.   Der Pandurenstein und anderes.
6408   Wiesbaden, Verlag des Volksbildungs-
vereins zu Wiesbaden, 1918.
45 p.

(Wiesbadener Volksbücher, Nr. 86)

NL 0352125 DLC-P4

WC   Lienhard, Friedrich, 1865-1929
14527   Parsifal und Zarathustra; Vortrag.
Stuttgart, Greiner & Pfeiffer, 1914.
46 p.

1. Wagner, Richard, 1813-1883. Parsifal.
I. Title(1)
cdu

NL 0352126 CtY MH

Lienhard, Friedrich,1865-1929.
Phidias; schauspiel in drei aufzügen. 2 aufl.
Stuttgart, Greiner & Pfeiffer. [pref.1918]
88p.

NL 0352127 OC1

Lienhard, Friedrich, 1865-1929.
Rudolf Eucken und sein Zeitalter. Studien von Professor D.
Dr. Friedrich Lienhard, Dr. Alfred Beck, Professor Curt Hacker
und Professor Dr. Bruno Jordan...   Langensalza: H. Beyer &
Söhne, 1926.   84 p.   8°.   (Paedagogisches Magazin. Heft
1072.)

"Schriften aus dem Euckenkreis. Heft 21."

1. Eucken, Rudolf Christof, 1846-   2. Hacker, Curt. 3. Beck,
Alfred. 4. Jordan, Bruno, 1885-   5. Ser.
N.Y.P.L.   September 7, 1926

NL 0352128 NN

PT
2623   Lienhard, Friedrich, 1865-1929.
I 41S3   Der Sängerkrieg auf der Wartburg, ein
Festspiel. Mit Buchschmuck von Joseph
Sattler. Eisenach, Freunde der Wartburg,
1925.
58 p. illus. 24cm. (Freunde der
Wartburg e.v. Eisenach. »Veröffentlichungen»
Hft. 3)

Includes Jahresbericht. 1925.

I. Title.

NL 0352129 CoFS MH NN InU

Lienhard, Friedrich, 1865-   ed.
Schicksale einer verschleppten in Frankreich, von ihr
selbst erzählt und von kaiserl. regierungs-kommis-
sar in Elsass-Lothringen eidlich erhärtet, hrsg. von
Friedrich Lienhard und Paul Kannengiesser ... 8. tausend. Strassburg i. E., Strassburger druckerei und verlagsanstalt, 1915.
48 p. 21½cm.

1. European war, 1914-1918—Personal narratives. I. Kannengiesser,
Paul, 1853-   joint ed. II. Title.

                                        25-15341

Library of Congress   D640.L46

NL 0352130 DLC CtY NjP

PT
2623   Lienhard, Friedrich, 1865-1929.
.I41S3   Die Schildbürger; ein Scherzlied vom Mai
1900   [von] Fritz Lienhard. Leipzig, G. H. Meyer,
1900.
92 p. illus.

Added t. p.: Die Schildbürger; eine
Frühlingsdichtung.

NL 0352131 NBuU WU N

838
8334F21   Lienhard, Friedrich, 1865-1929.
Schiller...   Berlin, Schuster
,1905,
84p. front.,plates, ports.,facsims.
(part.fold.) S. (Die dichtung. bd.
XXVI)

NL 0352132 IaU NIC CtY MH CU NcU NjP

Lienhard, Friedrich, 1865-1929.
Schiller, von Fritz Lienhard. Berlin,
Schuster & Loeffler, 1911?
84 p. illus. (Die Dichtung, Bd.26)

1. Schiller, Johann Christoph Friedrich von,
1759-1805. I. Series.

NL 0352133 WaU

VOLUME 332

Lienhard, Friedrich, 1865-1929.
Schwester Beate; Erzählung. Hamburg,
Agentur des Rauhen Hauses ₍c1934₎
72 p.

NL 0352134 WaU

PT
2623
.I41S65 7. Aufl. Stuttgart, Greiner & Pfeiffer
[n.d.]
225 p.

Lienhard, Friedrich, 1865-1929.
Der Spielmann; Roman aus der Gegenwart

NL 0352135 NBuU N

---

4 PT Ger Lienhard, Friedrich, 1865-1929.
-2513 Der Spielmann; Roman aus der Gegenwort.
10. Aufl. Stuttgart, Greiner & Pfeiffer.
225 p.

NL 0352136 DLC-P4

Lienhard, Friedrich, 1865-1929.
Der Spielmann; Roman aus der Gegenwart, von Friedrich
Lienhard. Neunundfünfzigste Auflage. Stuttgart: Greiner &
Pfeiffer ₍1913₎ 225 p. 20cm.

149347B. 1. Fiction, German. I. Title.
N.Y.P.L. February 27, 1942

NL 0352137 NN IEN MH OC1 ICarbS PPGi PP

PT2623 Lienhard, Friedrich, 1865-1929.
.I41S65 Der Spielmann; Roman aus der
Gegenwart. 32. Aufl. Stuttgart,
Greiner & Pfeiffer ₍1913₎
225 p. 20 cm.

NL 0352138 TU

PT2623 Lienhard, Friedrich, 1865-1929
Il1S6 Der spielmann, Roman aus der Gegenwart.
1913 53.Aufl. Stuttgart, Greiner & Pfeiffer
₍1913₎
225p. 20cm.

NL 0352139 IaU

PT
2623 Lienhard, Friedrich, 1865-1929.
L72sp Der spielmann; roman aus der gegenwart
... 73.aufl. Stuttgart, Greiner & Pfeiffer [192-?]
4p.ℓ.,225p. 20cm.

NL 0352140 NRU

PT2623 Lienhard, Friedrich, 1865-1929.
.I23 Der Spielmann; Roman aus der Gegen-
.S7 wart. 82. Aufl. Stuttgart, Greiner
& Pfeiffer ₍1913₎
225p. 20cm.

NL 0352141 NNU-W

838
L72sp Lienhard, Friedrich, 1865-1929.
1922 Der spielmann; roman aus der gegenwart, von
Friedrich Lienhard. 96.aufl. Stuttgart, Greiner & Pfeiffer, 1922.
4 p.ℓ.,211 p. 19½ᶜᵐ
"Erstausgabe dieses buches ... 1913."

NL 0352142 MiU CLSU

Lienhard, Friedrich, 1865-1929.
Der spielmann. Roman aus der gegenwart.
100. Aufl. Stuttgart, 1924.
211 p. 20 cm.

NL 0352143 RPB

Lienhard, Friedrich, 1865-1929.
Thüringer tagebuch...69.Aufl. Stuttgart,
n.d.
20 cm.

NL 0352144 RPB

Lienhard, Friedrich, 1865-1929.
Thüringer tagebuch, von Friedrich Lienhard.
11.aufl. Stuttgart, Greiner & Pfeiffer ₍191-₎
196 p.

NL 0352145 OCU

Lienhard, Friedrich, 1865-1929.
Thüringer Tagebuch. 66. Aufl. Stuttgart,
Greiner und Pfeiffer ₍192-₎
iv, 196 p. illus. 20cm.

"Die Erstausgabe dieses Buches erschien im
Dezember 1903."

NL 0352146 WU NN

GERMAN
838
L624t Lienhard, Friedrich, 1865-1929
Thüringer Tagebuch. 72. Aufl.
Stuttgart, Greiner und Pfeiffer ₍1903₎
196 p. illus.

NL 0352147 MiD MH

838
L72th Lienhard, Friedrich, 1865-1929.
1923 Thüringer tagebuch, von Friedrich Leinhard.
84.aufl. Stuttgart, Verlagsanstalt Greiner &
Pfeiffer, 1923.
194 p.incl.illus.,plates. 19½ᶜᵐ

NL 0352148 MiU OOxM

PT
2623 Lienhard, Friedrich, 1865-1929.
.I41T5 Thüringer Tagebuch. Stuttgart, Greiner &
1923 Pfeiffer, 1923.
194 p.

"89. Aufl."

NL 0352149 NBuU N

Lienhard, Friedrich, 1865-1929.
... Thüringer tagebuch. Neue durchgesehene aufl. Mit
zwanzig bildern aus dem Thüringer wald. Hamburg, Agentur
des Rauhen hauses gmbh. ₍1935₎
180, ₍2₎ p. front., plates. 21½ᶜᵐ
"103. bis 105. tausend der gesamtauflage."

I. Title.
46-33130
Library of Congress PT2623.I 41T5 1935

NL 0352150 DLC WaU

PT
2623 Lienhard, Friedrich, 1865-1929
.I41T55 Till Eulenspiegel; Narrenspiel in drei
1902 Teilen [von] Fritz Lienhard. 3. durchgearb.
Aufl. Leipzig, G. H. Meyer, 1902.
182 p.

NL 0352151 NBuU N

LIENHARD, Friedrich.
Till Eulenspiegel;dramatische dichtung.
Stuttgart, Greiner & Pfeiffer, 1911. 3 teile
(in 1 vol.).

sm. 4°.
Contents: Eulenspiegels ausfahrt. 4e umgearbeitete aufl. 1910.- Der fremde. 3e aufl.
1910.-Eulenspiegels heimkehr. 4e aufl. 1911.

NL 0352152 MH IaU

PT2623 Lienhard, Friedrich, 1865-
.123T6 ... Till Eulenspiegel; dramatische dichtung in drei teilen ...
1920 Eulenspiegels ausfahrt, Der fremde, Eulenspiegels heimkehr.
Stuttgart, Greiner und Pfeiffer, 1920.
3 pt. in 1 v. 19½ᶜᵐ
At head of title: Friedrich Lienhard.
Each part has special t.-p.
5. aufl.

NL 0352153 ICU

838
L72t Lienhard, Friedrich, 1865-1929.
1925 ... Till Eulenspiegel; dramatische dichtung
in drei teilen ... Stuttgart, Greiner &
Pfeiffer, 1925.
3 pts.in 1 v. 1 illus.(music) 19½ᶜᵐ
Each part has special t.-p.
Parts 1,3, 6.durchgesehene aufl.; pt.2, 6.aufl.
CONTENTS.--Eulenspiegels ausfahrt; schelmenspiel in
drei aufzügen.--Der fremde; zwischenspiel in einem
aufzug.--Eulenspiegels heimkehr; schauspiel in drei
aufzügen.
I.Title.

NL 0352154 MiU NN

PT
2623 [Lienhard, Friedrich] 1865-1929.
L72tu Türmer-beiträge aus den jahrgängen I
bis XXIV (1898-1922) [no imprint]
139p. 19½cm.
First issued 1922 by Greiner & Pfeiffer in
Stuttgart "als festschrift zu jg.25, hrsg. von
Paul Bülow." (105p.)

I. Bülow, Paul, 1894- II. Der Türmer;
deutsche monatshefte. III. Title.

NL 0352155 NRU

VOLUME 332

PT
2623
I41
U5
Lienhard, Friedrich, 1865-1929.
Unter dem Rosenkreuz; ein Hausbuch aus dem
Herzen Deutschlands. [1. Aufl.] Stuttgart,
Greiner & Pfeiffer, 1925.
217p. 20cm.

NL 0352156   WU

Lienhard, Friedrich, 1865-1929.
Unter dem Rosenkreuz; ein Hausbuch aus dem Herzen
Deutschlands. 4. Aufl. Stuttgart, Greiner & Pfeiffer [1925]
217 p. 20 cm.

I. Title.

PT2623.I41U5 1925   61-55248 ‡

NL 0352157   DLC WaU

---

b
Hitler
coll.
Lienhard, Friedrich, 1865-1929.
Unter dem Rosenkreuz; ein Hausbuch aus
dem Herzen Deutschlands. 6. Aufl. Stuttgart, Greiner & Pfeiffer [1925]

217 p.

Dedication by Paul Opitz.

NL 0352158   DLC

Lienhard, Friedrich. 1865-1929.
Unter dem rosenkranz. Stuttgart, Greiner,
[1935?]
217 p.

NL 0352159   PPT PPG

L4094
.I41
.585
[Lienhard, Friedrich] 1865-1929.
Varthän hör Elsass-Lothringen? Av
några Elsassare; översättning av Axel
Lindquist. Stockholm, Bonnier [1917]
106 p. 18½ cm.

Preface signed by Friedrich Lienhard.

1. Alsace-Lorraine question. I. Lindquist, Axel, tr. II. Title.

NL 0352160   NjP NN

Lienhard, Friedrich, 1865-1929.
Von Weibes Wonne und Wert. Buelow, Paul,
Hrsg. Lpz., Koch, 1921.
190 p.

NL 0352161   PPG

PT
2623
.I41A6
1924
Lienhard, Friedrich, 1865-1929.
Von Weibes Wonne und Wert, Worte und
Gedanken. Hrsg. von Paul Bülow. Leipzig,
M. Koch [c1922]
192 p. illus. 22 cm.

I. Title.

PT2623.I 41A6   1924a   53-52340

NL 0352162   NBuU N

Lienhard, Friedrich, 1865-1929.
Von Weibes Wonne und Wert, Worte und Gedanken.
Hrsg. von Paul Bülow. Leipzig, M. Koch [c1924]
192 p. illus. 22 cm.

I. Title.

PT2623.I 41A6 1924a   53-52340 ‡

NL 0352163   DLC OC1 WU

PT395
I54
Lienhard, Friedrich, 1865-1929.
Die Vorherrschaft Berlins; litterarische
Anregungen [von] Fritz Lienhard. Leipzig,
G.H. Meyer, 1900.
52 p.   (Flugschriften der Heimat, Heft 4)

Bibliographical footnotes.

1. German literature - 19th cent. - Hist.
& crit. 2. Berlin, Ger. - Intellectual
life.

NL 0352164   CU MH

334.91
L719v
1902
Lienhard, Friedrich, 1865-1929.
Die Vorherrschaft Berlins; litterarische
Anregungen [von] Fritz Lienhard. 2. verm.
Aufl.   Berlin, Meyer & Wunder, 1902.
52p.

1. German literature--Hist. & crit.
2. Berlin. 3. Nationalism. I. Title.

NL 0352165   ICarbS MB OCU OO

PT
2623
I41
W3
Lienhard, Friedrich, 1865-1929
Wandernd Licht; aus Lienhards Schriften für
jeden Tag des Jahres ausgewählt von Paul
Bülow. 10. Aufl. Stuttgart, Greiner &
Pfeiffer [1933?]
213p. 13cm.

NL 0352166   WU

LIENHARD, Friedrich, 1865-1929.
Wartburg; dramatische dichtung in drei teilen
Stuttgart, Greiner & Pfeiffer, [1906].

sm. 4°.
Contents: Heinrich von Osterdingen; schau-
spiel. Die heilige Elisabeth, trauerspiel.
Luther auf der Wartburg, schauspiel.

NL 0352167   MH OCU DLC-P4 IaU

Lienhard, Freidrich, 1865-1929.
Wartburg; drei dramatische dichtungen...
Stuttgart, Greiner & Pfeiffer [1916]
viii, 119, 104, 102p.

NL 0352168   OC1

Lienhard, Friedrich, 1865-1929.
Wartburg. Drei dramatische dichtungen.
Stuttgart, 1918.
19 cm.
Original title pages bound in.

NL 0352169   RPB

PT
2623
.I41W3
1920
Lienhard, Friedrich, 1865-1929.
Wartburg; drei dramatische Dichtungen.
Stuttgart, Greiner und Pfeiffer, 1920.
3 v. in 1

Each vol. has also special t.p.
Contents.- Heinrich von Ofterdingen. 6.
Aufl.- Die heilige Elisabeth. 7. Aufl.-
Luther auf der Wartburg. 8. Aufl.

NL 0352170   NBuU N

PT
2623
.I41
W37
Lienhard, Friedrich, 1865-1929.
Wartburg. Drei dramatische Dichtungen.
Heinrich von Osterdingen. Die heilige Elisa-
beth. Luther auf der Wartburg. Stuttgart,
Greiner und Pfeiffer, 1921.
viii, 126, 110, 111p. 19cm.

I. Heinrich von Osterdingen. II. Die
heilige Elisabeth. III. Luther auf der
Wartburg. IV. Title.

NL 0352171   TNJ PPG

U. of Cin.
PT2623
.I41W3
1923
Lienhard, Friedrich, 1865-1929.
Wartburg, drei dramatische dichtungen; Heinrich
von Ofterdingen, Die heilige Elisabeth, Luther auf
der Wartburg.   Stuttgart, Greiner & Pfeiffer [1923]
viii,119,104,102 p.   music.   20cm.
Each play has special title-page.

NL 0352172   OCU

Lienhard, Friedrich, 1865-1929.
Was wir verloren haben —. Entrissenes, doch nie ver-
gessenes deutsches land. Original-zeichnungen von
Wilhelm Thiele ... mit einem geleitwort von general-
feldmarschall von Hindenburg, unter mitarbeit von
Friedrich Lienhard, Artur Brausewetter, Paul Warncke
hrsg. vom verleger. Berlin, F. Zillessen (H. Beenken)
[1920]

Lienhard, Friedrich, 1865-1929.
Wasgaufahrten; siebenundzwanzigste aufl.
Stuttgart, Greiner [1901-12]
129p.

NL 0352174   OOxM

DD
801
A347
L71
1912
Lienhard, Friedrich, 1865-1929.
Wasgaufahrten. Buchschmuck von Karl
Spindler. 4. durchgesehene Aufl. Stutt-
gart, Greiner & Pfeiffer, 1912.
viii,156 p. illus. 19cm.

1. Alsace--Descr. & trav. I. Title.

NL 0352175   NIC RPB

PT
2623
.I41W35
Lienhard, Friedrich, 1865-1929.
Wasgaufahrten. 28. Aufl. Stuttgart,
Greiner & Pfeiffer [1912?]
129 p.

NL 0352176   NBuU NRU OC1 N

VOLUME 332

Lienhard, Friedrich, 1865-1929.
Wasgaufahrten. 31.Aufl. Berlin, Singer [1912]
120 p. 20 cm.

Bound with his Thüringer Tagebuch [1903]

NL 0352177 NjP

50558.33.20

LIENHARD, Friedrich, 1865-1929.
Wasgaufahrten. Stuttgart, Greiner & Pfeiffer,
[192-].

20 cm. Illustr.
"Buchschmuck von Karl Spindler."

NL 0352178 MH WaU

Lienhard, Friedrich, 1865-1929.
Wasgaufahrten; 20. aufl. Stutt. Greiner,
[1920]
156p.

NL 0352179 OCU

4PN Lienhard, Friedrich, 1865-1929.
943 Wege nach Weimar; Beiträge zur
Erneuerung des Idealismus. 12. Aufl.
Stuttgart, Verlagsanstalt Greiner &
Pfeiffer [19 -
v. 1, 3, 5

NL 0352180 DLC-P4 PSC

LIENHARD, F[riedrich], 1865-1929.
Wege nach Weimar;gesammelte monatsblätter.
Stuttgart, Greiner & Pfeiffer, 1906-08.

6 vol. Ports.,plates and other illustr.
Contents: i.Heinrich von Stein - Emerson.-ii.
Shakespeare - Homer.- iii.Friedrich der Grosse.
- iv. Herder - Jean Paul.- v.Schiller.- vi.
Goethe.

NL 0352181 MH CU NjP

PT2623 Lienhard, Friedrich, 1865-1929.
.I23W4 Wege nach Weimar; Beiträge zur Erneuerung des
1910 Idealismus. [2.Aufl. n.p., Vorwort 1910.
6 v. in 3.

NL 0352182 ICU

---

804 Lienhard, Friedrich, 1865-1929.
L719w Wege nach Weimar; Beiträge zur Erneuerung
1911 des Idealismus. 2., neugestaltete Aufl.
Stuttgart, Greiner & Pfeiffer [1911]
6v. plates,ports. 19cm.
CONTENTS.- 1.Bd.Heinrich v.Stein. Emerson.- 2.Bd.
Shakespeare. Homer.- 3.Bd.Friedrich d.Grosse.- 4.Bd.
Herder. Jean Paul.- 5.Bd.Schiller.- 6.Bd.Goethe.

1.Literature - Addresses, essays, lectures. 2.German literature - Addresses,
essays, lectures. I.Title. LC.

NL 0352183 CLSU CU MB MH OU

Lienhard, Friedrich, 1865-1929.
Wege nach Weimar; beiträge zur erneuerung
des idealismus. Stuttgart, Greiner und Pfeiffer,
[1910-1911, repr.] 1918-1919.
6 v. illus., ports. 19 cm.
Vol. 1-3, 5-6: "4. Aufl.": v. 4: "3. Aufl."
"Die sechs bände 'Wege nach Weimar', plan-
mässig als ein ganzes angelegt, erschienen zunächst in monatsheften (1905-1908) ... In der
zweiten auflage (1910-1911) wurde dann die volle
buchform hergestellt, durch gruppierung der
zusammengehöri gen aufsätze.

Die dritte (1916-1918) und folgenden auflagen
blieben im ganzen unverandert. Nur 'Königin
Luise' wurde hinzugefügt [bd. 3]"
Contents. - bd. 1. Heinrich von Stein.
Emerson. 1918. - bd. 2. Shakespeare. Homer.
1918. - bd. 3. Friedrich der Grosse. 1919. -
bd. 4. Herder. Jean Paul. 1918. - bd. 5.
Schiller. 1918. - bd. 6. Goethe. 1919.

NL 0352185 OCU

LIENHARD, FRIEDRICH, 1865-1929.
Wege nach Weimar. Beiträge zur erneuerung des
idealismus. 13.aufl. Stuttgart,Greiner &
Pfeiffer,192-.
6v. ports. 21cm.

Bd.2-3,5-6: 12.aufl.; bd.4: 11.aufl.
Contents.--1.bd.Heinrich von Stein, Emerson.
-2.bd.Shakespeare, Homer. -3.bd.Friedrich der
grosse. -4.bd.Herder, Jean Paul. -5.bd.Schiller.
-6.bd.Goethe.

NL 0352186 PU

Lienhard, Friedrich, 1865-1929.
Wege nach Weimar. 3.aufl. Stuttgart, Greiner,
1921.
6v.

NL 0352187 PPT

PN Lienhard, Friedrich, 1865-1929, comp.
6037 Wege nach Weimar; Beiträge zur Erneuerung
.L54 des Idealismus. 11. Aufl. Stuttgart,
1923 Greiner & Pfeiffer, 1923.
6v. illus. 20cm.

Contents.- 1. Bd. Heinrich von Stein--
Emerson.- 2. Bd. Shakespeare - Homer.- 3. Bd.
Friedrich der Grosse.- 4. Bd. Herder - Jean
Paul.- 5. Bd. Schiller.- 6. Bd. Goethe.

NL 0352188 TNJ NcU PSC OC1 PPGi

3469 Lienhard, Friedrich, 1865-1929.
.I68
3952 Wer zuletzt lacht... Ein schlossidyll.
10.aufl. Stuttgart, Greiner [1921]
83 p. 15½ cm.

NL 0352189 NjP PPGi

PT Lienhard, Friedrich, 1865-1929.
2623 Wer zuletzt lacht ... ein schlossidyll.
I41 12. Aufl. Stuttgart, Greiner & Pfeiffer
W4 [1921]
83p. 16cm.

NL 0352190 WU

LIENHARD, Friedrich, 1865-1929.
Wer zuletzt lacht; ein schlossidyll. 15. auf
Stuttgart, Greiner & Pfeister, [1921].

NL 0352191 MH

Lienhard, Friedrich, 1865-1929.
Westmark; Roman aus dem gegenwärtigen Elsass, von
Friedrich Lienhard... Stuttgart: Greiner und Pfeiffer, 1918.
200 p. 50. ed. 12°.

175003A. 1. Fiction, German. 2. Title. October 31, 1925
N. Y. P. L.

NL 0352192 NN OC1W OOxM MdBJ OC1

Lienhard, Friedrich, 1865-1929.
Westmark; roman aus dem gegenwärtigen Elsass, von
Friedrich Lienhard. 53. aufl. Stuttgart,
Greiner & Pfeiffer [1918]
vii, 186 p. 20 cm.

NL 0352193 CU

PT Lienhard, Friedrich, 1865-1929.
2623 Westmark; Roman aus dem gegenwärtigen
I21 Elsass. Stuttgart, Greiner und Pfeiffer,
W5 1919.
200 p. 20cm.
"24. Aufl."

NL 0352194 NIC

Lienhard, Friedrich, 1865-1929.
Westmark. Roman aus dem gegenwärtigen
Elsass...32.aufl. Stuttgart, 1920.
20 cm.

NL 0352195 RPB

PT2623 Lienhard, Friedrich, 1865-1929.
.I41W4 Westmark, Roman aus dem gegenwärtigen
1920 Elsass. 37. Aufl. Stuttgart, Greiner
und Pfeiffer, 1920.
200 p. 20 cm.

"Dieses Werk wurde im Herbst 1916, nach
einem Aufenthalt im oberen Elsass, zunächst
als dramatischen Skizze entworfen; dann in
Romanform umgewandelt und um Weihnachten 1918
vollendet."

NL 0352196 TU

Lienhard, Friedrich, 1865-1929.
Westmark. Roman aus dem gegenwärtigen
Elsass. Von Friedrich Lienhard. 40. Aufl.
Stuttgart, 1920.
20 cm.

NL 0352197 CtY

Lienhard, Friedrich, 1865-1929.
Westmark, Roman aus dem gegenwärtigen Elsass. 41.
Aufl. Stuttgart, Greiner und Pfeiffer, 1921.
200 p. 20 cm.
"Dieses Werk wurde im Herbst 1916, nach einem Aufenthalt im
oberen Elsass, zunächst als dramatischen Skizze entworfen; dann in
Romanform umgewandelt und um Weihnachten 1918 vollendet."

I. Title.
PT2623.I 41W4 1921 49-33751*

NL 0352198 DLC

VOLUME 332

PT
2623
I41
W45
   Lienhard, Friedrich, 1965-1929
     Westmark; Roman aus dem Elsass. 50. Aufl.
   Stuttgart, Greiner & Pfeiffer, 1923.
     200p. 20cm.

NL 0352199 WU

   Lienhard, Friedrich, 1865-1929.
     Westmark, Roman aus dem Elsass. 51. Aufl. Stuttgart,
Greiner & Pfeiffer, 1923.
     186 p. 20 cm.

   I. Title.
   PT2623.I 41W4 1923   53-52349 ‡

NL 0352200 DLC NBuU N

838
L719w
1930
   Lienhard, Friedrich, 1865-1929
     Westmark; roman aus dem Elsass.
   59.aufl.   Stuttgart, Greiner ₍1930?₎
     186p. D.

NL 0352201 IaU

832
L624wi
1905
   LIENHARD, FRIEDRICH, 1865-1929.
     Wieland der Schmied, dramatische dichtung,
von Fritz Lienhard, mit einer einleitung über
bergtheater und Wielandsage. Stuttgart,
Greiner & Pfeiffer, 1905.
     xix, 86p. 20cm.

NL 0352202 TxU OrU NN ICarbS

   Lienhard, Friedrich, 1865-1929.
     Wieland der Schmied; dramatische Dichtung. ₍In seven
scenes.₎ Mit einer Einleitung über Bergtheater und Wielandsage. Stuttgart: Greiner & Pfeiffer, 1910. xx, 86 p. 2. ed.
12°.

   1. Drama (German). 2. Title.
N.Y.P.L.   June 5, 1913.

NL 0352203 NN NBuU RPB IaU MH N

832.91
L71w
1913
   Lienhard, Friedrich, 1865-1929.
     Wieland der Schmied; dramatische Dichtung
von Friedrich Lienhard mit einer Einleitung
über Bergtheater und Wielandsage. 3., durchgesehene Aufl. Stuttgart, Greiner & Pfeiffer,
1913.
     xvi,90p. 21cm.

NL 0352204 TNJ CtY

   Lienhard, Friedrich, 1865-1929.
     Wieland der schmied; dramatische dichtung;
mit einer einleitung ueber bergtheater un
Wielandsage. 10 aufl. Stuttgart, Greiner
& Pfeiffer [pref. 1912-1913]

NL 0352205 OC1

   Lienhard, Friedrich, 1865-1929.
     Wohin gehört Elsass-Lothringen? Zürich, Rascher & cᵒ,
1915.

   LIENHARD, Friedrich, 1865-1929.
     Zeichnungen von Ellen Tornquist,mit begleit-
wort von Friedrich Leinhard. [2e aufl.] 1919.

NL 0352207 MH

AP30
.Z95
   Lienhard, Friedrich, 1865-1929, ed.
     Das zwanzigste Jahrhundert; deutsch-nationale Monatshefte
für sociales Leben, Politik, Wissenschaft, Kunst und Literatur.
     Berlin ₍etc.₎ H. Lüstenöder ₍etc.₎

   Lienhard, Fritz.
     Ueber die juristische natur des urheberrechts und die
uebertragbarkeit desselben nach schweiz. recht ... Bü-
lach, Druck von F. Scheuchzer, 1889.
     79, ₍1₎ p. 21ᶜᵐ.
     Inaug.-diss.—Zürich.
     "Verzeichniss der hauptsächlich benutzten literatur": p. 78.

   1. Copyright. 2. Copyright—Switzerland. 3. Publishers and publishing—Switzerland.
                           11-16841
   Library of Congress   Z637.L65

NL 0352209 DLC

   Lienhard, Fritz, 1865-1929.
     See
   Lienhard, Friedrich, 1865-1929.

   Lienhard, Fritz, 1871-
     Der Gottesbegriff bei Gustav Theodor Fechner.
Darstellung und Kritik ... Bern, 1920.
     23 cm.
     Inaug.-Diss. - Bern.
     Lebenslauf.
     "Literatur", p. ₍iii₎-iv.

NL 0352211 CtY PU

TL
205
.L72
1930
   Lienhard,Gabriel.
     Automobile,par Gabriel Lienhard ... à l'usage
des constructeurs d'automobiles et d'aéroplanes,
ingénieurs et chefs d'ateliers. 18.éd. Paris,
Dunod, 1930.
     5 p.l.,₍iii₎-xiv,₍2₎,380,A1-A76,xxxii p.
illus. 15 cm. ₍Agendas Dunod₎
     "Législation du travail,par G.Courtot": p.A1-
A67.
     "Bibliographie": verso of leaf following
p.xiv (first group)

NL 0352212 MiU

LIENHARD, GABRIEL.
   Construction automobile à l'usage des constructeurs
d'automobiles et d'aéroplanes, ingénieurs et chefs
d'ateliers. 11.éd. Paris, Dunod, 1923. xv, 487, lxiv p.
(p. ₍xxxiii-lxiv advertisements₎ illus. 15cm. (Agendas Dunod)

   Earlier editions by M.C. Favron.

   1. Automobiles—Handbooks, manuals, etc., 1923. I. Favron, M.C.
Construction automobile.   II. Series.

NL 0352213 NN

   Lienhard, George H   *comp.*
     ... The cross-word puzzle dictionary, compiled by George
H. Lienhard ... Houston, Tex., Lienhard publishing company, 1933.
     48 p. 18½ᵐ.
     At head of title: First edition.

   1. English language—Glossaries, vocabularies, etc. 2. Crossword puzzles.
                             33-15619
   Library of Congress   GV1507.C7L5
                      ₍a44d1₎   793.73

NL 0352214 DLC

   ₍Lienhard, Hans₎
     Entwurf eines schweizerischen tier-
schutzgesetzes. ₍Zürich, n.p. ₍1955₎
     1 p.l., 8 numb. 1. 30cm.

NL 0352215 MH-L

   Lienhard, Hans.
     ... Entwurf eines tierschutzgesetz-
es ... Zürich, Rechtshilfe-verlag,
1955.
     2 p.l., 7 numb. 1. 30cm. (Rechts-
hilfe-bücher, heft 91)

NL 0352216 MH-L

   Lienhard, Hans, *ed.*
     Die Gesetze der geistigen Welt; unsere Aufgabe, diesseits
und jenseits. Zürich, Verlag Geistige Loge, 1949.
     63 p. (p. 63 advertisement) 21 cm.
     "Besteht im wesentlichen nur aus Auszügen von Vorträgen des
Geistes Josef in der Geistigen Loge ... Die Uebermittlung erfolgte
durch das ... Medium Frau B₍eatrice₎."—p. 58.

   1. Spiritualism. I. Beatrice, medium. II. Josef, spirit. III. Title.
     BF1263.L5   133.93   A 50-2989
   Harvard Univ. Library
for Library of Congress   ₍3₎†

NL 0352217 MH DLC

   Lienhard, Hans.
     ... Grundriss des schweiz. staatsrech-
tes ... Zürich, Rechtshilfe-verlag, 1952.
     20 numb. 1. 15cm. (Rechtshilfe-bücher,
heft 74; Rechtslehre für jedermann, heft
24)
     Multigraphed copy.

NL 0352218 MH-L

VOLUME 332

Lienhard, Hans.
... Grundriss des strafprozessrechts ... Zürich, Rechtshilfe-verlag, 1952.
20 numb. l. 15cm. (Rechtshilfe-bücher, heft 71; Rechtslehre für jedermann, heft 21)
Multigraphed copy.

NL 0352219 MH-L

Lienhard, Hans.
Der Schlüssel der Einweihung; die Übungen der orientalischen Freimaurer und der Alchimisten. Zürich, 1950.

NL 0352220 MH

Lienhard, Hans.
Schöpferische Selbstversenkung; ein Weg zu Selbsterkenntnis und Selbstverwirklichung. Zürich, Buch- und Bildungsgenossenschaft, 1949.
16 p. (Buch und Bildung, 1)

NL 0352221 MH

Lienhard, Hans.
Die Uebungen der Jesuiten; eine systematische Selbst-Disziplinierung. Zurich, Buch- und Bildungsgenossenschaft, 1949.
16 p.

NL 0352222 DCU

Lienhard, Hans.
... Wie führe ich meine prozesse? (Grundriss des schweiz. zivilprozessrechtes) ... Zürich, Rechtshilfe-verlag, 1952.
16 numb. l. 15cm. (Rechtshilfebücher, heft 69; Rechtslehre für jedermann, heft 19)
Multigraphed copy.

NL 0352223 MH-L

Lienhard, Hans, fl. 1926.
Untersuchungen über die Wasserstoff-Ionen-Konzentration in der normalen und pathologischen Kuhmilch. [Zürich, 1926.]
Inaugural-Dissertation - Zürich.

NL 0352224 MH CtY

Lienhard, Heinrich, 1822-1893.
Californien unmittelbar vor und nach der entdeckung des goldes. Bilder aus dem leben des Heinrich Lienhard von Bilten, Kanton Glarus in Nauvoo, Nordamerika. Ein beitrag zur jubiläumsfeier der goldentdeckung und zur kulturgeschichte Californiens ... Zürich, Fäsi & Beer, 1898.
318 p. front. (port.) 22½ᶜᵐ.

1. California—Descr. & trav. 2. California—Hist. 3. California—Gold discoveries.

Library of Congress   F865.L7 1898

24—8625

MsU NN ICN
NL 0352225 DLC CU NNC NjP CaBVaU CaBViPA OU MiU CtY

Leinhard, Heinrich, 1822-1893.
Californien unmittelbar vor und nach der entdeckung des goldes. Bilder aus dem leben des Heinrich Lienhard von Bilten, Kanton Glarus in Nauvoo, Nordamerika. Ein beitrag zur jubiläumsfeier der goldentdeckung und zur kulturgeschichte Californiens.. Zürich, Fäsi & Beer, 1898.
Microcard edition (8 cards) (Travels in the West and Southwest) microprinted by LCP Louisville, 1968.
1. California—Descr. & trav. 2. California—Hist. 3. California—Gold discoveries. I. Title. II. Ser.

NL 0352226 ViU ICRL

Lienhard, Heinrich, 1822-1893.
Californien unmittelbar vor und nach der entdeckung des goldes. Bilder aus dem leben des Heinrich Lienhard von Bilten, kanton Glarus, in Nauvoo, Nordamerika. Ein beitrag zus [!] jubiläumsfeier der goldentdeckung und zur kulturgeschichte Californiens ... Zürich, E. Speidel, 1900.
318 p. front. (port.) 21½ᶜᵐ.

1. California—Descr. & trav. 2. California—Gold discoveries.

Library of Congress   F865.L7 1900   Rc-1062

NL 0352227 DLC ICJ CtY

Lienhard, Heinrich, 1822-1903.
I knew Sutter, by Heinrich Lienhard; translated from the original German by students of German at C. K. McClatchy senior high school. Sacramento, Calif., The Nugget press, 1939.
ix p., 3 l., 3-25 p., 1 l. incl. front. (port.) 17 cm.
"285 copies have been printed and bound for private distribution. This copy is no. 2."
A translation of chapter x of the author's "Californien unmittelbar vor und nach der entdeckung des goldes," published at Zurich in 1898 cf. Pref.
1. Sutter, John Augustus, 1803-1880.   I. Sacramento, Calif. C. K. McClatchy senior high school.   II. Title.

F865.S954   923.873   39-30826 rev

NL 0352228 DLC OkU CU-B NN

Lienhard, Heinrich, 1822-1903.
A pioneer at Sutter's fort, 1846-1850; the adventures of Heinrich Lienhard ... translated, edited, and annotated by Marguerite Eyer Wilbur from the original German manuscript. Los Angeles, The Calafia society, 1941.
3 p. l., xix p., 1 l., 291 p. front. (facsim.) plates, ports. 25½ cm. (Calafia series, no. 3)
Map on lining-papers.
A German edition was published in Switzerland in 1898 under title: Californien unmittelbar vor und nach der entdeckung des goldes. cf. p. xiv.
Bibliography: p. 276-277.
1. California—Descr. & trav. 2. California—Gold discoveries. I. Wilbur, Marguerite Knowlton (Eyer) 1889—   ed. II. Title.

F865.L72   917.94   42-11300 rev

CaBViPA OrU
NL 0352229 DLC CSmyS UU NjP CU-M NNC PP CSmH CU

Lienhard, Hermann, 1851-
Franco-Chilean arbitral tribunal, *Lausanne*, 1894-1901.
... Sentencia del Tribunal franco-chileno ... [Lima] Imprenta del estado, 1902.

Lienhard, Hermann, 1922-
Das Spiegelhaus, Gedichte. Salzburg, O. Müller [1955]
119 p. 20 cm.

I. Title.

PT2623.I 413S6   55-38004 ‡

NL 0352231 DLC CtY NN NcD

Lienhard, Hermann, 1922-
Die Verwandlung; Gedichte. Klagenfurt, Kleinmayr, 1948.
83 p.

NL 0352232 MH

881   Lienhard, Max Kurt, 1924-
A8po.Y8i   Zur Entstehung und Geschichte von Aristoteles' Poetik. Zürich, Juris-Verlag, 1950.
107p. 21cm.

Abhandlung—Zürich.
Vita.
Bibliography: p.102-104.

1. Aristoteles. Poetica.

NL 0352233 IU MiU NcD OU CtY MH OCU NNC NN

Lienhard, Otto E[rnst], Assistenzarzt d. Heilstätte: Aus der Lungenheilstätte Vogelsang b. Magdeburg. (Chefarzt: Schudt). Über kutane Tuberkulinbehandlung nach Ponndorf. Leipzig 1918: Edelmann. 19 S. 8°
Leipzig, Med. Diss. v. 21. Juni 1918, Ref. v. Strümpell
[Geb. 19. Juni 89 Schillersdorf E.-L.; Staatsangeh.: Elsaß-Lothringen; Vorbildung: L. Straßburg Reife 08; Studium: Straßburg 10 S.; Coll. 21. Juni 18; Approb. 4. Aug. 14.]   [U 18, 1132.]

NL 0352234 ICRL CtY DNLM

W 4   LIENHARD, Paul, 1927-
Z96   Untersuchungen zur Struktur der
1954   akuten hirntraumatischen Psychosen. Zürich, 1954.
24 p.
Inaug.-Diss. - Zürich.
"Erscheint im Schweizer Archiv für Neurologie und Psychiatrie, Bd. 74, 1954."
1. Psychoses - Traumatic

NL 0352235 DNLM

Lienhard, Richard.
Das Wettbewerbsmoment im Urheberrecht. Schleitheim, 1944.
vii, 55 p. 23 cm.
Inaug.-Diss.—Bern.
Bibliography: p. v-vii.

1. Copyright. 2. Copyright—Switzerland. 3. Competition, Unfair. 4. Competition, Unfair—Switzerland.   I. Title.

52-57575

NL 0352236 DLC

Lienhard, Romain, 1916-
Essai sur l'esprit fiscal en France d'après la législation de l'impôt sur le revenu. Zurich, AG. Fachschriften-Verlag & Buchdr., 1944.
147 p. 22 cm.
Thèse—Zürich.
Curriculum vitae.
"Bibliographie": p. 143-146.

1. Finance—France—Hist. 2. Taxation—France—Hist.   I. Title: L'esprit fiscal en France.

HJ1085.L5   49-44186*

NL 0352237 DLC NNC CtY

VOLUME 332

Lienhard, W.
    ... Le rôle et la valeur de l'ordre public en droit privé interne et en droit privé international ... par W. Lienhard ... Paris, Librairie du Recueil Sirey (société anonyme) 1934.
    4 p. l., 251 p. 24ᶜᵐ.
    Thèse—Dijon.
    "Bibliographie": p. ₁247₁-248.

    1. Public policy (Law) — France. 2. International law, Private — France. I. Title.

                       42–42225

NL 0352238   DLC NNC

Lienhard, W.
    ... Le rôle et la valeur de l'ordre public en droit privé interne et en droit privé international. Préface de m. P. Louis-Lucas ... Paris, Librairie du Recueil Sirey, 1935.
    xv, 251 p. 24ᶜᵐ.
    "Bibliographie": p. ₁247₁-248.

    1. Law—France. 2. International law, Private. I. Title. II. Title: L'ordre public, Le rôle et la valeur de.

                       37–17922

    Library of Congress   341.5

NL 0352239   DLC CtY

Lienhard-Egen, Ludwig, 1910-
    Der kimbrische Kernkreis; volkhafte Dichtung im Nordraum. Niederdeutsche Übersetzung von St.St. Blicher: "Ä Bindstouw". Würzburg,1940.
    235p. 21cm.
    Inaug.-Diss. - Berlin.
    Bibliography:p.214-235.
    Vita.

    1. Germanic literature - Hist. & crit. cdu.

NL 0352240   CtY MH

Lienhard-Riva, Alfredo.
    ... Armoriale ticinese; stemmario di famiglie ascritte ai patriziati della repubblica e cantone del Ticino, corredato di cenni storico-genealogici. Con 580 stemmi policromi ordinati in xxix tavole e 1074 illustrazioni in nero nel testo. ₁Losanna₁ Pubblicato sotto il patronato della Società araldica svizzera, auspice il Dipartimento cantonale della pubblica educazione, 1945.
    xxxi, 517 p., 1 l. col. front., illus. (incl. facsims.) xxix col. pl. (coa₁ of arms) 32 x 24½ᶜᵐ.
    "Fonti e bibliografia": p. xxv–xxix.
    1. Heraldry—Switzerland—Ticino. 2. Ticino (Canton)—Geneal. I. Società suisse d'héraldique. II. Ticino (Canton) Dipartimento della pubblica educazione. III. Title.
    CR2187.T54L5   929.8   A 46–5737
    Harvard univ. Library
    for Library of Congress   ₁3₁†

NL 0352241   MH DLC NN

Lienhard & Salzborn, photographers.
    [Views in Graubünden.]   Chur, n.d.
    21 mounted cabinet photographs in case.

NL 0352242   NIC

Lienhard und Gertrud
    see under   [Pestalozzi, Johann Heinrich] 1746-1827.

Lienhardt (Bruno). *Die Aetherbehandlung der Peritonitis. 23 pp. 8°. Zürich, B. Schwabe & Co. 1921.

NL 0352244   DNLM CtY

Avery
AA
1005
L62
Lienhardt, Carl.
    Sämmtliche Kirchen, Capellen und Denksäulen der inneren Stadt Wien. Mit kurzem erläuternde Texte und einem Vorworte von Carl Lienhardt. Wien, M. Gottlieb, 1885.
    ₁1 l.₁, 12 p. 28 illus. on 20 l. (1 fold.) 18 x 27 cm.

    At head of title: Erstes Album; hrsg. von Künstlern und Geschichtsforschern.
    Cover title: Die Kirchen Wien's.
    Plate III lacking.

NL 0352245   NNC

Lienhardt (Franz). *Beiträge zur Kenntnis der hereditären Lues, insbesondere der hereditärluetischen Knochenleiden. [Zürich.] 97 pp. 8°. Einsiedeln, C. & N. Benziger, 1884.

NL 0352246   DNLM

Lienhardt, H. F.
    Infectious abortion investigations.   Topeka, B. P. Walker, 1925.
    23 p. 8°.
    Kansas State Agric. Coll. Agric. Exper. Station, Tech. Bull. 14.
    1. Kitselman, C. H. 2. Sawyer, C. E.

NL 0352247   DNLM

Lienhardt, Friedrich
    see   Lienhard, Friedrich, 1865-1929.

Lienhardt, Georgius
    see   Georgius, Lienhart, Abbot of Roggenburg.

Lienhardt, Hans.
    Die österreichische Währungspolitik seit 1945. ₁Neuchâtel, 1952₁
    102 p. 22 cm.
    Thèse—Neuchâtel.
    Bibliography: p. ₁97₁–99.

    1. Currency question—Austria. I. Title.

    HG959.L5   57–21977

NL 0352250   DLC NNC CtY NN

Lienhardt, Hans.
    Ein Riesenverbrechen am deutschen Volke und die ernsten Bibelforscher, von Hans Lienhardt... Weissenberg i Bay.: Grossdeutscher Verlag₁, 1921₁. 46 p. 2. ed. 8°.

    417833A.   1. Jews—Anti-Semitic   SCHIFF COLLECTION.
    Anti-Semitic writings.   3. International   writings.   2. Jews in Germany—
    N. Y. P. L.   Bible Students Association.
                                         June 17, 1929

NL 0352251   NN

Lienhardt, Herbert Frederick, 1894-   joint author.
Aubel, Cliff Errett, 1890-
    The effects of low-phosphorus rations on growing pigs. By C. E. Aubel ... J. S. Hughes ... and H. F. Lienhardt ...
    (In U. S. Dept. of agriculture. Journal of agricultural research. v. 52, no. 2, Jan. 15, 1936, p. 149–159. illus., diagr. 23ᶜᵐ. Washington, 1936)

Lienhardt, Herbert Frederick, 1894-   joint author.
Aubel, Cliff Errett, 1890-
    The requirements of phosphorus in the ration of growing pigs ... by Cliff Errett Aubel ... ₁Topeka, 1936₁

NL 0352254   DNLM CtY

Lienhardt (Paul). *Ueber die Häufigkeit der Herzaffektionen nach den Beobachtungen der medizinischen Poliklinik in Zürich. [Zürich.] 38 pp. 8°. Einsiedeln, Benziger & Co., 1921.

NL 0352254   DNLM CtY

Lienhart, Antoine.
    Contribution expérimentale à l'étude de la thermodynamique des solutions macromoléculaires. Paris, Jouve, 1954.
    76, ₁4₁ p. illus., diagrs. 25 cm.
    Thèse—Strasbourg.
    Bibliography: p. ₁78₁

    1. Thermodynamics. 2. Solution (Chemistry)

    QD543.L5   56–44322

NL 0352255   DLC CtY

Lienhart, Constant, 1850-
    Les uniformes de l'armée française, recueil d'ordonnances de 1690 à 1894. Leipzig: M. Ruhl ₁1895-1905₁. 5 v. of col'd pl. 4°.
    Text lacking. Title from cover.
    By Lienhart and R. Humbert.

    1. Military uniforms, France.   2. Humbert, René.
    N. Y. P. L.   November 9, 1911.

NL 0352256   NN DNW

Lienhart, Constant, 1850-   , and René Humbert.
    Les uniformes de l'armée française depuis 1690 jusqu'à nos jours. — Leipzig. Ruhl. 1897-1906. 5 v. Plates. 4°.
    Most of the plates are colored.

    G3940 — Jt. auth. — France. Army and navy. Army. — Uniforms. Military and naval.

NL 0352257   MB

Lienhart, Ernst Eugen.
    Die Bürgschaft und andere Sicherungsgeschäfte. 2. Aufl. Zürich, Rechtshilfe-Verlag, 1949.
    16 p. 15 cm. (Rechtshilfe-Bücher, Heft 7)

    1. Security (Law)—Switzerland. 2. Suretyship and guaranty—Switzerland.

                      49–51584*

NL 0352258   DLC

Lienhart, Ernst Eugen, ed.

Switzerland. *Laws, statutes, etc.*
    ... Der Bundesstrafprozess der Schweiz, grundriss und gesetzestext; Bundesgesetz über die bundesstrafrechtspflege vom 15. juni 1934, in kraft getreten 1. januar 1935. Zürich, Schweizer druck- und verlagshaus, 1935.

VOLUME 332

Lienhart, Ernst Eugen.
... Das darlehen und andere finanzierungsgeschäfte nach schweizerischem recht. Wie beschaffe ich mir betriebs-kapital? ... Zürich (und Leipzig) Verlag Gropengiesser, abteilung Bildungsverlag (1943)

40 p. 21ᶜᵐ. (Rechtslehre für jedermann, hft. 11)

At head of title: Dr. E. E. Lienhart ...
Pages 39-40, advertising matter.
Bibliography: p. 36-37.

1. Loans—Switzerland.

47-37041

NL 0352260 DLC

Lienhart, Ernst Eugen.
... Der dienstvertrag im schweizerischen recht: was arbeitgeber und arbeitnehmer von ihren rechtsbeziehungen wissen müssen, das schweizerische arbeitsrecht ... Zürich (und Leipzig) Verlage Gropengiesser, Abteilung Bildungsverlag (1943)

35 p. 21ᶜᵐ. (Rechtslehre für jedermann, hft. 10)

At head of title: Dr. E. E. Lienhart ...
Bibliography: p. 34.

1. Hire—Switzerland. 2. Labor laws and legislation—Switzerland.

47-36271

NL 0352261 DLC

Lienhart, Ernst Eugen.
Grundriss des schweiz. strafrechts ...
Zürich, Rechtshilfe-verlag, 1952.

16 numb. 1. 15cm. (Rechtshilfe-bücher, heft 70; Rechtshilfe für jedermann, heft 20)

Multigraphed.

NL 0352262 MH-L NNU-W NNU

Lienhart, Ernst Eugen.
... Der handelsreisende im schweizerischen recht, ausweiskarten und anstellungsverhältnis der handelsreisenden. Der rechtsberater für handelsreisende und geschäftsinhaber ... Zürich (und Leipzig) Verlag Gropengiesser, abteilung Bildungsverlag (1943?)

39 p. 21ᶜᵐ. (Rechtslehre für jedermann, hft. 15)

At head of title: Dr. E. E. Lienhart.
Pages 38-39, advertising matter.
Bibliography: p. 36.

1. Commercial travelers—Switzerland. I. Switzerland. Laws, statutes, etc.

HF5441.L5   47-36847

NL 0352263 DLC

4K   Lienhart, Ernst Eugen.
Swiss.   Die interkantonale Auslieferung.
102   Zürich, Art Institut O. Füssli,
         1933.
                136 p.

NL 0352264 DLC-P4 MiU-L ICRL

Lienhart, Ernst Eugen.
... Das kleine kreditschutzbuch; wie sich der kaufmann vor kreditverlusten schützt. Zürich, Verlag der rechtshilfe-gesellschaft, 1940.

16 p. 15cm.

At head of title: E.E. Lienhart.

NL 0352265 MH-L

Lienhart, Ernst Eugen.
... Das lehrbuch für die eintreibung von forderungen. (Schuldbetreibung und konkurs) Das rechtliche inkasso in der Schweiz ... Zürich, Bildungsverlag, Gropengiesser (1946)

64 p. 21ᶜᵐ. (Rechtslehre für jedermann, schrift 18)

At head of title: Dr. E. E. Lienhart.
Part C published in 1939 under title: Das rechtliche inkasso in der Schweiz.
"Quellen": p. 59.

1. Executions (Law)—Switzerland. 2. Bankruptcy—Switzerland.

47-18431

NL 0352266 DLC

Lienhart, Ernst Eugen, *ed.*
... Das neue Schweizerische bürgschaftsrecht; Bundesgesetz über die revision des zwanzigsten titels des Obligationenrechts: Die bürgschaft; vom 10. dezember 1941, mit einleitung und sachregister. Zürich, Verlag der Rechtshilfe-gesellschaft, 1942.

20 p. 15ᶜᵐ.

At head of title: Dr. E. E. Lienhart.
Page 19, advertising matter.

1. Suretyship and guaranty—Switzerland. I. Switzerland. Laws, statutes, etc. II. Title.

42-20123

NL 0352267 DLC

Lienhart, Ernst Eugen.
... Das rechtliche inkasso in der Schweiz. 2. aufl. Zürich, Verlag der Rechtshilfe-gesellschaft, 1939.

16 p. 21ᶜᵐ.

At head of title: Dr. E. E. Lienhart.

1. Executions (Law)—Switzerland. 2. Collection laws—Switzerland.

47-37054

NL 0352268 DLC

Lienhart, Ernst Eugen.
... Das schweizerische erbrecht, die gesetzlichen erben, die verfügungen von todes wegen, der erbgang. Wie errichte ich ein testament? ... Zürich (und Leipzig) Verlage Gropengiesser, Abteilung Bildungsverlag (1943)

48 p. diagr. 21ᶜᵐ. (Rechtslehre für jedermann, hft. 4)
At head of title: Dr. E. E. Lienhart ...
"Literaturverzeichnis": p. 46.

1. Inheritance and succession—Switzerland.

47-36269

NL 0352269 DLC

Lienhart, Ernst Eugen.
Das schweizerische Familienrecht; Ehe, Verwandtschaft, Vormundschaft. Was jedermann von den familienrechtlichen Beziehungen wissen muss. (Von) E. E. Lienhart. Zürich, Verlage Gropengiesser, Abt. Bildungsverlag (1942)

40 p. 21 cm. (Rechtslehre für jedermann, Heft 3)

Bibliography: p. 35.

1. Domestic relations—Switzerland—Popular works. I. Title. (Series)

65-85320

NL 0352270 DLC

Lienhart, Ernst Eugen.
Das schweizerische Haftpflichtrecht; die Haftung aus unerlaubter Handlung und ungerechtfertigter Bereicherung. Die Haftpflicht des Familienhauptes, Geschäftsherrn, Tierhalters, Fahrzeughalters usw. Wie entsteht eine Schadenersatzpflicht? (Von) E. E. Lienhart. Zürich, Verlage Gropengiesser, Abt. Bildungsverlag (1943)

35 p. 21 cm. (Rechtslehre für jedermann, Heft 7)

Bibliography: p. 34.

1. Torts—Switzerland. 2. Liability (Law)—Switzerland. I. Title. (Series)

65-85318

NL 0352271 DLC

Lienhart, Ernst Eugen.
... Das schweizerische handelsrecht; die handelsrechtlichen teile des obligationenrechtes mit einleitung und sachregister. (Bundesgesetz vom 18. dezember 1936. in kraft seit 1. juli, 1937) Zürich, Rechtshilfe-gesellschaft, 1937.

197 p. 204ᵐᵐ.

At head of title: Dr. E. E. Lienhart.

1. Commercial law—Switzerland. 2. Corporation law—Switzerland. I. Switzerland. Laws, statutes, etc. II. Title.

39-29546

NL 0352272 DLC

Lienhart, Ernst Eugen.
Das schweizerische Mietrecht; was Mieter und Vermieter von ihren Rechtsbeziehungen wissen müssen. Der Mietvertrag und verwandte Verträge: Pacht, Leihe (von) E. E. Lienhart. Zürich, Verlage Gropengiesser, Abt. Bildungsverlag (1943)

31 p. 21 cm. (Rechtslehre für jedermann, Heft 9)

Bibliography: p. 25.

1. Landlord and tenant—Switzerland—Popular works. I. Title. (Series)

65-85319

NL 0352273 DLC

Law   Lienhart, Ernst Eugen, ed.

Switzerland. *Laws, statutes, etc.*
Die schweizerische Militärgesetzgebung; Gesetzestexte mit Einleitung und Anmerkungen (von) E. E. Lienhart. Zürich, Schweizer Druck- und Verlagshaus, 1936.

Lienhart, Ernst Eugen.
Das schweizerische Patentrecht; was man vom Schutz und der Verwertung von Erfindungen wissen muss. 2. Aufl. Zürich, Rechtshilfe-Verlag, 1949.

16 p. 15 cm. (Rechtshilfe-Bücher, Heft 11)

1. Patent laws and legislation—Switzerland—Compends.

50-15694

NL 0352275 DLC

Lienhart, Ernst Eugen.
Das schweizerische Personenrecht, insbesondere das Vereinsrecht. Wie gründe und leite ich einem Verein? Mit Mustern und Formularen. (Von) E. E. Lienhart. Zürich, Verlage Gropengiesser, Abt. Bildungsverlag (1942)

32 p. 21 cm. (Rechtslehre für jedermann, Heft 2)

Bibliography: p. 30.

1. Persons (Law)—Switzerland. 2. Unincorporated societies—Switzerland. I. Title. (Series)

65-88668

NL 0352276 DLC

Lienhart, Ernst Eugen.
... Das schweizerische sachenrecht, insbesondere das liegenschaftsrecht. Was jeder von den rechtsverhältnissen an grundstücken wissen muss. Der rechtsberater für den grundbesitzer ... Zürich (und Leipzig) Verlage Gropengiesser, Abteilung Bildungsverlag (1943)

40 p. 21ᶜᵐ. (Rechtslehre für jedermann, hft. 5)

"Literatur": p. 38.

1. Real property—Switzerland—Compends.

47-34128

NL 0352277 DLC

VOLUME 332

Lienhart, Ernst Eugen, *ed.*
... Das schweizerische versicherungsrecht; die bundesgesetze, bundesbeschlüsse, verordnungen und Bundesratsbeschlüsse über das private und öffentliche versicherungswesen, nachgeführt bis zum 1. april 1938, mit einleitung, anhang und sachregister. Aarau, H. R. Sauerlander & co. ₁1938₎

290 p. 19ᵐ.

At head of title: Dr. E. E. Lienhart.
"Schrifttum": p. 259–276.

1. Insurance law—Switzerland. I. Switzerland. Laws, statutes, etc. II. Title.

40-38364

NL 0352278   DLC NNC

Lienhart, Ernst Eugen.
Der thurgauische Strafprozess. Kreuzlingen, Anker ₁1934₎

75 p. 23 cm.

1. Criminal procedure—Thurgau (Canton) I. Title.

49-31084*

NL 0352279   DLC

Lienhart, Ernst Eugen.
... Das tier im schweizerischen recht, ein rechtsbuch für tierfreunde und tierhalter. Was jeder tierbesitzer vom gesetz wissen muss ... Zürich (und Leipzig) Verlage Gropengiesser, Abteilung Bildungsverlag ₁1943₎

63 p. 21ᵐ. (Rechtslehre für jedermann, hft. 25)

At head of title: Dr. E. E. Lienhart ...
Errata slip inserted.
Bibliography: p. 62.

1. Domestic animals—Switzerland—Law. 2. Animals, Treatment of. 3. Game-laws—Switzerland.

47-36270

NL 0352280   DLC

Lienhart, Ernst Eugen.
... Das versicherungswesen in der Schweiz, privatversicherung und sozialversicherung, was jedermann vom versicherungswesen wissen muss ... Zürich, Gropengiesser ₁1944₎

62 p. diagr. 21ᵐ. (Rechtslehre für jedermann, hft. 13)

At head of title: Dr. E. E. Lienhart ...
Pages 61–62, advertising matter.
Bibliography: p. 57–58.

1. Insurance law—Switzerland. 2. Insurance, Social—Switzerland.

47-19417

NL 0352281   DLC NNC

W 4
S892
no. 533
1950

LIENHART, François.
Mise au point de microméthodes permettant l'étude systématique des spiritueux de consommation courante au cours de leur distillation; application à la mirabelle. ₁Strasbourg, 1950₎

80 p. illus. (Strasbourg. Université. Faculté de pharmacie. Thèse, 1949/50, no. 533)
1. Brandy

NL 0352282   DNLM

870
L624†

Lienhart, Gertrud, 1906-
Tiberius, Caligula, Claudius, Nero: quid extra munera imperatoria scripserint, et quomodo litteris faverint, aut obtrectaverint, fragmentis et testimoniis collectis demonstratur ... Endingen, Buchdruckerei E. Wild, 1934.

70p.
Inaug.-diss.--Freiburg.
Vita.

1. Tiberius, emperor of Rome, B.C.42-A.D.37. 2. Caligula, emperor of Rome, 12-41. 3. Claudius, emperor of Rome, B.C.10--A.D.54. 4. Nero, emperor of Rome, 37-63.

NL 0352283   IU MiU PBm CtY MdBJ OrU ICRL NNC

4DD-430

Lienhart, Hans, 1858-
Elsässische Ortsneckereien, ein Beitrag zum Studium von Land und Leuten unter Mitwirkung von Freunden und Kennern des Elsass. Heidelberg, C., Winter, 1927.

246 p. (Schriften der Elsass-Lothringischen Wissenschaftlichen Gesellschaft zu Strassburg. Reihe A. Alsatica und Lotharingica, 2).

NL 0352284   DLC-P4 ICU MH

Lienhart, Hans, 1858-
... Gruss und anrede im Elsass ... von dr. Hans Lienhart ... [Stuttgart, 1896]

p. [11]-25. 22 cm.
Caption title.
"Besondere beilage des Staats-anzeigers für Württemberg."
"Vortrag gehalten in der hauptversammlung des zweigvereins Strassburg des Allgem. Deutschen sprachvereins am 13. märz, 1895."

1. German language- Dialects- Alsace.

NL 0352285   CU

Lienhart, Hans, 1858-
Laut- und flexionslehre der mundart des mittleren Zornthales im Elsass. Strassburg, K. J. Trübner, 1891.

pp. viii, 74. (Alsatische studien, I.)

Germ. lang.-Dial.-Zornthal||Series|AcS 185772

NL 0352286   MH CtY CU ICRL

Lienhart, Hans, 1858-   joint author.
Martin, Ernst Eduard, 1841-1910.
Wörterbuch der elsässischen mundarten, bearb. von E. Martin und H. Lienhart. Im auftrage der Landesverwaltung von Elsass-Lothringen ... Strassburg, K. J. Trübner, 1899-1907.

Lienhart, Hermann. Drenglyndi. Skáldsaga. Porsteinn Finnbogason þýddi. Reykjavík, Sögusafnið—Þorvaldur Kolbeins, 1933. 8°. pp. 207. IcF88L741

NL 0352288   NIC

Lienhart, Hermann.
Zwei fanden ihr Glück, Roman. Breslau, Drei-Kronen-Verlag ₁1939₎

256 p. 19 cm.

I. Title.

PT2623.I42Z4

49-42981*

NL 0352289   DLC

4K
Swiss.
79

Lienhart, Johann Paul, 1900-
Der Schweizerische Militärpflichtersatz. Zürich, 1923.
107 p.

NL 0352290   DLC-P4 ICRL CtY

Lienhart, Josef.
Die Reichsbank von 1876–1933 auf Grund ihrer Bilanzen und Erfolgsrechnungen. Würzburg, K. Triltsch, 1936.

viii, 228 p. diagrs, tables. 21 cm.

Bibliography: p. 206–209.

1. Reichsbank, Berlin.

HG3054.L5

50-50538

NL 0352291   DLC NN

Lienhart, Marcelle Claps

see

Claps-Lienhart, Marcelle.

Ia693
927

Lienhart, Maria, 1905-
Aufkommen der zusammengesetzten Epitheta in der englischen Literatur ... Freiburg,W. Wienken,1927.

70p.,1ℓ. 23cm.
Inaug.-diss. - Freiburg im Breisgau.
"Bibliographie": p.[4-6]
Lebenslauf.

1.English language - Adjectives. 2.Epithets. 3.English language - Compound words.

NL 0352293   CtY ICRL MH IU

W
4
N17
1944/45

Lienhart, Odile Marie Gabrielle Fabiola, 1920-
La maladie d'Ehlers-Danlos. Étude clinique anatomo-pathologique et génétique. Nancy, Société d'impressions typographiques, 1945.

114 p. (Nancy. Université. Faculté de médecine. Thèse. 1944/45. no. 30)

Bibliography: p. ₁109₎-114.

NL 0352294   DNLM

Lienhart, Robert.
Le secret de l'élevage du pigeon carneau. Problème de l'hérédité des pigeons jaunes, illustré de six planches hors texte, en couleurs, par Robert Lienhart ... Nancy, L'auteur, 1928.

54, ₍2₎ p. 6 l. VI col. pl., diagrs. 25¼ᵐ.
Illustration mounted on cover.
Half-title: Pages de zootechnie.
Each plate accompanied by leaf with descriptive letterpress.
"Liste explicative des termes scientifiques employés dans cette étude": p. ₁53₎-54.

1. Pigeons. 2. Heredity.

Library of Congress   SF465.L5

29-10567

NL 0352295   DLC

LIENHART, THÉOBALD, 1765-1831.
De antiquis liturgiis et de Disciplina arcani; tractatus historico-dogmaticus ... Argentorati, Typis F.G.Levrault, regis typographi, 1829.

liv, 339, ₁1₎ p.

NL 0352296   DDO PPPD

VOLUME 332

Lienhart, Théobald, 1765-1831.
Institutiones theologiæ dogmaticæ in usum seminarii argen-tinensis, a Theob. Lienhart ... editæ ... Argentorati, typis F. G. Levrault, 1819-21.
3 v. 21ᶜᵐ.
Vol. 3 wanting in L. C. set.

1. Catholic church—Doctrinal and controversial works. 2. Theology, Doctrinal. I. Title.
36-23419
Library of Congress   BX1751.L67   230.2

NL 0352297 DLC

Lienhout, Gheraert van
see Gheraert,

LIENIG, Friederike.
Lepidopterologische fauna von Lievland und Curland. Mit ammerkungen von P.C.Zeller. 1846.
4., pp. 127.

NL 0352299 MH-Z

Lienig, Georg.
...Eine Studienreise durch deutsche Geflügelhöfe, von Georg Lienig... Berlin: F. Pfenningstorff[, 1907]. 43 p. illus. (incl. plans.) 8°. (Aus Theorie und Praxis der Geflügelzucht. Jahrg. 1, Heft 1.)

1. Poultry—Housing. 2. Ser.
N. Y. P. L.   July 2, 1925

NL 0352300 NN ICRL

Lienig, Paul, 1859-
Die Grammatik der provenzalischen Leys d'-amors, verglichen mit der Sprache der Trouba-dours. Erster Teil (Phonetik) ... Breslau [1890]
Inaug.-Diss. - Breslau.
Vita.

NL 0352301 CtY NjP

PC3228 Lienig, Paul, 1859-
.L7   Die grammatik der provenzalischen Leys d'amors vergli-chen mit der sprache der troubadours. Von Paul Lienig ... 1. teil: Phonetik. Breslau, W. Koebner, 1890.
[6], 115 p. 22½ᶜᵐ.
No more published.

1. Leys d'amors. 2. Provençal language—Phonology.

NL 0352302 ICU NIC PU MH ICN

Liening, Ernst, 1911-
Geopolitische und geoökonomische Gesichtspunkte und Tendenzen in den modernen Aussenwirtschaftsbeziehungen. Hamburg, H. Schimkus, 1940.
57, xxi, [6] p. 29 cm.
Inaug.-Diss.-Rostock.
Vita.
Bibliography: p. [1]-[5] at end.

1. Commercial policy. I. Title.

HF1411.L5   55-55471

NL 0352303 DLC NIC CtY MH

LIENING, Martin, 1878-
Die personifikation unpersönlicher haupt-wörter bei den vorläufern Shakespeares (Lyly, Kyd, Marlowe,Peele, und Greene). Ein beitrag zur grammatik und poetik der Elisabethinischen zeit. Inaugural-dissertation, Münster. Borna-Leipzig. 1904.
"Lebenslauf", p. 103.

NL 0352304 MH NcD CtY PU NjP

Liening, Martin, 1878-   ed.
Schoeningh englische schulausgaben
see under title

Liening, Max, 1911-
... Epididymitis und Arthritis als Komplika-tionen bei der Gonorrhoe des Mannes und ihre Behandlung. (Nach den Erfahrungen der letzten drei Jahre an der Universitätshautklinik Köln) ... Köln, 1936.
Inaug.-Diss. - Köln.
Lebenslauf.
"Literaturverzeichnis": p. 25-26.

NL 0352306 CtY

Lienk, Siegfried Eric, 1916-
Revision of the genus Torymus in America north of Mexico (Hymenoptera, Torymidae) Urbana [1951]
270 l. 28 cm.
Thesis--University of Illinois.
Typewritten (carbon copy)
Vita.
Bibliography: leaf 269.
----- ----- Thesis copy.

NL 0352307 IU

Lienk, Siegfried Eric, 1916–
Revision of the genus *Torymus* in America north of Mexico (Hymenoptera, Torymidae) Ann Arbor, Univer-sity Microfilms, 1951.
([University Microfilms, Ann Arbor, Mich.] Publication no. 2718)
Microfilm copy of typescript. Positive.
Collation of the original: 270 l. illus.
Thesis--University of Illinois.
Abstracted in Microfilm abstracts, v. 11 (1951) no. 4, p. 1186-1187.
Vita.
Bibliography: leaf 269.
1. Torymus. I. Title.
Microfilm AC-1 no. 2718   Mic A 51-459

Michigan. Univ. Libr.
for Library of Congress

NL 0352308 MiU DLC

4PQ   Lienne, Aristide.
Fr.   Deux chants aérophiles. Genève,
2004   1853.
8 p.

NL 0352309 DLC-P4

... Les liens économiques entre la Pologne, la Lithuanie et les provinces ruthènes
see under [Tennenbaum, H   ]

Liens entre nations
see under   Comité d'action économique et douanière, Paris.

Les liens moraux de l'Amerique et de Bulgarie
see under Mishev, Dimitri, 1854-1932.

BX4700 Liento, Giovanni Luise.
A415N6   Relazione, mandata dal sig. Gio: Luise Liento ... del sacro sacco di s. Francesco d'Assisi, santo Amato ... e s. Guglielmo ... cosi descritto in uno libro del ... Francesco Noja ...   Venetia Per il Prodocimo, 1709.
2 p.l., 34 p. 15cm. in cover 20cm. [With Noia, Francesco. Discorsi critici su l'istoria della vita di s. Amato. 1707]

I. Noia, Francesco.

NL 0352313 CU

Lientz, Thelma.
The black box, by Thelma Lientz. New York, A. L. Burt company [*1929]
249 p. front. 19½ᶜᵐ. [Mystery and adventure series for girls]

I. Title.
Library of Congress   PZ7.L617B1   29-11021

NL 0352314 DLC

Lientz, Thelma.
Kay and the secret code, by Thelma Lientz ... New York, A. L. Burt company [*1930]
254 p. front. 19½ᶜᵐ. [Mystery and adventure series for girls]

I. Title.
Library of Congress   PZ7.L617Kay   30-11623

NL 0352315 DLC

Lienz, Anton Linder-
see Linder-Lienz, Anton.

N1733 Lienz. Museum der Stadt.
A7   Osttiroler Heimatmuseum, Schloss Bruck,
1951   Lienz. [Hrsg. vom Stadtamt Lienz in deutscher, italienischer und englischer Sprache. Innsbruck, Druck: Buchdruckerei Tyrolia, 1951]
24 p. 8 plates. 16.5cm.
Cover title.

NL 0352316 MWiW-C

DB879
L575L5
Lienzer Buch; Beiträge zur Heimatkunde von Lienz und Umgebung. [Festschrift zur 700-Jahr-Feier der Stadt Lienz] Innsbruck, Wagner, 1952.
287 p. illus., 33 plates, map. 24 cm. (Schlern-Schriften, 98)

1. Lienz, Austria. (Series)
A 53-3850
Harvard Univ. Library
for Library of Congress

NL 0352317 MH MoU TxU DLC NN

VOLUME 332

Lienzo de Tlaxcala.
Lienzo de Tlaxcala, manuscrito pictórico mexicano de mediados del siglo XVI. Próspero Cahuantzi, editor. México, D. F., Librería Anticuaria G. M. Echaniz ¡prólogo 1939¡

21 p. 81 plates (part col.) 24 x 30 cm.

Alternate pages blank.

1. Manuscripts, Mexican—Facsimiles. 2. Picture writing, Mexican. 3. Mexico—Hist.—To 1810. I. Cahuantzi, Próspero, ed.

F1219.L585   52-52057

NL 0352318   DLC MH-P OU CtY IU OC1 ICU

F1219 .M63

Lienzo de Tlaxcala.
Mexico. *Junta colombina.*
Homenaje á Cristóbal Colón. Antigüedades mexicanas; publicadas por la Junta colombina de México en el cuarto centenario del descubrimiento de América … México, Oficina tipográfica de la Secretaría de fomento, 1892.

Lienzo de Tlaxcala.., 1892
see under   Chávero, Alfredo, 1841-1906, ed. and tr.

Lienzo de Zacatepec
see
Codice Martinez Gracida.

Lieo Sisěwok.
เทริศฐั ¡โดย¡ ธวรรม. ¡พระนคร¡ บรรณาคาร ¡1953¡
463 p. 17 cm.

I. Title.
Title romanized: Sěttbini.

PL4209.L5S4   79-257153

NL 0352322   DLC

Lieou, Hiang
see
Liu, Hsiang, 77?–6? B. C.

Lieou, Ngo
see
Liu, Ê, 1857-1909.

Lieou, Pai-yu
see
Liu, Pai-yü.

Lieou Tche
see
Lew Che, fl.1724

Lieou, T'ie-yun
see
Liu, Ê, 1857-1909.

Lieou-Tsee-Lin
see
Lew Che, fl. 1724

Lieou, Yong-Choen.
Syndrome sympathique cervical posterieur et arthrite chronique de la colonne vertebrale cervicale.
Inaug. diss. Strasbourg, 1928.
Bibl.

NL 0352329   ICRL

Liep, Georg.
De Taciti Agricola. Commentatio critica … Crucenaci, 1861.
1. p. l., 19 p. 24.5 cm.
Programm - K. Gymnasium zu Kreuznach.
"Schulnachrichten": separately paged (37 p., incl. table) at end.
1. Tacitus, Cornelius. Agricola.

NL 0352330   CtY NjP

Liep, Peter.
Kahlberger Klänge. Essen-Kettwig, Welt-Verlag, 1949
45 p. illus. (Elbinger Hefte; eine kulturelle Schriftenreihe, 3)

NL 0352331   MH

LIEPA, ALEKSANDRS.
Rīgas privatdetektivi; kriminalgroteska. Illustrējis Vilis Ciesnieks. [Stockholm] Zelta Ābele, 1955.
188 p. illus. 20cm.

1. Detectives, Private—Anecdotes, facetiae, satire, etc. I. Title.

NL 0352332   NN OC1 MH

Liepa, Mārtiņš, 1874-
Jord- og arbejderspørgsmaalene i Rusland [ved] M. Leepa. Rønne, Arbejderpartiets bogtr., 1911
41 p. (Socialistisk bibliothek, 2.aarg.,nr.4)

NL 0352333   MH

Liepa, Osvalds.
…Mēmais miljonārs; viencēliens.   Rīgā: Autors, 1933.
15 p. 20½cm.

1. Drama, Lettish. I. Title.
N. Y. P. L.   October 5, 1939

NL 0352334   NN

Liepa, Osvalds.
…Vieglie lemeši; komēdija trijos cēlienos.   Rīgā: F. Vītuma izd. ¡1937¡ 61 p. 20½cm.

1. Drama, Lettish. I. Title.
N. Y. P. L.   September 25, 1940

NL 0352335   NN

Liepa, Rita, 1914-
Don Huana svētdiena. Rīgā, Rozes apgāds, 1944
93 p.
Short stories

NL 0352336   MH

LIEPA, RITA, 1914-
Pegazs un kaza; skices. Börnsenē, Apgāds Māra, 1946. 71 p. 14cm.

Microfiche (neg.) 2 sheets. 11 x 15cm. (NYPL FSN 15, 237)

1. Fiction, Lettish. I. Title.

NL 0352337   NN

Liepa, Rita, 1914-
Sveša vasara; romāns. [Stockholm] Daugava, 1955
336 p.

NL 0352338   MH NNC OC1 CtY NN

Hvd48 1 L626

Liepa, Zenta.
Mēness akmens. [n.p.] Gauja, 1949.
101p. 15cm.

NL 0352339   CtY

Liepāja.
Liepājas pilsētas budžets …
Liepājā, 19
v. tables. 29ᵐ.

1. Budget—Liepāja.
41-40253
Library of Congress   HJ9055.4.L5B2
¡2¡   332.109474

NL 0352340   DLC

Liepāja.
Liepājas pilsētas statistiskā gada grāmata 1929-1933. Sastādijis Z. Rozentāls.   ¡Liepājā¡ Liepājas pilsētas valdes izdevums, 1934. 87 p. incl. tables. 22cm.
No more published.

1. Latvia—Stat.
N. Y. P. L.   May 21, 1936

NL 0352341   NN

VOLUME 332

Liepāja.
Liepājas 300 gadu jubilejas piemiņai, 1625–1925. ₍Liepāja₎ Liepājas pilsētas valdes izdevums ₍1925₎ 154 p. incl. tables. illus. (incl. facsims., ports.) 31½cm.

Printed in double columns.
Pages 68–154 are full page illus.

800327A. 1. Liepāja, Latvia—Hist.   2. Liepāja, Latvia—Views.
N.Y.P.L.   January 24, 1936

NL 0352342   NN IEN CSt

Liepāja.
₍Ordinances and proclamations issued from May 7, 1915 to July 23, 1917 by various offices (i. e.: Militärpolizeimeister, Stadthauptmann, etc.) during the time of the German occupation of Liepāja, in regard to rationing, registration of civilians, regulations, etc., etc. Notices concerning civilians arrested, their sentences and executions. Forms to be filled out for the securing of ration-cards₎ Libau, 1915–17.   90 mounted broadsides in box.   64cm.

Also: Extrablatt der "Libauschen Zeitung." Libau, den 12 Dezember 1916 (abends), 1 mounted broadside; and a proclamation, dated and signed: Libau, den 27. Juni 1919. H. P. Gough, General-Leutnant der Britischen Armee, 1 mounted broadside printed in Latvian, German and Russian.
The broadsides are for the greater part in German and Latvian. Some in German, Latvian and Russian; one in German, Latvian, Polish and Lithuanian. A few in German or Russian only.

1. European war, 1914-1918—   Latvia—Liepāja.
N.Y.P.L.   May 7, 1942

NL 0352344   NN

Law

Liepāja. *Gorodskaía uprava.*
Контрактъ о сооруженіи и эксплоатаціи водопровода въ Либавѣ. ₍Въ Либавѣ, 1898₎
86 p. 18 cm.

1. Liepāja—Water-supply.   2. Smreker, Oskar.   i. Title.
Title transliterated: Kontrakt o sooruzhenii i éksploatatsii vodoprovoda.
                                                           56–54538

NL 0352345   DLC

HJ9514
.L5A53

Liepāja. *Gorodskaía uprava.*
Таблица торговымъ сборамъ, взимаемымъ въ гор. Либавѣ съ привозныхъ и вывозныхъ товаровъ, съ 1 сентября 1895. Tabelle der vom 1. September 1895 ab in Libau zu entrichtenden Handelsabgaben von Ein- und Ausfuhrwaaren. ₍Либава, 1899₎
87 p. 22 cm.

1. Octroi—Liepāja.   i. Title.   ii. Title: Tabelle der vom 1. September 1895 ab in Libau zu entrichtenden Handelsabgaben.
Title transliterated: Tablitsa torgovym sboram.

HJ9514.L5A53   56–54494

NL 0352346   DLC

Liepājas kuǵu vadītāju, mēchaniķu un zvejniecības skola, Liepaja, Latvia.
...Gada pavasari.
19

₍Liepājā, 19   22cm.
no.   illus.

Cover-title.
At head of title: Liepājas jūrskola.

1. Seamen—Training—Latvia.
N.Y.P.L.   May 17, 1940

NL 0352347   NN

Liepājas 300 gadu jubilejas pieminai
see under   Liepaja.
Liepajas 300 gadu jubilejas piemina...

Liepe, Alfred, *1890-* Die sichernden Massnahmen im System des Strafgesetzbuches. [Maschinenschrift.] VII, 119 S. 4°. — Auszug: o. O. (1924).   2 Bl. 8°
Kiel, R.- u. staatswiss. Diss. v. 3. Febr. 1925   [U 25. 5128

NL 0352349   ICRL

Liepe, C. Wolfgang.
See
Liepe, Wolfgang, 1888–

---

ar W
10077
Liepe, Else, 1903-
Der Freigeist in der deutschen Literatur des 18. Jahrhunderts.   Kiel, 1930.
67 p.   21cm.

Diss.—Kiel.

1. German literature—18th cent.—Hist. & crit. 2. Free thought. I. Title.

NL 0352351   NIC MH MdBJ ICRL PU DLC NjP CtY

Liepe, Emil.
... Paul Kuczynski und seine werke.   Kritische studie, von Emil Liepe ...   Langensalza, H. Beyer & söhne, 1912
40 p.   21cm.   (Musikalisches magazin, hft. 43)
Sonderabdruck aus dem dezember- und januarheft der "Blätter für haus- und kirchenmusik."

1. Kuczynski, Paul, 1846-1897.

                                                           12-5792

Library of Congress   ML55.M7

NL 0352352   DLC NN

Film
3513
Item 43
Music
Lib'y
Liepe, Emil.
... Paul Kuczynski und seine werke.   Kritische studie, von Emil Liepe ...   Langensalza, H. Beyer & söhne, 1912.
40 p.   21cm.   (Musikalisches magazin, hft. 43)
Sonderabdruck aus dem dezember- und januarheft der "Blätter für haus- und kirchenmusik."
Microfilm (negative)   New York, New York Public Library, 1963.   1 reel (various items)   35mm.

anal.   1. Kuczynski, Paul, 1846-1897   I. Series.

NL 0352353   TxU

Liepe, Heinrich, 1888-
S21g   Temperaturschwankungen der Meeresoberfläche
03   von Ouessant bis St.Paul-Fels.   Halle.a.S.,1911.
L624   Inaug.-Diss. - Halle-Wittenberg.

NL 0352354   CtY PU

LIEPE, Heinrich, *1888-*
Temperaturschwankungen der Meeresoberfläche von Ouessant bis St.Paul-Fels.   Halle a.S. 1911 Mittler, Berlin.

15 S., 2 Taf. 4°
(Aus: Annalen d. Hydrogr. u. marit. Meteorol. Jg. 39, H.9.)

NL 0352355   MH MiU ICRL

Liepe, Hermann, *1877-*
Technisches Taschenwörterbuch in italienischer und deutscher Sprache, unter besonderer Berücksichtigung auch der neueren Technik, wie Luftfahrt, Rundfunk u. dergl., hrsg. von Hermann Liepe unter Mitarbeit von Maurizio Lorandi. 2. neu bearb. und verm. Aufl. Berlin, G. Siemens ₍1943₎
2 v. 16 cm.
Added t.-p. in Italian.

1. Technology—Dictionaries—Italian. 2. German language—Dictionaries—Italian. 3. Technology—Dictionaries—German. 4. Italian language—Dictionaries—German. i. Lorandi, Maurizio. ii. Title.

T9.L54 1943   48–10910*

NL 0352356   DLC CLU

Liepe, Hermann, 1877–
Technisches Taschenwörterbuch in deutscher und italienischer Sprache. 3. neu bearb. und verm. Aufl. Berlin, G. Siemens, 1948.
2 v. 15 cm. (Siemens Technische Taschenwörterbücher, Bd. 7)
Vol. 2 has title: Technisches Taschenwörterbuch in italienischer und deutscher Sprache.
Contents.—1. T. Deutsch-Italienisch.—2. T. Italienisch-Deutsch.

1. Technology—Dictionaries—Italian. 2. German language—Dictionaries—Italian. 3. Technology—Dictionaries—German. 4. Italian language—Dictionaries—German. i. Title.

T9.L54 1948   603   49–17947 rev*

NL 0352357   DLC

Liepe, Karl Heinrich
see   Liepe, Heinrich, 1888–

Liepe, Karl Martin, 1921–
Die Schiedsgerichtsbarkeit im Dawes-Plan und im Londoner Schulden-Regelungs-Abkommen. ₍n. p.₎ 1954.
xix, 156 p. 30 cm.
Inaug.-Diss.—Mainz.
Vita.
Bibliography: p. x–xviii.

1. Arbitration, International. 2. European War, 1914-1918—Reparations. 3. International Conference on German External Debts, London, 1952. i. Title.

JX1952.L62   58–20411

NL 0352359   DLC

LIEPE, Wolfgang, *1888-*
Elisabeth von Nassau-Saarbrücken; die kulturellen und literaturgeschichtlichen grundlagen ihrer schirftstellerischen tätigkeit. Ein kapitel zur entstehungsgeschichte des deutschen prosaromans.   Einladungsschrift. Halle (S.), E.Karras, 1919.

NL 0352360   MH CtY

Liepe, Wolfgang, 1888–
Elisabeth von Nassau-Saarbrücken; entstehung und anfänge des prosaromans in Deutschland, von dr. Wolfgang Liepe ...   Halle a. S., M. Niemeyer, 1920.
xv, ₍1₎ 277, ₍1₎ p. 24½cm.
Issued in part, 1920, as the author's habilitations-schrift, Halle, 1919.

1. Elisabeth, countess of Nassau-Saarbrücken, d. 1456. 2. Romances, German—Hist. & crit. 3. German fiction—Early modern (to 1700)—Hist. & crit. 4. Literature, Comparative—French and German. 5. Literature, Comparative—German and French.

Library of Congress   PT1517.E43L5

                                                           23–15905

NL 0352361   DLC CU CtY PU MiU OU NcD ICRL NN IU NjP

VOLUME 332

Ddl
932ℓ
Liepe, Wolfgang, 1888-
   Natur und Kunst im bildnerischen Erlebnis
Goethes. Rede gehalten bei der Goethefeier der
Christian-Albrechts-Universität Kiel am 27.
April 1932 ...
   1p.ℓ.,15,[1]p.,1ℓ. 22x18cm. (Wissenschaft-
liche Gesellschaft für Literatur und Theater,
X, 1)

   I.Ser.   1.Goethe,Johann Wolfgang von - Anniversaries,etc. 1932.   2.Goethe,Johann Wolfgang
von - Esthetics.

NL 0352362   CtY

Liepe, Wolfgang, 1888 Das Religionsproblem im neueren Drama
von Lessing bis zur Romantik. ⟨Teildr.⟩ Halle a. d. S.
1913: Karras. VIII, 69 S. 8° ¶ Soll vollst. ersch. als:
Hermaea. H. 12.
   Halle, Phil. Diss. v. 28. Nov. 1913, Ref. Strauch
   [Geb. 27. Aug. 88 Schulzendorf, Pr. Brandenburg; Wohnort: Halle a. S.;
Staatsangeh.: Preußen; Vorbildung: G. Potsdam Reife 06; Studium: Berlin 6,
Paris 2, Berlin 1, Halle 4 S.; Rig. 5. Mai 13.]   [U 13.3616

NL 0352363   ICRL CtY CU NIC MH MiU PU

830.9082 Liepe, Wolfgang, 1888-1962.
H426   Das Religionsproblem im neueren Drama
v.12   von Lessing bis zur Romantik. Halle, Max
           Niemeyer, 1914.
              267p. 24cm. (Hermaea. Ausgewählte Arbei-
           ten aus dem Germanischen Seminar zu Halle,
           XII)
              1.German drama--18th century--Hist. & crit.
           2.German drama--19th century--Hist. & crit.
           3.Religion in literature. I.T. II.Series.

NL 0352364   CtU

PT641 Liepe, Wolfgang, 1888-
.L74   Das religionsproblem im neueren drama von Lessing bis
       zur romantik, von Wolfgang Liepe. Halle, M. Niemeyer,
       1914.
          xviii, 267, [1] p. 22½ᶜᵐ. (Added t.-p.: Hermaea; ausgewählte arbeiten aus dem
       Germanischen seminar zu Halle ... XII)
          Issued in part as author's inaug.-diss., Halle, 1913.
          "Literaturverzeichnis": p. [xv]-xviii.

          1. German drama—18th cent.—Hist. & crit. 2. Religion in literature.

   IaU NNU-W PHC MiDW CU MH NN IU
NL 0352365   ICU CaBVaU MiU NcU PU PBm OCU OO OU NjP

Liepe, Rolf, 1901-
   ... Ueber die Dickdarmpassage röntgenologisch
differenzierbarer kugeliger Fremdkörper.
Rostock, 1934.
   Inaug.-Diss. - Rostock.
   Lebenslauf.
   "Schrifttum": p. 12.

NL 0352366   CtY

Liepelt, Adolf: Bevölkerungs- und gesundheitspolitische Auswir-
kungen der künstlichen Fehlgeburt. [Maschinenschrift.] 78 S.
4° [Lag nicht vor.] — Auszug: (Rostock 1923: Winterberg).
1 Bl. 8°
   Rostock, Med. Diss. v. 19. Dez. 1923 [1925]   [U 25.7840

NL 0352367   ICRL

Liepelt, Adolf.
   Über den umfang und die bedeutung der polizeigewalt im
nationalsozialistischen staat, von dr. Adolf Liepelt. Würzburg, K. Triltsch, 1933.
   vii, 71 p. 21ᶜᵐ.
   Issued also as inaugural dissertation, Würzburg.
   "Schrifttum": p. iv-vii.

   1. Police—Germany. 2. Germany—Pol. & govt.—1983—   3. National socialism.

   Library of Congress   HV8207.L54   40-17949
                                                351.740943

NL 0352368   DLC

Liepelt, Adolf.
   Über den Umfang und die Bedeutung der Polizeigewalt im
nationalsozialistischen Staat, von Dr. Adolf Liepelt. Würzburg: K. Triltsch, 1938. vii, 71 p. 21cm.

   "Schrifttum," p. iv-vii.

   1. Germany—Govt.—Powers.
   N. Y. P. L.   March 19, 1940

NL 0352369   NN CtY IU MnU PU

WP
580
L719s
1952
LIEPELT, Adolf Oskar.
   Die Symptomatologie des Klimakteriums
und ihre Beziehungen zur Gesamtmedizin.
Stuttgart, Enke, 1952.
   50 p. (Zeitschrift für Geburtshilfe,
Bd. 136, Beilageheft)
   1. Menopause   Series: Zeitschrift
für Geburtshilfe und Gynäkologie, Bd. 136,
Beilageheft

NL 0352370   DNLM

Liepelt (Hellmuth) [1891-]. *Ueber die
Methoden der Analgesierung in der Gynäkologie und Geburtshilfe. 67 pp. 8°. Breslau. 1920.

NL 0352371   DNLM ICRL

FILM
7164
Liepelt,Helmut,1922-
   Die ideelle Einheit des Till Eulenspiegel-Epos
von Gerhart Hauptmann. 1951.
   66 ℓ.
   Inaug.-Diss.--Bonn.
   Vita.
   Includes bibliography.
   Microfilm (negative) of typescript.   1 reel.

   1.Hauptmann,Gerhart Johann Robert,1862-1946.
Till Eulenspiegel   I.Title.

NL 0352372   MiU NNC

Liepelt (Joannes Gustavus Samuel Theodorus)
[1835-]. *De aneurysmate aortae thoracicae
descendentis observatio. 32 pp. 8°. Berolini,
G. Schade, 1860.

NL 0352373   DNLM

Liepelt (Konrad). *Ueber den Einfluss von
Antipyrin und Chinin auf den Gaswechsel des
gesunden Menschen. [Jena.] 15 pp. 8°.
Leipzig. J. B. Hirschfeld. 1899.

NL 0352374   DNLM ICRL

Liepert, Joseph.
   Aristoteles und der zweck der kunst. Passau,
Druck von Dr. Bressl und J. Bucher, 1862.
   29 p. 27 cm.
   Program - Lyceum, Gymnasium und Lateinische
schule zu Passau.

NL 0352375   OCU NjP ViU

Liepert, Joseph.
   Beiträge zu Horaz. Strauging, 1885.

NL 0352376   NjP InGrD

PR
2807
.L72
Liepert,Joseph.
   Shakespeares "Hamlet." ... von J.Liepert
... Straubing, C. Attenkof, 1892.
   34 p. 23ᶜᵐ.
   Separate from Programm,K.Gymnasium,Straubing.

   1.Shakespeare,William. Hamlet.

NL 0352377   MiU NcU PU-F

Liepin', Petr Petrovich
   see
Liepiņš, Pēteris, 1986-

Liepin, T
   ... Genetics of soft wheats
      see under Filipchenko, IUrii Aleksandro-
   vich, 1882-1930.

B.F.
891.93
L719d
Liepiņa, Marija, 1892-
   Dzimtene; tautas luga 5 cēlienos. Drama-
tizējums pēc J. Jansevska romāna. Riga,
Izdevis A. Gulbis, 1933.
   64p. mounted port. 21cm.

NL 0352380   IEN NN

Liepiņa, Marija, 1892-
   ...Dzīves vētrās; romāns.   Rīgā: "Zelta grauds" [1937]
195 p. 20½cm.

   1. Fiction, Lettish. I. Title.
   N. Y. P. L.   December 6, 1938

NL 0352381   NN

Liepiņa, Marija, 1892-
   Iedzimtais grēks; drāmatizējums pēc Ivandes Kaijas [pseud.]
romāna. Rīgā: A. Gulbis, 1934. 67 p. 19½cm.

   1. Drama, Lettish. I. Lūkiņa, An-   tonija (Melders-Millers), 1876-
II. Title.
   N. Y. P. L.   April 26, 1938

NL 0352382   NN

VOLUME 332

Liepiņa, Marija, *1892-*
...Mīlas untumi; skatu luga 3-os cēlienos.   Rīgā: "Zelta grauds" [1937]   62 p.   20½cm.

1. Drama, Lettish.   I. Title.
N. Y. P. L.   September 25, 1940

NL 0352383 NN

Liepiņa, Milda, 1894–
...Intelliģences pārbaudes.   Rīgā: Praktiskās paidagogijas institūts, 1935.   56 p. incl. tables.   illus.   22½cm.   (Praktiskās paidagoģijas institūts, Riga. [Raksti. Sējums] 3.)

1. Intelligence—Testing.   I. Ser.
N. Y. P. L.   July 1, 1937

NL 0352384 NN

Liepiņš, Bernhards, comp.
Kokneses-Krapes draudze. Vēsturisks apskats Kokneses baznīcas 250 gadu atcerei. Sarakstijis skolotājs Bernhards Liepiņš [Koknese] Izdevusi Kokneses-Krapes ev.-lut. dr. valde, 1937. 97 p. incl. tables.   illus. (incl. ports.)   22cm.

"Izlietotā literatūra." p. [99]

1. Kokneses-Krapes evangeliskā   luteriskā draudze.
N. Y. P. L.   January 27, 1941

NL 0352385 NN

Liepiņš, Bernhards.
Vadonis pa Koknesi, sarakstijis B. Liepiņš.   Koknesē: J. Sprogis, 1931.   42 p.   illus., plan.   17cm.

857528A. 1. Koknese, Latvia—   Descr.
N. Y. P. L.   December 4, 1936

NL 0352386 NN

Liepiņš, Jānis, 1894–
8. [i. e. Astotā] Daugavpils kājnieku pulka vesture. Cēsīs, 8. Daugavpils kājnieku pulka izdevums, 1930.
153 p. illus. 24 cm.

1. Latvia. Armija. 8. Daugavpils kājnieku pulks. 2. Latvia—Hist.—1918-1940.

DK511.L18L5   67–36868 rev ‡

NL 0352387 DLC

Liepiņš, Olģerts, 1906-
Dēklas ratiņš; stāsti. [Geesthacht] Arvīds Sēlzemnieks, 1948.
172 p.

NL 0352388 MH CtY NIC

Balt 9750.158.120

Liepiņš, Olģerts, 1906-
Jodu gadi; stāsti. Bŏrnsenē [i.e.Bŏrnsen bei Hamburg] V.Beķera apgāds, 1947.
131 p.

NL 0352389 MH NIC OU

Liepiņš, Olģerts, *1906-*
...Olivers Kromvels, Anglijas republikas protektors; monografija.   Rīgā: A. Gulbis, 1934.   237 p.   20½cm.

784074A. 1. Cromwell, Oliver, 1599–   1658.
N. Y. P. L.   February 7, 1936

NL 0352390 NN

Liepiņš, Olģerts, *1906-*
Hvd48   Piemineklis; stāsts. [Geesthacht] A. Sēl-
1   zemnieks, 1947.
L628   77p. illus. 15cm.

NL 0352391 CtY

Liepiņš, Olģerts, *1906-*
Vēlā liesma; romāns. [Waverly, Iowa] Latvju grāmata, 1951.
287 p. 21 cm.

1. World War, 1939–1945—Fiction.   I. Title.

PG9048.L53V4   54–15434 ‡

NL 0352392 DLC NN OCl CtY MH

Liepiņš, Pēteris, 1886–
Pētera Liepiņa kapu kopiņas; dzejas.   Rīgā: Autors, 1931. 100 p.   23½cm.

856450A. 1. Poetry, Lettish.   I. Title.
N. Y. P. L.   November 18, 1936

NL 0352393 NN

Liepiņš, Reinholds.
...Galvas pilsētas Rīgas izbūve un saimniecība.   Rīgā: Rīgas pilsētas darbinieku biedrība, 1937.   21 p.   26½cm.

1. Riga—Descr.   I. Rīgas pilsētas   darbinieku biedrība.
N. Y. P. L.   June 11, 1943

NL 0352394 NN

[Liepiņš, Reinholds]
...Sirds un saules dziesma: Dievs, svētī Latviju! Valsts himnas vēsture latviskas sirds skatījumā. (Monografija.)   Rīgā: Latvijas vidusskolu skolotāju kooperātivs [1934]   29 p.   illus.   20½cm.

Author's pseud., Sudrabrīts, at head of title.

886150A. 1. Hymns, National—   Latvia. 2. National music—
Latvia. I. Title: Dievs, svētī   Latviju!
N. Y. P. L.   June 7, 1937

NL 0352395 NN

Liepkalne, Alma, pseud.
see [Lindberga, Alma]

Liepke, Andreas Siegfried
see Liepke, Siegfried, 1912-

W 4   LIEPKE, Karl Dankward, 1914-
L53   Über einen akuten Verblutungstod bei
1951   Rachenmandeloperation, durch ein
        cavernöses Haemangiom der Schädelbasis.
        [Leipzig, 1951]
        33 ℓ. illus.
        Inaug.-Diss. - Leipzig.
        Typewritten copy.
        1. Angioma 2. Nasopharynx -
Neoplasms 3. Tonsillectomy

NL 0352398 DNLM

Liepke, Siegfried, 1912-
... Beitrag zur Kenntnis der Genitaltuberkulose (an Hand der Fälle der Universitäts–Frauenklinik zu Leipzig von 1925-1935) ... [Zeulenroda, Thür., 1937]
Inaug.-Diss. - Leipzig.
Lebenslauf.

NL 0352399 CtY

Liepman, A   J
Westerbork en Theresiënstadt.   Boxtel, H. Bogaerts [1945]
31 p. 18 cm.

1. Westerbork (Concentration camp) 2. Terezín (Concentration camp)
D805.N4L48   A F 49–294*
Hoover Library
for Library of Congress   [1]†

NL 0352400 CSt-H DLC

Liepman, Adolph Johannes, 1889-
De heerser; toneelspel...door A. J. Leipman...   Alkmaar, Vink [1947]   75 p.   19cm.

1. Drama, Dutch.
N. Y. P. L.   December 13, 1951

NL 0352401 NN

LIEPMAN, Adolph Johannes, 1889-
In den greep van het noodlot; tooneelspel in 4 bedrijven, door A.J.Liepmann...   Dordrecht: Fa.C.Morks Czn. [1938] 72 p.   20cm.

1. Drama, Dutch. I. Title.

NL 0352402 NN

Liepman, Hans Peter, 1913-
An analytic design method for a two-dimensional asymmetric curved nozzle. Ann Arbor, University Microfilms, 1953.
([University Microfilms, Ann Arbor, Mich.] Publication no. 5696)
Microfilm copy of typescript. Positive.
Collation of the original: x, 100 l. diagrs.
Thesis—University of Michigan.
Abstracted in Dissertation abstracts, v. 13 (1953) no. 5, p. 737-738.
Bibliography: leaves 107-109.
1. Nozzles. 2. Aerodynamics. I. Title.
Microfilm AC-1 no. 5696   Mic A 53–1382

Michigan. Univ. Libr.
for Library of Congress

NL 0352403 MiU DLC

Liepman, Heinz
see
Liepmann, Heinz, 1905-

VOLUME 332

Liepmann, A   J
    see   Liepman, Adolph Johannes, 1889–

Liepmann, Adolf, bacc. jur., Referendar: Der Kinderhandel und seine Bekämpfung.   Leipzig-Reudnitz 1917: Vogel
95 S. 8°
Leipzig, Jur. Diss. v. 26. Febr. 1917
[Geb. 21. Aug. 93 Halberstadt; Wohnort: Leipzig; Staatsangeh.: Sachsen; Vorbildung: König-Albert-G. Leipzig Reife 13; Studium: Lausanne 1, Leipzig 5 S.; Rig. 28. Jan. 16.]   [U 17. 473

NL 0352406 ICRL

Liepmann, Clara Maria, joint author.

Van de Wall, Willem, 1887–
    Music in institutions, by Willem Van de Wall ... assisted by Clara Maria Liepmann ...   New York, Russell Sage foundation, 1936.

Liepmann, Clara Maria.
    Die Selbstverwaltung der Gefangenen.
— Mannheim. Bensheimer. 1926. x, (1), 226 pp. [Hamburgische Schriften zur gesamten Strafrechtswissenschaft. Heft 12.]
24½ cm., in 8s.
Literaturverzeichnis, pp. 221–226.

N5763 — T.r. — S.r. — Prisons and prison discipline. — Self-government. In prisons.

NL 0352408 MB

Liepmann, Clara Maria.
    Die Selbstverwaltung der Gefangenen, von Clara Maria Liepmann...   Mannheim: J. Bensheimer, 1928.   x, 226 p.   4°.
(Hamburgische Schriften zur gesamten Stafrechtswissenschaft. Heft 12.)

Bibliography, p. 221–226.

1. Criminals, Juvenile—Communities,   Selfgoverning.
N. Y. P. L.
                                              January 8, 1929

NL 0352409 NN InU OClW MH

LIEPMANN, Eduard.
    Die monopolorganisation in der tapetenindustrie, eine wirtschaftswissenschaftliche untersuchung. Darmstadt, A. Koch, 1913.

NL 0352410 MH

Liepmann, Franciscus.
    De neutralitate.   Berolini, n.d.
36 p.   O.

NL 0352411 RPB

Liepmann, Hans W.
    Lessing und die mittelalterliche philosophie: studien zur wissenschaftlichen rezeptions- und arbeitsweise Lessings und seiner zeit, von Hans W. Liepmann. Stuttgart. W. Kohlhammer, 1931.

xvi, 162 p.   22cm.   (Added t.-p.: Tübinger germanistische arbeiten, hrsg. von prof. dr. Hermann Schneider. 13. bd.)
Issued also as the author's inaugural dissertation, Tübingen, 1931.
"Quellen und literatur": p. [xi]–xvi.

1. Lessing, Gotthold Ephraim, 1729–1781.
                                              A C 34–3921

Title from Univ. of Chi-   cago PT2415.L7 Printed by L. C.

NRU IU MH NN NBC
NL 0352412 ICU MU NcU TxU CU CLSU LU CaBVaU PU MiU

Liepmann, Hans Wolfgang, 1914–
    Experiments in transonic flow
    see under   California Institute of Technology,
Pasadena.

Liepmann, Hans Wolfgang, 1914–
    Introduction to aerodynamics of a compressible fluid, by Hans Wolfgang Liepmann and Allen E. Puckett ...   New York, J. Wiley & sons, inc.; London, Chapman & Hall, limited [1947]
ix, 262 p.   illus., diagrs.   23½cm.   (Galcit aeronautical series)
"References": p. 254–255.
1. Aerodynamics. 2. Compressibility.   I. Puckett, Allen E., joint author.
TL573.L5   629.1323   47–2378

                  MtBC OrPR OrCS NcD NcGU NcRS TU TxU ICU ICJ ViU
NL 0352414 DLC WaS WaSpG CoU NN CU KEmT CaBVaU MtU

Liepmann, Hans Wolfgang, 1914–
    Investigations of effects of surface temperature and single roughness elements on boundary-layer transition, by Hans W. Liepmann and Gertrude H. Fila. Washington, U. S. Govt. Print. Off., 1947 [i. e. 1949]
ii, 12 p.   diagrs.   30 cm.   ([U. S.] National Advisory Committee for Aeronautics. Report no. 890)
Cover title.
"References": p. 12.
1. Boundary layer.   I. Fila, Gertrude H., joint author.
TL521.A33 no. 890   532.5   49–46866*
——— Copy 2.   QA913.L55

NL 0352415 DLC

Liepmann, Hans Wolfgang, 1914–
    On reflection of shock waves from boundary layers, by H. W. Liepmann, A. Roshko and S. Dhawan. Washington [U. S. Govt. Print. Off.] 1952 [i. e. 1953]
ii, 29 p.   illus.   30 cm.   ([U. S.] National Advisory Committee for Aeronautics. Report 1100)
Cover title.
Bibliography: p. 29.
1. Boundary layer. 2. Aerodynamics, Supersonic.   I. Title.
(Series)
TL521.A33 no. 1100   *629.123 629.13237   53–61064
——— Copy 2.   TL574.B6L5

NL 0352416 DLC

TL574 Liepmann, Hans   Wolfgang, 1914–
F6L5   On the application of statistical concepts to the buffeting problem. Rev.   Santa Monica, Douglas Aircraft Corp., 1952.
31 ℓ.   illus.   29 cm.

        1. Flutter (Aerodynamics) I. McDonnell Douglas Corp. II. Title.

NL 0352417 NcRS

Liepmann, Hans Wolfgang, 1914–
    Die schallgeschwindigkeit in flüssigem sauerstoff als funktion der siedetemperatur bei frequenzen von 7,5 und 1,5x 10⁶ Hz. ...
Basel, 1938.
Inaug. Diss. – Zürich, 1938.
Lebenslauf.

NL 0352418 ICRL CtY

533.6 Liepmann, Hans Wolfgang, 1914–
L719s   Summary of characteristics methods for steady state supersonic flows, by H.W. Liepmann and Ellis Lapin. [Santa Monica, Calif., Douglas Aircraft Co.] 1949.
33p. illus. 29cm.

        1.Aerodynamics, Supersonic. I.Lapin, Ellis, joint auth. II.Douglas Aircraft Company, Inc., Santa Monica, Calif. III.

NL 0352419 CLSU

Liepmann, Heinrich, 1904–
    Tariff levels and the economic unity of Europe; an examination of tariff policy, export movements and the economic integration of Europe, 1913–1931, by H. Liepmann ... with an introduction by Sir Walter Layton; translated from the German by H. Stenning. London, G. Allen & Unwin ltd. [1938]
424 p.   3 diagr. on fold. l.   22½cm.
"First published in 1938."
Bibliography: p. 416–420.
1. Tariff—Europe. 2. Europe—Commercial policy. 3. Europe—Econ. condit.—1918—   I. Stenning, Henry James, 1889–   tr. II. Title.
                                              39–15815
Library of Congress   HF2036.L56
                                              337.094

NL 0352420 DLC CU CaBVaU TU DAU NcD MH

Liepmann, Heinrich, 1904–
    Tariff levels and the economic unity of Europe; an examination of tariff policy, export movements and the economic integration of Europe, 1913–1931, by H. Liepmann ... with an introduction by Sir Walter Layton. Translated from the German by H. Stenning. New York, The Macmillan company, 1938.
424 p.   3 diagr. on fold. l.   22cm.
"First published in 1938."
Bibliography: p. 416–420.
1. Tariff—Europe. 2. Europe—Commercial policy. 3. Europe—Econ. condit.—1918—   I. Stenning, Henry James, 1889–   tr. II. Title.
                                              43–45371
Library of Congress   HF2036.L56 1938 a
                                              337

                  PBm PHC
NL 0352421 DLC CaBVaU WaS MH NIC FMU ICJ ViU PU

Liepmann, Heinz, 1905–
    Case history. New York, Beechhurst Press [1950]
334 p.   21 cm.
A novel.

        I. Title.

        PZ3.L62255Cas   50–11135

NL 0352422 DLC

Liepmann, Heinz, 1905–
    Death from the skies; a study of gas and microbial warfare, by Heinz Liepmann (with the scientific assistance of Dr. H. C. R. Simons, London) ... London, M. Secker & Warburg ltd, 1937.
286 p.   19cm.
"Translated from the German by Eden and Cedar Paul."
American edition (Philadelphia, London, J. B. Lippincott company) has title: Poison in the air.
Bibliography: p. 275–286.
1. Gases, Asphyxiating and poisonous—War use. 2. Bacteria, Pathogenic. 3. Air defenses.   I. Simons, H. C. R. II. *Paul, Eden, 1865– tr. III. Paul, Cedar, joint tr. IV. Title. V. Title: Microbial warfare.
                                              38–386
Library of Congress   UG447.L52 1937 a
                                              623.452

NL 0352423 DLC OCl NcD NN ICJ

833.9   Liepmann, Heinz, 1905–
L719wX   Fires underground; a narrative of the secret struggle carried on by the illegal organizations in Germany under penalty of death. Translated by R.T.Clark.   London, G.G.Harrap [1936]
287p. 21cm.

        Translation of Wird mit dem Tode Bestraft.

        I. Clark, Robert Thomson, 1889–   tr. II. Title.

NL 0352424 IEN CSt-H DAU CLSU NNC

VOLUME 332

Liepmann, Heinz, 1905–
Fires underground; a narrative of the secret struggle carried on by the illegal organizations in Germany under penalty of death, by Heinz Liepmann. Translated by R. T. Clark ... Philadelphia, London, J. B. Lippincott company, 1936.
300 p. 19½ cm.

1. Germany—Hist.—1933–1945—Fiction.   I. Clark, Robert Thomson, 1880–   tr.   II. Title.   *Translation of ... wird mit dem tode bestraft.*

PZ3.L62255Fi   36—18563

WU OCH
NL 0352425   DLC NN MB MH ScU CoU NcD CU OrSaW WaS

Liepmann, Heinz, 1905–
... Der frieden brach aus, roman. Wien, Phaidon-verlag [1930]
333, [1] p. 20ᶜᵐ.

I. Title.
Library of Congress   PT2623.I 43F7 1930   31—29516
Copyright A—Foreign   13224
                           [2]   833.91

NL 0352426   DLC IEN NcU CtY NN

Liepmann, Heinz, 1905–
... Die hilflosen; roman. Frankfurt a. M., Rütten & Loening, 1930.
4 p. l., 11–298 p. 20ᶜᵐ.

I. Title.
Library of Congress   PT2623.I 43H5 1930   30—27723
Copyright A—Foreign   8494
                                                       833.91

NL 0352427   DLC WaS MH IEN NN MB

Liepmann, Heinz, 1905–
... Das leben der millionäre. Paris, "Die Zone," 1934.
2 p. l., 7–123 p. 18½ᶜᵐ.
CONTENTS.—New-York hat sechzig gulden gekostet.—Girard, der grausamste wohltäter der welt.—Kleines rezept für massenmörder.—Der kronprinz der welt.—Der könig der pferdediebe.—Der mann mit dem besten gewissen der welt.—Der 24. september 1871.—Der grosse alte mann.—Der mann, gegen den Napoleon ein stümper gewesen ist.—Der mann, der den weltkrieg entschieden hat.—Der mann, der die stadt plünderte.—Ein philosoph baut automobile.—Marshall Fields warenhaus.—Der mann, der die indianer vernichtete.—Die kronprinzen der U. S. A.

1. Millionaires. 2. Capitalists and financiers—U. S.   I. Title.
                                                       43—32633
Library of Congress   HG181.L5

NL 0352428   DLC IEN NN MH

Liepmann, Heinz, 1905–
Murder—made in Germany; a true story of present-day Germany, by Heinz Liepmann; translated by Emile Burns. New York and London, Harper & brothers, 1934.
viii p., 1 l., 258 p. 21½ᶜᵐ.
"First edition."

1. Germany—Hist.—1933—   —Fiction.   I. Burns, Emile, tr.   II. Title.
Library of Congress   PZ3.L62255Mu   34—3724

NL 0352429   DLC NIC ViU NNJ NN WaSp MB

Liepmann, Heinz, 1905–
... Nächte eines alten kindes, roman. Wien, Phaidon-verlag, 1929.
222, [1] p. 18½ᶜᵐ.

I. Title.
Library of Congress   PT2623.I 43N3 1929   29—28086

NL 0352430   DLC WaS NN IU

Liepmann, Heinz, 1905–
Nights of an old child; a novel, by Heinz Liepmann; translated from the German by A. Lynton Hudson. Philadelphia, London, J. B. Lippincott company [*1937]
260 p. 21ᶜᵐ.

I. Hudson, Lynton Alfred, 1886–   tr.   II. Title.
Library of Congress   PZ3.L62255N1   37—5031
——— Copy 2.
Copyright A 103955   833.91

NL 0352431   DLC OrU CU WaS NBuU PP NN OEac

Liepmann, Heinz, 1905–
... Les nuits d'un vieil enfant, traduit de l'allemand par Guy Fritsch-Estrangin et Denise van Moppès. Paris, B. Grasset [1930]
234 p., 1 l. 18½ᶜᵐ.

I. Fritsch-Estrangin, Guy, tr.   II. Van Moppès, Denise, joint tr.   III. Title.
Library of Congress   PT2623.I 43N33   31—11643
Copyright A—Foreign   11182
                                                 833.91

NL 0352432   DLC

Liepmann, Heinz, 1905–
Peace broke out, by Heinz Liepmann. London, Chatto & Windus, 1932.
vi, 310 p., 1 l. 19½ᶜᵐ.
"Translated from the German by Emile Burns."

I. Burns, Emile, tr.   II. Title.
Library of Congress   PZ3.L62255Pe   32—29912
                                                 833.91

NL 0352433   DLC

LIEPMANN, HEINZ, 1905–
...Peace broke out.   New York, H. Smith and R. Haas, 1932.
vi, 310 p.   19½ cm.

"Translated from the German by Emile Burns."

661771A. 1. Fiction, German. 2. Inflation and deflation—Germany—Fiction. I. Burns, Emile, 1889–   , translator.
II. Title.

NL 0352434   NN CU WaTC

Liepmann, Heinz, 1905–
Poison in the air [by] Heinz Liepmann; translated from the German by Eden and Cedar Paul. Philadelphia, London, J. B. Lippincott company [*1937]
308 p.   21ᶜᵐ.
Published in England under title: Death from the skies.
Bibliography: p. [297]–308.

1. Gases, Asphyxiating and poisonous—War use. 2. Bacteria, Pathogenic. 3. Air defenses.   I. *Paul, Eden, 1865–   tr.   II. Paul, Cedar, joint tr.   III. Title.
Library of Congress   UG447.L52   37—19850
——— Copy 2.
Copyright A 109200   [5–5]   623.452

NL 0352435   DLC NIC OrU OrPS NcD PBa ViU NN MB

IK254   Liepmann, Heinz, 1905–
R3L5   Rasputin; Heiliger oder Teufel [von] Heinz
            Liepmann. Berlin, G. Weiss [195–?]
               302 p.   illus., ports.

               1. Rasputin, Grigoriĭ Efimovich, 1871–1916. 2.
            Russia – Pol. & govt. – 1894–1917. I. Title.

NL 0352436   CU IaU

Liepmann, Heinz, 1905–
...Smierć made in Germany; powieść. Autoryzowany przekład dra I. Bermana. We Lwowie: "Sigma" [1933]   313 p.
19cm.

10774B. 1. Germany—Hist., 1933.   —Fiction. 2. Fiction, German.
I. Berman, I., tr. II. Title.
N. Y. P. L.   February 29, 1940

NL 0352437   NN

Liepmann, Heinz, 1905–
Das vaterland; ein tatsachen roman aus dem heutigen Deutschland, von Heinz Liepmann. Amsterdam, P. N. Van Kampen & zoon n. v., 1933.
295 p. 20ᶜᵐ.

1. Fascism—Germany—Fiction.   I. Title.   A C 34–1628
Title from N. Y. Pub.   Libr. Printed by L. C.

NL 0352438   NN CU NcU OU InU IEN

Liepmann, Heinz, 1905–
... Wanderers in the mist, translated from the German by Emile Burns. New York and London, Harper & brothers, 1931.
3 p. l., 3–294 p. 20ᶜᵐ.
"First edition."

I. Burns, Emile, tr.   II. Title.   *Translation of Die hilflosen.*
                                                 31—7183
Library of Congress   PZ3.L62255Wan
——— Copy 2.
Copyright A 34958   [5]   833.91

NL 0352439   DLC NN PU

Liepmann, Heinz, 1905–
... wird mit dem tode bestraft, von Heinz Liepmann. Zürich, Europa-verlag, 1935.
246, [1] p. 20½ᶜᵐ.

1. Germany—Hist.—1933–   —Fiction.   I. Title.   36–14247
Library of Congress   PT2623.I 43W5 1935
Copyright A—Foreign   30069
                           [2]   833.91

NL 0352440   DLC IaU OrPR NcU IEN NcD CtY NN

Liepmann, Herbert.
Ueber die behandlung der grippe-pneumonie mit intravenoeser resorcin-injektion. (Auszug). Breslau, 1920.
Inaug.-diss. - Breslau.

NL 0352441   ICRL

Liepmann, Hugo Karl, 1863–1925.
Drei Aufsätze aus dem Apraxiegebiet. (Kleine Hilfsmittel bei der Untersuchung von Gehirnkranken [1905]. Die linke Hemisphäre und das Handeln [1905]. Ueber die Funktion des Balkens beim Handeln und die Beziehungen von Aphasie und Apraxie zur Intelligenz.) Berlin, S. Karger, 1908.
80 p.   8°.

NL 0352442   DNLM MH PPC NcD

VOLUME 332

Liepmann, Hugo Karl, 1863-1925.
Ein fall von reiner sprachtaubheit, von ... H. Liepmann ... Breslau, Schletter, 1898.
1 p. l., 50 p. illus. (incl. facsims.) fold. tab. 23½ᶜᵐ. (*On cover:* Psychia-
trische abhandlungen; hrsg. von dr. C. Wernicke. hft. 7/8)

1. Aphasia. 2. Deafness.

Library of Congress   RC321.P9 hft. 7/8

                                                    3-19339

NL   0352443   DLC DNLM ICJ

Liepmann, Hugo Karl, 1863-1925.
... Festschrift für Hugo Liepmann
see under title

Liepmann, Hugo Karl, 1863-1925.
Die "freie Selbstbestimmung" bei der Wahl des Aufenthalt-
sortes nach dem Reichsgesetz über den Unterstützungswohnsitz,
von Prof. Dr. phil. et med. H. Liepmann ... Halle a. S., C. Marhold, 1913.
56 p. 23¼ᶜᵐ.   (*On verso of t.-p.:* Sammlung zwangloser Abhandlungen aus
dem Gebiete der Nerven- und Geisteskrankheiten ... Bd. x, Heft 5)

NL   0352445   ICJ DNLM

Liepmann, Hugo Karl, 1863-1925.
Das krankheitsbild der aprazie ("Motorischen
asymbolie") Auf grund eines falles von einseitiger
... Berlin, Karger, 1900.
78p.

NL   0352446   MiU PPC

Liepmann, Hugo Karl, 1863-1925.
Die mechanik der Leucipp-Democritschen atome unter besonderer berücksichtigung der frage nach dem ursprung der
bewegung derselben ... Berlin, Buchdruckerei von G. Schade
(O. Francke) 1885.
69, ₁1₁ p. 22½ᶜᵐ.

Inaug.-diss.—Leipzig.
Vita.

1. Atoms. 2. Cosmogony.
                                                    6—40616
Library of Congress   QC173.L7

NL   0352447   DLC NjP CU MiU NjP NIC

LIEPMANN, Hugo Karl, 1863-1925.
Die mechanik der leucipp-democritschen atome
unter besonderer berücksichtigung der frage
nach dem ursprung der bewegung derselben.
Leipz., 1886.
pp. 69 †
"Vita", after p. 69.

NL   0352448   MH

Liepmann (Hugo Karl) [1863-1925]. "Ueber
die Delirien der Alkoholisten. 33 pp., 1 l. 8°.
Berlin, L. Schumacher. 1896.

NL   0352449   DNLM ICRL

WM   Liepmann, Hugo, Karl, 1863-1925.
L721u   Ueber Störungen des Handelns bei
1905   Gehirnkranken. Berlin, Karger, 1905.
             161 p. illus.

NL   0352450   DNLM MH PPC NNC MiU ICU NIC CU-M NNNPsI

Liepmann, Hugo Karl, 1863-1925.
Über Ideenflucht; Begriffsbestimmung und psychologische
Analyse, von Dr. phil. et med. H. Liepmann ... Halle a.d.S.,
C. Marhold, 1904.
84 p. 23½ᶜᵐ.   (*On verso of t.-p.:* Sammlung zwangloser Abhandlungen aus
dem Gebiete der Nerven- und Geisteskrankheiten ... v. Bd., Heft 1 (*i.e.* IV. Bd.,
Heft 8)

Bibliographical foot-notes.

NL   0352451   ICJ NIC DNLM NNNAM MSotcA

Liepmann, Hugo Karl, 1863-1925.
Der weitere Krankheitsverlauf bei dem einseitig Apraktischen
und der Gehirnbefund auf Grund von Serienschnitten. Von Prof.
Dr. H. Liepmann, ... Mit 12 Abbildungen im Text und 4
Tafeln. Berlin, S. Karger, 1906.
₁2₁, 49 p. illus., iv pl. 26½ᶜᵐ.
"Sonder-Abdruck aus der Monatsschrift für Psychiatrie und Neurologie, Bd. XVII u.
XIX."
Bibliographical foot-notes.

NL   0352452   ICJ CtY-M

LIEPMANN, JACOB, 1803-1865.
Der Ölgemälde-Druck, erfunden und beschrieben.
Berlin, L. Sachse, 1842.   viii, 47 p.   6 engr. plates (1 col.)
26cm.

1. Printing, Color.   2. Paintings--Reproductions.   3. Printing--Technique.

NL   0352453   NN NNC

Liepmann, Käthe.
Public utility house building: I-II. By Dr. Käthe Liepmann.
(*In* International labour review, Genevr. July, Aug., 1929. v. 20,
p. ₁15₁-34, ₁207₁-229)

1. Housing.   I. Title.

Library, U. S. Dept. of   Labor   L 29-128

NL   0352454   DL MiU

Liepmann, Kate K
The journey to work; its significance for industrial and
community life, by Kate K. Liepmann, PH. D., with a foreword by A. M. Carr-Saunders ... London, K. Paul, Trench,
Trubner & co., ltd. ₁1944₁
xii, 199 p. incl. tables. fold. maps, fold. diagr. 22½ cm. ₁Inter-
national library of sociology and social reconstruction. Editor: Dr.
Karl Mannheim₁
"First published 1944."
"The study has been approved by the University of London for the
award of the degree of Ph. D."—Pref.
Bibliographical foot-notes.
1. Traffic engineering. 2. Industries, Location of. 3. Cities and
towns—Planning.   I. Title.

HD7395.T72L5   331.83   44—3511

                                          ICarbS GAT NcU
NL   0352455   DLC MtU PU MH ViU NcD CU MB NBuU MiU AU

HD7392   Liepmann, Kate K
.T72L51   The journey to work; its significance for
            industrial and community life. With a fore-
            word by A. M. Carr-Saunders. New York, Oxford
            Univ. press, 1944.
            xii, 199 p. tables, fold. maps, fold. diagr.
            (International library of sociology and social
            reconstruction)
            Bibliographical foot-notes.

            1. Communication and traffic. 2. Industries,
            Location of. 3.   Cities and towns--Plan-
            ning.

NL   0352456   ICU NIC LU OrPR OrU OrP WaS OCU

Liepmann, Klaus.
The language of music. New York, Ronald Press Co.
₁1953₁
376 p. illus. 24 cm.

1. Music—Analysis, appreciation.   I. Title.

MT6.L43   781   52-12521 ‡

             OWorP WU OrU IdPS MtBC MtU WaS
             OCLU TU MiU PSt Or CoGrS CoU NBuC OrSaW MeB
             ICU OOxM NN TxU NcD PWcS OC1ND OU NcC OC1W OO
NL   0352457   DLC WaOrCS OrPS IEG AAP WaT IdU MB

qM787   Liepmann, Klaus.
L62p   Popular dances from the seventeenth century.
            For string quartet or string orchestra. Bos-
            Ton, Boston Music Co. ₁c1953₁
            score (32p.) and 6 parts. 31cm.

            For 3 violins, viola, violoncello and bass.

            1. String sextets (3 violins, viola, violoncel-
            lo, double bass), Arranged. 2. Music, Popular
            (Songs, etc.) 3. Dance music—To 1800. I.
            Title.

NL   0352458   IU OO MiU

Liepmann, Klaus, *arr.*
Songs and marches by famous composers, arr. for violin
and piano. New York, G. Schirmer, ₁1948₁
score (24 p.) and part. 31 cm.

1. Violin and piano music, Arranged.   I. Title.

M222.L6S6   48-10404*

NL   0352459   DLC

Liepmann, Kurt, Kammergerichtsrefer.: Die Pfändbarkeit
des Anspruchs auf Berichtigung des Grundbuchs. Berlin
1910: Ebering. 49 S. 8°
Heidelberg, Jur. Diss. v. 9. Mai 1910, Ref. Endemann
[Geb. 21. Juli 87 Oschersleben; Wohnort: Berlin; Staatsangeh.: Preußen;
Vorbildung: Friedrichs-Gymn. Berlin Reife O. 06; Studium: Heidelberg 2,
Berlin 4 S.; Rig. 3 März 10.]   [U 10. 1926

NL   0352460   ICRL MH-L

Liepmann, Leo.
Der kampf um die gestaltung der englischen währungsver-
fassung von der ersten bis zur zweiten Peel's-act, 1819-1844.
(Currency principle und banking school) Ein beitrag zur
geschichte des englischen geld- und bankwesens, von dr. L.
Liepmann ... Berlin, Junker und Dünnhaupt, 1933.
vi p., 1 l., 238 p. incl. tables. 24ᶜᵐ.
"Literaturverzeichnis": p. ₁234₁-238.

1. Currency question—Gt. Brit. 2. Banks and banking—Gt. Brit.
I. Title.

                                          A C 33-3346
Title from Yale Univ.   Printed by L. C.

NL   0352461   CtY NcD

VOLUME 332

Liepmann, Moritz, 1869-1928.
...American prisons and reformatory institutions; a report ₍by₎ M. Liepmann. Tr. by Charles O. Fiertz... ₍N.Y., 1928₎
91p.
Caption title.
Reprinted from Mental Hygiene, Vol. XII, No.2, April, 1928, pp.225-315.

NL 0352462 NcD-L OrU

Liepmann, Moritz, 1869-1928.
Amerikanische gefängnisse und erziehungsanstalten; ein reisebericht von M. Liepmann. Mannheim ₍etc.₎ J. Bensheimer, 1927.
xii, 76 p. 25ᶜᵐ. (Added t.-p.: Hamburgische schriften zur gesamten strafrechtswissenschaft, hrsg. von d⁻ M. Liepmann ... hft. 11)

1. Prisons—U.S. I. Title.

Library of Congress   HV9473.L5   33-3552
                                     365.973

NL 0352463 DLC PU MH NN

LIEPMANN, M₍oritz₎
Die anträge der deutschen antiduell-ligua. ₍Heidelberg, 1904.₎

"Sonderabdruck aus der MONATSSCHRIFT für kriminal-psychologie und strafrechtsreform", 2, p. 119-33.
Autograph dedication.

NL 0352464 MH-L

LIEPMANN, M₍oritz₎
Die bedeutung Adolf Merkels für strafrecht und rechtsphilosophie. n.t.p.

NL 0352465 MH-L

Liepmann, Moritz, 1869-1928.
Die Bedeutung der Reichsverfassung für die geistige Kultur Deutschlands, von M. Liepmann... Hamburg: W. Gente, 1920. 39 p. 18cm.

1. Germany. Constitution.   2. Germany—Civilization, 20th cent.
N. Y. P. L.   December 17, 1943

NL 0352466 NN InU MH

Liepmann, Moritz, 1869-1928.
Die beleidigung, von dr. M. Liepmann ... Berlin, Puttkammer & Mühlbrecht, 1909.
132 p. 19ᶜᵐ. (Added t.-p.: Das recht; sammlung von abhandlungen für juristen und laien ... bd. II-III)
"Literatur-uebersicht": p. ₍7-9₎

1. Libel and slander. ₍1. Libel and slander—Germany₎ I. Title.
                                       31-7465

NL 0352467 DLC CtY ICU MH

Liepmann, Moritz, 1869-1928.
... Der deutsche Strafgesetzentwurf. Korreferat auf der Jahresversammlung des Vereins für Psychiatria, 23. September 1922 in Leipzig. Von M. Liepmann ... Berlin, Walter de Gruyter & Co. ₍1922?₎
₍185₎-199 p. 21½cm.
Caption title.
"Separatabdruck aus der 'Zeitschrift für Psychiatrie usw.' Bd. 79."

NL 0352468 MH-L

FL8   Liepmann,Moritz,1869-1928.
G3.9   Duell und Ehre; ein Vortrag. Berlin, O.
L7175d   Liebmann, 1904.
1904   61 p. 19cm.

1.Dueling - Germany.

NL 0352469 MiU-L MH-L

Liepmann, Moritz, 1869-1928.
... Einfache Beleidigung. (§ 185 RStrGB.) Bearb. von Professor Dr. Liepmann ... ₍Berlin, Otto Liebmann, 1906₎
₍217₎-373 p. 26cm.
Caption title.
At head of title: Die Beleidigung.
(Abschnitt 14 des II. Teiles des RStrGB.) I.
On cover: Sonderabdruck aus der Vergleichenden Darstellung des deutschen und das

ausländischen Strafrechts ... hrsg. ... von ... Dr. Karl Birkmeyer, Dr. Fritz van Calker, Dr. Reinhard Frank ... ₍u.a.₎
Bibliographical footnotes.

NL 0352471 MH-L

Liepmann, Moritz, 1869-1929.
Einleitung in das strafrecht. Eine kritik der kriminalistischen grundbegriffe von dr. Moritz Liepmann ... Berlin, O. Häring, 1900.
xii p., 1 l., 212 p. 22ᵐ.

1. Criminal law. 2. Law reform. I. Title.
                                     36-16761

NL 0352472 DLC ICU MH CtY PU PU-L

LIEPMANN, M₍oritz₎
Die einschränkung des wahrheitsbeweises bei beleidigungs-klagen. Wien, n.d.

"Sonderabdruck aus der OESTERREICHISCHEN zeitschrift für strafrecht", 1, 1910. p. 205-43.
Autograph dedication.

NL 0352473 MH-L

LIEPMANN, Moritz.
Der fahrlässige falscheid des zeugen. Kiel, Leipzig, 1907.

45 p.
"Sonderabdruck aus Festgabe der kieler juristenfakultät zu Albert Hänels fünfzigjährigem doktor-jubiläum", 341-383.

NL 0352474 MH-L

LIEPMANN, M₍oritz₎.
Der friedensvertrag und der völkerbund. Hamburg, 1920.

27 p.

NL 0352475 MH-L NN

Liepmann, Moritz, 1869-1928.

Galin, Leo.
... Gerichtswesen und strafsystem im revolutionären Russland (dargestellt auf grund der ereignisse bis anfang 1920) mit vorworten von prof. E. Lederer ... und prof. M. Liepmann ... Berlin, F. Vahlen, 1920.

LIEPMANN, M₍oritz₎.
Der kieler hafen im seekrieg. Berlin, 1906.

49 p.

NL 0352477 MH-L CtY

Liepmann, Moritz, 1869-1928.
Kommunistenprozesse; ein rechtsgutachten, von dr. M. Liepmann ... München, Drei masken verlag, 1928.
71, ₍1₎ p. 22½ᵐ.
"Inhaltsverzeichnis" on p. 2 of cover.

1. Communism—Germany. 2. Kommunistische partei Deutschlands. I. Title.
Library of Congress   HX279.L75   29-6767

NL 0352478 DLC NN

Liepmann, Moritz, 1869-1928.
Krieg und kriminalität in Deutschland, von dr. Moritz Liepmann ... Stuttgart, Berlin ₍etc.₎ Deutsche verlagsanstalt; New Haven, Yale university press, 1930.
xiii, ₍1₎, 197 p. diagrs. 25ᶜᵐ. (Added t.-p.: ₍Carnegie endowment for international peace. Division of economics and history₎ Wirtschafts- und sozialgeschichte des weltkrieges. Deutsche serie)
"Literatur": p. ₍171₎-197.

1. Crime and criminals—Germany. 2. European war, 1914-1918—Influence and results. I. Title.
Library of Congress   HC56.C385   no. 10   30-29461
——— Copy 2.   HV6973.L5
                              ₍a38m1₎   (330.9) 364.943

DNW CSt-H NN ViU ICJ MB MH
CaQMM MU DAU NNUN PP PHC PSC OC1 OO OU PBm PU NcD
NL 0352479 DLC MtU OrPR IdU CaBVa MtBC WaS CaBVaU

Liepmann, Moritz, 1869-1928.
Die kriminalität der jugendlichen und ihre bekämpfung. Vortrag gehalten auf der "Versammlung norddeutscher frauenvereine" am 11. september 1908 in Kiel, von professor M. Liepmann-Kiel. Tübingen, Mohr, 1909.
2 p. l., 48 p. 21½ᶜᵐ.

1. Juvenile delinquency — Germany. 2. Juvenile courts — Germany. 3. Law reform—Germany. I. Title.
                                     36-21731
Library of Congress   HV9158.L5   364

NL 0352480 DLC MiU CtY ICJ

Liepmann, Moritz, 1869-1928, ed.

Merkel, Adolf, 1836-1896.
Die lehre von verbrechen und strafe, von Adolf Merkel ... Auf der grundlage des "Lehrbuchs des strafrechts" in verbindung mit den übrigen schriften des verfassers, hrsg. und mit einer einleitung versehen von dr. M. Liepmann ... Stuttgart, F. Enke, 1912.

VOLUME 332

Liepmann, Moritz, 1869–1928.
... Die pflege des völkerrechts an den deutschen universitäten; eine denkschrift von geh. justizrat prof. dr. Liepmann ... Berlin, H. R. Engelmann, 1919.
30 p. 23ᶜᵐ. (Monographien zum völkerbund, hrsg. von der Deutschen liga für völkerbund. Hft. 6)
"Anhang. Verzeichnis der an den deutschen universitäten während des weltkrieges über völkerrecht, internationales privatrecht u. s. w. angekündigten vorlesungen": p. ₁16₁–30.

1. International law—Study and teaching.   ɪ. Title.   A 20–762
Carnegie endow. Int. peace.   Library
for Library of Congress   JX1975.M72 hft. 6
—— Copy 2.   JX1293.G3L4
          ₁a45c1₁†

NL 0352482   NNCE ICRL DLC

Liepmann, Moritz, 1869–1928.
Die rechtsphilosophie des Jean Jacques Rousseau. Ein beitrag zur geschichte der staatstheorieen, von dr. jur. et phil. M. Liepmann ... Berlin, J. Guttentag, 1898.
144 p. 22½ᶜᵐ.

1. Rousseau, Jean Jacques, 1712–1778. 2. State, The. 3. Law—Philosophy. ɪ. Title.
          42–29925

NL 0352483   DLC CU ICU MH-L MH MNS IaU

Liepmann, Moritz, 1869–/928.
Die Reform des deutschen Schwurgerichts. ₁Heidelberg, C. Winter, 1909?₁
₁155₁–263 p. (Schwurgerichte und Schöffengerichte, hrsg. von W. Mittermaier und M. Liepmann, Bd. 2, Heft ₁2₁)

Caption title.

NL 0352484   NNC-L

Liepmann, Moritz, 1869–1928.
Die reform des deutschen strafrechts; kritische bemerkungen zu dem "Strafgesetzentwurf", von prof. dr. M. Liepmann. ₁Hamburg, W. Gente, 1921₁
3 p. l., ₁lx₁–xlv, ₁2₁, 151 p. 22½ᶜᵐ. (*Added t.-p.:* Hamburgische schriften zur gesamten strafrechtswissenschaft ... hft. 2)

1. Criminal law—Germany. 2. Law reform—Germany. ɪ. Title.
          40–18303

NL 0352485   DLC MH NN

Liepmann, Moritz, 1869–/928, joint ed.

Mittermaier, Wolfgang, 1867–   *ed.*
Schwurgerichte und schöffengerichte; beiträge zu ihrer kenntnis und beurteilung, hrsg. von dr. W. Mittermaier ... und dr. M. Liepmann ...
Heidelberg, C. Winter, 1908–

Liepmann, Moritz, 1869–1928.
Die staatstheorie des "Contrat social" ...
Halle a. S., C.A. Kaenmerer & co., 1896.
56, [2] p. 23 cm. [Halle. Universität.
Dissertationen. v. 45, no. 15].
Inaug.-diss. - Halle.
Vita.

NL 0352487   CU MH PU ICRL CtY

Liepmann, Moritz, 1869–1928.
Das Strafverfahren und die Organisation der Strafgerichte. Berlin, F. A. Herbig, 1926.
39 p. 19 cm. (Schriftenreihe der Vereinigung für Jugendgerichte und Jugendgerichtshilfen, Heft 6)

1. Criminal procedure—Germany—Popular works. ɪ. Title.
(Series: Deutsche Vereinigung für Jugendgerichte und Jugendgerichtshilfen. Schriftenreihe, Heft 6)
          52–54174

NL 0352488   DLC MH-L

343.2   Liepmann, Moritz.
L624t   Die todesstrafe; ein gutachten mit einem nachwort.   Berlin, 1912.
220p. tables.

"Sonderabdruck aus den Verhandlungen des XXXI. Deutschen juristentages."

NL 0352489   IU OU MH-L PU PU-L CtY

I   LIEPMANN, MORITZ, 1869–1928, ed.
747   Von Kieler Professoren; Briefe aus drei
.463   Jahrhunderten zur Geschichte der Universität Kiel. Herausgegeben zur Erinnerung an das 250jährige Jubiläum der Universität in ihrem Auftrag von Dr. M. Liepmann.   Stuttgart, Deutsche Verlags-Anstalt, 1916.
xviii,430p. 26cm.

NL 0352490   ICN MH IU

Liepmann, Moritz, 1869–1929.

Mattil, Friedrich.
Die wahrnehmung berechtigter interessen durch die presse; eine kritische studie über ihre voraussetzungen und ihre grenzen, de lege lata und de lege ferenda, von dr. F. Mattil ... Mit einer einleitung über die grundgedanken des § 193 des Strafgesetzbuches, von professor M. Liepmann† ... Hamburg, Broschek & co., 1929.

Liepmann, Moritz, 1869–1928.
Was sollen wir lernen aus diesem krieg?
Kiel, 1915.

NL 0352492   NjP

Liepmann, Paul.
Kritische erörterungen und vorschläge zur strafprozess-reform, von dr. jur. Paul Liepmann ... Berlin, F. Vahlen, 1909.
2 p. l., 86 p. 22½ᶜᵐ.

1. Criminal procedure—Germany. 2. Law reform—Germany.
          42–30868

NL 0352493   DLC PU-L

Liepmann, Paul.
Summarisches strafverfahren in England und strafverfahren in Schottland. Von dr. jur. Paul Liepmann ... und dr. jur. Wolf Mannhardt ... Berlin, J. Guttentag, g. m. b. h., 1908.
184 p. 23ᶜᵐ. (*On cover:* Beiträge zur reform des strafprozesses ... bd. ɪɪ. hft. 2)
"Gebrauchte literatur und abkürzungen": p. ₁9₁–11.

ɪ. Mannhardt, Wolf, 1864–   joint author.
          11–28809

NL 0352494   DLC PU-L

Liepmann, Paul, 1876–
... Ueber das vorkommen von talgdrüsen im lippenrot des menschen ... Königsberg, Liedtke, 1900.
36 p., 2 l.

Inaug.-diss., Königsberg, 1900.
Vita.
"Litteratur": p. ₁33₁–36.

1. Sebaceous glands. 2. Lips.

NL 0352495   NNC CtY MH ICRL DNLM

Liepmann (Philippus). * De duplicitate uteri et vaginae. 24 pp., 2 l., 1 pl. 4°. *Berolini, typ. F. Nietack, 1830.* [P., v. 1602.]

NL 0352496   DNLM PPC

W 4   LIEPMANN, Roger, 1918–
L992   Les stations climatiques du Moyen-
1948   Atlas central. Lyon, Impr. des beaux-arts, 1948.
86 p. illus. (Lyons. ₁Université₁ Faculté ₁mixte₁ de médecine et de pharmacie. Thèse. 1947/48. no. 187₁

NL 0352497   DNLM CtY-M

Liepmann, Rudolf.
... Die polizeilichen aufgaben der deutschen wehrmacht, von dr. jur. Rudolf Liepmann. Mit kartenskizze der wehrkreiseinteilung. Leipzig, T. Weicher, 1926.
vi, 88 p. fold. map. 26ᶜᵐ. (Leipziger rechtswissenschaftliche studien ... hft. 16)
"Die arbeit wurde als Leipziger dissertation im august 1924 abgeschlossen und konnte seitdem nur in einzelheiten ergänzt und fortgeführt werden."—Vorwort.

1. Germany—Army. 2. Police—Germany. ɪ. Title.
          26–23612

NL 0352498   DLC CU-L NN

Liepmann, Werner, 1912–
Der heutige stand der enterokokken-erkrankungen.
... Bonn, 1937. 41 p.
Inaug. Diss. - Bonn, 1937.
Lebenslauf.
Literatur-Angaben.

NL 0352499   DNLM

LIEPMANN, Wilhelm Gustav, 1878–
Die abtreibung; eine medizinisch-soz-iologische studie in bildlichen darstellungen für ärzte, juristen und soziologen. Berlin, Wien, 1927.

4°.

NL 0352500   MH-L

WP   LIEPMANN, Wilhelm Gustav, 1878–
qL719a   Atlas der Operations-Anatomie und
1912   Operations-Pathologie der weiblichen Sexualorgane mit besonderer Berücksichtigung des Ureterverlaufes und des Suspensions- und Stützapparates des Uterus. Berlin, Hirschwald, 1912.
48 p. and atlas (35 plates)
Text inserted at front of atlas.

NL 0352501   DNLM ICJ PPC

VOLUME 332

WP
17
fL719a
1924
LIEPMANN, Wilhelm Gustav, 1878-
Atlas der Operations-Anatomie und Operations-Pathologie der weiblichen Sexualorgane mit besonderer Berücksichtigung des Ureterverlaufes und des Suspensions- und Stützapparates des Uterus. 2. verm. Aufl. Berlin, Urban & Schwarzenberg, 1924.
175 p. illus.

NL 0352502 DNLM PPC ICJ

618.2
L624g-S
1926
Liepmann, Wilhelm Gustav, 1878-
Clinica obstetrica; la práctica de la obstetricia en veinte lecciones, para médicos y estudiantes, con 313 figuras, algunas en colores, intercaladas en el texto, por el Dr. Guillermo Liepmann ... 4.ª ed., tr. directamente del Alemán por el Dr. Víctor Conill y Montobbio ... Barcelona, Salvat editores, S. A., 1926.
xxv, 387 p. illus. (partly col.) 27½ cm.
Bibliographical foot-notes.

Translation of his Das geburtshilfliche seminar, praktische geburtshilfe, in 20 vorlesungen, für aerzte und studierende.

1. Obstetrics. I. Conill y Montobbio, Victor, tr. II. Title. III. Title: Das geburtshilfliche seminar, praktische geburtshilfe.

NL 0352504 MoSU

Liepmann, Wilhelm Gustav, 1878-
Die frau, was sie von körper und kind wissen muss, von dr. W. Liepmann ... 1.-10. tausend ... Stuttgart [etc.] Union deutsche verlagsgesellschaft [*1914]
2 v. illus, plates (part col.) diagrs. 19cm. (Half-title: Die bücher der frau. [bd. 1-2])
Part of plates accompanied by guard sheets with outline drawings.

1. Woman—Health and hygiene. 2. Obstetrics—Popular works.
I. Title.

Library of Congress   RG121.L7   14-11808

NL 0352505 DLC OC1

Liepmann, Wilhelm Gustav, 1878-
Geburtshelfer und Röntgenbild; erweiterung und erneuerung der geburtshilfe durch die Röntgendiagnostik, von ... dr. Wilhelm Liepmann ... und dr. Gerhard Danelius ... Mit 160 abbildungen. Berlin und Wien, Urban & Schwarzenberg, 1932.
viii, 271 p. illus. 27¼cm.
"Literatur": p. 263-264.

1. Obstetrics. 2. Pregnancy—Signs and diagnosis. I. Danelius, Gerhard, joint author. II. Title.
S G 32-67

Library, U. S. Surgeon-   General's Office

NL 0352506 DI-GS ICJ

Liepmann, Wilhelm Gustav, 1878-
Der geburtshilfliche phantomkurs ... Von dr. med. Wilhelm Liepmann ... Berlin [etc.] Urban & Schwarzenberg, 1922.
3 p. l., 311 p. illus. 22cm.

1. Obstetrics.

NL 0352507 MiU ICRL PPC ICJ

Liepmann, Wilhelm Gustav, 1878-
Der geburtshilfliche phantomkurs in 172 federzeichnungen für ärzte und studierende, von ... dr. med. Wilhelm Liepmann ... Zweite, vermehrte und verbesserte auflage. Berlin, Wien. Urban & Schwarzenberg, 1931.
x, 316, [1] p. incl. illus., plates. 22cm.

1. Obstetrics. 2. Obstetrics—Surgery. I. Title.
A 31-1382 Revised

Title from Columbia   Univ.
Library of Congress   RG725.L5 1931
Copyright A—Foreign   14860
618.8

NL 0352508 NNC DNLM ICJ OrU-M

WQ
300
L719g
1910
LIEPMANN, Wilhelm Gustav, 1878-
Das Geburtshilfliche Seminar; praktische Geburtshilfe in achtzehn Vorlesungen für Ärzte und Studierende. Berlin, Hirschwald, 1910.
xxiv, 331 p. illus.

NL 0352509 DNLM CtY ICJ PPC

WQ
300
qL719g
1918
LIEPMANN, Wilhelm Gustav, 1878-
Das geburtshilfliche Seminar; praktische Geburtshilfe in neunzehn Vorlesungen für Ärzte und Studierende. 2. verb. und verm. Aufl. Berlin, Hirschwald, 1918.
xxiv, 423 p. illus.

NL 0352510 DNLM

WQ
300
qL719g
1921
LIEPMANN, Wilhelm Gustav, 1878-
Das Geburtshilfliche Seminar; praktische Geburtshilfe in zwanzig Vorlesungen für Ärzte und Studierende. 3. verb. & verm. Aufl. Berlin, Hirschwald, 1921.
xvi, 387 p. illus.
Contains errata slip.

NL 0352511 DNLM PPC

WQ
300
qL719g
1924
LIEPMANN, Wilhelm Gustav, 1878-
Das Geburtshilfliche Seminar; praktische Geburtshilfe in zwanzig Vorlesungen für Ärzte und Studierende. 4. verb. & verm. Aufl. Berlin, Hirschwald, 1924.
xvi, 412 p. illus.

NL 0352512 DNLM ICJ

Liepmann, Wilhelm Gustav, 1878-
Gegenwartsfragen der Frauenkunde, Vorlesungen gehalten an der Berliner Friedrich-Wilhelm-Universität. Unter Mitarbeit von Paul Gornick und einem Beitrag von Maria Seyring. Leipzig, S. Hirzel, 1933.
244 p. illus. 24 cm.

1. Woman—Social and moral questions.

HQ1210.L5   54-47570 ‡

NL 0352513 DLC DNLM

Liepmann, Wilhelm Gustav, 1878-
Grundriss der gynäkologie, von dr. Wilhelm Liepmann ... Mit 5 tafeln und 62 figuren im text. Berlin, S. Seemann, 1914.
vi, 164 p., 1 l. illus., v pl. 18cm. (On cover: Seemanns grundrisse)
M. 3.80
Interleaved.

1. Woman—Diseases.
14-17266

Library of Congress   RG111.L5

NL 0352514 DLC

Liepmann, Wilhelm Gustav, 1878-
Grundriss der Gynäkologie, von Professor Dr. Wilhelm Liepmann ... III. Auflage. Berlin, S. Seemann, 1920.
viii, 170 p. illus, v pl. 18cm. (On cover: Seemanns Grundrisse)

NL 0352515 ICJ ICRL NNC DNLM

WP
qL719g
1911
LIEPMANN, Wilhelm Gustav, 1878-
Der gynäkologische Operationskursus and der Leiche; mit besonderer Berücksichtigung der Operations-Anatomie, der Operations-Pathologie, der Operations-Bakteriologie und der Fehlerquellen; in sechszehn Vorlesungen. Berlin, Hirschwald, 1911.
xx, 456 p. illus.

NL 0352516 DNLM PPC ICJ

WP
qL719g
1912
LIEPMANN, Wilhelm Gustav, 1878-
Die gynäkologische Operationskursus; mit besonderer Berücksichtigung der Operations-Anatomie, der Operations-Pathologie, der Operations-Bakteriologie, und der Fehlerquellen; in sechzehn Vorlesungen. 2., neubearb. und verm. Aufl. Berlin, Hirschwald, 1912.
xx, 488 p. illus.

NL 0352517 DNLM PPJ MiU

WP
660
q L719g
1920
LIEPMANN, Wilhelm Gustav, 1878-
Der gynäkologische Operationskursus; mit besonderer Berücksichtigung der Operations-Anatomie, der Operations-Pathologie, der Operations-Bakteriologie und der Fehlerquellen; in sechzehn Vorlesungen. 3. neudurchgesehene Aufl. Berlin, Hirschwald, 1920.
xx, 488 p. illus.

NL 0352518 DNLM PPC

Liepmann, Wilhelm Gustav, 1878-
Der gynäkologische Operationskursus, mit besonderer Berücksichtigung der Operations-Anatomie, der Operations-Pathologie, der Operations-Bakteriologie und der Fehlerquellen. In sechzehn Vorlesungen. 4. verb. Aufl. Berlin, A. Hirschwald, 1924.
xiii, 475 p. illus. (part col.), plates.
"Literatur": p. [454]-455.

NL 0352519 ICJ ICRL DNLM

Liepmann, Wilhelm Gustav, 1878-
Gynäkologische psychotherapie; ein führer für ärzte und studierende von dr. med. Wilhelm Liepmann ... In 10 vorlesungen mit 4 kunstbeilagen von Richard Fuhry und 20 abbildungen im text. Berlin, Wien, Urban & Schwarzenberg, 1924.
vii, 208 p. illus., 4 pl. 25½cm.

1. Woman—Diseases. 2. Therapeutics, Suggestive. I. Title.

Library of Congress   RG103.L5   25-8209

NL 0352520 DLC FU PPC

Liepmann, Wilhelm Gustav, 1878-
Das gynäkologische seminar; praktische gynäkologie mit besonderer berücksichtigung der sozialen frauenkunde, in 15 vorlesungen für ärzte und studierende, von dr. Wilhelm Liepmann ... Mit 305 zum teil mehrfarbigen abbildungen im text und auf 24 tafeln. Berlin, Wien, Urban & Schwarzenberg, 1931.
viii, 368 p. illus. (part col.) 24 col. pl. 28½cm.

1. Woman—Diseases. I. Title.   31-22664

Library of Congress   RG101.L5
Copyright A—Foreign   12685
618.1

NL 0352521 DLC ICJ PPC

VOLUME 332

Liepmann, Wilhelm Gustav, 1878–
... Jugend und Eros; sexualpsychologische Lebensfragmente junger Menschen. Dresden: C. Reissner, 1930. 222 p. 21cm.

120425B.   1. Sex—Psychology.   2. Sex—Ethics.
N.Y.P.L.   September 29, 1941

NL 0352522   NN WaU ViU

Liepmann, Wilhelm Gustav, 1878–   ed.
Kurzgefasstes Handbuch der gesamten Frauenheilkunde. Gynäkologie und Geburtshilfe für den praktischen Arzt, herausgegeben von Dr. W. Liepmann ... Band II–[III] ... Leipzig, F. C. W. Vogel, 1914.
2 vol. illus. (part col.), col. plates. 27½ᶜᵐ.
Includes bibliographies.
Contents.— Bd. 2. Frankl, O. Pathologische Anatomie und Histologie der weiblichen Genitalorgane in kurgefasster Darstellung. v, 302 p. 34 pl.—Bd. 3. Fraenkel, L. Normale und pathologische Sexualphysiologie des Weibes. Jaschke, R. T. Physiologie und Pathologie der Geburt. vii, [1], 827 p. 19 pl.
No more published.

NL 0352523   ICJ DNLM DLC

Liepmann, Wilhelm Gustav, 1878–
Leichengeburt bei Ichthyosauriern. Eine paläobiologische Studie, von Dr. Wilhelm Liepmann... Berlin: W. de Gruyter & Co., 1926. 11 p. incl. table. illus., 3 pl. 8°. (Heidelberger Akad. der Wissenschaften. Sitzungsb. Mathematisch-naturwissenschaftliche Klasse. Jahrg. 1926, Abhandl. 6.)
Bibliography, p. 11.

1. Ichthyosaurus.
N.Y.P.L.   May 9, 1927

NL 0352524   NN

10fs   Liepmann, Wilhelm Gustav, 1878–
L719   Psychologie der Frau; versuch einer
ps   synthetischen, sexualpsychologischen
1920   Entwicklungslehre, in zehn Vorlesungen
gehalten an der Friedrich-Wilhelms-Universität zu Berlin. Mit einer Tafel und 10
Textabbildungen. Berlin, Urban & Schwarzenberg, 1920.
315 p. illus., plate, diagr.

Bibliographical references included in
"Anmerkungen und Hinweise": p.309-315.

NL 0352525   CU MH PPC NNC ICJ

Liepmann, Wilhelm Gustav, 1878–
Psychologie der frau; versuch einer synthetischen, sexualpsychologischen entwickelungslehre, in zehn vorlesungen gehalten an der Friedrich-Wilhelms-universität zu Berlin von W. Liepmann. Mit zwei tafeln und 10 textabbildungen. 2., umgearb. aufl. Berlin, Wien, Urban & Schwarzenberg, 1922.
6 p. l., 322 p. illus., II pl., diagr. 25½ᶜᵐ.

1. Sex. 2. Sex (Psychology) 3. Woman. I. Title.

Library of Congress   HQ21.L4 1922   **25-8104**

NL 0352526   DLC N NBuU NcU MiU IU PU-L

WBB   LIEPMANN, Wilhelm Gustav, 1878–
L719t   Tabellen zu klinisch-bakteriologischen
1909   Untersuchungen für Chirurgen und
Gynäkologen, nebst einer kurzen
Anleitung zur Ausführung der "Dreitupferprobe." Berlin, Hirschwald, 1909.
1 v. (chiefly illus.)
Identical forms.

NL 0352527   DNLM

Liepmann (Wilhelm Gustav) [1878–].
* Ueber suprasymphysären Querschnitt. 33 pp.,
11. 8°. *Berlin, E. Ebering,* 1901.

NL 0352528   DNLM ICRL CtY

Liepmann, Wilhelm Gustav, 1878–
Weltschöpfung und Weltanschauung. Berlin, Wegweiser-Verlag, 1923.
247 p. illus. 19 cm.
Includes bibliography.

1. Cosmology.   I. Title.

BD513.L55   53–52496 ‡

NL 0352529   DLC NNC TU

BD 513   Liepmann, Wilhelm Gustav, 1878–
L55   Weltschöpfung und Weltanschauung. 2.
1926   verm. und verb. aufl. Berlin, Verlag
Quelle & Meyer, 1926.
243 p. illus. 19 cm.

1. Cosmology.   I. Title.

NL 0352530   CaBVaU

XS3   Liepmann & Friedländer, complainant.
F1L71   Abdruck der gerichtlichen Verhandlungen in Sachen der Nachfolger der Handlung Liepmann & Friedländer in Hamburg, Kläger, Appellanten und Ober-Appelanten, gegen die Handlung Salomon Spiro, die beiden Söhne Levi Salomon und Beer Salomon Spiro, so wie gegen den Spiroischen Creditoren-Ausschuss, Beklagte, Appellanten, resp. Ober-Appellanten. Frankfurt a/M., Heller und Rohm, 1824.
69 p. 23 cm.
1. Germany - Frankfort on the Main. I. Spiro, Salomon, defendant.   II. ti.

                                        65

NL 0352531   OCH

ML97   Liepmannssohn, Leo, firm, booksellers, Berlin.
.L72   ⁅Auction catalogs of music and autographs
of musicians⁆

1. Music--Bibliography--Catalogs. 2. Musicians--Autographs.

NL 0352532   ICU

Liepmannssohn, Leo, firm, booksellers, Berlin.
... Autographen von musikern, schriftstellern, gelehrten, naturforschern, bildenden künstlern und historischen personlichkeiten, sowie von handschriftlichen und gedruckten tabulaturen. Versteigerung am 15. und 16. November 1929. Berlin, L. Liepmannssohn [1929]
3 p. l., 58 p. front. (port.) VIII plates facsims. (music) 27.5 cm. (Versteigerungskatalog 56).
1. Catalogues. Booksellers'. 2. Auctions. Book. 3. Music-Bibliography-Catalogs. 4. Autographs-Catalogs. 5. Musicians-Autographs.

NL 0352533   MB

Liepmannssohn, Leo, firm, booksellers, Berlin.
Autographen von Musikern, Schriftstellern, Gelehrten, Bildenden Künstlern, Schauspielern, historischen Persönlichkeiten und Naturforschern. Ausstellung den 6.–8. Dezember 1932 von 10–5 Uhr. Versteigerung, Freitag, den 9. Dezember 1932, vormittags 10 3/4 Uhr und nachmittags 4 Uhr ... Berlin, 1932.
56 p. ports., facsims. 28 cm. (At head of title: Versteigerungs-Katalog, 63).
1. Autographs. 2. Composers - Autographs. 3. Musicians - Autographs.

NL 0352534   NcD

Liepmannssohn, Leo, firm, booksellers, Berlin.
... Autographen. z. T. aus dem Besitz eines bekannten Sammlers im Auftrage von Leo Liepmannssohn ... Versteigert durch ... W. Haehnel. [Berlin, L. Liepmannssohn] 1921.
24 cm.
Cover title.
At head of title: 46. Autographen-Versteigerung.
Contents. - I. Musiker. - II. Historische Autographen. - III. Schriftsteller. - IV. Bildende Künstler.

NL 0352535   CtY

Liepmannssohn, Leo, firm, booksellers, Berlin.
Catalogue d'une collection remarquable d'ouvrages et de brochures, de gravures et de cartes relatifs à l'histoire de France (Histoire.-Topographie.-Linquistig [ ]. - Auteurs provinciaus [ ] etc. qui se trouvent en vente aux prix marques. P. 1872.
(No. 34.)

NL 0352536   MH

Liepmannssohn, Leo, firm, booksellers, Berlin.
Catalogue n°. 36 de la librairie ancienne et moderne de L. Liepmannssohn ... Voyages et autres ouvrages relatifs aux pays hors d'Europe.
[Paris. 187–?] 24 pp. 20½ cm.

N2127 — Catalogues. Booksellers'.

NL 0352537   MB

Liepmannssohn, Leo, firm, booksellers, Berlin.
... Deutsche Literatur von den frühesten Zeiten bis zur Gegenwart: Literaturdenkmäler und Portraits ... nebst einer wichtigen Abteilung, enthaltend musikalische Kompositionen deutscher Dichtungen. Berlin [19—?]
3 v. 21.5 cm.
Cover-title.
At head of title, 1.T.: Katalog 161; 2.T.: Katalog 164; 3.T.: 166.
Contents. - 1.T. A–H. - 2.T. I–P. - 3.T. Q–Z.

NL 0352538   CtY

ML97   Liepmannssohn, Leo, firm, booksellers, Berlin.
.L71   ...Katalog...
Berlin, [19–

NL 0352539   DLC CU MB

Liepmannssohn, Leo, firm, booksellers, Berlin.
Katalog der von... Carl Bernstein... hinterlassenen Büchersammlung enthaltend Werke der klassischen deutschen Literaturperiode...
see under Bernstein, Carl.

VOLUME 332

ML 152
L5 K3
Liepmannssohn, Leo, firm, booksellers, Berlin.
Katalog einer Autographen-Sammlung bestehend
aus wertvollen Musik-Manuskripten und Musiker-
Briefen aus den Nachlassen von Julius Stockhausen
und Wilhelm Taubert und des Musikverlegers
Maurice Schlesinger aus Paris (1798-1871) sowie
aus Autographen von Dichtern, Schriftstellern,
Schauspielern, Bildenden Künstlern, Fürsten,
Staatsmannern, Kriegsleuten und Reformatoren.
Versteigerung am 4. und 5. November 1907 durch
den vereideten und öffentlich angestellten
Versteigerer Werner Haehnel. Berlin [1907]

120 p. facsims. (incl. music) 25 cm. (Autographen-Versteigerung Nr. 37)

Cover title.

1. Music - Bibl. 2. Bibliography - Rare
books. 3. Catalogs, Booksellers' - Germany.

NL 0352542   OU MB

ML150
.L72
LIEPMANNSSOHN LEO, firm, booksellers, Berlin.
Musikbibliographie und Notation. Berlin
[n.d.]
43 p. illus. (Its Katalog 223)

1. Music--Bibliography--Catalogs.

NL 0352543   ICU NcU NcD

Liepmannssohn, Leo, firm, booksellers, Berlin.
... Musiker-autographen. Versteigerung am
8. März 1929. Berlin, L. Liepmannssohn [1929].
2 p. l., 32 p. 27 cm. (Versteigerungs-
katalog 53).
1. Catalogues. Booksellers'. 2. Auctions.
Book. 3. Music--Bibliography--Catalogs.
4. Autographs--Catalogs. 5. Musicians--Auto-
graphs.

NL 0352544   MB

Leipmannssohn, Leo, firm, booksellers, Berlin.
... Musiker-autographen, darunter viele eig-
enhändige musikmanuscripte. Berlin, L. Leipmannssohn [193-?]
1 p. l., 62 p. 23.5 cm. (Katalog 228).
1. Music--Bibliography--Catalogs. 2. Auto-
graphs--Catalogs. 3. Musicians--Autographs.
4. Catalogues. Booksellers'.

NL 0352545   MB

Liepmannssohn, Leo, firm, booksellers, Berlin.
Musiker-Biographien. Katalog 222. Berlin,
[ca. 1930]
125 p. 23 cm.
"Nachtrag zu den Abteilungen I und II": p. 121.
Contents.-I. Allgemeine Musiker-Biographie.-
II. Spezielle biographische Literatur.-III. Gesamtausgaben von Werken musikalischer Klassiker
und musikalische Serienwerken.
1. Music - Bibliography - Catalogs. 2. Composers - Bibliography. 3. Musicians - Bibliography. I. Title.

NL 0352546   NcD

Liepmannssohn, Leo, firm, booksellers, Berlin.
Musikgeschichte. Katalog 224 ... Berlin
[ca. 1932].
91 p. 23 cm.
Contents.-I. Musikgeschichte. Geschichte der
Oper und des Theaters. Allgemeine Biographie. -
II. Exotische Musik.-III. Gesamtausgaben von
Werken musikalischer Klassiker. Musikalische
Serienwerke.
1. Music - History and criticism - Bibliogra-
phy - Catalogs. I. Title.

NL 0352547   NcD ICU

Liepmannssohn, Leo, firm, booksellers, Berlin.
Musikliteratur. Katalog 234: Gesamtausgaben
von Werken musikalischer Klassiker, musikalische
Serienwerke und Musikzeitschriften, Neuausgaben
alter Musikwerke und Bibliotheksgewerke aus allen
Gebieten der Musikliteratur. Berlin [ca. 1934]
29 p. 23 cm.
1. Music - Bibliography - Catalogs. I. Title.

NL 0352548   NcD

Liepmannssohn, Leo, firm, booksellers, Berlin.
Musikmanuskripte Wolfgang Amadeus Mozarts,
aus dem Besitz von Andre Erben
See under Mozart, Wolfgang Amadeus, 1791-1844

Liepmannssohn, Leo, firm, booksellers, Berlin.
Opern, oratorien und grössere gesangswerke
in partituren; stimmenmaterial zu opern und
vokalwerken ... Berlin [1922?]
103 p. front., illus. (Katalog 185).

NL 0352550   IU

Liepmannssohn, Leo, firm, booksellers, Leipzig.
... Katalog 175 enthaltend eine anzahl seltener
älterer werke aus allen gebieten der musikliteratur vom 15. bie zum ende des 18. jahrhunderts
darunter eine kosthare sammlung gedruckter und
handschriftlicher lauten- und orgel-tabulaturen.
Berlin, L. Liepmannssohn [190-?]
66 p. illus. (facsims.) 8 plates. 24 cm.
1. Catalogs, booksellers'. 2. Music-Bibliography-Catalogs. 3. Autographs-Catalogs.
4. Musicians-Autographs-Catalogs.

NL 0352551   MB

Liepmannssohn, Leo, firm, booksellers, Berlin.
Katalog 185, [189, 192-193] [Berlin, L.
Liepmannssohn, 1919?]
4 v. in 1 20-23 cm.
Contents. - Katalog 185. Opern, Cratorien und
grössere Gesangswerke in Partituren. - Katalog
189, 192-193. Vokalmusik mit Klavier- oder
Orgelbegleitung.

NL 0352552   CtY

[Liepmannssohn, Leo], firm, booksellers, Berlin.
Literarische Autographehen: Schriftsteller,
Dichter, Gelehrte, Naturforscher. [Berlin, L.
Liepmannssohn, 1926].
42-56 numb. l. plate. 25.5 cm.
Caption-title.
Apparently proofsheets of p. 42-56 of a
catalogue.

NL 0352553   CtY

Xv73
L62
930
Liepmannssohn, Leo, firm, booksellers, Berlin.
... Seltenheiten aus allen Gebieten der Musikliteratur vom 14. bis zur Mitte des 19. Jahrhunderts, nebst einer Sammlung kostbarer Tabulaturen. Berlin, L.Liepmannssohn[1930?]
1p.l.,154p. 9 plates.incl.facsims. on 5l.
23cm.
Tafel 9, printed on recto of back cover.
At head of title: Katalog 221.

NL 0352554   CtY CSt

Liepmannssohn, Leo, firm, booksellers, Berlin.
... Spanische und portugiesische werke über musik,
liturgie, theater und tanz. Ouvrages espagnols et portugais, relatifs à la musique ... [Greifswald, H. Adler]
1900.
28 pp. 8°.
Cover-title.
Katalog 144.
Z6816.Z9L7   1-14437-M1

NL 0352555   DLC

Ka LIEPMANNSSOHN, Selig Louis
Des Gerechten Andenken...Predigt bei der
...Gedaechtnissfeier des...Dr. Israel Jacobsohn...Neukirchen, published by the author,
1829. 24 p. 17 cm.
P.21-24 "Der Christ im Jacobstempel zu
Seesen", poem by Augustin, Domprediger...
1.Jacobsohn, Israel. 2.Sermons-German.
3.Sermons-Memorial. 4.History-Germany-Seesen
5.Seesen School (See Sulamith,v.3,pt.1,no.
6)

NL 0352556   NNJ

Liepmannssohn, S[elig] L[ouis]
Israelitische Predigt-Bibliothek, nebst
Aufsaetzen über Cultus-Angelegenheiten... Im
Vereine mehrerer israelitischer Prediger...
Bd.1 Lippstadt:Lange,1842.
iv.

NL 0352557   OCH

Liepmannssohn, Selig Louis.
Rede zur confirmation, in dem Israelitischen
Tempel zu Bergholzhausen am 26. Juli 1823
gehelten. [Bergholzhausen,1823]
24p.

NL 0352558   OCH

Liepmannssohn, S[elig] L[ouis]
Trauungs-Reden, in der Synagoge zu Neukirchen
bei Rietberg gehalten. Samlg. 1. Muenster: the
author.,1836.
iv.

NL 0352559   OCH

Liepmannssohn, Selig Louis.
Volksbuch für Israeliten. Mit einem Portrait:
Moses Mendelssohn. Wesel, A. Prinz, 1841.
1 v. 12°.
1. Jahrgang.

NL 0352560   NN

VOLUME 332

Liepmannssohn, Selig Louis.
Welche Anforderungen hat man an ein gutes Lehrer-Seminar zu stellen? Vorlesung veranlasst durch die beabsichtigte Reorganisation des israelitischen Vereins zu Münster, gehalten im Kreise einiger befreundeten Lehrer ... von S. L. Liepmannssohn ... Horn bei Lippstadt, 1867.
15 p. 18 cm.

NL 0352561 CtY

Liepmannssohn & Dufour, firm, book dealers, Paris.
Catalogue d'une jolie collection de livres anciens et modernes et d'une série de journaux et pamphlets politiques, dont la vente aura lieu le mercredi 20 avril ... Paris, Liepmannssohn et Dufour, 1870.
28 p. 23 cm.
Volume of pamphlets.

NL 0352562 NNC

Liepmannssohn & Dufour, firm, book dealers, Paris.
Catalogue no. 29 d'une belle collection de livres anciens & modernes relatifs à la musique en vente aux prix marqués chez Liepmannssohn & Dufour... ₍Paris, 1869₎ 74 p. 21cm.

"En grande partie de la bibliothèque de...A. Choron."
Imperfect: t.-p. wanting; title from caption.

1. Music—Bibl.   Card revised
N. Y. P. L.   December 29, 1947

NL 0352563 NN

Liepsner, Frank Wright, 1880–   joint author.

Reed, John Byron, 1880–
... The by-products of rice-milling. By J. B. Reed ... and F. W. Liepsner ... Washington ₍Govt. print. off.₎ 1917.

LIEPUKAS.
Graudus Verksmai, arba Pasibudinimas prie Apmislijimo Lietuvos vargu. Philadelphia, Spauda "Kovos", 1909. 16 p. 17cm.

1. Jesus Christ --Passion--   Poetry. 2. Hymns,
Lithuanian. I. Title.

NL 0352565 NN

LIEPUKAS.
Kanticzkos apie peklos kanczias. Surašé Liepukas. Bitténai, Išdu ív. Valento brostvos, Spaudinta pas M. Janku, 1907. 40 p. 13cm.

1. Hymns, Lithuanian.   I. Title.

NL 0352566 NN

Liepukas.
Keplos kančios; eilės. Chicago, Ill.: "Lietuvos," 1909.
28 p. 12°.

1. Poetry (Lithuanian). 2. Title.
N. Y. P. L.
                        N. Y. PUBLIC LIBRARY   May 16, 1911.

NL 0352567 NN OCI

Lièpvre. Ordinances.
Coutumes du Val-de-Lièpvre, S^te. Croix et S^te. Marie-aux-Mines. De l'an 1586. Nancy: Thomas, père & fils, 1761. 42 p. 16°

1. Municipal charters and ordinances
—France. 3. Sainte-Croix. Ordi-   —France. 2. Law, Customary
Mines. Ordinances.   nances. 4. Sainte Marie-aux-
N. Y. P. L.
                                        August 25, 1926

NL 0352568 NN

Lier,   police sergeant.
... Saar basin. The case Lier. Geneva, 1923.
1 p. l., 3 numb. l. 33^cm.
Caption title.
At head of title: ... League of nations.
Official no.: C.647.1923.I.
Mimeographed.
Petition dated Aug. 31, 1923 from M. Lier to the Council of the League of nations requesting to be reinstated in the police force, and observations dated Sept. 17, 1923 from the chairman of the Governing commission to the Secretary-general of the League of nations.

1. Police — Saar valley. 2. Saar valley — ₍Officials and employees₎
I. Saar (Territory) Regierungskommission. II. League of nations.

Woodrow Wilson memorial   library
for Library of Congress   ₍2₎

NL 0352569 NNUN-W

Lier, A   H   H   van.
Mijnen en mensen in Spanje; de praktijk van het national-syndicalisme. Utrecht, Dekker & Van de Vegt, 1953.
392 p. plates, maps (1 fold.) diagrs., tables. 25 cm.

Issued also as thesis, Amsterdam.
Part of illustrative matter in pocket.
Summary and conclusions in English.
Includes bibliographies.

1. Mining industry and finance—Spain. 2. Miners—Spain.
I. Title.
HD9506.S7L5 1953   55–42809

NL 0352570 DLC

Lier, A   H   H   van.
Spanje, een land van tegenstellingen. Meppel, J. A. Boom, 1952.
344 p. illus. 24 cm. (Terra-bibliotheek, 10)
Includes bibliography.

1. Spain—Civilization.
DP17.L5   54–28960 ‡

NL 0352571 DLC ICU TxU NN

Lier, A   J   S   van.
De fundatie van de Vrijvrouwe van Renswoude, binnen de stad Utrecht, overzicht van twee eeuwen geschiedenis 1754, 26 April, 1954. Utrecht, W. de Haan, 1954.
230 p. illus. 25 cm.

1. Utrecht. Ambachtskinderhuis.   I. Title.
HV777.U8L5   55–31096 ‡

NL 0352572 DLC MH NN

LIER, Adolf Leonhard.

See LIER, Leonhard, 1864–

Lier, Bernard Louis Philip van, 1871–
Invloed van de verwerping eener erfenis op de legitime ... door Bernard Louis Philip van Lier ... Amersfoort, J. Valkhoff, 1894.
74 p. 21½^cm.
Proefschrift—Utrecht.
"Stellingen": p. ₍67₎–74.

1. Inheritance and succession—Netherlands.   I. Title.
                                        34–25422

NL 0352574 DLC MB

Lier, Bertus van, 1906–
Buiten demaatstreep. Amsterdam, G. A. van Oorschot, 1948.
173 p. plates, ports., facsim., music. 21 cm.
"Errata": slip inserted.

1. Music—Addresses, essays, lectures.   I. Title.
ML60.L43   50–31050

NL 0352575 DLC NN ICU CtY NjR

M2003   Lier, Bertus van, 1906–
.L53   ₍The Holy song. Piano-vocal score. English
H6   & Dutch₎
1949a   The Holy song (The song of songs) Het
          hooglied, for three solo voices, chamber
          choir, chamber orchestra. Vocal score by
          Marius Flothuis. ₍Amsterdam, Donemus, c1949₎
          85p. 32 x 32cm. (Donemus audio-visual
          series, 1967, no.1)
          Reprinted from original edition, 2 score
          pages to the page.
          Program   notes in Dutch & English

NL 0352576 NcU

LIER, BERTUS VAN, 1906–
Kleine suite, voor viool en piano [1935] Amsterdam, Broekmans & Van Poppel [193–] Pl. no. 7281. 1 v. 34cm.

Score: violin and piano (15 p.) and part.

1. Suites (Violin and piano).   I. Title.

NL 0352577 NN

M786.41   Lier, Bertus van, 1906–
L719s2   ₍Sonatina, piano, no.2₎
Music   Sonatina nr. 2 for piano. Amsterdam,
lib.   Donemus; New York, C. F. Peters Corporation
           c^c1948₎
           9p. 31cm.

           Cover title.

NL 0352578 NcU

Lier, Bertus van, 1906–
₍Quartet, 2 violins, viola & vlc., no. 1₎
...Strijkkwartet no. 1 ₍1928–29₎... ₍Amsterdam, Donemus, c1949₎ Pl.no. BIII 2. 18 p. 23cm.
Miniature score.

1. Chamber music, 20th cent.—   Quartets. 2. Violin in quartets (2
violins, viola, violoncello).

NL 0352579 NN

VOLUME 332

M1001 Lier, Bertus van, 1906-
L54   [Symphony, no. 2]
no.2   2e [i.e. tweedie] symphonie (1930)
          Amsterdam, Donemus, c1948.
          miniature score (76 p.)

          Reproduced from holograph.

          1. Symphonies.

NL 0352580   WaU NN MH

LIER, Bruno, 1878-
Ad topica carminum amatoriorum symbolae:
Progr. Stettin, Druck von Herrcke & Lebeling,
1914.

          pp. 56 †.

NL 0352581   MH NjP

Lier, Bruno, 1878-
          Topica carminum sepulcralium latinorum ... Tubin-
gae, ex officina H. Laupp, jr., 1902.
          30, [2] p. 21cm.
          Inaug.-diss.—Greifswald.
          Vita.

          Library of Congress   5-31961

NL 0352582   DLC ICRL NjP NIC PU NN

RA   Lier, E
781   Turnspiele für Deutschlands Jugend. Zum
L71   Gebrauch für Volks- und Bürgerschulen, sowie
1885   für höhere Lehranstalten... 2. Aufl. Mit
          zahlreichen in den Text gedruckten Abbildungen.
          Langensalza, Schulbuchhandlung von F. G. L.
          Gressler, 1885.
          viii, 96 p. illus. 19cm.

          1. Gymnastics. 2. Games. 3. Schools—
Exercises and   recreations.

NL 0352583   NIC

Lier, Eduard Henri Benjamin van.
Over de interfibrillaire stof in de lederhuid bij
zoogdieren. Utrecht, 1909.
In. Diss.

NL 0352584   ICRL PU MiU MH

Lier, Eduard Sigismund Jacob van.
          The ionic theory of excitability. Utrecht, 1955.
          154 p. illus. 25 cm.
          Proefschrift—Leyden.
          "Stellingen" ([2] l.) inserted.
          Bibliography: p. 148-151.

          1. Excitation (Physiology)   I. Title.

          QP341.L48   64-41617

NL 0352585   DLC CtY DNLM MiU

Lier, Ernst.
Die behandlung der knieschusswunden im felde.
Inaug. diss. JEna, 1884 (Chemnitz)
Bibl.

NL 0352586   ICRL DNLM MH

Lier (E[rnst] Heinrich]). Die Haut als Vermit-
tler der Erkältungskrankheiten. 31 pp. 8º.
Hamburg & Leipzig, L. Voss, 1887.
Repr. from: Monatsh. f. prakt. Dermat., Hamb. 1887, vi.

NL 0352587   DNLM NNC

Lier, Evald.
          Glada värmlandshistorier; skisser och historier från
Värmlands gränsbygd. Stockholm, Wahlström & Wid-
strand [1955]
          129 p. illus. 23 cm.

          1. Tales, Swedish—Värmland.   I. Title.

                                              A 56-2422

Minnesota. Univ. Libr.
for Library of Congress   [8]

NL 0352588   MnU

W 6   LIER, Franciscus Abrahamus van.
P3   Positiones physico-medicae inaugurales, de
v.1932 aëre, aquis, locis et incolis regionis
no.3   Drenthiae, eorumque diaeta, moribus, sanitate
          et morbis ... Lugduni Batavorum, Apud Jacobum
          Douzy, 1784.
          11 p. 24 cm.
          Diss. - Leyden.

NL 0352589   DNLM

Lier, Frank George.
          A comparison of the three-dimensional shapes
of cork cambium and cork cells in the stem of
Pelargonium hortorum Bailey. 1952.
          312-328, 371-392 p. diagrs., tables. 25cm.

          Thesis, Columbia university.
          Two articles reprinted from Bulletin of the
Torrey botanical club, vol. 79, no. 4, July,
1952 and no. 5, September, 1952.
          Bibliography: p. 391-392.

NL 0352590   NNC

f
MT 268   Lier, Fritz.
.L72   Grundübungen für die linke Hand
          des Geigers. Preliminary exercises for
the left hand. Wilhelmshaven,
Heinrichshofen [n.d.]
          8 p.
          Caption title:
Geminiani-Campagnoli-Griffe.

          1. Violin—Studies and exercises. I.
Geminiani, Francesco, 1687-1762. II.
Campagnoli, Bartolomeo, 1751-1827. III.
Title. IV. Title: Preliminary exercises
for the left hand.

NL 0352591   ICU

Lier, Gustaaf Adolf van.
          Die durchlässigkeit der rothen blutkörperchen für die
anionen von natriumsalzen ... [Utrecht, Stoomsnelpers-
drukkerij L. E. Bosch en zoon] 1901.
          98 p. 23½ cm.
          Inaug.-diss.—Bern.

          1. Erythrocytes.

          QP91.L71   7—21892

NL 0352592   DLC DNLM

LIER, H.   A.
          Der augsburgische humanistenkreis mit beson-
derer berücksichtigung Bernhard Adelmann's von
Adelmannsfelden. Augsburg, 1880.

          pp. 68-108.
          From the Zeitschrift des historischen vereins
für Schwaben und Neuburg.

NL 0352593   MH

Lier (Hans). *Die funktionelle Prognose der
offenen und subkutanen Sehnenverletzungen
der Finger und der Hand. [Zürich.] 18 pp.
8º. *München*, J. F. Bergmann, Berlin, J.
Springer, 1921.

NL 0352594   DNLM ICRL CtY

TP248 Lier, Hein.
.C4L7   Het caseinesol ... Amsterdam, H. J. Paris, 1924.
          [8], 119, [3] p. tables (part fold.) diagrs. 23½ᶜᵐ.
          Proefschrift—Utrecht.

          1. Casein.

NL 0352595   ICU CtY ICRL MH

Lier, Heinrich.
          Le chauffage et la ventilation, par Henri Lier [et] Henri
Liebetrau. Lausanne, F. Rouge, 1943.
          24 p. illus. 29 cm. (Contributions à l'étude de la création de
possibilités de travail. Questions techniques, no 4)
          At head of title: La construction en temps de guerre.

          1. Heating. 2. Ventilation.   I. Liebetrau, Heinrich, joint author.
(Series)
          TH7226.L513   697   48-42902*

NL 0352596   DLC

Lier, Heinrich.
          ... Heizung und lüftung, von Hch. Lier ... [und] Hch. Liebe-
trau ... Zürich, Polygraphischer verlag a.-g. [1943]
          24 p. diagrs. 29½ᶜᵐ. (Schriftenreihe zur frage der arbeitsbeschaffung
... Bautechnische reihe, nr. 4)
          At head of title: ... Bauen in kriegszeiten.

          1. Heating. 2. Ventilation.   I. Liebetrau, Heinrich, joint author.
                                              46-12743
          Library of Congress   TH7226.L5
                                              697

NL 0352597   DLC

Lier, Heinrich, 1901-
          Zur kenntnis der saponine. Ueber das sapogenin
der weissen seifenwurzel, (Gypsophila-Sapogenin).
Inaug. diss. Zuerich, 1927.

NL 0352598   ICRL CtY

284.2492   Lier, Helperus Ritzema van, 1764-1793.
Z47l   The power of grace illustrated in six
          letters from a minister of the Reformed Church
          to John Newton, rector of St. Mary Woolnoth,
          London. Tr. from the original Latin by
          William Cowper. Edinburgh, Printed by H.
          Inglis for Campbell and Wallace, 1792.
          xv, 195 p. 16 cm.
          Letters signed: Christodulus.

          I. Cowper,   William, 1731-1800, tr.
          II. Newton,   John, 1725-1807. III.
Title.

NL 0352599   N NjP PPPrHi

VOLUME 332

Ex
3693
.7
.789

₍Lier, Helperus Ritzema van₎ b.1764-1793.
The power of grace illustrated in six letters, from a minister of the Reformed church to John Newton. Translated from the original Latin by William Cowper. London, Printed for J. Johnson, 1792.
179 p. 17 cm.

1.Newton, John, 1725-1803. I.Cowper, William, 1731-1800, trans. II.Title.

NL 0352600   NjP CSmH MWA MiU-C TxU MH NIC InU CtY

₍Lier, Helperus Ritzema van ₎ 1764-1793.
The Power of Grace illustrated, in Six Letters from a minister of the Reformed Church to John Newton, Rector of St. Mary Woolnoth, London. ... Translated from the original Latin by William Cowper, of the Inner Temple, Esq. ... ...Philadelphia: Printed by Neale and Kammerer, Jun. ... 1796.
142 p.

NL 0352601   NjP PSC MH PHi MWA MiU-C

*NC7
L6254
784v

Lier, Helperus Ritzema van, 1764-1793.
Verhandeling over het algemeen en byzonder gebruik der aërostatische machine, en de verschynselen, die dezelve ons kunnen opleveren. Door Helperus Ritzema van Lier ...
Te Groningen, By Lubbartus Huisingh, boekverkoper aan de Breede Markt.1784.
8°. 2p.l.,128p. 22.5cm.
Original printed wrappers preserved; bound in half green morocco.

NL 0352602   MH

Lier, Hendrik Willem van.
Over de parhaemoglobinaemieen. ₍On parahemoglobinemia₎ Utrecht, Zuidam, 1933.
102p.
Proefschrift--Groningen

NL 0352603   ICRL OU

Lier, Henri Jacobus Duparc Van
see   Duparc Van Lier, Henri Jacobus.

Lier, Hermann Arthur, 1837-1914.
Seidlitz, Woldemar von, 1850-1922.
Allgemeines historisches porträtwerk. Eine sammlung von 600 porträts der berühmtesten personen aller völker und stände seit 1300, nach auswahl von dr. Woldemar von Seidlitz, mit biographischen daten ... München, Verlagsanstalt für kunst und wissenschaft, vormals F. Bruckmann, 1884-90.

Lier, Hermanus Hubertus van.
Ndy30
S8
953L
Mijnen en mensen in Spanje; de praktijk van het nationaal-syndicalisme. Utrecht₍1953₎
392p. illus.,maps(part.fold.,part col.) charts,tables. 24cm.
Part of illustrative matter in pocket.
Academisch proefschrift - Amsterdam.
Summary and conclusions in English: p.379-384.
Stellingen: 2ℓ. inserted.
Bibliography: p.385-392.

NL 0352606   CtY NNC MH NN

Lier, Isaäcus van.
* De dentitione sana et morbosa. [Utrecht.] Amstelodami, typ. van Embden et socii [1828]. viii, 120 p. 8°.

NL 0352607   DNLM

₍Lier, Isidore Charles van,₎ 1833-1877.
Het ministerie en de materiële belangen van Nederland in het algemeen en bijzonder van de hoofdstad, door Ij en Amstel ₍pseud.₎. Amsterdam: J. Visser, 1858. 60 p. 8°.

1. Economic history, Netherlands.   2. Industry and state, Netherlands.
3. Economic history, Netherlands: Amsterdam.
N. Y. P. L.   August 31, 1917.

NL 0352608   NN

Lier, Isidore Charles van, 1833-1877, ed.
Lipman, Samuel Philippus, 1802-1871, ed.
Nederlandsch constitutioneel archief van alle koninklijke aanspraken en parlementaire adressen, enz. Verzameld en uitgegeven door mr. S. P. Lipman. Amsterdam, J. C. van Kesteren en A. Zweesaardt en zoon, 1846-64.

₍Lier, Isidore Charles van,₎ 1838-1877.
De tariefsherziening. Een ernstig woord aan onze kamers van koophandel en fabrieken, industriëlen en handelaren, door Ij en Amstel ₍pseud.₎. Amsterdam: J. Visser, 1860. 2 p.l., 90, 35 p. 8°.

1. Tariff, Netherlands. 2. Title.
N. Y. P. L.   September 6, 1917.

NL 0352610   NN

Lier (Jacob). Verhandeling over de Brightsche nierziekte. 87 pp. 8°. *Utrecht, J. van Boekhoren.* 1865.

NL 0352611   DNLM

PG5020
.K15
v.9,
etc.

Lier, Jan, 1852-1916.
Feuilletony. V Praze, Nákl. F. Šimáčka, 1885-1889.
3 v. (Kabinetní knihovna, sv. 9, 33, 40)

NL 0352612   ICU OCl

PG5038
.L5N6
1883

Lier, Jan, 1852-1916.
Novely. V Praze, J. Otto, 1883-1886.
v. 18 cm. (Salonní bibliotéka, čís. 26,42, 45)

NL 0352613   MB OCl CU NN

Lier, Jan, 1852-1916.
...Pokuta. Praha: J. R. Vilímek₍, 1902₎. 131 p. 16°.
(Vilímkova knihovna.)

192486A. 1. Fiction, Bohemian.   2. Title.
N. Y. P. L.   July 21, 1926.

NL 0352614   NN

398.3
D656t

Lier, Jan, 1852-1916.
Roman Lutnových; novela. V Praze, Nákl. České grafické akc. společnosti "Unie," 1919. 119p. 18cm. (His Sebrané spisy, sv.1)

1091996   I. Lier, Jan, 1852-1916. Sebrane spisy, sv.1. II. Title.

NL 0352615   TxU

Lier, Jan, 1852-1916.
S ptačí perspektivy, novely, napsal Jan Lier ... V Praze, Nákl. České grafické unie a. s., 1920.
152 p., 1 l. 19ᶜᵐ. (Added t.-p.: Sebrané spisy Jana Liera, vydává dr. Václav Brtník. Sv. 4)
CONTENTS.—Numerus clausus v Čermné.—Kroesus.—Falešný prorok. Pamětní deska.—Můj přítel Gerson.

I. Title.
Library of Congress   PG5038.L5S2   45-48072

NL 0352616   DLC OCl

PG 5038
.L5
1919

LIER, JAN, 1852-1916.
Sebrané spisy. Vyd. Václav Brtník. V Praze, Nákl. České grafické unie a.s., 1919-
v.
Contents:

NL 0352617   InU DLC

Lier, Jan, 1852-1916.
Vidiny a pravda, novely napsal Jan Lier ... V Praze, Nákl. Česke grafické akc. společnosti "Unie," 1919.
228 p. 19ᶜᵐ. (Added t.-p.: Sebrané spisy Jana Liera, vydáva dr. Václav Brtník. sv. 2)
"Vydání lišt od prvního časopiseckého tisku."—Pref., p. 5.
CONTENTS.—Kvas.—Hero a Leander.—V pohnuté době.

I. Brtník, Václav, 1895-   ed. II. Title.
Library of Congress   PG5038.L5V5   44-14984

NL 0352618   DLC

LIER, Jan Nicolaas.
Thoriumspectra en hun Zeeman-effect. Amsterdam, N.V.Noord-Hollandsche Uitgevers Maatschappij,1939.
24 cm.
Academisch proefschrift - Amsterdam.
"Stellingen" inserted.

NL 0352619   MH CtY

Lier, Jan van, 1751-
De kolonisten, or, Bijzondere leidingen der goddelijke voorzienigheid omtrent twee jonge vrienden, Jan van Lier en Gerrit Noorddijk
see under title

VOLUME 332

GN796 **.N4L7** Lier, Jan van, fl. 1760-1785.
Oudheidkundige brieven, bevattende eene verhandeling over de manier van begraven, en over
de lykbusschen, wapenen, veld- en eertekens, der
oude Germanen, en in het byzonder de beschryving
van eenen alouden steenen grafkelder ... by het
boerschap Eext, in het landschap Drenthe, ont-
dekt ... Uitgegeeven en met een voorreden en
aantekeningen vermeerderd door A. Vosmaer. 's-
Gravenhage, P. van Thol, 1760.
xix, 206 p. 5 fold. plates.

1. Mounds--Netherlands--Drenthe. 2. German
antiquities.

NL 0352621   ICU

QL **666** **.06** **L72** Lier, Jan van, fl. 1760-1785.
Verhandeling over de slangen en adders die
in het landschap Drenthe gevonden worden. Met
byvoeging van eenige aanmerkingen en
byzonderheden, tot deze en andere slangsoorten
betrekkelyk ... Amsterdam, Uitg. by de Erven
Houtuin en L. Huising, 1, 1781.
3 p.l., 372 p., 1 l. 3 col. plates. 27 cm.
Added t.-p. engraved, with portrait of author
incorporated in colored border; Verhandeling
over de Drentsche slangen en adders.
Title also in French; text in Dutch and
French in parallel columns.
1. Squamata--Netherlands--Drenthe.

NL 0352622   MiU MH CU

Lier, Joannes Henricus Petrus van.
... De jure venti ... submittit Joannes
Henricus Petrus van Lier ... Groningae,
L. Huisingh, 1781.

2 p.l., 33 p., 1 l. 23cm.

Diss.- Groningen.

NL 0352623   MH-L

RC524 **L54** **1916** LIER, Johan Leon van.
De seniele paranoia. Amsterdam, H.G.
Van Dorssen, 1916.
149p. 25cm.
Proefschrift - Leyden.
"Stellingen": [4]p., inserted.
Bibliography: p. [146]-149.
acc. no. 7765 cat. " LC " SG ...

1. Senile psychosis 2. Paranoia I.
Title Prov. Dusser de Barenne, Joannes
Gregorius, 18 85-1940

NL 0352624   CtY-M PPC DNLM

Lier, Johann Jacob, resp.
... De speciali jvris fevdalis altero ivs
domini in fevdvm et vasallvm nvnc explicante ...
see under Hildebrand, Heinrich,
1668-1729, praeses.

Lier, Juan Carlos.
El pasajero de medianoche. Portada de Ricardo Warecki.
Rosario ¡Editorial "Las Provincias"¡ 1949.
168 p. 20 cm.

I. Title.

A 52–468

New York. Public Libr.
for Library of Congress ¡1¡

NL 0352626   NN

LIER, K. [U.]   *Ein kasuistischer Beitrag
zur Frage der chronischen Form der Wilson-
Broeq'schen Erkrankung   [Halle-Wittenberg]
19p.   8:   Bleicherode-H., 1935.

NL 0352627   DNLM CtY

WM **L723o** **1902** LIER, L   van, *1851-1917.*
Oefeningen bij het hygiënisch
spreken en bij het stamelen.
's-Gravenhage, Ykema, 1902.
111 p.

NL 0352628   DNLM

Lier, L. van, *1851-1917.*
Oefeningen voor stotteraars. 100 pp.
8°. 's-Gravenhage, J. Ykema, 1902.

NL 0352629   DNLM

Lier, L. van, 1851-1917.
Oefeningen voor stotterende kinderen, door L. Van
Lier ... Utrecht, W. Leijdenroth van Boekhoven, 1912.
119 p. illus. 22½cm.
Illus. t.-p.

1. Stammering.

E 13–362

Library, U. S. Bur. of   Education RC424.V2

NL 0352630   DHEW ICJ

Lier, L   van, *1851-1917.*
Spreken en spraakgebreken (hygiënisch spreken — stotteren —
114900 stamelen), door L. van Lier, ... 's-Gravenhage, J. Ykema,
1902.
95, viii p. diagrs. 20cm.
———. Oefeningen woor stotteraars, door L. van Lier, ...
's-Gravenhage, 1902.
64 p. illus. 20cm.
———. Oefeningen bij het hygiënisch spreken en bij het stamelen, door L. van Lier, ... 's-Gravenhage, 1902.
111 p. 20cm.
Bound together.

NL 0352631   ICJ DNLM

Lier, L   van, 1851-1917.
Voor slecht sprekenden en spraakgebrekkigen.
s'Gravenhage, C. Brouver [1905].
82 p. 8°.
For biography see Ziekenhuis, Amst., 1917,
viii, 17 (J. Kuiper).

NL 0352632   DNLM

LIER, Leonhard, 1864-
Studien zur geschichte des Nürnberger fast-
nachtspiels. i. Inaug.-diss., Leipzig. Nürnberg, 1889.

pp. (2), 74 +
Life, after p. 74.
Contents:-i. Das Nürnberger fastnachtspiel
bis zu Hans Sachs.-Von Hans Sachs bis zu J.
Ayrer.

NL 0352633   MH NIC ICU OCU NjP OCl OClW ICRL

Lier, Lion van.
Vergiffenis. Oorspronkelijk tooneelspel in
een bedrijf, door Lion van Lier ... Amsterdam,
G.T. Bom, 1876.
68 p. 17½cm.
"Bekroond op den Internationalen wedstrijd van tooneellet-
terkunde, uitgeschreven door de Provinciale tooneel-
commissie te Antwerpen, en aldaar gehouden in September
1874."
No.4 in a made-up volume of plays published independ-
ently, with collective title, Nederlandsche tooneelstuk-
ken, in manuscript on cover.
I. Title.

NL 0352634   MiU

Lier, Marianne, 1910-
Das bäuerliche anerbenrecht nach der
gesetzgebung der deutschen länder in der
zweiten hälfte des 19. jahrhunderts. ...
Halle, 1935.
Inaug. Diss. - Halle-Wittenberg, 1935.
Lebenslauf.
Verzeichnis des verwendeten schrifttums.

NL 0352635   ICRL CtY

DP44 **L7** Lier, Mauritius van.
Specimen antiquarium inaugurale de inscriptionibus salpen-
sana et malacitana ...   Traiecti ad Rhenum, typis I. van
Boekhoven, 1865.
xii, 125, [1], xxi p.   2 fold. tables.   25cm.
Proefschrift—Utrecht.

1. Inscriptions, Latin—Spain.

NL 0352636   ICU MH ICRL NjP

W 6 **P3** LIER, N   Ez. van.
Eenige woorden aangaande de nieuwe
bijdragen tot de Bestrijding der vaccine,
van Dr. Abraham Capadose. Amsterdam,
Tetroode, 1824.
24 p.
1. Capadose, Abraham, 1795-1874.
Bestrijding vaccine

NL 0352637   DNLM

WC **588** **L719k** **1824** LIER, N   Ez. van.
Kritische aanmerkingen op de Bestrij-
ding der vaccine van Dr. Abraham
Capadose. Amsterdam, Tetroode, 1824.
128 p.

NL 0352638   DNLM

Lier, Nathan E. F. van.
* De vi vitali in universum, speciatim vero de
vitalitate sanguinis. Lovanii, typ. vid. J.
Meyer [1819].
93 p. 4°.

NL 0352639   DNLM

Lier, Otto, 1885-
Über Flächenscharen, die durch Berührungstransformation
in Kurvenscharen überführbar sind.   Berlin: R. Trenkel, 1909.
2 p.l., 69(1) p., 1 l.   8°.

Doctoral dissertation, Greifswald.
Gift of Carnegie Institution of Washington.

1. Surfaces.—Transformation of.   2. Surfaces (Curved).
N.Y.P.L.   N. Y. PUBLIC LIBRARY   January 3, 1911.

NL 0352640   NN RPB IU ICRL

VOLUME 332

Lier (Paul) [1894–   ]. *Etude sur les formes
douloureuses de la tuberculose rénale. [Paris.]
59 pp. 8°. Toulouse, 1921, No. 198.

NL 0352641   DNLM CtY

Z1207
L5   Lier, R., & Co., booksellers, Florence.
     Early Americana, geography & voyages, natural and physical
     sciences.   Milano, R. Lier & Co., 1923.
     67 p.   26cm.   (Its Catalogue, 3)
     Cover title.

NL 0352642   CU-B

Lier, R., & co., booksellers, Florence.
     Early medical books.   Firenze, 1923-32.
     12 v. in 1.   illus.

NL 0352643   ICJ KU-M MH-A CSmH

Lier, R., & co., booksellers, Florence.
     Unique collection of editiones principes of works of Galileo
Galilei, offered for sale by R. Lier & c°. ... Firenze ... [Fi-
renze, Tip. B. Coppini & c., 1931]
     2 p. l., 24 p., 2 l.   illus. (facsims.)   iv pl. on 2 l.   25½ᶜᵐ.
     Prices: leaf 2, at end.

     1. Galilei, Galileo, 1564–1642—Bibl.

Library of Congress   Z8321.Z9L7   31-21111
                                               012

NL 0352644   DLC CtY ICJ

Lier, R., & co., booksellers, Florence.
     ... William Harvey 1628-1928.   Florence, R.
Lier & c°. [1928]
     16 p. incl. port., facsim.   32ᶜᵐ.
     "List II. 1928".
     Foreword signed: Stephen d'Irsay.
     "Last acquisition" slip attached to p. 3.
     CONTENTS.--I. Works by Harvey.--II. Works on Harvey.
--[III] Portraits.

     1. Harvey, William, 1578-1657--Bibl.   I. Irsay, Stephen
d', 1894-1934.

NL 0352645   MiU NIC CtY-M OCl

Z6676
L62
1953   Lier, R. A. T., firm, booksellers, Florence.
     Old medicine and science.   Firenze, 1953.
     38 p.   (Its Catalogue 24)

     1. Catalogs, Booksellers' - Italy. 2. Medi-
cine - Early works - Bibliography. 3. Medicine
- Bibliography - Catalogs. 4. Science - Bibliography - Catalogs.

NL 0352646   NNC-M

Lier, Richard, 1900-
     ... Die Ansichten über die Entstehung der
Ganglien und ihre Behandlung ...   Eisleben,
1927.
     Inaug.-Diss. - Halle-Wittenberg.
     Lebenslauf.
     "Literaturverzeichnis": p. [30].

NL 0352647   CtY MiU

LIER, RUDIE VAN.
     Præhistorie; proza.   ['s-Gravenhage] 't Verguld
blazoen [1946]   109 p.   19cm.   (Het Zwarte lam)

     "Uitgegeven in 300 exemplaren."

     1. Dutch literature--   Misc.   I. Het Zwarte
lam. II. Title.

NL 0352648   NN CtY

GN 2
.A56   LIER, RUDOLF ASVEER JACOB VAN, 1914-
no.37   The development and nature of society in the
     West Indies.   [Amsterdam] 1950.
     10 p.   (Koninklijk Instituut voor de Tropen
     --Afdeling Culturele en Physische Anthropologie.
     [Mededelingen] no. 37

          Koninklijk Instituut voor de Tropen.   [Me-
     dedelingen] no. 92)

     1. Surinam--Social conditions. I. Title. Ser.

NL 0352649   InU NN FU NcD

Wason   Lier, Rudolf Asveer Jacob van, 1914-
GN2   The development and nature of society
A52   in the West Indies.   [Amsterdam]
no. 37   Indisch Instituut, 1950.
               19,4 p.   23cm.   (Koninklijke
           Vereeniging Indisch Instituut, Amsterdam.
           Mededeling no. XCII. Afdeling Culturele
           en Physische Anthropologie no. 37.
           (voorheen Afd. Volkenkunde))

NL 0352650   NIC CaBVaU NN

Lier, Rudolf Asveer Jacob van, 1914–
     Ontwikkeling en karakter van de Westindische maat-
schappij.   's-Gravenhage, M. Nijhoff, 1950.
     38 p.   23 cm.
     Rede—Leyden (aanvaarding van het ambt van buitengewoon hoog-
leraar in de sociologie en de cultuurkunde van Suriname en de Nederlandse Antillen) 1950.
     Bibliographical references included in "Aantekeningen" (p. [37]-
38)

     1. Dutch Guiana—Soc. condit.

HN321.D8L48   309.188   51-15106 rev

NL 0352651   DLC NN IEN ICU NSyU

Lier, Rudolf Asveer Jacob van, 1914–
     Samenleving in een grensgebied, een sociaal-historische
studie van de maatschappij in Suriname.   's-Gravenhage,
Nijhoff, 1949.
     425 p.   25 cm.
     Bibliography: p. [389]-396.

     1. Dutch Guiana—Soc. condit.   I. Title.

HN321.D8L5   50-18458 rev

NL 0352652   DLC ICU NN MB CtY NNC IEN PU TxU CU

Wason   Lier, Rudolf Jacob van, 1876-
TN113   Die mijnbouw in Nederlandsch-Indië.
D9L71   Amsterdam, Koloniaal Instituut, 1918.
               58 p.   illus.   map.   22cm.

     1. Mines and mineral resources--Indonesia
I. Title.

NL 0352653   NIC NN

WB
53835   Lier, Rudolf Jacob van, 1876-
     De steenkolenindustrie.   Haarlem,
H. D. Tjeenk Willink, 1917.
     87 p.   illus.   (Onze koloniale mijnbouw, 3)

     1. Coal mines and mining - Indonesia.
I. Ser.
cdu   sa

NL 0352654   CtY NIC NN

Lier, S. A. E. van, comp.

Belgium.   (Territory under German occupation, 1914–1918)
     Laws, statutes, etc.   German legislation for the occupied
     territories of Belgium.   (Indexes)
     ... Index to series xiv-xvii.   Flanders: 3 January 1918-
9 November 1918 (nrs. 1-101)   Walloon: 3 January 1918-5 November 1918 (nrs. 1-88)   The Hague, M. Nijhoff, 1919.

LIER, Salomo Jacobus van.
     De conditione resolutoria, secundum codicem
legum civilium....   Trajecti ad Roenum, n.d.

     (4)+62+(2) p.
     Inaug.-diss. --- Utrecht, 1828.

NL 0352656   MH-L

Judaica   Lier, Sebastian, 1690?-1742.
Mc16   Dissertatio philologica de proselytis
3   Judaeorum ...   Hafniae, Typis Joh. Georg.
2   Höpfneri[1720]
            [10]p.   19cm.   [Dissert. jud. historiae]
            Diss. - Copenhagen (Janus Storm, respon-
            dent)

     I. Storm, Jens, 1802-1768, respondent.

NL 0352657   CtY

Lier, Sigismund Karel Dorotheus Maurits van.
     Doorhaling van voogdij-hypotheek ...   Utrecht, J. van
Boekhoven, 1890.
     5 p. l., 103 p.   23ᶜᵐ.
     Proefschrift—Utrecht.

     1. Guardian and ward—Netherlands. 2. Mortgages—Netherlands.
I. Title.

                                               27-21972
Library of Congress

NL 0352658   DLC MH MB

HN87
.C3L44   Lier, Th   J   A   M   van.
     De sociale boodschap der pauselijke encyclieken.   Den
Haag, Albani [1949]
     231 p.   19 cm.   (De Volkspaedagogische bibliotheek, 15)
     "Literatuurlijst": p. 229-231.

     1. Church and social problems—Catholic church. 2. Encyclicals,
Papal.   (Series)

                                               A 50-4131
Harvard Univ. Library
for Library of Congress   [1]

NL 0352659   MH DLC OU DCU CtY

VOLUME 332

Lier, Th   van, *ed.*
De Arbeidsbemiddelingswet 1930 en hare uitvoering, **door** Th. van Lier ... met een inleiding van Anth. Folmer ... Alphen aan den Rijn, N. Samson n. v., 1932.
xiii, 242 p. 25^{cm}.

1. Employment agencies—Netherlands. 2. Labor laws and legislation—Netherlands. I. Netherlands (Kingdom, 1815–   ) Laws, statutes, etc. II. Title.

Library of Congress   HD5942.L5
                                        41-25900

NL 0352660   DLC NN

Lier, Th   van.
Maatregelen tot beperking van den arbeid en de bevoegdheden van vreemdelingen, door Th. van Lier ... met een voorwoord van Ir. R. A. Verweij ... Alphen aan den Rijn, N. Samson n. v., 1934.
xvi, 241 p. 25^{cm}.

1. Aliens—Netherlands. 2. Labor laws and legislation—Netherlands. I. Title.

Library of Congress   JX4270.N4L5
                                        41-27370

NL 0352661   DLC

Lier, Th. van.
De sociaal-economische beteekenis van het Nederlandsch-Belgisch verdrag, door Th. van Lier.   Roermond: J. J. Romen & Zonen, 1926. 124 p. incl. tables. 8°.

1. Belgium—For. rel.—Netherlands. 2. Netherlands—For. rel.—Belgium. 3. Belgium—Economic rel.—Netherlands. 4. Netherlands—Economic rel.—Belgium.
N. Y. P. L.
                                        October 21, 1927

NL 0352662   NN CU

Lier, Tilman.
...Pietje; eine niederrheinische Lausbubengeschichte. Köln, B. Pick, 1949. 233 p. illus. 19cm. (Erzähler der Gegenwart)

524660B. I. Title.

NL 0352663   NN

4F   Lier, W   F   van.
306   Aanteekeningen over het geestelijk leven en de samenleving der Djoeka's, Aukaners Boschnegers, in Suriname. Met een inleiding en gegevens van C. H. de Goeje ₍   19 ₎
132-294 p.

NL 0352664   DLC-P4 IEN

Lier, Werner, 1912–
Untersuchungen über das vorkommen herzwirksamer substanzen bei den Magnoliaceen. ... Dresden, 1937. 44 p.
Inaug. Diss. - Techn. Hochschule Braunschweig, 1937.
Lebenslauf.

NL 0352665   ICRL

Lier, Belgium. Institut J. B. Carnoy. Bibliothèque.
... Catalogue de la bibliothèque. Lierre, 1905
31 numb. l. 20.5 cm.

NL 0352666   CtY

Lier, Belgium. Rentmeester.
Rekening der Stad Lier . . . 1377 . . . 1394. Medegedeeld door F. H. Mertens.
(In Historisch genootschap, Utrecht. Codex diplomaticus Neerlandicus. Serie 2, deel 4, afd. 1, pp. 215-248, afd. 2, pp. 246-263. Utrecht, 1857, 6o.)

F6316 — Mertens, Frans Hendrik, ed.

NL 0352667   MB

British Tracts 1648 L61
The lier laid open in a letter, first written to a friend in the country, at his desire, for his private satisfaction: and now printed for the publick. Touching a late pamphlet, intituled, **The manifold practises and attempts of the Hamiltons; and particularly, of the present Duke of Hamilton, (now generall of the Scottish army) to get the crown of Scotland.** London, 1648.
16p. 18cm.

1. Nedham, Marchamont, 1620-1678. The manifold practises and attem   pts of the Hamiltons.
Chronology cd

NL 0352668   CtY NNC CSmH

Lier bygdeboknemnd.
Liers histoire
see under title

Liera B   , Guillermo.
El ejido, por el ingeniero Guillermo Liera B. ... México, D. F. ₍Ediciones "Ala izquierda" de la Cámara de diputados del Congreso de la unión₎ 1936.
95 p. incl. port. 21½^{cm}.

1. Commons—Mexico. 2. Agriculture—Mexico. I. Title.

Library of Congress   HD825.L5
                                ₍2₎   39-21722
                                            333.0972

NL 0352670   DLC IU

Liera B   , Guillermo.
... México en Colombia; ciclo de conferencias sustentadas por el ing. Guillermo Liera B., en la Sociedad colombiana de ingenieros, de Bogotá, Colombia. México, D-A-P-P, 1938.
84 p. 20^{cm}.
At head of title: Secretaría de agricultura y fomento.

1. Mexico—Economic policy. I. Mexico. Secretaría de agricultura y fomento. II. Title.

Library of Congress   HC135.L5
                                            39-30063
                                            330.972

NL 0352671   DLC LNHT CSt-H NN DPU

Lieras, Antonio Alvarez, 1892–
see   Alvarez Lieras, Antonio, 1892–

Lierau, Max.
Das Botanische museum und Bot. laboratorium für waarenkunde zu Hamburg. Eine uebersicht seiner sammlungen und einrichtungen.   Cassel. 1888 ['89].
15 p. 8°.
"Separatabdruck aus Botanisches centralblatt, 1889, xxxviii, 431, 476, 521, 558.

NL 0352673   MH-A

PC 2517 .L72   Lierau, Max, 1860–
Die metrische technik der drei sonettisten Maynard, Gombauld und Malleville verglichen mit derjenigen Fr. Malherbe's. I. teil ... ₍Von₎ Max Lierau ... Greifswald, J. Abel, 1882.
2 p. l., 30 p. 21^{cm}.
Inaug.-diss.—Greifswald.
Vita.
"Die vollständige arbeit wird im verlage von J. Abel in Greifswald erscheinen": Foot-note, p. 28. Never published?
1. French language—Rime. 2. Malherbe, François de, 1555-1628. 3. Maynard, François de, 1582-1646. 4. Gombauld, Jean Ogier de, 1570 (ca.)-   1666. 5. Malleville, Claude de, 1597-1647. ₍Full name: Maximilian Lierau₎

NL 0352674   MiU

Lierau, Walter.
Die neue Türkei; wirtschaftliche Zustände und Aussichten. Berlin, E. S. Mittler, 1923.
59, ₍2₎ p. map. 23 cm.
Bibliography: p. ₍60₎

1. Turkey—Econ. condit.—1918–   I. Title.

HC405.L46   52-56018

NL 0352675   DLC RPB DNW ICN NN MH OU

JX5244 S8L719   Lierau, Wolf-Dieter, 1911–
Der U-bootkrieg im weltkrieg; eine völkerrechtliche untersuchung... Berlin, Druck G. Buschhardt, 1935.
1 p. l., vi, 61 p., 1 l. 21^{cm}.
Inaug.-diss. - Göttingen.
Lebenslauf.
"Literatur-verzeichnis": p. iii-vi.

1. European war, 1914-1918 - Naval operations - Submarine. 2. War, Maritime (International law) 3. Submarine war-   fare. I. Title.

NL 0352676   CSt-H NN ICRL DLC-P4 CtY

---

333 L625
Lierde, Jacques Jean-Baptist Petrus van.
Een economische-analytische studie van het landgebruik in Zuid-Afrika, met speciale verwijzing naar de bezitvormen in de naturellengebieden gezien in het licht van de beoogde economische ontwikkeling. Pretoria, 1954.
vii, 414, iii l. tables, diagrs. (fold. in pocket) 33^{cm}.
Thesis, Pretoria.
Bibliography: l. ₍i₎-iii at end.

NL 0352677   NNC

Lierde, Juliana van.
Metingen over de thermo-diffusie en de inwendige wrijving in enkele gasmengsels bij lage en zeer lage temperaturen. Antwerpen, Standaard-Boekhandel, 1947.
78 p. diagrs. 27 cm. (Verhandelingen van de Koninklijke Vlaamse Academie voor Wetenschappen, Letteren en Schoone Kunsten van België. Klasse der Wetenschappen, jaarg. 9, no. 24)
Bibliography: p. 78.

1. Heat—Conduction. 2. Gases. 3. Friction. 4. Low temperature research. (Series: Vlaamsche Academie voor Wetenschappen, Letteren en Schoone Kunsten van België, Brussels. Klasse der Wetenschappen. Verhandelingen, jaarg. 9, no. 24)

Q56.V45 jaarg. 9, no. 24   56-19689

NL 0352678   DLC NIC

VOLUME 332

616.5
L719d

Lierde, Léon van.
La dermatologie aux Etats-Unis d'Amérique
Préface de Clément Simon. Bruxelles, Les Editions "Acta Medica Belgica" [1950?]
72 p. 24 cm.

Includes bibliographies.
Author's autograph presentation copy to Professor A.C.Curtis.
1.Dermatology.

NL 0352679 MiU PV DNLM

QV
60
L719p
1951

LIERDE, Léon van.
La prescription dermatologique; formes
pharmaceutiques, concentrations, formules
classiques. Paris, Maloine, 1951.
xx, 242 p. (Les Petits precis)
1. Drugs - Therapeutic use
2. Formularies 3. Skin - Diseases - Treatment

NL 0352680 DNLM ICJ

Lierde, Petrus Canisius van, *Bp.*, 1907-
Achter de bronzen poort; het centraal bestuur van Christus' Kerk. Haarlem, De Toorts, 1954.
216 p. plates. 26 cm.
"Lijst van citaten": p. 213–214.

1. Catholic Church—Government. I. Title.

A 55–5758

Catholic Univ. of   America. Library
for Library of Congress   [1]

NL 0352681 DCU

Liere, Adolf Richard Hermann
see Liere, Richard, 1881-

Liere, Adriaan van, 1879- joint author.

Weinhardt, Karl.
Universal-korrespondenz; systematisches handbuch der
privat- und handelskorrespondenz in acht sprachen. Von
Karl Weinhardt ... Max Henry Ferrars ... J. E. Pichon
... dr. G. M. Lombardo ... A. van Liere ... O. Pirrss ...
dr. Manuel Pedroso ... A. de Carvalle ... Freiburg (Baden) J. Bielefeld, 1914.

BV480
.L7

LIERE,CARL.
Geschichte und erklärung der gangbarsten evangelisch-
deutschen kirchenlieder, unter besonderer bezugnahme
auf die volksschule und ihre lehrer...von Carl Liere
...und Wilhelm Rindfleisch... Berlin,Nicolai,1851.
xiv,543,[2]p. 23cm.

1.Hymns,German--Hist.& crit.

NL 0352684 ICU NN

LIERE, Richard, 1881-
Beiträge zur Kenntnis des Aloins. Dresden
1909: Beyer,

43 S.

NL 0352685 MH-C PU CtY ICRL

Liere, Walter.
Pioniere im Kampf; Erlebnisberichte aus dem Polenfeld-
zuge 1939, im Auftrage der Pionierabteilung des Oberkom-
mandos des Heeres bearbeitet und hrsg. von Oberstleutnant
Liere. Berlin, W. Limpert [*1940]
93 p. illus. 20 cm.

1. World War, 1939-1945—Campaigns—Poland. I. Title.

D765.L54   55–47651 ‡

NL 0352686 DLC CoU

631.4
L625b
1948

Liere, Willem Johannis van, 1918-
De bodemgesteldheid van het Westland.
Soil conditions in the Westland. 's-Gravenhage, Staatsdrukkerij, 1948.
152p. illus.,maps. (part col.) and portfolio (10 fold. maps) 24cm.

Proefschrift-Landbouwhogeschoool te Wagen-
ingen.
"Stellingen" slip inserted at end.
Summary and legends in English.
"Literatuur": p. 150-152.
1. Soil. Nether-   lands. I. Title.
II. Title: Soil   conditions in the
Westland.

NL 0352687 KU

459.3
L62

Lieres, Li v.
Pilze und Blumen: Geschenke des waldes.
Halle (Saale) Marhold [1950?]
50 p.

1. Forest botany. 2. Mushrooms. Germany.

NL 0352688 DNAL

[Lieres, Vita von]
Die initialen des Johannes Zainer in Ulm aus
dem Vocabularius bibliae des Henricus de Hassia.
[1923]
[42] p. illus. 16 [.]

Text signed: Vita von Lieres.
"Den mitgliedern der Frankfurter bibliophilen-
gesellschaft zum 25. febr. 1923 gewidmet von
Olga und Paul Hirsch, Frankfurt am Main. Privatdruck in 200 gezählten abzügen. Dies ist nr.
199."
Presentation copy.   to Dr. Lohmann-Haupt, with
the inscription and   signature of Paul Hirsch.

NL 0352689 NNC ICN

Case
Wing
fZC
1
.505

LIERES, VITA VON.
Kalender und Almanache, von Dr. Vita von
Lieres ... [Bielefeld, 1926]
16p. illus. 31cm.

"Sonderabdruck des in der 'Zeitschrift
für Bücherfreunde,' Jahrgang 1926, Heft 6 erschienen Aufsatzes für die Mitglieder der
Frankfurter Bibliophilen-Gesellschaft ...
200 ... Exemplaren ... No.23."

69–201

NL 0352690 ICN

Z5095
.L7
Rare bk

Lieres, Vita von.
Kalender und almanache ... [Frankfurt] 1926.
cover-title, 16 p. plates, facsims.
"Sonderabdruck des in der 'Zeitschrift für
bücherfreunde', jahrgang 1926, heft 6 erschienenen
aufsatzes für die mitglieder der Frankfurter bibliophilen-gesellschaft. Von 200 numerierten exemplaren
ist dies no.29."
Based upon an exhibition of almanacs and calendars
sponsored by the society in 1926.

NL 0352691 ICU

Lieres und Wilkau, Ernst Oskar.
Die aufrechnung gegen den eingeklagten teil einer for-
derung.
Inaug. diss. Breslau, 1914. (Streigau)

NL 0352692 ICRL

Lieres und Wilkau, Otto Gottfried von.
Das Führerprinzip bei der Neuordnung der G.m.b.H. ... von
Otto Gottfried von Lieres und Wilkau ... Erlangen-Bruck: M.
Krahl, 1938. v, 68 p. 22cm.

Inaugural-Dissertation — Erlangen, 1938.
"Literaturverzeichnis," p. [iv]-v.

1. Corporations—Germany.   2. Management—Germany.
N. Y. P. L.   September 25, 1940

NL 0352693 NN NIC

Lieres und Wilkau, Viktoria von, 1881-
Beiträge zur geschichte der pferdedarstellung
in der altgriechischen vasenmalerei ... von Vik-
toria von Lieres und Wilkau ... Strassburg, J. H.
E. Heitz, 1914.
30 p., 1 l. 27cm.
Inaug.-diss.—Bonn.
Vita.

1. Horses (in art) 2. Vases, Greek. I. Title: Die pferdedarstellung in der altgriechischen vasenmalerei.

NL 0352694 ViU Vi MH CU ICRL DLC NjP

Lierheimer, Bernard Maria, O.S.B., 1826-1900.
Der Fastenprediger; ein sechsfacher Cyklus
von Predigten für die heilige Fastenzeit, von
P. Bernard Maria Lierheimer, O.S.B., K. Eggert
[u.a.] Regensburg, G.J. Manz, 1890-
v. 22 cm.

NL 0352695 PLatS MnCS

4BT-109

Lierheimer, Bernard Maria, pater, 1826-1900.
Gnade und Sakramente; Kanzelvorträge.
Regensburg, Verlags-Anstalt vorm. G. J. Manz,
1887.
459 p.

NL 0352696 DLC-P4

Lierheimer, Bernhard Maria, O.S.B., 1826-1900.
Das heilige Busssakrament in zusammenhängenden Kanzelvorträgen dargestellt. Regensburg,
G.J. Manz, 1874.
xvi, 340p 21cm

NL 0352697 MnCS PLatS

Lierheimer, Bernard Maria, *pater*, 1826–1900.
Jesus für uns. Predigten über das heilige messopfer, von p.
Fr. Xav. Lierheimer ... Regensburg. G. J. Manz, 1872.
xii, 319 p. 21cm.

1. Mass—Sermons. 2. Catholic church—Sermons. 3. Sermons, German. I. Title.
[Secular name: Franz Xaver Lierheimer]
37–22611

Library of Congress   BX2230.L47
     [2]   265.3

NL 0352698 DLC MnCS

VOLUME 332

BZ 104 L74 1890 Lierheimer, Bernard Maria, 1826-1900.
Jesus in uns; Predigten über die heilige Kommunion. 2., verm Aufl. Regensburg, G. J. Manz, 1890.
xvi, 274 p. 22 cm.

1.Communion, Holy - Sermons.
[Secular name - Franz Xaver Lierheimer.]

NL 0352699 IMunS MH

Lierheimer, Bernard Maria, O.S.B., 1826-1900.
Jesus mit uns. Predigten über das heiligste Sakrament des Altars. Regensburg, G.J. Manz, 1871.
xii, 252 p. 21 cm.

NL 0352700 PLatS MnCS

4-BR 613 Lierheimer, Bernard Maria, pater, 1826-1900.
Die Kirche Jesu Christi nach ihrem Bestande, ihrer Aufgabe und Wirksamkeit, mit besonderer Berücksichtigung der Gegenwart. Regensburg, G.J. Manz, 1865.
365 p.

NL 0352701 DLC-P4 MnCS PLatS

Lierheimer, Bernard Maria, O.S.B., 1826-1900.
Kleine anreden vor der heiligen Communion. 2 verm. aufl. München, Hermann Manz, 1871.
6-132 p. 14 cm.
Copy 2: 3 verm. aufl. Regensburg, G.J. Manz, 1892.
86 p. 22 cm.

NL 0352702 PLatS

Lierheimer, Bernard Maria, Father, 1826-1900.
Leben der ehrwürdigen Dienerin Gottes, Schwester Maria von Jesu ...
see under Antonio Maria da Vicenza, Father, d. 1890.

Lierheimer, Bernard Maria, O.S.B., 1826-1900.
Leib und seele. Vorträge gehalten in der königl St. Michaels Hofkirche zu München von Fr. Xav. Lierheimer. Regensburg, G.J. Manz, 1864.
xvi, 455 p. 21 cm.

NL 0352704 PLatS MnCS

Lierheimer, Bernhard Maria, O.S.B., 1826-1900.
Der leidene Jesus; Fastenbetrachtungen gehalten in der St. Michaels-Hofkirche zu Muenchen. von Dr. Franz Xaver Lierheimer. Regensburg, Georg Joseph Manz, 1865.
122 p. 21 cm.
Bound with: Stufler, Johann, S.J.: Die theorie der freiwilligen Verstocktheit. Innsbruck, F. Rauch, 1905.

1. Jesus Christ - Passion - Sermons.
2. Sermons, Lenten. 3. Sermons, German. I.Titl.

NL 0352705 PLatS

Lierheimer, Bernard Maria, O.S.B., 1826-1900.
Die letzen worte des Welterlösers. Fastenpredigten. Regensburg, G.J. Manz, 1878.
vii, 135 p. 21 cm.
Bound with Mach, Jose, S.J. Die sieben worte Jesu am kreuze. Regensburg, G.J. Manz, 1880.

NL 0352706 PLatS

Lierheimer, Bernard Maria, O.S.B., 1826-1900.
Der Papst und seine lehramtliche Unfehlbarkeit; neun Kanzelvorträge, von Fr. Xav. Lierheimer. Regensburg, Fr. Pustet, 1871.
iv, 134p. 20cm.

NL 0352707 PLatS

Lierheimer, Bernard Maria, O.S.B., 1826-1900.
Die parabeln und wunder in dem Sonntagsevangelien des kirchenjahres. Kanzelvorträge. Regensburg, G.J. Manz, 1868.
xvi, 386 p. 21 cm.

NL 0352708 PLatS

Lierheimer, Bernard Maria, pater, 1826-1900.
Scheurer, J B.
Sermons on the blessed sacrament, and especially for the forty hours' adoration. From the German of Rev. J. B. Scheurer, D. D. Edited by Rev. F. X. Lasance ... New York, Cincinnati [etc.] Benziger brothers, 1900.

Lierheimer, Bernhard Maria, O.S.B., 1826-1900.
Die Vollkommenheiten Gottes; zur Belehrung und Erbauung für das christliche Volk erklärt. Regensburg, G.J. Manz, 1866.
270p 19cm

NL 0352710 MnCS PLatS

Lierheimer, Bernard Maria, pater, 1826-1900, tr.
Rogacci, Benedetto, 1646-1719.
... Von dem einen nothwendigen. Aus dem italienischen übersetzt von F. X. Lierheimer ... Regensburg, G. J. Manz, 1857-59.

Lierheimer, Bernard Maria, O.S.B., 1826-1900.
Die zehn gebote Gottes in zusammenhängenden kanzelvorträgen ausführlich erklärt von Fr. Xav. Lierheimer. Regensburg, G.J. Manz, 1869-70.
3 v. 21 cm.

NL 0352712 PLatS CU

Lierheimer, F.X.
see Lierheimer, Bernard Maria, pater, 1826-1900.

Lierheimer, Franz Xaver
see Lierheimer, Bernard Maria, pater, 1826-1900.

Lierke, E. Erfolge der kalidüngung im obstbau. 8°. pp. 36. il. n. p., 1902.

NL 0352715 MBH

Lierke, E.
Die Kalisalze, deren Gewinnung, Vertrieb und Anwendung in der Landwirtschaft. 22 p. 11 pl. 3 p. of tables. Q. Stassfurt: R. Weicke, 1901.

NL 0352716 ICJ

Lierke, E.
The manuring of rubber trees. (In: International Rubber Congress, II. London, 1911. The rubber industry... London [1911]. 8°. p. 169-179.)

1. India rubber.
N. Y. P. L. June 5, 1913.

NL 0352717 NN

Lierke, E.
The potash controversy. Statement on behalf of German potash syndicated dated January 20, 1911 ... [No imprint]

NL 0352718 MiU

Lierke, E.
The potash supply, with special reference to the United States; lectures by E. Lierke and W. Inkster ... given on the occasion of the visit of the American commission on co-operative systems of European countries to Stassfurt-Leopoldshall, June 16th, 1913. Berlin, Kalisyndikat, g. m. b. h., 1913.
59 p. illus. fold. map. fold. plan, diagrs. 18½cm.

1. Potash. I. Inkster, W. II. Kalisyndikat, g. m. b. h.
G S 13-735
Library, U. S. Geol. survey 443 L62

NL 0352719 DI-GS ICJ TxU

531.8 L52p Lierke, E
Praktische düngetafeln. Graphische darstellung und zahlenmässige angabe des boden-nährstoff-bedarfs der wichtigsten kulturpflanzen und zusammensetzung der wichtigsten düngemittel. Im auftrage der Consolodierten alkali-werke in Westeregeln zusammengestellt von E. Lierke ... Berlin, P. Parey, 1887.
58p. tables(1 fold.) fold.col.diagr.

1. Fertilizers and manures.

NL 0352720 IU DNAL CtY

Lierke, E.
Wall-charts of the use of commercial and other fertilizers in Germany [1924] charts I-IV. 106½ x 83cm.

NL 0352721 DNAL

Liermain, Marcel, 1908-
... La nausée, symptome duodénal ... Paris, 1936.
Thèse - Univ. de Paris.
"Bibliographie": p. [95]-112.

NL 0352722 CtY

VOLUME 332

Lierman, *Mrs.* Emily C.
Stories from the clinic, by Emily C. Lierman. New York city, Central fixation publishing co., '1926.
3 p. l., 9–259 p. illus. (incl. ports.) 20ᶜᵐ.

1. Eye—Diseases and defects.   I. Title.

Library of Congress   RE51.L5   26–3969

NL 0352723   DLC FU DNLM CtY-M

Liermann, Bernt, 1909–
Der niedergang des böttcher-handwerks als produktions-gewerbe. ... 64 p.
Inaug. Diss. - Halle, [1934?]
Lebenslauf.
Bibliography.

NL 0352724   ICRL CtY MiU PU

Liermann, Erich, 1911–
... Johann Segebarth; ein beitrag zur pommerschen literaturgeschichte ... von Erich Liermann ... Dresden, M. Dittert & co., 1938.
114 p.   21ᶜᵐ.

Thesis, Greifswald.
"Literaturverzeichnis": p. 111–113.

1. Segebarth, Johann Peter Christoph, 1833–1919

NL 0352725   NNC ICRL CtY

4K Ger.   Liermann, Hans, 1893–
66   Das deutsche Volk als Rechtsbegriff im Reichs-Staatsrecht der Gegenwart.   Berlin, F. Dümmler 1927.
251 p.

NL 0352726   DLC-P4 MH NN DGU CtY

Liermann, Hans, 1893–
... Deutsches evangelisches kirchenrecht, von dr. Hans Liermann ... Stuttgart, F. Enke, 1933.
vi, 404 p. 22ᶜᵐ. (Bibliothek des öffentlichen rechts. bd. v)

1. Ecclesiastical law—Germany. 2. Church and state in Germany.
3. Protestant churches—Germany.   I. Title.
                                        36–34251

NL 0352727   DLC

Liermann, Hans, 1893–
Franken und Böhmen, ein Stück deutscher Rechtsgeschichte.   Erlangen, Kommissionsverlag von Palm & Enke, 1939.
100 p. illus., plates, ports. 25 cm.
Bibliography: p. 92–100.

1. Law, Frankish. 2. Law—Bohemia—Hist. & crit.
                                        50–53570

NL 0352728   DLC MH

Liermann, Hans, 1893–
Grundlegendes kirchlichen Verfassungsrecht nach lutherischer Auffassung. [1. Aufl.]   Berlin, Lutherisches Verlagshaus, 1954.
23 p. 22ᶜᵐ.   (Luthertum; eine Schriftenreihe. 11)

NL 0352729   NjPT

Liermann, Hans, 1893–   *ed.*
Kirchen und Staat.   München, Isar Verlag, 1954–55.
2 v. 23 cm. (Veröffentlichungen des Instituts für Staatslehre und Politik e. V. Mainz, Bd. 5)
Federal and state legislation of various periods.

1. Ecclesiastical law—Germany (Federal Republic, 1949–) 2
Church and state in Germany (Federal Republic, 1949–)   I.
Title.   (Series: Institut für Staatslehre und Politik, Mainz. Veröffentlichungen, Bd. 5)
                                        55–17325 rev

          PU ICU CU FU CtY-D OU ICMcC MB
NL 0352730   DLC CaBVaU NBuU OCIW ICU NjPT NN NcD MH

Liermann, Hans, 1893–
Das Minderheitenproblem, von Dr. Hans Liermann... (In: Harms, B., editor.   Volk und Reich der Deutschen.   Berlin, 1929. 8°.   Bd. 3, p. [85–]105.)

560066A. 1. Nationality.
N. Y. P. L.   December 28, 1931

NL 0352731   NN

Liermann, Hans, 1893–
Sind die preussischen Brüdergemeinen Körperschaften des öffentlichen Rechts? ein Rechtsgutachten...   Herrnhut, Als Handschrift gedruckt im Auftrag der Deutschen Unitäts-Direktion [1937]
48 p. 25ᶜᵐ.

Bibliographical footnotes.

NL 0352732   NjPT

Liermann, Hans, 1893–
... Staat und Evangelisch-protestantische landeskirche in Baden während und nach der staatsumwälzung von 1918, von dr. jur. Hans Liermann ...   Lahr in Baden, M. Schauenburg, k. g., 1929.
87 p. 24ᶜᵐ. (Veröffentlichungen des Vereins für kirchengeschichte in der Ev. landeskirche Badens, II.)

1. Vereinigte evangelisch-protestantische landeskirche Badens.
2. Church and state in Baden. 3. Protestants in Baden.   I. Title.
                                        31–29569

Library of Congress   BR857.B3L5
                                        284.14346

NL 0352733   DLC CBPac CSt NcD MH

2A4   Liermann, Heinz, 1909–
O3
B5   Endliche Gruppen, deren kommutatorgruppenordnung eine primzahl p≠2 ist. Leipzig.
22   B. G. Teubner, 1939.
Physical   [184]–207p. 24 cm. (German mathematical
Sciences   dissertations—Berlin, v. 22)
Library
          Thesis—Berlin
          Vita
          "Sonderabdruck aus den 'Schriften des Mathematischen Instituts und des Instituts für angewandte Mathematik   der Universität Berlin /Band 4."

NL 0352734   RPB CtY ICRL

Liermann, Heinz, 1909–
... Endliche gruppen, deren kommutatorgruppenordnung eine primzahl p ∓ 2 ist. Leipzig und Berlin, B. G. Teubner, 1939.
1 p. L. p. [183]–207. 24ᶜᵐ. (Schriften des Mathematischen Instituts und des Instituts für angewandte mathematik der Universität Berlin, hrsg. von L. Bieberbach ... bd. 4, hft. 7)
Issued also as the author's dissertation, Berlin, 1938.
Bibliographical foot-notes.

1. Groups, Theory of.
                                        A C 39–2179

Iowa. State coll. Library
for Library of Congress   [2]

NL 0352735   IaU

LIERMANN, Kurt, 1900–
Beiträge zur vergleichenden anatomie der wurzeln einiger pharmazeutisch verwendeter umbelliferen. Inaug.-diss., Basel. Borna-Leipzig, R. Noske, 1926.

Illustr.
"Literaturverzeichnis", pp. 97–98.
"Curriculum vitae", at end.

NL 0352736   MH ICRL CtY

Liermann, Otto, 1867–
... Altdeutsches lesebuch mit anmerkungen, bearbeitet von dr. Otto Liermann ... und dr. Wilhelm Vilmar ... 4. verb. aufl. Leipzig, Frankfurt a. M., Kesselring (E. v. Mayer) 1920.
xviii, 416 p.   21ᶜᵐ. (Added t.-p.: Deutsches lesebuch für höhere lehranstalten (Sexta bis prima nebst zwei vorschulteilen.) In verbindung mit prof. H. Butzer ... [u. a.] hrsg. von dr. O. Liermann)
Series title at head of t.-p.: Deutsches lesebuch für höhere lehranstalten. Obere stufe: obersecunda bis prima.   I.
First published 1909.
Bibliographical foot-notes.
1. German literature—Old High German. 2. German literature—Middle High German.   I. Vilmar, Wilhelm, 1870–   joint author.
II. Title.

Library of Congress   PT1372.L5 1920
                                        42–11910

NL 0352737   DLC

PT1372   Liermann, Otto, 1867–
L5   Altdeutsches Lesebuch mit Anmerkungen,
1926   bearb. von Otto Liermann und Wilhelm Vilmar. 5. verb. Aufl.   Frankfurt a. M., Kesselring, 1926.
xviii,432 p. illus. (His Deutsches Lesebuch für höhere Schulen, neubearbeitet und in Verbindung mit H. Gerber ... [et al.] herausgegeben. [Obere Stufe, 1])

Bibliographical footnotes.

--- ----- Wörterbuch mit grammatischem Anhange zu dem Altdeutschen Lesebuche, bearb. von Otto Liermann und Wilhelm Vilmar. 5. verb. Aufl.   Frankfurt a. M., Kesselring, 1926.
150 p.

Contents.- Mittelhochdeutsches Wörterbuch.- Zur Grammatik.- Auswahl von Büchern zu Vertiefung in die deutsche Muttersprache (p. [148]–150)

NL 0352739   CU

Liermann, Otto, 1867–
Analecta epigraphica et agonistica.   Halle, 1889.
Inaug. diss.- Halle.

NL 0352740   ICRL PU

Liermann, Otto, 1867–
[Analecta epigraphica et agonistica]
(In Halle. Universität. Dissertationes philologicae halenses ... Halis Saxonum, 1889. 22½ᶜᵐ. vol. x. 2 p. l., [7]–241, [1] p.)
Title of work and name of author given in table of contents of whole volume.
Issued also, in part, as the author's thesis, Halle.

1. Inscriptions, Greek.
                                        A C 37–1920

Yale univ. Library
for Library of Congress   [2]

NL 0352741   CtY InU NIC OCU CU NjP

VOLUME 332

Liermann, Otto, 1867-
AC831
F761
1901
Stack
Henricus Petreus Herdesianus und die
Frankfurter Lehrpläne nebst Schulordnungen
von 1579 und 1599; eine kulturhistorische
Studie.   Frankfurt a. M., 1901.
lxiii p.
"1901. Progr. No. 423."
Programmschrift - Goethe-Gymnasium,
Frankfurt am Main.
Accompanies Schulnachrichten.

1. Herdesianus, Henricus Petreus, 1546-1615.
2. Frankfurt am   Main. Gymnasium.

NL 0352742   CSt NNC

LIERMANN, Otto, 1867-
Politische und sozialpolitische vorbildung
durch das klassische altertum; ein vortrag.
Heidelberg, 1901.
pp. 21.
"Sonderabdruck aus jahrga 1901, heft 1.,des
Humanistischen gymnasiums."

NL 0352743   MH

Liermann, Otto, 1867-
Reformschulen nach Frankfurter und Altonaer System. Ein
Handbuch mit Unterstützung von Fachgenossen, herausgegeben
von Dr. Otto Liermann, ... Erster Teil: Die Casseler November Konferenz von 1901 über Fragen des Reformschulunterrichts.
Nebst einem Anhang: Übersicht über den Bestand an Reformschulen und einige Lehrpläne. Berlin, Weidmannsche Buchhandlung, 1903.
v, [2], 140 p. 1 table. 25½ᶜᵐ.
No more published.

NL 0352744   ICJ CU

Liermann (Wilhelm) [1864-   ]. * Bakterio-
logische Untersuchungen über putride Intoxica-
tion. [Freiburg.] 14 pp., 1 l. 8°. *Leipzig,*
J. B. Hirschfeld, 1890.
Repr. from: Arch. f. exper. Path. u. Pharmakol., Leipz.,
1890, XXVII.

NL 0352745   DNLM

Liermann, Wolfgang, 1901-
... Die blutdrucksenkende wirkung der anti-
pyretica ... Emsdetten (Westf.) 1932.
Münster
diss.
1932

NL 0352746   MiU

Liermant (Louis-Charles-Remy). * Sur l'apo-
plexie considérée en général. 16 pp 4°. : *Paris,*
1811, No. 40, v. 83.

NL 0352747   DNLM

Liern, Rafael F
    see   Liern y Cerach, Rafael Maria, 1832?-
1897.

Liern, Rafael María
    see   Liern y Cerach, Rafael María, 1832?-
1897.

LIERN, Vicente Vives y.
    See VIVES Y LIERN, Vicente.

[Liern y Cerach, Rafael María] 1832?-1897.
    Á orillas del mar. Letra de Amalfi. [pseud.]
Madrid, 1874.

NL 0352751   MH

Liern y Cerach, Rafael Maria, 1832-1897.
    Á tí suspiramos
        see under   Fernández Caballero, Manuel,
1835-1906.

Liern y Cerach, Rafael María, 1832-1897.
    El aceite de bellotas, lectura de una zarzuela peliaguda, casi
casi en un acto...por Don Rafael Maria Liern...   Madrid: J.
Rodriguez, 1874.   11 p.   12°.

1. Drama (Spanish). 2. Title.
N. Y. P. L.   October 1, 1919.

NL 0352753   NN

Liern y Cerach, Rafael María, 1832?-1897.
    El aceite de bellotas; lectura de una zar-
zuela peliaguda, casi casi en un acto. 2.
ed. Madrid, Impr. de J. Rodríguez, 1892.
13p.
    Microcard edition.

NL 0352754   ICRL

Liern y Cerach, Rafael María, 1832?-1897.
    Aiguarse la festa. Improvisacion en un acto y en verso,
original.   Valencia: Ferrer de Orga, 1864.   28 p.   12°.
    In: NPL p. v. 360, no. 1.

1. Drama (Spanish). 2. Title.
N. Y. P. L.   April 10, 1912.

NL 0352755   NN MH

Liern y Cerach, Rafael María, 1832?-1897.
    ... Aiguarse la festa; improvització en un acte
i en vers ...   [Valencia, Impremta Valencianista,
1918?]
15p.   23cm.

    At head of title: Teatro Valencia.
    Running title: El cuento del Dumenge.
    In: Teatre Valencià. v.9, no. 12.
    With this is bound Jacinto Benavente's La senda
de l'amor. Tr. de Carles Salvador.

    I. Benavente y   Martínez, Jacinto, 1866-
1954.

NL 0352756   NcU

Liern y Cerach, Rafael María, 1832?-1897.
He77   La almoneda del diablo, comedia de magia en
26   tres actos y un prólogo, escrita por Don
24   Rafael M. Liern, musica de Don Leandro Ruiz
       ... 9.ed. Madrid, Imprenta de José Rodriguez,
       1876.
       116p. 18½cm. [Binder's title: Teatro
       español, 24]
       Without music.
       "Refundida por su autor y ejecutada en el
       Teatro del Circo el 16 de enero de 1864."

NL 0352757   CtY NN

Liern y Cerach, Rafael Maria, 1832-1897.
    Una alumna de Baco, juguete cómico en un acto y en prosa,
original.   Madrid: J. Rodriguez, 1876.   24 p.   8°.   (El
teatro.)
    In : NPL p. v. 305, no. 1.

1. Drama (Spanish). 2. Title.
N. Y. P. L.   May 2, 1911.

NL 0352758   NN DLC

Liern y Cerach, Rafael María, 1832?-1897.
    Una alumna de Baco, juguete cómico en un acto y
en prosa, original de Don Rafael María Liern.
Madrid, José Rodríguez, 1876.
24p.
    Microcard edition.

NL 0352759   ICRL FU LU OrU

Liern y Cerach, Rafael María, 1832-1897.
    Americanos de pega, juguete cómico-lirico en un acto, original
de Don Rafael María Liern, música de D. Rafael Aceves y D.
Angel Rubio...   Madrid: J. Rodriguez, 1873.   27 p.   12°.
    Without music.

1. Drama (Spanish). 2. Title.
N. Y. P. L.   June 2, 1921.

NL 0352760   NN InU

Liern y Cerach, Rafael María, 1832?-1897.
    Americanos de pega; juguete cómico-lírico
en un acto. Original de Rafael María Liern.
Música de Rafael Aceves y Angel Rubio. Madrid, Impr. de J. Rodríguez, 1873.
27p.
    Microcard edition.

NL 0352761   ICRL

Bonaparte
Collection LIERN Y CERACH, RAFAEL MARÍA, 1832-1897.
No.4576   Amors entre flors y freses, ó Un rato en
           l'Hort del santisim. Juguete cómico bilingue,
           en un acto y en verso   Valencia,J.Rius,1861.
           39p. 22cm.

           Binder's title: Rafael Maria Liern.

NL 0352762   ICN

Liern y Cerach, Rafael Maria, 1832?-1897.
    Un animal raro. Comedia en un acto en
prosa.   Madrid, Centro General de Admini
stracion, 1863.
    49 p. 12°.   (Centro General de Adm.
Galeria dram).

NL 0352763   NN

VOLUME 332

MC
Liern y Cerach, Rafael María, 1832?-1897.
Un animal raro; comedia en un acto en prosa.
Original de D. Rafael María Liern. Madrid,
Centro General de Administración, 1863.
49p.
Microcard edition.

NL 0352764   ICRL

Liern y Cerach, Rafael Maria, 1832?-1897.
Artistas para la Habana; juguete cómico en un acto y en
verso. Con música del maestro F. A. Barbieri.   Madrid: J.
Rodriguez, 1887.   32 p.   3. ed.   12°.   (Administración
lírico-dramática.)
In: NPL p. v. 369, no. 15.

1. Drama (Spanish).   2. Madan y   Garcia, Augusto E., jt. au.   3. Barbieri, Francisco A., composer.   4. Title.
N. Y. P. L.   April 25, 1912.

NL 0352765   NN

PQ
6226
.T4
v. 4
Liern y Cerach, Rafael María, 1832-1897.
Aurora de libertad; apropósito patriótico en un acto y en verso improvisado
por Rafael M. Liern. Madrid, Imp. de J.
Rodriguez, 1868.
22 p. (In Teatro español. ₍Madrid,
etc., 1787-1935₎ v. 4, ₍16₎)
"Estrenado en el teatro de Novedades de Madrid el 17 de
Octubre de 1868 y en el Principal de Barcelona el 4 de los mismos."

NL 0352766   MiEM NN

Liern y Cerach, Rafael Maria, 1832?-1897.
Azulina. Zarzuela fantástica de gran espectáculo, en tres
actos, escrita en prosa y verso, con el pensamiento de una obra
francesa. Música del maestro B. de Monfort.   Madrid: J. Rodriguez, 1876.   64 p.   12°.
With autograph of author. In: NPL p. v. 351, no. 3.

1. Drama (Spanish).   2. Monfort,   Benito de, composer.   3. Title.
N. Y. P. L.   June 12, 1911.

NL 0352767   NN MH

Liern y Cerach, Rafael Maria, 1832?-1897.
El baron de la Castaña
    see under   Arché, Jose Vicente, b. 1829.

Liern y Cerach, Rafael Maria, 1832?-1897.
Una broma de sabó, apropósito bilingüe en un acto y en verso,
original.   Madrid: J. Rodriguez, 1867.   33 p.   12°.
In: NPL p. v. 283, no. 15.

1. Drama (Spanish).   2. Title.
N. Y. P. L.   March 10, 1911.

NL 0352769   NN MH

MC
Liern y Cerach, Rafael María, 1832?-1897.
Una broma de Sabó; apropósito bilingüe en
un acto y en verso. Original de Don Rafael
María Liern. Madrid, Impr. de J. Rodríguez,
1867.
33p.
Microcard edition.

NL 0352770   ICRL

Liern y Cerach, Rafael María, 1832?-1897
He77
26
31
El can-cán-¡atrás paisano! revista de teatros,
en dos actos, en prosa y verso, original de Don
Rafael Maria Liern ... Madrid, Impr. de J.
Rodriguez, 1869.
49p., 1l. 20cm. [Binder's title: Teatro
español, 31]
"Estrenada ... en el teatro de Variedades, el
10 de abril de 1869."
"Obras del mismo autor": 1l. at end.

NL 0352771   CtY

Liern y Cerach, Rafael María, 1832?-1897.
El can-cán-¡Atrás paisano! Revista de teatros,
en dos actos, en prosa y verso, original de Don
Rafael María Liern. Madrid, José Rodríguez, 1869.
49p.
Microcard edition.

NL 0352772   ICRL OrU LU FU

Liern y Cerach, Rafael Maria, 1832?-1897.
Carracuca!!! Juguete cómico-lírico-famélico en un acto y en
verso, original. Música de Benito de Monfort.   Madrid: J. Rodriguez, 1876.   29 p., 1 l.   8°.   (El teatro contemporáneo.)
In: NPL p. v. 283, no. 20.

1. Drama (Spanish).   2. Monfort,   Benito de, composer.   3. Title.
N. Y. P. L.   March 9, 1911.

NL 0352773   NN MH

Liern y Cerach, Rafael Maria, 1832?-1897.
Una casa de fieras. Juguete cómico en un acto y en prosa,
original.   Madrid: J. Rodriguez, 1873.   23(1) p.   3. ed.   8°.
(El teatro contemporáneo.)
In: NPL p. v. 283, no. 13.

1. Drama (Spanish).   2. Title.
N. Y. P. L.   March 10, 1911.

NL 0352774   NN

Liern y Cerach, Rafael María, 1832?-1897.
Una casa de fieras; juguete cómico en un
acto y en prosa. Original de Don Rafael
María Liern. 4. ed. Madrid, Impr. de J.
Rodríguez, 1877.
23p.
Microcard edition.

NL 0352775   ICRL

Liern y Cerach, Rafael María, 1832?-1897.
He77
26
32
Una casa de fieras; juguete cómico en un
acto y en prosa, original de Rafael María
Liern ... 3.ed. Madrid, Impr.de J.Rodriguez,
1890.
2p.l.,[7]-26,[2]p. 20cm. [Binder's title:
Teatro español, 32]
"Estrenado en el teatro de Novedades ...
á beneficio del primer actor del género cómico
don Ascensio Mora, el día 28 de enero de 1869."
"Obras del mismo autor": 2p. at end.

NL 0352776   CtY

Liern y Cerach, Rafael María, 1832?-1897.
Una casa de fieras, juguete cómico en un
acto y en prosa, original de Rafael María Liern.
3d. ed.   Madrid, José Rodríguez, 1890.
26 p.
Microcard edition.

NL 0352777   ICRL MoU

Liern y Cerach, Rafael Maria, 1832?-1897.
La Casaca; caricatura inverosimil en un acto y en prosa y
verso, original. Música del maestro Rubio.   Madrid: J. Rodriguez, 1888.   36 p.   12°.   (El teatro.)
In: NPL p. v. 355, no. 1.

1. Drama (Spanish).   2. Rubio,   Angel, composer.   3. Title.
N. Y. P. L.   June 9, 1911.

NL 0352778   NN MH

Liern y Cerach, Rafael María, 1832-1897.
El castañar español, consejo en un acto y en prosa y verso,
escrito por Amalfi ₍pseud.₎, música arreglada por Don Leandro
Ruiz...   Madrid: J. Rodriguez, 1873.   19 p.   8°.
Without music.

1. Drama (Spanish).   2. Title.
N. Y. P. L.   June 6, 1921.

NL 0352779   NN

Liern y Cerach, Rafael María, 1832-1897.
Cibeles y Neptuno, juguete comico-lirico-semi-fantastico en
dos actos en prosa y verso, letra de Don Rafael Maria Liern, música
de los maestros Rubio y Nieto...   Madrid: J. Rodriguez, 1880.
47 p.   12°.

1. Drama (Spanish).   2. Title.
N. Y. P. L.   September 30, 1919.

NL 0352780   NN MH

Liern y Cerach, Rafael Maria, 1832?-1897.
Una coincidencia alfabética, comedia en un acto y en prosa,
original.   Madrid: J. Rodriguez, 1867.   36 p.   2. ed.   8°.
(El teatro.)
In: NPL p. v. 283, no. 19.

1. Drama (Spanish).   2. Title.
N. Y. P. L.   March 10, 1911.

NL 0352781   NN MH

Liern y Cerach, Rafael Maria, 1832?-1897.
La comedianta Rufina. Zarzuela en un acto y
en verso. Musica de Benito de Monfort.   Madrid
J. Rodriguez, 1874.
24 p.   8°.   (El Teatro Contemporáneo.)
With author's autograph.
In: NPL p. v. 93 no. 14.

NL 0352782   NN

Liern y Cerach, Rafael María, 1832?-1897.
Una conversión en diez minutos, comedia en
dos actos y en prosa, original de Don Rafael
María Liern. Madrid, José Rodríguez, 1855.
42 p.
Microcard edition.

NL 0352783   ICRL FU MoU

Liern y Cerach, Rafael María, 1832?-1897.
He77
26
38
El cotillón de tapioca; juguete cómico-
lírico en un acto en prosa y verso, original
de Rafael María Liern, música del maestro
Mangiagalli ... Madrid, Impr.de J.Rodriguez,
1889.
31,[3]p. 20cm. [Binder's title: Teatro
español, 38]
Without music.
"Estrenado ... en el teatro de Apolo el día
19 de abril de 1889."
"Obras del mismo autor": p.[33-34]

NL 0352784   CtY NN

VOLUME 332

₁Liern y Cerach, Rafael María,₁ 1832–1897.
Cuadros vivos. Juguete cómico-lírico, en un acto y en prosa, letra de Amalfi ₁pseud.₁ música de varios autores... Madrid: G. Alhambra, 1874. 20 p. 8°. (Biblioteca dramática.)

In: NPL p. v. 308, no. 30.

1. Drama (Spanish). 2. Title.
N. Y. P. L. April 11, 1917.

NL 0352785 NN MH

Liern y Cerach, Rafael María, 1832 ?–1897.
Los de Cuba
For libretti, see under Falcón y Segura, Manuel.
For scores, see under Rubio, Angel, 1846–1906.

Bonaparte
Collection LIERN Y CERACH, RAFAEL MARÍA, 1832–1897.
No.4574 De femater á lacayo. Pieza en un acto y en verso 2. edicion. Valencia, J. Rius, 1859. 40p. 22cm.

Binder's title: Rafael Maria Liern.

NL 0352787 ICN MH

Liern y Cerach, Rafael María, 1832–1897.
Desde Céres á Flora, viaje fantástico de gran espectáculo, en un prólogo y tres jornadas, original de Don Rafael María Liern... Madrid: J. Rodriguez, 1869. 120 p. 8°.

Deck list

1. Drama (Spanish). 2. Title.
N. Y. P. L. September 18, 1918.

NL 0352788 NN CtY MH DLC

Liern y Cerach, Rafael María, 1832?–1897.
Desde Céres a Flora, viaje fantástico de gran espectáculo, en un prólogo y tres jornadas, original de Don Rafael María Liern. Madrid, Jose Rodríguez, 1869. 120p.
Microcard edition.

NL 0352789 ICRL OrU LU FU

Liern y Cerach, Rafael Maria, 1832?–1897.
El destierro del amor; zarzuela semifantástica. Madrid, 1878.

(El teatro contemporáneo.)

NL 0352790 MH NN

MC
Liern y Cerach, Rafael María, 1832?–1897.
El destierro del amor; zarzuela semifantástica, en dos actos y en verso. Letra de D. María Rafael Liern. Música de los maestros D. Angel Rubio y D. Casimiro Espino. Madrid, Impr. J. Rodríguez, 1878. 61p.
Microcard edition.

NL 0352791 ICRL MoU LU

Liern y Cerach, Rafael María, 1832?–1897.
Don Abdon y Don Senen, juguete-cómico-lirico en un acto y en verso. Música de los maestros A. Rubio y C. Espino. Madrid: J. Rodriguez, 1878. 27 p. 8°. (El teatro contemporáneo.)

In: NPL p. v. 374, no. 6.

1. Drama (Spanish). 2. Rubio, Casimiro, composer. 4. Title.
N. Y. P. L.

Angel, composer. 3. Espino,
April 17, 1912.

NL 0352792 NN

Liern y Cerach, Rafael Maria, 1832–1897.
Don Pompeyo en carnaval
see under Arché, Jose Vicente, b. 1829.

Liern y Cerach, Rafael María, 1832?–1897.
Doña Juana Tenorio, imitacion burlesca de escenas de Don Juan Tenorio, en un acto y en verso, original de Don Rafael María Liern. Madrid, Jose Rodríguez, 1876. 24p.
Microcard edition.

NL 0352794 ICRL LU MoU

Liern y Cerach, Rafael María, 1932?–1897.
Dos canarios de café. Zarzuela cómica en un acto. Letra de d. Rafael M. Liern. Música del Mtro. A. Rubio. Madrid, Unión musical española. [n.d.] 4 p.

B69505

Dos canarios de café.

NL 0352795 MoU

Liern y Cerach, Rafael Maria, 1832?–1897.
Dos canarios de café; zarzuela cómica en un acto y en prosa, original. Con música de Angel Rubio. Madrid: R. Velasco, 1899. 26 p., 1 l. 3. ed. 12°. (El teatro.)

In: NPL p. v. 355, no. 2.

1. Drama (Spanish). 2. Rubio,
N. Y. P. L.

Angel, composer. 3. Title.
June 9, 1911.

NL 0352796 NN MH

Liern y Cerach, Rafael María, 1832–1897.
Dos cómicos de provincias, zarzuela en un acto, letra de Don Rafael Maria Liern, música de Don F. Aceves... Madrid: J. Rodriguez, 1875. 23 p. 8°.

Without music.

1. Drama (Spanish). 2. Title.
N. Y. P. L. May 27, 1921.

NL 0352797 NN MH

MC
Liern y Cerach, Rafael María, 1832?–1897.
Dos cómicos de provincias, zarzuela en un acto. Original de Don Rafael María Liern. Música de F. Aceves. Madrid, Impr. de J. Rodríguez, 1875. 23p.
Microcard edition.

NL 0352798 ICRL

PQ
6226
.T4
v.15
Liern y Cerach, Rafael María, 1832–1897.
Dos tontos de capirote; fin de fiesta en un acto y en prosa original de Rafael María Liern. Escrito expresamente para Mariano Fernández. Madrid, Imp. de J. Rodriguez, 1870.
33 p. (In Teatro español, etc., 1787–1935₁ v. 15, ₁11₁)

"Representado por primera vez en el Teatro Español el día 24 de Diciembre de 1869 (Noche-buena)"

I. Title.

NL 0352799 MiEM MoU NN

Liern y Cerach, Rafael María, 1832?–1897.
Dos tontos de capirote, fin de fiesta en un acto y en prosa, original de Don Rafael María Liern. Madrid, José Rodríguez, 1870. 33p.
Microcard edition.

NL 0352800 ICRL FU LU

Liern y Cerach, Rafael María, 1832?–1897.
Dos y tres...dos, juguete cómico en un acto y en verso, original. Madrid: J. Rodriguez, 1869. 2 p.l., (1)8-34 p. 8°.

In: NPL p. v. 353, no. 33.

1. Drama (Spanish). 2. Title.
N. Y. P. L. June 14, 1911.

NL 0352801 NN

Liern y Cerach, Rafael María, 1832?–1897.
Efectos de la gran vía; apróposito. Madrid, 1887.

(El teatro.)

NL 0352802 MH NN

Bonaparte
Collection LIERN Y CERACH, RAFAEL MARÍA, 1832–1897.
No.4575 Les elecsions d'un poblet. Pieza en un acto, y en verso Valencia, J. Rius, 1859. 43p. 22cm.

Binder's title: Rafael Maria Liern.

NL 0352803 ICN MiEM MH

Bonaparte
Collection LIERN Y CERACH, RAFAEL MARÍA, 1832–1897.
No.4578 En les festes d'un carrer. Pieza de costumbres valencianas en un acto y en verso Valencia, J. Rius, 1861. 47p. 22cm.

Binder's title: Rafael Maria Liern.

NL 0352804 ICN

MICD
862
Liern y Cerach, Rafael María, 1832?–1897.
La escala del crimen, melodrama en tres actos y seis cuadros, en prosa, por los señores Don Rafael María Liern y Don Augusto E. Mádan y García. Madrid, José Rodríguez, 1877. 67 p.

A58705

La escala del crimen.

NL 0352805 MoU MH

VOLUME 332

Liern y Cerach, Rafa el María, 1832?-1897.
La escala del crimen, melodrama en tres actos y
seis cuadros, en prosa, por los señores Don Rafael
María Liern y Don Augusto E. Mádan y García.
Madrid, José Rodríguez, 1877.
67p.

Microcard edition.

NL 0352806   ICRL FU

862.5
L719e   Liern y Cerach, Rafael María, 1832?-1897.
La espada de Satanás, comedia de magia en
cuatro actos. Música del maestro Cristóbal
Oudrid. Madrid, J. Rodríguez, 1867.
109 p. 21 cm.

Without music.

NL 0352807   ICarbS MH

Liern y Cerach, Rafael María, 1832-1897.
Espinas de una rosa, juguete cómico-lírico en un acto y en
prosa y verso, letra de Don Rafael M. Liern, música del maestro
Don Apolinar Brull... Madrid: C. Rodriguez, 1882. 24 p.
12°.

Libretto.

1. Drama (Spanish). 2. Title.
N. Y. P. L.   September 30, 1919.

NL 0352808   NN

Liern y Cerach, Rafael María, 1832?-1897.
Esta casa es muy de ustedes: apropósito en un acto, en prosa
y verso, para inauguración de teatros, original. Música del maestro Ángel Rubio. Madrid: J. Rodriguez, 1888. 30 p. 8°.
(El teatro.)

In: NPL p. v. 283, no. 18.

1. Drama (Spanish). 2. Rubio,   Ángel, composer. 3. Title.
N. Y. P. L.   March 9, 1911.

NL 0352809   NN MH

Liern y Cerach, Rafael María, 1832?-1897.
Los feos
see under   Fernández Caballero, Manuel,
1835-1906.

Bonaparte
Collection LIERN Y CERACH, RAFAEL MARÍA, 1832-1897.
No.4579   La flor del camí del Grau. Juguete bilingüe
en un acto y en verso   Valencia,La opinion,
1862.
39p. 22cm.

Binder's title: Rafael María Liern.

NL 0352811   ICN

Liern, y Cerach, Rafael María, 1832?-1897.
Francia y Prusia, juguete en un acto, ó ratito de conversacion,
escrito á propósito de la guerra actual.   Madrid: J. Rodriguez,
1870. 14 p. 8°. (El teatro contemporáneo.)

In: NPL p. v. 283, no. 22.

1. Drama (Spanish). 2. Title.
N. Y. P. L.   March 10, 1911.

NL 0352812   NN MH DLC

Liern y Cerach, Rafael María, 1832?-1897.
Francia y Prusia, juguete en un acto ó ratito de
conversación escrito á propósito de la guerra
actual por D. Rafael M. Liern. Madrid, José Rodríguez, 1870.
14p.

Microcard edition.

NL 0352813   ICRL FU MoU

Liern y Cerach, Rafael María, 1832?-1897.
La gata de oro; zarzuela mágico-fantástica en dos actos, en
prosa y verso, original. Música de Angel Rubio.   Madrid: J.
Rodriguez, 1891. 78 p. 8°. (El teatro.)

In: NPL p. v. 354, no. 19.

1. Drama (Spanish). 2. Rubio,   Angel, composer. 3. Title.
N. Y. P. L.   June 16, 1911.

NL 0352814   NN MH

Liern y Cerach, Rafael María, 1832?-1897.
La gata de oro, zarzuela magico-fantastica en
dos actos, en prosa y verso ... musica de Don
Angel Rubio. Madrid, Jose Rodriguez, 1891.
78p.

Microcard edition.

NL 0352815   ICRL MoU LU

He77   Liern y Cerach, Rafael María, 1832?-1897.
26   La granadina; juguete cómico-lírico en un
53   acto y en verso, original de D. Rafael M.ª
Liern y D. Augusto Madan, música del maestro
D. Gregorio Mateos ... Madrid,R.Velasco,
imp.,1890.
32p.,1l. 20cm. [Binder's title: Teatro
español, 53]
Without music.
"Estrenado ... en el teatro de Apolo la
noch[e] del 7 de julio de 1890."

NL 0352816   CtY NN

Liern y Cerach, Rafael María, 1832-1897.
Las hijas de Fulano
see under   Fernández Caballero, Manuel,
1835-1906.

Liern y Cerach, Rafael María, 1832?-1897.
El hijo del murciélago; diálogs de unas cuan-
tas escénas. Madrid, J. Rodríguez, 1889.

(El teatro.)

NL 0352818   MH

Liern y Cerach, Rafael María, 1832?-1897.
El laurel de plata; cuento cómico-fantástico en tres actos,
escrito sobre el pensamiento de una obra francesa.   Madrid: J.
Rodriguez, 1868. 102 p., 1 l. 8°. (El teatro.)

In: NPL p. v. 369, no. 7.

1. Drama (Spanish). 2. Title.
N. Y. P. L   April 25, 1912.

NL 0352819   NN

Liern y Cerach, Rafael María, 1832?-1897.
El laurel de plata, cuento cómico-fantástico en
tres actos, escrito sobre el pensamiento de una
obra francesa por Rafael María Liern. Madrid,
José Rodríguez, 1868.
102p.

Microcard edition.

NL 0352820   ICRL MoU FU

Liern, y Cerach, Rafael María, 1832?-1897.
El marqués del Pimenton, proverbio cómico lirico en un acto,
original y en verso. Música del maestro Monfort.   Madrid: J.
Rodriguez, 1882. 24 p. 8°. (El teatro contemporáneo.)

In: NPL p. v. 354, no. 18.

1. Drama (Spanish). 2. Monfort,   Benito, composer. 3. Title.
N. Y. P. L.   June 15, 1911.

NL 0352821   NN

Liern y Cerach, Rafael María, 1832?-1897.
Matrimonios al vapor, juguete cómico en dos actos y en verso,
original.   Madrid: J. Rodriguez, 1877. 54 p. 8°. (Administración lírico-dramática.)

In: NPL p. v. 354, no. 12.
By Liern y Cerach, Rafael María, and Mádan y García,
Augusto E.

1. Drama (Spanish). 2. Mádan y   García, Augusto E., jt. au. 3. Title.
N. Y. P. L.   June 19, 1911.

NL 0352822   NN MH DLC

Liern y Cerach, Rafael María, 1832?-1897.
Matrimonios al vapor, juguete cómico en dos
actos y en verso, original de los señores Don
Rafael María Liern y D. Augusto E. Mádan y García.
Madrid, José Rodríguez, 1877.
54p.
Microcard edition.

NL 0352823   ICRL FU MoU

Liern, y Cerach, Rafael María, 1832?-1897.
Un milord de Ciempozuelos, extravagancia cómica en un acto
y en prosa, original.   Madrid: J. Rodriguez, 1872. 23(1) p.
12°.

In: NPL p. v. 354, no. 29.

1. Drama (Spanish). 2. Title.
N. Y. P. L.   June 14, 1911.

NL 0352824   NN MH DLC

Liern y Cerach, Rafael María, 1832?-1897.
Un milord de Ciempozuelos, extravagancia cómico
en un acto y en prosa, original de D. Rafael María
Liern. Madrid, José Rodríguez, 1872.
23p.

Microcard edition.

NL 0352825   ICRL OrU FU LU

Bonaparte
Collection LIERN Y CERACH, RAFAEL MARÍA, 1832-1897.
No.4581   La mona de Páscua. Juguete bilingüe en un
acto y en verso   Valencia,La opinion,1862.
34p. 22cm.

Binder's title: Rafael María Liern.

NL 0352826   ICN

VOLUME 332

Liern y Cerach, Rafael María, 1832?-1897.
..¡El mundo en un armario!! juguete en un acto
y en prosa, original de D. Rafael María Liern.
Madrid, José Rodríguez, 1870.
30 p.
Microcard edition.

NL 0352827   ICRL MoU FU

Liern y Cerach, Rafael María, 1832?-1897.
Oro molido; cogido al vuelo. Madrid, R.
Velasco, 1895.

Port.

NL 0352828   MH NNH

Bonaparte
Collection LIERN Y CERACH, RAFAEL MARÍA, 1832-1897.
No.4580   Una paella.   Juguete bilingüe en un acto
y en verso   Valencia,La opinion,1862.
31p. 22cm.

Binder's title: Rafael Maria Liern.

NL 0352829   ICN

Liern y Cerach, Rafael María, 1832?-1897.
La paloma azul. Madrid, 1865.

NL 0352830   MH

Liern y Cerach, Rafael María, 1832?-1897.
La paloma azul, comedia de magia en cuatro
actos, original de D. Rafael María Liern. Madrid,
José Rodríguez, 1865.
117p.

Microcard edition.

NL 0352831   ICRL LU FU

Liern y Cerach, Rafael María, 1832?-1897.
M1503
.M2765P3 Mangiagalli y Vitali, Carlos, 1842-1896.
Un par de lilas. Juguete cómico-lírico en un acto. Letra de
d. Rafael M. Liern. Música del mtro. Carlos Mangiagalli ...
Madrid–Bilbao, Sociedad anónima Casa Dotesio ₁18—₎

Liern y Cerach, Rafael María, 1832?-1897.
Para dos perdices...juguete cómico-lírico en un acto y en
verso. Madrid: J. Rodríguez, 1891. 29 p. 12°. (El
teatro.)
With autograph of author.
In: NPL p. v. 369, no. 13.
By Liern y Cerach, Rafael María, 1832?-1897.

1. Drama (Spanish). 2. Rubio,   Angel, jt. au. 3. Title.
N.Y.P.L.   April 25, 1912.

NL 0352833   NN MH

Liern y Cerach, Rafael María, 1832?-1897.
Pedro el veterano; episodio lírico-dramá-
tico. Madrid, 1874.

(El teatro.)

NL 0352834   MH NN

Liern y Cerach, Rafael María, 1832?-1897.
Pepa, Pepe y Pepin: extravagancia inverosímil, cómico-lírica
en un acto y en prosa y verso. Música del maestro Ángel Rubio.
Madrid: J. Rodríguez, 1888.   30 p.   8°.   (El teatro.)

In: NPL p. v. 283, no. 14.

1. Drama (Spanish). 2. Rubio, An-   gel, composer. 3. Title.
N.Y.P.L.   March 9, 1911.

NL 0352835   NN MH

Liern y Cerach, Rafael María, 1832?-1897.
Pepito París, juguete cómico-lírico en un
acto, en prosa y verso... musica del maestro
Ángel Rubio...   Madrid, J. Rodríguez, 1887.
37 (1) p.   12°.   (El teatro).
In NPL p. v. 160, no. 10.

NL 0352836   NN MH

Liern y Cerach, Rafael María, 1832?-1897.
Pizpereta; juguete cómico-lírico. Madrid,
R. Velasco, 1890.

(El teatro.)

NL 0352837   MH

Liern y Cerach, Rafael María, 1832?-1897.
El principe lila, aproposito cómico-lirico-bailable en dos actos
para inauguracion de teatros. Letra de R. M. Liern, música de los
señores Aceves y Rubio.   Madrid: J. Rodríguez, 1873.   59(1) p.
8°.

In: NPL p. v. 371, no. 11.

1. Drama (Spanish). 2. Aceves, com-   poser. 3. Rubio, Angel, composer.
4. Title.
N.Y.P.L.   April 13, 1912.

NL 0352838   NN InU

Liern y Cerach, Rafael María, 1832?-1897.
El príncipe lila, apropósito cómico-lírico-
bailable en dos actos para inauguración de
teatros, letra de Don Rafael María Liern, música
de los señores Aceves y Rubio. Madrid, José
Rodríguez, 1873.
59p.

Microcard edition.

NL 0352839   ICRL MoU

Liern y Cerach, Rafael María, 1832?-1897.
He77
26   ... El proceso del can-can. Revista
78   fantástica de bailes en dos actos, escrita por
Amalfi[pseud.]Música del Mtro. D. Francisco
A.Barbieri ... Madrid,Imprenta de G.Alhambra,
1874.
37p. 20cm. (Biblioteca dramática)
Binder's title: Teatro español, 78.
Without music.
"Estrenada en el jardin del Retiro, el dia
8 de Julio de 1873."

NL 0352840   CtY

¡Liern y Cerach, Rafael María,₁ 1832-1897.
El proceso del Can-can. Revista fantástica de bailes en dos
actos, escrita por Amalfi ₁pseud.₎. Música del maestro Don Francisco A. Barbieri...   Madrid: Imp. que fué de G. Alhambra á
cargo de I. Moraleda, 1877. 37 p. 2. ed. 12°. (Biblioteca dramática.)

In: NPL p. v. 276, no. 17.

1. Drama (Spanish). 2. Title.
N.Y.P.L.   April 20, 1917.

NL 0352841   NN MH

Liern y Cerach, Rafael María, 1832-1997.
He77
26   El que fuig de Deu; juguete bilingüe-cómico-
78   lírico en un acto y en verso, original de
Rafael Maria Liern; música del maestro Monfort ... Valencia,Librerias de J.Mariana
y Sanz,editor[etc.]1878.
22p. 20cm. [Binder's title: Teatro español
78]
"Estrenado ... en el teatro de la Princesa,
á beneficio del primer actor cómico D.
Ascensio Mora, la noche del 31 de enero de
1874."

NL 0352842   CtY

Liern y Cerach, Rafael María, 1832?-1897.
El regreso del cacique; juguete cómico-lirico en un acto y en
verso, original. Música del maestro Angel Ruíz.   Madrid: J.
Rodriguez, 1893.   30 p.   8°.   (El teatro.)

In: NPL p. v. 354, no. 4.

1. Drama (Spanish). 2. Ruiz,   Angel, composer. 3. Title.
N.Y.P.L.   June 20, 1911.

NL 0352843   NN MH

Liern y Cerach, Rafael María, 1832?-1897.
El regreso del cacique, juguete cómico-lírico en
un acto y en verso, original de Rafael María Liern,
música del maestro Angel Ruíz. Madrid, José Rodríguez, 1893.
30p.
Microcard edition.
In the MIDWEST INTER-LIBRARY CENTER

NL 0352844   ICRL LU MoU

Liern y Cerach, Rafael María, 1832?-1897.
El rosal de la belleza. Madrid, 1883.

NL 0352845   MH

Liern y Cerach, Rafael María, 1832?-1897.
El rosal de la belleza, espectáculos lírico-
fantástico en tres actos, en p osa y verso, letra
de Don Rafael María Liern, música del maestro
Mangiagalli.   Madrid, Cosme Rodríguez, 1883.
79 p.
Microcard edition.

NL 0352846   ICRL MoU LU

Liern y Cerach, Rafael María, 1832?-1897.
Rubio, Angel, 1846-1906.

La salsa de Aniceta. Zarzuela en un acto. Letra de R. M.
Liern. Música del mtro. Angel Rubio ... ₁Madrid, Unión
musical española, 18—₎

Liern y Cerach, Rafael María, 1832-1897.
Sesión de honor; apropósito para la función en honra de
Eduardo Escalante, ilustre sainetero, original y en verso de Rafael
María Liern...   Valencia: Ferrer de Orga ₁1896?₎.   23 p.
8°.

1. Drama (Spanish). 2. Title.
N.Y.P.L.   May 23, 1921.

NL 0352848   NN

VOLUME 332

Liern y Cerach, Rafael María, 1832?-1897.
    Setiembre del 68 y abril del 69: revista de
teatros cómico-lírico-bailable. Madrid, J.
Rodríguez, 1869.

    (Galería dramática y lírica.)

NL 0352849   MH NjR

Liern y Cerach, Rafael María, 1832?-1897.
    Setiembre del 68 y abril del 69, revista de
teatros cómico-lírico-bailable en dos actos y en
prosa y verso, original de Don Rafael María Liern,
música de Don José Vicente Arche. Madrid, José
Rodríguez, 1869.
    54p.
    Microcard edition.

NL 0352850   ICRL MoU LU

Liern y Cerach, Rafael María, 1832?-1897.
    Siemprevivas; artículos y poesías. [Madrid?
imp. de "La Correspondencia Militar], 1900.

    Port.

NL 0352851   MH

Liern y Cerach, Rafael María, 1832?-1897.
    El talento y la virtud; juguete lírico infantil en un acto y dos
cuadros, letra de R. M. Liern, música del maestro A. Rubio.
Madrid: Zozaya [190-?]. 23 p. 12°.

    In: NPL p. v. 373, no. 12.

1. Juvenile literature.—Drama (Span-   ish. 2. Rubio, Angel, composer.
3. Title.
N. Y. P. L.   April 13, 1912.

NL 0352852   NN MH

862.5
L719
   Liern y Cerach, Rafael María, 1832-1897.
    [Teatro. Madrid, 1871-1893]
    7 pamphlets in 1 v. 22 cm.

    A made up volume of plays issued in different
series by various publishers.

    Contents.—¡El teatro en 1876!—El príncipe
Lila.—El diamante negro.—Una casa de fieras.—
Artistas para la Habana.—La salsa de Aniceta.—
Un par de Lilas.

NL 0352853   ICarbS

Liern y Cerach, Rafael María, 1832?-1897.
    Teatro. [Madrid, 1855-1895]
    21 pamphlets in 2 v. 20cm.

    Binder's title. Each play has separate t.-p.
          Contents
Vol.1 [1] Aurora de libertad. 1868.
    [2] Una coincidencia alfabética. 1867.
    [3] Una conversión en diez minutos. 1855.
    [4] Cuadros vivos. 1874.
    [5] Desde Céres á Flora. 1869.
    [6] Efectos de la gran vía. 1887.

    Vol.1 [7] Las hijas de Fulano. 1874.
    [8] El laurel de plata. 1868.
    [9] Para dos perdices. 1891.
    [10] Pedro el veterano. 1874.
    [11] Pepa, Pepe y Pepín. 1888.
    Vol.2 [12] Pepito París. 1897.
    [13] El regreso del cacique. 1893.
    [14] La serpiente de los mares. 1879.
    [15] ¡El teatro en 1876! 1871.

Continued in next column

Continued from preceding column

    Vol.2 [16] Los titiriteros. 1874.
    [17] ¡Viva la paz! 1876.
    [18] Vivir al día. 1876.
    [19] ¡Y... sin contrata! 1895.
    [20] ¡A ti suspiramos! por R. M. Liern y Salvador
M. Granés. 1889.
    [21] Matrimonios al vapor, por R. M. Liern y
Augusto E. Madan y García. 1877.
    i. Granés, Salvador María, 1840-1911, jt au. ii
Madan y García, Augusto E 1833-1915, jt a

NL 0352856   FMU

867.5
L719t
   Liern y Cerach, Rafael María, 1832?-1897.
    El teatro en el bolsillo. (colección
de tipos teatrales) Ilustraciones de Heredia.
Madrid, Imp. de la Revista de Navegación
y Comercio, 1895.

    314 p. 14cm. (Biblioteca ilustrada de
autores contemporáneos, 10.)

NL 0352857   FU

Liern y Cerach, Rafael María, 1832?-1897.
    El teatro en 1876; revista fantástica de
teatros, dividida en dos épocas. Madrid, J.
Rodríguez, 1871.

    (El teatro.)

NL 0352858   MH NN DLC

¡Liern y Cerach, Rafael María,¡ 1832-1897.
    El testamento azul. Zarzuela en tres actos, letra de Amalfi
[pseud.]; música, la del acto primero del Mtro. Barbieri, la del
segundo del Mtro. Oudrid, y la del tercero del Mtro. Aceves....
Madrid: G. Alhambra, 1874. 55 p. 8°. (Biblioteca
dramatica.)

1. Drama (Spanish). 2. Title.
N. Y. P. L.   September 18, 1918.

NL 0352859   NN MH

Liern y Cerach, Rafael María, 1832?-1897.
    Los titiriteros. Arreglado á la escena es-
pañola por Amalfi, [pseud.]. Madrid, 1874.

NL 0352860   MH

**Bonaparte
Collection** LIERN Y CERACH, RAFAEL MARÍA, 1832-1897.
No.4577   La toma de Tetuan. Improvisacion lírico-
bilingüe en un acto y en verso; letra de d.
Rafael María Liern, música de d. Joaquín Miró.
Valencia, J. Rius, 1861.
    36p. 22cm.

    Binder's title: Rafael Maria Liern.
    Without the music.

NL 0352861   ICN

Liern y Cerach, Rafael María, 1832?-1897.
    La venida del Mesías, apropósito político-electoral en un acto
y en verso, original. Madrid: J. Rodriguez, 1872. 29 p. 8°.
(El teatro contemporáneo.)

    In: NPL p. v. 283, no. 17.

1. Drama (Spanish). 2. Title.
N. Y. P. L.   March 10, 1911.

NL 0352862   NN

Liern y Cerach, Rafael María, 1832?-1897.
    La venida del Mesías; apropósito político-
electoral en un acto y en verso. Original
de D. Rafael María Liern. Madrid, Impr. de
J. Rodríguez, 1872.
    29p.

    Microcard edition.

NL 0352863   ICRL

LIERN Y CERACH RAFAEL MARÍA, 1832?-1897
    La verdad sospechosa; comedia ... de ...
Juan Ruiz de Alarcon. Madrid, Rodríguez y
Odriozola, 1896.
    87 p. (El teatro)

    Cover imprint: Madrid, F. Fiscowich, 1896.

    I. Ruiz de Alarcón y Mendoza, Juan, ca. 1580-1639
La verdad sospechosa. II. Title.

NL 0352864   InU

Liern y Cerach, Rafael María, 1832?-1897.
    La verda sospechosa, comedia en tres actos y en
verso del immortal Don Juan Ruiz de Alarcon, re-
fundida y arreglada por Rafael María Liern.
Madrid, Sucesores de Rodríguez y Odriozola, 1896.
    87p.
    Microcard edition.

NL 0352865   ICRL MoU FMU LU

Liern y Cerach, Rafael María, 1832?-1879.
    ¡Viva la paz! Apropósito patriótico en
un acto y en verso. Original de Don Rafael
María Liern. Madrid, Impr. de J. Rodríguez,
1876.
    27p.
    Microcard edition.

NL 0352866   ICRL

Liern y Cerach, Rafael Maria, 1832?-1897.
    Vivir al dia, comedia en tres épocas y en
verso. Madrid, J. Rodriguez, 1876.
    96 p. 8°. (El teatro).
    In: NPL p. v. 198, no. 9.

NL 0352867   NN MH

Liern y Cerach, Rafael María, 1832?-1897.
    Vivir al día, comedia en tres épocas y en
verso, original de Don Rafael María Liern.
Madrid, José Rodríguez, 1876.
    96 p.
    Microcard edition.

NL 0352868   ICRL FU LU MoU

Liern y Cerach, Rafael María, 1832?-1897.
    Y...sin contrata! Juguete cómico-lírico en un acto, en prosa
y verso, original. Música del maestro Angel Ruiz. Madrid: R.
Velasco, 1895. 27 p. 8°. (Administración lírico-dramática.)

    In: NPL p. v. 284, no. 17.

1. Drama (Spanish). 2. Ruiz, Angel,   composer. 3. Title.
N. Y. P. L.   March 9, 1911.

NL 0352869   NN MH

VOLUME 332

Liern y Cerach, Rafael María, 1832?-1897.
¡Y ... sin contrata! juguete cómico-lírico en un acto, en prosa y verso ... música del maestro Ángel Ruiz.   Madrid, R. Velasco, 1895.
27 p.
Microcard edition.

NL 0352870   ICRL MoU LU

[Liernar, Johann Carl] *fl.* 1730.
Christiani Liberi [pseud.] Kurtze, doch gründliche untersuchung der conventional- oder collegial-rechten der evangelischen kirchen und deren rechtmässigen verwaltung ... Franckfurth und Leipzig, J. C. Schröter, 1742.
12 p. l., 157, [2] p. 17ᵐ.
The first edition appeared in 1733, with the fictitious imprint: Freystadt [i. e. Eisenach, Wittekind] cf. Weller, Die falschen und fingirten druckorte. Leipzig, 1864.
1. Ecclesiastical law—Germany. 2. Church and state in Germany. I. Title: Kurtze, doch gründliche untersuchung der conventional- oder collegial-rechten der evangelischen kirchen ...
Library of Congress   BV764.G3L5   42-34738

NL 0352871   DLC

Liernur, Alexander Gerard Marie.
Hexenbesen. Ihre morphologie, anatomie und entstehung ... Rotterdam, Nijgh & van Ditmar's uitgevers-maatschappij, 1927.
57 p. illus., pl. 25ᶜᵐ.
Proefschrift—Utrecht.
"Stellingen" [3] p., laid in.
"Literatur" : p. 11-23.

1. [Witches' brooms]
Library, U. S. Dept. of   Agriculture 464L62   Agr 28-1668

NL 0352872   DNAL ICRL ICU CtY

                                                    KPG 56
Liernur, Alexander Gerard Marie.
Die pneumatische Canalisation in der Praxis, deren Beschreibung, entwickelungsgeschichte und gegenwärtige Ausdehnung nebst Beleuchtung der Bedenken dagegen.   Frankfurt A.M., Liernur & De Bruyn-Kops, 1873.

NL 0352873   MH DNLM

Liernur, Charles Thieme, ed.
Archiv für rationelle Städteentwässerung...
see under title

Liernur, Charles Thieme.
——. Erläuternde Berechnungen zu dem im Auftrag des Magistrats ausgearbeiteten Project einer pneumatischen Canalisation am Alexander-Platz in Berlin. 27 pp. 8°. *Berlin, A. Neuendorff,* 1871.

NL 0352875   DNLM

Liernur, Charles Thieme.
The Liernur sewerage system, judged by T. Hawksley [et al.]
    see under   Liernur & De Bruijn Kops, firm, Amsterdam.

Liernur (Charles Thieme). Offener Brief an die Theilnehmer der XLII. Versammlung deutscher Naturforscher und Aerzte zu Dresden 1868 als Antwort auf die Aeusserungen des Dr. Georg Varrentrapp in Frankf. a. M. 28 pp. 8°. *Prag, A. Renn,* 1868.

                                              KF 3985
Liernur, Charles Thieme.
Open letter to the members of the Glasgow philosophical society, on the sewage question; especially with reference to the system of keeping faecal matter out the common sewers, and of removing it by pneumatic force and in tubular drains, for the purpose of immediate utilisation in its natural state. Glasgow, 1869.

Cover-title.

NL 0352878   MH

WAA   LIERNUR, Charles Thieme.
L721p   Die pneumatische Canalisation in
1873   der Praxis; deren Beschreibung,
            Entwickelungsgeschichte und gegen-
            wärtige Ausdehnung, nebst Beleuchtung
            der Bedenken dagegen.   Frankfurt a. M,
            Liernur & De Bruyn-Kops, 1873.
            140 p.

NL 0352879   DNLM

Liernur, Charles Thieme
——. Die pneumatische Kanalisation und ihre Gegner. Eine Widerlegung der Hobrecht'schen Kritik über das Liernur'sche System und seine Anwendung in Prag. 30 pp. 8°. *Frankf. a. M., F. Bosseli,* 1870.

NL 0352880   DNLM

Liernur, Charles Thieme, ed.
Rationelle Städteentwässerung...
    see   Archiv für rationelle Städteent-
wässerung.

                                              KE 6577
[Liernur, Charles Thieme]
A report on the drainage of the rural sanitary district of the Chorlton Union on Captain Liernur's system. Accompanied with five drawings. [Manchester, Johnson & Rawson, printers, 1875]

Signed: Liernur & De Bruyn Kops.

NL 0352882   MH

Liernur, Charles Thieme.
——. Stelselmatige bodemverontreiniging contra pneumatische rioleering. Een onderzoek naar de aanhangige voorstellen ter verbetering van den openbaren gezondheidstoestand te Amsterdam. 59 pp. 8°. *Amsterdam, Schellema & Holkema,* 1879.

NL 0352883   DNLM

K   Liernur, Charles Thieme.
TD   Ueber das Canalisiren von Städten auf
653   getrenntem Wege. Vortrag, gehalten zu Frank-
L71   furt a.M. am 24. Juli 1879 zufolge Einladung
          der Sielbau-Commission vor der Stadtverord-
          netenversammlung.   Frankfurt a.M., Druck von
          R. Baist [1879]
          46 p. 23cm.

          With this is bound the author's Rationelle
          Städteentwässerung. Berlin, 1883.

          1. Sewage disposal.

NL 0352884   NIC DNLM

LIERNUR, Christoph Adolph.
Brevis inquisitio in resuscitatos hodiernorum irenicorum conoau unionem evangelicorum et reformatorum concernentes.   Artentorati.[1704]

4°. pp. (8), 32.

NL 0352885   MH

Liernur (Christoph Adolph)
Pfaltz-Zweybrück-evangelisches Gesang-Buch, welches ... ausgefertigt worden von ... Liernur. *Zweybrücken: J. C. Geiss,* 1747. 4 p.l., 916 pp., 12 l., 20 pp. 19°.
Imperfect: wanting one or more pages at end.

NL 0352886   NN

VM35   Liernur, Christoph Adolph, comp.
F15   Pfaltz-Zweybrück-evangelisches Gesang-Buch,
1763   welches auf gnädigsten Befehl des ... Herrn Christian
          des Vierten, Pfaltz-Grafen bey Rhein ... zur Beförderung öffentlicher und Privat-Andacht ausgefertiget worden. Von ... Christoph Adolph Liernur ...
          Zweybrücken, Johann Christian Geiss, 1763.
          4 p.l., 561, [47] p.   17 cm.

NL 0352887   NNUT

Liernur, Francis.
Cold storage for the suburbs of Paris and the provinces. (In: International Congress of Refrigeration, II. Vienna, 1910. Reports and proceedings. English edition.   Vienna, 1911. 4°. p. 498-499.)

1. Refrigeration, etc., France : Paris.
N. Y. P. L.   October 14. 1912.

NL 0352888   NN

TC917   Liernur, G. A.
.A3
1888   Egypt. *Wizārat al-Ashghāl al-'Umūmīyah.*
          ... Notes on the Wady Rayan, by Mr. G. A. Liernur, Col. Western and Col. Sir C. C. Scott Moncrieff ... Cairo, National printing office, 1888.

W 4   LIERNUR, George Martinus Antonius.
L68   Over het verschil in waarde van
1872   resectie en amputatie. Amsterdam,
          Kesteren, 1872.
          58 p.
          Akademisch proefschrift - Leyden.

NL 0352890   DNLM

Liernur, W.
Voetbal omnia vincit! Oorspronkelijk blijspel in één bedrijf. Baarn: J. F. van de Ven [1910].   31 p.   12°.

1. Drama (Dutch). 2. Title.
N. Y. P. L.   February 9, 1911.

NL 0352891   NN

W 6   LIERNUR & De Bruijn Kops, firm Amsterdam
P3   The Liernur sewerage system, judged
          by T. Hawksley [et al.] Amsterdam,
          1883.
          49 p.
          1. Liernur, Charles Thieme.
          I. Hawksley, Thomas, 1807-1893

NL 0352892   DNLM

VOLUME 332

Liernur & De Bruijn Kops.
A report on the drainage of the rural sanitary
district of the Chorlton Union on Captain Liernur's
system
       see under   [Liernur, Charles Thieme]

The Liernur sewerage system judged by T.
Hawksley, ...
       see under   Liernur & De Bruijn Kops,
firm, Amsterdam.

PQ2623
.I46P6
   Lierre, Georges.
     Poèmes. ₁Le Puy₎ Les Cahiers du nouvel humanisme
₁1950₎
     39 p. 20 cm.

                                 A 51-3103
     Illinois. Univ. Library
     for Library of Congress   ₁1₎

NL 0352895   IU

   Lierre, Henri.
     La question de l'absinthe. Paris, Impr. Vallée, 1867.
     68 p. 20 cm.

     1. Absinthe. 2. Temperance. I. Title.

     HV5036.L6   48-37407*

NL 0352896   DLC DNLM

Lierre (Paul). Traitement de l'incontinence
nocturne d'urine chez l'enfant. 98 pp., 1 l. 8°.
Toulouse. 1902. No. 459.

NL 0352897   DNLM ICRL

   Lierre, *Belgium*
     see Lier, *Belgium.*

   Liers, Emil E
     An otter's story; illustrated by Tony Palazzo. New York,
Viking Press, 1953.
     191 p. illus. 22 cm.

     I. Title.

     QL795.O8L5   599.744478   53-8175 ‡

     GU WaU MiU WaS WaSp Or OrCS OrP OrU IdPI OrMonO MoU
NL 0352899   DLC OO OOxM IU OClW OCl OClMA ScU MB OU

   Liers, Hugo.
     Abriss der lateinischen syntax. Waldenburg,
1902.

NL 0352900   NjP

   Liers, Hugo.
     Annahme und Verweigerung d. Schlacht in
Altertum. n.p., 1893.

NL 0352901   NjP

                    Soc 7226.300
   Liers, Hugo.
     Chronik und Mitglieder-Verzeichniss der Loge Glück
auf zur Brudertreue zu Waldenburg in Schlesien während
der ersten 50 Jahre ihres Bestehens. Im Auftage des
Beamten-Collegiums zusammengestellt. Waldenburg,
Ferd'nand Domel's Erben [1897?]

     54 p.

NL 0352902   MH

   Liers, Hugo.
     De aetate et scriptore libri fertur Demetrii
Phalerei peri hermeneias. n.p., 1880.

NL 0352903   NjP

   LIERS, Hugo.
     De aetate et scriptore libri qui fertur
Demetrii Phalerei peri hermeneias. Vratislaviae, apud G. Koebnerum, 1881.

     pp. (4), 35+

NL 0352904   MH

   Liers, Hugo.
     Das kriegswesen der alten, mit besonderer berücksichti-
gung der strategie. Von dr. phil. Hugo Liers ... Breslau, W. Koebner, 1895.
     viii, 391 p. 23½ᶜᵐ.

     1. Military art and science—Greece. 2. Military art and science—Rome.
I. Title.

NL 0352905   MiU NjP CU PU MH MB

---

*B29
.A2L68 Liers, Hugo.

     Rhetoren und philosophen im kampfe um
die staatsweisheit, von ... dr. Liers ...
Waldenburg I. Schl., 1888.
     1 p.l., 12 p. 26½cm.

     Programm - Städtisches evangelisches
gymnasium, Waldenburg in Schlesien.
     No more published?
     Contents. - I. Isokrates und die
sophisten. - II. Sokrates und seine
schüler. Aristoteles. - III. Die

     alexandrinische zeit. Philodemus und
Dionys.
     Placed with other foreign theses and
monographs in philosophy in a non-serial
collection, with title: ₁Dissertations
and other monographs in philosophy₎

NL 0352907   OCU

   LIERS, Hugo.
     Die Theorie der Geschichts-schreibung des
Dionys von Halikarnass. Waldenburg, i.Schl.
1886.

     4°.

NL 0352908   MH CU NjP

   Liers, Ilse, 1901-
     ... Ein Beitrag zur Frage der Schwangerschaft
und Tuberkulose... Hamburg, 1931.
     Inaug. -Diss. - Hamburg.
     Lebenslauf.
     Published also in Beiträge zur Klinik der
Tuberkulose. Bd. 78.
     "Literaturverzeichnis": p. 183.
     [Full name: Ilse Dorothea Liers]

NL 0352909   CtY

Liers (Julius Adolphus) [1840-]. *De placenta praevia. 32 pp. 8°. Berolini, G. Lange,
[1864].

NL 0352910   DNLM

                    Soc 6876.135
   Liersch, Arvid.
     Die Freimaurerei in Neuwied in der zweiten Hälfte
des achtzehnten Jahrhunderts; ein Beitrag zur freimaure-
rischen Geschichte des Rheinlands. Neuwied, Heuser
[1899]
     vi, 94 p.

NL 0352911   MH

   Liersch, Carl
     see   Liersch, Karl, 1855-

831Sa16
DL
     Liersch, Charlotte, 1901-
     Motivgeschichtliche und stilistische unter-
suchungen zur alemannischen Magdalenenlegende
... von Charlotte Liersch ... Marburg-Lahn,
R. Friedrich's universitäts-buchdruckerei,
1936.
     55, ₁1₎ p. diagr. 24ᶜᵐ.

     Thesis, Marburg.
     "Literatur": p. ₁5₎.
     1. Saelden Hort. 2. Alemannische Magdalenen-
legende.

NL 0352913   NNC ICRL CtY

   Liersch, Herbert, 1911-
     Beitrag zur klinik des brustdrüsenkrebses beim
manne unter mitteilung der beobachtungen an der
chirurgischen universitätsklinik Breslau. ...
Breslau, 1936. 49 p.
     Inaug. Diss. - Breslau, 1936.
     Lebenslauf.
     Literaturverzeichnis.

NL 0352914   CtY MiU

---

arW
38518
     Liersch, Karl, 1855-
     Die Gedichte Theodulfs, Bischofs von Or-
leans. Halle, E. Karras, 1880.
     77 p. 22cm.

     1. Theodulfus, Bp. of Orleans, d. 821.

NL 0352915   NIC CU NjP MWelC NIC

Liersch (L[udwig] W[ilhelm]) [1830-].
Brillen und Augengläser. Anleitung zur Auswahl und zum Gebrauche derselben. vi, 64 pp.,
1 l. 16°. *Leipzig, J. J. Weber.* 1859.

NL 0352916   DNLM

VOLUME 332

Liersch, Ludwig Wilhelm, 1830–

——. Die linke Hand. Eine physiologische und medicinisch-praktische Abhandlung für Aerzte, Pädagogen, Berufsgenossenschaften und Versicherungsanstalten. 47 pp. 8°. *Berlin, R. Schoetz.* 1893.

NL 0352917   DNLM MH-L

Liersch, Ludwig Wilhelm, 1830–

——. Die Schule von Salerno. 16 pp. 8°. *Leipzig, F. C. W. Vogel.* 1902.

NL 0352918   DNLM

WW   LIERSCH, Ludwig Wilhelm, 1830–
L721s   Der symptomencomplex Photophobie;
1860   eine ophthalmiatrische Studie. Leipzig,
         Wigand, 1860.
              iv, 138 p.

NL 0352919   DNLM MB

Liersch, Paul, 1910–
    Wodurch wird die prognose der offenen
schädelbrüche getrübt? ... Würzburg, 1933.
21 p.   8°.
    Inaug. Diss. –Würzburg, 1933.
    Lebenslauf.

NL 0352920   DNLM

Liersch (Walter). ² Ein Fall von Bleilähmung an den oberen und den unteren Extremitäten. [Erlangen.] 24 pp. 8°. [*Amberg, C. Grübler.* 1892.]

NL 0352921   DNLM

Lierse, Erna Krahn-
    see Krahn-Lierse, Erna.

Lierse, Heinz Günther, 1907–
    Der sitz der juristischen personen des
handelsrechts. ... Breslau, 1934.   52 p.
    Inaug. Diss. – Breslau, 1934.
    Lebenslauf.
    Bibliography.

NL 0352923   ICRL

Liersel, C.
    Nouveau traité de la chasse et de la pêche
    see under   René, Adolphe.

4D–484   Liersemann, Heinrich, 1868–
         Alle Mann an Bord! Unsere blauen Jungen im
         Weltkriege. Berlin, A. Weichert [c1917]
              223 p.

NL 0352925   DLC-P4

4VA–19   Liersemann, Heinrich, 1868–
         Erinnerungen eines deutschen Seeoffiziers.
         2. Aufl.   Rostock i. M., C. I. E. Volckmann
         (Volckmann & Wette) 1902.
              258 p.

NL 0352926   DLC-P4 NN

Liersemann, Heinrich, 1868–
    Klar zum gefecht! Unsere blauen jungen im welt-
kriege, 1914/15, von Heinrich Liersemann ... farbenbil-
der und zeichnungen von Oskar Theuer. Berlin, A. Wei-
chert [1915]
    271, [1] p. incl. illus., group of ports. col. front. (port.) col. plates. 22ᶜᵐ.

    1. European war, 1914–   —Juvenile literature.   I. Title.

Library of Congress   D581.L5   16–16111

NL 0352927   DLC

Liersemann, Heinrich, 1868–
    Wir von der »Möwe«! Husarenstreiche zur see,
von Heinrich Liersemann ... Mit 9 bildern.
Leipzig, G. Fock g.m.b.h. [1916]
    198 p.   front., plates (incl. ports.) 21½ᶜᵐ.

    1. Möwe (Steamship) 2. European war, 1914–1918—
Naval operations.

NL 0352928   MiU DLC-P4 NjP IU NN

Liersemann, Karl Heinrich, 1835–1896.
    Lehrbuch der arithmetik und algebra, von dr.
Karl Heinrich Liersemann ... Leipzig, B. G.
Teubner, 1871.
    iv, 173, [1] p., 1 l.   21ᶜᵐ.

    1. Arithmetic. 2. Algebra.

NL 0352929   ViU CtY

Liersemann, Karl Heinrich, 1835–1896.
    Disquisitiones variae circa superficies secundi
gradus uno centro praeditas...   Vratislaviae,
H. Lindne [1859]
    23 [3] p.   21 cm.   (German mathematical
dissertations. Breslau. v. 1).
    Inaug.-diss.--Breslau.
    Vita.

NL 0352930   RPB

Lierta, Juan Maria Jordán de Urriés, *marqués* de

see

Ayerbe, de Lierta y de Rubi, Juan Maria Jordán de Urriés
y Ruiz de Arana, *marqués* de, 1851–

Lierta, Juan Nepomuceno Jordan de Urries
y Ruiz de Arana, marques de Ayerbe y
    see   Ayerbe y Lierta, Juan Nepomuceno
Jordan de Urries y Ruiz de Arana, marques de.

Lierta, Pedro Jordan Maria de Urries, **marques**
    de Ayerbe y
        see   Ayerbe y Lierta, Pedro Jordan
    Maria de Urries, marques de.

4K   Liertz, Lorenz.
Swiss   Das Engelberger Talrecht; eine
84   rechtsgeschichtliche Studie.   En-
         gelberg, R. Hess, 1906.
              42 p.

NL 0352934   DLC-P4 MH-L

Liertz, Max.
    ... Adolf Damaschke und die deutsche
bodenreform, ...
        see under   Liertz, Werner.

Liertz, Rhaban, 1885–
    Albert der Grosse; Gedanken über sein Leben und aus
seinen Werken. Münster, Regensberg, 1948.
    277 p. 25 cm.

    Bibliography: p. 285–287.

    1. Albertus Magnus, Saint, Bp. of Ratisbon, 1193?–1280.   I. Title.

    BX4700.A375L5   51–30393

NL 0352936   DLC DCU CtY-D OC1ND

Liertz, Rhaban, 1885–
    ... Erziehung und seelsorge, ihr gewinn aus seelenaufschlies-
sender forschung. München, J. Kösel & F. Pustet, 1927.
    90 p. 19ᶜᵐ.

    1. Religious education. 2. Psychology, Religious.   I. Title.

    Library of Congress   BV1471.L5   27–25926
    Copyright A—Foreign   34604

NL 0352937   DLC

Liertz, Rhaban, 1885–
    Harmonien und Disharmonien des menschlichen Trieb- und
Geisteslebens, von Dr. med. Rhaban Liertz. München: J. Kösel
& F. Pustet, 1925. 257 p. 8°.

    274993A. 1. Hygiene, Mental.   2. Dreams, Mental. 3. Instinct.
    4. Sex—Psychology.
    N. Y. P. L.   December 31, 1926

NL 0352938   NN

Liertz, Rhaban, 1885–
    Kwellingen en ziekten van den geest, behandeling en
genezing. Met een voorwoord van F. Geelen. Hilversum,
P. Brand [1943]
    126 p. 21 cm.

    1. Psychiatry.

    RC601.L6   616.8   48–37741*

NL 0352939   DLC DNLM MnU

VOLUME 332

Liertz, Rhaban, 1885-
BD   Die Naturkunde von der menschlichen Seele
422   nach Albert dem Grossen [von] Rhaban Liertz.
G3   Köln, J. P. Bachem [1932]
L5   140p. illus. 21cm. (Schriften zur
    praktischen Erziehungskunde, 1. Bd.)

    1. Soul   2. Mind and body   3. Albertus,
    Magnus, Saint, Bp. of Ratisbon, 1193?-1280
    I. Title

NL   0352940   WU

Liertz, Rhaban, 1885-
    Psychoneurosen, fragmente einer verstehenden
    erziehungskunde.   München, Kösel [c.1928]
    478 p.   O.

NL   0352941   NcD

LIERTZ, Rhaban, 1885-
BX   Der selige Albert der Grosse als
4700   Naturforscher und Lehrer, zum
.A375   650jährigen Gedächtnis seines
L52x   Todestages, von Dr. Rhaban Liertz.
    München, Galesianer [1931]
    62 p. illus. 16 cm.
    Bibliography: p. [55]-58.
    Cover title reads: Der heilige
    Albert der Grosse ...

    1. Albertus Magnus, Saint, Bp. of
    Ratisbon, 1193?-1280.   I. Title

NL   0352942   OKentU

LIERTZ, Rhaban, 1885-
WI   Ueber die Lage des Wurmfortsatzes.
L719u   Berlin, Hirschwald, 1909.
1909   146 p. illus.

NL   0352943   DNLM IU-M ICJ PPC

Liertz, Rhaban, 1885-
    *Ueber die Lage des Wurmfortsatzes.
    II. Die Lage des Wurmfortsatzes beim Fötus
    und bei Kindern. 12 pp. 8°. München,
    C. Wolf & Son, 1910.

NL   0352944   DNLM

Liertz, Rhaban, 1885-
    Über Seelenaufschliessung. Ein Weg zum Erforschen
    des Seelenlebens. 2. unveränderte Aufl. Paderborn, F.
    Schöningh, 1927.
    3, 178 p. 22 cm.

    1. Psychoanalysis.

    BF173.L5 1927   51-55038

NL   0352945   DLC

Liertz, Rhaban, 1885-
    Vor den toren der ehe; ein buch für alle, die
    das glück der ehe suchen, von Dr. med. Rhaban
    Liertz. Recklinghausen G.W. Visarius, (pref. 1926)
    111 p.

NL   0352946   PV

LIERTZ, Rhaban, 1885-
HQ   Vor den Toren der Ehe; ein Buch für
734   alle, die das Glück der Ehe suchen. 2.
L719v   Aufl. Recklinghausen, Visarius [1938]
1938   112 p. (Visarius Bücher)
    1. Marriage

NL   0352947   DNLM

LIERTZ, Rhaban, 1885-
WM   Wanderungen durch das gesunde und
9   kranke Seelenleben bei Kindern und
L719w   Erwachsenen. München, Kösel & Pustet,
1923   1923.
    ix, 168 p.   illus.

NL   0352948   DNLM NNC-M OCIW-H

Liertz, Rhaban, 1885-
    Wanderungen durch das gesunde und kranke seelenleben bei
    kindern und erwachsenen, von dr. med. Rhaban Liertz. 5. aufl.,
    13. bis 16. tausend. München, J. Kösel & F. Pustet, k. g., 1924.
    ix, 169 p. illus. 21½ᶜᵐ.

    1. Psychology, Pathological.   I. Title.

    Library of Congress   RC343.L6 1924   43-30032

NL   0352949   DLC

Liertz, Rhaban Anton Maria Leopold
    see   Liertz, Rhaban, 1885-

Liertz, Rolf, 1927-
    Die absatzwirtschaftliche Bedeutung des Sortimentsgross-
    handels für die Distribution von Arzneimitteln. [Berlin?
    1955]
    iv, 119, x l. 30 cm.
    Diss.—Freie Universität Berlin.
    Vita.
    Bibliography: leaves [i]-x.

    1. Drug trade—Germany.

    HD9668.5.L5   59-30111

NL   0352951   DLC NIC CtY

Liertz, Werner.
    Adolf Damaschke und die deutsche Bodenreform; ihre
    Ziele und Wege. [Ein Gedenkblatt zur 50. Wiederkehr der
    Begründung des Bundes Deutscher Bodenreformer, 3. April
    1898-3. April 1948. 1. Aufl.] Düsseldorf, L. Schwann
    [1948]
    52 p. 23 cm.

    1. Damaschke, Adolf Wilhelm Ferdinand, 1865-1935.   2. Land
    tenure—Germany.

    HD655.D23L5   333.3   49-26665*

NL   0352952   DLC NjP

Liertz, Werner.
    Handbuch des arztrechts, herausgegeben von Werner Liertz
    ... und dr. med. Hans Paffrath ... Düsseldorf, L. Schwann
    [1938]
    xvi, 572 p. 23ᶜᵐ.

    1. Medical laws and legislation—Germany. 2. Physicians—Germany.
    I. Paffrath, Hans, 1898-   joint author. II. Title.

                 42-27894

NL   0352953   DLC

Liertz, Werner.
    Volksheimstätten und die Bekämpfung des Bodenpreis-
    wuchers. Düsseldorf, L. Schwann [1946]
    45 p. 23 cm.

    1. Land tenure—Germany.   I. Title.

    HD655.L5   51-15001

NL   0352954   DLC NN CU NNC

Lierval, Eugène.
    Culture pratique du phlox, par Lierval, horticulteur.
    Paris, Librairie d'horticulture de E. Donnaud [1866]
    2 p. l., 85 p. 5 pl. 16ᶜᵐ. (On cover: Bibliothèque de l'horticulteur et
    de l'amateur de jardinage)

    1. Polemoniaceae. [1. Phlox]

                       Agr 26-150
    Library, U. S. Dept. of   Agriculture 97L622

NL   0352955   DNAL MBH NN

Lierzang aan de Britten
    see under   Brender à Brandis, Gerrit,
    1751-1802.

Lierzang, aen de ...Heeren F. J. J. Eisinga, S. H.
Roorda van Eisinga, H Buma, [and others]... protes-
teerende leden in den Raed van Friesland, tegens de reso-
lutie van den 1. Sept. 1779 voor de bepaelde convooijen.
Leyden: L. Herdingh, 1780. 10 pp. 8°.

NL   0352957   NN

Lierzang den Erfprinse van Oranje ...erfstadhouder
van Gelderland, Holland en Westfriesland...op zyn ge-
boortedag den 8. van Lente-maand 1748 toegewyd.
[Signed L. Trip] *Groningen*: W. Febfns, 1748. 1 p.l.,
8 pp. 12°.
    In: GAD p. v. 24.

NL   0352958   NN

Lierzang op de verklaarde onafhanglijkheid der Noord-Ameri-
kaansche Staaten. [Dordrecht, 1782] 8 p. 20cm. (8°.)
    Knuttel 19971.
    Caption-title.
    Dated: Dordrecht 8 April 1782.

    977598A.   1. Poetry, Dutch.   2. United States—Hist.—Revolution
    —Poetry.
    N. Y. P. L.   August 17, 1939

NL   0352959   NN

Lies, B   Eugenia.
    Forms, their design and use, by B. Eugenia Lies ... New
    York, N. Y., American management association, °1929.
    30 p. incl. forms. fold. diagr. 23ᶜᵐ. ([American management asso-
    ciation] Institute of management series: no. 13]
    "To be presented at the Institute of management meeting in New York,
    May 10, 1929."—p. 3.

    1. Office supplies. 2. Printing. Practical—Make-up.   I. Title.

    Library of Congress   HF5371.L5   37-25510
    ——— Copy 2.
    Copyright A 10628   651.65

NL   0352960   DLC

VOLUME 332

Lies, Camilla E.
The rival queens. A fairy operetta.
Libretto by Camilla E. Lies, music by
Chas. H. McCurrie. As given by 96
children of Alameda in aid of the Children's
hospital, San Francisco ... Alameda,
Cal., c1896–97.
63 p. 34 cm.

NL 0352961 RPB

Liés, Eugene, tr.
The female minister; or, A son's revenge. Tr. from the original by Eugene Liés and Eugène Plunkett. New-York, Harper & brothers, 1846.

Liés, Eugene.
The preludes. A collection of poems. By Eugene Liés ... New-York, C. L. MacArthur, 1846.
56, ₁lvii₎–lviii p. front. 18¼ᶜᵐ.
Includes two poems in French, and "Seventeen selections from the first book of the Odes of Horace" (p. ₁37₎–56)

I. Horatius Flaccus, Quintus. II. Title.

28–4760

Library of Congress PS2246.L42

NL 0352963 DLC CtY ViU NcD CSmH

Liés, Eugene, tr.
Beauvoir, Eugène Auguste Roger de Bully, *called* Roger de, 1806–1866.
Safia; or, The magic of Count Cagliostro. A Venetian tale, tr. from the French of Roger de Beauvoir, by P. F. Christin and Eugene Lies. New York, Harper & brothers, 1845.

LIÉS, Eugene, of San Francisco?
Gustave Touchard, plaintiff, vs. The city and county of San Francisco, defendant. Argument for plaintiff Eugene Liés, solicitor for plaintiff; Delos Lake, of counsel. San Francisco, B. F. Sterett, printer, 1867.

pp. (2) 44.
Cover-title.
At head of title:- "In the Circuit court of the United States Distric of California.

NL 0352965 MH-L

Liés, Eugene, of San Francisco?
In the Supreme Court Of The State of California. Edgar O. Brown, Plaintiff And Respondent, vs. The City & County Of San Francisco et al. Defendants And Appellants. Brief On Behalf of Respondent. [by] Eugene Liés, Of Counsel For Respondent. San Francisco, J.B. Painter, Book And Job Printer, 1860.
1a. 4to. In the original buff, printed paper covers. Front cover loose.
Purchased from John Howell, July 8, 1925.

NL 0352966 CSmH

Liés, Eugene, of San Francisco?
Society of California pioneers, *San Francisco.*
... Inaugural ceremonies at the opening of the new "Pioneer hall," eighth of January, 1863. Inaugural address, by President O. P. Sutton. Oration by Eugene Liés, esq. San Francisco, Alta California book and job office, 1863.

Lies, Eugene Theodore, 1876–
The day nursery as a factor in the problem of relief and family rehabilitation, by Eugene T. Lies... (Read before the National Federation of Day Nurseries, May 2, 1916.) ₁n. p., 1916.₎
8 l. 24°.
Caption-title.

1. Crèches. 2. Title.
N. Y. P. L. October 25, 1918.

NL 0352968 NN

790 Lies, Eugene Theodore, 1876–
L71h High light report on a study of private group work agencies of Cleveland together with their relationships to other leisure time agencies ... Cleveland, Ohio, The Welfare federation of Cleveland, 1935.
73p. tables (1 fold.) diagrs. Q.

Autographic reproduction of typewritten copy.

NL 0352969 IaU DL MiD OC1

Lies, Eugene Theodore, 1876–
How you can make democracy work, by Eugene T. Lies ... New York, Association press, 1942.
x, 131 p. 21ᶜᵐ.
Bibliography: p. 129–131.

1. Social problems. 2. Citizenship. 3. Democracy. I. Title.

42–19486

Library of Congress HN64.L517
₁20₎ 323.35

PPG PSt PPT WaSp WaS
NL 0352970 DLC CaBVaU Or OrP MiU PP OLak OC1 OEac

Lies, Eugene Theodore, 1876–
The leisure of a people. Report of a recreation survey of Indianapolis, conducted under the auspices of the Council of social agencies and financed by the Indianapolis foundation; directed by Eugene T. Lies ... ₁Indianapolis, C. E. Crippin and son, inc.₎ 1929.
1 p. l., x, 3–571 p. incl. plans, tables, diagrs. (1 double) plans (part fold.) fold. tables. 23ᶜᵐ.
Bibliography: p. 563–571.
1. Indianapolis—Amusements. 2. Leisure. 3. Social surveys. I. Council of social agencies, Indianapolis. II. Indianapolis foundation. III. Title. IV. Title: Recreation survey of Indianapolis.

A 40–1818

Enoch Pratt free library
for Library of Congress ₁2₎

NL 0352971 MdBE PSt ICU IU OU

Lies, Eugene Theodore, 1876–
The new leisure challenges the schools ₁by₎ Eugene T. Lies.
(*In* National education association of the United States. Addresses and proceedings, 1934. p. 467–468)

1. Leisure. I. Title.

E 35–422

Library, U. S. Office of Education L13.N212 1934
Library of Congress [L13.N4 1934]

NL 0352972 DHEW

BJ1498 Lies, Eugene Theodore, 1876–
.N35 National recreation association.
The new leisure challenges the schools. Shall recreation enrich or impoverish life? Based on a study made for the National recreation association by Eugene T. Lies; with a foreword by John H. Finley, LL. D. Washington, D. C., National education association of the United States ₁1933₎

Lies, Eugene Theodore, 1876–
Public outdoor relief in Chicago. [By] Eugene T. Lies, general superintendent, United Charities of Chicago. Chicago, Ill., [United Charities of Chicago], 1916.
10 p. 24ᶜᵐ.
Caption title.
"No. 59, Reprints and addresses of the National Conference of Charities and Correction, 1916 meeting at Indianapolis."

NL 0352974 ICJ

Lies, Eugene Theodore, 1876–
Chicago. *Municipal markets commission.*
Report to the mayor and aldermen, by the Chicago Municipal markets commission, on a practical plan for relieving destitution and unemployment in the city of Chicago. Chicago ₁H. G. Adair, printer₎ 1914.

Lies, Eugene Theodore, 1876–
Study of the leisure-time problem and recreation facilities in Cincinnati and vicinity, made by Eugene T. Lies, special representative, National recreation association. Prepared for the Public recreation commission, City of Cincinnati, Ohio ... Cincinnati, O., The Cincinnati bureau of governmental research, 1935.
2 v. tables. charts. 27ᶜᵐ. (₁Cincinnati bureau of governmental research₎ Report no. 65)
Mimeographed.
Bibliography: v. 2, leaves 379–383.
1. Leisure. 2. Cincinnati—Amusements. I. Title.

A 36–1127

Univ. of Chicago BJ1498.L7 (Ed) Printed by L. C.

NL 0352976 ICU OU OC1 OCU OrU

Liesau, Franz
see
Liesau, Oscar Franz, 1877–

W 4 Liesau, Herbert, 1914–
M96 Ausheilung cystischer Tumoren nach
1940 Frakturen. München, Schneider, 1940.
30, ₁4₎ p.
Inaug.-Diss. - Munich.
Bibliography: p. ₁31₎–₁33₎

NL 0352978 DNLM MnU

Liesau (Hermann). *Der Einfluss der Castration auf den weiblichen Organismus, mit besonderer Berücksichtigung des sexuellen und psychischen Lebens. 165 pp. 8°. Freiburg i. B., C. Lehmann, 1896.

NL 0352979 DNLM PU

W 4 LIESAU, Karl, 1911–
F82 Ausnutzungsversuche mit Obst und
1938 Gemüse. Frankfurt a. M., 1938.
12, 2 p.
Inaug.-Diss. - Frankfurt.
1. Fruit 2. Vegetables

NL 0352980 DNLM

VOLUME 332

Liesau, ₍Oscar₎ Franz, 1877–
  Studien zur altfranzösischen synonymik mit zugrunde-
legung der varianten des fablel L'Auberee ... Greifswald, Druck von J. Abel, 1900.

36 p. 23½ᶜᵐ.
Inaug.-diss.—Greifswald.
Lebenslauf.

1. French language—Old French—Synonyms.

                                                  G–1990

Library of Congress   PC2886.L7   *

NL 0352981   DLC CtY NjP PU CU MH

Liesau, Otto Franz, 1908–
  Zur biologie von didymella lycopersici, dem
erreger der tomatenkrebskrankheit ... Dessau,
1932. 34 p.
  Inaug. Diss. -Bonn, 1932.
  Lebenslauf.
  Bibliography.

NL 0352982   ICRL

Liesbert, Arthur, 1878–
  Die philosophie Giovanni Picos della
Mirandola; ein beitrag zur philosophie der
frührenaissance. (Einleitung. Kapitel I.
Kapitel II, abschnitt C.)... [Berlin, E.
Ebering] 1908.
  49, [1] p.   23 cm.
  Inaug.-diss. - Berlin.
  Lebenslauf. Name originally: Arthur Levy.
  "Verzeichnis der fertiggestellten werke
Picos": p. [7]
  1. Pico della Mirandola, Giovanni, 1463-1494.

NL 0352983   CU

Liesch, Auguste, ed.
  Luxemburg (Grand duchy) Courts.
  Pasicrisie luxembourgeoise. Recueil de la jurisprudence
luxembourgeoise en matière civile, commerciale, criminelle, de
droit public, fiscal, administratif et notarial ... t. ₁-
₍1872/1880₎-
  Luxembourg, Imprimerie T. Schroell, 1881-19

NL 0352986   ICJ

LIESCH, Bruce A
  Records of wells, water levels, and quality
of ground water in the Sammamish Lake area,
King county, Washington.
      [Tacoma, Wash.?] 1955. 193p. maps.
(1 fold.) fold.diagr. tables.

      At head of title: United States, Department
of the Interior, Geological survey, Water
resources division, Ground water branch.

NL 0352985   WaS

Liesch, J B   M912.43 M200
  Carte du Grand-Duché de Luxembourg, dressée par J. B. Liesch,
vérificateur chef de Bureau du cadastre, de concert avec plusieurs
collaborateurs de la même administration. ... [Bruxelles,
Établissement géographique de Bruxelles, 1862.]
  1 map in 9 sections. 67½ x 56½ᶜᵐ. - 69½ x 56ᶜᵐ.
  Scale, 1:40 000.
  "Dessinée par Pellering."

NL 0352986   ICJ

---

410   Liesche, Hermann.
L62e   Einfluss der französischen sprache
       auf die deutsche.   Dresden, 1871.
       100p.

       Gymn.-progr.—Neustadt-Dresden.

NL 0352987   IU

Liesche, Kurt, 1902–
  Studien über bildung und zersetzung von humusstoffen.
  Landw. jahrb. bd. 68, p. 435–488.   Berlin, 1928.
  Also issued as inaugural dissertation, Leipzig, 1928.

1. Humus.
                                          Agr 29–1255
Library, U. S. Dept. of   Agriculture 1SL23 bd. 68

NL 0352988   DNAL ICRL MH CtY ICJ

Liesche, Otto, 1878–
  Molargewichtsbestimmungen. Allgemeine theorie des mo-
largewichtes; die praxis der ebullioskopie und der kryoskopie.
Von Otto Liesche ... (Mit 38 abbildungen und 3 kurven.)
  (In Abderhalden, Emil, ed. Handbuch der biologischen arbeitsmethoden ... Berlin, 1920–   25ᶜᵐ. abt. III, Physikalisch-
chemische methoden. t. 4, 1. hälfte (1928) p. ₍569₎–722. illus., tables
(part fold.) diagrs.)
  Bibliographical foot-notes.

  1. Molecular weights. 2. Ebullition. 3. Cryoscopy.
                                              A C 36–3124
Title from Ohio State   Univ.
Library of Congress   [QH324.A3 1920 abt.3, t. A]
                      ₍2₎   (574.072)

NL 0352989   OU

Liesche, Otto, 1878–
  Rechenverfahren und rechenhilfsmittel mit anwendungen
auf die analytische chemie, von prof. dr. Otto Liesche ... Stuttgart, F. Enke, 1932.
  viii, 201 p. illus., diagrs. 24½ᶜᵐ. (Added t.-p.: Die Chemische analyse ... hrsg. von Wilhelm Böttger ... xxx. bd.)
  "Nomographische literatur": p. ₍194₎

  1. Mathematics. 2. Chemistry, Analytic. ₍2. Chemistry—Analysis—
Methods₎ 3. Nomography (Mathematics)
                                          Agr 32–381
U. S. Dept. of agr. Library   3B7M33 bd. 30
  for Library of Congress   QD75.C5 bd. 30
———— Copy 2.   QA39.L49
                      ₍a45c1₎†   (543.082) 510.84

NL 0352990   DNAL OrCS ViU MiHM NN NIC DLC PU

QD305 Liesche, Otto, 1878–
.A6L7   I. Ueber die akroleindarstellung nach wohl-
        neuberg. II. Beitraege zur kenntnis deer phenyl-
        hydraz one des acetaldehydes und des acetones.
        Weida, 1904.
        82p.
        Inaug. diss. Leipzig.

NL 0352991   DLC CtY PU

Liesching (Carol. Ludov. Guil.) * De gan-
grena. 43 pp. 4°. *Gottinge, Dieterich,* 1811.

NL 0352992   DNLM PPC

Liesching, Christian Friedrich, respondent.
    ... Dissertatio mathematica de triglyphis,
qvam ...
      see under Krafft, Georg Wolfgang,
1701-1754, praeses.

Liesching (Christoph. Fridericus). * Tripes
Heitersbacensis primam considerationem histo-
rico-dogmaticam defendendam sumsit. 44 pp.
1 pl. sm. 4°. *Tubinga, lit. Bauhof- et Franckia-
niis.* ₍1755₎.

NL 0352994   DNLM NNNAM PPC

BV   Liesching, Fanny Gregson, 1865-1893.
3277   Letters from Ceylon, by Fanny Gregson. With
L5   preface by the Rev. J. Elder Cumming, and a
        brief sketch by her father. London, Marshall
        Brothers ₍1893?₎
        xv, 208 p. illus.

        1. Missions—Ceylon. I. Title.

NL 0352995   NSyU

Liesching, G F   respondent.
  Consideratio historico-iuridica eorum quae in
Pacificatione Westphalia expediri nequiverant ...
    see under Hoffmann, Gottfried Daniel,
1719-1780, praeses.

BJ55   Liesching, Louis F
14h   A brief account of Ceylon ... Jaffna, Ripley
        & Strong, printers, 1861.
        xp., ₁ℓ., 151, [1] p., ₁ℓ. 17½cm.
        "List of works quoted or consulted": 1ℓ.
        preceding p.1.

NL 0352997   CtY

Liesching, Louis F.
  Personal reminiscences of Laurence Oliphant.
A note of warning. London, Marshall Brothers
[1891]
  40 p.

NL 0352998   PPL

JGN   Liesching, Louis F
PR   Through peril to fortune; a story of
4889   sport and adventure by land and sea.
L4T4   London, New York, Cassell, Petter,
        Galpin [1880]
        224 p. illus.

NL 0352999   MoU

Liesching (Theodor) [1853–]. * Ueber
Schenkelhalsbrüche. 19 pp., 1 pl. 8°. *Würzburg, Stürtz.* [1892].

NL 0353000   DNLM ICRL

Lieschke, Edgar, 1905–
  ... Die Hyperemesis gravidarum, eine
Schwangerschaftstoxikose ... Leipzig,
1931.
  Inaug.-Diss. - Leipzig.
  Lebenslauf.
  "Literatur": p. 18-19.

NL 0353001   CtY

Lieschke, Gerhard.
  Die eisentherapie bei den sekundären
anaemien der pferde. Berlin ₍n.d.₎
  32 p. 22 cm.

NL 0353002   DNAL

VOLUME 332

Leeschke, Gottfried, appr. Arzt, Unterarzt im Feldart.-Reg.
Nr. 58: Lipom und Trauma. Berlin: Ebering (1911)
46 S. 8° ¶ (Ersch. auch als Buch ebd.)
Berlin, Med. Diss. v. 29. Mai 1911, Ref. Hildebrand
[Geb. 25.Okt. 84 Plauen i. V.; Wohnort: Minden; Staatsangeh.: Sachsen;
Vorbildung: Realgymn. Plauen Reife O. 05; Studium: Berlin K. W. A. 10 S.;
Coll. 23. Mai 11; Appob. 27. Mai 11.]   [U 11. 100

NL 0353003   ICRL CtY NNC DNLM

Lieschke, Reinhard: Einfluß der Rachitis auf Kiefer und Zähne.
[Maschinenschrift] 39 S. 4°. — Auszug: Berlin (1922): Ebering.
2 Bl. 6°
Berlin, Med. Diss. v. 29. Sept. 1922 [1923]   [U 23. 196

NL 0353004   ICRL

Lieschke (Wolfgang Carl Moritz) [1891–   ].
*Beiträge zur Kenntnis der Lebererkrankun-
gen im Kindesalter. 88 pp. 8°. Berlin, E.
Ebering, 1917.

NL 0353005   DNLM CtY

Liesde, J.   de.
Gevaar! Gevaar! En geen vrede! Een woord tot
de slapenden en in slaap gewiegden, door J. de
Liesde ... Te Zutphen, bij A.E.C. van Someren.
1844.

[4], 110 p.   21.3cm.
No.6 in bound volume of pamphlets.

1.Dutch in the U.S.   I.Title.

NL 0353006   MiU-C

Liese, Adolph.
Ein dienstjahr in der einklassigen volksschule.
Berlin, 1886.
D.
Bound with Gelmini, Andrea. Studi psicologici
sul fanciullo. 1886.

NL 0353007   RPB CtY

Liese (Arthur) [1819–   ]. *De enuresi. 29
pp. 8°. Berolini, typ. fratrum Schlesinger, [1848].

NL 0353008   DNLM

Liese, Engelbert, 1906–
Der zeemaneffekt an den bandenspektren des
calciumbromids und strontiumchlorids sowie den
linienspektren des arsens und iridiums. ...
Bonn, 1936.
Inaug. Diss. - Bonn, 1936.
Lebenslauf.
Literatur-Verzeichnis.

NL 0353009   ICRL

---

ar W   **Liese, Ernst,** 1870–
53569   Des J. A. Comenius Methodus linguarum
no.1   novissima. Inhalt und Würdigung. Bonn,
         C. Georgi, Univ.-Buchdr., 1904.
         101 p. .22cm.

         Inaug.-Diss.--Erlangen.

         1. Comenius, Johann Amos, 1592-1670.

NL 0353010   NIC ICRL MH MdBJ NN PU CtY

Liese, Ernst, 1886–
Vom geiste in deutschen schulen und beim deutschen lehrer,
ein beitrag zur volkbewussten gestaltung von unterricht und
erziehung, von dr. Ernst Liese ... 2. aufl. der "Volksschule
nach dem kriege." Halle (Saale) H. Schroedel, 1934.

111, [1] p. 23½°.

"Verzeichnis der benutzten schriften": p. [112]

1. Education—Germany.   I. Title.
                                                      42-44608

Library of Congress   LA724.L5

NL 0353011   DLC CtY IaU

. 1886 (July)–
Liese, Ernst, Über das Bandenspektrum des Quecksilbers.
Leipzig: J. A. Barth 1912. 32 S. 8° ¶ (Aus: Zeitschrift f.
wiss. Photogr. Bd 11.)
Bonn, Phil. Diss. v. 22. Nov. 1912, Ref. Kayser
[Geb. 1. Juli 86 Olpe i. W.; Wohnort: Cöln; Staatsangeh.: Preußen; Ver-
bildung: Kaiser-Wilhelms-Gymn. Cöln Reife O. 06; Studium: Bonn 4, Frei-
burg i. B. 1, Bonn 6 S.; Rig. 26. Juni 12.]   [U 12. 4884

NL 0353012   ICRL MH PU

Liese, Erwin, 1892-
Über Quecksilbersubstitutionsprodukte des
p-Amidobenzoësäureäthylesters ...
[Berlin, 1915]
32 p.   22 cm.
Inaug.-Diss. - Berlin.
Lebenslauf.

NL 0353013   CtY

Liese (Franciscus Josephus Napoleon) [1808–   ].
*De epilepsia. 52 pp. 8°. Berolini, typ. Nic-
tschlanis. [1832.

NL 0353014   DNLM PPC

Liese (Grover Bernhard) [1888–   ]. *Ein
Fall von Vorderkammer- und Korneoskleral-
zyste mit Endothelauskleidung. 47 pp. 8°.
Heidelberg, Rössler & Herbert, 1918.

NL 0353015   DNLM CtY ICRL

Liese, Günter, 1915–
Der Einfluss der amerikanischen Porzellanzölle auf den
deutschen Haushaltporzellanexport nach den Vereinigten
Staaten von Amerika. München, 1954.

v, 154 L. illus. 30 cm.

Typescript (carbon copy)
Inaug.-Diss.—Munich.
Vita.
Bibliography: leaves 151-154.

1. Tariff on pottery—U. S. 2. Pottery—U. S. 3. Pottery—Germany.

HF2651.P8U57   59-30106

NL 0353016   DLC

Liese, Helmut, 1908–
Die conditio indebiti des öffentlichen rechts
und der rechtsweg. ... Tübingen, 1934.   84 p.
Inaug. Diss. - Tübingen, 1934.
Lebenslauf.
Bibliography.

NL 0353017   ICRL

PT1105   **Liese, Hermann,** ed.
.N3
         Nationalsozialistische deutsche arbeiter-partei. *Reichspro-
         pagandaleitung. Hauptkulturamt.*
            Das deutsche hausbuch, herausgegeben in verbindung mit
         dem Winterhilfswerk des deutschen volkes vom Hauptkul-
         turamt in der Reichspropagandaleitung der NSDAP. Berlin,
         F. Eher nachf., 1943.

NL 0353018 ...

GT4985   **Liese, Hermann.**
.R43
         Nationalsozialistische Deutsche Arbeiter-Partei. *Reichs-
         propagandaleitung. Hauptkulturamt.*
            Deutsche Kriegsweihnacht. [Für den Inhalt verantwort-
         lich: Hermann Liese. 4. Aufl.] München, F. Eher Nachf.
         [1944]

DD253   **Liese, Hermann.**   FOR OTHER EDITIONS
.N322   SEE MAIN ENTRY
1943   [Nationalsozialistische deutsche arbeiter-partei. *Reichs-
         propagandaleitung. Hauptkulturamt]*
         Ich kämpfe. [München, F. Eher nachf., 1943]

Liese (Hugo) [1846–   ]. *Ueber die heredi-
täre Syphilis. 25 pp., 1 l. 8°. Breslau, H.
Lindner, 1869.

NL 0353021   DNLM

Liese, Johannes, 1891–1952.
   Beiträge zur Kenntnis des Wurzelsys-
tems der Kiefer (Pinus silvestris) nebst
Beobachtungen an anderen Baumwurzeln.
Habilitationsschrift zur Erlangung der
venia legendi der Forstlichen Hochschule
Eberswalde.   Berlin, Springer, 1926.
67 p. plates. tables.   O.

NL 0353022   NcD

TA424   **Liese, Johannes,** 1891–   ed.
.T7
1950   Troschel, Ernst, ed.
           Handbuch der Holzkonservierung. 3., neubearb. Aufl.
        Unter Mitwirkung von Kurt Bach [et al.] Hrsg. von
        Johannes Liese. Berlin, Springer, 1950.

Liese, Johannes, 1891–1952.
   Holzschutz. Hrsg. von Walter Liese und Cecilie Gröger.
Berlin, Verlag Technik, 1954.
140 p. illus. 22 cm.

1. Wood—Preservation.   I. Title.

TA422.L46   57-21457 †

NL 0353024   DLC DNAL

Liese, Johannes, 1891–1952.
   Die Rostpilzerkrankungen der Waldbä-
ume. n.p., n.p., 1928.
v.p. illus. plates   O.

Reprint from Mitteilungen der Deutscher
Dendrologischen Gesellscjaft. N.40. 1928.

NL 0353025   NcD

VOLUME 332

Liese, Johann Anton Eduard.
De vi, quam morbi cerebri in functiones sensuum exercent. Berolini, Nietackianis, ₍1836₎
34 p.
Inaug. Diss.

NL 0353026   PPC

Liese, Josef
Die Rechtsnatur des Vorkaufsrechts und seine Formbedürftigkeit bei Grundstücksveräusserungen ... von Josef Liese ... Emsdetten, Heinr. & J. Lechte, 1935.

5 p.l., 29 p. 22½cm.
Inaug.-Diss. - Erlangen.
"Literaturverzeichnis": 3d - 5th prelim. leaf.

NL 0353027   MH-L

LIESE, Joseph.
Der altfranzösische roman "Athis et Prophilias" verglichen mit einer erzählung von Boccaccio (x.8). Görlitz, 1901.

4°. pp. 19.
Progr. d. städt. realsch. "1901, no. 243".

NL 0353028   MH

Hie   Liese, Joseph.
012   Der Minnesinger Reimar von Brennenberg; sein
L62   Geschlecht und seine Lieder. Posen, 1897.
     Pamphlet
L   "Beilage zum Jahresbericht des Königlichen Marien-Gymnasiums zu Posen. 1897. Progr. Nr. 169".

    1. Reimar von Brennenberg, 13th century.
    cdu

NL 0353029   CtY CU NcD

Liese, Joseph, 1867-1939.
Das Aachener Land in der Steinzeit. Aachen, J.A. Mayer, 1930.

119 p. (Aachener Beiträge zur Heimatkunde, 8)

NL 0353030   MH

Liese, Joseph, 1867-1939.
... Das klassische Aachen ... Aachen, J.A. Mayer, 1936-39.
2v. in 1. plates, ports., facsims., plan. 23cm. (Aachener beiträge zur heimatkunde, hrsg. von prof. dr. Max Eckert-Greifendorff. XVII, XX)

Contents. - I. Johann Arnold von Clermont (1728-1795), sein geschlecht und sein schaffen im Vaalser paradies". - II. Theodor Christian von Clermont, Helene Elisabeth Jacobi geb. von Clermont, Goethes "Dorothea".
1. Clermont   family. I. Aachener beiträge zur heimat-   kunde. II. Title.

NL 0353031   WU

Liese, Julius Gustav Robert, 1866-
Die Flexion des Verbums bei Spenser. Halle, C.A. Kaemmerer & Co. 1891.
51p. 23cm.
Inaug.-Diss.--Friedrichs Univ., Halle-Wittenberg.
Vita.

    1. Spenser, Edmund - Language - Grammar.

NL 0353032   KAS PBm ICRL NcD MiU NjP IU CU MH

Liese, Kurt.
Ueber die messung der dichtigkeit vagabundierender ströme im erdreich ... Halle a. S., Druck von W. Knapp, 1906.
2 p. l., 27, ₍1₎ p. illus. 28½ᶜᵐ.
Inaug.-diss.—Technische hochschule, Karlsruhe.

1. Electric currents.

                       9-20588
Library of Congress   QC615.L7

NL 0353033   DLC ICRL PU CtY

Liesche, Richard, publisher.
Atlas der einheimischen Schmetterlinge & Raupen ... Teil 1-2, Tafeln, 12.
Annaberg, Liesche, K.D.

NL 0353034   PPG

Liese, Robert
    see   Liese, Julius Gustav Robert, 1866-

Liese, Walther, joint author.

Bradtke, Franz, 1884-
Hilfsbuch für raum- und aussenklimatische messungen, mit besonderer berücksichtigung des katathermometers, von Franz Bradtke und Walther Liese, mit 20 zahlentafeln und 30 abbildungen im text. Berlin, J. Springer, 1937.

NL 0353038   DNLM

Liese (Wilhelm). *Ueber einen Fall von Lippen- und Kieferspalte mit besonderer Berücksichtigung der Zwischenkieferfrage. 16 pp. 8°. Leipzig, A. Edelmann, 1893.

HV   Liese, Wilhelm, 1876-
16   Geschichte der caritas, von Prof. Dr. Wilh.
.L71   Liese... Freiburg i. Br., Caritas-verlag, 1922.
     2 v.
     "Jubiläumswerk des Deutschen caritasbandes, 1897-1922."
     "Verzeichnis der benutzten bücher": bd. II., p. ₍245₎-278.

    1. Charities - History. I. Deutsches caritasband

NL 0353039   DCU CU-L NRCR ICU CtY DCU MH

Liese, Wilhelm, 1876-
Handbuch des Mädchenschutzes. Insbesondere für Priester und die Mitglieder charitativer Vereine. Freiburg im Breisgau, Charitasverband für das katholische Deutschland, 1904.
VII, 313 p. 16°. (Charitas-Schriften, Heft 13.)

NL 0353040   NN

Liese, Wilhelm, 1876-
⁷⁹⁴⁸ Das hauswirtschaftliche Bildungswesen in Deutschland, von Dr. Wilhelm Liese. Herausgegeben von "Arbeiter Verband für soziale Kultur und Wohlfahrtspflege. M. Gladbach, Zentralstelle des Volksvereins für das Kath. Deutschland, 1906.
vii, 104 p. 23½ᶜᵐ.

NL 0353041   ICJ

Liese, Wilhelm, 1876-
⁷⁹⁴⁸ Das hauswirtschaftliche Bildungswesen in Deutschland. Von Dr. Wilhelm Liese. Herausgegeben vom Verband für Soziale Kultur und Wohlfahrtspflege (Arbeiterwohl). 2. Auflage. M. Gladbach, Volksvereins-Verlag, GmbH., 1910.
[v]-xvi, 153 p. 22ᶜᵐ.
"Literatur," p. xiii-xvi.

NL 0353042   ICJ IU

Liese, Wilhelm, 1876-
Die katholischen orden Deutschlands und der völkerkrieg 1914/15. Statistik ihrer kriegsarbeit vom 1. august bis 31. dezember 1914, veranstaltet vom Caritasverband für das kathol. Deutschland, e. v., und bearbeitet von professor dr. W. Liese ... Freiburg i. Br., Caritasverband, 1915.
31 p. 23½ᶜᵐ.

1. Monasticism and religious orders — Germany. 2. European war, 1914-1918—Hospitals, charities, etc. I. Deutscher caritasverband. II. Title.
                      35-22049 Revised
Library of Congress   D622.L5
         ₍r42b2₎   940.31522

NL 0353043   DLC

Liese, Wilhelm, 1876-
Die katholischen Wohltätigkeits-Anstalten und sozialen Vereine in der Diözese Paderborn. Zusammengestellt von W. Liese. Freiburg i. Br.: Charitasverband für das katholische Deutschland, 1906. vii, 216 p. 16°. (Charitas-Schriften. Heft 17.)

1. Charities.—Associations, Germany: Paderborn.
N. Y. P. L.   July 17, 1911.

NL 0353044   NN

282.43   Liese, Wilhelm, 1876-
M381BL Konrad Martin, Professor und Bischof.
    Paderborn, Verlag der Bonifacius-Druckerei
    [1936]
    xii, 250 p. illus., port. 24 cm.

    1. Martin, Konrad, 1812-1879.

NL 0353045   ICarbS OCX MH

362.50943 Liese, Wilhelm, 1876-
W567BL Lorenz Werthmann und der Deutsche Caritasverband. Freiburg i. Br., Caritasverlag, 1929.
    xi, 627 p. front. 23 cm.

    1. Werthmann, Lorenz, 1858-
    2. Deutscher Caritasverband. 3. Charitable societies. 4. Catholic Church in Germany.

NL 0353046   ICarbS DCU

Liese, Wilhelm, 1876-
Wohlfahrtspflege und caritas im Deutschen Reich, in Deutsch-Österreich, der Schweiz und Luxemburg, mit einem ortskataster und alphabetischem register der einschlägigen katholischen einrichtungen, von dr. theol. Wilhelm Liese ... Mit 1 grundriss und 24 trachtenbildern. M₍ünchen₎ Gladbach, Volksvereins-verlag, gmbh., 1914.
2 p. l., ₍ix₎-xv, 477 p. 4 pl. 24ᶜᵐ.
"Literaturverzeichnis": p. ₍419₎-435.
1. Charities—Germany. 2. Charities—Austria. 3. Charities—Switzerland. 4. Charities—Luxemburg. 5. Church charities. 6. Catholic church—Charities.
Library of Congress   HV275.L4
                      14-10552

NL 0353047   DLC CSt CtY NN MB

VOLUME 332

Liese, Wolfgang, 1911–
... Über die Entstehung der sog. malacischen Gewebsveränderungen der Kniegelenksmenisken .. Wiesbaden, 1937.
Inaug.-Diss. - Berlin.
Lebenslauf.
"Literatur-Angabe": p. 15.

NL 0353048 CtY

LIESEBERG, Friedrich, 1898–
Beiträge zur bestimmung der zerfallswärme des wasserstoffs. Inaug.-diss., Heidelberg, Heppenheim (Bergstr.), G.Otto, 1926.

pp. 51+. Diagrs.
"Lebenslauf", at end.

NL 0353049 MH CtY ICRL

Liese, Edith, 1891–1937.
The small white bird ₍by₎ Edith Liese. ₍New York, The Harbor press₎ 1937.

₍158₎ p. incl. front. (port.) 19ᵐ.
"200 copies printed."
Poems.

ɪ. Title. 37-24078

Library of Congress PS3523.I 32 1937
———— Copy 2.
Copyright A 109437 ₍3₎ 811.5

NL 0353050 DLC KyU

Liesegang, Carl.
Deutsche Berg- und Hüttenleute in Süd- und Mittelamerika. Beiträge zur Frage des deutschen Einflusses auf die Entwicklung des Bergbaus in Lateinamerika. ₍Hamburg, Hansischer Gildenverlag₎ 1949.

119 p. plates, port. 23 cm. (Hamburger romanistische Studien. B. Ibero-amerikanische Studien, Bd. 19)

Bibliography: p. 100–119.

1. Mining engineers. 2. Engineers, German. 3. Mines and mineral resources—Spanish America. ɪ. Title. (Series: Hamburger romanistische Studien. B. Ibero-amerikanische Reihe, Bd. 19)

TN139.L5 622 51-17603

NL 0353051 DLC ICU CoU LNHT TxU NN MH CtY TU WaU

Liesegang, Eduard, firm, Düsseldorf.
... Ed. Liesegang, Fabrik für Projektions-Apparate, Kinematographen und Lichtbilder, gegründet 1854, Düsseldorf... Charlottenburg: W. Raue, 1926. 35 p. illus. (incl. ports.) 4°. (Industrie und Handel. Bd. 19.)

"Verantwortlich für die Redaktion: F. P. Liesegang."

1. Optical lantern. 2. Liesegang, Franz Paul, 1873– , editor.
3. Ser.
N.Y.P.L. October 25, 1928

NL 0353052 NN NNC

Liesegang, Eduard, firm, Düsseldorf.
Die geschichte der firma Ed. Liesegang, Düsseldorf. Zur feier ihres 75 jährigen bestehens am 2. dezember 1929. ₍1929?₎
28 p. illus., ports., facsim. 28½ᶜᵐ.

1. Liesegang, Eduard, firm.

NL 0353053 NNC

LIESEGANG, Eduard, firm, Düsseldorf.
Liesegang; ein fortschrittliches Unternehmen mit reicher Tradition. [Düsseldorf, 1954?] [14] p. illus. 15 x 21cm.

Caption title.

NL 0353054 NN

Liesegang, Eduard, firm, Düsseldorf.
Verzeichniss von photographischer literatur aus dem verlage von Ed. Liesegang, Düsseldorf. ₍1896?₎
24 p. illus. 16½ᶜᵐ.

1. Photography - Bibliography.

NL 0353055 NNC

Liesegang, Erich, 1860–1931.
Hartwig, Otto, 1830–1903.
Aus dem leben eines deutschen bibliothekars. Erinnerungen und biographische aufsätze von Otto Hartwig. Mit dem bildnis des verfassers. Marburg, N. G. Elwert, 1906.

Z671 Liesegang, Erich, 1860–1931, ed.
.B62 Blätter für volksbibliotheken und lesehallen. 1.– jahrg. jan./feb. 1900–
Leipzig, O. Harrassowitz, 1900–

Law Liesegang, Erich, 1860–1931, ed.
Magdeburg. Schöffenstuhl.
Magdeburger Schöffensprüche. Im Auftrage und mit Unterstützung der Savigny-Stiftung hrsg. und bearb. von Victor Friese und Erich Liesegang. 1. Bd., Abth. 1–4. Berlin, G. Reimer, 1901.

Liesegang, Erich, 1860–1931.
Niederrheinisches städtewesen, vornehmlich im mittelalter. Untersuchungen zur verfassungsgeschichte der clevischen städte; von Erich Liesegang. Breslau, W. Koebner, 1897.

xx, 758, ₍2₎ p. 23ᶜᵐ. (Untersuchungen zur deutschen staats- und rechtsgeschichte, hrsg. von dr. Otto Gierke. 52. hft.)

1. Cities and towns, Medieval. 2. Municipal government—Germany—Hist. ɪ. Title.

Library of Congress JS5360.L7 3–3126

NL 0353059 DLC MB

LIESEGANG, Erich, 1860–1931.
Die parochialgerichte der stadt Köln. Bonn, 1885.

(4)+40 p.
Inaug.-diss. ——— Göttingen.

NL 0353060 MH-L ICRL

LIESEGANG, Erich, 1860–1931.
Recht und verfassung von Rees; ein beitrag zur städtegeschichte des Niederrheins.

(In WESTDEUTSCHE zeitschrift für geschichte und kunst. Ergänzungsheft 6, 1890.)

NL 0353061 MH

Liesegang, Erich, 1860–1931, joint author.
Kohler, Josef, 1849–1919.
Das römische recht am Niederrhein ... Von J. Kohler ... und E. Liesegang ... Stuttgart, F. Enke, 1896–

Liesegang, Erich, 1860–1931.
Die sondergemeinden Kölns. Beitrag zu einer rechts- und verfassungsgeschichte der stadt. Von Erich Liesegang. Bonn, M. Cohen & sohn, 1885.

2 p. l., 189, ₍1₎ p. 24ᵐ.

1. Cologne—Pol. & govt. 5-9521

Library of Congress JS5368.C7G46

NL 0353063 DLC

Liesegang, Erich, 1860–1930.
Zur Geschichte des klevischen Städtewesens unter dem ältesten Herrscherhaus. (In: Hist. Verein f.d. Niederrhein ... Veröffentl. Köln, 1909. 8°. v. 2 p. 64–109.)

NL 0353064 NN

LIESEGANG, Erich, 1860–1931.
Zur verfassungsgeschichte der stadt Köln vornahmlich im 12 und 13 jahrhundert. n.p., n.d.

NL 0353065 MH

Liesegang, Erich, 1860–1931.
Zur Verfassungsgeschichte von Magdeburg und Salzwedel. n. t.-p. ₍Leipzig₎
69 p. 22cm.

Caption title.
"Sonderabdruck aus den Forschungen zur Brandenburgischen und Preussischen Geschichte. 3. Band 2. Hälfte."

1. Magdeburg—Hist. 2. Salzwedel, Ger.—Hist.

NL 0353066 NIC

Liesegang, Erich, 1860–1931.
Zur Verfassungsgeschichte von Neuruppin. (Sonderabzug aus den Forschungen zur Brandenburgischen und Preussischen Geschichte, Bd. 5. Leipzig, 1892)
83 p. 8°.

NL 0353067 CtY

Liesegang, Franz Paul, 1873–
Die fernphotographie. Düsseldorf, E. Liesegang, 1897.
134 p. illus., plates, diagrs. 22cm.

Bibliographical footnotes.
Contents.—Das prinzip der telephotographischen systeme.—Die konstruktion der teleobjektive und deren anwendung.—Telestereoskop-aufnahmen.—Fernaufnahmen mit einfachen hilfsmitteln.—Auge und camera.—Die geschichte der telephotographie.

NL 0353068 NNC NjP ICJ NN ViU

Liesegang, Franz Paul, 1873– joint ed.
Forschungen zur geschichte der optik (Beilagehefte zur Zeitschrift für instrumentenkunde) ... bd. 1– Berlin, J. Springer. 1928–

VOLUME 332

Liesegang, Franz Paul, 1873 –
Handbuch der praktischen Kinematographie. Die verschiedenen Konstruktions-Formen des Kinematographen, die Darstellung der lebenden Lichtbilder sowie das kinematographische Aufnahme-Verfahren. Von F. Paul Liesegang. .... Mit 125 Abbildungen. Leipzig, E. Liesegang (M. Eger), 1908.
vii, 294 p. front., illus. 22½ᶜᵐ.

NL 0353070 ICJ PU NN PU-Math PPF

Liesegang, Franz Paul, 1873 –
Handbuch der praktischen kinematographie; die verschiedenen konstruktions-formen des kinematographen, die darstellung der lebenden lichtbilder, sowie das kinematographische aufnahme-verfahren. ₃3. aufl.₃ Düsseldorf, Liesegang, 1912.
xii, 480 p. illus., diagrs. 23cm.

Bibliography: p. ₃457₃-464; ₃481₃

NL 0353071 NNC CLSU

TR
850
L5
Liesegang, Franz Paul, 1873-
Handbuch der praktischen Kinematographie. Die Konstruktions-Formen, die Darstellung der lebenden Lichtbilder, das Aufnahme-Verfahren und die Anwendungen des Kinematographen. von F. Paul Liesegang. 5. verm. Aufl. Düsseldorf, E. Liesegang, 1918.
590 p. illus. 23 cm.

Includes bibliography.
1. Cinematography - Handbooks, manuals, etc.

NL 0353072 WU NNC

Liesegang, Franz Paul, 1873 –
Handbuch der praktischen Kinematographie; die Bauart, Wirkungsweise und Handhabung des Kinematographen, das Aufnahmeverfahren und die Anwendungen des Kinematographen. Von F. Paul Liesegang... Leipzig: E. Liesegang, 1919. viii, 353 (1) p. diagrs., illus. 6. ed., rev. 8°.
"Deutsche Literatur," p. ₃330₃334.

1. Moving pictures.
N. Y. P. L. July 7, 1920.

NL 0353073 NN MiU

Liesegang, Franz Paul, 1873-
Handbuch der praktischen kinematographie, ... Halle, 1928

TR850
.L6

NL 0353074 DLC PPF

Liesegang, Franz Paul, 1873 –
Die Kinematographie vor 25 Jahren. Mounted clippings from the Photographische Industrie, 1913. Düsseldorf, 1913. 3 l. 4°.

1. Levison, Wallace Goold. 2. Moving pictures.—Kinematograph, 1888.
N. Y. P. L. September 19, 1913.

NL 0353075 NN

TR
848
L5
Liesegang, Franz Paul, 1873-
Das lebende Lichtbild; Entwicklung, Wessen und Bedeutung des Kinematographen, von F. Paul Liesegang. Düsseldorf, E. Liesegang, 1910.
68 p. (p. 56-68 advertisements) illus. 22 cm.

1. Moving-pictures - Hist. 2. Cinematography - Hist. I. Title

NL 0353076 WU NNC ICJ

Liesegang, Franz Paul, 1873 –
Lichtbild- und Kino-Technik. M. Gladbach: Lichtbilderei Volksvereins-Verlag G. m. b. H., 1913. 73 p. illus. 8°. (Lichtbühnen-Bibliothek. Nr. 1.)

1. Moving pictures.—Kinematograph
N. Y. P. L. September 27, 1913.

NL 0353077 NN

Liesegang, Franz Paul, 1873 –
Die richtige Ausnutzung des Objectives. Wie erreicht man in jedem Falle bei scharfer Tiefenzeichnung die grösstmöglichste Lichtstärke? 44 p. 1 il. table. O. Düsseldorf: E. Liesegang. 1896.

NL 0353078 ICJ ViU

Liesegang, Franz Paul, 1873 –
... Vom geisterspiegel zum kino; vortrag zu einer reihe von 66 grösstenteils nach alten quellenbildern sowie originalzeichnungen hergestellten lichtbildern, von F. Paul Liesegang... Düsseldorf, Ed. Liesegang, 1918.
44 p. diagr. 22ᶜᵐ. (Reihe 927)

Author presentation copy with inscription.

1. Chronophotography.

NL 0353079 NNC

TR145
.H22
bd. 6
Liesegang, Franz Paul, 1873–
Wissenschaftliche anwendungen der photographie ... Wien, J. Springer, 1931-33.

Liesegang, Franz Paul, 1873–
Wissenschaftliche Kinematographie; einschliesslich der Reihenphotographie. (Neubearbeitung des zweiten Teiles der 5. Auflage des Handbuchs der praktischen Kinematographie.) Von F. Paul Liesegang, unter Mitarbeit von Dr. Karl Kieser und Prof. Oswald Polimanti... Leipzig: E. Liesegang, 1920. viii, 352 p. diagrs., illus. 8°.
Bibliography, p. 311-329.

1. Moving pictures. 2. Moving pictures in education. 3. Moving pictures in science. 4. Kieser, Karl, 1878– , jt. au. 5. Polimanti, Oswald, jt. au.
N. Y. P. L. January 20, 1922.

NL 0353081 NN CLSU WU

Liesegang, Fritz, 1871-
Ein beitrag zur behandlung der coxitis tuberculosa ... Berlin, Vogt ₃1894₃
32, ₃2₃ p.

Inaug.-diss., Berlin, 1894.
Lebenslauf.
"Litteratur": p. ₃33₃

1. Hip-joint - Tuberculosis.

NL 0353082 NNC

Liesegang, Fritz, 1888–
Ländliche arbeiterverhältnisse im kreise Teltow ... ₃Piatkow, Druck: O. Friese₃ 1925.
65 p. 1 l. 22ᶜᵐ.

Inaug.-diss.—Berlin.
Lebenslauf.
"Benutzte literatur": p. 63-65.

1. Agricultural laborers. ₃1. Agriculture—Labor₃ 2. Agriculture—Teltow. ₃2. Teltow—Agriculture₃

Agr 28-895

Library, U. S. Dept. of Agriculture 283L62

NL 0353083 DNAL CtY PU ICRL DNLM

Liesegang, Hans.

Nolte, Otto, 1887–
Bemerkung zu vorstehenden ausführungen.
Landw. vers. stat. bd. 114, p. 299-300. Berlin, 1933.

Liesegang, Hans.
Über die düngewirkung einiger kalisalze für sich bzw. als gemisch. diagr.
Landw. vers. stat. bd. 114, p. 295-297. Berlin, 1933.
Erwiderung auf die darlegungen des herrn prof. dr. O. Nolte in dieser zeitschrift bd. 109 ₃1929₃ s. 332.

1. Potash. 1. Nolte, Otto, 1887– Das minimum.
Agr 33-236

Library, U. S. Dept. of Agriculture 105.8L23 bd. 114
Library of Congress [87.L293 bd. 114]

NL 0353085 DNAL OU

Liesegang, Hans.
Untersuchungen über aufnahmevermögen und bedarf an kali bei buchweizen, gerste, hafer und gelber lupine. (Wirkung des phonolith- und düngesalzkalis.) diagrs.
Landw. vers. stat. bd. 114, p. 303-320. Berlin, 1933.

1. Fertilizers and manures. 2. Grain. ₃1, 2. Fertilizers for cereals₃ 3. Potash.
Agr 33-239

Library, U. S. Dept. of Agriculture 105.8L23 bd. 114
Library of Congress [87.L293 bd. 114]
₃2₃

NL 0353086 DNAL OU

Liesegang, Hans.
Untersuchungen über den nährstoffverbrauch und den verlauf der nahrungsaufnahme verschiedener gemüsearten.
Landw. jahrb. bd. 67, p. 663-698. Berlin, 1928.

1. Fertilizers and manures. 2. Vegetables. ₃1, 2. Fertilizers for vegetables₃
Agr 29-1256

Library, U. S. Dept. of Agriculture 18L23 bd. 67

NL 0353087 DNAL

Liesegang, Hans.
Untersuchungen über die rückwirkungen der kaliversorgung auf chlorophyllgehalt, assimilationsleistung, wachstum und ertrag der kartoffeln. Unter mitwirkung von Th. Remy von dr. H. Liesegang. illus.
Landw. jahrb. bd. 64, p. 213-240. Berlin, 1926.
"Nachtrag. Von Th. Remy": p. 232-240.

1. Potash. 2. Potatoes. 3. Fertilizers and manures. ₃2, 3. Potatoes—Fertilizers₃ 1. Remy, Theodor J., 1868–
Agr 28-513

Library, U. S. Dept. of Agriculture 18L23 bd. 64

NL 0353088 DNAL

Liesegang, Hans.
Untersuchung von wiederholten bodenauszügen nach der methode von Th. Saidel-Bukarest zur beurteilung der kalilöslichkeit im boden. diagr.
Landw. vers. stat. bd. 111, p. 261-269. Berlin, 1931.

1. Soils. 2. Potash. ₃1, 2. Soils, Potash in₃ 3. ₃Soil solubility₃ 1. Saidel, Teodor.
Agr 31-557

Library, U. S. Dept. of Agriculture 105.8L23 bd. 111
Library of Congress [87.L293 bd. 111]

NL 0353089 DNAL OU

VOLUME 332

Liesegang, Hans.
Weitere untersuchungen zur austauschazidität der mi-
neralböden. diagrs.
Landw. vers. stat. bd. 99, p. 191-230.   **Berlin, 1922.**

1. Soils. ₁1. Soil acidity₎

                                                    Agr 23-88
Library, U. S. Dept. of   Agriculture 105.8L23 bd. 99

NL 0353090 DNAL OU

Liesegang, Hans Friedrich, 1906-
Das anordnungsrecht des arbeitgebers und
betriebsvereinbarungen... 1932.   41 p.
Inaug. Diss. -Greifswald, 1932.
Lebenslauf.
Bibliography.

NL 0353091 ICRL MiU

Liesegang, Helmuth.
De extrema odysseae parte dissertatio. Bielefeld, 1855.

4°. pp. 24.

NL 0353092 MH NjP

AC831   Liesegang, Helmuth.
C56-   I.De Taciti vita et scriptis. II.Quo consilio
1897   Tacitus Germaniam scripsisse videatur. Cleve,
pt. 2   1897.
             11 p.
          "Progr. Nr. 445."
Stack   Programmschrift - Königliches Gymnasium,
          Cleve.
          Accompanies Schulnachrichten (pt. 1)

          1.Tacitus, Cornelius.

NL 0353093 CSt NjP

Liesegang, Helmuth.
De XXIV. Iliadis rhapsodia dissertatio.
Pars I., II. [n.p.] 1862-67.

NL 0353094 NjP PBm

Liesegang, Johannes.
Da liegt Musike drin; Berliner Geschichten und Bilder
Feldpost-Ausg. Berlin, Buchwarte-Verlag ₍°1941₎
106 p. illus. 19 cm.
"Ungekürzte Feldpost-Ausgabe des Originalwerks."

1. German language—Dialects—Berlin—Texts. I. Title.

PF5788.L5 1941   52-54382

NL 0353095 DLC

LIESEGANG, [Johannes].
Det fiel mir ooch noch uff;heitere Geschichten
und Bilder. Berlin,Buchwarte-Verlag L.Blanvalet
[1939].

19 cm. Illustr.
"8.bis 12.Tausend."

NL 0353096 MH CtY

Liesegang, Johannes.
Det fiel mir ooch noch uff; Berliner
Geschichten und Bilder von
Liesegang. Feldpost-Ausgabe. Berlin,
Buchwarte-Verlag L. Blanvalet 1943.
110 p.   illus.   18 cm.
100.-128. Taus.

NL 0353097 CtY

Liesegang, Johannes.
Det fiel mir uff, heitere geschichten und bilder von Liesegang.
Berlin, Buchwarte-verlag L. Blanvalet ₍1940₎
133, ₍1₎ p., 1 l. illus. 19ᶜᵐ.
"41. bis 50. tausend."

ɪ. Title.

                                             46-29603
Library of Congress   PT2623.I 46D4
                              ₍2₎   837.91

NL 0353098 DLC

4PT   Liesegang, Johannes.
Ger.-   Familie Pieselmanns Feldpostbriefe.
4296   Feldpost-Ausg. Berlin, Buchwarte-Verlag,
         L. Blanvalet [c1940]
         105 p.

NL 0353099 DLC-P4

4PT   Liesegang, Johannes.
Ger.-   Die Feldpostbriefe der Familie Pieselmann.
3010   Berlin, Buchwarte-Verlag, L. Blanvalet [c1940]
         106 p.

NL 0353100 DLC-P4

Liesegang, L   Hermann.
Chlorsilber-Schnelldruckpapier, von L. Hermann Liesegang.
Düsseldorf: E. Liesegang, 1901. 52 p. front. 20cm.

403057A. 1. Photography—printing   —Paper.
N. Y. P. L.   August 25, 1934

NL 0353101 NN

Liesegang, Mara.
Die heilige Quelle; Lieder. [Medingen bei Dresden,
Die Gralsburg, c.1922]

NL 0353102 MH

Liesegang, Paul, 1873-
    see Liesegang, Franz Paul, 1873-

Liesegang, Paul Eduard, 1838-1896.
Die Bromsilber-Gelatine. Ihre Bereitung und Anwendung zu
photographischen Aufnahmen, zu Abdrücken und zu Vergrösse-
rungen. Von Dr. Paul E. Liesegang... Düsseldorf: E. Liesegang, 1882. 74 p. illus. 12°. (Liesegang's Bibliothek
für Photographen. Nr. 28.)

1. Photography—Gelatine process.
N. Y. P. L.   September 25, 1928

NL 0353104 NN

Liesegang, Paul Eduard, 1838-1896.
Die Bromsilber-Gelatine. Ihre Bereitung und Anwendung
zu photographischen Aufnahmen, zu Abdrücken und zu Ver-
grösserungen. Von Dr. Paul E. Liesegang...   Düsseldorf:
E. Liesegang, 1884. 156 p. 4. ed., enl. 8°.

1. Photography—Gelatine process.
N. Y. P. L.   March 6, 1928

NL 0353105 NN

Liesegang, Paul Eduard, 1838-1896.
Die Bromsilber-Gelatine. Ihre Bereitung und Anwendung
zu photographischen Aufnahmen, zu Abdrücken und zu Ver-
grösserungen. Von Dr. Paul E. Liesegang... Düsseldorf: E.
Liesegang, 1889. 198 p. diagrs., illus. 6. ed., enl. 8°.

1. Photography—Gelatine process.
N. Y. P. L.   April 7, 1928

NL 0353106 NN

Liesegang, Paul Eduard, 1838-1896.
Die Bromsilber-Gelatine. Ihre Bereitung und Anwendung.
Von Dr. Paul E. Liesegang. Achte Auflage. Mit 74 Abbildungen. Düsseldorf, E. Liesegang's Verlag, 1898.
iv, 193 p. illus., diagrs. 20½ᶜᵐ.

NL 0353107 ICJ

Liesegang, Paul Eduard, 1838-1896.
Die Collodion-Verfahren. Von Dr. Paul E. Liesegang. Achte
vermehrte Auflage des betreffenden Abschnittes im Handbuch
der Photographie... Düsseldorf: E. Liesegang, 1884. 218 p.
illus. 8°.

1. Photography—Collodion process.
N. Y. P. L.   March 6, 1928

NL 0353108 NN

TR   Liesegang, Paul Edward, 1838-1896.
390   Handbuch der photographie auf collodion
L71   Von Paul E. Liesegang. 2., sehr verm.
         aufl. Berlin, T. Grieben, 1860.
         1 p. l., v, 106 p. 17 cm.

         1. Photography - Printing processes. 2.
         Collodion.

NL 0353109 DSI

Liesegang, Paul Eduard.
Handbuch der photographischen Verfahren mit Silberver-
bindungen. Von Dr. Paul E. Liesegang... Düsseldorf: Verlag
des Photographischen Archivs, 1881. xii, 544 p. incl. diagrs.,
table. illus., pl. 7. ed., enl. 8°. (Liesegang's Bibliothek
für Photographen. Nr. 1.)

59454A. 1. Photography.—Hand-   books, 1881.
N. Y. P. L.   October 24, 1922.

NL 0353110 NN

Liesegang, Paurl Edward,1838-1896.
Handbuch des practischen photographen.
...10. verm. ausg. Mit 298 abbildungen. Düsseldorf, Liesegang,1887.
[1032]p.

Five parts; separate paging.

NL 0353111 MiU

VOLUME 332

Liesegang, Paul Edward, 1838–1896.
Handbuch des practischen photographen. Von dr. Paul E. Liesegang ... 11. verm. ausg. Mit 278 abbildungen. Düsseldorf, E. Liesegang, 1889.
₁1034₁ p. illus. 21ᶜᵐ.
Five parts; separate paging.
CONTENTS.—Einleitung.—I. abth. Der photographische apparat und dessen verwendung zur aufnahme von porträts, ansichten und reproductionen.—II. abth. Die collodionverfahren.—III. abth. Die bromsilbergelatine.—IV. abth. Der silberdruck.—V. abth. Der kohledruck.—Anhang. Namen- und hauptregister.
1. Photography—Handbooks, manuals, etc.
23–4786
Library of Congress   TR146.L5 1889

NL 0353112   DLC

Liesegang, Paul Eduard, 1838–1896.
Illustrirtes handbuch der photographie, von Paul E. Liesegang... 4. umgearb. aufl... Berlin, T. Grieben, 1864.
viii, 296 p. illus., diagrs. 18½ᶜᵐ.
(Liesegang's illustrirte bibliothek für photographen, no. 1)

Added t.-p.: Handbuch der photographie, von Paul E. Liesegang.
1. Photography.

NL 0353113   NNC

Liesegang, Paul Eduard, 1838–1896.
Der Kohle-Druck und dessen Anwendung beim Vergrösserungs-Verfahren. Nebst einer Notiz über Photomikrographie. Von Dr. Paul E. Liesegang... Düsseldorf: Verlag des Photographischen Archivs₁, 1877?₁. 151 p. illus. 5. ed. 12°.
(Liesegang's Bibliothek für Photographen. Nr. 12.)

1. Photography—Printing—Carbon   process.
N. Y. P. L.   April 2, 1921

NL 0353114   NN

Liesegang, Paul Eduard, 1838–1896.
Der Kohle-Druck und dessen Anwendung beim Vergrösserungs-Verfahren. Von Dr. Paul E. Liesegang... Düsseldorf: E. Liesegang, 1889. 142 p. illus. 9. ed., rev. 8°.

1. Photography—Printing—Carbon   process.
N. Y. P. L.   April 7, 1928

NL 0353115   NN

Liesegang, Paul Eduard, 1838–1896.   773.1 L62
⁂ Der Kohle-Druck. Von Dr. Paul E. Liesegang. (Mit Ergänzungen von Raph. Ed. Liesegang.) Zwölfte Auflage. Mit 24 Holzschnitten. Leipzig, E. Liesegang, 1902.
iv, 161 p. 24 illus. 21¼ᶜᵐ.

NL 0353116   ICJ

4597   Liesegang, Paul Eduard, 1838–1896.
.585
        A manual of the carbon process of permanent photography, and its use in making enlargements, &c...tr. from the sixth (rev.) German ed. by R.B.Marston... London, Low, 1878.
        7,146 p. mounted front.illus.(incl. diagrs.) 20 ᶜᵐ.

        1.Photography-Enlarging. 2.Photography-Printing processes-Carbon. I.Marston, Robert Bright,   1853- tr.

NL 0353117   NjP NN MiU DSI

Liesegang, Paul Edward, 1838–1896.
Notes photographiques: collodion humide, émulsion au collodion, émulsion à la gélatine, papier albuminé, procédé au charbon, agrandissements, photomicrographie, ferrotypie, construction des galeries vitrées. Par M. Paul E. Liesegang... Dusseldorf: Verlag des Photographischen Archiv ₁sic, etc., etc.₁ 1878. vii, 152 p. incl. diagrs. front. (photo), illus. 19½cm.
"Printed in France."

——— Deuxième édition, revue et augmentée. ₁1880₁ viii, 160 p. ₁Liesegang's illustrirte Bibliothek für Photographen. No. 22₁

937431A. 1. Photography.
N. Y. P. L.   July 14, 1938

NL 0353118   NN ICJ

TR
440   Liesegang, Paul Edward, 1838–1896.
L71   Der photographische kohle-druck. Swan's tuschverfahren. Ein neues einfaches verfahren, photographien in kohle oder haltbarn pigmenten darzustellen. Beschrieben von dr. Paul E. Liesegang. 2., durchgesehene aufl. Berlin, T. Grieben, 1868.
        60 p. illus. 19 cm.
        Advertisements: p. 57-60.

        1. Photography - Printing processes - Carbon.

NL 0353119   DSI NNC

Liesegang, Paul Eduard, 1838–1896, ed.

Photographisches archiv. Berichte über den fortschritt der photographie ...

Düsseldorf, E. Liesegang, 18

Liesegang, Paul Eduard, 1838–1896.
...Der Pigment-Druck (Kohledruck), von Dr. P. Liesegang, nebst Ozotypie-, Ozobrom-, Ölpigment- und ähnlichen Verfahren. 14. umgearbeitete und ergänzte Auflage, von Hans Spörl... Leipzig: M. Eger₁, 1911₁. 192 p. illus. 8°. (Photographischer Bücherschatz. Bd. 1.)

1. Photography—Printing—Carbon   process. 2. Spoerl, Hans, 1867-
editor. 3. Ser.   February 21, 1928
N. Y. P. L.

NL 0353121   NN

Liesegang, Paul Edward, 1838–1896. Kohledruck.

Spörl, Hans, 1867-
    ... Der pigmentdruck (kohledruck) von Hans Spörl ... 3. verb. aufl.—mit 26 abbildungen—(15. aufl. von dr. Paul Liesegangs Kohledruck nebst ozotypie-, ozobrom-, ölpigment- und ahnlichen verfahren) Leipzig, E. Liesegangs verlag, M. Eger, 1920.

Liesegang, Paul Eduard, 1838–1896.
    Die projektions-kunst für schulen, familien und öffentliche vorstellungen, nebst einer anleitung zum malen auf glas und beschreibung optischer, magnetischer, chemischer und electrischer versuche. 8. umgearb. und vermehrte aufl. ... Mit 98 holzschnitten. Düsseldorf, E. Liesegang, 1882.

    2 p.l.,195 p. illus.,diagrs. 20ᶜᵐ. (Liesegang's bibliothek für photographen,nr.16)

    1.Lantern projection.

NL 0353123   MiU

₁Liesegang, Paul Edward₁ 1838–1896.

Die projections-kunst für schulen, familien und öffentliche vorstellungen; nebst einer anleitung zum malen auf glas und beschreibung optischer, magnetischer, chemischer und electrischer versuche. 10. verm. aufl. Mit 130 abbildungen. Düsseldorf, Ed. Leisegang's verlag, 1896.
2 p.l., 293 p., illus., diagrs. 20ᶜᵐ.

1. Lantern projection. I. Title.

NL 0353124   ViU MiU NIC

Liesegang, Paul Edward, 1838–1896.   778.34 L62
⁴⁴⁴⁴ Die Projektions-Kunst für Schulen, Familien und öffentliche Vorstellungen, mit einer Anleitung zum Malen auf Glas und Beschreibung chemischer, magnetischer, optischer und elektrischer Experimente. Von Dr. Paul Ed. Liesegang. Mit 153 Abbildungen. XI. Auflage, vollständig umgearbeitet und vermehrt von F. Paul Liesegang und Dr. V. Berghoff. Leipzig, E. Liesegang, [1903].
iv, 312, [4] p. 153 illus. 22½ᶜᵐ.

NL 0353125   ICJ

Liesegang, Paul Edward, 1838–1896.
Die projektions-kunst und die darstellung von lichtbildern für schulen, familien und öffentliche vorstellungen, mit einer anleitung zum malen auf glas und beschreibung chemischer, magnetischer, optischer und elektrischer experimente. Von dr. Paul Ed. Liesegang ... 12. durchgesehene aufl., vollständig umgearb. und verm. in 11. aufl. von F. Paul Liesegang. Leipzig, E. Liesegang's verlag M. Eger, 1909.
307 p. illus., table, diagrs. 22cm.
1. Lantern projecti on. I. Liesegang, Franz Paul,
1873-   ed. II.   Title.

NL 0353126   ViU NN MB

Liesegang, Paul Eduard, 1838–1896.
Der Silber-Druck und das Vergrössern photographischer Aufnahmen. Von Dr. Paul E. Liesegang. Achte vermehrte Auflage des betreffenden Abschnittes im Handbuch der Photographie ... Düsseldorf: E. Liesegang, 1884. 182 p. illus. 8°.

1. Photography—Printing.   March 6, 1928
N. Y. P. L.

NL 0353127   NN

Liesegang, Paul Eduard, 1838–1896.
    Der silber-druck und das vergrössern photographischer aufnahmen. 10. verm. aufl. Düsseldorf, Ed. Liesegang's verlag ₁1898₁
    216 p. illus. 20cm.

NL 0353128   NNC

Liesegang, Raphael Eduard, 1869-
    Die Achate, von Raphael Ed. Liesegang. Mit 60 abbildungen. Dresden u. Leipzig, Verlag von T. Steinkopff, 1915.
iv p., 1 l., 118, ₁4₁ p. illus. 23½ᶜᵐ.
Bibliographical references.

1. Agates. I. Title.

                                         G S 25-100
Library, U. S. Geological   Survey 170 L62

NL 0353129   DI-GS NIC CU ICJ NN MiU NjP

VOLUME 332

Liesegang, Raphael Eduard, 1869–
Beiträge zu einer kolloidchemie des lebens, von Raphael Ed. Liesegang. Dresden, T. Steinkopff, 1909.
2 p. l., 148 p. 23⁰⁰.

1. Colloids. 2. Physiological chemistry.

Library of Congress   QP525.L6

10–2956 Revised

NL   0353130   DLC ViU OClW MiU ICJ NjR NjP CU

Liesegang, Raphael Eduard, 1869–
Beiträge zu einer kolloidchemie des lebens. (Biologische diffusionen). Von dr. Raphael Ed. Liesegang. 2. vollkommen umgearb. aufl. Dresden und Leipzig, T. Steinkopff, 1922.
39 p. illus. 23⁰⁰.

1. Physiological chemistry. (1. Chemistry, Physiological) 2. Colloids.

Agr 23—77

U. S. Dept. of agr. Library   386.2L62
for Library of Congress   (a41c1)

NL   0353131   DNAL ICRL ICU PPC DNLM NN

QP
525
L5
1923

Liesegang, Raphael Eduard, 1869–
Beiträge zu einer Kolloidchemie des Lebens. (Biologische Diffusionen) 3. umgearb. Aufl. Dresden, Steinkopff, 1923.
40 p. illus.

1. Colloids. I. Title.

NL   0353132   MiEM NcU IU

Liesegang, Raphael Eduard, 1869–
Beiträge zum Problem des electrischen Fernsehens. x,[4], 130 p. 14 il. O. (Probleme der Gegenwart, vol. 1.) Düsseldorf: E. Liesegang, 1891.
No title-page. Title taken from inside cover.

NL   0353133   ICJ

Liesegang, Raphael Eduard, 1869–
Biologische kolloidchemie, von dr. Raphael Ed. Liesegang ... Dresden und Leipzig, T. Steinkopff, 1928.
xii, 127 p. 22⁰⁰. (Added t.-p.: Wissenschaftliche forschungsberichte. Naturwissenschaftliche reihe. bd. xix (i. e. xx))

1. Colloids. 2. Biological chemistry. I. Title.

Library of Congress   QD549.L45

28–19202

NL   0353134   DLC DNLM CU PU-BZ ICJ NN

Liesegang, Raphael Eduard, 1869–
Chemische Reactionen in Gallerten. 65 p. il. sq. D. Düsseldorf: E. Liesegang, 1898.

NL   0353135   ICJ

Liesegang, Raphael Eduard, 1869–
Chemische reaktionen in gallerten. Von dr. Raphael Ed. Liesegang ... 2. umgearb. aufl. ... Dresden und Leipzig, T. Steinkopff, 1924.
4 p. l., 90 p. illus. 23½⁰⁰.
Bibliography: p. (85)–88.

1. Chemical reactions. 2. Colloids.

Library, U. S. Dept. of   Agriculture 386L622

Agr 25–493

NL   0353136   DNAL FMU CU OCU NjP

Liesegang, Raphael Eduard, 1869–
...Le développement des papiers photographiques à noircissement direct, par R.-Ed. Liesegang; traduit de l'allemand par V. Hassreidter... Paris: Gauthier-Villars et fils, 1898. 78 p. 19cm. (Bibliothèque photographique.)

1. Photography—Developing and   developers. I. Hassreidter, V.,
tr. II. Ser.
N. Y. P. L.   July 22, 1941

NL   0353137   NN NNC

Liesegang, Raphael Eduard, 1869–   771.14 L621
Elektrolyse von Gallerten und ähnliche Untersuchungen. 29 p. O. Düsseldorf: E. Liesegang, 1899.

NL   0353138   ICJ

Liesegang, Raphael Eduard, 1869–
Geologische diffusionen, von Raphael Ed. Liesegang. Mit 44 abbildungen. Dresden und Leipzig, T. Steinkopff, 1913.
vi p., 1 l., 180 p. illus. 24½⁰⁰.

1. Geology. 2. Diffusion.

Library of Congress   QE515.L4

14–2434

NL   PPAN NjP ICJ MB NN
0353139   DLC CU TxU KU CtY IdU DI-GS GU MiU OCU

566.1
L62g

Liesegang, Raphael Eduard, 1869–
... Glas. [Dresden] 1928.
p.251-258. (Kolloidtechnische sammelreferate. I)

Caption title.
"Sonder-abdruck aus 'Kolloid-Zeitschrift' bd.XLIV, hft.3 (1928)."
Bibliographical footnotes.

NL   0353140   IU

Liesegang, Raphael Eduard, 1869–
Glas, von Raphael Ed. Liesegang. Mit 12 Abbildungen.
(In Liesegang, R. E., ed. Kolloidchemische Technologie. 2. Auflage. Dresden und Leipzig, 1932. 26½⁰⁰. p. (702)–744. illus.)
Bibliographical foot-notes.

NL   0353141   ICJ

Liesegang, Raphael Eduard, 1869–
Innere Rhythmen im Pflanzenreich. n. t.-p. (Naumburg a. d. S.: Lippert & Co., G. m. b. H.) 1913. 10 p. illus. 12°.
Repr.: Naturwissenschaftliche Wochenschrift. N. F., Bd. 12.

1. Botany (Physiological), etc. 2.   Botany.—Chemistry in.
N. Y. P. L.   April 14, 1914.

NL   0353142   NN

Liesegang, Raphael Eduard, 1869–
Kolloid-fibel für mediziner. Dresden, T. Steinkopff, 1936.
33, [1] p. 21cm.

NL   0353143   CaBVaU

Liesegang, Raphael Eduard, 1869–
Kolloidchemie 1914–1922; bearbeitet von Dr. Raphael Ed. Liesegang... Dresden: T. Steinkopff, 1922. viii, 100 p. 8°. (Wissenschaftliche Forschungsberichte. Bd. 6.)
Bibliographical footnotes.

1. Colloids—Bibl. 2. Ser.
N. Y. P. L.   September 10, 1925

NL   0353144   NN IU-M OCU ViU MH NBuU NjP ICU

Liesegang, Raphael Eduard, 1869–
Kolloidchemie, von dr. Raph. Ed. Liesegang ... 2. völlig umgearb. und stark verm. aufl. Dresden und Leipzig, T. Steinkopff, 1926.
xii, 176 p. 22½⁰⁰. (Added t.-p.: Wissenschaftliche forschungsberichte. Naturwissenschaftliche reihe ... bd. vi)

1. Colloids. I. Title.

Library of Congress   QD549.L48   1926

27–19064

NL   0353145   DLC KU CU MiU NcU DNLM ICJ NjP

Liesegang, Raphael Eduard, 1869–
Kolloidchemie des glases. Dresden und Leipzig, T. Steinkopff, 1931.
2 p. l. (201)–744 p. illus.

Sonderabdruck aus der Kolloidchemischen technologie ...

NL   0353146   PSt NcU

Liesegang, Raphael Eduard, 1869–   ed.
Kolloidchemische technologie; ein handbuch kolloidchemischer betrachtungsweise in der chemischen industrie und technik. Unter mitarbeit von dr. R. Auerbach ... W. Clayton ... dr. E. Eichwald (u. a.) ... hrsg. von dr. Raph. Ed. Liesegang ... Mit 419 abbildungen und zahlreichen tabellen. Dresden und Leipzig, T. Steinkopff, 1927.
viii p., 1 l., 1047 p. illus., diagrs. 26½⁰⁰.
Bibliographies interspersed; bibliographical foot-notes; index of authors cited (p. (1030)–1041)
1. Colloids. 2. Chemistry, Technical. I. Auerbach, Rudolf. II. Clayton, William. III. Eichwald, Egon, 1883– IV. Title.

Library of Congress   TP149.L5

28–18391

NL   0353147   DLC IU ICJ NN MnU NIC IaU MnU

Liesegang, Raphael Eduard, 1869–   ed.
Kolloidchemische technologie; ein handbuch kolloidchemischer betrachtungsweise in der chemischen industrie und technik. Unter mitarbeit von dr. R. Auerbach ... dr. E. Berliner ... dr. A. Chwala (u. a., ... hrsg. von dr. Raph. Ed. Liesegang ... 2., vollständig umgearbeitete auflage ... Dresden und Leipzig, T. Steinkopff, 1932.
viii, 1085 p. illus., diagrs. 26½⁰⁰.
Issued in 13. lfg. 1931.
Date on t.-p.: 1932.
1. Chemistry, Technical. (1. Chemistry, Technology) 2. Colloids. I. Auerbach, Rudolf. II. Berliner, E. III. Chwala, August, 1881– IV. (Title)

Agr 31–1239

Library, U. S. Dept. of   Agriculture 388L622

NL   0353148   DNAL NcU MiU CtY CLU ICJ IU NN

VOLUME 332

Liesegang, Raphael Eduard, 1869–
Kolloide in der technik, bearbeitet von dr. Raphael Ed.
Liesegang ... Dresden und Leipzig, T. Steinkopff, 1923.
4 p. L, 157 p. 21½ᶜᵐ. (*Added t.-p.:* Wissenschaftliche forschungsbe-
-ichte. Naturwissenschaftliche reihe ... bd. IX)
"Eine auswahl des wichtigsten, was in- und ausland seit 1914 in jedem
einzelnen zweige der naturwissenschaften geleistet hat, soll in je einem
bändchen dieser 'Wissenschaftlichen forschungsberichte' ... in gedrängter
form geboten werden."—3d prelim. leaf.
Bibliographical foot-notes.

1. Colloids. 2. Colloids—Bibl.   I. Title.

Library of Congress   QD549.L5   26–3308

NL 0353149   DLC MiU OCU NcU CLSU ICJ MH NjP DP NN

Liesegang, Raphael Eduard, 1869–
Kolloide in der technik, von Raphael Ed. Liesegang ... 2.,
völlig neu bearb. aufl. Dresden und Leipzig, T. Steinkopff,
1943.
vii, ₍1₎, 128 p. 21½ᶜᵐ. (*Added t.-p.:* Wissenschaftliche forschungsberichte. Naturwissenschaftliche reihe ... bd. 9)

1. Colloids. 2. Colloids—Bibl.   I. Title.

Library of Congress   QD549.L5 1943   44–10
    ₍2₎   541.3452

NL 0353150   DLC NcRS NcD NN OU OrU NBuU

Liesegang, Raphael Eduard, 1869–
Kolloide in der technik, von Raphael Ed. Liesegang ... 2.,
völlig neu bearb. aufl. Dresden und Leipzig, T. Steinkopff,
1943;Ann Arbor,J.W. Edwards,1944.
vii, ₍1₎, 128 p. 21½ᶜᵐ. (*Added t.-p.:* Wissenschaftliche forschungsberichte. Naturwissenschaftliche reihe ... bd. 9)

NL 0353151   ICJ CU

QP
525
.L49
Liesegang, Raphael Eduard, 1869–
Kolloid-Fibel für Mediziner.   Dresden, Steinkopff, 1936.
33 p.

1. Colloids. I. Title.

NL 0353152   MiEM IU-M

Liesegang, Raphael Eduard, 1869–
Kolloid-fibel für mediziner, von dr. dr. Raphael Ed. Liesegang ... 2., völlig neubearb. aufl. Dresden und Leipzig, T
Steinkopff, 1942.
27 p. 22ᶜᵐ.

1. Colloids.   I. Title.

Library of Congress   QP525.L63 1942   43–22890
    ₍2₎   612.0144625

NL 0353153   DLC IU WU NjP MiU WU-M

Liesegang, Raphael Eduard, 1869–
Kolloid-Fibel für Mediziner. 3., völlig neubearb. Aufl.
Dresden, T. Steinkopff, 1944.
32 p. 23 cm.

1. Colloids.   I. Title.

QP525.L63 1944   52–57219 ‡

NL 0353154   DLC CtY TxHR NcD NNC-M DNLM ICRL

Liesegang, Raphael Eduard, 1869–
Kolloid-Lehre; Einführung in einfachsten Versuchen.
Büdingen, Natura-Verlag ₍1951₎
118 p. Illus. 26 cm.

1. Colloids.   I. Title.

QD549.L52   52–30992 ‡

NL 0353155   DLC CtY

Liesegang, Raphael Eduard, 1869–   joint ed.

Medizinische kolloidlehre; physiologie, pathologie und therapie in kolloidchemischer betrachtung ... herausgegeben von
prof. dr. L. Lichtwitz ... dr. dr. Raph. Ed. Liesegang ...
prof. dr. Karl Spiro ...   Dresden und Leipzig, T. Steinkopff,
1935.

[**Liesegang, Raphael Eduard,** 1869–   ]
Messias. [Leipzig, 1907]
77 p.

NL 0353157   MH

Liesegang, Raphael Eduard, 1869–
Der Monismus und seine Konsequenzen. Düsseldorf,
Liesegang, 1892–

(Probleme der Gegenwart, 2)
Contents:– 1. Die organologie.

NL 0353158   MH

Liesegang, Raphael Eduard, 1869–
Photographie, von Dr. Raphael Ed. Liesegang ...
(*In* Liesegang, R. E., *ed.* Kolloidchemische Technologie. 2. Auflage.
Dresden und Leipzig, 1932. 26¼ᶜᵐ. p. ₍1028,–1047₎)
Bibliographical foot-notes.

NL 0353159   ICJ

771
L625p
Liesegang, Raphael Edward, 1869–
Photographische Chemie. Düsseldorf,
E. Liesegang, 1894.
182 p. illus.

With this are bound: Paar, Jean.
Leitfaden der Retouche; Schnauss,
Hermann. Photographischer Zeitvertreib.

1. Photographic chemistry.

NL 0353160   WaU NNC NN

Liesegang, Raphael Eduard, 1869–
Photographische chemie (in allgemeinver-
ständlicher darstellung) 2. aufl. Düsseldorf, E. Liesegang, 1898.
172 p. diagrs., tables. 21cm.

1. Photographic chemistry.

NL 0353161   NNC CU

Liesegang, Raphael Eduard, 1869–
... . Photographische Chemie. In allgemein verständlicher
Darstellung. Von R. Ed. Liesegang. Dritte, vollständig neu
bearbeitete Auflage. Von Dr. Karl Kieser. Leipzig, E. Liese-
gangs Verlag, M. Eger, 1909.
160 p. diagrs. 20½ᶜᵐ. (Photographischer Bücherschatz Bd. IX.)
On cover: Liesegang's photographischer Bücherschatz.
Advertisements, p. 158–160.

NL 0353162   ICJ NBuG

TR
16.6
L621p
Liesegang, Raphael Eduard, 1869–
Photographische Physik (mit Ausnahme der
Optik) Düsseldorf, E. Liesegang's Verlag,
1899.
84 p.

1. Photography – Developing and developers.
2. Photography – Printing processes. I. Title

NL 0353163   CLU NNC ICJ

Liesegang, Raphael Eduard, 1869–
Der photographische Prozess; Photographie und Rontgeno-
graphie; von Dr. Raphael Ed. Liesegang ...   Frankfurt a.M.:
Keim & Nemnich, 1924. 4 p.l., 55 p.   8°.   (Radiologische
Praktika. Bd. 3.)
Bibliography, p. 49–50.

189748A. 1. Photography—Chem-   istry. 2. Ser.
N. Y. P. L.   June 23, 1925

NL 0353164   NN MnU ICJ DNLM

LIESEGANG, Raphael Edouard, 1869–   3926.8
Das Phototel. Beiträge zum Problem des electrischen Fernsehens.
[Düsseldorf, 1891.] x, (3), 130 pp. Illus. [Probleme de
Gegenwart. Bd. 1.] 8°.

NL 0353165   MB MdAN

Liesegang, Raphael Eduard, 1869–
Saskia; Drama. Osnabrück, Buchdr.Liesecke, 1921

NL 0353166   MH

Liesegang, Raphael Eduard, 1869–
Spezielle methoden der diffusion in gallerten. Von Raphael
Ed. Liesegang.
(*In* Abderhalden, Emil, *ed.* Handbuch der biologischen arbeits-
methoden ... Berlin, 1920– 25ᶜᵐ. abt. III, Physikalisch-
chemische methoden. t. B (1929) p. ₍33₎–130. Illus., diagrs.)
Bibliographical foot-notes.

1. Diffusion. 2. Colloids.   A C 36–3150

Title from Ohio State   Univ.
Library of Congress   [QH324.A3 1920 abt. 3, t. B]
    ₍2₎   (574.072)

NL 0353167   OU

Liesegang, Raphael Eduard, 1869–
Strahlentherapie, in kolloidchemischer
betrachtung. Dresden, T. Steinkopff, 1934.
p. [873]–914, illus. tables, O.
"Sonderabdruck aus Der medizinischen
kolloidlehre, hrsg. von prof. dr. L. Lichtwitz,
dr. Raph. Ed. Liesegang und prof. dr. Karl
Spiro."

NL 0353168   NcU

VOLUME 332

Liesegang, Raphael Eduard, 1869–
Trocknungserscheinungen bei Gelen. (In: Gedenkboek aangeboden aan J. M. van Bemmelen. Helder, 1910. 8°. p. 33-35.)

1. Gelatine.
N. Y. P. L.   April 23, 1914.

NL 0353169   NN

Liesegang, Raphael Eduard, 1869–
Über die Schichtungen bei Diffusionen. Eine Voruntersuchung von Raphael Ed. Liesegang. Düsseldorf, H. Ohligschläger, 1907.
56, [4] p. illus. 22½.

NL 0353170   ICJ MiU

Liesegang, Wilhelm.
Die reinhaltung der luft. Von prof. dr. phil. W. Liesegang ...
(In Ergebnisse der angewandten physikalischen chemie. Leipzig, 1935. 24ᵐ. 3. bd., p. 1-109 incl. tables)
"Literaturverzeichnis": p. [100]-109.

1. Air—Purification.   I. Title.

A C 38-2275

Northwestern univ. Library
for Library of Congress   [2]

NL 0353171   IEN

M/0420 **Liesegang, Wilhelm.**
L719v   Das Verhalten von Abgasen in der Luft. (From Kleine Mitteilungen für die Mitglieder des Vereins für Wasser-, Boden- und Lufthygiene E. V.)
p. 185-215. 23½cm.

(Control of exhaust gas in the air).

NL 0353172   DAS

Liesel, Nikolaus.
The Eucharistic liturgies of the Eastern churches. Translation: David Heimann. Photography: Tibor Makula. Art and layout: Brother Placid. Collegeville, Minn., Liturgical Press [1963]
310 p. illus. maps. 32 cm. (Popular liturgical library)
Translation of Die Liturgien der Ostkirche.

1. Liturgies. 2. Lord's Supper (Liturgy) 3. Catholic Church—Oriental rites. I. Title.

BX4710.63.L513 1963   264.015   63-3837

NL 0353173   DLC CU

Liesen, Bernhard.
AC831 Zur Klostergeschichte Emmerichs bei Beginn
E49   des XVI. Jahrhunderts. Emmerich, 1891.
1891   xiii, 14 p.
"1891. Progr. Nro. 435."
Programmschrift - Königliches Gymnasium, Emmerich.

1. Emmerich, Ger. - Convent - History.

NL 0353174   CSt

Liesen, Ferdinand.
Beitrag zur symptomatologie der kleinhirntumoren unter beruecksichtigung eines besonderen falles. Inaug. diss. Kiel, 1920.

NL 0353175   ICRL

Liesen (Friedrich Wilhelm) [1887-   ]. *Ein kasuistischer Beitrag zur Frage der Schussverletzungen der Harnblase. 31 pp. 8°. Giessen, O. Kindt. 1915.

NL 0353176   DNLM ICRL

Liesen, Paul, 1878–
... Über das vorkommen von *Ascaris lumbricorides* [!] im menschlichen körper, speciell in der freien bauchhöhle ... Bonn, Druck von E. Eisele, 1904.
33 p. 21½ᶜᵐ.
Inaug.-diss.—Bonn.
Vita.
Aus der Chirurgischen universitäts-klinik zu Bonn.
"Litteratur": p. [30]-31.

1. Ascaris lumbricoides.

Library of Congress   RC227.A8L7   6-20670

NL 0353177   DLC DNLM

Liesen, Walter, 1911–
... Eine Statistik über die primären Hirngeschwülste im Sektionsmaterial des Greifswalder Pathologischen Instituts in den Jahren 1919-1935 ... Greifswald, 1936.
Inaug.-Diss. - Greifswald.
Lebenslauf.
"Literaturverzeichnis": p. 17-18.

NL 0353178   CtY MiU

Liesen, Wilhelm
see Liesen, Friedrich Wilhelm, 1887–

Liesenberg, Carl, 1866–
Persönliche, geschäftliche, politische reklame; lehrbuch der reklamekunst, deren wesen, bedeutung und konsequenzen. Von Carl Liesenberg. Neustadt an der Haardt, Pfälzische verlagsanstalt, 1912.
4 p. l., 288 p. front. (port.) 23ᶜᵐ. M. 7.50

1. Advertising.

Library of Congress   HF5821.L5   12-8832

NL 0353180   DLC CtY ICJ NN

Liesenberg, Carl, 1866–
Peter Josef Löllgen; ein leben im gesetz von nehmen und geben, von Carl Liesenberg. Neustadt an der Haardt, Pfälzische verlagsanstalt, 1927.
3 p. l., 362 p. 22½ᶜᵐ.

I. Title.

Library of Congress   PT2623.O34Z8   27-11093

NL 0353181   DLC

PA   **Liesenberg, Friedrich.**
6205   Die Sprache des Ammianus Marcellinus.
Z5   1. Kap. Der Wortschatz (das Nomen)
L72   Blankenburg a. H., 1888-89.
       2 v. in 1. 25cm.

Accompanies "Programm" (Jahresbericht) --Herzogliches Gymnasium zu Blankenburg am Harz.

1. Ammianus Marcellinus.

NL 0353182   NIC ViU MH NjP PU CU CtY

PF5519 **Liesenberg, Friedrich.**
S8L7   Die Stieger mundart, ein idiom des Unterharzes, besonders hinsichtlich der lautlehre dargestellt, nebst einem etymologischen idiotikon ... Halberstadt, J. Hoerling's wwe. (F. Schilling) 1890.
[1], vii, 225 p. 21ᶜᵐ.
Inaug.-diss.—Göttingen.

1. German language—Dialects—Stiege.

NNU

NL 0353183   ICU CU NIC MH NN PBm PU CtY MiU ICU TxU

NA4817 **LIESENBERG, KURT, 1898–**
.L7   Der einfluss der liturgie auf die frühchristliche basilika... Neustadt an der Haardt, Pfälzische verlagsanstalt, 1928.
v, 213 p. illus. (incl. plans) 24cm.
Inaug.-diss.--Freiburg i.B.
"Quellennachweis": p. [209]-213.

1. Basilicas. 2. Church architecture--Hist. 3. Christian antiquities. 4. Liturgies.

NL 0353184   ICU MiU DDO ICRL CLU IU PU MH PBm CtY

Liesenborghs, Joseph.
L'ovrfre d'â quai. Comèdèye mahèye di chants è deux ackes. Liége, C. Gothier, 1899.
52 p. 12°. (Théatre Wallon.)

NL 0353185   NN

Liesenborghs, Joseph.
Truc di pauve. Comèdèye èn ine acke. Liége: La Meuse, 1899.
31 p. 8°. (Théate Wallon.)

NL 0353186   NN

Liesenborghs, Joseph.
Vingince. Comèdèye èn ine acke, mahèye di chants. Liége, C. Gothier, 1898.
48 p. 12° (Théate Wallon)

NL 0353187   NN

Liesener, Carl Ottokar, 1887–
... Über den Zusammenhang von Lebercirrhose und Milztumor en ... Greifswald, 1914.
24 p., 1 l. 22.5 cm.
Inaug.-Diss. - Greifswald.
Lebenslauf.

NL 0353188   CtY MiU

DD   **Liesener, Paul**
43   Deutschland. Frankfurt, P. List [1953]
L71d   63p. illus. maps. 23cm. (Harms lebendige Erdkunde. Arbeitshefte. Heft 1)
1953

1. Germany- Descr. & trav. - 1945-

NL 0353189   NRU

VOLUME 332

Br64
741

Liesenfeld, Franz, 1875-
Klemens Wenzeslaus der letzte Kurfürst von
Trier, seine Landstände und die französische
Revolution. Entwickelung der Krisis im Frühjahre
1792 bis zum Ausbruch der Feindseligkeiten ...
Trier, 1912.

Inaug.-Diss. - Bonn.
Lebenslauf.
"Die ganze Arbeit wird als XVII. Ergänzungsheft
der Westdeutschen Zeitschrift ... erscheinen."
"Quellen- und Literaturverzeichnis": p. iv-vi.

NL 0353190   CtY NN ICN MH ICRL PU

Liesenfeld, Peter.
Die ideal-ehe, moralisch einwandfreier und sicherer weg
natürlicher empfängnisverhütung nach dr. K. Ogino u. prof.
dr. H. Knaus, allgemeinverständlich bearb. von P. Liesenfeld.
1. aufl. Köln-Rhein, Dr. Weiler & co., 1932.

98 p. forms. (1 fold.) 22ᶜᵐ.

Folded form laid in.
Date of imprint changed in ink to 1933.
"Quellen-nachweis": p. 97-98.

1. Birth control. 2. Conception—Prevention. 3. Ogino, Kyusaku,
1881-   4. Knaus, Herman. I. Title.
                                                    33-18283
Library of Congress   HQ766.L47
Copyright A—Foreign   18275
                              ₍2₎   612.63

NL 0353191   DLC

Liesenfelt, Matilda M.
The Liesenfelt crochet book.
Hammond, [c1916]

TT820
.L6

NL 0353192   DLC

Liesenfelt, Matilda M.
The Liesenfelt yoke book. [Hammond, Ind., M. E.
Liesenfelt, ᵗ1915]

₍15₎ p. illus. 21½ x 28ᶜᵐ. $0.10
On verso of t.-p.: Arranged and collected by Matilda M. Liesenfelt.

1. Crocheting. I. Title: Yoke book.
Library of Congress   TT825.L5
                                                    16-3162

NL 0353193   DLC ICJ

Liesenhoff, A
Freiherr Karl von Oeynhausen, 1895.

NL 0353194   DI-GS

Liesenhoff, Karl Heinz Helms-
see **Helms-Liesenhoff, Karl Heinz,** 1912-

Lieser, Ernst.
Das Lagergeschäft und der Lagerschein
(Warrant) nach dem Handelsgesetzbuche
vom 10. Mai 1897 ... von Ernst Lieser ...
Fürth, A. Schröder, 1899.

58 p. 21½ᶜᵐ.

Inaug.-Diss. - Erlangen.
Bibliographical footnotes.

NL 0353196   MH-L ICRL NIC

Lieser, Franz.
Die konstitution der zahne bei patienten
mit schwerer lungentuberkulose.
Inaug. Diss., 1933.

NL 0353197   PPWI CtY

Lieser, Harry.
Kartelle und konjunktur in ihrer wechsel-
seitigen beeinflussung, von dr. Harry Lieser.
Wien und Leipzig, M. Perles, 1934.

79, [1] p. diagr. 23 cm.
"Literaturverzeichnis": p. 78-79.
1. Trusts, Industrial. 2. Prices. 3. Business
cycles.

NL 0353198   CU

Lieser, Heinrich, 1892-
... Über das perforierende Aneurysma luicum
der Aorta abdominalis mit Nierenlagermassen-
blutung ...   München, 1931.
Inaug.-Diss. - München.
Lebenslauf.

NL 0353199   CtY PPWI

Lieser, Helene, ed.
Müller, Adam Heinrich, *ritter von Nitterdorf,* 1779-1829.
... Versuche einer neuen theorie des geldes, mit erklä-
renden anmerkungen versehen von dr. Helene Lieser.
Jena, G. Fischer, 1922.

NA9070
L5
Arch.
Library

Lieser, Karl
Strasse, Platz und Hauptbau; ihre gegenseitigen ästhetischen
Beziehungen.   Heidelberg, C. Winter, 1929.
51 p. 38 illus., plans.

1. Plazas. 2. Market places. 3. Cities and towns -
Planning. I. Title.

NL 0353201   CU NN IU MH NNC

Lieser, Ludwig, 1890-
Vinzens von Beauvais als Kompilator und Philosoph; textkritische Untersuchung der Zitate aus
der antiken und patristischen Literatur im Speculum naturale, Buch 23 bis 27 (Seelenlehre) Köln,
1927.
36 p. 22 cm.
Inaug.-Diss.—Cologne.
Lebenslauf.
"Die vollständige Arbeit erscheint ... als I.

Heft des III. Bandes der 'Forschungen zur Geschichte der Philosophie und Pädagogik'."

1. Vincent de Beauvais, d. 1264. Speculum
maius. 2. Soul.

NL 0353203   TxU IU

Lieser, Ludwig, 1890-
Vinzenz von Beauvais als kompilator und philosoph; eine
untersuchung seiner seelenlehre im Speculum maius, von dr.
Ludwig Lieser. Leipzig, F. Meiner, 1928.

2 p. L. ₍ii₎-x, 204 p. 23½ᶜᵐ. (On cover: Forschungen zur geschichte
der philosophie und der pädagogik ... III. bd., hft. 1)
"Literaturverzeichnis": p. ₍vi₎-x.

1. Vincent de Beauvais, d. 1264. Speculum maius. 2. Soul.
                                                    32-8512
Library of Congress   B765.V44L5
                              ₍2₎   189.4

NL 0353204   DLC DCU ICJ

PR1195
O 3L48

Lieser, Paul, 1907-
Die englische Ode im Zeitalter des Klass-
izismus. Grossenhain i. Sa., 1932.
102 p. 21 cm.
Inaug.-Diss. - Bonn.
Lebenslauf.
"Bibliographie": p. [99]-102.
Cover title.

1. English poetry - 18th cent. - Hist. &
crit. 2. Odes.

NL 0353205   CoU PU ICRL CtY

Lieser, Theodor.
Beitraege zur Chemie der Cellulose, insbesondere der Hydro-
und Oxycellulose, sowie des Cellulosedithiocarbonates ... von
Theo Lieser...   Rostock: Adlers Erben, G.m.b.H., 1926. 52 p.
8°.

Dissertation, Zurich, 1926.
Lebenslauf.

1. Cellulose—Derivatives.
N. Y. P. L.   July 14, 1927

NL 0353206   NN CtY ICRL

Lieser, Theodor.
Kurzes Lehrbuch der Cellulosechemie. Berlin-Nikolassee,
Gebr. Borntraeger, 1953.
288 p. illus. 23 cm.

1. Cellulose. I. Title.
                              QD321.L72   53-22351 ‡

NL 0353207   DLC NN

IJ76
L625u

Liesering, Eugen, 1903-
Untersuchungen zur Christenverfolgung des
Kaisers Decius. Würzburg, R. Mayr, 1933.
64 p. 23 cm.

Inaug.-diss. - Würzburg.
Lebenslauf.
Includes bibliography.

1. Persecution - Early church. 2. Rome -
Hist. - Decius,   249-251.

NL 0353208   CtY-D ICRL PU MiU NNC

Liesering, Ludwig.
Neue Schule für B-Trompete (Cornet à pistons u. Flügel-
horn). Nouvelle méthode pour la trumpette ₍sic₎ en Si ♭ (cornet
à pistons et bugle). New school for the trumpet ₍sic₎ in B♭ (♭
cornet and bugle). Von Ludwig Liesering... Leipzig: D.
Rahter ₍1934₎ Publ. pl. no. 4509. 2 v. in 1. illus., tables.
31cm. (Elite Edition. No. 795-796.)

Preface, table of contents and explanatory text in German, French and English.

                                        JUILLIARD FOUNDATION FUND.
778318A. 1. Trumpet—Methods.   2. Cornet—Methods. 3. Saxhorn.
Methods.
N V P I   November 8, 1935

NL 0353209   NN

Liesganig, Joseph, 1719-1799.
Dimensio graduum meridiani Viennensis et
Hungarici augg. jussu et auspiciis per acta
a Josepho Liesganig ... Vindobonae, Prostat
apud Augustinum Bernardi, 1770.
₍22₎, 262, ₍2₎ p. X plates. 25cm.

1. Arc measures.

NL 0353210   NNC CSt WU CU PPAmP

VOLUME 332

911.4374 Liesganig, Joseph, 1719-1799.
L62k   Koenigreich Galizien und Lodomerien,
1824   herausgegeben im Jahre 1790 von Liesganig.
        Nach den vorzüglichsten neuern Hülfsquel-
        len vermehrt und verbessert von dem K. K.
        Oest. Generalquartiermeisterstabe im
        Jahre 1824. ₍n.p., 1824?₎
          32 double maps. 28cm.

          Scales vary.

NL 0353211   IU

Liesganig, Joseph, 1719-1799.
    Tabulae memoriales praecipua arithmeticae
tum numericae tum literalis, geometriae, etiam
curvarum, et trigonometriae, atque utriusque ar-
chitecturae elementa complexae, in usum audito-
rum, conscriptae a Josepho Liesganig ... Viennae, Austriae, typis J. T. Trattner, anno 1754.
    ₍84₎ p. 18 fold.pl. (incl. plans, diagrs.) fold.tab.
22ᶜᵐ.
    Pages ₍15-16₎ folded.

    1. Mathematics—Early works to 1800. 2. Architecture—
Early works to 1800. 3. Military architecture. I. Title.

NL 0353212   MiU

Liesganig, Joseph, 1719-1799.
    Tabulae memoriales praecipua arithmeticae tum
numericae tum literalis, geometriae, etiam curvarum
et trigonometriae, Viennae, 1755.
    8°

NL 0353213   NN

Lieshout, Adrianus Jacobus van.
    Onderzoek naar de levensomstandigheden der bevolking
van plattelandsgemeenten, in opdracht van de Stichting
Maatschappelijk Werk ten Plattelande. Uden. Eindhoven,
Uitgeverij "Het Hooghuis," 1948.
    392 p. illus., maps, diagrs. 25 cm.
    At head of title: Instituut voor Sociaal Onderzoek van het Neder-
landsche Volk.
    Issued also as thesis, Amsterdam, under title: Uden; onderzoek
naar de levensomstandigheden der bevolking van een Oostbrabantsche
plattelandsgemeenschap.
    Bibliographical footnotes.
    1. Uden, Netherlands—Soc. condit.

    .HN520.U3L5   49-24203 rev*

NL 0353214   DLC ICU

Lieshout, Adrianus Jacobus van.
    Uden; onderzoek naar de levensomstandigheden der
bevolking van een Oostbrabantse plattelandsgemeenschap.
₍Amsterdam₎ 1948.
    392 p. illus., maps, diagrs. 25 cm.
    Academisch proefschrift—Amsterdam.
    Published also under title: Onderzoek naar de levensomstandig-
heden der bevolking van plattelandsgemeenten.
    "Stellingen": ₍2₎ p. inserted.
    Bibliographical footnotes.
    1. Uden, Netherlands—Soc. condit.
    HN520.U3L5 1948a   50-21282

NL 0353215   DLC MH OU

Lieshout, Adrianus Kornelis Wytze Antonius van, 1906-
    De snelheid van de polymorfe omzetting; nieuwe onder-
zoekingen over de tinpest ... door Adrianus Kornelis Wytze
Antonius van Lieshout ... Utrecht, Amsterdam, Drukkerij
J. van Boekhoven ₍1934₎
    xi, 150 p. incl. illus., tables, diagrs. 24½ᶜᵐ.
    Proefschrift—Utrecht.
    "Stellingen" (2 leaves) laid in.

    1. Tin. 2. Chemical reaction—Velocity. I. Title. II. Title: Tin-
pest.
                                          36-35425
    Library of Congress   QD181.S7L5 1934
                           ₍2₎   546.81

NL 0353216   DLC OU CtY ICRL

Lieshout, D   J
    Na-oorlogse financiering van woningwetwoningen, 1919-
1948-1950. 3. druk. Arnhem, G. W. van der Wiel ₍1951₎
    160 p. tables. 21 cm. (VUGA uitgave)

    1. Housing—Netherlands—Finance.   I. Title.

    HD7344.A3L5 1951   53-38235

NL 0353217   DLC

B   Lieshout, Eustatius van, Father, 1880-1943.
693   La théorie Plotinienne de la vertu; essai
.Z7   sur la genèse d'un article de la Somme théo-
L71   logique de saint Thomas. Freiburg, Schweiz,
       Studia Friburgensia, 1926.
         viii, 203 p. 24 cm.

         Thèse—Fribourg.
         "Sources ₍et₎ littérature": p. ₍v₎-viii.

         1. Plotinus. 2. Virtue. 3. Thomas Aquinas,
Saint - Virtue.

NL 0353218   DCU IaU IU

B693   Lieshout, Eustatius van, Father, 1880-1943
Z7L5   La théorie plotinienne de la vertu;
       essai sur la genèse d'un article de la
       Somme théologique de Saint Thomas, par
       H. van Lieshout. Freiburg, Schweiz,
       Studia friburgensia, 1926.
         203p. 22cm. (Studia friburgensia,
       travaux publiés sous la direction des
       Dominicains professeurs à l'Université
       de Fribourg (Suisse)

         Bibliography: p. ₍vii₎-x.

NL 0353219   IaU IMunS

Lieshout, Hubertus van
    see
Lieshout, Eustatius van, *father*, 1880-1943.

Lieshout, Ruurd van.
    De wisselwerking in de theorie van de bêta radioactiviteit.
's-Gravenhage, Excelsior ₍1953₎
    111 p. diagrs., tables. 25 cm.
    Proefschrift—Amsterdam.
    Summary in English.
    "Stellingen": ₍2₎ p. inserted.
    Bibliography: p. 109-111.

    1. Radioactivity. 2. Beta rays.

    QC794.L5   57-46703

NL 0353221   DLC CtY

Liesi, Rafael.
    Tunnustus. [Lahti] Tekijän kustantama [1948]

    85 p. port.
    Essays

NL 0353222   MH

D   LIESIGK, HANS,   ed.
09   ₍Brandenburgische kirchengeschichte, von dr.
.74   H. Liesigk und dr. A. Blumenfeldt₎   Leipzig,
       Quelle, 1927.
no.43   47p. (Religionskundliche quellenbücherei...
       ₍43₎)

         "Schriftenverzeichnis": p. 5-6.

NL 0353223   ICN

PC2129 Liesigk, Hans, joint author.
.G3M3 Mädel, H
         Le petit employé de poste. Einführung in das Postfran-
       zösisch für Polizeibeamten-, Reichswehr- und Postschulen,
       von H. Mädel und H. Liesigk. Berlin, L. Oehmigke, 1922.

NL ...

D   LIESIGK, HANS,   comp.
09   ₍Religiöse lyrik der letzten jahrzehnte;
.74   ausgewählt von dr. H. Liesigk und prof. W. Op-
       permann₎   Leipzig, Quelle, 1926.
no.27   47p. (Religionskundliche quellenbücherei...
       ₍27₎)

         "Schriftenverzeichnis": p. 47.

NL 0353225   ICN

Liesin, Abraham
    see
Liessin, Abraham, 1872-1938.

232.99 Lieske, Aloisius, 1902-
G821Yl   Die Theologie der Christusmystik Gregors
        von Nyssa. ₍n.p., 1948₎
          340p.

          Cover title.
          "Zeitschrift für katholische Theologie.
        Sonderabdruck aus Jahrgang 70 (1948) Heft
        I-III."
          1. Gregorius, Saint, Bp. of Nyassa, fl. 379-
        394. 2. Jesus Christ—Mystical body.
        I. Title: Christusmystic.

NL 0353227   ICarbS

Lieske, Aloisius, 1902-
    Die theologie der Logosmystik bei Origenes, von p. Aloisius
Lieske, s. j. Münster in Westfalen, Aschendorff, 1938.
    xv, 230 p. 24ᶜᵐ. (Added t.-p.: Münsterische beiträge zur theologie,
hrsg. von F. Diekamp und R. Stapper. hft. 22)
    Issued also as thesis, Pontificia università gregoriana.
    "Literaturverzeichnis": p. ₍x₎-xv.

    1. Origenes. 2. Logos.   I. Title.

                                          A 41-3130
    Catholic univ. of America.   Library
       for Library of Congress   ₍2₎

NL 0353228   DCU CU OWorP CLSU DDO TNJ-R ICU

Lieske, Ernst, appr. Tierarzt: Über Zystennieren beim Schwein.
    Giessen 1911: v. Münchow. 40 S. 8°
    Gießen, Veterinär-Med. Diss. v. 30. Dez. 1911, Ref. Bostroem
    [Geb. 9. Okt. 83 Guben; Wohnort: Gießen; Staatsangeh.: Preußen; Vor-
    bildung: Gymn. Guben Reife O. 04; Studium: Gießen 6, Berlin Tierärztl.
    Hochsch. 3 S.; Rig. 10. März 11.]   [U 12.1387]

NL 0353229   ICRL MBCo DNLM

Lieske, Georg Rudolf
    see Lieske, Rudolf, 1886-

Lieske, Gerhard.
    Abschied von Regine; Roman.
    Lahr, Schauenburg (1949).
      339 p. 12.

NL 0353230   PPG

VOLUME 332

BX
8061
M72
L5
Lieske, H   William
Log cabin memorial; a Lutheran historical building, birthplace of the Lutheran Church, Missouri Synod, in Kansas, 1861. State roadside park-junction of highways US-40 and K-57, 2 1/2 miles east of Junction City, Kan. Great Bend, Kan., Kansas Lutheran Historical Society, 1955.
16 p. illus.

NL 0353231   KMK KU

Lieske, Hans.
Das abzahlungsgeschaeft und seine zivilrechtliche regelung...
Inaug. diss.   Leipzig, 1906.
Bibl.

NL 0353232   ICRL

LIESKE, Hans.
Die berücksichtigung geistiger minderwertigkeit in den vorarbeiten zur strafprozessreform. Berlin, 1913.

27 p.
"BEITRÄGE zur forensischen medizin...herausgegeben von Hans Lungwitz, " I.

NL 0353233   MH-L

Film
S454
LIESKE, Hans.
Die Berücksichtigung geistiger Minderwertigkeit in den Vorarbeiten zur Strafprozessreform. Berlin, Adler, 1913.
27 p. (Beiträge zur forensischen Medizin, Bd. 1, Heft 6)
Film copy.

NL 0353234   DNLM

Lieske, Hans.
Du und das Strafrecht. Leipzig, Dürr & Weber, 1920.
79 p. 20 cm. (Zellenbücherei, Nr. 39)

I. Title.

PT2623.I 48D8   53-52346 ‡

NL 0353235   DLC

LIESKE, Hans.
Das problem krimineller bekämpfung der ansteckung mit geschlechtsleiden. Würzburg,1917.

4°. 60 p.
"Würzburger abhandlungen aus dem ge samtgebiet der praktischen medizin. . . hrag.von Joh. Müller und Otto Seifert, bd.17, hft.3."

NL 0353236   MH-L

Lieske, Hans.
Rechtsunterricht für den Hausbedarf. Leipzig, Dürr & Weber, 1920.
94 p. 20 cm. (Zellenbücherei, Nr. 25)

1. Civil law—Germany—Popular works.   I. Title.

53-49464 ‡

NL 0353237   DLC

Lieske, Hugo: Das höfische Leben und die ritterliche Gesellschaft bei Heinrich von Freiberg. [Maschinenschrift.] 135 S. 4°. —
Auszug: Greifswald 1922: Adler. 4 S. 8°.
Greifswald, Phil. Diss. v. 16. Aug. 1922   [U 22. 9974

NL 0353238   ICRL CaBVaU

QD341
.A6L7
Lieske, Paul, 1875-
Beiträge sur kenntnis des phenylpropargylaldehyds.
Kiel, 1903.
62p.
Inaug diss. Kiel.

NL 0353239   DLC CtY PU DNLM MB MH

Lieske, Rudolf, 1886-
... Bakterien und strahlenpilze, von dr. Rudolf Lieske ... Mit 65 textfiguren. Berlin, Gebrüder Borntraeger, 1922.
2 p. l., 88 p. illus. 26½ᵐᵐ. (Handbuch der pflanzenanatomie ... hrsg. von K. Linsbauer ... II. abt. I. t.: Thallophyten. bd. VI)
"Literatur": p. [62]-65, 85.

1. Bacteria. 2. Actinomyces.
Library of Congress   QK641.H3 bd. VI   23-11480

NL 0353240   DLC NNBG CU MiU OO OU NcD PPC

1886-
Lieske, Rudolf. Beiträge zur Kenntnis der Physiologie von Spirophyllum ferrugineum Ellis, einem typischen Eisenbakterium. Mit 2 Textfig. Leipzig: Borntraeger 1911. 37 S. 8° ¶(Aus: Jahrbücher f. wiss. Botanik. Bd 49, H. 1.) Leipzig, Phil. Diss. v. 7. Febr. 1911, Ref. Pfeffer, Chun
[Geb. 6. Sept. 86 Dresden; Wohnort: Dresden-Altstadt; Staatsangeh.: Sachsen; Vorbildung: Annensch. Dresden Reife O. 06; Studium: Dresden Techn. Hochsch. 3, Leipzig 6 S.; Rig. 22. Nov. 10.]   [U 11. 3247

NL 0353241   ICRL OCU MH CtY

1886-
Lieske, Rudolf, Dr. phil., a. Dresden: Brasilianische Studien. Mit 5 Textfig. Leipzig: Borntraeger 1914. 25 S. 8° ¶Aus: Jahrbücher f. wiss. Botanik. Bd 53.
Mit: Einladung zur ... Probe-Vorlesung ... d. 21.Febr. 1914... Thema: Die photosynthetische und chemosynthetische Assimilation des Kohlenstoffes, Heidelberg (1914):Hörning. 1 Bl.8°
Heidelberg, Naturwiss.-math. Hab.-Schr. v. 1914   [U 14. 3943

NL 0353242   ICRL MH CtY

Lieske, Rudolf, 1886-
Kurzes lehrbuch der allgemeinen bakterienkunde, von dr. Rudolf Lieske ... Mit 118 abbildungen im text. Berlin, Gebrüder Borntraeger, 1926.
viii, 338 p. illus. 25ᵐᵐ.

1. Bacteria. 2. Bacteriology.
Library of Congress   QR41.L6   26-19253

NL 0353243   DLC MtBC PU-BZ CU DNAL DNLM PPPCPh PU-D

Lieske, Rudolf, 1886-
Morphologie und biologie der strahlenpilze (actinomyceten) von dr. phil. Rudolf Lieske ... mit 112 abbildungen im text und 4 farbigen tafeln. Leipzig, Gebrüder Borntraeger, 1921.
ix, 292 p. illus., 4 col. pl. 26ᵐᵐ.
"Die strahlenpilze als krankheitserreger bei menschen und tieren": p. [194]-280.
"Literatur": p. [271]-285.

1. Actinomyces. 2. Actinomycosis.   I. Title: Strahlenpilze.
A 22—1182
Stanford univ. Library
for Library of Congress   [a40d1]

NL 0353244   CSt NcU LU MiU DNLM PPC ICJ NjR

Lieske, Rudolf, 1886-
Serologische Studien mit einzelligen Grünalgen von Rudolf Lieske. Vorgelegt von G. Klebs. Heidelberg: C. Winter, 1916. 48 p. 8°. (Heidelberger Akad. der Wissenschaften. Sitzungsb. Mathematisch-naturwissenschaftliche Klasse. Abteil. B. Jahrg. 1916. Abhandl. 3. diagrs.)

1. Algae. 2. Serum. 3. Klebs,   Georg, 1857- .
N. Y. P. L.   January 12, 1921.

NL 0353245   NN

Film
1240
no. 17
LIESKE, Rudolf, 1886-
Untersuchungen über die Physiologie denitrifizierender Schwefelbakterien. Heidelberg, Winter, 1912.
28 p. (Heidelberger Akademie der Wissenschaften. Mathematisch-naturwissenschaftliche Klasse. Sitzungsberichte. Abt. B. Biologische Wissenschaften. Jahrg. 1912, Abhandlung 6)
Film 1240
Film copy.

NL 0353246   DNLM NN

Lieske, Rudolf, 1906-
Tiecks abwendung von der romantik (teildruck) ... von Rudolf Lieske ... Berlin, E. Ebering [1932]
51, [1] p. 23ᵐᵐ.
Inaug.-diss.—Berlin.
Lebenslauf.
Issued also in full as Germanische studien, hft. 134.
Bibliography: p. [50]-51.

1. Tieck, Johann Ludwig, 1773-1853. 2. Romanticism—Germany.
I. Title.
33-20895
Library of Congress   PT2540.L52   833.73

NL 0353247   DLC ICRL PU

Lieske, Rudolf, 1906-
... Tiecks abwendung von der romantik, von dr. Rudolf Lieske. Berlin, E. Ebering, 1933.
150 p., 1 l. 24½ᵐᵐ. (Germanische studien ... hft. 134)
Issued also in part (51 p.) as inaugural dissertation, Berlin.
Bibliography: p. [147]-148.

1. Tieck, Johann Ludwig, 1773-1853. 2. Romanticism—Germany.
I. Title.
33-20894
Library of Congress   PT2540.L5   833.73
[2]

ViU NcU OrU CaBVaU
NL 0353248   DLC KU TxU MU CU MoKU CLSU NcD OU CtY

Lieske (Walter) [1876-]. *Beitrag zur Untersuchung der Merkfähigkeit im hohen Greisenalter. [Rostock.] 40 pp. 8°. Bonn, E. Eisele [1907]

NL 0353249   DNLM ICRL MH

Lieskier (Christiaan-Everhard). *Keering bij stuitligging. [Amsterdam.] 3 p. l., 76 pp., 1 l. 8°. Tilburg, A. Arts 1903.

NL 0353250   DNLM

VOLUME 332

Liesker, G   J.
Die staatswissenschaftlichen anschauungen Dirck Graswinckel's ...   Freiburg (Schweiz), Buchdruckerei Gebrüder Fragnière, 1901.

ix, 268 p., 2 l. 23cm.

Inaug.-diss.—Freiburg (Schweiz)
Contents.—Vorwort. —Litteratur und leben. —Graswinckel's nationalökonomische anschauungen. —Graswinckel's öffentlichrechtliche anschauungen. —Anhänge.

1. Graswinckel, Dirk, 1600-1666. 2. Economics. 3. Political science.

NL 0353251   CU MH

Lieskin, E
see
Leskin, E

Lieskov, Nikolaĭ Semenovich
see Leskov, Nikolaĭ Semenovich, 1831-1895.

Lieskov, O   V
Передові методи варкп сталі. Київ, Держ. вид-во техн. літ-ри Украïни, 1951.

Microfilm copy (negative) made in 1956 by the Library of Congress. Collation of the original, as determined from the film: 30, ₃₁ p. illus.
Bibliography : p. ₃2₁

1. Steel—Metallurgy.   ι. Title.
        Title transliterated: Peredovi metody varky stali.

Microfilm Slavic 698 T   Mic 57-5304

NL 0353254   DLC

Lieskov, Serge, tr.
Scènes de la révolution Russe
see under title

Lieskova, Marīi͡a Aleksandrovna
see
Leskova, Marīi͡a Aleksandrovna, d. 1900.

Liesli; a Swiss tale
see under [Heun, Karl Gottlieb Samuel]

Лѣсная почва и клпматъ. Отъ 56 градуса сѣверной шпроты къ сѣверу. С.-Петербургъ, Электропечатня К. А. Четверикова, 1906.

35 p. 25ᶜᵐ.

Forest soil and climate.

1. Forest soils. 2. Soil and climate.
                                        Agr 10-1257
                title transliterated:
                Lisnaïa ...
Library, U. S. Dept. of   Agriculture 99L624

NL 0353258   DNAL

[Liesner, Christian]
'Der galante und in dieses Welt-Leben recht sich schickende Mensch/vormahls aus der italiänischen Sprache sein[er] Güte wegen in die teutsche übersetzet von Arione; jetzo aber was die Methode un[d] den Stylum betrifft/ mercklich gebessert/und in Frag-und Antwort gestellet von Fortunander[pseud.] Leipzig, C.Hülsse,1706.
7p.ℓ.,393,[4]p. 16½cm.
Title printed in red and black.
Added engraved t.-p.

Zg17
L62
706

NL 0353259   CtY

[Liesner, Christian]
Der galante und in dieses Welt-Leben recht sich schickende Mensch/vormahls aus der italiänischen Sprache sein[er] Güte wegen in die teutsche übersetzet von Arione; jetzo aber was die Methode un d den Stylum betrifft/mercklich gebessert/und in Frag- und Antwort gestellet von Fortunander [pseud.] Leipzig, C. Hülsse, 1706.
7p.ℓ.,393,[4]p. 17cm.
Title printed in red and black.
Added engraved t.-p.
(German Baroque Literature, No.1685, reel No. 599, Research Publications, Inc.)
Microfilm.

FILM
4333
PT
Reel
599

NL 0353260   CU

Liesner, Gerhard, joint author.

Henke, Carl.
Um Finnlands Freiheit, von Carl Henke ₍und₎ Gerhard Liesner. Berlin, Verlag Tradition W. Kolk, 1932.

DK459
.H45

Liesner, Gerhard, joint ed.

₍Senftleben, Eduard₎ ed.
Unter dem Roten kreuz im weltkriege; das buch der freiwilligen krankenpflege. Berlin, C. A. Weller ₍*1934₎

Liess, Andreas, 1903-
Carl Orff, Idee und Werk. ₍Zürich₎ Atlantis Verlag ₍1955₎

171 p. port., music. 20 cm. (Atlantis Musikbücherei)

"Verzeichnis Orffscher Werke": p. 164-167.

1. Orff, Carl, 1895-   A 56-2179

Oregon. Univ. Libr.
for Library of Congress   ₍3₎

TxFTC WU
NL 0353263   OrU MB MiD ICN ICU NN IU TxU PP NcU IaU

Liess, Andreas, 1903-
... Claude Debussy: das werk im zeitbild, von Andreas Liess ... Strassburg ₍etc.₎ Heitz & co., 1936.

2 v. 25½ᶜᵐ. (Sammlung musikwissenschaftlicher abhandlungen, hrsg. unter leitung von K. Nef, bd. 19)

Paged continuously.
Part 2 wrongly numbered on t.-p. as v. 18 of series (correctly numbered on cover)
"Literaturbeispiele": v. 2, p. 425.

Contents.—1. t. Das zeitbild.—2. t. Das werk und die zeit.

1. *Debussy, Claude, 1862-1918. 2. Music—Hist. & crit.—Modern. 3. Music—Philosophy and esthetics.
                                        37-2479
Library of Congress   ML410.D2SL74
                    ₍3₎   780.81

CaBVaU
NL 0353264   DLC WU TxU NcU NcD MB MH IaU ViU OU

Liess, Andreas, 1903-
... Claude Debussy und das deutsche musikschaffen. Würzburg-Aumühle, K. Triltsch ₍1939₎

61 p. illus. (music) 21ᶜᵐ. ₍Kleine deutsche musikbücherei, bd. 11₎

1. *Debussy, Claude, 1862-1918. 2. Impressionism (Music) 3. Music, German.

Library of Congress   ML410.D2SL75   41-27522
                    ₍2₎   780.81

NL 0353265   DLC NN IEN

Liess, Andreas, 1903-
Deutsche und französische Musik in der Geistesgeschichte des neunzehnten Jahrhunderts. Vorwort von Maurice Boucher. Wien, Berglandverlag ₍*1950₎

98 p. 22 cm.

Bibliography : p. ₍100₎

1. Music—Hist. & crit.—19th cent.

ML196.L5   51-32879

NL 0353266   DLC NIC PP ICU MH NN

Liess, Andreas, 1903-
Franz Schmidt, Leben und Schaffen. Graz, H. Böhlaus, 1951.

175 p. ports. 22 cm.

"Verzeichnis der Werke nach Gattungen": p. 162-165. "Verzeichnis der Druckwerke": p. 166.
"Literatur über Franz Schmidt": p. 169-170.

1. Schmidt, Franz, 1874-1939.

                                    A 52-3006
Oregon. Univ. Libr.
for Library of Congress   ₍3₎

ML410
.S2614L5

NL 0353267   OrU OCU ICU NN DLC

Liess, Andreas, 1903-
Fuxiana. Wien, Bergland Verlag ₍1958₎
95p. illus. 18cm. (Österreich-Reihe, Bd.53)

1. Fux, Johann Joseph, 1660-1741.

ML410
F99L45

NL 0353268   IaU

Liess, Andreas, 1903-
La Gioconda; ein Gedenkbuch. Wien, Berglandverlag ₍c1951₎
65 p. 30 plates.

1. Gioconda, La, 1923-1948.

GV1785
G5L5

NL 0353269   CU

Liess, Andreas, 1903-
Johann Joseph Fux, ein steirischer Meister des Barock. Nebst einem Verzeichnis neuer Werkfunde. Wien, L. Doblinger ₍*1948₎

90 p. port., music. 24 cm.

"Verzeichnis der in den Jahren 1942-1947 neu aufgefundenen Werke und Manuscripte": p. ₍57₎-89.
Bibliography: p. 90.

1. Fux, Johann Joseph, 1660-1741.

ML410.F99L47   50-21874

KU IEN IaU CoU
NL 0353270   DLC TxU ICU NcU NN IU OU MiU OBerB IaU

VOLUME 332

Liess, Andreas, 1903–
Johann Michael Vogl, Hofoperist und Schubertsänger. Graz, H. Böhlaus Nachf., 1954.
224 p. illus., ports., music. 22 cm.
"Die wichtigste Original-Literatur über Vogl": p. 201–202.
Four songs by J. M. Vogl (16 p., 21 cm.) in pocket.

1. Vogl, Johann Michael, 1768–1840. 2. Schubert, Franz Peter, 1797–1828. 3. Music—Austria—Vienna.

A 55–1265

Oregon. Univ. Librar₎
for Library of Congress   ₍2₎

NL 0353271   OrU CaBVaU DLC IaU MB NN NcU NcD TxU CoU

V
29
.55316
LIESS, ANDREAS, 1903–
Joseph Marx, Leben und Werk. Mit einem Titelbild, 12 Bildern im Text und 24 Notenbeispielen. Graz, Steirische Verlagsaufstalt, 1943.
247p. illus., port., facsims., music. 23cm.

NL 0353272   ICN MnU IEN MH NjP PP

Liess, Andreas, 1903–
... L. van Beethoven und Richard Wagner im Pariser musikleben, von dr. Andreas Liess. Hamburg, Hoffmann und Campe ₍1939₎
94 p. 19ᶜᵐ. (Added t.-p.: Geistiges Europa; bücher über geistige beziehungen europäischer nationen)
Series title in part at head of t.-p.
"Nachwort des herausgebers" signed: A. E. B. ₍i. e. A. E. Brinckmann₎

1. Beethoven, Ludwig van, 1770–1827. 2. Wagner, Richard, 1813–1883. 3. Paris—Intellectual life. I. Brinckmann, Albert Erich, 1881– ed.

A 41–3220

Minnesota. Univ. Libr.
for Library of Congress   ₍2₎

NL 0353273   MnU

Liess, Andreas, 1903–
... L. van Beethoven und Richard Wagner im Pariser musikleben, von dr. Andreas Liess. Hamburg, Hoffmann und Campe ₍1942₎
96 p. 19ᶜᵐ. (Added t.-p.: Geistiges Europa; bücher über geistige beziehungen europäischer nationen. Begründer und herausgeber: ... A. E. Brinckmann)
"11.–25. tausend."
Series title in part at head of t.-p.

1. Beethoven, Ludwig van, 1770–1827. 2. Wagner, Richard, 1813–1883. 3. Music—France—Paris.

46–32982

Library of Congress   ML410.B43L5
₍2₎   780.81

NL 0353274   DLC NcD MiU CtY CLU NN

ML197
.L46
Liess, Andreas, 1903–
Die Musik im Weltbild der Gegenwart; Erkenntnis und Bekenntnis. Lindau im Bodensee, Frisch & Perneder ₍1949₎
266 p. music. 21 cm.

1. Music—Hist. & crit.—20th cent. 2. Music—Philosophy and aesthetics. I. Title.
ML197.L46   780.904   50–32579

NL 0353275   DLC OrU

Liess, Andreas, 1903–
Die Musik im Weltbild der Gegenwart; Erkenntnis und Bekenntnis. Wien, F. Perneder ₍1949₎
266 p. music. 22 cm.

1. Music—Hist. & crit.—20th cent. 2. Music—Philosophy and aesthetics. I. Title.
ML197.L46 1949a   780.904   51–19567

NL 0353276   DLC NcD PP NN TxU

Liess, Andreas, 1903–
Die trio-sonaten von J. J. Fux, an hand der manuskripte der Wiener Nationalbibliothek; eine studie zum dynamischen geschichtsbild im süddeutschen spätbarock, von dr. Andreas Liess. Berlin, Junker und Dünnhaupt, 1940.
101, ₍1₎ p., 1 l., 49 p. 24½ᶜᵐ. (Added t.-p.: Neue deutsche forschungen. Abt.: Musikwissenschaft ... hrsg. von Joseph Müller-Blattau, bd. 9)
Half-title: Neue deutsche forschungen, hrsg. von Hans R. G. Günther und Erich Rothacker, bd. 263.
Bibliography included in "Anmerkungen" (p. ₍99₎–101)
"Notenanhang": 1 l., 49 p.

1. Fux, Johann Joseph, 1660–1741.   I. Title.

41–20748

Library of Congress   ML410.F99L5
₍2₎   787

NL 0353277   DLC NcU ICU IaU NIC MH NN ICN IU

Liess, Andreas, 1903–
... Wiener barockmusik, von Andreas Liess ... Mit 24 bildtafeln und zahlreichen notenbeispielen. Wien, L. Doblinger (B. Herzmansky) komm.-ges., 1946.
236 p. 24 pl. (incl. ports., facsims. ₍incl. music₎) on 12 l. 24½ᶜᵐ.
(Added t.-p.: Wiener musik-bücherei, bd. 3)
CONTENTS.—Die instrumentalmusik Österreichs im 17. jahrhundert.—Die oper in Wien.—J. J. Fux und der ausklang des Wiener hochbarock.—Notenbeispiele (p. ₍119₎–225)—Literaturverzeichnis (p. 227–228)

1. Music—Austria—Vienna. 2. Music—Hist. & crit.—16th-17th cent. 3. Instrumental music (Scores)—To 1800. 4. Vocal music (Scores)—To 1800. I. Title.
ML246.8.V6L5   780.9436   47–2596

GU WU
NL 0353279   DLC PP NcU CLSU MB NN TxU ICU MiU NIC NcD

Ließ, Bernhard: Aus d. dermatol. Universitätsklinik Breslau. Dir.: Neißer. Stellvertr. Dir.: Bruck. ˉEin Fall von Pityriasis rubra pilaris. Breslau 1912: Breslauer Genossensch.-Buchdr. 23 S. 8°
Breslau, Med. Diss. v. 3. Juni 1912, Ref. Bruck, Minkowski
₍Geb. 22. Febr. 78 Mossn; Wohnort: Frankfurt a. O.; Staatsangeh.: Preußen; Vorbildung: Gymn. Meseritz Reife O. 98; Studium: Berlin K. W. A. 10 S.; Coll. 22. Mai 12; Approb. 18. Okt. 04.₎   ₍U 12. 668₎

NL 0353280   ICRL DNLM

LIESS, Eberhard, 1902–
Untersuchungen über die quanten-energiewerte des unsymmetrischen kreisels und des Kramers-Pauli'schen molekülmodells. Inaug.-diss., Breslau, Ohlau i. Schl., H. Eschenhagen, [1928?]

pp. 21+ Diagr.
At head of title: Physikalisches institut der universität Breslau.
"Lebenslauf", at end.

NL 0353281   MH ICRL CtY

Liess, Emil.
Was ist sozialismus? Sieben vorträge von Emil Liess. ₍San Francisco, 1899₎
8 p. l., 117 p. 21½ᶜᵐ.
"Vierte, unveränderte auflage. Druck und verlag der S. F. Tageblatt publishing society", which appears on t.-p., is covered by label.

1. Socialism. 2. Labor and laboring classes.
2–16121
Library of Congress   HX86.L7

NL 0353282   DLC NN ICU

Liess,Felix,1908–
Die entwicklung der siebenbürgischsächsischen banken en der nachkriegszeit ... von diplomkaufmann Felix Liess ... Eisfeld i. Thür., C. Beck, 1937.
viii,90,₍6₎ p. tables (part fold.) 2 diagr. 22ᶜᵐ.
Inaug.--diss.--Erlangen.
Lebenslauf.
"Literaturverzeichnis": p. ₍1₎–5, at end.

1.Banks and banking--Transylvania.

NL 0353283   MiU CtY ICRL

Liess, Hermann.
Das Res.-infanterie-regiment nr. 71 im weltkriege 1914-1918; nach den amtlichen kriegstagebüchern und persönlichen aufzeichnungen bearb. von Hermann Liess ... Mit 10 karten, 8 textskizzen und 61 abbildungen. Oldenburg i.O./ Berlin, G. Stalling, 1925.
246, [5] p. illus. ₍incl. plans₎ fold. maps. 22 cm. (Added t.-p.: Erinnerungsblätter deutscher regimenter ... Truppenteile des ehemaligen preussischen₍k₎ ontingents ...)

NL 0353284   CSt-H

Liess, Johannes.
Die endoskopie beim rinde, ihre klinische bedeutung u. praktische ausführung, von dr. med. vet. habil. Johannes Liess ... Mit 32 abbildungen. Hannover, M. & H. Schaper, 1936.
167 p. illus., diagrs. 24½ᶜᵐ.
"Schrifttumverzeichnis": p. 163–167.

1. Endoscope and endoscopy. 2. Cattle—Diseases—Diagnosis. I. Title.
37–5186
Library of Congress   SF961.L5
Copyright A—Foreign   33050
₍2₎   619.2

NL 0353285   DLC DNLM

Liess, Johannes.
... Geburten im viehstall, von professor dr. J. Liess ... Berlin, Reichsnährstand verlags-ges. m. b. h. ₍*1937₎
47 p. illus. 23½ᶜᵐ. (Arbeiten des Reichsnährstandes. bd. 23)

1. Veterinary obstetrics. I. Title.
37–19016
Library of Congress   SF887.L5
Copyright A—Foreign   35821
₍2₎   636.082456

NL 0353286   DLC IaAS DNAL

Liess, Johannes.
... Vergleichende untersuchungen über die brauchbarkeit verschiedener flotationsmedien zum nachweis von parasiteneiern im kot der haustiere ... Alfeld (Leine) Buchdr. P. Dobler, 1925.
64 p. pl. 22ᶜᵐ.
Inaug.-diss.—Tierärztl. hochschule, Hannover.
"Literatur-verzeichnis": p. ₍57₎–61.

1. Parasites. ₍1. Parasite eggs₎
Agr 28–1146
Library, U. S. Dept. of   Agriculture 436L624

NL 0353287   DNAL

Liess, Otto, 1871–
... Ein beitrag zur kenntnis der wirkung der formaethrolpräparate ... Göttingen, Druck der Dieterich'schen univ.-buchdr. (W. F. Kaestner) 1909.
32, ₍2₎ p. 21½ᶜᵐ.
Inaug.-diss.—Bern.
Lebenslauf.
"Litteratur": page after p. 32.

1. Formethrol.
Agr 11–1459
Library, U. S. Dept. of   Agriculture 448L622

NL 0353288   DNAL DNLM PU

Liessart, Eléonore Paul Constant du Chambge de, baron
   see Du Chambge de Liessart, Eléonore Paul Constant, baron.

VOLUME 332

Liesse, André, 1854–
Les emprunts de guerre de l'Allemagne.   Paris: Berger-Levrault, 1916.   54 p., 1 l.   16°.   (Pages d'histoire, 1914–1916. [fasc.] 110.)

Author's name at head of title.

1. European war, 1914–   .—Finance, Germany, 1914–16. 3. Title. 4. Series. N. Y. P. L.   Germany. 2. Debt (Public), Germany, 1914–16.   January 18, 1917.

NL   0353290   NN MB PU CtY

Liesse, André, 1854–
Les entreprises industrielles, fondation et direction, par André Liesse ...   Paris, Librairie de l'enseignement technique, 1919.

vii, 205 p.   19ᶜᵐ.

"Ce livre a pour origine les conférences que nous avons faites, en 1916–1917, au Conservatoire national des arts et métiers."—Avant-propos.

1. Industry. 2. Efficiency, Industrial. 3. Executive ability. 4. Capital. I. Title.

Library of Congress   HD2326.L5   21–17305

NL   0353291   DLC ICU ICJ NN

Liesse, André, 1854–
... Evolution of credit and banks in France from the founding of the Bank of France to the present time, by André Liesse ...   Washington, Govt. print. off., 1909 [1910]

267 p. fold. tab. 23ᶜᵐ.   (U. S. 61st Cong., 2d sess. Senate. Doc. 522)

At head of title: National monetary commission. Issued also, 1911, in Publications of National monetary commission. vol. xv. [no. 1]

1. Banks and banking—France. 2. Credit—France. 3. Finance—France. I. U. S. National monetary commission. II. Title.

Library of Congress   HG3028.L5   10–35929

PPAmP PPT ICJ MH
NL   0353292   DLC CaBVaU WaS OrP CU MiU OU OFH NcD

Liesse, André, 1854–
... Evolution of credit and banks in France from the founding of the Bank of France to the present time, by André Liesse ...   Washington, Govt. print. off., 1909 [i. e. 1911]

267 p. fold. tab. 23ᶜᵐ.   (Publications of National monetary commission. vol. xv. [no. 1])

[U. S.] 61st Cong., 2d sess. Senate. Doc. 522.
Issued also separately, 1909 [i. e. 1910]

1. Banks and banking—France. 2. Credit—France. 3. Finance—France. I. U. S. National monetary commission. II. Title.

Library of Congress   HG471.A4 1911 vol. 15, no. 1   12–35283

NL   0353293   DLC NjP WaTC NIC OC1FRB PPT PHC

Liesse, André, 1854–   ed.
HJ1089
.S3
Say, Léon, 1826–1896.
... Les finances de la France sous la troisième république ...   Paris, Calmann Lévy, 1898–1901.

Liesse, André, 1854–
... Leçons d'économie politique, par André Liesse ...   Avec une préface de M. Courcelle-Seneuil.   Paris: A. Girard & E. Brière, 1892.

x, 216 p.   18ᶜᵐ.   (École spéciale d'architecture)

1. Economics.   I. Courcelle-Seneuil, Jean Gustave, 1813–1892.

Library of Congress   HB173.L7   5–35167†

NL   0353295   DLC NBuU

FOR OTHER EDITIONS SEE MAIN ENTRY
Liesse, André, 1845– ed.
Courcelle-Seneuil, Jean Gustave, 1813–1892.
... Les opérations de banque, traité théorique et pratique. 9. éd. rev. et mise à jour, par André Liesse ...   Paris, Guillaumin & cⁱᵉ, 1905.

Liesse, André, 1854–
L'organisation du crédit en Allemagne et en France.   Paris: Berger-Levrault, 1915.   170 p., 2 l., 4 tables (3 fold.).   Chart. 16°.   (Pages d'histoire, 1914–1915. [fasc.] 58.)

Author's name at head of title.

1. European war, 1914–   .—Finance, .—Finance, France. 3. Credit, Series. N. Y. P. L.   Germany. 2. European war, 1914– Germany. 4. Credit, France. 5.   June 6, 1916.

NL   0353297   NN OU PU

Liesse, André, 1854–
L'organisation du crédit en Allemagne et en France. [4e mille.] Paris. Berger-Levrault. 1915. 170, (11) pp. [Pages d'histoire. Whole no. 58. Ser. 8. La guerre et la presse mondiale. Vol. e (1).] 17½ cm., in 8s.

L1018 — S.r.c. (2) — European War, 1914– . Economic aspects. — Credit. — France. Fin. — Germany. Fin.

NL   0353298   MB CtY OU DNW MH-BA

Liesse, André, 1854–
Portraits de financiers ... par André Liesse ...   Paris, F. Alcan, 1908.

xvi (i. e. xvii), 348 p.   18½ᶜᵐ.

CONTENTS.—Ouvrard.—Mollien.—Gaudin.—Le baron Louis.—Corvetto.—Jacques Laffitte.—De Villèle.

1. Finance—France. 2. Capitalists and financiers—France.

NL   0353299   MiU NNC NjP NN MH-BA ICU KU RP IEN NcD NIC

Liesse, André, 1854– ed.
Leroy-Beaulieu, Paul, 1843–1916.
Précis d'économie politique, par Paul Leroy-Beaulieu ... revu par André Liesse ... 49. mille.   Paris, Delagrave, 1922.

Liesse, André, 1854–
Union coloniale française, *Paris.*
... Préparation aux carrières coloniales. Conférences faites par MM. Le Myre de Vilers—Dr. Treille—L. Simon—E. Fallot—J.-B. Malon—Paris—L. Fontaine—Maurice Courant—Gérome—André Liesse, 1901–1902. Petit manuel d'hygiène des colons; par le Dr. Reynaud. Préface par M. J. Chailley-Bert. Paris, A. Challamel, 1904.

HB105
.S3L7
LIESSE, ANDRÉ, 1854–
Un professeur d'économie politique sous la restauration, J.-B. Say au Conservatoire des arts et métiers, par André Liesse... Paris, Guillaumin et cie, 1901.
56 p. 19½ cm.

1. Say, Jean Baptiste, 1767–1832.

NL   0353302   ICU

Liesse, André, 1854–
... La question sociale, par André Liesse.   Paris, L. Chailley, 1894.

3 p. l., [3]–247 p. 20ᶜᵐ.   (*On cover:* La vie nationale; bibliothèque des sciences sociales & politiques, dirigée par mm. Charles Benoist et André Liesse)

Series title in part at head of t.-p.

1. Social problems. 2. Socialism.   I. Title.

Library of Congress   HN17.L5   42–7319

NL   0353303   DLC MB ICJ

HN
17
L71q
Liesse, André, 1854–
La question sociale. Paris, L. Chailley, 1895.
247 p. 20cm. (La Vie nationale; bibliothèque de la politique et de la science sociale) Series title in part at head of t.p.

1. Social problems. 2. Socialism.

NL   0353304   NRU

Liesse, André, 1854–   *7577.152.163
Social legislation.
(*In* Fiftieth anniversary, The, of the French Republic. Pp. 30–36. New York. 1921. [International Conciliation. No. 163.])

M2314 — France. Social science.

NL   0353305   MB

Liesse, André, 1854–
Die soziale Frage. Autorisierte Übersetzung aus dem Französischen von L. A. Hauff. Zittau, Verlag der Pahl'schen Buchhandlung, A. Haase, 1896.
x, 203 p. 23cm. (Bibliothek des sozialen und politischen Wissenschaften Frankreichs, Bd. 1) Translation of La question sociale.

1. Social problems. 2. Socialism.

NL   0353306   NRU

Liesse, André, 1854–
La statistique; ses difficultés; ses procédés; ses résultats, par André Liesse ... [Paris] Guillaumin et cⁱᵉ, 1905.
viii, 182 p. 18½ᶜᵐ.

1. Statistics.

Library of Congress   HA29.L7   5–15108

NL   0353307   DLC OCU ICJ NN MB

Liesse, André, 1854–
La statistique; ses difficultés—ses procédés; ses résultats, par André Liesse ... 2. éd. rev. et augm. Paris, F. Alcan, 1912.
viii, 192 p. diagrs. 19ᶜᵐ.

1. Statistics.

Library of Congress   HA29.L7 1912   12–16632

NL   0353308   DLC

VOLUME 332

Liesse, Andre, 1854–
La statistique; ses difficultes - ses
procedes; ses resultats, par Andre Liesse...
3. ed.rev.
Paris, F.Alcan, 1919.
viii,192 p. diagrs. 19 cm.

NL 0353309 DL

Liesse, André, 1854–
La statistique; ses difficultés—ses procédés; ses résultats, par
André Liesse ... 4. éd. rev. et augm. Paris, F. Alcan, 1927.
viii, 213 p., 1 l. diagrs. 19ᶜᵐ.

1. Statistics.

Library of Congress   HA29.L7 1927   37-29173
                           [2]   311

NL 0353310 DLC NN

Liesse, André, 1854–
La statistique; ses difficultés - ses procédés;
ses resultats ... 5. éd. Paris, F. Alcan,
1933.
viii, 213 p., 1 l. incl. diagrs. 19 cm.
1. Statistics.

NL 0353311 CtY

Liesse, André, 1854–   ed.
Garnier, Joseph i. e. Clément Joseph, 1813–1881.
Traité d'économie politique; exposé didactique des
principes et des applications de la science économique ...
9. éd. rev. et augm. par A. Liesse ... Paris, Guillaumin
et cie., 1889.

Liesse, André, 1854–   ed.
Garnier, Joseph i. e. Clément Joseph, 1813–1881.
Traité d'économie politique, sociale ou industrielle,
exposé didactique des principes et des applications de la
science économique, par Joseph Garnier ... 10. éd., rev.
et augm. par Robert Doucet ... avec les notes de la 9. éd.
par André Liesse ... Paris, Garnier frères, 1907.

Liesse, André, 1854–
Le travail aux points de vue scientifique, industriel et
social. Par André Liesse ... Paris, Guillaumin et cie.,
1899.
2 p. l., iii, 525 p. 22ᶜᵐ.

1. Labor and laboring classes.

                                           1-F-3645
Library of Congress   HD4901.L4

NL 0353314 DLC CU MB N WU

Liesse, Georges.
Le football dévoilé, par Georges Liesse & Jean Cornilli.
[Lodelinsart (Charleroi) Londot, 1954]
xx, 85 p. illus. 20 cm. (Éditions Pax)

1. Soccer.   I. Cornilli, Jean, joint author.   II. Title.
                                           A 55-1435
Ohio State Univ. Libr.
for Library of Congress   [1]

NL 0353315 OU

Liesse, H.
Le Pierrot d' à côte ...
see under   Lagye, Alexandre.

Liesse (Marcel) [1893–   ]. *Contribution à
l'étude de la réaction myotonique du tra-
pèse. 33 pp. 3°. Paris, 1923. No. 87.

NL 0353317 DNLM CtY

Liesse. Legend.
... Comment Ihyma ge Nᶠᵉ Dame de Liesse autrement ditte
de Lience fut trouuee auec les miracles. Notre-Dame de Liesse,
sa légende, d'après le plus ancien texte connu, avec un épilogue
de m. Georges Goyau ... [Nogent-le-Rotrou, Les presses de
Daupeley-Gouverneur] 1934.
3 p. l., [9]–89 p., 2 l. 20 pl. incl. front., facsim. 19ᶜᵐ.
At head of title: Comte de Hennezel d'Ormois.

I. Hennezel d'Ormois, Jehan Marie François, comte de, 1876–   ed.
II. *Goyau, Georges, 1869–1939.

Library of Congress   BT660.L5A3   42-35288

NL 0353318 DLC

Liesse. Legend.
Notre-Dame-de-Liesse, mère de grace. Légende,
pèlerinage et translation de la statue au Gesù de
Montréal. Montréal, Beauchemin & Valois, 1878.
80 p.

NL 0353319 MH

Liesseline, Ethel (McDonald) de
see
De Liesseline, Ethel (McDonald)

LIESSEM, Hermann Joseph, 1841–
Bibliographisches verzeichnis der schriften
Hermanns van dem Busche. [II], III. 2 pt.
Köln, 1888–89.
4°
(Progr.d.kaiser Wilhelm-gym", 1888, nr.4.
1889,nr.4.
For teil I. see his "Herman van dem Busche",
1884. 4°.

NL 0353321 MH

Liessem, Hermann Joseph, 1841–
De Hermanni Bvschii vita et scriptis ... Bonnae, typis
Caroli Georgii, 1866.
2 p. l., 80, [3] p. 21ᶜᵐ.
Inaug.-diss.—Bonn.
Vita.

1. Busche, Hermann von dem, 1468–1534.
                                           32-5101
Library of Congress   PA85.B85L5   928.79

NL 0353322 DLC ICRL NIC NNC

LIESSEM, Hermann Joseph, 1841–
Hermann van dem Busche. Sein Leben und seine
Schriften. Ie te [1e abth.] Progr. Köln,1884.
4°. pp. 1–2
For continuation, see his "Biliographisches
verzeichnis der schriften Hermanns van dem
Busche." 1888. 4°.

NL 0353323 MH

C43   Liessem, Hermann Joseph, 1841–
K834uH1 Die quodlibetischen disputationen
an der universität Köln.   Koln, 1886.
p. 58–70.   (Programm des Kaiser
Wilhelm-gymnasiums zu Köln)

NL 0353324 IU

Liessem, J. J., comp.
Poesie fürs haus; eine auswahl von gedichten, besonders aus der neueren zeit, ... Köln
am Rhein, Bachem, n.d.
517p. illus.

NL 0353325 OC1ND

Liessem, J. J.
Das rote Glückwunsch-Büchlein; Festwünsche zum neuen
Jahre, zu Namenstagen und Geburtstagen, zu Hochzeiten, Jubi-
läen und anderen Gelegenheiten, Album-Sprüche, mit einem An-
hang französischer und englischer Glückwünsche.   Köln: J. P.
Bachem [, 19—?]. 136 p. 8°.

1. Title. 2. Recitations.
N. Y. P. L.   January 27, 1933

NL 0353326 NN

Liessem, J. J.
Das rote Glückwunsch-Büchlein; Festwünsche zum neuen
Jahre, zum Namens- und Geburtstagen, zu Hochzeiten, Jubiläen
und anderen Gelegenheiten, Album Sprüche; mit einem Anhang
französischer und englischer Glückwunsche.   Cöln: J. P. Bachem
19—?]. 3-134 p. 12°.

NL 0353327 NN

Liessem (Nicolaus) [1809–   ]. *De morborum prodromia. 2 p. l., 30 pp., 2 l. 8°. Bonnæ,
ex off. Meeriana, 1832.

NL 0353328 DNLM PPC

Liessem, T
Kölsch Thiater
see under
Cologne. Kölner Rosenmontagszug, 1953.

Liessin, Abraham, 1872–1938.
... לידער און פאעמען. [1938–1888] מיט צייכמנונען פון
מארק שאגאל ... ניו יארק, ארויסגעגעבן פון "פארווערטס
אסאסיאיישאן". [New York 1938.]
3 v. fronts. (ports.) illus. (facsims.) mount. plates. 22ᶜᵐ.
At head of title: אברהם וואלט [א. ליעסין]

I. Chagall, Marc, 1887–   illus.   Title transliterated: Lider un poemen.
[Name originally: Abraham Walt]
                                           A 46-2316
New York. Public library
for Library of Congress   PJ5129.L535L5

NL 0353330 NN DLC CtY CaBVaU

VOLUME 332

Liessin, Abraham, 1872–1938.
... זכרונות וחויות. עם מבוא מאת ב. כצנלסון. הוצאת
עם עובד", תש"ג. [Tel-Aviv, "Am'oved," 1942/43]
39, 239 p. port. 19½ ". (כתבים נבחרים. ספר א') *(Added t.-p:* "מבחר א. קריב.
Preliminary matter paged with Hebrew characters.
1. Authors—Correspondence, reminiscences, etc.   I. Kariv, Abraham, 1900–   tr.   II. Katzenelson, Berl, 1887–
Title transliterated: Zikhronoth ...
[*Name originally:* Abraham Walt]
45–13906
Library of Congress   PJ5129.L535Z52

NL 0353331 DLC

Liessin, Abraham, 1872–1938.
זכרונות און בילדער. ציקא ביכער פארלאג.
[New York, 1954]
x, 313 p. illus., ports. 22 cm.
(ל. מ. שטיין פאלקס-ביבליאטעק ביים אלוועלטלעכן יידישן קולטור-קאנגרעס)
Half title: געקליבענע ווערק
Added t. p.: Selected works.
1. Socialism in the U. S. 2. Authors, Yiddish.
Title transliterated: Zikhroynes un bilder.
Name originally: Abraham Walt.
HX84.L5A3   59–59771

NL 0353332 DLC

Liesske, C. Rob.
Dante und seine Stellung zu Kirche, Schule und Staat seiner zeit. Dresden, Adler und Dietze, 1858.

NL 0353333 NIC PU

Liessman, Charles, 1878–   ed.
North Dakota. *Laws, statutes, etc.*
The compiled laws of the state of North Dakota, 1913; together with annotations: (1) explanatory and critical notes of the compiler; (2) notes of judicial decisions by which the various sections have been construed; (3) references to pertinent and important notes in annotated reports. Also the Constitution of the United States and of the state of North Dakota, with the amendments thereto. By authority of the Legislative assembly ... Rochester, N. Y., The Lawyers co-operative publishing company, 1914.

JK6425   Liessman, Charles, 1878–   ed.
1933
.A6   **North Dakota.** *Constitution.*
The constitution of the state of North Dakota with all amendments adopted to and including September 22, 1933. Published under legislative authority. By Robert Byrne, secretary of state. Edited by Charles Liessman, deputy. [Bismarck, Bismarck tribune, 1933]

Law   Liessman, Charles, 1878–   comp.
North Dakota. *Constitution.*
The Constitution of the State of North Dakota, with all amendments adopted to and including June 27, 1950, by Thomas Hall, secretary of state. Compiled by Charles Liessman. [Bismarck? 1950?]

Law   Liessman, Charles, 1878–   ed.
North Dakota. *Laws, statutes, etc.*
Corporation laws of the state of North Dakota, general and co-operative. Rev. to July 1, 1925. Issued by Robert Byrne, secretary of state. Edited by Charles Liessman, deputy. [Fargo, 1925]

JK1963   Liessman, Charles, 1878–   ed.
.N9A3
1930   **North Dakota.** *Laws, statutes, etc.*
Election laws of the state of North Dakota. 1930. Pub. under legislative authority by Robert Byrne, secretary of state. Ed. by Charles Liessman, deputy. [Fargo, Knight printing co., 1930]

Law   Liessman, Charles, 1878–   comp.
FOR OTHER EDITIONS
SEE MAIN ENTRY
North Dakota. *Laws, statutes, etc.*
Election laws of the State of North Dakota, 1948. Comp. by Charles Liessman. [Bismarck] T. Hall, Secretary of State [1948]

———— Supplement. 1950–
[Bismarck]

Liessmann, Elmer M.
Illinois. *Laws, statutes, etc.*
Compilation of tax laws and judicial decisions of the state of Illinois. Made by Albert M. Kales, Elmer M. Liessmann, under the direction of the Special tax commission ... pursuant to an act of the General assembly, approved June 10, 1909 ... [n. p., 1911?]

LIESSMANN, Elmer M.
Law of Persons and Domestic Relations.
167 p.
(In MODERN American Law, vol. 3, cop. 1914, p. 341-507.)
Same. Leading illustrative cases. 86 p. (In MODERN American Law, vol. 3, cop. 1914, p. 705-790.)

NL 0353341 MH-L

Liessmann, Elmer M.
Illinois. *Industrial board.*
Opinions and decisions of the Industrial board of Illinois...
Chicago, 1916–

Liessner [Elias] [1862–   ]. "Ein Beitrag zur Kenntniss der Kiemenspalten und ihrer Anlagen bei amnioten Wirbelthieren. 33 pp., 1 l. 8°. *Dorpat, Schnakenburg,* 1889.

NL 0353343 DNLM CU

Liestal. Kantonsbibliothek Baselland.
Catalogo generale della Biblioteca cantonale fino a tutto il 1912. Ordinato per materie.
[IX. Manoscritti e libri preziosi. [A] Manoscritti. Bellinzona, Tipografia e litografia cantonale, 1915.
37-47 l. 29ᶜᵐ.
Photostat (negative)

NL 0353344 NNC

LIESTING, Gerardus Theodorus Henricus
Vrijheid en gezag; autonomie van de mens en de Christelijke vrijheid.
Nijmegen, Brakkenstein, 1955.
40p. 22.3cm.

NL 0353345 MH-AH

UG30.2   Liesting, Gerardus Theodorus Henricus
L719   De zin van het laatste avondmaal volgens de Nieuw-Testamentische teksten; beeld of werkelijkheid ... door Gerardus Theodorus Henricus Liesting ... Brakkenstein-Nijmegen, Drukkerij Sint Joseph, 1948.
xii, 215p. 25cm.
Academisch proefschrift - Nijmegen.
"Stellingen", [3]p., laid in.
"Literatuurlijst": p.x-xii.

NL 0353346 NNUT DLC-P4 NjPT CtY

Liestmann, Wulf, 1904–
Beitrag zur kenntnis des nitrierhärtungsverfahrens ... Düsseldorf, 1933. 13 p.
Inaug. Diss. - Techn. Hochschule Berlin, 1933.
Lebenslauf.

NL 0353347 ICRL

*F601.5   [Liestøl, Aslak]
.M66   The Bergen runes and the Kensington inscription.
v.40
(In Minnesota history. St. Paul. 26cm. v.40(1966) p.59. illus.)

NL 0353348 MnHi

LIESTØL, ASLAK.
Cryptograms in Runic carvings; a critical analysis.
(IN: Minnesota history. St. Paul. 26cm. v. 41, no. 1 (spring, 1968) p. [34]-42. illus.)
1. Runic inscriptions. 2. Northmen in America.

NL 0353349 NN

GR220   LIESTØL, KNUT, 1881-1952, ed.
.L69   Aktstykke til soga um nordisk folkeminnegransking. Tridje samling ved Knut Liestøl.
n.p., [n.pub., n .]
[133]-143 p.
Reprinted from Saertrykk av Maal og minne, hefte 4, 1934.
I. Asbjørnsen, Peter Christen, 1812-1885. II. Tc. Folklore cd.

NL 0353350 InU

Liestøl, Knut, 1881-1952.
Draumkvæde: a Norwegian visionary poem from the Middle Ages. Oslo [Aschehoug] 1946.
144 p. 24 cm. (Studia Norvegica, no. 3)
Bibliographical footnotes.
1. Draumkvæde.   (Series)
GR1.S85 no. 3   65–82194
ICN MH NNC WaU MiU
NL 0353351 DLC InU CaBVaU CLU FMU KU ViU OU NIC CU

Liestøl, Knut, 1881-1952, ed.
Eventyr
see under Asbjørnsen, Peter Christian, 1812-1885.

VOLUME 332

Liestøl, Knut, 1881- 1952, ed.

Folklore fellows.
FF communications, edited for the Folklore fellows ...
no. 1–
Helsinki, Suomalaisen tiedeakatemian kustantama, 1911–

PT8623   Liestøl,Knut,1881- 1952
f.A3L7   Folkedikting, av professor dr.Knut Liestøl.
[Bergen,1927]
p.119-148. illus.(ports.) 32½x27ᶜᵐ.

Caption title.
"Særtryk av "Norske bygder",bd.II:Vestagder,
1.halvbind".

NL 0353354   ICU

Liestøl, Knut, 1881- 1952, ed.
Fylling, Peder Carolus Jonssøn, 1818–1890.
Folkesagn, ved Knut Liestøl. Oslo, Norsk folkeminnelag,
1942.

Liestøl, Knut, 1881- 1952, ed.
... Folkevisor, utgjeven av Knut Liestøl ... Folksägner och
folksagor, utgiven av C. W. von Sydow ... Stockholm, A.
Bonnier; [etc., etc., 1931]
7 p. l., [3]-295, [1], xxviii, [4] p. VIII pl. 25½ᶜᵐ. (Added t.-p.: Nordisk
kultur. [IX])
Series title also at head of t.-p.
Added t.-p. in Danish: ... Folkeviser. Folkesagn og folkeeventyr.
København, J. H. Schultz; [etc., etc.]
Part 2. ed. by C. W. von Sydow, has half-title: Sagor och sägner.
Contains bibliographies.
1. Folk-songs, Scandinavian. 2. Folk literature—Scandinavia. 3. Leg-
ends, Scandinavian. I. Sydow, Carl Wilhelm von, 1878–   ed.

Title from Yale Univ.   Printed by L. C.

A C 34–263

NL 0353356   CtY MU IU OCU NcD TU TxU PU OU ICN MnU NN

Liestøl, Knut, 1881- 1952.
Die guten Ratschläge in der Hervararsaga. Von Knut Lie-
stöl. (In: Festschrift; Eugen Mogk zum 70. Geburtstag. Halle
an der Saale, 1924. 8°. p. 84–98.)

1. Hervarar saga.
N. Y. P. L.   January 13, 1927

NL 0353357   NN

1881- 1952.
Liestøl, Knut, A Ingolv-episoden i Viga-
Glums saga. *In* Nordiskt folkminne. Studier tillägnade C. W. von Sydow. Stockholm, 1928. pp. 207-14.   420B84no

NL 0353358   NIC

Liestøl, Knut, 1881- 1952.
Jøtnarne og joli. *In* Festskrift til H. F. Feilberg... København, 1911. 8°. p. 192-205.

1. Christmas in folklore.
N. Y. P. L.   April 23, 1912.

NL 0353359   NN

Liestøl, Knut, 1881-1952.
Knut Liestøl in memoriam. [Knut Liestøls folkemin-
neoppskrifter, utg. av] Norsk folkeminnelag. Oslo, 1955.
111 p. port. 23 cm. (Norsk folkeminnelags skrifter, nr. 76)
Bibliography: p. [109]-111.

1. Folk literature, Norwegian. I. Norsk folkeminnelag.
(Series: Norsk folkeminnelag. Skrifter, nr. 76)

PT8601.L5   58-40000

NL 0353360   DLC NN NcD

Liestøl, Knut, 1881-1952, jt. comp.
Laerebok i gamalnorsk ...
see under Eskeland, Severin, 1880-

439.83   Liestøl, Knut, 1881-1952.
L62m   Målreising.   Oslo, O. Norlis, 1927.
118p. 22cm.

1. Norwegian language (Nynorsk)--Hist.

NL 0353362   IU NIC WU

Liestøl, Knut, 1881–
Moltke Moe. Oslo, Aschehoug, 1949.
163 p. illus., ports. 22 cm.

1. Moe, Moltke, 1859–1913.

A 50–5913

Minnesota. Univ. Libr.
for Library of Congress   [1]

NL 0353363   MnU TxU NN CU

Liestøl, Knut, 1881- 1952, ed.

Moe, Moltke, 1859–1913.
... Moltke Moes Samlede skrifter; utgitt ved Knut Liestøl
(with a summary in English) ...   Oslo, H. Aschehoug & co.; Cambridge, Mass., Harvard university press; [etc.,
etc.] 1925–

Liestøl, Knut, 1881- 1952.
... Norges litteraturhistorie. Norrøn litteratur og millomal-
derleg folkedikting, av Knut Liestøl. Fra reformasjonstiden
til våre dager, av Edvard Stang. Oslo, Gyldendal, Norsk forlag, 1938.
383, [1] p. illus. (incl. ports., facsims.) 20½ᶜᵐ. (De Tusen hjems bibliotek. [7])

1. Norwegian literature—Hist. & crit.   I. *Stang, Edvard, 1902–
                                            43-30079
Library of Congress   PT8360.L5
                              [2]   839.8209

NL 0353365   DLC

839.8   Liestøl, Knut, 1881- 1952, ed.
N787   NORSK folkedikting...   Oslo, Det
norske samlaget, 1936,
v. 25cm.

Contents.- I. Eventyr, ved P. Chr.
Asbjørnsen, Jørgen Moe og Moltke Moe.
På nynorsk med ei innleiding av Knut
Liestøl.
1. Folk-lore of Norway. 2. Norwegian
literature. Collections. I. Liestøl,
Knut, 1881-   ed. II. Norske samlaget.

NL 0353366   MnU IU

LIESTØL,Knut, 1881- 1952.
Norsk folkedikting. 2e utgaava. Oslo,Noregs
Ungdomslag og Student-Mållaget,1922.

19 cm.
"Norske folkeskrifter,62."

NL 0353367   MH

Liestøl, Knut, 1881- 1952.
Norske ættesogor, av Knut Liestøl. Med bilete og 1
kart. Kristiania, O. Norli, 1922.
182 p. illus., map. 21ᶜᵐ.
CONTENTS.— Fyreord.— Innleiding.— Robyggjelaget.— Skraddarsoga.—
Nokre andre ættesogor.— Attersyn og resultat.— Tillegg: Varianter til
Skraddarsoga.

1. Folk-lore—Norway. 2. Robyggjelaget, Norway. 3. Norway—Geneal.
I. Title. II. Title: Skraddarsoga.

Library of Congress   GR220.L5   25-3701

NL 0353368   DLC CaBVaU NIC IU

M1772   **Liestøl, Knut,** 1881- 1952.
.N89N6   Norske folkedansar ... Utgjeve av Noregs ungdomslag.
Oslo [Noregs boklag] 1934–

Liestøl, Knut, 1881- 1952.
Norske folkeviser fra middelalderen, med indledninger
og anmerkninger ved Knut Liestøl og Moltke Moe.
Kristiania, J. Dybwad, 1912.
4 p. l., 91 p. 21ᶜᵐ.   kr. 1.50
"Anmerkninger" (xxvii, [1] p.) in pocket.

1. Moe, Moltke *i. e.* Ingebret Moltke, 1859–   joint author.

Library of Congress   13-699

NL 0353370   DLC NIC CU OC1

PT8690   **Liestøl, Knut,** 1881- 1952.
.L53   Norske folkeviser fra middelalderen, med
1919   indledninger og anmerkninger, ved Knut Liestøl
og Moltke Moe. 2.opl. Kristiania, J. Dybwad,
1919.
91p. 21cm.

1. Folk-songs, Norwegian. I. Moe, Miltke i.e.
Ingebret Moltke, 1859-   joint author.

NL 0353371   NcU MH

398.8   **Liestøl, Knut,** 1881-1952.
L719n   Norske folkeviser. Folkeutgave ved Knut
Liestøl og Moltke Moe. Utg. godkjend av
Kirke- og Undervisnings-departementet.
Kristiania, J. Dybwad, 1920-24.
3v. 20cm.

1. Folk-songs, Norwegian. 2. Folk literature,
Norwegian. 3. Legends, Norwegian. I. Moe,
Moltke, 1859-   joint author. II. Title.

NL 0353372   IEN WaU ICU NIC CU MH

VOLUME 332

Liestøl, Knut, 1881-1952.
Norske trollvisor og norrøne sogor, av Knut
Liestøl. Kristiania, O.Norlis forlag, 1915.
247,⎣3⎦ p. 24ᶜᵐ.
CONTENTS.--Innleiding.--Aasmund Fraegdegjaeva.--Stein-
finn Fefinnsson.--Kappen Illugjen.--Ormaalen unge.--
Raasmund unge.--Iven Erningsson.--Episke drag i troll-
visone.--Ymse andre sogor og visor.--Norsk sogefortel-
jing og visedikting.--Avstyttingar.--Etterord.

1.Folk-songs,Scandinavian. 2.Sagas. I.Title: Trollvisor,Norsk.

NL 0353373   MiU PBm InU NN IU RPB NIC MH OCl CU

439.8
L625   Liestøl, Knut, 1881-1952.
Nynorsk og bokmal i dag, foredrag
på årsmøtet i Noregs ungdomslag 25.
juni 1938. Oslo, Noregs boklag, 1938.
30 p. 18cm.
1. Norwegian language. I. Title.

NL 0353374   MnU

Liestøl, Knut, 1881-1952.
... The origin of the Icelandic family sagas, by Knut Liestøl.
Oslo, H. Aschehoug & co.; Cambridge, Mass., Harvard uni-
versity press; ⎣etc., etc.⎦ 1930.
ix, 261 p. 19½ᶜᵐ. (Added t.-p.: Instituttet for sammenlignende kul-
turforskning. ⎣Publikasjoner⎦ ser. A: Forelesninger. x)
"Translated from the Norwegian by A. G. Jayne."
"Abbreviations. Editions of the sagas": p. ⎣255⎦-256.

1. Sagas.   I. Jayne. Arthur Garland, 1882-   tr. II. Title.

Library of Congress   PT7269.A4L5   31-7593
                                     ⎣2⎦   (572.062) 839.6

NL 0353375   IaU TU AAP NIC MU CaBVaU
              DLC ViU MB NN PBm PU CtY ICU TxU CU IU

Liestøl, Knut, 1881-1952.
P. Chr. Asbjørnsen, mannen og livsverket. Oslo, J. G.
Tanum, 1947-
v. illus., ports., facsims. 25 cm.
"Litteratur": v. 1, p. 268-272.

1. Asbjørnsen, Peter Christen, 1812-1885.

PT8802.Z5L5   928.3982   48-11467*

NL 0353376   DLC MH NcU NN MnU CtY

⎣Liestøl, Knut,⎦ 1881-1952.
Reykdœla saga; tradisjon og forfattar. (In: Festskrift til
Finnur Jónsson, 29. Maj 1928. København, 1928. 4°.
p. ⎣29-⎦44.)

Signed: Knut Liestøl.

1. Reykdœla saga.
N.Y.P.L.   January 18, 1929

NL 0353377   NN

Liestøl, Knut, 1881-1952
Saga og folkeminne. Oslo, O. Norlis,
1941.
281 ⎣4⎦ p. port.

NL 0353378   MiD

Liestøl, Knut, 1881-1952.
Asbjørnsen, Peter Christen, 1812-1885.
... Samlede eventyr; norske kunstneres billedutgave ...
Oslo, Gyldendal norsk forlag, 1936.

Liestøl, Knut, 1881-1952.
Scottish and Norwegian ballads. Oslo ⎣Aschehoug⎦ 1946.
16 p. 24 cm. (Studia Norvegica, no. 1)
Bibliographical footnotes

1. Literature, Comparative — Scottish and Norwegian. 2. Literature, Comparative —Norwegian and Scottish.   I. Title.   (Series)

GR1.S85 no. 1   65-82197

                   CLU NIC MH
NL 0353380   DLC MiU NNC WaU InU KU OU CaBVaU FMU ViU

Liestøl, Knut, 1881-1952.
Segner, med ei innleiing og merknader av
Knut Liestøl. [Oslo, det Norske samlaget,
1939]
240 p. 25 cm.
Added title-page: Norsk folkedikting.

NL 0353381   MH

Liestøl, Knut, 1881-1952.
... Upphavet til den islendske aettesaga, av Knut Liestøl.
Oslo, H. Aschehoug & co.; Cambridge, Mass., Harvard university press; ⎣etc., etc.⎦ 1929.
246 p. 20ᶜᵐ. (Added t.-p.: Instituttet for sammenlignende kultur-
forskning. ⎣Publikationer⎦ ser. A: Forelesninger. xa)

1. Sagas.   I. Title.

Library of Congress   PT7181.L5   30-18674

NL 0353382   DLC FTaSU MH NIC NN CtY ICU CU OU NIC

Liestøl, Knut, 1881-1952.
Uppruni Islendinga sagna. Bjørn
Guðfinnsson Islenzkaði. Reykjavík,
Bókadeild Menningarsjóðs, 1938.
222 p. 19cm.
Bibliographic footnotes.
Translation of Upphavet til den islendske
aettesaga.

1. Sagas - History and criticism. I.
Guðfinnsson, Bjørn, 1905-   tr. II.
Title.

NL 0353384   FU NIC MH CaBVaU

GR220
.L75   LIESTØL,KNUT,1881-
Utval av norske folkevisor til skulebruk, ved
Knut Liestøl og Moltke Moe. Oslo, Dybwad, 1928.
109 p.

1. Folk-lore--Norway. 2. Norwegian ballads &
songs. I. Moe,Moltke.1859-1913,jt.au. II. Tc.

NL 0353385   InU

PT8690
L48   Liestøl, Knut, 1881-1952,
Utval av norske folkeviser til skulebruk.
⎣Af⎦ Knut Liestøl og Moltke Moe. 8. oppl.
Oslo, J. Dybwad, 1947 ⎣c1934⎦
111 p.

1. Folk-songs, Norwegian. I. Moe, Moltke,
1859-1913, joint comp.

NL 0353386   CU

Lœstvichnik, Ioann, *Saint*
see
Joannes *Climacus, Saint, 6th cent.*

---

fSB443
.L5   Liesveld, John H.
Organization policies and operation
procedures ⎣manual⎦ Kansas City, Mo.,
Liesveld Inc., n. d.
paging irregular. illus. 29 cm.
Loose-leaf.

1. Florists.   2. Small business--
Management.

NL 0353388   AAP

Liesveld, John H
The retail florist. New York, Macmillan, 1951.
xii, 898 p. 16 plates. 22 cm.

1. Florists.   I. Title.

SB443.L5   658.9359   Agr 51-542
U. S. Dept. of Agr. Libr. 96.04L62
for Library of Congress   ⎣15⎦†

Or OrCS IdU CaBVa CaBVaU CaBViP MtBC
NL 0353389   DNAL WaT WaS Wa TxU NN MEkT CU NcRS DLC

N 5064
.L719   LIESVILLE,A   R   DE
Les artistes normands au Salon de 1874
⎣-1878⎦ Paris, H. Champion, 1874-1878⎦
5 v.

1. Paris--Salon, 1874-1878. 2. Artists--Norman.

NL 0353390   InU

Liesville, A   -R   de
Catalogue des mollusques vivants aux environs
d'Alençon. Paris, 1856.
16 p. 8°.

NL 0353391   MH-Z

Liesville, A   R   de
Coup-d'oeil général sur l'exposition historique de l'art ancien (palais du Trocadéro par
A.R.de Liesville. Paris,H.Champion,1879.
193 pp. 20 1/2cm.

NL 0353392   MH

VOLUME 332

Liesville, A R de.   Arc 1660.3F
Histoire numismatique de la révolution de 1848, ou Description raisonnée des médailles, monnaies, jetons, repoussés, etc. relatifs aux affaires de la France. Tom. i. 1*-9* livr. Paris, H. Champion, 1877-83.
pp. xii, 336.
No more published.

Planches. Paris, H. Champion, 1877-83.
f°. pp. (3). 108 plates.   Arc 1660.3F

Numismatics-France   767

NL 0353393   MH IaU

Lieszkovszky, József, 1850-1888.
Nádasdi, Zrinyi és Frangepán a vérpadon, 1671. Budapest, A Szerző, 1884.
139 p.

1. Hungary - Hist. - 1526-1683. I. Nádasdi, Ferenc, gróf, 1625-1671. II. Zrinyi, Péter, gróf, 1621-1671. III. Frangepán, Ferenc Kristóf, d. 1671.

NL 0353394   NNC

PC   **Liet, Albert**
2137   Traité de prononciation française; théorie et pratique. Paris, Boyveau et Chevillet, 1900.
+L54   144p. 26cm.

1. French language - Pronunciation I. Title

NL 0353395   WU MB MH OCU CU

Liet-Veaux, Georges.
Les associations syndicales de propriétaires. Paris, Recueil Sirey, 1947.
vii, 248 p. 22 cm. (Les Cahiers administratifs. Nouv. sér.)
Includes legislation.

1. Agriculture, Cooperative—France. 2. Soil conservation—France. 3. Real property—France. I. France. Laws, statutes, etc. Loi sur les associations syndicales. II. Title. (Series)

50-29502

NL 0353396   DLC MH NjR MoSU

Liet-Veaux, Georges.
La continuité du droit interne; essai d'une théorie juridique des révolutions. Paris, Recueil Sirey ₍1942₎
467 p.

Thesis - Rennes.
Issued also without thesis note.
Bibliography: p. ₍7₎-12.

1. Revolutions.

NL 0353397   NNC

Liet-Veaux, Georges.
... La continuité du droit interne, essai d'une théorie juridique des révolutions. Préface de Charles Rousseau ... Paris, Recueil Sirey, 1943.
2 p. l., 467, ₍1₎ p. 21½ᵐ.
"Bibliographie": p. ₍7₎-12.

1. Revolutions.   I. Title.
45-17353
Library of Congress   JC491.L45
                         ₍2₎   321.002

NL 0353398   DLC

JN2595   **Liet-Veaux, Georges.**
L719   Droit constitutionnel. Paris, Rousseau, 1949.
         342 p. 17 tables. 18ᶜᴹ. (Manuels élémentaires Rousseau)
         Imperfect: t.-p. wanting. Title from cover.
         "Constitution de la République française": p. ₍289₎-317.

1. France - Constitutional law. 2. France - Constitutional history. I.France. Constitution. I.Title.

NL 0353399   CSt-H NjP

Liet-Veaux, Georges.
Manuel élémentaire de droit constitutionnel. ₍Paris, Rousseau, 1949₎
342 p. 18 cm. (Manuels élémentaires Rousseau)
"Addenda": viii p. inserted.
"Constitution de la République française": p. ₍289₎-317.

1. France—Constitutional law. I. France. Constitution, 1946.
51-30771

NL 0353400   DLC ViU TU

Liet-Veaux, Georges.
La profession d'architecte; statut juridique. Préf. de Jacques Duvaux. Paris, Librairies techniques, 1954.
530 p. 23 cm.

1. Architects—Legal status. laws, etc.—France. I. Title.
56-21656

NL 0353401   DLC NNC MH-L

Liet-Veaux, Georges.
... Le régionalisme constitutionnel... ou, Le moyen de parvenir à une solution d'ensemble après quatre ans de révolution législative. Préface de Lucien Romier. Paris, Librairie générale de droit et de jurisprudence, 1943.
cover-title, 1 p. l., ii, 71, ₍1₎ p. 21½ᵐ.

1. Local government—France. 2. Administrative and political divisions—France. I. Title.
45-21775
Library of Congress   JS4895.L5
                         ₍2₎   352.044

NL 0353402   DLC MnU CU MiU MH

Liet-Veaux, Georges.
Traité de remembrement urbain et de reconstruction collective; associations syndicales de reconstruction et de remembrement, coopératives de reconstruction, par G. Liet-Veaux, M. Seguin ₍et₎ G. Planadevall. Préf. de M. Lerebours-Pigeonnière. Paris, Éditions du Moniteur des travaux publics, 1949.
497 p. 24 cm. (Bibliothèque du bâtiment et des travaux publics)
Includes legislation.
1. Cities and towns—Planning—France. 2. Reconstruction (1939-1951)—France. 3. Cooperative societies—France. 4. France. Laws, statutes, etc. Loi sur les associations syndicales.
A 57-3478
New York Univ.   Libraries NA9197
for Library of Congress   ₍2₎

NL 0353403   NN MH

Lietaert, Albert.
[De ware Jozef. Libretto. Dutch]
De ware Jozef; ₍operette in drie bedrijven, door Jozef de Seyn. Muziek van Albert Lietaert. Antwerpen, J. Janssens, 1952. 91 p. 20cm.

I. Seyn, Jozef de. De ware Jozef. II. Title.

NL 0353404   NN MH

Law   **Lietaert Peerbolte, L.**

Netherlands (*Kingdom, 1815- *) *Laws, statutes, etc.*
De Armenwet voor gemeentebesturen en instellingen toegelicht ₍door₎ Lietaert Peerbolte. Bewerkt in 6. druk door J. J. v. Wermeskerken. Alphen aan den Rijn, N. Samsom, 1950.

Lietaert Peerbolte, L.

Elenbaas, J N.
Handboek voor de beoefening van het nederlandsche administratieve recht, voornamelijk ten dienste van zelfonderricht voor aspirantburgemeesters, secretarissen en ambtenaren ter secretarie, door J. N. Elenbaas ... Uitgegeven vanwege de Nederlandsche vereeniging voor gemeentebelangen. Alphen aan den Rijn, N. Samson n. v., 1934-36 ₍v. 1, '36₎

Lietaert Peerbolte, L.
De huurcommissiewet en de huuropzegingswet. 2d. ed. Alphen a.d. Rijn, 1919.
140 p.

NL 0353407   PU-L

Lietaert Peerbolte, L.
Warenwet en haar uitvoering
see under Goester, L E

Lietaert Peerbolte, L.
Wijziging Huurcommissiewet en Huuropzeggingswet. Alphen a.d. Rijn. N. Samsom, 1923.
51 p.

NL 0353409   PU-L

Lietaert Peerbolte, Maarten, 1905-
The orgastical experience of space and metapsychologic psychagogy; an outline of practical mental and social hygiene. Leiden, A. W. Sijthoff, 1955.
150 p. 25 cm.
Bibliographical footnotes.

1. Sex (Psychology) 2. Psychoanalysis. I. Title.
BF692.L53   131.34   57-28692

NL 0353410   DLC IEN MH DNLM

Lietaert Peerbolte, Maarten, 1905-
... Peredur, de zoeker, zijn ontwikkeling in des levens tempel. 's-Gravenhage, H. P. Leopold, 1945.
v p., 1 l., 163 p. front., plates. 21ᵐ.
At head of title: Dr. M. Lietaert Peerbolte.

I. Title.
PT5854.L52P4   839.3135   A F 47-141
Columbia univ. Libraries
for Library of Congress ₍4₎†

NL 0353411   NNC ICRL NN DLC ICU

VOLUME 332

WM 460 L719p 1954
LIETAERT PEERBOLTE, Maarten, 1905–
Prenatal dynamics; a psychoanalytical approachment to the trauma of birth, prenatal traumata and conception. A contribution to female psychology and to extra-sensional perception. Leiden, Sijthoff, 1954.
ix, 182 p.
Five of the chapters appeared as periodical articles.
1. Psychoanalysis   Title

NL 0353412   DNLM IEN

Liétard, Alfred, 1872–1912.
... Au Yun-nan. Les Lo-lo p'o, une tribu des aborigènes de la Chine méridionale; par Alfred Liétard ... Münster i. W., Aschendorff, 1913.
viii, 272 p. illus. 25½ᶜᵐ. (... Anthropos-bibliothek ... t. 1, 5. fasc.)
CONTENTS.—Nom, division et distribution des Lo-lo.—Vie physique des Lo-lo.—Vie psychique des Lo-lo.—La langue des Lo-lo p'o.

1. Lolos. 2. Lolo language—Grammar.   I. Title: Les Lo-lo p'o.

14-10498

Library of Congress   GN1.A72

NL 0353413   DLC ICJ WaU OrU WU MiU NIC IU CU MH-P NN

PL20 L833 L62
Liétard, Alfred, 1872–1912.
Notions de grammaire Lo-Lo. (Dialecte A-Hi) Hanoi, D'extrême-orient, 1909.
24p. 26cm.
Extrait du Bulletin de L'école française d'extrême-orient.

NL 0353414   CtY

LIETARD, Gustave Alexandre, 1833–
Empédocle considéré comme philosophe et comme médecin.   [Paris?]1888.
19p. 25cm.
1. Empedocles

NL 0353415   CtY-M

WBI L719e 1860
LIÉTARD, Gustave Alexandre, 1833–
Études cliniques sur les eaux de Plombières. Paris, Masson, 1860.
vii, 106 p.

NL 0353416   DNLM

---

4 R 173
Liétard, Gustave Alexandre, 1833–
Lettres historiques sur la médecine chez les Indous.   Paris, V. Masson, 1862.
76 p.

NL 0353417   DLC-P4 ICJ

Liétard, Gustave Alexandre, 1833–
——. Menus-propos sur la profession médicale. Paris, G. Masson & Cie., [1900].
17 pp. 8°.

NL 0353418   DNLM

4R 171
Liétard, Gustave Alexandre, 1833–
Suçruta.   Paris, G. Masson [   ] 634-673 p.

NL 0353419   DLC-P4

Liétard, Thomas Philippe de Hennin-, *comte de Boussu*
see
Boussu, Thomas Philippe de Hennin-Liétard, *comte de, Cardinal,* 1679–1759.

Lietbert, Abbot of St. Ruf.   –1110.
Lietberti abbatis S. Rufi Epistolæ.
(In Patrologiæ cursus completus. Series secunda. Vol. 157, col. 715-720. Lutetiæ Parisiorum. 1854.)

NL 0353421   MB

Lietbert, St., Bp. of Cambray.   –1076.
Charta de constituendis canonicis regularibus in ecclesia S. Auberti. 2 pp. (Migne, J. P., Patrol. s. Lat. v. 146, p. 1438.)—Gesta. 9 pp. (Frankfort Soc. Scriel, v. 7, p. 489.)

NL 0353422   MdBP

PR L53.5 838
Lietch, D   Ross
Poetic frangments. By D. Ross Lietch, M. D. Tynemouth, J. Philipson, 1838.
232p. 21cm.
"Errata" inserted.

NL 0353423   CtY-M

Lieth, C. L. T.
Neues Elementarbüchlein zur leichten und gründlichen Erlernung des Lesens, eingetheilt in drei Lieferungen. 47th ed. Elberfeld, Sam. Lucas, 1853–
v.

Center has: v.1 only.

NL 0353424   ICRL

Lieth, E.   D.   Van der
see
Van Der Lieth, E   D

Lieth, F. H. von der
Commentatio de liene sano et morboso.
Inaug. Diss. Kiel, 1879

NL 0353426   ICRL

Lieth, Gallus, praeses.
Conclusiones scholastico-positivae ex universa theologia...   Ratisbonae, typis Joannis Baptistæ Lang, 1740.
467p 24cm

Dissertation — Regensburg (Josephus Rolland & Augustinus Duncan, defendentes.)

NL 0353427   MnCS

Lieth, Heinrich von der, fl. 1800–1815.

Brobergen, Lotte von, d. 1784.
Lotte von Brobergen: geschichte einer liebe in briefen aus der Werther-zeit, nach originalen hrsg. von Margarete Böing.   Berlin, Gebrüder Paetel (G. Paetel) 1913.

Lieth, Herbert v. d.
Das vermieterpfandrecht im verhältnis zum pfändungspfandrecht. ... Eisfeld i. Thür., 1936.   88 p.
Inaug. Diss. – Erlangen, 1936.
Literaturverzeichnis.

NL 0353429   ICRL

I lieti amanti. Primo libro de Madrigali a cinque voci, di diversi eccellentissimi musici, novamente composti, & dati in luce [basso] Venetia, G. Vincenzi & R. Amadino, 1586.
Contains 20 madrigals by D. Lodovico Agostini, Innocentio Alberti, Alberto l'hocca, Lelio Bertani, Hippolito Fiorino, Andrea Gabrieli, Alfonso Ganassi, Ruggiero Giovanelli, Paulo Isnardi, Luzzasco Luzzaschi, Luca Meranzio, Rinaldo del Mel, Alessandro Milleville, Constanzo Porta, Andrea Rota,

Alessandro Striggio, Marcello Tosoni, Oratio Vecchi, Paolo Virchi and Giaches Wert.

NL 0353430   CU

Lietke, Arthur *i. e.* Eduard Arthur, 1865–
Über die flächen, für welche eine krümmungscentralfläche ein kegel zweiten grades ist ... Königsberg, Hartungsche buchdruckerei [1890]
2 p. l., 36, [2] p.   diagrs. on 2 fold. pl. 21ᶜᵐ.
Inang.-dis.—Königsberg.
Vita.

1. Surfaces.   4-23650†

Library of Congress   QA645.L71

NL 0353431   DLC DNLM NjP RPB ICRL

Lietke, Eduard Arthur
see
Lietke, Arthur i.e. Eduard Arthur, 1865–

Lietmann, Heinrich.
Fischvermehrung; die gebräuchlichsten künstlichen und halbkünstlichen methoden und einrichtungen der fischvermehrung bei den in betracht kommenden nutzfischen, von fischzuchtmeister H. Lietmann ... mit 26 abbildungen. Berlin, Reichsnährstandsverlag, 1943.
46 p.   illus. diagrs.   20½ᶜᵐ.

1. Fish-culture.
SH21.L5   A F 47–3373
Colorado.   State agr. coll.   Library
for Library of Congress   [2]†

NL 0353433   CoFS DLC MiU

VOLUME 332

Lietmann, Heinrich.
　　Teichwirtschaft und Fischzucht im deutschen Osten. ₂2. Aufl.₎ Königsberg (Pr.) Reichsnährstandsverlag, Zweigniederlassung Ostpreussen ₍1943₎
　　74 p. illus. 21 cm. (Die Landwirtschaft in Ostpreussen)

　　1. Fish-culture—Prussia. East (Province) ɪ. Title. (Series)
　　SH79.L5 1943　　　639.31　　　A F 48–4061*
　　Colorado. State Agr.　　Coll. Library
　　for Library of Congress　　₍1₎†

　　NL 0353434　CoFS CU DLC

Lietmann, Heinrich.
　　Teichwirtschaft und Fischzucht im deutschen Osten. ₂2. Aufl.₎ Königsberg (Pr.) Reichsnährstandsverlag, Zweigniederlassung Ostpreussen ₍1943₎
　　74 p. illus. 21 cm. (Die Landwirtschaft in Ostpreussen)

　　1. Fish-culture—Prussia. East (Province) ɪ. Title. (Series)
　　SH79.L5 1943　　　639.31　　　A F 48–4061*
　　Colorado. State Agr.　　Coll. Library
　　for Library of Congress　　₍1₎†

　　NL 0353435　CoFS DLC

Lietnikov, A₍leksĕĭ Vasil'evich₎ 1837–1888.
　　Ueber die bedingungen der integrabilität einiger differential-gleichungen ... Dresden, Druck von B. G. Teubner, 1867.
　　46 p. 22½ᵐ.
　　Inaug.-dis.—Leipzig.

　　1. Differential equations.

　　Library of Congress　　QA372.L6　　　4–26382†

　　NL 0353436　DLC

FILM　　**Lieto, Bartholomeo,** 16th cent.
M787.6　　Dialogo qvarto di mvsica. Doue si ragiona
L62d　　sotto un piaceuole discorso delle cose pertinenti per intauolare le opere di musica esercitarle con uiola a mano ouer liuto con sue tauole ordinate per diuersi gradi alti e bassi. ₍Napoli₎ 1559₎
　　Microfilm copy made about 1949 of original in the British Museum. Positive.
　　Collation of the original as determined from the film: ₍19₎l.
　　Signatures: A–E⁴ (E⁴ and verso of E³ blank? not filmed)
　　Colophon: Stampato in Napoli per Matthio Cancer dil mese d'aprile M.D.LIX.

　　1. Lute music—To 1800. 2. Viol music—To 1800. 3. Tablature (Musical notation) I. Title.

　　NL 0353438　IU

WW　　**LIETO VOLLARO, Agostino de.**
141　　Elementi di semeiologia e diagnostica
L719e　　delle malattie dell'occhio e degli annessi
1934　　oculari. 2. ed., riordinata e notevolmente ampliata. Torino, Unione tip.-editrice torinese, 1934.
　　x, 453 p. illus. (Trattato di semeiologia fisica e diagnostica chirurgica, 11)
　　1. Eye - Diseases - Diagnosis
　　2. Eye - Examination　　Series

　　NL 0353439　DNLM

Il Lieto, pseud.
　　Memorie istoriche per servire alla vita di Vincenzio Monti ...
　　　　see under title

Lĭetopis' Dvinskaĭa
　　see Dvinskaĭa letopis'.

Lĭetopis' Nestora
　　see
　　Povest' vremennykh let.

Лѣтопись о многихъ мятежахъ и о разореніи Московскаго государства отъ внутреннихъ и вѣшнихъ непріятелеп п отъ прочихъ тогдашнихъ временъ многихъ случаевъ, по преставленіи Царя Іоанна Васильевича; а паче о междугосударствованіи по кончинѣ Царя Ѳеодора Іоанновича, и о учиненномъ исправленіи книгъ въ царствование благовѣрнаго Государя Царя Алексѣя Михайловича въ 7163⁄1655 году. Собрано изъ древнихъ тѣхъ временъ описанieвъ. Въ Санктпетербургѣ, 1771.
　　386 p. 20 cm.

　　1. Russia—Hist.—1533–1613. 2. Russia—Hist.—1613–1680. *Title transliterated:* Lĭetopis' o mnogikh mĭatezhakh.
　　DK111.L5 1771　　　55–53758
　　——Copy 2. Bound with Irodionov, Petr. Историческія ... извѣстія до города Торопца ... касающихся. Въ Санктпетербургѣ, 1788; and Sumarokov, A. P. Первый и главный стрѣлецкій бунтъ. ₍Санктпетербургъ₎ 1768.

　　NL 0353444　DLC

Лѣтопись о многихъ мятежахъ и о разореніи Московскаго государства отъ внутреннихъ и вѣшнихъ непріятелей и отъ прочихъ тогдашнихъ временъ многихъ случаевъ по преставленіи Царя Іоанна Васильевича; а паче о междугосударствованіи по кончинѣ Царя Ѳеодора Іоанновича и о учиненномъ исправленіи книгъ въ царствование благовѣрнаго Государя Царя Алексія Михайловича въ 7163 (1655) году. Собрано изъ древнихъ тѣхъ временъ описаніп. Изд. 2. Москва, Въ Тип. Компаніи типографической, 1788.
　　366 p. 23 cm.

　　1. Russia—Hist.—1533–1613. 2. Russia—Hist.—1613–1680. *Title transliterated:* Lĭetopis' o mnogikh mĭatezhakh.
　　DK111.L5 1788　　　56–50068

　　NL 0353445　DLC

Lĭetopis' po Ipatskomu spisku
　　see
　　Ipat'evskaĭa letopis'.

Лѣтопись происходящихъ въ расколѣ событій. 1886–

Москва, Тип. Э. Лиссшера и Ю. Романа ₍etc.₎
　　v. 22 cm. annual.
　　"Отдѣльный оттискъ ... журнала Братское слово."

　　1. Raskolniks—Periodicals. *Title romanized:* Lĭetopis' proiskhodiashchikh v raskolie sobytii.
　　BX601.L53　　　79–616886

　　NL 0353447　DLC

Lĭetopis' raskola za 1876–1879 gody.
Лѣтопись раскола за 1876–1879 годы; ₍статьи, напечатанныя въ "Московскихъ вѣдомостяхъ," 1877–1879 г. Н. Субботинъ₎. Москва, Тип. Э. Лисснеръ и Ю. Романъ, 1880.
　　151 p. 15 cm.
　　Includes bibliographical references.

　　1. Raskolniks. I. Subbotin, Nikolaĭ Ivanovich, 1827–1905, comp. II. Moskovskiĭa vĭedomosti.
　　BX601.L533　　　72–218070

　　NL 0353448　DLC

Лѣтопись самовидца о войнахъ Богдана Хмельницкаго и о междоусобіяхъ, бывшихъ въ Малой Россіи по его смерти. Доведена продолжателями до 1734 года. ₍Москва, 1846₎
　　ii, 72 p. 25 cm.
　　Edited by O. Bodĭanskiĭ.

　　1. Ukraine—Hist. 2. Chmielnicki, Bohdan, Hetman of the Cossacks, 1593–1657. ɪ. Bodĭanskiĭ, Osip Maksimovich, 1808–1877, ed. *Title transliterated:* Lĭetopis' samovidĭsa o voinakh Bogdana Khmel'nitĭskago
　　DK508.7.L5　　　56–52906

　　NL 0353449　DLC

Лѣтопись сибирская, содержащая повѣствование о взятіи Сибирскія земли русскими при царѣ Іоаннѣ Васильевичѣ Грозномъ, съ краткимъ изложеніемъ предшествовавшихъ оному событій. Издана съ рукописи XVII вѣка. Санктпетербургъ, Въ Тип. Департамента народнаго просвѣщенія, 1821.
　　ix, 88 p. port. 21 cm.
　　Edited by G. I. Spasskiĭ.

　　1. Siberia—Hist.—Sources. ɪ. Spasskiĭ, Grigoriĭ Ivanovich, d. 1864, ed. *Title transliterated:* Lĭetopis' sibirskaĭa.
　　DK752.L5　　　62–38124

　　NL 0353450　DLC

Lĭetopisĕts, pseud.
　　see
　　Strakhov, Nikolaĭ Nikolaevich, 1828–1896.

Лѣтописецъ руской отъ пришествія Рурика до кончины царя Іоанна Васильевича. Издалъ Н. Л. Въ Санктпетербургѣ, Въ Тип. Горнаго училища, 1792.
　　v. 21 cm.
　　Erroneously ascribed to Feofan Prokopovich. Cf. V. S. Sopikov. Опытъ россійской библіографіи. 1904; Russ. biog. slovar', v. 25, p. 445.

　　1. Russia—Hist.—To 1533. ɪ. Feofan, Abp. of Novgorod, 1661–1736, supposed author. ɪɪ. L'vov, Nikolaĭ Aleksandrovich, 1751–1803, ed.
　　Title transliterated: Lĭetopisĕts ruskoĭ ot prishestvīĭa Rurika.
　　DK70.L55　　　54–53336

　　NL 0353452　DLC

Лѣтописецъ Соловецкаго монастыря, въ коемъ повѣствуется о началѣ построенія его, о бывшихъ въ немъ начальникахъ ... и о другихъ многихъ произшествіяхъ по 1760 годъ. Москва, Иждивеніемъ Г. Бороздина, Въ Унив. тип., у В. Окорокова, 1790.
　　94 p. 20 cm.

　　1. Solovetskiĭ stavropigial'nyĭ monastyr'. *Title transliterated:* Lĭetopisĕts Solovetskago monastyrĭa.
　　BX583.S6L5　　　56–48716

　　NL 0353453　DLC

VOLUME 332

Лѣтописи русской литературы и древности ... т. 1–5, апр. 1859–окт. 1863. Москва, Въ типографіи Грачева и комп., 1859–63.
5 v. col. plates. 24½ᵐ. irregular.
Edited by Nikolaĭ Tikhonravov.
Each volume consists of three parts: ɪ. Изслѣдованія. ɪɪ. Матеріялм. ɪɪɪ. Смѣсь и библіографія.
No more published.
Indexes:
    Vols. 1–5, 1859–63. 1 v.
1. Russian literature—Hist. & crit.—Period. 2. Russian literature (Collections) 3. Russia—Hist.—Sources. 4. Russia—Antiq. ɪ. Tikhonravov, Nikolaĭ Savvich, 1832–1893, ed.
    Title transliterated: Lĭetopisi russkoĭ literatury i drevnosti.

Library of Congress   PG2900.L5   44–50215

NL 0353454   DLC OrU

Лѣтописный и лицевой изборникъ дома Романовыхъ; юбилейное изданіе въ ознаменованіе 300-лѣтія царствованія [1613–1913. Литературно-историч. отдѣлъ подъ ред. кн. М. С. Путятина; худож. подъ ред. С. И. Вашкова. Москва, Изд. С. С. Ермолаева; складъ изд. А. А. Левенсонъ, 1913]-
    v. illus. (part col., part mounted) maps, col. ports. 45 cm.
    Includes music.
1. Romanov, House of. 2. Russia—Hist. ɪ. Putiâtin, M. S., kniâz, ed.
    Title transliterated: Lĭetopisnyĭ i litŝevoĭ izbornik doma Romanovykh.

DK113.L5   64–53533

NL 0353455   DLC

Лѣтоструй; календарь на българитѣ (г. 2–3; 1910–11) [Солунъ]
    (2) v. illus., ports. 20 cm.
    Began publication in 1909.
    Issued by Bŭlgarska matitsa.
    Vol. 3, 1911, includes the statute of Bŭlgarska matitsa.

1. Almanacs, Bulgarian. ɪ. Bŭlgarska matitsa.
    Title transliterated: Lĭetostruĭ.

AY1038.B8L5   62–56325

NL 0353456   DLC

Lietsjes for it selskip "Gysbert Japix" to Haerlem ... Haerlem, P. Kuipers [1898]
    66 p., 1 ll. 14 cm.
    Friesland prov. bibl. Cat., p., 305.
    Works by: E. Halbertsma, W. Dykstra, G. Japiks, H. Sytstra, J.H. Halbertsma, J.G. v. Blom, H. de Jong, J.J. Hof, H.G.v.d. Veen, T.G.v.d. Meulen and others.
    Introduction signed: J.B. Schepers.

NL 0353457   PU

Liette, Pierre de, d. 1729.
E78
.N76C3 **Cadillac, Antoine de la Mothe,** 1656 (*ca.*)–1730.
    The western country in the 17th century; the memoirs of Lamothe Cadillac and Pierre Liette, ed. by Milo Milton Quaife. Chicago, Lakeside Press, 1947.

G338.0983
L625p **LIETTI, MARIO**
1950   ... Problemas chilenos ... 2. ed. Santiago de Chile [Tipografía "Chilena"] 1950.
    cover-title, 29p. 19cm.
    CONTENTS.—Reciprocidad.—Abaratamiento de la vida.—La casa propia y el juego del fútbol.—La industria del aceite de oliva.—La industria de la seda natural.—Criaderos de moluscos.—Cultivo y producción del té.—Exportaciones agrícolas italianas.
    1. Chile - Indus. 2. Chile - Economic policy. I. Title.

NL 0353459   TxU

Lietŭkis, Lietuvos žemės ūkio kooperatyvų sąjunga. ...Apyskaita.
19

Kaunas, 19   4°.
    no.
    19   , cover-title; full title reads: Lietuvos žemės ūkio kooperatyvų sąjungos (LIETŬKIO). Vytauto didžiojo metų apyskaita.
ɪ. Co-operation, Agricultural—Assoc.   and org.—Lithuania.
N.Y.P.L.   September 13, 1932

NL 0353460   NN

Lietŭkis, Lietuvos žemės ūkio kooperatyvų sąjunga.
    Vidaus degimo variklių tepimas. [Redagavo J. Gensas] Kaunas, 1939.
    240 p. illus., fold. col. map. 16 cm.

1. Automobiles—Handbooks, manuals, etc. ɪ. Gensas, J., ed. ɪɪ. Title.
    TL151.L5   59–58808

NL 0353461   DLC

Lietus, Fortunius.
    De Lucernis antiquorum reconditis libr. sex ... amplissimo atque excellentissimo D. Raimundo Ianforti. Patavium, Cadorinus, 1652.
    4 p.

NL 0353462   PPD

Lietuva
    see
Lithuania.

LIETUVA, Kaunas. sausio 12, 1925–sausio 31, 1928 (incomplete)
Kaunas.   v.

Microfilm.

Daily.
Issues for 1925–28 called 1st– 10th year.
Ceased publication with Jan. 31, 1928.

NL 0353464   NN

LIETUVA; politikos žurnalas, nr. 1–8; liepa rugsėjas, 1952–1956. New York. 8 no. in 2 v.
24cm.

    Irregular.
    Published by the Committee for a free Lithuania (no. 1 by the Lithuanian consultative panel) in cooperation with the Research and publications service, National committee for a free Europe.

    Title also in English: Lithuania, political magazine.
    Text in Lithuanian with English summary.

ɪ. Periodicals—U.S., Lithuanian. 2. Lithuania—Per. and soc. publ. ɪ. Committee for a free Lithuania. ɪɪ. National committee for a free Europe. ɪɪɪ. Title: Lithuania; political magazine.

NL 0353466   NN

Lietuva ir jos reikalai. Tautiškas Lietuvos katekizmas.
— Vilnius. M. Kuktos spaustuve. [190–?] 20 pp. 17 cm.
    The title is on the cover.

    By B. J....is.

K5030 — T.r. — Lithuania. Pol. hist. — Lithuania. Lang. Works in Lithuanian.

NL 0353467   MB

Lietuva; kraštas ir tauta. [Redagavo A. Stanys] Augsburgas, 1946.
    62 p. illus. 21 cm.

1. Lithuania. ɪ. Stanys, A., ed.

DK511.L2lA2   55–34898 ‡

NL 0353468   DLC PU OKentU

Lietuva tironu pančiuose
    see under   Audrūnos, Jonas.

Lietuva vaizduose. Views of Lithuania. [Hanau, L.T.B. Hesseno apygardos komiteto leidinys, 1949]
    1 v. (unpaged, chiefly illus., maps) 14 x 21 cm.
    On cover: Lithuania.
    Lithuanian, English, French, and German.

1. Lithuania—Descr. & trav.—Views. ɪ. Title: Views of Lithuania.

DK511.L212lA7   64–36729

NL 0353470   DLC

Lietuvai vaduoti sąjunga
    see also
Amerikos lietuvių tautinė sąjunga.

Lietuvininkų kalendorius. [1]–   1952–
München.
    v. illus., ports. 22 cm.
    Published by Mažosios Lietuvos Tarybos Spaudos komisija.
    Edited by A. Puskepalaitis.

1. Almanacs, Lithuanian—Germany. 2. Lithuanians in Germany. ɪ. Puskepalaitis, Albertas, ed. ɪɪ. Mažosios Lietuvos Taryba.
    AY1039.L5L54   53–20273

NL 0353472   DLC

PG8537
L5   **Lietuvio vaiko pradžiamokslis; skaitymo ir rašymo knygutė vaikeliams su vaizdeliais. Vaizdelius piešė A. Žmuidzinavičius ir kiti. Vilnius, M. Šlapelienės lietuvių knygyno komisijos sankrova, 1918.
    70 p. illus. (part col.)

1. Lithuanian language - Chrestomathies and readers. I. Žmuidzinavičius, A., illus.

NL 0353473   CU

WA   Lietuvis, A., pseud.
11115   Augis darbininkų judejimo Lietuvoje. Parašė A. Lietuvis ir N.N. Plymouth, Pa., Spauda "Vienybes Lietuvninku", 1900.
    58p.

1. Labor and laboring classes - Lithuania.

NL 0353474   CtY

VOLUME 332

LIETUVIS, Memmingen. [Liepos] 23, 1949-
[birželio] 16, 1950 (incomplete)
Memmingen [Germany]   v.   53cm.

Film reproduction. Negative.
Semiweekly (some issues combined), July 23-Dec. 23, 1949; weekly,
Jan. 5-June 16, 1950.
Title also as: The Lithuanian.
Issues for 1950 also numbered within the year.
I. Title: The Lithuanian,   Memmingen.

NL 0353475   NN

Lietuviška giesmių knyga. Episkopalės metodistų bažnyčios¡...
Kaunas: Sutaisé ir išleido "Krikščionystés sargo," 1923.   196 p.
16°.

602464A. 1. Hymns, Lithuanian.
N. Y. P. L.   August 19, 1932

NL 0353476   NN

Lietuviškoji enciklopedija ... Kaune, Leidėjas "Spaudos
fondas" ¡1933¡–
    v. illus. 25ᶜᵐ.
Editor: v. 1-   Vaclovas Biržiška.

    1. Encyclopedias and dictionaries, Lithuanian. 2. Lithuania—Bio-bibl.
    I. Biržiška, Vaclovas, ed.
                                              37-32253
Library of Congress   AE60.L5
                        ¡3¡   039.475

NL 0353477   DLC WU NN OC1 PU

Lietuviškų draugysčių sąryšis, *Cleveland*
    see
    Clevelando lietuviškų draugysčių sąryšis.

Lietuviškų juostų raštai. Kaune, Žiedas ¡1928¡
    ¡1¡ L, 40 plates (in portfolio) 24 x 32 cm.
    Cover title.
    Preface signed: P. Galaunė.

    1. Embroidery, Lithuanian.   I. Galaunė, Paulius.
    NK9256.L5   58-52784

NL 0353479   DLC

LIETUVISZKOS dainos isz visur surinktos.   Plymouth,
Pa., Kasztu ir spaustuveje J. Paukszczio, 1893.
496 p. 22cm.

Pref. signed Jūzas Pauksztys.

1. Poetry, Lithuanian--Collections. 2. Folk songs, Lithuanian.
I. Pauksztys, Jūzas.

NL 0353480   NN MH

Lietuvių archyvas; bolševizmo metai. ¡Paruošė J. Prunskis¡
Brooklyn, 1952.
436 p. 24 cm.
Reprinted from Lietuvių archyvas, v. 1-3, 1942.

    1. Lithuania—Pol. & govt. 2. Lithuania—Hist.—Sources. 3. Com-
munism—Lithuania.   I. Prunskis, Joseph, 1907-   ed.

DK511.L27L48   54-20938 ‡

NL 0353481   DLC NN IU PU

Lietuvių archyvas; bolševizmo metai. v. 1-4; 1942-43. Vil-
nius.
4 v. illus., ports. 25 cm.
Vols. 1-3 published in Kaunas.
Vol. 1: 3d ed.
Issued by Studijų biuras.
Editors: 1942, J. Balčiūnas.—1943, P. Babickas.

    1. Lithuania—Pol. & govt. 2. Lithuania—Hist.—Sources. 3. Com-
munism—Lithuania.   I. Balčiūnas, J. M., ed. II. Babickas, Petras,
1903-   ed. III. Studijų biuras, Vilna.

DK511.L27L47   54-46726

NL 0353482   DLC IU PU

Z2537   Lietuvių Bibliografinė Tarnyba.
.K76
    Knygų lentyna. –18. m. (nr. –141);
    spalis/gr. 1965. Danville, Ill., Jungtinių Amerikos Val-
    stybių Lietuvių Bendruomenės Kultūros Fondas ¡etc.¡

LIETUVIŲ BIBLIOGRAFINĖ TARNYBA.
    Lietuvių Knyga tremtyje, 1945-1948. Neumuen-
    ster, International exchange agency, Correspondence
    & advertisement [1948] 52 p. 16cm.

    1. Bibliography, Lithuanian.   I. Title.

NL 0353484   NN

Lietuvių dailė. ¡Redakcinė komisija: T. Černiauskas et al.
Dailininkas V. Jurkūnas. Sudarė P. Gudynas, E. Jurénas¡
Vilnius, Valstybinė grožinės literatūros leidykla, 1954.
xxxv, 107 p. (p. 1-96 illus.) 30 cm.
Lithuanian and Russian.
Added t. p.: Литовское изобразительное искусство.

    1. Art—Lithuania.   I. Černiauskas, T., ed. II. Gudynas, P.
    III. Title: Litovskoe izobrazitel'noe iskusstvo.

N7255.L5L5   55-23634

NL 0353485   DLC NN

Lietuvių darbininkų literatūros draugija
    see
    American Lithuanian Literary Association.

325.247505 Lietuviu dienos. Lithuanian days. v.1-
LI
        Los Angeles.
            v. illus. 33cm. monthly (except
        July and Aug.)

        Issues for   called also
        "Combined with California Lithuanian."
        Text in Lithuanian or English.

NL 0353487   IU OC1 NN

Lietuvių enciklopedija. ¡Boston¡ Lietuvių enciklopedijos
leidykla ¡*1953-
    v. illus., ports., maps. 25 cm.
    Vols. 1-4 edited by Vaclovas Biržiška.
    Some volumes accompanied by supplements.

    1. Encyclopedias and dictionaries, Lithuanian.   I. Biržiška,
    Vaclovas, 1884-   ed.
    AE60.L5L5   55-20366

        CtY IU OC1 WaU
NL 0353488   DLC CU PU NN DNLM KU OU NNC InU NNC MB

Lietuvių kalbos institutas, *Vilna*
    see
    Lietuvos TSR Mokslų akademija, *Vilna. Lietuvių kalbos
    institutas.*

Lietuvių kalbos ir literatūros institutas, *Vilna*
    see
    Lietuvos TSR Mokslų akademija, *Vilna. Lietuvių kalbos
    ir literatūros institutas.*

Lietuvių kalbos rašybos žodynas; rašyba, skyryba, kirčiavi-
mas, lyčių vartojimas, lietuvių kalbos tarmės, vardynas,
žodynas. Redagavo K. Gasparavičius ¡et al. Patvirtintas
vartoti mokyklose. Kaune¡ Valstybinė enciklopedijų,
žodynų ir mokslo literatūros leidykla, 1948.
438 p. 25 cm.

    1. Lithuanian language—Orthography and spelling.   I. Gaspara-
vičius, K., ed.
PG8545.L5   54-40648

NL 0353491   DLC PSt

Lietuvių kalbos vadovas
    see under   Skardžius, Pranas, 1899-

Lietuvių kalbos žodynas. Redagavo J. Balčikonis. ¡Kaune¡
Valstybinė enciklopedijų, žodynų ir mokslo literatūros leidykla ¡19
    v. 25 cm.
    At head of title, v.   : Lietuvos TSR Mokslų akademija. Lietuvių
    kalbos institutas; v. 3-   : ... Lietuvių kalbos ir literatūros insti-
    tutas.

    1. Lithuanian language—Dictionaries.   I. Balčikonis, Juozas,
    1885-   ed. II. Lietuvos TSR Mokslų akademija, Vilna. Lietuvių
    kalbos institutas.
    PG8675.L48   57-36137 rev

NL 0353493   DLC WaU KU OU CU InU ICU

Lietuvių katalikų spaudos draugija, *Chicago*
    see Lithuanian Catholic Press Society, *Chicago.*

Lietuvių Knyga tremtyje, 1945-1948
    see under   Lietuvių Bibliografinė Tarnyba.

Lietuvių Kulturos fondo Australijos valdyba.
    Atolas; LKF metrastis
    see under title

Lietuvių literatūros institutas, *Vilna*
    see
    Lietuvos TSR Mokslų akademija, *Vilna. Lietuvių litera-
    tūros institutas.*

VOLUME 332

Lietuvių mokslo draugija, Vilna.

DK511
.L2A245

Lietuvių tauta. kn.
-4, sąsiuvinys 3. Vilnius, Ruch'o spaustuvė, 19 -32.

LIETUVIŲ pasakos. Vaikų rinkinys. Vilnius, J.
Zavadzkio spaustuvėje, 1905. 72 p. 22cm.
("Aušros" išleidimas)

1. Folk tales, Lithuanian.

NL 0353499 NN

Lietuvių patariamoji grupė
see
Lithuanian Consultative Panel.

Lietuvių Romos katalikų kunigų vienybė Amerikoje
see
Lithuanian Roman Catholic Priests' League of America.

Lietuvių Romos katalikų susivienijimas Amerikoje
see
Lithuanian Roman Catholic Alliance of America.

Lietuvių skautų tuntas "Lituanica," *Chicago*
see
Lituanica, Lietuvių skautų tuntas, *Chicago*.

Lietuvių socialdemokratų partija
see
Lietuvos socialdemokratų partija.

Lietuvių studentų sąjunga JAV
see
Lithuanian Student Association.

Lietuvių studentų tautininkų korporacija Neo-Lithuania.
Lietuvių studentų tautininkų korporacija Neo-Lithuania,
1922-1964; kamieno žodis, pasaulėžiūra, istoriniai bruožai,
atžalos. [Atsakingasis redaktorius Antanas Diržys. Chicago, 1955]
327 p. illus., ports. 27 cm.
Bibliographical footnotes.

I. Diržys, Antanas, 1906– II. Title.

LA853.L48L47 68–115416

NL 0353506 DLC

Lietuvių susivienijimas Amerikoje
see
Lithuanian Alliance of America.

Lietuvių tauta. kn.
-4, sąsiuvinys 3. Vilnius, Ruch'o spaustuvė, 19 -32
v. illus., ports. 27 cm.
Began publication in 1907. Cf. Union list of serials.
"Lietuvių mokslo draugijos raštai."
No more published?

1. Lithuania. 2. Folk-lore, Lithuanian. I. Lietuvių mokslo
draugija, Vilna.

DK511.L2A245 67–34851

NL 0353508 DLC

Lietuvių tautos atstovų mitingas, *Moscow*
see
Miting predstavitelei litovskogo naroda, *Moscow*, April,
1942

Lietuvių tautosakos archyvas
see
Lithuania. *Lietuvių tautosakos archyvas.*

LIETUVIŲ-UKRAINIEČIŲ DRAUGIJA.
Lietuvių-Ukrainiečių draugijos įstatai. Kaunas,
1928. 10 p. 13cm.

NL 0353511 NN

Lietuvių vaizbos butas, *Chicago*
see
Lithuanian Chamber of Commerce of Illinois.

Lietuvos aero klubas.

Lietuvos sparnai. sausio mėn. 1935–
[Kaunas, 1935–

Lietuvos aero klubas.

TL526
.L7P9

Pyragius, Jonas, ed.
Paukščių keliais; pirmiesiems civilinės aviacijos žingsniams Lietuvoje paminėti. Kaunas, Lietuvos aero klubo
leidinys, 1933.

LIETUVOS AIDAS, Kaunas. vasario 1, 1928-
gruodžio 23, 1936 (incomplete)
Kaunas [Lithuania] 1925-36. v. illus.,
ports. 47cm.

Film reproduction. Positive.

Daily (except Sunday).
File begins with v. 3, continuing the numbering of an earlier
newspaper with the same   name, published 1917-18 in
Wilno.

NL 0353515 NN

Lietuvos albumas
see under Gira, Liūdas, 1884-1946, ed.

Lietuvos atgimimo patriarcho d-ro Jono Basanavičiaus gyvenimo vaizdų albumas su biografija. [Surinko, spaudai
paruošė ir redagavo Kostas Radziulis. Kaune, V. D. U.
studentų "Šarūno" korporacija, 1937]
79 p. illus., ports. 25 cm.

1. Basanavičius, Jonas, 1851-1927. I. Radziulis, Kostas, ed.

DK511.L28B3 55–53897

NL 0353517 DLC

914.75
A939L

Lietuvos automobilių klubas.
Lithuania, guiding facts for tourists.
Kaunas [Printed by "Spindulys", 193-?]
80p. illus., fold. map. 26cm.

1. Lithuania - Description and travel.

NL 0353518 NcU MB OC1 PP PU CU

HG
3129
.L44A3

Lietuvos bankas.
... Apyskaita. (4.-7. metai) 1926-1929.
[Kaunas? 1927-30]
4 v. 29 cm.

NL 0353519 DLC

Lietuvos bankas.
Balance sheet ... 1927-   Kaunas,
1928-
v. annual.

NL 0353520 MH-BA

HC337
.L5A15

Lietuvos bankas.
... Biuletenis. [nr. 1]
1928-   Kaunas, 1928-
nos. in v. diagrs. 31cm.

NL 0353521 DLC

Lietuvos bankas.
Bulletin.

Kaunas [19
nos. in v. tables, diagrs. 32½ᶜᵐ. semiannual.

1. Banks and banking—Lithuania. 2. Lithuania—Econ. condit.
46–31737

Library of Congress   HG3135.7.L5
[2]   330.9475

NL 0353522 DLC

Lietuvos bankas.
Lietuvos bankas (Bank of Lithuania) [London, Printed
by Eyre and Spottiswoode, 1922]
23 p. 25 cm.
Errata slips inserted.
CONTENTS.—Law of the Bank of Lithuania.—Byelaws of the Bank
of Lithuania.—Law of the monetary unit.

HG3135.7.L53 53–48829

NL 0353523 DLC CtY

VOLUME 332

332.1   Lietuvos bankas.
L621   Lietuvos bankas, first decade, 1922-1932.
    Kaunas, 1932.
       74p. illus., plates, ports., tables, diagrs.

NL   0353524   IU

Lietuvos bankas.
    Pirmasis dešimtmetis, 1922–1932. Kaunas, 1932.
    74 p. illus., ports. 25 cm.

HG3135.7.L55   61–56108

NL   0353525   DLC NN

Lietuvos bibliografijos institutas, Kaunas
    see Kaunas. Lietuvos bibliografijos
institutas.

Lietuvos bibliotekininkų draugija.

Bibliografijos žinios ... 1.–   metai. 1928–
Kaunas, 1928–

W 3   LIETUVOS dantų gydytojų kongresas. Kaunas,
LI431   1938.
1938   Darbai. Kaunas, 1939.
       235 p. illus.
       Summaries in German.
       1. Dentistry - Congresses

NL   0353528   DNLM

LIETUVOS EKONOMINE KONFERENCIJA.
    [Programas.]
[nr.] 1

Kaunas, 1931   23cm.
   no.

1. Economics—Congresses—Lithuania.

NL   0353529   NN

Lietuvos eksportas ir eksporteriai. Lithuanian **exports &**
exporters.
1927–
Kaune.
    v. illus., ports., map, tables. 25 cm. annual.
    Editor: 1927– D. Gruodis.
    Lithuanian, English, French, and German.

    1. Lithuania—Comm. 2. Lithuania—Comm.—Direct. ɪ. Gruodis,
Donnas, 1896–   ed. ɪɪ. Title: Lithuanian exports & exporters.

HF3635.7.L48   53–56164 rev

NL   0353530   DLC NN

[Lietuvos franciškonai; istorijos bruožai/ir paminklinic
Šv. Antano vienuolyno pašventinimo iškilmių programa.
Brief history of the Franciscan Fathers and dedication
program. Kennebunk Port, Me. [1948]

NL   0353531   MH

46
Akl T   Lietuvos gyvulininkystes mokslinio ty-
    rimo institutas.
     Tipiniai racionai kiaulėms.   Vilnius,
Valstybine politines ir mokslines literaturos
leidykla, 1955.
    145 p.
     Russian title: Tipovye ratsiony dlia
svinei.

NL   0353532   DNAL

45
Akl   Lietuvos gyvulininkystes mokslinio tyri-
    mo institutas.
     Tipiniai racionai lietuvos juodgalvių
veislės avims.   Vilnius, Valstybine politines
ir mokslines literaturos leidykla, 1955.
    45 p.
     Russian title: Tipovye ratsiony dlia
litovskoi chernogolovoi porody.

NL   0353533   DNAL

47
Akl Tr   Lietuvos gyvulininkystes mokslinio tyri-
    mo institutas.
     Tipiniai racionai vištoms ir žąsims.
Vilnius, Valstybine politines ir mokslines
literaturos leidykla, 1955.
    28 p.
     Russian title: Tipovye ratsiony dlia kur i
gusei.

NL   0353534   DNAL

43
Akl2 T   Lietuvos gyvulininkystes mokslinio tyri-
    mo institutas.
     Tvartine-ganykline galvijų laikymo sistema
Lietuvos TSR sąlygomis; mokslinė konferencija
1954 m. kovo 19-20 d.   Vilnius, Valstybine
politines ir mokslines literaturos leidykla,
1954.
    114 p.
     Russian title: Stoilovo-pastbishchnaia
sistema soderzhaniia skota v usloviiakh
Litovskoi SSR.

NL   0353535   DNAL

DK511   Lietuvos istorijos draugija, Kaunas.
.L2P75
    Praeitis. 1.–2. t. Kaunas, 1930–33.

Lietuvos istorijos metraštis.
    Vilnius, Lietuvos TSR Mosklų akademija, istorijos insti-
tutas.
     v. illus. 22 cm. annual.
     Summaries in Russian.

    1. Lithuania—History—Periodicals.   ɪ. Lietuvos TSR Mosklų
akademija, Vilna. Istorijos institutas.

DK511.L2A247   73–641391
                           MARC S

NL   0353537   DLC

Lietuvos kariuomene
   see
Lithuania. *Kariuomenė.*

    Lietuvos kariuomenės kūrėju savanorių sąjunga.
DK511
.L27R85
    Ruseckas, Petras, 1883–   *ed.*
     Savanorių žygiai; nepriklausomybės karų atsiminimai.
Kaunas [Išleido Lietuvos kariuomenės kūrėjų savanorių
sąjunga] 1937–

HX8   Lietuvos Komunistų partija. Centro Komitetas.
.K565
    Коммунист.
    Вильнюс

HX8   Lietuvos Komunistų partija. Centro Komitetas.
.K588
    Komunistas.
    Vilnius, Lietuvos KP CK Laikraščių ir žurnalų leidykla.

    Lietuvos Komunistų partija. Centro Komitetas.
Propagandos ir agitacijos skyrius.

    Блокнот агитатора.
    [Вильнюс]

Lietuvos Komunistų partija. *S"ezd*
   see
Lietuvos Komunistų partija. *Suvažiavimas.*

Lietuvos Komunistų partija. *Suvažiavimas.*
    Съезд Коммунистической партии Литвы.
    Вильнюс, Госполитнаучиздат.
     v. 20 cm.

    1. Kommunisticheskaiā partiiā Sovetskogo Soiūza. 2. Lithuania—
Economic policy.   ɪ. Title.   *Title transliterated:* S"ezd Kom-
munisticheskoi partii Litvy.

JN6745.A98K55   65–34274

NL   0353544   DLC

Lietuvos Komunistų partija. *TSentral'nyi Komitet*
   see
Lietuvos Komunistų partija. *Centro Komitetas.*

Lietuvos kooperatyvų kongresas.
    ... Lietuvos kooperatyvų kongresai. ɪ–v-jo kooperatyvų kon-
gresų rezoliucijos ... Kaunas [Spaudė koop. raidės spaustuvė
Kaune] 1939.
    134 p., 1 l. illus. (ports.) diagrs. 23ᶜᵐ.
    At head of title: Lietuvos kooperatyvų taryba.

    1. Cooperation—Congresses. 2. Cooperative societies—Lithuania.
ɪ. Lietuvos kooperatyvų taryba.

                           42–51806

    Library of Congress   HD3517.6.A28

NL   0353546   DLC

VOLUME 332

Lietuvos kooperatyvų taryba.

Lietuvos kooperatyvų kongresas.
... Lietuvos kooperatyvų kongresai. ɪ–v-jo kooperatyvų kongresų rezoliucijos ... Kaunas ¡Spaudė koop. raidės spaustuvė Kaune¡ 1939.

Lietuvos lenkintojų kampanija. ¡1906¡

NL 0353548 MH

TC801
.Z4   Lietuvos matininkų ir kultūrtechnikų sąjunga.
Žemėtvarka ir melioracija.
Kaunas, 19

JS6130
.5
.A1S3   Lietuvos miestų sąjunga.
Savivaldybė; mėnesinis Lietuvos savivaldybių laikraštis. birž.
1923–
¡Kaunas, 1923–

Lietuvos miškų ūkio institutas
see
Lietuvos miškų ūkio mokslinio tyrimo institutas.

Lietuvos miškų ūkio mokslinio tyrimo institutas.
Darbai.
Kaunas, 195
v. illus. 27 cm.
Vols.   have added title pages: Труды.
Summaries in Russian.

1. Forests and forestry—Societies, etc.

SD1.L52   59–47077

NL 0353552   DLC NN DNAL MiU

Lietuvos miškų ūkio mokslinio tyrimo institutas.
Труды (*transliterated:* Trudy)
see its
Darbai.

Lietuvos mylėtojas, *pseud.*
see
Szlupas, John, 1861–1944.

Lietuvos periodika
see   Nepriklausomos Lietuvos periodika,
1929/30–

Lietuvos praeitis
see under   Kaunas. Antano Smetonos lituanistikos institutas. Lietuvos istorijos skyrius.

Lietuvos šaulių sąjunga.
Į Lietuvą Vytauto Didžiojo metais. Kaunas, 1930.
95 p. illus. 22 cm.

1. Lithuania—Descr. & trav.   ɪ. Title.

DK511.L2I.A22   56–53575 ‡

NL 0353557   DLC PU CU

Lietuvos šaulių sąjunga.
1928 ¡i. e. Tūkstantis devyni šimtai dvidešimt aštuntųjų¡ m. vasario 16; 10 metų Lietuvos Nepriklausomybės sukaktuvėms paminėti. Redagavo A. Marcinkevičius. Kaunas, 1928.
288 p. illus. 24 cm.

1. Lithuania—Hist.—Addresses, essays, lectures.   ɪ. Marcinkevičius, Aleksandras, ed.   ɪɪ. Title.

DK511.L27I.A485   57–55233 ‡

NL 0353558   DLC

Lietuvos šaulių sąjunga.
1930 ¡i. e. Tūkstantis devyni šimtai trisdešimtųjų¡— Vytauto Didžiojo—metų Vasario 16; Lietuvos Nepriklausomybės 12 metų sukaktvėms paminėti. Redagavo A. Marcinkevičius. ¡Viršelį ir vinjetes piešė K. Šimonis¡ Kaunas, 1930.
106 p. illus., ports., map. 24 cm.

1. Lithuania—Hist.—Addresses, essays, lectures.   ɪ. Marcinkevičius, Aleksandras, ed.   ɪɪ. Title.

DK511.L2I.A23   58–50413

NL 0353559   DLC

Lietuvos savivaldybes 1918–1928
see under   Lithuania.   Savivaldybes departamentas.

¡Lietuvos socialdemokratų partija¡
Hilferuf des litauischen Volkes. Stuttgart, 1948
38 p.
Five texts published by the Party from 1945 to 1947

NL 0353561   MH

Lietuvos Socialdemokratų Partija.
Dėl laisvos Lietuvos
see under title

LIETUVOS SOCIALDEMOKRATŲ PARTIJA.
Lietuvos socialdemokratų partijos XII-sis suvažiavimas (Kaune, 1925 m. balandžio 17, 18 ir 19d.)   Kaune, "Raidės" spaustvė, 1925.
72p. 16cm.

Bound with Krupavičius, Mykolas.
Lietuvių politinės partijos. ¡Kaunas,n.d.¡

NL 0353563   PU

Lietuvos sparnai. sausio mėn. 1935–
¡Kaunas, 1935–
v. illus., diagrs. 29½ᶜᵐ. monthly.
Organ of the Lietuvos aero klubas.
Editors: Jan.–Feb. 1935, Jonas Pyragius.—Mar. 1935—   Juozas Krygeris.

1. Aeronautics—Period. 2. Aeronautics—Lithuania.   ɪ. Lietuvos aero klubas.

Library of Congress   TL504.L5   41–40567

NL 0353564   DLC

Lietuvos sutartys su svetimomis valstybemis
see under   Lithuania.   Treaties, etc.

Lietuvos TSR
see
Lithuanian S. S. R.

Lietuvos TSR knygų metraštis
see
Lietuvos TSR Knygų rūmai.
Knygų metraštis.

Lietuvos TSR Knygų rūmai.
Knygų metraštis; valstybinė bibliografija. 1947 m. sausio/kovo mėn.–
Kaunas, Valstybinė enciklopedijų, žodynų ir mokslo literatūros leidykla.
v. 22 cm. quarterly (except 1948, annual)
Title varies: 1947, Lietuvos TSR knygų metraštis.
Vols. for 1947–   have added title pages: Книжная летопись Литовской ССР.

1. Lithuanian literature—Bibl.—Period.   ɪ. Title.

Z2537.L48   61–43669

NL 0353568   DLC

Lietuvos TSR Knygų rūmai.
Lietuvos TSR periodika, 1940–1950; jubiliejinis leidinys. Vilnius, Valstybinė politinės ir mokslinės literatūros leidykla, 1952.
77 p. 22 cm.
Added t. p.: Периодика Литовской ССР.
Table of contents also in Russian.

1. Newspapers—Lithuania—Bibl. 2. Periodicals—Lithuania—Bibl. 3. Lithuanian newspapers—Bibl. 4. Lithuanian periodicals—Bibl. ɪ. Title.

Z6956.L5L47   61–48563

NL 0353569   DLC

Z6956
.L5L5   **Lietuvos TSR Knygų rūmai.**
Lietuvos TSR periodinių leidinių metraštis; valstybinė bibliografija. 1951–
Vilnius.

Z2537
.L53   **Lietuvos TSR Knygų rūmai.**
Lietuvos TSR spauda; valstybinė suvestinė bibliografija. 1940/55–
Vilnius, Valstybinė politinės ir mokslinės literatūros leidykla.

VOLUME 332

PN
5278
.L5
L72

Lietuvos TSR Knygų rūmai.
Lietuvos TSR spaudos statistika. Статистика печати Литовской ССР. 1940/55–
Vilnius.
v. 22 cm.
Vol. for 1940/55 has added t. p. and table of contents in Russian.

1. Press—Lithuania—Stat. I. Title.

PN5278.L5L5   58–44675 rev

NL 0353572   DLC PU MiU

Lietuvos TSR Knygų rūmai.
Статистика печати Литовской ССР (*transliterated:* Statistika pechati Litovskoĭ SSR)
see its
Lietuvos TSR spaudos statistika.

AI 19
.L5Z8

Lietuvos TSR Knygų rūmai.
Žurnalų ir laikraščių straipsnių metraštis; Lietuvos TSR valstybinės bibliografijos organas.

Vilnius, Valstybinė politinės ir mokslinės literatūros leidykla.

Lietuvos TSR Mokslų akademija, *Vilna.*
Darbai. Serija A. Труды. Серия А. 1–
1955–
Vilnius, Valstybinė politinės ir mokslinės literatūros leidykla.
nos. in   v.   illus., maps. 26 cm.   irregular.
Supersedes in part the academy's Žinynas.
Lithuanian or Russian; summaries in Lithuanian or Russian.

AS262.V422   59–19995

NL 0353575   DLC OrU

Lietuvos TSR Mokslų akademija, *Vilna.*
Darbai. Serija B. Труды. Серия Б. 1–
1955–
Vilnius, Valstybinė politinės ir mokslinės literatūros leidykla.
v. illus., maps. 26 cm.   irregular.
Supersedes in part the academy's Žinynas.
Lithuanian or Russian; summaries in Lithuanian or Russian.

1. Science—Societies, etc. 2. Agriculture—Societies, etc. 3. Engineering—Societies, etc.

Q4.L52   59–19939

NL 0353576   DLC NN PPiU TxU

Lietuvos TSR Mokslų akademija, *Vilna.*
Leidinys. nr. 1–
Vilnius, 1945–
v. 15 cm.

AS262.L4824   62–26112

NL 0353577   DLC

S469
.L5L5

Lietuvos TSR Mokslų akademija, Vilna.
Lietuvos TSR žemės ūkio tolesnio išvystymo klausimai. ¡Redakcinė komisija: Vyr. redaktorius V. Lašas; redakcinės komisijos nariai: J. Kriščiūnas et al.¡ Vilnius, Valstybinė politinės ir mokslinės literatūros leidykla, 1954.

Lietuvos TSR Mokslų akademija, *Vilna.*
Литовская ССР. ¡Ответственные редакторы: К. К. Белюкас, Ю. И. Булавас, И. В. Комар¡ Москва, Гос. изд-во геогр. лит-ры, 1955.
389, ¡3¡ p.   illus., maps (2 fold.)   21 cm.
At head of title: Академия наук Литовской ССР. Институт географии Академии наук СССР.
Bibliography: p. 878–¡890¡

1. Lithuania.   I. Bieliukas, K., ed.   II. Akademiıa nauk SSSR. Institut geografii.   III. Title.   *Title transliterated:* Litovskaıa SSR.

DK511.L2I.A14   56–35388

NL 0353579   DLC CaBVaU TU

Lietuvos TSR Mokslų akademija, *Vilna.*
План научно-исследовательских работ.
Вильнюс.
v. 26 cm.

Title transliterated: Plan nauchno-issledovatel'skikh rabot.

AS262.L483   61–34665 rev

NL 0353580   DLC DNLM

Lietuvos TSR Mokslų akademija, *Vilna.*
Statutas. Patvirtintas Lietuvos TSR Liaudies Komisarų Tarybos 1945 m. balandžio 14 dienos nutarimu nr. 208. Vilnius, 1945.
18 p.   15 cm.   (*Its* Leidinys nr. 1)

(Series: Lietuvos TSR Mokslų akademija, Vilna. Leidinys nr. 1)

AS262.L4824 nr. 1   62–26113

NL 0353581   DLC

Lietuvos TSR Mokslų akademija, *Vilna.*
Труды. Серия А (*transliterated:* Trudy. Seriıa A)
see its
Darbai. Serija A.

Lietuvos TSR Mokslų akademija, *Vilna.*
Труды. Серия Б (*transliterated:* Trudy. Seriıa B)
see its
Darbai. Serija B.

Lietuvos TSR Mokslų akademija, *Vilna.* Вестник (*transliterated:* Vestnik)
see its Žinynas.

Lietuvos TSR Mokslų akademija, *Vilna.*
Žinynas. Вестник. 1–
1947–
Kaune, Valstybinė enciklopedijų, žodynų ir mokslo literatūros leidykla.
(/) v. ports. 26 cm.
Editor: 1947–   J. Žiugžda.
Summaries in Russian.

I. Žiugžda, Juozas, ed.

AS262.V42   52–21491

NL 0353585   DLC NN

LIETUVOS TSR MOKSLŲ AKADEMIJA, Vilna.
Žinynas. 1–4/5, 7–8
Vilnius ¡etc.¡ Valstybinė politinės ir mokslinės literatūros leidykla ¡etc.¡ 1947–51.   v.   ports. 26cm.

Film reproduction. Negative.
Irregular.
After no. 9, 1953, superseded by Lietuvos TSR mokslų akademija, Darbai.

Serija A, and Lietuvos TSR mokslų akademija, Darbai, Serija B (see those entries).
Text in Lithuanian with summaries in Russian. Occasional articles in Russian.
Name of academy and title also in Russian: Академия наук Литовской ССР. Вестник.)   (Akademiya nauk litovskoi SSR. Vestnik.)

1. Societies, Learned—Lithuania.   I. Lietuvos TSR mokslų akademija. Vestnik.

NL 0353586   NN

Lietuvos TSR Mokslų akademija, *Vilna. Biologijos institutas.*
Darbai. Труды. 1. t.–
¡Kaune¡ 1951–
v. illus. 25 cm.

1. Biology—Societies, etc.

QH301.L53   57–26017

NL 0353587   DLC

Lietuvos TSR Mokslų akademija, *Vilna. Biologijos institutas.*
Труды (*transliterated:* Trudy)
see its
Darbai

QL671
.P73

Lietuvos TSR Mokslų akademija, Vilna. Biologijos institutas.
Pribaltiiskaıa ornitologicheskaıa konferentsiıa.
Труды. 1.–   конференция; 1951–
Рига ¡etc.¡ Изд-во Академии наук Латвийской ССР ¡etc.¡

Lietuvos TSR Mokslų akademija, *Vilna. Biologisches Institut*
see
Lietuvos TSR Mokslų akademija, *Vilna. Biologijos institutas.*

Lietuvos TSR Mokslų akademija, *Vilna. Central Library*
see
Lietuvos TSR Mokslų akademija, *Vilna. Centrinė biblioteka.*

Lietuvos TSR Mokslų akademija, *Vilna. Centrinė biblioteka.*
Lietuvos TSR Mokslų akademijos ir jos darbuotojų knygų ir straipsnių bibliografija. 1941/54–
Vilnius.
4 v. 21 cm.
Title varies: 1941/54, Lietuvos TSR Mokslų akademijos ir jos mokslo darbuotojų leidinių bibliografija; knygos.
1941/54–   have added title page: Библиография изданий Академии наук Литовской ССР и ее научных сотрудников: книги; Библиография книг и статей Академии наук Литовской ССР и ее сотрудников.
Lithuanian and Russian.
1. Lietuvos TSR Mokslų akademija. Vilna—Bibl.   I. Title.

Z5055.L52L5   57–35837 rev

NL 0353592   DLC NBuG NN CtY IU CSt DNLM InU

VOLUME 332

Lietuvos girių milžinai
  see under Ščesnulevičius, K

Lietuvos gydytojų kongresas. *5th, Kaunas, 1937.*
  Darbai. Redaktorius V. Vaičiūnas. Kaunas, Lietuvos
gydytojų sąjungos Centro valdybos leidinys, 1937.
  393 p. illus. 23 cm.

  1. Medicine—Congresses.   I. Vaičiūnas, V., ed.   II. Lietuvos
gydytojų sąjunga.
  R106.L5 1937   60–57902

NL 0353594 DLC

R106
.L5
1937
Lietuvos gydytojų sąjunga.

Lietuvos gydytojų kongresas. *5th, Kaunas, 1937.*
  Darbai. Redaktorius V. Vaičiūnas. Kaunas, Lietuvos
gydytojų sąjungos Centro valdybos leidinys, 1937.

W 3
LI434
1924
LIETUVOS gydytojų suvažiavimas. 3d,
  Kaunas, 1924.
    Trečiasis Lietuvos gydytojų
  suvažiavimas, spalių mėn. 2–4 d.
  1924 m. Kaunas, 1926.
    245 p. illus.
    1. Medicine - Congresses.

NL 0353596 DNLM

Lietuvos gyvulininkystes mokslinio tyrimo
  institutas. Darbai, 1, 1954–
    Title changed to Lietuvos gyvulininkystes
  ir veterinari jos mokslinio tyrimo institutas
  Darbai, with v 2, 1955; changed to Lietuvos
  gyvulininkystes mokslinio tyrimo institutas
  Darbai with v 5, 1961.

NL 0353597 CU

43
Ak12
Lietuvos gyvulininkystes mokslinio ty-
  rimo institutas.
    Tipiniai racionai buliams-reproduktoriams.
  Vilnius, Valstybine politines ir mokslines
  literatūros leidykla, 1955.
    36 p.

    Russian title: Tipovye raciony dlia
  bykov-reproduktorov.

NL 0353598 DNAL

**Lietuvos TSR Mokslų akademija, Vilna. Centrinė biblio-
teka.**
  Lietuvos TSR Mokslų akademijos leidinių bibliografija.

Vilnius.
    v. 21 cm. annual.
    Lithuanian or Russian.
    Continues its Lietuvos TSR Mokslų akademijos ir jos darbuotojų
knygų ir straipsnių bibliografija.

  1. Lietuvos TSR Mokslų akademija, Vilna—Bibliography—Yearbooks.   I. Title.
  Z5055.L52L5   73–641253
                                         MARC-S

NL 0353599 DLC NNBG

Lietuvos TSR mokslų akademija. Dirvožemio ir
  žemdirbystės institutas

  See

Lietuvos TSR mokslų akademija. Žemdirbystės ir
  dirvožemio institutas.

Lietuvos TSR Mokslų akademija, *Vilna. Ekonomikos ir
teisės institutas*
  see also
  Lietuvos TSR Mokslų akademija, *Vilna. Istorijos ir
  teisės institutas.*

W 1
LI34
LIETUVOS TSR Mokslų akademija, Vilna.
  Eksperimentines medicinos ir onkologijos
  institutas
    Darbai.
    1. –   1948–
    Vilnius.
      v. illus., port.
      Issue for 1948 has no vol. numbering,
    but constitutes t. 1.
      Summaries in Russian.
      1. Neoplasms - Period. 2. Research -
  Medical - Period.

NL 0353602 DNLM

Lietuvos TSR Mokslų akademija, *Vilna. Fiziko-tekhniche-
skiĭ institut*
  see
  Lietuvos TSR Mokslų akademija, *Vilna. Fizikos-technikos institutas.*

Lietuvos TSR Mokslų akademija, *Vilna. Fizikos-technikos
institutas.*
  Darbai.
  Vilnius. Valstybinė poįitinės ir mokslinės literatūros leidykla,
19

    v. diagrs. 26 cm.

  Vols.   have added title pages in Russian: Трудм.
  Lithuanian and Russian; summaries in Lithuanian and Russian.

  1. Science—Societies, etc. 2. Engineering—Societies, etc.
  Q60.L5   58–22791

NL 0353604 DLC

Lietuvos TSR Mokslu adakemija, *Vilna. Fizikos-technikos
institutas.*
  Труды (*transliterated:* Trudy)
  see its
  Darbai.

Lietuvos TSR Mokslų akademija, *Vilna. Geological and
Geographical Institute*
  see
  Lietuvos TSR Mokslų akademija, *Vilna. Geologijos ir
  geografijos institutas.*

Lietuvos TSR Mokslų akademija, *Vilna. Geologijos ir geografijos institutas.*
  Moksliniai pranešimai. t. 1–
Vilnius, Valstybinė politinės ir mokslinės literatūros leidykla, 1955–
    v. illus., maps (part fold.) 27 cm.
    Vols. 1–   have added title pages: Научные сообщения; v. 4–
  have also added title pages : Scientific reports.
    Lithuanian or Russian.
    "Regioninio pasitarimo Pabaltijo ir Baltarusijos kvarterinių dari-
nių tyrimo klausimais darbai" : v. 4.
    1. Geology—Societies, etc. 2. Geography—Societies, etc.   I. Re-
gional'noe soveshchanie po izuchenii chetvertichnykh otloshenii Pri-
baltiki i Belorussii, Vilna and Kaunas, 1955.
  QE1.L448   58–18595

NL 0353607 DLC CLU

Lietuvos TSR Mokslų akademija, *Vilna. Geologijos ir geografijos institutas.*
  Научные сообщения (*transliterated:* Nauchnye soob-
  shcheniiā)
  see its
  Moksliniai pranešimai.

Lietuvos TSR Mokslu akademija, *Vilna. Geologijos ir geografijos institutas.*
  Scientific reports
  see its
  Moksliniai pranešimai.

Lietuvos TSR Mokslų akademija, Vilna.
  Gyvulininkystės ir veterinarijos institutas
    see Lietuvos gyvulininkystės mokslinio
  tyrimo institutas.

Lietuvos TSR Mokslų akademija, *Vilna. Institut biologii*
  see
  Lietuvos TSR Mokslų akademija, *Vilna. Biologijos institutas.*

Lietuvos TSR Mokslų akademija, *Vilna. Institut ėkonomiki
i prava*
  see
  Lietuvos TSR Mokslų akademija, *Vilna. Ekonomikos ir
  teisės institutas.*

Lietuvos TSR Mokslų akademija, *Vilna. Institut für Geologie und Geographie*
  see
  Lietuvos TSR Mokslų akademija, *Vilna. Geologijos ir
  geografijos institutas.*

Lietuvos TSR Mokslų akademija, *Vilna. Institut geologii i
geografii*
  see
  Lietuvos TSR Mokslų akademija, *Vilna. Geologijos ir
  geografijos institutas.*

Lietuvos TSR Mokslų akademija, *Vilna. Institut istorii*
  see
  Lietuvos TSR Mokslų akademija, *Vilna. Istorijos institutas.*

VOLUME 332

Lietuvos TSR Mokslų akademija, *Vilna. Institut litovskogo îăzyka i literatury*
see
Lietuvos TSR Mokslų akademija, *Vilna. Lietuvių kalbos ir literatūros institutas.*

Lietuvos TSR Mokslų akademija, *Vilna. Institut melioratsii*
see
Lietuvos TSR Mokslų akademija, *Vilna. Melioracijos institutas.*

Lietuvos TSR mokslų akademija. Institut zemledeliya i pochvovedeniya

See

Lietuvos TSR mokslų akademija. Žemdirbystēs ir dirvožemio institutas.

Lietuvos TSR Mokslų Akademija, Vilna.
Institut zhivotnovodstva i veterinarii
see   Lietuvos gyvulininkystes mokslinio tyrimo institutas.

Lietuvos TSR Mokslų akademija, *Vilna. Institute of Geology and Geography*
see
Lietuvos TSR Mokslų akademija, *Vilna. Geologijos ir geografijos institutas.*

Lietuvos TSR Mokslų akademija, *Vilna. Instytut Geologii i Geografii*
see
Lietuvos TSR Mokslų akademija, *Vilna. Geologijos ir geografijos institutas.*

DK190
.L5

Lietuvos TSR Mokslų akademija, Vilna. Istorijos institutas.
Lithuanian S. S. R. *Vidaus reikalų ministerija. Archyvų skyrius.*
Документы штаба М. И. Кутузова, 1805-1806; сборник. ₍Под общей ред. Жюгжда, Ю. И.₎ Вильнюс, Гос. изд-во полит. лит-ры, 1951.

Lietuvos TSR Mokslų akademija, *Vilna. Istorijos institutas*
see also
Lietuvos TSR Mokslų akademija, *Vilna. Istorijos ir teisēs institutas.*

Lietuvos TSR Mokslų akademija, *Vilna. Istorijos ir teisēs institutas.*
Lietuvos TSR istorijos šaltiniai. Redakcinē kolegija: K. Jablonskis ₍et al.₎ Vilnius, Valstybinē politinēs ir mokslinēs literatūros leidykla, 1955–
v. 27 cm.
Contents.—1. t. Feodalinis laikotarpis.

1. Lithuania—Hist.—Sources.   i. Jablonskis, Konstantinas, 1892- ed. ii. Title.
DK511.L2I424   56–31275 rev

NL   0353624   DNLM NN ICU CU NN   DLC

Lietuvos TSR Mokslų akademija, *Vilna. Istorijos ir teisēs institutas.*
Teisinių terminų žodynas. Sudarē A. Žiurlys. Redakcinē kolegija: J. Bulavas ₍et al.₎ Vilnius, Valstybinē politinēs ir mokslinēs literatūros leidykla, 1954.
238 p. 20 cm.
Errata slip inserted.

1. Law—Dictionaries—Lithuanian. 2. Lithuanian language—Dictionaries—Russian.   i. Žiurlys, A.   ii. Bulavas, J., ed.   iii. Title.
56–38277

NL   0353625   DLC

Lietuvos TSR Mokslų akademija, *Vilna. Istorijos ir teisēs institutas*
see also
Lietuvos TSR Mokslų akademija, *Vilna. Istorijos institutas.*

BX8070
.L727K7

Lietuvos TSR Mokslų akademija, Vilna. Lietuvių kalbos institutas.
Luther, Martin, 1483–1546.
Pirmoji lietuviška knyga. ₍Redaktorius Jonas Kruopas, dailēs redaktorius Mečislovas Bulaka. Kaune₎ Valstybinē enciklopedijų, žodynų ir mokslo literatūros leidykla ₍1947₎

Lietuvos TSR Mokslų akademija, *Vilna. Lietuvių kalbos institutas*
see also
Lietuvos TSR Mokslų akademija, *Vilna. Lietuvių kalbos ir literatūros institutas.*

Lietuvos TSR mokslu akademija, Vilna. Lietuvių kalbos ir literaturos institutas.
Adomas Mickevicius ir lietuviu literatura
see under   Mykolaitis, Vincas, 1893–1967.

Lietuvos TSR Mokslų akademija, *Vilna. Lietuvių kalbos ir literaturos institutas.*
Dabartinēs lietuvių kalbos žodynas. Apie 45,000 žodžių. Redakcinē kolegija: J. Balčikonis ... J. Kruopas (atsak. redaktorius) ₍et al.₎ Vilnius, Valstybinē politinēs ir mokslinēs literatūros leidykla, 1954.
xvi, 990 p. 23 cm.

1. Lithuanian language—Dictionaries.   i. Balčikonis, Juozas, 1885-   ii. Kruopas, J., ed.   iii. Title.
PG8675.L5   55–24424 rev

DS CU MB NSyU TxU CoU CLSU IU
NL   0353630   DLC CSt NNC NIC PU OU NN NcD ICU CtY CLU

Lietuvos TSR mokslu akademija, Vilna.
Lietuvių kalbos ir literaturos institutas.
Kristijoro Donelaičio rankrasčiai
see under   Donelaitis, Kristijonas, 1714-1780.

Lietuvos TSR Mokslų akademija, *Vilna. Lietuvių kalbos ir literatūros institutas.*
Lietuvių tautosakos rinktinē. ₍Ats. redaktorius K. Korsakas. Paruošē Tautosakos sektoriaus kolektyvas: Amb. Jonynas et al. Dailininkas T. Kulakauskas. Vilnius₎ Valstybinē grožinēs literatūros leidykla, 1954.
558 p. illus., ports. 23 cm.
Includes unacc. melodies.

1. Folk-lore, Lithuanian.   i. Jonynas, Amb.   ii. Korsakas, Kostas, 1909- ed.   iii. Title.
GR203.L5L5   55–28022

NL   0353632   DLC NN KU InU CU

Lietuvos TSR Mokslų akademija, *Vilna. Lietuvių kalbos ir literatūros institutas.*
Očerk istorii litovskoĭ sovetskoĭ literatury. ₍Redakcionnaíà kollegiíà: M. K. Dobrynin i dr.₎ Moskva, 1955.
258 p. 23 cm.
On leaf preceding t. p.: Akademiíà nauk SSSR. Institut mirovoĭ literatury. Akademiíà nauk Litovskoĭ SSR. Institut litovskogo íàzyka i literatury.

1. Lithuanian literature—Hist. & crit.   i. Dobrynin, M. K., ed.   ii. Akademiíà nauk SSSR. Institut mirovoĭ literatury.   iii. Title.
          Title transliterated: Ocherk istorii litovskoĭ sovetskoĭ literatury.
PG8701.L56   56–22147 ‡

NL   0353633   DLC OkU

Lietuvos TSR Mokslų akademija, *Vilna. Lietuvių kalbos ir literatūros institutas.*
Tarybinē lietuvių literatūra ir kritika; bibliografinē rodyklē. 1945/55–
Vilnius.
v. 20 cm.
Subtitle varies slightly.

i. Title.
Z2537.L5   58–16118 rev

NL   0353634   DLC CU MiU CtY OU CoU NNC

Lietuvos TSR Mokslų akademija, *Vilna. Lietuvių kalbos ir literatūros institutas*
see also
Lietuvos TSR Mokslų akademija, *Vilna. Lietuvių literatūros institutas.*

Lietuvos TSR Mokslų akademija, *Vilna. Lietuvių literctūros institutas.*
Darbai. Труды. 1–
1947–
Kaune, Valstybinē enciklopedijų, žodynų ir mokslo literatūros leidykla.
v. 26 cm.
Editor: 1947–   K. Korsakas.
Summaries in Russian.

1. Lithuanian literature—Societies, etc.   i. Korsakas, Kostas, 1900- ed.
PG8701.L55   52–21085 rev

NL   0353636   DLC

Lietuvos TSR Mokslų akademija, *Vilna. Lietuvių literatūros institutas.*
Lietuvių literatūra kovoje prieš klerikalizmą; literatūrinis rinkinys. ₍Redagavo K. Korsakas. Vilniuje₎ Valstybinē grožinēs literatūros leidykla, 1951.
398 p. 21 cm.

1. Lithuanian literature (Selections: Extracts, etc.)   i. Korsakas, Kostas, 1900- ed.   ii. Title.
PG8713.L5   57–38063 ‡

NL   0353637   DLC

Lietuvos TSR Mokslų akademija, *Vilna. Lietuvių literatūros institutas.*
Puškinas ir lietuvių literatūra. Redagavo K. Korsakas. ₍Kaune₎ Valstybinē grožinēs literatūros leidykla ₍1950₎
147 p. illus. 20 cm.
Added t. p. in Russian; table of contents also in Russian.

1. Pushkin, Aleksandr Sergeevich—Appreciation—Lithuania.   i. Korsakas, Kostas, 1900- ed.
PG3355.7.L5L5   53–31450 ‡

NL   0353638   DLC

VOLUME 332

Lietuvos TSR Mokslų akademija, *Vilna. Lietuvių literatūros institutas.*
　Senoji lietuviška knyga; pirmosios lietuviškos knygos 400 metų išleidimo sukakčiai paminėti. ₍Redakcinė kolegija: K. Korsakas, P. Pakarklis, J. Kruopas. Atsakingasis redaktorius V. Mykolaitis. Kaune₎ Valstybinė enciklopedijų, žodynų ir mokslo literatūros leidykla ₍1947₎
　　888 p. plates. 25 cm.
　　Table of contents also in Russian.
　　Bibliographical footnotes.
　　1. Mažvydas, Martynas, 1520(ca.)–1563.　2. Luther, Martin. Catechismus, Kleiner.　i. Mykolaitis, Vincas, 1884–　ed.　ii. Title.

BX8080.M36L5　　　　　　　　　　　58–36612

NL　0353639　DLC CU NN

Lietuvos TSR Mokslų akademija, *Vilna. Lietuvių literatūros institutas.* Труды (*transliterated:* Trudy)
see its Darbai.

Lietuvos TSR Mokslų akademija, *Vilna. Lietuvių literatūros institutas*
see also
Lietuvos TSR Mokslų akademija, *Vilna. Lietuvių kalbos ir literatūros institutas.*

Lietuvos TSR Mokslų akademija, *Vilna. Melioracijos institutas.*
　Artimiausi melioracijų uždaviniai Tarybų Lietuvoje; straipsnių rinkinys. Redagavo J. Čeičys ir K. Ramanauskas. Vilnius, Valstybinė politinės ir mokslinės literatūros leidykla, 1954.
　　138 p. 22 cm.

　　1. Reclamation of land—Lithuania.　2. Drainage—Lithuania.　i. Čeičys, J., ed.　ii. Ramanauskas, K., ed.　iii. Title.

TC978.L5L5　　　　　　　　　　57–30203

NL　0353642　DLC CU

Lietuvos TSR Mokslų akademija, *Vilna. Obshchee sobranie*
see
Lietuvos TSR Mokslų akademija, *Vilna. Visuotinis susirinkimas.*

Lietuvos TSR Mokslų akademija, *Vilna. TSentral'naiā biblioteka*
see
Lietuvos TSR Mokslų akademija, *Vilna. Centrine biblioteka.*

Lietuvos TSR Mokslų Akademija, Vilna.
　Visuotinis susirinkimas.
　Lietuvos TSR mokslų akademijos visuotinio susirinkimo pirmoji sesija, 1946. II. 20–23. Vyriausiasis redaktorius: J. Žiugžda, Redakcinės kolegijos nariai: J. Matulis [et al.] [Kaunas] Valstybinė enciklopedijų, žodynu ir mokslo literatūros leidykla [1947]
　　167 p. 25 cm.
　　At head of title: Lietuvos TSR mokslų akademija.

Continued in next column

Continued from preceding column

　　Partial contents. – Matulis, J. Pagrindinės Lietuvos TSR mokslų akademijos darbo gairės –Žiugžda, J. Tarybiniu mokslininkų darbo linkmė –Bulavas, J. Lietuvos TSR mokslų akademijos įkūrimas ir atstatymas. –Budrys, D. Lietuvos ūkio karo metu sugriovimas ir jo atstatymo perspektyvos. –Bieliukas, K. Lietuvos energetikos bazės. –Lašas, V. Mitybos tyrimo klausimu. –Dalinkevičius, J. Mineraliniai Lietuvos TSR resursai. –Minkevičius, A. Kulfūrinių augalų

parazitiniai grybai. –Grybauskas, K. Vietos vaistingujų augalų kultūra. Ivanauskas, T. Kailinių žvėrelių auginimas ir aklimatizacija.

NL　0353647　PU

Lietuvos TSR mokslu akademija, Vilna.
Žemdirbystės ir dirvožemio institutas.
Nemuno žemupio užliejamosios pievos

see under

Nemuno žemupio užliejamosios pievos.

Lietuvos TSR periodinių leidinių metraštis; valstybinė bibliografija. 1951–
Vilnius.
　　v. 21 cm. annual.
　　Issued by Lietuvos TSR Knygų rūmai.
　　Vols. for 1951–　have added title pages: Летопись периодических изданий Литовской ССР.

　　1. Lithuanian periodicals—Bibl.　2. Periodicals—Lithuania—Bibl.　3. Lithuanian newspapers—Bibl.　4. Newspapers—Lithuania—Bibl.　i. Lietuvos TSR Knygų rūmai.

Z6956.L5L5　　　　　　　　　　61–44592

NL　0353649　DLC

Lietuvos TSR Politinių ir mokslinių žinių skleidimo draugija.
　Paskaitos.
　₍Kaune₎ 19
　　v. 21 cm.
　　Title from p. 3 of cover; each issue has special t. p. only.

AS262.L515　　　　　　　　　　58–53123

NL　0353650　DLC

PG8501　　**Lietuvos TSR Rašytojų sąjunga.**
P4
　　Pergalė; literatūros, meno ir kritikos žurnalas.
　　₍Vilnius₎

　　　　Lietuvos TSR Rašytojų sąjunga.
PG8771
.R1S6　　Советская Литва; альманах.
　　₍Каунас₎ Гос. изд-во худож. лит-ры Литовской ССР ₍19

Lietuvos TSR spauda; valstybinė suvestinė bibliografija. 1940/55–
Vilnius, Valstybinė politinės ir mokslinės literatūros leidykla.
　　v. in illus. 27 cm.
　　Period for 1940–55 in 2 v.; later quinquennial.
　　At head of title, v. 1, pt. 1–　: Lietuvos TSR Kultūros ministerija.
　　Vols. 1, pt. 1–　have added title pages: Печать Литовской ССР.
　　Issued by Lietuvos TSR Knygų rūmai.

　　1. Lithuanian literature—Bibl.—Period.　2. Lithuania—Bibl.—Period.　3. Lithuania—Imprints.　i. Lietuvos TSR Knygų rūmai.

Z2537.L53　　　　　　　　　　63–35648

NL　0353653　DLC NN DNLM OU MiU MH

Lietuvos TSR Tarybinių Rašytojų sąjunga
see
Lietuvos TSR Rašytojų sąjunga.

Lietuvos TSR VRM
see
Lithuanian S. S. R. *Vidaus reikalų ministerija.*

Lietuvos TSR VRM Archyvų skyrius
see
Lithuanian S. S. R. *Vidaus reikalų ministerija. Archyvų skyrius.*

Lietuvos TSR Valstybinė centrinė biblioteka, *Kaunas*
see
Vilna. Lietuvos TSR Valstybinė respublikinė biblioteka.

Lietuvos TSR Valstybinis akademinis operos ir baleto teatras, *Vilna*
see
Vilna. Lietuvos TSR Valstybinis akademinis operos ir baleto teatras.

Lietuvos TSR žemės ūkio tolesnio išvystymo klausimai. ₍Redakcinė komisija: Vyr. redaktorius V. Lašas; redakcinės komisijos nariai: J. Kriščiūnas et al.₎ Vilnius, Valstybinė politinės ir mokslinės literatūros leidykla, 1954.
　　370 p. 27 cm.
　　At head of title: Lietuvos TSR Mokslų akademija.
　　Proceedings of a joint conference of Lietuvos TSR Mokslų akademija, Lietuvos TSR Žemės ūkio ir paruošų ministerija, Lietuvos Žemės ūkio akademija and Lietuvos Veterinarijos akademija.
　　Lithuanian or Russian.
　　Errata slip inserted.
　　1. Agriculture—Lithuania.　i. Lašas, Vladas, 1892–　ed.　ii. Lietuvos TSR Mokslų akademija, Vilna.

S469.L5L5　　　　　　　　　　56–15747

NL　0353659　DLC CU

Lietuvos TSR žurnalų ir laikraščių straipsniai
see
Žurnalų ir laikraščių straipsnių metraštis.

Lietuvos Tarptautinio Intelektualinio Bendradarbiavimo Tautine Komisija
see **Lithuania.** *Tarptautinio Intelektualinio Bendradarbiavimo Tautine Komisija.*

VOLUME 332

Lietuvos tarybinių Rašytojų sąjunga
see
Lietuvos TSR Rašytojų sąjunga.

Lietuvos Tarybu Socialistine Respublika

see under

Bol'shaĭa sovetskaĭa entsiklopediĭa.

Lietuvos Tarybų Socialistinės Respublikos dešimtmetis. ¡Vilniuje¡ Valstybinė politinės ir mokslinės literatūros leidykla, 1950.
112 p. illus. 20 cm.

1. Lithuania—Pol. & govt.

DK511.L27L49   56–22865 ‡

NL 0353664   DLC

Lietuvos tautinė olimpijada. *1st, Kaunas, 1938.*
Pirmoji Lietuvos tautinė olimpijada. The first Lithuanian national olympiad. Redagavo V. Kemežys. Foto montažai Ged. Orento. ¡Kaunas, Kūno kultūros rūmų leidinys¡ 1938.
67 p. illus., ports. 24 cm.
Lithuanian and English.

1. Sports—Lithuania.   I. Kemežys, Vincas, 1899–   ed.

GV648.L5L53 1938   59–56978

NL 0353665   DLC NNC NN

Lietuvos teisininkų tremtinių draugija.
Lietuvos sovietizacija 1940-1941 m.
Augsburgas, Lietuvos teisininkų tremtinių draugija, 1949.
48 p.   21 cm.
"Bankrašǒio teisėmis."
At head of title: X.Y.

NL 0353666   PU

Lietuvos sovietizacija 1940-1941 m
see under   Lietuvos teisininkų tremtinių draugija.

Lietuvos telefonų abonentų sąrašas.

Kaunas.
v. fold. map. 24 cm.
Title varies: 19   Telefonų abonentų knyga.
Issues for 19   accompanied by separately paged supplements
with special title pages.

1. Telephone—Lithuania—Direct.

HE9275.7.L5   52–21991

NL 0353668   DLC

LIETUVOS ūkininkas.
Kaunas.   no.   illus., ports.   f°.

Film reproduction. Positive.

Weekly (some issues in combined form).
"Lietuvos valstiečių liaudininkų sąjungos laikraštis."
Includes various separately-paged supplements.

Ceased publication in 1940?

1. Agriculture--Per. and soc. publ. 2. Agriculture--Lithuania.
I. Lietuvos valstiečių liaudininkų sąjunga.

NL 0353670   NN

Lietuvos ūkis; mėnesinis visuomenės ūkio ir finansų laikraštis ... Finansų ministerijos leidinys ... ¡1.¡–6. tomas (¡1.¡–7. metai); gruodis 1921–gruodis 1928. Kaunas, Valstybės spaustuvė ¡etc., 1921–28¡
6 v. in 2. 31ᶜᵐ.
No more published.

1. Lithuania—Econ. condit.—Period.   I. Lithuania. Finansų ministerija.

Library of Congress   HC337.L5A16   41–27106

NL 0353671   DLC

Lietuvos ūkis ir rinka. Litauens wirtschaft und markt. Leidžia Centralinis statistikos biuras ... nr. 1–10/11; sausis/kovas 1930–balandis/rugsėjis 1932.   Kaunas ¡"Spindulio" b-vės spaustuvė, etc., 1930–32¡
3 v. in 1. maps, tables, diagrs. 32ᶜᵐ. quarterly (irregular)
Lithuanian and German.
Supersedes Lietuvos ūkis and Tautos ūkis.
No more published?

1. Lithuania—Econ. condit.—Period. 2. Lithuania—Comm.—Period.
I. Lithuania. Centralinis statistikos biuras. II. Title: Litauens wirtschaft und markt.

Library of Congress   HC337.L5A162   42–27621

NL 0353672   DLC

Lietuvos universitetas, *Kaunas*
see **Kaunas.** Universitetas.

                            Soc 827.41.20(11)
Lietuvos valstiečių Liaudininkų Sąjunga.
Dr. Kazys Grinius. Documentation in Commemoration held on June 24, 1955, at the Carnegie Endowment International Center in New York City ¡in Cooperation with the International Peasant Union¡ NY, 1955

37 p. illus. (International Peasant Union documents, 11)
Cover title: Commemoration of Dr. Kazys Grinius

NL 0353674   MH

Lietuvos valstiečių liaudininkų sajunga.
Lietuvos ūkininkas
see under title

Lietuvos žemdirbystės institutas, *Dotnuva*
see
Dotnuva, Lithuania. Lietuvos žemdirbystės institutas.

Lietuvos žemdirbystės mokslinio tyrimo institutas, *Dotnuva*
see
Dotnuva, Lithuania. Lietuvos žemdirbystės institutas.

Lietuvos žemės ūkio akademija, *Kaunas*
see
Kaunas. Lietuvos žemės ūkio akademija.

Lietuvos žemės ūkio kooperatyvų sąjunga
see
Lietūkis, Lietuvos žemės ūkio kooperatyvų sąjunga.

Lietuvos žemės ūkis ir statistika. Redagavo A. Musteikis. ¡Dillingen¡ Mūsų kelias ¡1948¡
143 p. illus. 15 cm.

1. Lithuania—Statistics.   I. Musteikis, Antanas, 1900–   ed.
II. Title.

HA1448.L5L53   65–76925

NL 0353680   DLC

LIETUVOS žinios; politikos visuomenes ir literaturos dienraštis. saus. 4-liepos 12, 1915 (incomplete) Vilna, 1915. 1 v.   51cm.

Film reproduction. Positive.

1. Periodicals,   Lithuanian.

NL 0353681   NN

Lietz, A., Company
See
Lietz, firm, math. instr. makers, San Francisco.

Lietz (Alexander). * Ueber die Vertheilung des Phosphors in einzelnen Pilzen unter Berücksichtigung der Frage nach dem Lecithingehalt derselben. 36 pp. 8°. *Jurjew, C. Mattiesen,* 1893.

NL 0353683   DNLM

Lietz, Ernst: Gliom der Rautengrube, das durch einen Hydrocephalus internus radiologisch einen Hypophysentumor vortäuschte. [Maschinenschrift.] 25 S. 4°. — Auszug: Königsberg i. Pr. 1923: Petzelberger. 1 Bl. 8°
Königsberg, Med. Diss. v. 15. Dez. 1923 [1925]   [U 25.5876

NL 0353684   ICRL

Lietz, Franz: Die Organisation des ländlichen Immobiliarkredits in der Provinz Westpreussen. ⟨T. 1 bis 3.⟩ (Berlin: Ebering 1910.) 88 S. 8° ¶(Ersch. vollst. als Buch ebd.)
Berlin, Phil. Diss. v. 14. Okt. 1910, Ref. Sering, Wagner
[Geb. 25. Sept. 70 Dirschau; Wohnort: Charlottenburg; Staatsangeh.: Preußen; Vorbildung: Realgymn. Danzig Reife M. 90; Studium: Berlin 8 S.; Rig. 23. Juni 10.]   [U 11.273

NL 0353685   ICRL CtY PU

VOLUME 332

Lietz, Gerhard, 1908–
Das symbolische in der dichtung Barlachs ...
von Gerhard Lietz ... Lengerich i. W., Lenge-
richer handelsdruckerei [1937]
92 p.   diagr.   21cm.

Thesis, Marburg.
"Literatur": p. 5-6.

1. Barlach, Ernst, 1870-1938.

NL 0353686   NNC ICRL NIC MH CtY CU

FILM   Lietz, Gerhard, 1908–
PT   Das Symbolische in der Dichtung Barlachs.
no.43   Marburg, 1934[1937?]
        92p.

Inaug. Diss. – Marburg.

Microfilm (negative).   1 reel.   35mm.

1. Barlach, Ernst, 1870-1938. I. Title.

NL 0353687   CLSU CoU

PT2603   Lietz, Gerhard, 1908–
A53252   Das Symbolische in der Dichtung Barlachs.
1934a   Lengerich [1937]
         92 p.   21cm.

Inaug. Diss. – Marburg.
Lebenslauf.
Includes bibliography.
Xerox copy.   47ℓ.   21x30cm.

1. Barlach, Ernst, 1870-1938.

NL 0353688   CoU

Lietz, Günter, 1911–
... Die Aufgaben des Zahnarztes für die
Volksgesundheit im ernährungsphysiologischen
Sinne ...   Bottrop i. W., 1937.
Inaug.-Diss. – Berlin.
Lebenslauf.
"Schrifttum": p. 22-24.
[Full name: Günter Werner Willi Lietz]

NL 0353689   CtY

Lietz, Gustav, 1903–
Über die löslichkeit der edelgase in wasser.
Inaug. Diss.   Bonn, 1931.
Bibl.

NL 0353690   ICRL CtY

Lietz, Heinrich.
Wir bauen eine Kolonialausstellung, eine praktische Anleitung für Schulen. [1. Aufl.] Hrsg. vom Reichskolonial-
bund. Berlin [1937]
46 p. illus. 24 cm.
Bibliography : p. 45-46.

1. Germany—Colonies—Study and teaching.   I. Title.

JV57.G4L5   53-47439

NL 0353691   DLC MH

Lietz, Heinz.
Die alternativermaechtigung des glaeubigers nach
geltendem recht.
Inaug. diss. Leipzig, 1929.
Bibl.

NL 0353692   DLC

HD2859   Lietz, Heinz, 1908–
L719   Die stellung der politischen parteien zu der
konzentrationsbewegung in der deutschen wirtschaft ... Leipzig, Druck von Frommhold &
Wendler, d.r.g.m., 1932.

3 p.l.,114 p.,1 l.   23cm.

Inaug.-diss. – Halle-Wittenberg.
Reproduced from type-written copy.
Lebenslauf.
"Eiteratur": 2d and 3d prelim. leaves.

1. Corporations   – Germany. 2.Political
parties – Germa   ny. 3.Germany – Pol. &
govt. – 1918–   I.Title.

NL 0353693   CSt-H MH PU MiU NNC CtY ICRL

Lietz, Helene Volchert
see
Volchert-Lietz, Helene.

Lietz, Hermann, 1868-1919
D.L.E.H., das 1.[– 15.] Jahr im Deutschen Land-
Erziehungsheim. Leipzig, Voigtländer, 1901– [v.1,
1910]

illus.
Library lacks. Jahr 13, T.2 and Jahr 14
Title varies. Jahr 15, T.1 has title: Die Deutsche
Nationalschule

Imprint varies: pt.3-5, Berlin, Dümmler; pt.6,
Schloss Bieberstein, Haubinda und Ilsenburg; pt.7,
Schloss Bieberstein und Haubinda
Das 1.u.2. Jahr: 2.Aufl.

NL 0353696   MH

LIETZ, H[ermann], 1868-1919.
D.L.E.H. Das dreizehnte jahr in Deutschen
land-erziehungsheimen. Teil I. Leipzig, R.
Voigtländer, 1911.

Port. of Berta von Petersenn and plates.

NL 0353697   MH

373.43   Lietz, Hermann, 1868-1919
L71d   D.L.E.H. Das zwölfte Jahr in
1910   Deutschen landerziehungsheimen...
         Leipzig, Voigtländers verlag, 1910.
         2v. in 1. plates, fold.table. O.

NL 0353698   IaU

Lietz, Hermann, 1868–   L373·43 31
D. L. E. H. Die deutschen Land-Erziehungs-Heime. Gedanken und Bilder, von Dr Hermann Lietz. Leipzig, R. Voigtländer, 1910.
[8], 148 p. incl. illus., plates. 26½cm.

NL 0353699   ICJ ICRL MH IU

Lietz, Hermann, 1868-1919.
Des Vaterlandes Not und Hoffnung, Gedanken und Vorschläge zur Sozialpolitik und Volkserziehung 1919. Neu
hrsg. von Alfred Andreesen. Haubinda, Thür., H. Lietz,
1934.
viii, 115 p. 21 cm.

1. Education—Germany.   I. Title.

LA721.8.L52   52-57712

NL 0353700   DLC

Lietz, Hermann, 1868-1919.
Deutsche land-erziehungsheime; erziehungs-
grundsätze und einrichtungen, ... [Leipzig,
Voigtländer, 1909.]
37p.

NL 0353701   OCU

LIETZ, Hermann, 1868-1919.
Deutsche Land-Erziehungs-Heime; grundsätze
und einrichtungen. [Leipzig, R.Voigtländer,
1913.]

pp. 51.   Table and illustr.

NL 0353702   MH

Lietz, Hermann, 1868-1919.
Deutsche land-erziehungsheime in Schloss Bieberstein,
Haubinda i. Thüringen, Ilsenburg i. Harz. Das achte
jahr, 1905/1906. Von Hermann Lietz. Leipzig, R. Voigtländer [1906]
112 p. front., pl. 25cm.

1. Agriculture—Teaching—Germany.

                                         E 13-146

Library, U. S. Bur. of   Education S535.G3L6

NL 0353703   DHEW

LIETZ, Hermann, 1868-1919.
The Deutsche Land-Erziehungs-Heime; principles
and institutions. Translated from the German.
Osterwieck/Harz, A.W. Zickfeldt, 1913.

pp. 48.   Illustr.

NL 0353704   MH

LC93   Lietz, Hermann, 1868-1919
G4L5   Deutsche Nationalerziehung; Auswahl aus
seinen Schriften, besorgt von Alfred Andreesen.
2.unveränderte Aufl.   Weimar, H.Lietz
[Vorwort 1938.]
viii, 139p.   22cm.

1. Education and state – Germany. 2. Education
Germany. I. Title

NL 0353705   IaU N MH NN WU IEN DLC MH

Lietz, Hermann, 1868-1919.
Die deutsche nationalschule; beiträge zur schulreform
aus den deutschen landerziehungsheimen, von Hermann
Lietz ... Leipzig, R. Voigtländer, 1911.
95, [1] p. incl. tables. fold. tab. 24cm.

Illus. t.-p.
"Ein teil der 'Erläuterungen' erschien bereits im XII. Jahrbuch der
deutschen land-erziehungsheime": p. 6.

1. Education—Germany.

                                         E 12-627

Library, U. S. Bur. of   Education LA722.L7

NL 0353706   DHEW MH

VOLUME 332

Lietz, Hermann, 1868-1919.
　　Die deutsche nationalschule; beiträge zur
schulreform aus den deutschen landerziehungsheimen, von Hermann Lietz. I. 2. aufl.
Vekkenstedt a. d. Ille, Verlag des Land-
waisenheims, 1920.
　　xii, 90, [2] p.　incl. tables. fold. tab.
24 cm.　[Pamphlets on "deutsche nationalschule"
no. 5]
　　"Hrsg. von Alfred Andreesen."
　　No more published.
　　I. Andressen, Alfred, 1886-　ed.

NL 0353707　CU

Lietz, Hermann, 1868-1919.
　　Das deutsche Volkshochschulheim. Warum und wie es
werden muss. Von Dr. Hermann Lietz...　Langensalza: H.
Beyer & Söhne, 1919.　66, 8 p.　pl.　8°.　(Paedagogisches
Magazin. Heft 708.)
　　"Die deutsche Volkshochschule. Sammlung von Beiträgen hrsg. von Professor
Dr. W. Rein. Heft. 7."

1. People's high schools, Germany.　　　　2. Series.
N. Y. P. L.　　　　　　　　　　　　November 18, 1921.

NL 0353708　NN NNU-W

Lietz, Hermann, 1868-1919.
　　Emlohstobba: fiction or fact? Pictures of the school
life of the past, present, or future ... tr. from the German
with the author's sanction, with a preface by W. Rein ...
　　(In Reddie, Cecil. Abbotsholme ...　London, 1900.　8°.　p. 257-407)

1-3662

NL 0353709　DLC

LB1026
.L72　Lietz, Hermann, 1868-1919.
　　Emlohstobba, roman oder wirklichkeit?
Bilder aus dem schulleben der vergangenheit, gegenwart oder zukunft? Von dr.
phil. Hermann Lietz... Mit 22 tafeln in
autotypie.　Berlin, Dümmler, 1897.
　　vip., 1 l., 192p.　front., plates.
21½cm.

　　1.Education, Secondary. 2.Education -
Germany. 3.Education - Experimental methods. I.Title.

NL 0353710　NNU-W

LA722
.L73　Lietz, Hermann, 1868-1919.
　　Die ersten drei deutschen land-erziehu-
ungs-heime zwanzig jahre nach der begründung; ein versuch ernsthafter durchführung deutscher schulreform, von
Hermann Lietz.　2. aufl.　Veckenstedt
am Harz, Verlag des Land-waisenheims an
der Ilse, 1919.
　　104p.　illus.　20cm.

　　1.Education - Germany.　I.Title.
II.Title: Land-erzeihungs-heime.

NL 0353711　NNU-W

LA722
.L732　Lietz, Hermann, 1868-1919.
　　...Ein erstes deutsches kriegs-waisen-
heim auf dem lande; das Land-waisenheim
a. d. Ilse b. Veckenstedt a. Harz.
Veckenstedt am Harz, Verlag des Land-
waisenheims an der Ilse, 1918.
　　48p.　illus.　20cm.

　　1.Education - Germany.　2.Land-waisen-
heim, Veckenstedt am Harz.　I.Title.

NL 0353712　NNU-W

Lietz, Hermann, 1868-1919.
　　Das fünfzehnte jahr in deutschen landerziehungs-hei-
men; beiträge zur schulreform, 2. t., von Hermann Lietz.
Leipzig, R. Voigtländer, 1913.
　　96 p.　front., plates.　25ᶜᵐ.
　　1. t. pub. under title: Die deutsche nationalschule.

　　1. Education—Germany.

E 14-389

Library, U. S. Bur. of　　　　Education

NL 0353713　DHEW MH

BT101
.A1L5　Lietz, Hermann, 1868-1919, comp.
　　...Gott und welt; stimmen von führern
der menschheit.　Veckenstedt a. Harz,
Verlag des Land-waisenheims an der Ilse,
1919.
　　367,[1]p.　plates.　20cm.
　　"Von Gott und welt zeugen nachfolgende
werke, die in diesem buch benutzt wurden".
p.366-367.

　　1.God.　I.Title.

NL 0353714　NNU-W

940.5311G　Lietz, Hermann, 1868-1919.
L7197g　　Gott, Volk, Vaterland; Worte von Hermann Lietz,
　　　　zusammengestellt von Alfred Andreesen.　Weimar,
　　　　H. Lietz-Verlag [1938?]
　　　　48 p.　20 cm.

　　　　Includes bibliography.

　　　　1. Education. Germany. I. Andreesen, Alfred, 1886-
　　　　comp. II. Title.

NL 0353715　N NN IaU CtY MH

PT 2623
I48　　Lietz, Hermann, 1868-1919.
H439　　Heim der Hoffnung, von H.L.　Leipzig,
1911　　R. Voigtländer [1911]
　　　　68 p.　18 cm.

NL 0353716　CaBVaU

4L-18
Lietz, Hermann, 1868-1919.
　　Lebenserinnerungen. Von Leben und Arbeit
eines deutschen Erziehers. Veckenstedt am
Harz, Verlag des Land-Waisenheimes [1920]
316 p.

NL 0353717　DLC-P4 OCU

Lietz, Hermann, 1868-1919.
　　Lebenserinnerungen. Von leben und arbeit eines
deutschen erziehers.　3. aufl... Mit bild des
verfassers und schriftennachweis.　Beckenstedt am
Harz, Waisenheimes, 1922.
　　323p.　21cm.
　　"Herausgegeben von Erich Meissner, mit
buchschmuck von Rudolf André."
　　"Bibliographischer anhang" p. 318-319.

　　I. Meissner, Erich, editor.　I. Title.

NL 0353718　NNF

Lietz, Hermann, 1868-1919.
　　Lebenserinnerungen.　Neu hrsg. und durch Briefe und
Berichte ergänzt von Alfred Andreesen. 4./5. Aufl.　Wei-
mar, 1935 [1936]
　　215 p.　illus., ports., facsim.　22 cm.
　　Bibliography: p. 211-214.

　　r. Andreesen, Alfred, 1886-　　ed.

LB775.L46 1936　　　　　　50-50310

NL 0353719　DLC ICU MiD CtY

LA722
.L74　Lietz, Hermann, 1868-1919.
　　... Lehr- und arbeitspläne der deutschen volks-einheitschule; beiträge zur
schulreform aus den deutschen land-
erziehungsheimen.　Veckenstedt am
Harz, Verlag des Land-Waisenheims a.d.Ilse,
1919.
　　8p.　fold.chart.　21cm.
　　Title vignette.

　　1.Education - Germany. 2.Public schools
- Germany.　　　I.Title.

NL 0353720　NNU-W

LIETZ, [Hermann], 1868-1919.
　　Leitsätze zur reform der deutschen mittelschulen. (bezw. höheren lehranstalten).　n.p.,
[1910].

　　pp.(10).
　　"Aus dem XIII.jahrbuch der Deutschen land-
erziehungsheime. Teil I. 1910."
　　"Begründung und weitere ausführung dieser
Leitsätze ist zu finden im zweiten teil des XII
und ersten teil des XIII. Jahrbuches der Deutschen land-erziehungs 'me. 1910."

NL 0353721　MH

PT 2623
I48　　Lietz, Hermann, 1868-1919.
M33　　Das Märchen vom Gärtner und der blauen
1910　　Blume, von HL.　[n.p., 1910?]
　　　　13 p.

NL 0353722　CaBVaU

Lietz, Hermann, 1868-1919.
　　Die probleme im begriff der gesellschaft bei Auguste
Comte im gesamtzusammenhange seines systems ...
Jena, G. Neuenhahn univ.-buchdr., 1891.
　　97 p.　22ᶜᵐ.
　　Inaug.-diss.—Jena.

　　1. *Comte, Auguste, 1798-1857. 2. Sociology.

15-19696 Revised

Library of Congress　　　　HM55.C8L5

NL 0353723　DLC NjP OO ICRL PU ICU MH

VOLUME 332

Lietz, Hermann, 1868-1919.
Das sechzehnte jahr in deutschen landerziehungsheimen, von Hermann Lietz. Leipzig, R. Voigtländer,
1914.
vii, 119, [1] p. front. 25⁻ᵐ.

1. Education—Germany. [2. Landerziehungsheime]

E 17-557

Library, U. S. Bur. of   Education LA722.L62 1914

NL 0353724 DHEW

LB1033 **LIETZ,HERMANN,**1868-1919.
.L72   Ein tag im neuen schulstaat Emlohstobba. Von dr.
phil.Hermann Lietz... Berlin,F.Dümmler,1897.
[2],77 p. 22 pl.(incl.front.) 21½cm.

NL 0353725 ICU

Lietz, Hermann, 1868-1919.
... Das vierzehnte jahr in deutschen landerziehungsheimen, von dr. H. Lietz. Leipzig, R. Voigtländer, 1912.
96 p. pl. 24½ᵐ.
At head of title: D. l. e. h.

1. Education—Germany.

E 14-390

Library, U. S. Bur. of   Education

NL 0353726 DHEW

Lietz, Joachim, 1904-
Beiträge zur Kenntnis der Pyromorphit-
Mimetesit-Vanadinit-Gruppe ... Leipzig, 1931.
Inaug.-Diss. - Hamburg.
"Sonderabdruck aus der 'Zeitschrift für
Kristallographie' Band 77 ... 1931."
Lebenslauf.
"Literaturverzeichnis": p. 497-498.

NL 0353727 CtY MiU

Lietz, Joseph, 1897-
Beitraege zur zytologie der gattung mentha.
Inaug. diss. Berlin, 1930. (Muenchen)
Bibl.

NL 0353728 ICRL CtY OU

W 4   **Lietz, Martin,** 1914-
R511   Messungen über die Länge des Canalis
1940   pterygopalatinus. Berlin, Pfau [1940]
13, [3] p.

Inaug.-Diss. - Berlin.
Bibliography: p. [15]

NL 0353729 DNLM

Lietz, Paul S

[Selections]
"Authors Autograph."

Vasco de Giurova: Oidor made bishop.
Viceroy Toledo and the University of
San Marcos.

NL 0353730 WaSpG

Lietz, Ulrich, 1906-
Inhalt der jagdberechtigung... Marburg, 1931.
39 p.
Inaug. Diss. -Marburg, 1931.
Lebenslauf.
Bibliography.

NL 0353731 ICRL CtY

Lietz, *firm, math. instr. makers, San Francisco.*
(1896. *The A. Lietz company*)
The cyclotomic transit; description of a novel surveying instrument made by the A. Lietz company ... San
Francisco, California. [San Francisco?] 1896.
cover-title, 12 p. illus. 23ᵐ.

1. Transit (Instrument)

Library of Congress   TA575.L7

5-38922†

NL 0353732 DLC

Lietz, *firm, math. instr. makers, San Francisco.*
(1938. *The A. Lietz company*)
... General catalog ...
San Francisco, The A. Lietz company [°19
v. illus. (part col.) 23ᵐ.

1. Surveying—Instruments—Catalogs. 2. Drawing materials—Catalogs.

88-13361

Library of Congress   TA581.L65
———— 2d set.
Copyright   526.91005

NL 0353733 DLC

Lietz, *firm, math. instr. makers, San Francisco.*
(1893. *The A. Lietz company*)
Manual of modern surveying instruments and their
uses ... Together with a catalogue and price list of scientific instruments, particularly those of the civil engineer and surveyor. Made by the A. Lietz company ...
San Francisco ... [San Francisco] The Company [1893]
vii, [1], 111, [72], x p. illus., plates. 23½ᵐ.
CONTENTS.—pt. I. Description of the establishment. The A. Lietz company ...—pt. II. Description of instruments. With remarks on their proper
use, care, preservation and adjustments.—pt. III. Professional papers
published by the A. Lietz company. 1893.—pt. IV. Illustrated catalogue
and price list.
1. Surveying—Instru-   ments.

6-250†

Library of Congress   TA581.L71

NL 0353734 DLC

Lietz, *firm, math. instr. makers, San Francisco.*
(1897. *The A. Lietz company*)
... Manual of modern surveying instruments and their
uses ... Together with a catalogue and price list of scientific instruments, particularly those of the civil engineer
and surveyor, made by the A. Lietz company ... San
Francisco ... Written and ed. by Otto von Geldern ...
[San Francisco] The Company, 1897 [1896]
vii, [3], 200, x p. illus. 23ᵐ.
At head of title: Revised edition ...
CONTENTS.—pt. I. Description of the establishment. The A. Lietz company ...—pt. II. Description of instruments. With remarks on their proper
use, care, preservation and adjustments.—pt. III. Professional papers
published by the A. Lietz company. 1896.—pt. IV. Illustrated catalogue
and price list.
1. Surveying—Instru-   ments.

6-249†

Library of Congress   TA581.L72

NL 0353735 DLC DN-Ob

Lietz, *firm, math. instr. makers, San Francisco.*
... Manual of modern surveying instruments and their uses,/con-
taining useful information for the civil engineer and surveyor.
Together with a catalogue and price list of scientific instruments,
... , made by the A. Lietz Company, ... 1899. Third edition.
vii,[3],200,x p. il. O. [San Francisco 1898.]

NL 0353736 ICJ

Lietz, *firm, math. instr. makers, San Francisco.*
(1908. *The A. Lietz company*)
... Manual of modern surveying instruments and their
uses, together with a catalogue & price list of scientific instruments made by the A. Lietz company ... San Francisco ... [10th ed.] San Francisco, The A. Lietz company, 1908.
204 p. illus. 23ᵐ.

1. Surveying—Instruments.

8-2416

Library of Congress   TA581.L76

NL 0353737 DLC ICJ

Lietz, *firm, math. instr. makers, San Francisco.*
Manual A of modern surveying instruments, and their uses;
together with a catalogue and price list of scientific instruments
...made by the A. Lietz Company... San Francisco, 1911-12.
320 p. incl. diagrs., plates., tables. illus. 11. ed. 8°.

1. Surveys—Instruments and apparatus   —Catalogues.
N. Y. P. L.   November 29, 1927

NL 0353738 NN

Lietz, *firm, math. instr. makers, San Francisco.*
(1915. *The A. Lietz company*)
Nautical instruments; catalogue and price list.
San Francisco, Cal.
1 v. illus., diagrs. 23ᵐ.
Only latest issue in Library is kept on shelf.

1. Nautical instruments—Catalogs.

CA 16-81 Unrev'd

Library of Congress   VK585.L5

NL 0353739 DLC

Lietz, firm, math, instr. makers, San Francisco
Solar Ephemeris 1912. Published by the A. Lietz
Co., manufacturers of surveying and nautical in-
struments, drawing materials.
San Francisco, Cal., n.d.
3 pl. on 2 f., (20) p. 14 cm.

NL 0353740 DN-Ob

Lietz, firm, math. instr. makers, San Francisco.
Solar Ephemeris 1919....
San Francisco, Cal., n.d.
1 no. 14½cm.

NL 0353741 DN-Ob

Lietzau, Friedrich Otto.
Historia trium monstrorum ... Regiomonti,
[1825].
[23] p. 8°.

NL 0353742 MH-Z

VOLUME 332

WB
L719L
1847
LIETZAU, Friedrich Otto.
Die Lehre von den Fiebern und den Entzündungen. Berlin, Duncker und Humblot, 1847.
2 v. (His Lehrbuch der speciellen Therapie, Bd. 1-2)

NL 0353743   DNLM

Lietzau, Friedrich Otto, ed.
Über die Eingeweidebrüche
see under Kirby, John, M.R.C.S.
[supplement]

Lietzau, Friedericus Otto
see Lietzau, Friedrich Otto.

JN3970
A1L71
Lietzau, Hans, 1900-
Die staatsrechtliche stellung der politischen partei ... Borna-Leipzig, Grossbetrieb für dissertationsdruck von R. Noske, 1934.
xiv,148 p.,1 l. 20½ᶜᵐ
Inaug.-diss.- Jena.
Lebenslauf.
"Literatur": p.ix-xiv.

1.Political parties - Germany. 2.Germany - Pol.& govt. -   1918-

NL 0353746   CSt-H ICRL CtY

Lietzau, Willy.
... Beiträge zur kenntnis der disruptiven entladung, von dr. Willy Lietzau. [Fribourg (Suisse) Imprimerie Fragnière frères, 1904.
41 p. incl. tables, diagrs. VIII fold. pl. 23½ᶜᵐ. ([Mémoires de la Société fribourgeoise des sciences naturelles; Mathématiques et physique, vol. I, fasc. 1)
Issued also as the author's thesis, Fribourg.

1. Electric discharges. 2. Condensers (Electricity)
Title from John Crerar   Libr.   A C 33-2231
Library of Congress   [Q67.F82 vol. 1, pt. 1]

NL 0353747   ICJ PPAmP

97.45
L62
Lietze, A.
New production of caladiums with many coloured leaves, by A. Lietze... Rio de Janeiro [192-?]
76 p. 23cm.

NL 0353748   DNAL

Lietze, Ernst.
The graphic method applied to machine designing. A number of diagrams for determining the dimensions of machine parts, with their construction, derivation and use. By Ernst Lietze, M. E. Cincinnati, O., 1885-
no. diagrs. 35ᶜᵐ.
Blue prints.

1. Machinery—Design.

Library of Congress   TJ235.L7   6-24308†

NL 0353749   DLC

Lietze, Ernst.
Modern heliographic processes: a manual of instruction in the art of reproducing drawings, engravings, manuscripts, etc., by the action of light; for the use of engineers, architects, draughtsmen, artists, and scientists. With thirty-two illustrations on wood and ten specimen heliograms. By Ernst Lietze... New York, D. Van Nostrand company, 1888.
viii, 143 p. incl. illus., tables. 10 prints mounted on 5 l. 26½ᶜᵐ.
Bibliography: p. iv.

1. Photography—Reproduction of plans, drawings, etc. 2. Photography—Printing processes.
Library of Congress   TR920.L71   9-5452

NN MiHM
NL 0353750   DLC MtBC NIC CU OU OCl OCU DN CLU ICJ MH

Lietze, Martin: Wirtschaftsgeographie der Rhön. Berlin 1914: Marschner. 100 S. 8° ¶ Auch als: Geogr. Arbeiten. H. 10. Rostock, Phil. Diss. v. 4. Juli 1914, Ref. Ule
[Geb. 14. Nov. 90 Rathenow; Wohnort: Rostock; Staatsangeh.: Preußen; Vorbildung: RG. Rathenow Reife 09; Studium: Rostock 1, Berlin 3, Rostock 6 S.; Rig. 28. Mai 14.]   [U 14. 4589]

NL 0353751   ICRL CtY PU MH

QD305
.A2L72
Lietzenmayer, Otto.
Ein beitrag zur kenntniss der chelidonsaure und aepfelsaure.
Erlangen, 1878-
67p.
Inaug. diss. Erlangen.

NL 0353752   DLC

---

ar W
54512
no.7
Lietzenmayer, Richard.
Selbsthilfe- und Deckungs-Verkauf unter besonderer Berücksichtigung der oberstrichterlichen Entscheidungen. Ebingen, Druck der Buchdr. A. Widmaier [1918?]
137 p. 23cm.

Inaug.-Diss.--Erlangen.

NL 0353753   NIC ICRL

Lietzke, A   F
Theoretical and experimental investigation of heat transfer by laminar natural convection between parallel plates. Washington, U. S. Govt. Print. Off., 1955 [i. e. 1956]
[, 7 p. diagrs. 30 cm. ([U. S.] National Advisory Committee for Aeronautics. Report 1223)
Cover title.
Bibliography: p. 7.

1. Heat—Transmission.   (Series)
TL521.A33 no. 1223   *629.123 629.1323   56-61126
——— Copy 2.   QC321.L5

NL 0353754   DLC

W 4
J86
1939
Lietzke, Arno, 1913-
Über Kollaps-Behandlung der Lungentuberkulose unter besonderer Berücksichtigung der Plombierung mit Polyviol. Freiburg im Breisgau, Waibel, 1939.
29 p. illus.

Inaug.-Diss. - Freiburg im Breisgau.
Bibliography: p. 25-29.

NL 0353755   DNLM

Lietzmann, Alfred, 1853-
Zur geschichte des diabetes mellitus...
Inaug. Diss.   Berlin, 1877

NL 0353756   ICRL

Lietzmann, Eugen, 1863-
Ueber die permeabilitaet vegetablischer zellmembranen...
Inaug. Diss. Berlin, 1887 (Regensburg)

NL 0353757   ICRL

DD
103
.L5
Lietzmann, Friedrich Christian Johann, 1792-
Freiwilliger Jäger bei den Totenkopfhusaren siebzehn Jahre Leutnant im Blücherhusaren-Regiment. Erzählungen aus dem deutschen Befreiungskrieg, aus kleiner pommerscher Garnison und von der Grenzwacht gegen den polnischen Aufstand 1831. Hrsg. von Karl Litzmann. Berlin, R. Eisenschmidt, 1909.
217 p. illus. 21 cm.
At head of title: Aus dem schriftlichen Nachlass eines kolberger Veteranen.
Includes bibliography.

NL 0353758   WU

QB64 Lietzmann, H.
.L7   Anleitung zur himmelsbeobachtung mit kleinen fernrohren, von H. Lietzmann. Mit 59 abbildungen im text. Jena, G. Fischer, 1922.
[4], 58, [2] p. incl. illus., tables, diagrs. 23ᶜᵐ.

1. Astronomy.

NL 0353759   ICU

LIETZMANN, HANS.
Torbole am Gardasee; ein Führer für Fremde. Torbole, 1953. 43 p. illus., map (part. fold.) 17cm.

1. Torbole, Italy.

NL 0353760   NN

---

*Lietzmann, Hans, 1875-1942.

Fendt, Leonhard, 1881-
... Die alten perikopen, für die theologische praxis erläutert von d. dr. Leonhard Fendt ... mit einem vorwort von Hans Lietzmann. Tübingen, J. C. B. Mohr (P. Siebeck) 1931.

Lietzmann, Hans, 1875-1942.   FOR OTHER EDITIONS SEE MAIN ENTRY

Bible. *N. T. Galatians. German. 1932.*
... An die Galater, erklärt von d. Hans Lietzmann ...
3. aufl. Tübingen, Mohr, 1932.

Lietzmann, Hans, 1875-1942.   FOR OTHER EDITIONS SEE MAIN ENTRY

Bible. *N. T. Corinthians. German. 1931.*
... An die Korinther I · II, erklärt von d. Hans Lietzmann ...
3. aufl. Tübingen, Mohr, 1931.

VOLUME 332

BT
990
L5

Lietzmann, Hans, 1875-1942.

Die Anfänge des Glaubensbekenntnisses. Aus der Festgabe für A. von Harnack zum siebzigsten Geburtstag... Tübingen, J. C. B. Mohr, 1921. p.226-242.
Cover title.
Bibliographical references.

NL 0353764   MoSCS CBPL DDO

IJ70
L625a

Lietzmann, Hans, 1875-1942.
Die anfänge des problems kirche und staat. ⌈Berlin, Verlag der Akademie der wissenschaften, in kommissin bei W. de Gruyter, 1938⌉
xxxvii-xlvii p. 27 cm.

Detached from Sitzungsberichte der preussischen Akademie der wissenschaften, 1938. Offentliche sitzung zur feier des jahrestages   könig Friedrichs II.

NL 0353765   CtY-D

BR1720 Lietzmann, Hans, 1875-1942.
.A56L7   Apollinaris von Laodicea und seine schule. Texte und untersuchungen von Hans Lietzmann. I. Tübingen, J. C. B. Mohr (P. Siebeck) 1904.
xvi, 323 p. 23cm.
No more published.

1. Apollinarius, bp. of Laodicea, d. ca. 390. 2. Theology—Early works to 1500.

NcD
    RPB GEU-T OO InStme OO CSt PPiPT CBPL CU IEG NcU
NL 0353766   ICU NN TxFTC NcD MH CtY MiU PPPD PU DDO

Lietzmann, Hans, 1875-1942, ed.

Apollinaris, *bp. of Laodicea, d. before 392.*
... Apollinaristische schriften syrisch, mit den griechischen texten und einem syrisch-griechischen wortregister, herausgegeben von dr. Johannes Flemming ... und lic. Hans Lietzmann ... Berlin, Weidmannsche buchhandlung, 1904.

Lietzmann, Hans, 1875-1942.
Ausgewählte Predigten
see under title

Lietzmann, Hans, 1875-
The beginnings of the Christian church, by Hans Lietzmann; translated by Bertram Lee Woolf. London, ⌈ Nicholson and Watson, limited, 1937.
xv, 17-406 p. front. (port.) 20½ cm. (Half-title: The international library of Christian knowledge, ed. by W. A. Brown and B. L. Woolf)
"The present work ... is the first volume of a projected 'History of the early church.' "—p. vi.
"Literature": p. 390-401.
1. Church history—Primitive and early church. 2. Bible. N.T.—History of contemporary events, etc. 3. Christian literature, Early—Hist. & crit.   I. Woolf, Bertram Lee, 1884-   tr. II. Title.

Full name: Johannes Carl Alexander Lietzmann.

BR129.L53 1937   270.1   37—21255

PPT PBm ICU KyU KyLxCB
NL 0353769   DLC CaBVaU OrU WaWW PPEB PPP OClW NN NcD

Lietzmann, Hans, 1875-1942.
The beginnings of the Christian church; translated by Bertram Lee Woolf. New York, Scribner, 1937-50.
3 v. front. (port.). (The International library of Christian knowledge)
Contents. - v. 1, The beginnings of the Christian church. - v. 2, The founding of the church universal. v. 3, From Constantine to Julian.

NL 0353770   DDO

BV239 Lietzmann, Hans, 1875-1942.
F6   The beginnings of the christian church by
I   Hans Lietzmann. Translated by Bertram Lee Woolf. New York, Charles Scribner's Sons, 1949.

303 p.
"Literature":p.⌈297⌉-298.
"A short bibliography for English readers": p.⌈299⌉-300.

1.Church of contemporary events, etc. 2.Christian literature, Early-Hist.& Crit. 3.Bible-History of contempo   rary events, etc.-N.T. I. Woolf, B.L.,1884.   II.Title. III.Series:History of the early church.I.

NL 0353771   MBtS MiU OO CU PPWe MH MB ICU

Lietzmann, Hans, 1875-1942.
The beginnings of the Christian Church. Translated by Bertram Lee Woolf. New York Meridian Books ⌈1950?⌉
303 p. 23 cm.
Translation of Die Anfänge, published as v. 1 of the author's Geschichte der alten Kirche.

NL 0353772   KEmT OrPR

Lietzmann, Hans, 1875-1942.
The beginnings of the Christian Church. Translated by Bertram Lee Woolf. New York, Scribner ⌈1952⌉
303 p. 23 cm.
Translation of Die Anfänge, published as v. 1 of the author's Geschichte der alten Kirche.

1. Church history—Primitive and early church. 2. Bible. N.T.—History of contemporary events, etc. 3. Christian literature, Early—Hist. & crit.   I. Title.

Full name: Johannes Carl Alexander Lietzmann.

BR129.L53 1952   53-3008 ‡

NL 0353773   DLC OU NBuG PSt

270.1 Lietzmann, Hans, 1875-1942.
L62aN   The beginnings of the Christian Church.
1953   Translated by Bertram Lee Woolf. 3d ed., rev. London, Lutterworth Press ⌈1953⌉
303p. 22cm.

Translation of Die Anfänge, published as v.1 of the author's Geschichte der alten Kirche.
1. Church history. Primitive and early church. 2. Bible. N.T. History of contemporary events,etc.   3. Christian literature, Early. Hist.   & crit. I. Title.

NL 0353774   KU ICMcC MH-AH ViU NNC TNJ MiU

BT
1405
L53

Lietzmann, Hans, 1875-1942.
Ein beitrag zur Mandäerfrage, von Hans Lietzmann. Berlin, Walter de Gruyter, 1930.
15 p. 25 cm. (Sonderausgabe aus den Sitzungsberichten der preussischen Akademie der Wissenschaften. Phil-hist. klasse. 1930. XXVII.)
Reprint from the Proceedings of the Akademie der Wissenschaften, Berlin.

1. Mandaeans. I. Title. (Series: Akademie der Wissenschaften, Berlin. Philosophisch-Historischen Klasse. Sitzungsberichte, 1930, Nr. 27.)

NL 0353776   NRCR

LIETZMANN, HANS, 1875-1942.
Bericht über die mit Unterstützung der K. G. d. W. vorgenommene Catalogisierung der Catenenhandschriften ... ⌈n.p., n.d.⌉

4 p.
"Aus den Nachrichten der K. Gesellschaft der Wissenschaften zu Göttingen. Geschäftliche Mitteilungen. 1899. hft.1."

NL 0353777   DDO

Lietzmann, Hans, 1875-1942.
Bilderanhang.
(In Wendland, J. T. P. Die hellenistisch-römische Kultur in ihren Beziehungen zu Judentum und Christentum. Pp. 180-190. Tübingen. 1907.)

NL 0353778   MB

Lietzmann, Hans, 1875-
... Die briefe des apostels Paulus...
Tübingen, 1910-21.
see under Bible. N.T. Epistles of Paul. German. 1910-21.

(also with dates 1910-13, 1911-13, and 1913)

Lietzmann, Hans, 1875-1942.
... Die Briefe des Apostels Paulus, I. (Die 4 Hauptbriefe) Tübingen (Handbuch zum N.T.)
see under Bible. N.T. Epistles of Paul. German. 1906-10. (Also: 1910)

Lietzmann, Hans, 1875-1942.
Die Briefe des Apostels Paulus, erklärt von Hans Lietzmann und Martin Dibelius. Tübingen (Handbuch zum N.T.)
see under Bible. N.T. Epistles of Paul. German. 1910-13. (Also with date 1910-21)

PB 3023
.L 5
1911

Lietzmann, Hans, 1875-1942.
Byzantinische legenden, deutsch von Hans Lietzmann. Jena, E. Diederichs, 1911.
1 p.l., 100, [2] p., 1 l. illus. 26½cm.

1. Legends, Byzantine. 2. Saints - Legends. 3. Byzantine literature - Translations into German. 4. German   literature - Translations from By-   zantine literature.

CtY NcD TxFTC
NL 0353782   MdBJ NIC CaBVaU NN DDO OC1 MiU MH NNC ICU

Lietzmann, Hans, 1875-1942.
Catenen. Mitteilungen über ihre geschichte und handschriftliche überlieferung von lic. Hans Lietzmann. Mit einem beitrag von prof.dr. Hermann Usener. Freiburg i.B. ⌈Leipzig und Tübingen, J.C.B.Mohr (Paul Siebeck) 1897.
vi p.,1 l.,85 p. 25cm.
"Julian von Halikarnass von H.Usener": p.⌈28⌉-34.

1.Catenae. 2.Julianus,bp.of Halicarnassus. I. Usener,Hermann Karl,1834-1905.

NBuU NNC CLSU CSt PPT InNd IEG
NL 0353783   MiU PPLT PPWe DDO CtY-D TxFTC TxDaM-P

VOLUME 332

GG
L719
Lietzmann, Hans, 1875- 1942.
... Christliche Literatur ... Leipzig
und Berlin,B.G.Teubner,1923.
1p.l.,36p. 25cm. (Gercke, Alfred, ed.
Einleitung in die Altertumswissenschaft
... 1.Bd.,5.Hft.)
"Ausgaben und Abhandlungen": p.32-36.

NL 0353784   NNUT OCU TxFTC MH NcD

Lietzmann, Hans, 1875-1942, ed.
Corpus der griechisch-christlichen Inschrif-
ten von Hellas. Herausgegeben von H.Lietzmann,
Nikos A.Bees und G.Sotiriu. Athen, 1941.

29 cm.
At head of title: Christlich-archäologische
Gesellschaft zu Athen.
Contents:-Bd.1. Die griechisch-christlichen
Inschriften des Peloponnes. Lief.1. Isthmos-
Korinthos.

NL 0353785   MH OCU

Lietzmann, Hans, 1875-   ed.
Teaching of the twelve apostles.   FOR OTHER EDITIONS
SEE MAIN ENTRY
... Die Didache, mit kritischem apparat, herausgegeben von
Hans Lietzmann. 4. aufl. Berlin, W. de Gruyter & co., 1936.

FT42
L625p
Lietzmann, Hans, 1875-1942.
Das doppelantlitz der nachapostolischen zeit.
₍Berlin, Verlag der Akademie der wissenschaften,
in kommission bei W. de Gruyter, 1932₎
379-380 p. 27 cm.

Bound with the author's Petrus römischer
märtyrer. ₍Berlin, 1936₎
Caption title.
Detached from Sitzungsberichte der

Preussischen akademie der wissenschaften, 1932,
20. Sitzung der philosophisch-historischen
klasse.

1. Apostolic age. I. Title. II. Series.

NL 0353788   CtY-D

Lietzmann, Hans, 1875- 1942, ed.
... Die drei ältesten martyrologien, herausgegeben von lic.
Hans Lietzmann ... Bonn, A. Marcus und E. Weber, 1903.
16 p. 20ᶜᵐ. (Kleine texte für vorlesungen und übungen, 2)
CONTENTS.—Die depositiones des Chronographen von 354.—Das mar-
tyrolog von Carthago.—Das syrische martyrolog.

1. Martyrologies.
₍Full name: Johannes Carl Alexander Lietzmann₎
Title from Univ. of Mich.   Printed by L. C.   A C 34-2537

NL 0353789   MiU OC1 NIC IEG MH NNUT

Lietzmann, Hans, 1875- 1942, ed.
Die drei ältesten Martyrologien. 2.Aufl. Bonn,
Marcus und E.Weber, 1911.

18 p. (Kleine Texte für theologische und philologisch
Vorlesungen und Übungen, 2)
Contents:- Die Depositiones des Chronographen von 354.
- Das Martyrolog von Carthago. - Das syrische Martyrolog

NL 0353790   MH PLatS NNC ICU OC1 OCU ViU DDO NcD

Lietzmann, Hans, 1875-1942, ed.
Knopf, Rudolf, 1874-1920.
... Einführung in das Neue Testament; Bibelkunde des
Neuen Testaments; geschichte und religion des urchristentums,
von Rudolf Knopf ... 4. aufl., unter mitwirkung von professor d. Hans Lietzmann neu bearb. von professor d. dr. Heinrich Weinel. Giessen, A. Töpelmann, 1934.

Lietzmann, Hans, 1875-1942.
Einführung in das römische Brevier
see under Catholic Church. Liturgy and
ritual. Breviary. German. [Miscellaneous]

*Lietzmann, Hans, 1875-   FOR OTHER EDITIONS
SEE MAIN ENTRY
Bible. N. T. Romans. German. 1928.
... Einführung in die textgeschichte der Paulusbriefe. An
die Römer, erklärt von d. Hans Lietzmann ... Dritte auflage.
Tübingen, J. C. B. Mohr (P. Siebeck) 1928.

CB
3
W301
1925/26
Lietzmann, Hans, 1875-1942.
Die Entstehung der christlichen Liturgie
nach den ältesten Quellen.
(In Warburg Institute. Vorträge der Bibliothek Warburg. Nendeln/Liechtenstein. 24 cm.
v.5 (1925-1926), p. ₍45₎-66)

(Series: Warburg Institute. Vorträge der
Bibliothek Warburg, 1925/26)

NL 0353794   CU-S

BW935
.L714
v.4
Lietzmann, Hans, 1875-1942.
The era of the church fathers.
Tr. by Bertram Lee Woolf.   N.Y.,
Meridian books ₍pref. 1950₎
212 p. 22ᶜᵐ. (His, A history of
the early church. 4)

Bibliographies: p. ₍203₎-207.

I Woolf, Bertram Lee, 1884-
II Lietzmann, Hans, 1875-1942. A
history of the early church. 4

NL 0353795   NjPT

BR
165
L719
v.4
Lietzmann, Hans, 1875-1942.
The era of the Church Fathers (A history of the Early Church, vol. IV).
Translated by Bertram Lee Woolf. London, Lutterworth Press ₍1951₎
212 p. 22cm.

1. Church history--Primitive and
early church. 2. Fathers of the Church.
I. Lietzmann, Hans, 1875-   . Geschichte der alten Kirche--English, v. 4.

NL 0353796   NIC NcRS

Lietzmänn, Hans, 1875-1942.
The era of the church fathers. Translated by Bertram
Lee Woolf. New York, Scribner's, 1952.
212 p. 22 cm. (His A history of the early church, v. 4)
"Literature": p. ₍203₎-205.

1. Church history—Primitive and early church. I. Title.
Full name: Johannes Carl Alexander Lietzmann.

BR205.L493   270.1   A 53-1349 rev
Duke Univ. Library
for Library of Congress   ₍r58f1₎†

OrU
NL 0353797   LU ICU NjPT ViU NNC CtY-D DDO PU NBuG Or OrPR DLC
NcD InU MB PPPD PSt OU PHC CU ScU KEmT

Lietzmann, Hans, 1875-1942.
The era of the church fathers. Translated
by Bertram Lee Woolf. ₍2d ed.,rev.₎ London,
Lutterworth Press ₍1955₎
212 p. 23 cm. (His A history of the
early church, v.4)

"First published in 1951. Second edition,
revised, 1953. Second edition reprinted 1955."
Translation of Die Zeit der Kirchenväter
published as v.4 of the author's Geschichte der

alten Kirche.
"Literature": p. ₍203₎-205. "Suggestions
for further reading": p. 206-207.

NL 0353799   ICMcC ViU MB NNC ICU KU

Lietzmann, Hans, 1875-1942.
The founding of the church universal (The beginnings
of the Christian church: volume II) By Hans Lietzman;
translated by Bertram Lee Woolf. London, Nicholson and
Watson, limited, 1938.
3 p. l., ix-xvi, 17-432 p. 20¼ cm. (Half-title: The international
library of Christian knowledge, ed. by W. A. Brown and B. L. Woolf)
Bibliography: p. 419-422.
1. Church history—Primitive and early church. 2. Christian literature, Early—Hist. & crit. I. Woolf, Bertram Lee, 1884-   tr.
II. Title.
₍Full name: Johannes Carl Alexander Lietzmann₎

Library of Congress   BR165.L47   38-24886
₍a50j½₎   270.1

WaS OrU OKentU Or
NL 0353800   DLC DDO ScU KyWAT PPEB NcD MH OC1 OO ICU

BW935
.L714
1949
v.2
Lietzmann, Hans, 1875-1942.
The founding of the church universal. Tr. by Bertram Lee Woolf.
₍2d ed.₎   N.Y., Meridian books
₍pref. 1949₎
328 p. 23ᶜᵐ. (His, A history of
the early church. 2)

Bibliographies: p. ₍318₎-321.
I Woolf, Bertram Lee, 1884-   , tr.
II Lietzmann, Hans, 1875-1942. A history
of the early   church. 2

NL 0353801   NjPT

Lietzmann, Hans, 1875-1942.
The founding of the church universal; a History
of the early church, volume II. By Hans
Lietzmann; tr. by Bertram Lee Woolf. London,
Lutterworth press ₍1950₎
328 p. 22.5 cm.
"First published in 1938; second edition,
revised, 1950."
Bibliography: p. [318]-321

NL 0353802   OO

Lietzmann, Hans, 1875-1942.
The founding of the church universal; a history of the
early church: volume II. Translated by Bertram Lee
Woolf. ₍2d ed.₎ New York, Scribner, 1950.
328 p. 23 cm.
Includes bibliographies.

1. Church history—Primitive and early church. 2. Christian literature, Early—Hist. & crit. I. Title.
Full name: Johannes Carl Alexander Lietzmann.

BR165.L483 1950   270.1   53-1474

KU MB
NL 0353803   DLC ViU LU ICU MiU MH InU NBuG PPWe KEmT

Lietzmann, Hans, 1875-1942.
The founding of the church universal. A history of the early church, vol.II. Translated
by Bertram Lee Woolf. ₍3d ed., rev.₎ London,
Lutterworth Press ₍1953₎
328p. 23cm.

Bibliography: p.₍320₎-321. "Literature":
p.₍318₎-319.

NL 0353804   TxU MiU MiDW

VOLUME 332

Lietzmann, Hans, 1875–1942.
The founding of the church universal; a history of the
early church: volume II. Translated by Bertram Lee
Woolf.   London,
Lutterworth Press ₍1955₎.
328 p. 23 cm.

Includes bibliographies.

NL 0353805   MiU ICMcC NRCR OrPR

Lietzmann, Hans, 1875–1942.
Från fornkyrkan; nyare fynd och
forskningar. Olaus-Petri-föreläsningar
vid Uppsala Universitet. Översättning...
av Erik Gren. Stockholm, Svenska
Kyrkans Diakonistyrelses Bokförlag,
₍1935₎
₍78₎p., 16 p of il., facsim., O.

NL 0353806   PPLT

Lietzmann, Hans, 1875–1942.
From Constantine to Julian; a History of the early church,
volume III. Translated by Bertram Lee Woolf. London,
Lutterworth Press ₍1950₎.
340 p. 23 cm.
"Corrigenda et emendanda" slip inserted.
Translation of Die Reichskirche bis zum Tode Julius, published
as v. 3 of the author's Geschichte der alten Kirche.
Bibliography : p. ₍329₎–333.

1. Church history—Primitive and early church.   I. Title.
Full name: Johannes Carl Alexander Lietzmann.

BR205.L512   270.2   51–1229

NL 0353807   CtY-D NcD NIC NNC PPWe OO PPEB NRCR OrSaW
               DLC OrU ScU KU InStme NjPT OrPR MB ICN

Lietzmann, Hans, 1875–1942.
From Constantine to Julian. Translated by Bertram Lee
Woolf. New York, Scribner, 1950.
340 p. 23 cm. (His A history of the early church, v. 3)
Translation of Die Reichskirche bis zum Tode Julius.
"Corrigenda et emendanda" slip inserted.
Bibliography : p. ₍329₎–333.

1. Church history—Primitive and early church.   I. Title.
Full name: Johannes Carl Alexander Lietzmann.

[BR205.L   ]   A 53–9944
Wellesley College. Libr.
for Library of Congress   ₍5₎

NL 0353808   MWelC KEmT NBuG MH DCU NNC OrP KyLxCB

BR165   Lietzmann, Hans, 1875–1942.
.L6932   From Constantine to Julian; a History of the
         early church, volume III. Translated by Bertram
         Lee Woolf. London, Lutterworth Press ₍1953₎.
         340 p.
         "First published in 1950; second edition, re-
         vised, 1953."
         Includes bibliography.

NL 0353809   ICU ICMcC ViU PAtM MtU

Lietzmann, Hans, 1875–1942.
From Constantine to Julian; a History of the early church,
volume III. Translated by Bertram Lee Woolf. London,
Lutterworth Press ₍1955₎
340 p. 23 cm.
"Corrigenda et emendanda" slip inserted.
Translation of Die Reichskirche bis zum Tode Julius, published
as v. 3 of the author's Geschichte der alten Kirche.
Bibliography : p. ₍329₎–333.

NL 0353810   MiU

Lietzmann, Hans, 1875–1942 ed.
... Fünf festpredigten Augustins in gereimter
prosa
see under Augustinus, Aurelius, Saint,
bp. of Hippo. Sermons (Two or more) German.
1905.

Div.S. Lietzmann, Hans, 1873–1942.
922.443
H299L   Gedächtnisrede auf Adolf von Harnack.
         Berlin, Verlag der Akademie der Wissenschaften,
         In Kommission bei W. de Gruyter, 1931.
         12 p. 26 cm.

         "Sonderausgabe aus den Sitzungsberichten der
         Preussischen Akademie der Wissenschaften,
         Öffentliche Sitzung vom 22. Januar 1931."
         1. Harnack, Adolf von, 1851–1930. I. Title.

NL 0353812   NcD

BX8080   Lietzmann, Hans, 1875–1942.
H56L5   Gedächtnisrede auf Karl Holl. ₍Berlin,
         Verlag der Akademie der Wissenschaften,
         In Kommission bei W. De Gruyter₎ 1927.
         15 p. 26ᶜᵐ (Sitzungsberichte der Preussi-
         schen Akademie der Wissenschaften, 86–37)
         Cover title.
         "Öffentliche Sitzung zur Feier des Leibni-
         zischen Jahrestages vom 30. Juni ₍1927₎"
         "Verzeichnis der im Druck erschienen
         Schriften Karl Holls": p.11–15.

         1. Holl, Karl,   1866–1926.

NL 0353813   CSt

---

*Lietzmann, Hans, 1875–1942.

Holl, Karl, 1866–1926.
... Gesammelte aufsätze zur kirchengeschichte ... Tübingen, Mohr, 1928–32 ₍v. 1, '32₎

Lietzmann, Hans, 1875–1942.
Geschichte der alten kirche, von Hans Lietzmann ... Berlin
und Leipzig, W. de Gruyter & co., 1932–
v. 23ᶜᵐ.
"Literatur": v. 1, p. ₍318₎–319; v. 2, p. ₍330₎–331.
CONTENTS.—v. 1. Die anfänge.—v. 2. Ecclesia catholica.

1. Church history—Primitive and early church.   I. Title.
₍Full name: Johannes Carl Alexander Lietzmann₎
36–11330
Library of Congress   BR165.L48
270.1

NL 0353815   NRCR ViRUT CtY NIC ICU MB
               DLC ICLT OCU MU IaU NcD CLU PPLT PPDrop

Leitzmann, Hans, 1875–1942.
Geschichte der alten kirche. Berlin &
Leipzig, W. de Gruyter, 1936–1938.
3 v.
Contents: 1, Die anfänge (2 aufl.).– 2, Ecclesia
catholica.– 3, Die Reichskirche.

NL 0353816   DDO

Lietzmann, Hans, 1875–1942.
Geschichte der Alten Kirche. Berlin,
W. de Gruyter, 1936–53 [v. 1, 1937] 4 v.
24cm.

Vols. 1,4: 2. Aufl.
Includes bibliographies.
Contents.—1. Die Anfänge.—2. Ecclesia
catholica.—3. Die Reichskirche bis zum
Tode Julians.—4. Der Zeit der Kirchenväter.
1. Church history—   Undivided church,
to 1054.

NL 0353817   NN

Lietzmann, Hans, 1875–1942.

Geschichte der Alten Kirche.   Berlin,
Walter de Gruyter, 1937–1944.
4v. 23cm.

1. Church history – Primitive and early
church. i. Title.

NL 0353818   MoSCS

270.1   Lietzmann, Hans, 1875–1942.
L719g   Geschichte der alten Kirche. Berlin und
1953   Leipzig, W. de Gruyter, 1953.
Theol.   4 v. 22cm.
         Vol.1, 3d ed.; v.2–4, 2d ed.
         Contents.—v.1. Die Anfänge.—v.2. Ecclesia
         catholica.—v.3. Die Reichskirche.—v.4. Die Zeit
         der Kirchenväter.

         1. Church history—Primitive and early church.

NL 0353819   TxDaM TxU OU CU

IK   Lietzmann, Hans, 1875–1942.
C766   Der glaube Konstantins des Grossen. Berlin,
xL62   Verlag der Akademie der Wissenschaften, in
         kommission bei W. de Gruyter, 1937.
         263–275 p. illus. 27 cm. (Sitzungsbe-
         richte der Preussischen Akademie der wissen-
         schaften. Philosophisch-historische klasse,
         1937, 28–29)

         Includes "Klassensitzung am 2. dezember"
         (p. 259–260) and   "Gesamtsitzung am 9.

         dezember" (p. 261–262)
         Bibliographical footnotes.

         1. Constantinus I, the Great, emperor of
         Rome, d.337. I. Series: Akademie der wissen-
         schaften, Berlin.   Philosophisch-historische
         klasse. Sitzungs⟋   berichte, 1937, 28–29.

NL 0353821   CtY-D DDO

PA   Lietzmann, Hans, 1875–1942.
3316   Griechische Papyri. Bonn, A. Marcus
L71   und E. Weber, 1905.
         16p. 20cm. (Kleine Texte für
         theologische und philologische Vorlesungen
         und Ubungen. 14)

         1. Manuscripts, Greek (Papyri)—
         Collections.

NL 0353822   NIC MH CtY OCU

Lietzmann, Hans, ₍1875–
PA3316
.L5   ... Griechische papyri, ausgewaehlt und erklaert von
         d. Hans Lietzmann ... 2. aufl. Bonn, A. Marcus und
         E. Weber, 1910.
         32 p. 19½ᶜᵐ. (Kleine texte für theologische und philologische vorle-
         sungen und übungen. 14)

                                        14–2246

NL 0353823   DLC

VOLUME 332

Lietzmann, Hans, 1875–   ed.
... Griechische papyri, ausgewaehlt und erklaert von d. Hans Lietzmann ... 2. aufl. ... Bonn, A. Marcus und E. Weber, 1924.
32 p. 19¹ᶜᵐ. (Kleine texte für theologische und philologische vorlesungen und übungen ... 14)

  NcD DLC
NL 0353824 NBuU IEG RPB WaU OWorP DDO ICU OCU NNC

---

*Lietzmann, Hans, 1875–1942¸ed.
Handbuch zum Neuen Testament, in verbindung mit W. Bauer, M. Dibelius ... ¡u. a.¸ herausgegeben von Hans Lietzmann ... ¡2. aufl.¸ Tübingen, J. C. B. Mohr (P. Siebeck) 1912–

CH2   Lietzmann, Hans, 1875–1942.
L625   Hans Lietzmann. ¡Leipzig, F. Meiner, 1926?¸
    41, 16 p. port. 24 cm.

    Caption title.
    Also paged 77–117.
    Reprinted from Die religionswissenschaft der gegenwart in selbstdarstellungen, bd. 2, winter 1925/26.
    "Leseproben aus der Wissenschaft der

    gegenwart in selbstdarstellungen": 16 p. at end.
    Bibliographical footnotes.

NL 0353827 CtY-D

Lietzmann, Hans, 1875–1942.
    Histoire de l'église ancienne. Traduction française du professeur André Jundt, revue par l'auteur. Préface de Maurice Goguel. Paris, Payot, 1936–49.
    4 v. in 2. (Bibliothèque historique)

    Includes bibliographies.

NL 0353828 NNC

BR   Lietzmann, Hans, 1875–1942.
165   Histoire de l'Église ancienne. Traduction
.L484 française du André Jundt, revue par l'auteur.
    Paris, Payot, 1937–50 ¡v. 1, 1950¸
    4v. 23cm. (Bibliothèque historique)

    Contents.––v.1. Les commencements. Préf. de Maurice Goguel.––v.2. Ecclesia catholica.––v.3. L'Église, de l'empire jusqu'a la mort de Julien. ––v.4. L'Époque des Père de l¡Église jusqu'au V siècle.

NL 0353829 NPurMC NjP

LIETZMANN, HANS, 1875–
    ...Histoire de l'Église ancienne... Traduction française d'André Jundt.   Paris, Payot, 194–
    1 v.
    At head of title : Bibliothèque historique.

NL 0353830 DDO

BR162 Lietzmann, Hans, 1875–1942.
L719h   A history of the early church. Translated
19– by Bertram Lee Woolf. London, Lutterworth
GU Press ¡19–
    v. 23cm.

    CONTENTS.– v.1. The beginnings of the christian church. v. 2. The founding of the church universal. 3d ed., 1953, reprinted 1960.– v.3. From Constantine to Julian. 2d ed. 1953. Reprinted 1960.
    v.4. The era of the church fathers. 2d ed., 1953, reprinted   1958.

NL 0353831 GU

    Lietzmann, Hans, 1875–1942.
270.1   A history of the early church; tr. by
L719gaE Bertram Lee Woolf. New York, Scribner,
    1937–52.
    4 v. 20ᶜᴹ. (The international lbrary of Christian knowledge)
    Contains bibliographies.
    Contents.– v.1.The beginnings of the Christian church.– v.2.The founding of the church universal.– v.3.From Constantine to Julian.– v.4. The era of the church fathers.

    1.Church his   tory - Primitive and
early church.   2.Bible,N.T. - History of
contemporary   events, etc.

NL 0353832 CSt PHC PPLT

BR165 Lietzmann, Hans, 1875–1942.
L483   A history of the early church. Translated by Bertram Lee Woolf. London, Lutterworth Press ¡1949–
    v.

    Bibliography: v.1, p.¡297¸–300; v.2, p. ¡318¸–321; v.3, p.¡329¸–333.

    Contents.– v.1. The beginnings of the Christian church. ¡Rev. throughout¸– v.2. The founding of the Church universal. ¡2d ed., rev.¸– v.3. From Constantine to Julian.

NL 0353833 CU IEN MH TxU

BR   Lietzmann, Hans, 1875–1942.
165   A history of the early Church. Tr. by Bertram
.L69 Lee Woolf. New York, Scribner's, 1949–52.
E5   4 v. 22cm.
1949   Bibliography at end of each volume.
    Contents.– v.1. The beginnings of the Christian Church. 2.ed. – v.2. The founding of the Church universal. 2.ed. – v.3. From Constantine to Julian, –v.4. The era of The Church Fathers.
    1. Church history - Primitive and early Church. I.Title.

NL 0353834 DCU ICarbS

BR129 Lietzmann, Hans, 1875–1942
.L532   A history of the early church. Tr. by Bertram Lee Woolf. ¡2d. ed.¸ New York, Scribner's, 1950– ¡v.1, 1952¸
    v. 23cm.
    Translation of Die Anfänge, published as v.1 of the author's Geschichte der alten Kirche.
    Some vols. are 3rd ed., published by Lutterworth Press, London. Others are the 1st edition, 1950.
    Includes bibliography.

    Contents.– 1. The beginnings of the Christian church.– 2. The founding of the church universal.– 3. From Constantine to Julian.– 4. The era of the church fathers.

    1. Church history - Primitive and early church. 2. Bible. N.T. - History of contemporary events, etc. 3. Christian literature, Early - Hist. & crit. I-   IV. Title entries for each
title in contents   note. S

NL 0353836 PSt PPDrop

LIETZMANN, Hans
    A History of the Early Church. Translated by Bertram Lee Woolf. London, Lutterworth Press, 1951.
    1.Church History. 2.Translator.
Library has:

    Vol.IV. The Era of the Church Fathers.

NL 0353837 NNJ Ge

---

270   Lietzmann, Hans, 1875–1942.
L625rE2 ¡A history of the early church¸ Translated by Bertram Lee Woolf. ¡2d ed. revised¸ New York, Meridian Books ¡1953¸
    2 v.

    Translation of Reichskirche.
    Contents:- ¡v.1¸ The beginnings of the Christian church.- v.2. The founding of the church universal.- v.3. From Constantine to Julian.- v.4. The era of the church fathers.

NL 0353838 WaU WaS OrSaW

Lietzmann, Hans, 1875–1942.
    A history of the early church. Translated by Bertram Lee Woolf. London, Lutterworth Press ¡1955¸
    4v. 23cm.

    Vol.1–2:3d ed.,rev.;v.3–4:2d ed.,rev.
    Vol.1 issued without series title.
    Translation of Geschichte der alten Kirche.
    Contents.–v.1. The beginnings of the

    Christian church.–v.2. The founding of the church universal.–v.3. From Constantine to Julian.–v.4. The era of the church fathers.

    1. Church history––Primitive and early church. I. Woolf, Bertram Lee, 1884–   tr.

NL 0353840 ICMcC

GJ3   Lietzmann, Hans, 1875–1942.
Ir2   Der jenaer Irenäus-papyrus. ¡Göttingen,
X462 1912¸
    ¡292¸–320 p. illus., fold. facsims. 25 cm.

    "Aus den nachrichten der K. Gesellschaft der wissenschaften zu Göttingen. Philologisch-historische klasse. 1912."

NL 0353841 CtY-D MB

Lietzmann, Hans, 1875–1942, joint author.
Beyer, Hermann Wolfgang, 1898–
    ... Die jüdische katakombe der Villa Torlonia in Rom, bearbeitet von Hermann Wolfgang Beyer und Hans Lietzmann. Mit 11 textabbildungen und 31 tafeln. Berlin ¡etc.¸ W. de Gruyter & co., 1930.

Lietzmann, Hans, 1875–1942, ed.
    Kleine Texte für theologische und philologische Vorlesungen und Ubungen
      see Kleine Texte für Vorlesungen und Ubungen.

Lietzmann, Hans, 1875–1942, ed.
    Kleine Texte für theologische Vorlesungen und Ubungen
      see Kleine Texte für Vorlesungen und Ubungen.

VOLUME 332

Lietzmann, Hans, 1875–1942, ed.
Kleine Texte für Vorlesungen und Ubungen
see under title

Lietzmann, Hans, 1875–1942, ed.

Clementine liturgy.
... Die Klementinische liturgie aus den Constitutiones apostolorum VIII, nebst anhängen, herausgegeben von d. Hans Lietzmann ... Bonn, A. Marcus und E. Weber, 1910.

Lietzmann, Hans, 1875–1942.
... Die landmauer von Konstantinopel; vorbericht über die aufnahme im herbst 1928, von Hans Lietzmann. Mit 10 tafeln und 15 textbildern. Berlin, Verlag der Akademie der wissenschaften, in kommission bei Walter de Gruyter u. co., 1929.
33, [1] p. illus., x pl. (part fold.; incl. plan) 29½ cm. (Abhandlungen der Preussischen akademie der wissenschaften. Jahrg. 1929. Philosophisch-historische klasse. nr. 2)
"Wichtigste literatur": p. 18.
1. Istanbul—Fortifications. 2. Inscriptions, Greek—Istanbul.
I. Title.
Full name: Johannes Carl Alexander Lietzmann.

AS182.B34 1929, Nr. 2   A C 39–3521
Princeton Univ. Libr.
for Library of Congress   [a58c½]†

NL 0353847   NjP OCU DDO CtY-D DLC

Div.S. Lietzmann, Hans, 1875–1942.
722
fA669D   Die Landmauer von Konstantinopel. Berlin,
   W. de Gruyter, 1929–43.
Bd.8
   2 v. illus., plans, plates. 30–37 cm.
   Vol. 1: Abhandlungen der Preussischen Akademie der Wissenschaften. Jahrg. 1929, Philosophisch-historische Klasse, Nr. 2.
   Vol. 2: Archäologisches Institut des Deutschen Reiches. Denkmäler antiker Architektur, Bd.8.
   Vol. 2: Aufnahme. Beschreibung und Geschichte von B. Meyer-Plath und A. M. Schneider.

   1. Constantinople. Fortifications. 2. Inscriptions, Greek. Constantinople. I. Meyer-Plath, B. Die Landmauer von Konstantinopel. II. Schneider, Alfons Maria. III. Title.

NL 0353849   NcD

Lietzmann, Hans, 1875–   comp.
... Lateinische altkirchliche poesie, ausgewählt von d. Hans Lietzmann ... Bonn, A. Marcus und E. Weber, 1910.
64 p. 19ᵐ. (Kleine texte für vorlesungen und übungen, 47–49)

1. Christian poetry, Early. 2. Latin poetry (Collections)
[Full name: Johannes Carl Alexander Lietzmann]
A C 34–2558
Title from Univ. of Mich.   Printed by L. C.

NL 0353850   MiU ICU NNUT ViU PSC PU PPLT CtY NNUT WaU

PA6124
.L7   Lietzmann, Hans, 1875–   comp.
   Lateinische altkirchliche poesie. Berlin,
   W. de Gruyter & Co., 1938.
   64 p. 19 cm. (Kleine Texte für
   Vorlesungen und Ubungen, 47–49)

   1. Christian poetry, Early. 2. Latin poetry (Collections). (Series)
   [Full name: Johannes Carl Alexander Lietzmann]

NL 0353851   IEG CtY-D NcD

*Lietzmann, Hans, 1875–1942, ed.

Simeon, *Stylites, Saint.* **Legend.**
   Das leben des heiligen Symeon Stylites in gemeinschaft mit den mitgliedern des Kirchenhistorischen seminars der Universität Jena, bearb. von Hans Lietzmann. Mit einer deutschen übersetzung der syrischen lebensbeschreibung und der briefe von Heinrich Hilgenfeld. Leipzig, J. C. Hinrichs, 1908.

Lietzmann, Hans, 1875–1942.
   Das Leiden Unseres Herrn Jesu Christ. Sieben original-Holzschnitte von Hans Lietzmann. Den Brüdern, die im Grossen Krieg für uns gelitten haben und gestorben sind, gewidmet... [Berlin?] 1916. 1 p.l., 7 pl. 60cm.

202302B. 1. Jesus Christ in art.   2. Wood engravings, German.
N. Y. P. L.   November 17, 1942

NL 0353853   NN

GM3
T542   Lietzmann, Hans, 1875–1942.
xL62   Die liturgie des Theodor von Mopsuestia.
   Berlin, Verlag der Akademie der wissenschaften in kommission bei W. de Gruyter, 1933.
   24 p. 26 cm.

   Also paged [915]–936.
   "Sonderausgabe aus den Sitzungsberichten der preussischen akademie der wissenschaften.

   Phil.-Hist. klasse. 1933. XXIII."
   Bibliographical footnotes.

   1. Theodorus, bp. of Mopsuestia, d.ca.428.

NL 0353855   CtY-D

*Lietzmann, Hans, 1875–1942, ed.

... Liturgische texte ... Bonn, A. Marcus und E. Weber, 1903–

Div.S. Lietzmann, Hans, 1875–1942.
922.4
L973LIE   Luthers Ideale in Vergangenheit und Gegenwart. Bonn, A. Marcus und E. Weber, 1918.
   16 p. 20 cm.

   Rede—Jena (Reformationsfeier, 1917)

   1. Luther, Martin, 1483–1546.

NL 0353857   NcD

Lietzmann, Hans, 1875–1942.
   Mass and Lord's supper. A study in the history of the liturgy. Translation, with appendices by Dorothen H. G. Reeve. Introduction and supplementary essay by Robert Douglas Richardson. Leiden, E. J. Brill 1953–
   v. 24½ cm. 18.00 (v. 1.–v. 7)   Ne 69–83 (v. 1)
   Cover title.
   Issued in parts.
   Translation of Messe und Herrenmahl.

   1. Liturgies, Early Christian.   I. Richardson, Robert Douglas.
   II. Title.
BV185.L513   264.01′1   76–528383
       MARC

FTaSU CtY CMenSP KAS DCU
NBuU MH-AH MCE NRCR LU KyLxCB GU ODW OC1JC FU MB
PPLT NcU PSt OO IaU PU MH DDO NNJ WaSpG MBtCA OCH
NL 0353858   DLC ViU MShB-W IU MiU ViU NcD PPWe ICU OU

BS2600 Lietzmann, Hans, 1875–1942.
.L7   Der menschensohn; ein beitrag zur neutestamentlichen theologie von Hans Lietzmann. Freiburg i. B. und Leipzig, J. C. B. Mohr (P. Siebeck) 1896.
   vii, 95 p. 22½ᵐ.

   1. Jesus Christ. 2. Theology, Biblical.

   CSt NcD NRCR NNUT PPLT NcD PPEB CU TxFTC
NL 0353860   ICU GEU-T TxDaM MoSCS IU TNJ-R MH-AH

Lietzmann, Hans, 1875–1942.
   ... Messe und Herrenmahl, eine studie zur geschichte der liturgie, von Hans Lietzmann. Bonn, A. Marcus und E. Weber, 1926.
   xii, 263 p. 22ᶜᵐ. (Arbeiten zur kirchengeschichte, hrsg. von Karl Holl und Hans Lietzmann. 8)
   Bibliographical foot-notes.

   1. Lord's supper (Liturgy)   I. Title.
     [Full name: Johannes Carl Alexander Lietzmann]
BV185.L5   A F 47–490
Union theol. sem. Library
for Library of Congress   [4]†

PPDrop MH NN ICN ICU
NL 0353861   NNUT DLC TU MB NcD RPB DDO CtY NjP MiU

BR
141   Lietzmann, Hans, 1875–1942.
.A7   Messe und Herrenmahl; eine Studie zur
v.8   Geschichte der Liturgie. 3. Aufl. Berlin,
   de Gruyter, 1955.
   xii, 263 p. (Arbeiten zur
   Kirchengeschichte, 8)
   Bibliographical footnotes.

   1. Lord's Supper (Liturgy)   I. Title.

NL 0353862   NBuU CBGTU MU NIC CLSU CSt NcD PU IEG

Lietzmann, Hans, 1875–1942, ed.
   ... Das Muratorische fragment und die Monarchianischen prologe zu den Evangelien, herausgegeben von lic. Hans Lietzmann ... Bonn, A. Marcus und E. Weber, 1902.
   16 p. 19ᶜᵐ. (Kleine texte für vorlesungen und übungen, 1)

   1. Bible. N. T. — Canon. 2. Bible. N. T. Gospels — Criticism, interpretation, etc. I. Muratori, Lodovico Antonio, 1672–1750. II. Title: Die Monarchianischen prologe.
     [Full name: Johannes Carl Alexander Lietzmann]
     A C 34–2536
Title from Univ. of Mich.   Printed by L. C.

KyLxCB
NL 0353863   MiU OC1 NcD MH-AH CU NNUT ICU MH PPiPT

LIETZMANN, HANS, 1875–1942, ed.
   Das muratorische Fragment und die monarchianische Prologe zu den Evangelien. 2. Aufl. unveränd. Berlin, W. de Gruyter, 1933.

   16 p. (Kleine Texte für Vorlesungen und Übungen, 1)

NL 0353864   DDO

Lietzmann, Hans, 1875–1942, ed.
   Ordo Missae secundum Missale Romanum
   see under Catholic Church. Liturgy and ritual. Ordinary of the Mass.

Leitzmann, H[ans] 1875–1942.
   Papyrus Jenensis nr. 1. Lpz. 1907.
   [3] p. 23 cm. (Zeitschrift für wissenschaftliche theologie. v. 50. p. 149–151)
   Caption title.

NL 0353866   CU

VOLUME 332

Lietzmann, Hans, 1875-1942.
Paulus. Berlin, Leipzig, W. de
Gruyter, 1934.
32 p. 23 cm. (Der Weg der Kirche,
heft 5)

1. Paul, Saint, apostle. I. Title.

NL 0353867 NRCR IaU MH-AH CtY-D RPB TxFTC

FT42
L625p
Lietzmann, Hans, 1875-1942.
Petrus römischer märtyrer. ₍Berlin, Verlag
der Akademie der wissenschaften, in kommission
bei W. de Gruyter, 1936₎
392-410 p. 27 cm.

Caption title.
Detached from Sitzungsberichte der
Preussischen akademie der wissenschaften, 1936,
29. Sitzung der philosophisch-historischen
Klasse(?)

NL 0353868 CtY-D MBtS

Lietzmann, Hans, 1875-1942.
Petrus und Paulus in Rom; liturgische und archäologische studien, von Hans Lietzmann; mit 6 plänen. Bonn,
A. Marcus und E. Weber, 1915.
xii, 189, ₍1₎ p. illus. 23ᵐᵐ.

1. Church history—Primitive and early church. I. Title.
₍Full name: Johannes Carl Alexander Lietzmann₎
24-14696

Library of Congress BR165.L5

CU
NL 0353869 DLC NcD CtY OO OClW PPLT ICMcC ICN NjPT

Lietzmann, Hans, 1875-1942.
... Petrus und Paulus in Rom; liturgische und archäologische
studien von Hans Lietzmann. 2. neubearb. aufl. Mit 13 tafeln.
Berlin und Leipzig, W. de Gruyter & co., 1927.
viii, 315, ₍1₎ p. 1 illus., 13 fold. pl. (incl. plans) 22½ᵐᵐ. (Arbeiten zur
kirchengeschichte ... 1)
Folded plates in pocket.

1. Church history—Primitive and early church. I. Title.
₍Full name: Johannes Carl Alexander Lietzmann₎
28-3810
Library of Congress BR165.L5 1927

NL 0353870 DLC MH-AH NRCR NjPT NcD DDO PPWe

Lietzmann, Hans, 1875-1942.
Die preussische Agende im Auszug.
see under Evangelische Kirche der
Altpreussischen Union. Liturgy and ritual.

Lietzmann, Hans, 1875-1942.
Das Problem Staat und Kirche im weströmischen Reich.
Berlin, Akademie der Wissenschaften in Kommission bei
W. de Gruyter, 1940.
10 p. 30 cm. (Abhandlungen der Preussischen Akademie der
Wissenschaften. Jahrg. 1940. Philosophisch-historische Klasse, Nr.
11)
1. Church and state. 2. Church history—Primitive and early
church. (Series: Akademie der Wissenschaften, Berlin. Philoso-
phisch-historische Klasse. Abhandlungen, Jahrg. 1940, Nr. 11)
Full name: Johannes Carl Alexander Lietzmann.
AS182.B34 1940, Nr. 11 A 50-1460

Stanford Univ. Library
for Library of Congress

NL 0353872 CSt PU CtY-D DLC

---

*Lietzmann, Hans, 1875-1942, joint ed.
Bible. O. T. Amos. Hebrew. 1905.
... Der prophet Amos, hebräisch und griechisch, heraus-
gegeben von d. Johannes Meinhold ... und lic. Hans Lietzmann
... Bonn, A. Marcus und E. Weber, 1905.

Lietzmann, Hans, 1875-1942.
Der prozess Jesu, von Hans Lietzmann ... Berlin, Akademie der wissenschaften in kommission bei W. de Gruyter u. co.,
1931.
12 p. 25½ᵐᵐ.
Double paging (original paging retained)
"Sonderausgabe aus den Sitzungsberichten der Preussischen akademie der wissenschaften. Phil.-hist. klasse. 1931. XIV."

1. Jesus Christ—Trial. I. Title.
₍Full name: Johannes Carl Alexander Lietzmann₎
41-23461
Library of Congress BT440.L55
232.962

NL 0353874 DLC PPWe

LIETZMANN, HANS, 1875-1942.
Der Psalmencommentar Theodor's von Mopsuestia.
₍Berlin₎ Verlag der Königlichen Akademie der
Wissenschaften, in Commission bei G. Reimer ₍1902₎
13 p.
Sonderabdruck aus den Sitzungsberichten der
Akademie der Wissenschaften, Berlin. Philos.-
hist. Klasse. 1902, 17.
Cover title.
Pages also numbered 334-346.

NL 0353875 DDO DCU-H NNUT

Lietzmann, Hans, 1875-1942, ed.
Usener, Hermann Karl, 1834-1905.
Religionsgeschichtliche untersuchungen, von Hermann
Usener ... Bonn, F. Cohen, 1911-

Lietzmann, Hans, 1875-1942, ed.
Das Sacramentarium gregorianum nach dem
Aachener urexemplar
see under Catholic Church. Liturgy and
ritual. Sacramentary. [Hadrianum]

Lietzmann, Hans, 1875-1942.
Schallanalyse und textkritik, von Hans Lietzmann. Tübingen, Mohr, 1922.
39 p. 24½ᵐᵐ.
Review of Wolfgang Schanze's Das Neue Testament schallanalytisch
untersucht: 1. stück, Der Galaterbrief (Leipzig, 1918) reprinted from
Göttingische gelehrte anzeigen, 1919, no. 5-6, p. 223-229; no. 11-12,
p. 401-419.
"Epilogus. Antwort auf E. Sievers' schrift 'H. Lietzmann und die
schallanalyse'": p. 28-39.
Double paging (original paging retained)
1. Bible. N. T.—Criticism, Textual. 2. Schanz, Wolfgang. Der Galaterbrief: Das Neue Testament schallanalytisch untersucht. 3. *Sievers, Eduard, 1850- H. Lietzmann und die schallanalyse. I.
Title.
₍Full name: Johannes Carl Alexander Lietzmann₎
28-22513
Library of Congress BS2385.L5

NL 0353878 DLC NjPT CtY-D

---

*Lietzmann, Hans, 1875-1942, joint author.
Franchi de' Cavalieri, Pio Pietro, 1869-
Specimina codicvm graecorvm vaticanorvm collegervnt
Pivs Franchi de' Cavalieri et Iohannes Lietzmann. Bonnae,
A. Marcvs et E. Weber; ₍etc., etc.₎ 1910.

Mnk31
L62
Lietzmann, Hans, 1875-1942, ed.
... Symbole der alten Kirche, ausgewählt
von Lic. Hans Lietzmann ... Bonn, A. Marcus
und E. Weber, 1906.
32p. 20½cm. (Kleine Texte für theologische
Vorlesungen und Übungen ... 17-18)

1. Creeds - Early church. 2. Creeds -
Collections. I. Title.

NL 0353880 CtY OO MH

Lietzmann, Hans, 1875-1942, ed.
... Symbole der alten kirche, ausgewählt von Hans Lietzmann. 2. aufl. Bonn, A. Marcus und E. Weber, 1914.
40 p. 19ᵐᵐ. (Kleine texte für vorlesungen und übungen, 17-18)
Bibliography: p. ₍3₎

1. Creeds, Ecumenical. I. Title.
₍Full name: Johannes Carl Alexander Lietzmann₎
Title from Univ. of Mich. Printed by L. C. A C 34-2546

NL 0353881 MiU WaU

JK30
L625s
Lietzmann, Hans, 1875-1942, ed.
Symbole der alten kirche. 4. aufl. Berlin,
W. de Gruyter, 1935.
40 p. 21 cm. (Kleine texte für vorlesungen
und übungen, 17/18)

"Die 4. aufl. ist ein photomechanischer neudruck der 2. aufl."
Bibliography: p. ₍3₎

NL 0353882 CtY-D DDO

Lietzmann, Hans, 1875- ed.
...Synopse der drei ersten Evangelien.
Tübingen, 1936
see under Bible. N. T. Gospels.
Greek. Harmonies. 1936.

---

*Lietzmann, Hans, 1875- ed.
Bible. N. T. Gospels. Greek. Harmonies. 1936.
... A synopsis of the first three Gospels. 9th ed. A complete
revision of earlier editions, by Hans Lietzmann ... English
edition, prepared in conjunction with the above by Frank
Leslie Cross ... Tübingen, Mohr, 1936.

BR60
.L7
Lietzmann, Hans, 1875-1942, ed.
...The three oldest martyrologies, ed. by Hans
Lietzmann... Cambridge[Eng.]Deighton,Bell and
co.,1904.
16p. 19ᵐᵐ. (Materials for the use of theo-
logical lecturers and students... 2)

NL 0353885 ICU

CB
3
W301
1922/23
Lietzmann, Hans, 1875-1942.
Der unterirdische Kultraum von Porta
Maggiore in Rom.
(In Warburg Institute. Vorträge der
Bibliothek Warburg. Nendeln/Liechtenstein.
24 cm. v.2 (1922-1923), pt.1, p.₍66₎-70)

NL 0353886 CU-S

VOLUME 332

*Lietzmann, Hans, 1875-1942, ed.

Melanchthon, Philipp, 1497-1560.
... Der unterricht der visitatoren 1528, herausgegeben von Hans Lietzmann. Bonn, A. Marcus und E. Weber, 1912.

NL 0353888   OC1

Lietzmann, Hans, 1875-1942.
Die vorlage der gotischen Bibel.
[1],250-278p. [Berlin, 1914?]

Caption-title.
Extract from Zeitschrift für deutsches altertum und deutsche litteratur, v.56.

NL 0353888   OC1

Lietzmann, Hans, 1875-1942, ed.

Usener, Hermann Karl, 1834-1905.
Das weihnachtsfest, von Hermann Usener; kapitel I-III. 2. aufl. Bonn, F. Cohen, 1911.

OD11.5 **Lietzmann, Hans,** 1875-1942.
L625w   **Der weltheiland; eine jenaer rosenvorlesung mit anmerkungen.** Bonn, A. Marcus und E. Weber, 1909.
59 p. 20 cm.

Bibliographical references included in "Anmerkungen" (p. [35]-59)

NL 0353890   CtY-D NcD MH NNUT IU PU DDO CtY OCH

BS2320 **Lietzmann, Hans,** 1875-1942.
L71   **Wie wurden die Bücher des Neuen Testaments**
W64   **heilige Schrift? 5. Vorträge.** Tübingen, J. C. B. Mohr, 1907.
119 p. 22 cm. (Lebensfragen. Schriften und Reden, herausgegebe von Heinrich Weinel, 21)

1. Bible. N.T.—Canon. 2. Bible. N.T. Gospels—Criticism, interpretation, etc.

ICU CtY-D
NL 0353891   PPiPT TNJ-R PPT NcD MH PPEB CBPac TxFTC

Lietzmann, Hans, 1875- ed.
... Die Wittenberger und Leisniger kastenordnung, 1522, 1523, herausgegeben von lic. Hans Lietzmann ... Bonn, A. Marcus und E. Weber, 1907.
24 p. 19cm. (Kleine texte für vorlesungen und übungen, 21)
"Die Wittenberger ordnung ist am 24 jan. 1522 auf betreiben ihres verfassers Karlstadt worden."—p. [3]
The "Leisniger kastenordnung" is Luther's "Ordnung eines gemeinen kastens" edited from the original edition published in Wittenberg in 1523.
1. Poor laws—Germany. I. Karlstadt, Andreas Rudolf, 1480 (ca.)-1541. II. Luther, Martin, 1483-1546. III. Title. IV. Title: Leisniger kastenordnung.
[Full name: Johannes Carl Alexander Lietzmann]
A C 34-2548
Title from Univ. of Mich.   Printed by L. C.

NL 0353892   MiU MoU PPLT PU

Lietzmann, Hans, 1875-1942, ed.
... Die Wittenberger und Leisniger kastenordnung, 1522, 1523, herausgegeben von lic. Hans Lietzmann. 2. **Aufl.** Berlin, W. de Gruyter, 1935.
24 p. 19cm. (Kleine texte für vorlesungen und übungen, 21)

NL 0353893   NcD

Leitzmann, Hans, 1875-1942.
... Die zeit der Kirchenväter.   Berlin, W. de Gruyter & co., 1944.
iv, 200 p. 23 cm. (His Geschichte der alten kirche, v. 4)
"Literatur": p. [193]-194.

NL 0353894   OO OCH PPWe

Lietzmann, Hans, 1875-1942.
... Zeitrechnung der römischen kaiserzeit, des mittelalters und der neuzeit für die jahre 1-2000 nach Christus, von d. Hans Lietzmann ... Berlin, Leipzig, W. de Gruyter & co., 1934.
127 p. incl. tables. 16cm. (Sammlung Göschen. [1085])
Bibliography: p. [4]

1. Chronology. 2. Calendar. I. Title.
[Full name: Johannes Carl Alexander Lietzmann]
35-12143
Library of Congress   CE6.L5
529

NL 0353895   DLC CLU TNJ CU PPWe CtY

LIETZMANN, HANS, 1875-1942.
Zeitrechnung der römischen kaiserzeit, des mittelalters und der neuzeit für die jahre 1-2000 nach Christus...   Berlin, W. de Gruyter & co., 1946.

127 p.   tables.   (Sammlung Göschen. bd. 1085)

NL 0353896   DDO InStme PU

Lietzmann, Hans, 1875-1942.
Zur Datierung der Josuarolle, von Hans Lietzmann...
(In: Mittelalterliche Handschriften.   Leipzig, 1926.   4°.
p. [181-]185.   facsim.)

Caption-title.

305057A. 1. Bible. O. T. Greek.   Septuaginta. Codex vaticanus.
Joshua.   Seotember 7, 1927
N. Y. P. L.

NL 0353897   NN

GN3   **Lietzmann, Hans,** 1875-1942.
X   Zur entstehungsgeschichte der briefsammlung
L625   Augustins. Berlin, Akademie der wissenschaften in kommission bei W. de Gruyter, 1930.
35 p. 26 cm.

"Sonderausgabe aus den Sitzungsberichten der preussischen Akademie der wissenschaften. Phil.-hist. klasse. 1930. XXIII."
Bibliographical footnotes.

NL 0353898   CtY-D

Lietzmann, Hans, 1875-1942, ed.
Zur Geschichte der orientalischen Taufe und Messe im II.und IV.Jahrhundert. 2.Aufl. Bonn, Marcus und Weber, 1909.

16 p. (Liturgische Texte, 1)
Kleine Texte für Vorlesungen und Übungen, 5.

NL 0353899   MH CtY

FX92 **Lietzmann, Hans,** 1875-1942.
L625z   **Zur Menschensohnfrage.** [Freiburg i.B., J.C.B. Mohr, 1899]
14 p. 24 cm.

Caption title.
"Theologische arbeiten aus dem Rheinischen wissenschaftlichen prediger-verein. Neue folge. Zweites heft. Separat-abdruck."
Bibliographical footnotes.

NL 0353900   CtY-D

Lietzmann, Heinrich, 1904-
Die strafrechtspflege im Saargebiet.
Inaug. diss. Marburg, 1928.
Bibl.

NL 0353901   DLC

Lietzmann, Heinz.
Die haftung der eisenbahn für verlust und beschädigung von frachtgut, nach dem Internationalen übereinkommen über den eisenbahnfrachtverkehr vom 23. oktober 1924 unter berücksichtigung des deutschen und französischen eisenbahnfrachtrechts ... von Heinz Lietzmann .. Magdeburg, Haenel [1931?]
xvii, 113 p. 21 cm.

Thesis, Würzburg.
Bibliography.

NL 0353902   NNC ICRL

Lietzmann, I   C   H
Die herstellung der leder in ihren chemischen und physikalischen vorgängen, wissenschaftlich begründet von I.C.H.Lietzmann...   Bonn, C.Georgi. 1870.
vi p.,1 1.,300 p.   illus.,fold.table.   22 1/2 cm.

1. Tanning. 2. Leather.

NL 0353903   DP DSI

Lietzmann, I   C   H
Die herstellung der leder in ihren chemischen und physikalischen vorgängen. Von I.C.H. Lietzmann...   Zweite umgearbeitete auflage...
Berlin, T.Grieben, 1875.
vi p.,1 1.,448 p.   illus.   19cm.

1. Tanning. 2. Leather.

NL 0353904   DP

Lietzmann,I   C   H.
Die herstellung der leder in ihren chemischen und physikalischen vorgängen. Von I.C.H.Lietzmann ... 3.aufl. Mit 13 mikroskopischen ansichten. Berlin, T.Grieben, 1880.
2 p.l.,448 p. illus.,tables. 19½cm.

1.Tanning.

NL 0353905   MiU

Lietzmann, Irmgard, 1906-
*Zwei Fälle von Akropachie ohne nachweisbares Grundleiden. 28p. 8.°
Berl. 1932.

NL 0353906   DNLM CtY

VOLUME 332

D
581
L53
1922

Lietzmann, Joachim, 1894–
     Auf verlbrenem Posten, unter der Flagge des Grafen Spee. München-Grünwald, Haus Lhotzky, 1922.
     195p. illus. 20cm.

     1. European War, 1914–1918 – Naval operations, German. 2. European War, 1914–1918 – Personal narratives, German. I. Title.

NL 0353907   MU NN

Lietzmann, Joachim, 1894–
     Auf verlorenem Posten, unter der Flagge des Grafen Spee. München-Grünwald, Haus Lhotzky [1935, ᶜ1930]
     191 p. illus., ports., fold. map. 21 cm.

     1. European War, 1914–1918—Naval operations, German. 2. European War, 1914–1918—Personal narratives, German. I. Title.

     D581.L53 1935   50–40008

NL 0353908   DLC CtY WaU

D581
.B86

Lietzmann, Joachim, 1894–

Busch, Fritz Otto, 1890–   *ed.*
     Unsere marine im weltkrieg; herausgegeben von korvettenkapitän a. d. Fritz Otto Busch, korvettenkapitän a. d. Georg Günther frh. v. Forstner, unter mitarbeit von kontreadmiral a. d. Hermann Lorey, korvettenkapitän Joachim Lietzmann. Mit 145 bildern, 46 gefechtsskizzen und wegekarten im text. 1.–10. tausend. Berlin, Brunnen-verlag, W. Bischoff [ᶜ1934]

Lietzmann, Johannes Carl Alexander
     see
Lietzmann, Hans, 1875– 1942.

4K
Ger
799

Lietzmann, Kurt, 1903–
     Das Verhältnis des Betruges zu den Aneigungsdelikten der §§ 242, 246. Borna, R. Noske, 1939.
     58 p.

NL 0353911   DLC-P4

Lietzmann, Walther, 1880–
     ... Altes und neues vom kreis, von dr. W. Lietzmann ... Mit 52 figuren und 41 aufgaben. Leipzig und Berlin, B. G. Teubner, 1935.
     iv, 47 p. illus., diagrs. 18½ᶜᵐ. (Mathematisch-physikalische bibliothek. Reihe I, hrsg. von W. Lietzmann und A. Witting. 87)
     "Zur literatur": p. 45–47.

     1. Circle.   I. Title.
                            35–14249
     Library of Congress   QA484.L5
                                     513.21

NL 0353912   DLC CU

QA 484
.L 719

LIETZMANN, WALTHER, 1880–
     Altes und neues vom Kreis. 2., durchgesehene Aufl. Leipzig, B. G. Teubner, 1951.
     54 p. illus. (Mathematisch-Physikalische Bibliothek. Reihe I)

     1. Circle. Math.cds. No sec.cds. in PC.

NL 0353913   InU OU NcD NBuU MiU

Lietzmann, Walther, 1880–
     Anschauliche Einführung in die mehrdimensionale Geometrie. München, R. Oldenburg, 1952.
     220 p. illus. 24 cm.

     1. Hyperspace.   I. Title.

     QA691.L56   513.8   53–20558 ‡

NL 0353914   DLC OrCS NBC ViU OU NN MB NcD NjP

Lietzmann, Walther, 1880–
     Anschauliche Topologie. München, Oldenbourg, 1955.
     171 p. illus. 24 cm.

     1. Topology.   A 55–5136
     Princeton Univ. Libr.
     for Library of Congress

NL   MoU CLU MeB CU NBC
0353915   NjP OU NN OrU OrCS MH CtY MiU ICU FMU

510.1
L62a

Lietzmann, Walther, 1880–
     ... Aufbau und grundlage der mathematik ... Berlin, 1927.
     89p. diagrs. (Lietzmann. Mathematisches unterrichtswerk, ergänzungsheft 3)

NL 0353916   IU CU

510.21
L62a4

Lietzmann, Walther, 1880–
     Aufgabensammlung und leitfaden für arithmetik, algebra und analysis. Ausgabe A: für gymnasien ... auf grund von E. Bardeys aufgabensammlung, bearb. von dr. W. Lietzmann. 4.aufl. Leipzig, 1925.
     2v. tables, diagrs. (Added t.-p.: Mathematisches unterrichtswerk für höhere knabenschulen)

     Vol.2, 2d ed., ed. by Dr. W. Lietzmann and Dr. P. Zuhlke.

NL 0353918   IU

510.21
L62ab4

Lietzmann, Walther, 1880–
     Aufgabensammlung und leitfaden für arithmetik, algebra und analysis. Ausgabe B. für realanstalten ... auf grund von E. Bardeys aufgabensammlung, bearb. von dr. W. Lietzmann. 4.verb. aufl. Leipzig, 1924.
     2v. tables, diagrs. (Added t.-p.: Mathematisches unterrichtswerk für höhere knabenschulen)

NL 0353919   IU

Lietzmann, Walther, 1880–

     Aufgabensammlung und Leitfaden für Arithmetik, Algebra und Analysis; Ausgabe B: für Anstalten realer Richtung, Oberstufe ... von W. Lietzmann und P. Zühlke. [2 parts in 1 vol] 8., durchgesehene Aufl. Leipzig und Berlin, B.G. Teubner, 1930.

     vi, 242, 111 p. diagrs. 23cm.
     At head of title: W. Lietzmann, Mathematisches Unterrichtswerk für höhere Knabenschulen.

NL 0353920   CaBVaU

510.92
L62a

Lietzmann, Walther, 1880–
     ... Aus der mathematik der alten, quellen zur arithmetik, planimetrie, stereometrie und zu ihren anwendungen ... Leipzig, 1928.
     65p. front., illus., plate, diagrs. (Lietzmann. Mathematisches unterrichtswerk, ergänzungsheft 4)

     Biographical notes: p.[63]–65.

NL 0353921   IU CU

510.97
L62a

Lietzmann, Walther, 1880–
     ... Aus der neueren mathematik, quellen zum zahlbegriff und zur gleichungslehre, zum funktionsbegriff und zur analysis. ... Leipzig, 1929.
     78p. plates, diagrs. (Lietzmann. Mathematisches unterrichtswerk, ergänzungsheft 5)

NL 0353922   IU

Lietzmann, Walther, 1880–
     ... Die ausbildung der mathematiklehrer an den höheren schulen Deutschlands ... Leipzig und Berlin, B. G. Teubner, 1915.
     cover-title, p. [311]–328. 25ᶜᵐ. (Berichte und mitteilungen, veranlasst durch die Internationale mathematische unterrichtskommission. 1. folge, XI)
     Contains bibliographies.

     1. Mathematics—[Study and] teaching—Germany. 2. Education, Secondary. [2. Mathematics—Teaching—Secondary schools]
                                    E 16–126
     Library, U. S. Bur. of   Education   QA11.L6

NL 0353923   DHEW

Lietzmann, Walther, 1880–

Deutscher ausschuss für den mathematischen und naturwissenschaftlichen unterricht.
     ... Bericht über die tätigkeit des Deutschen ausschusses für den mathematischen und naturwissenschaftlichen unterricht im jahre 1911, erstattet von dem geschäftsführenden sekretär, dr. W. Lietzmann ... Leipzig und Berlin, B. G. Teubner, 1912.

Lietzmann, Walther, 1880–
     Berichte und Mitteilungen
        see under   International Commission on the Teaching of Mathematics.

QA491
.L47

Lietzmann, Walther, 1880–
     Elementare Kugelgeometrie mit numerischen und konstruktiven Methoden; mit 157 Figuren. Göttingen, Vandenhoeck & Ruprecht, 1949.
     viii, 292 p. illus., diagrs. 24 cm. (Studia mathematica; mathematische Lehrbücher, Bd. 3)
     Bibliography: p. 290. Bibliographical footnotes.

     1. Sphere. 2. Geometry, Differential.   (Series)
                                     A 60–2458
     Columbia Univ.   Libraries
     for Library of Congress   [1]

NL   NcRS WU
0353926   NNC DLC NcU NIC MiU CSt NBC NBuU NcD OU

VOLUME 332

QA43
.B3

Lietzmann, Walther, 1880–
Ergebnisse zu Barday-Lietzmann: Aufgaben-sammlung für Arthmetik... B.G. Teubner, 1915.
v, 63, [1] p. 22 cm.

NL 0353927 DLC

510.7
L62e

Lietzmann, Walther, 1880–
Erkenntnislehre im mathematischen unterricht der oberklassen. Charlottenburg, 1921.
·67p.

NL 0353928 IU

Lietzmann, Walther, 1880–
Frühgeschichte der Geometrie auf germanischem Boden. Breslau, F. Hirt, 1940.
96 p. illus. 22 cm.

1. Geometry—Hist.   I. Title.

QA447.L5   50–52086

NL 0353929 DLC OkU NjP NcD ICU NNC RPB ICRL DSI

Lietzmann, Walther, 1880–
... Funktion und graphische darstellung; mit 99 figuren im text. Breslau, F. Hirt, 1925.
190 p. illus., diagrs. 21½ᶜᵐ.

1. Functions. 2. Graphic methods.
Library of Congress   QA331.L5   25–7647

NL 0353930 DLC NjP

510
L72m3ga

Lietzmann, Walter, 1880–
Geometrische aufgabensammlung. Ausgabe A: für gymnasien... von Dr. W. Lietzmann... Leipzig [etc.] B.G. Teubner, 1916-18.
2 v. illus. incl. diagrs. 23 cm.
(Mathematisches unterrichts-werk für höhere knabenschulen)

NL 0353931 MiU

510
L72m3gb

Lietzmann, Walter, 1880–
Geometrische aufgabensammlung. Ausgabe B: für realanstalten... von Dr. W. Lietzmann... Leipzig [etc.] B.G. Teubner, 1916-20.
2 v. illus. incl. diagrs. 23 cm.
(Mathematisches unterrichts-werk für höhere knabenschulen)

NL 0353932 MiU

Lietzmann, Walther, 1880–

Weinreich, Hermann, 1884–
... H. Weinreich: Die fortschritte der mathematischen unterrichtsreform in Deutschland seit 1910. W. Lietzmann: Der Pariser kongress der Internationalen mathematischen unterrichtskommission vom 1. bis 4. april 1914. Leipzig und Berlin, B. G. Teubner, 1915.

Lietzmann, Walther, 1880–
... Kegelschnittlehre, von dr. W. Lietzmann ... Mit 36 figuren im text. Leipzig und Berlin, B. G. Teubner, 1933.
iv, 46 p. diagrs. 18½ᶜᵐ. (Mathematisch-physikalische bibliothek, reihe I ... 79)

1. Conic sections.   I. Title.

Library of Congress   QA485.L75   33–25025
                                                513.22

NL 0353934 DLC

Lietzmann, Walther, 1880–
... W. Lietzmann, Der kongress in Mailand vom 18. bis 20. september 1911. R. Schimmack, Über die verschmelzung verschiedener zweige des mathematischen unterrichts ... Leipzig und Berlin, B. G. Teubner, 1912.
cover-title, [89]–127, [1] p. 25ᶜᵐ. (Berichte und mitteilungen, veranlasst durch die Internationale mathematische unterrichtskommission. VII)

1. International congress on the teaching of mathematics. 1st, Milan, 1911. 2. Mathematics—Teaching. I. Schimmack, Rud.
                                                E 12–770
Library, U. S. Bur. of   Education QA1.I 66L6

NL 0353935 DHEW

Lietzmann, Walther, 1880–
Lebendige Mathematik. 2. Aufl. Würzburg, Physica-Verlag, 1955.
435 p. illus. 22 cm.

1. Mathematics—Addresses, essays, lectures. I. Title.

QA7.L7   1955   58–20068 ‡

NL 0353936 DLC CSt NIC MiU

Lietzmann, Walther, 1880–
... Lustiges und merkwürdiges von zahlen und formen; beispiele aus der unterhaltungsmathematik, mit 102 figuren im text und 3 tafeln auf kunstdruckpapier. Breslau, F. Hirt, 1922.
187, [1] p. front., illus., plates. 21½ᶜᵐ.
Bibliography: p. 8–11.

1. Mathematical recreations.   I. Title.
Library of Congress   QA95.L67   23–560

NL 0353937 DLC CU OO MiU NIC

Lietzmann, Walther, 1880–
... Lustiges und merkwürdiges von zahlen und formen; beispiele aus der unterhaltungsmathematik, mit 107 figuren im text und 3 tafeln auf kunstdruckpapier. 2., durchgesehene und erweiterte aufl. Breslau, F. Hirt, 1923.
195, [1] p. front., illus., plates. 21½ᶜᵐ.
Bibliography: p. 9–10.

1. Mathematical recreations.   I. Title.
Library of Congress   QA95.L67 1923   24–20392

NL 0353938 DLC MiU

Lietzmann, Walther.
... Lustiges und merkwürdiges von zahlen und formen ... mit 203 figuren im text und 20 tafeln. 3. durchgesehene und erweiterte aufl. Breslau, F. Hirt, 1928.
vi, 307, [1] p. illus., xx pl. (incl. front.) diagrs. 21½ᶜᵐ.
Bibliography: p. 4–5.
CONTENTS.—I. hft. Allerlei unterhaltungsmathematik.—II. hft. Von den zahlen.—III. hft. Von den geometrischen formen.

1. Mathematical recreations.   I. Title.
Library of Congress   QA95.L67 1928   29–6717

NL 0353939 DLC NcD CU PSC NN WaU

Lietzmann, Walther, 1880–
... Lustiges und merkwürdiges von zahlen und formen; allerlei unterhaltungsmathematik, von den zahlen, von den geometrischen formen; mit 203 figuren im text und 20 tafeln. 4., durchgesehene und ergänzte aufl. Breslau, F. Hirt, 1930.
vi, 307 p. illus., xx pl. (incl. front.) diagrs. 21½ᶜᵐ.

1. Mathematical recreations.   I. Title.
Library of Congress   QA95.L67 1930   31–559
Copyright A—Foreign   9210
                                                793.74

NL 0353940 DLC MoU NcD CtY

Lietzmann, Walther, 1880–
... Lustiges und merkwürdiges von zahlen und formen; allerlei unterhaltungsmathematik, von den zahlen, von den geometrischen formen. 6. aufl. Breslau, F. Hirt, 1943.
vi, 296 p. illus. (incl. diagrs.) xvi pl. (incl. front., port.) 21½ᶜᵐ.
"Schriften": p. 4–5. Bibliographical foot-notes.

1. Mathematical recreations.   I. Title.   A 46–4980
Yale univ. Library
for Library of Congress   QA95.L67 1943
                           [2]†   793.74

NL 0353941 CtY IU DLC

510.87
L62l
1950

Lietzmann, Walter, 1880–
Lustiges und Merkwürdiges von Zahlen und Formen. 7. neubearb. Aufl. Göttingen, Vandenhoeck & Ruprecht [1950]
276p. illus., diagrs. 22cm.

Includes bibliographies.

1. Mathematical recreations. I. Title.

NL 0353942 IU PU-Math NBuU

Lietzmann, Walther, 1880–
Lustiges und Merkwürdiges von Zahlen und Formen. 8., durchgesehene Aufl. Göttingen, Vandenhoeck & Ruprecht [1955]
276 p. illus.

NL 0353943 MH

Lietzmann, Walther, 1880–
Mathematik in erziehung und unterricht, von dr. W. Lietzmann ... unter mitarbeit von dr.-ing. U. Graf ... Leipzig, Quelle & Meyer, 1941–
v. diagrs. 23½ᶜᵐ.
CONTENTS.—1. bd. Ziel und weg.

1. Mathematics—Study and teaching. I. Graf, Ulrich, 1908– joint author. II. Title.
                                                45–29046
Library of Congress   QA11.L48
                                                510.7

NL 0353944 DLC

Lietzmann, Walther, 1880–
... Mathematik und bildende kunst. Breslau, F. Hirt, 1931.
149, [1] p. illus., diagrs. 21½ᶜᵐ.

1. Composition (Art) 2. Architecture. 3. Sculpture. 4. Painting. I. Title.
Library of Congress   N7430.L5   31–2587
Copyright A—Foreign   9367
                           [2]   701

NL 0353945 DLC NN NNC PSC

VOLUME 332

Lietzmann, Walther, 1880–   joint author.

QA39
.H46
    Heye, Karl.
     ... Mathematisches unterrichtswerk für höhere schulen ...
2. aufl. ... Leipzig und Berlin, B. G. Teubner, 1940–

NL 0353947   IU NjP

510.7   Lietzmann, Walther, 1880–
L62m   Methodik des mathmatischen unter-
     richts.   Leipzig, 1919.
      2v. illus., diagrs.   (Handbuch des
     naturwissenschaftlichen und mathema-
     tischen unterrichts hrsg. von ... dr.
     J. Norrenberg. 7.bd., 1.teil.)

NL 0353948   IU NjP

Lietzmann, Walther, 1880–
   ... Methodik des mathematischen Unterrichts, von Dr. W.
Lietzmann ... 1.–[3.] Teil. ... Leipzig, Quelle & Meyer, 1923–
1926.
   3 vol. illus., plates, diagrs. 24½cm. (*In* Handbuch des naturwissenschaftlichen und mathematischen Unterrichts. VII. Band, 1.–3. Teil.)
    Pt. 1, 2, second edition.
    "Kurze biographische Angaben über einige ... Mathematiker und Schul-
männer," pt. 3, p. [218]–227.
    Includes bibliographies.
    Contents.—1. Tl. Organisation, allgemeine Methode und Technik des Unter-
richts. 1926. x, [2], 360 p.—2. Tl. Didaktik der einzelnen Gebiete des mathematischen Unterrichts. 1923. xii, 367 p.—3. Tl. Didaktik der angewandten
Mathematik. 1924. xi, 234 p.

NL 0353948   ICJ MH

Lietzmann, Walter, 1880–
   ... Methodik des mathematischen unterrichts,
von dr. W. Lietzmann ... Leipzig, Quelle,
1926–
    v. illus.,plates,diagrs. 25cm. (Handbuch
des naturwissenschaftlichen und mathematischen
unterrichts. bd.7)

     Contents.–v.1: Organisation, allgemeine methode
und technik des unterrichts. 2.,umgearb. und verm.
aufl.–v.2: Didaktik des rechnens, der arithmetik,
algebra und analysis. 3., neubearb. aufl.–

NL 0353949   NBC

QA11
.L5
    Lietzmann, Walther, 1880–
     Methodik des mathematischen Unter-
     richts.   Leipzig, Quelle & Meyer,
     1926-1933.
      2v. diagrs. 25cm. (Handbuch des
     naturwissenschaftlichen und mathema-
     tischen Unterrichts, Bd. VII,T.1-2)
     1.T., 2. umgearb. und verm. Aufl.
     1926; 2.T., 3. neubearb. Aufl. 1933.
     Contents.–I.Organisation, allge-
     meine Methode und Technik des Unter-
     richts.–II.Didaktik des Rechnens, der
     Arithmetik,   Algebra und Analy-
     sis.

NL 0353950   NNU-W

Lietzmann, Walther, 1880–
    Methodik des mathematischen Unterrichts. Heidelberg,
Quelle & Meyer, 1953.
    2 v. 25 cm.
    Vol. 2 published separately in 1951.
    CONTENTS.—Bd. 1. Der Unterricht.—Bd. 2. Der Lehrstoff.

    1. Mathematics—Study and teaching.   I. Title.

    QA11.L482   54–20365 ‡

NL 0353951   DLC

Lietzmann, Walther, 1880–
    Methodik des mathematischen Unterrichts, der Lehrstoff.
Heidelberg, Quelle & Meyer, 1951.
    208 p. 25 cm.

    1. Mathematics—Study and teaching.   I. Title.

    QA11.L484   51–33507

NL 0353952   DLC

Lietzmann, Walther, 1880–
    ... Neue erlasse in Bayern, Württemberg und Baden, von W.
Lietzmann ... E. Geck ... H. Cramer ... Mit einem schlusswort
zu bd. II, von A. Thaer. Leipzig und Berlin, B. G. Teubner,
1913.
    v. [4], 49 p. 26ᶜᵐ. (Abhandlungen über den mathematischen unter-
richt in Deutschland, veranlasst durch die Internationale mathematische
unterrichtskommission, hrsg. von F. Klein. bd. II. [Die höheren schulen
in Süd- und Mitteldeutschland] hft. 8)
    Contents and t.-p. of bd. II inserted after p. v.

    1. Mathematics—Teaching—Germany.   I. Geck, Erwin, joint author.
II. Cramer, Hans, joint author.

                            E 13—1057

   U. S. Off. of educ.   Library   QA11.I 6G3
     for Library of Congress   [a41b1]

NL 0353953   DHEW

Lietzmann, Walther, 1880–
    ... Die organisation des mathematischen unterrichts
an den höheren knabenschulen in Preussen, von dr. Walther Lietzmann ... Mit 18 figuren im text. Leipzig und
Berlin, B. G. Teubner, 1910.
    vi p., 1 L, 204 p. diagrs. 26ᶜᵐ. (Abhandlungen über den mathemat-
ischen unterricht in Deutschland veranlasst durch die Internationale
mathematische unterrichtskommission hrsg. von F. Klein. bd. I. [Die höheren
schulen in Norddeutschland] hft. 2)

    1. Mathematics — Teaching — Prussia.   2. Mathematics — Teaching —
Secondary schools.

                            E 11–910

   Library, U. S. Bur. of   Education QA11.I5

NL 0353954   DHEW NN

Lietzmann, Walther, 1880–
    ... Die organisation des mathematischen unterrichtes
in den preussischen volks- und mittelschulen, von dr. W.
Lietzmann ... Leipzig und Berlin, B. G. Teubner, 1914.
    iv p., 1 L, 106 p. 25ᶜᵐ. (Abhandlungen über den mathematischen un-
terricht in Deutschland veranlasst durch die Internationale mathematische
unterrichtskommission, hrsg. von F. Klein. bd. v [Der mathematische elementarunterricht und die mathematik an den lehrerbildungsanstalten]
hft. 6)

    1. Mathematics—[Study and] teaching—[Prussia]

                            E 14–450

   Library, U. S. Bur. of   Education QA11.I 6G3

NL 0353955   DHEW MiU OCU OU

Lietzmann, Walther, 1880–
    ... Der Pythagoreische lehrsatz; geometrische und arithme-
tische beweise, von dr. W. Lietzmann ... 5. umgearb. aufl.
Mit 39 figuren im text und auf 2 tafeln, sowie einer titeltafel.
Leipzig und Berlin, B. G. Teubner, 1937.
    iv, 43 p. front., diagrs. 18ᶜᵐ. (Mathematisch-physikalische biblio-
thek, reihe I, hrsg. von W. Lietzmann und A. Witting. 3)
    "Einiges über die literatur zum Pythagoreischen lehrsatz": p. 41–43.

    1. Pythagorean proposition.   38–15388

   Library of Congress   QA460.P8L52   t. 1   1937

NL 0353956   DLC

Lietzmann, Walther, 1880–
    ... Der pythagoreische lehrsatz, mit einem ausblick auf
das Fermatsche problem, von dr. W. Lietzmann ... mit 4[?]
figuren im text. Leipzig und Berlin, B. G. Teubner, 1912.
    2 p. l., 72 p. diagrs. 18½ᶜᵐ. (Mathematische bibliothek, hrsg. von W.
Lietzmann und A. Witting. 3)   M. 0.80
    "Einiges über die literatur zum pythagorischen lehrsatz": p. 70–72.

    1. Pythagorean proposition.   2. Fermat's theorem.   I. Title.

                            12–5500

   Library of Congress   QA459.L6

NL 0353957   DLC NN PU-Math

Lietzmann, Walther, 1880–
    ... Der pythagoreische lehrsatz, mit einem
ausblick auf das Fermatsche problem, von dr.
W. Lietzmann ... mit 55 figuren im text.
Leipzig und Berlin, B.G. Teubner, 1917.
    iv, 69, [1] p. diagrs. 18.5 cm.
    (Mathematische bibliothek, hrsg. von W.
    Lietzmann und A. Witting. 3)   M. 0.80
     2., durchgesehende und verm. aufl.

NL 0353958   CU

QA3
.M3
v.3
1930
    Lietzmann, Walther, 1880–
     ... Der pythagoreische lehrsatz, mit einem ausb-
     lick auf das Fermatsche problem, von dr. W. Lietz-
     mann ... 4. durchgesehan aufl ... Leipzig und Ber-
     lin, B. G. Teubner, 1930.
      iv, 72 [3] p. diagrs. 18½ᶜᵐ. (Mathematische-
     physikalische bibliothek, hrsg, von W. Leitzmann un
     A. Witting, 3)
     "Einiges über die literatur zum pythagorischen
     lehrsatz": p. 70–72.
     1. Pythagorean pro   position. 2. Fermat's
     theorem. I. Title   II. Ser.

NL 0353959   ViU CU

QA459
P8
L6
1951
    Lietzmann, Walther, 1880–
     Der Pythagoreische Lehrsatz mit einem
     Ausblick auf das Fermatsche Problem. 6.,
     überarbeit. Aufl.   Leipzig, B.G. Teubner,
     1951.
      95p. diagrs. 20 cm. (Mathematisch-
     physikalische Bibliothek. Reihe I. 2/3)

     Bibliography: p.92-95.

NL 0353960   RPB MiU

Lietzmann, Walther, 1880–
    Der Pythagoreische Lehrsatz, mit einem Ausblick auf das
Fermatsche Problem. 7. Aufl. Stuttgart, B. G. Teubner,
1953.
    95 p. illus. 20 cm. (Mathematisch-physikalische Bibliothek,
Reihe I, 2/3)

    1. Pythagorean proposition. 2. Fermat's theorem.   I. Title.

    QA460.P8L5 1953   55–25925 ‡

       PU OrCS
NL 0353961   DLC TU NN OU NcD PBL CLSU NBuU CLU ScU

Lietzmann, Walther, 1880–
    ... Riesen und zwerge im zahlenreich; plaudereien für
kleine und grosse freunde der rechenkunst, von dr. W.
Lietzmann ... mit 18 figuren im text. Leipzig und Berlin,
B. G. Teubner, 1916.
    2 p. l., 56 p. illus. 18½ᶜᵐ. (Mathematische bibliothek hrsg. von W.
Lietzmann und A. Witting. 25)   mk. 0.80

    1. Mathematical recreations.   I. Title.

    Library of Congress   QA95.L68   22–17464

NL 0353962   DLC GAT OrU

VOLUME 332

Lietzmann, Walther, 1880-
...Riesen und zwerge im zahlenreich; plandereien fuer kleine und grosse freunde der rechenkunst... mit 18 figuren im text. Leipzig und Berlin, Teubner, 1918.
56 p. (Mathematishce bibliothek ..Lietzmann & Witting. 25)

NL 0353963 MiU CU

Lietzmann, Walther, 1880-
... Riesen und zwerge im zahlenreich, von dr. W. Lietzmann ... Dritte durchgesehene und vermehrte auflage, mit 17 figuren im text. Leipzig und Berlin, B. G. Teubner, 1932.
2 p. l., 60 p. incl. illus., tables. 18½ᶜᵐ. (Mathematisch-physikalische bibliothek, hrsg. von W. Lietzmann und A. Witting. 25)

1. Mathematical recreations.   I. Title.

Title from N. Y. Pub.   Libr.   A 34-37
Library of Congress   [QA95.L   ]

NL 0353964 NN

QA95
L52
1951
pam
Lietzmann, Walther, 1880-
Riesen und Zerge im Zahlenreich. 4., neu bearb. Aufl. Leipzig, B. G. Teubner, 1951.
57 [1] p. illus. 20cm. (Mathematisch-Physikalische Bibliothek. Reihe I, [Heft] 25)

1. Mathematical recreations.   I. Title.

NL 0353965 OrCS

Lietzmann, Walther, 1880-
... Riesen und zwerge im zahlenreich, von dr. W. Lietzmann ... Fünfte auflage, mit 9 abbildungen. Stuttgart, B.G. Teubner, 1953.
59, [1] p. incl. illus., tables. 19½cm. (Mathematisch-physikalische bibliothek. Reihe I, hrsg. von W. Lietzmann. 25)

1. Mathematical recreations.   I. Title.

CLSU NcD
NL 0353966   TxU CLU CSt PU RPB WU CtY NBuU MWelC OU

Lietzmann, Walther, 1880-   tr.

International commission on the teaching of mathematics.
... Rundschreiben des Hauptausschusses [Leipzig und Berlin, B. G. Teubner, 1909-

Lietzmann, Walther, 1880-
Schulreform und mathematischer Unterricht. Heidelberg, Quelle & Meyer, 1949.
127 p. 28 cm.

1. Mathematics—Study and teaching.   I. Title.

QA11.L49   50-55371

NL 0353968 DLC NBC

512.81
L62s
Lietzmann, Walther, 1880-
Sonderlinge im Reich der Zahlen.   Bonn, F. Dümmler, 1948.
175p.   19cm.

1. Numbers, Theory of.

NL 0353969 IU

Lietzmann, Walther, 1880-
Sonderlinge im Reich der Zahlen. 2. durchgesehene und verm. Aufl. Bonn, F. Dümmler [1954]
214 p. 20 cm.

1. Mathematical recreations. 2. Mathematics—Problems, exercises, etc. I. Title.

QA95.L685 1954   56-28752 ‡

NL 0353970 DLC NN

Lietzmann, Walther, 1880-
... Stoff und methode des raumlehreunterrichts in Deutschland; ein literaturbericht, von dr. Walther Lietzmann ... Mit 38 figuren im text. Leipzig und Berlin, B. G. Teubner, 1912.
viii, 88 p. illus., diagrs. 25½ᶜᵐ. (Abhandlungen über den mathematischen unterricht in Deutschland, veranlasst durch die Internationale mathematische unterrichtskommission, hrsg. von F. Klein, bd. v [Der mathematische elementarunterricht und die mathematik an den lehrerbildungsanstalten] hft. 2)
"Literaturverzeichnis": p. 80-86.
1. Geometry—Teaching—Germany.

                                  E 12-1371
Library, U. S. Bur. of   Education QA11.I 6G3

NL 0353971 DHEW OU MiU OCU

Lietzmann, Walther, 1880-
... Stoff und methode des rechenunterrichts in Deutschland, ein literaturbericht, von dr. Walther Lietzmann ... Mit 20 figuren im text. Leipzig und Berlin, B. G. Teubner, 1912.
iv, vii, 125, [1] p. illus., diagrs. 25½ᶜᵐ. (Added t-p.: Abhandlungen über den mathematischen unterricht in Deutschland, veranlasst durch die Internationale mathematische unterrichtskommission, hrsg. von F. Klein. 5. bd. Der mathematische elementarunterricht und die mathematik an den lehrerbildungsanstalten, hft. 1)
Series title also at head of t-p.
Pages i-iv contain an introduction to bd. 5 of this series by F. Klein.
"Literaturverzeichnis": p. [108]-122.
1. Arithmetic—Teaching—Germany.

                                  E 12-92
Library, U. S. Bur. of   Education QA11.I 6G3

NL 0353972 DHEW

Lietzmann, Walther, 1880-
... Stoff und methode im mathematischen unterricht der norddeutschen höheren schulen auf grund der vorhandenen lehrbücher, von dr. Walther Lietzmann ... Mit einem einführungswort von F. Klein. Leipzig und Berlin, B. G. Teubner, 1909.
xii, 102 p. diagrs. 26ᶜᵐ. (Abhandlungen über den mathematischen unterricht in Deutschland veranlasst durch die Internationale mathematische unterrichtskommission hrsg. von F. Klein. bd. i, hft. 1)
"Literaturverzeichnis": p. [92]-102.
1. Mathematics—Study and teaching.

Library of Congress   QA11.L5   9-29479

NL 0353973 DHEW DLC NN

Lietzmann, Walter, 1880-
International commission on the teaching of mathematics.
...Titel und inhaltsübersicht zur ersten und zweiten folge der Berichte und mitteilungen. E. und K. Körner: Gesamtregister der schriften des deutschen unterausschusses der Internationalen mathematischen unterrichtskommission ... W. Lietzmann: Zusammenstellung der bis ostern 1917 auf veranlassung der IMUK im auslande veröffentlichten arbeiten. F. Klein und W. Lietzmann: Zum abschluss der Berichte und mitteilungen. Leipzig und Berlin, B. G. Teubner, 1917.

514
L62t
Lietzmann, Walther, 1880-
Trigonometrie und analytische geometrie der ebene für die VI.-VIII. klasse der gymnasien und die VI.-VII. klasse der realschulen, bearb. von dr. W. Lietzmann ... und dr. J. Jarosch ...   Wien, F. Deuticke, 1927.
184p. illus., diagrs.   [Their Mathematisches unterrichtswerk für mittelschulen]

1. Trigonometry. 2. Geometry, Analytic. I. Jarosch, Julius, joint author.

NL 0353975 IU

Lietzmann, Walther, 1880-
... Trugschlüsse, gesammelt von dr. W. Lietzmann ... 3. stark verm. aufl. des ersten teiles von "Wo steckt der fehler?" Mit 27 figuren im text. Leipzig und Berlin, B. G. Teubner, 1923.
2 p. l., 54 p. diagrs. 18½ᶜᵐ. (Mathematisch-physikalische bibliothek, hrsg. von W. Lietzmann und A. Witting. 53)

1. Mathematical recreations.   I. Title.

Library of Congress   QA95.L72   24-31256

NL 0353976 DLC

512.81
L719u
Lietzmann, Walter, 1880-
Ueber das biquadratische reciprocitätsgesetz in algebraischen Zahlkörpern. Göttingen, Druck der Dieterich'schen Universitäts-Buchdruckeri, 1904.
93 p.

Inag.-Diss. - Göttingen, 1903.
Lebenslauf.

1. Numbers, Theory of. I. Title.

NL 0353977 NcU NjP ICJ MB NN NNU CtY

510.7
L62w
Lietzmann, Walther, 1880-
Über die beurteilung der leistungen in der schule; Mathematisches, psychologisches, pädagogisches.   Leipzig, 1927.
116p. illus., diagrs.

NL 0353978 IU

510.9
L62z
Lietzmann, Walther, 1880-
... Überblick über die geschichte der elementarmathematik ...   Leipzig, Teubner, 1926.
68p. illus. (incl. ports.) (Lietzmann, Mathematisches unterrichtswerk, ergänzungsheft 1)

NL 0353979 IU NjP RPB CLU

Lietzmann, Walther, 1880-
Überblick über die Geschichte der Elementarmathematik. 2. durchgesehene und verm. Aufl. Leipzig, Teubner, 1928
80 p. illus. (Lietzmann/Mathematisches Unterrichtswerk. Ergänzungsheft 1)

NL 0353980 MH CU

Lietzmann, Walther, 1880-
Die Versammlung in Brüssel
see under   International Commission on the Teaching of Mathematics.

VOLUME 332

Lietzmann, Walther, 1880-　　ed.
Zeitschrift für mathematischen und naturwissenschaftlichen
unterricht. (*Indexes*)
... Verzeichnis des gesamtinhalts von band 33 bis 60 ...
herausgegeben von dr. W. Lietzmann ... Leipzig und Berlin,
B. G. Teubner, 1930.

NL　0353983　DLC

Lietzmann, Walther, 1880-
... Von der Pythagoreischen gleichung zum Fermatschen
problem, von dr. W. Lietzmann ... 5. umgearb. aufl. des
zweiten teiles von "Der Pythagoreische lehrsatz". Mit 17
figuren und 38 aufgaben. Leipzig und Berlin, B. G. Teubner,
1937.
48 p. diagrs. 18½ᶜᵐ. (Mathematisch-physikalische bibliothek, reihe
I, hrsg. von W. Lietzmann und A. Witting. 91)

1. Pythagorean proposition. 2. Fermat's theorem.
38-15515
Library of Congress　　QA460.P8L52　t. 2　1937
513.14

NL　0353983　DLC

Lietzmann, Walther, 1880-　　tr.
International commission on the teaching of mathematics.
... Vorbericht über organisation und arbeitsplan der
Kommission. Ausgearb. von H. Fehr ... [Leipzig, B. G.
Teubner, 1909?]

HG995　**Lietzmann, Walther,** 1880-
L62　　**Was ist Geld?** Leipzig, B.G. Teubner, 1918.
55 p. illus. 19ᶜᵐ. (Mathematisch-physikalische Bibliothek, 30)

Bibliography: p.55.

1.Money. 2.Money - Germany. I.Title.

NL　0353985　NjP

QA9
.L52　**Lietzmann, Walther,** 1880-
Das Wesen der Mathematik. Braunschweig, F. Vieweg,
1949.
vii, 168 p. diagrs. 22 cm. (Die Wissenschaft; Einzeldarstellungen aus der Naturwissenschaft und der Technik, Bd. 102)
Bibliographical footnotes.

1. Mathematics—Philosophy. 2. Logic, Symbolic and mathematical. I. Title. (Series)
A 50-3916
Rochester. Univ. Libr.　QA9.L52
for Library of Congress　　[1]

NL　0353986　NRU DLC OU RPB NjP ICJ NIC

Lietzmann, Walther, 1880-
... Wo steckt der fehler? Mathematische täuschun-
gen und fehler, gesammelt von dr. W. Lietzmann ... und
Viggo Trier ... 3. stark verm. aufl., mit 35 figuren im
text. Leipzig und Berlin, B. G. Teubner, 1923.
iv, 48 p. diagrs. 18½ᶜᵐ. (Mathematisch-physikalische bibliothek, hrsg.
von W. Lietzmann und A. Witting. 52)
An enlarged edition of the second part of Wo steckt der fehler? 1913.
The 3d edition (1923) of the first part has title: Trugschlüsse, gesammelt
von dr. W. Lietzmann.
1. Mathematical recreations. I. Trier, Viggo Peter, 1862-1916, joint
author. II. Title.
Library of Congress　　QA95.L7　1923
24-31261

NL　0353987　DLC NcD

Lietzmann, Walther, 1880-
Wo steckt der Fehler? Mathematische Trugschlüsse und
Warnzeichen. Leipzig, B. G. Teubner, 1950.
182 p. diagrs. 20 cm.
First ed. (1913) by W. Lietzmann and V. Trier. Pt. 1, by W.
Lietzmann, also published separately in 1923 under title: Trug-
schlüsse.

1. Mathematical recreations. I. Title.

QA95.L7　1950
51-20461

NL　0353988　DLC NcD NjP NN ICU OU OO NBC

Lietzmann, Walther, 1880-
Wo steckt der Fehler? Mathematische Trugschlüsse und
Warnzeichen. 3., durchgesehene und erweiterte Aufl. Stuttgart, B. G. Teubner, 1953.
184 p. illus. 20 cm.

1. Mathematical recreations. I. Title.

QA95.L7　1953　　510.76　54-17970 ‡

OrCS
NL　0353989　DLC MiU OU NcRS MB MH ScU NBuU PU CLU

Lietzmann, Walther, 1880-
... Wo steckt der fehler? Trugschlüsse und schüler-
fehler, gesammelt von dr. W. Lietzmann ... und V. Trier
... Mit 24 figuren im text. Leipzig und Berlin, B. G.
Teubner, 1913.
2 p. l., 57, [1] p. diagrs. 18½ᶜᵐ. (Mathematische bibliothek, hrsg.
von W. Lietzmann und A. Witting. 10)　M.0.80

1. Mathematical recreations. I. Trier, Viggo Peter, 1862-　joint
author. II. Title.
Library of Congress　　QA95.L7
13-23450

NL　0353990　DLC GU NjP

Lietzmann, Walther, 1880-1959.
... Wo steckt der fehler? Trugschlüsse und schüler-
fehler, gesammelt von dr. W. Lietzmann ... und V. Trier
... Mit 29 figuren im text. Leipzig und Berlin, B. G.
Teubner, 1917.
iv, 53 [1] p. diagrs. 18½ᶜᵐ. (Mathematische bibliothek, hrsg.
von W. Lietzmann und A. Witting. 10)　M.0.80
"2., verm. und verb. aufl."

NL　0353991　NIC CU

Lietzow, F. W., comp.
Armour grain company, Chicago.
... Private code ... comp. by F. W. Lietzow ... [Chi-
cago?] ᶜ1909.

Lietzow, Paul, 1842-1905.
Nord- und südgermanen. Leben und lieben in
Dänemark. Von Paul Lietzow, Berlin, B.
Behr's buchhandlung (E. Bock) 1871.
iv, 226 p. 21 cm.
Title vignette (printer's mark)

NL　0353993　CU

Lieu, Dakuin Keetau
see
Liu, Ta-chün, 1890-1962.

Lieu, Tran-van-
see
Tran-van-Lieu.

Le lieu-de-santé de Rouen, réimprimé avec une introduction par le Dᵣ G. Panel. Rouen, Imprimerie L. Gy, 1905.
lxxv, 28 p. fold. pl., 4 plans (3 fold.) 22½ᶜᵐ. (*Half-title:* Société
rouennaise de bibliophiles. [Publications. 58])
With reproduction of original t.-p.: Recit de ce qvi s'est passé en
l'Establissement des Hospitaux de saint Louis & de S. Roch de la ville
de Rollen; Pour les malades & convalescents de la peste. Avec la Description particuliere, & la figure de de [!] tous les bastimens commencés
en l'année 1654. Paris, Chez C. Savrevx, 1654.
"N° 25. M. Bouis."

1. Rouen—Hospitals. 2. Plague—Rouen. 3. Contagion and conta-
gious diseases—Hospitals. I. Panel, Gustave, 1862-　ed.
28-497
Library of Congress　　AC20.87　vol. 58　Provisional

NL　0353996　DLC MH OU MiU

Lieu Notre Dame lès Romorantin (*Cistercian abbey*)
see
Romorantin, France. Lieu Notre Dame lès Romorantin
(*Cistercian abbey*)

Film
1239　**Lieuallen, R　　E**
The Jeffersonian and Jacksonian conceptions in
higher education. [Stanford, Calif.] 1954.
iv, 171ℓ.

Thesis (Ed.D.) - Stanford University.
Bibliography: leaves 160-171.
Microfilm. Ann Arbor, Mich., University Micro-
films, 1955. 1 reel. 35mm.

1. Education, Higher. 2. Jefferson, Thomas,
Pres. U.S., 1743-1826. 3. Jackson, Andrew, Pres.
U.S., 1767-1845.

NL　0353998　TxU

Lieuallen, R　　E
A manual for school building construction, prepared by R. E.
Lieuallen ... Salem, Or., Rex Putnam, superintendent of public instruction, 1947.
1 p. l., iv, 90 p. incl. tab., diagr. 23ᶜᵐ.

1. School-houses—Oregon. I. Oregon. Office of superintendent of
public instruction.
LB3218.O7L5　　371.6　47-32101

NL　0353999　DLC ICJ TxU OrPS OrU OrCS MtU

843L625
OE　[**Lieudé de Sepmanville, Cyprien Antoine,**
de]
Épitre au roy, par le premier marguiller
de la paroisse de Fontenoy. Fontenoy,
1745.

16 p. 21cm.

In verse.
"Tous les écrits qui pararent à cette
époque, à l'occasion de la bataille de
Fontenoy, n'ont point tous le poème
de Voltaire pour objet ... néanmoins

dans presque tous ces derniers il est ou
question de Voltaire, ou il est fait
allusion à son poème." -Querard. Les
supercheries littéraires devoilées.
2. ed. v.1, col. 501.
1.Fontenoy, Battle of, 1745. Poetry. 2.
Voltaire, François Marie Arouet de, 1694-
1778. Poème de Fontenoy. Parodies.
etc. I. Title.

NL　0354002　MnU ICN

VOLUME 332

[Lieudé de Sepmanville, Cyprien Antoine de]
Lettre a madame la marquise de *** sur la
tragedie de Mérope, de m. de Voltaire. Sur la
comedie nouvelle de l'Ecole des meres. Et sur
les francs-maçons.
A Bruxelles,M.DCC.XLIV.

14p. 19.5cm.
Signed at end: L******
Lettered on spine: La merope franc.

*FC7
V8893
744ma

NL 0354003   MH

Lieudé de Sepmanville, [François Cyprien Antoine]
baron, 1762–1817.
Détail particulier pour la carte de la Gonave, ajoutée
en 1788 au pilote de l'isle de Saint-Domingue. Par M. de
Lieudé de Sepmanville ... [Paris, Imprimerie royale,
1788]

10 p. 25½ x 19^{cm}. [With Puységur, A. H. A. de Chastenet, comte de.
Détail sur la navigation aux côtes de Saint-Domingue et dans ses débouquemens. Paris, 1787]

1. Pilot guides—Haiti.

Library of Congress   VK973.S3P9   5-25913

NL 0354004   DLC MB

Lieude de Sepmanville, François Cyprien
Antoine, baron, 1762-1817.
Puységur, Antoine Hyacinte Anne de Chastenet, *comte de*,
1752-1807.
Instructions nautiques sur les côtes et les débouquemens de
Saint-Domingue, avec le détail de la position des principaux
points qui ont servi de base à la construction des cartes publiées,
en 1787, au Dépôt général des cartes et plans de la marine et
des colonies; par m. de Chastenet-Puységur. Pub., pour la
première fois, par ordre du roi, en 1787. Paris, Imprimerie
royale, 1821.

Lieudé de Sepmanville, François Cyprien
Antoine, baron, 1762-1817.
Puységur, Antoine Hyacinte Anne de Chastenet, *comte
de*, 1752-1807.
A treatise upon the navigation of St. Domingo: with
sailing directions, for the whole extent of its coasts,
channels, bays and harbours. (Undertaken by order of
the King) By M. de Chastenet Puységur. Tr. from the
French by Charles de Monmonier. Baltimore, Printed
for the translator, by W. Pechin, 1802.

Lieurade, Jean Marc Louis, 1915-
... À propos d'un cas de maladie de Hodgkin
... Paris, 1940.
Thèse - Univ de Paris.

NL 0354007   CtY CtY-M DNLM MnU

Lieurade, Louis Géraud Paul Marie, 1904-
... Le cancer du sein dans ses relations
avec la grossesse et l'allaitement ...
Bordeaux, 1926.
25 cm.
Thèse - Univ. de Bordeaux.
Bibliographie: p. [79]-84.

NL 0354008   CtY

Lieurance, Iva G
America's best low-cost homes ...
see under Garlinghouse, L. F., company
Topeka, Kan.,

Lieurance, Iva G
Colonial homes ...
see under Garlinghouse, L.F., company,
Topeka, Kansas.

Lieurance, Iva G
De luxe small homes
see under Garlinghouse, L.F., company,
Topeka, Kan.

Lieurance, Iva G
Low budget homes
see under Garlinghouse, L.F., company,
Topeka, Kan.

Lieurance, Iva G
New American homes
see under Garlinghouse, L.F., company.

LIEURANCE, IVA G
New brick homes.   Topeka, Kans., Garlinghouse co. c1937.
48 p.

NL 0354014   Or

Lieurance, Iva G
New small homes
see under Garlinghouse[L. F.] company.

---

q784.3 Lieurance, Thurlow, 1878-1963.
L62a   At the foot of the mound: Scene characteristic from the American Indian. For
soprano with flute ad libitum. Philadelphia, Theodore Presser co. [c1917]
2v.

Contents:- v.1 The red birds sing o'er
the crystal spring.- v.2 The owl's bleak
call.

NL 0354016   IU

---

q784.3 Lieurance, Thurlow, 1878-1963
L62at   At the sundown. From the Red Willow
Pueblos.   Philadelphia, Theodore Presser
co., c1915.
5p.   (Indian songs)

NL 0354017   IU

Lieurance, Thurlow, 1878-
...By the waters of Minnetonka; an Indian love song (Sur
les eaux du Minnetonka), avec accompagnement de violon ou
flûte, ad. lib. Paroles anglaises de J. M. Cavanass, paroles françaises de Louis Poterat. Musique de Thurlow Lieurance...
Paris: Chappell S. A., cop. 1914.] Publ. pl. no. C. S. A. 537².
2 parts. f°.

Voice, piano, violin (or flute) in score, and violin (or flute) part. English and
French words.

1. Songs, American. 2. Songs, arias,   JUILLIARD FOUNDATION FUND.
I. Cavanass, J. M. II. Poterat, Louis,   etc., with various instruments,
Sur les eaux du Minnetonka.   translator. III. Title. IV. Title:
April 20, 1932

NL 0354018   NN MB OrP

---

q786.4 Lieurance, Thurlow, 1878 -
L62b   By the waters of Minnetonka; an Indian
love song. Piano solo.   Philadelphia,
Theodore Presser co. c1915.
4p.

NL 0354019   IU

---

q784.3 Lieurance, Thurlow, 1878-
L62by   By the waters of Minnetonka, an Indian
love song. High voice with violin and
flute ad lib.   Philadelphia, Theodore
Presser co., c1917.
2v.

Contents:-
v.1 Voice and piano.
v.2 Violin or flute.

q784.3 ---- ---- Low voice with violin and
L62byl   flute ad lib.   Philadelphia, Theodore
Presser co., c1914.
2v.

Contents:-
v.1 Voice and piano.
v.2 Violin or flute.

NL 0354021   IU

---

sVM   LIEURANCE, THURLOW, 1878-
1669   By the waters of Minnetonka. An Indian love
L 72b   song. High voice, with violin and flute ad lib.
Philadelphia, T.Presser Co.[c1917]
7p. 31cm.

Poems by J.M.Cavanass.
Plate no.: 14561-6.

NL 0354022   ICN

Lieurance, Thurlow, 1878 -

By the waters of Minnetonka, an Indian love
song. Presser [c1921]
5 p.

Organ.

NL 0354023   OrP

---

qM786.413 Lieurance, Thurlow, 1878-
L62b
By the waters of Minnetonka; an Indian
love song. Piano solo, concert edition.
Philadelphia, Theodore Presser Co.[1925]
5p. 31cm.

1. Piano music. I. Title

NL 0354024   IU

[Lieurance, Thurlow] 1878-
[By the waters of Minnetonka. Arr. for orch.]
... By the waters of Minnetonka. [n. p., 193-?] 10 f. 59½cm.

Full score.
Photostatic reproduction of manuscript.
Caption-title.
At head of title: Einar Swan.
Running footnote: Raymond Paige.
On cover: Thurlow Lieurance.

1. Orchestra—Arr. I. Swan,   Einar. II. Paige, Raymond.
III. Title.   April 30, 1941

MUSIC DIV.

NL 0354025   NN

VOLUME 332

q784.3 Lieurance, Thurlow, 1878-
L62b   By the weeping waters.   Philadelphia,
Theodore Presser co., c1916.
5p.   (Indian songs)

NL 0354026   IU

q786.4 Lieurance, Thurlow, 1878-
L62by   By the weeping waters. Piano solo.
Philadelphia, Theodore Presser co. c1916.
5p.   (Indian Music no.14234)

NL 0354027   IU

Music   Lieurance, Thurlow, 1878-
-R7812d   Drama from the Yellowstone, a musical
drama introducing Mr. Thurlow Lieurance's
Harris   "Four songs from the Yellowstone", also his
Collection   "The bird and the babe" (A lullaby), "By weeping waters" and "Where cedars rise" For mixed
quartette and chorus. Text by Charles O. Roos
and Juanita E. Roos; music by Thurlow Lieurance.
Philadelphia, T. Presser, c1921.
42 p.   27 cm.

NL 0354028   RPB

Lieurance, Thurlow, 1878-1963.
[Songs from green timber]
Eight songs from green timber. Lyrics
by Charles O. Roos. Philadelphia, T.
Presser, c1922.
39 p.
1. Title: Songs from green timber.

NL 0354029   DLC RPB OrP

M1621   Lieurance, Thurlow, 1878
.L54F5
Five songs for medium voice by Thurlow Lieur-
ance ... Kansas City, Mo., J. W. Jenkins' sons
music co., c1907.
15 p. 31 1/2cm.
Words by Wm. Felter.
Piano accompaniment.
CONTENTS.—The way to slumberland.—Alone.—
To be near dear heart.—Pansies.— Loveland.
1. Songs, English. 2. Songs (Medium voice)
with piano. I. Felter, William.

NL 0354030   MB

Lieurance, Thurlow, 1878-1963.
From the Dalles to Minnetonka; five
impressions for the pianoforte. Presser,
c1926.
Contents: At nightfall. By the cabin window.
By the waters of Minnetonka. Indian flute call
and reverie. To a ghost flower.

NL 0354031   OrP

Lieurance, Thurlow, 1878 —   No. 6 in **W.54.L4.2
George and his father. [Words by] Chas. Clarke, Jr. [Music by]
Thurlow Lieurance. [With pianoforte accompaniment.]
= Philadelphia. Theodore Presser Co. [1915.] (3) pp. [Encore
songs.] 31 cm.
Refers to George Washington.
The W copy belongs to "The Walter Updike Lewisson Collection of Wash-
ingtoniana."

D8457 — Double main card. —   Lieurance, Thurlow. (M1) —
Clarke, Charles, Jr. (M2) — T.r. Song.. .) — Washington, George. Music. (1)
— Songs. With music. (1)

NL 0354032   MB

Lieurance, Thurlow, 1878-
Indian love songs, arranged for three part
chorus of women's voices... Philadelphia,
Presser, c1925.
38p.   0.

NL 0354033   OO OrU OrP

Lieurance, Thurlow, 1878-
Indian melodies for violin and piano, by Thurlow Lieurance
... Philadelphia: T. Presser Co., cop. 1917. Publ. pl. no. I. M.
11. 2 parts in 1 v. f°.
Violin and piano in score and violin part.

1. Violin and piano. 2. Title.   July 1, 1919.

NL 0354034   NN IU OC1 ICN NBuG

Lieurance, Thurlow, 1878-1963.
Indian music ... n.p., 1903.
[4] p.   25 cm.
Cover-title.
From Southern Workman, August, 1903.

NL 0354035   RPB

ML3557   Lieurance, Thurlow, 1878-1963.
L53   Indian music [by] Thurlow Lieurance, Charles
Wakefield Cadman, Arthur Nevin ...   Philadel-
phia, Theodore Presser co. c1928.

1p.l.,28p.   illus.(ports.)   16cm.
(The Etude musical booklet library)

I. Cadman, Charles Wakefield, 1881-
jt. author.   II. Nevin, Arthur, 1871-
jt. author. 1. Indians of North America.-
Music.

NL 0354036   NBuG Or

M32.8   Lieurance, Thurlow, 1878-1963.
L5415   [Indian songs. Indian flute call and love
song]
Indian songs: Indian flute call and love
song. Philadelphia, T.Presser [c1914]
3p. 35cm. (Publisher's no.11854)
Originally for flute.
"This melody and flute call was recorded on
the Northern Cheyenne reservation, near Lame
Deer, Montana, April 2, 1912, at the Trader's
store."
1. Indians of   North America - Music.
2. Piano music,   Arranged.

NL 0354037   IaU IU

q786.4 Lieurance, Thurlow, 1878-
L62i   Indian suite. For pianoforte solo.
Philadelphia, Theodore Presser co. c1914.
5p.

NL 0354038   IU

qM784.3 Lieurance, Thurlow, 1878-
L62l   A lone owl is calling. Words by Juanita
E. Roos. Philadelphia, T. Presser c1924.
5p. 32cm. (His Under northern skies
no.3)

For voice and piano.

1. Songs (High voice) with piano. I. Title

NL 0354039   IU

Lieurance, Thurlow, 1878-1963.
[Indian songs]
Nine Indian songs, with descriptive notes, by Thurlow
Lieurance. Philadelphia, T. Presser [c1913]
27 p. illus. 31 cm.

1. Indians of North America—Music. 2. Songs (Medium voice)
with piano.
M1669.L54N5   44-44442
—— Copy 3.   ML30.4c no. 1215 Miller

NL 0354040   DLC RPB NN IU MB OC1 ICN OrU CaBVa OrP

q784.3 Lieurance, Thurlow, 1878-1963.
L62ra   Rainbow land. With violin and 'cello
ad lib.   Philadelphia, Theodore Presser
co., c1916.
2v.   (Indian songs)
Contents:-
v.1 Voice and piano.
v.2 Violin and cello.

NL 0354041   IU

q784.3 Lieurance, Thurlow, 1878-
L62r   Rue. [Vocal solo] (Violin or flute obbligato) Philadelphia, Theodore Presser
co., c1916.
2v.
Contents:
v.1 Voice and piano.
v.2 Violin or flute.

NL 0354042   IU

q784.3 Lieurance, Thurlow, 1878-1963.
L62sa   The sacrifice, an Indian mourning
song.   Philadelphia, Theodore Presser
co., c1915.
5p.   (Indian songs)

NL 0354043   IU

Lieurance, Thurlow, 1878-
Singing children of the sun, a book of Indian songs for
unison singing, by Thurlow Lieurance. Philadelphia, Theodore Presser co., c1943.
47 p. 23 cm.
With piano accompaniment.

1. Indians of North America—Music. 2. Songs (Medium voice) with
piano. I. Title.
Library of Congress   M1669.L54S5   44-32051

NL 0354044   DLC

Lieurance, Thurlow, 1878-1963.
Sioux Indian fantasie, for flute and
piano. Philadelphia, T. Presser [c1921]
score (6 p.) and part.

NL 0354045   DLC CU

q784.3 Lieurance, Thurlow, 1878-
L62s   A Sioux serenade.   Philadelphia,
Theodore Presser co., c1916.
3p.   (Indian songs)

NL 0354046   IU

VOLUME 332

Lieurance, Thurlow, 1878 –

Sometime, words by Wm. Felter. Windsor
Music Co., c1903.
3 p.

NL 0354047   OrP

Lieurance, Thurlow, 1878-1963.

Songs from the Yellowstone, by Thurlow Lieurance...
Philadelphia: T. Presser co., c1921. 18 p. 30½cm.
For 1 voice with piano acc. 1 song with flute obbligato. English words.

1. Song cycles. 2. Songs, Eng-   BISPHAM BEQUEST.
lish—U. S. composers. I. Title.
October 5, 1939

NL 0354048   NN RPB NBuG

---

sVM   LIEURANCE, THURLOW, 1878-1963, arranger.
1669   Songs of the North American Indian, with
L 72s   preface and explanatory notes.   Philadelphia,
         Theodore Presser Co. c1920;
         38p. port., illus. 31cm.

Violin or flute accompaniment in two songs.
Contents.—By the waters of Minnetonka (J.M.
Cavanass)—By the weeping waters.—Canoe song.—
Dying Moon-Flower.—From an Indian village.—From
Ghost Dance canyon.—In mirrored waters.—Indian
spring bird (Alfred   Fletcher)—A rose on
an Indian grave.

CaBVa
NL 0354049   ICN NN OC1 MB RPB NcD WaT CSt OrP OrU

Lieure, J.
Administration financière des lycées nationaux de
garçons et de jeunes filles d'après les documents officiels,
par J. Lieure ... Avec une préface de M. Étienne Port,
inspecteur général de l'instruction publique. Paris,
Boudignon, Sartiaux & cⁱᵉ, 1918.
1 p. l., xi, [1], 608 p. 22ᶜᵐ.
Earlier edition published under title: Comptabilité des lycées nationaux
de garçons et de jeunes filles d'après les documents officiels, par E. Guille-
min.
1. Public schools—France. 2. Education—France—Finance. 3. Education, Secondary. [2, 3. Secondary education—France—Finance]   I. Title.
E 20-248
Library, U. S. Bur. of   Education   LB2909.L62

NL 0354050   DHEW

Jad63   Lieure, Jules, 1866–
C3   Les bâtiments de l'Abbaye aux Hommes, fon-
912L   dée par Guillaume le Conquérant, aujourd'hui
         le lycée Malherbe. Eaux-fortes et texte de
         J. Lieure, clichés de A. Ravizé. Caen, L.
         Jouan, 1912.
         8 p. 34 plates. 25 cm.

NL 0354051   CtY MH

NE   Lieure, Jules, 1866–
647   L'école française de gravure, par J.
.L5   Lieure. Paris, La Renaissance du livre
         [1928-31]
         2 v. illus. (A travers l'art fran-
         çais)
         CONTENTS.--[1] Des origines à la fin du
         XVIe siècle.--[2] XVIIe siècle.

NL 0354052   MoU

Lieure, Jules, 1866–
...L'école française de gravure, des origines à la fin du XVIᵉ
siècle, par J. Lieure.   Paris: La Renaissance du livre[,] 1928[,].
190 p.   facsims., plates.   12°.   (À travers l'art française.)
Bibliographical footnotes.

442628A.   1. Engraving, French—   Hist.
November 11, 1929

NL 0354053   NN NjP PP OC1MA InU MdBWA CtY MH PPPM

Lieure, Jules, 1866–
...L'école française de gravure, xviiᵉ siècle, par J. Lieure.
Paris, La Renaissance du livre [1931]
201 p., 1 l. xxiv pl. (incl. ports.) 19¼ᶜᵐ. (A travers l'art français)

1. Engraving—France.   I. Title.
32-6015
Library of Congress   NE647.L5
760.944

NL 0354054   DLC NcU

Lieure, Jules, 1866–
La gravure en France au xviᵉ siècle. La gravure dans le
livre et l'ornement. Paris, G. Vanoest, 1927.
62 p. 72 plates. 34 cm.

1. Engraving—France. 2. Illustration of books.   I. Title.
NE647.L53   Rosenwald Coll.   51-8337

MiU PP ICU NjP MH NcU MiDA PBm ICN OOxM OC1MA
NL 0354055   DLC CSt CtY NNC ViU TxU CaBVaU PU OC1

Lieure, Jules, 1866–
Jacques Callot, par J. Lieure; introduction de F. Courboin
... Paris, Éditions de la Gazette des beaux-arts, 1924–29.
2 pt. in 5 v. plates (part fold.) ports., facsims. 33ᶜᵐ.
Each plate accompanied by guard sheet with descriptive letterpress.
Part 2 issued in 12 "fascicules," 1923-27.
Errata slip inserted (ptie. 2, t. 1)
"Bibliographie": ptie. 1, t. II, p. 90–116.
CONTENTS.—1. ptie. t. I. La vie artistique. 1929. t. II. La vie ar-
tistique, appendice. 1929.—2. ptie. Catalogue de l'œuvre gravé. t. I-III.
1924-27.
1. Callot, Jacques, 1592–1635.
42-5712
Library of Congress   NE650.C3L5

NcGU
NL 0354056   DLC NN OC MH GU NjP NBB OC1 NIC MoU PP

Lieure, Jules, 1866–
...La lithographie artistique et ses diverses techniques; les
techniques, leur évolution. Paris, J. Danguin, 1939.
5 p. l., [13]–104 p., 1 l. plates. 23 x 18ᶜᵐ.
At head of title: J. Lieure.

1. Lithography—Technique.   I. Title.
40-21695
Library of Congress   NE2425.L45
763

NL 0354057   DLC OC1MA NjP

HE970   Lieury, Robert, joint author.
.A8
Audouin, Émile.
... General average. York-Antwerp rules, 1924. An account of the Stockholm conference, 1924, and a study of the
1924 rules, by mm. Audouin, Gervais and Lieury ... Translation edited by Arnold W. Knauth ... Baltimore, American
maritime cases, inc., 1925.

---

965   Lieussou, Aristide, 1815-1858.
L721e   Études sur les ports de l'Algérie par A.
         Lieussou.   Paris, Imp. P. Dupont, 1850.
         107p. maps (1 fold.)

Presentation copy.

1. Harbors—Algeria.   I. Title.

NL 0354059   IEN

Lieussou, Aristide, 1815-1858.
Études sur les ports de l'Algérie, par A. Lieussou ... 2. éd.,
publiée par les Départements de la guerre et de la marine.
Paris, Imprimerie administrative de P. Dupont, 1857.
189 p. incl. illus., tables. maps (2 fold.) 24ᶜᵐ.

1. Harbors—Algeria.
[Full name: Jean Pierre Hippolyte Aristide Lieussou]
32-32389
Library of Congress   TC319.A4L5 1857   627.20965

NL 0354060   DLC

Lieussou, Aristide, 1815-1858.
... Recherches sur les variations de la marche des pen-
dules et des chronomètres, suivies d'un projet d'organisation du service des chronomètres appartenant à la marine,
par M. Aristide Lieussou ... Paris, Impr. de P. Dupont,
1854.
179, [1], [2] p. incl. tables. 23½ᶜᵐ.
At head of title: Dépôt général de la marine.
"Extrait des Annales hydrographiques (1853)"
1. Chronometer.
19-18004
Library of Congress   QB107.L5

NL 0354061   DLC DN-Ob DN ICJ ICU

PQ   Lieussou, Georges, 1857–
2338   ... L'inspirée; comédie en un acte.
L72i   Paris, P. Ollendorff, 1902.
         42p. 18½cm.

NL 0354062   NRU CtY

PQ   Lieussou, Georges, 1857–
2338   ... Spécialités pour divorces; comédie
L72s   en un acte. Paris, P. Ollendorff, 1902.
         28p. 18½cm.

NL 0354063   NRU

Lieussou, Jean Pierre Hippolyte Aristide
see Lieussou, Aristide, 1815-1858.

Lieutard, Eugène Victor.
Généalogie des études des notaires de l'arrondissement
de Sisteron, par Eugène Victor Lieutard ... Paris, E.
Lechevallier, 1891.
50 p. 19½ᶜᵐ.

1. Sisteron, France—Geneal. 2. Lawyers—Sisteron, France.   I. Title.
20-15859
Library of Congress   CS597.S5L5

NL 0354065   DLC

VOLUME 332

Rare Book Dept.
Lieutaud,
xXG
.3561　　Epître a la lanterne. Par m. Lieutaud ...
.22　　[Paris] Chez Devaux,libraire,au Palais royal,
no.8　　N°.181. [179-]

　　　　8p. 21cm.
　　　　Caption title; imprint from p.8.
　　　　Verse.

NL 0354066　　MB IaU

Lieutaud, seigneur d'Aiglun.
　　Memoire sur les degradations des terres,
occasionnées par les torrens et par les
inondations. Amsterdam; Paris, Vve
Hérissant, 1782.
　　36 p. 8°.

NL 0354067　　DNLM

Lieutaud, Albert, joint tr.

Stevenson, Robert Louis, 1850-1894.
　　... L'Ile au trésor; traduction intégrale avec une préface de l'auteur traduite en français pour la première
fois. Traduction d'Albert Savine et d'Albert Lieutaud.
Paris, A. Michel [1924]

845L62 Lieutaud, Albert.
Of1923　　La lanterne à la main; essais ...
　　　　Paris, 1923.
　　　　153p.

NL 0354069　　IU

Lieutaud (Édouard). * Sur les phénomènes de
l'accouchement naturel. 30pp. 4°. *Paris*, 1836.
No. 359. v. 304.

NL 0354070　　DNLM

Lieutaud, Jacques, 1660(ca.)-1733.
　　La connoissance des temps, ou Calendrier et epheme-
rides ... calevlées pour Paris, et pour l'année 1693 ...
A Paris, Chez E. Michallet [1692?]
　　5 p. l., 115, [1] p. incl. tables. fold. diagr. 14cm.
　　Illustrated half-title.

　　1. Ephemerides.

NL 0354071　　MiU

Lieutaud, Jacques, 1660(ca.)-1733.
　　Connoissance des temps pour l'année
1705. Au meridien de Paris, publiée
par l'ordre de l'Academie Royale des
Sciences, et calculée par Mr. Lieutaud,
de la même Academie. A Paris, Chez
J. Boudot, 1705.
　　107 p.　fold. plates, fold. map,
tables.　19cm.

　　Added title page, engr.
　　1. Almanacs, French.

NL 0354072　　MnU

Lieutaud, Jacques, 1660(ca.)-1733.
　　Connoissance des temps, pour l'annee 1707, au
meridien de Paris...Paris, Boudot, 1706.　187p. YA 2916

NL 0354073　　DLC

Lieutaud, Jacques, 1660(ca.)-1733.
　　Connoissance des temps pour l'année 1715. au
meridien de Paris, publiée par l'ordre de l'Academie rofale des sciences, et calculée par m.
Lieutaud ...
　　A Paris, Chez Jean Mariette, ruë s. Jacques,
aux Colonnes d'Hercules. M. DCC. XIV. Avec privilege du Roi.　[1714]

　　2 p.l., 3-194 p. illus. (diagrs.) 2 fold.pl.,
fold.map. 15.5cm. (12mo)

　　Engraved half-title.
　　"Fautes à corriger": p.192.
　　"De l'imprimerie de la veuve d'Antoine Lam-
bin"--p.194.

NL 0354075　　MB

Lieutaud, Joseph, 1703-1780.
　　Anatomie historique et pratique. Nouv.
éd., augmentée de diverses remarques historiques et critiques, et de nouvelles planches
par M. Portal. 2 v. 12, xvi, 688 pp., 6 pl.; viii,
336, 247 pp., 4 pl. 8°. *Paris, P.-F. Didot jeune,*
1776-7.

NL 0354076　　DNLM

Lieutaud, Joseph, 1703-1780.
　　Compendio della medicina pratica, che contiene
l'istoria delle malattie, e la maniera di trattarle: con osservazioni, e riflessioni critiche
intorno ai punti piu' rilevanti. Tr. dalla lingua francese. Venezia, G. Pasquali, 1762.
　　2 v. in 1.

NL 0354077　　ICJ

Lieutaud, Joseph, 1703-1780.
　　Compendio della medicina pratica ...
Venezia, G. Pasquale, 1774.
　　2 v.

NL 0354078　　DNLM

Lieutaud, Joseph, 1703-1780.
　　Compendio della medicina pratica, che contiene l'istoria delle malattie, e la maniera
di trattarle: ... tr. dalla lingua Francese
... Bassano,A spese Remondini di Venezia,
1789.
　　2v. in 1.　19 1/2cm.

　　1. Medicine - Practics.

NL 0354079　　CtY-M

Lieutaud, Joseph, 1703-80.
　　—. Elementa physiologiæ, juxta solertiora,
novissimaque physicorum experimenta, et accu-
ratiores anatomicorum observationes concinnata.
7 p. l., 335 pp. 8°. *Amstelodami, typ. fratrum
Detonnes,* 1749.

NL 0354080　　DNLM NNNAM

QM21
L72
LIEUTAUD,JOSEPH,1703-1780.
　　Essais anatomiques contenant l'histoire exacte de
toutes les parties qui composent le corps de l'homme,
avec le manière de dissequer,par Mr.Lieutaud... Paris,P.-M.Huart,1742.
　　xxi,[3],724,[16]p. VI fold.pl. 20½cm.
　　Title vignette;head and tail pieces.

　　1.Anatomy,Human--Early works to 1800.

NL 0354081　　ICU DNLM MBCo CtY-M WaU PPC

Adelmann
QM
21
L72
Lieutaud, Joseph, 1703-1780.
　　Essais anatomiques, contenant l'histoire
exacte de toutes les parties qui composent
le corps de l'homme, avec la maniere de
disequer. Paris, P.-M. Huart, 1742.
　　xxi, 724 p. 6 fold. plates. 20cm.

　　1. Anatomy, Human--Early works to 1800.
　　2. Dissection. I. Title.

NL 0354082　　NIC NNNAM PPJ WU

WZ
260
L625e
1766
Rare
LIEUTAUD, Joseph, 1703-1780
　　Essais anatomiques, contenant l'histoire
exacte de toutes les parties qui composent
le corps de l'homme; avec la maniere de les
découvrir & les démontrer... Nouvelle édition, revue & augmentée. Paris, Chez D'
Houry [etc.] 1766.
　　[4], xxii, [2], 730, xxvi p. 6 plates.
19.8 cm.
　　Pages 545-560 are misbound preceding page
529.
　　1. Anatomy[--　　18th cent.] 2. Blad-
der--Anatomy &　　histology 3. Dissection I. Title

NL 0354083　　CLU-M WU-M

Lieutaud, Joseph, 1703-1780.
　　Essais anatomiques contenant l'histoire
exacte de toutes les parties qui composent le
corps de l'homme ... Paris, 1767.
　　xxii, 730 xxvi p. 6 pl. (80

NL 0354084　　NNNAM

R128 Lieutaud, Joseph, 1703-1780.
.7　　Historia anatomico-medica, sistens numerosissima cadaverum
.L67 humanorum extispicia, quibus in apricum venit genuina
morborum sedes; horumque reserantur causæ, vel patent
effectus. Opus quadripartitum ... Auctore Josepho Lieutaud
... Recensuit & suas observationes numero plures adjecit,
uberrimumque indicem nosologico ordine concinnavit Antonius
Portal ... Parisiis, apud Vincent, 1767.

　　2 v. 26cm.

　　1. Medicine—Early works.

NL 0354085　　CLU-M MnCS WU MnU KyU
　　　　　　　　ICU CU PPC PPL MH ViU NNNAM DNLM NcD-MC

WZ
260
L721H
1779
Lieutaud, Joseph, 1703-1780.
　　Historia anatomico-medica, sistens numerosissima cadaverum humanorum extispicia,
quibus in apricum venit genuina morborum
sedes, horumque referantur causae, vel
patent effectus. Recensuit & suas observationes numero plures adjecit, uberrimumque
indicem nosologico ordine concinnavit
Antonius Portal... Editio prima Veneta.
Venetiis, Apud Thoman Bettinelli, 1779.

　　2 v.　26 cm.

　　1. Pathology. I. Portal, Antoine, 1742-
1832, ed. II. Title: Historia anatomico-
medica.

NL 0354087　　WU-M DNLM

VOLUME 332

Lieutaud, Joseph, 1703–1780.
Iosephi Lieutaud ... Historia anatomico-medica, sistens numerosissima cadaverum humanorum extispicia, quibus in apricum venit genuina morborum sedes, horumque reserantur caussae, vel patent effectus. Recensuit quondam, et suas observationes numero plures adiecit, uberrimumque indicem nosologico ordine concinnavit, Antonivs Portal ... Recudi iam nunc curavit, correxit, et supplementis locupletavit, Ioannes Christ. Travg. Schlegel ... Longosalissae, impensis I. S. Zolling, 1786–87.
2 v. in 1. 21¼ᶜᵐ.
1. Anatomy, Pathological. 2. Pathology—Early works to 1800. I. Portal, Antoine, 1742– 1832, ed. II. Schlegel, Johann Christian Traugott, 1746– 1824, ed. III. Title: Historia anatomico-medica.
Library of Congress   RB24.L5   35–36247

NL 0354088   DLC

Lieutaud, Joseph, 1703–1780.
Iosephi Lievtavd, ... , Historia anatomico-medica, sistens nvmerosissima cadavervm hvmanorvm extispicia, qvibvs in apricvm venit genvina morborvm sedes, horvmqve reserantvr cavssae, vel patent effectvs. Recensvit qvondam, et svas observationes nvmero plvres adiecit, vberrimvmqve indicem nosologico ordine concinnavit, Antonivs Portal, ... Recvdi iam nvnc cvravit, correxit, et svpplementis locvpletavit, D. Ioannes Christianvs Travgott Schlegel, ... Volvmen I–III. Gothae, C. G. Ettinger, et Amstelodami, I. St. van E. Holtrop et soc., 1796–1802.
3 vol. 20ᶜᵐ.

NL 0354089   ICJ MiU

RBS26. **Lieutaud, Joseph.**
Inbegriff der ganzen medicinischen praxis in zween theilen.
Leipzig: J. F. Judinius, 1777–1779.

NL 0354090   NNNAM

Lieutaud, Joseph, 1703–1780.
Inbegriff der ganzen medicinischen Praxis.
Leipzig, Junius, 1778.
558 p.

NL 0354091   PPC

B615.1
L625G **Lieutaud, Joseph,** 1703–1780.
Inbegriff der ganzen medicinischen Praxis. Verbesserte und abgekürzte Aufl.
Frankenthal, Im Verlag einer typographischen Gesellschaft, 1785.

6 v. in 3.   19cm.

Tr. of Précis de la matière médicale.

NL 0354092   MnU DLC

BENJ **LIEUTAUD,** Joseph, 1703–1780
WZ   Observations anatomiques sur la structure de
260   la vessie. [Paris] 1753.
L625o   26 p.   24.9 cm.   (In portfolio)
1753   Detached from Mémoires de l'Academie Royale
RARE   des Sciences, 1753.
          [1. Bladder] I. Title II. Mémoires de
        l'Academie Royale des Sciences, 1753.

NL 0354093   CLU-M

R615.1 **Lieutaud, Joseph,** 1703–80
1766   Précis de la matiere medicale, contenant les connoissances les plus utiles sur l'histoire, la nature, les vertus & les doses des médicamens, tant simples qu'officinaux, usités dans la pratique actuelle de la médecine, avec un grand nombre de formules éprouvées, traduction de la seconde partie du Précis de la médecine pratique, publié en Latin.
Paris, Vincent, 1766.
890p. 21cm.

NL 0354094   OC PPC

Lieutaud, Joseph, 1703–80.
Précis de la matière médicale, contenant les connoissances les plus utiles sur l'histoire, la nature, les vertus et les doses des médicamens, tant simples qu'officinaux, usités dans la pratique actuelle de la médecine, avec un grand nombre de formules éprouvées. Traduction de la seconde partie du Précis de la médecine pratique, publié en latin par ... 4 pts. in 3 v. 16°.
Paris, Vincent, 1768.

NL 0354095   DNLM RPB

RM **Lieutaud, Joseph,** 1703–1780
84   Précis de la matiere medicale, contenant les
L5   connoissances les plus utiles sur l'histoire,
1770   la nature, les vertus & les doses des médicamens ... Traduction de la seconde partie du Précis de la médecine pratique, publié en latin. Nouv. éd., corrigée, augm., & à laquelle on a ajouté un Traité des alimens & des boissons. Paris, Didot, 1770.
2v. 21cm.
Translation of the second part of Synopsis universae praxeos medicae.
1. Materia   medica – Early works to 1800 I. Title

NL 0354096   WU KyU DNLM

Lieutaud, Joseph, 1703–1780.
Précis de la matière médicale, contenant ce qu'il importe de savoir sur la nature, les propriétés & les doses des médicaments, tant simples qu'officinaux; un grand nombre de formules, & un traité des aliments. Par m. Lieutaud ... Nouv. éd., rev. par l'auteur ... Avignon, J. A. Joly, 1793.
4 v. 18ᵐᵒ.
A translation of the second part of the author's Synopsis universae praxeos medicae.
1. Materia medica—Early works to 1800. I. Title.   39–33462
Library of Congress   RM84.L5 1793

NL 0354097   DLC

RS79 **Lieutaud, Joseph,** 1703–1780.
.L7   Précis de la matière médicale, contenant ce qu'il importe de savoir sur la nature, les propriétés & les doses des médicaments, tant simples qu' officinaux; avec un grand nombre de formules. Par M. Lieutaud ... Nouv. éd., rev. par l'auteur ... Paris, T. Barrois le jeune, 1781.
2 v. 20ᵐᵐ.

1. Materia medica.

NL 0354098   ICU KyU

Lieutaud, Joseph, 1703–1780.
Précis de la medecine pratique, contenant l'histoire des maladies... & remarques critiques sur les points les plus intéressans. À Paris, chez Vincent, 1759.
xxiii, 764 p.   20 cm.
Imperfect: t.p. partly mutilated.

1. Medicine - Early works to 1800. I. T.

NL 0354099   NjP

Lieutaud, Joseph, 1703–80.
Précis de la médecine pratique, contenant l'histoire des maladies, et la manière de les traiter, avec des observations et remarques critiques sur les points les plus intéressans. 2. éd. xvi, 798 pp. 8°. *Paris, Vincent,* 1761.

NL 0354100   DNLM PPC KyU PPL ICJ

Lieutaud, Joseph, 1703–1780.
18th cent.   Précis de la medecine pratique, contenant l'historie des maladies, et la maniere de les traiter ... Nouvelle édition.   Tome Premier [Second] A Paris, Chez Vincent, 1765.
2v. 17cm.

NL 0354101   CtY-M

Lieutaud, Joseph, 1703–1780.
Précis de la médecine pratique, contenant l'histoire des maladies, & la maniere de les traiter, avec des observations & remarques critiques fur les points les plus intéressans... 3e éd., rev. & aug... Paris, Vincent, 1769.
2 v. 20½cm.

NL 0354102   MShM KyU DNLM

616.09 **LIEUTAUD,** Joseph, 1703–1780.
L625p   Précis de la medecine pratique,
1776   contenant l'histoire des maladies & la maniere de les traiter; avec des observations & des remarques critiques sur les points les plus intéressants. Nouv. éd. rev. Paris, Vincent, 1776.
2 v.

1. Pathology - Early works to 1800.

NL 0354103   WaU MnU CtY-M DNLM

Lieutaud, Joseph, 1703–1780.
Précis de la médecine pratique ... Nouv. ed. Paris, P.-F. Didot, 1777.
2 v.

NL 0354104   DNLM

616.08 **Lieutaud,** Joseph, 1703–1780.
L72p   Précis de la médecine pratique, contenant l'his-
1787   toire des maladies, & la maniere de les traiter, avec des observations & remarques critiques sur les points les plus intéressants. Par mr. Lieutaud ... Quatrieme édition, revue & augmentée par l'auteur. Tome premier-[troisieme] Rouen, la veuve de Pierre Dumesnil, 1787.
3 v. 17 cm.

NL 0354105   MiU MH DNLM NNNAM ICJ

WZ **LIEUTAUD,** Joseph, 1703–1780
270   Proposals for publishing by subscrip-
L721sZ tion, the first part of the Synopsis of the
1816   universal practice of medicine, exhibiting a concise view of all diseases ... By Joseph Lieutaud ... Now first translated from the Latin, by Edwin A. Atlee ... [Philadelphia, Published by Edward and Richard Parker; Abraham Bowman, printer, 1816]
[viii p. 23 cm.

Continued in next column

VOLUME 332

Continued from preceding column

Imprint supplied from the "Synopsis"
as published in 1816.
"Conditions" (p. viii) dated "3d mo.
25th 1816. "
"Extract from the author's preface":
p. [ii]-viii.

I. Atlee, Edwin Augustus, 1776-1852,
tr. Title

NL 0354108   DNLM

W 4 LIEUTAUD, Joseph, 1703-1780, praeses
A31   Quaestiones II^ae medicae ex Hyppocratis & Galeni libris
1746 depromptae, propositae a ... Josepho Begue ... praeside D.
L 1   Josepho Lieutaud ... Aquis-Sextiis, Typis viduae Renati
      Adibert [1746]
        7 p. 24 cm.
        Diss. - Aix (R. M. Saint Mihiel, respondent)

        1. Hippocrates. Aphorismi. Bk. 4. 2. Galenus. I.
      Begue, Joseph, proponent. II. Saint Mihiel, René Mathurin,
      respondent

NL 0354109   DNLM

Lieutaud, Joseph, 1703-1780.
    Synopsis of the universal practice of medicine. Exhibiting
a concise view of all diseases, both internal and external:
illustrated with complete commentaries. By Joseph Lieutaud
... Translated from the Latin, by Edwin A. Atlee ... Philadelphia. Published by Edward and Richard Parker, no. 178
High street. Abraham Bowman, printer. 1816.
    3 p. l., viii, 641, [1] p. 22½^cm.

    1. Medicine—Practice. I. Atlee, Edwin Augustus, 1776-1852, tr.
II. Title.
                                                  34-34662

    Library of Congress   RC46.L65

NL 0354110   DLC PSC PPL ICJ KyU OClW-H NBuG MiU NcU
             NNNAM DNLM OKentU CtY-M PPJ PU NcD

R616 Lieutaud, Joseph, 1703-80
1820   Synopsis of the universal practice of
C   medicine, exhibiting a concise view of
      all diseases, both internal and external,
      illustrated with complete commentaries,
      translated from the Latin by E.A.Atlee.
      Philadelphia, Parker, 1820.
      641p.23cm.

NL 0354111   OC NNNAM MH

Lieutaud, Joseph,1703-1780.
    Synopsis universae praxeos-medicae, in binas
partes divisa... Auctore ...Amstelodami,Sumpt-
ibus fratrum De Tournes,1745.
    2 pts. in 1 v.   26p.

NL 0354112   MiU

R   Lieutaud, Joseph, 1703-1780.
128   Synopsis universae praxeos-medicae, in
.7   binas partes divisa, quarum prior contractum
L72+ omnium morborum, tùm internorum, tùm exter-
      norum conspectum exhibet; altera verò rem
      medicamentariam; vel promptuarium selectis-
      simorum medicaminum, emporeticorum, offici-
      nalium & magistralium, perpetuis commenta-
      riis illustratum, sistit ...   Amsteloda-
      mi, Sumptibus Fratrum De Tournes, 1765.
      2 v. 26cm.

NL 0354113   NIC NNNAM DNLM NIC

Lieutaud, Joseph, 1703-1780.
    Synopsis universae praxeos medicae, in
binas partes divisa.   Patavii, J. Manfré, 1777.
    2 v.

NL 0354114   DNLM

NL 0354115   DNLM

Lieutaud (Louis) [1871-   ]. *Contribution
à l'étude du pneumothorax, et en particulier de
sa guérison. 82 pp. 8°. Paris, 1898, No. 247.

NL 0354116   DNLM

Lieutaud (Paul-Émile). *De l'hydrarthrose.
34 pp. 4°. Paris, 1881, No. 149

Lieutaud, Paul Marie, 1896-
    ... Les péricystites phlegmoneuses. Travail
de la Clinique des maladies des voies urinaires
de l'Hôpital Necker...   Paris, 1929.
    24 cm.
    Thèse - Univ. de Paris.
    "Bibliographie": p. [85] - 86.

NL 0354117   CtY

Lieutaud, Roquil-

see

Rauquil-Lieutaud.

Lieutaud, Soliman, b. 1795.
    Liste alphabétique de portraits français gravés jusque
et y compris l'année 1775, faisant le complément de celle
de la Bibliothèque historique de la France du P. Lelong,
cinq volumes in-folio. 2. éd., rev., cor., et considérablement augm., par Soliman Lieutaud. Paris, 1846.
    vi, 105 p. 31½^cm.
    "Imprimé à deux cents exemplaires."

    1. France — Biog. — Portraits — Catalogs. 2. Engravings — Catalogs.
I. Lelong, Jacques, 1665-1721. Bibliothèque historique de la France. II. Title: Portraits français gravés.
                                                  13-10717

    Library of Congress   NE270.L4

NL 0354119   DLC NN IEN

Lieutaud, Soleman, b. 1795.
    Liste alphabetique des portraits des
personnages nés dans l'ancien duché de
Lorraine ...   Paris, 1852.

NL 0354120   PPPM

Lieutaud, Soliman, b. 1795.
    Liste alphabétique de portraits dessinés, gravés et lithogra-
phiés de personnages nés en Lorraine, pays Messin et de ceux qui
appartiennent à l'histoire de ces deux provinces, avec une courte
notice biographique sur chaque personnage, l'indication du format
des portraits et les noms des artistes dont ils sont l'œuvre...par
Soliman Lieutaud...   Paris: L'auteur, 1862.   viii, 240, 53 p.
2. ed. rev. and enl.   4°.
    no. 30 of 200 copies printed.

182158A. 1. Portraits, French   —Lorraine—Catalogues. 2. Lorraine—Biog.   June 18, 1925

NL 0354121   NN

Lieutaud, Soliman, b. 1795.
    Liste des portraits dessinés, gravés ou lithographiés
des députés à l'assemblée nationale de 1789, avec l'indication de leur format et le nom des artistes à qui ils sont
dus, précédés d'une courte notice biographique sur chaque personnage, par Soliman Lieutaud. Paris, L'auteur,
1854.
    1 p. l., ii, 218 p. 24½ x 16^cm.

    1. France—Biog.—Portraits. 2. France—Hist.—Revolution. 3. Engrav-
ings—Catalogs. 4. Drawings—Catalogs.
                                                  13-4902

    Library of Congress   NE270.L5

NL 0354122   DLC

Lieutaud, Victor, 1844-

Marseille. Bibliothèque municipale.
    Catalogue de la Bibliothèque de Marseille. Ouvrages relatifs
à la Provence. Essai d'introduction & de classement méthodique, par V. Lieutaud ... Marseille, Imprimerie et lithographie Gravière fils, 1877.

Lieutaud, Victor, 1844-
    Un amour; pouèmo en trento tindet, qu'a
gagna lou brout de roure argentau i Jo-
Flourau de Barcilouno, 2 de mai 1880, pèr
Vitou Liéutaud. Marsiho, Bérard, 1882.
    63 p.

NL 0354124   WaU MH

Liéutaud, Vitou.
    ... Au roc de Castelano ; odo courounado a Saragousso
i grand jo flourau de la courouno d'Aragoun lou 19 d'òu-
tobre 1900, emé un reviramen en lengo franceso. Caste-
lano, Encò d'A. Gauthier, 1904.
    32 p. 22½^cm.
    Title vignette.

                                                  5-34358

NL 0354125   DLC CU

Lieutaud, Vitou.
    ... Le Poil, canton de Sénez, arrondissement de Castelane
(B.-A.) (Pèou, Pèu, Pèl, Pèn) Histoire féodale, toponymique
et religieuse. Sisteron, A. Clergue, 1903.
    cover-title, 44 p. 23^cm.

    1. Poil, Le, France. 2. Castelane, Seigneurs de.
                                                  5-6323 Revised
    Library of Congress   DC801.P7L7

NL 0354126   DLC

A Lieutenant.
    Another view of the British navy
    see under   Another view of the British navy.

The lieutenant, and the crooked midshipman
    see under   [Collingridge, Augustus]

Lieutenant Bird's letter from the shades
    see under   Bird, T., pseud.

VOLUME 332

A lieutenant colonel.

The **Christian** corporal. A dialogue between a corporal and a soldier. Written by a lieutenant colonel. Edinburgh, Printed for the booksellers, 1816.

A lieutenant - colonel.
    Indian deficits and their remedy
       see under title [supplement]

Lt.-Col. Charles Lyon Chandler. [Cambridge. Mass., Printed by Welch, Bigelow, and company, 1864?]
  40 p. port. 19ᵐ.
A collection of newspaper extracts, letters, etc.

1. Chandler, Charles Lyon, 1839-1864.

Library of Congress   E601.C45   8—20227

NL 0354132   DLC MeB ViU TxU MH NcD NjP

Lieutenant-Colonel David Du Bose Gaillard ...
    see under   [Fries, Amos Alfred] 1873-

Lieutenant-colonel de l'état-major général.
    Considérations sur les défenses naturelles
et artificielles de la France...
       see under title

UA649
.B86

A lieutenant-colonel in the British army.

The **British** army, by a lieutenant-colonel in the British army, with an introduction by Major-General F. Maurice ... London, S. Low, Marston & co., (limited) 1899.

Lieut. Col. Jacob Reed
    see under   [Reed, Willoughby H   ]
1856-   comp.

Lieutenant Colonel Joseph Bridgham Curtis
    see under   [Curtis, George William]
1824-1892.

Lieut.-Col. **M. F. McTaggart**, D.S.O.; an appreciation, with fore-word by Lieut.-Col. R. S. Timmis.   Manchester: Cornish & Barber ltd., 1936.   79 p. incl. front. (port.), plates.   23cm.

893098A. 1. McTaggart, Maxwell-   Fielding, 1874-1936. 2. Horseman-ship. I. Timmis, Reginald Symonds,   1884- .   N. Y. P. L.   July 12, 1937

NL 0354138   NN

A lieutenant-colonel of the army.
    The corporal and soldier
       see under title

Lieutenant-Colonel Patrick Ferguson.

Extract from Living age,   Oct.7, 1882.

NL 0354140   NcU

---

s.c.
p92
F38B

Lieutenant-Colonel Patrick Ferguson. A career of the American Revolution. (In: Blackwood's Magazine, Sept., 1882. p. 316.-330)

1. Ferguson, Patrick, 1744-1780.

NL 0354141   ScU MdBP

Lieut.-Colonel Robert Horn, D.S.O., M.C. ...
    see under [Horn, Myra (Macandrew)]

DS479
.1
.M9L7

Lt.-Col. Sir A. Lakshmanaswami Mudaliar commemoration volume. [Madras] The Committee, 1948.
  342 p. illus.

1. Mudaliar, Sir Arcot Lakshmanaswami, 1887-

NL 0354143   ICU HU

Lieut.-Col. William French, C. B. E., D. S. O., M. C. In memoriam, 1884-1955.   [Maidstone, Kent] Privately printed [in the Dept. of printing, Maidstone college of art, 1955] 3 l 20cm.

56R0694. 1. French, William, 1884-   1955.

NL 0354144   NN

Un lieutenant de chasseurs
    see
Thomas, Louis, 1885-

Un lieutenant de vaisseau.
    Considérations sur les marines à voiles et à vapeur de France et d'Angleterre
       see under [La Roncière le Noury, Camille Adalbert Marie Clément, baron de] 1813-1881.

LIEUT. Eric Reginald Dennis, M.C. killed in action "somewhere in France" April 5th, 1917. [Hali., Priv. pr., 1917?] unp. front. (port.) 23 cm.

NL 0354147   CaNSWA

A lieutenant from Norwich.
    A short survey of the western counties
       see under title

Un lieutenant-général.
    Lettre d'un lieutenant-général à M. le comte de L***
       see under title

DC
202
.1
B11

Le lieutenant-général baron E. Hulot, 1774-1850. Notice biographique, documents historiques et militaires, ordres du jour, lettres [par E. B.]   Paris, Spectateur militaire, 1884.
  84 p. 23cm.
  Pref. signed by E. B.

1. Hulot, Étienne, baron, 1774-1850.
2. France--History, Military--19th cent.
I. E., E.

NL 0354150   NIC MH DNW

Lieutenant General D.H. Hill.   N.p., n.d.
  1.Hill, Daniel Harvey, 1821-1889.

NL 0354151   NcU

Un lieutenant general de province.
    Lettre d'vn lieutenant general de province à vn des premiers magistrats de France
       see under title

Lieutenant-General Theophilus Hunter Holmes, C.S.A.   N.p.,n.d.
  1.Holmes, Theophilus Hunter, 1804-1880.

NL 0354153   NcU

Lieutenant-general Wm. Tecumseh Sherman
    see under [Reid, Whitelaw] 1837-1912.

---

*EC65
A100
648L25

Lieutenant Generall Cromwell's last vvill & testament: with the military directions he gave his field-officers a little before his death.
  London.Printed in the year,1648.
  1p.ℓ.,6p. 19cm.
  Abbott 243.
  Title vignette.
  A prose satire on Cromwell, dated by Thomason 27 July 1648.

NL 0354155   MH MnU CtY InU

Lieut. Gov. Gore
and Upper Canada. 18 pp. (*Fraser's Mag.* v. 47, 1853, p. 627.)

NL 0354156   MdBP

VOLUME 332

E
179
U11
v.29
no.19
Lieut.-Gov. Higgins, Republican candidate for governor. What President Roosevelt, the Hon. Elihu Root, the Hon. Cornelius N. Bliss and others say about him. [New York, 1904]

32 p. 20cm.

1. Higgins, Frank Wayland, 1856-1907. 2. Campaign literat   ure, 1904—Republican.

NL 0354157   NIC

The lieutenant governor of Massachusetts. Why John N. Cole of Andover should be the Republican nominee as told by "The Committee of 5000" and the press of Massachusetts. Political data in appendix. [n.p., 1908]

[32] p. port. 15cm.

NL 0354158   MH

Lt. Governor Spotswood and the Virginia burgesses.
(In Southern literary messenger. v. 17. p. 585-604)

NL 0354159   Vi

A lieutenant in the Bengal cavalry.
Letters, political, military, and commercial...
see under   Civis, pseud.

CbB
T237
Lieut. James W. Tayloe. Charles F. Tayloe.
[n.p., n.d.]
[1]p. 32 x 20 cm.
Printed on silk.
Eulogy of James and Charles Tayloe of ington, N.C.

1. Tayloe, James W   1846?-1857?
2. Tayloe, Charles F   1823-1857?

NL 0354161   NcU

The **Lieutenant** John A. Larkin, Jr., Memorial Scholarship established at Princeton University, 1945. [New York? 1946]

[33] p. ports., facsims. 28 cm.

Foreword signed: Henrietta Kleberg Larkin [and] John Adrian Larkin.

1. Larkin, John Adrian, 1922-1945. 2. Princeton University. Lieutenant John A. Larkin, Jr., Memorial Scholarship. I. Larkin, Henrietta Rosa (Kleberg) II. Larkin, John Adrian, 1891-1948.

CT275.L2753L4   920   48-15079*‡

NL 0354162   DLC WHi TxU

Lieutenant Joshua Hewes
see under   Putnam, Eben, 1868-

Lieutenant Murray [pseud.]

See

[Ballou, Maturin Murray] 1820-1895.

A lieutenant of the left wing.
Sketch of the Seminole war, and sketches during a campaign. By a lieutenant of the left wing. Charleston [S. C.] D. J. Dowling [etc.] 1836.

The lieutenant of the Tower's speech and repentance at the time of his death... [1615]
see under   [Helwys, Sir Gervase] 1561-1615.

LIEUTENANT RICHARD STOCKTON BULLITT [of the] 110[th infantry] 28th division. [Philadelphia? 1919?]
23 p. illus., port. 25cm.

Cover title.

1. European war, 1914-1918--   Biog., Indiv. 2. Bullitt, Richard Stockton, 1896-1918.

NL 0354167   NN

Lieutenant Samuel Woodfill, Kentucky's outstanding world war soldier

See *under*

[Hardin, Bayless *Evans*] *1912-*

Lieutenant Z.

... L'armée aux grèves. Grève générale des mineurs (octobre–novembre 1902) par le lieutenant Z. Paris, G. Bellais, 1904.

Lieutier (Aimé). *De l'action de la belladone sur la sécrétion gastrique et de son application au traitement de l'hyperchlorhydrie. 86 pp. 8°. Paris, 1904. No. 450...

NL 0354170   DNLM

Lieutier (Louis-Michel-Théodore). *L Du traitement de la néphrite simple, de la néphrite calculeuse et de la néphrite granuleuse. II. [etc.] 34 pp. 4°. Paris, 1839. No. 142, v. 345.

NL 0354171   DNLM

Lieutier, Paul.
...Bourg-la-Reine, essai d'histoire locale.   Paris, Letouzey & Ané, 1914.   x, 306 p. plates. 23cm.

"Bibliographie," p. ix-x.

577431B. 1. Bourg-la-Reine, France   —Hist.   May 25, 1951

NL 0354172   NN MH

Lieutier, Paul.
...Louis Mandrin; pièce historique en trois actes en vers. Paris: R. Chiberre, 1925.   110 p.   12°.

1. Drama, French. 2. Mandrin,   Louis, 1724-1755—Drama.
                                               August 26, 1926

NL 0354173   NN

Lieuwe, Denys van
     see   Denis le Chartreux.

HD9574
V4L5
★★
Lieuwen, Edwin, 1923-
A history of petroleum in Venezuela. [Berkeley, 1952]
viii,340 l. maps.

Thesis (Ph.D. in History) - Univ. of California, Jan. 1952.
Bibliography: p.329-340.

NL 0354175   CU

Lieuwen, Edwin, 1923–
Petroleum in Venezuela; a history. Berkeley, University of California Press, 1954.

160 p. maps (1 fold.) 24 cm. (University of California publications in history, v. 47)

Based on thesis—University of California.
Bibliography: p. [145]-151.

1. Petroleum industry and trade—Venezuela. I. Title. (Series: California. University. University of California publications in history, v. 47)

E173.C15 vol. 57   338.2728   A 54—9420
—— Copy 2.   HD9574.V4L5
California. Univ. Libr.
for Library of Congress   †

TxU
NL 0354176   PU OCU NN PSt OU ViU TxU TU DI CU-B DLC ICJ OOxM LU   CU WaTC MtBuM IdPI WaS CaBVaU CaBViP PP

Lieuwen, J. C.

VK563
.N44
Netherlands (*Kingdom, 1815-*   ) *Departement van Marine.*
Zeevaartkundige tafels, voorzien van een korte verklaring van de inrichting en het gebruik; uitg. op last van het Ministerie van Marine. Bewerkt door P. Haverkamp. 's-Gravenhage, Staatsdrukkerij- en Uitgeverijbedrijf, 1948-49.

Lieuwen, John, 1894–
Sweat en tears. Holland, Mich., Printed by Steketee-Van Huis Print. House, *1947.

168 p. 20 cm.

I. Title.
PN6110.H8L5   817.5   48-12335*‡

NL 0354179   DLC

Lieuwen, John, 1894–
Troebel en fon, by John Lieuwen. With 24 pen drawings by the author.   Corsica, S.D., the Corsica globe publishers [Pref. 1938]
3 p.l., [9]-122 p. incl. plates. 22 cm.
Poems in Holland-American dialect.

NL 0354180   CU

VOLUME 332

Lieux, André, 1900–
... Le rachitisme est-il une maladie par carence? ...   Lyon, 1922
25.5 cm.
Thèse - Univ. de Lyon.

NL 0354181   CtY

42
L622   Lieux, Pierre, 1925–
L'élevage et l'entraînement du cheval de pur sang anglais.   Paris, Foulon, 1950.
64 p.

Thèse - École nationale vétérinaire d'Alfort.

1. Race horses.

NL 0354182   DNAL

Lievx commvns, et tres-elegantes sentences: avec plusieurs comparaisons & similitudes sur vne partie d'icelles. Ausquels sont comprins les plus beaux traicts dont on peut vser en amour, & en autres discours.   Lyon, P. Colomby, 1603.
141 p. 14 cm.
Also published under title: Les marguérites des lieux communs et excellentes sentences. Lyon, 1604.
"Epistre de Penelope a Vlisse ... Traduitte des vers latins d'Ouide, par L. S. D. P.": p. 133–141. The translation, erroneously attributed to Philippe Desportes, is by Jacques Davy Du Perron. cf. J. Lavaud in his edition of Desportes' Imitations de l'Ariosto, 1936, p. 177.
1. Quotations, French. I. Ovidius Naso, Publius. II. Du Perron, Jacques Davy, Cardinal, 1556–1618, tr. III. Desportes, Philippe, d. 1606, supposed tr.

PN6302.L5   20–19628 rev

NL 0354183   DLC

Lieux de Genève
see   International Civil Defence Organization. (supplement)

Liev, Ziskind.
פּױלין–אַ שענבֿהיין פֿאַר מענטשן. ניו יאָרק, ביאַליסטאָקער.
נאַמיד-דזשאַרעי אין שטענטסמאַכאַװװער הילפס-קאָמיטעטמן צו שמיצן
די פֿאַליטישע אַרעסטירטע אין פּױלין.
[New York] 1933.
71 p. illus. 22 cm.

1. Political crimes and offenses—Poland.
Title transliterated: Poyln.

HV6295.P6L5   60–55980 ‡

NL 0354185   DLC

[Lievaart, Inge]
Biecht van een Christen aan zijn volk [door] Anna Terweel [pseud.] Oegstgeest, In Signo Piscium, 1944.
[12] p. 25 cm.

"De oplage is groot 250 exemplaren. No. 146."
In verse.

I. Title.

A 48–3530*

Harvard Univ. Library
for Library of Congress

NL 0354186   MH IEN

Lievain, O
L'hystérectomie totale intra-isthmique

see under

Carron, Claudio E

LIEVANA, CARMEN ISABEL
El gran mariscal de Ayacucho, d. Antonio José de Sucre; conferencia leída en el Ateneo Femenino.   La Paz, Bolivia, Escuela Tipográfica Salesiana, 1930.
iv, 21p. 24cm.

1. Sucre, Antonio José de, pres. Bolivia, 1795–1830.

NL 0354188   TxU

Liévana, Pedro de, d. 1602.
Don Pedro de Liévana, primer poeta de Guatemala. (Siete composiciones inéditas del siglo XVI) Publicalas con una advertencia A. R. Rodríguez Moñino ... Badajoz, Centro de estudios extremeños, 1934.
15 p. 22ᶜᵐ.

I. Rodríguez Moñino, Antonio R., 1910– ed.

35–20550

Library of Congress   PQ7499.L5A13   861 39

NL 0354189   DLC

W 4
M61
1950   LIEVANA PALMA, Arturo
Informe médico-sanitario del municipio de Tultepec, edo. de México, y la enterocolitis el la primera infancia; enfermedad de mayor incidencia en el lugar. México, Ortega, 1950.
45 p.
Tesis - Univ. de México.
1. Digestive system - Diseases - Children 2. Public health - Mexico - Mexico (State)

NL 0354190   DNLM

Lievana Palma, Gilberto.
La suspensión provisional en el juicio de amparo. México, 1948.
87 p. 23 cm.

Tesis (profesional)—Univ. Nacional Autónoma de México.
"Bibliografía": p. 87.

1. Amparo (Writ)—Mexico. I. Title.

49–16829*

NL 0354191   DLC

304
L722a   **Liévano, Carlos.**
Asuntos públicos ... Bogotá, Imprenta Eléctrica, 1913.
61 p. 24 cm.

Contents: Prácticas democráticas. Crítica al Congreso de 1909. El derecho de propiedad en tiempo de guerra. Causas de la emigración. Autonomía municipal. Por los fueros del poder judicial. Nueva emisión. La baja del oro. Los nuevos impuestos. Va la prueba. Rafael Rocha Gutiérrez.

NL 0354192   NcU

Liévano, Ernesto Hoffman
see   Hoffman Liévano, Ernesto.

Lievano, Eudaldo Xavier Bouchot
see   Bouchot Lievano, Eudaldo Xavier.

Liévano, Félix J.
see
Liévano Danies, Félix J.

Liévano, Indalecio, 1833–1913.
Exploraciones y estudios de las mejores lineas para construir caminos carreteros y ferrocarriles de Bogotá al río Magdalena. Bogotá, Zalamea hnos., 1885.
(4), 82 p. f°. Map and tables.
Cover-title: Carreteras y ferrocarriles de Bogotá al río Magdalena.

NL 0354196   MH

Gz
385.986
L625I   LIÉVANO, INDALECIO, 1835–
Informe sobre el camino carretero de Bogotá al Río Magdalena, por la ruta de Siete Vueltas, según el trazado del señor Poncet. Diversas rutas que se pueden adoptar para construir caminos carreteros. Ferrocarril al Magdalena, con dos ramificaciones: la una que sale al Río Magdalena a un punto comprendido entre Conejo i Guarumo, i la otra al alto Magdalena al pueblo de Guataquí, por Indalecio Liévano ... Bogotá, Imprenta de La Nación, 1866.
2p l.,58p.   fold. map. 22cm.

NL 0354197   TxU NNH

Liévano, Indalecio, 1833–1913.
Instruccion popular sobre meteorolojia agricola, i especialmente sobre el añil i el café, por Indalecio Lievano ... Bogota, Impr. de la nacion, 1868.
18 p. 18½ᶜᵐ.
Publicacion del 'Diario oficial.' "

1. Meteorology, Agricultural. 2. Indigo. 3. Coffee.

12—11297

Library of Congress   S600.L6

NL 0354198   DLC

Liévano, Indalecio, 1833–1913.
Investigaciones científicas, por Indalecio Liévano ... Bogotá, F. Mantilla, 1871.
85, [3] p. diagrs. on 2 fold. pl. 22½ cm.

CONTENTS.—Teoría de las paralelas sin postulado.—Números inconmensurables.—Varios principios de aritmética.—Teorema de la proporcionalidad de las cantidades.—Teorema que establece la identidad de dos polinomios iguales.—Solucion completa del problema de interes compuesto.—Estudios filosoficos.

1. Parallels (Geometry) 2. Arithmetic—Problems, exercises, etc.

9—20695

Library of Congress   QA481.L6

NL 0354199   DLC

LIÉVANO, Indalecio, 1833–1913.
Tratado de aljebra. Adaptado para la enseñanza en todos los colejios. Bogota, Imp.de Medardo Rivas,1875.

NL 0354200   MH

Liévano, Indalecio, 1833–1913.
Tratado de aritmética, por Indalecio Liévano ... 2. ed., mejorada i aumentada ... Bogotá, Impr. de M. Rivas, 1872.
xv, 206 p., 1 l. 22½ᶜᵐ.

1. Arithmetic—1846–1880.

2—27609

Library of Congress   QA103.L7225

NL 0354201   DLC

VOLUME 332

Liévano, Indalecio, 1833-1913.
Tratado de aritmetica... 3. ed. Bogota,
Imp. de Zalamea, etc., 1878.

NL   0354202   MH

Liévano, Julio, joint ed.

Colombia (*Republic of Colombia, 1886-   *) *Laws, statutes, etc.*
Recopilacion de las leyes y disposiciones vigentes sobre tierras baldías. Ed. oficial. Bogotá, Impr. de M. Rivas, 1884.

Liévano, Manuel Laverde
see   Laverde Liévano, Manuel.

Liévano, Roberto.
En torno a Silva; selección de estudios e investigaciones sobre la obra y la vida íntima del poeta. Bogotá, Editorial El Gráfico, 1946.
73 p. illus., ports. 22 cm.

1. Silva, José Asunción, 1865-1896.   I. Title.

PQ8179.S5Z73   928.6   49-19075*

NL   0354205   DLC CaBVaU NcU OC1 CtY ICU

Liévano, Roberto, ed.
Honor a un colombiano
see under title

Liévano, Roberto.
El mensaje inconcluso (poesías) Bogotá, Dirección de Extensión Cultural y Bellas Artes, 1947.
154 p. 20 cm.

I. Title.

PQ8179.L45M4   861.6   48-13874*

NL   0354207   DLC MU NcD NcU IU NNC DPU CtY

Liévano, Roberto.
Viejas estampas. Bogotá, Ediciones del Concejo, 1948.
110 p. 25 cm.

CONTENTS.—Tertullas literarias de antaño.—Retablos coloniales.—La conjuración septembrina.

1. Colombia—Hist. 2. Colombia—Intellectual life.   I. Title.

F2271.L53   918.6   49-19177*

NL   0354208   DLC IaU ICU NN TxU FMU

Liévano, Vicente, comp.

Chiapas, *Mexico. Laws, statutes, etc.*
Código de las leyes de hacienda del estado, nuevamente arreglado con sus adiciones y reformas, por acuerdo del ejecutivo del mismo, por Vicente Liévano. Tuxtla Gutiérrez, Chiapas, Imprenta del gobierno, 1919.

Liévano, Vicente, ed.

Chiapas, *Mexico. Laws, statutes, etc.*
Nueva codificación de las leyes, decretos y reglamentos del orden judicial, arreglada por acuerdo del gobierno del estado de Chiapas, por Vicente Liévano. Tuxtla Gutiérrez, Imprenta del gobierno, 1927.

Liévano, Vicente.

Chiapas, *Mexico. Laws, statutes, etc.*
Nuevo codigo de las leyes de hacienda del estado, arreglado por acuerdo del ejecutivo del mismo, por el jefe de la sección 1ª de la Tesorería general, Vicente Lievano, y revisado por el tesorero y director general de rentas, Lic. Ausencio M. Cruz. Tuxtla Gutierrez, Chiapas, Impr. del gobierno, 1909.

F2235
.3
.L58   **Liévano Aguirre, Indalecio.**
Bolívar. ₍2. ed.₎ Bogotá, Editorial "El Liberal" ₍1950?₎
520, ₍7₎ p. 24 cm.
Bibliography: p. ₍527₎

1. Bolívar, Simón, 1783-1830.

A 51-1111

Yale Univ. Library
for Library of Congress

NL   0354212   CtY NBuU TxU FMU IaU DPU NcU ViU NcD DLC

Liévano Aguirre, Indalecio.
...Bolívar. Bogotá, "El Liberal" [1952?]
520 p. 24cm.
2. ed.
"Bibliografía," p. [527]

1. Bolívar, Simón, 1783-1830.

NL   0354213   NN

Liévano Aguirre, Indalecio.
... Rafael Núñez; prólogo del doctor Eduardo Santos. 2. ed., corr. Bogotá, Medellín, Librería Siglo xx, 1944.
2 p. l., ₍7₎-429 p. 24½ᵐ. (Ediciones Librería Siglo xx)
"Bibliografía": p. ₍423₎-424.

1. Núñez, Rafael, pres. Colombia. 1825-1894. 2. Colombia—Pol. & govt.—1803-1885. 3. Colombia—Pol. & govt.—1886—

Library of Congress   F2276.N7647 1944   45-21216

923.186

NL   0354214   DLC CSt NcU FU MB KU

Liévano Aguirre, Indalecio.
... Rafael Núñez; prólogo del doctor Eduardo Santos. ₍Bogotá₎ Librería Siglo XX ₍1946₎ xv, 438 p. 24cm. (Ediciones Librería Siglo XX)
3. ed.
"Bibliografía," p. 433-434.

523717B. 1. Núñez, Rafael, pres.   Colombia, 1825-1894.
August 30, 1950

CaBVaU
NL   0354215   NN NcU CU ViU MH TxU IU IaU CtY NBuU

Liévano Aguirre, Nicolás.
Hacia la nueva reforma política. Bogotá, Impr. Municipal, 1953.
58 p. illus. 19 cm. (Colección Estado nacional)

1. Political science.   I. Title.

JC271.L47   320   54-17926 ‡

NL   0354216   DLC IaU MH DPU

Law   **Lievano Baraya, Félix José,** ed.

Colombia. *Laws, statutes, etc.*
Compilación aérea nacional (aviación militar, aviación civil y militar, radiocomunicaciones, correos, aduanas, convenciones internacionales) 1916-1948 ₍por₎ Félix José Lievano Baraya y José Antonio Sánchez Bernal. Bogotá, Impr. del Ministerio de Guerra, 1949.

Liévano Danies, Félix J.
... Principios o fundamentos de la economía política: depresión económica, sus causas, desarrollo y remedios que deben aplicarse. Bogotá, Rep. de Colombia, Tip. Augusta ₍1935₎
96, 2 p. 17ᵐ.
Includes advertising matter.

1. Money. 2. Economics. 3. Currency question—Colombia.   I. Title.

Library of Congress   HB179.L6   36-28640

330

NL   0354218   DLC

Lieve, H   L
Predikant achter prikkeldraad ₍door₎ H. L. Lieve ... ₍en₎ K. R. ter Steege ... Nijkerk, G. F. Callenbach n. v. ₍1946₎
219 p., 1 l. 21ᵐ.

1. World war, 1939-1945—Prisoners and prisons, German. 2. World war, 1939-1945—Personal narratives, Dutch. 3. World war, 1939-1945—Jews. 4. Amersfoort (Concentration camp)   I. Steege, K. R. ter, joint author. II. Title.
D805.N4L5   A F 47-3005
Hoover library, Stanford   univ.
for Library of Congress   †

NL   0354219   CSt-H NN DLC

PT5404
.B7   **Lieve, R. W.,** joint author.

Brands, G   A
Gouden aren, leesboek voor gymnasia, middelbare scholen en scholen van voortgezet lager onderwijs door G. A. Brands en R. W. Lieve. Met illustr. van B. Midderigh-Bokhorst ₍et al.₎ 's Gravenhage, G. B. van Goor Zonen, 1947-

---

PT5060
.B65
1949   **Lieve, R. W.,** joint author.

Brands, G   A
Overzicht der Nederlandse letteren, door G. A. Brands en R. W. Lieve. 3. vermeerderde druk. 's-Gravenhage, G. B. van Goor, 1949.

W 4
P23
1955
no. 121   **LIEVEAUX, André Georges,** 1926-
Polypes fibreux intra-cavitaires de l'utérus; indications thérapeutiques; techniques chirurgicales. Paris, 1955.
42 p. (Paris. ₍Université₎ Faculté de médecine. Thèse, 1955, no. 121)
1. Fibroma 2. Uterus - Neoplasms

NL   0354222   DNLM

VOLUME 332

Wason
DS646.6
L72

Lievegoed, Ant.   J   ,
    De Planclade; moderne Molukkenvaart.
₍Semarang? 1924?₎
    75 p. 21 cm.

"Overdruk van de reisschetsen van Ant.
J. Lievegoed in De Locomotief van 8, 14, 22,
23, 24, 26, 27, 28, 30 3n 31 Mei 1924."

1. Moluccas--Descr. & trav.   I. Title.

NL   0354223   NIC

B583 **Lievegoed, Antonius Adrianus Wilhelmus Maria.**
.L7   Eenige termen der stoïsche kennisleer bij Marcus Aurelius
Antoninus ... Amsterdam, H. J. Paris, 1924.
    ₍11₎, 71 p. 23ᶜᵐ.
    Proefschrift—Amsterdam.

1. Aurelius Antoninus, Marcus, emperor of Rome. 2. Stoics.

NL   0354224   ICU IU MH NcD

Lievegoed, Bernardus Cornelis Johannes.
    Het arbeidsveld der sociale paedagogie. Utrecht, W. de
Haan, 1955.
    32 p. 25 cm.
    Rede—Nederlandsche Economische Hoogeschool, Rotterdam (aan-
vaarding van het ambt van bijzonder hoogleraar in de sociale paedagogie vanwege de Stichting tot Bevordering der Sociale Paedagogie)
1955.

1. Educational sociology.   I. Title.

LC71.L5   65–49616 ‡

NL   0354225   DLC

Lievegoed, Bernardus Cornelis Johannes.
    Maat — rhythme — melodie, grondslagen voor een thera-
peutisch gebruik van muzikale elementen ... Door Bernardus
Cornelis Johannes Lievegoed ... Utrecht, Uitgeversmaatschappij W. de Haan n. v. ₍1939₎
    173 p. illus. (music) 2 pl. on 1 l., diagr. 25ᶜᵐ.
    Proefschrift—Leyden.
    With summary in Dutch, German, English and French.
    "Lijst van geraadpleegde literatuur" : p. ₍172₎–173.
    "Ziektegeschiedenissen" : p. ₍120₎–159.
    "Stellingen" : 2 leaves, laid in.
    1. Music, Influence of. 2. Music, Physical effect of. 3. Music—
Psychology. 4. Children, Abnormal and backward.   I. Title.

Library of Congress   ML3920.L693M2
                                            40–21451
                                            780.13

NL   0354226   DLC CtY NNC

Lievegoed, Bernardus Cornelis Johannes.
    Ontwikkelingsphasen van het kind. Utrecht, W. de Haan,
1946.
    199 p. illus. 25 cm.

1. Child study.   I. Title.

BF721.L53   55–36608

NL   0354227   DLC CtY

R147
.P2S4

Lievegoed, Bernardus Cornelis Johannes.

Sleeswijk, Jan Gerard, 1879–   *ed.*
    Paracelsus herdacht, 1493–1541. Twee voordrachten:
Paracelsus als hervormer der geneeskunde en als synthetisch
denker, door R. A. B. Oosterhuis. Hippocrates, Paracelsus,
Goethe, door B. C. J. Lievegoed, met een woord vooraf van
J. G. Sleeswijk. Den Haag, W. P. van Stockum, 1941.

Lieven, Alexander, Baron von, 1843–1922
D285.8   Der General Baron Otto Heinrich von Lieven
L59L5   und seine Gemahlin, die Staatsdame Charlotte
Stack   geb. Freiin von Gaugreben, Fürstin. Riga,
W.F.Häcker, 1915.
    36 p. illus. 27cm.

1.Liven, Otto Heinrich, Baron von, 1726–
1781. 2.Liven, Charlotte (Gaugreben), kniaginia, 1743–1828.   SC

NL   0354229   CSt

Lieven, Alexander, *baron* von, 1843–1922.
    Urkunden und nachrichten zu einer familiengeschichte der
barone, freiherren, grafen und fürsten Lieven ... Gesammelt
von baron Alexander Lieven. Mitau, Druck von J. F. Steffenhagen und sohn, 1910–11.
    2 v. illus. (incl. coats of arms) 22ᵐ.
    Imprint on label mounted on cover of v. 1: Riga, Commissions-verlag
von Jonck & Poliewsky.
    CONTENTS.—I. Die Lieven in Livland von 1269–1389, in Estland von
1389–1713, in Schweden seit 1653.—II. Die Lieven in Kurland und in den
grenzgebieten von Littauen seit 1507.

1. Lieven family.
                                            43–47055
    Library of Congress   CS887.L5   1910

NL   0354230   DLC

Lieven, Anatole, *prince* de
    see
Liven, Anatoliĭ Pavlovich, *kniaz'*, 1872–

Lieven, Anton
Lieven, Anton   Aerztlicher Ratgeber für Aachener Thermalkuren, unter Berücksichtigung
von Kuren in der Heimat.. 44 pp. 12°.
Aachen, H. Köster, 1905.

NL   0354232   DNLM

Lieven, Anton
    Guide populaire du baigneur et du touriste à
Aix-la-Chapelle et Borcette...   Aix-la-Chapelle,
O. Müller, 1900.
    16.5 cm.
    Fold. map. in pocket.

NL   0354233   CtY

4DD
3028

Lieven, Anton
    Populärer Führer durch Bad Aachen,
Burtscheid und Umgebung, für
Kurgäste und Touristen. 5. Aufl.
Aachen, P. Urlichs [   ]
    112 p.

NL   0354234   DLC-P4

Lieven, Anton
—— Popular guide for the use of the Aix-
la-Chapelle waters. 90 pp. 12°. Aachen,
F. G. Mosengel [1911].

NL   0354235   DNLM

Lieven, Anton
—— Die Syphilis der Mund- und Rachenhöhle.
112 pp., 1 pl. 8°. Jena, 1900.
Forms 2. lfft. v. 4, of: Klin. Vortr. a. d. Geb. d. Otol.
u. Pharyngo-Rhinol. Jena.

NL   0354236   DNLM

Lieven, Anton
—— . Die Syphilis der oberen Luftwege unter
besonderer Berücksichtigung der differentiellen
Diagnose und der lokalen Therapie. I. Teil.
Die Syphilis der Nase. 28 pp. 8°. Jena, G.
Fischer, 1898.
Forms 10. lfft. v. 2, of: Klin. Vortr. a. d. Geb. d. Otol.
u. Pharyngo-Rhinol. Jena.

NL   0354237   DNLM

Lieven (Anton). *Ueber den Einfluss einiger
Arzneimittel auf Blutkreislauf und Blutvertheil-
ung. [Würzburg.] 17 pp., 1 l. 8°. Wesel,
W. Romen, 1889.

NL   0354238   DNLM

DA20
.R91
3d ser.,
vol. 60, 62

Lieven, Dar'ia Khristoforovna (Benckendorff)
    kniaginia, 1785–1857.

Aberdeen, George Hamilton-Gordon, *4th earl of,* 1784–1860.
    The correspondence of Lord Aberdeen and Princess Lieven,
1832–1854 ... Edited for the Royal historical society by E.
Jones Parry ... London, Offices of the Royal historical society,
1938–39.

Lieven, Dar'ia Khristoforovna (Benckendorff) *kniaginia,*
1785–1857.
    Correspondence of Princess Lieven and Earl Grey, edited
and translated by Guy Le Strange ... London, R. Bentley
and son, 1890.
    3 v. fronts. (2 port., fold. facsim.) facsim. 23ᶜᵐ.
    Letters of Princess Lieven translated from the French.
    CONTENTS.—I. 1824 to 1830.—II. 1830 to 1834.—III. 1834 to 1841.
    1. Europe — Hist. — 1815–1848 — Sources. 2. Europe—Politics—1815–
1848. 3. Gt. Brit.—Hist.—19th cent.—Sources.   I. Grey, Charles Grey,
2d earl, 1764–1845, joint author. II. Le Strange, Guy, 1854–1933, ed.
and tr.
                                            15–12047 Revised
    Library of Congress   D352.8.L65
                                ₍r43g2₎   920.7

        OC1 DCU-IA PPL PU NjP WaU
NL   0354240   DLC CaBVaU NN TNJ MdBP NNC CtY MiU OCU

DB80
.8
.M55
1942

Lieven, Dar'ia Khristoforovna (Benckendorff)
    kniaginia, 1785–1857.

Metternich-Winneburg, Clemens Lothar Wenzel, *fürst von,*
1773–1859.
    Geist und herz verbündet; Metternichs briefe an die gräfin
Lieven. Wien, W. Andermann ₍1942₎

Lieven, Dar'ia Khristoforovna (Benckendorff) *kniaginia,*
1785–1857.
    Letters of Dorothea, princess Lieven, during her residence in
London, 1812–1834; edited by Lionel G. Robinson; with two
photogravure portaits. London, New York ₍etc.₎ Longmans,
Green, and co., 1902.
    xx p., 1 l., 414 p. 2 port. (incl. front.) 23½ᶜᵐ.
    1. Gt. Brit.—For. rel.—Russia. 2. Russia—For. rel.—Gt. Brit. 3. Eu-
rope—Politics—1815–1848. 4. Gt. Brit.—Pol. & govt.—1800–1837.   I.
Robinson, Lionel G., ed. and tr.
                                            3–1262 Revised
    Library of Congress   D352.8.L62
                                ₍r43g2₎   -920.7

        PP PU
NL   0354242   DLC MeB GU NcD MB WaU OO OCU OC1 MiU

DB80
.8
.M55
1909

Lieven, Dar'ia Khristoforovna (Benckendorff)
    kniaginia, 1785–1857.

Metternich-Winneburg, Clemens Lothar Wenzel, *fürst von,*
1773–1859.
    Lettres du prince de Metternich à la comtesse de Lieven,
1818–1819; publiées, avec une introduction, une conclusion et
des notes, par Jean Hanoteau; préface de m. Arthur Chuquet
... Paris, Plon-Nourrit et cⁱᵉ, 1909.

VOLUME 332

Lieven, Dar'ía Khristoforovna (Benckendorff) *kníā͠, iníā,*
1785–1857.
The Lieven-Palmerston correspondence, 1828–1856; translated and edited by Lord Sudley, with a preface by Sir John Squire. London, J. Murray ₍1943₎.

xiv, 316 p. front., plates, ports. 22½°°.

"First edition, 1943."
"Errata" slip inserted.
1. Europe—Politics—1815–1848. 2. Gt. Brit.—Pol. & govt.—19th cent.
3. Gt. Brit.—Soc. life & cust. ɪ. Palmerston, Emily Mary (Lamb)
Temple, viscountess, 1787–1869. ɪɪ. Sudley, Arthur Paul John Charles
James Gore, viscount, 1903— ed. and tr. ɪɪɪ. Title.

Harvard univ. Library   A 43–2346
for Library of Congress   D352.8.L68.

          †   920.7

   DLC MB
NL 0354244   MH NjP OrP OrU OKentU NcD FMU TU CtY

Lieven, Dar'ía Khristoforovna (Benckendorff) *kníāginíā,*
1785–1857.
The private letters of Princess Lieven to Prince Metternich, 1820–1826, edited and with a biographical foreword by Peter Quennell, assisted in translation by Dilys Powell ... London, J. Murray ₍1937₎.

xxii, 386 p. incl. plates, facsims. (1 double) front., plates, ports. 23°°.

1. Metternich-Winneburg, Clemens Lothar Wenzel, fürst von, 1773–
1859. ɪ. *Quennell, Peter, 1905— ed. and tr. ɪɪ. Powell, Dilys,
joint tr.   38–5637 Revised

Library of Congress   D352.8.L67 1937
          ₍r43d2₎   920.7

   NNC OU OCl PPL
NL 0354245   DLC CaBVaU IdU OrP OrU WaSpG TxU OrU CtY

Lieven, Dar'ía Khristoforovna (Benckendorff) *kníāginíā,*
1785–1857.
The private letters of Princess Lieven to Prince Metternich, 1820–1826, edited and with a biographical foreword by Peter Quennell, assisted in translation by Dilys Powell ... New York, E. P. Dutton & co., inc. ₍°1938₎.

xxii, 386 p. incl. plates, facsims. (1 double) front., plates, ports. 23½°°.

"First edition."
1. Metternich-Winneburg, Clemens Lothar Wenzel, fürst von, 1773–
1859. ɪ. *Quennell, Peter, 1905— ed. and tr. ɪɪ. Powell, Dilys,
joint tr.   38–3251 Revised

Library of Congress   D352.8.L67 1938
          ₍r43d2₎   920.7

  NcRS WaU OClJC OCU OClW PU OO NN NcGU
NL 0354246   DLC WaS IdU NIC KyLx ViU CtHC PSt CtY

Lieven, Dar'ía Khristoforovna (Benckendorff) *Kníāginíā,*
1785–1857.
The private letters of Princess Lieven to Prince Metternich, 1820–1826. Edited by Peter Quennell. London, J. Murray ₍1948₎.

xx, 321 p. illus., facsims., ports. 21 cm. (Albemarle library)
First published 1937.

ɪ. Metternich-Winneburg, Clemens Lothar Wenzel, Fürst von,
1773–1859. ɪɪ. Quennell, Peter, 1905— ed. and tr. ɪ. Title.

[D352.8]   909.8'0924   67–4338/CD
Printed for Card Div.
Library of Congress

NL 0354247   AU NcU TU IU NNC PV LU NSyU NFQC

Lieven, Dar'ía Khristoforovna (Beckendorff)
  kníāginíā, 1785–1857.
D352.8
L65   Das Tagebuch der Fürstin Lieven, mit politischen Skizzen und einigen Briefen. Hrsg. mit Erläuterungen von Harold Temperley. ₍Übersetzung aus dem Englischen von Thea Nowak. 1. Auf ₎ Berlin, Verlag für Kulturpolitik, 1926.
     316 p. 23cm.
    "Bücher- und Quellenverzeichnis": p. ₍311₎–316.

     1. Europe - Politics - 1815–1848. I. Temperley, Harold William Vazeille, 1879— ed

NL 0354248   CSt IaU

Lieven, Dar'ía Khristoforovna (Benckendorff) *kníāginíā,*
1785–1857.
The unpublished diary and political sketches of Princess Lieven, together with some of her letters, edited with elucidations by Harold Temperley ... London, J. Cape ltd., 1925.

288 p. front., ports., facsim. 23°°.

"Index to books and authorities": p. 280–283.

1. Europe—Politics—1815–1848.   ɪ. Temperley, Harold William
Vazeille, 1879— ed.   25–19519 Revised 2

Library of Congress   D352.8.L6 1925
          ₍r43f2₎   920.7

  MiU OCl NcD PU
NL 0354249   DLC WaSpG GU CU-S MeB CtY WaU NN MB OCU

Lieven, Dorothea de
see
Lieven, Dar'ía Khristoforovna (Benckendorff) *kníāginíā,*
1785–1857.

LIEVEN, Franz, 1883–
Über ureteritis cystica. Ein beitrag zur kenntnis ihrer genese. Inaug.-diss., Bonn, 1909₍

NL 0354251   MBCo ICRL DNLM MH

Soc
DS
517.9   Lieven, H   of Riga
L5   Hurra-Bansai. Erlebnisse eines Arztes während des russisch-japanischen Feldzuges. Mit zweihundertneunundsechzig Illustrationen nach Originalaufnahmen des Verfassers und vier Kartenskizzen.   Berlin, Dietrich, 1905.
     372p. illus., maps

     1. Russo-Japanese War, 1904–1905 - Medical and sanitary affairs. I. Title.

NL 0354252   FTaSU NN DNW WaU CtY DLC-P4

---

f871   Lieven, Hugo.
C7.Y11   Die consecutio temporum des Cicero. Eine grammatische untersuchung. Riga, 1872.
     55p.

NL 0354253   IU NjP CtY

Lieven, Just Bubbe-
   see   Bubbe-Lieven, Just.

Lieven, Maximilian, Fürst
HD8529   Die Arbeitsverhältnisse den Grossgrund-
C6L54   besitzes in Kurland, von Fürst Maximilian Lieven.   Mitau, J.F. Steffenhagen, 1900–
Stack   v. 30cm.

     Contents.-Bd.1.Die Enquête vom Frühjahr 1899 und ihre Resultate. Lieferungen.-

     1.Labor and laboring classes - Courland.
2.Peasantry - Courland. I.Title.

NL 0354255   CSt InU ICJ

Lieven (Parcival), Baron [1860–]. *Ueber
den Blutdruck bei den verschiedenen Formen
des Pneumothorax. Experimentelle Untersuchungen. 53 pp., 1 l. 8°. Dorpat, H. Laakmann, 1893.

NL 0354256   DNLM

Lieven (Paul). *Ein Beitrag zur Aetiologie
der Geschwüre der Vaginalportion. 26 pp. 8°.
Würzburg, Stahel, 1864.

NL 0354257   DNLM ICRL

Kress
Room   Lieven, Paul, prince
     Über vertheilung des grundbesitzes ... Dorpat, Gedruckt in der Universitätsbuchdruckerei von J.C.Schünmann's wittwe, 1844.
     2 p.l., 94, [1] p. 21.5 cm.

     Thesis - Dorpat.

     1.Dissertations, Academic. 2.Land tenure -
Esthonia. 3.Esthonia.

NL 0354258   MH-BA

Lieven, Peter, prince
     see   Lieven, Petr Aleksandrovich, kniaz, 1887–

Lieven, Peter von, *d.* 1943.
... Im einklang mit dem Ewigen. Zürich, Rascher, 1944.
217, ₍1₎ p., 1 l. 20¾°.

"1. auflage."
"Copyright 1943."

1. Eternity. 2. Love.   ɪ. Title.
BD422.G3L5   47–16911

NL 0354260   DLC

Lieven, Quirin, ed.
     Ausführungsbestimmungen (grundbestimmungen) zum gesetz über das branntweinmonopol vom 8. April 1922
     see under   Germany (Federal Republic, 1949–) Laws, statutes, etc.

Law   Lieven, Quirin, ed.

   Germany. *Laws, statutes, etc.*
     Gesetz über das Branntweinmonopol vom 8. April 1922. Textausg. unter Berücksichtigung der Änderungen bis 1. Juli 1948, bearb. von Quirin Lieven ₍und₎ Hans-Joachim Hoppe. Düsseldorf, K. Stamm ₍1948₎

Law   Lieven, Quirin, ed.

   Germany. *Laws, statutes, etc.*
     Gesetz über das Branntweinmonopol vom 8. April 1922. Stand 1. Februar 1949. Kommentar von Quirin Lieven ₍und₎ Hans-Joachim Hoppe. Düsseldorf, K. Stamm ₍1949₎

Lieven, Quirin, 1881–
     Das nichtige und das anfechtbare Rechtsgeschäft nach dem Rechte des Bürgerlichen Gesetzbuches ... von Quirin Lieven ... Borna-Leipzig, R. Noske, 1909.

     viii, 58 p. 22cm.

     Inaug.-diss. - Erlangen.
     "Literaturverzeichnis": p. ₍vii₎–viii.

NL 0354264   MH-L NIC ICRL NN MH

VOLUME 332

Lieven (Samuel P.) *Nonnulla de tæniis, imprimis de Bothriocephalo lato, ejusque appellendi methodo peculiari.* 59 pp. 8°. *Dorpat, typ. J. C. Schuenmanni, 1834.*

NL 0354265   DNLM

Lieven, Sophie, *Fürstin von,* 1880–
    Eine Saat, die reiche Frucht brachte; aus der Erweckungs-Bewegung in Petersburg um die Wende des 19. Jahrhunderts. Basel, Brunnen-Verlag ₍1952₎

112 p. 19 cm.

1. Revivals—Russia.   ɪ. Title.

BV3777.R8L5   54–24159 ‡

NL 0354266   DLC CtY-D MH

Lieven, Theodor Karl.
    Heio! Emmerich! Geschichtliche Erzählung für die Jugend aus der Zeit der Vorbereitung zum Antritt der Herrschaft der Germanen in Europa (3. Jahrhundert) Mit Bildschmuck von Kurt Lange. Hildesheim, F. Borgmeyer ₍193–?₎

174 p. illus. 19 cm.

ɪ. Title.

PZ35.L52   55–53051 ‡

NL 0354267   DLC

Lieven (Theodorus Jacobus.) *Tuberculosis ventriculi casus duo.* 30 pp. 8°. *Halis Sax., formis Ploetzianis. 1863.*

NL 0354268   DNLM

Lieven, Wilhelm.
    Das rote Russland; augenblicks-bilder aus den tagen der grossen russischen revolution; tagebuchblätter von dr. Wilhelm Lieven. Mit sechzehn abbildungen. 6. bis 10. tausend. Berlin, A. Scherl ₍1918₎

212 p. plates, ports., fold. facsim. 19ᶜᵐ.

1. Russia—Hist.—Revolution. 1917–   ɪ. Title.

DK265.L4   21–21245

NL 0354269   DLC DNW CtY NN NcD ICJ

Lieven, Wilhelm.
    Russlands zerfall und die erneuerung des Baltikums, von dr. med. Wilhelm Lieven. Berlin, K. Curtius ₍1919₎

31 p. 22ᶜᵐ.

1. Russia—Hist.—Revolution. 1917–   2. Baltic provinces.
ɪ. Title.

                                   34–6752

Library of Congress   DK265.L44   947.084

NL 0354270   DLC CSt-H

Mann SF 487 L72

Lievens, F
    La situation actuelle des recherches sur l'élevage des poussins en batterie. Louvain, Librairie René Fonteyn, 1936.
    110 p. diagrs., tables. 24 cm. (Institut de Zootechnie de Louvain. Bulletin no. 25)

        1. Poultry.   I. Title. II. Series: Louvain. Univer   sité catholique. Institut
de zootechnie.   Bulletin. no. 25.

NL 0354271   NIC

Lievens, Gerard.
    Christelijcke en vriendelijcke aensprake der predicanten van Nimmegen
        see under title

Lievens, Gerard, fl. 1669.
    Disputatio Medica Inauguralis De Syncope...
Lugduni Batavorum: J. Elzevier, 1669.
    Copinger 2849

NL 0354273   PU DNLM

Lievens, Jan, 1546– (ca) 1599.

Plinius Caecilius Secundus, C.
    C. PlinI Panegyricvs liber Trajano dictvs, cvm annotationibus antehac ineditis Dominici Bavdii. Iis accedunt commentarius Justi Lipsii, integræ notæ Joannis Livinæi, Jani Gruteri, Conradi Rittershusii, ac selectæ variorum. Lvgdvni Batavorum, ex officina Hackiana, 1675.

BR65 .C45D4 1612

Lievens, Jan, 1546 (ca.)–1599, tr.

Chrysostomus, Joannes, *Saint, patriarch of Constantinople, d.* 407.
    Divi patris Ioannis Chrysostomi ... De virginitate liber, in gratiam stvdiosæ iuuentutis græcè & latine editus; interprete Ioanne Liuineio Gandensi. Monachi, ex typographéo Nicolai Henrici, impensis Ioannis Hertsroy, 1612.

---

* PA6138 .P315 1599

Lievens, Jan, ca. 1546–1599, ed.
    XII panegyrici veteres, ad antiquam quà editionem, qua Scripturam infinitis locis emendati, aucti. Johannes Livineius Belga, gandensis, recensebat, ac notis illustrabat. Antverpiae, ex officina Plantiniana, Apud Joannem Moretum, 1599.
    397 p. 18cm.
    "Notae," 285–397 p.
    Publisher's device on title page.
    1. Latin literature (Collections) I. Plinius Caecilius Secundus, C. II. Claudianus Mamertus, d. ca. 474. III. Theodosius I, the Great, Emperor of Rome, 346?–395. IV. Constantinus I, the Great, Emperor of Rome, d. 337 V. Constantius II, Emperor of the east. VI. Title.
    361.

NL 0354276   ViU MH

Lievens, Jan, 1546(ca.)–1599, ed.
    XII. panegyrici veteres... Nuper quidem ope Ioh. Livineii, nunc vero opera Iani Grvteri. Praeter quorum notas, accedunt etiam coniecturae Valentis Acidalii & Conradi Rittershvsii. Francofvrti, Typis N. Hoffmanni, Impensis I. Rhodij, 1607.
    615 p.

    I. Grvterus, Janus, 1560–1627, ed.

NL 0354277   NjP MdBP PBm

Lievens, Jef
    Herrie in Heidebroek. Retie, Kempische Boekhandel ₍1955₎

162 p.

NL 0354278   MH DLC-P4

LIÉVENS, LEON.
    Méthode de voix labiale idéale; la voix sur les lèvres, applicable aux chanteurs des deux sexes. Illustrée de 55 gravures.   Paris [1913] 63 p. 27cm.

    1. Singing—Methods, 1901–   (In French).

NL 0354279   NN

Liévens, Léon.
    Méthode de voix labiale idéale, applicable aux chanteurs des deux sexes. Illustrée de 55 gravures. ₍2. éd.₎ Paris ₍ᶜ1925₎

64 p. illus., music. 24 cm. (La voix sur les lèvres)

1. Singing—Methods.   ɪ. Title.

MT835.L5 1925   63–58869/MN

NL 0354280   DLC

Liévens, Léon.
    ... La vérité vocale sur la voix humaine parlée, déclamée, chantée ... ₍Yvetot, Imprimerie commerciale₎ ᶜ1925.

cover-title, 119, ₍1₎ p. illus., plates. 24ᶜᵐ.

1. Voice. 2. Singing and voice culture.   ɪ. Title.

                                  26–23237

Library of Congress   MT821.L43

NL 0354281   DLC

Liever, David
    see Liwer, David.

Lievermann, C. Siegfried.
    ... Ueber einige Nitroverbindungen des Thiodiphenylaminsulfoxyds... von Dipl. Ing. C. S. Lievermann.   Genf: J. Studer & Sohn, 1917. 29 p. 8°.
    Dissertation, Lausanne, 1917.

1. Sulphoxides.
                                   January 10, 1923.

NL 0354283   NN PU

Lievevrouw-Coopman, Lodowijk, 1862–
    Blonde Marie... Drama in vier bedrijven. Antwerpen, G.J. & E. Janssens, 1901.
    72 p. 12°. (Vlaamsche tooneelverzameling, Gemengde rollen, no. 215)

NL 0354284   NN

VOLUME 332

Lievevrouw-Coopman, Lodewijk, 1862-
De gedachtenlezer... Kluchtspel in drie
bedrijven.   Antwerpen, G.J. & E. Janssens
[1901]
    64 p.   12°.   (Vlaamsche tooneelverzame-
ling. Gemengde rollen, no. 203)

NL 0354285   NN

Lievevrouw-Coopman, Lodewijk, 1862-
Gents woordenboek. Gent, Drukkerij Erasmus,
1950-1955.
    2 v. (Koninklijke Vlaamse academie voor
taal- en letterkunde. Reeks 6, nr. 68)

1. Flemish language - Dialects - Ghent.
I. Vlaamse academie voor taal- en letterkunde.
[Uitgeven] VI. reeks. [Bekroonde werken] 68.
II. Title.

NL 0354286   NNC NcU ICU MH

Lievevrouw-Coopman, Lod[ewijk], 1862-
Meisjesgrillen; blijspel in een bedrijf.   Antwerpen: Gebroe-
ders Janssens, 1911. 40 p.   3. ed.   12°.   (Vlaamsche
Tooneel-verzameling. Gemengde rollen. no. 350.)

1. Drama (Flemish). 2. Title.
                                               October 19, 1911.

NL 0354287   NN

Lievevrouw-Coopman, Lodewijk, 1862-
Naakte beelden. Tooneelstuk in één bedrijf.
Antwerpen, G.J. & E. Janssens [1901]
    31 p.   sq. 12°.   (Vlaamsche Tooneelver-
zameling. Reeks 173 no. 195)

NL 0354288   NN

Lievevrouw-Coopman, Lodewijk, 1862-
... Oude gentsche typen en andere zantingen, door Lod.
Lievevrouw-Coopman. 2. en verzamelde uitgave. Gent-Dede-
berg, Drukkerij & boekbinderij "De Dageraad" [1944?]
    46 p., 1 l. Illus. (incl. music) plates, ports. 24°°. (Roman- en novel-
lenbibliotheek "Het Morgenrood." 6)
    At head of title: ... Volkskundige sprokkelingen.
    "Pater Kerckhove": p. 35–43.

1. Ghent—Soc. life & cust. 2. Kerckhove, Isidor van de, 1790–1871.
I. Title.
DH811.G48L5   914.93   A F 47–50
Newberry library
for Library of Congress   †

NL 0354289   ICN NN CU DLC MH

Lievevrouw-Coopman, Lod[ewijk], 1862-
Roodkapje; blijspel in een bedrijf.   Antwerpen: Gebroeders
Janssens, 1910. 36 p.   3. ed.   12°.   (Vlaamsche Tooneel-
verzameling; Gemengde Rollen. no. 346.)

1. Drama (Flemish). 2. Title.
                                               August 23, 1911.

NL 0354290   NN

Lievevrouw-Coopman, Lod[ewijk], 1862-
Smokkelaarsvolk; drama in vier bedrijven.   Gent: V
Roegiers-van Schoorisse, 1912. 47 p.   8°.

1. Drama (Dutch). 2. Title.
                                               January 13, 1913.

NL 0354291   NN

Lievevrouw-Coopman, M.
Het volkskind zijne opvoeding en zijn onderwijs, door
M. Lievevrouw-Coopman ... Gent, Drukkerij I. Vander-
poorten, 1895.
    2 p. l., [3]–134 p. 24°°.
    "Door de Koninklijke academie van Belgie met een prijs 'De Kein'
bekroond."

1. Education. 2. Children—Education.

                                               E 11–1039
Library, U. S. Bur. of   Education LB775.L59

NL 0354292   DHEW

Liévin de Hamme, père.
Ancient and modern Palestine, by Mary B. Rotthier; from
the French of Brother Liévin de Hamme ... 4th ed., rev. and
enl. ... New York, The Meany printing co. [°1898]
    2 v. fronts., plates, ports., map, plans (part fold.) 18°°.
    First French edition, 1869.

1. Palestine—Descr. & trav.   I. Rotthier, Mary B., tr.
                                  [Secular name: Édouard Colleman]
                                          99–1574 Revised
Library of Congress   DS107.L72

NL 0354293   DLC NN PLatS DHN

Liévin de Hamme, père.
    Guida indicatrice dei santuari e
luoghi storici di Terra Santa. Traduzione dal francese del padre Cipriano
da Treviso. Venezia, Antonelli, 1870.
    752 p. illus. 17°°.

    1. Palestine - Descr.& trav.- Guide-
books.

NL 0354294   NjP

LIÉVIN de HAMME, pere.
    Guide-indicateur des sanctuaires et lieux his-
toriques de la Terre Sainte. 2e. Louvain, F.
et J. Lefever, 1876.

    3 vol. Maps, plans.

NL 0354295   MH CtY ArLSJ

LIÉVIN de HAMME, père.
    Guide-indicateur des sanctuaires et lieux
historiques de la Terre Sainte. 3e éd.
Jerusalem, impr. des PP. Franciscains, 1887.

    3 vols. Maps, plans, illustr.

NL 0354296   MH CtY DHN

Liévin de Hamme, père.
    Guide-indicateur des Sanctuaires et lieux
historiques de la Terre-Sainte. 4 ed. revue,
augmentée et enriche de vues, de cartes et de
plans nouveaux. Troisième partie.   Jérusalem,
Imprimerie des PP. Franciscains, 1897.

    viii, 353? p. illus., maps. p. 18cm.
    Defective copy: pp. 272-353 missing.

1. Palestine—Description and travel—Guidebooks.

NL 0354297   PLatS NN

Liévin de Hamme, père.
    Guide to the Holy Places and historical
sites in the Holy Lnad, by Brother Liévin de
Hamme...   Ghent, C. Poelman, 1875.
    [vi], vii, 623 p.

NL 0354298   DHN

Liévin de Hamme, père.
    Das Heilige Land und seine heilig-
thümer. Ein pilgerführer. Aus der 2.
verm.aufl.des französischen originals
übers.und mit benutzung neuer angaben
und ergänzungen des verfassers bearb.
von P.Franz Joseph Costa-Major. Mainz,
Kirchheim, 1887.
    3 v. illus., maps. 18 °°.

NL 0354299   NjP

Liévin de Hamme, père.
    The pilgrim's handbook to Jerusalem and its neighbourhood, by
Wilfrid C. Robinson from the French by Brother Liévin de Hamme...   London, Burns and Oates [etc., etc., 1890]   336 p.
illus., map. 16cm.
    Imperfect: p. [333]–336 mutilated.
    Real name: Ed Colleman.

290282B. 1. Palestine—Guidebooks,   1890.   April 20, 1945

NL 0354300   NN DHN

595.323 Liévin, Albert Karl Ludwig, 1810-1881.
L62b   Die Branchiopoden der Danziger Gegend. Ein
Beitrag zur Fauna der Provinz Preussen. Mit
11 Tafeln in Steindruck.   Danzig, Druck der
Gerhard'schen Officin, 1848.
    52p. plates. 27cm. (Neueste Schriften der
Naturforschenden Gesellschaft in Danzig. 4.Bd.,
2. Heft)

NL 0354301   IU MH NN

Liévin, Albert Karl Ludwig, 1810–1881.
    Danzig und die Cholera. Ein statistisch-topographischer Ver-
such, von Dr. A. Liévin. ... . Danzig, A. W. Kafemann, 1868.
    [2], 96 p. incl. tables. I fold. plan. 30°°.

NL 0354302   ICJ

Liévin (Albert [Carl Ludwig]) [1810–81]. °De
epidemia Halensi anni mdccexxxiv. 32 pp., 1 l.
8°. Halæ, typ. C. Granerti, 1835.

NL 0354303   DNLM PPC

Lievin, Albert Karl Ludwig, 1810-
—— Die Geburtsziffer und die Kindersterb-
lichkeit in Danzig in den Jahren 1862–73. 1 l.
fol. [Danzig, A. W. Kafemann, n. d.]

NL 0354304   DNLM

Lievin, Albert Karl Ludwig, 1810-
—— Die Mortalitätsverhältnisse in Danzig in
den Jahren 1884, 1885. 2 sheets. 4° & fol.
Danzig, A. W. Kafemann, 1885–6.
Sheet for 1884 is repr. from: Danziger Zeitung, No. 15148.

NL 0354305   DNLM

VOLUME 332

Liévin [Albert Karl Ludwig] [1810–]. Die
Sterblichkeit in Danzig vor und seit dem Jahre
1872. 1 l. roy. 8°. [Danzig. 1876.]

NL 0354306　　DNLM

Lievin, Albert Carl Ludwig, 1810–
——. Ueber die Sterblichkeit in Danzig in den
Jahren 1863 bis 1879. 38 pp. 12°. [Danzig,
1880.]

NL 0354307　　DNLM

Liévin, Auguste.
Applications numériques de la nouvelle méthode de calcul des grandes constructions continues, par Auguste
Liévin ... Paris, Le Constructeur de ciment armé, 1923.
iv, 144 p. diagrs. 24ᶜᵐ.

1. Structures, Theory of. 2. Building. ɪ. Title.
Library of Congress　　TG260.L5　　24–3939

NL 0354308　　DLC ICJ

TA683
.T318
1941
Liévin, Auguste.
Tédesco, Napoléon de.
Cálculo rápido del cemento armado, sin fórmulas algébricas,
por N. de Tédesco ... Revisado y corregido por Augusto
Liévin ... 2. ed., rev. y corr. por el dr. Buenaventura Bassego-
da ... Barcelona, J. Montesó, 1941.

Liévin, Auguste.
Méthodes de calculs des constructions complexes; théorie et
applications, par Auguste Liévin ... Paris, Le Constructeur de
ciment armé, 1933.
1 p. l., 250 p. tables, diagrs. 24ᶜᵐ.

1. Structures, Theory of. 2. Strains and stresses.　　A C 35–330
Title from Iowa State　　College. Printed by L. C.

NL 0354310　　IaAS

625
L62n
Liévin, Auguste.
Notes techniques relatives a la construction des chemins de fer.　[Paris?]
n.d.
79p. tab.

Autographed from manuscript copy.

NL 0354311　　IU NN

Liévin, Auguste.
Nouvelle méthode de calcul des grandes constructions continues, par Auguste Liévin... Paris: Le Constructeur de
ciment armé, 1921. vi, 209 p. diagrs. 8°.

1. Girders, Continuous. 2. Strains　　and stresses.　May 28, 1925

NL 0354312　　NN

Liévin, Auguste.
... Sur le calcul des constructions complexes.
Paris, 1933.
Thèse – Univ. de Nancy.

NL 0354313　　CtY

625.6
L62t
Liévin, F　　, and Heude, H
Tramway à vapeur à voie de 0,60ᵐ de
Pithiviers à Toury. 1.– Description
du tracé, du matériel fixe et du matér-
iel roulant. Détail des dépenses par
F. Liévin. 2.– Examen critique des
résultats obtenus par H. Heude.
Paris, 1894.
52p. fold.pl.

NL 0354314　　IU

Liévin (Heinrich) [1850–]. Ueber die
Grösse und Begrenzung des normalen Gesichts-
feldes. 31 pp. 8°. Königsberg, E. J. Dalkowski. 1877.

NL 0354315　　DNLM

Liévin, Henri Victor, 1898–
... De l'examen du rhino-pharynx à l'école...
Lille, 1924.
24,5 cm.
Thèse – Univ. de Lille.

NL 0354316　　CtY

Lievin, Isaak, 1901–
Zur kenntnis der organoquecksilberverbindungen...
Inaug. diss.　Berlin, 1928

NL 0354317　　ICRL CtY

Liévin, Jean.
Les meilleures professions pour faire fortune après la guerre
... Paris: Les éditions pratiques et documentaires [cop. 1916].
63(1) p.　8°.

Cover-title.
Author's name at head of title.

1. Occupations.—Choice of. 2. Eu-　　ropean war. 1914– .—Economic
aspects.　　June 1, 1918.

NL 0354318　　NN

Liévin, Louis.
Le centre gauche devant l'opinion. Compte
rendu ausc électeurs 1871–1875. Paris,
C. Schiller, 1878.
86 p.　'2°.

NL 0354319　　NN

Liévin, Madeleine.
... Recherches sur les stilliréactions de l'antimoine ...
Paris, Jouve, 1940.
145 p. illus. 24 cm. (Paris. Université. Faculté de pharmacie.
Thèse. [1989/40?] sér. U. no. 50)

1. Antimony.　ɪ. [Series]　　Med 48–1205
U. S. Army Medical Libr.　[W4P232　1940]
for Library of Congress

NL 0354320　　DNLM CtY ViU IU MnU

LIÉVIN, Omer.
Les solutions alcalines d'iode. [Thèse, Paris]
Roubaix, A.Delplanque, 1923.

Diagrs.

NL 0354321　　MH-C CtY

Liévin, Omer.
... Les solutions alcalines d'iode, par Omer Liévin ...
Lille, Facultés catholiques; Paris, A. Hermann; [etc.,
etc., 1923]
1 p. l., 144, [2] p. diagrs. 25ᶜᵐ. (Mémoires et travaux pub. par des
professeurs des Facultés catholiques de Lille, fasc. xxɪv)
Bibliographical foot-notes.

1. Iodine. 2. Alkalies. ɪ. Title.
Library of Congress　　QD181.I 1L65　　26–16843

NL 0354322　　DLC CtY

ar W
53076
no.13
Liévin, Walter.
Ueber alimentäre Glykosurie. Einhundert
Versuche an Gesunden und Kranken. Erlangen,
E. T. Jacob, 1897.
51 p.　22cm.

Inaug.--Diss.--Erlangen.

NL 0354323　　NIC DNLM ICRL

Liévois, Françoise.
La délinquance juvénile, cure et prophylaxie. Paris,
Presses universitaires de France, 1946.
171 p.　23 cm. (Bibliothèque de l'École pratique de psychologie et
de pédagogie)
The author's thesis, 1944, with added material, including legisla-
tion through 1945.
"Bibliographie": p. [167]–168.

1. Juvenile delinquency—France. ɪ. France. Laws, statutes,
etc. (Series)
48–21334*

NL 0354324　　DLC CLU InU MH-L

Lièvre (André). Comment on défend son vin.
La lutte contre les maladies et altérations des
vins. 76 pp. 12°. Paris. [1901].
Collection "Comment on défend", no. 49.

NL 0354325　　DNLM

Lièvre, Anton Val de
see　Val de Lièvre, Anton.

Lièvre, Auguste François, 1828–1898.
Angoulême, histoire, institutions & monuments
Angouleme, Coquemard, 1885.
150 p.　illus., fold. plan.　19 cm.
1. Angoulême, France. Hist. (SA)
2. Angoulême, France. Descr. (SA) I. Main
cd. (SA)

NL 0354327　　NjP

VOLUME 332

Lièvre, Auguste François, 1828–1898.
Les chemins gaulois et romains entre la Loire et la Gironde, les limites des cités, la lieue gauloise, par A. F. Lièvre. 2. éd. Niort, L. Glouzot, 1893. 127 p. map. 25cm.

307953B. 1. Roads, Roman—France.   2. Roads—France.   December 11, 1945

NL 0354328   NN MH

Lièvre, Auguste François, 1828-1898.
Geschiedenis van de Protestanten en de hervormde kerken in Poitou. Naar het Fransch van Auguste Lièvre. Uitgegeven van wege de Evangelische maatschappij. Arnhem, G. W. van der Wiel, 1859.
2 p. l., 312 p.   18½ᶜᵐ.
Foreword signed G. J. v. d. H.
According to the Catalogus der bibliotheek van de Maatschappij der Nederlandsche letterkunde te Leiden, this was published in the Evangelische bibliotheek, 1859, v.
1. Protestant churches—France. 2. Poitou—Church history.   I. Evangelische maatschappij, Amsterdam. II. G. J. v. d. H. III. H., G. J. v. d.

NL 0354329   MiU

Lièvre, Auguste François, 1828–1898.
Histoire des protestants et des églises réformées du Poitou, par Auguste Lièvre ... Paris, Grassart; [etc., etc.] 1856–60.
3 v. illus., fold. map. 23ᵐ.

1. Protestant churches—Poitou. 2. Protestants in Poitou.
12–16801
Library of Congress   BX9456.P7L7

CtY CU
NL 0354330   DLC TNJ-R WU FTaSU MiU MdBP MB NcD OC1

Lièvre, Auguste François, 1828–1898.

Dez, Pierre.
... Histoire des protestants, et des églises réformées du Poitou. Nouv. éd., entièrement refondue ... La Rochelle, Impr. de l'Ouest, 1936–

LIÈVRE, Auguste François, 1828-1898.
Les huîtres nourries en eau douce dans l'ancienne Aquitaine (problème d'archéologie et de zooéthique.) Paris, [etc.], J.Baer, 1883.
Cover-title, 7 p. 24 p.
"Extrait de la Revue archéologique, août, 1883".

NL 0354332   MH

BR   Lièvre, Auguste François, 1828–1898.
1608   Les martyrs poitevins. Toulouse, Société
F8   des livres religieux, 1874.
L72   305 p. 19cm.

1. Martyrs--France--Poitou. I. Société des livres religieux de Toulouse. II. Title.

NL 0354333   NIC

WA   Lièvre, Auguste François, 1828-1898.
15905   Les martyrs poitevins. Toulouse, Société
            des Publications Morales et Religieuses, 1910.
            288 p.
            2. éd.

1. Huguenots in France - Hist. 2. Poitou - Church history.

NL 0354334   CtY MH

LIÈVRE, Auguste François, 1828-1898.
La misère et les épidémies à Angoulême aux XVIe et XVIIe siècles. Angoulême. 1886.

"Tirage à 225 exemplaires.
"Extrait du BULLETIN DE LA SOCIÉTÉ ARCHÉOLOGIQUE ET HISTRIQUE DE LA CHARENTE, 1886."

NL 0354335   MBCo MnU NjP

Lièvre, C. A., tr.

Barker, Aldred Farrer, 1868–
"Wool and the textile industries: raw material to finished fabric," in English, French, Italian and Spanish, with a technical glossary. A series of articles on the textile industries specially written to introduce the technical words and phrases with which those engaged in the wool industry should be conversant. By Aldred F. Barker ... tr. by C. A. Lièvre ... [Leeds, 1919]

Lièvre, Daniel.
Une éruption volcanique au Japon. Higashi Kirishima, 15 Mars 1896. Par Daniel Lièvre... Havre, 1896.
30 p. illus. 23 cm. [Pamphlets on geology. v. 4, no. 10]
"Extrait du Bulletin de la Société de géographie commerciale."
1. Volcanoes. Japan.

NL 0354337   CU

[Lièvre, Daniel]
... I vulcani del Giappone. Milano, Societa editrice Sonzogno [1900]
cover-title, 32 p. incl. illus., maps. 22ᶜᵐ. (Biblioteca illustrata dei viaggi intorno al mondo per terra e per mare. N. 75)

"Questa relazione è tolta da una series di notizie stampate nel Bollettino della Società geografica dell'Hayre, nel 1896-97-98, sotto i titoli di: Una eruzione vulcanica nel Giappone, Passeggiate giapponesi e coreane, da Daniel Lièvre."

NL 0354338   NNC

Lièvre (Edeau-Heuri-Louis) [1888–   ]. *Contribution à la géographie médicale.* Notes et observations recueillies au Rio Nunez (1887-8) 75 nn. 4°. *Bordeaux,* 1891. No. 27.

NL 0354339   DNLM

Lièvre, Édouard, 1829–1886.
Art gems. A series of thirty high-class engravings from pictures by the most eminent painters, ancient and modern. Produced under the direction of Édouard Lièvre, with notices of the artists and their works. London [etc.] H. Sotheran, J. Baer and co., 1873.
2 p. l., 60 p. 30 pl. (incl. front.) 34½ᵐ.

1. Paintings. 2. Engravings.   I. Title.
17–27817
Library of Congress   ND1170.L5

NL 0354340   DLC CSmH MB NN

Lièvre, Édouard, 1829–1886.
Les arts décoratifs à toutes les époques, par Édouard Lièvre ... Paris, Vᵛᵉ A. Morel & cⁱᵉ, 1870.
2 v. 120 pl. (chiefly col.) 47ᵐ.
In portfolios.
Portfolio of v. 1 dated 1868, that of v. 2, 1872.
Introduction signed: Alfred Darcel.

1. Art objects. 2. Design, Decorative. 3. Decoration and ornament.   I. Title.
Library of Congress   NK1115.L6   12–33718

NL 0354341   DLC CtY NN

Lièvre, Édouard, 1829–1886.
Les collections célèbres d'œuvres d'art, dessinées et gravées d'après les originaux, par Édouard Lièvre; textes historiques et descriptifs par mm. F. de Saulcy ... Adrien de Longpérier ... [etc.] Paris, New York [etc.] Goupil & cⁱᵉ, 1866–69.
2 v. 100 pl. (incl. fronts.) 25½ᵐ.
Colored initials.

1. Art objects.
Library of Congress   NK1115.L7   1866 a   10–19719

NL 0354342   DLC NjN MU MiU NN MdBWA CU

Lièvre, Édouard, 1829–1886.
... Eaux-fortes et gravures des maîtres anciens, tirées des collections les plus célèbres et publiés avec le concours de Édouard Lièvre; notes par Georges Duplessis ... [1.-4. sér.] Paris, Amand-Durand; [etc., etc.] 1874–81.

Lièvre, Édouard, 1829–1886, illus.

Mantz, Paul, 1821–1895.
Hans Holbein, par Paul Mantz; dessins et gravures sous la direction de Édouard Lièvre. Paris, Librairies-impr. réunies [1879]

Lièvre, Édouard, 1829–1886.   .8
Meubles d'art. Œuvres décoratives choisies dans les collections célèbres. Paris. Goupil. [1880.] 30 plates. [Bibliothèque des beaux-arts.] F°.
The plates are accompanied by explanatory text.

*D5462 — S.r. — Furniture.

NL 0354345   MB

Lièvre, Edouard, 1829-1886.
Musée graphique pour l'étude de l'art dans ses applications. Paris. n.d.
2v. plates. 67cm.

NL 0354346   MdBWA

Lièvre, Edouard, 1829-1886.
Le musée universel. (Oeuvres d'art, anciennes et moderne; tableaux, dessins, sculptures, gravures, curiosites, etc.) Paris, 1868.
3 v. fol.

NL 0354347   CtY

VOLUME 332

Lièvre, Édouard, 1829–1886.
Works of art in the collections of England, drawn by Edward Lièvre ... and engraved by Bracquemond, Courtry, Flameng, Greux, Le Rat, Lhermitte, J. Lièvre, Muzelle, Rajon, Randall and Valentin. London. Holloway and son [187–?]
2 p. l. [8]–49 l. l pl. 53½cm.
"Only 500 copies printed."

1. Art objects—England. 2. Art objects—Private collections.
12–12345

Library of Congress   NK480.A1G7

NL 0354348   DLC CtY CU NcRS PPD NN CSmH

Lièvre, Édouard le, marquis de la Grange
see   La Grange, Adelaide Édouard le Lièvre, marquis de, 1796–1876.

Lièvre (Gaëtan). *Les causes finales sources des indications en thérapeutiques.* 95 pp. 8°. Paris. 1904. No. 30.

NL 0354350   DNLM

Lièvre, Henri.
... Une forme de la concentration commerciale. Les entreprises à succursales multiples dans l'industrie et le commerce du vêtement. [Paris, Imp. Villain et Bar, 1934]
235, [3] p. 25½cm.
Stamped on cover and t.-p.: En vente chez l'auteur ... St-Nazaire (L. I.) et en librairie.
Errata leaf laid in.

1. Chain stores. 2. Department stores. 3. Clothing trade.
A 38–542

New York. Public library
for Library of Congress

NL 0354351   NN

Lièvre, Henri, 1902–
... Les distomatoses à Fasciola hepatica...
Alger [1932.
Thèse – Univ. d'Alger.
"Index bibliographique": p. [249]–287.

NL 0354352   CtY

Lièvre, Jacques André, 1905–
Comment traiter la sciatique. Paris, Éditions médicales Flammarion [1954]
124 p. 21 cm.

1. Sciatica.   I. Title.
RC420.L5   55–15214 ‡

NL 0354353   DLC CtY-M DNLM

Lièvre, Jacques André, 1905–
... L'ostéose parathyroïdienne et les ostéopathies chroniques... [Paris, 1931]
Thèse – Univ. de Paris.
"Bibliographie": p. [369]–383.

NL 0354354   CtY

Lièvre, Jacques André, 1905–
... L'ostéose parathyroïdienne et les ostéopathies chroniques. Paris, Masson et cie, 1932.
3 p. l., 389 p. illus., XVI pl. on 8 l. 25 cm.
Errata slip attached to t.-p.
"Bibliographie": p. [369]–383.

1. Bones—Diseases. 2. Parathyroid glands.   I. Title.   II. Title: Les ostéopathies chroniques.
RD684.L5   616.71   34–21235 rev

NL 0354355   DLC PPC DNLM OU

Lièvre, Louis.
... Le collectivisme aux cent visages. Paris, Tallandier [°1934]
2 p. l. [7]–222 p. 23cm. (Collection du temps présent, publiée sous la direction de Jean de Granvilliers)

1. Collectivism.   I. Title.
Library of Congress   HX266.L66   35–4164
Copyright A—Foreign   25937
                                    335

NL 0354356   DLC MH NN

Lièvre, Louis.
... La monnaie et le change en Bourgogne sous les ducs Valois. Dijon, Imprimerie veuve P. Berthier, 1929.
2 p. l., ix, 170 p. 25cm.
"Bibliographie": p. [v]–ix.

1. Money—Burgundy. 2. Money—France—Hist. 3. Valois, House of.   I. Title.
Library of Congress   HG990.B8L5   30–21324

NL 0354357   DLC MH CtY

Lièvre, Louis.
... Politique et religion. Paris, J. Tallandier [1930]
224 p. 18½cm. (Collection du temps présent)
"2e édition."

1. Religion.   I. Title.
Library of Congress   BL65.P7L5 1930   31–20763
Copyright A—Foreign   6965
                                    261

NL 0354358   DLC ViU NNUT

Lièvre, Louis.
... Le procès de notre époque. Paris, J. Tallandier [1932]
189, [2] p. 22½cm. (Collection du temps présent ...)

1. Civilization. 2. Social conditions. 3. Economic conditions—1918–   I. Title.
                                    33–7514
Library of Congress   HN15.L53
Copyright A—Foreign   18838
                                    301

NL 0354359   DLC CU

Lièvre, Louis, *writer on stenotypy.*
...Nouvelle méthode de sténographie mécanique apprise sans professeur sur la machine à écrire Smith Premier... Lyon: P. Legendre & Cie., 1903. 24 p. 8°.
Cover-title.

1. Stenotypy.
May 18, 1926

NL 0354360   NN

Lièvre (Louis) [1876–]. *Du décollement épiphysaire traumatique de l'extrémité inférieure du tibia.* 54 pp., 4 pl., 1 l. 8°. *Paris, 1901, No. 297.*

NL 0354361   DNLM

LIÈVRE, Lucien R[oger].
Thèse de droit comparé; l'estoppel et la theorie francaise de l'apparence dans les relations juridiques.   Cambridge, Mass., 1938.

4°. (Typewritten).
Thèse --- Harvard Law School.

NL 0354362   MH-L

Lièvre, Lucienne Gauthier
see   Gauthier-Lièvre, Lucienne.

PQ1755
.M7
1950
Corneille, Pierre, 1606–1684.
Mélite, pièce comique. Texte de la première éd. (1633) publié avec les variantes par Mario Roques et Marion Lièvre. Lille, Giard, 1950.

Lièvre, Marion, ed.

Lièvre (Paul). *De la hernie étranglée et de l'hémorrhagie consécutive chez les femmes opérées à l'époque menstruelle.* 46 pp., 3 l. 4°. *Montpellier, J. Martel ainé, 1868, No. 18.*   c.

NL 0354365   DNLM

Lièvre, Pierre.
... Le commerce international des bois. Thèse pour le doctorat ... par Pierre Lièvre ... Paris, L. Laveur, 1909.
2 p. l., 115, [1] p.

NL 0354366   CaBVaU

Lièvre, Pierre, 1882–
... Une amitié.   Paris, c1920.
18 cm.

NL 0354367   CtY

T840.81   **Lièvre, Pierre,** 1882–
G453zL   André Gide. Paris, Le Divan, 1927.
46p. 19cm.

"Cette brochure a été tirée seulement sur pur fil Lafuma, à 250 exemplaires numérotés. No.73."

1. Gide, André Paul Guillaume, 1869–1951.

NL 0354368   NcU IEN WU NcU CU

VOLUME 332

PQ1779   Lièvre, Pierre, 1882-
L54   Corneille et son oeuvre; quatre causeries pour la radio à
     l'occasion du tricentenaire du Cid.   Paris, Le Divan, 1937.
     62 p.

     "300 exemplaires ... No 231."
     With author's autograph.

     1. Corneille, Pierre, 1606-1684.

NL   0354369   CU CtY OC1 MWelC NIC

Lièvre, Pierre, 1882-
     ... L'éducation des filles. ₁Paris₁ Gallimard ₁°1932₁
143, ₁1₁ p.   17ᶜᵐ.
Drama.

     I. Title.
                              32-22965
   Library of Congress   PQ2623.I 47E4 1932
   Copyright D pub. 16292   842.91

NL   0354370   DLC MiU OU

840.904   Lièvre, Pierre, 1882-1939.
L722e   Esquisses critiques.   Paris, La Renaissance
     du livre, 1921-1929.
     3v. (Bibliothèque internationale de
     critique: Lettres et arts)

     Imprint varies. Vols. 2-3: Paris, Le Divan.
     Series 2 has series note: Les Quatorze no.
     6.

     1. French literature--19th century--History
     and criticism.   2. French literature--
     20th century--   History and criticism.
     I. Title.

     WaU ICU RPB CtY MB IaU OCU PSt NjP OrPR CU
NL   0354371   ICarbS GASC LU IU MiU NBC OC1 OU CtY MiD

Lièvre, Pierre, 1882-
     ... L'extravagante punie. Paris, Gallimard ₁1931₁
4 p. L., ₁11₁-142 p., 1 l.   16½ᶜᵐ.

     I. Title.
   Library of Congress   PQ2623.I 47E8 1931   32-7167
   Copyright A--Foreign   14996
                              843.91

NL   0354372   DLC OU OC1 NN

PQ   Lièvre, Pierre, 1882-
2623   Iphigénie; ou, Le sacrifice d'Agamemnon;
I47   tragédie en cinq actes. Paris, La Renaissance
I6   du livre ₁1916?₁
     120p. illus. 20cm.

     I. Title   II. Title: Le sacrifice d'Agamemnon₁

NL   0354373   WU OU

Lièvre, Pierre.
     Iphigénie; ou, Le sacrifice d'Agamemnon.   (Revue de Hol-
lande.   Paris, 1917.   4°.   Année 2, tome 4, p. 673-714, 793-
818.   illus.)

     A play, in five acts.
     Signed: Pierre Lièvre.

1. Drama (French). 2. Title.
                             June 25, 1917.

NL   0354374   NN

Lièvre, Pierre, 1882-
     ... Iphigénie; ou, Le sacrifice
d'Agamemnon, tragédie en cinq actes.
Paris ₁1925?₁

     129p.   front., illus.   20cm.

NL   0354375   RPB

3266   Lièvre, Pierre, 1882-
.41   ...Jeunesse se fane... Paris, Le Divan,
.349   1925.
     124 p.   18½ ᶜᵐ.   (Les soirées du
divan)

NL   0354376   NjP

Lièvre, Pierre, 1882-
     ... Maurras. Paris, Le Divan, 1925.
2 p. L., ₁7₁-82 p., 1 l.   14½ᵐ.
585 copies printed. "500 exemplaires sur alfa bouffant numérotés 1 à
500. Nᵒ 373."

     1. *Maurras, Charles, 1868-   38-12362
   Library of Congress   PQ2625.A954Z75
                              928.4

NL   0354377   DLC MH CU NN OCU

808.1   LIÈVRE, PIERRE, 1882-
L626n   Notes et réflexions sur l'art poétique.
     Paris, B. Grasset, 1911.
     174 p.

     Author's autograph presentation copy to
     Victor Émile Michelet.

     1. Poetry.   I. Title: Art poétique.

NL   0354378   WaU CaBVaU

Lièvre, Pierre, 1882-
     ... Ouvrages galants et moraux. Paris, Gallimard, Éditions
de la Nouvelle revue française ₁1929₁
3 p. L., ₁9₁-225 p., 2 l.   19ᶜᵐ.
Plays.
CONTENTS.--Ah ! que vous me plaisez.--Quelle horreur !--Les dangers
du tête-à-tête.

     I. Title.
   Library of Congress   PQ2623.I 47O8 1929   29-22358

NL   0354379   DLC MH

Lièvre, Pierre, 1882-
     Paul Valéry. Paris, Le Divan, 1924.
     77 p.

     1. Valéry, Paul, 1871-1945.

NL   0354380   NNC CU IEN MiU NcU NN WU MH

PQ   Lièvre, Pierre, 1882-
2623   Le roman sournois.   Paris, P.-V.
J47R7   Stock, 1909.
     127 p.   15cm.

NL   0354381   NIC

Fr   Lièvre, Pierre, 1882-
L722s   Supplément au Paradoxe sur le comédien de
IN: Diderot. Cuivres et bois originaux de C.
spec   Brandel.   Paris, Éditions du Trianon, 1929.
     118p.   illus., ports. 18cm.   (Suppléments
     à quelques oeuvres célèbres, 8)

     1. Acting.   2. Jouvet, Louis, 1887-   I.
     Diderot, Denis, 1713-1784. Le paradoxe sur
     le comédien. II. Title.   (Series)

NL   0354382   IEN CU

Lièvre, Pierre, 1882-1939, ed.

Corneille, Pierre, 1606-1684.
     ... Théâtre ... Texte établi et annoté par Pierre Lièvre.
₁Paris, Éditions de la Nouvelle revue française, 1934₁

Lièvre, Pierre, 1882-
     ... La vie et le roman; roman. Paris, Gallimard ₁1939₁
3 p. L., ₁9₁-221 p., 1 l.   19ᶜᵐ.

     I. Title.
                                39-18910
   Library of Congress   PQ2623.I 47V5 1939
   Copyright A--Foreign   43575
                              843.91

NL   0354384   DLC CtY

Lièvre, Pierre, 1905-
     ... Les indications thérapeutique de la
     d'arsonvalisation à ondes courtes; applications
     locales et fièvre artificielle...   Paris, 1939.
     Thèse - Univ. de Paris.

NL   0354385   CtY

Lièvre, Roger Lucien.
     ... La protection des actionnaires dans les sociétés anonymes
     ... par R. Lucien Lièvre ... Alençon, Imprimerie alençonnaise,
     1939.
2 p. L., ₁vii₁-viii, 176 p.   25½ᵐ.
Thèse--Univ. de Paris.
"Bibliographie"; ₁167₁-174.

     1. Stock companies--France. 2. Stock companies--U. S. 3. Securi-
ties--France. 4. Securities--U. S. 5. Corporation law--France. 6. Corporation law--U. S. 7. Comparative law.   I. Title.
                              41-25028
   Library of Congress   HG4929.A2L5
                           658.11440944

NL   0354386   DLC

Lièvre-Brizard, Colette, 1895-
     Poèmes. ₁Paris₁ Porte étroite, 1951.
33 p.   24 cm.

     PQ2623.I 48P6   52-18546 ‡

NL   0354387   DLC NN

Pam.   Lievsay, John Leon.
Coll.   Bacon versified. ₁Cambridge, Mass., 1951₁
24628   223-238 p.   23 cm.

     "Reprinted from the Huntington library
     quarterly, vol. 14, no. 3, May, 1951."
     Bibliographical footnotes.

NL   0354388   NcD

VOLUME 332

Lievsay, John Leon
A Cavalier library—1643, by John L. Lievsay and Richard B. Davis.

(*In* Virginia. University. Bibliographical Society. **Studies in bibliography.** Charlottesville. 26ᶜᵐ. v.6 (1953-54) p.[141]-160)

1. Bludder, Sir Thomas, b. 1590? 2. Libraries, Private—England. I. Davis, Richard Beale, 1903- joint author.

NL 0354389   ViU

Pam.
Coll.   **Lievsay, John Leon.**
Daniel Tuvill's "Resolves". [Chapel Hill,
24641   N. C., 1949]
196-203 p. 23 cm.

Cover title.
"Reprinted from Studies in philology, 46,
2, April, 1949."
Bibliographical footnotes.

NL 0354390   NcD

Lievsay, John Leon, joint author.

Emery, Clark.
Practice in reading and writing [by] Clark Emery ... John L. Lievsay ... [and] Henry F. Thoma ... Boston, New York [etc.] Houghton Mifflin company [1942]

Pam.
Coll.   **Lievsay, John Leon.**
"Silver-tongued Smith," paragon of Eliza-
24629   bethan preachers. [Cambridge, Mass., 1947]
13-36 p. 24 cm.

"Reprinted from the Huntington Library quarterly, vol. 11, no. 1, November, 1947."
Bibliographical footnotes.

NL 0354392   NcD

Pam.
Coll.   **Lievsay, John Leon.**
Some renaissance views of Diogenes the
24627   Cynic. [Washington, 1948]
447-455 p. 24 cm.

Caption title.
"Reprint from Joseph Quincy Adams memo-
rial studies. The Folger Shakespeare Library,
Washington, 1948."
Bibliographical footnotes.

NL 0354393   NcD

CR   **Lievyns, A.**
5059   Fastes de la Légion-d'honneur.
L72+   Biographie de tous les décorés, accompagnée
de l'histoire législative et réglementaire
de l'ordre par MM. Lievyns, Verdot, Bégat.
Paris, Bureau de l'administration, 1842-47.
5 v. 27cm.

1. Légion d'honneur—Biog. I. Title.

NL 0354394   NIC

Liewald, Friedrich
Streptopolymethinfarbstoffe aus 3,6,7,8-
tetrahydro-4-amino-acenaphthen und 4'-
amino-4-methyl-diphenyl-sulfoxyd als beitrag zu
dem problem: farbe, konstitution und optische
aktivität. ... Dresden, 1935.
Inaug. Diss. - Techn. Hochsch. Dresden, 1935.

NL 0354395   ICRL

PG   **Liewehr, Ferdinand,** 1896-
4101   Einführung in die historische Grammatik
L72   der tschechischen Sprache. Brünn, R.M.
Rohrer, 1933-
v. 24cm.

Cover title.
Contents.—1. T. Lautlehre.

1. Czech   language—Grammar,
Historical.

NL 0354396   NIC CtY NN IU InU MH CaBVaU

Liewehr, Ferdinand.
...Die Ortsnamen des Kuhländchens, von Dr. Ferdinand Liewehr... Reichenberg: Gebrüder Stiepel, Ges. m.b.H., 1926. 88 p. incl. tables. 8°. (Deutsche Universitaet, Prague. Slavisti-scher Arbeitsgemeinschaft. Veröffentlichungen. Reihe 1: Unter-suchungen. Heft 1.)

Bibliography, p. 7-10.

1. Geography—Names—Czecho-   Slovakia. 2. Ser.
February 21, 1930

NL 0354397   NN IU CtY CU MH InU

Liewehr, Ferdinand, *ed.*
Slavistische Studien. Franz Spina zum sechzigsten Ge-burtstag von seinen Schülern. Reichenberg, Gebr. Stiepel, 1929.
201 p. illus., port. 24 cm. (Veröffentlichungen der Slavistischen Arbeitsgemeinschaft an der Deutschen Universität in Prag. 1. Reihe: Untersuchungen, Heft 5)
CONTENTS.— Zur vergleichende Forschung über die slavischen Zehnsilbler, von R. Jakobson. — Sočivica, von G. Gesemann. — Die Hochzeitsbräuche der Serbokroaten in ihren Hauptelementen, von E. Schneeweis.—Beiträge zur tschechischen Sondersprachenkunde, von E. Rippl.—Sprachliches Allerlei, von R. Zasche.—Das Drümel, von J. Hanika.—Deutsch-slavische Kulturüberschichtungen am Bauern-haus der Sudeten- und Karpathenländer, von B. Schier.—Deutsche Übersetzer moderner tschechischer Lyrik, von W. Hauffen.—Neruda

und die tschechische Volkskunde, von F. Longin.—Die nationalen Verhältnisse in den Prager Kreisen zur Zeit der Aufklärung, von E. Lemberg.—Ost-West in der tschechischen Entwicklung, von W. Gold-schmid.—Ein Beitrag zu den tschechisch-deutschen Literaturbezie-hungen, von F. Velčovsky.—Die neuere tschechische Literatur in ihrer Stellung zu den Juden, von H. Waldhas.—Zum Wesen der tschechi-schen Idylle, von O. Stonjek.—Beiträge zur slavischen Sprachwissen-schaft, von F. Liewehr.

1. Slavic studies—Addresses, essays, lectures. I. Spina, Franz, 1868-1938. II. Title. (Series: Prague. Universität. Veröffent-lichungen der Slavistischen Arbeitsgemeinschaft. 1. Reihe: Unter-suchungen, Heft 5)

PG14.S6   65-71949

NL 0354399   DLC MH IU ICU NN CSt

Liewehr, Ferdinand.
Slawische Sprachwissenschaft in Einzeldarstellungen. Wien, R. M. Rohrer, 1955.
129 p. 20 cm.
Bibliographical footnotes.
CONTENTS. — Wandlungen der Sprachbetrachtung.—Wie erklärt sich die Gleichstimmigkeit der vor- und früheinzelsprachlichen Laut-prozesse des Slawischen?—Zur Bildung der slawischen Präterita.—Betrachtungen zur altostslawischen Lautentwicklung.

1. Slavic languages—Addresses, essays, lectures.

PG15.L5   A 56-1398
Harvard Univ. Library
for Library of Congress   [a60b½]†

ICU MiU NcU WU DLC
NL 0354400   MH CaBVaU NN IU CSt PU OC1W OCH CLU CtY

Liewehr, Ferdinand, editor.
...Tschechische und slowakische Studien, redigiert von Fer-dinand Liewehr. Reichenberg: Verlag Gebrüder Stiepel, G.m.b.H., 1930. 259 p. 8°. (Deutsche Universität, Prague. Slavistische Arbeitsgemeinschaft. Veröffentlichungen. Reihe 1, Heft 7.)

Bibliography, at end of some chapters.
Contents: BRECHENSBAUER, A. Zum Todesproblem in der neueren tschechischen Literatur. REPP, F. Kritische Bemerkungen zum alttschechischen Vévoda Arnošt. KATHOLNIGG, F. Die tschechische Lyrik der Gegenwart und die Deutschen. STREIT, E. Der Anteil Schlesiens an der tschechischen Literatur. EMERITZY, A. Svetozár Hurban-Vajanský.

1. Bohemian literature—Hist. and   crit. I. Ser.
September 2, 1931

NL 0354401   NN ICU CaBVaU MiU CU MH

PG1244 **Liewehr, Ferdinand,** 1896-
.L7   Zur Chronologie des serbokroatischen Akzentes.
Prag, Taussig und Taussig, 1927.
48 p.

1. Serbo-Croatian language—Accents and accen-tuation.

NL 0354402   ICU InU PBm

Liewen, Berndt Guilielmus von, respondent.
De Pelasgis, Graeciae aboriginibus...
see under Arvedson, Andreas Arvidus, praeses.

1799   **Liewen, Carl Gustaf**
Sweden [Circulare-bref til Krigs-rätterne.
7   Nov. 8, 1799] Begins: Wi, Carl Gustaf
Liewen... så ock samtelige ledamöter
uti Kongl. Maj:ts Krigs-Hof-Rätt
[Stockholm, Kongl. Tryckeriet, 1799]

[3] p. 23cm. [Sweden Documents
relating to trade etc. 1799:7]

NL 0354404   MnU

Liewendahl, Frej, 1902-
Ålåndska segelleder och ankarplatser, av Frej
Liewendahl. Åbolands skärgård, segelleder och
ankarplatser, av S.A.Merivirta. [Karlshamn,
Lagerblad boktryckeri, 1954]

91 p. illus.
Särtryck ur SXK:s Årsskrift, 1954

NL 0354405   MH

ar W   **Liewer, Hans,** 1899-
54547   Die wirtschaftliche Entwicklung von
no.5   Benrath-Reisholz. Coburg, Druckerei des
Coburger Tageblatt, 1926.
134 p. tables. 22cm.

Inaug.-Diss.—Erlangen.

NL 0354406   NIC MH CtY MiU PU ICRL

Liewied, P
Wie erwerbe ich ein Patent? [Wien, Steffel-Verlag, 1946]
32 p. 15 cm. (Kleinbuchreihe "Wirtschaft," Nr. 1)

1. Patent laws and legislation—Austria—Popular works.
I. Title. (Series)

51-36309

NL 0354407   DLC InLP NN

VOLUME 332

Liewschitz, Moses, 1882–
Beitrag zur erkennung der pyelitis.
Inaug. diss. Berlin, 1906.
Bibl.

NL 0354408   ICRL DNLM

Liez, François, 1898–
... Thrombo angéite oblitérante...
Bordeaux, 1927.
24 cm.
Thèse - Univ. de Bordeaux.
"Bibliographie": p. [47]–48.

NL 0354409   CtY

Liez, Heinrich.
Die verteilung der mittleren höhe in der Schweiz ...
Bern, Haller'sche buchdruckerei, 1903.
3 p. l., 38 p. 2 fold. pl., 5 fold. tab. 23ᶜᵐ.

Inaug.-diss.—Bern.
On cover: Aus dem Geographischen institut der Universität Bern.
"Sonderabdruck aus dem Jahresbericht der Geographischen gesellschaft von Bern, XVIII."

1. Switzerland—Altitudes.

Library of Congress   GB498.63.L7
6–39548

NL 0354410   DLC PU NN

Liezen, Lammert.

G4124
.S539
1950
.P8
Public Letter Bureau, *Sheboygan, Wis.*
Graphic shopping guide of Sheboygan, Wisconin. Prepared ... by Public Letter Bureau, Lammert Liezen, proprietor. Sheboygan ₍1950₎

Liezen-Mayer, Alexander, 1839–1898, illus.

Goethe, Johann Wolfgang von, 1749–1832.
Faust; a tragedy by Johann Wolfgang von Goethe. The first pt. Tr., in the original metres, by Thomas James Arnold ... with 50 illustrations after original designs by Alexander Liezen Mayer ... and with vignettes, ornamental borderings, etc., by Rudolf Seitz. Munich, T. Stroefer; New York, G. Kirchner & co. ₍1877?₎

Liezen-Mayer, Alexander, 1839–1898, illus.

Goethe, Johann Wolfgang von, 1749–1832.
Faust. Eine tragödie, von Goethe. Mit zeichnungen von Adolf Schmitz, in holz geschnitten von R. Brend'amour. Berlin, G. Grote, 1868.

Liezen-Mayer, Alexander, 1839–1898, illus.

Schiller, Johann Christoph Friedrich von, 1759–1805.
Schiller's Song of the bell. With illustrations by Alexander Liezen Mayer and Edmund H. Garrett. Boston, Estes and Lauriat, 1883.

Liezen-Mayer, Alexander, 1839–1898, illus.

Schiller, Johann Christoph Friedrich von, 1759–1805.
The song of the bell, by Friedrich von Schiller, tr. by William H. Furness, with 32 illustrations after original paintings by Alexander Liezen Mayer and with vignettes, ornamental borderings, etc., by Rudolf Seitz. Munich, T. Stroefer; New York, G. Kirchner & co. ₍1879₎

Liezen-Mayer, Alexander, 1829–1898, illus.

Goethe, Johann Wolfgang von, 1749–1832.
Songs and scenes from Goethe's Faust. Illustrated from designs by A. Liezen Mayer and Ad. Lalauze. Engraved by George T. Andrew and others. Boston, Estes and Lauriat, 1884.

344.1
J83.9
L722s
LIEZENBERG, Jacobus Laurentius.
Studia Flaviana, observationes criticae in Flavi Josephi antiquitates judaicas.
Schiedam, H.A.M. Roelants, 1899.
102p. 23.5cm.

Thesis–Leiden.

NL 0354417   MH-AH NN NjP PU

Liezeray, Henri.
Leabar gabala₎ Livre des invasion
see under   [Leabhar gabhala]

Liezeris, Jānis.
...Ziedu vieglumā. ₍Rīga₎ "Latvju grāmata," 1935.   110 p.
20½cm.

Poems.

886153A. 1. Poetry, Lettish.   I. Title.   June 7, 1937
N. Y. P. L.

NL 0354419   NN

Lif, Sh   B
Американская агрессия в Корее. ₍Москва₎ Гос. изд-во полит. лит-ры, 1951.
114 p. 20 cm.
Author's pseud., Л. Перов, at head of title.

1. Korean War, 1950–1953.   I. Title.
Title transliterated: Amerikanskaîa agressiîa v Koree.

DS918.L46   52–33208 rev

NL 0354420   DLC

Lif, Sh   B
Экономическое разоружение Германии; стенограмма публичной лекции. Москва ₍Правда₎ 1945.
22 p. 22 cm.
At head of title: Всесоюзное лекционное бюро при Комитете по делам высшей школы при СНК СССР.

1. Germany—Econ. condit.—1918–1945.   I. Title.
Title transliterated: Èkonomicheskoe razoruzhenie Germanii.

HC286.3.L53   54–41199 ‡

NL 0354421   DLC

Germanit. - Serbian.

Lif, Sh   B
Економско разоружање Немачке. Д. Орлов: О противницима економско разоружања Немачке. Београд, 1947.
31 p. 21 cm. (Политичка библиотека, 12)

1. Germany—Econ. condit.—1918–1945.   I. Orlov, D. O protivnicima razoruřanja Nemačke. II. Title. III. Title: O protivnicima razoruřanja Nemačke.
Title transliterated: Ekonomsko razoruřanje Nemačke.

HC286.3.L538   58–49786 ‡

NL 0354422   DLC

Lif, Sh   B
Кризите на капиталистическата система в световното стопанство. София, Центр. кооперативен съюз, 1947.
30 p. 18 cm.

1. Economic history - 20th cent. 2. Business cycles.
Title transliterated: Krizite na kapitalisticheskata sistema v svetovnoto stopanstvo.

HC54.L55   50–55172

NL 0354423   DLC

Lif, Sh   B
Die Lage des Proletariats in den USA ₍von₎ B. Lif. ₍Übersetzung aus dem Russischen von Eduard Wöhrmann₎ Berlin, Tribüne, 1952.
47 p. 22 cm.
Added original t. p. in Russian, with imprint: Москва, 1949.

1. Labor and laboring classes—U. S.   I. Title.

HD8072.L546   66–32961

NL 0354424   DLC IEN RPB

Lif, Sh   B
Положение пролетариата в США. Стенограмма публичной лекции, прочитанной в Москве. Москва ₍Правда₎ 1949.
36 p. 22 cm.
At head of title: Всесоюзное общество по распространению политических и научных знаний.

1. Labor and laboring classes—U. S.
Title transliterated: Polozhenie proletariata v SShA.

HD8072.L54   50–39384

NL 0354425   DLC WaU-L

Lif, Sh   B
Положението на пролетариата в САЩ. ₍Превела: Д. Казанджиева₎ София, ₍Българска Комунистическа партия ₍1950₎
65 p. 17 cm.

1. Labor and laboring classes—U. S.   I. Title.
Title transliterated: Polozhenieto na proletariata v SASht.

HD8072.L543   56–31003 ‡

NL 0354426   DLC

---

4 HD-
1064
Lif, Sh   B
Postaveni proletariatu v USA. [Z ruskeho originalu prelozili Jarmila Kubeckova a Ota Jagos. 1. vyd.] Praha, Orbis, 1950.
72 p. (Mala knihovna sovetske vedy, sv 28)

NL 0354427   DLC-P4

Lif, Sh   B
(Sensō to Nihon keizai)
戰爭ト日本經済 ₍大連₎ 滿鐵·調査部 昭和 16, 1941₎
5, 444 l. 26 cm.
Cover title.
At head of title: 滿鐵 (rubber stamped)
Translation of Voina i èkonomika îAponii.
Bibliography: leaves 437–444.

1. Japan—Economic conditions—1918–1945.   I. Minami Manshū Tetsudō Kabushiki Kaisha. Chosabu. II. Title.

HC462.8.L5316   72–805454

NL 0354428   DLC

VOLUME 332

Lif, Sh   B
... Война и экономика Японии; под общей редакцией академика Е. С. Варга. ₍Ленинград₎ Политиздат при ЦК ВКП(б) 1940.
246, ₍2₎ p. incl. tables. 22½ᶜᵐ.
At head of title: Институт мирового хозяйства и мировой политики Академии наук СССР. Ш. Лиф.
"Мы пользуемся данными главным образом за 1936, 1937 и 1938 гг."—p. ₍4₎
"Основные источники": p. 244-₍247₎
"Закон о мобилизации военной промышленности ... (введен в силу 10 ноября 1937 г.) ... ₍и₎ Закон о всеобщей мобилизации страны, принятый Японским парламентом 24 марта 1938 г.": p. 239-244.
1. Japan—Econ. condit.—1918-¹·^ε. ɪ. Varga, Eugen, 1879-
ed. ɪɪ. Akademiíà nauk   SSSR. Institut mirovogo khozíaĭstva i mirovoĭ politiki.   ɪɪɪ. Title. *Title transliterated:*
Voĭna i ėkonomika   ĬÀponii.
Library of Congress   HC462.L72   43-37692

NL 0354429   DLC

Lifa-lichtfilterfabrik, Augsburg.
Lifa light filter handbook. 5th ed. Augsburg, Lifa light filter works ₍1922₎
83 p. incl. front. (diagr.) illus., plates, tables, diagrs. 21ᶜᵐ.

29 pages of plates, printed on both sides, in folder at back.

1. Photography.

NL 0354430   NNC

Lifa-Lichtfilterfabrik, Augsburg.
Lifa-Licht-Filter handbuch. Ed 4. Augsburg, Kellner, 1927.
82 p. tab. O.

NL 0354431   PPF

Lifanov, I   A
Организация чаши водохранилища; затопления и подтопления в гидротехническом строительстве. Под ред. П. И. Василенко. Москва, Гос. энерг. изд-во, 1946.
224 p. illus. 22 cm.
Bibliography: p. 210-212.

1. Flood dams and reservoirs.   *Title transliterated:* Organizatsiíà chashi vodokhranilishcha.
TC167.L5   50-20460

NL 0354432   DLC

Lifanov, I   A
Водохранилища гидроэлектростанций. Москва, Гос. энерг. изд-во, 1955.
69 p. illus. 20 cm. (В помощь гидроэнергетическим строителям, вып. 21)
Includes bibliography.

1. Reservoirs. 2. Water-power electric plants. ɪ. Title. (Series: V pomoshch' gidroénergeticheskim stroĭkam, vyp. 21)   *Title transliterated:* Vodokhranilishcha gidroélektrostantsiĭ.
TD395.L5   56-24078
Library of Congress

NL 0354433   DLC

Z7164
.S67L4

Lifanov, M. I.

Leningrad. Publichnaíà biblioteka.
О переходе от социализма к коммунизму; рекомендательный указатель литературы. Под ред. Л. П. Маркузе. Ленинград, 1949.

Lifar, Serge, 1905-
A l'aube de mon destin chez Diaghilew, sept ans aux Ballets russes. Paris, A. Michel ₍1949₎
154 p. illus., ports. 24 cm.
Follows the author's Du temps que j'avais faim.

1. Diàgilev, Sergeĭ Pavlovich, 1872-1929. 2. Ballet. ɪ. Title.

GV1785.L5A3   927.933   49-25749*

NL 0354435   DLC NSyU CLU CtY ICU NN

Lifar, Serge, 1905-
Alexandre le Grand
see under   Gaubert, Philippe, 1879-1941.

Lifar, Serge, 1905-
Auguste Vestris, le dieu de la danse. Paris, Nagel ₍1950₎
253 p. illus., ports. 23 cm. (Collection "Arts")

1. Vestris, Auguste, 1760-1842.

GV1785.V48L5   927.933   51-18580

NL 0354437   DLC NN OU IU NSyU CaOTP NcGU

Lifar, Serge, 1905-
Ballet, traditional to modern, by Serge Lifar ... Translated by Cyril W. Beaumont. London, Putnam ₍1938₎
6 p. l., 3-302 p. front., illus., plates, ports. 22ᶜᵐ.
"First published November, 1938; reprinted December, 1938."

1. Ballet. 2. Dancing—Hist. ɪ. Beaumont, Cyril William, 1891- tr. ɪɪ. Title.   *Translation of* La danse. Les grands courants de la danse académique.
                                 39-15975 Revised
Library of Congress   GV1787.L45 1938 a
                       ₍r42g3₎   792.8

NL 0354438   DLC WaT CaBVa LU MiU TxU OU OCl OClW NN

Lifar, Serge, 1905-
... Carlotta Grisi. Paris, A. Michel ₍1941₎
3 p. l., 9-126 p., 1 l. illus. (facsim.) xvi pl. (incl. ports.) on 8 l. 20ᶜᵐ.
"Bibliographie": p. 122-124.

1. Grisi, Carlotta, 1819-1899.

GV1785.G73L5   927.933   47-34799

NL 0354439   DLC OU FU IU CtY NN

Lifar, Serge, 1905-
Carlotta Grisi; tr. from the French, with an introd. by Doris Langley Moore. London, J. Lehmann ₍1947₎
87, ₍1₎ p. plates, ports. 24 cm.
Bibliography: p. 87-₍88₎

1. Grisi, Carlotta, 1819-1899.   ɪ. Moore, Doris (Langley-Levy) 1903- tr.

GV1785.G73L52   927.933   48-22886*

TxU NcGU NcU
NL 0354440   DLC WaT CaBVa IU OU TU CaOTP KEmT MH

Lifar, Serge₎ 1905-   *ed.*
Centenaire de Pouchkine, 1837-1937. Exposition Pouchkine et son époque, Paris. ₍Paris, Imp. Coopérative Étoile, 1937₎
1 p. l., 7-94 p., 1 l. front., illus., plates, ports., facsims. 19ᶜᵐ.
"Édité par S. Lifar."
Contents.—Préface, par Serge Lifar.—Guide de l'exposition "Pouchkine et son époque," par Serge Lifar et Modeste Hofmann.—Discours prononcés à l'occasion de l'inauguration de l'exposition "Pouchkine et son époque" à la salle Pleyel, le 16 mars 1937: ɪ. Discours de m. Nicolas Pouchkine. ɪɪ. Discours de m. Modeste Hofmann.—La vie et l'œuvre de Pouchkine, par m. Modeste Hofmann.—Trois commémorations de Pouchkine, par Serge Lifar.
1. Pushkin, Aleksandr Sergeevich—Anniversaries, etc. ɪ. Hofmann, Modeste, 1887- ɪɪ. Title. ɪɪɪ. Title: Exposition Pouchkine et son époque. ɪᴠ. Title: Pouchkine et son époque.
Library of Congress   PG3354.L5   44-1961
                                928.917

NL 0354441   DLC CtY NNC WU MH MU NcD CoU MiU

Lifar, Serge, 1905-
... La danse. Les grands courants de la danse académique. Avec trente-six clichés hors texte et dans le texte. Paris, Denoël ₍1938₎
2 p. l., 7-349, ₍1₎ p. front., illus., plates, ports. 22½ᶜᵐ.

1. Ballet. 2. Dancing—Hist. ɪ. Title.   40-5079
Library of Congress   GV1787.L44
                                792.8

NL 0354442   DLC CtY CLSU CU NcD NN

LIFAR, SERGE, 1905-
La danse. [Paris, Éditions de La revue choréographique, 1952] 11 p. illus. 39cm.
Cover title: Méditations sur la danse.

1. Dancing. ɪ. Title: Méditations sur la danse.

NL 0354443   NN NcGU

LIFAR, SERGE, 1905-
Danza académica. Con dibujos de Monique Lancelot. [La versión española ha sido realizada por Alicia Simonet. Madrid] Escelicer [1955] 226 p. illus., plates. 25cm. (Colección El David. 2)

1. Ballet—Instruction. ɪ. Colección El David. ɪɪ. El David, Colección.

NL 0354444   NN

Lifar, Serge, 1905-
2e [i. e. Deuxième] exposition Pouchkine et son époque, organisée par S. Lifar, 26 juin-10 juillet 1949 [catalogue] Paris, Lycée russe de Paris [1949]
15 p.

NL 0354445   MH

Lifar, Serge, 1905-
Дягилевъ и съ Дягилевымъ. Парижъ, "Домъ книги" ₍1939₎
499, ₍3₎ p. incl. front. illus., plates, ports., facsims. 26 cm.

1. Diàgilev, Sergeĭ Pavlovich, 1872-1929.   *Title transliterated:* Diàgilev i s Diàgilevym.

GV1785.D5L47   49-31637

NL 0354446   DLC

Lifar, Serge, 1905-
Du temps que j'avais faim. Paris: Librairie Stock ₍cop. 1935₎ 245 p. pls., ports. 12°.

1. Lifar, Serge. 2. Title.   January 14, 1936

NL 0354447   NN OU NBuG CtY CFlS

VOLUME 332

Lifar, Serge, 1905–

PG3343
.E8
1937a   Pushkin, Aleksandr Sergeevich, 1799–1837.
Евгеній Онѣгинъ, романъ въ стихахъ. Сочиненіе Алексаидра Пушкина. Съ комментаріями М. Л. Гофмана, С. М. Лифаря и Г. Л. Лозинскаго, подъ редакціей М. Л. Гофмана. Юбилейное изданіе. Парижъ, Въ типографіи "Étoile," 1937.

Lifar, Serge, 1905–
... Giselle, apothéose du ballet romantique. Paris, A. Michel ₁1942₎
300 p., 1 l. illus. (incl. facsim.) plates, ports., diagrs. 21ᵐ.

1. Adam, Adolphe Charles, 1803–1856. Giselle. 2. Saint-Georges, Jules Henri Vernoy de, 1801?–1875. Giselle. 3. Gautier, Théophile, 1811–1872. Giselle. i. Title.
GV1790.G5L5   A F 47–4370
New York. Public library
for Library of Congress   †

NL 0354449   NN NSyU OU KMK CtY NNC DLC

M1523
.J68G8   Lifar, Serge, 1905–

Jolivet, André, 1905–
₁Guignol et Pandore; arr.₎
Guignol et Pandore, ballet en un acte de Serge Lifar. Paris, M. Eschig ₁1949, ᶜ1948₎

Lifar, Serge, 1905–
Histoire du ballet russe, depuis les origines jusqu'à nos jours. Paris, Nagel ₁1950₎
322 p. illus., ports. 22 cm. (Collection "Arts")

1. Ballet—Hist. 2. Dancing—Russia—Hist.
GV1787.L454   792.8   51–450

NL 0354451   DLC ICU ICN NIC PU NN OU MH OKentU

Lifar, Serge, 1905–
A history of Russian ballet from its origins to the present day. Translated by Arnold Haskell. London, Hutchinson ₁1954₎
328 p. illus. 24 cm.

1. Ballet—Hist. 2. Dancing—Russia—Hist.
GV1787.L4542   792.8   54—2694 ‡
₁55c2₎

CaBVa CaBVaU OrCS
NN PP OU OC1 IEN MB OCU OOxM MiU PPD PPT WaT WaS
NL 0354452   DLC GU TxU OkU UU NcD MB MiD NIC IaU

Lifar, Serge, 1905–
A history of the Russian ballet from its origins to the present day. Translated by Arnold Haskell. New York, Roy Publishers ₁1954?₎
328 p. illus. 24 cm.

1. Ballet—Hist. 2. Dancing—Russia—Hist.
[GV1787]   792.8   55–9309 ‡
Printed for U. S. Q. B. R.
by Library of Congress

NL 0354453   Or CaBViP OrP Wa LU PP ViU

Lifar, Serge, 1905–
Hommage à Balanchine: George Balanchine
see under title

Lifar, Serge, 1905–
Исторія русскаго балета отъ XVII вѣка до "Русскаго балета" Дягилева. Парижъ, 1945.
302 p. illus., ports. 25 cm.

1. Ballet—Hist. 2. Dancing—Russia—Hist.
          Title transliterated: Istorīi͡a russkago baleta.
GV1787.L456   1945   51–18424

NL 0354455   DLC OrCS MtU CSt VtU

Lifar, Serge, 1905–
Lifar on classical ballet. With an introd. by Arnold L. Haskell and a foreword by Karsavina. Drawings by Monique Lancelot. ₁Translated from the French by D. M. Dinwiddie₎ London, A. Wingate ₁1951₎
212 p. illus., 36 plates. 22 cm.
Translation of Traité de danse académique.

1. Ballet dancing.
GV1788.L514   792.8   52–3199

OrP WaS OrCS
NL 0354456   DLC FU LU NcU NSyU IU NIC NcGU CaBViP

Lifar, Serge, 1905–
Le livre de la danse. Illustré par Aristide Maillol ₁et al.₎ Paris, Éditions du Journal musical français, 1954.
226 p. illus. 24 cm.

1. Ballet. i. Title.
GV1785.L5A32   54–40201 ‡
Library of Congress

NL 0354457   DLC CtY NN FTaSU

792.82
L 693   Lifar, Serge, 1905–
Le Manifeste du Chorégraphe. Paris, Messageries Hachette, 1935.
38 p.   19 cm.

1. Ballet - Choriography. I. Title.

NL 0354458   MWAC MH NN ScU

Lifar, Serge, 1905–
Мой путь к хореотворчеству. Парижъ ₁Cooperative Étoile₎ 1938.
22 p. 5 plates. 24 cm.
An excerpt from the 2d ed. of the author's "Танец, современные течения академического танца." cf. pref.

1. Ballet. i. Title.
        Title transliterated: Moĭ put' k khoreotvorchestvu.
GV1787.L46   49–30520*

NL 0354459   DLC

Lifar, Serge, 1905–
La musique par la danse, de Lulli à Prokofiev. Paris, R. Laffont ₁1955₎
166 p. 19 cm.

1. Ballet. 2. Dance music—Hist. & crit. i. Title.
ML3460.L5   55–30806 ‡

NL 0354460   DLC NcGU NSyU OrU NN

Lifar, Serge, 1905–
... Pensées sur la danse; illustré par Aristide Maillol, avec un avant-propos de Paul Valéry. ₁Paris₎ Bordas ₁1946₎
3 p. l., 3–61 p., 3 l. incl. front., plates. 33ᶜᵐ.

1. Dancing. i. Maillol, Aristide Joseph Bonaventure, 1861–1944, illus.
GV1595.L47   793.3   47–20786

NL 0354461   DLC NBu NN CSt CU

Lifar, Serge, 1905–

Pushkin, Aleksandr Sergeevich, 1799–1837.
... Письма Пушкина къ Н. Н. Гончаровой. Юбилейное изданіе (второе) 1837–1937. Парижъ ₁Издалъ С. Лифаръ, 1936₎

DK216
.P8
1935   Lifar, Serge, 1905–

Pushkin, Aleksandr Sergeevich, 1799–1837.
... Путешествіе въ Арзрумъ во время похода 1829 года. Подъ редакціей и съ примѣчаніями проф. М. Л. Гофмана и со вступительной статьей Сергѣя Лифаря. 2. изд. ₁Парижъ₎ Изданіе С. Лифаря, 1935.

Barnard
GV
1785
.D5
L5
1940   Lifar, Serge, 1905–
Serge Diaghilev, his life, his work, his legend; an intimate biography. London, Putnam ₁1940₎
556 p. plates, ports. 22cm.

1. Diagilev, Sergeĭ Pavlovich, 1872–1929.

NL 0354464   NNC CU CSt

Lifar, Serge, 1905–
Serge Diaghilev, his life, his work, his legend; an intimate biography by Serge Lifar ... New York, G. P. Putnam's sons ₁ᶜ1940₎
xiv, 399 p. front., plates, ports. 24½ᵐ.

1. Diagilev, Sergeĭ Pavlovich, 1872–1929. 2. Ballet.
Library of Congress   GV1785.D5L5   40–33124
Copyright   927.93

MiU NcC PP OrU
NL 0354465   DLC OrSaW CaBVa WaS Or WaSp OrP OC1JC

VOLUME 332

792.8
D536Yℓ
Lifar, Serge, 1905–
Serge Diaghilev, his life, his work, his legend; an intimate biography. London, Putnam [1945]
xvi,556p. ports. 23cm.

1. Diagilev, Sergieĭ Pavlovich, 1872-1929.
2. Ballet.

NL 0354466　IEN CaBVaU CLSU CaQMM

Lifar, Serge, 1905–
Serge de Diaghilev: sa vie, son œuvre, sa légende. Préf. par Jean-Louis Vaudoyer. Monaco, Éditions du Rocher [1954]
321p. illus. 21 cm.
First published under title: Дягилевъ и съ Дягилевымъ (transliterated: Diagilev i s Diagilevym)

1. Diagilev, Sergeĭ Pavlovich, 1872-1929. 2. Ballet.

GV1785.D5L49　　　54-25758 ‡

NL 0354467　DLC MiU NN MB OCl LU NSyU

Lifar, Serge, 1905–
Страдные годы, моя юность въ Россіи. Парижъ [Складъ изд. "Домъ книги"] 1935.
328 p. ports. 19 cm.

ɪ. Title.　　　*Title transliterated:* Stradnye gody.

GV1785.L5A33　　　54-52120

NL 0354468　DLC WU CSt

Lifar, Serge, 1905–
Танец; основные течения академического танца. 2. доп. изд. Парижъ, Étoile, 1938.
253 p. illus. 26 cm.

1. Ballet. 2. Dancing—Hist. ɪ. Title.
　　　　　　　Title transliterated: Tanets.
GV1787.L4367 1938　　　53-54528 ‡

NL 0354469　DLC CSt

Lifar, Serge, 1905–
... Terpsichore dans le cortège des muses. Paris, P. Lagrange [1943]
125 p., 1 l. incl. plates. front. 23 x 17½ᵐ.

1. Dancing. 2. Ballet. ɪ. Title.
　　　　　　　　　　　　　46-6050
Library of Congress　　GV1781.L5
　　　　　　　　　　　　　793.3

NL 0354470　DLC CaBVaU NSyU NN CtY

Lifar, Serge, 1905–
Traité de chorégraphie. Dessins et lithographies de Monique Lancelot. [Paris] Bordas, 1952.
231 p. illus. 24 cm.

1. Ballets—Choregraphies. ɪ. Title.

GV1788.L49　　　792.8　　　53-18571 ‡

NL 0354471　DLC NSyU NN MB PP OU LU NcGU

Lifar, Serge, 1905–
Traité de danse académique; dessins de Monique Lancelot. [Paris] Bordas, 1949.
226 p. illus. plates. 24 cm.

1. Ballet dancing. ɪ. Title.

GV1788.L5　　　792.8　　　49-28858*

NL 0354472　DLC CaBVaU MB NSyU PU OU CtY ICU

Lifar, Serge, 1905–
Traité de danse académique. Dessins de Monique Lancelot. [Éd., rev. et complétée. Paris] Bordas, 1952 [i. e. 1953]
231 p. illus. plates. 24 cm.

1. Ballet dancing. ɪ. Title.

GV1788.L5 1953　　　54-31698

NL 0354473　DLC NcGU MiU CSf NN

Lifar, Serge, 1905–
Третій праздникъ Пушкина. Парижъ, 1937.
24 p. port. 14 cm.

1. Pushkin, Aleksandr Sergeevich—Anniversaries, etc.
　　　　Title transliterated: Tretiĭ prazdnik Pushkina.

PG3353.L5　　　52-55325

NL 0354474　DLC MH CSt

Lifar', Sergeĭ Mikhaĭlovich
see
Lifar, Serge, 1905–

Lifchitz, Déborah, *ed. and tr.*
... Textes éthiopiens magico-religieux. Paris, Institut d'ethnologie, 1940.
x, 254 p. 27ᵐ. (Université de Paris. Travaux et mémoires de l'Institut d'ethnologie. xxxviii)
Ethiopic and French on opposite pages.
"Mgr. S. Grébaut m'a aidée dans la traduction de certains textes."—Préface.
Contents.—Introduction: ᴀ. Brèves indications sur l'usage magique des textes religieux. ʙ. Les textes magico-religieux en Abyssinie.—L'Enseignement des arcanes et la Mystagogie.—Le Rempart de la croix.—La Louange de la Trinité.—Le Glaive de la Trinité.—La Langue de Jacob.
"Bibliographie": p. [245]-250.
1. Ethiopic language—Texts. 2. Ethiopic literature—Translations into French. 3. French literature—Translations from Ethiopic. 4. Manuscripts, Ethiopic. 5. Amulets. 6. Magic—Ethiopia. ɪ. Grébaut, Sylvain, 1881– joint tr. ɪɪ. Title.
Library of Congress　　　PJ9008.L5　　　40-31214
Copyright A—Foreign　　　49082
　　　　　　　　　　　　　　　　　　492.8

NcD OCH DDO RPB PPDrop MB MH CSt TxFTC
NL 0354476　DLC NSyU UU MoU CU CaBVaU OU ICarbS NcU

Lifczis, Annie R., *joint tr.*
Die prozellanstadt...
see under Peregudov, Aleksandr Vladimirovich.

PG3476
.N67S65
Lifczis, Annie R., *joint tr.*
Novikov-Priboĭ, Aleksei Silych, 1877–1944.
... Die salzige taufe; roman einer seefahrt. Autorisierte übersetzung aus dem russischen von Boris Krotkow und Annie R. Lifczis. Mit 60 holzschnitt-illustrationen von Karl Rössing. Berlin, Büchergilde Gutenberg, 1933.

Life, Andrew C
[Algae and related subjects - collected works]
[1901-1905?]
2 no. in 1 v. 26 cm.
Table of contents in volume.
1. Algae - Collected works.

NL 0354479　CU

Life, Mrs. Cora Smith, *joint author.*
Coble, Mary Ferguson.
Introduction to ornithological nomenclature, by Mary Ferguson Coble ... and Cora Smith Life ... Los Angeles, Wm. B. Straube printing co. [*1932]

Life, Henry.
A few thoughts for consumptives; by Henry Life ... Milton [Pa.] Morton & Bound, printers, 1869.
12 p. 21ᵐ.

1. Consumption.
　　　　　　　　　　　　　　7-34965†
Library of Congress　　RC311.L71

NL 0354481　DLC

Life, Henry.
The science of the tides, as illustrated and supported by the test of experiment. By Henry Life, ᴍ. ᴅ. New-York, S. W. Green, printer, 1875.
30 p. illus. 18¼ᵐ.

1. Tides.
　　　　　　　　　QB419.L72　　　6-11063†

NL 0354482　DLC DNLM NN

Life. v. 1–　　　Nov. 23, 1936–
[Chicago, Time, inc., 1936–
v. illus. (part col., incl. ports.) 35ᵐ. weekly.
Editors: Nov. 23, 1936–　　H. R. Luce and others.

ɪ. Luce, Henry Robinson, 1898–　ed.
　　　　　　　　　　　　　　37-8367
Library of Congress　　AP2.L547
　　　　　　　　　　　　　　051

CaBVaU KyLoU NcD ICN MoU DAU MNS CtNIC Nh OClW OCU OU TxLT ICN NdU OAkU NIC FM CU-Riv NcRS PHC KT AzTeS NIC NN ViU MB PHC PU PSC PPT PHi PBm
NL 0354483　DLC DNAL PCarlD WaTC WaS MtBC OrP MeP

Film
13-275
Life. v. 1–
Nov. 23, 1936–
[Chicago] Time inc.
v. illus. 35 cm. weekly.

Microfilm. Ann Arbor, Mich., University Microfilms, 1971. reels. 35 mm. (Current periodical series. Publication no. 1127)

NL 0354485　OU PSt OrCS

Life. International ed.
see
Life international.

VOLUME 332

DC
133.8   Life. Chicago.
L72a   Age of enlightenment. [New York] Time, 1947,
          15p. illus.(part col.),ports.(part col.)
          36cm. (Its History of western culture, 5)
          Cover title.
          "From Life, September 15,1947."
          Limited to France.

NL   0354487   NRU

Life (Chicago).
     [American art museums.   Chicago,Life,1950].
     4p.illus.Q.

     Excerpt from Life, August 20, 1950.

NL   0354488   CaBViP

Life. Chicago.
     The American heritage, it is ours because men dared be free.
     [New York] Time, inc., c1941.   10 l.   illus.   36cm.
     "Reprinted from Life, Nov. 10, 1941 with additional pictures and text."

     1. Monuments—U. S. 2. Historic   houses—U. S. I. Title.
                                                              April 17, 1946

NL   0354489   NN

Life (periodical) Chicago.
     American life and times, 1900-1950 ...
     mid-century issue ... Chicago,Time,inc.
     1950.   100p.illus.(part col.)   (v.28,
     no.1, January 2, 1950)

     Cover-title.
     Contents:

NL   0354490   CaBVa

Life. Chicago.
     Art exhibition by men of the armed forces, sponsored by Life.
     [New York] Time inc., 1942]

     3, [2] p. 1 illus., 6 pl. (part col.) on 3 l. 35½ᵐᵐ.
     Cover-title.
     "The 117 works of art listed in this catalogue and exhibited at the
     National gallery of art in Washington, D. C. during July [1942] were
     selected from over 1500 entries submitted for Life's art competition for
     men of the armed forces."

     1. Paintings, American—Exhibitions. 2. World war, 1939-1945—Pic-
     torial works—Exhibitions. 3. Art—Exhibitions. Traveling. i. U. S.
     National gallery of art.

     Library of Congress   ND212.L5   43–1253 Revised

                              [r46d2]   759.13917

NL   0354491   DLC LU MH OC1MA

Life (Periodical) Chicago.
     ... The battle of the tanks ... [1945]
     [3] p. illus.

     From Life, March 26, 1945, p. 41-42, 44.

     1. Tanks (Military science)

NL   0354492   NNC

Life (Chicago)
     Christianity.   Chicago, Time, 1955.
     168 p.   illus.(part.col.)   35 cm.

     Special double issue of Life, v. 39,
     no. 26, v. 40, no. 1, 1955.

     1. Christianity - 20th cent. I. Title.

NL   0354493   KAS

L535.6   Life. Chicago.
L626   Color; it is the response of vision to wave
            lengths of light. [Chicago, Time, 1944]
            p.[39]-[50] col.illus. 37cm.

            Caption title.
            Detached from Life, July 3, 1944.

            1. Color.

NL   0354494   OrU

TR785
.U62   Life. Chicago.
1942   U.S. Bureau of aeronautics (Navy dept.)
             Commence shooting! Prepared by the Photographic section,
          Bureau of aeronautics, with the collaboration of the editors of
          Life magazine and of the March of time newsreel. [New
          York] Time, inc., c1942]

[Life (Chicago)].
     The condor's last stand.   [Chicago,Life,1951].
     3p.illus.Q.

NL   0354496   CaBViP

PN4888
.C5M3   Life. Chicago.

          Magazine Audience Group.
          Continuing study of magazine audiences. Report.

          [Chicago?] Life.

Life (Periodical)

     Cranbrook academy of art, Bloomfield Hills, Mich.
        Cranbrook-Life exhibition of contemporary American paint-
     ing. May 17–June 2, 1940, Cranbrook academy of art, Bloom-
     field Hills, Michigan. [Bloomfield Hills, Cranbrook press,
     c1940]

D769
.1
.T5   Life (Chicago)

          Time, the weekly news-magazine.
             December 7, the first thirty hours, by the correspondents of
          Time, Life, and Fortune. New York, A. A. Knopf, 1942.

Life. Chicago.

     Yale-Life conference on house building technics, New Haven,
     1939.
        Digest of papers presented at the Yale-Life conference on
     house building technics, Department of architecture, School of
     the fine arts, Yale university, New Haven, Connecticut. [New
     York, Time, inc., c1939]

Life (Periodical) Chicago.
     Earliest dinosaurs; diggers unearth a small
     species that lived 200 million years ago.
     [1947]
        p. 49-50, 52. illus. 35cm.

     From Life, August 11, 1947.
     Skeletons discovered by Dr. Edwin H. Colbert
     and associates.

NL   0354501   NNC

DA
670   Life. Chicago.
L72e   The Edwardians. [New York] Time, 1947.
             22p. illus.(part col.),ports.(part col.)
             36cm. (Its History of western culture, 6)
             Cover title.
             "Reprinted from the November 17,1947 issue."

NL   0354502   NRU

Life. (Chicago)
     Exhibitions.   New York.
        v. illus.   23 cm.   annual.
        Issue for 1947/48 called Photographic
     exhibitions catalogue 4.
        1. Photography - Exhibitions.

NL   0354503   IU

F726.6   Life (Chicago)
L626f   Four great churches... Photographed for
1953   Life by Dmitri Kessel. [Chicago, 1953]
            28[43]p. col.illus. 36cm.

            Excerpt from Life, Dec. 28, 1953.

            1. Ulm. Münster. 2. Venice. San
         Marco (Basilica) 3. Wells, Eng. Cathedral
         4. Bourges, France. Saint Etienne (Cathe-
         dral) I. Kessel, Dmitri, photographer.
         II. Title.

NL   0354504   KU

Life (Chicago)
     ... The geography of reading
        see under   Magazine Audience Group.

Life, Chicago.
     A guide to your Life Round table on the pur-
     suit of happiness.   [New York, Time inc.,
     c1948]
        50 p.   25 cm.
        Title on cover.

NL   0354506   OC1MA

Life. (Chicago).
     How Life gets the story: behind the scenes in
     photo-journalism

        see under

     Rayfield, Stanley.

---

051   Life. Chicago.
LIF21i   It's Life! [New York, c1951]
            1 v. unpaged. illus., map. 19cm.

            Cover title.

            1. Life (Periodical)

NL   0354508   IU

PC4111   Life. Chicago.
.T635
         Time, the weekly news-magazine.
            Let's learn Spanish with Time; word lists, prepared and
         produced by the Radio programs department of Time and Life
         magazines ... [Chicago, Time, inc., c1943]

VOLUME 332

q728
L621
Life. Chicago.
Life houses. Here are eight new homes planned
and built for U.S. 1940. ⟨Chicago, Time, inc.,
1940⟩
p.76-90. illus.(incl.plans)

Caption title.
"Reprinted from July 1 ⟨1940⟩ issue of Life".

1. Architecture, Domestic--Designs and plans.
2. Architecture, Domestic--U.S. I. Title.

NL 0354510   IU

Life (*Chicago*)
Memorable Life photographs. Foreword and comment by
Edward Steichen. New York, Museum of Modern Art
⟨°1951⟩
1 v. (chiefly illus.) 36 cm.

1. Photography, Journalistic. 2. Photographs. I. Steichen,
Edward, 1879-   II. Title.

TR820.L5   779   52-10476 rev

ViU NcRS NN IU CaBVa OrPR Wa WaS
NL 0354511   DLC MB CoU MeB TxU MdBP CU FTaSU DSI

Life (Chicago)
Michelangelo's Sistine ceiling
see under   Buonarroti, Michel Angelo,
1475-1564.

D
118
L72m
Life. Chicago.
The Middle Ages. [New York] Time, 1947.
38p. illus.(part col.),ports. 36cm. (Its
History of western culture. 2,3)
Caption title.
"From Life, April 7 and May 26,1947."

NL 0354513   NRU

ND205
.B6
1940
folio
Life. Chicago.   FOR OTHER EDITIONS
                                  SEE MAIN ENTRY
Boswell, Peyton, 1904-
Modern American painting. With 89 illus. in full color
selected from the series on contemporary American artists
pub. in Life. New York, Dodd, Mead, 1940.

Life. Chicago.
The new world ... ⟨Chicago, 1947⟩
⟨6⟩ p.incl.illus.,plates,facsims.(part col.)
35.5cm.

Article about illustrations in The new
world,by Stefan Lorant.Separated from Life,
March 10,1947.

1.Bry,Theodore de,1528-1598,engr. 2.White,John,fl.
1585-1595. I.Lorant,Stefan,1901-   . The new world.

NL 0354515   MiU-C

DO51
L6273
Life (Periodical) Chicago.
The pace of Life. ⟨New York, Time, incor-
porated, c1940⟩
1 v. illus., diagrs. 38 x 43½cm.

Cover-title.

NL 0354516   NNC MH ICU IU

Life (*Chicago*)
Picture history of Western man.   New York, Time inc.,
1951.
806 p. illus. (part col.) ports. (part col.) maps (part col.) 36 cm.
Bibliography: p. ⟨296⟩-300.

1. Civilization, Occidental.   I. Title.

CB245.L5   901   51-7649

CaBVaU OrAshS
MtBuM WaE WaSp WaTC OrCS OrP Wa WaS WaT WaSpG OrPS
MdBP MiU TxU NcU OrPR KyLx OrStbM IdU MtBC LU OrU
DSI IdB IdPI MeB KEmT Or ViU TU MB MH NN GU CU MiU
NL 0354517   DLC PSt NBuC TxU NNC CaBVa CaBViP NSyU

Life (*Chicago*)
Picture history of World War II.   New York, Time, inc.,
1950.
vii, 368 p. illus. (part col.) ports. (part col.) maps. 37 cm.

1. World War, 1939-1945—Pictorial works.   I. Title.

D743.2.L48   940.53084   50-10501

WaT OrPS OrStbM Wa WaWW WaSp
IdB CaBVaU CaBViP OrCS OrP WaE WaS OrAshS Or CaBVa
CSt MsU ViU NcU NN AU PSt OCIU NcU MtBuM MtU IdU
NL 0354518   DLC MiD MH MB PSC PSt PV PP PBL PU PPD

Life (Periodical) Chicago.
Plutonium laboratory; ⟨historic research on
man-made element used in atomic bombs was done
at University of Chicago's "new chem"; photographs for Life by F. W. Goro. ⟨1946⟩
69-⟨83⟩ p. illus. (part col.) 35ᶜᵐ.

From Life, vol. 21, no. 2, July 8, 1946.

1. Plutonium.

NL 0354519   NNC

G1019
H321L7
f
Life. Chicago.
... A preview of Look at the world by
Richard Edes Harrison. ⟨New York⟩ Time inc.,
1944.
⟨1⟩,56-61 p. illus.(incl.port.,maps,part.
col., 1 double) 35ᶜᵐ.

Hoover
Library
"Reprinted from the Feb. 28th issue of
Life."

1. Harrison, Richard Edes. Look at the
world. 2. Atlases. I. Title.

NL 0354520   CSt-H

Life. (Chicago)
**Michigan-Life conference on new technologies in transpor-
tation,** *University of Michigan,* 1939.
Proceedings of the Michigan-Life conference on new tech-
nologies in transportation, November 1-2-3, 1939. Ann Arbor,
Mich., The University ⟨1940⟩

Life (Chicago)
The promise and purpose of Life.
⟨New York, Time, inc. n.d.⟩
8 pamphlets in folder. illus. 35 cm.
(in box)
Contents.-1. Events and politics.-2. Art
and beauty.-3. History and civilization.-4.
Science and nature.-5. The lively arts.-6.
Better living.-7. Sport and adventure.-8.
Human experience.

1. Life (Chicago). I. Title.

NL 0354522   AAP MtBC

Life (Periodical) Chicago.
⟨R. Buckminster Fuller's Dymaxion world map.
⟨Chicago, 1943⟩
⟨5⟩ p. illus., maps (part col.)

Detached from Life, 14:41-55 Mr. 1, 1943.

I. Fuller, Richard Buckminster, 1895-

NL 0354523   MiD

DG
533
L72r
Life . Chicago.
Renaissance man. [New York, Time, 1947]
69-83p. illus.(part col.),ports. 32cm. (Its
History of western culture, 1)
Caption title.
"Reprinted from Life, March 3,1947."
A 15th century Italian, Aeneas Piccolomini,
later Pope Pius II, selected as the prototype.

NL 0354524   NRU

Life (periodical) Chicago.
The search for the bones of St.
Peter ... Photographed for Life by
Nat Farbman. ⟨Chicago,Time,inc.1950⟩
65-85p.illus.plates(part col.) (Life,
vol.28, no.13, Mar 27, 1950 p.65-85)

Caption title.
Includes extracts from a report
written ... by Monsignor Ludwig Kaas.

NL 0354525   CaBVa

Life (Periodical) Chicago.
⟨Selections from the special number on Russia.
New York, Time, inc., 1943⟩
19-116 p. illus. (part col.) ports. 25½cm.

From Life, March 29, 1943.

1. World war, 1939-   - Russia. 2. World
war, 1939-   - Pictorial works. 3. Russia -
History - Pictorial works.

NL 0354526   NNC

---

*fAC9
B4356
LZ999
Life. Chicago.
Stephen Benét: the ultimate objectives of free
men are to be discovered in their arts and
letters.
(In Life. Chicago,1943.   35.5cm.,in case
37cm.   vol.14, no.14, p.22)

The magazine's editorial for the week of
April 5, 1943.
In half blue morocco case labeled on spine:
Miscellaneous magazines ...

NL 0354527   MH

Life (Chicago).
A study of duplication

see under

Politz (Alfred) Research, Inc., New York.

Life (Chicago)
A study of four media, their accumulative
and repeat audiences

see under

Politz (Alfred) Research, inc., New York.

VOLUME 332

Life (Chicago)
A study of the accumulative audience of Life
see under Politz (Alfred) Research,
inc., New York.

Life (Periodical) Chicago.
... Thomas Jefferson, 1743-1943. [New York,
Time, inc., 1943]
62-75 p. illus., ports. (part col.) 35½ᶜᵐ.

Caption-title.
From Life, April 12, 1943.

1. Jefferson, Thomas, pres. U. S., 1743-1826.

NL 0354531   NNC

fLA209   Life (Chicago)
.2   U. S. schools; they face a crisis;
L5   special issue. [Chicago, Time, inc.,
1950]
192 p. illus.

Cover-title.
Extract from Life, v.29, no.16,
Oct. 16, 1950.

NL 0354532   CU

L629.13   Life (Periodical) Chicago.
L62   U. S. tests rockets in New Mexico. [1946]
31-35 p. illus.

From Life, vol. 20, no. 21, May 27, 1946.

1. Rockets (Aeronautics)

NL 0354533   NNC

Oversize   Life (Chicago)
ND   The Van Eyck altarpiece. [New York, 1949]
673   [13] p. illus. (part col., 2 double]
E87L5   36 cm.
Art   At head of title: Art masterpieces from
Collection   Life.
Reprinted from Life issue of April 18,
1949.
Photos. by Fernand Bourges.

1. Eyck, Hubert van, 1366-1426. 2. Eyck,
Jan van, 1390-   1440. 3. Altarpieces.
I. Title.

NL 0354534   NBuU MdBJ

Life. Chicago.
Virginia has the most beautiful campus in the
country.
(In Life. New York, 1937. 36ᶜᵐ. vol.2, no.
23. June 7, 1937. p.[48-49] incl. col. illus.)
Caption title.
Detached copy.
Title in contents of the magazine issue: Vir-
ginia campus.

1. Virginia. University—Description—Views.
I. Title. II. Title: Virginia campus.

NL 0354535   ViU

Life. Chicago.
War art, a catalogue of paintings done on the war fronts by
American artists for "Life." [Chicago, Time inc., 1943]
cover-title, 35 p. illus. (part col., incl. ports.) 35¼ᵐ.
"At the close of the exhibitions of these paintings in the great museums of the U. S., Life will turn these pictures over to the U. S. government that they may be a permanent record of this war, forever available to the American public."—p. 2.
Includes brief biographical sketches of the artists.

1. Paintings, American—Exhibitions. 2. Art—Exhibitions, Traveling.
World war, 1939-1945—Pictorial works—Exhibitions. 4. World war,
1939-1945—U. S. 5. Artists, American.   I. Title.

43-14854 Revised
Library of Congress   ND212.L527
[r46f3]   756

NL 0354536   DLC WaS CU OC1 OO OC1MA MdBWA MB

D769   Life. Chicago.
.1
.T5   Time, the weekly news-magazine.
1941   War comes to the U. S.—Dec. 7, 1941; the first 30 hours as
reported to the Time-Life-Fortune news bureau from the U. S.
and abroad. [New York? 1941?]

Life . Chicago.
The war world. New York, 1939.
104 p. illus. maps.

Special issue, September 25, 1939.

NL 0354538   OC1

QE 11   Life (Chicago)
.L 52   Die welt in der wir leben; die naturge-
1955 Q   schichte unserer erde. München [etc.] Th.
Knaur nachf. [c1955]
304 p. illus. (part col.) col. maps,
col. profiles. 36cm.

"Von der redaktion Life und von Lincoln
Barnett."
"Titel der originalausgabe: The world we
live in; überset-   zung und textgestaltung
von Fritz Bolle."

NL 0354539   MdBJ

Life (Chicago).
Why insects change form; a young Harvard scien-
tist discovers the cause of metamorphosis. [Chi-
cago,Life,1952].
8p.illus.sq.Q.

From Life, vol.32, February 11, 1952.

NL 0354540   CaBViP

Life (Chicago)
The world we live in, by the editorial staff of Life and
Lincoln Barnett. New York, Time, inc.; [distribution by
Simon & Schuster] 1955.
304 p. illus. (part col.) col. maps, col. profiles. 36 cm.
" 'The world we live in' series appeared in Life at intervals of
approximately two months from December 8, 1952 to December 20,
1954 ... 'The world we live in' book is basically a compilation of the
thirteen parts of the series."

1. Natural history. 2. Natural history—Pictorial works.
I. Barnett, Lincoln Kinnear, 1909-   II. Title.

QH45.L69   574.084   55—13583

PSt OOxM
WaSpG DI MiD OC1W OC1Ur OCU ViU OO NN KyLx ICJ PU
UU KyMdC KyU PBL OrPS OrStbM OrU Wa WaE WaS WaT
PPAN OC1 OU TU ViU FU KyLx KEmT KyMurT KyU-H NBuC
OrAshS OrP PWcS MtBuM NcD PBm PSt PV PBa MdBP MiHM
TxU NcC CaBVa CaBViP CaBVaU IdB MtBC MtU Or OrCS
NL 0354541   DLC WaSp PPT PHC MiU PSC NIC MB CU IU

Life (Chicago)
The world's great religions
see under title

Life. v. 1-103; Jan. 4, 1883-Nov. 1936. [New York, Life
magazine, inc., etc., 1883-1936]
103 v. in 117. illus. (part col.) plates (part col.) 27-30ᵐ.
Weekly, 1883-Nov. 1931; monthly, Dec. 1931-1936.
Founded and for many years edited by J. A. Mitchell.
Absorbed by Judge.
L. C. set incomplete: Nov. 1935 wanting.

I. Mitchell, John Ames, 1845-1918, ed.
7-21211 Revised
Library of Congress   AP101.L6

COMC
AzTeS CtH PCaD KT PPL PP PU NjP MH MB OC1W OO MiU
NL 0354544   DLC OrCS PPiU CaOTRC NN InU CaOOG I

Film   Life. v. 1-6; Jan. 1883-Dec. 1885. [New York,
2053   Life magazine, inc., 1883-1885]
6v. illus. (part col.) plates (part col.)
Weekly.
Founded and edited by J. A. Mitchell.
"Periodical preservation plan."
Microfilm. Cleveland, Ohio, Micro Photo Division,
Bell & Howell [n.d.] 1 reel.

I. Mitchell, John Ames, 1845-1918, ed.

NL 0354545   TxU DLC NN

Life. New York.
Auto fun; pictures and comments from "Life" ... New
York, T. Y. Crowell & co. [1905]
71 l. incl. illus., plates. 17½ x 23ᵐ.

1. Automobiles—Anecdotes, facetiae, satire, etc.   I. Title.
5-26778 Revised
Library of Congress   PN6231.A8L5

NL 0354546   DLC DSI

Life. New York.
Life's book of animals; drawings by E. W. Kemble, T. S.
Sullivant ... and others. New York, Doubleday & McClure
company, 1898.
80 p. illus. 18½ x 25½ᵐ.

1. Animal pictures. 2. Wit and humor, Pictorial.   I. Title.
98-255 Revised
Library of Congress   NC1428.L52

NL 0354547   DLC MB ViU OKentU

Life (Periodical) New York.

Hoover, Ellison.
Cartoons from Life, by Ellison Hoover; foreword by
Robert Benchley. New York, Simon and Schuster, 1925.

Life. New York.
Life's comedy. 1st-[2d] series. New York,
1897.
2 v. 30 x 24 cm.

NL 0354549   CtY

VOLUME 332

Life. New York.
The comedy of Life ... New York, Life publishing company, 1907.
1 p. l., ₍118₎ p. of illus. 29½ᶜᵐ.

ɪ. Title.
7–38424 Revised
Library of Congress   NC1428.L47

NL 0354550   DLC

Life. New York.
Masson, Thomas Lansing, 1866–
Dogs from "Life," by Thomas L. Masson ... Garden City, New York, Doubleday, Page & company, 1920.

Life. New York.
Masson, Thomas Lansing, 1866–   *ed.*
Dogs from "Life". Second litter, edited by Thomas L. Masson ... Garden City, N. Y., Doubleday, Page & company, 1926.

Life. New York.
Drawings from "Life"
see under   ₍Gibson, Charles Dana₎ 1867–

Life. New York.
Fun from Life. New York, F. A. Stokes & brother, 1889.
1 p. l., 62 p. illus. 18 x 22½ᶜᵐ.

1. Wit and humor, Pictorial.   ɪ. Title.
11–25476 Revised
Library of Congress   NC1428.L48

NL 0354554   DLC OrU

Life (*New York*)
The good things of Life ... ₍1st₎–10th series. New York, White, Stokes, & Allen ₍etc.₎ 1884–93.
10 v. illus. 22 x 27 cm.

1. Wit and humor, Pictorial.   ɪ. Title.
NC1428.L5
11–25475 rev 2

NIC RPB
NL 0354555   DLC CaBVaU MH PSC PU PP NcU IEN CLU MB

Life. New York.
Life's Dog Calendar
see under title

Life. New York.
Men, women and mirth ... New York, Life publishing company ₍1909₎
₍120₎ p. illus. 29½ᶜᵐ.

1. Wit and humor, Pictorial.   ɪ. Title.
9–18979 Revised
Library of Congress   NC1428.L53

NL 0354557   DLC WaS NcD

Life. New York.
Herford, Oliver, 1863–1935, *ed.*
Poems from "Life" with introductory words by Oliver Herford, and orchestration by Charles B. Falls. New York, The Macmillan company, 1923.

NC38   **Life.** New York.
.L6   Life's prints.   New York, Life ₍1908₎
119p. illus.

Reproductions from Life.
Catalog of prints for sale.

1. Pictures - Catalog. I. Title.

NL 0354559   NcU MoKU

Life. New York.
Rhymes & roundelays from "Life." New York, Doubleday, Page & co., 1902.
xiv, 146 p. incl. front., illus. 17½ᶜᵐ.

1. American wit and humor.   ɪ. Title.
2–21110 Revised 2
Library of Congress   PS595.H8L5

CtY
NL 0354560   DLC WaS MtU OrU NcU NcD OrU OClW PU MB

Life. New York.
Short stories from Life; the 81 prize stories in "Life's" shortest story contest, with an introduction by Thomas L. Masson ... Garden City, New York, Doubleday, Page & company, 1916.
xx, 346 p., 1 l. 19½ᶜᵐ.

1. Short stories, American.   ɪ. Masson, Thomas Lansing, 1866–
16–17415 Revised
Library of Congress   PZ1.L63

ViU NN
NL 0354561   DLC AAP CaBViP WaTC OrU MsU OrU LU OO

Life. New York
The social comedy ... New York, Life Publishing Company, 1902.
1 v. (unpaged, chiefly illus.) 30 cm.

1. American wit and humor, Pictorial.
2. Caricatures and cartoons - U. S.
I. Title.

NL 0354562   MoKU

Life. New York.
The social comedy ... ₍3d ed.₎ New York, Life publishing company, 1902.
1 p. l., ₍118₎ p. of illus. 29½ᶜᵐ.

1. Wit and humor, Pictorial.   ɪ. Title.
8–7174 Revised
Library of Congress   NC1428.L55

NL 0354563   DLC PP

Life. New York.
The social comedy ... New York, Life publishing company, 1906. 4th ed.
1 p. l., ₍118₎ p. of illus.

NL 0354564   MiU

Life. New York.
The spice of Life.   New York and London, White and Allen ₍ᶜ1888₎
64 p. illus. 21 x 26ᶜᵐ.

1. Wit and humor, Pictorial.   ɪ. Title.
11–25478 Revised
Library of Congress   NC1428.L58

NL 0354565   DLC

Life. New York.
Taken from Life. Verses. New York, Doubleday & McClure co., 1897.
xiii, 146 p. incl. front. illus. 17½ᶜᵐ.

1. American wit and humor.   ɪ. Masson, Thomas Lansing, 1866–
comp. ɪɪ. Title.
22–24202 Revised
Library of Congress   PS595.H8L49

NL 0354566   DLC CSmH ViU

PS595 **Life.** New York.
.H8L49   Taken from Life. Verses. New York, Doubleday
1898   & McClure Co., 1898.
xiii, 146 p. incl. front. illus. 17½ cm.
"Fourth edition."

1. American wit and humor. I. Masson, Thomas
Lansing, 1866—   comp. ₚ. II. Title.

NL 0354567   ViU MH

Life. New York.
Taken from Life; verses.   New York, Doubleday & McClure co., 1901.

"5th ed."

NL 0354568   MH NBuG

T917.64
.L628t   **LIFE.** New York.
That Texas number of Life, starring the Lone Star State.   [New York, Life Pub. Co.] 1912.
1747-1790p. illus. 28cm.

Cover title.
Life, v.60, no.1559, September 12, 1912.

1. Texas.

NL 0354569   TxU

Life. New York.
Life's verses, illustrated by H. W. McVickar, F. G. Attwood, Jessie McDermott, C. G. Bush, and others. New York, Mitchell & Miller ₍ᶜ1885₎
88 p. illus. 22ᶜᵐ.
Edited by John Ames Mitchell.

1. American wit and humor.   ɪ. Mitchell, John Ames, 1845–1918, ed.
ɪɪ. Title.
30–3419 Revised
Library of Congress   PS595.H8L48

NL 0354570   DLC InU NjP RPB NNU-W CSmH NN

VOLUME 332

Life. New York.
Life's verses. 2d ser. Illustrated by F. G. Attwood, Alfred Brennan, O. Herford ... and others. New York, White, Stokes, & Allen, 1886.
56 p. illus. 22^{cm}.
Edited by John Ames Mitchell.

1. American wit and humor.   I. Mitchell, John Ames, 1845–1918, ed.
II. Title.
30–3420 Revised

Library of Congress   PS595.H8L47

NL 0354571   DLC RPB

Life (*New York*)
War as viewed by Life. [New York, Life publishing company, 1914]
[82] p. illus. (part col.) 43½ x 29¼ cm.

1. War. 2. Caricatures and cartoons.   I. Title.

NC1070.L5   14–18046 rev 2

NL 0354572   DLC WaS

Life; digest of outstanding reading. v. 1–   **Apr. 1, 1938–**
West Melbourne [Fitchett brothers pty., ltd., 1938–
v. 20^{cm}. monthly.
Title varies: Apr.–July 1938 (v. 1, no. 1–4) Australian life; a digest of reading of outstanding interest (subtitle varies slightly)
Aug. 1938–   Life; digest of outstanding reading.
Editor: Apr. 1938–   J. C. Fitchett.
Supersedes Life; a record for busy folk ... (later Life)

Library of Congress   AP7.L62   41–16349
                                            052

NL 0354573   DLC

052   **Life;** or, Religion & politics. no.1–16;
LIF   Apr.3–July 17, 1834. Birmingham, Printed by J. Allen.
189p. front. 18cm. weekly.

"By Leo Ironface, merchant."

NL 0354574   IU

The life. Boston, Colby & Rich [187–?]
68 p. diagr. 20^{cm}.

1. Conduct of life.
                                            34–10944
Library of Congress   BJ1571.L63
                                            170

NL 0354575   DLC NN

Life; a photo-play (motion picture)
see under   Buchanan, Thompson, 1877–1937.

Life aboard the U. S. S. Denver; a biography of the CL 58, 1942–1945. [Baltimore, etc., Thomsen-Ellis-Hutton co., 1946]
39 p. illus., map. 28cm.

534276B. 1. Warships, U. S.—   Denver. 2. World war, 1939–1945—
Naval hist. and operations—Pacific.
                                            July 24, 1950

NL 0354577   NN

Life according to Jones. By Enlightened selfishness [pseud.]. With a foreword by the Rt. Hon. George N. Barnes...   London: Co-operative Prtg. Soc., Ltd., 1918.   346 p., 1 l.   12°.
Contents: Foreword. Introductory. Birth and babyhood. Sense and the senses. Youth and development. Religion and dogma. I and my neighbour. God, angels, and immortality. Maturity, marriage, and maternity. Politics and economics. Labour and leisure.

1. Essays (English). 2. Enlightened   selfishness, pseud.
                                            April 30, 1919

NL 0354578   NN NjP

The life, achievements, and death of General Sir Ralph Abercrombie, (contemporary of the great Nelson,) who died March 28, 1801, of a wound received in defeating the French Army at Alexandria. To which is added, particulars of the glorious death of General Wolfe, and a parallel between the three most renowned heroes of modern times, Abercrombie Wolfe, and Nelson. London: Printed for Thomas Tegg and T. Hughes, by J. Hartnell, 1806.
28 p. 18[cm]. (On cover: The entertainer. v.3 [no.2])
Chap-book.
1. Chap-books. 2.   Abercromby, Sir Ralph, 1734–
1801. 3. Wolfe, Jam-   s, 1728–1759. 4. Nelson,
Horatio Nelson, visc   ount, 1758–1805. I. Ser.

NL 0354579   ViU

WILLIAM
ANDREWS
CLARK
MEMORIAL
LIBRARY

The life, actions, and amours, of Ferdinando, marquiss of Palleotti, lately executed at Tyburn, for the murther of his servant: wherein are contain'd, the true origin of that ancient and illustrious family ... and the reasons which might have induced the government, had they so thought fit, to have changed the execution of his sentence into a more honourable punishment. Written by a gentleman that was conversant with him abroad, and during   his abode here in England, and his confinement in Newgate ... London Printed, and sold by William Boreham ... 1718.
39 p.   20^{cm}.

Signatures: A–E⁴.
Bound in half calf.

NL 0354581   CLU-C ICN InU IU

Mann
BF   **Life adjustment booklet**[s]. Chicago,
698   Science Research Associates, Inc.
L72   v. illus. 24 cm.

1. Personality. I. Science Research Associates, Chicago.

NL 0354582   NIC

HF5381   **Life adjustment series.**
.P742
Prosser, Charles Allen, 1871–
Practice book on selecting an occupation, by C. A. Prosser ... and R. H. Palmer ... Bloomington, Ill., McKnight & McKnight, ᶜ1936.

The Life, adventures, and amours, of Sir R——— P———, who so recently had the honour to present the F——— address at the English court ... London, Printed and sold by J. Brough, 1770.
1p.l., 70p. 19cm.
"The scandalous 'Life, Adventures, and Amours of Sir R[ichard] P[errott]', published anonymously in 1770 ... war ... an ebullition of private malice." – DNB.

NL 0354584   CtY CLU DFo

Life, adventures and anecdotes of "Beau" Hickman, Prince of American bummers...
see under   [Trout, James Samuel]

The LIFE, adventures and eccentricities of the late Lord Camelford, to which is added the particulars of the late fatal duel, genuine extracts from His Lordship's will, &c. &c. &c. London, Sold by R. Lace [1804]
20 p. 19.5cm.

Photostat copy of original in the Library of Royal united service institution, London.

NL 0354586   CaBVaU

The life, adventures, and opinions of Col. George Hanger, 1801
see under   Combe, William, 1742–1823.

Life, The, adventures, and opinions of a Liverpool policeman, and his contemporaries. Part 1...   Liverpool: Booker & Co., 1841.
iv, 725 p., 17 pl.   8°.

1. Fiction (English).   September 14, 1914.

NL 0354588   NN ICN

The life, adventures & pyracies of the famous Captain Singleton ...
see under   [Defoe, Daniel] 1661?–1731.

The life, adventures, & serious remonstrances of a Scotch guinea note, containing a defence of the Scotch system of banking, and a reply to the late letters of E. Bradwardine Waverley [pseud.]. By the author of the "Letters of a plain man." Edinburgh, Printed for Waugh & Innes; [etc., etc.] 1826.
iv p., 1 l., [5]–21 p. 21^{cm}.

1. Currency question—Scotland. 2. Banks and banking—Scotland. 3. Croker, John Wilson, 1780–1857.   I. Letters of a plain man, Author of.
                                            CA 10–5130 Unrev'd

Library of Congress   HG2999.S4L6

NL 0354590   DLC MH-BA CtY

The life, adventures and surprising deliverance of Duncan Cameron
see under   Cameron, Duncan, fl. 1756.

The life, adventures and vicissitudes of Mary Charlton
see under   Charlton, Mary.

VOLUME 332

The life, adventures, intrigues, and amours
of the celebrated Jemmy Twitcher. Exhibiting
many striking proofs to what baseness the human
heart is capable of descending. The whole
faithfully compiled from authentick materials
...

*EC75
A100
770l2

London: Printed for Jonathan Brough, at the
Bible, near Temple bar, Strand. [1770?]

8°. 2p.ℓ., 92p. 21.5cm.
Imprint date from BM.
Satirical biography of John Montagu, 4th earl
of Sandwich.

NL 0354593   MH

Life, adventures, strange career and assassination
of Col. James Fisk, jr. The Fisk-Stokes tragedy.
see under [Barclay, George Lippard]

Life after dark
    see [Clarke, William] 1800-1838.
    Every night book; or, Life after dark.

Y157.1
L626

Life after death; or, A descriptive account
of the most remarkable apparitions, spirits,
ghosts or spectres of persons that have really
appeared after their decease. Carefully collected from the most authentic accounts. [London,
1725?]

56 p. 20cm.

Authorship ascribed to Daniel Defoe. cf.
Dealer's catalog, Bodley Book Shop, New York.
Supplementary list no. 20, 1960.
1. Apparitions. 1. Defoe. Daniel,
1661-1731, sup- posed author.

NL 0354596   MnU

LIFE after death; or, The history of
apparitions, ghosts, spirits or spectres.
Consisting of variety of true stories, attested by people of undoubted veracity...
London, 1758.

2 p.ℓ., [111]-vi, [7]-70 p. 20cm.

Illustrated t.-p.

1. Ghosts.

NL 0354597   MnU MH

Life Agency Management Conference, *Ohio State Univer-
sity, Columbus.*
Proceedings. 1st-
1950-
[Columbus]
    v. 25 cm. (Ohio State University publications. College of
Commerce conference series)
    Conference sponsored by the University's College of Commerce and
Administration.
    Edited by the Bureau of Business Research.
    1. Insurance, Life—Congresses. 1. Ohio. State University,
Columbus. Bureau of Business Research. (Series: Ohio. State
University, Columbus. College of Commerce and Administration.
College of Commerce conference series)

               A 51-10624

Ohio State Univ. Libr.
for Library of Congress

IU TxU
NL 0354598   OU Or OrCS OrU CaBVa IdPI IdU MtU NIC

Life agents brief
    see

The **Spectator** life agents brief.

Life (The) almanack and diary of the Briton Life
Association, Limited. / Head office, 429 Strand.
London. 118 pp. 12°. *London, Fealx, Chiffriel
& Co., 1885.*

NL 0354600   DNLM

Life along the Connecticut river; introduction by Charles
Crane, text by Marion Hooper, photography by Lewis Brown,
Ralph Day, Newell Green, R. D. and M. E. Snively & Cort-
landt Luce. Brattleboro, Vt., Stephen Daye press, 1939.

120 p. front., illus. (incl. map) 32 x 24ᶜᵐ.

1. Connecticut river. 2. Connecticut valley — Descr. & trav. — Views.
I. Crane, Charles Edward, 1884– II. Hooper, Marion. III. Brown,
Lewis, illus. IV. Day, Ralph, illus. V. Green, Newell, illus. VI. Snively,
R. D., illus. VII. Snively, M. E., illus. VIII. Luce, Cortlandt, illus.

Library of Congress   F12.C7L5   39–27348

Copyright A 129427   917.4

PBm PP
NL 0354601   DLC MB OKentU CaOTP CU IaU OU OCl OEac

Life among the Indians. New York, Great American
engraving and printing co., 1886.

80 p. illus. 24ᶜᵐ.
Imprint on cover: New York city. Kicapoo Indian printing office.
Includes advertising matter (Indian medicines)

1. Indians of North America.

            CA 26–282 Unrev'd

Library of Congress   E77.L72

NL 0354602   DLC CU NjP CtY

Ayer
250
L68
1890

LIFE among the Indians. [New Haven, Conn.]
ca.1890? 80p. illus. 24cm.

"Caution to the public" signed: Healy &
Bigelow, Indian agents.
Includes advertising matter (Kickapoo Indian
medicines)

NL 0354603   ICN

Life among the lawless.

    See

[Arrington, Alfred W] 1810-1867.
    The rangers and regulators of the Tanaha, or
life among the lawless.

Life among the Mormons; or, The religious,
social, and political history of the Mormons,
from their origin to the present time
see under [Mayhew, Henry] 1812-1887.

LIFE among the Mormons. O. (From Put-
man's monthly, Aug. to Dec., 1855)

NL 0354606   ICN

Life among the Mormons... By an officer of the
U.S, Army...
    see under Waters, William Elkanah, 1883-

M
615.88
L722

Life among the Shakers [pamphlet advertising Shaker
medicines. New York? 1880]
7 p. illus. 29 cm.

Caption title.
Includes an account of a visit to the Shaker settlement by
Mary F. Carr.

1. Medicines. Patent, proprietary, etc. 2. Shakers.
I. Carr, Mary Frances.

NL 0354608   N MWA

M
615.88
L722a2

Life among the Shakers [pamphlet advertising Shaker
medicines. New York? 1895?]
32 p. 14 cm.

Includes an account of a visit to the Shaker settlement
by Mary F. Carr.

1. Medicines.   Patent, proprietary, etc. 2. Shakers.
I. Carr, Mary   Frances.

NL 0354609   N

The LIFE, amours and exploits of Nell Gwinn,
the fortunate orange girl, who became the
bosom friend and mistress of King Charles.
II. Otley, W.Walker, [17-?]

nar.16°. pp.24.
In the original paper bindings as
issued.

NL 0354610   MH

Case
Y
1565
.L 614

The LIFE, amours, and secret history of Fran-
celia, late D....ss of P.......h, favourite
mistress to King Charles II. With a compleat
key. London, A.Amey, 1734.
67, [1]p. front. 19cm.

NL 0354611   ICN

Life and accident insurance. A recently organ-
ized and ably managed association. broadside.
New York, 1886.
*Repr. from : Commercial World and U. S. Exporter, N.
Y., Jan. 2, 1886.*

NL 0354612   DNLM

Life and accident insurance cases...
prior to 1871 down to 1875. N.Y.,
Hurd & Houghton, 1871-1877.
vol. 1-5

NL 0354613   OClW

The **life** and achievements of Gov. Louis Kossuth, and a complete history of the late Hungarian war for independence!... By
an officer of the army. New York: W. Lord, 1852. 56 p.
illus. 23cm.

1. Kossuth, Lajos, 1802-1894.   2. Hungary—Hist.—Uprising of
1848-1849. I. An officer of the   army.
                            December 30, 1943

NL 0354614   NN

VOLUME 332

The life and achievements of Rob Roy MacGregor, the celebrated Scotch freebooter!—containing an account of the proscription of his name and race; his great actions, and uncommon prowess in battle: the various engagements he was concerned in, and a view of the manners and customs of the Scots in the sixteenth and seventeenth centuries: being a complete history of this wonderful man!   London, Bailey, n.d.
    32 p.

NL 0354615   CaBVa

BF1995   Life and action, the great work in America.
.L5   v. 1, no. 1, spring 1909. v. 4-5, Dec.
    1912 - Sept./Oct. 1914.   Chicago, The
    Indo-American magazine [1909]-14.
    3 v. in 2.   19 cm.
    Vol. 1, no. 1 has title: The Indo-American magazine.

    L. C. number 10-28386

NL 0354616   DLC

Life and action, the great work in America; the Indo-American magazine. v. I—   The first-
year's numbers reprinted in book form ... Chicago, The
Indo-American magazine company, 1910-
    v. 20 cm.

    Vols. I—   1st edition.
    Originally issued in parts; vol. I, no. 1, has title: The Indo-American magazine.

    1. Theosophy—Period.

    BF1995.L6   11—725

NL 0354617   DLC WHi ICRL TxDaM-P ICJ

PR   The life and actions of Caius Julius Caesar in
3347   Aegypt, &c. Collected from the best historians
C2   illustrating the history of Caesar and Cleopatra;
L5   from whence the plot of Mr. Cibber's new tragedy
Cage   is taken ... London, Printed and sold by J.
    Roberts and A. Dodd, 1724.
    [8] 16 p.   A-C⁴. includ. front. 8vo.

NL 0354618   DFo MH-AH NcU

The LIFE and actions of Frederic the victorious king of Prussia. Compiled from original
Memoirs and documents. London, J. Wilkie,etc.,
1758.

    pp. xi, 466-. Port. map, and plans,
2 plates of "Explanation of the plan of the
battle of Crevelt inserted with plan, between
pp. 398-399.
    Formerly owned by Thomas Carlyle with his
book plate and MS note

NL 0354619   MH

The life and actions of Frederick III, king
of Prussia; containing also the origin of the house
of Brandenburgh; with the lives of the electors
of that family. London, 1759.

NL 0354620   PPL

xB   The life and actions of Lewis Dominique
C3281Ed   Cartouche: who was broke alive upon the wheel
    at Paris, Nov.28. 1721. n.s. Relating at large
    his remarkable adventures, desperate enterprises,
    and various excapes. With an account of his
    behaviour under sentence, and upon the scaffold;
    and the manner of his execution. Translated
    from the French.   London, Printed for J.
    Roberts, 1722.
    88p. 19cm.

    Translation by Defoe of Histoire de la vie
    et du procès de Louis Dominique Cartouche? Or
    of various articles in French newsletters? Cf.
    Brit. Mus. Cat.; William Lee, Daniel Defoe:
    his life and recently discovered writings.
    1869. v.1, p.360.

    CSmH DFo
NL 0354622   IU CLU-C MB CU-S MH OCU MH-L TxU CtY

PR   Life and actions of Mahomet, the famous
975   Oriental impostor, giving an account of the
L62a   superstitious absurdities attending his birth
    ... To which is prefixed, a sketch of the
    history of Constantinople, the whole exhibit-
    ing the manners & customs of the Turks. Lon-
    don [18—]
    36 p. front.
    Imperfect copy: title page closely trimmed,
    part of imprint cut away.

NL 0354623   CLU

The **life** and actions of Napoleon Bonaparte, emperor of
the French, king of Italy, and protector of the Confederation
of the Rhine.   Norwich, Printed by J. F. Fairchild, 1810.
    208 p. 17ᵐ.

    1. Napoléon I, emperor of the French, 1769-1821.
                                           44-11094
    Library of Congress   DC203.L68

NL 0354624   DLC MWA NBu MiD RPB CtY MiU-C NBuG MnU

The **life** and actions of Robert Emmet, leader of the insurrection
of 1803, including his trial, and the celebrated speech delivered by
him upon that occasion. Stereotyped ed.   Dublin: C. M. Warren
[1840] 108 p. 14cm.

    1. Emmet, Robert, 1778-1803.   January 31, 1944

NL 0354625   NN

The **life and actions** of that distinguished naval
hero, Admiral Nelson; who fell in the battle of Trafalgar, October 21.1805. By an officer. [Hudson,
Published by William E.Norman book-seller,no.2 Warren street. N.Elliot,printer,Catskill. 1808.
    70 p. 14.4cm.

    1.Nelson,Horatio Nelson,viscount,1758-1805.2.
Trafalgar (Cape) Batt le of,1805.I.An officer.

NL 0354626   MiU-C

The **life** and actions of that notorious old bawd Susannah
Wells, and Mary Squires, (an old travelling gipsey,) who were
both convicted at Justice-hall in the Old-Baily, on Thursday
the 22d of February, 1753, for a felony and robbery on Elizabeth Canning, who was confin'd in the house of the said Wells,
and almost starv'd, having nothing to support her for twenty-
nine days, but mouldy crusts and stinking water. London, F.
Clifton, 1753.
    24 p. 17½ᵐ.
    1. Wells, Susannah, d. 1763. 2. Squires, Mary, d. 1762. 3. Canning,
Elizabeth, 1734-1773.
                                           45-48428

NL 0354627   DLC

Bd.w.   The life and actions of the famous Mr. Jonathan
B3259.2   Wilde. Gloucester, Printed by R. Raikes and
    Company, [1725?]
    24 p. B-D⁴. illus. 8vo.
    John Stackhouse copy; Luttrell family library
copy.

NL 0354628   DFo

The life and actions of the late renowned
    prelate & souldier Christopher Bernard
    van Gale, Bishop of Munster, Prince of
    the Holy Empire, administrator of Corvay,
    Marquess of Stromberg
    see under   [Vries, Simon de] b. 1630,
supposed author.

R.B.R.   The life and actions of the noted William
    Hawke. With a particular narrative of all the
    robberies he committed in and near London
    before and after his return from transporta-
    tion, his behaviour after condemnation and
    at Tyburn, at which place he justly forfeited
    his life on Friday, the 24th of June last,
    in the 24th year of his age. To which is
    annexed, a genuine discovery of that infamous
    set of sharpers in London, called Swindlers
    ... Together with a new edition of the life

    and important discoveries of John Poulter,
    alias Baxter, who a few years since was con-
    nected with the greatest set of villains,
    sharpers, and gamblers in England ... Lon-
    don, Printed by W. Creswell [1774?]
    48 p. 21 cm.
    1. Hawke, William, 1744-1774. I. Poulter,
John, 17¹ᶜ

NL 0354631   NcD

The life and activities of Captain Newton Knight
    and his company
    see under   [Knight, Thomas Jefferson]

... The life and administration of ex-President
Fillmore
    see under   [Williams, Edwin] 1797-1854.

Life and advent hymns.
    see under   Brooks, Cyrus E

Life and adventure in the south Pacific
    see under   [Jones,   ] a roving printer.

VOLUME 332

PR
3455
.L7
1760

The life and adventures of a cat. The 2d ed.
London, Printed for W.Mynors, 1760.
[2],190 p. 17 cm.
Caption title: The history of a cat.
The work has been ascribed to Henry Fielding
cf.Cross,W.L. The history of Henry Fielding,
v.3,p.348-349.

I.Fielding,Henry,1707-1754,supposed author.

NL 0354636   MiU TxU MH InU CSmH

Life and adventures of a fly. London, E.
Newbery [1789]
121, [7] p.
By S.J., i.e. Stephen Jones?

NL 0354637   MWA

Life and adventures of a fly. Boston, Printed
and sold by Samuel Etheridge, 1797.
95 p. 12 cm.
Attributed to Stephen Jones - cf. Supplement to Evans.

NL 0354638   MWA

Life and adventures of a cheap jack
see under   [Green, William] of Brighton.

Life and adventures of A   no. 1, America's
most celebrated tramp
see under   [Livingston, Leon Ray] 1872-

The life and adventures of a lap-dog
see   [Coventry, Francis] d. 1759.
The history of Pompey the little; or, The life
and adventures...

Life and adventures of a soldier's widow
see under   [Orvis, Sarah R. J.]

The life and adventures of Alexander Selkirk,
the real Robinson Crusoe
see under   [Howell, John] 1788-1863.

The life and adventures of Anthony Leger, esq.; or,
The man of shifts ... London, Printed and sold by T.
Wilkins, 1789.
3 v. 16¼ᵐᵐ.

Library of Congress   PZ3.L6261

7-3533

NL 0354644   DLC PSt

The life and adventures of Arthur Clenning ...
see under   [Flint, Timothy] 1780-1840.

The life and adventures of Arthur Spring; the murderer of Mrs. Ellen Lynch and her sister, Mrs. Shaw.
With the complete trials, speeches, and conviction of the
murderer ... Philadelphia, T. B. Peterson [1853]
1 p. l., 7-109 p. illus. (incl. ports.) 24½ᵐᵐ.

1. Spring, Arthur, 1814-1853? 2. Shaw, Mrs. Honora (Donovan) 1807?-
1853. 3. Lynch, Mrs. Ellen (Donovan) 1822-1853.

CA 22-144 Unrev'd

Library of Congress   HV6248.S62L5

NL 0354646   DLC PHi

The life and adventures of Mr. Bampfylde-Moore Carew, commonly
called the king of the beggars. Being an impartial account of his
life, from his leaving Tiverton School, at the age of fifteen, and entering into a society of gipsies...with his travels twice through
great part of America. Giving a particular account of the origin,
government, laws, and customs of the gipsies...and a dictionary
of the cant language, used by the mendicants.   London: Sold by

T. Forster, R. Armstrong, J. Digby, and W. Locke, 1779.   246 p.
front. (port.) 18cm. (12°.)
See: Sabin 27615.
The authorship has been ascribed variously to Thomas Price, Robert Goadby, Mrs.
Goadby and Carew himself. There are numerous versions with varying titles.

1. Carew, Bampfylde Moore, 1693-
3. Gipsies. 4. Indians, N. A.
Thomas, of Poole, supposed au.
supposed au. III. Goadby, Mrs.

BANCROFT COLLECTION.
1770? 2. Beggars and begging.
5. Criminal slang, English. I. Price,
II. Goadby, Robert, 1721-1778,
Robert, supposed au. *Revised*
October 8, 1932

NL 0354648   NN TxU ViW MWA

The life and adventures of Mr. Bampfylde-Moore Carew, commonly called the King of the beggars ... With
his travels twice through great part of America. Giving
a particular account of the origin, government, laws, and
customs of the gipsies; with the method of electing their
king; and a dictionary of the cant language used by mendicants. London, R. Whiston [etc.] 1782.
iv, [5]-240 p. 17½ᵐᵐ.

1. Carew, Bampfylde-Moore, 1693-1770? 2. Gipsies. 3. Gipsies—Language. 4. U. S.—Descr. & trav.

10—969

Library of Congress   HV4547.C3

NL 0354649   DLC CtY InU PBm PPL MiU-C

The life and adventures of Mr. Bampfylde-Moore Carew, commonly called the king of the beggars. Being an impartial account
of his life, from his leaving Tiverton school...and entering into a
society of gipsies... With his travels twice through great part of
America. Giving a particular account of the origin, government,
laws, and customs of the gipsies; with the method of electing their
king: And a dictionary of the cant language, used by the mendicants.   London: Printed for J. Wren and W. Hodges, 1785.
244 p.   12°.

1. Gipsies. 2. Criminals.—Language   of. 3. Indians, North America.
September 24, 1920.

NL 0354650   NN MH ICarbS NNC CtY

The life and adventures of Mr. Bampfylde-Moore Carew, commonly called the king of the beggars. Being an impartial account
of his life, from his leaving Tiverton school, at the age of fifteen,
and entering into a society of gipsies...with his travels twice
through great part of America. Giving a particular account of
the origin, government, laws and customs of the gipsies; with the
method of electing their king. And a dictionary of the cant language, used by the mendicants.   London: Printed for J. Wren
and W. Hodges, 1786.   197 p., 1 l.   18cm. (12°.)

Continued in next column

Continued from preceding column

See: Sabin 27615.
Last leaf blank.
The authorship has been ascribed variously to Thomas Price, Robert Goadby, Mrs.
Goadby and Carew himself. There are numerous versions with varying titles.

217366B. 1. Carew, Bampfylde
begging. 3. Gipsies. 4. Indians,
I. Price, Thomas, of Poole, supposed
supposed au. III. Goadby, Mrs.

Moore, 1693-1770? 2. Beggars and
N. A. 5. Criminal slang, English.
au. II. Goadby, Robert, 1721-1778,
Robert, supposed au.
June 18, 1943

NL 0354652   NN PP WHi

The life and adventures of Bampfylde-Moore Carew, commonly
called the king of the beggars: being an impartial account of his
life, from his leaving Tiverton school at the age of fifteen, and
entering into a society of gipsies...with his travels twice through
great part of America: giving a particular account of the origin,
government, laws, and customs of the gipsies, with the method of
electing their king: and a dictionary of the cant language used by
the mendicants.   London: Printed for T. Martin, 1788.   203 (?) p.
17½cm. (12°.)

See: Sabin 27615.
The authorship has been ascribed variously to Thomas Price, Robert Goadby, Mrs.
Goadby and Carew himself. There are numerous versions with varying titles.
Imperfect: p. 9-10 and 203 slightly mutilated (the latter leaf so mutilated that it is
impossible to determine whether numbered or not).

889912A. 1. Carew, Bampfylde
begging. 3. Gipsies. 4. Indians,
I. Price, Thomas, of Poole, supposed
supposed au. III. Goadby, Mrs.

Moore, 1693-1770? 2. Beggars and
N. A. 5. Criminal slang, English.
au. II. Goadby, Robert, 1721-1778,
Robert, supposed au.
September 30, 1937

NL 0354654   NN TxU MdBJ CtY NjP OCl

The LIFE and adventures of Bampfylde-Moore Carew, commonly called the king of the beggars: being
an impartial account of his life, from his leaving
Tiverton school at the age of fifteen, and entering into a society of Gipsies...the great number of characters and shapes he has appeared in...with his travels
twice through great part of America: giving a particular account of the origin, government, laws, and

customs of the Gipsies; with the method of electing
their king: and a dictionary of the Cant language,
used by the mendicants.   London, Printed for John
Taylor, 1789.   204 p.   18cm.(12°)

Sabin 27615.   See: Howes: U.S.-iana, 1962, C132.
Page 171 wrongly numbered 117.

The authorship has been ascribed variously to Thomas Price, Robert
Goadby, Mrs. Goadby and Carew himself. There are numerous versions
with varying titles.
"A dictionary of the Cant language," p. [193]-204.

Ford Collection
1. Carew, Bampfylde Moore, 1693-1770? 2. Beggars and begging.
3. Gipsies. 4. Indians, N.A. 5. Criminal slang. I. Price, Thomas, of
Poole, supposed author.   II. Goadby, Robert, 1721-1778,
supposed author. III. Goadby,   Mrs. Robert, supposed author.

NL 0354657   NN PU CtY

The life and adventures of Bampfylde-Moore
Carew, commonly called the king of the beggars: being an impartial account of his life, from his
leaving Tiverton school at the age of fifteen, and
entering into a society of gipsies; wherein the
motives of his conduct are related and explained:
the great number of characters and shapes he has
appeared in through Great Britain, Ireland, and
several other places of Europe: with his travels
twice through great part of America: giving a particular account of   the origin, government,

laws, and customs of the gipsies, with the method
of electing their king: and a dictionary of the
cant language used by the mendicants.   London:
Printed for W. Cavill, 1791.
222,[6] p. 18ᶜᵐ.
Signatures: A-T⁶.
Bound in old half calf.

NL 0354659   CLU-C NN

VOLUME 332

HV4547
C3
1793

The life and adventures of Bampfylde-Moore Carew,
commonly called the King of the beggars ...
With his travels twice through great part of
America. Giving a particular account of the
origin, government, laws, and customs of the
gipsies; with the method of electing their king;
and a dictionary of the cant language used by
mendicants. London, Printed for J. Buckland,
C. Bathurst, and T. Davies, 1793.
2 p. l., [53]-235, [5] p. 17.5 cm.
1. Carew, Bampfylde-Moore, 1693-1770? 2. Gipsies.
3. Gipsies - Language. 4. U. S. - Descr. & trav.

NL 0354660   TxHU

The life and adventures of Bampfylde-Moore Carew,
commonly called the King of the beggars. Being an impartia[l]
account of his life, from his leaving Tiverton school at the ag[e]
of fifteen, and entering into a society of gipsies ... with hi[s]
travels twice through great part of America: giving a
particular account of the origin, government, laws, and customs
of the gipsies, with the method of electing their king. And a
dictionary of the cant language used by the mendicants. London, J. Buckland [etc.] MDCCXCIV.

242, [6] p. 19 cm.

One of the numerous versions with varying titles, the authorship of
which has been ascribed variously to Thomas Price, Robert Goadby, Mrs.
Goadby and Carew himself.

1. Carew, Bampfylde-Moore, 1693-1758. 2. Gipsies. 3. Cant. I.
Price, Thomas, supposed author. II. Goadby, Robert, 1721-1778, supposed author. III. Goadby, Mrs. Robert, supposed author.

35-34391

Library of Congress   HV4547.C3 1794

NL 0354662   DLC

The life and adventures of Bamfylde Moore Carew, the King of
the beggars, being an impartial account of his life from leaving
Tiverton school at the age of fifteen, and entering into a society
of gypsies, with the great number of characters and shapes he has
appeared in through Great Britain, Ireland, and several parts of
Europe: with his travels twice through great part of North
America, giving a particular account, of the origin, government,
laws, and customs of the gypsies, ... : and a dictionary of the
cant language, used by the mendicants. London, Printed for
W. Wright, [18--?].
182 p. 15 cm.

"A dictionary of the cant language," p. 177-182.
"Thomas Price, an educated man who was the original compiler of the life ... as-
serts in the preface that his narrative is selected wholly from the journals which Mr. Ca-
rew constantly kept of his travels." — Moore, Devonshire, p. 700.
There are numerous versions with varying titles, and probably by various compilers.
The first authentic edition of the "Life" was probably The life and adventures of
Bampfylde-Moore Carew, the noted Devonshire stroller ... Exon, Printed by the
Farleys for J. Drew, 1745.
"An apology for the life of Mr. Bampfylde-Moore Carew ... " London, 1749, is
ascribed to Robert Goadby and is based on the earlier narrative.

NL 0354664   ICJ

R745.k

The life and adventures of Bamfylde-Moore[!]
Carew, commonly called the King of the
beggars: being an impartial account of his
life, from his leaving Tiverton school at the
age of fifteen, & entering into a society of
gipsies; wherein the motives of his conduct
are related and explained ... London, Printed
by R. Bassam[1800?]
1 p. l., ii, [5]-182 p. front. (port.) 14½ cm.
Numerous versions exist, variously ascribed
to Robert Goadby, Mrs. Goadby, Thomas Price,
and Carew himself.
"A dictionary of the cant language":
p. 177-182.

NL 0354665   CtY

The life and adventures of Bampfylde-Moore Carew,
commonly called the King of the beggars ... being a true
account of his life from his leaving Tiverton school at the
age of fifteen, and entering into a society of gipsies ... with
his travels twice through great part of America: giving a
particular account of the origin, government, laws and customs of the gipsies ... to which is added a Dictionary of the
cant language used by the mendicants. Bath, Printed and
sold by J. Browne; London, Sold by Crosby and Letterman,
1802.

1 p. l., 124 p. front. (port.) 18 cm.
"Thomas Price, an uneducated man, who was the original compiler
of the life ... asserts in the preface that his narrative is selected
wholly from the journals which Mr. Carew constantly kept of his
travels."—Moore, Devonshire, p. 700.
There are numerous versions with varying titles, and probably by
various compilers. The first authentic edition of the "Life" was probably The life and adventures of Bampfylde-Moore Carew, the noted
Devonshire stroller ... Exon, Printed by the Farleys for J. Drew, 1745.
"An apology for the life of Mr. Bampfylde-Moore Carew" ... London, 1749, is ascribed to Robert Goadby, and is based on the earlier
narrative.
"A dictionary of cant terms": p. 117-124.

1. Carew, Bampfylde Moore, 1693-1758. 2. Gipsies. 3. Cant—Dictionaries. I. Price, Thomas, supposed author. II. Goadby, Robert,
1721-1778, supposed author. III. Goadby, Mrs. Robert.

HV4547.C3 1802   17-21619

NL 0354668   DLC KMK

HV
4547
.C3
1806

C55447

The life and adventures of Bampfylde-Moore
Carew, commonly called the King of beggars;
being an impartial account of his life,
from his leaving Tiverton School, at the
age of fifteen, and entering into a society
of gipsies ... and a dictionary of the cant
language used by the mendicants. London,
Printed for J. Brambles [etc.] by H. Mozley,
1806.
167 p.

"Thomas Price,   an uneducated man, who

was the original compiler of the life ...
asserts in the preface that his narrative is
selected wholly from the journals which Mr.
Carew constantly kept of his travels."--Moore,
Devonshire, p. 700.

#Carew, Bampfylde Moore, 1693-1758.
#Gipsies.
#Cant--   Dictionaries.
   Price Thomas,   supposed author.

NL 0354670   MoU OrP

The life and adventures of Bampfylde-Moore Carew, commonly
called the king of the beggars. Being an impartial account of his
life, from his leaving Tiverton School at the age of fifteen, and entering into a society of gipsies ... with his travels twice through
great part of America: containing a particular account of the
origin, government, laws, and customs, of the gipsies, with the
method of electing their king, and a dictionary of the cant language used by the mendicants. Derby: H. Mozley, 1811?].
159 p., 5 l. front. 17½ cm.

The authorship has been ascribed variously to Thomas Price, Robert Goadby, Mrs.
Goadby and Carew himself. There are numerous versions with varying titles.

136373A. 1. Carew, Bampfylde Moore,   1693-1770? 2. Beggars and begging. 3. Gipsies. 4. Indians, N. A.   5. Criminal slang, English. I. Price,
Thomas, of Poole, supposed au.   II. Goadby, Robert, 1721-1778,
supposed au. III. Goadby, Mrs.   Robert, supposed au.   *Revised*
                                                October 5, 1932

NL 0354672   NN DLC

HV
4547
C27
1820

The life and adventures of Bampfylde-Moore Carew,
commonly called the King of the beggars. Being an impartial
account of his life, from his leaving Tiverton school at the age
of fifteen, and entering into a society of gipsies ... with his
travels twice through great part of America: cont. a particular account of the origin, government, laws, and customs
of the gipsies, with the method of electing their king. And a
dictionary of the cant language used by the mendicants.
Derby [Eng.] H. Mozley [1820?]
159 p. illus. 19 cm.

NL 0354673   NIC

The life and adventures of Bampfylde Moore Carew..
New York, 1823. pl.
31 p.

NL 0354674   MWA

The life and adventures of Bampfylde Moore Carew,
commonly called the King of the beggars. Being an impartial account of his life, from his leaving Tiverton
school at the age of fifteen and entering into a society of
gipsies; wherein the motives of his conduct are related
and explained. London, Printed for the book-sellers,
1835.
144 p. front. (port.) 18½ cm.

Numerous versions exist, variously ascribed to Robert Goadby, Mrs. Goadby, Thomas Price, and Carew himself.
"A dictionary of the cant language": p. 141-144.

1. Carew, Bampfylde Moore, 1693-1758. 2. Gipsies. I. Price, Thomas,
of Poole, supposed author. II. Goadby, Robert, 1721-1778, supposed author.
III. Goadby, Mrs. Robert, supposed author.

NL 0354676   MiU ICN

Case
E
5
.C 1838

The LIFE and adventures of Bampfylde-Moore
Carew, the noted Devonshire stroler and dog-
stealer; as related by himself, during his passage to the plantations in America...   Exon,
Printed by the Farleys, for J. Drew, 1745.
[1], v, 164 p.   21 cm.

The authorship of this version has been ascribed to Thomas Price.
Armorial bookplate: C. H. Wilkinson.

NL 0354677   ICN TxFTC ViU MH CSmH MB

Micro-
fiche
s417

The life and adventures of Bampfylde-Moore Carew,
the noted Devonshire stroller [sic] and dog-stealer; as
related by himself, during his passage to the plantations
in America. Containing, a great variety of remarkable
transactions in a vagrant course of life, which he followed
for the space of thirty years and upwards. [Vignette]
Exon: Printed by the Farley's, for Joseph Drew, bookseller, opposite Castle-Lane, 1745.

Microcard edition (4 cards).

First edition, first issue.
Author's copy with his ms. note at foot of p. 49.
Sabin cf. 27815.

1. Carew, Bampfylde Moore, 1693-1758.

NL 0354678   ViU OU UU MoU TxU ICRL MsU

HC4547
.C3
1931

The life and adventures of Bampfylde-Moore
Carew.

The King of the beggars, Bampfylde-Moore Carew,
edited by C. H. Wilkinson ... Oxford, The Clarendon press,
1931.

The life and adventures of Bampfylde Moore
Carew ...
     see also   The life of Bampfylde Moore
Carew ...

Life and adventures of Billy Purvis
see under   [Arthur, Thomas] biographer.

VOLUME 332

Life and adventures of Broncho John,...

　　see under

[Sullivan, John H]

Life and adventures of Calamity Jane
　　see under　Canary, Martha, 1852-1903.

The life and adventures of Capt. John Avery
　　see under　[Broeck, Adrian van,
pseud.]

ZclO
878l1

The life and adventures of Chan Reticker,
"the California boy," from his career as a mail
rider over the plains of California to the
present day ... Lexington, Ky., Transylvania
Printing and Publishing Company, 1878.
　　cover-title,40p. 19cm.
　　Advertising matter on versos, and p.[2-4] of
cover.
　　An undoubtedly fictional account, serving as
advertising for Reticker's show, a prototype
of the Wild West show.
　　Original wrap-　　pers.

NL 0354684　　CtY

The life and adventures of Chanticleer, the intelligent
rooster. An interesting story in verse for children. From the
German, by Mrs. Louise Pollock. With eight illustrations.
Boston, A. Williams & co., 1862.
　　96 p. front., plates. 20¾[m].
　　Cover-title: The Chanticleer.

　　I. Pollock, Louise, d. 1901, tr. II. Title: The Chanticleer.
　　　　　　　　　　　　　　　　　　44-14176
　　Library of Congress　　PZ8.3.L6

NL 0354685　　DLC RPB

The life and adventures of Chanticleer, the intelligent rooster.
An interesting story in verse for children. From the German, by
Mrs. Louise Pollock... Boston: A. Williams & co., 1863.
96 p. front., plates. 20½cm.

　　21097B. 1. Juvenile literature—
tr.　　　　　Poetry, German. I. Pollock, Louise,
　　　　　　　　　　　　　　October 10, 1940

NL 0354686　　NN NBuG

Life and adventures of Charles Anderson Chester, the
notorious leader of the Philadelphia "killers," who was
murdered, while engaged in the destruction of the California house, on election night, October 11, 1849 ... Philadelphia, Printed for the publishers, 1850.
　　2 p. l., 11-36 p. front., illus. 21½[m].

　　1. Chester, Charles Anderson, d. 1849. 2. Philadelphia—Riot, 1849.
　　　　　　　　　　　　　　　　　　11-30529
　　Library of Congress　　F158.44.L69

NL 0354687　　DLC MB MWA N NjP CU ViU PHi

Life and adventures of Charles Anderson
Chester, the notorious leader of the Philadelphia "killers," who was murdered, while
engaged in the destruction of the California house, on election night, October 11,
[1849]...　Philadelphia, Printed for the
publishers, 1852.
　　11-36 p. front., illus. 22 cm.

NL 0354688　　TU

Life and adventures of Charles Ball,] a black
man who lived forty years in Md.,S. Carolina and
Georgia as a slave, under various masters, and
was one year in the navy ... with observation
on the state of the morals amongst the cotton plants
and perils and sufferings of a fugitive slave.
Lewistown, Pa., 1836.

NL 0354689　　PPL

The life and adventures of Christopher Hawkins
　　see under　　Hawkins, Christopher,
1764-1837.

The life and adventures of Claude Duval, the dashing highwayman. By the author of "Dick Clinton"... &c., &c.　New York:
Dick & Fitzgerald [187-?]　106 p.　22½cm.

　　Printed in double columns.

37729B. 1. Fiction, English.　　　　I. Dick Clinton, Author of.
II. Title: Claude Duval.　　　　　　　　September 30, 1940

NL 0354691　　NN

Life and adventures of Colonel Daniel Boon
　　see under　[Filson, John] 1753?-1788.

PN6157
K6L722
x

The life and adventures of Colonel David Crockett, of West
Tennessee. Cincinnati, Pub. for the Proprietor, 1833.
202+ p. 19cm. [Koundakjian collection]
　　Copy imperfect: ms. note on front lining papers states "Last
page missing." The text of the main work is complete, but
"Billy Buck," p.197-202 is incomplete.
　　In the copyright notice on p.[ii] J. S. French is given as
proprietor.
　　The author was unknown to Crockett, who wrote his "Narrative" to correct the wrong impressions produced by this publication. Cf. Pref. to Crockett's Narrative. Doubtfully ascribed
to J. S. French by E. A. Poe. Cf. Southern literary messenger,
v. 2, 1835-36, p.589.
　　Also issued New York, 1833, under title: Sketches and
eccentricities of Col.　　David Crockett of west Tennessee.

　　1. Crockett, David, 1786-1836. I. French, James Strange,
1807-1886, supposed author. (Series)

NL 0354694　　CU-B IU MiU-C AU CU TxU CtY CSmH OClWHi

Nqg25
G5
861T

...Life and adventures of Colonel Burnaby,
late of the Royal Horse Guards. London,
The General Publishing Company [1885?]
cover-title,16p. illus.(port.) 20cm.
[Binder's title: Yelverton case, etc.]

　　At head of title: One penny.

　　1. Burnaby, Frederick Gustavus, 1842-1885.

NL 0354695　　CtY

The life and adventures of Colonel Jack, a
notorious highwayman
　　see　Defoe, Daniel, 1661?-1731.
The history and remarkable life of the truly
honourable Colonel Jack.

The life and adventures of Common Sense
　　see under　[Lawrence, Herbert] fl. 1769.

Life and adventures of Dandy Jack, the celebrated equestrian performer
　　see under　Uncle Tobias, pseud.

The life and adventures of David Lewis
　　see under　Lewis, David, 1790-1820.

...The life and adventures of Dick Clinton, the masked highwayman... By the author of "Nat Blake"...etc., etc.　New
York: Dick & Fitzgerald [187-?]　104 p. illus. 22½cm.

　　At head of title: [Co]mpanion to "Jack Sheppard."
　　Caption-title: Dick Clinton: or, The masked highwayman.
　　Printed in double columns.

37732B. 1. Fiction, English. I. Nat　　Blake, Author of. II. Title:
Dick Clinton. III. Title: The masked　　highwayman.
N. Y. P. L.　　　　　　　　　　　October 1, 1940

NL 0354700　　NN

The life and adventures of Dr. Dodimus Duckworth,
A.N.Q.
　　see under　[Greene, Asa] 1789-1838.

The life and adventures of Doctor Updike Underhill
　　see under　[Tyler, Royall] 1757-1826.
The Algerine captive.

The life and adventures of Don Bilioso de l'Estomac
　　see under　[Mead, Richard] 1673-1754.

M-film
810.8
Am35
156-15

The life and adventures of Ebo Jube; in
connexion with, and as more fully illustrated
by, what befel his master, Charley Brief, at
various times, and in different parts of the
world. Part I.　New York, A. Sherman,
1852.
　　69 p. illus.

　　Microfilm (positive) Ann Arbor, Mich.,
University Microfilms, 1971. 15th title of 16.
35 mm. (American fiction series, reel 156.15)

NL 0354704　　KEmT CU DLC

The life and adventures of Guzman d'Alfarache;
or, The Spanish rogue
　　see under　[Alemán, Mateo] 1547-1614?

VOLUME 332

941.58
C692
v.6
no.2   The life and adventures of Henry Lanson,/the only son of a wealthy planter in
the West Indies ...   London [1800?]
42p. front.

[Collins pamphlets. v.6, no.2]

NL 0354706   IU

The life and adventures of Henry Thomas, the
western burglar and murderer
see under [Howard, H   R   ]

Life and adventures of Horace Greeley, the
Chappaqua sage and mongrel candidate for President of the United States. [New York?] 1872.
cover-title, 32 p. illus. 14 x 9cm.

Preface signed: B. C. R.

NL 0354708   NNC

The life and adventures of Indiana, the
virtuous orphan
see under [Collyer, Mary (Mitchell)
d. 1763, supposed author.

The life and adventures of Jack of the mill:
commonly called Lord Othmill
see under Howitt, William, 1792-1879.

823
L5263l   The life and adventures of Jack Sheppard.
[London, G. Purkess, ca.1840]
215p. illus. 22cm.

In ms. inside front cover: Gothic novel
<ca.1840> 27 penny nos. published by G. Pur-
kess.

NL 0354711   IU

The life and adventures of James Kelly
O'Dwyer. London, Richard Bentley, 1852.

3v. 20cm.

Fiction.

NL 0354712   FU

821
L623   The life and adventures of James Lovewell,
Esq., of the Bengal Civil Service, from the
period of his proceeding to Haileybury College,
to the time of his retiring from the service
of the Honourable East India Company, as judge
and magistrate. In eight cantos. By the
author of "Shigram Poh" and "Occasional poems."
Calcutta, Printed at the India Gazette Press,
1829.
xii, 280p. 22cm.

Author's autograph copy.
"Occasional poems, on various subjects"
(127p.) bound in at end.

I. Title: Occasional poems.

NL 0354714   IU

The life and adventures of James Ramble, esq.:
interspersed, with the various fortunes of
certain noble personages deeply concerned
in the northern commotions in the year 1715
see under Kimber, Edward, 1719-1769.

LIFE and adventures of Jefferson Davis.
Chicago, and New York, J. Smith & company,
1865.

24°. pp.14. Wdct.

NL 0354716   MH

The life and adventures of Joe Thompson...
see under [Kimber, Edward] 1719-1769.

The life and adventures of John A. Murrell,
the great western land pirate, with twenty-
one spirited illustrative engravings
see under [Howard, H   R   ]

The life and adventures of John Edwin, comedian
see under Edwin, John.

The life and adventures of John James Audubon,
the naturalist [book review]
see under Edinburgh review. [supplement]

The life and adventures of John Marston Hall
see under [James, George Payne
Rainsford] 1801?-1860.

The life and adventures of Joseph Balsamo ...
see under [Barberi,   ] [Supplement]

The life and adventures of Joseph T. Hare,
the bold robber and highwayman
see under [Howard, H   R   ]

Life and adventures of Josh Billings, with a characteristic
Sketch of the humorist, by Francis S. Smith. Also one hundred illustrated aphorisms ... New York, G. W. Carleton &
co.; [etc., etc.] °1883.
92 p. illus. 19ᶜᵐ.

Portraits on covers.
"A sketch of 'Josh Billings' by Francis S. Smith": p. 63-67.

1. Shaw, Henry Wheeler, 1818-1885. i. Smith, Francis Shubael,
b. 1819. ii. Carleton, Geo. W., & co., publishers.

Library of Congress   PS2808.L5   30-10775

NL 0354724   DLC AU ICU MH NN

---

arU
1029   The life and adventures of Lady Anne, by the
author of "The blue silk workbag," "Harcourt family," etc. New ed., with a preface by the Bishop of Lincoln. London,
Simpkin, Marshall [1874]
xii, 135 p. 15cm.

I. The blue silk workbag, Author of.

NL 0354725   NIC

PR3991
.A7
B6
1913   The life and adventures of Lady Anne, the
little pedlar, by the author of The blue
silk workbag, Harcourt family, etc. A new
ed., with introductory note by Elizabeth
Wordsworth. London, A.R. Mowbray; Milwaukee,
Young Churchman Co. [1913?]
161p. illus. 17cm.

NL 0354726   NcU

The life and adventures of Lazarillo de Tormes
see under Lazarillo de Tormes. English.

The life and adventures, of Martin Douglas
see under Douglas, Martin, b.ca.1777.

The life and adventures of Miss Emma
Howard, a model of female virtue. By
the author. New York, George C.
Holbrook, 1853.
38 p. 22½cm.

NL 0354729   NcD MH

FILM
4274
PR
v.2
reel
L7   The life and adventures of Miss Emma Howard,
a model of female virtue. New York, G. C.
Holbrook, 1853.
38 p. (Wright American fiction, v.II,
1851-1875, no.1548, Research Publications
Microfilm, Reel L-7)

NL 0354730   CU

PS
991
.A1
L722   The life and adventures of Miss Robinson Crusoe.
Chapters IX-XIV. [Boston, E.Littell, 1846]
3 pts.in 1 v. 25 cm.
Detached from Littell's Living age,v.11,
Oct.-Dec.,1846,p.55-56,285-287,367.
Chapters 1-8 appeared in Littell's Living age,
v.10,July-Sept.,1846.

I.Title: Miss Robinson Crusoe.

NL 0354731   MiU

823
L6265   The life and adventures of Miss Sally Jones, the
original Bath beauty, or Girl of the town; a
narrative founded upon facts, giving an account
of her many intrigues and pursuits in fashionable life, from her birth to the time of her
late residence in Bond-Street. Principally
written by the lady herself. London,
Printed by J. Bailey [n.d.]
22p. col.illus. 17cm.

Running title: Sally Jones, the Bath beauty.
Bound with Tales of the baroni. London
[1820?]

I. Title: Sally Jones, the Bath beauty.

NL 0354733   IU

VOLUME 332

The life and adventures of Mr. Duncan Campbell
see   Defoe, Daniel, 1661?-1731.
    History of the life and adventures of Mr. Duncan
Campbell.

The life and adventures of Mr. Francis Clive...
    see under   [Gibbes, Mrs. Phebe]

The life and adventures of Mr. Jethro Ludlow,
    of Oxford
    see under   Ludlow, Jethro, pseud.?

The life and adventures of Mrs. Christian Davies, commonly call'd Mother Ross; who, in several campaigns under King William and the late Duke of Marlborough, in the quality of a foot-soldier and dragoon, gave many signal proofs of an unparallell'd courage and personal bravery. Taken from her own mouth when a pensioner of Chelsea-hospital, and known to be true by many who were engaged in those great scenes of action. London, R. Montagu, 1740.

"The authorship ... has, on no reasonable grounds, been sometimes attributed to Defoe."—Dict. nat. biog., vol. xiv, p. 133.
Partly included in Women adventurers. Edited by Ménie Muriel Dowie. London, 1893.

1. Davies, Mrs. Christian (Cavenaugh) 1667-1739. 2. Gt. Brit.—Army—Military life. 3. Gt. Brit.—History, Military—Stuarts, 1603-1714. I. Defoe, Daniel, 1661?-1731, supposed author.

Library of Congress   U767.L72

19—1610

InU TxU MWiW-C CLU-C CtY PU PPRF
NL 0354738   DLC NBuG NN NjP ICN MiDW OCU MB CSmH

---

*P.11 The life and adventures of Mrs. Christian
.2163 Davies, commonly called Mother Ross; who, in several campaigns under King William and the late Duke of Marlborough, in the quality of a foot soldier and dragoon, gave many signal proofs of an unparallelled courage and personal bravery. Taken from her own mouth when a pensioner of Chelsea-Hospital, and known to be true by many who were engaged in those great scenes of action. London: Printed for C. Welch, 1740.
    iv, 262 p.   18.5cm.

Although sometimes attributed to Daniel Defoe, this is not accepted as his by Moore.
Pages 207, 217, & 225 misnumbered 107, 117 & 125.

NL 0354740   MB

The life and adventures of Mrs. Christian Davies.   (In his: Roxana; or, The fortunate mistress. and Mrs. Christian Davies. London, 1910. 18cm.   p. [351]-502.)

NL 0354741   NN

The life & adventures of Mrs. Christian Davies commonly called Mother Ross. With an introd. by the Hon. Sir John Fortescue. London, P. Davies, 1928.
    196 p. (soldiers' tales)

NL 0354742   CaBVaU CLU-C IU ICN MH KyU

The life & adventures of Mrs. Christian Davies, commonly called Mother Ross. ⟨By Daniel Defoe⟩ with an introduction by the Hon. Sir John Fortescue. New York, R. M. McBride & company, 1929.
    xv, 196 p. 21½ᵐ.   (Half-title: Soldiers' tales, ed. by Hon. Sir John Fortescue)
Printed in Great Britain.
Contains reproduction of the t.-p. of the original edition.
"The authorship ... has, on no reasonable grounds, been sometimes attributed to Defoe."—Dict. of nat. biog., vol. xiv, p. 133.
1. Davies, Mrs. Christian (Cavenaugh) 1667-1739. 2. Gt. Brit.—Army—Military life. 3. Gt. Brit.—History, Military—1689-1714. I. Defoe, Daniel, 1661?-1731, supposed author.

32-12014

Library of Congress   U767.L72 1929

923.542

NL 0354743   DLC MiD NN OU

The life and adventures of Nicholas Nickleby
    see under   [Dickens, Charles] 1812-1870

Life and adventures of Oliver Twiss (sic) [1839]
    see under   Bos, pseud.

The life and adventures of Paul Jones. New York, Dewitt and Davenport [184-?]
    64 p. 24½ᵐ.

1. Jones, John Paul, 1747-1792.

CA 28-1096 Unrev'd

Library of Congress   E207.J7L716

NL 0354746   DLC

The life and adventures of Paul Jones. New York, W. H. Graham, 1846.
    64 p. 22ᵐ.

1. Jones, John Paul, 1747-1792. I. Graham, William H., New York, pub.

11-22485

Library of Congress   E207.J7L72

NL 0354747   DLC MiU-C

The life and adventures of Percival Mayberry...
    see under   [Ingraham, Joseph Holt] 1809-1860.

The life and adventures of Peter Wilkins
    see under   [Paltock, Robert] 1697-1767.

The life and adventures of Philip Quarll...
    see under   Longueville, Peter, fl. 1727, supposed author.

The life and adventures of R. D. Romaine
    see under   [Payson, George]
    The new age of gold, etc.

Life and adventures of Robert, the hermit of Massachusetts, who has lived 14 years in a cave, secluded from human society
    see under   [Trumbull, Henry].

The life and adventures of Robin Hood.
n.p., n. d.
    pp. 5-46. Wdcts.
    Imperfect: - title - page and preliminary pages wanting.   25257.6.5

NL 0354753   MH

The LIFE AND ADVENTURES OF ROBIN HOOD. [illus.] Glasgow: Printed for the booksellers, 1855. Price One Penny. (New and Improved Series, No. 34.) * KVD p.v.20, no.95
14.5 x 9 cm. 24 p. Illustrations.
In prose.

NL 0354754   NN

Life and adventures of Robin Hood. Philadelphia, J. B. Perry, 1865.
    70 p. illus. 14½ cm.
    Illus. t.-p.

1. Robin Hood.

PR2127.L5

12—36172

NL 0354755   DLC

---

ar V
6444   The life and adventures of Robin Hood and his merry men. Philadelphia, Rodgers [18--]
    263 p. illus. 16cm.

1. Robin Hood.

NL 0354756   NIC

PR 2127 The LIFE AND ADVENTURES OF ROBIN HOOD AND HIS
.L723   merry men. New York, Hurst and Co. [19--?]
    263 p.

NL 0354757   InU

The life and adventures of Robinson Crusoe
    see   Defoe, Daniel, 1661?-1731.
    Robinson Crusoe.

The life and adventures of Roderick Douglas
    see under   [Mackintosh, D   B   ]

The life and adventures of Roxana, the fortunate mistress
    see   Defoe, Daniel, 1661?-1731.
    The fortunate mistress.

VOLUME 332

Life and adventures of Sam Bass, the notorious Union Pacific and Texas train robber; together with a graphic account of his capture and death, sketch of the members of his band, with thrilling pen pictures of their many bold and desperate deeds, and the capture and death of Collins, Berry, Barnes and Arkansas Johnson. Dallas, Tex., 1878.   89 p.   8°.

1. Bass, Samuel, 1851-1878.   2. Train robbers.
January 27, 1927

NbUC ICN CtY NNC NcD NjP MH-L CtU IaU MnHi MeB
NL   0354761   NN MH-L TxU IEdS CoD OU N MnU NjP IU

MICROFILM   **Life** and adventures of Sam Bass, the notorious
300   Union Pacific and Texas train robber; to-
12   gether with a graphic account of his capture
and death, sketch of the members of his band,
with thrilling pen pictures of their many
bold and desperate deeds, and the capture
and death of Collins, Berry, Barnes and
Arkansas Johnson.   Dallas Commercial Steam
Press. 1878.
89p.
Microfilm copy. Made by Southwestern Microfilm. Positive

1. Bass, Sam. 1851-1878. 2. Brigands and
robbers. 3. Crime and criminals--Texas.

NL   0354763   TxFTC

Life and adventures of Sam Bass, the notorious
Union Pacific and Texas train robber; together
with a graphic account of his capture and death -
sketch of the members of his band, with thrilling
pen pictures of their many bold and desperate
deeds, and the capture and death of Collins, Berry, Barnes, and Arkansas Johnson.   Dallas, Tex.,
Dallas commercial steam print, 1878.   [Austin?
Tex., 193-?]
89p.   22½cm.
1. Bass, Sam,   1851-1878.

NL   0354764   TxU

976.4   **Life** and adventures of Sam Bass, the
B293Z   notorious Union Pacific and Texas train
robber, together with a graphic account
of his capture and death - sketch of
the members of his band, with thrilling
pen pictures of their many bold and
desperate deeds, and the capture and
death of Collins, Berry, Barnes, and
Arkansas Johnson.   Dallas, Texas,
Dallas Commercial Steam Print, 1878;
Houston, Texas, The Frontier Press
[1952]
89 p.   illus.,   21 cm.

NL   0354765   LU TxU

The life and adventures of Sm. Denmore Hayward,
who was found guilty of burglary, and suffered the
penalty of his crime at the Old Bailey, on Tuesday
Nov. 27, 1821.   23p. col.front.(port.)   London,
J. L. Marks [1821]

A chap-book.

NL   0354766   OC1

The life and adventures of Sir Bartholomew
Sapskull
    see under   [Donaldson, William] fl. 1768.

PR   The Life & adventures of that most eccen-
3991   tric character James Hirst of Rawcliffe,
A1L613   Yorkshire; his amusing tricks at school;
his apprenticeship; death of his sweet-
heart; his speculations; his leap into
the horse-pond when hunting on his favourite bull "Jupiter" ... his encounter
with two footpads; extract from his will
and codicil thereto; &c., &c.   Knottingley, E. W. Hepworth [1840?]
47 p.   fold.front.

NL   0354768   CLU

The LIFE and adventures of that eccentric
character, James Hirst of Rawcliffe, Yorkshire,
Knottingley, W.S.Hepworth; etc., etc., [cir,
1850]

pp.47+. Front.

NL   0354769   MH

The life and adventures of that most witty
and ingenious Spaniard, Lazarillo de Tormes
    see under   Lazarillo de Tormes. *English*.

Life and adventures of that valiant outlaw Robin Hood
... together with the history of Little John, and his merry
men all.   To which is added, several admired songs from
Robin Hood's garland. London, W. Cole [1829]
28 p.   fold. col. front. 18½ᶜᵐ. [With Fraser, John. The humorous
chap-books of Scotland. New York, 1873-[74] Copy 2]

6-39399†

NL   0354771   DLC

Life and adventures of the accomplished forger and
swindler, Colonel Monroe Edwards.   New York, H. Long
& brother [1848]
152 p. incl. front. (port.) illus. 24ᶜᵐ.

1. Edwards, Monroe, b. 1808.

14-17402

Library of Congress   HV6698.Z9E3¹⁻

NL   0354772   DLC PHi PPL TxHU NBu TxU NN

Life and adventures of the Burdett twins.   (Fanny and Major.)
New York. Torrey & Clark. 1881. 16 pp. 14 cm.

K8717 — Burdett, Fanny, 1859-. — Burdett, Major, 1859-. — Dwarfs.

NL   0354773   MB

The **life** and adventures of the celebrated Alexander Farnese, prince of Parma, commander in chief of the Spanish
forces, at the siege of Antwerp, &c. In the year 1545 [i. e.
1585]. Being a narrative of his enterprising exploits; particularly by forming a bridge over the river Scheld, to intercept
the communication between the besieged city and the maritime
provinces ... Translated from the Spanish. London, A.
Young, 1803.
1 p. l., [7]-44 p. front. 18ᵐ.

1. Alessandro Farnese, duke of Parma and Piacenza, 1545-1592.
2. Antwerp—Siege, 1584-1585.

28-15653

Library of Congress   DH194.L5

NL   0354774   DLC

The **life** and adventures of the celebrated Walking
Stewart: including his travels in the East Indies, Turkey,
Germany, & America. By a relative ... London, E.
Wheatley, 1822.
16 p. front. (port.) 22ᵐ.
Possibly by William Thomas Brande.

1. Stewart, John, 1749-1822.   I. Brande, William Thomas, 1788-1866,
supposed author.   25-6386
Library of Congress   CT788.S765L5
                                        [Political pamphlets, v. 63, no. 5]
                                        JA36.P8 vol. 63

NL   0354775   DLC MiU-C CtY NN

Life and adventures of the famous Colonel Blood, who
seized on the person of the Duke of Ormond, and con-
veyed him to Tyburn, with the intention of putting him
to death on a common gibbet, and who afterwards, in the
disguise of a priest, with several of his daring associates,
obtained admittance into the Tower of London, which
they robbed of the crown, ball, sceptre, and other regalia;
but who was afterwards pardoned by King Charles II.
who settled on him a handsome pension for life. London,
Hodgson and co. [1825?]
24 p. fold. col. front. 17½ᶜᵐ.
1. Blood, Thomas,   1618?-1680.
                                        15-12521
Library of Congress   DA447.B5L5

NL   0354776   DLC CoCA

The **life** and adventures of the famous Moll
Flanders ...
    see   Defoe, Daniel, 1661?-1731.
    The fortunes and misfortunes of the famous
Moll Flanders.

Life and adventures of the Indian chiefs, warriors and squaws, of
the Winnebago tribe, now exhibiting at Barnum's American Museum, New York.   New York: Wynkoop, Hallenbeck & Thomas,
1863.   8 p.   12°.

1. Indians (N. A.): Winnebago.   November 9, 1915.

NL   0354778   NN

The **life** and adventures of the Marchioness
Urbino
    see under   [Noake, Dorothy]

The **life** and adventures of the Old lady of
Threadneedle street
    see under   [Reid, William] political
economist.

The **Life** and adventures of Theodore Smartville...
London, 1851.
    21 cm.   [Bound with The Ladies' cabinet of
fashion, Ser. 3, v. 17]

NL   0354781   CtY

...The **life** and adventures of Three Fingered Jack, the terror
of Jamaica.   London: Printed for O. Hodgson [18—]   24 p.
col'd front.   21cm.

At head of title: Hodgson's edition.
Original covers bound in.
"Hodgson's list of pamphlets," p. [1] of cover.
With bookplate of Charles Todd Owen, and armorial bookplate of Victor Cutter
Macomber.

NL   0354782   NN

VOLUME 332

Life and adventures of Timothy Murphy, the
benefactor of Schoharie
see under   [Sigsby,   ]

The life and adventures of Tom Thumb
see under   Tom Thumb.

Life and adventures of Wat Tyler, the good and the
brave ... London, H. G. Collins, 1851.
iiii–viii, ₍9₎–174 p. 17½ᶜᵐ.

1. Tyler, Wat, d. 1381.

Library of Congress   DA231.T9L7   4-34694

NL 0354785   DLC NjR NcU NN

The life and adventures, songs, services and
speeches of Private Miles O'Reily
see under   [Halpine, Charles Graham]
1829-1868.

Life and alone. Boston, Lee and Shepard, 1870.
1 p. l., 5–407 p. 18ᶜᵐ.

Library of Congress   PZ3.L6237   7-19392†

NL 0354787   DLC ViU MB

Life and alone.   Boston, Lee and Shepard, 1870.
407 p. (Wright American fiction, v.II,
1851-1875, no.1549, Research Publications
Microfilm, Reel L-7)

NL 0354788   CU

The life and amours of Charles Lewis Elec-
tor Palatin. Done out of French.   London,
Printed for Thomas Nott ... and are to be
sold by Randal Taylor ... 1692.
5 p.l.,143 p. 14½ᶜᵐ.

Translation of La vie et amours de comte
Louis, electeur Palatine.
Signatures: A⁵, B-G¹².
Bound in half calf.

NL 0354789   CLU-C CtY CSmH

Rare
PN   The life and amours of Mrs. Waylett, of
2598   the Haymarket, Adelphi, and Olympic
W35   Theatres. ₍London, Printed and pub-
L72   lished by W. P. Chubb, 182-?₎
16 p. 22cm.

Caption title; t. p. wanting?
With this is bound The theatre. v. 1,
no. 6, and v. 1, no. 9. ₍London₎ 1828.

1. Waylett,   Harriet Cooke, 1798-
1851.

NL 0354790   NIC

The Life and amours of Owen Tideric Prince
of Wales
see under [Curli,   de]

Life and Andrew Otway
see under [Southwold, Stephen] 1887-

The life and anecdotes of John Philpot Curran
see   Cut and come again! The life and
anecdotes of John Philpot Curran ...

The life and anecdotes of the Black Dwarf
see under   Chambers, William, 1800-1883.

The life and approaching death of William
Kiffin./ Extracted out of the visitation
book by a church member.   London, T. Bateman, 1659.
₍2₎,5 p. 19ᶜᵐ.

A satire.
From the Isaac Foot collection.

NL 0354795   CLU-C

LIFE and art in photograph.
no. 1–

London: Chatto & Windus [etc., 1934   26cm.
v. plates.

1. Photographs.

NL 0354796   NN NhD OO OU

Life and art of Joseph Jefferson, with some account
of his ancestry and of the Jefferson family of actors.
N.Y., 1894.
ix, 319 p. il. 8°

NL 0354797   MWA

973.84   The life and assassination of President Gar-
G18W£i   field, together with the life of the cowardly
assassin Guiteau. President Garfield's war
record and life in full. From canal-boy to
the first office in the gift of the people.
Philadelphia, Barclay ₍1881₎
111p. illus. 24cm.

1. Garfield, James Abram, Pres. U.S., 1831-
1881. 2. Guiteau, Charles Julius, 1840(ca.)-
1882.

NL 0354798   IU

E687   The Life and assassination of President Gar-
.9   field, together with the life of the coward-
.L72   ly assassin, Guiteau. President Garfield's
war record and life in full. From canal-boy
to the first office in the gift of the people.
Philadelphia, Barclay ₍1883₎
19–111 p. illus.

1. Garfield, James Abram, Pres. U.S., 1831-
1881. 2. Guiteau, Charles Julius, 1841-1882.

NL 0354799   ICU MiD-B OClWHi

The life and astonishing adventures of Peter
Williamson, who was carried off when a child
from Aberdeen and sold for a slave
see under   Williamson, Peter, 1730-1799.

The life and astonishing transactions of John Daniel
see under   [Morris, Ralph]

Life and battles of Henry C. Gilliland for seventy
years
see under   Gilliland, Henry C   1845-

The life and battles of Jack Johnson
see under   [Fox, Richard Kyle] 1846-

Life and battles of James J. Corbett ...
see under   [Sullivan, James E   ]

Life and battles of James J. Corbett, the champion
pugilist of the world ...
see under   [Fox, Richard Kyle] 1846-1922.

Life and battles of Joe Collins (Tug Wilson)
champion pugilist of England
see under   [Harding, William Edgar]
1848-

The life and battles of John Morrissey. With portraits
from life of John Morrissey, John C. Heenan, Yankee
Sullivan and Bill Poole ... New York, E. James ₍1879₎
cover-title, 24 p. incl. ports. 19½ x 12ᶜᵐ.
From the New York clipper.

1. Morrissey, John, 1831-1878. 2. Boxing.

CA 7-6241 Unrev'd

Library of Congress   GV1132.M8L7

NL 0354807   DLC

VOLUME 332

Life and battles of Yankee Sullivan, embracing full and accurate reports of his fights with Hammer Lane, Tom Secor, Harry Bell, Bob Caunt, Tom Hyer, John Morrisey ... Philadelphia, A. Winch [1854]

1 p. L, [9]–96, [2] p. 14ᵐ.

In double columns.

1. Ambrose, James, 1813–1856. 2. Boxing.

Library of Congress   GV1132.S9L7   5–29629†

NL 0354808   DLC CtY NN

The **life** and beauties of Fanny Fern [pseud.] ... Philadelphia, T. B. Peterson [185–?]

x, [11]–330 p. 18¼ᵐ.

An unfriendly sketch of Fanny Fern (Mrs. Parton) apparently occasioned by her "Ruth Hall." Includes selections from her writings.

1. Parton, Mrs. Sara Payson (Willis) 1811–1872. I. Parton, Mrs. Sara Payson (Willis) 1811–1872.

Library of Congress   PS2523.P9Z7   42–26968

NL 0354809   DLC CLSU NcGU

The **life** and beauties of Fanny Fern [pseud.] ... New York, H. Long and brother, 1855.

x, [11]–330 p. 19ᵐ.

An unfriendly sketch, apparently occasioned by Fanny Fern's "Ruth Hall"; with selections from her writings. In original red cloth. Motto on t.-p. differs from that in another issue of same year.

1. Parton, Mrs. Sara Payson (Willis) 1811–1872. I. Parton, Mrs. Sara Payson (Willis) 1811–1872.

Library of Congress   PS2523.P9Z7 1855   24–17271 Revised

NL 0354810   PBL NNU-W ICU DLC MeB WaS ViW WaWW TxU MdBP NN MB MWA

The **life** and beauties of Fanny Fern [pseud.] ... New York, H. Long and brother, 1855.

x, [11]–330 p. 18ᵐ.

An unfriendly sketch of Fanny Fern (Mrs. Parton) apparently occasioned by her "Ruth Hall"; includes selections from her writings. The motto on t.-p. differs from that of another issue of same year.

1. Parton, Mrs. Sara Payson (Willis) 1811–1872. I. Parton, Mrs. Sara Payson (Willis) 1811–1872.

Library of Congress   PS2523.P9Z7 1855 a   34–30560

NL 0354811   OCl DLC ScU T ICU IaU TU TxU OClWHi ODW NcD

B C976*l*

The **life** and beauties of the Right Honourable John Philpot Curran; with numerous interesting anecdotes, &c. 4th ed. Dublin, J. M'Cormick [n.d.] 144p. 15cm. (The national library for Ireland, v.2)

1. Curran, John Philpot, 1750–1817.

NL 0354812   KU IU

DA948 .3C9 .L5

The **life** and beauties of the Right Honourable John Philpot Curran; with numerous interesting anecdotes, &c. 6th ed. Dublin, J. M'Cormick, [18—] 144p. 15cm. With this is bound The beauties of the principal speeches of Henry Grattan, M. P. with a memoir of his life.

1. Curran, John Philpot, 1750–1817 2. Ireland -   Hist. - 18th century.

NL 0354813   NNU

B C97613

The **life** and beauties of the Right Honorable John Philpot Curran; with numerous interesting anecdotes, etc. 3d ed.   Dublin [1846?] 144p.

NL 0354814   IU

DK169 .S815

Life & campaigns of General Suworow, conqueror of Italy, by an officer. London: Printed for T. Hirst, by Brook and Lancashire, Huddersfield, 1801. 164 p. 20 cm.

1. Suvorov, Aleksandr Vasil'evich, kniaz' Italiiskii, 1729?–1800.

NL 0354815   ViU

Bo67 816

The **life** and campaigns of Napoleon Bonaparte ... containing details of his military achievements/... a circumstantial account of the decisive battle of Waterloo; with particulars of his exile to St. Helena, conversations with Dr. Warden, and his employment in the island. Embellished with a portrait. To which is annexed, The consequences of the French revolution. Haddington, Printed by and for G. Miller and son 1816? 74, 3 –119p. col. front. (port.) 19½cm.

NL 0354816   CtY

Life and campaigns of Napoleon Bonaparte: giving an account of all his engagements, from the siege of Toulon to the battle of Waterloo
   see under   [Reid, William Hamilton] d. 1826, comp.

The **life** and campaigns of Victor Moreau. Comprehending his trial, justification and other events, till the period of his embarkation for the United States. By an officer of the staff. Tr. from the French. New York, Printed for D. Bliss, 1806.

viii, [9]–288 p. incl. front. (port.) 17½ᵐ.

Translated by John Davis.
Identical with another issue of the same year "published by I. Riley & co. ... Feb. 1806". The copyright notice, dated 10th of January, in which D. Bliss is entered as proprietor, is the same in both issues.
1. Moreau, Jean-Victor Marie, 1763–1813. I. Davis, John, of New York, tr.

    DC146.M8L52   5–23406

NL 0354818   PPL MB DGU ICarbS NcU TxU OClWHi WHi MiU-C NjP PP ViU DLC CSmH NjR PPL NBu NjR NN MH MdBE MWA

The **life** and campaigns of Victor Moreau. Comprehending his trial, justification and other events, till the period of his embarkation for the United States. By an officer of the staff. Tr. from the French. New York, I. Riley & co., Feb. 1806.

viii, [9]–288 p. incl. front. (port.) 17½ᵐ.

Tr. by John Davis.
Identical with another issue of the same year "printed for David Bliss ... Southwick & Hardcastle, printers." The copyright notice, dated 10th of January, in which D. Bliss is entered as proprietor, is the same in both issues.
1. Moreau, Jean Victor Marie, 1763–1813. I. Davis, John, of New York, tr.

Library of Congress   DC146.M8L5   5–23407

NL 0354819   DLC OU ViU

Life (The) and career of James Greenacre, partly written by himself, and compiled from authentic sources, giving an account of his family [etc.]. 28 pp., 1 pl. 12°. *London, J. Duncombe & Co.,* [1837]

NL 0354820   DNLM

Life and casualty insurance company of Tennessee [Burton, Andrew Mizell]

John Smith and his success and sparks from live wires. Nashville, Foster & Parkes co. for Life and casualty insurance company of Tennessee [1923]

HG8963 .L66A12

Life and casualty mirror

Nashville, Tenn., The Life and casualty insurance company [19 v. illus. (incl. ports.) 23–28cm. weekly.

Caption title.

I. Life and casualty insurance company of Tennessee.

NL 0354822   DLC

The **life** and character of a strange he-monster, lately arrived in London from an English colony in America, and is often to be seen upon the Royal Exchange, gratis.

This work is available in this library in the Readex Microprint edition of Early American Imprints published by the American Antiquarian Society.
This collection is arranged according to the numbers in Charles Evans' American Bibliography.

NL 0354823   DLC

LIFE and Character of a Strange He-Monster, lately arriv'd in London, from an English Colony in America. And is often to be seen upon the Royal Exchange, Gratis. [L.]. 1726.

pp.21.

NL 0354824   MH

Life and character of Ambrose E. Burnside.

NL 0354825   KyLx

The **life** and character of Bishop Moore of Virginia...
   see under   [Henshaw, John Prentiss Kewley] 1792–1852.

Life and character of Bonaparte from his birth to the 15th of August, 1804
   see under   Burdon, William, 1764–1818.

The **life** and character of Charles duke of Shrewsbury. In a letter to a noble lord. By a gentleman that was privy to the most material passages. London: Printed for St. J. B. and sold by the booksellers of London and Westminster. 1718.

1 p.l., 36 p. 21½ᵐ. (With [Defoe, Daniel] Memoirs of publick transactions in the life and ministry of His Grace the D. of Shrewsbury ... London, 1718)

First edition, variant imprint.
Signatures: A–D⁴, E³.

NL 0354828   CLU-C InU MB CtY CSmH

VOLUME 332

Life and character of Colonel David Franson,
   compiler from previously published biographies.
   1874. [Philadelphia] Sunday Republic, Print
   [1874].
     15 p.   24 mo.   illus.   Bound in one-half
dark blue roan, blue boards. Original blue paper.
The Nicholson Collection, September, 1922.

NL 0354829   CSmH PHi

411   Life and character of Dr.Franklin ...
L58   p.[631]-633. port. 22cm.
         From The Political magazine and parliamentary
      naval, military and literary journal ... v.1,
      Oct., 1780.

NL 0354830   CtY

Life and character of Edward Austin Sheldon
      see under   [Skinner, Charles Rufus] 1844-
1928.

Life and character of Frederick Augustus Rauch
      see under   Nevin, John Williamson,
1803-1886.

Life and character of Gerhard Tersteegen
      see under   Tersteegen, Gerhard, 1697-
1769.

PR   The life and character of Harvey, the famous
3291   conjurer of Dublin. Containing Harvey's notions
L51   and opinions about superstition, enthusiasm, re-
Cage   ligion [etc.] ... To which is added an account
      of two real fortunetellings, and some prophecys
      of Harvey's ... Dublin, Printed, and re-printed,
      in London, 1728.

      72 p.   B⁴, [2d]B-I⁴. 8vo.

NL 0354834   DFo

Lilly   THE LIFE AND CHARACTER OF JAMES BUTLER ...
DA 501 With a particular account of all his battles
O 73 L 72 ... Together with the particulars of the mar-
      riages, descents, and deaths of the said
      family, ever since King Henry II's reign.
      The whole publish'd from authentick manuscripts
      ... London, R. Walker, 1729.
        2 p.l.,35 p.   8vo(19 cm.)

        BM 9:464.
        Typesigned T.B. on p. 8.
        Disbound.

NL 0354835   InU MH

14454   The life and character of James Butler,
.689   late Duke, Marquis and Earl of Ormond...
.58   with a particular account of all his
      battles; and an impartial relation of the
      rise...of that illustrious family...pub.
      from authentick manuscripts. Dublin,
      Printed and sold by J.Hoey, 1730.
        24 p. 18 cm.

        Dedication   signed: T.B.

NL 0354836   NjP

The life and character of Jane Shore.
*EC7   Collected from our best historians, chiefly
R7926   from the writings of Sir Thomas More; who was
714ta   her cotemporary, and personally knew her.
      Humbly offer'd to the readers and spectators of
      her tragedy, written by Mr. Rowe. Inscrib'd to
      Mrs. Oldfield ...
      London,Printed:and sold by J.Morphew near
      Stationers-hall,and A.Dodd at the Peacock with-
      out Temple-Bar.MDCCXIV.   Price six pence.
        2p.l.,20p. 22.5cm.
        Bound with   Rowe's The tragedy of
        Jane Shore,   [1714].

NL 0354837   MH IaU CtY TxU CLU-C

The life and character of Jane Shore.
*EC7   Collected from our best historians, chiefly
R7926   from the writings of Sir Thomas More; who was
714t   her cotemporary, and personally knew her.
      Humbly offer'd to the readers and spectators of
      her tragedy written by Mr. Rowe. Inscrib'd to
      Mrs. Oldfield ... The second edition.
      London,Printed:and sold by J.Brown at the
      Black Swan without Temple-Bar,W.Taylor at the
      Ship in Pater-noster row,N.Cliffe in Cheapside,
      J.Morphew near Stationers-hall,and A.Dodd at
      the Peacock with-   out Temple-Bar.1714.
      Price six pence.

        2p.l.,20p. 23.5cm.
        Apparently largely printed from the same
      setting of type as the first edition.
        Bound with Rowe's The tragedy of Jane Shore,
      [1714].

NL 0354839   MH DFo IU

      The life and character of Jane Shore,
   collected from our best historians, chiefly
   from the writings of Sir Thomas More, who
   was her cotemporary, and personally knew her.
   Humbly offer'd to the readers and spectators
   of her Tragedy written by Mr.Rowe. Inscrib'd
   to Mrs. Oldfield. 3d ed. London, Printed
   and sold by W.Lewis [etc.] 1714.
     46 p. 1 illus. 17 cm.

NL 0354840   NjP DFo

ar V   The life and character of John Barber, esq.;
3766   late lord-mayor of London, deceased... 2d ed.
      London, Printed for T. Cooper [1741?]
        60 p. 20cm.

        No. 3 in vol. lettered: Dumourier unmasked.
      Viette.

        1. Barber, John, 1675-1741?

NL 0354841   NIC ICN NjP CtY MB CLU-C

      The life and character of John Barber, esq;
   late lord-mayor of London, deceased ... The
   second edition. London: Printed for T. Cooper,
   at the Globe in Pater-Noster-Row, and sold at
   the Pamphlet-Shops in London and Westminster
   [1746?]
     [4], 60 p. 20cm.

     Bound with An impartial history of the life
   ... of Mr. John Barber. 1741.

NL 0354842   NNC

The life and character of John Philips...
      see under   [Sewell, George] d. 1726.

Life and character of Lewis Cass.
   Albany, 1848.
     64p. 8°

NL 0354844   MWA

The life and character of Major Pitcairn ...
      see under   [Hudson, Charles] 1795-1881.

The life and character of Marcus Portius Cato
   Uticensis
      see under   [Theobald, Lewis] 1688-1744.

The life and character of Mr. John Philips...
      see under   [Philips, John] 1676-1709.

The life and character of Mrs. Mary Moders
      see under   Carleton, Mary (Moders)
1642-1673.

The life and character of Moll King, late
   mistress of King's coffee-house in Covent-
   Garden ... containing a true narrative of this
   well-known lady ... also, the flash dialogue
   between Moll King and Old Gentleman Harry...
   To the whole is added, an epitaph and elegy,
   wrote by one of Moll's favourite customers,
   and a key to the flash dialogue.   London,
   Printed by G. Brice, 1747.
     16 p.   20 cm.
     King, Mrs. Moll (Crispin) 1796-1747.

NL 0354848   CU

Life and character of Rev. D. Howe Allen,
   D. D., professor of Theology in Lane seminary.
   memorial sermon, delivered at the anniversary.
   May 11, 1871, Cincinnati, 1871.

NL 0354849   OClWHi

...Life and character of Robert Fulton...   [Boston: Carter
and Hendee, 1818?]   74-120 p. 20cm.   (Scientific tracts.
v. 2. no. 4-5.)

     Caption-title.
     Issued in two parts.

                                    HANFORD COLLECTION.
710330A. 1. Fulton, Robert, 1765-   1815. I. Ser.
                                    September 20, 1934

NL 0354850   NN

VM   Life and character of Robert Fulton.
140   [Boston, Carter and Hendee, 183-?]
.F9   [73]-120 p. 19 cm. (Scientific tracts,
L72   v.2,no.4-5)
         Caption title.

         1.Fulton,Robert,1765-1815.

NL 0354851   MiU

VOLUME 332

Life and character of S. H. Stearns. 1839
   see under   Stearns, William Augustus, 1805-
1876.

The life and character of Sir William Temple,
bart.
   see under   [Giffard, Martha (Temple) Lady.
1638-1722.

The life and character of that eminent and learned
prelate, Dr. Edward Stillingfleet
   see under   Goodwin, Timothy.

Life and character of the chevalier John Paul Jones,
1857
   see under   Sherburne, John Henry, 1794-
1850?

Life and character of the founders of the Columbia,
Tennessee, athenaeum
   see under   [Smith, William A   ]

Life and character of the Hon. John C. Calhoun, with
illustrations: containing notices of his father and uncles,
and their brave conduct during our struggle for independence, in the American revolutionary war. New-York,
J. Winchester; [etc., etc.,] 1843.
   24 p. illus. 23ᶜᵐ.

   1. Calhoun, John Caldwell, 1782-1850.

   Library of Congress   E340.C15L7
                                                7-15668

NL 0354857   DLC MWA MB CtY NcD PHi NN

The **life** and character of the late Lord Chancellor Jefferys ... London, Printed by A. Moore, 1725.
   8 p. l., 47 p. 19½ᶜᵐ.
   Attributed to A. Moore. - cf. Halkett and Laing.

   1. Jeffreys, George Jeffreys, 1st baron, 1648-1689.

   Library of Congress   DA447.J4L7
                                                4-33707†

NL 0354858   DLC MH MnU MB MsSM CtY InU

*Defoe
30
.725   The **life** and character of the late Lord Chan-
.A10Lc   cellor Jefferys. The 2d ed. London, Printed
           for J. Pottinger, and J. Seymour, 1764.
           54 p. 21cm.

           1. Jeffreys, George Jeffreys, baron, 1648-1689.

NL 0354859   MB CLL MH MdBP

...Life and character of the late Mr. Cornelius...   [Boston,
1832.] 250-264 p. 8°.
   Caption-title.
   Excerpt: Quar. register. v. 4, no. 4. May, 1832.

411416A. 1. Cornelius, Elias, 1794-   1832.
                                                        May 15, 1929

NL 0354860   NN

x285.6
As78a   The life and character of the late Reverend
1770   and learned Mr. Thomas Boston ... To which is add-
           ed, an elegy on his much lamented death: also, a'
           elegy on his son's death.   Edinburgh, Printed:
           and sold at the printing house in the West-Bow,
           1778.
           22p. 16cm.

             Bound with Associate Presbytery (Scotland)
           Act, declaration and testimony. Glasgow, 1770.
           Closely trimmed, with loss of some page num-
           bers.

NL 0354861   IU

The Life and character of the Reverend Benjamin
Colman. Boston, 1749.
   238 p.   8°.

NL 0354862   MWA

Life and character of the Reverend Sylvester
Judd. Boston, Crosby, Nichols, 1854.

   1. Judd, Sylvester, 1813-1853.

NL 0354863   ViU

The life and character, rise and conduct of Count
Brühl...
   see under   [Justi, Johann Heinrich Gottlob]
1720-1771, supposed author.

The life and choice writings of George Lippard
   see under   Lippard, George, 1822-1854.

The life and comical transactions of Lothian
Tom, wherein is contained a collection of roguish
exploits done both in Scotland and England. 8p.
[n.p., n.d.]

   A chap-book.

NL 0354866   OC1

Life and confession of Ann Walters, the female murderess!
Also the execution of Enos G. Dudley, at Haverhill, N. H.,
May 23d, 1849. To which is added th[ᵢ] confession of Mary
Runkle, who was executed for murder. [Boston] Printed for
the proprietor, 1850.
   32 p. illus. 22ᶜᵐ.

   1. Walters, Mrs. Ann (Smith) 1812-1844. 2. Dudley, Enos G., d. 1849.
   3. Runkle, Mrs. Mary.
                                                        6—33810
   Library of Congress   HV6248.W3L5

NL 0354867   DLC Nh CtY

Life and confession of Asenath the daughter of
Pentephres of Heliopolis, narrating how all-
beautiful Joseph took her to wife; prepared by
Mary Brodrick from notes supplied by Sir Peter
Le Page Renouf. London, Philip Wellby, 1900.
   37 p.

   Note: -The apocryphal story translated and
abridged from the oldest Greek text.

NL 0354868   MiD

The life and confession of Bridget Dergan, who murdered Mrs. Ellen Coriell, the lovely wife of Dr. Coriell,
of New Market, N. J. To which is added her full confession, and an account of her execution at New Brunswick. Philadelphia, Barclay & co. [1867]
   1 p. l., 21-49 p. incl. illus., 2 port. 25ᶜᵐ.

   1. Deignan, Bridget, 1843-1867.
                                                        25-2454
   Library of Congress   HV6248.D35L5

NL 0354869   DLC PP MnU NN

CT104   The Life and confession of George B. Jarman
.J29L   who was executed for murder in New Brunswick,
           N. J. on Friday the 8th of August, 1828. Together
           with original pieces in prose and poetry, composed
           by him while in prison. New Brunswick, N. J.,
           Jacob Edmonds, William Packer & Aaron Slack
           [1828?]
           8 p. 21 cm.

           1. Jarman, George B   , 1780-1828.

NL 0354870   NjR

The life and confession of Isaac Heller
alias Isaac Young who was executed at Liberty, Union County, Ia. on the 29th of April,
1836 for the murder of his wife and three infant children, ... Liberty. C. V. Duggins
--Printer. 1836.
   13 x 18.5 cm. 22 p., 1 blank leaf.
   [Heller, Isaac, d. 1836.

NL 0354871   In

The life and confession of John Johnson, the murderer
of James Murray, together with some particulars of his
family, not generally known ... New-York, Brown &
Tyrell, 1824.
   26 p. 1 illus. 21½ᶜᵐ.

   1. Johnson, John. 2. Murray, James, d. 1823.
                                                        15-3283
   Library of Congress   HV6248.J6L5

NL 0354872   DLC

The life and confession of John Tuhi
   see under   Tuhi, John.

The life and confession of Johnson Green
   see under   Green, Johnson, 1757-1786.

VOLUME 332

Life and confession of Stephen Dee Richards, the murderer of nine persons, executed at Minden, Nebraska April 26, 1879. With a brief sketch of the following murderous miscreants and their crimes: the famos I. P. Olive and his gang, tried and convicted for lynching and burning Ketchum and Mitchell, Dr Geo. J. St. Louis, the wife poisoner and suicide. W. J. M'Elvoy, the boy murderer, Orlando Casler, the murderer of his friend and guest. Henry Schlencker, the murderer of Florence Booth. (Lincoln, Neb., The State journal co., 1879)
72 p. 18¼ᶜᵐ.
Title vignette (portrait)
1. Richards, Stephen Dee, 1856–1879. 2. Crime and criminals.
20–607
Library of Congress HV6248.R5A3

NL 0354875 DLC

Life and confessions of Harvey N. Thorpe
see under Thorpe, Harvey N

In The life and confessions of Humphrey Humbug
L626 ... with a brief account of his family from 1
935 anno mundi to 1835 anno Christi. Related by himself. London, A. J. Attwood, 1835.
2 p.ℓ., iii, [1], 100 p. 19½ cm.

NL 0354877 CtY ICU

The Life & Confessions of Martha Grinder, The Poisoner. Pittsburgh. 1866.
23 p.

NL 0354878 DLC OClWHi

The life and conversation of Richard Bentley, delivered in his own words, for the most part from his own writings ... London, Printed for J. Morphew, 1712.
(⁵), 6–14, 6–14, (1) p. 18¼ᶜᵐ.
Added t.-p. in Latin; Latin and English on opposite pages.
Pages 6–14 numbered in duplicate.
A lampoon.

1. Bentley, Richard, 1662–1742.

NL 0354879 MiU ICN MoSW TxU CtY

The **life** and correspondence of Francis Bacon, viscount St. Albans, lord chancellor of England ... London, Saunders, Otley, and co., 1861.
xxiv, 568 p. 20¼ᶜᵐ.
Ascribed to J. F. Foard. cf. Halkett & Laing; Allibone suppl.
Occasioned by Hepworth Dixon's Personal history of Lord Bacon.
Book-plate of Dr. Ernest Lewis McEwen.

1. Bacon, Francis, viscount St. Albans, 1561–1626. 2. Dixon, William Hepworth, 1821–1879. Personal history of Lord Bacon. I. Foard, J. F., supposed author.
32–24212
Library of Congress B1197.L55 921.2

NL 0354880 DLC NjP

The life and dangerous voyages of Sir Francis Drake, with the surprising of Nombre de Dios, and the manner of his gaining large quantities of gold and silver. And a large account of that voyage, wherein he encompassed the whole world. And the voyage which he made with Francis Knolls and others, with their taking St. Iago, Sancto Domingo, Carthagena and St. Augustin. With the last voyage in which he died. London, Printed by John Willis and Jos. Boddington [17– –?]
1 p.ℓ., 162 p. 15 cm.

NL 0354881 CU RPJCB

The life and dangerous voyages of Sir Francis Drake, with the surprising of Nombre de Dios, and the manner of his gaining large quantities of gold and silver. And a large account of that voyage wherein he encompassed the whole world. And the voyage which he made with Francis Knolls and others, with their taking the towns of St. Iago, Sancto Domingo, Carthagena and St. Augustin. With the last voyage in which he died. London: Printed for

H. Dean ... and sold by most booksellers of London and Westminster [171–?]
164 p. incl. front. 15ᵃ.
Signatures: A–G¹²(A₁, frontispiece; G₆ incorrectly signed G₅; G₁₁–₁₂, advertisements)
Title within double line border.
Bound in old calf.

NL 0354883 CLU-C

DA The life and dangerous voyages of Sir Francis
86.22 Drake, with the surprising of Nombre de Dios ...
D7 and a large account of that voyage wherein he
L5 encompassed the whole world ... London, Printed
Cage for H. Dean (1722?)

164 p. A–F¹², G¹⁰. 12mo. illus.
Dated 1700? in British Museum Catalogue and 1750? in Library of Congress Catalog; however, sig. A1r contains an advertisement for a book published in 1722.
Based on N. Crouch's The English hero.

NL 0354884 DFo

The life and dangerous voyages of Sir Francis Drake, with the surprising of Nombre de Dios, and the manner of his gaining large quantities of gold and silver. And a large account of that voyage wherein he encompassed the whole world. London, H. Dean (1750?)
164 p. incl. front. (port.) 14ᶜᵐ.

1. Drake, Sir Francis, 1540?–1596.

Library of Congress DA86.22.D7L7
4–25900†

NL 0354885 DLC CtY

BP520 Life and death. [n.p., Theosophical league,
.H6 n.d.].
v. 1, [4] p. 19 cm.
no. 20 Houdini pamphlets: theosophy, v. 1, no.
Houdini 20.
Coll.

NL 0354886 DLC

Life and death; a novel
see under [Francis, Samuel Ward] 1835–1886.

Life and death: as taught in Scripture. London, E. Stock, 1868.
2 p. l., 124 p. 19ᶜᵐ.

1. Eschatology.
42–29012
Library of Congress BT821.L53

NL 0354888 DLC

The life and death, birth and burial, of O. Cromwel the late usurper, faithfully described
see [Heath, James] 1629–1664.
Flagellum: or the life and death...

Life and death in Hollywood
see under [Rosenthal, George S]

942.05 The life and death of Anne Bullen, queen consort
An7W1 of England. (London) Printed by G. Smeeton, 1820.
50 p. front. (port.)

Title in red and black with vignette.

1. Anne Boleyn, queen consort of Henry VIII, 1507–1536.

NL 0354891 IU PPL RPJCB WHi WaU MdBG RPB CtY

Life, The, and death of Captain John Porteous. (Edinburgh? 1737?) 4 p.l., (1)4–96 p. 12°.
t.-p. missing.

1. Porteous, John. 2. Riots, Gt. Br.: Scotland: Edinburgh, 1736.
3. Trials, Gt. Br., 1736. June 27, 1911.

NL 0354892 NN TxU MH CtY NjP

Life and death of Captain Thomas Stukeley
see
Captain Thomas Stukeley.

The life & death of Captain William Bedloe, one of the chief discoverers of the horrid Popish plot... London, G. Larkin, 1681. 125 p. front. 17cm.

292282B. 1. Bedloe, William, 1650– 1680. March 30, 1945

NL 0354894 NN MH MnU ICN CtY

Case The LIFE and death of Charles the First, king
F of Great Britain, France and Ireland: containing
4552 an account of his sufferings; his tryal, sentence,
.506 and dying words on the scaffold; and his
farewel and advice to his children, and the whole
nation... London, Printed by J. Bradford (16– –?)
16 p. 20cm.

Binder's title: Charles the First &c.
Illustrated t.-p. (port.)
Armorial bookplate of John Trotter Brockett.

NL 0354895 ICN

The life and death of Cock Robin
see under Cock Robin.

VOLUME 332

The life and death of Cormac the skald
    see under   Kormaks saga.

PN2598
G3
L5

The Life and death of David Garrick, esq.;
the celebrated English Roscius. Giving an
account of his figure, face, voice, and education. His great powers both in tragedy
and comedy are considered, and Messrs. Alleyn, Mohun, Hart, Nokes, Leigh, Betterton,
Wilks, Cibber, and Barry, compared with Mr.
Garrick. Also Mr. Garrick's celebrated
speech on his retiring from the stage in 1776.
The procession and ceremony at his funeral,
substance of his will, account of the jubilee at Stratford upon Avon, with part of the
ode and songs on that occasion; his best
prologues, epilogues, bon mots, repartees,
etc. To which   is added, the life of

Edward Alleyn, the celebrated comedian in the
reigns of Queen Elizabeth and James the First,
founder of Dulwich College, and who was called
the Roscius of his time. Also a curious anec-
dote of Alleyn, Shakespeare, and Ben Jonson.
By an old comedian. London, Printed and sold
by J. Pridden ₍etc.₎ 1779.
    2 p.₍., 64 p. 19 cm.

    Imperfect copy: p.9-16 wanting.

NL 0354899   CU-A NIC MH CSmH

The life and death of Dr. Martin Luther
    see under   [Hayne, Thomas] 1582-1645.

Life and death of Edward, Prince of Wales.
(Harleian Misc., v. 8, p. 163-178).

NL 0354901   MnHi

E
5
J 719

The LIFE and death of Ernest Jones, the
Chartist reformer: a memoir…   Manchester,Hey-
wood₍1869?₎
    14p. (with Davies, D.P. A short sketch
of the life and labours of Ernest Jones… 1857)

    Manuscript notation on title-page: Issued
January 27, 1869.

NL 0354902   ICN

The life and death of Fair Rosamond
    see under   Fair Rosamond.

FILM
FP
1115

The Life and death of Gamaliell Ratsey,a famous
theefe of England,executed at Bedford the 26.
of March last past,1605. ₍London, Printed for
J.Trundle, 1605₎
    Caption title.
    Title page lacking? Manuscript t.p.,by former
owner,prefixed in original copy in Bodleian
Library.
    Short-title catalogue no.20753 (carton 1115)

    1.Ratsey,Gamaliel,d.1605.

NL 0354904   MiU NNC ViU

PR
1121
.C69
v.3

The life and death of Gamaliel Ratsey,a famous
thief of England. Executed at Bedford the 26
of March last past. 1605. ₍Reprinted,
London, 1866₎
    ii p.,reprint: ₍2₎,44 p.   21 cm. (In
Collier,J.P.,ed. Illustrations of old English
literature. London,1866. v.3)
    11 p. (editor's Introd.) follow the t.p.
which is part of the reprint.
    "Ratseys repentance,which he wrote with his
owne hand when hee was in New-gate" ₍in verse₎:
p.₍35₎-44.
    1.Ratsey,Gamaliel,d.1605.   I.Collier,John
Payne,1789-   1883,ed.

NL 0354905   MiU OU

… The life and death of Gamaliel Ratsey, a famous thief,
of England, executed at Bedford the 26th of March last past.
1605. ₍London₎ Pub. for the Shakespeare association by H.
Milford,Oxford university press,1935.
    xii p., 1 l., facsims. (₍44₎ p.; 2 p. l., ₍43₎ p.) 23ᶜᵐ. (Shakespeare asso-
ciation. Facsimiles. no. 10)
    Introduction signed: S. H. Atkins.
    Facsimiles of two pamphlets published shortly after Ratsey's death
in 1605. "The life and death of Gamaliel Ratsey" is reproduced from
the original copy now in the Bodleian library and "Ratseis ghost" from
the copy in the John Rylands library, Manchester.
    1. Ratsey, Gamaliel, d. 1605.   I. Atkins, S. H., ed.   II. Title: Ratseis
ghost.
                                                    35—17955
    Library of Congress   HV6248.R385L5 ₍1605n₎
                                        ₍38d1₎   923.4142

FMU
CaOTP TU PU PPL ViU NN PBm OClW OU PHC FU NcD CU NIC
NL 0354906   DLC CaBVaU WaSpG KEmT OrPR ICarbS OOxM

---

*EBB65H
v.1

The life and death of George of Oxford: to
a pleasant new tune, called, Poor Georgy.
[London] Printed for P.Brooksby in West-
smithfield.[ca.1683]
    broadside. 2 illus. 21x32cm.
    Crawford 118.
    Includes also George's confession.
    No.143 in a two volume set from the Huth
collection (lot 433) lettered on spine: Black
letter broadside ballads …

NL 0354907   MH

STC
11090

The life and death of Griffin Flood informer…
Wherein is…declared the murther of John Chipper-
ford…for which…Griffin Flood was pressed to
death the 18. day of January last past. London,
Printed for I. T., 1623.

    A-C⁴ (A1, probably blank, lacking; A2, title-
page, in facsimile) 4to.

NL 0354908   DFo

The Life And Death Of Hector. One, and the
first of the most Puissant, Valiant, and Renowned Monarches of the world, called the
Nyne worthies
    see under   Lydgate, John, 1370?-1451?

The │life and death of…Henrietta Maria
     de Bourbon.
     London, for S. Speed 1669. 12mo.

     Purdy copy

NL 0354910   MWiW-C

Rare Book
Room
By7A
685L

The life & death of Henrietta Maria de
Bourbon, queen to that blessed King & Martyr
Charles I. mother to … K. Charles II … London,
Printed for Dorman Newman at the Kings Armes in the
Poultrey, 1685.
    4p. l., 108, [6]p₍ front₎ 14cm.
    Signatures: [A]¹ B-F¹².
    Frontispiece-portrait of Henrietta Maria
and Charles I.
    "Books printed for Samuel Speed bookseller":
p. [109]-114.
    Imperfect: front-   ispiece bled.

NL 0354911   CtY MnU

The life and death of Henrietta Maria de Bourbon,
queen to that blessed king and martyr, Charles I., mother
to His late glorious Majesty of happy memory, K. Charles
II., and to our present most gracious soveraign, James II.
… London, Printed for D. Newman, 1685; Re-printed
and sold by G. Smeeton, 1820.
    2 p. l., 41 p. front. (port.) 20½ x 16½ᶜᵐ. (In Smeeton, George … His-
torical and biographical tracts. Westminster, 1820. v. 1 [no. 8])

    Subject entries: Henrietta Maria, queen consort of Charles I, king of Eng-
land, 1609-1669.
                                                    2-23813

    Library of Congress, no.   DA385.S974.

NL 0354912   DLC MB PPL MiU NIC ViU

The life and death of Isabella Turnbull and Ann
Wade
    see under   [Wilson, Samuel].

The life and death of Jack Sheppard; a drama…
    see under   [Greenwood, Thomas Longdon]
1806-1879.

Life and death of Jack Straw
    see
Jack Straw.

The life and death of James A. Garfield from
the tow path to the White House
    see under   [Ogilvie, John Stuart] 1843-
1910.

The life and death of James Arminius and Simon
Episcopius
    see under   Bertius, Petrus, 1565-1629.

923.4173
B635L

The life and death of James L. Blair, original
general counsel of the Louisiana purchase
exposition. A resume of the great exposure
which startled the entire country. St. Louis,
Allied printing, Trades union label council
[1904]
    128 p. plates, ports., facsim. 17cm.

NL 0354918   NcD

VOLUME 332

The life and death of Jane Shore; containing the whole account of her amorous intrigues with King Edward the IVth, and the Lord Hastings: her penitence, punishment and poverty. To which are added, other amours of that king and his courtiers; with several antient love poems, written by the wits of those times. Also an heroical epistle from King Edward IV. to Jane Shore, with her answer. London: Printed and are to be sold by J. Roberts ... 1714.
1 p.l.,24 p.   22ᶜᵐ.

First edition.
Signatures: 1 leaf unsigned, B-D⁴.
"An heroical epistle from King Edward IV. to Jane Shore, alter'd from Drayton", p.17-24.
Bound in half maroon morocco.

NL 0354920   CLU-C CSmH CtY

The life and death of Jane Shore.
The life and death of Mrs. Jane Shore, concubine to Edward IV. [London,1750?]
24p. 17cm.

By28
Sh784
750*l*

NL 0354921   CtY OCl

The life and death of Jane Shore, concubine to Edward IVth. York, Printed and sold by J. Kendrew [179-?]
24 p. 16cm.

Rare
PR
1187
G23

No. 33 in vol. lettered: Chap books.

1. Chap books. 2. Shore, Jane, d. 1527?

NL 0354922   NIC

Life and death of Jay Gould and how he made his millions. New York, Ogilvie [1892]

208 p.   illus. (The peerless series, 65)
Microfilm, positive, of Harvard College Library copy

NL 0354923   MH

Life, The, and death of Jennie Wren. Illustrated . . . by Harrison Weir.
— [Lowell. Baker. 1850.] (24) pp. Plates. [Pleasure books for young children.] 17½ cm.
The title on the cover is: Death of Jenny Wren.
Appended is: The frog who would a-wooing go.
Bound with the original paper covers.

N2943 — S.r. — Weir, Harrison Wi. ...n, illus., 1824-1906. — Frog, The, who would a-wooing go.

NL 0354924   MB RPB

The life and death of Jenny Wren. Illustrated with drawings by Harrison Wier. And The story of a frog who whoud a wooing go. New York, Elton & co. [186-?]

"Pleasure books for children."

NL 0354925   MH ICU MiDW

The life and death of John Atherton lord bishop of Waterford and Lysmore within the kingdome of Ireland, borne neare Bridgwater in Somersetshire. Who for incest, buggery, and many other enormous crimes, after having lived a vicious life, dyed a shamefull death and was on the fifth of December last past, hanged on the gallows greene at Dublin ... London Printed, 1641.
[8] p. illus. 18½x14½ᶜᵐ.

Signature: A⁴.
In verse.
Bound in old vellum.

NL 0354927   CLU-C InU ICN NjP CtY NcD

The life and death of Jonathan Wild...
see Defoe, Daniel, 1661?-1731.
The life of Jonathan Wild.

The life and death of Judas Iscariot, or The lost and undone Son of Perdition. Glasgow, Printed for the booksellers [18--? repr.1877]
24 p. 19cm. (John Cheap, the chapman's, library [v.2, no.19])

"Ascension of Our Lord and Saviour Jesus Christ": p.19-24.
Published also under title: The lost and undone Son of Perdition; or The life and death of Judas Iscariot.
1. Judas Iscariot. 2. Jesus Christ - Ascension

NL 0354929   OCU OCl NN

The life and death of King Charles the Martyr, parallel'd with our Saviour in all his sufferings. Who was murdered (before his own palace at Whitehall) the 30th of Jan. 1648. With some observations upon his cruel and bloudy persecutors. ... London, n.p., printed in the year, 1649.
6 p. 9cm. (Bound with other 17th century pamphlets.)

1. Charles I, king of Great Britain, 1600-1649. I. Title.

NL 0354930   NcD

The life and death of King James V. of Scotland. From the French, printed at Paris, 1612. In which is the beginning of the reformation in that kingdom: an account of the sufferings of the renowned Lady Jean Douglas, &c. II. The navigation of that king round Scotland, the Orkney and western isles, in which is the distances of the havens; the dangers, and how to avoid them; the soundings, courses, the times of full sea, and the courses of the tides, &c. from the mouth of the Humber to Carlisle.   London, Printed for W. Taylor, 1710;

Edinburgh, Re-printed for D. Webster, 1819.
xxiv, [25]-100 p. 20 cm. [Bound with Webster, David. A collection of rare and curious tracts on witchcraft and the second sight... 1820].
1. James V, king of Scotland, 1512-1542.

NL 0354932   CU

Life, The, and death of King James the Fifth of Scotland; in which is the beginning of the Reformation in that kingdom: an account of the sufferings of the renowned Lady Jean Douglas, &c. From the French, printed at Paris, 1612.   Glasgow: J. Wylie & Co., 1819. 81-164 p. nar. 12°. (Miscellanea Scotica. v. 4.)

1. James V., king of Scotland.   2. Reformation, Gt. Br.: Scotland.
3. Scotland.—History, 1513-42.
January 22, 1913.

NL 0354933   NN

The life and death of King James the First of Scotland
see under   Stevenson, Joseph, 1806-1895.

Drama   The life and death of King John.
PR3291   [No imprint, 1740?]
A1L5
80p. 18cm.

1. John, king of England, 1167?-1216.—Drama.

NL 0354935   NBuG

The life and death of King John. [n.p., 179-?]
2 p. l., [9]-80 p. 17 1/2cm. [With Don Juan ... Boston, 1795.]

NL 0354936   MB

DA412   The life and death of King Richard the second,
.A1   who was deposed of his crown, by reason of his
no.733   not regarding the councell of the sage and wise
Rare bk   of his kingdom, but followed the advice of of
room   wicked and lewd councell, and sought as farre as
in him lay, to deprive many good English subjects of their lives and estates, who stood wholly for the good of the commonalty; but at a Parliament holden, his counsellors were all called, whereof some fled, others received condigne punishment according to the   law. Published by a well-

wisher to the Common-wealth, being worthy the observation of all men in these times of distractions. London, Printed for G. Tomlinson, and T. Watson, 1642.
8 p. 17½cm.
Closely trimmed.
[English tracts, 1640-1660. no.733]

1. Richard II,   king of England, 1367-1400.

NL 0354938   ICU MnU NNUT CSmH MH PU DFo

[The life and death of Lady Jane Grey, with some extracts from her writings. 12p. London, F. Collins [etc., 18-]

A chap-book.

NL 0354939   OCl DFo

... The life and death of Lady Jane Grey: with some extracts from her writings. New York, The American tract society [183-]
32 p. incl. illus., pl. 11ᶜᵐ.
At head of title: No. 8.
On cover: Series III. No. VIII.

1. Dudley, Lady Jane, known as Lady Jane Grey, 1537-1554.
I. American tract society.

Library of Congress   DA345.1.D9L5   41-37765

NL 0354940   DLC

PZ262   The life and death of Lady Jane Grey ...
.L71   Philadelphia, American Sunday school union [183-?]
183-   32 p. illus. 11cm.

NL 0354941   ICU

VOLUME 332

...The life and death of Lady Jane Grey. Bristol: J. Chilcott, 1835. 16 p. 16°. (Church of England Tract Soc. [Tract] no. 11.)

436074A. 1. Grey, Lady Jane, 1537-   1554.   February 27, 1930.

NL 0354942   NN

The life and death of Lady Jane Grey; prepared for the American Sunday school union, and revised by the Committee of publication. Philadelphia, American Sunday-school union [187-?]
35 p. incl. front., illus. 14½cm.
With this is bound: Story of Samson, the strongest man. Philadelphia [187-?]

1. Dudley, Lady Jane, known as Lady Jane Grey, 1537-1554. I. American   Sunday-school union.

NL 0354943   ViU

Witchcraft
BF
1563
T86

The life and death of Lewis Gaufredy: a priest of the Church of the Accoules in Marseilles in France, (who ... committed many most abhominable sorceries, but chiefly vpon two very faire young gentle-women ... hee was ... burnt aliue ... the last day of April, 1611. Together with the 53 articles of his confession ... Translated ... out of two French copies ... London, Printed by T. C. for R. Redmer, 1612.

[34] p. 19cm.

No. 11 in vol. lettered: Tracts of witches.

1. Witchcraft. 2. Gaufrédy, Louis, 1562-1611.

NL 0354945   NIC DFo

FILM

The life and death of Lewis Gaufredy: a priest of the Church of the Accoules in Marceilles in France, (who after hee had giuen himselfe soule and bodie to the Diuell) committed many most abhominable sorceries, but chiefly vpon two very faire young gentle-women, Mistris Magdalene of the Marish, and Mistris Victoire Corbier, whose horrible life being made manifest, hee was arraigned and condemned by the Court of Parliament of Aix in Prouince, to be burnt aliue, which was performed

the last day of Aprill. 1611. Together with the 53 articles of his confession. To which is annexed, a true discourse of a most inhumaine murther, committed by foure women witches, vpon a young gyrle, of about tenne yeares olde, who were all executed the 28. of Iune last past. Translated and faithfully collected out of two French copies, the one printed at Paris,   the other at Roane,

anno.1612. London, Printed by T.C.[reed] for R. Redmer, 1612.
Short-title catalogue no.11687 (carton 838)

1. Gaufridi, Louis, 1562-1611. 2. Witchcraft--France.

NL 0354948   MiU

The life and death of Major Clancie, the grandest cheat of this age
     see under   [Settle, Elkanah] 1648-1724.

Life and death of Miss Abby Victoria Painter, who died December 9, 1818, aged twenty-two years./ Middlebury, Vt., pr. by J.W. Copeland. 1819.
16 p. no covers, sewn, 16 mo. pcm.

NL 0354950   VtMiS NjPT

The life and death of Mr. Badman...
     see under   [Bunyan, John] 1628-1688.

STC
11728

The life and death of Mr. Edmund Geninges priest,/ crowned with martyrdome at London, the 10. day of Nouember, in the yeare M.D.XCI ... At S. Omers by Charles Boscard, An. 1614.

102p., 1l., 103-110p. illus. 19.5cm.
Engr. t.-p.
Page 63 misnumbered 36.
Dedication signed: I. W. P. [i.e. John Wilson, priest?]
The title-page and full-page engravings are by Martin Baes

NL 0354952   MH DFo CSmH

The life and death of Mr. John Bunyan ...

This work is available in this library in the Readex Microprint edition of Early American Imprints published by the American Antiquarian Society.
This collection is arranged according to the numbers in Charles Evans' American Bibliography.

NL 0354953   DLC

The | LIFE | And | Death | Of | Mr. John Rowe | Of | Crediton in Devon. | [. . (3 lines).
London | Printed for Francis Tyton at the three | Daggers in Fleetstreet. 1673. | Line border. 13.4x8cm. (21),1-4,21-127,(4)p.
Preface by Theophilus Gale.
From the library of Walter W. Law.

NL 0354954   NNUT-Mc CLU-C

Div.S.
922.342
A436L

The Life and death of Mr. Joseph Alleine [sic] ... whereunto are annexed diverse Christian letters of his, full of spiritual instructions ... and his funeral sermon, preached by Mr. Newton. [n.p.] 1671.
126, 38, 167 p. 16 cm.
Each part has separate paging; two have special t.p.: "The life and death of ... Joseph Alleine ... 1672." and "A sermon preached at the funeral of Mr. Joseph Aleine ... London, Printed and ... sold by Nevil Simmons ... 1672."
Imperfect: closely trimmed with some loss of pagination;   wormed.

1. Alleine, Joseph, 1634-1668. I. Alleine, Joseph, 1634-1668. Christian letters full of spiritual instructions. II. Newton, George, 1602-1681. A sermon preached at the funeral of Mr. Joseph Aleine.

NL 0354956   NcD

---

*EC65
A&527
W672&ca

The life and death of Mr. Joseph Alleine, late teacher of the church at Taunton, in Sommersetshire, assistant to Mr. Newton. Whereunto are annexed diverse Christian letters of his, full of spiritual instructions tending to the promoting of the power of godliness, both in persons, and families. And his funeral sermon preached by Mr. Newton.
London, Printed for Nevil Simmons, at the Princes-Arms in St. Pauls church-yard, 1672.

3p.l., 126, 144p.; 31p. 17cm.
In the second count pages 15 & 59 and in the third count 29 are misnumbered 5, 39 & 10.
Errata: verso of 3d prelim. leaf.
"Christian letters, full of spiritual instructions" by Joseph Alleine: 144p.
"A sermon preached at the funeral of Mr. Joseph Alleine, by Mr. George Newton", with separate paging   and signatures and special t.-p.   31p. at end.

NL 0354958   MH CLU-C CU CtY ICU

The life and death of Mr. Tho. Wilson...
     see under   [Swinnocke, George] 1627-1673.

The life and death of Mr. Vavasor Powell...
     see under   [Bagshaw, Edward] 1629-1671, attributed author.

The life and death of Mrs. Jane Shore
     see   The life and death of Jane Shore.

Mhc8
1680
L62

The life and death of Mrs. Margaret Andrews,/ the only child of Sir Henry Andrews, baronet, and the Lady Elizabeth his wife, of Lathbury, in the county of Bucks, who died May 4th 1680, in the 14th year of her age ... London, N. Ponder, 1680.
12p.l., 102p. 14cm.

NL 0354962   CtY ICN

...The life and death of Mrs. Maria Bickford,/ a beautiful female, who was inhumanly murdered, in the moral and religious city of Boston, on the night of the 27th of October, 1845, by Albert J. Tirrell, her paramour, arrested on board the ship Sultana, off New Orleans, December 6th. By a clergyman, of Brunswick, Me. 2d ed., rev. Boston, 1845.

NL 0354963   OU

The life and death of moderation
     see   [Brathwaite, Richard] 1588?-1673.
The trimmer: or, The life and death...

The life and death of Monsieur Claude
     see under   [Ladevèze, Abel Rodolphe de]

The Life and Death of Mother Shipton
     see under   Head, Richard, 1637?-1686?

VOLUME 332

The life and death of Old Father Janus, the vile author of the late wicked Courant.

This work is available in this library in the Readex Microprint edition of Early American Imprints published by the American Antiquarian Society.
This collection is arranged according to the numbers in Charles Evans' American Bibliography.

NL 0354967   DLC

The life and death of Old Father Janus, the vile author of the late wicked Courant. A satyr. ₁Boston: Printed and sold by J. Franklin. 1726₁   7 p.   19½cm.

Photostatic reproduction.
Evans 2758.
Caption-title and colophon.
"'Old Father Janus' is the signature of a club who ₁sic₁ contributed to the New England Courant." — *Sabin 41003.*

111973B. 1. Satire, American.   WILBERFORCE EAMES COLL.
papers—U. S.—Mass.—Boston—New   2. Poetry, American. 3. News-
1697-1735. II. Title: Old Father   Engl₁a₁n₁d₁, Courant. I. Franklin, James,
N. Y. P. L.   Janus, The life and death of.
    July 22, 1941.

NL 0354968   NN MH MHi

The life and death of Old Father Janus, the vile author of the late wicked Courant. A satyr. ₁Colophon: Boston: Printed and sold by J. Franklin in Union-street. MDCCXXVI₁ ₁Boston, 1941₁

facsim.: 7 p. 21¼ᶜᵐ. ₁Photostat Americana. Second series ... Photostated at the Massachusetts historical society. No. 130₁

In verse.
Old Father Janus is the signature of a club which contributed to the New England courant, published by James Franklin. *cf.* Sabin, Bibl. amer., v. 10, p. 334.
One of 14 copies from the original in the Massachusetts historical society, October, 1941.
    1. The New England courant. I. Franklin, James, 1697-1735.
    II. Title: Old Father   Janus.
    42-11757
Library of Congress   PS700.A1L47 1726 a
    811.1

NL 0354969   DLC ViW RPJCB NcD MiU ViU

The life and death of Philip Herbert, the late infamous knight of Barkshire, once earle of Pembrock Moungeomerie, &c. who departed from this life to another January 23, 1649. Having, by a degenerate basenesse, betrayed his nobilitie; and entered himselfe a commoner, amongst the vere Scum of the Kingdom. Likewise a discourse with Charon in his voyage to Hell. With his arraignment, tryall and condemnation, before the three judges, AEacus, Minos and Raddamanthus. Also the entertainment and welcome made by his brethren, Pym, Dorslaus, Raynsborough, &c. with an ample testimonie

of their rejoycing at his Lordships arival. [London?] Printed in the first yeere of Phil. Harbert's infernall captivity, and (I hope) the last of State-Tyranny, [1650?]
    small 4 to. A, 4 ll.   Unbound.
    The Britwell copy, sale March 1923, no. 418.

NL 0354971   CSmH

The life and death of Pierce Gaveston, Earl of Cornwal grand favorite and prime minister to that unfortunate prince, Edward II. King of England, with political remarks, by way of caution to all crowned heads and evil ministers. By a true patriot.   London, G. Bickham, jun., 1740.
    1 p.l., viii, 9-43 p., 1 pl.   12°.

NL 0354972   NN MtU

The life and death of Queene Elizabeth, from the wombe to the tombe, from her birth to her buriall... Written in heroicall verse.   London, 1639.

NL 0354973   CSmH PU

Case
Y   The life and death of Queene Eliza-
17935   beth, from the wombe to the tombe, from
.51   her birth to her buriall... Written in
    heroicall verse.   London, 1639.

    Photostat reproduction (positive)
    Original in the Henry E.Huntington li-
brary.

NL 0354974   ICN PU CSmH

FILM   The life and death of Queene Elizabeth,from
    the wombe to the tombe,from her birth to her
    buriall. The many and mighty dangers,and mira-
    culous deliverances of the all-beloved,admired,
    and renowned Queene Elizabeth,of England,&c.
    Written in heroicall verse. London, Printed
    by I.Okes, 1639.
    Part of the text is in prose.
    University Microfilms no.20679 (carton 770)
    Short-title catalogue no.7587.

    1.Elizabeth,Queen   of England,1533-1603--
Poetry.

NL 0354975   MiU

The life and death of Ralph Wallis the cobler of Glocester: together with some inquiring into the mystery of conventicleism. London, Printed by E. Okes, for W. Whitwood, 1670.

    43 p. 20cm. ₁Stuart tracts. v.48, no.1₁

    1. Wallis, Ralph, d.1669. 2. Gt. Brit. History. 1670.

NL 0354976   MnU CtY NNUT-Mc MH

PZ163
.C95L7   Life and death of rich Mrs. Duck, a notorious
186-   glutton. Illustrated by Cruikshank. London, Read
    ₁186-?₁
    cover-title, 8 p. col. illus.

NL 0354977   ICU NN MH

The life and death of Robin Hood, complete in twenty-four songs
    see under   Robin Hood.

The life and death of Robin Hood, the renowned out-law ...
    see under   Robin Hood.

The life and death of Rosamond
    see under   Fair Rosamond. [Supplement]

The life and death of Sam, in Virginia
    see under   [Gardner]

The life and death of Sir Henry Vane, 1662
    see under   Sikes, George.

The life and death of Sir Hugh of the Grime.
*EBB65   [London] Printed for P.Brooksby,at the
    Golden-Ball,in West-smith-field,neer the
    Hospital-gate.[ca.1690]

    broadside. 1 illus. 19x32.5cm.
    Imperfect: top edge cropped, affecting one
line; mounted.

NL 0354983   MH

The life & death of Sir John Falstaff
    see under   [Shakespeare, William] 1564-1616.

The life and death of Sir Phillip Sidney, late Lord gouernour of Flvshing
    see under   [Phillips, John] fl. 1570-1591.

LIFE, The, and death of Sir Richard Whittington.
    N. p. N. d. 36 pp. Sm. 8°.

NL 0354986   MB

The life and death of Sr. Thomas Moore, who was lord chancelor of England to King Henry the Eighth
    see under   [More, Cresacre] 1572-1649.

The life & death of Socrates. London ₁etc.₁ J. M. Dent & sons, ltd.; New York, E. P. Dutton & co., 1923.
    ix, 178, ₁1₁ p. front. (port.) 16ᶜᵐ. (*Half-title:* The bedside series)

    CONTENTS.—Preface.—Introduction by George Grote.—Passages from the "Memorabilia" by Xenophon.—The trial and death of Socrates: Alcibiades' praise; The trial of Socrates from Plato's "Phaedo"; The death of Socrates from Plato's "Phaedo"; The message of Socrates from Plato's "Crito".

    1. Socrates. I. Xenophon. II. Plato.

Washington, D. C.   Public Library   W 23-13

NL 0354988   DWP CaBViP PSt NSyU

Life and death of Stephen Decatur, who fell in a duel with James Barron, March 22, 1820. Phila. ₁L1820?₁
    24 p.

NL 0354989   PHi PPL

VOLUME 332

Case
B
5
.M 35796
The LIFE & death of Stephen Marshall... / Written by the way of letter to a friend... London, 1680.
[6], 30p., 19cm.

Published also the same year with title: The Godly man's legacy to the saints upon earth. STC II L 2011.

NL 0354990　　ICN MH MnU CSmH MWA

BX9339
.A6L5
1672
The Life & death of that excellent minister of Christ, Mr. Joseph Alleine. London, Printed by J. Darby for N. Simons, 1672.

143 (i. e. 127) p. 17 cm.

Consists of articles written by Theodosia Alleine and others, with an introd. by Richard Baxter.
With this are bound, as issued: Alleine, Joseph. Christian letters ... [London, 1672 and Newton, George. A sermon preached at the funeral of Joseph Alleine. London, 1672.

1. Alleine, Joseph, 1634-1668.　I. Alleine, Theodosia.　II. Baxter, Richard, 1615-1691.
BX9339.A6L5　1672　　　　　　　48-34385*

NL 0354991　　DLC IU NjR CtY

---

x B
A423l
1673
The life & death of that excellent minister of Christ Mr. Joseph Alleine. London, Printed by J. Darby for N. Simmons, 1673.
127p. 17cm.

Consists of articles written by Theodosia Alleine and others, with an introd. by Richard Baxter.
Bound with Alleine, Joseph. Christian letters. London, 1673, and Newton, George. A sermon preached at the funeral of Mr. Joseph Alleine. London, 1673.

NL 0354992　　IU TxDaM PPPrHi MH

BX
5207
A4L5
The life and death of that excellent minister of Christ, Mr. Joseph Allein ... London, N. Simmons and T. Sawbridge, 1677.
301 [i. e. 311] p. 17cm.

CONTENTS.--The life and death ... [by various authors]--Christian letters ... [by Joseph Alleine]--A sermon preached at the funeral of Mr. Joseph Allein, by George Newton.

1. Alleine, Joseph, 1634-1668.　I. Alleine, Joseph, 1634-1668. Christian letters.　II. Newton, George, 1602-1681.

NL 0354993　　CBBD NNG MnU DFo

BX5207
.A4B28
The life & death of that excellent minister of Christ, Mr. Joseph Alleine. Late teacher of the church of Taunton in Somerset-shire ... London, Printed by J. Darby, for N. Simons [etc.] 1693.
127 p. 16½ᶜᵐ.
Partly written by Mrs. Theodosia Alleine. cf. p. [4]

1. Alleine, Joseph, 1634-1668.

NL 0354994　　ICU

The life and death of that holy and reverend man of God, Mr. Thomas Cawton
see under Cawton, Thomas, 1637-1677.

The life and death of that judicious divine
see under [Durham, William] 1611-1684.

The life and death of that renowned John Fisher
see under [Hall, Richard] 1537-1604.

The life and death of that reverend divine, and excellent historian, Doctor Thomas Fuller
see under [Fell, John] bp. of Oxford, 1625-1686.

The life and death of the B. Virgin [Mary]
see under [Fleetwood, William] bp. of Ely, 1656-1723.

---

*pEB7
A100
734l
The life and death of the Duke of Berwick. Newcastle: Printed and sold by John White. [1734?]

broadside. 2 illus. 24.5x35cm.
In verse.

NL 0355000　　MH

The LIFE and death of the eminently learned pious and painful minister of the Gospel, Dr. Samuel Winter, sometime provost of Trinity Colledge near Dublin in Ireland. Together with some rare examples of God's gracious answer to his prayers, upon several occasions. London, printed for Tho. Parkhurst, 1671.

24º. pp. (18), 75.
"The epistle to the reader" is signed J.W., probably John Weaver.
Imperfect: several lines of text on pp. 50-54 lined out with ink.

NL 0355001　　MH

The life and death of the English rogue; or, His last legacy to the world
see under [Head, Richard] 1637?-1686?

The life and death of the famous Thomas Stukely ...
see under [Johnson, Richard] 1573-1659?

The life and death of the godly man
see under [Bragge, Robert] 1622-1704.

The life and death of the late Rev. Joseph Alleine, of Taunton, Somersetshire. Written by his widow and other persons. London: L. B. Seeley & Son, print. print., 1826. iv, 220 pp. 32°.

NL 0355005　　NN PPAmS

The life and death of the merry deuill of Edmonton ...
see under [Brewer, Thomas] fl. 1624.

The life and death of the most blessed among women the Virgin Mary...
see under Taylor, John, 1580-1653.

The life and death of the notorius highway man, now hanging in chains at Hampstead
see [Head, Richard] 1637?-1686?
Jackson's recantation, or, The life and death of the notorious highway-man...

The life and death of the pipe of Kilbarchan
see under [Sempill, Robert] 1595-1668.

The life and death of the renowned John Fisher
see under Hall, Richard, 1537-1604.

Life and death of the Rev. Joseph Alleine... Written by the Rev. Richard Baxter, his widow, Mrs. Theodosia Alleine, and other persons. To which are added, his Christian letters, full of spiritual instructions... Reprinted from the corrected edition of 1815; with a recommendatory preface by Alexander Duff... Edinburgh: J. Lindsay & co. [etc., etc.] 1838. xxi, 296 p. 18cm.

"Christian letters," p. [135]-296.

1. Letters, English. 2. Christian life. I. Baxter, Richard, 1615-1691. II. Alleine, Theodosia (Alleine).
　　　　　　　　　　　　　　　Card revised
　　　　　　　　　　　　　　　February 29, 1940

NL 0355011　　NN

Life and death of the Rev. Joseph Alleine ... Written by Richard Baxter, his widow, Theodosia Alleine, and other persons. To which are added his Christian letters, full of spiritual instructions, tending to the promoting of the power of godliness both in persons and families. With a Recommendatory preface by Alexander Duff ... From the last Edinburgh ed. New York, R. Carter, 1840.
275 p. 20 cm.
Pub. in 1672 under title: The life & death of that excellent minister of Christ, Mr. Joseph Alleine.
1. Alleine, Joseph, 1634-1668.　I. Baxter, Richard, 1615-1691. II. Alleine, Theodosia.
BX9339.A6L5 1840　　922.542　　37-12137 rev*

NL 0355012　　DLC PPULC NNUT PPPrHi PPLT ICU

The life and death of Thomas Walsh
see under [Morgan, James]

The life and death of Thomas Woolsey, cardinal
see under [Cavendish, George] 1500-1561?

The LIFE and death of Tom Careless, to which is added the history of Will Worth and Nancy Wilmot; [poem] London, printed by J. Evans, [17-?]

pp. 8.

NL 0355015　　MH

VOLUME 332

The life and death of Tom Thumb. Ornamented with cuts
    see under   Tom Thumb.

The life and death of Tom Thumb the Great
    see   [Fielding, Henry] 1707-1754.
    The tragedy of tragedies; or, The life and death...

The **life** and death of two young ladies, contrasted. By a lady. To which is added, A short account of the life and death of R..... A...... late of Talbot, Maryland: also, A soliloquy on death, and two interesting letters. By the Rev. J. Fletcher ... Philadelphia: Printed for and sold by Daniel Danovan. 1806.
    53 p. 17½ᵐ.

    1. Death.   I. A lady.   II. Fletcher, John William, 1729-1785.

Library of Congress   BT825.L52
                                 39-10927

NL 0355018   DLC TxDaM

The **life** and death of two young ladies, contrasted, by a lady. To which are added, A short account of the life and death of R——A—— late of Talbot, Maryland: also, A soliloquy on death, and two interesting letters, by the Rev. J. Fletcher... Philadelphia: Printed by J. M. Sanderson, 1816. 60 p. 12°.

1. Death.—Preparation for.   2. Fletcher, J.
                                     January 27, 1921.

NL 0355019   NN ICN PHi MWA

BT 825 The **Life** and death of two young ladies, contrast-
L5   ed. By a lady. To which is added, A short
    account of the life and death of R—— A——,
    late of Talbot, Maryland ... New-York, N.
    Bangs and T. Mason, for the Methodist Episcopal
    Church, 1824.
    1 p. l., [5]-70 p. 14 cm.

NL 0355020   OU NcD

236.1   The life and death of two young ladies, con-
L626   trasted. By a lady. To which is added, A
1826   short account of the life and death of
    R—— A——, late of Talbot, Maryland. New
    York, Published by N. Bangs and J. Emory for
    the Methodist Episcopal Church, 1826.
    71p. 15cm.

NL 0355021   TxU

PZ114   The life and death of two young ladies, con-
.S94   trasted. [New York, J. Emory and B. Waugh, 1828?]
no.8   48 p.
    [Sunday School biography. 1828-1829. no.8]

NL 0355022   ICU

R.Rm.
BY1542 The life and death of two young ladies con-
.H63S7   trasted. [New York, B. Waugh and T. Mason,
    1836]
    48 p. 14 cm.

    Bound with: Religious experience of ...
    Eliza Higgins by Joshua Soule.

    1. Death of children.

NL 0355023   IEG

The life and death of William Bedloe
    see   The life & death of Captain
William Bedloe.

The life and death of William Lawd.
    see under   Waller, Edmund, 1606-1687,
supposed author.

The life and death of William Long Beard...
    see under   Lodge, Thomas, 1558-1625.

Life & death offered to the choice of the sons and
    daughters of Adam
    see under   Carter, R., minister, "Upton
cum Chalveii", Bucks. [Supplement]

Life and death; or, How to secure health and avoid sickness, presented by the   life insurance co. New York, A. Stoddart, [1868.
    cover-title, 23, [1] p. 21½ᵐ.
    "The blank pages of this book are designed to be filled by the companies using the same with matters pertaining to life insurance."—p. [4] of cover.

    1. Hygiene.   CA 10-3504 Unrev'd

Library of Congress   RA776.L72

NL 0355028   DLC

The life and defence of the conduct and principles of
    Edmund Bonner
    see under   Townsend, George, 1788-1857.

The life and depredations of David Hoggart
    see under   Hoggart, David, 1800-1821.

B
B9231   The life and deserved fall of George Villiers,
    duke of Buckingham, (prime minister to King James
    and King Charles I) ... To which is added, an es-
    say on the rights of British subjects in electing
    members of Parliament; and the fatal consequences
    that have attended those princes who have invaded
    them. London, Printed for J. Cox, 1735.
    112, 64p. front.(port.)

    Caption title for first part: The fate of fa-
    vourites; for the second part: The rights of the

Continued in next column

Continued from preceding column

subject in electing their representatives. The two parts were published separately in 1734 under these titles.
    1. Buckingham, George Villiers, 1st duke of, 1592-1628. 2. Representative government and representation. I. Title: Fate of favourites. II. Title: The rights of British subjects in electing members of Parliament. III. Title: The rights of the subjects in   electing their representatives.

NL 0355032   IU

Life and doctrine of Saint Catherine of Genoa
    see under   Caterina da Genova, Saint, 1447-1510.

The **life** and dreadful sufferings of Captain James Wilson, in various parts of the globe, including a faithful narrative of every circumstance during the voyage to the South Sea Islands, in the missionary ship Duff, for the propagation of the Gospel, with an authentic and interesting account of the sufferings and calamities of the missionaries, from the year 1797 to the present period. Portsea, G. A. Stephens, 1810.
    415p. fold.front.

NL 0355034   OCl

Life and dreams, poems
    see under   [Poucher, Emma E   ]

The life and dying confessions of James
    Hamilton
    see under   Hamilton, James, 1791-1818.

The life and dying testimony of Abram Combe in
    favour of Robt. Owen's new views of man and
    society
    see under   [Combe, George] 1788-1858.

G535 (The) **life** and dying words of Capt. Nicholas
L5   Wingfield, and Capt. Adams Hyde, who was
    executed at Execution-dock, on Wednesday
    the twenty-eighth of March, 1759. For
    piracy on the high-sea. London, Printed
    by T. Bailey [1759?]

    16p. 17½cm. in 20½cm.

    1. Wingfield, Nicholas.   2. Hyde, Adams.
    3. Pirates.

NL 0355038   NBuG

The life and eccentricities of L.S. Pilkington
    alias Jack Hawley ... Doncaster, E. Dale
    [1876]
    46 p. 12°.

NL 0355039   PHi

VOLUME 332

Life, The, and eccentricities of the late Dr. Monsey, F.R.S., physician
to the Royal Hospital at Chelsea. / With curious anecdotes of
persons of rank and consequence.
— London. Hughes. 1804. x, 108 pp. Vignette. 14 cm., in 6s.

M4306 —) Monsey, Messenger, 1693-1788.

NL 0355040   MB CSmH

The life and end of Thomas Awfeeld a seminary
preest and Thomas Webley a dyers seruant in
London, beeing both traitours who were condemned
as fellons for bringing seditious books into this
realme and dispersing of the same, among their
fauourers: for which they were executed at
Tibourne the 6.day of this monthe of Iuly.1585.
London, Imprinted for T.Nelson [1585]
   Short-title catalogue no.997 (carton 949)

   1.Awfeeld,Thomas,d.1585. 2.Webley,Thomas,
d.1585.

NL 0355041   MiU

The life and entertaining adventures of Mr.
Cleveland, natural son of Oliver Cromwell,
written by himself
      see under [Prévost, Antoine François,
called Prévost d'Exiles] 1697-1763.

The life and epistles of St. Paul
      see under [Bacon, Rev. Leonard] 1802-1881.

The life and errors of my uncle, and the amours
of my aunt
      see [Disraeli, Isaac] 1766-1848.
      Flim-flams! or, The life ...

Life and eternity
      see under [Leeser, Isaac] 1806-1868.

The life and eulogy of Daniel Webster
      see under [Clark, Lewis Gaylord]
1808-1873.

PZ   Life and examination of Charles Peace, charged with the
2.1   Bannercross murder. London, G. Purkess [1878]
C38   16 p. illus.

         Bound with Charles Peace. London [after 1880]
         At head of title: Police news edition.

         1. Peace, Charles Frederick, 1832-1879.

NL 0355047   CLU

Life and execution of Geo. Shaftesbury, who killed his father &
mother! and Marie Lavine, his paramour, the noted murderess.
Also, the execution of Madam Tiquet, and the trial and execution
of Prof. Webster, for the murder of Dr. Geo. Parkman!   Boston:
Pub. by Dr. H. B. Skinner, 1856.   30 p.   illus.   8°.

   Cover-title.

   1. Murder—Trials. 2. Shaftesbury,   George Lampanas, d. 1850.
3. Tiquet, Marie Angélique (Carlier),   1657-1699. 4. Webster, John
White, 1793-1850.
                                                       November 8, 1926

NL 0355048   NN N

The **life** and execution of Jack Kehoe, king of the "Mollie Maguires," together with a full account of the crimes
and executions of the other principals in that terrible organization. Fourteen Mollies hanged! Philadelphia, Pa.,
Barclay & co. [1886]
   1 p. l., 19-100 p. illus. (incl. ports.) 23½ᶜᵐ.

   1. Kehoe, John, d. 1878. 2. Molly Maguires.
                                                       17-9208
   Library of Congress   HV6452.P4 1886

NL 0355049   DLC

The life and exploits of Don Quixote, de la Mancha
      see under [Cervantes Saavedra, Miguel
de]

The life and exploits of Gen. Scott
      see under Soup [pseud.]

DA68.12   (The) life and exploits of His Grace, the Duke
W4L4   of Wellington, embracing, at one view, the
            whole military career of this illustrious
            warrior, including a complete history of the
            Peninsular war, with all the spirit-stirring
            incidents and anecdotes of that memorable
            contest.   With sixty engravings.   London,
            G. Berger [1843?]

            iv,444p.   illus.   19cm.

            Added t.-p., illus.

            1. Wellington,   Arthur Wellesley, 1st duke
            of, 1769-1852.

NL 0355052   NBuG

Rare Book
Collection
HV6248   The life and exploits of Jack Sheppard, the
.W5   notorious housebreaker, comprising his sev-
A1   eral escapes from prison, and a full account
1829   of his trial and execution. London, Printed
            and published by W.S. Johnson [n.d.]
            24 p. illus. (col.) 20 cm. (Johnson's edition)

            Bound with: The life and death of Jonathon
            Wild.

            1. Sheppard, John, 1702-1724.

NL 0355053   NcU

PR   The Life and exploits of Jack Sheppard, a
975   notorious housebreaker and footpad; giving
.52aexp   a full account of his numerous robberies: his
            escape from the New Prison; his commitment
            to Newgate; he is tried, and receives sen-
            tence of death; his wonderful escape from
            thence although loaded with irons; he is
            retaken, confined in the condemned cell, and
            chained to the floor; then removed to a
            stronger place in Newgate, called the Castle,
            from which place he escapes in the night; he
            is again taken, and secured in Newgate; after

Continued in next column

Continued from preceding column

which he is hung at Tyburn.   Derby, T.
Richardson [ca.1830?]
23 p. fold.col.front.

   1. Sheppard, Jack, 1702-1724.

NL 0355055   CLU CtY

The life and exploits of Robin Hood
      see under Robin Hood.

Life and exploits of S. Glenn Young, world-famous law
enforcement officer. Compiled by a friend and admirer from
data furnished by the hero, with the exception of the last chapter which was completed by another of the hero's intimate
friends ... Herrin, Ill., Mrs. S. Glenn Young [192-?]
   258 p., 1 l. illus. (incl. ports.) 21ᶜᵐ.

   1. Young, S. Glenn, 1886-1925. 2. Crime and criminals — Illinois —
Williamson co.
                                                       45-47870
   Library of Congress   HV7914.Y6L5

NL 0355057   DLC NNC IU

PR   The life & exploits of that extraordinary
2993   character, Sir John Falstaff, the hero of
.F2   Shakespear, and companion of Henry, prince of
L7   Wales; with an account of the numerous rob-
            beries & offences committed by them; particu-
            lars of his amorous adventures and gallant-
            ries at Windsor ... his conduct as a captain
            at the battle of Shrewsbury, between Percy
            and Hotspur; a humorous description of his
            soldiers; trial and conviction at Maidstone,
            &c. London, Printed and published by W.
            Mason [1814?]
            30 p. front.(port.) 16½ᶜᵐ.
            1.Shakespeare,Wil-   liam—Characters—
            Falstaff.

NL 0355058   MiU PU CtY MH

The **life** and exploits of ... the Duke of Wellington,
embracing ... the whole military career of this illustrious
warrior, including a complete history of the Peninsular
war. New York, J. Winchester, 1843.
   1 p. l., 64 p. 4°. (The New world. Extra ser. 4th ed.)

                                                       1-1529

NL 0355059   DLC NNC

Life and explorations of David Livingstone, L. L. D.,
complete so far as is known
      see under Roberts, John S., fl. 1868-1882.

Life and explorations of David Livingstone, the
great missionary explorer in the interior of
Africa
      see under Livingstone, David, 1813-1882.

VOLUME 332

The life and extraordinary adventures of Captain Socivizca, who was commander of a numerous body of robbers, of the race of the Morlachians ..., Containing many bloody rencounters which happened between his troops and the Turks ... To which is added a ... curious account of the manners and customs of the inhabitants of Wallachia; with a particular description of that country. The fifth edition. London: Printed and sold by T. Sabine₍a.d₎

31 p. front. 18½ᶜᵐ. (On cover: The entertainer v. 2 ₍no. 4₎)

1. Socivizca, Stan islaus, b. 1715. 2. Chapbooks. I. Ser.

NL 0355061   ViU

PR 974
.G3   The life and extraordinary adventures of Captain Socivizca commander of a numerous body of robbers, of the race of the Morlachians, commonly called Montenegrins, a people inhabiting P[...] Dominions of Venetian Dalmatia. Newcastle, M. Angus & Son, Printers.
24 p. 16 cm. [In Garret, William. A right pleasaunt and famous book of histories by William Garret. Vol. 1. no. 1].

NL 0355062   DLC

The life and extraordinary adventures of Captain Socivizca, who was commander of a numerous body of robbers, of the race of the Morlachians ... Containing many bloody rencounters which happened between his troops and the Turks ... To which is added a ... curious account of the manners and customs of the inhabitants of Wallachia; with a particular description of that country. The 2d ed. London, Printed for J. Lever ₍1778?₎

32 p. front. 23ᶜᵐ.

1. Socivizca, Stanislaus, b. 1715.

16-20227

Library of Congress   G530.S74

NL 0355063   DLC TxU

PR 974
.G 455   The life and extraordinary adventures of Captain Socivizca, Commander of a numerous body of robbers, of the race of the Morlachians, commonly called Montenegrins, a people inhabiting part of the Dominions of Venetian Dalmatia. London, Printed by T. Maiden, for Ann Lemoine. and J. Roe. 1806.
No. 5 in Chapmbooks. London, Printed for Ann Lemoine and J. Roe, by T. Maiden, 1805-1806.

NL 0355064   DLC

Life and extraordinary adventures of John H. Surratt, the conspirator. A correct account and highly interesting narrative of his doings and adventures from childhood to the present time. Philadelphia, Barclay & co. ₍ᶜ1867₎

1 p. l., 21-24, 37-40 p. pl., ports. 23ᶜᵐ.

Another edition with same t.-p. contains also "Trial of John H. Surratt, conspirator. for the murder of Abraham Lincoln", p. 43-136.

1. Surratt, John Harrison, 1844-1916.   I. Barclay and company, Philadelphia, pub.

12—3001

Library of Congress   E457.5.L71

NL 0355065   DLC NjP

Life and extraordinary adventures of John H. Surratt, the conspirator. A correct account and highly interesting narrative of his doings and adventures from childhood to the present time. Philadelphia, Barclay & co. ₍ᶜ1867₎

1 p. l., 21-24, 37-40, 43-136 p. front., plates, ports., map, plan. 24½ cm.

"Trial of John H. Surratt, conspirator, for the murder of Abraham Lincoln": p. 43-136.

1. Surratt, John Harrison, 1844-1916.

E457.5.L72   12-3002 rev
———— Copy 4. ₍With Townsend, G. A. The life, crime, and capture of John Wilkes Booth. New York, 1865. Copy 4₎
E457.5.T74   Copy 4

NL 0355066   DLC MB MiU-C NjP OClWHi

An
R974
807c
Rare
Books
Col   The life and extraordinary adventures of Lucy Amelia Gordon, who was well known, some years since, as the handsome servant maid of Grosvenor Square. A true narrative, written by herself.
Printed for and sold by J. Ker, No.90, High Holborn; by M'Gowen, 15, Church Street, Blackfriars Road. Sold also by T. Hughes, Stationers' Court; Willmott and Hill, 50, Borough; Perks, Stationer, 21, St. Martins Lane; S. Elliott, High Street, Shadwell; Barfoot, Norton Falgate: Dixon, Rochester;

T. Evans, 79, Long Lane; Howard & Evans, 42, Long Lane, West Smith-field; Kemmish, 17, King Street, Borough; Neil, No.448, Strand; and Champante & Whitrow, Jewry Street, Aldgate [n.d.] 38p. incl. front.(port.) 18cm. [With Ryder, Frances Mary. Cordelia ... London, 1807]

NL 0355068   TxU NBuU

The life and extraordinary adventures, the perils and critical escapes, of Timothy Ginnadrake.

See under

₍Fleming, Francis₎ fl. 1771.

Ib94
t815   The life and extraordinary confessions of Gibbs, the pirate, who was executed for murder at New York, on the 22nd April, 1831 ... Liverpool;Printed for James Scott, and may be had at his old book shop and news room, 54,Pool lane.1831.
18p. 15cm. [Penny histories]
"Taken from the New York journal of commerce."

NL 0355070   CtY ICN

The Life and fall of John Duke of Marlborough, from the reign of King Charles the Second, to this time: with the reasons of his being remov'd from all his offices and employments, and retiring out of England. Also the substance of the information against him in the court of exchequer, by the attorney-general, and his answer thereto, before his going out of England. London, Printed by J. Read [1712?]
12 p. 4 to. (Broadsides, pamphlets and newspapers relating to English history, 1656-1746, no. 116])

NL 0355071   InU

Life and finite individuality; two symposia. 1918
see under   Carr, Herbert Wildon, 1857-1931.

THE LIFE| AND DATE OF| CHRISTIANITIE, EN-| TREATING OF THE SA-| CRAMENT OF BAPTISME, DE-| VIDED INTO FIVE BOOKES.| Contayning the effects, the mater, the forme, the| Baptizer, and the partie Baptized: with the| reafons and vfe of all the auntient| rites and Ceremonies. |...Compofed, ₍65.09₎ gathered, and written| by O. A. ₍...ornament₎ With permiffion.| Anno M. DC. XIIII.
Colophon: A Douay, par Pierre Auroi, au Pelican d'or. Anno 1614.

A-O⁸, unsigned⁴. 8vo. 14x9cm.
Stained; wormholed.
Bookplate of Morgan Thomas; Harmsworth copy. Contemporary calf.

NL 0355074   DFo

The life and genuine character of doctor Swift, 1733
see under   Swift, Jonathan, 1667-1745.

Life and genius of Goethe
see under   [Bancroft, George] 1800-1891.

The life and gests of S. Thomas Cantilupe, bishop of Hereford
see under   [Strange, Richard] 1611-1682.

---

*Defoe
20
.715
.A1013   The life and glorious actions of His Grace James duke of Ormond: with his conduct in the campaign of 1712. London, Printed by R. Mathard, 1715.
24 p. 18cm.

1. Ormonde, James Butler, duke of, 1665-1745. 2. Spanish Succession, War of, 1701-1714.

NL 0355078   MB

The life and glorious actions of the most heroic and magnanimous Jonathan Wilde, generalissimo of the prig-forces in Great Britain and Ireland. Introduced with the most memorable passages in the lives of his ancestors, and concluding with his behaviour in Newgate... London, Printed for Whitridge, 1725

63 p. front.

NL 0355079   MH

The life and glorious actions of the Right Honourable Sir George Rook, K'. ₍London, 1707?₎ 136 p. nar. 16°.
Title-page wanting.
Half-title.

27412A. 1. Rooke, Sir George, 1650-1688-1704.   PROUDFIT COLLECTION. 1709. 2. Navy (British).—History.
February 9, 1922.

NL 0355080   NN ICN CtY InU NRU IU ICU CSmH

WILLIAM
ANDREWS
CLARK
MEMORIAL
LIBRARY   The life and glorious history of John d. and e. of Marlborough, prince of the empire, captain general of the confederate forces, &c. Containing a relation of the most important battles, sieges, and negotiations, manag'd under his auspicious conduct, both in the wars of Flanders and Ireland; with a full and particular account of the ever memorable battles of Hockstet and Schellenburg in Germany. As also his march to the Moselle in 1705. His return

to the Netherlands, and forcing the French line near Tirlemont; with other remarkable passages from his first advancement in the court of King Charles II. To this present time. The second edition. With the addition of His Grace's last glorious campaign, particularly the great and memorable battle of Ramellies. London: Printed for J. Chan- try ... 1707.

214 p.incl.front.(port.) 15ᶜᵐ.

Signatures: B⁶ (B₁, frontispiece), B-H¹², I⁵, K¹².
Book-plate of Olive Percival.
Bound in brown morocco, by Holden.

NL 0355083   CLU-C

VOLUME 332

**7
4549
.506** The LIFE anf glorious reign of Queen Elizabeth: containing her great victories by land
and sea, and her other successes against the
enemies of the Protestant religion. Likewise,
an account of Sir Francis Drake's voyage round
the world. Also, an account of the destruction
of the great fleet, call'd the Spanish armado.
With the life and death of the Earl of Essex.
London, J. Bradford, 1708.
16p. 19cm.

NL 0355084   ICN

The life and gospel experience of Mother Ann Lee...
see under [Blinn, Henry Clay] 1824-1905,
ed.

Life and habits of moths
see under [Kerlin, Harry J   ]

The life and habits of wild animals. Illustrated by designs by Joseph Wolf. Boston, D. Lothrop & co. [1877]
104 p. incl. front., plates. 1 pl. 26½ᶜᵐ.

1. Animals, Habits and behavior of.

Library of Congress   QL50.L71   4-29441

NL 0355087   DLC DSI

The life and happy death of Selina Pugh.
Rev. by the Committee of Publication of the
American Sunday-School Union. Philadelphia,
American Sunday-School Union [1835]
33 p. front. 15cm.

Bound with Schneider, Benjamin. Letters
from Asia Minor, respecting the Greeks and
Armenians. Philadelphia [1837]

I. American Sunday-School Union.

NL 0355088   FU

**W 1
LI39** LIFE and health. v. 1-3; Jan. 1896-Oct. ?
1898. New York.
3 v.
Absorbed the Home doctor in Apr. 1898
and from then until Oct. 1898 called Life
and health and home doctor.

NL 0355089   DNLM

Life and health; the national health magazine.

Oakland, Cal., Pacific press publishing co., 18
Washington, D. C., Review & herald publishing assn., 19
v. illus. 24-26ᶜᵐ. monthly.
Title varies: 18   Pacific health journal.
19   -May 1915, Life and health ...
June-Dec. 1915, Health and temperance.
Jan. 1916-   Life and health ...
Editors: 18   W. H. Maxson, M. C. Wilcox.-19   G. H. Heald.

1. Hygiene—Period.   I. Maxson, W. H., ed.   II. Wilcox, Milton
Charles, 1853-1935, ed.   II. Heald, George Henry, 1861-1934, ed.   IV.
Pacific health journal.   v. Health and temperance.

CA 7—1307 Unrev'd

Library of Congress   RA773.L6

NL 0355090   DLC OrU KU DNLM MiU FTaSU PPC

The life and heroic achievements of Sir William
Wallace, the Scottish patriot; and The life of
Robert Bruce, king of Scotland
see under   [Henry, the Minstrel] fl. 1470-
1492.

The life and heroic actions of Balbe Berton,
chevalier de Grillon [!]
see under   [Lussan, Marguerite de] 1682-
1758.

The life and history of a convict, being facts
written by himself. Containing a short narrative of the sufferings which attend the pursuit of
dishonest practices, giving a description of
the ways, customs, and usage, on board the
prison-ships, and the manner of conveying
convicts to Botany-Bay. With observations
on the effects of transportation, by the author...
London, 1814.
1 p. l., ii, [5]-53 p.   15.5 cm.

NL 0355093   CtY

The life and history of a pilgrim
see under [Wollaston, George]

The life and history of Belisarius, who conquer'd
Africa and Italy
see under [Oldmixon, John] 1673-1742.

Life and history of Cardinal Wolsey, containing a full account of
his origin, promotion to power, continuance in magnificence, and
sudden fall.   London: Knevett, Arliss, & Baker[, 1811].   72 p.
front.   16°.   (Juvenile library.)

437487A. 1. Wolsey, Thomas,   cardinal, 1475?-1530.
October 11, 1929

NL 0355096   NN CtY

**FILM
5561
PR** The life and history of George Barnwell; who,
from the highest character and credit fell to
the lowest depth ... London, Dean & Munday
[1820]
34 p. plates. On film.

Microfilm. Original in British museum.

I. Title: George Barnwell.

NL 0355097   CU

The life and history of Henry St. John,
viscount Bolingbroke, containing the whole series
of his conduct from his first entrance into Parliament. London, 1754.
port. 8°.

NL 0355098   MH

**944.03
L92W1i** The life and history of Lewis XIV. Present
king of France and Navarre. In eight parts ...
London, Printed for J. Morphew, 1709.
602, 72p.

1. Louis XIV, king of France, 1638-1715.

NL 0355099   IU OrU InU MB TxU MH MnU

The LIFE and history of Mary, Queen of Scots.
Glasgow, Published by Francis Orr & sons [1850?]
12 l. 16cm.

Weiss: Chapbooks, 442.
On t. p.: 165.
Pages incorrectly numbered, some numbers missing.
Without covers.

NL 0355100   NN MnU

**Ex
1081.
.502
.56
.1800** The life and history of Paul Jones, the English
corsair: giving an account of the extraordinary
perils, escapes, and voyages, of that bold and
determinate pirate and smuggler. Plymouth,
Printed and published by R. Bond [1800?]
30 p. illus. 18 cm.

1. Jones, John Paul, 1747-1792.

NL 0355101   NjP

The life and history of Paul Jones, the English corsair:
giving an account of the extraordinary perils, escapes, & voyages, of that bold and determinate pirate and smuggler ...
London, J. Lee [1810?]
34, [1] p. incl. fold. front. 17½ᶜᵐ.

Published also under title: The history of that bold, courageous, and
resolute seaman, Paul Jones.
"The malefactor. Written by David Service": p. [35]

1. Jones, John Paul, 1747-1792.

20—7032

Library of Congress   E207.J7L725 1810

NL 0355102   DLC

**British
Tracts
1742
L62** The life and history of Sarah, dutches of
Marlborough, containing her birth, family, and
education: her rise and progress at court for
many years past: also her courtship and marriage
with the present duke of Marlborough, and other
secret maters down to this present time, never
before publish'd. London, Printed by J. Read
[1742?]
8p. 17cm.
Title vignette (port.)

1. Marlborough, Sarah (Jennings) Churchill, duches
of, 1660-1744.

NL 0355103   CtY

The life and history of Swing, the Kent rickburner
see under Swing, Francis, pseud.

VOLUME 332

x942.07
B63Wl
The life and history of the Right Honourable Henry St. John, lord visc. Bolingbroke Containing, the whole series of his conduct from his first entrance into Parliament, to the death of Queen Anne, and from thence to the end of his life. In which the publick transactions of those times are set in a clear light and His Lordship's conduct during the negotiations of the famous Treaty of Utrecht, impartially stated. With many curious anecdotes of court intrigues and

ministerial stratagems ... Likewise some account of His Lordship's degradation, his attainder, his exile and restauration. Faithfully collected from the histories, memorials, records and annals of those times. To which is prefixed, His Lordship's effigy, curiously engraved. London, Printed for M. Cooper and C. Sympson, 1754.

104p. port. 19cm.

Closely trimmed.

1. Bolingbroke, Henry Saint-John, 1st viscount, 1678-   1751.

NL 0355107   IU DFo PPT ICN

Life and history of William O'Neal; or, The man who sold his wife. St. Louis, A. R. Fleming & Co., 1896.
55p. front. (port.)

1. O'Neal, William, 1827-

NL 0355108   TNDC NcD

The LIFE and humble confession of Richardson the informer. n.p., [1772: reprinted 18-?]

Illustr.
Broadside regarding Ebenezer Richardson, the informer, found in the library of the Historical Society of Pennsylvania at Philadelphia With additional matter by W.R. Cutter, librarian of the Woburn (Mass). Public Library. The original broadside is 13 1/2 x 8 in.

NL 0355109   MH PHi NN

The life and humorous adventures of William Grigg, of Snarlton in Suffolk
see under Grigg, William.

Life and imprisonment of Jefferson Davis
see under [Addey, Markinfield]

The Life and infamous actions of that perjur'd villain John Waller, who made his exit in the pillory ... London, W. James, 1732.

NL 0355112   CLL

The life and influence of Charles Carlton, 1821-1902
see under [Hay, Kenneth McKinley]

The life and influence of Dean Grosvenor. [1917]
see under Stires, Ernest Milmore, 1866-

The life and interesting anecdotes of Mr. Kean
see Cooke sleeps! - Kean lives. The life and interesting anecdotes of Mr. Kean ...

---

*Defoe
30
.729
.A10L2
The life and intrigues of the late celebrated Mrs. Mary Parrimore, the tall milliner of 'Change-Alley. Containing a series of uncommon adventures, no less surprising than entertaining: with an account of her writings, and a further illustration of Love upon tick: wherein the whole adventure is set in a true light, with the addition of several material particulars omitted in that pamphlet. London: Printed for A. Moore, 1729.
1 p.l., 78 p.   19.5cm.

NL 0355116   MB CSmH

The life and inventions of Thos. A. Edison. 1890
see under [Stieringer, Luther.]

Life and its aims
see under [Osborne, Elise]

Life and its Author. An Essay on Matters of Faith. In Verse. Norwich, [England].
22 p.   12°.   [In v. 461, College Pamphlets]

NL 0355119   CtY

Life and its Author. An Essay on Matters of Faith. In verse. [A later edition] Norwich, [England]
22 p.   12°.   [In College Pamphlets, v. 1721]

NL 0355120   CtY

Life and its maintenance. A symposium on biological problems of the day. London [etc.] Blackie and son, limited, 1919.
viii, 297 p. pl., 4 double maps, diagrs. 18½ᶜᵐ.
CONTENTS.—The problem of food, by W. M. Bayliss.—War bread and its constituents, by F. G. Hopkins.—Accessory food-factors (vitamines) in war-time diets, by E. M. Hume.—Alcoholic and other beverages in war-time, by A. R. Cushny.—The strategy of farming, past and future, by K. J. J. Mackenzie.—The possibilities of increased crop production, by Dr. E. J. Russell.—Grass-land and arable, by R. G. Stapledon.—Spraying problems, by A. S. Horne.—Birds and insects in relation to crops, by S. J. Hickson.—Co-operation in food supply, by A. G. Tansley.—The physiological aspects of flying, by Lieut.-Col. Martin Flack.—The anaerobic treatment of wounds, by R. C. McLean.—Substitution of raw materials. Paper, by F. W. Oliver.—Industrial efficiency and fatigue, by H. M. Vernon.—Fresh air and efficiency, by Henry Kenwood.

1. Agriculture—England. [1. England Agriculture] 2. European war, 1914-1918—Food question. [2. War and food supply] I. Bayliss, Sir William Maddock, 1860-1924. II. Cushny, Arthur Robertson, 1866-1926. III. Flack, Martin William. IV. Hickson, Sydney John, 1859- V. Hopkins, Sir Frederick Gowland, 1861- VI. Horne, Arthur Samuel. VII. Hume, E. Margaret. VIII. Kenwood, Henry Richard, 1862- IX. Mackenzie, Kenneth James Joseph. X. McLean, R. C. XI. Oliver, Francis Wall, 1864- XII. Russell, Sir Edward John, 1872- XIII. Stapledon, Reginald George, 1882- XIV. Tansley, Arthur George, 1871- XV. Vernon, Horace Middleton, 1870- XVI. Title: Fresh air and efficiency. XVII. Title: War bread.

Agr 20-740

U. S. Dept. of agr. Library   331.62
for Library of Congress   [a3711-]

NL 0355122   DNAL CaBVaU MiU DNLM ICJ MB NN

Life and its manifestations: past, present and future. A series of revelations from angelic sources, containing a new system of scriptural science and philosophy. Illustrated by examples. For private circulation only.
Manchester, Eng. [Heywood.] 1891, 92. 2 v. 21 cm., in 8s.

D8197 — Spiritualism. — Future life.

NL 0355123   MB

Life and its renewal.   [London: Printed by W. Clowes and Sons. 1864?]   16 p.   8°.

Half-title.
Criticism of: The renewal of life... By Thomas K. Chambers.
"Excerpt 'Meliora,' January. 1864."
In: VTZ p. v. 68, no. 19.

1. Chambers, Thomas King, 1818-   89: The renewal of life. 2. Alcohol.—Therapeutic use.
March 21. 1918.

NL 0355124   NN

Life and labor. v. 1-11, no. 8 (no. 1-126); Jan. 1911-Oct. 1921. [Chicago, National women's trade union league of America, 1911-21]
11 v. illus. (incl. ports.) 25½ᶜᵐ. monthly.
No numbers were issued for July and Aug. 1920 and Aug. and Sept. 1921.
Editors: 1911-July 1915, Alice Henry (with Stella M. Franklin).—Aug. 1915-Jan. 1916, Stella M. Franklin.—Feb.-Nov. 1916, Amy W. Field.—Dec. 1916-1921, Margaret D. Robins.
Superseded in Aug. 1922 by Life and labor bulletin.
1. Woman—Employment—Period. [1. Women in trade-unions—Period.] 2. Trade-unions—[U. S.]—Period. 3. [Woman—Employment] U. S. I. Henry, Alice, 1857-1943, ed. II. Franklin, Stella M., ed. III. Field, Amy Walker, ed. IV. Robins, Margaret (Dreier) ed. V. National women's trade union   league of America.
HD6050.L48   L 12-85 rev
U. S. Dept. of labor. Libr.
for Library of Congress   [r46h2]†

MB
NL 0355125   DL DLC WaS DNAL FU MNS WHi CU PP PBm ICJ

Life and labor bulletin; covering the activities of the National women's trade union league and some happenings in the labor movement. v. 1-10, no. 2; Aug. 1922-Feb. 1932. Washington [etc.] The National women's trade union league of America, 1922-32.
10 v. 31ᶜᵐ. monthly (irregular)
Caption title.
Supersedes Life and labor.
Subtitle varies slightly.
Superseded by another publication of the same title, no. 1 of which was published in Apr. 1933.
1. Woman — Employment — Period. 2. Trade-unions — Period. 3. Woman—Employment—U. S. 4. Trade-unions—U. S. I. National women's trade union league of America.
42-47108
Library of Congress   HD6050.L5
331.405

NL 0355125-1   DLC

LIFE and labor bulletin.
Chicago [etc.]

Microfilm. (master negative)

NL 0355126   NN

Life and labor bulletin; covering the activities of the National women's trade union league and some happenings in the labor movement. v. 1-10, no. 2; Aug. 1922-Feb. 1932. Washington [etc.] The National women's trade union league of America, 1922-32.
10 v. 31ᶜᵐ. monthly (irregular)
Caption title.
Supersedes Life and labor.
Subtitle varies slightly.
Superseded by another publication of the same title, no. 1 of which was published in Apr. 1933.
1. Woman — Employment — Period. 2. Trade-unions — Period. 3. Woman—Employment—U. S. 4. Trade-unions—U. S. I. National women's trade union league of America.
42-47108
Library of Congress   HD6050.L5
331.405

NL 0355127   DLC IU NcD WaS

VOLUME 332

The **life** and labors of Eliza R. Snow Smith; with a full account of her funeral services. Salt Lake City, Utah, The juvenile instructor office, 1888.

37, 24 p. 17½ᶜᵐ.

"Doctrines of the Church of Jesus Christ of Latter-day saints ... by Elder John Morgan": 24 p. at end.

1. Smith, Mrs. Eliza Roxey (Snow) 1804–1887.   I. Church of Jesus Christ of latter-day saints.   II. Morgan, John.

20–23356

Library of Congress   BX8695.S5L5

NL 0355128   DLC ICN NjP

Life and labors of Henry Gustavus Magnus.

(*In* Smithsonian institution. Annual report. 1870. Washington, 1871. 23½ᶜᵐ. p. ₍223₎–230)

"From the Archives des sciences physiques et naturelles, Geneva."

1. Magnus, Gustav i. e. Heinrich Gustav, 1802–1870.

S 15–281

Library of Congress   Q11.S66 1870
Library, Smithsonian   Institution

NL 0355129   DSI MiU OO OU DLC

Life and labors of Henry W. Grady, his speeches, writings, etc. ... Written and compiled under the immediate supervision of the publishers, from the most reliable sources ... Atlanta, Ga., H. C. Hudgins & co., 1890.

488 p. front., plates, ports. 20ᶜᵐ.

1. Grady, Henry Woodfin, 1851–1889.   I. Hudgins, H. C., & co., comp.

11–2778

Library of Congress   E664.G73L7

GAOC
NL 0355130   DLC WaTC GASC ViU ICRL NcD ICRL ViU PP

LIFE and labors of H^enry W. Grady, his speeches, writings, etc., New York, W. M. Goldthwaite, [cop. 1890].

Port. and plate.
Imperfect: Lacks pp. 99–116, 177–194.

NL 0355131   MH

Life and labors of Henry W. Grady; his speeches, writings, etc. ... Written and compiled under the immediate supervision of the publishers, from the most reliable sources. New York, W. M. Goldthwaite ₍*1890₎

Microfilm copy (positive) made in 1959 by Photoduplication Service, Library of Congress.
Collation of the original, as determined from the film: 488 p. illus., ports.
First published by H. C. Hudgins, Atlanta.

1. Grady, Henry Woodfin, 1850–1889.

Microfilm 6171 E   Mic 59–7943

NL 0355132   DLC

Life and labors of Rev. Reuben Gaylord
see under   [Gaylord, Mrs. Mary M (Welles)]

The life and labors of Rev. Thomas Walsh the Irish methodist preacher, a converted Roman Catholic. Ottawa, Holiness Movement Publishing House, 1906.

209p.

Preface signed A.M.

NL 0355134   CaOTU CaBVaU

Life (The) and labors of William Griesinger. 28 pp. 8°. [*Utica, N. Y.,* 1869.]
Repr. from: Am. J. Insan. Utica, N. Y., 1868–9, xxv.

NL 0355135   DNLM

Life and labour in Germany
see under   Labour party (Gt. Brit.) Commission on wages, hours of employment, working conditions, and the standard of living.

Life and labour of Rev. A. E. Garriso... ... N.p.n. pub. [1943]
130 p. incl. front. port.

NL 0355137   CaBViP

The life and labours of Adam Clarke, LL. D. To which is added an historical sketch of the controversy concerning the sonship of Christ, partiennial as connected with the proceedings of the Wesleyan-Methodist conference... London, J. Stephens, 1834.

xii, 520p. front. (port.) 18½cm.

Hare lettered on cover as author by binder.

1. Clarke, Adam, 1760?–1832.   2. Jesus Christ. Divinity.

NL 0355138   CtW MWA CLSU

The life and labours of Adam Clarke, LL. D... 2d ed. London, Longman, Brown, Green, and Longmans, 1842.

xi, 416p. front. (port.) 22½cm.

1. Clarke, Adam, 1760?–1832.

NL 0355139   CtW IMunS NjPT NcD RPB

... **Life** and letter of acceptance of Chester A. Arthur, the Republican candidate for vice-president. New York, 1880.

38 p. front. (port.) 16½ᵐ.

At head of title: Republican leaders.
Cover-title: Campaign sketch of Chester A. Arthur.

1. Arthur, Chester Alan, pres. U. S., 1830–1886.   I. Title: Republican leaders.

7—4194

Library of Congress   E692.L72

NL 0355140   DLC NN NjP

LIFE and letter of acceptance of Chester A. Arthur, the Republican candidate for vice-president. New York, 1880.   38 p. port. 17cm.   (Republican leaders)

Microfiche (neg.) 1 sheet. 11 x 15cm.   (NYPL FSN 11, 900)
In ms. on t. p.: By Edgar L. Murlin?

1. Arthur, Chester Alan, 21st. pres. U.S. I. Murlin, Edgar Lewis, 1848?–1937.

NL 0355141   NN

Life and letters. v. 1.–3; Sept. 1922–July 1925. **Girard, Kan.,** 1922–25.

3 v. in 1. illus. 37ᶜᵐ. monthly.

Caption title.
Emanuel Haldeman-Julius, editor.
Merged into the Haldeman-Julius weekly.

1. Haldeman-Julius, Emanuel, 1889–   ed.

27–16785

Library of Congress   AP2.L548

NL 0355142   DLC WaSpG MiU NcU NN

AP4
.L416
Life and letters and the London mercury. v. 1–65; June 1928–June 1950. London, Brendin Pub. Co. ₍etc.₎

v. in   18–25 cm.

Frequency varies.
Publication suspended May–Aug. 1935.
Title varies: June 1928–Apr. 1935, Life and letters.—Sept. 1935–June 1945, Life and letters today.—July 1945–Jan. 1946, Life and letters and the London mercury and bookman.
Editors: June 1928–Feb. 1934, D. MacCarthy (with H. Miles, Mar. 1923–Feb. 1934)—Apr.–Aug. 1934, H. Miles.—Sept. 1935–June 1950, R. Herring (with P. Townshend, Sept. 1935–spring 1937)
Absorbed the London mercury in May 1939.
L. C. set incomplete: v. 18, no. 11; v. 35, no. 62; v. 62–63 wanting.
1. Literature—Hist. & crit.—Period.   2. Books—Reviews.   I. Mac-Carthy, Sir Desmond, 1878–1952, ed.   II. Miles, Hamish, 1894–1937, ed.   III. Herring, Robert, ed.   IV. Life and letters today.

AP4.L416   31–33340 rev 2*

OrPS NSyU KU TxU MnU NcU NcD PHC MtU MNS KMK MB
NL 0355143   DLC ICN FU PSt MoS PPT NhD AAP NtN1C

Life & letters incorporating "To-day." v. 1–2 (no. 1–10); Nov. 1923–Aug. 1924. London & Manchester ₍Percy brothers, ltd., 1923–24₎

2 v. 24½ᶜᵐ. monthly.

Absorbed To-day (London, 1917–23) in Feb. 1924.
No more published.

37–6044

Library of Congress   AP4.L4162

052

NL 0355144   DLC NN

The life and letters of Captain John Brown ... [Publisher's announcement]
see under   Smith, Elder and co., publishers, London.

Life and letters of Dean Stanley
see under   [Ernle, Rowland Edmund Prothero, baron], 1852–

The life and letters of Elizabeth Prentiss, [1882]
see under   Prentiss, George Lewis, 1816–1903.

Life and letters of General Johann August Sutter
see under   Sutter, John Augustus, 1803–1880.

Life and letters of Henry William Thomas, mixologist
see under   [Wheeler, Charles Van Cise] 1866–   ed.

VOLUME 332

Life and letters of Herbert Spencer
see under   Duncan, David.

LIFE and letters of James Fisk, jr. and Miss
Mansfield. New York, Sullivan & co., [1872?]
pp.36.
Cover-title.

NL 0355151   MH

Life and letters of John C. Colt. 2d ed. ... [New
York, Dillon & Hooper, 1842]
16 p. 24½ᵐ.
Caption title: "Extra Tattler. October 21, 1842. Life and letters of John Caldwell Colt; condemned to be hung on the eighteenth of November, 1842, for the murder of Samuel Adams."
Portrait of John C. Colt on t.-p.   3-13293

NL 0355152   DLC

*
PS1917
.R61   The Life and letters of Lafcadio Hearn
1906   [book review]
[no.2]   (In The Athenaeum. London. 29½cm. no. 4136
(Feb. 2, 1907) p. 126-127)

1. Hearn, Lafcadio, 1850-1904. Life and letters.

NL 0355153   ViU

*
PS1917
.A41   Life and letters of Lafcadio Hearn
1906   [book review]
[no.1]   (In The Literary digest. New York. 30½cm.
vol. XXXIII, no. 23 (Dec. 8, 1906) p. 855)

1. Hearn, Lafcadio, 1850-1904. Life and letters. 2. Wetmore, Elizabeth (Bisland) 1861-1929, ed.

NL 0355154   ViU

Life and letters of Mandell Creighton
see under   Creighton, Louise (von Glehn)
1850-1936.

The life and letters of Marcus Tullius Cicero
see under   Cicero, Marcus Tullius.
Epistolae. English.

Life and letters of Mrs. Jeanette H. Platt
see under   [Platt, Cyrus] 1818-

BX4705
.D3L7   Life and letters of Rev. Mother Teresa Dease, foundress
and superior general of The institute of the Blessed Virgin
Mary in America.   Ed. by a member of the community.
Toronto, McClelland, Goodchild & Stewart [1916]
282 p. front. (port.) 20ᵐ.
Introduction signed: Dean Harris.

1. Dease, Mother Teresa, 1820-1889.

NL 0355158   ICU DCU CaOTP

[Life and letters of St. Paul. Translated by
John T.Tucker. West Central African mission,
A.B.C.F.M. Kamundongo, Sarah H.Bates memorial
press, 1917.
168 p. 20 cm.

NL 0355159   MH

The life and letters of Sydney Dobell, 1878
see under   Jolly, Miss Emily.

The life and letters of the Rev. Richard Harris Bar-
ham ...
see under   [Barham, Richard Harris Dalton]
1815-1887.

Life and letters of Wilder Dwight, 1868
see under   Dwight, Elizabeth Amelia (White)
1809-1883.

The life and letters of William Beckford, of Fonthill
see under   [Benjamin, Lewis Saul] 1874-1932.

Life and letters of William Fleming Stevenson
see under   [Stevenson, Elizabeth Montgomer
(Sinclair)]

Life and letters of William John Butler
see under   [Butler, Arthur John]

Life and letters to-day
see Life and letters and the London mercury.

Life and life-work of Mother Theodore Guérin
see under   [Mug, Mary Theodosia]
sister, 1860-

Life and light for heathen women
see
Life and light for woman.

Life and light for woman. v. 1-52; Mar. 1869-Dec. 1922. Bos-
ton, Press of Rand, Avery, & company [etc., 1869-1922]
52 v. illus., plates, ports., maps. 18-21ᵐ.
Quarterly, Mar. 1869-Dec. 1872; monthly, Jan. 1873-Dec. 1922.
Title varies: Mar. 1869-Dec. 1872, Life and light for heathen women
(this title continued on title-pages through v. 4, 1874)
Jan. 1873-Dec. 1922, Life and light for woman.
Published by the Woman's board of missions, the Woman's board of
missions for the Pacific, etc.
Merged into the Missionary herald.
L. C. set incomplete: Dec. 1922 wanting.
With v. 1-32 are bound: Annual reports of the Woman's board of
missions. Boston, 1869-1903.
1. Congregational churches—Missions—Period.   I. Woman's board
of missions. Boston.
Library of Congress   BV2612.L5   40-23876
266.58

MH CSmH ICN NBuG MB Nh WaU
NL 0355169   DLC WaS GEU NIC MNS MH-AH MiU IEG MiGr

[Life and list of the scientific writings of] Henry
James Clark. [7 pl. 8°. [n. p.], 1866.
Repr. from: Gen. Catalogue Mass. Agricul. Coll. 1866.

NL 0355170   DNLM

Life and literature. Tor.,
Nelson [c193 -
Library has: Book

NL 0355171   CaBVa CaBViP

Life and literature in the Soviet Union.
London: Pilot press [1942]   18½cm.
v.
Editors: 1942-   , I. G. S. Montagu and H. P. J. Marshall.

1. No subject. I. Montagu, Ivor   Goldsmith Samuel, 1904-   , ed.
II. Marshall, Herbert P. J., 1912-   ed.
February 9, 1943

NL 0355172   NN OO

Life and literature in the United States.
London, The Pilot press ltd., 1943   v. illus. 16-22cm.
In most numbers series title appears only on book jacket.
Editor : 1943   Michael Barsley.

1. No subject. I. Barsley, Michael,   ed.
July 11, 1945

NL 0355173   NN

Life and love and death
see under   [Hall, Bolton] 1854-1938.

Life and manners in Switzerland
see   Johnson, Anna Cummings, 1818-1892.
The cottage of the Alps; or, Life and manners in
Switzerland.

PR 974
.G3   The life and martial achievements of the most
Vol. IV   noble Arthur, Duke of Wellington, commander
in chief of the combined army at the Battle of
Waterloo. Falkirk, Printed and sold by T.
Johnston. 1817.
24 p. 16 cm.   [In Garret, William. A
right pleasant and famous book of histories.
Newcastle 1818. Vol. IV no. 3]

NL 0355176   DLC

VOLUME 332

The life and Martirdome of St. George
see under [Lowick, Thomas] 1582-

The life and martyrdom of Abraham Lincoln
see under [Williamson, David Brainerd] 1827-

....The life and martyrdom of John Hooper, bishop of Glocester and Worcester;/who was burnt at Glocester in the bloody reign of Queen Mary for his opposition to the antichristian doctrines of popery, and his zeal for the doctrines of the Bible and the Church of England ... ₍Bristol₎ Sold by J. Richardson ₍etc.₎, 1815₎ ₍2₎, 3-10 p. 19ᶜᵐ. (Bristol. Church of England tract society. No. XVIII)

Illustrated title-page.
1. Hooper, John   bp. of Gloucester, d. 1555.
I. Bristol, Er   Church of England tract
society. 18.

NL 0355179   NNC

The life and martyrdom of Mr. Maxfield, 1616
see under [Kellison, Matthew] 1560?-1642.

CT99
.C388Z8

Life and martyrdom of the holy and glorious martyr of Christ, St. Cecilia,/and those who were with her, Saints Valerian, Tiburtius and Maximus. Translated from the ancient acts ... New York, Langan & bro. [n. d.]
16 p.   23cm.

Illustrated t.-p.
I. Cecilia, Saint.

NL 0355181   DLC

The life and martyrdome of Thomas Becket, archbishop of Canterbury
see under Robert, of Gloucester, fl. 1260-1300, supposed author.

... Life and medical discoveries of Samuel Thomson
see under [Lloyd, John Uri] 1849-

---

x B
C5592 1

The life and memoirs of Elizabeth Chudleigh, afterwards Mrs. Hervey and Countess of Bristol, commonly called Duchess of Kingston. Written from authentic information and original documents.   London, Printed for R. Randall ₍1788₎ 36p. 2 ports. 28cm.

1. Chudleigh, Elizabeth, countess of Bristol, calling herself duchess of Kingston, 1720-1788.

NL 0355184   IU MiU-C CtY-M

---

x B
C5592 i

The life and memoirs of Elizabeth Chudleigh, afterwards Mrs. Hervey, and countess of Bristol, commonly called duchess of Kingston.   Dublin₎ Printed for H. Chamberlaine, 1789.
iii, 269p. port. 17cm.

1. Chudleigh, Elizabeth, countess of Bristol, calling herself   duchess of Kingston, 1720-1778.

NL 0355185   IU MH CtY

Life and memoirs of Gen. Ulysses S. Grant
see under [Abarbanell, Jacob Ralph]

The life and memoirs of Her Royal Highness Princess Charlotte of Saxe Coburg Saalfeld, &c. London, T. Kinnersley, 1818.
1 p. l., 596 p. 5 pl., 5 port. 21½ᶜᵐ.
Engr. t.-p., with vignette.
Also issued the same year under title: The life of the late Princess Charlotte ...

Subject entries: Charlotte Augusta, of Wales, princess, consort of Prince Leopold of Saxe-Coburg-Saalfeld, 1796-1817.   5-29471

Library of Congress, no.   DA506.A5L7.

NL 0355187   DLC NjP

The life and memoirs of Mr. Ephraim Tristram Bates, commonly called Corporal Bates, a brokenhearted soldier ... London: Printed by Malachi **** for Edith Bates, relict of the aforesaid Mr. Bates, and sold by W. Owen ... 1756.
WILLIAM v,7-238 p. 17ᶜᵐ.
ANDREWS
CLARK   First edition.
MEMORIAL Signatures: A-K¹²(K₁₂ advertisements)
LIBRARY   Armorial book-plate of Barlborough Hall
Bound in old sprinkled calf, rebacked; lettered on back: Corporal Bates.

NL 0355188   CLU-C IU MH

Life and memoirs of the late Maj. Gen. Lee, second in command to Washington. 1813
see under Lee, Charles, 1731-1782.

Life and memoirs of William Warren, Boston's favorite comedian, with a full account of his golden jubilee, fifty years of an actor's life. ₍Boston₎ Daly ₍1882₎
70 p. ports., facsim.

1. Warren, William, 1812-1888.

NL 0355190   NNC MWA CSmH PU

PN2287
W3L5

Life and memoirs of William Warren, Boston's favorite comedian. With a full account of his golden jubilee. Fifty years of an actor's life. [Boston] Published by James Daly [1886?]

70 p. fronts. (port., facsim.) ports. 17cm.
Material furnished by W. T. W. Ball and the Boston daily papers.
Facsimile tipped in at end.
1. Warren, William, 1812-1888. I. Ball, William T   W

NL 0355191   CSmH OClWHi

Life and memoirs of William Warren, Boston's favorite comedian. With a full account of his golden jubilee. Fifty years of an actor's life. ₍Boston: ₎ J. Daly₍, 1888?₎. 70 p.   facsims., front., ports. 16°.

1. Warren, William, 1812-1888.   2. Actors and acting—Biog.
November 16, 1926

NL 0355192   NN CU MB

Life and memoirs of William Warren, Boston's favorite comedian. With a full account of his golden jubilee. Fifty years of an actor's life. Boston, J. Daly ₍1889₎
1 p. l., 70 p. front., ports., facsim. 17½ᶜᵐ.

1. Warren, William, 1812-1888.
1-3474

Library of Congress   PN2287.W45A3
WU MH:
NL 0355193   DLC OClWHi RPB MH TU MB ViU WaU GU KU

The life and memorable actions of George Washington, general and commander of the armies of America. ₍Baltimore, Md.₎ Printed by and for George Keatinge, no. 207 Market street ₍1800₎
2 p.l., ₍4₎ -10, ₍4₎, ₍17₎ -96p. incl. front. (port.) 12.5 cm.

NL 0355194   CSmH PHi MHi

The life and memorable actions of George Washington, general and commander of the armies of America. A new ed. cor. Frederick-Town ₍Md.₎ Printed by M. Bartgis, 1801.
68, ₍2₎ p. incl. front. (port.) 15½ x 9ᶜᵐ.
Some of the early paragraphs of this biography are taken from the "Sketch of Mr. Washington's life and character," by John Bell, of Maryland, first printed in Charles H. Wharton's A poetical epistle to ... George Washington, Annapolis, 1779.

1. Washington, George, pres. U. S., 1732-1799. I. Bärtgis, Matthias, pub. II. Bell, John.
16-15453

Library of Congress   E312.L7

NL 0355195   DLC IEN MdHi

Life and memorials of Daniel Webster
see under [Lyman, Samuel P   ] 1804-1869.

Life (The) and meritorious transactions, of John Knox, the great Scottish reformer. *Glasgow*, ₍18—₎ 24 pp. 16°.
In: *C. p. v. 687.

NL 0355197   NN

The LIFE and meritorious transactions, of John Knox, the great Scottish reformer. Glasgow, Printed for the booksellers [1830?] 24 p. 16cm.

Weiss: Chapbooks, 448.
On t.-p.: 61.
Without covers.
*KVD p.v. 20, no. 97
---- Second copy.
1. Knox, John, 1505-1572.

NL 0355198   NN

VOLUME 332

The life and meritorious transactions,
of John Knox, the great Scottish reformer.
Glasgow, Printed for the booksellers [ca.
1840]

24 p.   17cm.   [Chap books. v.1, no.5]
"[No.] 61."
1.Knox, John, 1505-1572.

NL 0355199   MnU

The Life and meritorious transactions, of John
Knox, the great Scottish reformer.   Glasgow,
Printed for the booksellers [1840? Repr. 1877]
24 p.   port.   19 cm.   (John Cheap, the
Chapman's Library [v. 2, no. 1])
Caption title: The Life of John Knox.
1. Knox, John, 1505-1572.   I. Title:
The life of John Knox.

NL 0355200   OCU

The life and military achievements of Tousant Loverture, late general in chief of the armies of St. Domingo ...
with an impartial account of his political conduct ... to
which is added a melancholy and accurate description of
the rapacious, tyrannical and inhumane conduct of General Le Clerc, until his death: also his successor General
Rochambeau's actions, until the evacuation of that colony, and capture by the British, in the fall of 1803. [n.p.]
Printed for the author, 1804.
2 p. l., [3]-76 p. 21½cm.
1. Toussaint Louverture, Pierre Dominique, 1746?-1803. 2. Haiti—
Hist.—Revolution, 1791-1804.
15-4520
Library of Congress   F1923.T86
[Miscellaneous pamphlets, v. 375, no. 3]
AC901.M5 vol. 375

NL 0355201   DLC PHi PPL PPAmP

The life and military atchievements [sic] of Toussaint Loverture,
late general in chief of the armies of St. Domingo...with an
impartial account of his political conduct...to which is added a
melancholy and accurate description of the rapacious, tyrannical
and inhuman conduct of General Le Clerc...also his successor's
(Gen. Rochambeau) actions, until the evacuation of that colony,
and capture by the British, in the fall of 1803.   n.p., Printed
for the author, 1805.   64 p., 1 l.   2. ed.   8°.

1. Toussaint Louverture, Pierre   Dominique, 1746?-1803. 2. Haiti—
History, 1791-1804.
August 23, 1915.

NL 0355202   NN DPU TxU ICN MH

The life and military actions of His Royal
Highness Francis Eugene, Prince of Savoy ...
London: Printed and sold by T. Read ... 1735.
[8],220 p.   front.(port.)   18¼cm.

WILLIAM
ANDREWS
CLARK
MEMORIAL
LIBRARY

First edition.
Bound in old sprinkled calf.

NL 0355203   CLU-C

Life and military actions of this Royal Highness
Prince Eugene, of Savoy.   2 ed., corrected
and enlarged.   With an account of his death
and funeral.   London, 1736.
12°

NL 0355204   MdBP KU CLU-C

The life and military actions of His Royal Highness
Prince Eugene, of Savoy.   With an account of his death
and funeral ...   Dublin, Printed by and for J. Jones,
1737.
13 p. l., 224 p. 17cm.

1. Eugène i. e. François Eugène, prince de Savoie-Carignan, 1663-1736.
17-15257
Library of Congress   D274.E8L6

NL 0355205   DLC CtY TNJ

3A
333   The LIFE and military actions of His Royal
Highness Prince Eugene, of Savoy.   With an
account of his death and funeral ...
London,1739.
350p.   front.(port.)   15cm.

NL 0355206   ICN MH

E
464   Life and military career of "Stonewall"
C585   Jackson.   From authentic sources.
v.32   London, Bacon [1863?]
no.7   15 p.   24cm.

1. Jackson, Thomas Jonathan, 1824-1863.

NL 0355207   NIC

---

*
E467   Life and military career of "Stonewall"
.1   Jackson.   London, Bacon [1863]. Photoprinted
.J15L5   1952.
1863   15 p. on 10 l.   27 x 30cm.
1952ed.   Photocopy (positive) made Mar. 12, 1952, from
           the original in the collection of Roy Bird Cook,
           Charlestown, W. Va.

1. Jackson, Thomas Jonathan, 1824-1863.

NL 0355208   ViU

The life and military character of Maj. Gen. Scott,
illustrated with numerous anecdotes and spirited engravings.   Together with his views upon the principal moral,
social and political topics of the age.   With full particulars of the surrender of the castle and city of Vera Cruz.
New York, S. French, 1847.
cover-title, 36 p. illus. 24cm.
Text on pages 3 and 4 of cover (included in paging)

1. Scott, Winfield, 1786-1866.
13-19356
Library of Congress   E403.1.S4L73

NL 0355209   DLC MiU-C

923.542
fM347L   The life and military history of his Grace
           the Duke of Marlborough, Prince of the Roman
           Empire, and Generalissimo of the British
           Forces, in the late reign of her Majesty Queen
           Anne. Containing, a particular description of
           all the principal transactions of the war, and
           of all the battles, sieges, &c. in which that
           glorious and ever-successful general commanded.
           Letters of correspondence between his Grace

           and the court of Hanover; also letters that
           passed between his Grace and other great men,
           which the Duke left among other papers, de-
           signed to be published by Mr. Glover and Mr.
           Mallet, who were appointed by the late Dutchess
           of Marlborough, in her will, to write his life.
           Likewise letters from the emperor, the States
           General, King Charles III. of Spain, &c. to

           the Duke, with his Grace's answers. To which
           will be added, The last will and testament of
           the Duke of Marlborough, never before published
           The whole embellished and illustrated with a
           large variety of whole sheet copper plates,
           taken from the original designs, and engraved
           by the best hands; representing all the battles,
           and sieges, in which that General was concerned.

           London, M. Cooper, 1754.
           620, ix, [21] p.   fold. plates, port.,
           tables.   36 cm.

           1. Marlborough, John Churchill, 1st duke
           of, 1650-1722 2. Gt. Brit. History. 1660-
           1714 3. Gt. Brit. History. 1714-1837

NL 0355213   NcD

The life and military exploits of Pyrrhus
see under [Jourdan, Jean Baptiste]
1711-1793.

The Life and ministry of Benjamin Bosworth
Smith.   A memorial discourse, Sept. 24,
1884.   Louisville, 1884.
16 p.   8°.

NL 0355215   MWA

The life and miracles of Saint Philomena, virgin and martyr, whose sacred body was lately discovered in the catacombs
at Rome, and from thence transferred to Mugnano, in the kingdom of Naples.   Translated from the French ...   New York,
P. O'Shea, 1865.
xi, 185 p. front. 15cm.
For a discussion of the correct identification of the body referred to
in the title see Marucchi: Studio archeologico sulla celebre iscrizione di
Filumena scoperta nel cimitero di Priscilla (Nuovo bullettino di archeol.
crist. XII, 1906) and Butler: Lives of the saints, vol. VIII (1933).
1. Philomena, Saint.
41-42181
Library of Congress   BX4700.P75L5

NL 0355216   DLC

The life and miracles of Saint Wenefride
see under [Robert, of Shrewsbury] d. 1167.

The life and miracles of St. Winefride,to which is
added the life of St. Catherine...
see under [Robert, of Shrewsbury] d. 1167.

The life and missionary labours of that holy
man, Francis Xavier, commonly called the
Apostle of the Indies ...   New-York, Published
by Thomas Bakewell, Paul and Thomas, printers,
1814.
1 p.l., [iii]-vi, [7]-180p.   front. (port.)
Title page and front. mutilated.

1. Francisco Xavier, Saint, 1506-1552.

NL 0355219   PMA NjPT MWA DGU MH NjP CtY CaBVaU MdW

The life and most surprizing adventures of
Robinson Crusoe
see Defoe, Daniel, 1661?-1731
Robinson Crusoe.

The life and mysteries of the celebrated Dr. "Q."
see under [Alexander, Conlin]

The life and mysterious transactions of Richard Morris, esq.,
better known by the name of Dick Spot, the conjuror, particularly
in Derbyshire and Shropshire.   Written by an old acquaintance,
who was a critical observer of all his actions for nearly fifty
years ...   London: Printed by T. Maiden for A. Lemoine
[1798?]   38 p.   front.   17½cm.
Running title: The life of Dick Spot, the conjuror.
At foot of frontispiece: Printed for & under the direction of I. Roe, July 3, 1798.

171497B.   1. Morris, Richard.   I. Title: The life of Dick Spot.
October 19, 1942

NL 0355222   NN DLC-P4

VOLUME 332

4
Rare
Bks
    The life and mysterious trans-
actions of Richard Morris, better
known by the name of Dick Spot, the
conjuror, particularly in Derbyshire
and Shropshire, written by an old
acquaintance, who was a critical observer of all his actions, for near
fifty years. London, Printed for A.
Lemoine; and sold by T. Hurst, 1799.
    48 p.

M—Library of Congress

NL   0355223   DLC-P4

                        17437-35
    The life and opinions of Bertram Montfichet, written by him-
self. London, printed for C. G. Seyffert, [1761].
    2 vol. Fronts.
    An imitation of Sterne's Tristram Shandy.

Sterne–Imitations

NL   0355224   MH PBm NjP NNC

    The Life and Opinions of Bertram Montfichet,
Esq. ... London, Seyffert [1765]
    2 v. in 1.

NL   0355225   PU

Rare Book
Room
Im
St45
H760l
    The life and opinions of Miss Sukey Shandy,
of Bow-street, gentlewoman. In a series of
letters to her dear brother Tristram Shandy,
gent. ... London:Printed for R.Stevens,at
Pope's Head in Pater-noster-row.1760.
    2p ℓ.,163p. 16½cm.
    Signatures: 2ℓ. unsigned, B-L⁸M².
    In imitation of Laurence Sterne's The life
and opinions of Tristram Shandy.

NL   0355226   CtY MH

    Life & opinions of the celebrated George
      Buchanan
        see under   Lawson, John Parker.

    The life and opinions of Tristram Shandy,
      gentleman..   Vol. III.   1760.
        see under   Carr, John, 1732-1807.

    The life and particular proceedings of the Rev. Mr.
      George Whitefield
        see under   [Tucker, Josiah] 1712-1799.

---

*Defoe
30
.708
A10L2
    The life and penitent death of John Mawgridge,
gent. who was executed for the murder of Capt.
Cope. Penn'd from his own account of himself,
and approv'd by him, before his death ... London, Printed and sold by H. Hills, 1708.
    16 p. 19cm.

    1. Mawgridge, John, 1676-1708?   2. Crime and
criminals—Gt. Brit

NL   0355230   MB

Case
4A
694
    The LIFE and persecutions of Miss Beatrice
Claflin...from a narrative furnished by the
Ladies' philanthropical society...
Philadelphia, Published by Barclay & Co., [1880]
[2],19-64p. illus. 24cm.
    Captions to the illustrations in English
and German.
    Wright III,2249.
    This copy has a purple illustrated cover.
    At head of title: The great wrongs of the
shop girls.

NL   0355231   ICN

    The life and poetry of Edgar Poe.
      From- Littell's Living age, April 16, 1853.
      (From Chamber's Journal)
      157-161 p. 23 cm.

NL   0355232   RPB

    Life and political history of Sylvester Pennoyer,
      governor of Oregon
        see under   History Publishing Company.

LQ1
pam
    The life and political opinions of the
late Sam House; interspersed with curious
anecdotes and amorous intrigues of this
singular and distinguished character ...
The second edition. London,Printed for
the author by C.Buckton,and sold by J.
Ridgway[etc.,1785]
    vi,[5],-45p. fold.front. 20cm.

NL   0355234   NNUT

Slavery
E
441
M46
v.271
no.3
    The life and pontificate of Pope Pius IX.

    (In The Monitor; a Catholic family
weekly. [Sacramento?] 23cm. [1878?]
37 p.)

    May anti-slavery pamphlets, v. 271.

    1. Pius IX, pope, 1792-1878.

NL   0355235   NIC

    The life and posthumous writings of William
Cowper... By William Hayley... [Book
review]
        see under   Jeffrey, Francis Jeffrey,
Lord, 1773-1850.

Life and prophecies of Jeremiah. Written for the American Sunday-school union, and revised by the Committee of publication. Philadelphia, American Sunday-school union [1836]
81 p. 15ᶜᵐ.

    1. Jeremiah, the prophet.   I. American Sunday-school union.

                                       31-25337
  Library of Congress   BS580.J4L5   221.92

NL   0355237   DLC

    The life and prophecies of Mr. Alexander Peden..
        see under   [Walker, Patrick] 1666?-1745?

    Life and prophecies of Mother Shipton
        see under   Shipton, Ursula.

Life and public career of a prominent Pennsylvanian.
[John P. Elkin] [n. p., 1901?]
cover-title, [32] p. front. (port.) 23ᶜᵐ.
Personal estimates by friends and acquaintances.
Introd. signed: Charles H. Heustis.

Subject entries: Elkin, John Pratt, 1860-

                                       3-3179

NL   0355240   DLC PHi PPB

    The life and public career of Daniel Webster ...
        see under   [Lyman, Samuel P   ] 1804-
1869.

DS481
.S88
L72
    Life and public service of Dr. Nadirshaw H.E.
Sukhia, by admirers. [Bombay, S. H. Jhab-
vala, n.d.]
    671 p. port.

    1. Sukhia, Nadirshaw Hormusji Edalji, 1860-
I. Jhabvala, Shavaksha Hormusji.

NL   0355242   ICU

JS
7032
.S95
L72
    Life and public service of Dr.Nadirshaw
H.E.Sukhia ... by admirers. [Bombay,
S.H.Jhabvala, 1926]
    671,[74] p. geneal.table,port.
    Second group of pages in Gujarati.

    1.Sukhia,Nadirshaw H.E.,b.1860.   2.Bombay
--Pol.& govt.

NL   0355243   MiU

    Life and public services of Abraham Lincoln
        see under   [Williamson, David Brainerd]
1827-

    ... The Life and public services of Abraham Lin-
coln, sixteenth president of the United States,
together with his State papers, &c. By H. L.
Raymond. New York, Derby and Miller, 1865.
2. The Martyr's monument. New York, The American news company, 1865. [London, Elliot
Stock, 1866]
    p. [269]-515. 22.4 cm. 5|4 green morocco.
Caption-title.
Review.
Excerpt from: The London quarterly review, vol.
26, no. 52, July, 1866.

NL   0355245   CSmH

Life and public services of Gen'l Harris M. Plaisted.
Portland, Me., The New era publishing co., 1880.
cover-title, 31 p. 22ᶜᵐ.
Portrait on cover.

    1. Plaisted, Harris Merrill, 1828-1898.   I. The New era publishing co.,
Portland, Me., pub.
                                     17-16291
  Library of Congress   F25.P69

NL   0355246   DLC

VOLUME 332

...The life and public services of Gen. Lewis Cass: comprising his services in the War of 1812, in the Senate of the United States, in the Cabinet, in foreign diplomatic stations, and in the highest offices in Michigan. To which is added, The military and civil life of Gen. William O. Butler: comprising his services in the War of 1812, in various civil capacities, and in the war with Mexico which has recently terminated... Hartford: Belknap & Hamersley, 1848. 64 p. incl. front., plates, ports. illus. 8°.

At head of title: Cass and Butler.

1. Cass, Lewis, 1782–1866. 2. Butler, William Orlando, 1791–1880.

April 30, 1925

NL 0355247 NN LNHT WaU CtY MH

E340
C3L5

Life and public services of Gen. Lewis Cass, Democratic candidate for the Presidency. Together with a sketch of the life and services of Gen. William O. Butler, Democratic candidate for the Vice Presidency. Boston, J. B. Hall, 1848.
34 p. illus. 23 cm.

Cover title.
1. Cass, Lewis, 1782–1866. 2. Butler, William Orlando, 1791–1880. 3. Campaign literature, 1848 - Democratic.

NL 0355248 MeB MiU

Life and public services of Gen. Z. Taylor: including a minute account of his defence of Fort Harrison, in 1812; the battle of Okee-chobee, in 1837; and the battles of Palo Alto and Resaca de la Palma, in 1846 ... To which is added, sketches of the officers who have fallen in the late contest. Ed. by an officer of the U. S. A. New York, H. Long & brother, 1846.

3 p. l., ₍9₎–56 p. port., fold. maps, fold. facsim. 23ᶜᵐ.

On cover: Longs' illustrated edition.
1. Taylor, Zachary, pres. U. S., 1784–1850. 2. U. S.—Hist.—War with Mexico, 1845–1848.

13—22193

Library of Congress E422.L73

NL 0355249 DLC OkU ViU CU NN MB

Life and public services of Gen. Z. Taylor: including a minute account of his defence of Fort Harrison, in 1812; the battle of Okee-chobee, in 1837; and the battles of Palo Alto and Resaca de la Palma, in 1846 ... To which is added, sketches of the officers who have fallen in the late contest. Ed. by an officer of the U. S. A. New York, H. Long & brother, 1846.

56 p. front. (fold. facsim.) port., fold. maps. 23½ᶜᵐ.
On cover: Longs' illustrated edition.
Slightly enlarged from the original edition published the same year.
1. Taylor, Zachary, pres. U. S., 1784–1850. 2. U. S.—Hist.—War with Mexico, 1845–1848—Campaigns and battles.

13–24552

Library of Congress E422.L72

NL 0355250 DLC ViU

Cb73
230t

... Life and public services of Gen. Z. Taylor: including a minute account of his defence of Fort Harrison, in 1812; the battle of Okee-Chobee, in 1837; and the battles of Palo Alto, Montery, Resaca de la Palma, and others ... To which is added, sketches of the officers who have fallen in the late contest. Ed. by an officer of the U.S.A. New-York, E. Hutchinson, 1848.
50p. illus. 22½cm. (*In* Pictorial history of remarkable events in America ... New-York, 1849)
At head of title Part third.

NL 0355251 CtY

Life and public services of Gen. Z. Taylor: including a minute account of his defense of Fort Harrison, in 1812; the battle of Okee-Chobee, in 1837; and the battles of Palo Alto, Resaca de la Palma, and others ... To which is added, sketches of the officers who have fallen in the late contest. Ed. by an officer of the U. S. A. Also the life of Millard Fillmore ... New York, 1850.
3 p. l., 5–96 p. front. illus. (incl. ports.) plates. 22ᶜᵐ.
The larger part of this work was originally published in 1846.
"Battles of Mexico. Names of the killed, wounded, and missing ... of the American army": p. 81–96.
1. Taylor, Zachary, pres. U. S. 1784–1850. 2. U. S.—Hist.—War with Mexico, 1845–1848—Campaigns and battles. 3. U. S.—Hist.—War with Mexico, 1845–1848—Registers, lists, etc.

9–30731

Library of Congress E422.L78

NL 0355252 DLC CU

Life, The, and public services of Henry Clay. [Anon.] Portrait. (In The New World. [Extra number.] Pp. 1–16. New York. 1842.

K1739 — Clay, Henry. 1777–1852.

NL 0355253 MB

The life and public services of Hon. Abraham Lincoln
        see under [Bartlett, David Vandewater Golden] 1828–1912.

The life and public services of Hon. Horace Greeley, Liberal Republican candidate for president of the United States, and of Hon. B. Gratz Brown, candidate for vice president; with a record of the proceedings of the Cincinnati convention ... Chicago, New York ₍etc.₎ Goodspeed's empire publishing house, 1872.
74, ₍6₎ p. illus., port. 22ᶜᵐ.

1. Greeley, Horace, 1811–1872. 2. Brown, Benjamin Gratz, 1826–1885. 3. Campaign literature, 1872—Liberal Republican. I. Liberal Republican party. National convention, Cincinnati, 1872.

11—2798

Library of Congress E415.9.G8L69

NL 0355255 DLC MWA

The life and public services of Hon. James Buchanan, of Pennsylvania. 20th thousand. New York, Livermore & Rudd, 1856.
118 p. front. (port.) 19¼ᶜᵐ.
On cover: The authorized campaign edition.
Attributed to Edward F. Underhill. *cf.* G. T. Curtis, Life of James Buchanan ... 1883, vol. II, p. 136.

1. Buchanan, James, pres. U. S., 1791–1868. 2. Campaign literature, 1856—Democratic. I. Underhill, Edward Fitch, 1830–1898.

7–15652 Revised

Library of Congress E437.L72

NL 0355256 DLC ViU PSt TxU OC1WHi

Life and public services of Hon. Willis A. Gorman.
(*In* Minnesota historical society. Collections. St. Paul, 1880. 24ᶜᵐ. v. 3, p. ₍314₎–332)
CONTENTS.—Obituary notices compiled from various St. Paul journals.—Eulogy pronounced before the Ramsey Co. bar association, by ex-Governor C. K. Davis.

1. Gorman, Willis Arnold, 1816–1876. I. Davis, Cushman Kellogg, 1838–1900.

18–9208

Library of Congress F601.M66 vol. 3

NL 0355257 DLC MB MnHi MdBP

Life and public services of John Charles Fremont, nominee of the black Republicans for President.' 3d ed., authorized and rev. [Albion, N.Y., 1856?]
14p. illus. 4½x4cm.

NL 0355258 CtY

Life and public services of Major-General Butler (Benjamin F. Butler.) The hero of New Orleans ... Philadelphia, T. B. Peterson & brothers ₍1864₎
1 p. l., 17–108 p. 20ᶜᵐ.
Portrait of Butler on front cover.

1. Butler, Benjamin Franklin, 1818–1893.

7—15665

Library of Congress E467.1.B87L7

NL 0355259 DLC MB PPL MWA NIC NjP LNHT NcU

The **life** and public services of Major-General McClellan, which includes a complete summary of his report. Written by a gentleman who accompanied him through his campaigns. Philadelphia, Martin & Randall, 1864.
84 p. 20ᶜᵐ.

1. McClellan, George Brinton, 1826–1885.

22-16588

Library of Congress E467.1.M2L6

NL 0355260 DLC OC1WHi NIC

Life and public services of Major-General Meade. (George Gordon Meade.) The hero of Gettysburg; and commander of the Army of the Potomac ... Philadelphia, T. B. Peterson & brothers ₍1864₎
1 p. l., 19–80 p. 20ᶜᵐ.

1. Meade, George Gordon, 1815–1872. I. Peterson, T. B., & bros., Philadelphia, pub.

12–23828

Library of Congress E467.1.M38L7

NL 0355261 DLC OC1WHi NIC PU MB

The **life** and public services of Major General Zachary Taylor, with graphic accounts of the battles of Palo Alto; Resaca de la Palma; Monterey, and Buena Vista ... With all his letters and despatches. Philadelphia, G. B. Zieber & co., 1847.
60 p. incl. front., illus. 18½ᶜᵐ.

1. Taylor, Zachary, pres. U. S., 1784–1850. 2. U. S.—Hist.—War with Mexico, 1845–1848—Campaigns and battles.

13–22192

Library of Congress E422.L75

NL 0355262 DLC TxU CU-B Nh

The **life** and public services of Major General Zachary Taylor, with graphic accounts of the battles of Palo Alto; Resaca de la Palma; Monterey, and Buena Vista ... With all his letters and despatches. Philadelphia, New York, Turner & Fisher ₍1848?₎
60 p. incl. front., illus. 19¼ᶜᵐ.

1. Taylor, Zachary, pres. U. S., 1784–1850. 2. U. S.—Hist.—War with Mexico, 1845–1848—Campaigns and battles.

13–22550

Library of Congress E422.L77

NL 0355263 DLC

The life and public services of the Hon. James Knox Polk
        see under [Hickman, George H   ]

VOLUME 332

Life and public services of Winfield Scott, general-in-chief of the army of the United States. Comprising his early life, his services in the war of 1812 ... and ... in the Mexican war ... Philadelphia, Lippincott, Grambo & co., 1852.

1 p. l., ₍9₎-78 p. front. (port.) plates. 19½ᶜᵐ.

1. Scott, Winfield, 1786-1866.

13-18343

Library of Congress   E403.1.S4L74

NL 0355265   DLC NcU

The life and reign of Busiris, King of Egypt. London, Printed for S. Redmayne, and sold by A. Morris, ₍1719?₎

NL 0355266   DFo CtY

The life and reign of Edward I.
     see under   [Seeley, Robert Benton] 1798-1886.

The life and reign of Henry the Sixth. Giving a full account of the English glory abroad. Their factions at home. The fatal treaty of Tours. The loss of France, and, the civil wars in England. About the hereditary and parliamentary right, between the two houses of York and Lancaster. London: Printed for A. Baldwin, 1712. 59 p. 19cm.

95401. 1. Henry VI, king of England, Hist.—Henry VI, 1422-1461.   1421-1471.   2. Great Britain—
Revised
September 13, 1938

NNC
NL 0355268   NN MB CLU-C C-S ICU MH CSmH ICN NIC DFo

Life and reign of Henry VI, author of.
    The history of the life and reign of Edward II. Containing a full account of the tyrannical government of his favourites and minions
     see under title

The life and reign of Her late excellent Majesty Queen Anne...
     see under   Chamberlen, Paul, fl. 1738.

The life and reign of Her Most Sacred Majesty
     see under   [Boyer, Abel] 1667-1729, comp.

₍Y940.7
In6b₎

The LIFE and reign of Innocent XI, late pope of Rome, London, Printed for Abel Roper, 1690.

2 p.ℓ., 76 p.   front. (port.) 21cm.

"To the reader" signed: T.L.
1. Innocentius XI, pope, 1611-1689.
I. L   , T

NSchU CLU-C
NL 0355272   MnU NNUT-Mc MH IU DFo CSmH InU CtY ICN

The life and reign of King Richard the second...
     see under   [Howard, Sir Robert] 1626-1698.

The life and reign of Richard II. Containing a full account of the sudden rise and fall of his three chief favourites, the Treasurer, the Chancellor, and Robert earl of Oxford, &c. Of the several invasions made on the laws of this kingdom₍:₎, and the rights of the subject, and of the grand revolution which followed. By deposing of Richard II. and advancing of Henry IV. With seasonable and useful reflections. London: Printed, and sold by A. Baldwin ... 1713.
2 p.l., 72 p.   18ᵐ.

WILLIAM ANDREWS CLARK MEMORIAL LIBRARY

First edition.
Signatures: ₍A₎², B-K⁴ (₍A₁₎ verso, advertisements)
Bound in half brown cloth.

NL 0355275   CLU-C RPB MH InU NN

The life and reign of the emperor Napoleon III
     see under   [The Illustrated London news]

The life and reigne of King Charles...
     see under   [Bos, Lambert van den] 1610-1698.

The life and reign of King Charles, or the pseudo-martyr discovered
     see under   [Milton, John] 1608-1674, supposed author.

BP75
.M152

The life and religion of Mohammed.

Majlisī, Muḥammad Bāqir ibn Muḥammad Taqī, 1627 or 8-ca. 1699.
    The life and religion of Mohammed, as contained in the Sheeāh traditions of the Hyât-ul-Kuloob, tr. from the Persian by James L. Merrick. Boston, Phillips, Sampson, 1850.

Life and reminiscences of General Wm. T. Sherman
     see under   [Fletcher, Thomas Clement] 1827-1899.

Tzz
340.92
B611ℓ

The Life and reminiscenses [!] of Hon. W.H. (Wick) Blanton, by his friends. Gonzales, Tex., Published by the Gonzales county news, 1940.
5p.ℓ.,101p. front.,ports. 22cm.

1. Blanton, Wick Horace, 1871-1937.

NL 0355281   TxU NNC

Life and reminiscences of Jefferson Davis. By distinguished men of his time. Introductory by Hon. John W. Daniel ... Baltimore, R. H. Woodward & company, 1890.

vᵗⁱⁱ, xⁱⁱⁱ-xvⁱⁱⁱ, 3-308 p. plates, ports. 19½ᵗᵐ. (*In* Johnson, B. T., ed. A memoir of the life and public service of Joseph E. Johnston ... Baltimore, 1891)

1. Davis, Jefferson, 1808-1889.   1. Daniel, John Warwick, 1842-1910.
11. Woodward, R. H. & company, Baltimore, pub.

Library of Congress   E467.1.J74J6   1-13596

NL 0355282   DLC OClWHi PPWa CoU PP PWcS

Life and reminiscences of Jefferson Davis. By distinguished men of his time. Introductory by Hon. John W. Daniel ... Baltimore, R. H. Woodward & company, 1890.

xviii, 490 p. front., plates, ports. 22½ᶜᵐ.

1. Davis, Jefferson, 1808-1889.   1. Daniel, John Warwick, 1842-1910.
11. Woodward, R. H., & company, Baltimore, pub.

Library of Congress   E467.1.D25L7   7-21596

GU-De MdBP MB Vi NjP OU
NL 0355283   DLC WaWW WaTC CaBVaU KyHi MsU LU NcD

Life and reminiscences of Jefferson Davis. By distinguished men of his time. Introductory by Hon. John W. Daniel ... Baltimore, R. H. Woodward & company, 1890.
xviii, 490 p. front., plates, ports. 22½ᵐ.

Authorized facsimile: Ann Arbor, Mich., University Microfilms, 1970.

NL 0355284   NcGU

There are no cards for numbers NL 0355285 to NL 0356000

The life and sayings of Sam P. Jones
     see under   [Jones, Laura (McElwain)]

M
287.08
W514
v.2

The life and sayings of the Rev. Philip Henry ... London, T. Cordeux, 1814.
12p. 19cm.

Theol.   Bound with other Methodist pamphlets.

1. Henry, Philip, 1631-1696.

NL 0356002   TxDaM CtY

Life and scenery in Missouri
     see under   [O'Hanlon, John] 1821-1905.

Life and scenes among the Kickapoo Indians ... [1889?]
     see under   Healy & Bigelow, firm, New Haven.

VOLUME 332

Life and select writings of the venerable servant of God, Louis-Marie Grignon de Montfort, missionary apostolic, tertiary of the holy Order of St. Dominic, and founder of the Congregation of the Missionaries of the Holy Ghost of Saint-Laurent-sur-Sevre, and of that of the Daughters of Wisdom. Translated from the French by a secular priest of the Third Order of Penance of St. Dominic. London. Richardson. 1870. lxxxiv, (4), 422 pp. 19 cm., in 8s. The select writings are catalogued separately.

H3986 — Grignon de Montfort, Louis ..arie. 1673-1716. — Secular priest, A, of the Third Order of Penance of St. Dominic, pseud., tr.

NL 0356005   MB DCU PLatS MiD

Life and sentiments of James Hooper
        see under   Hooper, James, b. 1769.

Life and sermons of the Rev. C. H. Spurgeon,
        from original documents ...
        see under   Spurgeon, Charles Haddon,
        1834-1892.

E
457
W75
1864

The Life and services as a soldier of Major-General Grant, the hero of Fort Donelson, Vicksburg and Chattanooga; commander of the military division of the Mississippi; and captor of 472 cannon and over ninety thousand rebel prisoners. Philadelphia, T. B. Peterson & Brothers [1864] 19-108 p. 19 cm.

Bound with [Williamson, David Brainerd] Life and public services of Abraham Lincoln.

Philadelphia [1864]

1. Grant, Ulysses Simpson, Pres. U.S., 1822-1885.

NL 0356009   WHi NIC N OrHi CSmH ICN NBuG OClWHi MiU

Life and services of Col. Richard Lathers of New Rochelle, N. Y. *n. p.* [1897] 7 pp. 8°.
    Gift of Andrew H. Green.

NL 0356010   NN

...Life and services of David French Boyd...
        see under   [Gunby, Andrew Augustus]
        1849-1917.

Life and services of Elihu Burritt, together with an account of his funeral, local editorial notices, and obituary resolutions. New Britain, Conn., R. J. Vance & co., printers, 1879.
    20 p. 22cm.

1. Burritt, Elihu, 1810-1879.

                                            21-22125
Library of Congress   PS1219.B7Z6

NL 0356012   DLC

The life and services of Gen. Geo. B. McClellan...
        see under   [Hurlbert, William Henry]
        1827-1895.

Life and services of Gen. Pierce, respectfully dedicated to Gen'l Lewis Cass.   Baltimore, 1852.
    14 p.   21.7 cm.
    A miniature pamphlet 3.7 x 2.5 cm. in slip case 21.7 cm. high.
    1. Pierce, Franklin, pres. U. S., 1804-1869.
    2. Campaign literature, 1852 - Whig.

NL 0356014   MiU-C

Life and services of Gen. Pierce, respectfully dedicated to Gen'l Lewis Cass. Concord (N. H.) Gazette press, 1852.
    14 p. 18½cm.
    A miniature pamphlet 4½ x 2½cm, the leaves mounted as an inset on blank sheets.

    1. Pierce, Franklin, pres. U. S., 1804-1869. 2. Campaign literature, 1852—Whig.
                                            17-1841
    Library of Congress   E432.L69

NL 0356015   DLC CtY RPJCB NN CSmH

Life and services of Gen. Pierce, respectfully dedicated to Gen'l Lewis Cass. Philadelphia, B. King, jr., 1852.
    16 p. incl. front. 4½ x 3cm.

    1. Pierce, Franklin, pres. U. S., 1804-1869. 2. Campaign literature, 1852—Whig.
                                            19-7869
    Library of Congress   E432.L692

NL 0356016   DLC CSmH

E415
.9
.H5L7
Lincoln

LIFE and services of General Thomas J. Henderson... [Springfield? 1911]
    30 p. port., facsim. 23cm.
    Reprinted from the Journal of the Illinois state historical society.
    Includes a biography by J.W.Templeton.

    1.Henderson,Thomas Jefferson,1824-1911.

NL 0356017   ICU

E672
L54

Life and services of General U. S. Grant, conqueror of the rebellion, and eighteenth president of the United States ...   Washington, D. C., Philp & Solomons, 1868c.
    160p.   23½cm.

    1. Grant, Ulysses Simpson, 1822-1885.
    I. Philip & Solomons, pub.

NL 0356018   NBuG DNW Nh OClWHi OO CtY

The Life and Services of John E. Dawson, 1872

TNSB has this on 1 roll of positive and negative microfilm.

NL 0356019   TNSB

The life and services of Major-General the Marquis de Lafayette.
= New York. Beadle & Co. [1870.] 91 pp. Plate. Colored portrait on cover. [Lives of great Americans. No. 5.] 16 cm.
    The preface is signed E. P. H.

M9661 — S.r. — Lafayette. Mari Paul Joseph Roch Ives Gilbert de Motier, Marquis de, 1757-1834.

NL 0356020   MB NN MH

The life and services to literature of Jones Very
        see under   Essex Institute, Salem, Mass.

Rare
HV
6248
S538
1787

The life and singular adventures of Jack Shepherd ... who was executed at the Old Bailey on the 22d of November, 1786 ... a footpad, a highwayman, a housebreaker, a shoplifter, and a forger ... To which is added an appendix, containing several new and interesting facts relative to the three murderers .. executed ... December 18, 1786, with the confession of Richard Payne. A new   ed., corr. London, S. Bladon,   1787.

    viii, 62 p. 21cm.

    Publisher's advertisement: p. [i]

    1. Shepherd, Jack, d. 1786. 2. Walker, Michael, d. 1786.   3. Payne, Richard, d. 1786. 4. Cox,   John, d. 1786. I. Payne, Richard,   d. 1786.

NL 0356023   NIC NN

---

*A08
B6750
833t

The life and sketches of curious and odd characters. Illustrated with twenty-four engravings.
    Boston:Published by George Clarke.1833.
    192p.incl.front.,illus. 17cm.
    Woodcut illustrations by Abel Bowen.
    Brief biographies of various English eccentrics.
    Original printed pink boards.

NL 0356024   MH CtY

Life, The, and sketches of curious and odd characters.
— Boston. Gaylord. 1840. 3-192 pp. Illus. 16 cm., in 6s. English characters.
A manuscript note on the title-page ascribes the engravings to Abel Bowen.

H6374 — Great Britain. Biog. — Bowen, Abel, illus. 1790-1850. — Eccentrics.

NL 0356025   MB MH CtY

The life and speeches of Abraham Lincoln, and Hannibal Hamlin
        see under   Vose, Reuben.

Life and spirit of J. B. M. Champagnat, priest and founder of the society of the Little Brothers of Mary, by one of his first disciples; translated from the French.   London: Burns & Oates, Ld., 1887. 491 p.   pl., port., tables. 8°.

1. Champagnat, Joseph Benoit Mar-   cellin. 2. Little Brothers of Mary. N. Y. P. L.   December 5, 1916.

NL 0356027   NN MB ODaU

The Life and spiritual sufferings of that faithful servant of Christ, Jane Hoskens
        see under   Hoskens, Jane (Fenn),1694-

The life and strange surprising adventures of Major A. Ramkins
        see   Defoe, Daniel, 1661 ?-1731.
        The memoirs of Majr. Alexander Ramkins.

The life and strange surprizing adventures of Mr. D---- De F--
        see under   [Gildon, Charles] 1665-1724.

VOLUME 332

The life and strange surprizing adventures of
Robinson Crusoe ...
    see   Defoe, Daniel, 1661?-1731.
Robinson Crusoe.

The life, and strange, unparallel'd and unheard-of
voyages and adventures of Ambrose Gwinett,...
    see under   [Bickerstaffe, Isaac] d. 1812
supposed author.

The life and sufferings of Cecelia Mayo, founded on incidents
in real life. Boston, M. Aurelius, 1843. 36 p. illus. 18cm.

Fictitious account.

I. Title: Cecelia Mayo.
N. Y. P. L.   July 7, 1950

NL   0356033   NN CtY ICN IU ViU NNC CU DLC

The life and sufferings of Miss Emma Cole
    see under   Hanson, Emma (Cole)

Life (The) and surprising adventures of Bigenio,
an hermaphrodite, or man-woman and woman-
man. 93pp. 1 pl. 12°. *London, H. Smith.* [n.d.]

NL   0356035   DNLM

The life and surprising adventures of blue-
eyed Patty, the valiant female soldier, who was
the daughter of Mr. Samuel Freelove... 8p.
Wolverhampton, Printed by J. Hately [18-]

A chap-book.

NL   0356036   OC1

The life and surprising adventures of Captain Talbot, containing
a curious account of the various changes and gradations of this
extraordinary character... The whole forming a complete series
of singular incidents and entertaining adventures. London:
Printed by Barnard and Sultzer for Tegg and Castleman[, 1803].
4 p.l., 147 p.   12°.

1. Talbot, Silas, 1751-1813. 2. United   States—Hist.—Revolution—Military.
3. Navy, U. S.—Hist.—Revolution.
N. Y. P. L.   May 29, 1925

NL   0356037   NN MiU-C RPJCB

**The life and surprising adventures of
Colonel Blood; detailing the plots
and conspiracies in which he was
concerned... Forming a chain of the
most daring enterprises ever recorded in English history.   London,
Printed for T. Redriffe [1825?]
12p. front. D.**

NL   0356038   IaU

The life and surprizing adventures of Crusoe
Richard Davis ...
    see under   Bannac, Adolphus, supposed
author.

---

*Defoe
30
.761
.A10L   The life and surprizing adventures of Don Antonio de Trezzanio, who was self-educated, and
lived forty-five years in an uninhabited island
in the East-Indies. London, Printed for H. Serjeant, 1761.
158 p. plates. 15cm.
Ex libris (autograph notation on t. p.): Robert Southey. Keswick. 17 May 1830.

1. Voyages, Imaginary.

NL   0356040   MB

The life and surprising adventures of Frederick
Baron Trenck
    see under   Trenck, Frederich, freiherr
von der, 1726-1794.

The life and surprising adventures of Mirandor.
Translated from the Dutch... 1730. 2 v.

    see under [Heinsius, Nicolaas] 1656-1718

The life and surprising adventures of Robinson
Crusoe
    see under [Defoe, Daniel] 1661-1731.
Robinson Crusoe.

The life and surprising adventures of Robinson
Crusoe of York, mariner
    see   Defoe, Daniel, 1661?-1731.
Robinson Crusoe.

D94
t815   ~~The life and surprising adventures of Sir
William Wallace, the champion of Scotland.
Glasgow:Printed for M'Kenzie & Hutchison,
booksellers,16, Saltmarket.[1820?]
24p. 15cm. [Penny histories]
Title-vignette (woodcut of Sir William)~~

NL   0356045   CtY DLC NN

---

no. 25
The LIFE and surprising adventures of that renowned
hero, Sir W. Wallace. Durham, G. Walker,
Jun., printer, 1838.   24 p. 18cm.

Weiss: Chapbooks, 454.
"The tears of Scotland," p. 19-21. In verse.
"Peter, the wild boy," p. 21-22.
"Adventures of a leg of mutton," p. 22-24.
Without covers.

*KVD p. v, 16, no. 11.
---- Second copy.

1. Wallace, Sir William, ca. 1270-1305.

NL   0356047   NN

Life and surprising adventures of the celebrated
John Smith, first settler of Virginia
    see under [Davis, John] 1774-1854.

The life and surprising atchievements, real and
truly singular adventures of Samuel Simkins,
Esq.
    see under   Parkinson, Peter.

The life and surprising exploits of that notorious housebreaker and foot-pad, Jack Sheppard; containing his wonderful escapes from Newgate, and other prisons: to which is added,
his own account of himself, as he left it in manuscript for publication. London, Printed and sold by J. Bailey [n. d.]
36 p. col. front. 18°.

1. Sheppard, Jack, 1702-1724.

Library of Congress   HV6248.S56L5   46-43213

NL   0356050   DLC

PR3291
.L75
1766   The life and surprizing adventures of Don Antonio de
Trezzanio, who was self-educated, and lived forty-five years
in an uninhabited island in the East Indies. Written by
Salandio the Hermit ... Tr. from the Portuguese. London, Printed for H. Serjeant, 1766.
160 p. front., plates. 18cm.

NL   0356051   ICU

The life and teachings of Jesus Christ, in the
words of the King James Version ...
    see under   Bible. N.T. Gospels.
English. Harmonies. 1937? Authorized.
(New York, Coverdale Bible Press; Philadelphia,
Winston) Also: 1940? (N.Y., Coverdale Bible
Press)

The life and teachings of Our Lord. In Verse,
being a complete harmonized exposition of
the four Gospels, with original notes, textual
index, etc. ...
    see under   Coles, Abraham, 1813-1891.

Life and teaching of the masters of the Far East
    see under [Spalding, Baird T   ]

Life and teachings series.

Ananda Kutir, Sivananda Publication League, 194
v. ports. 19 cm.

1. Sivananda, Swami. I. Sivananda Publication League.

B133.S73L5   181.4   50-26332‡

NL   0356055   DLC

Life and the conditions of survival; the physical
basis of ethics, sociology and religion
    see under   Brooklyn ethical association.

**LIFE and theatrical career of John Mathews,
champion swordsman, showman, dogman, and
pantomimist.** 4 nos in 1 vol. [London,1874]

NL   0356057   MH

The life and theatrical excursions of William Robert Grossmith, the juvenile actor, who
appeared at the London theatres in the character of Richard III. &c. when but five years
and a half old; now in the tenth year of his
age ... Fourth edition. Reading, Printed and
published by M. Cowslade and Co., 1829.
22 p.

Critiques from newspaper articles in pocket.

NL   0356058   NNC MH NN

VOLUME 332

The life and time, of Col. Daniel
Boone, the hunter of Kentucky, with
sketches of his contemporaries; narrative
of St. Clair's defeat; Mrs. Merrill's
adventures, etc. ... New York, 1860.
96 p.

NL 0356059   OFH

LIFE and time of Jimmy Walker; outline of an original
screenplay, approved by James J. Walker.
[Hollywood, Calif.] 1941. 102 l. 28cm.

1. Moving picture plays--Texts and outlines. 2. Walker, James John,
1881-1946--Drama. 3. Cinema--Scripts. 4. Drama--Historical
characters--Walker, James   John, 1881-1946.

NL 0356060   NN

E
667
L72

Life and times of Andrew Johnson, seven
teenth president of the United States.
Written from a national stand-point, by a
national man.   New York, D. Appleton,
1866.
xii, 363 p. port. 20cm.

1. Johnson, Andrew, Pres. U. S., 1808-
1875.

NL 0356061   NIC TxFTC PLF NBC PP ICN IU NjP MB

Life and Times of Burke & Hare
see under   Burke, William, 1792-1829

The life and times of Captain John Piper
see under   Eldershaw, M. Barnard, pseud.

...The life and times of Charlemagne. [London:] Religious
Tract Soc.[, 1854?] 192 p. 15½cm.
(Religious Tract So-
ciety, London. Monthly series.)
Cover-title.

603517A. 1. Charlemagne, 742-814.   I. Religious Tract Society, London.
N. Y. P. L.   March 6, 1934

NL 0356064   NN

Life and times of Charlemagne. Rev. by Thomas O.
Summers. Nashville, Tenn., Published by A. H. Redford,
agent, for the M. E. Church, South, 1872.
188 p. 16 cm.

1. Charlemagne, 742-814.   I. Summers, Thomas Osmond, 1812-
1882, ed.
DC73.8.L53   52-54013 ‡

NL 0356065   DLC

The life and times of Christopher Carson
see under   [Ellis, Edward Sylvester]
1840-1916.

The life and times of Conrad the squirrel...
see under   [Noel, Lady Augusta]

B
01781

The life and times of Daniel O'Connell.
With the beauties of his principal
speeches.   Dublin, 1846.
144p.

Bound with The life and beauties of
... John Philpot Curran. 1846; The
beauties of the principal speeches of
Henry Grattan; Lives and times of the
United Irishmen: Lord Edward Fitzgerald;
Selections of Irish national poetry.

NL 0356068   IU

Life and times of Daniel O'Connell, with
sketches of his contemporaries. Compiled from
the works of W. J. O'N. Daunt, Mr. Fegan, R. L.
Sheil, etc. etc. Dublin, J. Mullany, 1867.
2 v.

1. O'Connell, Daniel, 1775-1847. I. Fagan,
William, 1801-1859, jt. au. II. Sheil, Richard
Lalor, 1791-1851, jt. au. III. Title.

NL 0356069   NNC MB

Life and times of Daniel O'Connell, with sketches of his contempo-
raries. Compiled from the works of O'Neill Daunt, John
O'Connell, Fagan, Sheil, etc. With An address to the people of
Ireland, by J. R. O'Flanagan.
— Dublin. Mullany. 1875. xx, (12), 780 pp. Portrait. 48½ cm.,
in 12s.
At head of title: Centenary of O'Connell.
The address by O'Flanagan is catalogued separately.

M3618 — O'Connell, Daniel, 1775-1847.

NL 0356070   MB

Life and times of David Humphreys, soldier-
statesman-poet, "belov'd of Washington ...
see under   Humphreys, Francis Landon,
1858-

Life and times of Francis the first, King of
France
see under   Bacon, James.

The life and times of Garibaldi, the Italian hero
and patriot
see under   [Blackett, Howard]

The life and times of George Robert Fitzgerald,
commonly called Fighting Fitzgerald
see under   Fitzgerald, George Robert,
1748-1786, defendant.

The life and times of Girolamo Savonarola
see under   [Heraud, John Abraham]
1799-1887.

Life and times of Hezekiah. P., 1863.

NL 0356076   PPL

The life and times of Hon. Elijah Stansbury
see under   [Hawkins, Archibald]
1766-1851.

The life and times of Hon. Schuyler Colfax, speaker of
the United States House of representatives and Republican candidate for the vice-presidency. By a distinguished historian. Comprising an authentic account of
the life and public services of this distinguished orator,
patriot and statesman. New York, E. B. Treat & co.;
Chicago, Ill., C. W. Lilley; [etc., etc.] ʻ1868.
cover-title, 50 p. incl. port. 20ᵐ.
Campaign biography.
1. Colfax, Schuyler, 1823-1885.

Library of Congress   E415.9.C68L7   7-19547

NL 0356078   DLC

The life and times of Hon. William P. Ross, of
the Cherokee nation
see under   [Ross, William Potter] 1820-
1891.

Life and times of John de Wycliffe ...   Philadelphia, American Sunday-school union; London, Religious tract society
[1851?]
viii, 9–192 p. 15ᵐᵐ.

1. Wycliffe, John, d. 1384.   I. American Sunday-school union.
                                                                32-30337
Library of Congress   BX4905.L5   922.342

NL 0356080   DLC NcD ViLxW FMU

Life and times of John de Wycliffe; rev. by Thos.
O. Summers, D.D.   Nashville, Tenn.,
Stevenson & Owen, 1856.
178 p. S.

NL 0356081   NcU

Life and times of John de Wycliffe, revised by Thos. O.
Summers, D. D. Nashville, Tenn., Southern Methodist publishing house, 1885.
viii, [9]–178 p. 15¼ᵐ.

1. Wycliffe, John, d. 1384.   I. Summers, Thomas Osmond, 1812-1882.
                                                                41-28892
Library of Congress   BX4905.L5 1885

NL 0356082   DLC

Life and times of John Wycliffe, the
morning star of the reformation. [Lon-
don] The Religious tract society, 1884.
160p. front.(port.),plates,facsim. 18½cm.
Second edition.

1. Wycliffe, John.

NL 0356083   NRU NNUT CtY

LS30
W97
X626

Life and times of John Wycliffe, the Morning
Star of the Reformation. [2d ed. London]
Religious Tract Society, 1884.
160 p. illus., facsim., port. 18 cm.

Bibliographical footnotes.

1. Wycliffe, John, d.1384.   I. Religious
Tract Society, London(2)

NL 0356084   CtY-D

The life and times of John Huss, Author of,
Life lessons in the school of Christian duty
see under   [Gillett, Ezra Hall] 1823-1875.

VOLUME 332

The life and times of John Kettlewell; with details
of the history of the Nonjurors
see under   Carter, Jane Frances Mary.

The life and times of John Tomline Walsh, with
biographical and historical sketches and
reflections on contemporary men and things.
Ed. by a member of his family.   Cincinnati,
Standard, 1885.
171 p.   D.

NL   0356087   NcD NcU NcWsW

Life and times of Joseph Gould
see under   Higgins, W   H
of Toronto.

The life and times of King George the Fifth and King Edward the Eighth; a pictorial record preceded by short biographies. London, P. R. Gawthorn, ltd. [1937]
2 p. l., 16, [341] p. incl. 339 p. of illus. front. (port.) 31ᶜᵐ.
A new edition of "King George the Fifth, his life and times, 1865-
1936" with additional material on King Edward the Eighth.

1. George v, king of Great Britain. 1865-1936. 2. Edward viii, king
of Great Britain, 1894-   3. Gt. Brit.—Hist.—George v, 1910-1936—
Pictorial works.
                                                              37-19584
Library of Congress   DA573.K48 1937
                               [3]   923.142

NL   0356089   DLC OU

The Life and times of King George vi, 1895-1952. London,
Odhams Press [1952]
159 p. illus., ports. 26 cm.

1. George vi, King of Great Britain, 1895-1952.   i. Odhams
Press, ltd.
DA584.L5   923.142   52-2389

NL   0356090   DLC MiU MB NcGU OCl IdU WaT CaBVaU CaBViP

The life and times of Leo the Tenth. Philadelphia c18-.
see under   American Sunday-school union.

Life and times of Leo the Tenth. N.Y., 1854.
Edited by D. P. Kidder.

I. Kidder, Daniel Parish, 1815-1891, ed.

NL   0356092   ODW

(The) life and times of Leo the tenth.
BX1315   London, The religious tract society [1880?]
L5
192p.   14½cm.   (The religious tract
society.   The monthly volume.   no. 54)

1. Leo X, pope, 1475-1521.

NL   0356093   NBuG

356871   The life and times of Lord Edward
Fitzgerald.   Dublin, 1867.
256p. ports.

NL   0356094   IU

The life and times of Martin Luther
see under   [Lee, Mrs. Hannah Farnham
(Sawyer)] 1780-1865.

The life and times of Queen Victoria; with which is incorporated
The domestic life of the queen, by Mrs. Oliphant.   London: Cassell and Co., Ltd. [18—?]   4 v.   illus., pl., port.   8°.

1. Victoria, queen of Great Britain.   CENTRAL RESERVE.
century.   2. Great Britain.—History: 19th
N. Y. P. L.   August 31, 1916.

NL   0356096   NN NIC MB PSt PPRCl

Life and times of Rev. Thomas M. Hudson,
of the Pittsburgh annual conference of the
Methodist Episcopal church
see under   Hudson, Thomas M., 1799-

The life and times of Rienzi ...
see under   [Du Cerceau, Jean Antoine]
1670-1730.

...The life and times of Robert Emmet, from authoritative
sources.   London: J. Ouseley, Ltd., 1908.   96 p.   port.
8°.   (The Irish library. no. I.)

193159A. 1. Emmet, Robert, 1778-
rebellion, 1803. 3. Ser.   1803. 2. Ireland—Hist.—Emmet's
N. Y. P. L.   September 17, 1925

NL   0356099   NN IU

The life and times of Sam written by himself
see under   [Chase, Henry]

The life and times of Selina, countess of
Huntingdon
see under   [Seymour, Aaron Crossley
Hobart] 1789-1870.

The life and times of Sir Philip Sidney
see under   [Davis, Sarah Matilda Henry]

Life and times of Sir Robert Peel
see under   [Taylor, William Cooke]
1800-1849.

The life and times of that excellent and renowned actor
Thomas Betterton ... with such notices of the stage and English history, before and after the restoration, as serve generally to illustrate the subject.   By the author and ed. of the
lives of "Mrs. Abingdon," "James Quin," etc., etc. London,
Reader, 1888.
2 p. l., 160 p. front. (port.) 20ᶜᵐ.

1. Betterton, Thomas, 1635?-1710.
                                                          1—21875
Library of Congress   PN2598.B6L4

NL   KMK PU MiU MB NjP CtY NcGU
0356104   DLC NcD TxU MH MWA MdBP MnCS NN NIC NNC

The Life and times of the Blessed Brother Solo-
BX   mon of the Institute of the Brothers of the Christian Schools.
4705   Paris, Procure Générale des Frères, 1927.
S669L5   204 p. illus. 19cm.

"Adapted and abridged from the French life of Brother
Solomon by Monseigneur Chassagnon (at Martinez, California)"

1. Solomon, Brother,. 1745-1792. 2. Brothers of the
Christian Schools.   I. Chassagnon, Hyacinthe. Life of
Brother Solomon.

NL   0356105   CMenSP

---

life and times of the Duke of Wellington...
the military career... his services in India...
the battle of Waterloo... Phil, Leary pref., 1842.

NL   0356106   PPA

Life and times of the Duke of Wellington; embracing the whole
military career of this illustrious warrior; his services in India, the
Peninsular war, and a full and complete account of the memorable
battle of Waterloo, with all the spirit-stirring incidents and anecdotes of these memorable contests...   Philadelphia: W. A. Leary
& co., 1850.   252 p.   front. (port.), illus.   16cm.

Bibliographical footnotes.

824463A. 1. Wellington, Arthur   Wellesley, 1st duke of, 1769-1852.
N. Y. P. L.   June 7, 1937

NL   0356107   NN

Life and times of the Rev. Philip Henry, M.A. ...
see under   [Henry, Matthew] 1662-1714.

The life and times of Thomas Cranmer
see under   [Lee, Mrs. Hannah Farnham
(Sawyer)] 1780-1865.

Bz84   The life and times of Thomas Francis Meagher
M464   ... [n.p.,1867?]
867ℓ   160p.incl.port.   22cm.
Caption-title.
Notes, p.[3] and 8, signed: J.C.W.

NL   0356110   CtY

The life and times of William P. Ross
see under   Ross, William Potter, 1820-1891.

PR   The life and times of William Shakspeare.
2894   With an account of his plays and their plots
.L72   ... London, W.S.Sonnenschein & co. [188-?]
xi,244 p.   front.,illus.(facsim.),pl.,2 port.
19cm.

1.Shakespeare,William,1564-1616.

NL   0356112   MiU

Life and times of Shakespeare: actor and dramatist.
London. Vickers. [1864?] 16 pp. Portrait. Autograph facsimile. 19 cm.

K2666 — Shakespeare, William. Biog. and crit.

NL   0356113   MB

The life and times of William Lilly
see under   Lilly, William, 1602-1681.

VOLUME 332

PR2894
.L5
1888
The life and times of William Shakspeare.
With an account of his plays and their plots.
2d ed. London, S. Sonnenschein, Lowrey,
1888.
xi, 244 p. 19cm.
Running title: Shakespeare and his contemporaries.

1. Shakespeare, William, 1564-1616. 2.
Shakespeare, William—Plots.

NL 0356114   ViU MiU

Life and tomorrow
see under [Craigie, Mrs. Pearl Mary—
Teresa (Richards)] 1867-1906.

The life and tragic death of Jesse James
see Jesse James: the life and daring
adventures...

456. The LIFE AND TRANSACTIONS of Mrs.
JANE SHORE, concubine to King Edward IV.
Containing an account of her parentage, wit
and beauty; her marriage with Mr. Shore; the
King's visits to her; her going to court, and
leaving her husband; her great distress and
misery after the king's death, &c. [Woodcut.]
Edinburgh: Printed for the booksellers in town
and country.   * KVD p.v.11, no.12
15.5 x 10 cm. 24 p.
In prose.

NL 0356117   NN

The life and transactions of Mrs. Jane
Shore, concubine to King Edward IVth.
Adventure of Allan Barclay, a private
soldier in the------ regiment. Love and
torture. Glasgow, Printed for the
booksellers [1840?]
24 p. 17cm. [Chap books. v.2,
no.5]
"[No.] 8."
1. Shore, Jane, d. 1527?

NL 0356118   MnU CSmH OCl

The life and travels of Alexander von Humboldt
see under [Stoddard, Richard Henry] 1825-
1903.

Life and travels of Elder William Conrad, being
a brief sketch of the nativity and marriage, call by
grace to the obtaining of eternal life, call to the
work of the ministry ... history of the old Baptist
church of Christ, at Williamstown and Forklick,
Grant county, Raysfork, Scott county and Twin Creek,
Harrison county, Ky. Cinc., Wrighton & co., 1876.

NL 0356120   OCU

The life and travels of James Tudor Owen;
Owen; who, amidst a variety of other interesting particulars, gives an account of his
being in an East Indian campaign; and his
singular adventures while among the Hindoos;
as also his voyage, shipwreck, and journey
with a troop of wild roving Arabs over
immense burning sands, and trackless desarts.
He embarks from the Egyptian shore for Ireland, and there, during the late war with
America, gains an ensigncy to go with the
British forces   against that country.

Is wounded in battle, and taken by the
Agiguans, a warlike nation inhabiting the
wilds of America ... London: Printed by S.
Fisher [1805]
42 p. front. 19cm.

1. Voyages and travels. 2. Tudor—Owen, James.

NL 0356121   ViU

The life and travels of John Pemberton, a
minister of the Gospel of Christ
see under [Hodgson, William]

The life and travels of Josiah Mooso. A life on the
frontier among Indians and Spaniards, not seeing the
face of white woman for fifteen years ... Winfield, Kan.,
Telegram print, 1888.
400 p. front. (port.) 20cm.
Mooso was of a Canadian family, and came to the U. S. in the thirties.
The greater part of the book relates to his adventures on the western frontier in the forties and early fifties. Settled in Cowley Co., Kan., about 1870.
1. Mooso, Josiah, b. 1803. 2. Frontier and pioneer life—The West.
3. Cowley Co., Kan. 4. Salvation army.

Library of Congress   F591.M82   12-27349

NL 0356122   DLC CaBViPA KMK UU NjP PPRF MnU CtY

The life and travels of Mungo Park; with the
account of his death ...
see under Park, Mungo, 1771-1806.

The life and travels of the apostle Paul. Prepared with
questions for the use of Sunday schools ... Boston, Lilly, Wait,
Colman, and Holden, 1833.
1 p. l., [vii]-xi, [13]-272 p. front. (fold. map) 16½cm.

1. Paul, Saint, apostle.

Library of Congress   BS2505.L5   39-10468

[2]   [922.1] 225.92

NL 0356124   DLC MH-AH CtY NN

Life and travels of Thomas Thumb, in the United States,
England, France, and Belgium. With illustrations of him
in his different costumes. Philadelphia, Lindsay and
Blakiston [1849]
1 p. l., 144 p. front., ports. 15½ x 12cm.
Added t-p., illus.

1. Stratton, Charles Sherwood, 1838-1883.

Library of Congress   GN69.5.S9L5   15-3356

NL 0356125   DLC OClWHi OrU

Life and trial for murder of Wilson Howard
see under [Erwin, Frederick Alphonso]

... The life and trial of Eugene Aram, who was executed
for the murder of Daniel Clark (of Knaresborough)
With some account of his family; the remarkable defence
he made on his trial; his own account of himself, written
after his condemnation; with the apology which he left
in his cell, for the attempt he made on his own life.
Containing also The dream of Eugene Aram, a poem, by
Thomas Hood, esq. Leeds [Eng.] J. Johnson; [etc., etc.,
187-?]
30 p. 17½cm. (Johnson's cheap library)
1. Aram, Eugene, 1704-1759. 2. Clark, Daniel, d. 1745.

16-21840

Library of Congress   HV6248.A7L4

NL 0356127   DLC OrU

qT364
J232Bt
1883r
The life and trial of Frank James. [New
York, Frank Tousey, 1883?]
21p. illus. 29cm. (The Wide awake li-
brary, special number, Sept. 28, 1883)
Caption title.
Facsimile reprint made by the Dime Novel
Club, 194-. Cf. Bragin, Charles. Catalogue
no.16. 1946. p.[3] of cover.

1. James, Frank, 1844-1915. I. Series.

NL 0356128   TxU KU NNC AU N CtY CU-B CU

The life and trial of John Rann, alias Sixteen-
string Jack, for robbery
see under Rann, John, 1750?-1774?
defendant.

920.7
B317
The life and trial of Mary Bateman, the
Yorkshire witch; traced from the earliest
thefts of her infancy... till her execution
at the New Drop, York; with a full account
of her trial. Containing also, the whole of
the letters written to William Perigo and
other very valuable and interesting particulars.
Leeds, J. Johnson [181-?]
32p. 18cm. in cover 21cm. (Cheap penny
series, no.5)

1. Bateman, Mary Harker) 1768-1809.
2. Witchcraft.   I. Series.

NL 0356130   OrU

HV6248
.B7L5   Life and trial of Perry Bowsher, convicted
Office of the murder of Edwin S. and Ann McVoy...
1878
1 pam.   8°

NL 0356131   DLC

The LIFE and trial of Richard Turpin a Notorious highwayman, containing a particular accoun
of his adventures. To which is added the Life
of Sawney Beane, the man eater. A new edition
with additions. London, printed by T.Maiden
for A Lemoine and J.Roe, [1803]
nar.12°. pp.38. Front-engraved.

NL 0356132   MH

The life and trial of Richard Turpin
see also The life of Richard Turpin [1807?]

Life (The) and trial of the child murderess,
Charlotte Winsor; containing her correct portrait as she appeared at the dock, sketch of the
cottage in which the murders took place, trial
at the Devon assizes, full account of her love
and dissolute habits, account of her three mar-
riages, supposed number of her victims, fearful

revelation of infanticide in England. 16 pp.
8°. London, [n. d.].
Bound with: TRIAL (The) and examination of Dr. Hunter [etc.]. 8°. London, [n. d.].

NL 0356134   DNLM

Life (The) and trial of the four prisoners connected with the Penge murder. Summing up!
Verdict! Sentence! And interesting particulars
never before published, with large and correct
portraits. "Police News" ed. 16pp. 8°. [Lon-
don, G. Purkess, 1877.]

NL 0356135   DNLM

VOLUME 332

Life and Trial of the unfortunate Spence Broughton, who suffered death at Tyburn near York, 1792 for robbing the Rotherham Mail. Taken in Court. 3d ed.　Lincoln, n. d.
20 p.　12°.
In vol. backtitled:- Pamphlets.

NL 0356136　MH-L

The life and trial of Thomas Muir, esq., advocate, of Huntershill, near Glasgow, one of the celebrated reformers of 1792-1793, who was tried for sedition before the high court of justiciary in Scotland, and sentenced to transportation for fourteen years ...　Rutherglen, P. Walsh, 1919.
p.[3]-93,18cm.

NL 0356137　CaBViPA

The life and trials of a young lady convert ...
　　see under　[Heggie, Cora M　A　]
1861-

Life and trip around the world of General U. S. Grant...　Chicago, Frank Roehr, ptr. & pub. n. d.
15 p. ports. (on cover)

Cover-title.
Printed in double columns.

NL 0356139　MiD-B

Life and triumphant death of Theodocia Maxey. Philadelphia, 1794.

NL 0356140　PPL

Beinecke Library
DA483
F85
L55
1717

The life and unaccountable actions of William Fuller, alias Esq; Fuller, alias Colonel, alias Sir William, alias William Baron Fuller, the notorious English cheat ...　The 2d ed. with large additions continued down to this present time. London, A. Bettesworth and J. Stone, [1717]
5 p.ℓ.,.182 [i.e.206] p. .14½ cm.
1st ed. pub. 1701 with title: The life of Wm. Fuller, alias Fullee, alias Fowler.
Errors in paging: 205-206 numbered 181-182.

1. Fuller, William, 1670-1733. I. The life of Wm. Fuller, alias Fullee ... 2d ed.

NL 0356142　CtY IU

The life and unparalleled voyages and adventures of Ambrose Gwinett
　　see under　[Bickerstaffe, Isaac] d. 1812?
supposed author.

---

x B
W668ℓ

The life and villainous actions of that notorious offender, Jonathan Wild, who was executed at Tyburn on Monday the 24th of May last. Containing a full account of his secret correspondence with thieves: the methods he took to make himself their head, and his manner of governing all sorts of thieves.　London, Printed for T. Catesby [1725?]
29p.　20cm.

Upper margins　　closely trimmed.

NL 0356144　IU TxU

---

439. The LIFE & VISIONS OF NICHOLAS HART. In which are particularly described the state of blessed spirits in the heavenly Canaan: and also a description of the condition of the damned in a state of punishment; as revealed to him in several visions or trances. Faithfully narrated by William Hill, senior, of Lincoln's Inn. London. And attested on oath by the said Nicholas Hart. Newcastle upon Tyne: Printed by J. Marshall, in the Old Flesh-Market. Where may also be had, a large and interesting collection of songs, ballads, tales, histories, &c. n. d.
17 × 9.5 cm. 24 p.　　* KVD p.v.12, no.1
In prose.
"Falkirk, Printed by T. Johnston."

NL 0356145　NN

The life and voyages of Christopher Columbus ... 1871
　　see under　[Lamartine, Alphonse Marie Louis de] 1790-1869.

... The life and voyages of Christopher Columbus, with many illustrations, being the Washington almanac for the year 1892.　New York, The Washington life insurance co. [1892?]
64 p. incl. front. (port.) illus. 21½cm.

1. Colombo, Cristoforo.　I. Washington life insurance company, New York.

18-13574

Library of Congress　　E111.L7

NL 0356147　DLC CSmH

The life and voyages of Verrazzano ...
　　see under　[Greene, George Washington]
1811-1883.

The life and wanderings of a mouse
　　see under　[Kilner, Dorothy] 1755-1836.

The life and wanderings of the hardy Norseman, Christian Jacobsen Drakenberg
　　see under　[Mönsted, P.]

The LIFE and wonderful adventures of Henry Lanson who was left on shore at an uninhabited island; his mode of life and discovery of the ruins of an ancient temple, and an oracle of the sun, made of pure gold, the manner he converted the natives of a nieghbouring island to Christianity.　London, printed for J. Kendrew, [1800?].

pp.40.　Front.

NL 0356151　MH

The LIFE and wonderful prophecies of Donald Cargill. Who was executed at the Cross of Edinburgh, on the 26th July, 1680. For his adherence to the Covenant, and work of reformation.　Glasgow, Printed for the booksellers [1830?]　24 p. 16cm.

Weiss: Chapbooks, 462.
On t. p.: 123.
Without covers.
In prose and verse.
1. Cargill, Donald, 1619?-1681.

NL 0356152　NN OCU MnU OC1

The life and words of Christ
　　see under　Geikie, John Cunningham, 1824-1906.

Life and work; a parish magazine
　　see　Life and work, the record of the Church of Scotland.

IIN1
.L5

Life and work; bulletin of the International Social Institute.
no. 1-
mai 1927-
Genève.

nos. in　v. ports. 23 cm. irregular.
Pub. in Zürich, May-Nov. 1927.
Some articles in English, some in French, some in German.
Ceased publication with no. 10 (June 1930) being superseded by the Institute's News letter. Cf. Union list of serials.

1. Church and social problems—Period.　I. International Social Institute.

HN1.L5　　50-43361

NL 0356155　DLC NN ICU

Life and work; daily bulletin of Universal Christian conference at Stockholm. no. 1-12; Aug. 19-30, 1925. [Stockholm] 1925.
1 v. illus. 39½ᶜᵐ.
Caption title.
No more published.
L. C. set incomplete: no. 10-11 wanting.

1. Universal Christian conference on life and work, Stockholm, 1925.

26-10914
Library of Congress　　BR41.U6A3

NL 0356156　DLC

Period.
1076

Life and work, the Record of the Church of Scotland. v.1-　1879-
Edinburgh.
v. 26cm. monthly.

Founded 1879 as Life and work; a parish magazine.
1901, absorbed Home and foreign mission record of the Church of Scotland, and Missionary record of the United Presbyterian Church.

1929, united with The Record of the United Free Church of Scotland.
Numerous irregularities in numbering.

1. Church of Scotland - Periodicals.
2. Scotland - Church history.

NL 0356158　MH-AH

Life and work of Abraham Lincoln.
See
[Hill, John Wesley] 1863-1936.
Speeches and writings of John Wesley Hill ...

The life & work of Benjamin Jowett, reminiscences & memorials by friends & pupils
　　see under　Westminster Gazette.

Life and work of Francis David
　　see under　[Boros, György]

The life and work of Francis Jacob Ruth
　　see under　[Crouse, J　] ed.

... The life and work of General John A. Sutter ...
　　see under　[Landis, Jacob B　]

VOLUME 332

Life and work of His Eminence D. Cardinal Dougherty and history of St. Charles Seminary. June 10, 1928.

143p. front. (col. port.) illus. 30cm.

At top of title page: Official jubilee volume.
1. Dougherty, Denis Joseph, Cardinal, 1865-1951. 2. Catholic church in Philadelphia. 3. Philadelphia (Archdiocese)--History. 4. Philadelphia, Pa. St. Charles Borromeo Seminary.

NL 0356164   PLatS

The life and work of Innocent, the archbishop of Kamchatka, the Kuriles and the Aleutian Islands, and later the metropolitan of Moscow
    see under   [Barsukov, Ivan Platonovich]

---

f N40   The Life and work of L. Alma Tadema [by Helen Zimmern].
L5   J.L.E. Meissonier [by Lionel Robinson,and] J.C. Hook [by F.G. Stephens] London, Art Journal Office, 1888.
32, 32, 32 p. illus., ports. 33cm. (The Art annual)

Each work has special t. p.

1. Alma-Tadema, Sir Lawrence, 1836-1912. 2. Meissonier, Jean Louis Ernest, 1815-1891. 3. Hook, James Clarke, 1819-1907. I. Zimmern, Helen, 1846-   /L. Alma Tadema. II. Robinson, Lionel. /J.L.E.   Meissonier.

NL 0356166   CU

The life and work of Mary Aikenhead, foundress of the Congregation of Irish sisters of charity, 1787-1858, by a member of the Congregation, with a preface by Father John Sullivan ... London, New York [etc.] Longmans, Green and co., 1924.

ix p., 1 l., 476 p. front., plates, ports., facsim. 22cm.

1. Aikenhead, Mary, 1787-1858. 2. Sisters of charity, Irish.

Library of Congress   BX4705.A4L5   24-12844

NL 0356167   DLC MiU NN

Life and work of Mother Mary St. Ignatius (Claudine Thévenet) (1774-1837), foundress of the Congregation of Jesus and Mary. With an account of the development of the Congregation. By a religious of Jesus and Mary.   Dublin, Clonmore and Reynolds [1953]   346 p.   illus., ports.   22cm.

Bibliography, p. 339-341.
1. Mary St. Ignatius, mother, 1774-1837. 2. Sisters of Jesus and Mary. I. A religious of Jesus and Mary.

NL 0356168   NN MiU IMunS

The life and work of Sir Isaac Pitman
    see under   Pitman, Sir Isaac and sons, publishers.

The life and work of the Redeemer, by the Very Rev. H. Donald M. Spence...the Most Rev. W. Alexander...the Rev. Professor Marcus Dods... [and others]   London [etc.] Cassell and co., 1901.   340 p.   illus. 21cm.

227654B. I. Jesus Christ—Life.
Maurice, 1836-1917.   I. Spence-Jones, Henry Donald
N.Y.P.L.   May 13, 1943

NL 0356170   NN MB

BX4700   The life and work of the Ven. J. B. de La Salle, the
.L3L5   founder of the Institute of the Brothers of the Christian Schools. By F.C.N.   New York, D. & J. Sadlier, 1883.
368 p.   port.   20 cm.
Bibliography: p. [v]-vi.

1. La Salle, Jean Baptiste de, Saint, 1651-1719. 2. Brothers of the Christian Schools.   I. N., F.C.   II. F.C.N.

BX4700.L3L5   48-41775*

Library of Congress   [1]

NL 0356171   DLC

Life and works of Abraham Lincoln. Commemorative edition. Ed. by Marion Mills Miller. [Prospectus]   n.p., n.d.
folded por., il.   31 x 23 cm.
Sheet printed on both sides in red and black.

NL 0356172   RPB

The life and works of Alfred Aloysius Horn
    see under   Horn, Alfred Aloysius, pseud.

The life and works of Gustave Satter. A biographical sketch in memoriam of the great pianist and composer. Savannah, Georgia, 1879. Macon, Ga., Seifert & Smith, printers, 1879.
23 p. 21½cm.

1. Satter, Gustav, 1832-
23-3685

Library of Congress   ML410.S2L4

NL 0356173   DLC MB ICN

PS   Life and works of Henry W. Longfellow.   Cam-
2281   bridge ed.   Cambridge, Mass., Tribune
.L5   Pub. Co., 1882.
80 p.   illus.   18 cm.

1. Longfellow, Henry Wadsworth, 1807-1882.

NL 0356174   WU

The life and works of Lord Byron: a collection of articles thereon which appeared in Blackwood's magazine, Eclectic magazine, Fortnightly review, Forum, Harper's magazine, Littell's Living age, National review and Nineteenth century.   Cleveland, 1915.

Contents:

Byron, George Noel Gordon,   6th baron

NL 0356175   CaBVa

The life and works of Ludwig van Beethoven. Beethoven centennial, 1827-1927
    see under   [Columbia Phonograph Company, New York.]

BT   Life and worship. v. 1-   (no. 1-
4002   Oct. 1929-
.L81   Alresford, Hants, Society of St. Gregory.
v.   24 cm.   quarterly.
Title varies: v. 1-12, Music and liturgy.-
v. 13-38, Liturgy.

1. Liturgy - Periodicals.

NL 0356177   DCU

The life and writings of Adolphus F. Monroe, who was hung by a blood-thirsty mob in Charleston, Ill., on the 15th day of February, 1856
    see under   [Aulick, Napoleon B   ]

Toner   Life and writings of Andreas Vesalius. [anon.]
1886   Philadelphia, northamerican medico-chirurgical review, 1861.
1-33 p.   8°.
[In Northamerican medico-chirurgical review, Jan. 1861]

NL 0356179   DLC

The life and writings of Carl Theodor Korner (written by his father) ...
    see under   [Koerner, Christian Gottfried]
1756-1831.

Life and writings of Dr. Jonathan Swift
    see under   [Delany, Patrick] 1685?-1768.

Life and writings of Gen. Nathaniel Lyon. 1861.

NL 0356182   KyLX

Life and writings of George Washington Doane
    see under   Doane, George Washington.

The life and writings of James Gordon Bennett, editor of the New-York herald ... New-York, 1844.
64 p.   21cm.

1. Bennett, James Gordon, 1795-1872. 2. New York herald.

Library of Congress   PN4874.B4L5   0—7162

NL 0356184   DLC NN PPL NBuG MWA

Life and writings of John Whitehead...
    see under   [Chalk, Thomas] 1787-1869, ed.

The life and writings of Miguel de Cervantes Saavedra
    see under   [Navarrete, Martín Fernández de] 1765-1844.

The life and writings of St. Peter
    see under   [Seeley, Robert Benton]
1798-1886.

The life and writings of the apostle Peter. Written for the American Sunday-school union, and revised by the Committee of publication. Philadelphia, American Sunday-school union [1836]
232 p.   front., illus.   15cm.
"Letters of the apostle Peter. Written about A.D. 64 and 65.": p. 211-232.

1. Peter, Saint, apostle.   I. Bible. N. T. Peter. English. 1836. II. Bible. English. N. T. Peter. 1836. III. American Sunday-school union.
34-19078

Library of Congress   BS2515.L5   [922.1]   225.92

NL 0356188   DLC NRCR

VOLUME 332

Life and writings of the late Mr. Justice Talfourd.
A criticism. (In North British Review. [London] 1856. 8°. v. 25, no. 49, p. 47-78)
Bd. with: [Plays and puritans ...] (In North British Review. [London, 1856] 8°. v. 25, no. 49)
Excerpt.

NL 0356189   NN

The life and writings of the Rev. William Dodd ...
see under Dodd, William, 1729-1777.

The life, anecdotes, and heroic exploits of
Israel Putnam, major-general in the
Revolutionary war
see under [Humphreys, David] 1752-1818.

The life, apprehensio[n] arraignement, and
execution of Char[les] Covrtney ...
see under Courtney, Charles, d. 1612.

372.891 Life around the world; a collection of
qL722   authentic facts about our international
         neighbors, written by natives of Mexico,
         Brazil, Turkey, Norway, and India.
         Cleveland, Bloch, °1955.
         [30] p. illus., maps. 28 cm.

         Cover title.
         Includes music.

         1. Geography. Text-books.

NL 0356193   N OC1

BV4510   Life as a fine art; co-education of the
.L626   mind - the heart - and the body. [New
         York, University of Re-Creation, 1941]
         24 p.

         1. Christian life - Addresses, essays, lec-
         tures. I. Title.

NL 0356194   CtHC

Life as a fine art. Happiness
     see Highley, Florence Barry.
     Happiness.

Life as a fine art; introduction to happiness
     see Highley, Florence Barry.
     Introduction to happiness.

Life as I saw it. London: K. Paul, Trench, Trubner & Co., Ltd.,
1924. 216 p. 8°.

180375A. 1. Church work, Social—   Gt. Br. 2. Catholic Church, Roman
—Converts.
N. Y. P. L.   May 28, 1925

NL 0356197   NN

AC
8   Life as it is. Bloomington, Ill., "ONO"
.L54   Publisher [°1930]
         79 p.   diagrs.

         "Copyright...Wm. E. Gates."
         Contents.–Universal physics.–Polarization.–
         The science and psychology of sex.–Science of
         health.–Philosophy of birth control.–Marriage.–
         A visitor from Venus.–Communion with other
         worlds.–Will astrology come back?–Prohibition
         or temperance.–Man's dominion.–Or (a poem)
         I. Gates, William E.

NL 0356198   INS

---

*
PZ2   Life as it is: or, A Peep into fashionable
.L547   parties. A novel. London: Printed at the
1808   Minerva-Press, for Lane, Newman and Co.,
         1808.
         3 v. 19cm.

NL 0356199   ViU

976.9485
p.v.1   Life as lived 150 years ago in old Fort Harrod.
No.4   n.p., n.d.
         4 p.
1291
         Program of a celebration at the Fort.

NL 0356199-1   KyHi

Life association news.

[Albany, National association of life underwriters, 19
  v. illus. 29½ᵐ. monthly.
Editorial office in New York.

1. Insurance, Life—Period.   I. National association of life underwriters.
Library of Congress   HG8751.L47   43–33801
                           [2]   368.305

NL 0356200   DLC OkS AzTeS MB OrP ICRL ICU

Life association of America, plaintiff.
    ... Life association of America against James
A. Rhodes. [New York? 1875]
    37 p. 25 cm.
    Caption title.
    At head of title: N. Y. Supreme court.

NL 0356201   CtY RPB Nh

Life association of America, *St. Louis.*
    Long term insurance with participation in dividends ...
St. Louis, The Life association of America [1872]
    cover-title, 5, [4] p. 20 x 9ᶜᵐ.

Library of Congress   HG8963.L73A4   CA 9–1891 Unrev'd

NL 0356202   DLC

---

ar W   Life Association of American, St. Louis.
6411   Tables giving reserves at the end of
         each policy year for ten years, on kinds of
         policies issued by the Life Association of
         America; also tables giving the reserves
         each year, until maturity, on continued
         payment and ten payment policies, issued at
         age 35, maturing at age 80 and in 35, 30, 25,
         20, 15 and 10 years. St. Louis, 1870.
         [24] p. 22cm.

         1. Insuran   ce, Life—Rates and
         tables.

NL 0356203   NIC CU

LIFE ASSOCIATION OF SCOTLAND.
    Princes street, Edinburgh; an illustrated account of its
origin and development. Issued by the Life association of
Scotland on the occasion of its centenary, 1938. [Edin-
burgh: G. Stewart and co. ltd., 1938] 85 p. incl. plates,
ports. 22½cm.

    Illustrated end papers.

4910B. 1. Edinburgh—Streets—Princes street.

NL 0356204   NN

LIFE assurance; its schemes, its difficultie
and its abuses. London,1852.

NL 0356205   MH

Life assurance. Memorandum of the procedure for effecting a life assurance; with observations on some of the points which require
to be considered by the directors of an association for the assurance of lives.
= [Edinburgh. Stark & Co. 1847?] 24 pp. 8°.

F7220 — Life insurance. — No main card.

NL 0356206   MB

YA24681 **Life** assurance... a family book. New York,1867.
         38p.

NL 0356207   DLC

The **Life** assurance agent's vade-mecum.
    Edinburgh, Trustees of the late James Wilkie.
    v. tables. 17 cm.

    1. Insurance, Life—Gt. Brit.—Rates and tables.
    HG8881.L67   55–18954

NL 0356208   DLC

Life assurance companies: their financial
condition discussed, with reference to impend-
ing legislation, in a letter addresses to the
Right Hon. W. E. Gladstone by an actuary.
London, E. Wilson, 1869.
23p.

    1. Insurance, Life—Gt. Brit.   I. An
actuary.

NL 0356209   ICarbS

Life assurance in business
    see under Joint Stock Companies'
    Journal, London.

W 1   LIFE Assurance Medical Officers' Asso-
LI39K   ciation
            Transactions. 1894—1914-15. London
            v.   W1 LI39K
            Issues for 1894-95 title: Report of
         the proceedings. —1896-99: Proceedings.
         Continued by the Transactions of the
         Assurance Medical Society.
            Title: Transactions of the Life
         Assurance Medical Officers' Association

NL 0356211   DNLM ICJ

519.5   Life assurance pamphlets.   n.p., n.d.
L626   11 pamphlets.

           Binder's title.

NL 0356212   IU

VOLUME 332

British Tracts 1795 L62

Life Assurance Society, for the Benefit of
Widows and Female Relations.
Life Assurance Society; for the benefit of
widows, and female relations. Established by
deed inrolled 1795. [London, 1795]
15 p. 20 cm.

NL 0356213 CtY

The life assurance text-book (formerly known
as The Insurance guide and handbook—vol.I)
Editor: R.C.Simmonds ... Assistant editor:
P.F.Hooker ... London, C.and E.Layton, 1929.
vii,360 p. tables. 21½ cm.
Seventh edition. The fifth and sixth editions (1912
and 1922 were issued as v.1 of The insurance guide and
hand-book; earlier editions had been published in one
volume.
"List of reading ..." at end of most of the chapters.

1.Insurance,Life. I.Simmonds,Reginald Claud,ed.
II.Hooker,Percy Francis,joint ed.

NL 0356214 MiU PPProM

Life assurer's handbook and key to life assurance
see under [The British empire mutual life
assurance society]

Life at Bowdoin
see under Bowdoin college.

Life at eighty as I see it
see under [Flake, Arthur] 1862–

Life at Phillips Exeter
see under Phillips Exeter Academy.

Life at high tide
see under Howells, William Dean, 1837–
1920, ed.

---

378 L72

Life at Portland State. Portland State
College.

I.Oregon. Portland State College.

NL 0356220 OrP

Life at sea, miscellaneous
articles.
(Form, naval misc.)
38,297

NL 0356221 DN

Life at the lees ... by X107. Boston, Hall's book shop,
1916.
66 p., 1 l. 18½ cm. $1.00
Verses, with Extracts from letters.

1. X107

Library of Congress PS3500.X4L5

16–15053

NL 0356222 DLC NcU MB ViU NcD

Life at Tung-sol. v. 1–   [July 1942]–
[Newark, Tung-sol lamp works, inc., 1942–
v. in illus. 35½ cm.

1. Tung-sol lamp works, inc.

45–26278

Library of Congress HD9697.U7T85

[2] 621.32065

NL 0356223 DLC NN

Life at Vassar; seventy-five years in pictures. Poughkeepsie,
Vassar cooperative bookshop [1940]
124 p. illus. (incl. ports., facsim.) pl. 27¼ cm.
Title vignette, with dates: 1865, 1940.
Foreword signed: Marion Bacon '22, editor.
"Published in celebration of the seventy-fifth anniversary of Vassar
college and in honor of Henry Noble MacCracken in the twenty-fifth year
of his presidency."

1. Vassar college. I. Bacon, Marion, ed.

40–10797

Library of Congress LD7183.L5

[6] 378.747

NcGU

NL 0356224 DLC OkU NIC GU OrU OU OCl OO ViU RPB

The Life-Bed, an invention for rendering
seamen's bedding a life preserver
see under Jennings, Henry Constantine,
1731–1819.

Life before him. A novel
see under [Bunce, Oliver Bell] 1828–1890.

Life below: in seven poems
see under [Raymond, George Lansing]
1839–

The life beyond, adapted from Mrs. Alfred Gatty
by M.A.T.
see under Gatty, Margaret (Scott) 1809–
1873.

Life beneath the waves and a description of the Brighton
aquarium ... London, Tinsley brothers, 1871.
iv p., 1 l., [7]–95, [1] p. plates, plan. 19 cm.

1. Marine fauna. 2. Zoology—Juvenile and popular literature. 3.
Brighton, Eng. Aquarium.

6–18555†

Library of Congress QL122.L72

NL 0356229 DLC

The Life, birth and character, of the Right
Honourable Robert earl of Oxford, Lord
High Treasurer of Great Britain, &c.
[London] Printed by Rich. Newcomb, in
Wine-Office-Court in Fleetstreet, 1711.
8 p. 18 cm.

1. Oxford, Robert Harley, 1st Earl of, 1661–
1724.

NL 0356230 CtY

Per. 1626

The Life boat; a weekly political pamphlet,
edited by William Hill, late editor of the
Northern star.
v. 1–
[Hull, Printed and Published by R. Johnson,
1843–
v. 22cm. weekly.
Vol. 1, no. 1-6 issued Dec. 2? 1843–Jan. 6,
1844.
Subtitle varies: a miscellany of politics and
literature.

NL 0356231 NNC

The Life-boat. An illustrated monthly journal devoted to chari-
table, philanthropic, health and soul-winning work. Hinsdale,
Ill., [Workingmen's Home and Life Boat Mission, 1905–1914].
Vol. 8, no. 6–vol. 17. June 1905–Dec. 1914. illus. 24 cm.
Caption title; no index.

NL 0356232 ICJ IEG

The Life boat; children's work for seamen. no. 1–
Jan. 1858–
New York, The American seamen's friend society, 1858–
19
v. illus. 21½ cm. monthly. [With The Sailors' magazine and seamen's friend]

1. American seamen's friend society.

CA 20–97 Unrev'd

NL 0356233 DLC NRAB PCC

The Life-boat; journal of the Royal national life-boat institution.
London, C. Knight [etc.] 18
v. illus., plates (part col.) maps, diagrs. 25 cm. quarterly.
Includes Annual reports of the institution.

1. Life-saving—Period. I. Royal national life-boat institution for the
preservation of life from shipwreck, London.

CA 6–317 Unrev'd

Library of Congress VK1300.L7

NL 0356234 DLC NN NjP DN

THE LIFE boat; a juvenile temperance magazine ...
Mont., 1852-53. v.1, no. 1-9, 12; v.2, no. 1-3.

NL 0356235 CaNSWA

The life boat. A poem
see under [David, John] 1761–1847.

The life boat; or, The stranded ships on the
bar of Memel, being an authentic and interesting
account of the remarkable deliverance of three
ships' companies by the crew of the Robert and
Margaret. London, Printed by Augustus Apple-
gath and Edward Cowper, n.d.
8 p. (In Miscellaneous pamphlets)
Title vignette.

NL 0356237 PMA

The life-boat service and the war
see under [Royal national life-boat
institution, London]

VOLUME 332

E467.1
.H2L7   The life, brilliant military career, and public
            services of General Winfield Scott Hancock ...
            Philadelphia, Barclay & co. [c1880]
              1 p. l., 19-64 p.   24 cm.
              Portrait on cover.
              1. Hancock, Winfield Scott, 1824-1886.
              I. Barclay & co., pub.

NL 0356239   DLC OClWHi

Life building method of the Ralston Health Club
  "all nature" course
    see under   Edgerly, Webster, 1852-1926.

Life by the fireside. 1853
    see under   [Kelty, Mary Ann] 1789-1873.

The life, campaigns and battles of General
  Ulysses S. Grant
    see under   [Larke, Julian K   ]

The life, campaigns, and public services of General Mc-
  Clellan. (George B. McClellan.) The hero of western
  Virginia! South Mountain! and Antietam! ... Phila-
  delphia, T. B. Peterson & brothers [1864]
    1 p. l., [17]-184 p. 19½ᶜᵐ.

  1. McClellan, George Brinton, 1826-1885.   I. Peterson, T. B., & brothers, Philadelphia, pub.

  Library of Congress   E467.1.M2L7   12-12846

        PPL PHi ViU PSC PV PU MB MH NBuU NIC
NL 0356243   DLC PLF OU MWA PBL OCh OClWHi MiU OClW

796.54   Life Camps, Inc.
qL722   Adventures in camping education at
         National Camp, a new outdoor school for
         advanced leadership training. New York,
         National Camp, Life Camps [1943?]
           15 p. illus. 31 cm.

           1. Camping. I. Title.

NL 0356244   N

SK601   Life Camps, inc.
.N6
1948   New York (City) Board of Education.
           Extending education through camping; report of the
         school camp experiment authorized by the Board of Educa-
         tion of the city of New York, conducted in cooperation with
         Life Camps, inc. [New York, Life Camps, 1948]

Life cases (including health and accident); the full texts of
  all higher court decisions, State and Federal, pertaining to
  all types of life, health and accident insurance. v. 1-15,
  1938/39-51/53; 2d ser., v. 1-
  1953/55-
  Chicago [etc.,] Commerce Clearing House.
    v. 25 cm. (Insurance case series)
    Contains exact reproductions of the decisions reported in the "cur-
  rent volume" of the Life, health and accident unit of the Insurance
  law reporters.
    INDEXES:
    Vols. 1-15, 1938/39-51/53, in v. 15.
    1. Insurance, Life—U. S.—Cases. 2. Insurance, Health—U. S.—
  Cases. 3. Insurance, Accident—U. S.—Cases.   I. Commerce Clearing House.   (Series)

                                               39-18284 rev*

NL 0356246   DLC NcD ViU-L WaU-L IU MB OU

British
Tracts   The life, character and death of Judas
1711   Iscariot, that traytor, who betray'd Our
L62   Blessed Lord and Saviour Jesus Christ ...
           London, Printed and sold by E. Midwinter,
           1711.
             [3]-24 p. illus. 15 cm.

             1. Judas Iscariot.

NL 0356247   CtY

E
5
.G86867   The LIFE, character, and death, of the most
           illustrious pattern of female vertue, the Lady
           Jane Gray, who was beheaded in the tower at 16
           years of age, for her stedfast adherence to the
           Protestant religion. Collected from the best
           historians.   London, J. Roberts, 1714.
             27p. 19cm.

NL 0356248   ICN MH DFo

The life, character, and genius of Ebenezer
  Elliott, the Corn law rhymer
    see under   [Phillips, George Searle]
1815-1889.

The life, character, and literary labours of
  Samuel Drew, A. M.
    see under   [Drew, Jacob Halls]

Life, civilization, the way of peace...
    see under   [Harris, Rufus Arnold] 1872-

The life, condemnation, dying address, and trial
  of the three Thayers. Who were executed for
  the murder of John Love, at Buffalo, N. Y.
  June 17th, 1825. Second edition. Boston:
  Printed by John G. Scobie, for the Publishers
  [1825]
    16p. 24cm.

NL 0356252   NBu

The life, confession, and atrocious crimes of Antoine
  Probst, the murderer of the Deering family. To which is
  added a graphic account of many of the most horrible and
  mysterious murders committed in this and other countries ...
  Philadelphia, Barclay & co. [1866]
    1 p. l., 37-85, [1] p. incl. plates, ports. front., pl., port. 24½ᶜᵐ.

    1. Probst, Anton, 1842-1866. 2. Dearing, Christopher, d. 1866.

                                               45-49746

NL 0356253   DLC MH-L MB PP NjP

The life, confession, and atrocious crimes of Antoine Probst,
  the murderer of the Deering family. To which is added a
  graphic account of many of the most horrible and mysterious
  murders committed in this and other countries ... Philadelphia, Barclay & co. [1866]
    1 p. l., 37-109 (i. e. 112) p. front., illus. (incl. ports.) 22ᶜᵐ.
    Irregularities in paging.
    "The trial [in a Court of oyer and terminer, Philadelphia, for the
  murder of Christopher Dearing,]": p. 60-92.
    1. Dearing, Christopher, d. 1866.   I. Probst, Anton, 1842-1866, de-
  fendant.   II. Pennsylvania. Court of oyer and terminer (Philadelphia
  co.)

                                               32-8616

NL 0356254   DLC

Life conservation studies
    see under   Heart Council of Greater
Cincinnati.

The life, crime and death of Charles J. Guiteau, the
  assassin of James A. Garfield, president of the United
  States ... New York, F. Tousey, 1882.
    16 p. incl. illus., ports. 42 x 30ᶜᵐ.
    Caption title.

    1. Guiteau, Charles Julius, 1841-1882.   I. Tousey, Frank, pub.

  Library of Congress   E687.9.G685   11-14849

NL 0356255   DLC

Life, crimes and confession of Bridget Durgan.
  P., 1857.

NL 0356256   PPL

... Life, crimes and confession of Mrs. Julia
  Fortmeyer
    see under   Fortmeyer, Mrs. Julia E
d. 1875.

...Life, crimes and execution of Peregrine
Hutton and Morris N.B.Hull, the mail robbers....
Phila., 1820.

NL 0356258   PPL

The life cry
    see under   [Linden, Ingvärd Marya] 1894-

W 1
LI39R   LIFE crystals. v. 1, no. 1-8; Jan.-Sept.
         1882. Oakland, Calif.
           128 p.

NL 0356260   DNLM CSmH

The life, death, and actions of the most chast,
  learned, and religious lady, the Lady Iane Gray
    see under   Dudley, Lady Jane, known as
Lady Jane Grey, 1537-1554.

Life, death and burial of Queen Victoria,
  Empress of India. [Cardiff, Wales, Western
  Mail, ltd.] 1901.
    32p. illus., ports.

    Cover-title.
    Queen's supplement to the Western mail,
  February 5th, 1901.
    Laid in: Jan. 23, 1901 issue of South Wales echo
  containing articles on the life and death of Queen
  Victoria.

NL 0356262   OCl

The life, death & misfortunes of the famous
  Moll Flanders
    see   Defoe, Daniel, 1661?-1731.
  The fortunes and misfortunes of the famous
  Moll Flanders.

The life, death and prophecies of Mother Shipton. The
  end of the world prophecied! Being a true account of
  her strange birth, the most important passages of her
  life, and her wonderful prophecies, now newly collected
  and explained ... Also many prophecies of the astrol-
  oger, William Lily, are indiscriminately interspersed;
  and the extraordinary vision of St. Maol Maodhog
  O'Morgair; known in his native Irish land as St. Malachy,
  referring to the liberation of Ireland from British rule.
  [Liverpool, Baskerville steam printing works, 187-]
    21, [2] p. 18½ᶜᵐ.
    1. Shipton, Ursula,   2. Prophecies.   I. Lily, William,
  1602-1681.   II. Malachy,   O'Morgair, Saint, 1094?-1148.   III.
  Title.

  Library of Congress   BF1815.S5L5   17-2315.

NL 0356264   DLC

VOLUME 332

The life, death, and renovation of Tom Thumb
see under [Dibdin, Charles] 1745–1814.

The life, deeds, and opinions of Dr. Martin
Luther. Hudson, 1818
see under Tischer, Johann
Friedrich Wilhelm, 1767–1842.

A life director of the American tract society.
An inquirer answered; a dialogue ...
see under title

AP62
.L6

Life en español. v. 1–
enero 5, 1953–
[Chicago, Time, inc.]
v. illus. (part col.) 36 cm. fortnightly.

"Esta edición ... se compone de material escogido de las ediciones
de Life, en inglés, y de material preparado especialmente para **Life**
en español."

I. Time, inc.

AP62.L5   54–36653

Library of Congress   [a55b1]

NL 0356268   DLC OU

The life, eulogy, and great orations of Daniel
Webster
see under Webster, Daniel, 1782–1852.

LIFE experiences of a detective, by an ex-detect-
ive. [Newton, Mass., Detectives' Museum
Publishing Co.] 1878.
51p. 21cm.

1. Detectives. Crime and criminals.

NL 0356270   KPT

Life, explorations, and public services of
John Charles Fremont ... Boston, Tickner and Fields
see under [Upham, Charles Wentworth]
1802–1875.

The life, explorations, and public services of **John
Charles Fremont.** New York, Livermore & Rudd, 1856.
115 p. front. (port.) 19½ᶜᵐ.
On cover: The authorized campaign edition.

1. Fremont, John Charles, 1813–1890.
                                                10–29827
Library of Congress   E415.9.F8L6

NL 0356271   DLC PBL MWA MB   CtY

The life, explorations, and public services of **John
Charles Fremont.** New York, Livermore & Rudd; Cincinnati, Truman & Spofford, 1856.
115 p. front. (port.) 19½ᶜᵐ.
On cover: The authorized campaign edition.

1. Fremont, John Charles, 1813–1890.
                                                10–29828
Library of Congress   E415.9.F8L61

NL 0356271-1   DLC Nh OrU

W 1   LIFE Extension Examiners, New York
LI39V   Proceedings. v. 1–3, no.6;
               Jan. 1939–Nov./Dec. 1941. New York.
               3 v. in 1. illus.

               1. Insurance, Life - period.

NL 0356272   DNLM ICJ MiDW OU

Life extension institute, incorporated.

Fisk, Eugene Lyman, 1867–1931.
Alcohol; its relation to human efficiency and longevity, by
Eugene Lyman Fisk ... authorized by the Life extension in-
stitute ... reviewed and criticised by members of the Hygiene
reference board and approved by a majority. New York and
London, Funk & Wagnalls company, 1917.

Life Extension Institute, Incorporated.
Employees welfare work that pays; how employers and employees are going fifty-fifty on a new life extension and insurance
service, by Harold A. Ley... [New York,] cop. 1922. 16 p.
illus. 8°.

Cover-title.

489755A. 1. Insurance, Group.   I. Ley, Harold Alexander, 1874– .
N. Y. P. L.   August 20, 1930

NL 0356274   NN

Life extension institute, incorporated.

[Fisk, Eugene Lyman] 1867–
Food, fuel for the human engine; what to buy, how to
cook it, how to eat it; the simple story of feeding the
family, based on the Diet squad experiment in cooperation with the New York city Police department. New
York city, Issued by the Life extension institute, 1917.

Life extension institute, inc.
The growing movement to prolong human life.
New York city, Life extension institute
(1914?)
16 p. 23 cm.

NL 0356276   DL

Life Extension Institute, Incorporated.
A home study course in health and culture of body and mind.
Prepared by Henry Wysham Lanier from the rules of health
formulated by the one hundred experts of the Hygiene Reference
Board of the Life Extension Institute... Lessons
New York: Review of Reviews Co.[, cop. 1917.]
diagr., illus., plates. 4°.

Cover-title.
Facsimile typewritten text.

Extra part: General instructions to students.
Contents: Lesson 1. Why not be well?
          Lesson 3. How to eat.
             Lesson 5–6. The process of feeding. Lesson 7. Air, sunlight and
weather. Lesson 8. Worry, work, fatigue. Lesson 9. Alcohol, smoking, beverages and
health. Lesson 10. Colds, hay-fever, headaches, infections, and how to gain immunity.
Lesson 11. The muscle system of the human body. Lesson 12. The perfect body built
by exercise. Lesson 13. First aid in emergencies.

1. Hygiene, Personal. 2. Lanier,   O'KEEFE COLLECTION.
N. Y. P. L.   Henry Wysham, 1873– , editor.
                                          October 29, 1925

NL 0356278   NN OU

Life Extension Institute, inc.
How to live; a ... journal of health and hygiene
see under title

RA776   Life extension institute, incorporated.
.F535
1946   Fisher, Irving, 1867–   FOR OTHER EDITIONS
                                        SEE MAIN ENTRY
           How to live; rules for healthful living based on modern
           science, by Irving Fisher ... and Haven Emerson ... Prepared
           in collaboration with the Hygiene reference board of the Life
           extension institute. 21st ed., completely rev. and rewritten.
           New York [etc.] Funk & Wagnalls [1946]

Life extension institute, incorporated.
How to live long ... New York, Life extension institute, 1923.
16 p. illus. 23ᶜᵐ.

1. Hygiene. I. Title.

                                        CA 24–623 Unrev'd
Library of Congress   RA776.L6

NL 0356281   DLC

Life extension institute, inc.,
The life extension institute, inc. New York
city (1914?)
cover-title, 14 p. 23 cm.

NL 0356282   DL

Life extension institute, incorporated.

Fisk, Eugene Lyman, 1867–
Manual of procedure in periodic physical examinations,
by Eugene Lyman Fisk ... compiled in collaboration with
a committee of the examining staff of the Life extension
institute. [New York] 1925.

Life Extension Institute, incorporated,
Menus, January 9th to [29th], inclusive. 25-cent a day experi-
ment conducted with twelve men in the New York Police Training
School. [New York, 1917.] 3 l. f°.

Caption-title.
Typewritten sheets.

1. Menus. 2. Prices of foodstuffs,   U. S., 1917. 3. Living expenses,
U. S. 4. Title: 25-cent a day experi- ment.
N. Y. P. L.   June 4, 1917.

NL 0356284   NN

Life extension institute incorporated.
Monthly health letter.
New York city [1917]

NL 0356285   DLC

Life extension institute incorporated.

Fisk, Eugene Lyman, 1867–
Periodic physical examination of employes: its eco-
nomic and social value; address delivered before the
National association of manufacturers May 26, 1915, by
Eugene Lyman Fisk ... [New York? 1915]

Life Extension Institute, inc.
Prolonging life as a function of life insurance; five years'
experience of the Life Extension Institute. New York,
1919.
47 p. 23 cm.

1. Insurance, Life—Medical examination.

HG8898.H4L5   368.3   49–37189*

NL 0356287   DLC ICJ NN CU DNLM

VOLUME 332

Life extension institute, incorporated.
The review of reviews course in physical training, health and life extension; from the rules of health formulated by the one hundred experts of the Hygiene reference board of the Life extension institute, in seven lessons ... New York, The Review of reviews company ₁1920₎

7 v. front., illus. 16ᶜᵐ.

1. Hygiene.   ɪ. Title.

Library of Congress   RA776.L73   20–3573

NL 0356288   DLC ICJ ViU

Life extension institute incorporated.
What to eat; how to use the science of modern dietetics for more efficient living. Pub. by the Review of reviews company under the auspices of the Life extension institute of New York ... ₁New York₎ ᶜ1917.

48 p. incl. front. plates. 20¼ᶜᵐ. $1.00

1. Diet.   ɪ. Title.

Library of Congress   RM216.L75   17–10376

NL 0356289   DLC ViU

The life, extraordinary adventures and vicissitudes of Walter Beverly, by sea and land. Written by himself ... London, R. Harrild, 1812.

1 p. l., ₁7₎–29 p. col. front. 17½ᶜᵐ.

ɪ. Beverly, Walter, pseud.

Library of Congress   PZ3.L6241   7–16055†

NL 0356290   DLC

The life, extraordinary adventures, voyages, and surprizing escapes of Capt. Neville Frowde, of Cork
    see under   [Kimber, Edward] 1719–1769.

A life for a life
    see under   [Craik, Dinah Maria (Muloch)] 1826–1887.

"Life from the dead." an authentic narrative. Published by the American tract society and sold at their depository. No. 144 Nassau Street near the City-Hall, New York ... [n.d.]
12 p.   17 cm.

NL 0356293   DLC

Life from the dead: being a national bellringing journal advocating the identity of the British nation with the lost ten tribes of Israel./ Ed. by Edward Hine. London, ₁1873–1880₎
₁v. 1–3, 5–7.₎

p. 1–32 of v. 2 is bound with v. 1.

NL 0356294   OCH ICarbS

Life, Great Trial, and Execution of Guiteau
    see under   Guiteau, Charles Julius, 1841–1882, defendant.

Life hazard and resuscitation in electrical engineering
    see under   [Copeland, Clem A   ]

Life, health and accident insurance law; index to papers and articles. v. ₁1₎–   1906–31—
New York, Association of Life Insurance Counsel.

v.   24 cm.

Subtitle varies.
Vol. 1 was issued by American Life Convention.
Indexes the Proceedings of the Legal Section of the American Life Convention, the Proceedings of the Association of Life Insurance Counsel and other legal papers.

1. Insurance law—U. S.—Bibl.   ɪ. American Life Convention. Legal Section. Proceedings.   (Indexes)   ɪɪ. Association of Life Insurance Counsel. Proceedings.   (Indexes)

Z7164.I 7L5   016.368   35–25985 rev 2*

                    NcD
NL 0356297   DLC ICU NNC FU-L WaU-L OrU-L ICJ NN OU

Life High and Low. With 6 colored plates by C. Williams.   London, printed for J. Stockdale, 1819.
12 mo.   Crimson straight-grained levant, gilt lines on sides and back, gilt top, uncut; bound by Zaehnsdorf.
Original Edition.
Halsey Library from F.T. Sabin, London, Nov. 1904.
I. Williams, C., illustrator.

NL 0356298   CSmH

Life high and low. By the author of the Greeks, Pigeons, Fashion, &c. London, printed for J. J. Stockdale, 1819.
pp. viii, ₁13₎–218. Colored plates by Charles Williams.
At head of title "Second edition."
This book may be consulted in the room of the Widener Collection.

||Williams

NL 0356299   MH CSmH ViU

828
L722X6   ... Life high and low. By the author of The Greeks, Pigeons, Fashion, To Night ... Embellished with humorous coloured plates. 6th ed.   London, Pr. for J.J. Stockdale, 1819.
viii, ₁13₎ –218p. col. front., col. plates. 19cm.

I. Williams, Samuel, 1788–1853, illus.

NL 0356300   LNHT

PR
3991
.A7   ... Life high & low. By the author of The
G79   Greeks,Pigeons,Fashion ... &c. ... Embel-
L7   lished with humorous coloured plates. Lon-
1819   don, Printed for J.J.Stockdale, 1819.
viii,₁13₎–218 p. col.front.,col.plates. 19½ᶜᵐ.
At head of title: Tenth edition.

1.Gt.Brit.—Soc.life & cust.

NL 0356301   MiU

... Life histories of North American birds with special reference to their breeding habits and eggs ...
    see under   Bendire, Charles Emil, 1836–1897.

Life history and abstract of work of Sir D'Arcy Power
    see under   Power, Sir D'Arcy, 1855–1941.

Life, history, and handcuff secrets of Houdini. ₁n. p., 1907†₎
63 p. illus., ports. 23 cm.

Cover title.
Caption title: Harry Houdini: the adventurous life of a versatile artiste.

1. Houdini, Harry, 1874–1926.

GV1545.H8H3 1907   63–56967
———— Copy 3. Bound with Harry Houdini: the adventurous life of a versatile artiste. ₁n. p., 1906?₎ Copy 2.
GV1545.H8H3 1906 copy 2

NL 0356304   DLC

Life, history, and handcuff secrets of Houdini. ₁Rev. ed. Leicester? Eng., 1913₎
32 p. illus., ports. 22 cm.

Cover title.
Caption title: Harry Houdini: the adventurous life of a versatile artiste.
Bound with Harry Houdini: the adventurous life of a versatile artiste. ₁n. p., 1906?₎ Copy 2.

1. Houdini, Harry, 1874–1926.

GV1545.H8H3 1906 copy 2   63–56972

NL 0356305   DLC

Life, history, and handcuff secrets of Houdini. ₁Rev. ed. Leicester? Eng., 1914₎
36 p. illus., ports. 22 cm.

Cover title.
Caption title: Harry Houdini: the adventurous life of a versatile artiste.

1. Houdini, Harry, 1874–1926.

GV1545.H8H3 1914   63–56974

NL 0356306   DLC

Life history and poetry of "Hairbreadth Harry". or, Old inner tubes come clean
    see under   [Moan, James Joseph] 1881–

The life, history and tryal of Harry Smythee ...
    see under   Clark, Jeremiah.

The life history of —— —— . A sample life history of a Californian of oriental parentage.
[n.p., 1927?]
11 p.   23.5 cm.
Used by the Institute of Pacific relations, at the 1927 conference at Honolulu?

NL 0356309   CSt-H

Life history of Colonel Luther S. Allard, patriot, editor and a man of many attainments
    see under   [Allard, Luther Stockton] 1861–   ed.

Life history of Thomas Orr, jr.
    see under   [Taylor, Lillie Jane Orr] 1870–

764.9
Univ   The LIFE hymnal; a book of song and service
1910/h   for the Sunday School. Boston, Universalist
Publishing House, 1910.
xlix, 140p. 20cm.

"The services in this book are compiled mainly from The Altar ... by J.G. Bartholomew"

NL 0356311   MH-AH

VOLUME 332

LIFE illustrated; a journal of entertainment, improvement and progress. New ser., v. 1, no. 1-9, 11-25, v. 2, no. 1-7, 13-v. 3, no. 26; Nov. 3-Dec. 29, 1855, Jan. 12-Apr. 19, May 3-June 14, July 26, 1856-Apr. 25, 1857 New York, Fowler and Wells. v. illus. 45cm.

Weekly.
New ser., v. 1-3, also numbered continuously no. 53-130.
Began publication in 1854. Absorbed by Phrenological journal and science of health in May, 1861.
1. Periodicals—U. S.

NL 0356312   NN MiU-C WHi ICN

FM
139   Life illustrated. v. 1-2, Nov. 1854-55; n. s. v. 1-11,
L722   Nov. 3, 1855-April 1861. New York.
13 v.

          Merged into Phrenological journal (139 P57)
          Microfilm (negative) of the original in the New York
          State Library. Albany, N. Y., New York State Library, 1963.
          reels. 35 mm.

          1. Phrenology.   Period.

NL 0356313   N

BX6913   Life immortal, the true way to spiritual life, by one
.C3H6   who is under divine guidance. First discourse.
no. 2   San Francisco, Donaldson publishing company
Houdini   [n. d.]
Coll.   36 p.   15 cm.
          Houdini pamphlets: Christian science, no. 2.

NL 0356314   DLC

Life imprisonment for exposing communists
     see under   [Pearson, Melford]

Life in a Canadian college. [n.p., 1853]
     392-402 p.   23 cm.

     Extracted from an unnamed journal, April 1853.

     1. Church schools - Quebec (Prov.) 2.
     Education -   Quebec (Prov.)

NL 0356316   CaBVaU

Life in a debtor's prison
     see under   [Thomson William Hamilton]

Life in a log cabin, with hard cider. [Political pamphlet in regard to the candidacy of W. H. Harrison.] Philadelphia: M. B. Roberts, 1840.   8 p.   8°.

1. United States.—Politics, 1840.   2. Harrison, William Henry, 9. president of the United States.
N. Y. P. L.   May 28, 1913.

NL 0356318   NN

Life in a man of war, or, Scenes in "Old Ironsides"
     during her cruise in the Pacific
     see under   Mercier, Henry James.

Life ... in a nutshell ...
     see under   [Francis, Edward Charles] 1908-

Life in a tub; with a description of the Turkish bath
     see under   Diogenes, pseud.

Is82   ... Life in a whale ship; or, The sports and
tl   adventures of a leading oarsman. Written by an
L626   American author, and based upon the cruise of an
          American whale ship in the south Atlantic and
          Indian oceans, during the years 1836-7-8: a
          cruise replete with incident and wild adventure,
          faithfully recorded. Boston, J. N. Bradley & co.,
          at the office of The daily mail and Universal
          Yankee nation [1841?]
               illus., plates. 24½cm.
          This publication will be continued weekly for

          six months, forming a book of 500 pages. - cf.
          Adv. on verso of cover to no. 4.
          Paged continuously.

NL 0356323   CtY CU

FILM
4274   Life in a whale ship; or, The sports and
PR   adventures of a leading oarsman,
v. 1   Romance of the deep! or, The cruise of
          the Aeronaut, being a faithful narrative
reel   of incidents of romance and wild adventure
L4   by sea and land. During a three years'
          voyage in an American whale ship.
          Worcester, Redding, 1846.
          pt. 1-4. (Wright American fiction, v. 1,
          1774-1850, no. 1665, Research Publications
          Microfilm, Reel L-4)
          I. Title: Romance of the deep.

NL 0356324   CU

SH   Life in a whaler; or, Perils and adventures
381   in the tropical seas. By Sailor Charley.
L72   London, Ward, Lock, and Tyler [1860]
          [201]-424 p. illus. 18cm.

          1. Whaling. I. Charley, Sailor. II.
          Sailor Charley.

NL 0356325   NIC IEdS MBU NjP MH

Life in Afrikanderland as viewed by an Afrikander; a
story of life in South Africa, based on truth, by "Cios"
[pseud.] London, Digby, Long & co., 1897.
xi, 274 p. 20cm.

1. Africa, South—Hist.—Fiction. 2. Boers.
                                        14-8159
Library of Congress   DT888.L5

NL 0356326   DLC IEN MdBP TxU CtY

Life in Algoma; or, Three years of a clergyman's
     life and church work in that diocese
     see under   [Burden, Harold Nelson] 1860-

Life in all ages.
n.p.   n.p., [19-?]
     8 l.

     Typewritten manuscript.
     Cover-title.

NL 0356328   OO

Life in America; or, The wigwam and the cabin
     see under   [Simms, William Gilmore]
1806-1870.

Life in America series. Boston,
Houghton Mifflin company, 19-
     v.

NL 0356330   OO

RC462   Life in an asylum: strange stories, sayings and
894l   doings of madmen. By an ex-attendant.
          London, Clay Brothers, 1894.
          2p. l., 43, [1]p. 19cm.

          1. Mentally ill.

NL 0356331   CtY-M

Life in Bombay, and the neighboring out-stations ...
London, R. Bentley, 1852.
1 p. l., [v]-xvi, 350 p. plates. 25cm.

1. Bombay.

Library of Congress   DS485.B61L7   5-7527†

NL 0356332   DLC MH HU CtY CaOTP KMK WU NcD CU

Life in Calcutta, by an old military officer. In three series
... Calcutta, Printed by the Bengal printing company, 1872.
1 p. l., vi, 396+ p. 22cm.

Contains only the 3 nos. of the 1st series and no. 1 of the 2d; each number has special t.-p. not included in paging.
Novel.

1. An old military officer.
                                        44-18749
Library of Congress   PZ3.L62415

NL 0356333   DLC

Life in California: during a residence of several
     years in that territory
     see under   [Robinson, Alfred] 1806-1895.

Life in Carolina and New England, during the
     nineteenth century ...
     see under   Middleton, Alicia Hopton,
1849-

LIFE in central Asia.
     (In Travel, adventure, and sport. Vol. 4, pp. 260-295. London
[1890.])

NL 0356336   MB

Life in death ...   Alaska, 1930
     see under   Lundblad, S.

Life in death: a metrical romance, in two parts. Louisville [Ky.] B. Casseday & co., 1849.
36 p. 18cm.

                                        30-23863
Library of Congress   PS991.A1L5   1871

NL 0356338   DLC MH

Life in Dixie's land; or, South in secession time
     see under   [Gilmore, James Roberts] 1822-
1903.

VOLUME 332

EErbd
942L
Life in Eritrea. 1st ed. [Asmara, Fotocelere
coloniale] 1942.
album of 360 mounted photos. 23x46cm.
"No.6."

1. Eritrea - Descr. & trav. - Views. I.
Fotocelere coloniale, Asmara.

NL   0356340   CtY

Life in Fejee
see under   Wallis, Mary Davis (Cook)

Life in Germany
see under   Head, Sir Francis [Bond] bart.

LIFE in Glenshie, being the recollections
of Elizabeth Ray, school teacher; a tale,
by the author of "My young master,"
Casting the lot," "In search of the super-
natural," &c. Montreal, J. Dougall, 1878.

167 p.   24 cm.

1. My young master, Author of.

NL   0356343   CaBVaU

Life in heaven...
see under   [Banks, William]

Life in Indiana at three score
see under   Bishop, John Mason,
1819-1890.

Life in India; or, Madras, the Neilgherries, and Calcutta.
Written for the American Sunday-school union. Philadelphia, American Sunday-school union [1855]
528 p. front., plates. 15¼ᶜᵐ.

1. India—Descr. & trav.

Library of Congress   DS412.L72
                                          4-28714

NL   0356346   DLC

Life in India; or, The English at Calcutta
see under   [Monkland, Mrs.   ]

Life in letters; American autograph journal. v. 1–
Oct. 1938–   [Merion Station, Pa., American autograph shop, 1938–
v. in   facsims. 18ᶜᵐ. monthly.

1. American letters.   I. American autograph shop, Merion Station,
Pa.
Library of Congress   PS672.L5
                                          43-8471
                           [3]   810.5

NL   0356348   DLC MiU NcD PPAmSWM ViU NN PHi COMC

Life in letter[s] and art-music ...
see under   [Johnson, Marjorie Belle]

Life in letters of William Dean Howells.

See under

[Howells, William Dean, 1837-1920]

Life in London: a drama ... depicting the day
and night scenes of Tom, Jerry, Logic & Co.
see under   Dibdin, Charles, 1768-1833.

Life in London; a play in three acts
see under   Dibdin, Charles, 1768-1833.

Life in London. A story of thrilling interest,
founded upon the scenes of happiness and
misery, virtue and vice
see under   [Reynolds, George William
MacArthur] 1814-1879.

Life in Louisiana
see   Boucicault, Dion, 1820?-1890.
"Octoroon," or Life in Louisiana.

Life in Mexico during a residence of 2 years in
that country...
see under   [Calderon de la Barca, Frances
Erskine (Inglis)] 1804-1882.

Life in New Sweden Two Hundred Years Ago; or,
Life in New Sweden. Phila., 1876.
253 p.

NL   0356356   PHi

Life in New York
see under   [Prime, Samuel Irenaeus]
1812-1885.

Life in New York, in doors and out of doors. Illustrated by 40 engravings, by ... William Burns. New
York, Bunce & brother, 1851.
[90] p., 1 l. illus. 23ᶜᵐ.

1. New York (City)—Indus. 2. Woman—Employment. 3. New York
(City)—Soc. condit.
                                          8-14199†
Library of Congress   HD6096.N6B8

NL   0356358   DLC MH

LIFE in New Zealand series. no. 1–
Palmerston North, N.Z., Policeman publications,
1947–   no.   illus.   23cm.

1. Juvenile literature--   Picture books.

NL   0356359   NN

Life in Normandy; sketches of French fishing,
farming, cooking
see under   [Campbell, Walter Frederick]
1798-1855.

[Life in other lands library; classroom pictures. Grand
Rapids] Informative Classroom Picture Publishers, 1945–
v. plates, ports., maps (part fold. col.) 31 cm.
Each vol. issued in portfolio.
Some volumes issued in Informative classroom picture series.
Includes volumes of all editions.
CONTENTS.—[1] Alaska.—   [3] Mexico.—[4] Brazil.—
[5] South America.—   [7] Australia.—[8] China.—
[9] India.
1. Civilization — Hist. — Pictorial works. 2. World history—Pic-
torial works. I. Informative Classroom Picture Publishers, Grand
Rapids.
CB13.L5   901   55-28040 rev

NL   0356361   DLC

Life in our villages
see under   [Millin, George Francis]

Life in Palestine.
[Tel-Aviv]
v. illus. 32 cm. irregular.
Published Feb. 1941-May 1948. Superseded by Life in Israel. Cf.
Union list of serials.

1. Palestine—Descr. & trav.—Period.

DS101.L5   *915.694   58-33662

NL   0356363   DLC DNAL NN

Lilly
PR 3991
.L 46
... Life in Paris; a drama, in three
acts: adapted to Hodgson's theatrical characters and scenes in the same. London, Hodgson and Co. [1822?]
24 p. 18 cm. (Hodgson's Juvenile
drama)

NL   0356364   InU

LIFE in Paris before the war and during the siege.
Together with reasons why the Germans beat the
French [With a French slang dictionary in French and
English]   London, Diprose & Bateman, printers,
1871. 112 p. 16cm.

1. Paris—Social life, 18th cent. 2. Paris—Hist., 1870-1871.
3. Slang, French—Dictionaries.

NL   0356365   NN

Life in Paris; comprising the rambles, sprees, and
amours of Dick Wildfire ...
see under   [Carey, David] 1782-1824.

LIFE in Paris, or The adventures of a marquis;
a new historical romance. By Vidocq, late chief
of police in Paris. London, E. Appleyard, 1848.

1. 8°. Plates.

NL   0356367   MH NjP

Life in Rochester, or Sketches from life
see under   [Chumasero, John Chamberlain]
1816-1903.

Life in Sing Sing, by number 1500. Indianapolis, The
Bobbs-Merrill company [1904]
4 p. l., 276 p. 19¼ᶜᵐ.

1. New York. Sing Sing prison, Ossining.

Library of Congress   HV9475.N78L5
                                          4—32162

NL   0356369   DLC OU ViU ICJ MB

VOLUME 332

Life in Santo Domingo
see under   Fabens, Joseph Warren, 1821-
1875.

308
Z
(Box 865
Life in Soviet Russia.
Russia's religious future. (Paris) 1935.
78 p. (Pamphlet series. no. 10)

"Translations from the Soviet Press."
"A quartely (!) bulletin prepared and issued by the Russian Orthodox Theological Institute and the Russian Student Christian
Movement abroad."

NL 0356371 NNC

Life in Soviet Russia; pamphlet series

no.

Paris, 193   nos. in   18 – 19cm.
"Prepared and issued by the Russian orthodox theological institute and the Russian
student Christian movement abroad."
"Translations from the Soviet press."
Ceased publication with no. 10.

1. Russia. 2. Russia—Soc. condit.   3. Religion—Russia. I. Pravoslavnyĭ
bogoslovski institut, Paris.   II. Russkoye studencheskoye
khristianskoye dvizheniye.
N. Y. P. L.   June 30, 1938

NL 0356372 NN DLC

DK266
.A2L5
... Life in soviet Russia; problems of
daily life-religion-culture-youth-class.
no.1-   Apr. 1932-
(Paris, 1932
v.   27cm.   monthly.

Issued by the Russian orthodox theological
institute and the Russian student Christian
movement abroad.
Caption title.
At head of title: Translated soviet press
clippings.
Superseded in   1933 by Life in soviet
Russia; pamphlet   series?

NL 0356373 DLC

Life in the Adirondacks, including the legend of **Sabaal.**
By one of the Q. C. (New York, C. A. Coffin, 1876)
(5)–23 p. 23ᶜᵐ.
"An extract from my diary."

1. Adirondack Mountains—Description and travel.

A 18–1910

Title from Harvard Univ.   Printed by L. C.

NL 0356374 MH MB PHi N

Life in the Antarctic. Sixty photographs by **members**
of the Scottish national Antarctic expedition. London (etc.) Gowans & Gray, ltd., 1907.
67 p. incl. front., plates. 15ᶜᵐ. (*Half-title:* Gowans's nature books, **no.**
10 ...)

Plates printed on both sides of leaf.
"Notes on some Antarctic mammals and birds. By W. S. Bruce,
F. R. S. E." p. (65)–67.

1. Antarctic regions. Zoology. I. Bruce, W. S. II. Scottish national
Antarctic expedition.

Agr 9-2093

Library, U. S. Dept. of   Agriculture 411L62

NL 0356375 DNAL CaOTP CaBVaU ICJ

Life in the back-woods: a guide to the successful hunting and trapping of all kinds of animals. New York,
F. M. Reed (1875)
28 p. 14¼ᵐᵐ.

1. Hunting. 2. Trapping.

Library of Congress   SK283.L72   12-36176

NL 0356376 DLC

Life in the Bronx
see also   Bronx life.
Bronx Westchester life.

Life in the county jail
see under   (Flagg, Daniel)

Life in the far west: a narrative of adventures in
the western wilderness
see under   (Jones, John Beauchamp) 1810-
1866.

Life in the forest
see under   American Baptist Publication Society.

Life in the insect world: or, Conversations upon insects, between an aunt and her nieces ... Philadelphia,
Lindsay & Blakiston, 1844.
vii, (9)–241 p. incl. plates. front. 17½ᵐ.

Subject entries: Entomology, Popular.

Agr 3-1141

Library, U. S. Dept. of   Agriculture, no. 422L62.

NL 0356381 DNAL FU CtHT-W MB

BY2070
.L72
LIFE in the itinerancy, in it's relations
to the circuit and station, and to the
minister's home and family. By one who,
long devoted to its toils and cares...
New York, Miller, Orton & Mulligan, 1856.
vi, 335 p. 20 cm.

1. Itinerancy (Church polity)--Methodist
Church. 2. Methodist Episcopal Church--
Clergy.

NL 0356382 IEG

Life in the Klondike gold fields
see under   (Ladue, Joseph)

Life in the land of the fire worshipper
see under   H*******, Charles de.

Life in the laundry
see under   (McCleary, George Frederick)

... **Life** in the making, by Wade Crawford Barclay, **Arlo**
A. Brown, Alma S. Sheridan, William J. Thompson,
and Harold J. Sheridan, approved by the Committee on
curriculum of the Board of Sunday schools of the Methodist Episcopal church and the Committee on curriculum of the General Sunday school board of the Methodist Episcopal church, South. New York, Cincinnati,
The Methodist book concern; Nashville, Dallas (etc.)
Smith & Lamar (*1917)
236 p. 19ᵐ. (Training courses for leadership, ed. by H. H. Meyer and
E. B. Chappell)
1. Sunday-schools. 2. Religious education. 3. Child study.   I. Barclay,
Wade Crawford, 1874-   II. Brown, Arlo Ayres, 1883-   III. Sheridan, Alma S. IV. Thomp-   son, William Joseph, 1864-
v. Sheridan, Harold J.

Library of Congress   BV1520.L5   17—30762

NL 0356386 DLC ICRL OC1U ViU OC1 OO NcD PU OCU

Life in the Mofussil; or, The civilian in Lower
Bengal
see under   (Graham, G   )

DJ71
.C6
Life in the Netherlands, by seventeen third grade
teachers. [c1932).

(Columbia university. Teachers college. Teachers
lesson unit series. c1931).No. 43.)

NL 0356388 DLC Or OrMonO

Life in the New world; or, Sketches of American
society
see under   (Sealsfield, Charles) 1793-1824.

Life in the nursery: sports of childhood by
land and water.
see under   American Sunday-School Union.

Is94
t1
v.4(1
Life in the nursery, the kind sister
(Philadelphia, American Sunday school union
(18--)
cover-title,12 numb.?. col.illus. 19cm.
In verse.
Printed on alternate rectos and versos;
illustrated paper cover.

I. American Sunday-school ur ion.

NL 0356391 CtY

Life in the nursery, the three dangerous steps.
Philadelphia, (n.d.)
cover title, [12] l.   col. illus.   20 cm.

NL 0356392 RPB

Life in the Royal Navy. By "A ranker" With ...
illustrations, by another "Ranker."
Portsmouth, G. Chamberlain, 1891.
x, 1 l., (1) 14-171 (1) p., 8 pl.   12°.
2. ed.

NL 0356393 NN PPL

914.98
L626
Life in the Rumanian people's republic,
Young Pioneers' palace. Bucharest, 1951.
1v. (unpaged) illus. 17x25 cm.

1. Rumania. Social conditions. I.
Title: Young Pioneers' palace.

NL 0356394 OrU

VOLUME 332

Life in the shop. A series of articles reprinted from "The Daily chronicle " ...
(London, 1898)
16 p. 34 cm.

NL 0356395   DL

Life in the sick-room. Essays
      see under   [Martineau, Harriet] 1802-1876.

Life in the singing world
      see under   [Brogan, Clara]

Life in the South; from the commencement of the
war
      see under   [Hopley, Catherine Cooper]

Life in the spheres; a series of messages received from the
spirit world, by W. C. Manchester, "Two worlds" publishing
co., ltd., 1922.
2 p. l., ii, 55 p. 19ᶜᵐ.

1. Intermediate state. 2. Immortality. 3. Spiritualism.   I. C., W.
II. W. C.

                                33-38477
Library of Congress   BF1301.L69   [159.96173] 133.93

NL 0356399   DLC

Life in the tent; or, Travels in the desert and
Syria
      see under   Woods, Mrs. Anne (Hindley)

Life in the Union army: or notings and reminiscences of a two years' volunteer a rythmical
history of the fifteenth New York volunteer
engineers. New York, 1864.

NL 0356401   RP RPB

Life in the United States; a collection of narratives of contemporary American life from first-hand experience or observation. New York, C. Scribner's sons, 1933.
viii p., 1 l., 324 p. 20ᶜᵐ.

"The twenty-seven narratives ... are the result of a prize offered by
Scribner's magazine."—Publishers' note.

1. Short stories, American.
Library of Congress   PZ1.L6314   33-24659

ViU PPL PBm IdB OrSaW WaU IdU
NL 0356402   DLC GU OU FU NcU LU ODW OU OCU NN MB

PS659
L5
1934
     Life in the United States; a collection of
     narratives of contemporary American life
     from first-hand experience or observation.
     London, J. Cape [1934]
     viii, 324 p. 20cm.

     1. Short stories, American.

NL 0356403   CoU

Life in the West. A merry Briton in pioneer
Wisconsin. A contemporary narrative reprinted
from Life in the West: Back-wood leaves and
Prairie flowers ...
      see Morleigh, pseud.
A merry Briton in pioneer Wisconsin.

Life in the West; back-wood leaves and prairie
flowers
      see under   Morleigh, pseud.

Life in the West; or, the curtain drawn, a novel ...
      see under   [Deale,   ]

Life in the West; or, The Moreton family. By the author of "The village boys." Written for the American
Sunday-school union. Philadelphia, New York [etc.]
American Sunday-school union [ᶜ1851]
100 p., 1 l., 105-258 p. incl. front., illus., pl. 15½ᶜᵐ.

Frontispiece wanting in L. C. copy.

I. Village boys, Author of.

                             12-36204
Library of Congress   PZ7.L62

NL 0356407   DLC MiU-C NIC IaU OClWHi NcD PU IU

Life in the wild west; a true story. By
Uncle John. [n.p.,190-?]
2p.l.,76p. 16cm.
Original wrappers.
Illus. t.-p.
Frontier life in the Niobrara river valley,
Nebraska.

NL 0356408   CtY

Uzn58
900ℓ
     Life in the woods; a guide to the successful
     hunting and trapping of all kinds of animals.
     Chicago,Ill.,Richardson & company[19--?]
     cover-title,63p. 15½cm.

NL 0356409   CtY

Life in town, or The Boston spy. /Being a series of
sketches illustrative of whims and women in the 'Athens
of America.' By an Athenian ... Boston, Redding and
company; New York, Burgess & Stringer; [etc., etc.] 1844.
24 p. front. 27ᶜᵐ.

On cover: In twelve monthly numbers, each complete in itself ... No. 1.
Sewing circles.

1. Boston—Soc. life & cust.

                           10-31049
Library of Congress   F73.44.L72

NL 0356410   DLC MH CU N ViU MB NjP

Life in Tuscany
      see under   Crawford, Mabel Sharman

Life in Whitehall during the ship fever times
      see under   [Wilson, David] 1818-1887.

Life insurance
      see under   [Bard, William]

Life insurance. Credit system. Being a **review of an**
official document of the Mutual benefit life **insurance**
company, of New Jersey. [n. p.] 1851.
15 p. 20ᶜᵐ.

Signed: Pro bono publico.

1. Mutual benefit life insurance company, Newark.

Library of Congress   HG8963.M76L7   7-6537†

NL 0356414   DLC

Life insurance; a Canadian handbook.
Tor.Macmillan,1945.
56p.front.illus.O.

NL 0356415   CaBViP

Life insurance adjustment bureau.
     Life insurance; a handbook for social
     workers ... New York, 1937)
     cover-title, 24 p. 19½cm.

NL 0356416   DL

Life insurance adjustment bureau.
     Life insurance, a handbook for social workers concerning the
examination, evaluation, and adjustment of life insurance. 3d
ed., 1940. New York, N. Y., The Life insurance adjustment
bureau [1940]
cover-title, 46 p. incl. forms. 23ᶜᵐ.

1. Insurance, Life. 2. Insurance, Life—U. S. 3. Insurance, Industrial—U. S.

                            42-13004
Library of Congress   HG8773.L7 1940
                          [2]   368.3

NL 0356417   DLC OU MH IU

Life insurance adjustment bureau
     Life insurance; a handbook for social workers
concerning the examination, evaluation, and
adjustment of life insurance. 4th ed. N. Y.
[The Author] 1946.
46 p.

NL 0356418   MiD

Life insurance advertisers association.
     Forum on company public relations, sponsored
jointly by the Life insurance advertisers association and the Institute of life insurance,
March 30-31, 1948. New York City. [1948]
cover-title, 174 p. ports., charts.

1. Publicity.
2. Insurance, Life.
I. Title: Public relations.
II. Institute of life insurance.   jt. au.

NL 0356419   NNC

HG8758
.L5
     Life Insurance Advertisers Association.
     Membership roster.
     New York.
     v. 23 cm. annual.
     Cover title.   Roster.

     1. Insurance, Life—Direct.

     HG8758.L5   67-4091 ‡

NL 0356420   DLC

VOLUME 332

LIFE INSURANCE AGENCY MANAGEMENT ASSOCIATION.
  Annual meeting. [1]-   ; 1946-
Chicago.   v.   illus.   23cm.

1. Insurance, Life--Congresses--
          U.S. --Ill. --Chicago.

NL   0356421   DLC MH-BA PPT CLSU PU-W

368.3   Life Insurance Agency Management Association
L7196c   Career underwriting, a life work.
         ₍Hartford, 1949₎
           63p. illus.,diagrs. Q.

           Earlier editions published by Life
         insurance sales research bureau.

           1.Insurance. Life. Agents. I.(Title)

NL   0356422   IaU PU-W OCl

368.3   Life Insurance Agency Management Association.
L62c   Covering the market, a survey of life in-
         surance ownership, buying and contact with
         agents among a representative sample of U.S.
         families.   Hartford, 1953.
           9p. tables. 28cm. (Research report,
         1953-5. File no. 940)

           "A market study."

           1. Insurance, Life--U.S. I. Title. (Se-
         ries)

NL   0356423   IU

**Life insurance agency management association
  Current practices; a summary bulletin of
  information**

NL   0356424   PU-W

---

368   Life Insurance Agency Management Association
L613h   How to make your agency well known; a
       public relations manual. Hartford, Conn.
       ₍1955₎
         102 p. illus.

         File no. 661.
         Published as part of the Manager's hand-
       book.

         1. Insurance, Life – Agents   I. T.

NL   0356425   MiD

S   Life Insurance Agency Management Association.
658.3   Human relations in management; leaders'
L722   manual. ₍Hartford, ᶜ1949₎
           44 p. 28 cm.

           "Published as part of the Manager's hand-
         book."

           1. Personnel management. I. Title.

NL   0356426   N

368.3   Life Insurance Agency Management Association.
L621   Introduction to programming. ₍1st ed.₎
         ₍Hartford, 1953₎
           iv, 89p. diagrs. 20cm.

           "An Agency Management Association Service
         published as part of the Manager's handbook."

           1. Insurance, Life

NL   0356427   IU NcU

Ref   Life Insurance Agency Management Association.
HG   Manager's handbook
8876   19-
.I43   Hartford, Conn.
          1 v. (loose-leaf) monthly.

          1. Insurance, Life - Agents. I. Title.

NL   0356428   NBuU

---

368   Life Insurance Agency Management Association
L613m3   Managing a district. ₍Hartford, Conn.,
        ᶜ1954₎
          1 v. (loose-leaf)

          1. Insurance, Life - Agents   I. Title

NL   0356429   MiD TU

    Life Insurance Agency Management Association.
      Managing an agency; principles and practices of **agency**
    management. ₍Hartford, 1949₎
      158 p. 24 cm.
      Includes bibliographies.

      1. Insurance, Life—Agents.   I. Title.

    HG8876.I47   368.3   49-6319*

NL   0356430   DLC OrPS InU MiD OrP CaBVa PPFML

    Life Insurance Agency Management Association.
      Managing an agency; principles and practices of **agency**
    management. ₍Hartford, 1953]
      158 p. 24 cm.
      Includes bibliographies.

NL   0356431   FU TU PSt MiD

368.3   Life Insurance Agency Management Associa-
L625m   tion.
1955   Managing an agency; principles and prac-
         tices of agency management. [Rev. ed.
         Hartford, 1955]
           4p.l.,161p. 24cm.

           Includes bibliographies.

           1. Insurance, Life - Agents. I. Title.

NL   0356432   TxU

LIFE INSURANCE AGENCY MANAGEMENT ASSOCIATION.
  Monthly survey of life insurance sales in the
United States and Canada. 1946-Nov. 1947, 1948-
Nov. 1949, 1950-date
Hartford.   v.   charts, tables (part fold.)
29cm.

  "File no. 821"

  Supersedes: Life insurance sales research bureau. Monthly survey of
ordinary life insurance sales in the United States. (Cataloged under an earlier
title; see the bureau's Monthly survey of life insurance sales.)
  Title varies: 1946-49, Monthly survey of life insurance sales in the
United States.

1. Insurance, Life--Stat.--U.S.   2. Insurance, Life--Stat.--Canada.

NL   0356434   NN IU ICU

Life insurance agency management association.
  Organization, constitution, committees,
member roster.
Hartford.
    v.

  Library has 1951 ed. only.

NL   0356435   MH-BA

368.306   Life Insurance Agency Management Association.
L625   Proceedings [of the] annual meeting.
Bus Ad
Eco RR   [Hartford?]
               v. 23cm.

             1. Insurance, Life - Agents. 2. Insurance,
           Life - Societies.

NL   0356436   TxU FTaSU

HG 8877   LIFE INSURANCE AGENCY MANAGEMENT ASSOCIATION.
.L 72
            Prospecting for recruits; an Agency
          Management Association service, pub. as part of
          the Manager's handbook. Hartford, Conn. ₍1953₎
            77 p.

            1. Insurance—Life—Agents. I. Title.
          Bus. cds.

NL   0356437   InU

368.3   Life Insurance Agency Management Association.
L6263w   What price business? A discussion of
         method and principle. Hartford, Conn.,
         1953,ᶜ1938₎
           103p. tables. 28cm.

           "This confidential report has not been
         prepared for general distribution or sale."

NL   0356438   OrU

368.3   Life Insurance Agency Management Association.
L625w   What price business? A discussion of
1953   method and principle. 3d print. Hartford,
         1953.
           103p. 28cm.

           "Supplement" (17p.) inserted.

           1. Insurance, Life. I. Title.

NL   0356439   TxU

Life insurance agents' vade mecum comprising premium rates at
all ages of issue (participating and nonparticipating) on ordinary
life, limited premiums life, ordinary endowment and term policies,
.... . Oak Park, Ill., U. S. A., A. J. Flitcraft, ᶜ1898-ᶜ1916.
    Library has edition 1, 5, 7, 11, 16-22, 24, 1898, 1901-1902, 1904, 1908-1914,
  1916. tables. 17ᶜᵐ.

    Subtitle varies.

NL   0356440   ICJ

Life insurance and silver dollars
    see under   [Hallock, James Collins] 1896-

338.205   Life insurance and the American public; a re-
LII   port by the Institute of Life Insurance. v.1-
           10, no.2; July 1943-Nov./Dec.1953. New
           York, N.Y.
             v. illus. 28cm.

             The "purpose is to give ... some idea of what
           the Institute ... is doing in public relations;
           and to bring to ... attention the mass of material
           that appears in the press and in the magazines
           about life insurance."
             Wanting: v.1-2,   no.7.

NL   0356442   IU

Life Insurance Association of America
    [Addresses and other pamphlets.]
    Continued.

NL   0356443   ICJ

VOLUME 332

Life Insurance Association of America.
Aims, services, committees, membership.

New York.
v. 22 cm.

HG8941.L5   55–35759 ‡

NL 0356444   DLC OrU

Life insurance association of America.
... Are you borrowing from your widow? New York, Association of life insurance presidents [1913?]
2 p. l., 33 p. incl. tables, diagrs. 23 cm.
At head of title: Betterment of life insurance service.
"Reprinted from Proceedings of the seventh annual meeting of the Association of life insurance presidents, New York, December 11–12, 1913."
CONTENTS.—Ultimate effect of an unrestricted right to borrow on life insurance policies, by A. E. Childs.—Growth of the policy loan problem, statistical evidence, by R. L. Cox.—General discussion: Policy loans, by W. J. Fischer.

1. Insurance, Life—Finance.   I. Childs, Arthur Edward, 1869–
II. Title.

HG8934.L49   15–16459 rev

NL 0356445   DLC NN

Life insurance association of America.
... Bequeathing our debts, what it means for policyholders to borrow on their life insurance policies—reduction of protection to widows and orphans—some possible remedies; views and suggestions of representatives, taken from their editorial pages, following the discussion on this subject by the Association of life insurance presidents. New York, Association of life insurance presidents, 1914.
24 p. 23 cm.
At head of title: Betterment of life insurance service.
1. Insurance, Life.   I. Title.

HG8934.L5   15–6824 rev

         OO OU NN IU
NL 0356446   DLC MH–BA NcD NIC Or PPULC PPProM NcD

HG8932
.L48

Life insurance association of America.
Betterment of life insurance service, need for better vital statistics; report of Health committee, Association of life insurance presidents ... submitted at the sixth annual meeting of Association of life insurance presidents at New York, Dec. 5, 1912. [New York, 1912]
cover-title, 7 p. 23 cm.

1. Insurance, Life—Stat. 2. Vital statistics.   I. Title. II. Title: Need for better vital statistics.

HG8932.L48   13–9234 rev

NL 0356447   DLC NcD Or NIC CU

Life insurance association of America.
Birth and death bookkeeping business methods applied to the health problem—registration of vital statistics not a fad of doctors and scientists but a fundamental need of the movement to prolong human life ... submitted by the Association of life insurance presidents. [New York, 1913]
cover-title, 12 p. 23 cm.
At head of title: Betterment of life insurance service.

1. Vital statistics. 2. Insurance, Life—Stat.   I. Title.

HA38.N7L5   13–19666 rev

NL 0356448   DLC CaBVaU Or

HG8837
L47

Life insurance association of America.
Board contracts, stock selling and promotion schemes. A synopsis of the laws and rulings of departments relating thereto. New York, Association of life insurance presidents, 1914.
27 p. 21 cm.

1. Insurance, Life—Addresses, essays, lectures.

HG8837.L47   20–2903 rev

NL 0356449   DLC NIC

HG
8850
L514

Life Insurance Association of America.
Chairman's address. 19 -
New York, 19 -
v. 22 cm.

1. Insurance companies—U.S.

NL 0356450   LU

HG4926
.A3L5

Life insurance association of America.
Digest of life insurance investment statutes of the United States ... prepared ... by the Association of life insurance presidents for the confidential use and information of its member companies only—covers the investment statutes of the states of the United States and the District of Columbia applicable to domestic, foreign and alien life insurance companies ... November 1, 1930. New York, N. Y., Association of life insurance presidents, *1930.
34 l. 35½ x 53½ cm.

1. Insurance, Life—U. S. 2. Insurance law—U. S. 3. Investments—U. S. 4. Law reports, digests, etc.—U. S.   I. Title.

HG4926.A3L5   332.63   52–51816

NL 0356451   DLC

Life Insurance Association of America.
Economic and investment report.
New York.
v. 23 cm.

1. United States—Economic conditions—1961–   2. Insurance companies—United States—Investments.   I. Title.

HC106.6.L5   338.4'7'368973   72–625368

NL 0356452   DLC NSyU

Law

Life Insurance Association of America.
Investment law manual, containing texts of statutes, with indices thereto, relating to investments by legal reserve life insurance companies of the United States. Prepared for the use of member companies. New York, 1949–
1 v. (loose-leaf) 25 cm.
"Will be kept current by replacement or new sheets."

1. Investments—U. S.   I. Title.

          49–1264*

NL 0356453   DLC

Life Insurance Association of America.
Laws ... relating to legal reserve life insurance companies in the United States and Canada
see under title

Life insurance association of America.
... Lengthening life through legislation; progress made in vital statistics registration laws in 1913; report of Health committee, the Association of life insurance presidents ... submitted at the seventh annual meeting of the Association of life insurance presidents, at New York, December 12, 1913. [New York, 1913]
cover-title, 11 p. 23 cm.
At head of title: Betterment of life insurance service.
1. Insurance, Life—U. S.   I. Title. II. Title: Vital statistics registration laws in 1913.

HG8931.L47   15–3599 rev

NL 0356455   DLC Or

HG8932
.L5

Life insurance association of America.
Movement to lengthen life; abstracts from some editorial comments on suggestions concerning ways to increase human longevity made to the Association of life insurance presidents by Dr. Irving Fisher ... and by Dr. Burnside Foster ... New York, The Association of life insurance presidents [1909?]
cover-title, 24 p. 23 cm.

1. Insurance, Life. 2. Longevity. 3. Hygiene, Public.   I. Fisher, Irving, 1867–1947.

HG8932.L5   12–10332 rev

NL 0356456   DLC NIC

Life Insurance Association of America.
Need for better vital statistics. Report of Health Committee, Association of Life Insurance Presidents
see its Betterment of life insurance service. *Need for better vital statistics*

Life Insurance Association of America.
Proceedings of the ... annual meeting. 1st–
1907–
[New York]
v. in   illus., ports., maps. 22–24 cm.
Title varies slightly.
Issues for 1907–1942–43 pub. under the association's earlier name: Association of Life Insurance Presidents.
INDEXES:
Vols. 1–10, 1907–16, in v. 10.
Vols. 1–15, 1907–21, in v. 15.
Index, cumulative from 1907, issued annually in v. 20–   1926–
1. Insurance, Life—Societies. 2. Insurance, Life—U. S.

HG8941.A7   368.306273   9–14082 rev 2*

         ICJ OrP MtU IdU MtBC WaS CaBVaU OrU–M WaSp CaBVa OrC
         NBuU–L MBU NN CtY CtNlC TxU LU NNC TU PBL Or WaWW Or
NL 0356458   DLC MoSW–L MB CtY–M PV NN MtU DNLM PHC

Life insurance association of America.
Publications of the Association of life insurance presidents. [New York, 1920]
[8] p. 23 cm.
Caption title.

1. Insurance, Life—Bibl.

Z7164.I 7L55   21–7526 rev

NL 0356460   DLC WaS

HG
8850
L5

Life Insurance Association of America.
Record of life insurance investments, a report to the membership.
New York.
v. 22 cm.

1. Insurance companies—U. S.—Investments.

HG8850.L5   58–18688

NL 0356461   DLC MH–L MH–BA LU

HG8912
.L5

[Life insurance association of America]
Reform in life insurance taxation. Insurance journals of two countries indorse conference held in New York, December 4th and 5th, 1908, and point out necessity for continued activity in this campaign for the policyholders. [New York, 1909]
cover-title, 7 p. 23 cm.
Conference on taxation, held at the second annual meeting of the Association of life insurance presidents, Dec. 4–5, 1908.

1. Insurance, Life—U. S.—Taxation.   I. Title.

HG8912.L5   9–20554

NL 0356462   DLC PPProM OOxM NN

S
368.3
qL719

Life Insurance Association of America.
A report in support of proposed amendments to Article 5, Section 81, of the New York insurance law. Submitted to the Joint Legislative Committee on Insurance Rates and Regulation of the State of New York, by Life Insurance Association of America and American Life Convention. [New York?] 1951.
v, 158 p. tables. 28 cm.

1. Investments. 2. Insurance. Life. New York (State) I.   American Life Convention. II. New   York (State) Legislature. Insurance Rates.

NL 0356463   N

VOLUME 332

Life Insurance Association of America.
Serving seventy million Americans, a report to
the membership of the Life Insurance Association
of America
see under   Fulton, James Arthur, 1874-

HD7125
.A54
American life convention.
Social security, a statement by the Social security commit-
tees of American life convention, Life insurance association of
America ₍and₎ the National association of life underwriters.
₍Chicago, 1945₎

Life insurance association of America.
... Some statistical reflections on the state of the nation in
1921. Life insurance as a mirror; interpretative addresses
on causes of death among policyholders, new business issued,
loans on insurance policies, distribution of investments, and
national physical and economic health.   Delivered at the
fifteenth annual meeting of the Association of life insurance
presidents, at New York, December 8 and 9, 1921. ₍New
York? 1921?₎
cover-title, 63 p. fold. tables, diagrs. 23 cm.
At head of title: Betterment of life insurance service.

CONTENTS.—Preface.—National health in the life insurance mirror,
by R. L. Cox.—New life insurance business of 1921; what it means,
by J. M. Holcombe.—Recent fluctuations in policy loans, by H. S.
Nollen.—A decade of life insurance investments, by A. S. Wing.

1. Insurance, Life — U. S. 2. Insurance, Life — Stat.   I. Title.
II. Title : Betterment of life insurance service.
HG8955.L5 1921
22–18031 rev

NL 0356467   DLC Or OrU NIC CaBVaU

HG8121
.A65
Life insurance Association of America.

American Life Convention.
State premium taxes, payable by foreign and alien life insurance companies in the United States, certain territories and
dependencies; recommended procedure, schedules, tax formulas,
texts of statutes, digests of rulings and decisions. Prepared for
the use of member companies by ₍a Joint Premium Taxation
Committee of₎ the American Life Convention and the Life Insurance Association of America. New York ₍1946₎

HG8912
.L53
Life insurance association of America.
State premium taxes; recommended procedure, tax sched-
ule, text of statutes, digest of rulings and decisions. New
York, N. Y., The Association of life insurance presidents
₍1942₎
1 v. 25½ x 19½ cm.
Loose-leaf.

1. Insurance, Life—U. S.—Taxation. 2. Insurance law—U. S.
I. Title.
HG8912.L53   368.30973   42–10465 rev

NL 0356469   DLC

Life Insurance Association of America.
Statutes relating to legal reserve life insurance
companies in the United States and Canada
see   Laws relating to legal reserve life
insurance ...

Life Insurance Association of America.
Committee on Civil Defense.
General aspects of civil defense, report.
New York, 1954.
vii, 86 p. illus., map

Bibliography: p. 49–59.

1. Civilian defense – U. S. I. Title

NL 0356471   MiD

Life insurance clearing company, *St. Paul, Minn.*
Agents' manual ... issued by the Life insurance clearing co. ... ₍St. Paul, Minn., The Life insurance clearing
company, ⁺1895₎
43 p. 18½ᶜᵐ.

Library of Congress   HG8881.L7   7–2703†

NL 0356472   DLC

Life insurance companies association.
... Japanese experience life tables, 1912–1927.
Monetary tables at 3 1/2 and 4 percent on
JPM(3) tables, conducted and published by the
Life insurance companies association.   Tokyo,
Marunouchi, 1932.
x, 239 p., 1 l.   incl. tables.   27 cm.
Japanese and English text.
1. Insurance, Life - Rates and tables. 2. Japan-
Statistics, Vital.

NL 0356473   CU

Life Insurance Companies Association, Tokio.
...Japanese pure endowment experience tables, 1912–1927,
conducted and published, by the Life Insurance Companies Asso-
ciation.   Tokyo, 1933.   viii, 73 p. incl. tables. chart. 27cm.
Title in Japanese at head of title.
Text in Japanese and English.

723407A. 1. Insurance, Life—Rates   and tables—Japan.
N.Y.P.L.   November 21, 1934

NL 0356474   NN OC1 CU

368.3 Life Insurance Companies of Massachusetts
L625s   Seminar--the next decade, The Life Insurance Companies of Massachusetts in cooperation with the Graduate School of Business
Administration, Harvard University, Boston,
Massachusetts, April 13–14, 1950   ₍Boston,
1950₎
1 v (various pagings) diagrs. 28cm.

1. Insurance, Life--U S   I Title   II Title: The next dec   ade

NL 0356475   IU NNC MiD NcU

Life insurance company of Virginia, Richmond.
A comparative statement showing the growth of
the Life insurance company of Virginia, Richmond,
Virginia, for the past 26 years, 1907 through
1932. Prepared by Davenport & co. ... Richmond,
Virginia. ... ₍Richmond, Va., 1933₎
₍4₎ p. 23 cm.

I. Davenport & co., Richmond, Va.

NL 0356476   Vi

Life insurance company of Virginia, Richmond.
The **Mortality** experience of industrial policyholders, 1916–
1920; a contribution to the public health movement in America, by the Colonial life insurance company of America,
John Hancock mutual life insurance company, Life insurance company of Virginia, Metropolitan life insurance company, Prudential insurance company of America. New
York, 1923.

LIFE INSURANCE COMPANY OF VIRGINIA.
Non-participating premium rates ordinary
and intermediate, together with tables of loans
and surrender values. Richmond, Va., [1908]

nar. 24°.

NL 0356478   MH

Life insurance compendium
see under ₍Flitcraft, Allen J   ₎
1854–1931.

IG9164
Z9L53
Life Insurance Corporation of India.
Report and accounts.
₍Bombay₎
v. in   28 cm. annual.
Report year ends Mar. 31; report year for   ends
Dec. 31.

HG9164.Z9L53   S A 68–749

NL 0356480   DLC

Life insurance courant.
Oak Park, Ill., A. J. Flitcraft,
v.   plates, ports. 29½ᶜᵐ. monthly.
Editors :   A. J. Flitcraft and others.

1. Insurance, Life—Period. 2. Insurance, Life—U. S.   I. Flitcraft,
Allen J., 1854-   ed.
CA 8—2264 Unrev'd
Library of Congress   HG8751.L5

FU FM PPT MH–BA ICRL NN Vi IEN WaS DNLM NIC OkS
NL 0356481   DLC MoSW N TxU CL AzTeS WvU OC Vi ICJ LU

Life insurance directory. 1st–   ed. 1943–
₍Calcutta₎ Chhaya Publication.
v. 19 cm.

1. Insurance, Life—India—Direct.
HG9162.L5   368.3058   52–18781 ‡

NL 0356482   DLC

HG
8018
I59
v.14
no.5
Life insurance dividends earned in the last
seven years. ₍New York, The De Vinne Press,
1886₎
11 p. 23cm.

1. Insurance, Life--Statistics.

NL 0356483   NIC

VOLUME 332

The life insurance educator. Series II
　　see under　[Weekly underwriter]

The life insurance educator; life insurance,
　　accident and health insurance
　　　see under　Weekly underwriter.

The **Life** insurance educator monthly; a practical magazine on the art in the sale of life insurance ... **with**
which is consolidated the "**Pink supplement**" of **the**
Insurance field. v. 1–　　Sept. 1904–
Louisville, Ky., The Insurance educator co. (incorporated) 1904–
　　v.　illus. (incl. ports.) 24–35ᶜᵐ.
Title varies: Sept. 1904–Mar. 1907, The Life insurance educator.
　Apr. 1907–Dec. 1913, The Life insurance educator monthly of the Insur-
　ance field.
Jan. 1914–　　　　The Life insurance educator monthly; a practical
　magazine ...

　1. Insurance, Life—Period.

Library of Congress　　　HG8751.L55　　　　8-4519 (rev. '25)

NL　0356486　　DLC ICJ I

Life insurance fact book. 1946–

[New York, 1946–
　　v.　diagrs. 23½ cm.　annual.
　Issued by the Statistical division of the Institute of life insurance,
New York.

　1. Insurance, Life — Yearbooks. 2. Insurance, Life — U. S.
ɪ. Institute of life insurance, New York. Statistical division.

HG8943.L5　　　　368.3058　　　*47-27134*

OrU-M OrAshS MB CU DNAL

OrP OrU WaE WaT WaTC WaU-L MtBC CaBVaU WaSpG
OFH OClW KyWA CaBVa IdB IdPS IdU MtU Or OrCS
NBuU MtBuM KU-L CtY NBuC CMenSP GU-L KEmT DI
CtNIC PJB NSyU PLF PPFr DI LN Wa WaWW Or PPiU-H
MH PHC NcD PPSOPR PPD MeB ICU MBCo DNLM NcU-H GEU
NL　0356487　　DLC NIC PV NNC ICJ TxU ICRL IaU TxLT

Life insurance failures
　　see under　[Brigham, Alasco Delancey]
supposed author.

Life insurance illustrated and objections consider-
　ed from a business standpoint
　　see under　[Smith, Matthew Hales] 1810–
1879.

Life insurance. Important facts, shewing the
　successive reductions that have taken place in
　the terms for the insurance of lives
　　see under　[Beaumont, John Thomas Barber]
1774-1841.

Life insurance in Great Britian and the United
　States, two articles from the Boston journal
n p., 1869.　　*YA 25016*
　15p.

NL　0356492　　DLC

The **Life** insurance independent.

Chicago, The Independent printing & publishing co.,
18　–1902; New York [Life insurance independent
publishing co., 1902–
　　v.　illus. 30ᶜᵐ.　monthly.
Title varies:　　　　　　The Chicago independent.
　　　　　　　The Life insurance independent.
Editors:　　　G. L. McKean.—Apr. 1903, J. A. Jackson.—May
1903–　　N. H. Weed.
Merger into the Insurance salesman, Aug. 1920.
　1. Insurance, Life—Period.　ɪ. McKean, Gideon L., ed. ɪɪ. Jackson,
Jacob Anderson, 1848–　ed. ɪɪɪ. Weed, Nathan Herbert, 1868–　ed. ɪv.
The Chicago independent.

Library of Congress　　　HG8751.L6　　　CA 8—2265 Unrev'd

NL　0356493　　DLC ICRL

Life insurance index.
　Philadelphia [etc.] The Spectator [etc.]
　　v. 15–28 cm.　annual.
　Title varies: 18　–80, The Policyholders' pocket index.—1881–
1982, The Life insurance policyholders pocket index.—1983–60, The
Spectator life index.

　1. Insurance, Life—U. S.—Stat. 2. Insurance, Life—Canada—Stat.
ɪ. The Spectator. Philadelphia.

HG8955.S88　　　　　　　0-2472 rev 2*

NL　0356494　　DLC MtU WaSp NN MiU PPFML

Life insurance. Its history in the United States
　during the last half century...
　　see under　[Byington, William W　　　]
1840-1899? comp.

Life insurance is light
　　see under　[Kingsley, Darwin Pearl]
1857-1932.

Life insurance, its nature, origin and progress
　　see under　[Norton, Charles Benjamin]
1825-1891.

Life Insurance Management Association.
　Clerical salaries in the life insurance business. Being the results of
　a survey of this and correlated subjects. [1932.]
— Fort Wayne. 1932. 1 v. Tables. 23 cm.

D2278 — Life insurance. — Salaries.

NL　0356498　　MB

Life Insurance Management Institute, *University of Illinois*
　see **Institute of Life Insurance Management,** *University*
of Illinois.

... **Life** insurance manual
　　see　Flitcraft ... life insurance **manual.**

Life Insurance Medical Research Fund, New York.
　Annual report
　　see its　Report.

HG
8754
q L722

LIFE Insurance Medical Research ,Fund,
　New York
　[Collection of publications]

　　　The library has a collection of miscellaneous publications of this organization
kept as received. These publications are
not listed nor bound separately.

NL　0356502　　DNLM

Life Insurance Medical Research Fund.
　Report. 1st–　　　　1945–
New York.
　　v. 23 cm. annual.
　Report year for 1945–　ends Dec. 31, for　　June 30.

　1. Medical research. [1. Research, Medical]

R850.L5　　　　　　　　Med 47-3186 rev
U. S. Armed Forces　　　　Medical Libr. [W1LI 406]
for Library of Congress　　[r55b1]†

MiDW-M NcU-H
NL　0356503　　DNLM DLC OrU-M ViRM NN NBuU CtY-M

NNgr10
L528

Life insurance news data; monthly press release.
　　　　　　New York, Institute
of life insurance,
　tables,diagrs. 47cm.

Broadsides.

NL　0356504　　CtY

The **Life** insurance policyholders pocket index
　see
Life insurance index.

---

ar W
5693

Life insurance principles and home
　office procedure. A series of
lectures delivered at the University
of Southern California, Los Angeles,
California, February and March, 1929.
[Los Angeles] The Pacific Mutual
Life Insurance Company of California,
1929.
144 p. 22cm.

NL　0356506　　NIC

Life insurance ratios
　see
Compendium of official life insurance reports.

Life insurance sales research bureau.
　Agency management. [Hartford, Conn., 19--]
1 v.

Manifold copy.
Loose-leaf.

NL　0356508　　MH-BA OrU

Life insurance sales research bureau.

Association of life agency officers.
　Annual meeting of the Association of life agency officers
and the Life insurance sales research bureau ...
[Chicago]

VOLUME 332

Life Insurance Sales Research Bureau.
Awards for leading agencies. [Hartford,
1939]
Cover title, 19 *l*. (Its Reference report
no.26)

File no.650.

NL 0356510   MH-BA

Life Insurance Sales Research Bureau.
Building new organization, a study of the
agency manager's problem of finding and select-
the right man. Hartford, Conn., c1942.
196 p.

1. Insurance - Agents. I. Title.

NL 0356511   TxHU

[Life insurance sales research bureau]
Career underwriting, a life work. [Hartford, 1941]
63 p. illus., diagrs. 27 cm.

1. Insurance as a profession.   I. Title.

HG8091.L5   368.069   45—44278

NL 0356512   DLC

368.3   Life insurance sales research bureau]
L6261c   Career underwriting, a life work. [Rev. ed.]
Hartford, Conn., The life insurance research bureau, 1944]
cover-title, 63p. illus., diagrs.

NL 0356513   IU PSt

Life Insurance Sales Research Bureau.
Change of residence of policyholders.
[Hartford, 1939]
Cover title, 13 *l*. (Its Reference report
no.25)

File no.734.

NL 0356514   MH-BA

Life insurance sales research bureau.
A comparative survey of advertising expendi-
tures by life insurance companies in 1934. Presented by Life insurance sales research bureau
in cooperation with Life advertisers association
... [Hartford, Conn., 1935]
23 *l*. incl. tables. IX charts. 28½ cm.

Mimeographed.

1.Advertising - Insurance, Life. I.Life
advertisers association.

NL 0356515   NNC

Life insurance sales research bureau.
Conservation at the source; increasing
profits by improving persistency. Hartford,
Conn. [1934]

NL 0356516   MH-BA

[Life insurance sales research bureau]
A guidebook to early production. [Hartford,
Conn., Life insurance sales reasearch bureau,
c1932]

NL 0356517   OrU

Life insurance sales research bureau.
Handbook of agency management.

Hartford, Conn.,
v.   23 cm.   monthly.

"A Research bureau service"
Scattered loose-leaf pages.

1. Insurance, Life - Agents. I. title.

NL 0356518   NNC

368.3   Life Insurance Sales Research Bureau.
L722h   "How to do it series". no.1-3. Hartford,
Conn. [1934]
3 v. diagrs. 28 cm.
Contents: -1. How to find the man you want.-
2-3. How to increase production from established
agents. pt.1-2.

1.Insurance, Life - Agents.

NL 0356519   CSt

Life insurance sales research bureau.
How to increase production from established agents; a work
book of methods and plans ... Hartford, Conn., Life insurance sales research bureau [c1934]
2 pt. diagrs., forms. 28 cm. (*On cover:* "How to do it" series. nos.
2-3)
CONTENTS.—pt. 1. Group methods.—pt. 2. "Individual" methods.

1. Insurance, Life—Agents.   I. Title.

                                                          34-14523
Library of Congress   HG8876.L48
Copyright AA 146654   [2]   368.3

NL 0356520   DLC

Life insurance sales research bureau.
How well does the aptitude index work?
A follow-up study of a thousand agents hired
in 1939 ... [n.p.] 1941.
74 p.incl.tables, charts, form.

NL 0356521   MH-BA

[Life insurance sales research bureau]
Increasing your income through profitable selling ... [Hart-
ford, Conn., Life insurance sales research bureau, c1937]
1 p. l., 49, [1] p. diagrs. 21¼ cm.

1. Insurance, Life—Agents.   I. Title.
                                                          41-37515
Library of Congress   HG8877.L5
                               [2]   368.3

NL 0356522   DLC

Life insurance sales research bureau.
John Doe's profits and costs; an analysis of
income and expenses in the John Doe General
Agency. Hartford, Conn., Life Insurance Sales
Research Bureau, 1929.
20 p.

NL 0356523   MH-BA

Life insurance sales research bureau.

Manager's magazine. v. 1-
Jan. 1926-
[Hartford, Life insurance sales research bureau, 1926-

Life Insurance Sales Research Bureau, New York.
...Manager's manual. Section 1   New York: Life Insurance Sales Research Bureau, 1923.   v.   diagrs., tables.
12°.

    Contents: Section 1. Your Future agents.

1. Insurance, Life.
N. Y. P. L.   November 1, 1924

NL 0356525   NN MB ICU DLC

Life insurance sales research bureau.
... Manager's manual ...   3d ed., completely rev.
and enl. Hartford, Conn., Life insurance sales research bureau, 1930-
v. diagrs., forms. 20½ cm.

1. Insurance, Life—Agents.   I. Title.

                                                 30-16476
Library of Congress   HG8876.L5 1930
Copyright A 25069   [2]   368.3

NL 0356526   DLC

Life Insurance Sales Research Bureau.
Monthly survey of life insurance sales, new paid-for ordinary
insurance...
1926-

Hartford, 1926-   obl. 4°.
nos.   illus.

For earlier years. see its: New paid for ordinary life insurance sales by states.

1. Insurance—Reports, stat., etc.
N. Y. P. L.   August 22, 1928

NL 0356527   NN

Life insurance sales research bureau.
Morale and agency management, a Research bureau service
... [Hartford, Conn., Life insurance sales research bureau,
c1940-
v. diagrs. 26½ cm.
CONTENTS.—I. Morale, the mainspring of management. Appendix.—
II. Morale, what it is and what it does. Appendix.—III. Morale, how to
build it.

1. Insurance, Life—Agents. 2. Psychology, Applied.   I. Title.

                                                 42-11133
Library of Congress   HG8876.L515
                               [2]   368.3

NL 0356528   DLC CSt FTaSU FU

Life insurance sales research bureau.
Morale-building starts at the top, a Research bureau service.
Hartford, Conn., Life insurance sales research bureau, c1940.
15 p. 27cm.

1. Insurance, Life—Agents.
N. Y. P. L.   May 31, 1949

NL 0356529   NN FU

Life Insurance Sales Research Bureau.
New ordinary paid for business (excluding group) of the
companies in the monthly sales survey.
1921-

[Hartford, 1922-   f°.
nos.
1921-   multigraphed.

1. Insurance — Reports, statistics, etc.
N. Y. P. L.   June 9, 1927

NL 0356530   NN

VOLUME 332

Life Insurance Sales Research Bureau.
New paid for ordinary life insurance sales by states. 1913/18–

Hartford₁ 1922?–
nos.   f°.

1. Insurance — Reports, statistics, etc.
N. Y. P. L.   June 9, 1927

NL 0356531   NN

Life insurance sales research bureau.
Organizing for sales . . . Hartford: Life insurance research bureau ₁1938₁ 119 p. illus. 28cm.

Copies numbered; this copy no. 515.

1. Salesmanship and salesmen—   U.S.
N. Y. P. L.   December 16, 1943

NL 0356532   NN MH-BA

Life insurance sales research bureau.
Plans for a national cooperative advertising campaign in the interest of ordinary life insurance for companies operating in the United States. Proposed by the cooperative advertising committees of the Life insurance sales research bureau and of the National association of life underwriters, April, 1929. ₁Hartford, Conn.₁ Cooperative advertising committees, c1929.
13 p. incl. form.

NL 0356533   MH-BA

Life insurance sales research bureau, N. Y.
Pooling our sales experience. A description of the aims, methods and program of the Life insurance sales research bureau. New York, Life insurance research bureau, 1923.
20 p. incl. maps, diagrs. 28ᶜᵐ.

1. Insurance, Life—Agents. 2. Salesmen and salesmanship. I. Title.

NL 0356534   MiU

HG8754
.L47   **Life insurance sales research bureau.**
. . . Report.
Hartford, Conn.,
v. diagrs. 28cm.

1. Insurance, Life.

NL 0356535   DLC MiU NN

Life Insurance Sales Research Bureau.
Retirement plans for field men. ₁Hartford, 1938₁
Cover title, 22 : *l.* (Its Reference report no. 23)

NL 0356536   MH-BA

368.3
L722   **Life insurance sales research bureau.**
The revolt of Ralph Day. ₁New York?₁ Life insurance sales research bureau, c1927₁
1 p. l., 30 p. illus. 21cm.

"First edition."

1. Insurance, Life. I. Title.

NL 0356537   CSt IU OCl

Life insurance sales research bureau.
Selection of agents; a method of relating personal history information to probable success in life insurance selling . . . ₁Hartford, Conn., Life insurance sales research bureau, c1937₁ 22 p. illus. 28cm.

1. Insurance, Life—Agents.
N. Y. P. L.   May 31, 1949

NL 0356538   NN

Life insurance sales research bureau.
Research agencies group.
Slants on supervision, by members of the Research agencies group, edited by H. G. Kenagy. Hartford, Conn., Life insurance sales research bureau ₁ᶜ1935₁

Life insurance sales research bureau.
Strategy in selling; selling yourself. ₁Hartford, Conn.₁ Life insurance sales research bureau, 1938.
88, ₁1₁ p. illus. 21½ᵐ.

1. Insurance, Life—Agents. I. Title.
    41–24812
Library of Congress   HG8876.L32

NL 0356540   DLC

Life insurance sales research bureau.
Volume of new paid-for ordinary life insurance in the United States, 1923–1941. ₁Hartford, Conn., 1942?₁
broadside. tab.

NL 0356541   MH-BA

Life Insurance Sales Research Bureau. Man Power Committee.
Report of man power committee prepared for the life insurance sales research bureau. 1931.

Committee composed of Morris Albert Linton et al.

NL 0356542   PPProM

Life insurance selling.
₁St. Louis, Life insurance publishing co., 19
v. illus. 28ᵐ. monthly.
Absorbed Selling insurance in 1937.

1. Insurance, Life—Period. 2. Insurance, Life—Agents.
    43–26920
Library of Congress   HG8751.L65
    ₍2₎   368.305

NL 0356543   DLC OkS NN

Life insurance selling.
Ideas that make dollars. Saint Louis, Mo., Life insurance selling ₁ᶜ1930₁
80 p. 20ᵐ.

1. Insurance, Life—Agents. I. Title.
Library of Congress   HG8876.L53   31–1457
Copyright A 32359   ₍2₎   368.3

NL 0356544   DLC

AP2
L5472   **Life** international. v. 1–
July 22, 1946–
₁Chicago, Time Incorporated₁
v. illus. 36 cm. biweekly.
Title varies: July 22, 1946–Apr. 14, 1958, Life. International ed.

AP2.L5472   051   49–28817 rev*‡

NL 0356545   DLC NN

---

*
M1
.S444   **Life is but a strife.** Composed for the
v.103, piano forte and respectfully dedicated to
no.22 Miss Elizabeth White. Baltimore, F₁ D. Benteen, ᶜ1846. Pl. no. 1019.
₁2₁ p. 35cm. ₁Sheet music collection, v. 103, no. 22₁
Caption title.
Webb.

1. Songs with piano.

NL 0356546   ViU

Life is life, and other tales and episodes
see under [Keats, Gwendoline]

Life is worth living (Television program)
BX890   FOR OTHER EDITIONS
.S53   SEE MAIN ENTRY
Sheen, Fulton John, *Bp.,* 1895–
Life is worth living. Illus. by Dik Browne. New York, McGraw-Hill ₁1953–

Life isn't a short story
see under [Aiken, Conrad] 1889–

The life, labours, and deliverances of a Forest of Dean collier
see under [Chilver, A   ]

The life, labours, and writings of Caesar Malan
see under [Malan, Caesar] the younger.

The life, labours, perilous adventures, and discoveries of Dr. Livingstone . . .
see under Stanley, Henry Morton, 1841–1904.

Life, last sickness and death of Robert Mott
see [Mott, Lydia P   ]
A brief account of the life, last sickness and death of Robert Mott.

Life, last words and dying speech of Stephen Smith. A black man, who was executed at Boston . . . October 12, 1797 for burglary. — *Broadside.* [Boston. 1797.] Size, 21½ × 13¼ inches. Illus.

M6545 — Broadsides. → Smith, Stephen, 1769?–1797.

NL 0356554   MB

Life lessons in the school of Christian duty
see under [Gillett, Ezra Hall] 1823–1875.

Life let us cherish. Published, at P. A. von Hagen & Cᵒ imported piano forte ware house Nᵒ 3 Cornhill Boston. Also by G Gilfert New York . . . ₁1800₁
₁1₁ l. 34 cm.

The song is frequently attributed to H. G. Nägeli, but was not composed by him. Cf. Schweizer Musiklexikon.

1. Songs (Medium voice) with piano. I. Nägeli, Hans Georg, 1773–1836, supposed composer. Freut euch des Lebens.

M1.A1L   M 54–809

NL 0356556   DLC RPJCB MiU-C RPB

VOLUME 332

W.C.L. Life let us cherish; with variations by Mo-
M780.88 zart. New York, W. Dubois, No. 126 Broad-
A512CE way ₍ca. 1820₎
.no.22   4 p.   34 cm.
Caption title.
The song with English words on p. 1 is
attributed to H. G. Nägeli. The same theme with
variations for piano, p. 2-4, not by Mozart. Cf.
Köchel, Anh. 289a, Mozart Verzeichnis, 1947, p.
901.
₍No. 22₎ in a vol. with binder's title:
Music ₍collected by₎ Sarah Pauleva.
1. Songs (High voice) with piano. 2.
Variations (Piano) I. Nägeli, Hans Georg,
1773-1836, supposed composer. Freut
des Lebens.

NL 0356557   NcD

W.C.L. Life let us cherish. Composed by Mozart.
M780.88 New York, Firth & Hall, 1 Franklin Sq.
M987D ₍1832₎
.no.9   1 l.   34 cm.
Caption title.
Not composed by Mozart. Cf. Köchel's
Mozart Verzeichnis, Anh. 289a. (3. Aufl.)
For voice and piano.
₍No. 9₎ in a vol. of piano music and songs
with binder's title: Music
1. Songs (Medium voice) with piano.

NL 0356558   NcD

LIFE let us cherish. Lord Wellington.   New York,
Firth & Hall [184-?] 1 l. 34cm.

Caption title.
For piano.

1. Dances (Piano) I. Title: Lord Wellington.

NL 0356559   NN

Life, letters and journals of George Ticknor
see under   Ticknor, George, 1791-1871.

Life, life work and influence of O. H. Greenleaf
see under   [Greenleaf, O   S   ]

Life-lights of song. Songs of God and
nature ... 1864 [pref. 1863]
see under   Page, David, 1814-1879, ed.

Life-lights of song. Songs of love & brotherhood.
... 1864 [pref. 1864]
see under   Page, David, 1814-1879, ed.

Life line ...
see also   Lifeline.

Life line magazine. v. 1–
Feb. 1908–
South Framingham, Mass., Life line publishing com-
pany, 1908–
v.   illus. 23½ᶜᵐ. monthly (irregular)
From Feb. 1908 to Jan. 1909 title reads: Life line.

1. Prostitution—Period.

                                        11-7621
Library of Congress   HQ301.L6

NL 0356565   DLC

The life-line of the Lone One; or, Autobiography of
the world's child
see under   [Chase, Warren] 1813-1891.

Life links in the warfare of Commissioner and
Mrs. Booth-Tucker.   London, Sal. Army,
1888.
119 p.   2 port.   sq. 24°.

NL 0356567   NN

A life-long spiritualist, pseud.
Mysteries...
see under
Lunt, Edward D.

955
L7234   A life-long story, or Am I my sister's keeper? Facts and
phases for the times. Dedicated to the women of England. By
one of themselves.   London, Simpkin, Marshall, 1859.
vii, xv, 456 p.   front.

I. One of themselves.

NL 0356569   CU

Life-lore: a monthly magazine of biology. Ed. by W.
Mawer. v. 1-2; July 1888–Mar. 1890. London ₍etc.₎
W. Mawer ₍etc.₎ 1889–90.
2 v. illus. 4°.
Cover-title: Life-lore: a monthly magazine of natural history.
No more published.

1. Natural history—Period.   I. Mawer, W., ed.

Library of Congress   QH1.L3   1-9693

NL 0356570   DLC

Life-lore: lessons from the childhood of Nolan Fairfield.
London. Longman, Brown, Green, & Longmans. 1847. iv, 188 pp.
Sm. 8°.

NL 0356571   MB

Life, love and light; practical morality for men
and women
see under   [Pollard, Alfred William] 1859–

A life, Love, and other poems. By R. F. T.   London, K. Paul,
Trench & co., 1889.   xii, 151 p.   19cm.

534065B.   I. T., R. F.
N. Y. P. L.   August 23, 1950

NL 0356573   NN

Life lyrics ... 1869
see under   Brown, Edward.

The life mask; a novel, by the author of "To M. L. G."
New York, Frederick A. Stokes company ₍1913₎
4 p. l., 3-346 p. 19½ᶜᵐ. $1.30

I. To M. L. G., Author of.

Library of Congress   PZ3.L6242   13-3301

NL 0356575   DLC

The life mask; a novel by the author of To M. L. G.   New
York: Frederick A. Stokes Co. ₍cop. 1913₎ 2 p.l., 346 p. 2. ed.
12°.

                              CENTRAL RESERVE.
1. Title.
N. Y. P. L.   October 27, 1915.

NL 0356576   NN

Life mask of Abraham Lincoln
see under   [Volk, Leonard Wells]
1828-1895.

The life, memoirs, military career and death of
General U. S. Grant
see under   [McMaster, John Bach] 1852–

Life military and civil of the Duke of Wellington
see under   Maxwell, William Hamilton,
1792-1850.

Life, ministry, last sickness and death of
Elias Hicks. n.p.[1830] 8p. Caption
title.
Includes (p.[5]-8) The last letter of
Elias Hicks, written to Hugh Judge of Ohio,
and just closed, when he was attacked with
the paralytic affection which terminated his
life.

NL 0356580   NN PSC-Hi MH

Life, ministry, last sickness, and death of
Elias Hicks.   Philadelphia, J. Richard,
printer, 1839.
30 p.   front. (port.)   9 cm.
"The last letter of Elias Hicks, written to
High Judge, of Ohio," p. [17]-30.

NL 0356581   PSC-Hi

A life-motif recorded in twenty-five years of service, 1916-1941.
₍n. p., 1941?₎   7 l.   illus.   23cm.
On cover: Rev. Chas. E. Coughlin, Silver jubilee, 1916-1941.

1. Coughlin, Charles Edward,   1891–
N. Y. P. L.   October 3, 1944

NL 0356582   NN

Life-notes; bulletin from the Cleveland Life
Underwriters Association. v.14, no.4 – v.18, no.10.
Dec 1943 - June 1948. [Cleveland, O.]
Monthly, Sept. - June inclusive.
Ceased publication.

NL 0356583   OCl

The life of a backwoodsman; or, Particulars of
the emigrant's situation in settling on the
wild land of Canada
see under   [Linton, John James Edmond-
stoune] 1804-1869.

The LIFE of a ballad singer; a tale of wonder
Written by herself. London, J. Ker. [17- ?]
pp. 38.

NL 0356585   MH

VOLUME 332

Life, The, of a bear. His birth, education and adventures. By the author of 'The life of an elephant.' New edition. London. Seeley & Co. 1901. (2), 226 pp. Plates. Sm. 8°.

G8238 — Bear.

NL 0356586　　MB ICJ

The Life of a Beau
　　see under　[Carey, Henry] 1687?-1743.

The life of a bear, Author of.
The life of an elephant
　　see under title

Wing
ZP　　　The LIFE of a bee. / Related by herself.
745　　　London, Printed by John Marshall [1798?]
.M 363　　xi, 71p. front. 16cm.

"To the reader": signed L.P.
Owner's autograph dated 1798.

NL 0356589　　ICN

The life of a boy; by the author of The panorama of youth
　　see under　Sterndale, Mrs. Mary.

The life of a celebrated Buccaneer
　　see under　Clynton, Richard

The life of a Christian which is a lamp kindled and lighted from the love of Christ, ...
　　see under　[Penington, Isaac] 1616-1679.

The life of a famous actress [Eleonora Duse]
　　see under　[Bracco, Antonio]

The life of a horse, supposed to be written by himself; Benevolence rewarded; The bird; Ingratitude punished; The accident; and The faithful dog ... Boston, Munroe and Francis; New-York, C. S. Francis, 1829.
43 p. incl. front., illus. 15½cm.

P26　　　Number [1] in a volume lettered: Story
.S85　　teller.
Toner
Coll.
Office　　　　　　　　　　　　　35M2264

NL 0356594　　DLC

The life of a lawyer. Written by himself. London, Saunders and Benning, 1830.

1 p. l., 421 p. 19ᵐ.

A fictitious autobiography. Authorship attributed by Halkett and Laing to Sir James Stewart; by Edinburgh, Faculty of advocates, Library, to James Stewart of Lincoln's Inn.

1. Legal novels. ɪ. Stewart, Sir James, supposed author. ɪɪ. Stewart, James, 1805-1860, supposed author.

30-30991

NL 0356595　　DLC

340.9
1626　　　The life of a lawyer, written by him-
　　　　　self. London, G. Routledge, 1843.
421p.

A fictitious autobiography. Authorship attributed by Halkett and Laing to Sir James Stewart; by Edinburgh Faculty of Advocates Library, to James Stewart of Lincoln's Inn.

I. Stewart, Sir James,　　b.1758? supposed
author. II. Stewart,　　James, 1805-1860,
supposed author.

NL 0356596　　PP NNU-W MH-L

823
1626　　　The life of a midshipman; a tale founded on
　　　　　facts, and intended to correct an injudi-
　　　　　cious predilection in boys for the life of
　　　　　a sailor [by E. N.] London, H. Colburn
　　　　　and R. Bentley, 1829.
xii, 264p. 21cm.

I. N., E. II. E. N.

NL 0356597　　IU

The life of a Negro slave
　　see under　Ball, Charles, negro slave.

The LIFE of a nobleman. London, W. Strange
n. d.

3 pts. 4°. 9 colored plates signed G.
Dawe.
Another copy, large paper.
These books may be consulted in the room of the Widener Collection.

NL 0356599　　MH

The life of a Norfolk dumpling, alias Norfolk ——————: containing, his birth, parentage, and rise... To which is added, some extraordinary stories, relating to a certain city, alias a South-Sea pudding: and, as an ornament to this work, is prefix'd, The Norfolk lanthorn. A new ballad. To the tune of, Which no body can deny. And the whole concluded with a speech of Sir Francis Wennington to a Parliament of Great Britain... Written by No-body, yet recommended by an unbiass'd Some-body, to the perusal of every-body. Dedicated to a gentleman of Heydon in York-

shire; who is taken notice of in his turn in this pamphlet. London: Printed for, and sold by all the booksellers and pamphlet-sellers in city, town, and country [, 1730?]. 4 p. l., 40 p. 8°.

An attack upon Walpole.

1. Walpole, Robert, 1st earl of Orford,　　1676-1745. 2. Great Britain—
Politics, 1727-1760.
N. Y. P. L.　　　　　　　　　　　　　May 13, 1931

NL 0356601　　NN IU ICN

Tzz
976.409　　Life of A.O. Babel, the original and famous Texas
B115Bℓ　　cowboy pianist. New York, Dick Pub. House [188-?]
　　　　　[32]p. illus. 17cm.

Cover title.

1. Babel, A.O., b.1858. 2. Horse-training.

NL 0356602　　TxU

T976.409
B115Bℓ　　Life of A.O. Babel, the original and famous
Photo-　　Texas cowboy pianist. New York, Dick Pub.
copy　　　House [188-?]
　　　　　[32]p. illus. 23cm.

Cover title.
Photocopy.

1. Babel, A.O., b.1858. 2. Horse-training.

NL 0356603　　TxU

The life of a patriot whom death deprived of his chance of signing...
　　see under　[Burdge (Franklin)] 1835-1908.

Life of a Political Trickster; or, the Duplicity & Treachery of Josiah A. Noonan, Postmaster at Milwaukee, exposed ... By "A Pure Man." Milwaukee, 1857.
26 p. 8°.　　[In v. 24, Biographical Pamphlets]

NL 0356605　　CtY

The life of a prig
　　see under　[Longueville, Thomas] 1844-1922.

The life of a recluse
　　see under　[Gibson, A.]

The life of a regiment; the history of the Gordon highlanders
　　see under　Gardyne, Charles Greenhill, 1831-1923.

The life of a sailor
　　see under　[Chamier, Frederick] 1796-1870.

The life of a satyrical puppy, called Nim...
　　see under　[May, Thomas] 1595-1650.

The life of a ship
　　see under　[Ballantyne, Robert Michael] 1825-1894.

The life of a showman; and the managerial struggles of David Prince Miller
　　see under　[Miller, David Prince]

The life of a Siberian sable hunter ...
　　see under　[Goodrich, Samuel Griswold] 1793-1860.

The life of a soldier: a narrative of twenty-seven years' service
　　see under　Lewin, Henry Ross, 1778-1843.

VOLUME 332

The life of a Soviet collective farmer. What is farm life like in Russia? How do farmers fare under Communism? ₍Washington₎ U. S. Dept. of Agriculture, Office of Foreign Agricultural Relations, 1951.

13 p. 27 cm.

"Published originally under copyright by the New York times."

1. Agriculture, Cooperative—Russia. I. U. S. Office of Foreign Agricultural Relations.

HD1491.R9L5   334.683   51–60634

NL 0356615   DLC DNAL

BF
1283
.Z9
L72

The life of a spiritualist medium, written by herself.... Los Angeles, Calif., Austin Pub. Co. ₍ᶜ1921₎

110 p. 20 cm.

1. Spiritualism.

NL 0356616   MiU

The life of a sportsman
     see under   [Apperley, Charles James]
1778–1843.

The life of a successful banker, by his Boswell. Illustrations by Spencer Wright. San Francisco, Paul Elder ₍1905₎

₍38₎p. front., illus. (part. col.) 24 cm.

"The Banker's response", a pamphlet of ₍7₎p. has been inserted at back of book.

"Edition limited to 55 copies"

1. Bankers. I. Boswell, pseud. II. The Banker's response (Title anal)

NL 0356618   RPB

The life of a travelling physician, from his first introduction to practice
     see under   [Lefevre, Sir George William]
1798–1846.

The LIFE of a tree; being a history of the phenomena of vegetation from the seed to the death of the plant. London, Soc. for prom. Christ. knowl., 1849.

sq. 16°. Front., plates and wdcts.

NL 0356620   MH

The life of a vagrant...
     see under   Basset, Josiah.

Life of a woman: or, The curate's daughter
     see under   [Haines, John Thomas]
1799?–1843.

BX
4659
.E4
K4

The life of Abba John Khamé; Coptic text edited and translated from the Cod. Vat. Copt. LX by M. H. Davis. Paris, Formin-Didot, 1919.

cover-title, ₍317₎–372 p. (Patrologia Orientalis. Tome XIV. Fasc. 2)

Bibliographical footnotes.

NL 0356623   NNC IEG TxFTC PPPD

Life of Abe Lincoln, of Illinois. Printed for the publishers, 1860. cover-title, ₍3₎,4–8p. 7x4cm.

NL 0356624   IHi CSmH

Life of Abraham Gothelf Kästner. ₍London, 1801.₎ 97–105 pp. Portr. 8°. Cut from the Philosophical magazine [*3356.1.9].

NL 0356625   MB

Life of Abraham Lincoln. [Chicago, 1860]
     see under   [Scripps, John Locke] 1818–1866.

... The life of Abraham Lincoln in verse
     see under   [Mathews, Stella Tyler]

Life of Abraham Lincoln, late president of the American republic. Reprinted from the 'Morning star' ... Manchester, A. Heywood & son; ₍etc., etc., 1865₎

16 p. 20ᶜᵐ.

1. Lincoln, Abraham. pres. U. S., 1809–1865.

3–10012

Library of Congress   E457.L725

NL 0356628   DLC OCIWHi

The life of Abraham Newland, esq.
     see under   [Collier, John Dyer]

The Life of Abram Antone; who was sentenced to be executed on the twelfth day of September, 1823, for the murder of John Jacobs. Taken in part from his own mouth. Morrisville [N. Y.] Printed at the office of the Republican monitor, 1823.

12 p. 21 1|2 cm. Orig. grey paper covers. Uncut.

Autograph of Simon Switcher on paper cover and p. [2].

1. Antone, Abram, 1750–1823. 2. Jacobs, John.

NL 0356630   CSmH N

The life of Absalom. Written for the American Sunday-school union and revised by the Committee of publication. Philadelphia, American Sunday-school union ₍ᶜ1844₎

89 p. front., plates. 15¼ᶜᵐ.

1. Absalom, son of David.   I. American Sunday-school union.

31–23622

Library of Congress   BS580.A35L5   221.92

NL 0356631   DLC ViU

The life of Achilles. Extracted from various authors; necessary to be perus'd by the readers and spectators of the new opera, call'd Achilles. Written by the late Mr. Gay. London, Printed: and sold by J. Roberts ... 1732.

27 p. 19½ᶜᵐ.

First edition.

Signatures: A–C⁴, D².

A topical life of Achilles, published in the same year as Gay's opera, to catch public appeal. Unbound, in   cloth case.

NL 0356632   CLU-C MH

The life of Adelina Patti
     see under   [Dalmazzo, G. M.]

The life of Admiral Blake. Containing an account of the gallant actions of that brave commander...
     see under   [Johnson, Samuel] 1709–1784.

The life of Admiral Lord Nelson ... With an authentic account of the ever memorable victory, in which he so nobly fell. ... Birmingham, Printed by Thomas Martin, 1805.

48 p. front. 18.5 cm.

1. Nelson, Horatio Nelson, viscount, 1758–1805.

NL 0356635   CtY

The life of Admiral Vernon. By an impartial hand. London, Printed for J. Fuller, 1758.

1 p. l., 250 p. 16½ᶜᵐ.

1. Vernon, Edward, 1684–1757.

Library of Congress   DA87.1.V5L7   4–37326

NL 0356636   DLC RPJCB

E
5
.A 258

The LIFE of Africaner, a Namacqua chief, of South Africa. Revised by the committee of publication. Philadelphia, American Sunday school union₍1830?₎

35p.

Attributed to John Campbell in British museum Catalogue.

"Happy death of a Madagascar youth": p.₍27₎–35.

NL 0356637   ICN TNF

The life of Africaner, a Namacqua chief, of South Africa. Rev. by the editors. New York, Pub. by B. Waugh and T. Mason, for the Sunday school union of the Methodist Episcopal church, 1833.

1 p. l., ₍5₎–32 p. 1 illus. 13ᶜᵐ. (On back cover: Sunday school and youths library)

"Happy death of a Madagascar youth": p. ₍25₎–32.

1. Afrikaner, Christian, Hottentot chief, d. 1823? 2. Missions—Africa, South.

30–1754

Library of Congress   BV3557.A3L5

NL 0356638   DLC

Life of Albert R. Parsons, with brief history of the labor movement in America
     see under   [Parsons, Mrs. Lucy E   ]

Life (The) of Alexander Pope, Esq *n. p., n. d.* 1 p.l., ix–lxxii pp., 1 pl. 12°.

Probably an introduction to some of Pope's Works. The plate has autographs of Swift, and Pope thereon.

Bd. with: Impartial (An) history of the life, character, amours, travels, and transactions, of Mr. John Barber....*London: E. Curl* 1741. 12°.

In: AN.

NL 0356640   NN

VOLUME 332

The life of Alexander Pope, esq; with a true copy of his last will and testament. London, C. Corbett, 1744.

3 p. l., 64 p. 17ᵐ.

1. Pope, Alexander, 1688-1744.

44-20841

Library of Congress   PR3633.L5

WU NIC MWiW-C MH MiU
NL 0356641   DLC PMA MB CSmH IU MH CtY TxU CtY DFo

The life of Alexander Smith, captain of the
island of Pitcairn
see under   [Sargent, Charles Lenox]

LIFE of Alexander Tardy, the poisoner or,
Pirate chief of St. Domingo.
The anonymous author of the above has
written another work entitled "Kit Clayton,
or The hero of the road." [18-?] (Call-
number:- AL 4322.35)

NL 0356643   MH

The life of Alexander I., emperor of Russia; including an
account of his restoring to life a Polish peasant by his per-
severance and personal exertion; for which a gold medal was
voted and presented to him by the Royal humane society of
London; and an historical sketch of the Russian empire. London, W. Mason, 1814.

24 p. col. front. (port.) 18¼ᵐ.

I. Alexander I, emperor of Russia, 1777-1825.

42-26662

Library of Congress   DK191.L5

NL 0356644   DLC

DF234
.L5S8   The life of Alexander the Great. Edited by
Thomas O. Summers. Nashville, Published by
E. Stevenson and F.A. Owen, Agents, for the
Methodist Episcopal Church, South, 1855.
177 p. 16cm.

1. Alexander the Great, 356-323 B.C.
I. Summers, Thomas Osmond, 1912-1382, ed.

NL 0356645   T NcD

DF234
.L5S8
1857   The life of Alexander the Great. Edited by
Thos. O. Summers. Nashville, Published by E.
Stevenson & F. A. Owen, Agents, for the Methodist Episcopal Church, South, 1857.
177 p. 15 cm.

1. Alexander the Great, 356-323 B.C. I.
Summers, Thomas Osmond, 1812-1882, ed.

NL 0356646   T

The life of Alfred Nobel
see under   [Nobelstiftelsen, Stockholm]

Life of Alfred the Great, with his maxims, and
those of his counsellors
see under [Haller, Albrecht von] 1708-1777.

The life of Ali Pacha
see under   [Beauchamp, Alphonse de]
1767-1832.

The life of Ambrose Barnes, sometime alderman of Newcastle.
Newcastle: Printed by T. and J. Hodgson for E. Charnley, 1828.
vi, 35 p., 1 fold. chart. 12°.   (Newcastle-upon-Tyne Typo-
graphical Soc. ₍Publ., no. 37.₎)

Extracted from a ms. signed M. R. and dated 1716, entitled: "Memoirs of the
life of Mr. Ambrose Barnes, late merchant and sometime alderman of Newcastle-
upon-Tyne."—*cf. Pref.*
Preface signed: C. S. ₍i.e. Sir Cuthbert Sharp.₎

1. Barnes, Ambrose, 1627-1710.   2. Sharp, Sir Cuthbert, 1781-1849,
editor. 3. R., M.
N. Y. P. L.   August 14, 1917.

NL 0356650   NN NNC OCl ICN MnU OU CtY

The life of an alcoholic, by an alcoholic; the
answer to anyone's liquor problem
see under [Proctor, Harry Daily] 1893-

Life, The, of an elephant. By the author of "The life of a bear." New
edition.
London. Seeley & Co., Ltd. 1897. (2), 228 pp. Plates. 18 cm.,
in 8s.

H6288 — Elephant.

NL 0356652   MB

The life of an elephant. By the author of 'The life of a bear.'
New edition. [4],228 p. 24 pl. D. New York: E. S. Gorham,
1901.

NL 0356653   ICJ

Life of an elephant, Author of.
The life of a bear. His birth, education and
adventures
see under title

271.99
V825ℓ   The life of an enclosed nun, by A Mother
Superior ... New York, The John Lane
company, London, A. C. Fifield, 1910.
124 p. front. (port.) 18cm.

1. Visitation nuns. I. A Mother Superior.

NL 0356655   MoSU

The life of an enclosed nun, by a mother superior ...
New York, The John Lane company; ₍etc., etc.₎ 1911.
124 p. front. (port.) 18ᶜᵐ. $1.00

I. A mother superior.

Library of Congress   BX4210.L5

11-4459

NL 0356656   DLC

The life of an insect ... Published under the direction of
the Committee of general literature and education, appointed
by the Society for promoting Christian knowledge. London, The Society for promoting Christian knowledge ₍1851₎
2 v. fronts., illus., plates. 14 x 10¼ᵐ.
Signed at end: R. E.
Dedication dated 1850.
CONTENTS.—pt. I, A history of the changes of insects from the egg to
the perfect being.—pt. II. An account of insect habits and manners.
1. Insects. I. E., R. II. R. E. III. Society for promoting Christian
knowledge, London. General literature committee.

6-16955 Revised

Library of Congress   QL467.L72
₍r37m2₎   595.7

NL 0356657   DLC MBH

The life of an officer, written by himself,
during a residence in Pennsylvania...
see under [Graydon, Alexander] 1752-1818.

The life of Andrew Hellman, alias Adam Horn. Containing full particulars of the murder of his first wife, his
escape from prison, and marriage with Malinda Horn, his
second victim; with an account of his trial and sentence,
and a complete review of his confession. To which is
added, a full account of the Staten Island murders. Philadelphia, J. B. Perry and H. Jordan ₍1844₎
67, 2 p. illus. (incl. ports.) pl. 15½ᵐ.
Last two pages devoted to the "Staten Island murder and arson" i. e.
the murder of Mrs. George Houseman and her child by Polly Bodine.

1. Hellman, Andrew, 1792-1843. 2. Bodine, Mary, defendant. 3. Houseman, Mrs. Emeline, d. 1843.

10-25320

NL 0356659   DLC ICU PP

The life of Andrew Jackson, president of the United
States. Illustrated with numerous cuts. By Major Jack
Downing ₍pseud.₎, of the Downingville militia ... Philadelphia, T. K. Greenbank, 1834.
2 p. l., ₍vii₎-xii, 263 p. incl. front., illus. 18 cm)

1. Jackson, Andrew, pres. U. S., 1767-1845. I. Smith, Seba, 1792-
1868, supposed author. II. Davis, Charles Augustus, 1795-1867, supposed author. III. Clarke, John, of Philadelphia, supposed author.

Library of Congress   E382.L72   13—18462

PPL PPA MnU MH OClWHi MB MiU NjR IEdS
NL 0356660   DLC MnU NIC NNC TxU NcD LU NcU CU PHi

... Life of Andrew Jackson: embracing anecdotes
illustrative of his character ...
see under   [Frost, John] 1800-1859.

The life of Andrew Marvell ...
see under   [Coleridge, Hartley] 1796-1849.

The life of Anne Catharine Emmerich
see under   [Schmöger, Karl Erhard]
d. 1883.

The life of Annie Besant
see under   [Wells, Geoffrey Harry] 1900-

The life of Anson Bunker, "the bloody hand" ...
see under   Bunker, Anson.

Life of Anthony Benezet. Phil., 1867.

NL 0356666   PHC

Life of Antonio Rosmini Serbati, founder of
the Institute of charity
see under   Macwalter, Gabriel Stuart.

The life of Aodh Ruadh O Domhnaill ...
see under   Leabhar Lughaidh Uí Chlérigh.

VOLUME 332

Life of Archibald Gardner, Utah pioneer of 1847
      see under   [Hughes, Delila (Gardner)]

The Life of Archibald McDonald, of Barisdale,
   who is to suffer for High-Treason, on the
   22d of May, at Edinburgh ...   Lond., 1754.
   8°.
   [By an impartial hand]

NL 0356670   CtY

BX4666
.H8
A3
       Life of Archbishop Hughes, with a full
   account of his funeral...sermon on Catholic
   emancipation, and his great speeches on the
   school question...   New York, American News
   Co., 1864.
   128p. port.

       I.Title: Sermon on Catholic emancipation.
   II.Title: School question.

NL 0356671   NcU

      Life of Archbishop Hughes, with a full account of
   his funeral, Bishop McCloskey's oration, and
   Bishop Loughlin's Month's Mind sermon. Also
   Archbishop Hughes' sermon on Catholic emancipation, and his great speeches on the School
   question, including his three days' speech in
   Carroll Hall; speech before the Board of Aldermen; letter to Mayor Harper, etc. ... 2 ed.
   New York, The American news company, 1864.
   7-128p. front. (port.) 20cm.
   1. Hughes, John, Abp., 1797-1864. 2. Religious
   education. 3. Catholic emancipation--Sermon.

NL 0356672   PLatS MH PPL NN

BX4705
.H79L5
       The life of Archbishop Hughes. (First
   archbishop of New York.) With a full account
   of his life, death, and burial; as well as his
   services in all pursuits and vocations, from
   his birth until his death. Born in Clogher,
   Ireland, 1798. Died in New York, Jan. 3,
   1864 ... Philadelphia, T. B. Peterson &
   brothers [c1864]
   1 p.l., p. 19-70. 21½cm.

   Portrait on   cover.

NNC
NL 0356673   DLC PHi ICN MB NNCoCi PV PLatS NcD CtY

   A life of Archbishop Laud
      see under   [Longueville, Thomas]
   1844-1922.

   The life of Archbishop Leighton: with brief
   extracts from his writings. New York, American
   tract society [18--]
   1v, [5]-142 p. 15½cm.

      1. Leighton, Robert, abp. of Glasgow, 1611-1684. I.
   American tract society.

NL 0356675   ViU NN FMU MA

   Life of Archbishop Secker
      see Chandler, Thomas Bradburn, 1726-
   1790.
      An appendix to the American edition of the Life
   of Archbishop Secker.

The life of Aristides, the Athenian
   see under   Theophrastus, pseud.

Life of Armelle Nicolas, commonly called the
   good Armelle; a poor maid servant in France ...
   see under   Jeanne de la Nativite, fl. 1650.

Life of Arthur, Duke of Wellington, &c. &c. &c.
   London, F. C. & J. Rivington, 1822.
   1 p.l., 194 p.
   Title page lacking. Typed page substituted.
   (Abridged from the Quarterly review, with
   consent of the proprietor)

NL 0356679   WaPS

Life of Arthur Tappan
   see under   [Tappan, Lewis] 1788-1873.

The life of Arthur Vandeleur, major, Royal
   artillery
      see under   [Marsh, Catherine] 1818-1912.

The life of Augustus von Kotzebue
   see under   [Cramer, Friedrich Matthias
   Gottfried] 1779-1836.

Life of B. F. Peter Claver of the Society of Jesus
   see under   [Fleuriau, Bertrand Gabriel]
   1693-1773.

... The life of Bacon
   see under   [Montagu, Basil] 1770-1851.

Life of Babajee. (Bombay. Book and Tract Soc.
   pub. Malirathi ser.) Bombay, 1844.
   12°

NL 0356685   NN CtY

xB
C272i
180-
       The life of Bamfylde Moore Carew, sometime
   king of the beggars; containing an accurate history of his travels, voyages, & adventures, from
   the time of his leaving school, and entering into
   the society of the gipsies. To which is added,
   a dictionary of the mendicants' cant phrases.
   London, T. Hughes [180-?]
   36p. col.port. 18cm.

   Portrait dated: 1804.
   1. Carew, Bampfylde Moore, 1693-1758.

NL 0356686   IU RPB

B
692
.255
       The LIFE of Bampfylde Moore Carew, sometime
   king of the beggars; containing an accurate history of his travels, voyages, and adventures,
   from the time of his leaving school, and entering
   into the society of the gipsies: also, a description of the origin, government, laws, and customs
   of the gipsies. To which is added, A dictionary
   of the mendicants' cant phrases. London, T.
   Hughes, 1804.
   104p. col.front. 14cm.   (with The elegant
   preceptor... 1806)
       The authorship   has been ascribed vari-
   ously to Thomas   Price, Robert Goadby,
   Mrs. Goadby and Carew himself.

NL 0356687   ICN CtY OC1

   The life of Bamfylde Moore Carew, sometime
   king of the beggars, containing an accurate
   history of his travels, voyages and adventures.
   35p. front.(port.) Edinburgh, Oliver & Boyd,
   1812.

   A chap-book.

NL 0356688   OC1 CtY

Nvg95
G6
74511
       The life of Bampfylde Moore Carew, sometime
   king of the beggars; containing an accurate
   history of his travels, voyages,and adventures
   ... Also, a description of the origin, government, laws and customs of the gipsies ...
   Philadelphia, W.M'Carty, 1813.
   1p.l.,94p. 14cm.

NL 0356689   CtY MWA

   The life of Bamfylde Moore Carew, some time king of the beggars, containing an accurate history of his travels, voyages, and
   adventures.   New-York, Published by S. King, 1828.   31 p.
   front. 20cm.

   See: Sabin 27615.
   Frontispiece colored by hand.
   "List of pamphlets, &c. printed and sold by S. King," front and back covers.

258336B. 1. Carew, Bampfylde Moore,   1693-1770? 2. Beggars and
begging. 3. Gipsies.
N. Y. P. L.   March 30, 1944

NL 0356690   NN CtY CSmH

   The life of baron Frederick Trenck...
      see under   Trenck, Friedrich freiherr von
   der, 1726-1794.

   The life of Bampfylde Moore Carew, sometime
   king of the beggars
      see also   The life and adventures of
   Bampfylde Moore Carew ...

DS
481
S26
L72
       [Life of Barrister Savarkar.   Madras, B. G.
   Paul, 1926]
   viii,144 p. illus. 21cm.

   Imperfect: t. p. wanting.

      1. Savarkar, Vinayak Damodar, 1883-

NL 0356693   NIC

ar W
10565
       The life of Bartolomeo Bergami, baron Fran-
   cini ...   London, Spilling and Whiteman
   [1820?]
   4 p. port. 21cm.

   Caption title.
   No. 4 in vol. lettered: Queen Caroline
   tracts.

      1. Bergami,   Bartolommeo, barone della
   Francina, d.   1841.

NL 0356694   NIC

   The life of Beethoven, including his correspondence
   with his friends, numerous characteristic
   traits, and remarks on his musical works
      see under   [Schindler, Anton Felix]
   1795-1864.

   The life of Belisarius
      see under   [Stanhope, Philip Henry
   Stanhope, 5th earl] 1805-1875.

VOLUME 332

The··LIFE of Benjamin Disraeli, earl of Beacons
field. New York, Harper & Brothers, cop.
1878.

1.8°. pp.14. Port.
(Franklin Square library,15)

NL 0356697 MH PPL

The life of Benjamin Franklin, LL. D. Poughnill, near
Ludlow ₍Eng.₎ G. Nicholson ₍1804?₎

1 p. l., 56 p. illus. 15ᶜᵐ.

Title vignette (portrait)

1. Franklin, Benjamin, 1706–1790. ₁. Nicholson, George, 1760–1825,
pub.

17–14992

Library of Congress   E302.6.F8L45

NL 0356698 DLC OrU PPAmP ICN CtY

Life of Benjamin Franklin. ₍Edinburgh: W. and R. Chambers,
183–?₎ p. ₍177–₎184. illus. f°. (Chambers's information
for the people. no. 23.)

Caption-title.

1. Franklin, Benjamin, 1706–90.
N. Y. P. L.   October 19, 1922.

NL 0356699 NN

412
L62
1876

... Life of Benjamin Franklin: embracing
anecdotes illustrative of his character ...
Boston,Lee and Shepard₍etc.,etc.₎1786.
viii,₍9₎-208p. front.,plates. 19cm. (The
Young American's library)
On cover: Eminent statesmen.
Published also under title: Pictorial life of
Benjamin Franklin ...
May have been written by H.H.Weld, or John
Frost.

NL 0356700 CtY

E302.6
.F8L7

Life of Benjamin Franklin, embracing
anecdotes illustrative of his character. Philadelphia, Lindsay & Blakiston ₍1846₎
208 p. illus.,ports. 18cm.
(The Young American's library)

Added t.p., illustrated.

LNHT NN WHi CSmH
NL 0356701 MnHi KyHi NNC MtU MH OKentU ICU MH

412
L62
1868

... The life of Benjamin Franklin: embracing
anecdotes illustrative of his character ...
Boston,Lee and Shepard,1868.
viii,9-208p. front.,plates. 18½cm. (The
Young American's library)
On cover: Library of eminent statesmen.
Published also under title: Pictorial life of
Benjamin Franklin ...
May have been written by H.H.Weld, or
John Frost.

NL 0356702 CtY MB MoU

412
L62
1869

... Life of Benjamin Franklin: embracing
anecdotes illustrative of his character ...
Boston,Lee and Shepard,1869.
viii,₍9₎-208p. front.,plates. 18½cm. (The
Young American's library)
On cover: Library of eminent statesmen.
Published also under title: Pictorial life
of Benjamin Franklin ...
May have been written by H.H.Weld, or John
Frost.

NL 0356703 CtY

412
L62
1870

... Life of Benjamin Franklin; embracing
anecdotes illustrative of his character ...
Boston,Lee and Shepard₍187-?₎
viii,₍9₎-208p. front.,plates. 18½cm. (The
Young American's library)
On cover: Library of eminent statesmen.
Copyright, 1846, by Lindsay & Blakiston.
Published also under title: Pictorial life of
Benjamin Franklin ...
May have been written by H.H.Weld, or John
Frost.

NL 0356704 CtY

Franklin
412
L62
1875

... Life of Benjamin Franklin: embracing
anecdotes illustrative of his character
... Boston, Lee and Shepard; New York,
Lee, Shepard and Dillingham, 1875.
2 p.l., iii-viii, 9-208 p. front., plates.
19 cm. (The Young American's library ₍of
eminent statesmen₎)
Published also under title: Pictorial life
of Benjamin Franklin.
May have been written by H.H. Weld, or John
Frost.

NL 0356705 CtY

The life of Benjamin Franklin. Illustrated by tales,
sketches and anecdotes. Adapted to the use of schools
... New-York, Collins & Hannay, 1832.
180 p. incl. front., illus. 15¼ᶜᵐ. (Half-title: ... American school biographies ...)
Title vignette.
Copyright by S. G. Goodrich; authorship disclaimed by him in his "Recollections."
"Essays of Dr. Franklin": p. ₍136₎-180.

1. Franklin, Benjamin, 1706-1790.

14-3378

Library of Congress   E302.6.F8L7

NL 0356706 DLC MWA ViU MiU-C ICU MB

E83
.F83135
XL7223
1836

The life of Benjamin Franklin. Illustrated
by tales, sketches, and anecdotes. Adapted
to the use of schools ... Philadelphia,
Desilver, Thomas & Co., 1836.
180 p. illus. 17 cm.

Copyright by Samuel G. Goodrich: authorship
disclaimed by him in this "Recollections".

1. Franklin, Benjamin, 1706-1790.

NL 0356707 WHi PPAmP MH CSmH PU ViU CtY ICU

The life of Benjamin Franklin. Illustrated by tales,
sketches, and anecdotes. Adapted to the use of schools
... Philadelphia, Thomas, Cowperthwait & co., 1838.
180 p. incl. front., illus. 17½ᶜᵐ.
Title vignette.
Copyright by S. G. Goodrich; authorship disclaimed by him in his "Rec-
ollections."
"Essays of Dr. Franklin": p. ₍136₎-180.

1. Franklin, Benjamin, 1706-1790.

7-9224

NL 0356708 DLC CU-A CoU OCl PU CtY

The life of Benjamin Franklin. Illustrated by tales, sketches, and anecdotes. Adapted to the use of schools.
With engravings. Philadelphia,
Thomas, Cowperthwait & co., 1841.
180 p. incl. front., illus. 17cm.
Title vignette.
Copyright by S. G. Goodrich; authorship disclaimed by him in his "Recollections."
1. Franklin, Benjamin, 1706-1790.
I. Goodrich, Samuel Griswold, 1793-1860,
supposed   author.

NL 0356709 MnU

The Life of Benjamin Franklin. Illustrated by
tales, sketches, and anecdotes. Adapted to the
use of schools. With engravings. Philadelphia, ... 1842.
180 p. 12°.

NL 0356710 MHi

412
L64
1844

The life of Benjamin Franklin. Illustrated by
tales, sketches, and anecdotes. Adapted to
the use of schools ... Philadelphia,Thomas,
Cowperthwait & co.,1844.
180p. incl.front.,illus. 15½cm.
Title vignette.
Copyright by S.G.Goodrich; authorship disclaimed by him in his "Recollections."
"Essays of Dr. Franklin": p.₍136₎-180.

NL 0356711 CtY PHC MWA

---

*
E302
.6
.F8L75
1848

The life of Benjamin Franklin. Illustrated
by tales, sketches, and anecdotes. Adapted
to the use of schools. Philadelphia: Thomas,
Cowperthwait, 1848.
180 p. plates. 16cm.
Copyright by S.G.Goodrich; authorship disclaimed
by him in his "Recollections."
"Essays of Dr. Franklin": p. ₍136₎-180.

1. Franklin, Benjamin, 1706-1790.

NL 0356712 ViU

The life of Benjamin Franklin. Illustrated by tales,
sketches and anecdotes. Adapted to the use of schools ...
Philadelphia, Thomas, Cowperthwait & co., 1851.
180 p. incl. front., illus. pl. port. 17ᶜᵐ. ₍With The life of Christo-
pher Columbus. Philadelphia, 1851₎
Title vignette.
"Essays of Dr. Franklin": p. 136-180.
Copyright by S. G. Goodrich; authorship disclaimed by him in his
"Recollections".

1. Franklin, Benjamin, 1706-1790.

2—8034

Library of Congress   E111.L74

NL 0356713 DLC CSmH ViU

The life of Benjamin Franklin. Illustrated by tales,
sketches, and anecdotes. Adapted to the use of schools
... Philadelphia, C. Desilver, 1860.
180 p. incl. front., illus. 3 pl., port. 19¼ᶜᵐ. ₍With The life of Chris-
topher Columbus. Philadelphia, 1860₎
Title vignette.
Copyright by S. G. Goodrich; authorship disclaimed by him in his
"Recollections."

1. Franklin, Benjamin, 1706-1790.

16-13254

Library of Congress   E111.L76

NL 0356714 DLC MnU

---

*
E111
.L74
1865

The life of Benjamin Franklin. Illustrated
by tales, sketches, and anecdotes. Adapted
to the use of schools, with engravings.
Philadelphia: Charles Desilver, 1865.
180 p. illus. 20cm. ₍With The life of
Christopher Columbus ... Philadelphia, 1865₎

1. Franklin, Benjamin, 1706-1790.

NL 0356715 ViU

The life of Benjamin Franklin, including a sketch of
the rise and progress of the war of independence, and of
the various negociations at Paris for peace; with the history of his political and other writings. London, Printed
for Hunt and Clarke, 1826.
407, ₍1₎ p. front. (port.) 17½ᶜᵐ.

Attributed by Ford (Franklin bibl.) to Leonard Woods.

1. Franklin, Benjamin, 1706-1790. ₁. Woods, Leonard, 1774-1854, supposed author.

Library of Congress   E302.6.F8L6   20-11338

NL 0356716 DLC NIC MiU-C ViU OCl CtY PHC PU MH MB

VOLUME 332

... The life of Benjamin Franklin, written by himself. Now first edited from original manuscripts, and from his printed correspondence, and other writings, by John Bigelow. London: 1879.

(*In* Edinburgh review, 1880. 21½ᶜᵐ. v. 151, p. 321-358)

At head of title: Art. II.
Review.

1. Franklin, Benjamin, 1706-1790. The life of Benjamin Franklin.

Library of Congress   E302.6.F7A2 1879 L   17-8420
———— Copy 2, detached.

NL 0356717   DLC

Toner 1885

Life of Benjamin S. Barton, M.D. [anon.]
[Philadelphia, H. Hall, 1816]
p. 273-287.   8°.
Note: p. 273-287 of the Portfolio, fourth series, v. 1. 1816.

NL 0356718   DLC

Life of Benjamin West.
— London. Wetton & Jarvis. [1821.] 164 pp. Illus. Portrait. [Select biography. Vol. 9.] Sm.8°.

G6741 — S.r. — West, Benjamin, American painter. 1738-1820.

NL 0356719   MB

The life of Benjamin West. [London, Wetton & Jarvis, 1821]

(American culture series, 43:11)
Microfilm copy (positive) made in 1956 by University Microfilms, Ann Arbor, Mich.
Select biography, v. 9.
Collation of the original, as determined from the film: 164 p. illus., port.
"A catalogue of pictures painted by the late Benjamin West, Esq. ... exhibited on at no. 14, Newman Street": p. [121]-144.
"A catalogue of the paintings of Mr. West": p. [145]-164.
1. West, Benjamin, 1738-1820. (Series: Select biography, v. 9)
Microfilm 01291 reel 43, no. 11 E   Mic 59-7411

NL 0356720   DLC KEmT ICRL

The life of Benjamin West, the great American painter, wirtten for children ...
see under   Forbes, Gerritt Van Husen, 1795-1863.

The life of Bernard Overberg, teacher of the Normal School ...
see under   [Krabbe, Caspar Franz, 1794-1866].

The life of Blessed John Berchmans, of the Society of Jesus
see under   [Frizon, Nicolas] d. 1737.

Life of Big Bertha (Mrs. Stanley) the confidence queen.
[San Francisco] Francis, Valentine & Co., Printers [1886?]
16 p.   port.   17cm.   [Pamphlets on California biography, v.1, no.8]

F860 C2 v.1:8 x

Cover title.

NL 0356724   CU-B

The life of blessed Henry Suso
see under   [Suso, Heinrich] 1300?-1366.

The life of Blessed Julie Billiart, foundress of the Institute of Sisters of Notre Dame
see under   Clare, James, 1827-1902.

Life of Blessed Madeleine Sophie Barat, foundress of the Society of the Sacred Heart. 1779-1865. 2d edition.
= Rochampton. 1908. 126 pp. 14 cm., in 16s.

N8596 — Madeleine Sophie, Saint, 179. 1865. — Society of the Sacred Heart of Jesus.

NL 0356727   MB WaSpG IMunS

Zan M363 W889h

The life of blessed Martin de Porres, (a Negro saint) of the Third Order of St. Dominic in the province of St. John Baptist of Peru. Translated from the Italian by Lady Herbert. New York, Catholic Publication Society Co., 1889.
xiv, 110p. 19cm.

1. Martín de Porres, 1579-1639.

NL 0356728   CtY ICN ODaU CtY KAS ViHaI DCU ICN

BW 908 G2 L72

Life of Blessed Michael Garicoïts, a classical saint. Revised and authorized by the Priests of the Sacred Heart of Jesus (of Betharram). Tr. by C. Otis-Cox, with introductory preface by His Eminence Cardinal Verdier. London, Sands, 1935.
xi, 223 p. front., plates 19 cm.

1. Garicoïts, Michel, 1797-1863. I. Priests of the Sacred Heart of Jesus of Betharram.

NL 0356729   IMunS

Life of Blessed Paul of the Cross...
see under   Finotti, Joseph Maria, d. 1879.

Life of Blessed Reginald of St. Giles, O. P.
see under   [Bayonne, Emmanuel Ceslas] 1832-1885.

By46 420f

The life of Boetius, recommended to the author of the Life of Julian ... London, Printed and are to be sold by W.Davis,1683.
4p.l.,101p. 15cm.
Signatures: A⁴,B-G⁸,H⁴(H4 blank)
Preliminary matter paged in ms. as p.1-7.
An answer to Samuel Johnson's Julian the Apostate, in which "the Duke of York was portrayed in the character of Julian." - Cf. Dict. of Nat. Biog, v.30,p.28.

NL 0356732   CtY DFo MH NNUT-Mc CLU-C

Life of Boston King
see under   King, Boston.

The life of Brigham Young... 1893
see under   [Anderson, Edward Henry] 1858-

Life of Buddha in frescoes, Mulagandhakuti Vihara, Sarnath
see under   [Nosu, Kosetsu]

The life of Bonaparte, First Consul of France... 1804
see under   [Corry, John] fl. 1825.

Life of Bonaparte, first consul of France, from his birth to the peace of Luneville
see under   [Dubroca, Louis]

GROSVENOR LIBRARY DC203 L65

Life of Buonaparte, in which the atrocious deeds, which he has perpetrated, in order to attain his elevated station, are faithfully recorded, by which means every Briton will be enabled to judge of the disposition of his threatening foe; and have a faint idea of the desolation which awaits this country, should his menaces ever be realized ... London, Printed for Tegg and Castleman [1800?]
vi[7]-286p. 18cm.

NL 0356738   NBuG

DA87.1 NbF3 18D—

Life of Buonaparte, in which the atrocities of the first consul are faithfully recorded as a warning to Britons against threatened invasion. London, Printed by Barnard and Sultzer for Tegg and Castleman [1805?]
36 p. port. 18 cm.

Bound with Fairburn's edition of the life of Admiral Lord Nelson. London [1805?]

1. Napoléon I, emperor of the French, 1769-1821.

NL 0356739   OU ViU

The life of Bonaparte, late emperor of the French, &c. &c. &c. from his birth until his departure to the island of St. Helena. By a citizen of the United States. Salem, Indiana, Printed by Patrick & Booth. 1818.
xii, [13]-257 p. 17ᶜᵐ.

1. Napoléon I, emperor of the French, 1769-1821.

Library of Congress   DC203.L7   4-13204

NL 0356740   DLC InU ViU InHi InGrD In MoSM

1885

Life of Cadioallader Calden, M.D. [anon.]
New York.
6 p. 12°. [From Allen's Biographical Dictionary]
[Toner Excerpts]

NL 0356741   DLC

N 979.511C E

Life of Captain Cook. [Edinburgh, Chambers, 1845]
32 p. port.

Running title.
Chambers's miscellany of useful and entertaining tracts, no.40.

1. Cook, James, 1728-1779.

NL 0356742   WaU CaBViP

The life of Captain James Cook. Dublin, Printed by J. Jones, 1824.
vi, [7]-179 p. incl. front., illus. 14ᶜᵐ.

1. Cook, James, 1728-1779.

Library of Congress   G246.C7L7   5-29011†

NL 0356743   DLC CtY CaBVaU

VOLUME 332

B910.4
C773

The life of Captain James Cook, the celebrated
circumnavigator, compiled from the most
authentic sources. Dublin, Printed by R.
Napper, 1831.
vi, [7]-173 p. front., plates. 14cm.

1. Cook, James, 1728-1779.

NL 0356744   NNC CU

The life of Captain James Cook; a new
edition. Lond.C.F.Cock,1831.
iv+170p.front.(pl.),3pl.T.

NL 0356745   CaBViPA

The Life of Captain James Whitney. Containing his
Most Remarkable Robberies and other
Adventures ... London, for A.R., 169⅞.
30 p.   small quarto.   Bound with Green,
Robert, The Behaviour and Execution of
Robert Green.
Note: The Bridgewater Library copy, 2 (20)
E 7.

NL 0356746   CSmH

4PZ
926

The life of Captain Macheath, the
bold highwayman. London, G. Purkess
[18]
214 p.

NL 0356747   DLC-P4 MH

Life of Captain Nathan Hale, the martyr-spy of the Revolution. Boston, American Tract Society [1874]
32 p. 13 cm.

1. Hale, Nathan, 1755-1776.

E280.H2L72 1874b   72-222853
Library of Congress   72 [2]   MARC

NL 0356748   DLC MH MB MWA

Life of Captain Nathan Hale, the martyr-spy of the revolution ...   New York, U. S. military post library association,
1874.
36 p. 14½cm.

1. Hale, Nathan, 1755-1776.   I. Military post library association of
the United States, New York, pub.

Library of Congress   E280.H2L72   11—14937

NL 0356749   DLC

... Life of Captain William Henry Allen [Excerpt
from The Portfolio, Third Series, Vol. III,
No. 1] [Philadelphia] January, 1814.
24 p.   8vo.
Harbeck Library, No. 278A.

NL 0356750   CSmH

The life of Cardinal Cheverus, archbishop of
Bordeaux, and formerly Bishop of Boston, in
Massachusetts
see under   [Hamon, André Jean Marie]
1795-1874.

The life of Carl Theodor Körner
see under   [Körner, Christian Gottfried]
1756-1831.

The life of Carlo, the famous dog of Drury-Lane
Theatre
see under   [Fenwick, Eliza]

The life of Caroline E. Smeldt, who died on the
21st September, 1817, ...
see under   [Waddel, Moses] 1770-1840.

The life of Caroline Gallup Reed
see under   [Reed, Sylvanus Albert] 1854-

WILLIAM
ANDREWS
CLARK
MEMORIAL
LIBRARY

The life of Carolus Gustavus of Bavaria,
Count Palatine at Kleeburg, King of Sweden.
The tenth of the name.   London, Printed
for the author, 1688.
[2],158 p. 17cm.
Signatures: A-K⁸.
Pages 47, 50-51, 54-55, 58-59, 62 incorrect-
ly numbered 37, 40-41, 44-45, 48-49, 52 re-
spectively.
Title within line border.   Marginal notes.
Bound in half   calf.

NL 0356756   CLU-C MH

Life of Carsten Niebuhr
see under   [Austin, Mrs. Sarah (Taylor)]
1793-1868.

The life of Cassem, the son of Hamid, a noble Arabian.

Editions of this work printed in America before 1801 are
available in this library in the Readex Microprint edition of
Early American Imprints published by the American Anti-
quarian Society.
This collection is arranged according to the numbers in
Charles Evans' American Bibliography.

NL 0356758   DLC

The LIFE of Cassem, the son of Hamid, a noble
Arabian. Translated from an Oriental manuscript.
London, Printed for J. Buckland, 1746.

21 cm.   pp.(1),iv,48.   Vignette (engraved).

NL 0356759   MH NjP PU

The life of Catharine II. empress of Russia
see under   [Castera, J   ]
1749-1838.

Augustan
HV 6248
.H3 L 5

The life of Catherine Hayes. Giving
a true and perfect account of her parentage,
birth, education ... from the time of her birth
to the hour of her death ... To which is added,
the lives of Thomas Wood and Thomas Billings
... London, Sold by J. Applebee [etc.], 1726.
40 p. front.

1. Hayes, Catherine, 1690-1726   2. Wood, Thomas,
ca. 1698-1726   3. Billings, Thomas, ca. 1698-1726
4. Crime and criminals--Gt. Brit.

NL 0356761   InU

Life of Catherine McAuley, foundress and first
superior of the Institute of religious Sisters of
mercy
see under   [Carroll, Mary Teresa Austin,
mother] d. 1909.

The life of Ceolfrid, abbot of the monastery at Wear-
mouth and Jarrow, by an unknown author of the eighth
century; tr. from the original, and ed. (with introductory essay and notes) by Douglas Samuel Boutflower ...
now first pub. in English; to which is added a reprint of
an article on the Codex amiatinus, by the late Rev. J. L.
Low (Church quarterly review).   Sunderland, Hills &
company; London, Simpkin, Marshall, Hamilton, Kent,
& co., ltd., 1912.
4 p. l., 120 p., 1 l. front. (facsim.) 23cm.
1. Ceolfrid, Saint, 642-716. 2. Codex amiatinus.   I. Boutflower, Douglas Samuel, ed. and tr.   II. Low, John Low, 1817?-1888.
                                                          18-3236
Library of Congress   BX4700.C64L5

NL 0356763   DLC RPB FMU MdBWA OCl MiU MB

The LIFE of Charles, prince of Lorrain.
Including the history of the house of Lorrain.
With a complete narrative of all the battles,
sieges, etc., from the commencement of the
war to this time. L. 1746.

Port.
Formerly owned by Thomas Carlyle; with
his book plate, autograph, MS. notes and
memoranda.

NL 0356764   MH PPL

The life of Charles XII. king of Sweden. Translated from the French. And now published with
additions and corrections. London: Printed by
W. M'Dowall, for J. Davis, Military chronicle
office, 1812.
1 p.l., 1v, [5]-142 p. 24cm. (In Interesting historical and biographical memoirs of the most remarkable events
and characters, copied from originals of undoubted authen-
ticity... v.2 London [1811?-1817,])
Supplement to the Royal military chronicle [v.4]

1. Karl XII, king of   Sweden, 1682-1718. I. Royal
military chronicle.   Supplement. II. Ser.

NL 0356765   ViU

The life of Charles F. Parham, founder of
the Apostolic faith movement
see under   [Parham, Sarah E   (Thistle-
thwaite)]

The life of Charles Freeman, once an American
slave ... [London, Sold at the Cosmorama, 209,
Regent Street, and to be had of all booksellers,
price 2d. ... [1855?]

8 p.   16.5cm.

1. Slavery in the U.S.-Fugitive slaves. 2. Freeman, Charles. I. Cosmorama, London.

NL 0356767   MiU-C

Life of Charlotte Elizabeth
see under   [Tonna, Mrs. Charlotte
Elisabeth (Browne) Phelan] 1790-1846.

Life of Christ. (Middle English poem)
Leben Jesu, ein fragment, und Kindheit
Jesu ...
see under   Horstmann, Carl, 1851-

VOLUME 332

Life of Christ (*Middle English poem*)
A stanzaic life of Christ compiled from Higden's Polychronicon and the Legenda aurea, ed. from ms. Harley 3909 by Frances A. Foster ... London, Pub. for the Early English text society by H. Milford. Oxford university press, 1926.
xliii, 456 p. front. (facsim.) 22½cm. (*Half-title: Early English text society. Original series. no. 166. 1926 (for 1924)*)
"A compilation made at Chester in the fourteenth century from two famous Latin works ... The result looks like a translation of the Legenda aurea with insertions from the Polychronicon."—p. ₍ix₎, xvii.
Missing parts supplied from Addit. ms. 38666, and Harl. 2250.
1. Jesus Christ—Poetry. I. Jacobus de Varagine. II. Higden, Ranulf, d. 1364. III. Foster, Frances Allen, 1887– ed. IV. British museum. Mss. (Harleian 3909) v. Title.
27—1550
Library of Congress   PR1119.A2 no.166

OU OCU MiU PBm MB MH ViU MBrZ PU PSC
NL 0356770   DLC CSaT OrU NjPT CaBVaU NcD NN PP PHC

•N8050   ₍Life of Christ.   No imprint, 1908?₎
L4
2 vols.   30cm.

Title from binding.

1. Jesus Christ.–Art.

NL 0356771   NBuG

The life of Christ.   Springfield, Ill., W.H. Cribb [c1928]
see under   [Cribb, William Harris] 1862–

N
8050   The life of Christ by Chinese artists.
.L5   London, Society for the Propagation of the Gospel, 1938.
52p. (chiefly illus.) 22cm.

1. Jesus Christ.   Art.

NL 0356773   OrU CBBD

The life of Christ by Chinese artists
₍24 pictures from original paintings on silk; foreword by Rosamund Essex₎ ₍London₎
Society for the propagation of the Gospel, 1939.

NL 0356774   ODW

N8050
L5   The life of Christ by Chinese artists.
Westminster, The Society for the Propagation of the Gospel, 1940.
52 p. illus. 22 cm.

1. Jesus Christ—Art.

NL 0356775   PPiPT OC1U

The life of Christ by Chinese artists.
Westminster, Society for the propagation of the gospel, 1941.
1 p. l., 52, ₍1₎ p., 1.l.incl. plates.   22ᶜᵐ.

Second edition, 16th impression.
"Introduction" signed: Rosamund Essex.
"About the pictures" signed: E. F.
1. Paintings, Chinese.
2. Jesus Christ – Art.

NL 0356776   NNC

A life of Christ for children ...   New York ₍etc.₎ Longmans, Green, and co., 1910.
ix p., 1 l., 77 p. front., 14 pl. 22ᶜᵐ. $1.00
10–2599
Library of Congress

A life of Christ for children; illustrated. 1913.

NL 0356778   OC1

The LIFE of Christ. Illustrated by choice passages from one hundred and thirty-eight eminent British and foreign divines; and embellished with seventy wood engravings after celebrated masters. ₍Compiled by T.T.₎ London, Ball, Arnold, and co. [1841] x, 288 p. illus. 23cm.

1. Jesus-Christ--Life. I. T., T., ed.

NL 0356779   NN MH–AH CtY

The life of Christ in Rembrandt's etchings.
N.Y., 1942

see under   New York. Metropolitan Museum of Art.

The life of Christ, our Lord and Savior
see under   Duryee, James E.

The life of Christian F. Swartz, an early missionary in India.
see under   American Sunday-school union.

The life of Christian F. Swartz, missionary at Travancore— 1750-1798.
London, Seeley, Jackson, and Halliday, 1855.
vi, 272 p. port., map. 18ᶜᵐ.

1 Schwartz, Christian Friedrich, 1726-1798

NL 0356783   NjPT WaU PPAmS

The life of Christopher Columbus.
Lond. Ward, L. & co. n. d. 369–383 pp. 8°.

NL 0356784   MB

The life of Christopher Columbus, illustrated by tales, sketches, and anecdotes. Adapted to the use of schools ... New York, Collins and Hannay, 1832.
vi, ₍7₎–187 p. incl. front., illus. 15ᶜᵐ.
Title vignette.
Half-title: A series of American school biographies publishing by Collins and Hannay.
Binder's title: Parley's Columbus.
Copyright by Samuel G. Goodrich; authorship disclaimed by him in his "Recollections".
1. Colombo, Cristoforo.
2—8030
Library of Congress   E111.L72

NL 0356785   DLC ViU OC1WHi MoU

The life of Christopher Columbus, illustrated by tales, sketches, and anecdotes. Adapted to the use of schools . . . ₍anon.₎ Philadelphia, Desilver, Thomas & co., ₍1836.
vi, 7-187 p. incl. front., illus. 16½ᶜᵐ.
Copyright by Samuel G. Goodrich; authorship disclaimed by him in his "Recollections."
Subject entries: Colombo, Cristoforo, 1446-1506.
2—8081
Library of Congress, no.   E111.L73.

NL 0356786   DLC PU

The life of Christopher Columbus, illustrated by tales, sketches, and anecdotes. Adapted to the use of schools. With engravings. Philadelphia, Desilver, Thomas & co., 1837.   vi, (1)8–187 p. incl. front. illus. 17cm.

Binder's title: Parley's Columbus.
Copyright by Samuel G. Goodrich; authorship disclaimed by him in his "Recollections."
With stamp of H. M. Washburn.

53R0323. 1. Columbus, Christopher.   I. Title: Parley's Columbus.

NL 0356787   NN ViU

The LIFE of Christopher Columbus, illustrated by tales, sketches, and anecdotes. Adapted to the use of schools. With engravings. Philadelphia, Thomas, Cowperthwait & co., 1838.
187p. incl. front. illus. 17cm.

Binder's title: Parley's Columbus.
Copyright by S.G. Goodrich; authorship disclaimed by him in his "Recollections."

NL 0356788   MnU ViU MH OO PU ICU MH RPB

Life of Christopher Columbus, illustrated by tales, sketches and anecdotes. Philadelphia, 1844.

NL 0356789   CtY OC1

The life of Christopher Columbus, illustrated by tales, sketches and anecdotes ... ₍anon.₎ Philadelphia, Thomas, Cowperthwait & co., 1851.
vi, ₍7₎-187 p. incl. front. (port.) illus. pl. 17ᵐ.
Title vignette.
Copyright by S. G. Goodrich; authorship disclaimed by him in his "Recollections".
1. Colombo, Cristoforo.
2—8082
Library of Congress   E111.L74

NL 0356790   DLC ViU CSmH CtY

Life of Christopher Columbus, illustrated by tales sketches and anecdotes. Philadelphia, 1857.

NL 0356791   CtY

E111
L76   The Life of Christopher Columbus. Illustrated
1859   by tales, sketches, and anecdotes. Adapted to the use of schools. Philadelphia, C. Desilver, 1859.
187 p. illus. 20cm.

Copyright by S. G. Goodrich; authorship disclaimed by him in his "Recollections."
With this is bound, The Life of George Washington, and, The Life of Benjamin Franklin.

NL 0356792   GU

VOLUME 332

The life of Christopher Columbus. Illustrated by tales, sketches, and anecdotes. Adapted to the use of schools ... Philadelphia, C. Desilver, 1860.
vi, ₍7₎-187 p. incl. front. (port.) illus. 3 pl. 19½ᶜᵐ.

Title vignette.
Copyright by S. G. Goodrich; authorship disclaimed by him in his "Recollections."

1. Colombo, Cristoforo.

16-13253

Library of Congress   E111.L76

NL 0356793   DLC CSmH MnU

---

*
E111
.L74
1865
The life of Christopher Columbus. Illustrated by tales, sketches, and anecdotes. Adapted to the use of schools. With engravings. Philadelphia: Charles Desilver, 1865.
187 p. illus. 20cm.
With this is bound The life of George Washington ... Philadelphia, 1865 and The life of Benjamin Franklin ... Philadelphia, 1865.
Bookplate of W. U. Oglesby, Lynchburg, Va.

1. Colombo, Cristoforo. I. Goodrich, Samuel Griswold, 1793-1860, supposed author.

NL 0356794   ViU

Life of Christopher Columbus.
Portrayed by 1200 characters, in Barnum & Bailey show. [N. Y. ?] Bailey. 1892. 31 pp. Illus. Portrs. 8°.

NL 0356795   MB

... The life of Christopher Columbus, the discoverer of America. Boston, B. H. Greene, 1840.
viii, ₍9₎-233 p. front., 1 pl. 16 cm. (American juvenile biography)

1. Colombo, Cristoforo, 1446-1506.

E111.L75   2--22061

NL 0356796   DLC

PR
3687
S7
Z5
1791
The life of Christopher Smart. ₍Reading, Eng., Smart and Cowslade, 1791₎
xliii, 15½cm.
Offprint of the Poems of the late Christopher Smart...Reading, Smart and Cowslade, 1791, v.1, p. i-xliii, The life of Christopher Smart.

1. Smart, Christopher, 1722-1771. I. Smart, Christopher, 1722-1771. Poems.

NL 0356797   IdU

Life of Claude A. Gunder, saved by the Blood from a drunkard's hell
see under   Gunder, Claude A., b. 1873.

The life of Collin Reynolds
see under   Barnard, Charles Francis, 1808-1884.

Life of Col. Aaron Burr, vice-president of the U. S. ...
see under   Todd, Charles Burr, 1849-

---

*
GN69
.5
.C43
1844
Life of Col. Chaffin. 2d ed. New York, Printed by J. W. Bell, 1844.
12 p.   19cm.
Cover title.
At head of title: An exact profile likeness.
Caption title: A sketch of the life, incidents of travel, notices of the press, &c. &c., of Col J. H. Chaffin.

1. Chaffin, Josephus Henry, 1825-   2. Dwarfs.

NL 0356801   ViU

... Life of Colonel Croghan ...
(In the Port folio. Philadelphia, 1815. 21½ᶜᵐ. 3d ₍i. e. 4th₎ ser., v. 5, p. 212-220)

1. Croghan, George, 1791-1849.

Library of Congress   AP2.P85 vol. 24   21-68

NL 0356802   DLC

Case
Y
1565
.L 624
The LIFE of Colonel Don Francisco ₍Francis Charteris₎ Containing the whole series of the most remarkable and unprecedented actions from his birth to the time of his receiving sentence of death for a rape... London, Printed for the author₍1730?₎
55p. incl. front. (port.) 20cm.

NL 0356803   ICN CLU-C CU NRU ICN CtY

AC901
.D8
The life of Col. Despard, with an account of the execution of him ... for high treason including the speech made by the Colonel on the platform.   Dublin, 1803.
12 p.   (Duane pamphlets, 18:4)

NL 0356804   DLC

Western
Americana
Zc52
842Li
Life of Col. Edwards, with eight engravings; a complete and authentic narrative of the life, exploits, travels and adventures ... together with the detection, conviction and confession of the great Southern forger ... Colonel Monroe Edwards, recently convicted in the Court of Oyer and Terminer of New York, and now imprisoned in the Egyptian Tombs awaiting sentence. [n. p., 1842]
31, [1] p. illus., ports. 23 cm.
Streeter   no. 1410.

NL 0356805   CtY MB

E415
.9
.F8L72
Life of Col. Fremont. ₍New York, Greeley & M'Elrath, 1856₎
32 p.   illus. (incl. port.) 23cm.

Caption title.
This issue dated at end: New York, Aug. 1st, 1856.

1. Frémont, John Charles, 1813-1890. I. Greeley & McElrath, pub.

WaU CU IU NNC CaBViP
NL 0356806   DLC WaU PHi OrU WaU CoD RPB MiU ICN

The life of Col. James Fisk, jr., with sketches of Edward S. Stokes, his assassin, Miss Helen Josephine Mansfield, his former mistress, and various incidents in the checkered career of a murdered millionare ₍!₎   New York, W. E. Hilton ₍187-?₎
1 p. l., ₍5₎-58 p. front., illus., plates (1 double) ports. 23½ᶜᵐ.

1. Fisk, James, 1835-1872. 2. Stokes, Edward S., 1841-   3. Mansfield, Helen Josephine, 1848-

27-10181

Library of Congress   CT275.F565L4

NL 0356807   DLC

The life of Col. James Fisk, jr. ... of Miss Helen Josephine Mansfield ... of Edward L. Stokes ... and Hon. Wm. M. Tweed ... with a sketch of the grand duke Alexis, of Russia ...   Chicago ₍etc.₎ J. W. Goodspeed; New York, H. S. Goodspeed & co., 1872.
1 p. l., ₍5₎-162 p. front., plates (1 fold.) ports. 22½ᶜᵐ.

1. Fisk, James, 1835-1872. 2. Mansfield, Helen Josephine, 1848- 3. Stokes, Edward S., 1841-   4. Tweed, William Marcy, 1823-1878. 5. Alexis, grand duke of Russia, 1850-   I. Goodspeed, Jerome Washington, comp.

CA 17-2172 Unrev'd

Library of Congress   CT275.F565L42

NL 0356808   DLC MiU NN CtY OClWHi NRU NN

The life of Col. James Gardiner
see under   ₍Doddridge, Philip₎ 1702-1751.

Life of Col. Michael Corcoran, 69th New-York Regiment.   [New York, 1861]
8 p.   24mo.   Bound in one-half dark blue roan, blue boards.
The Nicholson Collection, September 1922.

NL 0356810   CSmH

Life of Commander Henry James
see under   James, Henry, commander.

Life of Commodore Preble
see under   ₍Kirkland, John Thornton₎ 1770-1840.

The life of Confucius, reproduced from a book entitled Shêng chi t'u, being rubbings from the stone "Tablets of the Holy shrine" ...   Shanghai, Kwang Hsueh publishing house, Oxford university press, China agency ₍1934?₎
3 p. l., 1 illus., 108 pl. on 54 l., 1 l.   12½ x 19ᶜᵐ.
"Shêng chi t'u" transliterated from Chinese characters in title.
Plates, with explanatory letterpress in Chinese and English, illustrating the life and cult of Confucius. Some are reproductions of "rubbings" from stone monuments in the temple to Confucius at Ch'ü-fu, Shantung province.
"List of books on Confucius in the library of the North China branch of the Royal Asiatic society": 1 leaf at end.
1. Confucius and Confucianism.

Library of Congress   B128.CSL5   35-9017
                          ₍3₎   921.9

NL 0356813   DLC NcD NPV CtY NjP

A life of consecration
see under   ₍Legge, Alfred Owen₎

The life of Cornelia Connelly, 1809-1879, foundress of the Society of the Holy Child Jesus, by a member of the society; with a preface by Cardinal Gasquet ...   London, New York ₍etc.₎ Longmans, Green and co., 1922.
xvi, 486 p.   front., illus. (incl. facsim.) plates, ports. 22½ᶜᵐ.

1. Connelly, Mrs. Cornelia Augusta (Peacock) 1809-1879. 2. Society of the Holy Child Jesus.

Library of Congress   BX4705.C77L5   22--10878

NL 0356815   DLC PRosC PIm PV OCX

The life of Cornelia Connelly, 1809-1879, foundress of the Society of the Holy Child Jesus, by a religious of the society; with a preface by Cardinal Gasquet ... With portrait. 2d ed., abridged and rev. New York, London ₍etc.₎ Longmans, Green and co., 1924.
xvi, 260 p.   front. (port.) 19½ᶜᵐ.
Printed in Great Britain.

1. Connelly, Mrs. Cornelia Augusta (Peacock) 1809-1879. 2. Society of the holy Child Jesus.

Library of Congress   BX4705.C77L5 1924   25--8443

NL 0356816   DLC PRosC IaU DCU TxU

VOLUME 332

The life of Cornelius van Tromp, Lieutenant-Admiral of Holland and Westfriesland: containing many remarkable passages relating to the war between England and Holland. As also the sea-fights and other memorable actions of this great man, from the year 1650, to the time of his death. London: J. Orme, 1697. 533 p. 12°.

27413A. 1. Tromp, Cornelis, 1629– PROUDFIT COLLECTION.
N. Y. P. L. tory, 1650–91. 1691. 2. Navy (Dutch).—His-
February 9, 1922.

NL 0356817 NN InU CLU-C N DN ICN CtY PU

Life of Commodore John Paul Jones; and Memoirs of Captain Nathaniel Fanning
see under [Fanning, Nathaniel] 1755–1805.

The life of Count Louis Batthyányi the hero, prime minister of Hungary in 1848, who was ordered by the Austrian general Haynau to be executed and was shot in Pesth (Hungary) Oct. 6th, 1849. And the life of General Arthur Görgey, the traitor of Hungary in 1849. New York, G. B. Teubner, printer, 1858.

2 p. l, 14 p. 23½ .

1. Batthyány, Lajos, gróf, 1806–1849. 2. Görgei, Arthur, 1818–1912.
25–5847
Library of Congress DB936.L4

NL 0356819 DLC PPL PU PHi PPAmP

The life of Count Ulfeld, great master...
see under [Rousseau de la Valette, Michel]

Life of Cromwell [1859]
see under [Lamartine, Alphonse Marie Louis de] 1790–1869.

DS
282
.C97 The life of Cyrus. New York, Carlton & [?] n.d.
185 p.

1. Cyrus, the Great, King of Persia, 600?–529 B.C. 2. Iran–Hist.–Ancient to 640 A.D. 3. Legends, Jewish. I. Title.

NL 0356822 DAU

The life of Cyrus. Philadelphia, American Sunday-School Union [18--]
192 p. (Village and family library. 7)

First published simultaneously by American Sunday School Union and Religious Tract Society in 1847.

I. American Sunday School Union, Philadelphia. II. Religious Tract Society, London.

NL 0356823 NNC

935.092
'C997Z The life of Cyrus. Edited by Thos. O. Summers.
Theol. Nashville, Southern Methodist publishing house,
1880.
179p. 16cm.

1. Cyrus, the Great, king of Persia, d. B.C.
529. I. Summers, Thomas Osmond, 1812–1882, ed.

NL 0356824 TxDaM GeU NcD

The life of Czechoslovak village youth. [Praha, Orbis, 1954]
unpaged. illus. 15 x 21 cm.

1. Youth–Czechoslovak Republic. 2. Czechoslovak Republic–Rural conditions. I. Title: Czechoslovak village youth.

HQ799.C9L5 57-20707 ‡

NL 0356825 DLC

The life of Daniel
see under [Hooker, Mrs. Mary Ann (Brown)] 1796–1838.

Life of Daniel Boone. Dayton, O., Ells, Marquis & company, 1856.

vi, 7–288 p. incl. front., illus. (incl. ports.) pl. 18ᵐ.
Illustrated t.-p.

1. Boone, Daniel, 1734–1820.

CA 25–723 Unrev'd
Library of Congress F454.B765

NL 0356827 DLC KyHi WHi MoU CLSU

Life Of Daniel Boone And Other Heroes And Hunters Of The West. ... New York, W. L. Allison Company Publishers [182–?]
8vo. Brown cloth.
Brock Collection, October, 1922.
1. Boone, Daniel, 1734–1820.

NL 0356828 CSmH

The life of Daniel Dana, D. D.
see under [Dana, William Coombs] 1810–1873.

Life of Daniel Defoe... 1841
see under Chalmers, George, 1742–1825.

The LIFE of Daniel Lambert: with an account of men noted for their corpulence. And other interesting matters. New-York: Printed and sold by Samuel Wood & Sons [181–?] 46 p. 14½cm.

Imperfect: first two leaves wanting. Title from cover.

783726A. 1. Lambert, Daniel, 1770–1809.

NL 0356831 NN

The life of Daniel, the prophet
see under M'Gavin, William, 1773–1832.

... Life of Daniel Webster, the statesman and the patriot
see under [Frost, John] 1800–1859.

The life of Dante, Italy's greatest poet.
London [n.d.]
p. 161–[176] O.
By S. I. A.
Binder's title: Dante Vita A-C

NL 0356834 RPB

[Life of Dante; to which are added miscellaneous comments on Dante's life and works, ...]
see under [Chambers, William Henry] 1830–1906.

Life of David Belden
see under Belden, David, 1832–1888.

Life of David Bell Birney, major-general United States volunteers
see under [Davis, Oliver Wilson]

Life of David Crockett; the original humorist and irrepressible back-woodsman ...
see under Crockett, David, 1786–1836.

The life of David, king of Israel
see under [Hooker, Mrs. Mary Ann (Brown)] 1796–1838.

DT 731
.L9L5 The life of David Livingstone, by a class in the School of missions (1922) under direction of M. K. W. Heicher, Ph. D., First Presbyterian church, Cedar Falls, Iowa. Based upon the "Life of David Livingstone" by Sylvester Harne. Cedar Falls, Ia.... c 1923.

NL 0356840 DLC

PR974
.C4
Vol. 5 The life of David Love. Containing his birth, parentage, and education. With several curious transactions during his youth. Printed for the author by J. Marshall, Old Flesh-Market, Newcastle.
8 p. 16.5 cm. [In Chap books. London, 1777–1835, Vol. V, no. 5]
Part I.

NL 0356841 DLC

CT
275
P38
L5 The Life of David Patton. Dugway, Utah, Kraut's Pioneer Press [n.d.]
viii,72p.

1. Patton, David Wyman, 1800 (ca.)–1838.

NL 0356842 UU

The life of Denis M. Bradley, First bishop of Manchester
see under [Dowd, M H]

Rare Book
Room The life of Deval. Shewing how he came to be
Nvq49 a highway-man ... Together with his arraignment
G6 and condemnation. As also his speech and con-
670dy fession, at the place of execution. [London]
Printed by W.R. and are to be sold in Westsmith-field, next door to the Dolphin near Hosier-lane end, 1669[/70]
8p. 18½cm.
Signature: A⁴.
The highwayman's name is given on p.3 as "Lewis Deval, alias John Brown": his true name

was Claude Duval, and his execution took place on January 21st, 1669/70.

NL 0356845 CtY MnU

VOLUME 332

The life of Dick En–l–d, alias Captain En–l—d; of turf memory. With notes and illustrations ... London, T. Boosey, 1792.

2 p. l., ₍vii₎–xvi, 53 p. 21ᶜᵐ.

1. England, Richard.

Library of Congress   CT788.E7L5   44-19871

NL 0356846   DLC MH CLU CtY DFo

The life of Dr. Arnold
    see under   ₍Guyton₎ Mrs. Emma Jane
    (Worboise)

E
5
.C 1396   The LIFE of Dr. Archibald Cameron, brother
to Donald Cameron of Lochiel... Containing, I. The reasons which induced the doctor to list himself among the rebels. II. His principal business and employment in the chevalier's army. III. The genealogy of the Camerons... IV. A character and description of the antient Highlanders... With the proceedings against him at the Court of King's bench, his behaviour at the tower after sentence...the procession from the tower to the place of execution, and his behaviour there...
London, M. Cooper,   1753.
29p.   ports.   22cm.

NL 0356848   ICN

The life of Dr. Beilby Porteus
    see under   ₍Hodgson, Robert₎ d. 1844.

Life of Dr. Brigham. ₍Boston, D. Clapp, 184-9.
p. 250-255. 8°.
Signed: B. C. C.
From the Boston medical and surgical journal, 1849. V. XLI. No. 13.
1. Brigham, Amariah, 1798-1849.

NL 0356850   DLC

The life of Dr. Burnet
    see under   ₍LeClerc, Jean₎ 1657-1736.

The life of Doctor Culverwell, written by himself; being curiosities of thirty-five years' medical experience, embodied in the biography of the author
    see under   Culverwell, Robert James, 1802-1865.

1885   Life of Dr. Edwin Eldridge. ₍anon.₎
Elmira, Gazette, 1876.
₍From Elmira Gazette, Dec. 22, 1876₎
₍Toner Excerpts₎

NL 0356853   DLC

412
1   Life of Dr. Franklin.
From Brittanic magazine, v. 12, p. 433-440, 1807.

NL 0356854   CtY

The life of Doctor Franklin, and the Way to wealth; to which is added a collection of sacred poems, designed to promote in the rising generation, the principles of piety, industry, and economy.
    see under   Hulbert, Charles, 1778-1857.

The life of Dr. George Abbot, Lord Archbishop of Canterbury...

    see under

Oldys, William, 1696-1761.

The life of Dr. Henry Compton, Lord Bishop of London
    see under   Salmon, Nathaniel.

Toner
1885   The life of Dr. Jenner ₍anon.₎   ₍n. p., 1817?₎
p. 48-59.   8°.

NL 0356858   DLC

The life of Dr. Jim (by one who knows him). Together with the story of the Transvaal rising, with portraits of the principal actors in the drama of South Africa... ₍London₎ "The Sun", 1896.   28 p. incl. ports.   21cm.

1. Jameson, Sir Leander Starr,   1853-1917. 2. Transvaal—Hist.
—Jameson's raid, 1895-1896.
N.Y.P.L.   June 17, 1942

NL 0356859   NN

1885   Life of Dr. Joseph Warren.   ₍Philadelphia,
H. Perkins, 1835₎
6 p.   8°.   ₍From National Portrait Gallery, v. 1835₎

NL 0356860   DLC

1885   ₍Life of₎ Dr. Josiah Bartlett. ₍anon.₎   ₍Philadelphia, R. W. Pomeroy, 1823₎
p. 133-165.   8°.
Note: p. 133-165 of Biography of the signers to the declaration of independence. By John Sanderson. 8°. 1823. v. iii.

NL 0356861   DLC

The life of Dr. Oliver Goldsmith: written from personal knowledge, authentic papers, and other indubitable authorities ...
    see under   Percy, Thomas, D. D., Bishop of Dromore.

The life of Dr. Samuel L. Boicourt, of Louisville, Kentucky
    see under   Boicourt, Samuel L   b. 1807.

The life of ... Dr. Thomas Fuller
    see under   ₍Fell, John₎ 1625-1686.

The life of Dr. Thomas Morton, late bishop of Duresme
    see under   ₍Baddeley, Richard₎ fl. 1621.

The life of Dr. William Wagstaffe, to which is annexed, an account of his writings.   ₍n. p., n. d.₎
xivp.   20cm.   ₍With Memoirs of the life and character of Mr. John Locke. London, 1742₎

Written as an introduction to a collection of tracts by Wagstaffe.

1. Wagstaffe, William, 1685-1725

NL 0356866   IEN

The life of Don Quixote and his man Sancho Pancha
    see under   ₍Cervantes Saavedra, Miguel de₎
1547-1616.

The life of Donna Rosina, a novel
    see under   ₍Castillo Solórzano, Alonso de₎
fl. 1640.

266.092
M241   Life of Duncan Macpherson, a faithful standard-bearer; the story of the interesting life and work of Duncan Macpherson, city missionary, Auckland, New Zealand, by a friend.   Auckland, Clark & Matheson, 1914.
191p.   illus., ports.   19cm.

1. Macpherson, Duncan, b. 1839.

NL 0356869   TxU

The life of Edmund Kean
    see under   ₍Procter, Bryan Waller₎ 1787-1874.

E.E. Ayer
Collection   Life of Edward Herrick Castle, written and compiled from data possessed by himself at the request of his friends.   Chicago, M. G. Peck, 1893.
29p.   illus., pl., ports.   19cm.

Illustrated covers, including portrait.

NL 0356871   ICN

Rare
DA
26
E581
v.26
no.6   The life of Edward Seymour, Duke of Somerset, Lord General, and Lord Protector, of the realm, in the reigns of Henry VIII and Edward VI. With some parallel influences to the case of John Duke of M-----h, late great favourite of England. To which is added, the sudden fall of ... John Dudley, Duke of Northumberland. Wherein is contain'd the opinion of the judges at that time, in the point of altering the succession, as then settled by act of Parliament.   London, Printed for J. Baker,   1713.

42, ₍2₎ p.   19cm.

Publisher's catalogue: p. ₍43₎-₍44₎
No. 6 in vol. lettered: English history pamphlets, 26, 1712-15.

1. Somerset, Edward Seymour, 1st duke of, 1506?-1552. 2. Northumberland, John Dudley, 1st duke of,   1502?-1553.

NL 0356873   NIC MH CtY

The life of Edward II, with the fates of Gavestone and the Spencers
    see under   ₍Hubert, Sir Francis₎ d. 1629.

VOLUME 332

x813 The Life of Eleanor Moreland, in a letter to
L6261 her niece. Cambridge, Printed for the
trustees of the publishing fund, by Hilliard
and Metcalf. Sold by Cummings & Hilliard,
Boston, and by other agents of the publishing
fund, Jan. 1822.
64p. 18cm.

Wright 1668.

I. Moreland, Eleanor.

NL 0356875 IU MWA CU CtY DLC

Life of Elias Ruark Horner, pioneer circuit rider in the Pacific
Northwest... ₍Corvallis? Or.₎ 1915. 10 l. illus. 23cm.

"Published by the family..."

1. Horner, Elias Ruark, 1835–1914.
N. Y. P. L.   January 13, 1950

OrHi OrP WaS
NL 0356876 NN NNC ICU OrU WaPS OrSaW OrCS InU

The life of Elisha
    see under   [Hooker, Mary Ann (Brown)]
1796–1838.

The life of Ellwood Cooper. ₍n. p., 1913?₎
28,₍1₎ p. 18cm. ₍Pamphlets on California
biography. new ser. v.1, no.2₎

NL 0356878 CU-B

Life of Emanuel Swedenborg, with some account
    of his writings, together with a brief notice
    of the rise and progress of the New church
    see under   [Hobart, Nathaniel]

The Life of Emelia Geddie, Daughter of John
    Geddie, of Hiltoun, in Falkland, ...
    n.p., printed for Margaret MacDonald,
    n.d. [1810?]
        sm. 8vo.   Cream paper boards.
    Huth copy, pt. 3:3168.

NL 0356880 CSmH

The Life of Émile Zola (Motion picture script)
    "The life of Emile Zola." (Dialogue transcript.) ₍Burbank,
Cal.₎ c1937. ₍46₎ f. 33cm.

    Various paging.
    Reproduced from typewritten copy.
    Screen play by N. R. Raine, Heinz Herald and Géza Herczeg, from a story by
Heinz Herald and Géza Herczeg. Produced by Warner brothers.

    1. Moving picture plays—Texts   and outlines. 2. Zola, Émile, 1840–
1902—Drama. I. Herald, Heinz,   jt. au. II. Herczeg, Géza, jt. au.
III. Warner brothers pictures, inc. IV. Title.
N. Y. P. L.   March 7, 1939

NL 0356881 NN CLSU

The life of Enoch again revived, in which Abels
    offering is accepted
        see under   [Bayly, William] d. 1675.

The life of Erasmus
    see under   [Jortin, John] 1698–1770.

Life of Ethan Allen
    see under
        Sparks, Jared, 1789–1866.

The life of faith... New York: F. J. Huntington ₍etc.₎ 1864.
vi, 8–31 p. 11cm.

"Translated from the French, by some...Christian whose initials only are given
in the edition, published in London, 1860, of which this is a reprint."— Pref.
Translated by William Upton Richards.— cf. Brit. mus. Cat. of printed books.

1. Faith. I. Richards, William Upton, 1811–1873, tr.
N. Y. P. L.   April 20, 1938

NL 0356885 NN

The life of faith, exemplified and recommended, in
    a letter found in the study of J. Belcher ...
        see under   Eliot, Joseph, 1683–1694.

HP34.2 The life of faith exemplified; being thoughts
L62   on the principal scenes in the life and
         times of David, King of Israel. ₍Pref.
         signed C.H.M.₎ 3d ed., rev. Philadelphia
         H. Longstreet ₍pref. 1862₎
         199p.

         1. David, King of Israel. I. M., C.H.

NL 0356887 CSaT OO GEU

The life of faith exemplified in the eleventh chapter
    of St. Paul's Epistle to the Hebrews ...
        see under   Wesley, Charles.

The Life of Faith Library. London,
Marshall, n.d.
v.

    Contents: Grenfell, W. T. A man's
faith.

NL 0356889 OO

The life of Father Haskins, by a friend of the
    House of the angel guardian
        see under   [Kelly, William D   ]

Life of Father Mathew, the great apostle of temperance. ₍Bos-
ton, 1844?₎ 46 p. 8°.

    Caption-title.
    In: ZLH p. v. 10, no. 10.

1. Mathew, Theobald, 1790–1856.
N. Y. P. L.   November 11, 1919.

NL 0356891 NN

Life of Father Taylor, the sailor preacher
    see under   Boston port and seamen's aid
society.

YA The life of Felix Neff, pastor of the high
.S914 Alps. Prepared form Gillies' memoir of
Felix Neff... New York. n.d.
168p.

(Sunday school books; arr. numerically.)

NL 0356893 DLC

BX9459 Life of Felix Neff, pastor of the High Alps. Lon-
.N35L7 don, The Religious tract society[1836]
viii, 208 p. 14½cm.

1. Neff, Felix, 1798–1829.

NL 0356894 ICU PPPrHi

The life of Field Marshall the duke of
    Wellington.
        See under
Siddons, Joachim Hayward, 1800?–1885.

The life of Fisher transcribed from
    ms. Harleian 6382
        see under   [Hall, Richard] 1537–1604.

The life of Florence L. Barclay; a study in personality,
by one of her daughters. London and New York, G. P.
Putnam's sons, 1921.

306 p. front., plates, ports., facsim. 19ᶜᵐ.

1. Barclay, Mrs. Florence Louisa (Charlesworth) 1862–1921.

Library of Congress   PR6003.A66Z7   22–26236

NL 0356897 DLC ICN FMU TxU LU OrCS MB NN OCl MnU PP

813.5 The life of Florence L. Barclay; a study in personality,
B244ZL by one of her daughters. London and New York, G. P.
Putnam's sons ₍1927₎

310 p. (p. 307–310 advertisements) plates.
19 cm.
    "Popular edition August 1924... reprinted
May 1927."

NL 0356898 NcD

Life of Francis Marion, brigadier-general in the
    army of the United States
        see under   James, William Dobein.

The life of Francis of Lorrain, duke of Guise
    see under   [Valincour, Jean Baptiste
Henri du Trousset de] 1653–1730.

Life of ... Francis Schlatter, the great healer
    see under   [Stedman, Charles Reuben]

VOLUME 332

The life of Francis Xavier, apostle of the Indies ... Philadelphia, Printed by Hogan & M'Elroy, for A. Brodie, 1798.

1 p. l., ₁viii₁-xii, ₁13₁-192 p. front. (port.) 16½ᶜᵐ.

The first part of this abstract is taken from two accounts of St. Francis by different men; the rest is from Dominique Bouhours' "Life of St. Francis Xavier," tr. by Dryden, London, 1688. *cf.* Pref.

1. Francisco Xavier, Saint, 1506-1552.

4-29048

       NN ICU
NL 0356902   DLC NcGU NjR PMA MWH MWA CtY NNC PP PU

The life of François de Salignac de la Motte Fenelon, archbishop and duke of Cambray
    see under   [Ramsay, Andrew Michael]
1686-1743.

The life of Frederick the Second, king of Prussia
    see under   [Laveaux, Jean Charles Thibault de] 1749-1827.

The life of Frederick William von Steuben, major general in the revolutionary army
    see under   Kapp, Friedrich, 1824-1884.

B   The life of Fremont. Only unauthorised ed.
F872£i ₁New York₁ Levison & Haney ₁1856?₁
       17p. illus. 12cm.

       1. Fremont, John Charles, 1813-1890.
       I. Levison, William H., 1822-1857.

NL 0356906   IU

The life of Friedrich Schiller
    see under   [Carlyle, Thomas] 1795-1881.

... Life of Galileo Galilei: with illustrations of the advancement of experimental philosophy
    see under   [Bethune, John Elliot Drinkwater] 1801-1851.

Life of General Andrew Jackson ...
    see under   [Kendall, Amos] 1789-1869.

Life of Gen. Benjamin Harrison
    see under   Messaros, Waldo.

Life of General Booth. Nelson, n.d.
    see   General Booth. London [1913?]

Life of Gen. Cass
    see under   Hickman, George H

Life of Gen. Charles A. Browne.

NL 0356913   DN

The life of Gen. Francis Marion
    see under   [Weems, Mason Locke] 1759-1825.

Life of Gen. Franklin Pierce, the Democratic candidate for president. Trenton, Printed by M. R. Hamilton, 1852.

48 p. 21½ᶜᵐ.

1. Pierce, Franklin, pres. U. S., 1804-1869.

13-4014

Library of Congress   E432.L72

NL 0356915   DLC NjR

973.793 The Life of Gen. George B. M'Clellan.
M13£if   ₁n.p.₁, 186-₁
         16p. illus. 16cm.

         Caption title.

         1. McClellan, George Brinton, 1826-1885.

NL 0356916   IU

Life of General Goerge Washington
    see under   [Corry, John] fl. 1825.

LIFE of Gen. J.A.Garfield.- Speech of Gen. Garfield to the soldiers of the 18th brigade during the east Kentucky campaign. Incident of Gen. Garfield at the time of Pres. Lincoln's assassination. n.p., [1881]

sm.4°. pp.(4).
Port. of Pres. Garfield.
"Supplement to Sulphur bitter herald."

NL 0356918   MH

Life of General Jacob Brown. To which are added memoirs of Generals Ripley and Pike. New York, Nafis & Cornish; St. Louis, Mo., Nafis, Cornish & co., 1847.

iv, ₁5₁-256 p. incl. plates. 11½ᶜᵐ.

1. Brown, Jacob, 1775-1828. 2. Pike, Zebulon Montgomery, 1779-1813. 3. Ripley, Eleazer Wheelock, 1782-1839.

17-1535

Library of Congress   E353.1.B9L72

NL 0356919   DLC MWA NcD OClWHi NN CtHT-W

Life of General Jacob Brown. To which are added memoirs of Generals Ripley and Pike. New York, Sheldon Blakeman, 1856.
256p.

NL 0356920   MiD-B MH

Life of General James Wolfe, the conqueror of Canada
    see under   [Pringle, Sir John, bart.] 1707-1782.

... Life of General Lafayette; with anecdotes illustrative of his character ... Philadelphia, Lindsay & Blakiston ₁1847₁

1 p. l., viii, 9-208 p. front. (port.) plates. 18ᶜᵐ. (The young American's library)

Added t.-p., illustrated in colors, with portrait vignette.

1. Lafayette, Marie Joseph Paul Roch Yves Gilbert de Motier, marquis de, 1757-1834.

A 34-1333

Title from N. Carolina   Univ. Printed by L. C.

       PP PU PPLas
NL 0356922   NcU IdU NIC OKentU NcD MoU OEac OrU

WB   Life of General Lafayette: with anecdotes
26930   illustrative of his character. Boston, Lee and Shepard, 1868.
        208p. illus. (The Young American's library)

        1. Lafayette, Marie Joseph Paul Yves Roch Gilbert du Motier, Marquis de, 1757-1834.
        cdu

NL 0356923   CtY OrP

DC146   Life of General Lafayette: with anecdotes
.L2L5   illustrative of his character. Boston,
1876   Lee and Shepard, 1876.
        208 p. illus., port. 19cm. (The Young American's library. Famous generals. ₁4₁)

        1. Lafayette, Marie Joseph Roch Yves Gilbert de Motier, marquis de, 1757-1834.

NL 0356924   ViU

Life of General Lewis Cass: comprising an account of his military service in the North-west during the war with Great Britain, his diplomatic career and civil history. To which is appended, a sketch of the public and private history of Major-General W. O. Butler, of the volunteer service of the United States ... Philadelphia, G. B. Zieber & co., 1848.

viii, 11-210 p. 2 port. (incl. front.) 20ᶜᵐ.
Campaign biographies of the candidates for president and vice president on the Democratic ticket.
The sketch of Butler is expanded from The life and service of Gen. William O. Butler, by F. P. Blair, jr.

1. Cass, Lewis, 1782-1880. ₁. Zieber. 1866. 2. Butler, William Orlando, 1793-1880. G. B. & co., Philadelphia, pub.
                                                       7-15405
Library of Congress   E340.C3L7

       CtY MiU-C OClWHi PU MiU ViU PP PHi TxU
NL 0356925   DLC DNW MiU CaBViPA Nh MWA MnHi MtU

Beinecke The Life of General M.D. Stanley, an American
Library   militia general: the celebrated roué,
Za   swindler, pickpocket, and murderer. Who was
L627   executed at Vienna, Austria, September 17,
854   1853. Comprising details of bold deeds,
          daring adventures, and thrilling scenes in
          the career of a villain. Baltimore, Philadelphia [etc.] A.R. Orton, 1854 [c1853]
          1 p. l., [23]-49, [1] p. front., illus. 22 cm.
          Original wrappers.

NL 0356926   CtY

FILM   The life of General M. D. Stanley, an American
4274   militia general, the celebrated roué, swin-
PR   dler, pickpocket, and murderer, who was ex-
v.2   ecuted at Vienna, Austria, September 17,
reel   1853... Baltimore, A. P. Orton, 1854.
L8   49 p. illus. (Wright American fiction, v.II, 1851-1875, no.1551, Research Publications Microfilm, Reel L-8)

NL 0356927   CU

VOLUME 332

The life of General M. D. Stanley, an American militia general: the celebrated roué, swindler, pickpocket, and murderer. Who was executed at Vienna, Austria, September 17, 1853. Comprising details of bold deeds, daring adventures and thrilling scenes in the career of a villain. Baltimore ₍etc.₎ A. R. Orton, 1855.

1 p. l., 23-50 p. front. (port.) illus. 8°.

1-19599-M 4

NL 0356928   DLC PSt KMK ViU

M-film
810.8
Am35
37-3

The life of General M. D. Stanley, an American militia general... Comprising details of bold deeds, daring adventures and thrilling scenes in the career of a villain. Baltimore ₍etc.₎ A. R. Orton, 1855. 49 p. illus.

Microfilm (positive) Ann Arbor, Mich., University Microfilms, 1967. 3rd title of 7. 35 mm. (American fiction series, reel 37.3)

NL 0356929   KEmT

...LIFE of General Marion; embracing anecdotes illustrative of his character... Philadelphia: Lindsay & Blakiston [1847] ix, 10-208 p. front., plates. 18cm. (The young American's library.)

Added t.-p. illustrated in colors.
Wood engravings by Gilbert and Gihon.

42148B. 1. Marion, Francis, 1732-1795.

NL 0356930   NN LU ViU NcU

LIFE of General Marion. Embracing anecdotes illustrative of his character. Boston, Lee and Shepard, 1868.

18 cm. Ports.
"The young American's library."

NL 0356931   MH

... Life of General Marion: embracing anecdotes illustrative of his character. With illustrations. Boston, Lee and Shepard; New York, Lee, Shepard and Dillingham, 1875.

ix, 10-208 p. front., plates. 19ᶜᵐ. (The young American's library)
Armorial book-plate: Walter Shanly.

1. Marion, Francis, 1732-1795.

NL 0356932   MiU

E207
.M315
1876

Life of General Marion: embracing anecdotes illustrative of his character. Boston, Lee and Shepard, 1876.

208 p. plates, port. 19cm. (The Young American's library ₍of famous generals₎)

1. Marion, Francis, 1732-1795.

NL 0356933   ViU OrU OrP MsU

Life of General Markle. Phila., King & Baird, 1844.
12 p. illus.,port.

Phot.(pos.)

NL 0356934   MiD-B

Life of General Narciso Lopez; together with a detailed history of the attempted revolution in Cuba, from its first invasion at Cardinas ₍!₎, down to the death of Lopez, at Havana. By a flibustiero ₍pseud.₎ New York, De Witt & Davenport ₍1851₎

32 p. 25ᶜᵐ.
Portrait on cover.

1. Lopez, Narciso, 1798 or 9-1851. 2. Cuba—Hist.—Insurrection, 1849-1851. I. A flibustiero, pseud.

15-4525

Library of Congress   F1784.L86L7

NL 0356935   DLC MB CtY LU NcD NN

Life of General Sam Houston ... ₍Washington, Printed by J. T. Powers, 1856?₎

15 p. 24ᶜᵐ.
Caption title.

1. Houston, Samuel, 1793-1863.

11-10274

Library of Congress   F390.H855

NL 0356936   DLC NcD TxU OO MiU TU CU-B NNC NjP

Life of General Sam Houston
    see also   Life of Samuel Houston.

Life of General Scott. ₍New York, C. A. Alvord, printer, 1852₎

32 p. illus. 23½ᶜᵐ.
Caption title.

1. Scott, Winfield, 1786-1866.

10—13951

Library of Congress   E340.S4L7

NL 0356938   DLC ICN CtY Nh CU-B NNC ViU

973.5
Sco8W

Life of General Scott. ₍New York, A. H. Jocelyn, 1852₎
32 p. illus. 25cm.
Caption title.

NL 0356939   IU Mi TU TxU MiU-C ViU IEN

E340
.S4L6

Life of General Scott, to which are added, sketches of the lives of Croghan, Johnson, Dearborn, and Carroll. New York: Nafis & Cornish: St. Louis, Mo., Nafis, Cornish & Co., 1847.
1 p.l., 256p. front., illus. 12 cm.

Added t.-p., with vignette (port.)
Lettered on spine: Illustrated life of Gen. Scott.

1. Scott, Winfield, 1786-1866. 2. Croghan, George, 1791-1849. 3. Johnson, Richard Mentor, 1781-1850. 4. Dearborn, Henry, 1751-1829 5. Carroll, William, 1788-1844.

NL 0356940   NjR MiD-B N ICN InU OFH

Life of Gen. Sir R. Abercromby ... together with an accurate statement of the campaign in Egypt ... By an officer in the army. Ormskirk, J. Fowler, 1806.

101 p. front. (port.) 20½ᶜᵐ. ₍With Lloyd, Frederick. An accurate and impartial life of the late Lord Viscount Nelson. Ormskirk, 1806₎

1. Abercromby, Sir Ralph, 1734-1801.

4—25897

Library of Congress   DA87.1.N4L7

NL 0356941   DLC

Life of Gen. Sir R. Abercromby
    see also   Life of Sir R. Abercromby.

The life of General Sir William Napier ...
    see under   Napier, Sir William Francis Patrick, 1785-1860.

973.63
T219Zc

Life of General Taylor. From the best authorities. New York, Cornish, Lamport & Co., 1851.
256 p. illus. 12 cm.

1. Taylor, Zachary, Pres. U.S., 1784-1850.

NL 0356944   LU

The life of General Taylor, the hero of Okee Chobee, Palo Alto, Resaca de la Palma, Monterey, and Buena Vista. With numerous illustrative anecdotes and embellishments. Philadelphia, Lindsay and Blakiston, 1847.

viii, 9-214 p. front. (port.) plates. 18 x 14ᶜᵐ.
Also published under titles "Pictorial life of General Taylor" and "The people's life of General Zachary Taylor."

1. Taylor, Zachary, pres. U. S., 1784-1850.

13-22548

Library of Congress   E422.L74

NL 0356945   DLC NjP LU PMA NRU

... Life of General Taylor, the hero of Okee Chobee, Palo Alto, Resaca de la Palma, Monterey, and Buena Vista. Containing numerous anecdotes ... Philadelphia, Lindsay & Blakiston ₍1850?₎

viii, 9-227 p. front. (port.) plates. 17½ᶜᵐ. (The young American's library)
Slightly enlarged from an edition which appeared in 1847. Also published under titles "Pictorial life of General Taylor" and "The people's life of General Zachary Taylor".

1. Taylor, Zachary, pres. U. S., 1784-1850.

28-18674

Library of Congress   E422.L768

NL 0356946   DLC OU TxFTC NcD OKentU PPT CLU CtY PU

Life of General Taylor, the hero of Okee Chobee, Palo Alto, Resaca de la Palma, Monterey, and Buena Vista. Containing numerous anecdotes. Boston Lee and Shepard, 1869.

227 p. illus. 19cm. (The Young American's Library)

On cover: Library of famous generals.

1. Taylor, Zachary, pres. U. S., 1784-1850.

NL 0356947   MnU KMK

Life of General Taylor, the hero of Okee Chobee, Palo Alto, Resaca de la Palma, Monterey, and Buena Vista. Containing numerous anecdotes. Boston: Lee and Shepard, 1875. 2 p.l., iii-viii, 9-227 p., 7 pl., 1 port. 12°. (Young American's library.)

1. Taylor, Zachary, president of N. Y. P. L.

MILITARY SERVICE INST. the U. S.
November 15, 1911.

NL 0356948   NN OrP

E422
.L763
1876

Life of General Taylor, the hero of Okee Chobee, Palo Alto, Resaca de la Palma, Monterey, and Buena Vista; containing numerous anecdotes. Boston, Lee and Shepard ₍1876?₎

227 p. illus., port. 19cm. (The Young American's library. Famous generals ₍2₎)

1. Taylor, Zachary, Pres. U. S., 1784-1850.

NL 0356949   ViU

VOLUME 332

The life of General, the Right Honourable Sir
David Baird, bart. ...
    see under   [Hook, Theodore Edward]
1788-1841.

The life of General Tom Thumb.   Troy, N. Y., Published by
Moore & Nims ₁1856?₁   64 p.   1 illus.   56mm.

Sabin 92733.
"Charles Stratton...was born...in January, 1832, and is now twenty-four years old."
— *p. 6-7.*
Pages ₁22₁-64 comprise nursery rhymes and moral tales.

1. Stratton, Charles Sherwood,   1838-1883.

NL 0356951   NN MH NBuG NcD CtY

The life of General W. A. Bowles, a native of America—born of English parents, in Frederic County, Maryland, in the year 1764 ... London—printed: New-York—
Reprinted by Robert Wilson, no. 147 Pearl-street. 1803.

31 p. 22½ᶜᵐ.

₁Duane pamphlets, v. 1, no. 6₁
"From 'Public characters, for 1802.'"

1. Bowles, William Augustus, 1764-1805. 2. Creek Indians. 3. Cherokee Indians.
                             18-18229

Library of Congress   AC901.D8 vol.1

NL 0356952   DLC MWA ViU NcD PSt CaBVaU TxU OU

Life of General Warren; to which are added sketches of
the lives of DeKalb, Wayne and Morgan. New York,
Nafis & Cornish; St. Louis, Mo., Nafis, Cornish & co.,
1847.

1 p. l., iv, ₁5₁-256 p. incl. 8 pl. col. front. 12ᶜᵐ.
Added t.-p., illustrated in colors.

1. Warren, Joseph, 1741-1775. 2. Kalb, Jean, baron de, originally Johann Kalb, 1721-1780. 3. Wayne, Anthony, 1745-1796. 4. Morgan, Daniel, 1736?-1802.   I. Nafis & Cornish, New York, pub.
                             17-15501

Library of Congress   E263.M4W26

NL 0356953   DLC Vi CtY OO MiU

Life of General Warren; to which are added sketches of the lives of
De Kalb, Wayne and Morgan.   New York: Cornish, Lamport
& co., 1851.   iv, 6-256 p.   front., 12 pl.   11cm.

Added t.-p., with title vignette (port. of Warren.)

30599B. 1. Warren, Joseph, 1741-   1775. 2. Kalb, Jean, baron de,
originally Johann Kalb, 1721-1780.   3. Wayne, Anthony, 1745-1796.
4. Morgan, Daniel, 1736?-1802.
N. Y. P. L.   March 20, 1940

NL 0356954   NN MH

The life of Gen. Washington, commander in chief
of the American army during the late war,
and present president of the United States
    see under   [Morse, Jedediah] 1761-1826.

The life of General Washington, commander in chief of the
American forces. London, Printed for T. Allman, 1840.
. x, 440 p. front. 12½ᶜᵐ.
Title vignette.

1. Washington, George, pres. U. S., 1732-1799.
                                 A 32-1127
Title from Grosvenor   Libr. E312.L72 Printed by L. C.

NL 0356956   NBuG NN CSmH MB InU

E312
.L72
1843

The life of General Washington, Commander in
Chief of the American forces. London,
Printed for T. Allman, 1843.
x, 440 p. front. 13cm.
Title vignette.

1. Washington, George, pres. U. S., 1732-1799.

NL 0356957   ViU MB

The life of George Washington, late president and
commander in chief of the armies of the
United States of America
    see under   Corry, John, fl. 1825.

Life of Gen. George Washington, late president
of the United States of America, and commander
in chief of their armies, during the revolutionary
war
    see under   [Corry, John] fl. 1825.

... Life of General Winfield Scott, commander-in-chief
of the United States army ... New York, A. S. Barnes
& co.; Boston, Redding & co.; ₁etc., etc.₁ 1852.

191, ₁1₁ p. front. (port.) illus. (incl. maps, plan) 19ᶜᵐ.
At head of title: A. S. Barnes & co.'s pamphlet edition. Incidents taken
from Mansfield's Life of General Scott.

1. Scott, Winfield, 1786-1866.   I. Mansfield, Edward Deering, 1801-
1880.
                                  13-19340
Library of Congress   E403.1.S4L75

NL 0356960   DLC OkU CtY

Beinecke
Library
Zc50
851 L1

Life of General Worth; to which is added A
sketch of the life of Brigadier-General
Wool. New York, Cornish, Lamport & Co.,
1851.
3 p.l., [iii]-iv, [5]-256 p. incl. front.,
plates. 12 cm.
Added illus. t.-p.

1. Worth, William Jenkins, 1794-1849.
2. Wool, John Ellis, 1784-1869.

NL 0356961   CtY OKentU

Life of General Worth; to which is added
a sketch of the life of Brigadier-general Wool.
New York, Sheldon, Lamport & Blakeman, 1855.
1 p.l., iv, ₁5₁-256 p. front., plates 13cm.

Title-page duplicated.
Imperfect: frontispiece mutilated.

NL 0356962   NcD

The life of Gen. Zachary Taylor, and a history of the
war in Mexico, giving an account of the battles of Palo
Alto, Resaca de la Palma, Monterey, and Buena Vista,
with sketches of the lives of Ringgold, May, Yell, M'Kee,
Hardin, Henry Clay, jr., and others ... New York, W. H.
Graham, 1847.

64 p. incl. front. (port.) illus. 23½ᶜᵐ.

1. Taylor, Zachary, pres. U. S., 1784-1850. 2. U. S.—Hist.—War with
Mexico, 1845-1848—Campaigns and battles.
                                13-25499
Library of Congress   E422.L76

NL 0356963   DLC CU-B ICN MiU-C

E
422-
.L72
1848

The life of General Zachary Taylor, embracing
his military and civil career: including the
Mexican battles of Palo Alto, Resaca de la Palma,
Monterey, and Buena Vista, with his political
letters in reference to the presidency. To
which is added, a biographical sketch of Hon.
Millard Fillmore ... New York, Dewitt & Davenport, 1848.
64 p. incl. front. (port.) illus. 23ᶜᵐ.
Cover-title: The life of Gen. Zachary Taylor, and a
history of the war in Mexico ... with sketches of the
lives of Ringgold, May, Yell ... and others ... Buffalo,
G. H. Derby & co., 1848.
1. Taylor, Zachary,   pres. U. S., 1784-1850. 2. U. S.
—Hist.—War with   Mexico, 1845-1848—Campaigns
and battles.

NL 0356964   MiU

The life of George Barrington ... with the whole
of his celebrated speeches, taken from the
records of King's Bench, Old Bailey ...
[London, 1790]
56 p.   18 cm.   (Bd. in. Gay, John. The
beggar's opera. 1782.)

NL 0356965   RPB

The life of George Castriot, king of Epirus and Albania, commonly
called Scanderbeg; on which is founded the tragedy of the Christian hero. Being a most entertaining true history.   Edinburgh:
Printed by W. Ruddiman, jun., and Co., 1753.   33 p.   20cm.

710755A. 1. Castriota, Giorgio, called   Scanderbeg, 1403-1467.
N. Y. P. L.   September 24, 1934

NL 0356966   NN

Life of George Cheyne, M. D.
    see under   [Greenhill, William
Alexander] 1814-1894.

The life of George Frederic Cooke, esq. (the legitimate successor to Garrick, Macklin, and Henderson) late of the Theatre-
Royal, Covent-Garden; and of New York, Philadelphia, &c. Containing an account of the whole of his theatrical career from his
first treading the boards, down to his final dramatic exit, at Rhode
Island, in America ... Embellished with a   print, engraved by
Mr. G. Cruickshank   London: P. Egan ₁181-?₁   34 p.
col'd front.   22cm.

With bookplate of Albert M. Cohn.

224146B. 1. Cooke, George Frederick,   1756-1812.
N. Y. P. L.   May 6, 1943

NL 0356968   NN CSmH MB MH

Life of George Frederic Cooke; the characters he
performed.   London, 1813.
34 p.   8'.

NL 0356969   MB

The LIFE of George Herbert.   London, James
Burns, 1844.

24°.   pp. 30.   Front.

NL 0356970   MH

Life of George Herbert of Bemerton... / Pub.
under the direction of the Tract committee.
Lond., Soc. for promoting Christian knowledge,
1893.
320 p. port.

NL 0356971   MiD OrP IEG

VOLUME 332

The life of George Robert Fitzgerald ...
including several anecdotes of his family ...
to which is added a number of facts relative
to his tiral and execution ... London,
Printed for J. Ridgway, 1786.
194, iv p. front. (port.) 19cm.

1. Fitzgerald, George Robert, 1748?-
1786.

NL 0356972   FU MH-L

The life of George Meredith, by Robert
Esmonde Sencourt

see under

Sencourt, Robert, 1890-

The life of George S. Gordon, 1881-1942, by M. C. G.
see under   [Gordon, Mary C   (Biggar)]

Life of George Stephenson, founder of the
railway system ...
see under   Cleveland educational bureau.

British
Tracts   The life of George Villiers, Duke of Buckingham,
1740   (prime minister to King James and King Charles
162   the First) who was stabb'd by Felton, August
            23, 1628 ... London, Printed for T.Cooper,
            1740.
            viii, 3-112 p., incl.front.(port.) 18 cm.
            First published in 1734 with title: The fate
            of favourites.

            1. Buckingham, George Villiers, 1st duke of,
            1592-1628. I. The fate of favourites.

NL 0356975   CtY NN

... Life of George Washington, by Washington
Irving ... New York and London, G. P.
Putnam's sons [c1857]
see under   Irving, Washington, 1783-
1859.

The life of George Washington, commander in
chief of the armies, and late president of
the United States of America
see under   Corry, John, fl. 1825.

Life of George Washington: embracing anecdotes
illustrative of his character ...
see under   [Weld, Horatio Hastings]
1811-1888.

The life of George Washington, first president,
and commander in chief of the armies of the
United States of America
see under   Corry, John, fl. 1825.

Life of George Washington, first president of
the United States...
see under   [Condie, Thomas] 1775?-1814.

Life of George Washington. From the best
authorities. New York, Nafis & Cornish;
St. Louis, Mo., Nafis, Cornish & Co. [Reed
& Cunningham, Printers, New York] 1847.
iv, (1), 6-256 p. incl. plates, col. front.
and added t.-p. (col.) Bound in the original
brown cloth, gilt.
The Lewisson collection, September 1922.

NL 0356981   CSmH ODW OClWHi

The life of George Washington. Illustrated by tales,
sketches and anecdotes. Adapted to the use of schools ...
New York, Collins and Hannay [c1832]
vi, [7]-174 p. incl. front., illus. 15cm. (Half-title: ... American school
biographies ...)
Title vignette.
Copyright by S. G. Goodrich; authorship disclaimed by him in his
"Recollections."

1. Washington, George, pres. U. S., 1732-1799.

Library of Congress   E312.L72   15-2691

NL 0356982   DLC OClWHi PLF MSaE CSmH

E 312
L53   The LIFE of George Washington; illustrated
1832a   by tales, sketches and anecdotes. Adapt-
          ed to the use of schools. New York,
          Collins and Hannay, c1832.
          174 p. illus.
          Photocopy. Cleveland, Micro Photo
          [196-]

          1. Washington, George, pres. U. S.,
          1732-1799.

NL 0356983   CaBVaU

The Life of George Washington. Illustrated by
Tales, Sketches and Anecdotes. Adapted to the use
of schools. [Woodcut.] With Engravings. Boston.
Russell, Shattuck & Co. 1836.
16mo, pp. 174, including frontispiece and illustrations.

NL 0356984   NN CSmH PHi PU

The life of George Washington. Illustrated by tales,
sketches and anecdotes. Adapted to the use of schools ...
Philadelphia, Desilver, Thomas & co., 1837.
vi, [7]-174 p. incl. front., illus. 17cm.
Title vignette.
1st edition, New York, 1832.
Copyright by S. G. Goodrich; authorship disclaimed by him in his
"Recollections."

1. Washington, George, pres. U. S., 1732-1799.

Library of Congress   E312.L73   15-2690

NL 0356985   DLC KyHi NcD OClWHi PHi MWA MB CSmH

The life of George Washington, illustrated
by tales, sketches and anecdotes. Adapted to
the use of schools. Philadelphia, Thomas,
Cowperthwait & co., 1838.

Binder's title: Parley's Washington.
Copyright by S.G.Goodrich; authorship
disclaimed by him in his "Recollections."

NL 0356986   MH NNC CSmH OCl

W.30
G6   The life of George Washington. Illus. by
1840A   tales, sketches and anecdotes. Adapted to the
           use of schools. Philadelphia, Thomas, Cowper-
           thwait & Co., 1840.
           174 p. front., illus. 17cm.

           1. Washington, George, Pres. U. S.—Biog.

NL 0356987   MB N CSmH PHi MiU-C MH

The life of George Washington. Illustrated by tales,
sketches and anecdotes. Adapted to the use of schools ...
Philadelphia, Thomas, Cowperthwait & co., 1844.
vi, [7]-174 p. incl. front., illus. 16cm.
Title vignette.
1st edition, New York, 1832.
Copyright by S. G. Goodrich; authorship disclaimed by him in his
"Recollections."

1. Washington, George, pres. U. S., 1732-1799.

Library of Congress   E312.L737   15-2689

NL 0356988   DLC MWA CSmH

The life of George Washington. Illustrated by tales,
sketches and anecdotes. Adapted to the use of schools ...
Philadelphia, Thomas, Cowperthwait & co., 1848 [c1836]
vi, [7]-174 p. incl. front., illus. 16cm.
Title vignette.
1st edition, New York, 1832.
Copyright by S. G. Goodrich; authorship disclaimed by him in his
"Recollections."

NL 0356989   MeB PU MBAt

The life of George Washington. Illustrated by tales,
sketches and anecdotes. Adapted to the use of schools ...
Philadelphia, Thomas, Cowperthwait & co., 1851.
vi, [7]-174 p. incl. front., illus. pl., port. 17cm. [With The life of
Christopher Columbus. Philadelphia, 1851]
Title vignette.
Copyright by S. G. Goodrich; authorship disclaimed by him in his
"Recollections".

1. Washington, George, pres. U. S., 1732-1799.

Library of Congress   E111.L74   2—8083
                           [27c1]

NL 0356990   DLC

The life of George Washington. Illustrated by
tales, sketches and anecdotes. Adapted to the
use of schools ...   Philadelphia, C. Desilver,
1857.
vi, [7]-174 p. incl. front., illus. plates,
port. 19 cm. [With The life of Christopher
Columbus. Philadelphia, 1857]
Title vignette.
Copyright by S.G. Goodrich; authorship
disclaimed by him in his "Recollections."

NL 0356991   CtY

The Life of George Washington. Illustrated by tales,
sketches and anecdotes. Adapted to the use of schools
... Philadelphia, C. Desilver, 1860.
vi, [7]-174 p. incl. front., illus. 2 pl., port. 19½cm. [With The life of
Christopher Columbus. Philadelphia, 1860]
Title vignette.
Copyright by S. G. Goodrich; authorship disclaimed by him in his "Rec-
ollections."

1. Washington, George, pres. U. S., 1732-1799.

                                              17-8403
Library of Congress   E111.L76

NL 0356992   DLC MnU

---

*
E111
.L74   The life of George Washington. Illustrated
1865   by tales, sketches and anecdotes. Adapted
           to the use of schools, with engravings.
           Philadelphia: Charles Desilver, 1865.
           174 p. illus., port. 20cm. [With The life of
           Christopher Columbus ... Philadelphia, 1865]

           1. Washington, George, Pres. U. S., 1732-1799.

NL 0356993   ViU PHi

VOLUME 332

G 3701
83
L54
1807

The LIFE of George Washington. Maps and subscribers' names. Philadelphia, C.P. Wayne,
1807.
   1 v. of maps. 30 cm.
   Library's copy consists of double-leafed
maps numbered 1,3,5-7,9-10.

   1. Northeastern States - Maps. I. Washington, George, Pres. U.S., 1732-1799.

NL 0356994   CaBVaU ViU RPB NjR DSI

Life of George Wishart, (of Pitarrow)
the martyr
     see under   [Lawson, John Parker] d. 1852.

The life of Gerald Griffin...
     see under   [Griffin, Daniel]

Life of Gerard Hallock
     see under   [Hallock, William H   ]

Life of Gideon.
   N. Y. Carlton & Porter. 1856. 109 pp. Pls. 24ᵖ.

NL 0356998   MB

The life of God in the soul of man; or, The nature
and excellency of the Christian religion
     see under   [Scougal, Henry] 1650-1678.

E182
.G69

The life of Gould.

Gould, Roland Freeman, *b.* 1817.
   The life of Gould, an ex-man-of-war's-man, with incidents
on sea and shore, including the three-year's [sic] cruise on the
line of battle ship Ohio, on the Mediterranean station, under
the veteran Commodore Hull. Claremont, N. H., Printed by
the Claremont Manufacturing Co., 1867.

... The life of Gov. Louis Kossuth, with his public
speeches in the United States, and a brief history of the
Hungarian war of independence. Illustrated by handsome engravings. By an officer of the Hungarian army.
[Illustrated ed.] New York, W. Lord, stereotyper, 1852.
   184 p. incl. 3 pl., port. 22ᶜᵐ.

   Subject entries: 1. Kossuth, Lajos, 1802-1894. 2. Hungary—Hist.—Uprising of 1848-1849.
                                                    3-12897
   Library of Congress, no.   DB937.K86.

NL 0357001   DLC MdBP

Life of Greece; a pictorial publication.
   Oct./Nov.-Dec. 1945/Jan., Sept., Nov./Dec. 1946,
   July/Aug., Nov./Dec. 1947)   Boston, 1945-47.
   v.   illus.   28-30cm.

   Bimonthly.
   Oct./Nov.-Dec. 1945/Jan. 1946 also called v. 1¹⁻².
   Published by Life of Greece guild.

   1. Greece, Modern—Per.   and soc. publ.

NL 0357002   NN

The life of Gregory Lopez. 1841
     see under   Losa, Francisco de, 1536-1624.

The life of Grish Chunder Ghose, the founder and
first editor of the Hindoo patriot and The
Bengalee
     see under   Ghosh, Manmathanath.

Case
E
5
.C 60752

LIFE of Grover Cleveland. A record of incom-
petency, demagoguery and mediocrity. Always
against the people   Phila.,Pa.,J.D.Avil & co.
[1884]
   32p. 23cm.

   At head of title: Campaign of 1884.

NL 0357005   ICN OOxM MH

The life of Gustav Gottheil
     see under   [Gottheil, Richard James
Horatio] 1862-1936.

**EO65
A100
B688t

The life of H. H. With the relation at large
of what passed betwixt him and the taylors wife
in Black-friars, according to the original.
As likewise particular remarks of his behaviour
ever since. Which proves (tho times change) him
to be the same H. H. stil.
London, Printed for T.S. in the year 1688.

   9p.l.,54p. 15cm.
   "To the reader" signed: William Kiffen.
   "A premonition to the reader from the hand of
a friend" dated and signed: July 15, 1672.
Daniel King.

   Dedicatory epistle signed and dated: Henry
Hills ... Jan. 28. 1650[1651].
   No.3 in a volume labeled: Tracts.

NL 0357008   MH

The life of Hannah More, with selections from her
correspondence
     see under   Roberts, William, 1767-1849.

The Life of Harriet Stuart...
     see under   [Lennox, Charlotte (Ramsay)]
1720-1804.

The life of Haydn, in a series of letters written
at Vienna
     see under   [Beyle, Marie Henri] 1783-
1842.

The life of Helen Lucretia Cornaro Piscopia
     see under   Deza, Massimilliano, and others.

The life of Henri Masers de Latude, who was imprisoned thirty-five years. To which is added some account of the Bastille.

   The Pamphleteer. London, 1814. 22½ᶜᵐ. v. 3, p. [195]-216.

   1. Latude, Jean Henri Masers de, 1725-1805. 2. Bastille, Paris.

                                              CA 5—690 Unrev'd
   Library of Congress   AP4.P2 vol.3

NL 0357013   DLC

BX
7899
.A5
L4
L71
B5

The life of Henriette d'Osseville (in religion,
Mother Ste. Marie), foundress of the Institute of the Faithful Virgin. Arranged
and edited by John George MacLeod. London,
Burns and Oates, 1878.
   xvi, 229 p. 20cm. (Quarterly series, v.26)

   1. Le Forestier d'Osseville, Henriette,
1803-1858. 2. Daughters of the Faithful Virgin.
I. MacLeod, John George, ed. II. Series.

NL 0357014   DCU

The life of Henrietta Kerr, religious of the
Sacred Heart. Roehampton, 1886.
   384 p.
   Ed. by John Morris.

NL 0357015   MiD

The life of Henrietta Kerr
     see also   The life of Mother Henrietta Kerr

Life of Henriette Sontag, countess de Rossi. With interesting sketches by Scudo, Hector Berlioz, Louis Boer-
ne, Adolphe Adam, Marie Aycard, Julie de Margueritte,
Prince Puckler-Muskau, and Theophile Gautier. New
York, Stringer & Townsend, 1852.
   63, [1] p. front. (port.) 22½ᶜᵐ.

   1. Sontag, Henriette, comtesse Rossi, 1806-1854.

                                              10-28091
NL 0357017   DLC

The life of Henry Chichelé, archbishop of
Canterbury, founder of All Souls college,
in the University of Oxford
     see under   [Spencer, Oliph Leigh]

... Life of Henry Clay. [Washington, Kendall's expositor, 1844?]
   [81]-88 p. 24½ᶜᵐ. (<Tract no. 18>)

   1. Clay, Henry, 1777-1852. 2. Campaign literature, 1844—Democratic.
   I. Kendall's expositor, Washington, D. C.

                                              7-23569
   Library of Congress   E340.C6L6

NL 0357019   DLC

... Life of Henry Clay, the statesman and the
patriot ...
     see under   [Frost, John] 1800-1859.

VOLUME 332

The life of ... Henry Compton, late lord bishop
of London. London, A. Baldwin [1715?]
2 p.l., 84 p. 12°.
In: A p.v. 25.

NL 0357021 NN ICN

The life of Henry Longden, Minister of the Gospel
see under Longden, Henry, 1754-1812.

979.461
2c7t
Life of Henry P. Coon. ¿San Francisco?
168-?¿
14 p. 24 cm.

Caption title.

1. Coon, Henry Perrin, 1822-1884.

NL 0357023 N

... Life of Henry Phillips, sentenced to be executed at
Boston, March 13th, 1817, for the murder of Gaspard
Denegri. ¿Boston, Russell, Cutler & co., 1817¿
8 p. 23½°°.
Caption title.
"Russell, Cutler & co.'s publication. Annexed to their report of the
trial."

1. Phillips, Henry, 1791-1817. 2. Denegri, Gaspard, d. 1816.

CA 19-154 Unrev'd

Library of Congress HV6248.P5A3

NL 0357024 DLC NNCoCi

The life of Henry St. John, lord viscount
Bolingbroke
see under [Goldsmith, Oliver] 1728-1774.

... The life of Henry the Fifth
see under [Shakespeare, William]

The life of Henry the Second, King of England. Shew-
ing what troubles befel in his reign, concerning the wars be-
tween him and his subjects ... necessary to be observed in
these dangerous and distracted times of ours. London,
H. B., 1642.
(*In* The Harleian miscellany. London, 1808-13. 30 cm. v. 5
(1810) p. 502-504)
In editions of the Harleian miscellany in the Library of Congress:
London, 1744-46. 26 cm. v. 5 (1745) p. 474-477.
London, 1808-11. 22 cm. v. 5 (1810) p. 232-235.
1. Gt. Brit.—Hist.—Henry II, 1154-1189.
DA300.H28 vol. 5 A 64-888
Newberry Library
for Library of Congress ¿2¿†

NL 0357027 ICN DLC MnU NIC CtY

Life of Henry Wadsworth Longfellow. ¿Park
Place, N. Y., Knapp, Lithographers & Printers,
1888?¿
15p. 7cm.

"Packed in Duke's cigarettes."

1. Longfellow, Henry Wadsworth, 1807-1882.

NL 0357028 FMU

The life of Henry Ward Beecher
see under [Griswold, W C]

Life of Henry Welby, Esq.: who lived at his house
in Grub street, forty-foure yeares and, in that
space, was never seen by any. Aged 84 yeares.
London, 1637.

NL 0357030 PPL

DA497
.M4L7 The life of Her Grace, Sarah, late duchess dowager of
Marlborough. To which are annex'd, remarks on Her
Grace's last will. London, Printed for M. Cooper, 1745.
¿1¿, 102, 94 p. 20°°.
With this are bound 10 pamphlets on various subjects.
"A true copy of the last will and testament of Her Grace, Sarah, late duchess
dowager of Marlborough": 94 p. at end.

1. Marlborough, Sarah (Jennings) Churchill, duchess of, 1660-1744.

NL 0357031 ICU NSchU NjP

The life of Her late Majesty Queen Anne, as well before her accession to the throne as after. Together with
all the transactions of her reign ... wherein her conduct
during the last four years of her reign is not only vindicated, but shewn to be most beneficial and glorious ...
London, Printed for C. Rivington, 1721.
2 v. 20°°.
Subject entries: 1. Anne, queen of Great Britain, 1664-1714. 2. Gt.
Brit.—Hist.—Anne, 1702-1714. 3-26005

Library of Congress, no. DA495.L72.

NL 0357032 DLC NcU OC IU CtY CLU-C InU OrU

The life of Her majesty the Queen. [London, 1881]
p. 769-784. port. [Penny books for the
people] 8°.
By C. E. G.

NL 0357033 MB

British
Tracts
1678
L626
The Life of Herod the Great. Wherein his
inhumane cruelties are briefly but
accurately related. With an account of
his fatal and miserable end. ... London, Printed for Enoch Wyer, at the White
Hart in St.Pauls Church-Yard, 1678.
2 p.l., 36 p. 21 cm.

Wing: L-2031.

1. Herod I, the Great, king of Judea, d.
B.C.4.

NL 0357034 CtY CSmH

The life of Herr Gutenberg, dedicated to members of the
craft. ¿Buffalo, 1940¿
6 numb. l., 2 l. 20½°°.
Caption title.
Cover-title: Anniversary, five hundred years of printing, 1440-1940.
"Of this keepsake ... 110 copies have been privately printed, for dis-
tribution among my friends and members of the Buffalo club of printing
house craftsmen ... Done for the love of the craft by Emil Georg
Sahlin."—Leaf at end.
Printed on one side of leaf on opposite pages.

1. Gutenberg, Johann, 1397?-1468. I. Buffalo club of printing house
craftsmen.
40-82906
Library of Congress Z126.L71
¿2¿ 926.55

NL 0357035 DLC NN

The life of his grace, James, late duke of Ormond. Containing, I. An impartial account of his family ... II.
A just prospect of his Grace's conduct in all his employments ... III. An authentic account of his exile ...
London, Printed for T. Thompson, 1748.
172 p. 18°°.
Book-plate: Thomas Pitt.

1. Ormonde, James Butler, 2d duke of, 1665-1745.

NL 0357036 MiU

The life of His Grace, Philip, late
Duke of Wharton. [n.p.,n.d.]
35p. 20cm. [With Memoirs of the
life and character of Mr. John
Locke. London, 1742]

1. Wharton, Philip Wharton, Duke of,
1698-1731

NL 0357037 IEN

The life of His Grace the Duke of Wellington; containing details of the numerous and important
services in which he has been engaged in various
parts of the world. Together with a copious
account of the memorable battle of Waterloo.
London, T. Allman, 1846.
xi, [1], 436 p. front. (port.), plates.
13 cm.
Added engr. t.-p.

NL 0357038 CU

Life, The, of His Grace the Duke of Wellington ; containing details of
the numerous and important services in which he has been engaged in various parts of the world. Together with a copious account of the memorable Battle of Waterloo.
— London. Allman. 1848. x, 436 pp. Plates. 12½ cm., in 8s.

K9606 — Wellesley, Arthur, 1st Duk Wellington, 1769-1852. — Waterloo,
Battle of, 1815.

NL 0357039 MB

Life of His Holiness Pope Pius x, together with a sketch
of the life of his venerable predecessor, His Holiness Pope
Leo XIII, also a history of the conclave, giving a full account
of the rites and ceremonies connected with the election of a
successor to the see of St. Peter. With a preface by His
Eminence James, cardinal Gibbons ... New York, Cincinnati
¿etc.¿ Benziger brothers, 1904.
401 p. incl. front. (port.) illus. 21°°.
"The life of Pius x has been largely taken from the sketch by Rev.
Dr. Joseph Schmidlin ... and also from the more comprehensive life,
by Monsignor Anton de Waal."
1. Pius x, pope, 1835-1914. 2. Leo XIII, pope, 1810-1903. I. Schmidlin, Joseph, 1876- II. Waal, Anton de, 1836-1917.
4—14161
Library of Congress BX1375.L5

PPLas MB DCU PLatS MsU OrStbM
NL 0357040 DLC OCX MiDP OkU InStme ICU OClND PV

943.6
K1474bl
The LIFE of His Serene Highness,
Charles, prince of Lorrain... including,
the history of the illustrious house of
Lorrain... likewise, an authentic relation of the affairs of Germany, Prussia,
France, Spain, England, Holland, &c...
with a complete narrative of all the
battles, sieges, &c. from the commencement of the war to this time... London, Printed for M. Cooper ¿etc.¿ 1746.
vi, 360, ¿8¿ p. port. 17cm.
1. Karl Alexander, prince of Lorraine,
1712-1780. 2. Europe MnU 48-456
History, 18th century. 3. Austrian
succession, War of, 1740-1748.

NL 0357041 MnU PBm NIC

VOLUME 332

LIFE of Hon. George Canning, n.p., [1827?]

pp. 3-22.
The title-page is wanting.

NL 0357042   MH

973.8
L62

Life of Hon. Grover Cleveland ... with a
sketch of the life and public services of
Hon. Adlai E. Stevenson, together with the
"Gladstone-Blaine controversy," by Hon.
Roger Q. Mills; Free trade, by the Rt. Hon.
W. E. Gladstone, and Protection, by Hon.
James G. Blaine. To which is appended a
full account of the National Democratic
convention, at Chicago, June 21-23, 1892,
with Democratic platform adopted ... also
Reciprocity; The silver question; Behring

Sea and Chilian questions. [Official ed.]
Political pub. co. [c1892]
1 v. (various pagings) pl., ports.

NL 0357044   NNC ViU MiU

Life of Hon. James Black of Lancaster, Pa. [Lancaster, Pa.,
1895?] 5 l. 4°.

Type-written.

1. Black, James, 1823-93.
N. Y. P. L.   April 26, 1917.

NL 0357045   NN

F
867
B41L6

Life of Horace Bell. [n.p., after 1886]
18 p.

Caption title.

1. Bell, Horace, 1830-1918.

NL 0357046   CLU CSmH

Life of Horace Greeley. Including all the
"Recollections," corrections, deflections,
connections, reflections, objections, and
elections. Together with what he knows about
farming. From verdant infancy to a green old
age. By a professional biographer. [1872]
30 p. illus. 25cm.

Copy imperfect: pages lacking at end.

1. Greeley, Horace. 1811-1872.

NL 0357047   NNC MiD-B MWA

Life of Horace Mann, by his wife
    see under   [Mann, Mrs. Mary Tyler
(Peabody)] 1806-1887.

The life of Horace, with Dr. Bentley's preface,
Latin and English ...
    see under   [Suetonius Tranquillus, C.]

Life of Horatio, Lord Nelson...pub. under
direction of the committee of General literature
and education, appointed by the Society for
promoting Christian knowledge. Lond., Soc. for
promoting Christian knowledge, 1847.
182 p. illus.

NL 0357050   MiD

The life of Horatio Lord Viscount Nelson.
[London, Wetton & Jarvis, etc., 182- ?]

Added title-page: Select biography; a collection of lives of eminent men, who have been an
honor to their country. By various distinguished
writers.
Series title also at head of title-page.

NL 0357051   MH

Life, The, of ... Horatio ... Nelson ... comprehending authentic
and brief details of his glorious achievements under the British
flag; with an appendix, containing a short account of some of the
principal officers who fought under him; with a particular account
of his funeral ceremony.   Edinburgh: Denham & Dick, 1806.
2 p.l., [iii]-iv, (1)10-86 p., 1 port.   12°.

1. Nelson (1. viscount), Horatio   Nelson.
N. Y. P. L.   August 25, 1911.

NL 0357052   NN

Life of Hugh Macleod, assynt, embracing a report of his trial at
the Circuit Court, Inverness, on 23rd Sept., 1831, for the murder of
Murdoch Grant, pedlar, with evidence, including that of Kenneth
Fraser, "the dreamer," and an account of the execution.   Inverness: J. Noble, 1889.   49 p.   3. ed.   8°.

1. Murder trials—Gt. Br.—Scot-   land—Inverness, 1831. 2. Macleod,
Hugh, 1809-1831.   Hugh, 1809-1831.
N. Y. P. L.   June 29, 1925

NL 0357053   NN MH

The life of Hugh Price Hughes, by his daughter ...
    see under   [Hughes, Dorothea Price]

The life of ... Humphrey Prideaux ...
    see   The life of the Rev. Humphrey
Prideaux.

Life of Isaac Mason as a slave
    see under   [Mason, Isaac] 1822-

The life of Izaak Walton
    see under   [Zouch, Thomas] 1737-1815.

1886

Life of J. Marion Sims, M.D. [anon.]   Louisville,
Med. Jour., 1873.
p. 92-95.   8°.   [In Richmond & Louisville
Med. Journal, Jan. 1873]

NL 0357058   DLC

Life of J. Théophane Vénard, martyr in Tonquin;
or, what love can do
    see under   Venard, Jean Théophane, 1829-

The life of Jack Rann, otherwise Sixteen-String Jack, the noted
highwayman; who was executed at Tyburn, November 30, 1774.
London: Printed by and for Hodgson and co. [182-?]   24 p.
col'd front.   19½cm.

162664B. 1. Robbers and robberies   —Gt. Br. 2. Rann, John, d. 1774?
N. Y. P. L.   March 16, 1942

NL 0357060   NN CLU

Collection
KL61
.T7

The life of Jack Sheppard; giving a full
account of his early life, the various
robberies he committed; his capture ...
executed at Tyburn on Nov. 16th, 1724 ...
Illustrated with 10 views of the interior
of Newgate gaol ...   Leeds, J. Johnson;
Manchester, John Heywood, [18-]
18 [12] p.   illus.   16 1/2 cm.

Bound with: [Trials connected with
framebreaking. [Nottingham, 1817?]

1. Sheppard, John, 1702-1724.

NL 0357061   NcU

Life of Jack Sheppard, the notorious house and
gaol breaker.   24p.   Newcastle-on-Tyne, Bowman
[n.d.]

A chap-book.
Bound with this are 22 other chap-books.

NL 0357062   OCl

... The life of Jack Sheppard, a notorious housebreaker and footpad; giving a full account of his
various robberies ... Hung at Tyburn, and buried
in St. Martin's church-yard. To which is added
his own account of his surprising escapes, &c. as
he left in manuscript for publication ...
London: J. Bysh. [ca.1820].
24p. fold.col.front.   18½cm.
Title within border; at head of title: Bysh's
edition.
No.7 in a three-quarter red mor. vol. labelled:
Pamphlets.

NL 0357063   PPRF MH MnU

The life of Jack Sprat ...
    see under   Jack Sprat.

The life of Jacob, and his son Joseph. Written for the
American Sunday-school union, and revised by the Committee
of publication. Philadelphia, American Sunday-school union
[c1836]
191 p. incl. illus. (incl. maps)   front. 15cm.

1. Jacob, the patriarch. 2. Joseph, the patriarch.   I. American
Sunday-school union.

                                    31-25340

Library of Congress   BS580.J3L5   221.92

NL 0357065   DLC

---

*
BS580
.J3L5
1872

The life of Jacob, and his son Joseph.   Written for the American Sunday-School Union, and
revised by the Committee of Publication.
Philadelphia, American Sunday-School Union,
1872.
191 p.   illus. (incl. maps)   front.   16cm.

1. Jacob, the Patriarch. 2. Joseph, the
Patriarch.   I. American Sunday-School Union.

NL 0357066   ViU

[The life of Jacob Behmen
    see under   [Hotham, Durant] 1617?-1691.

VOLUME 332

The life of James, duke of Ormond; containing an account of the most remarkable affairs of his time, and particularly of Ireland under his government
see under   [Carte, Thomas] 1686-1754.

The **life** of James Allan, the celebrated Northumberland piper, and other branches of his extraordinary family. Containing a description of their singular mode of living and a faithful detail of his astonishing adventures and wonderful feats in England, Scotland, Ireland, France, India, Persia, Egypt, and other countries; embracing also a large number of most surprising and interesting anecdotes. Collected from sources of genuine authority. A new edition, improved. Blyth [Northumberland, Eng.] W. Guthrie, 1818. 384 p. front. (port.) 21cm.

42350B. 1. Allan, James, 1734?-1810.   July 19, 1940
N. Y. P. L.

NL 0357069   NN CtY NcD OC1

The life of James Bonnell
see under   [Hamilton, William] d. 1729.

E437
.L723   [Life of James Buchanan].
[n.p.] n.d.]

NL 0357071   DLC

The life of James Fitz-James, duke
of Berwick... London, 1738.

see under

[La Pause, Guillaume Plantavit de, abbé de
Margon] 1685- (ca.) -1760.

The life of James Gates Percival. [Review] from
the Saturday Review.
From- Living Age, Dec. 29, 1866. 22 cm.
p. 811-813.

NL 0357073   RPB

The LIFE of James Hervey. Rector of Weston-
Favell, Northamponshire. Portsmouth, N.H.
1764.

pp. 30.

NL 0357074   MH MWA NNUT

Rare
DA   The life of James, late Duke of Ormonde.
462   Containing: I. An historical and genealogical
073   account of His Grace's family. II. An impartial
L72   view of his conduct in his civil and military
        employments, with the history of his time, and an
        inquiry into the principles and measures of
        those parties, which he either supported or
        opposed. III. A succinct account of the most
        remarkable events that happen'd to him during
        upwards of thirty   years exile, from authen-
        tic materials.   London, Printed for M.

Cooper, 1747.
544 p. 20cm.

1. Ormonde, James Butler, 2d duke of, 1665-
1745.

TxU
NL 0357076   NIC PU NRU FU NSchU ViU CoU InU ICU ICN

Life of James Lawrence, esq. late a captain in the United States navy. To which is added, a collection of interesting papers, relating to the capture of the U. States frigate Chesapeake, by His Britannic Majesty's frigate Shannon: and the death and funeral of Captain Lawrence. Hartford: Printed and published by B. & J. Russell. State-street, 1814.

81 (i. e. 71) p. 14½cm.

Pages 62-71 wrongly numbered 72-81.

1. Lawrence, James, 1781-1813. 2. Chesapeake (Frigate) 3. Shannon (Frigate)
A 32-1550

Title from N. Y. Pub.   Libr. Printed by L. C.

NL 0357077   NN NBuHi N MH CSmH OCHP

1886   Life of James Macdonald, M.D. [anon.]
         Utica, Journal of Insanity, 1849.
         p. 71-92. 8°.

NL 0357078   DLC

The life of James Nayler, a fanatic enthusiast, who profanely and blasphemously personated Jesus Christ, at London, Bristol, &c. &c.
see under   [Pugh, Edward] d. 1813.

Life of James Robertson, D. D.
see under   [Gordon, Charles William] 1860-

Life of James Sangster and Speech of Eliakim Malcolm ...
[London? Ont., 1942?]

cover-title, 1 p. l., 4, 7 numb. l., 1 l. 29cm.

Type-written copy (carbon) made by Edwin Seaborn from newspaper clippings.

1. Sangster, James. 2. Brant co., Ont.   I. Malcolm, Eliakim.
II. Seaborn, Edwin, 1872-   43-3389
Library of Congress   CT310.S3L5
[3]

NL 0357081   DLC

Life of James Sharp, archbishop of St. Andrews. First printed in MDCLXXVIII. To which is now added, an account of his death, by an eye-witness. Glasgow: J. Wylie & Co., 1818. 1 p. l., vi, (1)8-109 p. nar. 12°. (Miscellanea Scotica. v. 2.)

I. Sharp, James, abp. of St. Andrews.
N. Y. P. L.   January 22, 1913.

NL 0357082   NN OC1

The life of James the Second, king of England, &c., collected out of memoirs writ of his own hand ...
see under   [Innes, Lewis] 1651-1738, supposed author.

The life of James II. late king of England. Containing an account of his birth, education, religion, and enterprizes
see under   [Jones, David] fl. 1676-1720.

Life of James W. Jackson, the Alexandria hero, the slayer of Ellsworth, the first martyr in the cause of southern independence; containing a full account of the circumstances of his heroic death, and the many remarkable incidents in his eventful life, constituting a true history, more like romance than reality. Pub. for the benefit of his family. Richmond, West & Johnston, 1862.

48 p. 21½cm.

1. Jackson, James William, d. 1861. 2. Ellsworth, Ephraim Elmer, 1837-1861. 3. Alexandria, Va.—Hist.—Civil war.
15-22445

Library of Congress   F234.A3J13

NL 0357085   DLC NIC NcD NcU OC1WHi NjP MBAt MB Vi

... **Life** of James Watt, from Chambers's "Miscellany": 1871. Contributed by Duncan J. Kerr ... A Newcomen publication, 1938. [New York] 1938]

40 p. incl. front. (port.) illus. 22½cm.

At head of title: The Newcomen society. American branch.

1. Watt, James, 1736-1819. 2. Steam-engines—Hist.   I. Kerr, Duncan John, 1883-   II. Newcomen society for the study of the history of engineering and technology, London. American branch.
41-5309
Library of Congress   TA140.W3L5
[2]   926.2

NL 0357086   DLC NIC MB NN ICJ

The LIFE of Jean Baptiste Poquelin de Moliere comic dramatist and satirist. London, Ward Lock & co., [18- ?]

pp. 81-96.   Port.
Cover serves as title-page.
At head of title: Ward & Lock's penny books for the people. Biographical series.
Signed. H.W.D.

NL 0357087   MH NNC

Life of Jean Paul F. Richter
see under   [Lee, Mrs. Eliza (Buckminster)]
1794-1864.

Life of Jefferson Davis. From authentic sources. By a South Carolinian. London, G. W. Bacon and co. [186-?]

iv, 123 p. front. (port.) 20cm.

1. Davis, Jefferson, 1808-1889.
13-19357
Library of Congress   E467.1.D26L68

NL 0357089   DLC NIC NcD NN

E467.1   The life of Jeff. Davis, in five expressive
D26L51   tableaux ... [New York? Published
         at 109 Nassau street [1868?]

1 l. (fold. and cut) illus. 16cm. in
20½cm.

1. Davis, Jefferson, 1808-1899.

NL 0357090   NBuG NBu

Life of Jefferson Davis, with an authentic account of his private and public career, and his death and burial. Together with the life of "Stonewall" Jackson. (Thomas Jonathan Jackson.) Including his glorious military career and his tragic death on the battlefield ... Philadelphia, The Keystone publishing co., 1890.

197 p., 1 l., [5]-300 p. plates, 2 port. (incl. front.) 19½cm.
This book is a new edition of "Life and imprisonment of Jefferson Davis" published in 1866, with the addition of new matter in the life of Davis, p. 96-146, 189-197, by Jas. W. Morton, jr.
The 2d part, bearing half-title "Life and military career of Thomas Jonathan Jackson", originally appeared in 1864 as "'Old Jack' and his foot-cavalry".

1. Davis, Jefferson, 1808-   1889. 2. Jackson, Thomas Jonathan, 1824-1863.   I. Morton, James W., jr.   II. Keystone publishing company.   [a34b1]
Library of Congress   E467.1.D26L52   5-36857

NL 0357091   DLC MH

Life of Jefferson S. Batkins, member from
Cranberry Centre
see under   [Jones, Joseph Stevens] 1811-
1877.

VOLUME 332

Life of Jemima, or, The confessions of an unfortunate bastard, who, by the antipathy of her parents, was driven to every scene of vice and prostitution! containing some particulars of her early years; with general remarks on public hospitals, an account of the interior of a madhouse, and its abuses; her escape thence and voyage to America, her unhappy marriage, and final settlement in England, as nurse in a hospital. London: Printed and sold by J. Bailey [1800?]
24 p. col. fold. front. 18½cm.
Chap-book.
Caption title: Je   mima, the unfortunate bastard.
Chap-books.   1. Title: The confessions of an
unfortunate bastard.   11. Title: Jemima, the unfortunate bastard.

NL 0357093   ViU

The **LIFE** of Jereboam O. Beauchamp who was hung at Frankfort, Kentuckay, for the murder of SolomonP. Sharpe   Frankfort, d'Unger & co., 1850.

Pamphlet.

NL 0357094   MH

The life of Jereboam O. Beauchamp
    see also   The avenger's doom.

B
E
       Life of Jesse Duncan Elliot, Esq. of the United States Navy. (n.p.) 1814.
(529) - 539 p.

Detached from The Port Folio, 3rd series, v. 4, no. 6, Dec., 1814.

1. Elliott, Jesse Duncan, 1782-1845.

NL 0357096   ViN CSmH

LIFE of Jesse H.Pomeroy, the boy fiend... Taunton, Mass.: Taunton Pub. Co., 1875. 26 p. illus. 19½cm.

Cover-title.

869256A. 1. Pomeroy, Jesse Harding, 1859–

NL 0357097   NN

The life of Jesus. Translation from the French
    see under   [Renan, Ernest] 1823-1892.

The life of Jesus ... Written for the Massachusetts Sabbath school society, and approved by the Committee of publication. Boston, Massachusetts Sabbath school society, 1853.
viii, [9]-214 p. incl. illus., plates. front. 19½ᶜᵐ.

1. Jesus Christ—Biog.—Juvenile literature.   1. Massachusetts Sabbath school society.

                                         34-8170
Library of Congress   BT302.L67

NL 0357099   DLC RPB CU

[Life of Jesus] First edition. For the American Zulu mission, South Africa. New York, American tract society, 1907.

22 p. plates. 16 cm.

NL 0357100   MH

The life of Jesus, edited by Charles M. Sheldon... [c1926]
    see under   Bible. N.T. Gospels. English. Harmonies. 1926?

Life of Jesus ... as pictured by master painters of the world ...
    see under   [Wilde, Myrtle K   ] comp.

Life, The, of Jesus Christ. [In the Pongwe language.] Cape Palmas, West Africa: Press of the A. B. C. F. Mission, 1840. 149(1)p. 24°.

1. Jesus Christ.—Life. 2. African   languages.—Pongwe.
N.Y.P.L.   October 2, 1912.

NL 0357103   NN CtY

The life of Jesus Christ, including his apocryphal history, from the spurious gospels, unpublished manuscripts, &c. &c., embellished with a head of Jesus
    see under   [Huttmann, William]

The life of Jesus, the Messiah. A sacred poem. ... 1874 [c1873]
    see under   Welles, Albert.

AC901
.M2
       Life of Jim Crow, showing how he got his inspiration as a poet ... his interview with General Jackson ... written by himself. Philadelphia, 1835.
23 p. [Markoe pamphlets, 27: 13]

NL 0357106   DLC

Life of "Jimmy" ...
    see under   [Hutchings, John Stidworthy]
1877-

The **LIFE** of Joab, the son of Zeruiah, compared with that of Andrew Jackson. Addressed to the sober and reflecting people of the Western country. By an old farmer. n.p., ? [1828]

Without title page. Caption title.
A campaign documents of the preseidential election of 1828.

NL 0357108   MH DLC

... The **life** of Joan of Arc, by Jules Michelet, and other biographies. [Reading, Pa.] The Spencer press [c1937]
1 p. l., vii-ix p., 1 l., 397 p. front. 21½ᶜᵐ. (Classic romances of literature. [vol. vii])
The biography of Mahomet is a selection from Gibbon's The history of the decline and fall of the Roman empire; the biography of Cromwell is a translation of a portion of Lamartine's Vies de quelques hommes illustres.
CONTENTS.—Joan of Arc, by Jules Michelet.—Mahomet, by Edward Gibbon.—Martin Luther, by C. K. J. Bunsen.—Frederick the Great, by T. B. Macaulay.—Oliver Cromwell, by Alphonse Lamartine.
1. Biography. 2. Jeanne d'Arc, Saint, 1412-1431. 1. Michelet, Jules, 1798-1874. Jeanne d'Arc. 11. Gibbon, Edward, 1737-1794. 111. Bunsen, Christian Karl Josias, freiherr von, 1791-1860. The life of Martin Luther. 1v. Macaulay, Thomas Babington Macaulay, 1st baron, 1800-1859. Frederic the Great. v. Lamartine, Alphonse Marie Louis de, 1790-1869.
Library of Congress   CT104.L4   37-21524 Revised
———— Copy 2.
Copyright A 107674   [37f2]   920.02

NL 0357109   DLC FMU PPT

BF1815
S7
L5
       The life of Joanna Southcott, the prophetess: containing an impartial account of her wonderful and astonishing writings, her miraculous conception, the coming of Shiloh, and of the numerous presents sent to her preparatory to her accouchement, particularly the superb crib!! made by Mr. Seddon ... London, John Fairburn, 1814.
38p. 21 cm.

NL 0357110   RPB NN

The life of Joaquin Murieta the brigand chief of California; being a complete history of his life, from the age of sixteen to the time of his capture and death at the hands of Capt. Harry Love, in the year 1853. San Francisco: Published at the office of the California police gazette." 1859.

71 p. illus. 31 cm.
Advs. on 3 unnumbered p. at end.
Photostat reproduction.

1. Murieta, Joaquin, 1829?-1853.

NL 0357111   CSmH

Life of John Allen, "The Wickedest Man in New York." By an Impartial Observer. N.Y., 1868.

32 p.

NL 0357112   PHi NN

R55
.T4
       The life of John Antes, a missionary in Egypt. Philadelphia, S.S. union.
16 p. illus. (Theologiacl pamphlets, 155:11)

NL 0357113   DLC

Life of John Beith, the blind Scottish newsman of New York
    see under   [Fraser, John]

BX
5199
B73L5
       The Life of John Bradford, Prebendary of St. Paul's. Martyred in Smithfield, July 1, 1555. London, Seeley, Jackson, and Halliday, Fleet Street, and B. Seeley, Hanover Street, London, 1855.
265 p. 17 cm.

1. Bradford, John, 1510?-1555.

NL 0357115   NRCR

The life of John Buncle, esq.; containing various observations and reflections, made in several parts of the world
    see under   [Amory, Thomas] 1691?-1788.

The life of John Bunyan ...
    see under   Bunyan, John, 1628-1688.

Life of John Bunyan. By the author of "Robert Dawson," "Jane Hudson," &c.
    see under   [Knight, Helen (Cross)]

VOLUME 332

B
C15211 Life of John C. Calhoun. Presenting
a condensed history of political events
from 1811 to 1843.   New York, 1843.
76p. front.(port.)

NL 0357119   IU DLC CSmH PHi PPAmP MiD-B CU MdBP

The life of John Calvin "the man of Geneva", for
young persons. By the author of "The story of
Martin Luther;" and "The story of Ulrich
Zwingle." London, J. F. Shaw [1864]
213 p.   illus.   17 cm.
1. Calvin, Jean, 1509-1564.

NL 0357120   IEG MH MnFS

Life of John Charles Fremont ... New York, Greeley
& McElrath, 1856.
cover-title, 32 p. incl. illus., ports. map. 23ᶜᵐ.
The map is on verso of back of cover.

1. Fremont, John Charles, 1813-1890.   I. Greeley & McElrath, pub.

Library of Congress   E415.9.F8L7   10—29592

NL 0357121   DLC ICN MnHi ICN IHi NN MB MH MeB MWA

The life of John Dennis, the renowned critick
in which are likewise some observations on most
of the poets and criticks, his contemporaries, not
written by Mr. Curll.   London, J. Roberts,
1734.
(2), 59 p.

NL 0357122   MH

The life of John Donne, Dr. in Divinty [sic], and
late dean of Saint Pavls Church London
see under   [Walton, Izaak] 1593-1683.

The life of John earl of Stair...
see under   [Henderson, Andrew] fl. 1734-
1775.

The life of John Egerton, late bishop of Durham
see under   [Bridgewater, Francis Henry
Egerton] 8th earl of, 1756-1829.

The life of John Eliot, the apostle of the Indians
see under   [Wilson, John] 1804-1875.

---

*XG
.389A
.360   The life of John Engelbrecht; containing an
account of his sufferings by reason of faithful-
ness to the trust committed to him by his lord
and master; his extraordinary call in the ministry; and wonderful visions; together with some
sentences out of his writings. Translated out of
the German original. By a friend to mankind.
Hallowell [Me.]: Printed by E. Goodale. 1819.

108 p. 14.5cm.
Shaw/Shoemaker 48490.

NL 0357127   MB CSmH

Life of John Ericsson. ₍New York, Knapp & Co., lithographers and printers, 1889?₎
15 p. 70 mm. (Histories of poor boys who have become rich,
and other famous people)
Distributed in packages of Duke's Cigarettes.
Colored port. and illus. on cover.

1. Ericsson, John, 1803-1889. 2. Bibliography—Microscopic and
miniature editions—Specimens.   I. The Knapp Company, Inc., New
York. II. Duke, W., Sons & Co., Durham, N. C. III. Series.

TA140.E74L54   73-213724

NL 0357127-1   DLC

The life of John Frederic Oberlin, pastor of Waldbach, in
the Ban de la Roche. Compiled for the American Sunday-
school union, and revised by the Committee of publication.
Philadelphia, American Sunday school union, 1830.
140 p. incl. front. pl. 18ᶜᵐ.

1. Oberlin, Johann Friedrich, 1740-1826.   I. American Sunday-
school union.

33-17056

Library of Congress   BX4827.O3L5   922.444

MiU ICJ ICN NjR PU NjP MnU CtW
NL 0357128   DLC NcD OC1WHi CtY NNUT OO PHi OOxM

The life of John Gay
see under   [Coxe, William] 1747-1828.

HV
6248
G46   The life of John Gilbert, who was executed
at Gloucester, April the 19th, 1776, for
breaking open the house of the Rev. Mr.
Roquet, and that of the Rt. H. the earl of
Wigton. To which are added several letters
that passed between him and the Rev. Mr.
Roquet of Bristol ... The public may depend
that none are genuine but those signed by Mr.
Mould. Gloucester, J. Pytt, [1776?]
16 p. 22cm.

NL 0357130   NIC

The life of John Gilpin, taken from divers manuscripts
in the possession of the family. To which is added, by
way of appendix, The celebrated history of his journey
to Edmonton ₍in verse by W. Cowper₎ as read by Mr.
Henderson, at Free-mason's-hall ... New ed. London,
S. Bladon, 1785.
2 p. l., ii, 140 p. fold. front. 16½ᶜᵐ.

1. Gilpin, John, pseud.   I. Cowper, William, 1731-1800.

Library of Congress   PZ3.L6244   7-16053†

NL 0357131   DLC NjP MH MBAt

Wordsworth
CT
788
H36   The life of John Hatfield, commonly called
the Keswick impostor, with an account of
his trial and execution for forgery; also
his marriage with "Mary of Buttermere."
To which is added A pastoral dialogue,
and the celebrated Borrowdale letter,
shewing the native dialect of this district. Keswick, J. Ivison ₍1849₎
iv,32,12 p. 18cm.

"A pastoral dialogue in the Cumberland

dialect; with a humourous epistle, by a
young shepherd ₍Isaac Ritson₎ ..." has
separate t. p.
Healey 2004.
With autograph: J. E. Hargreaves.
1. Hatfield, John, 1759-1803. 2. English
language--Dialects--Cumberland. I. Title:
A pastoral dialogue in the Cumberland dialect. II. Rit   son, Isaac, 1761-1789.
A humourous   epistle... III. Borrowdale letter.

NL 0357133   NIC

B
H362 The life of John Hatfield, commonly
called the Keswick impostor, with an
account of his trial and execution for
forgery; also his marriage with Mary of
Buttermere. To which is added a pastoral dialogue, and the celebrated Borrowdale letter, shewing the native dialect
of this district. And also, The wild
dog of Ennerdale.   Cockermouth [1881]
55p.

NL 0357134   IU

The life of John Howard, esquire, LL. D. and F. R. S. New-
castle upon Tyne, Printed by W. Thompson, M,DCC,XC.
1 p. l., 60 p. 21ᶜᵐ.
Title vignette.
"John Howard, esq., monody": p. 59-60.
With this are bound : Howard, John. Extracts selected from the
writings and observations of the late John Howard ... Newcastle,
M,DCC,XC. and Tyranny annihilated ... ₍London, 1792₎

1. Howard, John, 1726?-1790.

35-34396

Library of Congress   HV8978.H8L47

NL 0357135   DLC CtY CaBVaU

The life of John Howard, the philanthropist. Abridged
from authentic sources. By a friend of Sabbath schools.
New-York, B. Waugh and T. Mason, for the Sunday school
union of the Methodist Episcopal church, 1833.
128 p. incl. front. 13¼ᶜᵐ.

1. Howard, John, 1726?-1790.   I. Sunday-school union of the Methodist Episcopal church.

33-34929

Library of Congress   HV8978.H8L48   923.642

NL 0357136   DLC

The Life of John Howard, the philanthropist;
embracing an account of his great and
successful labours in meliorating the
condition of prisoners in European gaols,
Phila., Presbyterian board of publication,
₍18-?₎
o p. l., 154 p. 2 fronts   S.

NL 0357137   OO PHi NNUT-Mc PPPrHi

[The life of John Howard Payne]
see under   [Harrison, Gabriel]

Life of John Hullah, LL. D.
see under   [Hullah, Mrs. Frances (Rosser)]

... The life of John James Audubon. Iowa City, Ia.,
The University ₍1925₎
10 p. incl. port. 23½ᶜᵐ. (University of Iowa extension bulletin. Bulletin no. 116, January 15, 1925)

1. Audubon, John James, 1785-1851.

25-27077

Library of Congress   QL31.A9L5

NL 0357140   DLC OC1

Life of John Jay
see under   Renwick, Henry Brevoort, 1817-

VOLUME 332

Life of John Kaspar Lavater, minister
of St. Peter's church, Zurich,   Lond.
Religious tract soc. n.d.

NL 0357142   MA PPAmP

L & T	The life of John Kaspar Lavater, minister
2	of St. Peter's Church, Zurich. Philadelphia,
L58	American Sunday-School Union ₍etc., etc., n. d.₎
L	192 p. 15 cm.

NL 0357143   MWiW NNC PBL

The life of John Knox, the Scottish reformer.
    see under   American Sunday-school union.

... Life of John Lee Chapman. New York, Philadelphia ₍etc.₎ Metropolitan publishing company, 1872.
1 p. l., 3 p. front. (port.) 28¼ x 23ᶜᵐ.
At head of title: Biographical cyclopædia of Maryland. **Representative
men ...**

1. Chapman, John Lee, b. 1812.
                                            14-19557
Library of Congress   F189.B1C46

NL 0357145   DLC

The life of John Mary Decalogne, student in the
    University of Paris
    see under   [Proyart, Liévain Bona-
venture] 1743?-1808.

4	The life of John Metcalf; commonly
Rare	called Blind Jack of Knaresbrough:
Books	with many entertaining anecdotes of
	his exploits in hunting, card playing,
	&c., some particulars relating to the
	expedition against the rebels, in
	1745, in which he bore a personal
	share; and also, A succinct account of
	his various contracts for making
	roads, erecting bridges, and other

undertakings,in Yorkshire, Lancashire,
Derbyshire, and Cheshire, which, for
a series of years, brought him into
public notice, as a most extraordinary character. 6th ed. with considerable additions and amendments. London, Printed for the booksellers

72 p.

NL 0357148   DLC-P4 OU N MiU CtY ICU

Room	... The life of John Metcalf, commonly
Ib94	called Blind Jack of Knaresbro' ... Leeds:
t4	J.Johnson,publisher. Manchester:John Heywood
v.3	[18--?]
	30p. 17½cm.bd. to 20cm. (Johnson's cheap
	library edition, 2)
	[Binder's title: Chap books, III]
	Illustrated t.-p.
	Original wrappers bound in.

NL 0357149   CtY ICN OCl NcD

The life of John Metcalf, commonly called Blind
Jack of Knaresbrough, with many entertaining anecdotes of his exploits in hunting, card playing,
&c., some particulars relating to the expedition
against the rebels, in 1745, in which he bore a
personal share; and also, a succinct account of
his various contracts for making roads, erecting
bridges... 5th ed. with additions.   72p. front.
(port.) London, J. Kendrew [18-]

A chap-book.

NL 0357150   OCl

The life of John Metcalf, commonly
called Blind Jack of Knaresborough ...
A new ed., improved. London,E.Peck,1812.
iv,75p. front.(port.),fold.pl. 17½cm.
Differs considerably from 1795 ed.

NL 0357151   CtY

PR974	The life of John Metcalf, commonly called
.C506	Blind Jack of Knaresbrough: with an account of
Rare bk	his exploits in hunting, card-playing, &c: some
	curious particulars relating to the expedition
	against the rebels, in 1745, in which he bore a
	personal share: and also a succint account of
	his various contracts, for making roads, erect-
	ing bridges, and other undertakings ... which,
	for a series of years, brought him into public
	notice as a most extraordinary character. 3d
	ed. Knaresbrough, W. W. Langdale, 1829.
	62 p. front. (port.)
	₍Chap-books: miscellaneous,. London,
	etc., 180-?-29, no.11₎

NL 0357152   ICU

arV	The Life of John Metcalf, commonly called
22221	Blind Jack, of Knaresbrough... also a
	succinct account of his various contracts,
	for making roads... and other undertakings
	in Yorkshire, Derbyshire, and Cheshire ...
	5th ed. Knaresbrough, W. Langdale, 1842.
	60 p. port. 17cm.

Bound with The Original and only
authentic account of the trial of Eugene
Aram. Knaresbrough ₍1890?₎

1. Metcalf,   John, 1717-1810.

NL 0357153   NIC

The life of John Milton, containing, besides the
history of his works, several extraordinary
characters of men and book...
    see under   [Toland, John] 1670-1722.

LIFE of John Morrissey, the Irish boy who
fought his way to fame and fortune.
New York, The Great Publishing House,1878.

pp.28.

NL 0357155   MH

The life of John Newton ...
    see under   [Cecil, Richard] 1748-1810.

The life of John Oliver Hobbes [psued.] told in
her correspondence with numerous friends;
with a...
    see under   [Craigie, Mrs. Pearl Mary
Teresa (Richards)] 1867-1906.

The life of John Owen, D.D.   ₍London:₎ Religious Tract Soc.
₍1835?₎ 72 p. 24°.   (Christian biography.)

1. Owen, John, 1616-83. 2. Series.
N. Y. P. L.   May 25, 1916.

NL 0357158   NN

The life of John Paul Jones
    see under   [Kaler, James Otis] 1848-1912,
ed.

Life of John Paul Jones; and Memoirs of
Nathaniel Fanning; who served during part
of the American Revolution and died in the
service of the United States at Charleston,
South Carolina. Lexington, Ky., Printed
for W. Johnson, 1826.
iv, 247 p. 18cm.

NL 0357160   NNC

The life of John Philip Kemble, esquire, a proprietor, and
stage manager of Covent Garden theatre, interspersed with
family and theatrical anecdotes ... London, J. Johnston ₍etc.₎
1809₎
2 p. l., 52 p. fold. front. 22ᶜᵐ.

1. Kemble, John Philip, 1757-1823.
                                            43-47847
Library of Congress   PN2598.K5L5

NL 0357161   DLC NIC ICU MH CtY MH CSmH

Life of John Tauler of Strasburg. Temp.
1340
            see under   ₍Meisters Buoch.
English.₎

The life of John Travers Lewis...
    see under   [Lewis, Ada Maria (Leigh)]

Life of John Tyler, president of the United States, up
to the close of the second session of the Twenty-seventh
Congress: including some of his most important speeches
while a member of the House of representatives and of the
Senate of the United States, and his principal messages and other public papers as chief magistrate of the
Union ... New York, Harper & brothers, 1843.
viii, ₍9₎-256 p. front. (port.) 23½ᶜᵐ.

1. Tyler, John, pres. U. S., 1790-1862.

Library of Congress   E397.L72   3-33141

NcU ViU NN
NL 0357164   DLC MdBP OO TU AAP NIC WaWW MiD NcD

Life of John Tyler, president of the United States, up to the
close of the second session of the Twenty-seventh Congress:
including some of his most important speeches while a member
of the House of representatives and of the Senate of the United
States, and his principal messages and other public papers as
chief magistrate of the Union ... New-York, Harper &
brothers, 1844.
viii, ₍9₎-256 p., incl. front. (port.) 23½ᶜᵐ.
First edition, New-York, 1843.
With this copy are bound: (1) The life and times of Martin Van
Buren ... By William L. Mackenzie. Boston, 1846.—(2) The lives and
opinions of Benj'n Franklin Butler ... and Jesse Hoyt ... By William L.
Mackenzie. Boston, 1845.
1. Tyler, John, pres. U. S.,   1790-1862.

Library of Congress   E397.L73   3-33142

NL 0357165   DLC OrU ViW ViU NN NjP

VOLUME 332

Life of John Wesley. Edited by Thomas
O Summers. Nashville, Tenn., Publishing
house of the M. E. Church, South, 1871.
90 p., front.(port.) illus. 15 1/2 cm.

NL 0357166　　NcA-S

The life of John Wickliff
　　see under　[Tytler, Patrick Fraser]
1791-1849.

The life of John Wilkes, esq. in the manner of
Plutarch... 1773
　　see under　[Cradock, Joseph] 1742-1826.

The life of Johnson: with maxims and observations,
moral, critical, and miscellaneous, accurately
selected from the works of Dr. Samuel Johnson,
see under　Johnson, Samuel, 1709-1784.

---

*A
1835　　The life of Joice Heth, the nurse of Gen.
.L554　George Washington, (the father of our country,,
now living at the astonishing age of 161
years, and weighs only 46 pounds. Price six
cents. New-York: Printed for the publishers,
1835.
　12 p.　21cm.

1. Heth, Joice, 1674—　2. Washington,
George, Pres. U. S., 1732-1799.

NL 0357170　　ViU CSmH MHi MBAt

The life of Jonathan Wild, from his birth to
his death
　　see under　[Defoe, Daniel] 1661?-1731.

The life of Jonathan Wild the great
　　see under　[McCusker, Honor Cecilia]

BS580
.J6L5　The life of Joseph.　Nashville, Tennessee,
Thomas G. Bradford, 1811.
192 p. 18cm.

1. Joseph, the Patriarch.

NL 0357173　　T THi

The life of Joseph, a scripture narrative
　　see under　Miller, E

The life of Joseph: to which is added,
Pride in dress. New Haven:Published by
Is94　S.Babcock.1850.
t1　36p. incl.front.,illus. 15cm.
1　Imperfect: t.-p. wanting; title, as
above, taken from cover.

NL 0357175　　CtY

PR 3306
L53　The LIFE of Joseph Addison, Esq., extracted
1733　from ... the General dictionary. To
which is prefixed, the Life of Dr.
Lancelot Addison, his father. London,
N. Prevost, 1753.
112 p.

1. Addison, Joseph, 1672-1719. I.
Bayle, Pierre, 1647-1706. /A general
dictionary.

NL 0357176　　CaBVaU

The life of Joseph Balsamo, commonly called
Count Cagliostro ...
　　see under　Barberi,

The LIFE of Joseph Benson,abridged from authentic sources,by a friend of Sabbath schools.
New York,J.Emory and B.Waugh,1832.

13 cm.　pp.94.

NL 0357178　　MH

1447　Life of Joseph Chamberlain, by Rt.Hon.
.249　Viscount Milner,J.A.Spender, Sir Henry
.58　Lucy, J.Ramsay Macdonald,Harold Cox,
L.S.Amery... London, The Associated newspapers [1914?]
320 p. front.(port.) 16 cm.

1.Chamberlain,Joseph,1836-1914. I.
Milner,Alfred Milner,1st viscount,1854-
1925.

NL 0357179　　NjP

The life of Joseph Ritner, farmer of Washington County, Pennsylvania. May, 1835. [Washington] Pa., 1835. 10 p. 23cm.

1. Ritner, Joseph, 1780-1869.
N.Y.P.L　　　　　　　　　　　　　　January 27, 1941

NL 0357180　　NN

The life of Joseph the son of Israel
　　see under　[Macgowan, John] 1726-1780.

The Life of Judah Philip Benjamin. (New
Orleans) Louisiana State Museum, 1937.
26p. 23.5 cm.

1.Biography. 2.Benjamin, Judah Philip.
3.History-Louisiana.

NL 0357182　　NNJ

The life of Judas Iscariot ...

This work is available in this library in the Readex Micro-
print edition of Early American Imprints published by the
American Antiquarian Society.
This collection is arranged according to the numbers in
Charles Evans' American Bibliography.

NL 0357183　　DLC

The Life of Judas Iscariot, who betrayed
his Lord and Master. Embellished with
cubs.
Phila.:Printed in 1794.
pp.(29)32mo.

AAS:Evans 27222.

NL 0357184　　MWA

E302　Life of Judge Marshall. (In the Port folio, third
.M4.7　series, conducted by Oliver Oldschool, esq.
Toner Coll. [Philadelphia]. 1815.

NL 0357185　　DLC

The life of Joseph Addison, Esq; extracted from nº III.
and IV. of the General dictionary, historical and critical.
To which is prefixed, The life of Dr. Lancelot Addison ...
his father. London, Printed for N. Prevost, 1733.
1 p. l., vi, 112 p.　front. (port.)　15½ᶜᵐ.
Binder's title: Memoirs of L. & J. Addison, of Milstone.
Bibliographical foot-notes.
Armorial book-plate: Edward Duke.

1. Addison, Joseph, 1672-1719.　2. Addison, Lancelot, 1632-1703.

NL 0357186　　MiU IEN DFo ICN

There are no cards for numbers
NL 0357187 to NL 0358000

... Life of Kepler ...
　　see under　[Bethune, John Elliot
Drinkwater] 1801-1851.

The life of King Edward III of England
　　see under　[Cooke, Thomas] 1703-1756.

942.08　The life of King George V. Presenting in
G294　prose and pictures, the life and work of
L　a monarch beloved of his peoples.
London, Associated Newspapers, ltd.[1936?]
223p. illus.,ports. 25cm.

1. George V, King of Great Britain,
1865-1936.

NL 0358003　　OrU

YA　The life of King Hezekiah. Boston, Massachusetts
15366　sabbath school society, 1837.
51p.

NL 0358004　　DLC

DA
277.5　The life of Lady Halket. Edinburgh, Printed for
H2　Andrew Symson and Henry Knox, 1701.
cage
[8] 53 [6] p. 4⁴, A-H⁴, 4to.
Pencil drawing on vellum pasted in.
Books written by the Lady Halket, sig. H2r-H4v.
Dedication signed : S. C.

NL 0358005　　DFo CtY

The life of Lady Halket
　　see also　The life of the Lady Halket.

VOLUME 332

Life of Lady Jane Grey, and of Lord Guildford Dudley, her husband. This young lady at twelve years of age understood eight languages, was for nine days queen of England, and was beheaded in the Tower in the seventeenth year of her age, being at that time the most amiable and accomplished woman in Europe.

See *under*

ᵣGodwin, Williamᵢ 1756-1836.

The life of Lady Russell. Philadelphia, American Sunday-school union; London, Religious tract society ₁185-?₁

192 p. *15 cm.*

1. Russell, Lady Rachel (Wriothesley) Vaughan, 1636-1723. I. American Sunday-school union. II. Religious tract society.

33—25081

Library of Congress   DA447.R97L5

ᵣ45b1₁   920.7

NL   0358008   DLC PU PPL MeB

Life of Lafayette, including an account of the memorable revolution of the three days of 1830. Boston, Light & Horton; New York, Leavitt, Lord, and co.; ₁etc., etc.₁ 1835.

viii, 274 p. front. (port.) 16ᶜᵐ.

1. Lafayette, Marie Joseph Paul Roch Yves Gilbert de Motier, marquis de, 1757-1834. 2. France—History—July revolution, 1830.

A 35-136

Title from Lafayette   College. Printed by L. C.

NL   0358009   PEL NIC MB

Life of Lam-ang

see

Biag ni Lam-ang.

The life of Lamenther: a true history.

see under   [Wall, Anne]

The life of Lamoignon Malesherbes ...

see under   [Delisle de Sales, Jean Claude Izouard, called] 1741-1816.

... The life of Lancelot Andrewes, D. D. ... London, Joseph Masters, 1854.

1 p. l., 97 p. front. (port.) 16 cm.
At head of title: Biography of English divines.
1. Andrewes, Lancelot, bp., 1555-1626.

NL   0358013   NNUT

E
5
.L 295

The LIFE of La Perouse, the celebrated and unfortunate French navigator, including his voyage, shipwreck, & subsequent adventures in a desolate island, on the northern coast of Japan; where he was discovered by Madame La Perouse. 3d edition. On this interesting history is founded, the pantomimical drama of Perouse, or, The desolate island, performing, with unbounded applause, at the Theatre Royal, Covent Garden; an accurate description of which, including the songs, &c. is also added. Sommers Town, A. Neil, 1801.

64p. 17cm.

NL   0358014   ICN

D8475
.2
.L72

The Life of late Shett Damodher Thackersey Mooljee, published by Chhagunlal Jamndas. Bombay, 1895.

230 p. port.
Copy imperfect: p. 1-2 wanting.
Text in Gujarati.

1. Thackersey, Damodhar, 1847-1893. I. Chhagunlal Jamndas.

NL   0358015   ICU

Life of Latude, imprisoned 35 years in the Bastile

see under   Latude, Jean Henri Masers de, 1728-1805.

The life of Lavina Crawford

see under   Crawford, Lavina, 1820-1882.

The LIFE of Lavinia Beswick, alias Fenton, alias Polly Peachum, containing her birth and education, her intrigues at a boarding school, etc:, the whole interspers'd with convincing proofs of her ingenuity, wit, and smart repartee, and concluding with some remarkable instances of her humanity to the distressed. London, A. Moore, 1728.

PP ₁2₁, 48.

NL   0358018   MH

The life of Lazarillo de Tormes

see under   Lazarillo de Tormes. *English.*

The life of Leopold, late emperor of Germany, &c. containing the most remarkable transactions of Europe, as well relating to the Turks as Christians, for about sixty years, with variety of original papers, letters, treaties, characters, &c. London, Printed for T. Newborough ₁etc.₁ 1706.

2 p. L., 389, ₁7₁ p. 19¼ᶜᵐ.

Subject entries: 1. Leopold I, emperor of Germany, 1640-1705. 2. Holy Roman empire—Hist.—Leopold I, 1658-1705.

3-24127

Library of Congress, no.   DB67.L7.

NL   0358020   DLC ICU

The life of Leopold, late Emperor of Germany, &c. ... The second edition. London, Printed for James Knapton ₁etc.₁ 1708.

₁4₁, 389, ₁7₁ p. 20cm.

1. Leopold I, Emperor of Germany, 1640-1705. 2. Holy Roman Empire - History - Leopold I, 1658-1705.

NL   0358021   NNC NN

Life of Lewis Cass, and sketch of W. O. Butler

see   Life of General Lewis Cass.

Life of Lewis Cass with his Letters, etc.

see under   [Hickman, Georg H.]

THE LIFE of Lewis Charlton a poor old slave ...
Fred., Pitts, [n.d.] 28 p. 19 cm.

NL   0358024   CaNSWA

The life of Lewis of Bourbon, late prince of Conde

see under   [Coste, Pierre] 1668-1747.

Life of Lieut. Col. Blackader. ₁Philadelphia₁ Presbyterian Board of Publication, 1840.

118 p. 16 cm.

1. Blackader, John, 1664-1729. I. Presbyterian Church in the U.S.A. Board of Publication and Sabbath School Work.

NL   0358026   NcD NNUT

Life of Lieut. Col. Blackader, born 1664 died 1729. New ed. Phila., Pres. of Pub., n.d.

120 p.

NL   0358027   PPPrHi

Life of Lieut.-Col. Blackader, born 1664 — died 1729. London: Religious Tract Soc. ₁1835?₁ 72 p. 24°. (Christian biography.)

1. Blackadder, John, 1664-1729. 2.   Series.
N. Y. P. L.   May 25, 1916.

NL   0358028   NN MH

The life of Lieutenant Gen. T. J. Jackson

see under   [McGabe, James Dabney] 1842-1883.

Life of Lieutenant Michael Carlier, Trappist monk-soldier, a model of virtue in the cloister and a hero in the great war, translated from the original French

see under   [Daumont, Octave]

BX
7987
.S4
F49
E5

A life of light, Sister Mary Bonaventure (Anna Fink) School Sister of Notre Dame, by a religious of the same congregation, translated by another. Zurich, Regina-Verlag ₁c1934₁

426 p. illus. 22cm.

1. Fink, Maria Bonaventura, Sister, S.S.N.D.,   1894-1922.

NL   0358031   DCU

Life of Lincoln ᵣ1895₁

see   Abraham Lincoln. Boston ₁1895₁

The LIFE of Lincoln. Lincoln, Lamon, Holland, and Reed. [Signed C. F. B.] . [N. Y. 187-?]

Broadside.
"From the New York world."

NL   0358033   MH

ᵣLife of Linne, pub. by Linnea, incorporated, of Chicago, Illinois, n.dd.

NL   0358033-1   PPAmSwM

VOLUME 332

STC
17783

The life of Long Meg of Westminster: Containing
the mad merry prankes shee played in her life time,
not onely in performing sundry quarrels with diuers
ruffians about London: But also how valiantly she
behaued her selfe in the Warres of Bolloingne.
London: Printed for Robert Bird, 1635.

A-E⁴. (A1, blank, lacking.) 4to.
Running-titles read: The life and prankes of
Long Meg of Westminster.

NL 0358034   DFo

FILM

The life of Long Meg of VVestminster: containing the mad merry prankes shee played in
her life time, not onely in performing sundry
quarrels with diuers ruffians about London:
but also how valiantly she behaued her selfe
in the warres of Bolloingne. London, Printed
for R. Bird, 1635.
Short-title catalogue no.17783 (carton 966)
Microfilm.
I. Title: Long Meg of Westminster. II. Title:
Meg of Westminster.

NL 0358035   MiU

The life of Long Meg of Westminster: containing the mad
merry pranks she played in her life time, not onely in
performing sundry quarrels with divers ruffians about
London: but also how valiantly she behaued her selfe
in the warres of Bolloingne. London, Printed for Robert Bird, 1635. [Reprint]

4 p. l., 30 p. 25½ᶜᵐ. (In Miscellanea antiqua anglicana. London, R.
Triphook, 1816-[21] [v. 2, no. 5])

I. Title: Long Meg of Westminster. II. Title: Meg of Westminster.

18-19704

Library of Congress   DA310.M5 vol.2

NL 0358036   DLC CtY NcU PU PBm MB CSmH OU IaU

PR974
.G3
Vol. VI

The life of Long Meg, of Westminster, containing
the merry pranks she played in her lifetime
not only in performing sundry exploits with
divers Ruffians about London, but also how
valiantly she behaved herself at the Wars of
Bollogn.   Newcastle, printed by G. Angus, in
the Side.
24 p.   16 cm.
[In Garret, William. A right pleasaunt and
famous book of histories. Newcastle, 1818
Vol. VI no. 9]

NL 0358037   DLC

PR
973
H66+
1871a
v.2

The life of Long Meg of Westminster: the
mad merry pranks she played in her life time,
but also how valiantly she behaved herself in
the wars of Boulogne. Edited by Charles
Hindley.   London, Reeves and Turner, 1871.
xxix, 47 (i. e. 49) p. illus. 26cm. (In
Hindley, Charles, ed. The old book collec-
tor's miscellany. London, 1871-73. v. 2
(1872))
A modernized   version; with reproduction of the t.   p. of the 1635 ed.

NL 0358038   NIC MH CtY NNC PU MH

The life of Lord Anson. [London, Wetton &
Jarvis, 182- ?]

Added title-page: Select biography; a collection of lives of eminent men, who have been an
honor to their country. By various distinguished
writers.
Series title also at head of title-page.

NL 0358039   MH

---

ar W
27360

Life of Lord Byron. [London, J. Limbird,
1824]
p. 337-352 24cm.

Detached from The Mirror of literature,
amusement, and instruction, v. 3, no. 85,
supplementary no.
No. 1 in a vol. lettered: Byron.

1. Byron, George Gordon Noël Byron, 6th
baron, 1788-   1824.

NL 0358040   NIC

The life of Lord Chatham.
London. Ward, Lock & Co. [185-?] 157-272 pp. Portrait. 8°.
By S.T.A.

2 — Pitt, William, 1st Earl of Chatham.

NL 0358041   MB

DA536
.P2L5
1865

Life of Lord Palmerston: with an account
of his death and funeral. London, New York,
G. Routledge; 1865.
192 p.   17cm.

1. Palmerston, Henry John Temple, 3d viscount,
1784-1865.

NL 0358042   ViU

...The LIFE OF [woodcut] Louis Kos-
SUTH. Kirkintilloch: William M'Millan. n. d.
19 × 11 cm. 12 p.   * KVD p.v.17, no.10
At head of title: Only One Penny.

NL 0358043   NN

274.2
W716

Theol.

[The life of Louis-Philippe, king of the French]
32p. illus. 19cm.

Title page missing. Caption title.
"No. 1"

Bound with William of Orange and the Netherlands.

1. Louis Philippe, king of the French, 1773-
1850.

NL 0358044   TxDaM

LIFE of Louis Philippe, late king of the French; containing a correct account of his early education;
his trials & adventures during his travels in Europe
& America; his political career; abdication; and
revolution of 1848, with the causes which led to
that event. Glasgow, Printed for the booksellers,
1850.   24 p. 16cm. (New and improved series. No. 25)

Weiss: Chapbooks, 447.
Without covers.
1. Louis Philippe, King of the   French, 1773-1850.

NL 0358045   NN MnU

Life of Louis, prince of Condé, surnamed the
Great
        see under [Stanhope, Philip Henry
Stanhope] 5th earl, 1805-1875.

The life of Lucilio (alias Julius Caesar) Vanini,
burnt for atheism at Thoulouse
    see under   [Durand, David] 1680?-1763.

BR325
L5

(The) life of Luther ...   London, The
religious tract society; Philadelphia,
American Sunday school union [c1846]

x,11-192p.   15cm.   ([The religious
tract society.   The monthly volume.   no.10])
[YA.S44]

1. Luther, Martin, 1483-1546.

NL 0358048   NBuG DLC ViU MA NN

The life of Luther. 1858
        see under König, Gustav Ferdinand
Leopold, 1808-1869.

Life of Luther C. Ladd, the first martyr that fell a
sacrifice to his country, in the city of Baltimore, on the
19th of April, 1861, while bravely defending the flag of
the nation ... with an account of his parentage and a description of his home in Alexandria, N. H.; also, an account of the brilliant naval engagement at Port Royal.
By a citizen of Alexandria ... Belfast, Me., J. W. Dickinson, 1862.
viii, [9]-40 p. front. (port.) 22ᶜᵐ.
Ladd was a member of the 6th Massachusetts infantry.
1. Ladd, Luther Crawford, 1843-1861. 2. Port Royal (S. C.) expedition,
1861.
24-9653

Library of Congress   E513.5.6th L1

NL 0358050   DLC

Life of Luther C. Ladd, the first martyr that fell a sacrifice to his country, in the city of Baltimore, on the 19th
of April, 1861, while bravely defending the flag of the nation ... Also, an account of the brilliant naval engagement at Port Royal. By a citizen of Alexandria ... Concord [N. H.] P. B. Cogswell, printer, 1862.
viii, [9]-40 p. front. (port.) 22ᶜᵐ.
"The great naval and land battle. By an eye witness": p. [33]-40.
1. Ladd, Luther Crawford, 1843-1861. 2. Port Royal (S. C.) expedition,
1861.
12-40297

Library of Congress   E513.5.6thL

NL 0358051   DLC Nh

---

arV
16129

Life of Luther. Life of Calvin. London,
The Religious Tract Society [1856?]
2 v. in 1. 16cm.

1. Luther, Martin, 1483-1546. 2. Calvin,
Jean, 1509-1564.

NL 0358052   NIC

The life of Luther; or a brief history of the Reformation in Germany
        see under   American Baptist Publica-
tion Society.

The life of Luther written by himself
        see under [Luther, Martin] 1483-1546.

Life of Ma-ka-tai-me-she-kia-kiak, or Black Hawk.
    see under   Black Hawk, Sauk chief, 1767-
1838.

VOLUME 332

Life, The, of Macbeth: Containing a key to his character, secret amours, intrigues and atchievements [sic], during his reign. . . . London: Printed for the author, . . . [1768?] (1), 237 pp. 16 cm., in 6s.
This is vol. I of a projected work, A key to the drama, and was first published under that title [**G.3925.28; etc.]. Being unsuccessful, the remaining sheets were provided with a new title-page and issued as The life of Macbeth.

K4895 — Shakespeare, William. Macbeth. — Macbeth, King of Scotland. -1057.

NL 0358056   MB

The life of Madam de Maintenon ... 1753-1740.
     see under   [Caraccioli, Louis Antoine de] 1721-1803.

Life of Madame de La Peltrie (Magdalen de Chauvigny)
     see under   St. Thomas, Mother.

Life of Mme. de la Rochefoucauld, duchess of Doudeauville, founder of the Society of Nazareth. Tr. from the French. Boston, Houghton, Osgood and company, 1878.
336 p. 18½ᶜᵐ.
Tr. by Mrs. Cashel Hoey.

1. La Rochefoucauld, Bénigne Augustine Françoise (de Montmirail) duchesse de Doudeauville, 1764-1849. I. Hoey, Frances Sarah (Johnston) "Mrs. Cashel Hoey," 1830-1908, tr.

16-13000

NL 0358059   DLC OrP OClW OCl MiU NNUT NBuG PPFHi CoU

DC
130
M2L62
   The Life of Madame de Maintenon. Translated from the French. London, L. Davis, 1772.
   xi,263,125 p.

1. Maintenon, Françoise d'Aubigné, marquise de, 1635-1719.

NL 0358060   CLU NjP KyLx

... **Life** of Madame Du Barry. Girard, Kan., Haldeman-Julius company [°1922]
62 p. 13ᶜᵐ. (Ten cent pocket series no. 123, ed. by E. Haldeman-Julius)

1. Du Barry, Jeanne Bécu, comtesse, 1743-1793.

Library of Congress   DC135.D8L5   CA 22-567 Unrev'd

NL 0358061   DLC

The life of Madame Flore
     see under   Jackson, Frances, 1848-

The life of Madame Louise de France.
     see under   [Lear, Mrs. Henrietta Louisa (Farrer)] 1824-1896.

W
600
L722
1847
   LIFE of Madame Restell, with an account of her professional career, and secret practices; to which is added a view of the case now on trial before the Court of Sessions, by a physician of New York. New York, Smith, 1847.
   48 p. illus.
     1. Lohman, Anna (Trow) 1812-1878
   I. A physician of New York

NL 0358064   DNLM

The life of Mdlle. de Lamourous, commonly called "The good mother," foundress and first superioress of the House of Mercy at Bordeaux. London, Burns and Lambert, 1859.   56 p.   16cm. (The cheap family and educational library)

Bound, as issued, with: The life of Sœur Rosalie of the Daughters of St. Vincent de Paul. London, 1858.

1. Lamourous, Marie Thérèse   Charlotte de, 1754-1836.

NL 0358065   NN MoSU

Life of Mademoiselle Le Gras (Louise de Marillac), foundress of the Sisters of charity. Preceded by letters of Mgr. Mermillod ... and of Very Rev. A. Fiat ... Translated from the French by a Sister of charity. New York, Cincinnati [etc.] Benziger brothers, 1884.
368 p., 1 l. 19¼ᶜᵐ.

1. Le Gras, Louise (de Marillac) Saint, 1591-1660. 2. Sisters of charity of St. Vincent de Paul. 3. Sisters of charity. I. Sister of charity, tr.

34-23708

Library of Congress   BX4700.L5H5
Copyright 1884 : 10187   922.244

NL 0358066   DLC

Life of Mademoiselle Le Gras (Louise de Marillac) foundress of the Sisters of Charity.   New York: Benziger Bros., 1917.   3 p.l., (1)6-350 p.   12°.

1. Le Gras, Louise (de Marillac).   1591-1660. 2. Sisters of Charity of St. Vincent de Paul. N.Y.P.L.   August 31, 1918.

NL 0358067   NN

The life of Maecenas ... 1748
     see under   [Richer, Henri] 1685-1748.

The life of Maecenas ... corrected and enlarged by Ralph Schomberg ... 1766
     see under   Schomberg, Ralph, 1714-1792.

The life of Mahomet; or The history of that imposture which was begun, carried on, and finally established by him in Arabia ... To which is added, An account of Egypt. South Shields:Printed by W.Hallgarth,jun.at the Minerva press.1799.
ix,229[i.e.231]p. front.(port.) 17cm.
Signatures: π⁴. unsigned, A-U⁶.

NL 0358070   CtY

The **life** of Mahomet; or, The history of that imposture which was begun, carried on, and finally established by him in Arabia; and which has subjugated a larger portion of the globe, than the religion of Jesus has yet set at liberty. To which is added, An account of Egypt. 1st American ed. Worcester: Printed by Isaiah Thomas, jun. May—1802.
viii, [13]-154 p. 17ᶜᵐ.

1. Muhammad, the prophet. 2. Egypt.

Library of Congress   BP75.L5 1802
                      32-16715

NL 0358071   DLC PMA ICN MWA PBL CtY CSt MB NBu

The life of Mahomet; or, The history of that imposture which was begun, carried on, and finally established by him in Arabia, and which has subjugated a larger portion of the globe, than the religion of Jesus has yet set at liberty. 2d American ed. New-York: Published by Evert Duyckinck, no. 102 Pearl-street. J. C. Totten, printer. 1813.
vi, [7]-118 p. 14ᶜᵐ.

1. Muhammad, the prophet.

Library of Congress   BP75.L5 1813   32-11970
                  [2]   922.97

NL 0358072   DLC NcD NjR

The life of Mahomet, the famous oriental impostor. [London,Lee,printer,Half Moon street Bishopsgate,ca.1800?]
[3]-36p. front. 17cm. [Bound with The life of Mahomet. South Shields,1799]
Signatures: B₂₋₆C-D⁶.
Caption title.
Apparently an imperfect copy, lacking title-page or cover-title, and possibly other preliminary matter.
"Sketch of the history of Constantinople": p.[33]-36.

NL 0358073   CtY

The **Life** of Mahomet, together with the Alcoran at large, tr. out of Arabick into French by the Sieur De Ryer. Now faithfully English'd. London, Printed for J. and B. Sprint, 1718.
450 p. port. 20 cm.
The 4th vol. of a work of which the other 3 vols. have title: A compleat history of the Turks from their origin in the year 755 to the year 1718 ... London, 1719. This vol. was originally pub. separately in London, 1649, with title: The Alcoran of Mahomet, tr. out of Arabique into French by the Sieur Du Ryer. cf. Brit. Mus. Cat.
1. Muhammad, the prophet. I. Koran. English. II. Du Ryer, André, ca. 1580-ca. 1660, tr. III. A compleat history of the Turks from their origin in the year 755 to the year 1718.

BP75.L5 1718   49-44646*

NL 0358074   DLC

The life of Major General Andrew Burn of the Royal Marines. [Philadelphia] Presbyterian board of publication; W.S. Martien, publishing agent, 1840.
242 p., 16ᵐᵒ.

1. Burn, Andrew, 1742-1814.

NL 0358075   NjPT PBL

The life of Major-Gen. Geo. B. McClellan, late general-in-chief U. S. A.
     see under   [Victor, Orville James] 1827-1910.

The life of Major-Gen. Israel Putnam. To which is added, a biographical sketch of the late Major-General Anthony Wayne
     see under   [Humphreys, David] 1752-1818.

923.544
L161LI
   The life of Major-General the Marquis de Lafayette ... Easton, Pennsylvania, privately printed for the Maroon Club of Lafayette College, 1943.
   109 p. port. 21 cm.

1. Lafayette, Marie Joseph Paul Roch Yves Gilbert de Motier, Marquis de, 1757-1834

NL 0358078   NcD

VOLUME 332

The life of Major-General William Henry Harrison: comprising a brief account of his important civil and military services, and an accurate description of the council at Vincennes with Tecumseh, as well as the victories of Tippecanoe, Fort Meigs and the Thames.   Philadelphia, Grigg & Elliot ₁etc.₁ 1840.

96 p. front. (port.) 2 pl. 21½ᶜᵐ.

On p. ₁4₁ of cover, "Homage of justice", being various tributes to Gen. Harrison.

Apparently not the same as Isaac R. Jackson's "The life of William Henry Harrison", although some portions of the text are the same as in that work.
Another issue appeared in the same year having different frontispiece, 4 plates, different spacing of the lines of text, and without any printing on p. ₁4₁ of cover.

1. Harrison, William Henry, pres. U. S., 1773-1841. 2. Tippecanoe, Battle of, 1811. 3. Thames, Battle of, 1813. 4. Meigs, Fort, O.

Library of Congress   E392.L732   26-251̄7̄

KyBgW
NL 0358080   DLC NIC TU KyHi RPB OC1 InU PU NSchU

The life of Major-General William Henry Harrison: comprising a brief account of his important civil and military services, and an accurate description of the council at Vincennes with Tecumseh, as well as the victories of Tippecanoe, Fort Meigs and the Thames.   Philadelphia, Grigg & Elliot ₁etc.₁ 1840.

96 p. front. (port.) 4 pl. 22 cm.

Apparently not the same as Isaac R. Jackson's "The life of William Henry Harrison", although some portions of the text are the same as in that work.

Another issue appeared in the same year having different frontispiece, 2 plates, different spacing of the lines of text, and with various tributes to Gen. Harrison, "Homage of Justice", on p. ₁4₁ of cover.

1. Harrison, William Henry, pres. U. S., 1773-1841. 2. Tippecanoe, Battle of, 1811. 3. Thames, Battle of, 1813. 4. Meigs, Fort, O. I. Jackson, Isaac Rand, d. 1843.

E392.L73   11—19334

CLSU PP
NL 0358082   DLC MnHi CtY PPA NjR NN MB ViU MiU CSmH

The life of Mansie Wauch.   FOR OTHER EDITIONS
                                     SEE MAIN ENTRY
₁Moir, David Macbeth₁ 1798-1851.
The life of Mansie Wauch, tailor in Dalkeith, written by himself, with eight illustrations by George Cruikshank. Edinburgh and London, W. Blackwood and sons ₁1898 ?₁

BW
719   Life of Marcellin-Joseph-Benedict Cham-
C4   pagnat, Marist father, founder of the Institute
V7   of the Little Brothers of Mary or the Marist
         Brothers of the Schools, by one of his first
         disciples; tr. from the French third ed. Paris,
         Desclée, 1947.
           xxiv, 641p. plates, ports. 20cm.
         1. Champagnat, Marcellin Joseph Benoit, 1789-
         1840. 2. Marist brothers.

NL 0358084   IMunS CMenSP

The life of Margaret Fox
      see under   Fox, Margaret (Askew) Fell,
1614-1702.

Life of Marie-Catherine Putigny, lay-sister of
      the Visitation convent at Metz; from the French
      by a Sister of the same order.   Ilchester, Md.,
      College press, 1903.
        267 p.

NL 0358086   PPCCH

The life of Marie Lataste, lay-sister of the Congre-
      gation of the Sacred Heart
      see under   [Thompson, Edward Healy] 1813-
1891.

The life of Marlowe and the tragedy of Dido,
      queen of Carthage
      see under   Marlowe, [Christopher] 1564-
1593.

The life of Marmaduke Rawdon of York; or, Marmaduke
Rawdon the second of that name. Now first printed from the
original ms. in the possession of Robert Cooke ... Ed. by
Robert Davies ... ₁Westminster₁ Printed for the Camden
society, 1863.
   xiii, 204 p. incl. geneal. tab. 22½ x 17 cm. ₁Camden society. Publications, no. LXXXV₁

1. Rawdon, Marmaduke, 1610-1669. I. Davies, Robert, 1793-
1875, ed.

[DA20.C17 vol. 85]   A 17—1254
Chicago. Univ. Libr.
for Library of Congress   ₁a58y½₁†

MiU OCU NcU PU MB MU NBuU ViU
NL 0358089   ICU CaBVaU OrU WaSpG DLC CtY MH MdBP OU

The life of Marquis Cornwallis ... Brought down to the
period of his death ... 1805. Ormskirk, J. Fowler, 1806.
   1 p. l., 103-145 p. front. (port.) pl. 20½ᶜᵐ. ₁With Lloyd, Frederick. An
accurate and impartial life of the late Lord Viscount Nelson. Ormskirk,
1806₁

1. Cornwallis, Charles Cornwallis, 1st marquis, 1738-1805.

Library of Congress   DA87.1.N4L7   4-25896†

NL 0358090   DLC

Life of Marshal MᶜMahon, duke of Magenta; with the
pedigree of the MᶜMahon family, from their founder,
Brian Boroimhe, monarch of Ireland, down to the present century, from authentic historic documents. Dublin, Printed and published at the "Irishman" office,
1859.
   iv, ₁5₁-63, ₁1₁ p. front. (port.) 17½ᶜᵐ.
   "Marshal MᶜMahon, duke of Magenta. A biographical sketch" signed
D. H.: p. ₁5₁-14.

"The royal descent of the MᶜMahons of France signed Firinne: p. ₁15₁-28
"By Eugene Curry" in manuscript on cover.

1. MᶜMahon, Marie Edme Patrice Maurice de, duc de Magenta, 1808-1893.
2. MᶜMahon family. I. H., D. II. D. H. III. Firinne. IV. O'Curry, Eugene, 1796-1862.

NL 0358092   MiU

The life of Martin Boos...
      see under   Boos, Martin, 1762-1825.

Life of Martin Luther; including a concise,
but comprehensive history of the Reformation. 2d ed., enl.   Dublin: Printed by
M. Goodwin, 1826.

   Bound (?) with Barbauld, A. L. A. Hymns, in
prose, for children. London, 1825.

NL 0358094   CLU

The life of Martin Luther, the German reformer
      see under   König, Gustav Ferdinand
Leopold, 1808-1869.

Life of Mary Cherubina Clare of St. Francis (in the world) Mary of
the Conception Saraceni, a professed religious in the monastery of
St. Clare of Assisi. Translated from the Italian. With a preface
by Lady Herbert.
   London. Washbourne. 1874. xvi, 192 pp. Portrait. Sm. 8°.

G7618 — Herbert, Mary Elizabeth, Lady, prefacer. — Clarisses.

NL 0358096   MB

The life of Mary Dudley
      see under   Dudley, Mrs. Mary, 1750-1823.

Life of Mary F. McCray
      see under   [McCray, S   J   ]

The life of Mary Jemison, her father and mother
      killed, she captured by Indians, and living
      among them all her life
      see under   [Seaver, James Everett]

BX   Life of Mary Monholland, one of the pioneer
7977.3   sisters of the Order of Mercy in the West.
.M74   By a member of the Order. Chicago, J.S.
L7   Hyland, 1894.

           183 p. port. 20 cm.

           1. Monholland, Mary Francis de Sales,
         Mother, R.S.M., 1816-1888.

NL 0358100   DCU NN ICU ICN KAS

The life of Mary Mordant
      see under   [Marshall, Mrs. L   A   ]

Life, The, of Mary, mother of God; with, The feast of the Assumption; to which are added, the Rosary and the Scapular.   London:
T. Richardson & Son ₁18—?₁.   1 p.l., 9(1), 12, 6 p.   24°.

In: ZLH p. v. 2, no. 4.

1. Mary (Virgin).
N. Y. P. L.   May 14, 1912.

NL 0358102   NN

B
M393.L1   Life of Mary, queen of Scots; with
           a description of Queen Mary's room,
           castle guide, and table shewing the
           descent of Queen Victoria from
           Queen Mary. Written for the warden
           of Queen Mary's room.   Edinburgh,
           Published at Queen Mary's room ₁18--₁
           cover-title, 32p. table. D.

NL 0358103   IaU

Life of Mary Smith, the painter
      see   A brief sketch of the life of Mary
Smith, the painter.

The life of Mary, the Mother of our Lord and
      Savior
      see under   Gihon, Albert Leary.

VOLUME 332

Life of Mary Ward, foundress of the Institute of the B. V. M.
Compiled from various sources. With an introduction by the
Right Rev. Abbot Gasquet, o.s.b.
— London. Burns & Oates, Ltd. [1909.] xxv, 140 pp. Portraits.
Autograph facsimile. 18½ cm., in 8s.

*"This biography ... has been compiled chiefly
from that of Sister Mary Catherine Chambers"*

H3526 — Ward, Mary. 1585–1645. — Institute of Mary, York, England.

NL   0358106   MB MBtS CCamarSJ DCU OrStbM

The life of Masaccio...
    see under   [Patch, Thomas] d. 1782.

PZ 260   The Life of Master Watty & Miss Jessy
.L61   Supine; or, The evils of a bad
18--   education. Wellington: Printed and
          sold by F. Houlston [18--?]
          29 p. illus. 11 cm.

NL   0358108   ICU

Life of Maumer Juno of Charleston, S. C.
    see under   Whilden, Ellen Ann.

The life of Mère St. Joseph (Marie Louise Françoise
Blin de Bourdon) co-foundress and second superior general
of the Institute of Sisters of Notre Dame de Namur, by a
member of the same institute ... London, New York [etc.]
Longmans, Green and co., 1923.

    x, 285, [1] p. front., plates, ports. 22½ cm.
    "Based ... on the French edition published in 1920."—Note, p. v.
    Adapted and translated by Sister Frances de Chantal, s. n. d.
    1. Saint Joseph, mother, 1756–1838. 2. Sisters of Notre Dame de
    Namur.   i. Frances de Chantal, sister, 1875–   ed. and tr.

    BX4485.3.Z8L5   922.2493   23—18952

NL   0358110   DLC CMenSP PRosC PV

Life of Mère Thérèse, founder and first Superior-General of the Daugh-
ters of the Cross. From the French. With a preface by Cardinal
Vaughan.
— London. Burns & Oates. [1893.] xii, 302 pp. Portrait. Sm. 8°.

    Tombeur, Jeanne.

    — Daughters of the Cross.

NL   0358111   MB

The life of Merlin, sirnamed Ambrosivs
    see under   [Heywood, Thomas] d. 1641.

Case   The LIFE of Michael Adrian de Ruyter, Admiral
E   of Holland... London, Printed by J.B. for D.Newman,
5   1677.
.R 936 [1],115p. 16cm.

NL   0358113   ICN InU DFo MH CLU-C

Life of Millard Fillmore. New York, R. M. De Witt [1856]
    32 p. Illus. 22½ᵐ.
    Caption title.
    "Sketch of the life of Andrew Jackson Donelson": p. 29–32.

    1. Fillmore, Millard, pres. U. S., 1800–1874. 2. Donelson, Andrew
    Jackson, 1800–1871. 3. Campaign literature, 1856—American party.

                                                  29—4716

NL   0358114   DLC MdBP NBu

The life of Miss Anne Catley, celebrated singing performer
of the last century, including an account of her introduction to
public life, her professional engagements in London and Dublin, and her various adventures and intrigues ... Carefully
comp. and ed. from the best and most authentic records extant.
London, 1888.

    78 p. front. (port.) 20½ᵐ.

    1. Catley, Anne, 1745–1789.
    Library of Congress   ML420.C36   6—4765
    ——— Copy 2.   PN2598.C25L5

       GU CtY NcD PPT TxU ViU MiU NN MB
NL   0358115   DLC WU NIC PSt TU MiU MB WaT OClW CaOTP

The LIFE of Miss Anne Catley, celebrated singing
performer of the last century; including an account
of her introduction to public life, her professional
engagements in London and Dublin, and her various
adventures and intrigues. Carefully compiled and
edited from the best and most authentic records
extant. London, 1888.   78 p. port.   20cm.

    Microfiche (neg.) 2 sheets. 11 x 15cm. (NYPL FSN 14, 734)

    1. Catley, Anne.

NL   0358116   NN

Life, The, of Miss Catlane; or, the ill effects of a hasty marriage. In
a series of letters. Being a complete narrative of real characters.
To which is added, an essay on false friendship; or Satan's eye
tooth.
London: printed for the author. 1788. vii, (16), 215 pp. 16½
cm., in 6s.

NL   0358117   MB PU

Life of Miss Davis, the Farmer's Daughter of
Essex
    see under   Penn, James.

The life of Miss Fanny Bell
    see   The golden prize, pt. 1. The life
Miss Fanny Bell.

The life of Miss Jenny Cameron, the reputed
mistress of the deputy Pretender. London:
Printed for C, Whitefield, in White-Fryers, Fleet-
Street. MDCCXLVI [1746]

NL   0358120   PU

The LIFE of Miss Julia King of Boston.
New York, 1843.

    pp.31.

NL   0358121   MH

M-film   The life of Miss Marion Smith, being a faithful
810.8   narrative, written by her niece.   Boston,
Am35   1844.
4-11   12 p. illus., ports.

          Microfilm (positive) Ann Arbor, Mich.,
          University Microfilms, 1966. 11th title of 15.
          35 mm. (American fiction series, reel 4.11)

          1. Smith, Marion.

NL   0358122   KEmT CU

Biog.   LIFE of Miss Millie Lammar, the beautiful Cey-
L188ℓ   lonese mind-reader, containing also an expose of
        second-sight mysteries ... New York[188-?]
        [15]p. 17cm.
        1. Mind-reading. 2. Second sight.
        3. Lammar, Millie.

NL   0358123   CtY-M

The life of Miss Sylvia Hardy, the celebrated
Maine giantess, the wonder of America. ...
Written by one who has been intimately ac-
quainted with her for sixteen years. Boston,
William White, 1856.

NL   0358124   PPiU PHi

The Life of Mr. Alexander Kilham, Methodist
preacher ...
    see under   Kilham, Alexander, 1762-
1798.

The Life of Mr. Anthony a Wood, Historiographer
of the most Famous University of Oxford ...
    see under   [Rawlinson, Richard] 1690-
1775.

The life of Mr. Bayle. In a letter to a peer of Great
Britain. London, 1708.
    (*In* Bayle, Pierre. Miscellaneous reflections, occasion'd by the comet
    which appear'd in December 1680. London, 1708. 18ᵐ. vol. ii, 224 p.)
    "Books written by Mr. Bayle": p. 220–224.

                                                  6-26365†

NL   0358127   DLC CtY NjP

The life of Mr. Cleveland, natural son of Oliver
Cromwell
    see under   [Prévost, Antoine François]
called Prévost d'Exiles, 1697-1763.

The life of Mr. George Herbert
    see under   [Walton, Izaak] 1593-1683.

The life of Mr. Henry Longden
    see under   Longden, Henry, 1754-1812.

The life of Mr. James Quin, comedian. With the history of the stage from his commencing actor to his retreat
to Bath. Illustrated with many curious and interesting
anecdotes of several persons of distinction, literature, and
gallantry. To which is added a genuine and authentic
copy of his last will and testament. Dedicated to David
Garrick, esq. London, S. Bladon, 1766.
    2 p. l., 116 p. front. (port.) 17ᵐ.

    1. Quin, James, 1693-1766. 2. Theater—England—Hist.
    Library of Congress   PN2598.Q6L6 1766   13-18400

       PPL CtY
NL   0358131   DLC InU CaBVaU MH MB WaU NcD MiU OU OCU

The life of Mr. James Quin comedian, with the history of
the stage from his commencing actor to his retreat to Bath ...
to which is added a supplement of original facts and anecdotes
... with his trial for the murder of Mr. Bowen. London
[Reader] 1887.
    1 p. l., 107 p. front. (port.) 19½ᵐ.
    The first part is a reprint of the edition of 1766 and contains repro-
    duction of original t.-p.

    1. Quin, James, 1693-1766. 2. Theater—England—Hist.
                                                  1—18588
    Library of Congress   PN2598.Q6L6 1887

       CSmH
       OrU PBL TU MiU MB NN NjP CLSU NcD PU-F NjP PPiU TxU
NL   0358132   DLC PPT IEN TxU PPiU CSmH PU CaBVaU NNC

VOLUME 332

The life of Mr. John Bunyan. 8p. Chelsea, Printed by J. Tilling [18-]

Caption-title.
A chap-book.

NL 0358133 OC1

AC901   The life of Mr. John Bunyan. To which is added,
.M5   sin, no trifle. Philadelphia, Published by
    the Religious Tract Society of Philadelphia,
    William Bradford, Agent.
    12 p. (Miscellaneous pamphlets, 318:5)

NL 0358134 DLC

Life, A, of Mr. John Bunyan, written immediately after his death, and prefixed to what is called the third part of the Pilgrim's progress, first published in 1692, and now reprinted from a copy in the British Museum. With an explanatory advertisement by J. Ivimey. London: G. Wightman, 1832. 2 p.l., (i)iv-viii, 43 p. 24°.

Facsimile title-page also.

1. Bunyan, John. 2. Ivimey, Joseph,   editor.
N.Y.P.L.   July 5, 1913.

NL 0358135 NN

The life of Mr. John Dennis, the renowned critick. In which are likewise some observations on most of the poets and criticks, his contemporaries. Not written by Mr. Curll. London: Printed for J. Roberts ... 1734.
2 p.l., 3-59 p. 19½cm.

First edition.
Signatures: 1 leaf unsigned (half-title), A-G4, H2.
Letter from John Dryden to Dennis: p.12-18.

Unbound in brown cloth folder, by Rivière & son. *Cf.* Wise, T.J. The Ashley library. 1922-36. v.10, p.104.

NL 0358137 CLU-C MH

PR   The life of Mr. John Dennis, the renowned
3409   critick, in which are likewise some obser-
D3   vations on most of the poets and criticks,
Z6   his contemporaries. Not written by Mr.
    Curll. London, Printed for J. Roberts,
    1734.
    59p. 22cm.

Xerox copy.

1. Dennis, John, 1657-1734.

NL 0358138 CtU

PR   **The Life of Mr. John Dennis, the renowned**
3409   **critick, in which are likewise some obser-**
.D3   **vations on most of the poets and criticks,**
L5   **his contemporaries. Not written by Mr.**
    Curll. London, J. Roberts, 1734 [Ann Arbor,
    University Microfilms, 1960]
    59 p. (on double leaves) 23 cm.

1. Dennis, John, 1657-1734.

NL 0358139 WU MsU

The life of Mr. John Dennis, the renowned critick. In which are likewise some observations on most of the poets and criticks, his contemporaries. Not written by Mr. Curll. London, Printed for J. Roberts, 1734 [Ann Arbor, Mich., University Microfilms, 1961. facsim.(59p.) 21cm.

1. Dennis, John, 1657-1734.

NL 0358140 OkU

801.9
D411Y   **The Life of Mr. John Dennis, the renowned**
1964   **critick, in which are likewise some ob-**
    servations on most of the poets and
    criticks, his contemporaries. Not written
    by Mr. Curll. London, Printed for J.
    Roberts, 1734.
    59 p. 22cm.

Photocopy by University Microfilms, Inc., Ann Arbor, Mich., 1964.

1. Dennis, John, 1657-1734. 2. Criticism.

NL 0358142 FU

PR3409   **The life of Mr. John Dennis, the renowned**
D3L5   **critick. In which are likewise some obser-**
    vations on most of the poets and criticks,
    his contemporaries. Not written by Mr.
    Curll. London, J. Roberts, 1734.
    59p. 20cm.

Photocopy made in 1966 by Harvard University Library. 59p. on [118.l.] 13 x 20cm.

1. Dennis, John, 1657-1734.

NL 0358143 IaU OrPS

---

q821M64
BL626   The life of Mr John Milton.
1691f   facsim.: 9 sheets on 5 l.
    Photographic reproduction of fol.140r.-144r. in
    ms. Wood D.4 in the Bodleian library, Oxford.
    Caption title.
    Published in E. S. Parson's The earliest life
    of Milton, in the English historical review, v.
    17, 1902, p.95-110, where this manuscript is dat-
    ed between 1674 and 1691.
    1. Milton, John--Sources. I. Oxford. Univer-
    sity--Bodleian library--Mss.(Wood D.4)

NL 0358144 IU

Life of Mr. John Rowe, of Crediton, Devon: who was born in 1588, and died in 1660. London: Religious Tract Soc., 1835? 68 p. 24°. (Christian biography.)

Preface by the Rev. Theophilus Gale.

1. Rowe, John, 1588-1660. 2. Gale,   Theophilus, 1628-1678. 3. Series.
N.Y.P.L.   May 24, 1916.

NL 0358145 NN CLU

---

*Defoe
30
.723   The life of Mr. John Stanley. Viz. Of his par-
.A10L   ents: how served by officers in his education ...
    Of his going on the highway ... Oh his children
    by Mrs. Maycock; the exact account of stabbing
    her ... His defence, &c. at his trial ... Lon-
    don, Printed by J. Applebee, and sold by T. War-
    ner, 1723.
    viii, 54 p. 19cm.

1. Stanley, John, d. 1723. 2. Crime and criminals—Gt. Brit.

NL 0358146 MB

The life of Mr. Paschal, with his letters relating to the Jesuits ...
see under   Pascal, Blaise, 1623-1662.

The life of Mr. Rich. Hooker, the author of those learned books of the laws of ecclesiastical polity ...
see under   [Walton, Izaak] 1593-1683.

The life of Mr. Richard Savage, son of the Earl Rivers. ... To which are added the lives of Sir Francis Drake, and Admiral Blake. ...

See   under

[Johnson, Samuel, 1709-1784]

The life of Mr. Richard Savage, Who was condemn'd with ...

see under

[Beckingham, Charles, 1699-1731, attributed author]

---

x827
L626   The life of Mr. Robin Lyn, very noted in Great-
    Britain for his large dealings in foreign com-
    modities: containing his birth and parentage; his
    rise from a petty trader to a wealthy merchant;
    the way of his transacting private business, tho'
    contiguous to publick trade, and the prosperity
    of his sovereign's subjects; an account of his
    places of profit, badges of honour, and skill in

    state-physick and golden-specificks; and the
    particulars of his management as sub-governor and
    treasurer of an impoverished company. And, as an
    ornament to this work, is annexed, an inventory
    of his real and personal estate. London,
    Printed for the author and sold by the book-
    sellers of London and Westminster, 1729.
    48p. 21cm.

"A political satire on Robert Walpole, earl of Orford."- Brit. Mus. Cat.

1. Walpole, Robert, 1st earl of Orford, 1676-1745.

NL 0358153 IU CU MB

The life of Mr. Thomas Betterton
see under   [Gildon, Charles] 1665-1724.

The life of Mr. Thomas Firmin, late citizen of London. Written by one of his most intimate acquaintance. With A sermon on Luke x. 36, 37. preach'd on the occasion of his death. Together with An account of his religion, and of the present state of the Unitarian controversy. London, Printed, and sold by A. Baldwin, 1698.
1 p. l., 5-118, 83 p. 17½cm.
(Theological pamphlets, v. 133, no. 5)
"A sermon on Luke x. 36, 37" has special t-p.
"An account of Mr. Firmin's religion; and of the present state of the Unitarian controversy" (with special t.-p.) : 83 p. at end.
1. Firmin, Thomas, 1632-1697.

                              15-9165

NL 0358155 DLC PPL MdBP CtY CBPac

BX9869
.B6T7   The life of Mr. Thomas Firmin, late citizen of
    London. Written by one of his most intimate ac-
    quaintance. With a sermon, on Luke x. 36, 37.
    preached on the occasion of his death. London,
    1791.
    99 p. [With Toulmin, Joshua. A review of the
    life ... of the Rev. John Biddle. London, 1791]
    "Re-printed from the edition of 1698."

1. Firmin, Thomas, 1632-1697.

NL 0358156 ICU MeB MH

VOLUME 332

The life of Mr. William Shakespear.
Whose monument was lately erected in
Westminster-Abbey, at the expence of the
publick ... London:Printed in the year
1743.
37,[2]p. 17cm.
Signatures: [A]–E⁴
Advertisements: p.[38–39]

NL 0358157   CtY DFo

Life of Mr. William Whittingham, dean of Durham,
from a ms. in Antony Wood's collection, Bodleian library,
Oxford, with an appendix of original documents from the
Record office. Edited by Mary Anne Everett Green. ₁Westminster₎ Printed for the Camden society, 1870.
1 p. l., ii, 48 p. 22 cm. ₁The Camden miscellany, v. 6, no. 1₎
Forms part of the society's Publication no. civ.

1. Whittingham, William, d. 1579.   i. Green, Mary Anne Everett
(Wood) 1818–1895, ed.   ii. Oxford. University. Bodleian library.

Columbia Univ.   Libraries   A 41—1274
for Library of Congress   [DA20.C17   vol. 104]
              ₁a50e₂₄₎   (942.0062)

NL 0358158   NNC CaBVaU INS PU OCU PPPD PU CU MH MU

The life of Mr. Woolston, with an impartial account of his
writings. London, Printed for J. Roberts, 1733.
31 p. 19ᶜᵐ.
"Ascribed by Woog to Thomas Stackhouse."—Dict. nat. biog., v. 62,
p. 480.

1. Woolston, Thomas, 1670–1733.   i. Stackhouse, Thomas, 1677–
1752, supposed author.

Library of Congress   BR1725.W64L5   38–4812
                     ₍2₎   222

NL 0358159   DLC NjP IEN CtY CLU-C

The life of Mrs. Abington (formerly Miss Barton) celebrated comic actress, with full accounts of her various performances in the theatres of London and Dublin. Including
also interesting notes upon the history of the Irish stage and
copious notices, anecdotes, and criticisms of her theatrical contemporaries ... By the editor of the "Life of Quin." London, Reader, 1888.
1 p. l., 124 p. front. (port.) 20ᶜᵐ.

1. Abington, Frances (Barton) 1737–1815.

Library of Congress   PN2598.A2L5   1–18932 rev.
——— Large paper copy.   26¼ x 19¼ᶜᵐ

    NcD MiU MB NN PU-P PU
NL 0358160   DLC WaU OC1 NNC PSt PPL MH GU NcU CtY

Life of Mrs. Cameron
    see under   [Cameron, Mrs. Lucy Lyttelton
(Butt)] 1781–1858.

The life of Mrs. Dorothy Lawson

    See under

₁Palmer, William₎ 1591–1670.

E   ...The LIFE of Mrs. Hannah Childs, who long in
5   darkness lay, will now be brought to light.
.9   n.p.,n.d.
       27p.
Ce-Chi
       Binder's title: Individual biography.
       Caption title.

NL 0358163   ICN RPB MWA

CS71   The life of Mrs. Joseph Dorsett Bedle, founder, and
.B412   first regent of the Paulus Hook Chapter
1939   ₁Daughters of the American Revolution₎ 1842–
        1926. Presented by the Paulus Hook Chapter,
        Jersey City, New Jersey; Mrs. William Voorhees, recent; Eleanor Remsen Vredenburgh
        Micelli, Chairman, Genealogical records
        committee. Jersey City, 1939.
        19 l.   ports.   28 cm.

        Typewritten.

        1. Bedle, Alt ...nea (Randolph)

NL 0358164   NjR

The life of Mrs. Kendall.   n. p., 1947

     See under

₁Kendall, William₎

Life of Mrs. Mary D. James
    see under   [James, Joseph H.]

The life of Mrs. Sherwood ... Abridged for the Presbyterian board of publication. Philadelphia, Presbyterian board of publication ₍ᶜ1857₎
152 p.   front. (port.)   17½ᶜᵐ.
Preface signed: J. H.
Material selected from "The life of Mrs. Sherwood," edited by Sophia
Kelly.

1. Sherwood, Mrs. Mary Martha (Butt) 1775–1851.   i. Presbyterian
church in the U. S. A. Board of publication.   ii. Kelly, Mrs. Sophia
(Sherwood) Streeten, b. 1815.   iii. H., J.   iv. J. H.

                            21–3204

Library of Congress   PR5449.S4Z5 1857

NL 0358167   DLC MH MWA AU

Life of Mohammad ... 1853, 1858.
    see under   [Bowen, George] 1816–1888.

The life of Mohammed ... Philadelphia, American
Sunday-school union; London, Religious tract
society₎ ₍n.d.₎
     xiv, 15–192 p.   15½ᶜᵐ.
     "The American Sunday-school union have made an arrangement with the London Religious Tract Society, to publish,
concurrently with them, such of their valuable works as
are best suited to our circulation ... As they will be
substantially, reprints of the London edition, the credit
of their general character will belong to our English
brethren ...."—Verso of t.-p.

1. Muhammad, the prophet.   I. American Sunday-school
union.   II. Title.

NL 0358169   ViU MA

---

297   ┌─────────────────────────────────┐
Zm9p1l   │ The life of Mohammed...   Phil.,Amer-
        │ ican Sunday-school union₎etc.,etc.₎188–?₎
           Attributed to Humphrey Prideaux.

NL 0358170   N

The life of Moll Flanders
    see   Defoe, Daniel, 1661?–1731.
    The fortunes and misfortunes of the famous
Moll Flanders.

The life of Monsieur Des Cartes, containing the
history of his philosophy and works
    see under   [Baillet, Adrien] 1649–1706.

The life of M. Olier
    see under   [Faillon, Etienne Michel]
1800–1870.

Life of Moses.   London, I. T. Wood, n.d.
Illustrated broadsheet on cardboard,
15:11.5 cm.
    1. Art. 2. Moses. 3. Title.
    4. Bible-Pictures.

NL 0358174   NNJ

The life of Moses. Written by a friend of little children,
particularly for their use. Embellished with eight engravings. New York, W. Burgess, 1830.
iv, ₁5₎–108 p.   front., plates.   14½ᶜᵐ.

1. Moses.

Library of Congress   BS580.M6L5   36–37407
                    ₍2₎   221.92

NL 0358175   DLC

LIFE OF MOSES, the meekest man.
[Woodcut.] Be all my ways of modest kind. Of
humble, meek, and gentle mind. New-York:
Printed and sold by Mahlon Day, At the New
Juvenile Book-store, No. 374, Pearl-street.
n. d.   CHILDREN'S ROOM
8 x 4.8 cm. Paper covers. Illustrations.
In prose.

NL 0358176   NN

Life of most reverend Peter Richard Kenrick. 1891
    see under   O'Brien, Rev. John.

Life of Mother Catherine Aurelia of the Precious Blood,
foundress of the Institute of the precious blood, 1833–1905, by
a member of the institute; introduction by Rev. A. M. Skelly,
o. p.   St. Louis, Mo. and London, B. Herder book co., 1929.
xxii, 205 p.   front., pl., ports.   23ᶜᵐ.

1. Catherine Aurélie du Précieux Sang, Mere, 1833–1905. 2. Sisters
adorers of the precious blood.   I. A member of the institute.

Library of Congress   BX4705.C345L5   29—16326

NL 0358178   DLC WaSpG COSA CMenSP OrStbM

The life of Mother Clare Fey
    see under   Watterott, Ignaz, 1869–1922.

LIFE of Mother Elizabeth Boyle, one of Mother
Seton's first companions, and first superioress
of "The Sisters of Charity of Vincent de Paul"
in New York City. By A.M.M.G. Edited by James
Dougherty. Mount Loretto. Staten Island,
N.Y., press of the Mission of the Immaculate
Virgin,1893.

Ports. and plates.
On binding; Mount St. Vincent series, [1]

NL 0358180   MH

BX   Life of Mother Gamelin, foundress and first
4705   superior of the Sisters of Charity of Providence, by a Religious of her institute.
.G3   Translated from the French by Anna T. Sadler.
L513   Montreal, Mother House of Providence, 1912.
       xxii,274p. illus.,ports. 24cm.

       Errata: p.₍xxv₎

       1. Gamelin, Marie Emmelie Eugene Tavernier,
Mother, 1800–1851. 2. Sisters of Charity of
Providence. I. A religious of her institute.

NL 0358181   OrU WaS CaBVa DGC

VOLUME 332

The **life** of Mother Gin; containing, a true and faithful relation of her conduct and politicks, in all the various and important occurrences of state that she was engaged in during her time; her transactions with several eminent patriots and great m——s; particularly, in the four last years of the late q——n; with the secret motives, and true reasons of her fall; and a detection of the views of the authors of it. By an impartial hand. London, Printed for W. Webb, 1736.

31 p. 19¼ᵐᵐ. ₁With Holden, A. A vindication of a pamphlet ... intituled The tryal of the spirits ... London, 1736₁

1. Gin. 2. Liquor prob lem—Gt. Brit.

10-13663

Library of Congress HV5448.H8

NL 0358182 DLC NNNAM CLU-C CtY

BX 8013 .J4 K4 L7

The Life of Mother Henrietta Kerr, religious of the Sacred Heart. Edited by John Morris, S.J. 3d ed. Roehampton, 1892.
xii, 394 p. front. (mounted port.)
19 cm.
1. Kerr, Henrietta Mary Emma, 1842-1884. 2. Society of the Sacred Heart of Jesus. I. Morris, John, 1826-1893, ed.

NL 0358183 DCU PPCCH

The life of Mother Henrietta Kerr
see also The life of Henrietta Kerr.

M282.774 L72

Life of Mother M. Camilla Madden, O.S.D. Adrian, Mich., Sisters of St. Dominic, St. Joseph's College and Academy [192-?]
89p. illus.,ports. 24cm.

1.Camilla, Mother. 2.St. Joseph's College and Academy, Adrian, Mich. 3.Sisters of the Order of St. Dominic, Adrian, Mich. I.Sisters of the Order of St. Dom inic, Adrian, Mich.

NL 0358185 Mi

Life of Mother Margaret Mary Hallahan, foundress of the English Congregation of St. Catherine of Sienna of the Third order of St. Dominic. By her religious children. With a preface by ... the Bishop of Birmingham ... London, Longmans, Green, Reader, and Dyer, 1869.
xv, 539 p., 2 leaves, front. (port.)
22.5 cm.
1. Tertiaries (Dominicans) Congregation of St. Catharine of Sienna. 2. Hallahan, Margaret Mary. 3. Catholic church in England. Biography.

NL 0358186 NNUT

Life of Mother Marie-Hermine of Jesus, massacred in Shan-si (China) July 9th, 1900. ₁Quebec, 1910₁
89 p. illus. ports. 24 cm.

1. Marie-Hermine de Jésus, Mother, 1866-1900.

BV3427.M286A3 52-46464

NL 0358187 DLC NN

Life of Mother Mary of Saint Maurice, second superior-general of the society of Marie Reparatrice, by a religous of the same society... London & Edinburgh, Sands & co., 1922.

NL 0358188 NNF

The life of Mother Pauline von Mallinckrodt
see under [Servatia, sister] 1880-

Life of Mother St. Augustine O'Keefe, superioress of Ursuline convent, New Orleans. By an Ursuline nun ... ₁New Orleans₁ 1888.
cover-title, 12 p. 23ᶜᵐ.

1. O'Keeffe, Saint Augustine, mother, 1811-1888. 2. Charlestown, Mass. Ursuline convent. ɪ. An Ursuline nun.

37-17884

Library of Congress BX4705.O45L5
Copyright 1888: 32019 ₍2₎ 922.273

NL 0358190 DLC

The life of Mother Shipton
See *under*
₁Thompson, Thomas, fl. 1668.₁

Life of my patron saint. J.A. McGee, ₁1856₁

Variously paged, illus., plates, 15 cm.
Title page missing. Title taken from cover.

1. Saints, Women. 2. Wenefrida, O.S.B., Saint, d. 660.

NL 0358192 PLatS

... The life of My Savior
see under [Mary Catherine, sister]

Life of Napoleon Bonaparte ...

All entires are arranged by imprint date, regardless of subtitle.

The life of Napoleon Bonaparte, late Emperor of France, from his birth to his abdication, and arrival at Elba; including his parentage, military achievements, remarkable actions, speeches, battles, & victories... to which is added, a geographical description of the Island of Elba. London,W.Mason,n.d.
72p. 18½cm.

At head of title: Third edition, with a map of the Island of Elba.

Bound with Monkhouse, John. The last moments of Buonaparte... London,n.d.

NL 0358196 OClWHi

The Life of Napoleon Bonaparte. Philadelphia, American Sunday-school union, [n.d.]
192 p. 15 cm.
Originally published by the Religious tract society, London.
1. Napoleon I, Emperor of the French, 1769-1821. I. Religious tract society, London.

NL 0358197 IaU

DC203 L7

Life of Napoleon Bonaparte, emperor of the French, king of Italy and protector of the Rhenish confederation, from his birth to the present time. Hudson, Wm. E. Norman, 1810.

108p.incl.front. 15cm.

1. Napoleon I, emperor of the French, 1769-1821.

NL 0358198 NBuG NBu CoU NjP ICN

Life of Napoleon Bonaparte, emperor of the French, king of Italy, and protector of the Rhenish confederation. New York, E. Duyckinck, 1811.
108 p. incl. front. (port.) 14 cm.
Published, with additions, Hudson, N.Y., 1813 under title: Memoirs of the life and actions of Napoleon Bonaparte ...
P. 101-104 wanting.
1. Napoléon I, emperor of the French, 1769-1821.

NL 0358199 CtY MH

Life of Napoleon Bonaparte, emperor of the French, king of Italy, and protector of the Rhenish Confederation. New York, J. Tiebout, 1811.
108 p. port. 14 cm.
1. Napoleon I, emperor of the French, 1769-1821.

NL 0358200 MnU MWA

The life of Napoleon Bonaparte, emperor of the French ... 1812
see under H., J.

... The life of Napoleon Bonaparte. London, J. Wallis [1814]-18
see under [Heweston, W B]

944.05 N162X

The life of Napoleon Bonaparte, late emperor of France, from his birth in 1769 to his arrival in Elba; containing an account of his parents, education, preferment, battles, etc., interspersed with numerous and interesting anecdotes. 4th ed. with additions. Berwick, W. Lockhead, 1815.
584 p. front. (port.) fold. maps. 21 cm.

1. Napoleon I, emperor of the French, 1769-1821. 2. France--Hist.--1789-1815.

NL 0358203 MoSU

The Life of Napoleon Bonaparte, late emperor of France, from his birth to his abdication, and arrival at Elba; including his parentage, military achievements, remarkable actions, speeches, battles & victories. And a full account of his campaigns ... interspersed with anecdotes and biographical memoirs of the principal generals in the French armies. To which is added a geographical description of the Island of Elba. 1st American, from the 3d London ed. Boston, T.W. White, 1815.
71 p. 18 cm.
1. Napoléon I, emperor of the French, 1769-1821.

NL 0358204 RPB MBC CtY MiDA MWA MB

The life of Napoleon Bonaparte; late Emperor of the French, &c. &c. &c. from his birth, until his departure to the Island of St. Helena. By a citizen of Delaware. Wilmington,Printed for M.R. Lockerman by R. Porter, 1815.
275 p. 12mo

Early printing of the text which later became the first literary work printed in

Indiana, Salem, 1818. The Indiana text has title: The life of Bonaparte ... Py a citizen of the United States. Bound in contemporary calf.

NL 0358206 InU OSW NcU DeWI

VOLUME 332

Beinecke
Library
Bo67
816M

The life of Napoleon Bonaparte; late emperor
of the French, &c. &c. &c. from his birth, until his departure to the island of St. Helena.
By a citizen of the United States. Warren,
Published by James White, 1816.
xii, [13]-312 p. 21 cm.

1. Napoleon I, emperor of the French, 1769-
1821. I. A citizen of the United States.

NL   0358207   CtY IEN OClWHi ViU InU NjP

944.05
N162X
1817

The life of N. Bonaparte, late emperor of
France, from his birth in 1769 to his arrival
in Elba: containing an account of his parents,
education, talents, preferment, battles, ministers, generals, etc., interspersed with numerous, interesting and professional anecdotes. To which is added Parker's account of
the battle of Waterloo containing a detail of
all the principal events and occurences that
took place on Bonaparte's departure from Elba
until his arrival in St. Helena. 5th ed.
with additions. Berwick, W. Lockhead [1817]
584, 200 p.   front. (port.) maps.
21 cm. Napoleon I,   emperor of the French, 1769-
1821.

NL   0358208   MoSU

The LIFE of Napoleon Bonaparte, late emperor
of France, from his birth to his abdication, and
arrival at Elba, [etc., etc.]. Interspersed with
anecdotes and biographical memoirs of the
principal generals in the French armies. To
which is added a geographical description of
the Island of Elba. 1st American, from the 3d
London ed. Boston, T.W.White, 1817.

19 cm.   pp.71.

NL   0358209   MH

The life of Napoleon Bonaparte, from the best French and
English authorities ... including original correspondence, and
numerous anecdotes of his cotemporaries. Illustrated with
eighty engravings. London, M. Moore, 1839.
1 p. l., 646 p. front. (port.) illus. 22cm.

1. Napoléon I, emperor of the French, 1769-1821.

Library of Congress   DC203.L72   4—13182

NL   0358210   DLC OClWHi

Case
Y
148
.158

The LIFE of Napoleon Bonaparte.   [London,
Ryle & Paul,184-?]
12p. illus. 17cm.

Binder's title: Chap-books.
Caption title.

NL   0358211   ICN

Soc
DC
203
L7

The life of Napoleon Bonaparte, late Emperor
of the French, selected from the most authentic sources. With an introductory essay by
Dr. Channing.   Halifax, W. Milner, 1840.
440p. front.(port.)

Added t.p., engr., with vignette.

1. Napoléon I, Emperor of the French,
1769-1821. I. Channing, William Ellery,
1780-1842.

NL   0358212   FTaSU CtY

The life of Napoleon Bonaparte, late emperor
of the French, selected from the most
authentic sources. With an introductory
essay, by Dr. Channing.   Halifax, W. Milner,
1845.
lxxii, 440 p.   12.5 x 8.5 cm.

NL   0358213   PLF CtY

... Life of Napoleon Bonaparte, emperor of the
French, containing numerous anecdotes of his
court and times ...   Philadelphia, Lindsay
& Blakiston [c1845]
vi, 188 p. front., illus., plates. 18 cm.
(The young American's library)
1. Napoléon I, emperor of the French,
1769-1821.

NL   0358214   CU MWA

Life of Napoleon Bonaparte. N.Y.,1856.
256p. 32°

NL   0358215   MWA

Life of Napoleon Bonaparte. Emperor of the French.
From the best authorities. New York, P. J. Cozans, 1860.
iv, [5]-256 p. incl. plates, ports. 12½cm.

1. Napoléon I, emperor of the French, 1769-1821.

                                34–5727
Library of Congress   DC203.L73   923.144

NL   0358216   DLC

DC203
.L726
1876

Life of Napoleon Bonaparte, Emperor of the
French; containing numerous anecdotes of
his court and times. Boston, Lee and
Shepard [1876?]
188 p. illus. 19cm. (The Young American's
library. Famous generals [6])

1. Napoléon I, Emperor of the French, 1769-1821.

NL   0358217   ViU NN OrP

Life of Napoleon Bonaparte
   see also   Memoirs of the life and actions
of Napoleon Bonaparte.

The life of Napoleon Buonaparte: containing historical
sketches, and anecdotes illustrative of his public and private
character. Impartially selected and arranged from the most
authentic documents and publications. With a portrait of the
emperor. By an American. Elizabeth-town, N. J. Published
by Allen and Bryant. J. & E. Sanderson, printers. 1820.
vii, [9]–503 p. 22cm.
Portrait wanting.

1. Napoléon I, emperor of the French, 1769-1821. I. An American.

                                28–5518
Library of Congress   DC203.L725

ViLxW MWA NjR OMC NjP ViRVal
NL   0358219   DLC CSmH IaCrC MH MS MSa NPtw NcD CtY

The life of Napoleon Buonaparte, emperor of the
French. 1834
   see under   [Scott, Sir Walter] bart.,
1771-1832.

The Life of Napoleon III, ex-emperor of the French,
containing a full account of his birth, etc.
London, Diprose & Bateman, 1873.
On cover:-Diprose's edition.

NL   0358221   MH

The life of Ned Scarlet, the daring highwayman. By the author
of "Dick Clinton"...etc., etc.   New York: Dick & Fitzgerald
[187-?]   112 p. illus.   22½cm.
Printed in double columns.

37730B. 1. Fiction, English.   I. Dick Clinton, Author of.
II. Title: Ned Scarlet.
N. Y. P. L.   September 30, 1940

NL   0358222   NN

The life of Nelson
   see under   [Barker, Mathew Henry]
1790-1846.

The life of Nicholas Ferrar, M. A. and fellow of Clare-hall,
Cambridge. Designed particularly for youth. Philadelphia,
French & Perkins; Boston, Perkins & Marvin, 1833.
108 p. 14½cm.

1. Ferrar, Nicholas, 1592-1637.

                                37–23857
Library of Congress   BX5199.F4L5
                        [2]   922.342

NL   0358224   DLC ViW NjPT ViU

The life of Nicholas Ferrar, 1852
   see under   [Peckard, Peter] 1718?-1797.

The life of Nicholas Hart
   see under   [Hill, William, attorney]

BX
4705
P39
1869

The life of Nicholas Pavillon, Bishop of
Alet, of whom a short account has already
been presented to English readers by
Mrs. Schimmelpenninck in her "Select
memoirs of Port Royal," under the head
of "A tour to Alet." Chiefly translated
from the French by a layman of the Church
of England. Oxford, A. R. Mowbray,
1869.
xvi,346 p. port. 19cm.

NL   0358227   NIC OrU DNC

The life of Nicolas Herman...
   see under   Herman, Nicolaus, 1611-1691.

The life of Nicolas Mooney ... taken from his
own mouth
   see under   Mooney, Nicolas, 1721-1752.

The life of Nixon, the Cheshire prophet.
(In Nixon, Robert, the Cheshire prophet. Pp. 20-32. London.
[1714.])
By W. E.

L2381 — Nixon, Robert, the Cheshire prophet.

NL   0358230   MB

VOLUME 332

The life of Oliver Cromwel ⌠l680?⌡, ⌠17-?⌡
    see under   [Crouch, Nathaniel] 1632?-1725?

By44
69

The life of Oliver Cromwel, lord protector of
the common-wealth of England, Scotland, and
Ireland. Being an account of all the battles,
sieges ... wherein he was engaged ... and
likewise, of his civil administration ...
London, Printed by D. Pratt, [1715?]
    2 p.l., 137, [8] p. 14½ cm.
    Bookseller's catalogue at end contains Robin-
son Crusoe, first pub. 1714. Not to be confused with The history of Oliver Cromwell by
Nathaniel Crouch.

NL 0358232   CtY DFo

DA426
.K49
1741

The life of Oliver Cromwell.
                   FOR OTHER EDITIONS
                   SEE MAIN ENTRY
⌠Kimber, Isaac⌡ 1692-1755.
    The life of Oliver Cromwell, lord-protector of the com-
monwealth of England, Scotland, and Ireland. Impartially collected from the best historians, and several original manuscripts. The 4th ed., with additions. London,
Printed for J. Brotherton ⌠etc.⌡ 1741.

The life of Oliver Cromwell, lord protector of the common-
wealth of Great-Britain and Ireland. Containing a just account of all his military exploits, and surprizing success during
the civil wars of England ... By a gentleman of Oxford. London, Printed for T. Thompson, 1748.
    247 p. 18ᵐ.

    1. Cromwell, Oliver, 1500-1658.

                                    3-15592

Library of Congress   DA428.L72

NL 0358234   DLC ViU

DA
426
L5
Cage

    The life of Oliver Cromwell. Containing his
military exploits in England during the grand rebellion; his reduction of Scotland, and conquest
of Ireland: his civil government, policy, treaties
with, and respect paid him, by foreign princes and
states. With an account of the great actions performed by his brave generals and admirals in the
war with the Dutch and Spaniards. London, H. Woodgate and S. Brooks, 1760.
    [2] 164 p. [A]¹, B-G¹², H¹¹. ([A]1 possibly
printed as H12). 12mo.

NL 0358235   DFo CSmH MnU

Life of Oliver Wolcott. [anon.] Philadelphia,
R.W. Pomeroy, 1823.
    63-77 p. 1 port. 8°.
    p. 63-77 of Biography of the signers of
the Declaration of Independence, J. Sanderson,
v. 3, 1823.

NL 0358236   DLC

The LIFE OF one Jacob Bochmen. Wherein
is contained a perfect catalogue of his
workes. London, R. Whitaker, 1644.

    sm. 4°. pp.(8). Plate.

NL 0358237   MH

The life of Origen. London, Religious tract
society, 1840.
    100 p. T.

NL 0358238   PP

... The life of Oscar Wilde as prosecutor and
prisoner. London, Published for the proprietors
[1895]
    cover-title,⌠3⌡-16 p. 21ᵐ.

    At head of title: Just out. Complete.
    Cf. Clark, W.A. Wilde and Wildeiana. 1922-31.
v.5, p.68; [Millard, C.S.] Bibliography of Oscar
Wilde. London [1914] p.578-579, no.686.

NL 0358239   CLU-C

The life of Oscar Wilde as prosecutor and
prisoner
    see also   The life, trial and verdict of
Oscar Wilde..

The life of our Blessed Lord and Saviour Jesus
Christ. ⌠n.p., n.d.⌡
    728p.

    Includes also the Life of the Blessed Virgin
Mary, Lives of the Apostles and, the profane
history from the birth of Christ to the comple-
tion of the New Testament.
    Imperfect: title-page and pages 1-10 lacking.

NL 0358241   ICRL

YA
.S863

    The life of our blessed Lord and Saviour Jesus
    Christ...Vol. II. New York [n.d.].
    204p.
    (Sunday school books; arr. numerically)

NL 0358242   DLC

    The LIFE of our blessed Lord and Saviour Jesus Christ.
In prose and verse... Andover, Mass., Published by
the American tract society, and for sale at the General
depository & by agents of the society throughout the U.
States [1824?] 31 p. illus. 13cm.

    At head of title: No. 16.
    In original illustrated tan paper covers, with publishers' advertisements
on back.
    1. Jesus Christ--Life, Juvenile.   I. American tract society, Boston.

NL 0358243   NN RPB

    The LIFE of our blessed Lord and Saviour Jesus Christ.
In prose and verse... New-York, Published by the
American tract society, 150 Nassau-street [183-?]
31 (1) p. illus. 11cm.

    At head of title: No. 11. On cover: Series III. No. XI.
    In original illustrated green paper covers, with publishers' advertise-
ments on back.
    Imprint on cover has 144 Nassau-st.

    Presentation copy to Mary F. Harvey from her teacher, Caroline G.
Jones.

    1. Jesus Christ--Life, Juvenile. I. American tract society.

NL 0358245   NN

    Life of our blessed Lord & Saviour, Jesus Christ.
N.Y., 1852.
    Edited by D.P. Kidder.

    I. Kidder, Daniel Parish, 1815-1891, ed.

NL 0358246   ODW

BT300
L5

The life of our Blessed Savior, Jesus
    Christ. ⌠n.p., n.d.⌡
    154p. illus. 14cm.

    Title-page and pages after 154
lacking.
    Contains also brief biographies of
Saints Luke, John, Peter, James, Philip,
Bartholomew, Andrew, Thomas and Jude.

NL 0358247   RPB

The life of our Lord and Savior Jesus Christ,
Boston, 1844
    see under
[Chapman, Edwin.]

The life of Ovr Lord and Saviovr Iesvs-Christ ... 1634
    see under   Heigham, John, fl. 1639, comp.

The life of Our Lord, in the words of the four
    Evangelists ...
        see under   Bible. N.T. Gospels.
English. Harmonies. 18--? (N.Y., Anson)
Also: 1877? Authorized. (N.Y., Randolph)
See also similar or ident. title with date "1901?"
(N.Y., Whittaker)

Life of our president, Benjamin Harrison, together
with that of his grandfather, 1889
    see under   Morrison, J.E.

Is94
t l
v.1(1

The life of Our Savior. New Haven, Published
by S.Babcock,1840.
    8p. illus. 7½cm.
    Title vignette.

NL 0358252   CtY MiD

(The) life of Our Saviour, Jesus Christ;
extracted from the New Testament... for the
use of children
        see under   Bible. N.T. English.
Selections. 1835.   (also 1849)

The life of Paine
    see under   [Linton, William James] 1812-1897

---

*EC7
R3961
H741l

    The life of Pamela. Being a full and particu-
lar relation of the birth and advancement of
that fortunate and beautiful young damsel, who,
from the lowest degree of rural life, came to
be the mistress of a most splendid house and
fortune, by her steady adherence to the principles of virtue and honour. Shewing the various
arts that were used to seduce and betray her;
and in what manner she triumph'd in her innocence
and chastity: with what decency and propriety
she supported the exalted station to which she
was raised; and with what exemplary piety she

    finished a life that was attended with so many
hazardous attacks upon her constancy and virtue
...
    London:Printed for C.Whitefield,in White
Fryers.MDCCXLI.
    1p.l.,495p. front.,9 pl. 17cm.
    Pages 191 & 256 misnumbered 119 & 526.
    Erroneously attributed on binding to Fielding.
    The plates are by John Carwitham.
    Two extra en-   graved plates have been
inserted.

NL 0358256   MH CtY

VOLUME 332

Life of Pastor Fliedner of Kaiserswerth. Translated from the German (with the author's sanction) by Catherine Winkworth ... London, Longmans, Green, and co., 1867.

xxvi, 155 p. front. (port.) 18ᶜᵐ.

Original German edition appeared in the "Kaiserswerth almanack" for 1866. *cf.* Editor's pref.

1. Fliedner, Theodor, 1800–1864.   I. Winkworth, Catherine, 1827–1878, tr.

Library of Congress   BX8080.F55L5   5–2599

NL 0358257   DLC CtY MH MBAt

Life of Patrick Hamilton, abbot of Ferne ...
        see under   [Lawson, John Parker]
d. 1852.

The life of Patty Saunders. Written by herself
        see under   Saunders, Patty, pseud.

The life of Paul Jones. 1827?
        see   Fairburn's improved edition of the
life of Paul Jones.

Life of Paul Jones. [n. p., 1829.] 255–284 p. port. 8°.

Binder's title.
Excerpt.

471504A. 1. Jones, John Paul, 1747–   1792. 2. Navy, U. S.—Hist.—Biog.
N. Y. P. L.   October 29, 1930

NL 0358261   NN

The **life** of Paul Jones, containing his travels, voyages, and daring engagements, with numerous anecdotes of undaunted courage.... Hartford: Printed and published by B. & J. Russell, 1818. 60 p.
2. ed. 24°.

p. 7–8 mutilated.
Pages 50–51, 54–55, 58–59 wrongly numbered 62–63, 66–67, 70–71.

1. Jones, John Paul, 1747–1792.   2. Navy—U. S.—Hist.—Revolution.
N. Y. P. L.   July 18, 1925

NL 0358262   NN CSmH NcWfC

The **life** of Paul Jones, containing his travels, voyages, and daring engagements, with numerous anecdotes of undaunted courage. 30th ed. [n. p.] Printed for the publishers, 1831.

64 p. 11½ᶜᵐ.

Earlier editions appeared under various titles: The interesting life, travels, voyages, and daring engagements of ... Paul Jones ...; The life, travels, voyages ... of Paul Jones ...; The life, voyages, and sea battles of ... Paul Jones ...

1. Jones, John Paul, 1747–1792.

Library of Congress   E207.J7 I 655   17–24574

NL 0358263   DLC

Case
E
5   The LIFE of Paul Jones, the pirate, one of
.J 72747   the principal characters in the celebrated novel, "The pilot", by Sir Walter Scott, bart. With some highly interesting particulars of Captain Gustavus Cunningham, another pirate, contemporary with Paul Jones. Compiled from the London gazette, and other authentic sources. London, Hodgson & co.[1826?]

iv,[5]–24p. fold.col.front. 19½cm.

Front., obviously intended originally for another publication, has caption: Comodore Paul Jones, and imprint: London, Printed for T. Hughes, 1826.

NL 0358264   ICN CSmH MiU-C

The life of Paul Jones
        see also   The interesting life, travels, voyages, and daring engagements of ... Paul Jones.

The life of Paul Jones
        see also   The life, travels, voyages ...
of Paul Jones.

The life of Paul Jones
        see also   The life, voyages, and sea battles of ... Paul Jones.

The life of Peter Stuart, the "Ditton Doctor"
        see under   [Finigan, L   ]

The life of Peter the Great. Frederick-Town, 1813
        see under   Voltaire, François Marie
Aroute de, 1694–1778.

The life of Peter the Great. Trenton, 1813
        see under   [Banks, John] 1709–1751.

Life of Peter the Great ... 1882
        see under   [Wight, Orlando Williams]
1824–1888, ed.

The life of Peter the Great. New York [1903]
        see under   Barrow, Sir John, bart.,
1764–1848.

The life of Petrarch, collected from Memoires
pour la vie de Petrarch by Mrs. Dobson...

        See under

[Sade, Jacques Francois Paul Aldonce de] 1705–1788

Beinecke   The **Life** of Philip Melancthon. Printed for
Library.   the blind under the direction of S.G. Howe
Ma45   at the expense of the American Sunday School
M489X   Union: at the N.E. Institution for the
+L61   Education of the Blind. Boston, 1837.
50 numb. *l.* 15 x 26 cm.
Embossed in "Boston line" or "Howe type".
Imperfect: leaves 5, 8, 15, 17, 44 mutilated, with some loss of type; corners of page wanting on t.-p. and *l.* 1.

NL 0358274   CtY

Life of Philip Melancthon [!], the German reformer ... Philadelphia, Presbyterian board of publication, 1841.

198 p. 15½cm.

1. Melanchthon, Philipp, 1497–1560. I. Presbyterian church in the U. S. A. Board of publication.

NL 0358275   ViU ViLxW PPPrHi NWM NcD

BR
335   **Life** of Philip Melancthon, the German
.L72   reformer. ... Philadelphia, Presbyterian
board of publication [187–?]
202 p.

NL 0358276   MiU ViU

The **life** of Philip the Evangelist. By a Sunday-school teacher. Rev. by D. P. Kidder. New York, Lane & Tippett, for the Sunday-school union of the Methodist Episcopal church, 1846.

85 p. front. 16°.   1–14616—M 2

NL 0358277   DLC

Life of Philip, the Indian chief
        see under   [Savage, Sarah] 1785–1837.

The life of Pill Garlick
        see under   Temple, Sir Edmund.

The life of Pontiac the chief of the Ottawas, together with a full account of the celebrated siege of Detroit. New York, 1860.
102 p. incl. front. (map)

NL 0358280   OClWHi

BX
513   A **life** of Pope St. Gregory the Great, written
.W57   by a monk of the monastery of Whitby (probably
G24   about A.D. 713) Westminster [Eng.] Art and
Book Co., 1904.
x, 46 p. illus. 26 cm.
Printed from MS. Gallen, 567.
Ed. by Francis Aidan Gasquet, cardinal, 1846–1929.
1. Gregory I, the Great, Saint, Pope, 540 (ca.)–604. I. A monk of the monastery of Whitby II. Title.

NL 0358281   DCU NjP PP MH CtY OCl MiU ILS NIC NcD

The life of President Edwards.
        see under   American Sunday-school union.

The **Life** of Prince Eugene of Savoy, Generalissimo of the Emperor's army in Italy. Written originally in the German tongue, translated out of that into French and now into English. London, E. Castle and S. Buckley, 1702.

249 p. 19 cm.

1. Eugène, Prince of Savoie-Carignan, 1663–1736.

D274.E8L63   66–39837

NL 0358283   DLC CLU-C InU MnU

The life of Prince Eugene, of Savoy, 1812
        see under   Ligne, Charles Joseph, prince de] 1735–1814.

Life of Prince Talleyrand
        see under   [Villemarest, Charles Macime de]
1785–1852.

VOLUME 332

The life of Princess Louisa (Madame Louise)
see under   [Proyart, Liévain Bonaventure]
1743?-1808.

The life of Queen Anne
see under   [Boyer, Abel]

The Life of Quin, editor of.
The life of Mrs. Abington
see under title

The life of Rafaello Sanzio da Urbino
see under   [Duppa, Richard] 1770-1831.

A life of Ramón Lull, written by an unknown hand about
1811, and now first translated from the Catalan with notes and
an appendix by E. Allison Peers. London, Burns, Oates &
Washbourne ltd. ₍1927₎
vii, 86 p. 17ᵐ.
Latin text (Vita beati Raymundi Lulli ...) : p. 47-86.

1. Lull, Ramón, d. 1315.   I. Peers, Edgar Allison, ed. and tr.
II. Title : Vita beati Raymundi Lulli.   *Translation of* Vida
coetània.

Library of Congress   B765.L84V5   28-14916

NL 0358290   DLC NN IU OC1 ICU InStme OKentU

Life of Rear-Admiral John Paul Jones, compiled
from his original journals and correspondence
see under   Jones, John Paul, 1747-1792.

[Life of Red Hugh O'Donnell]
see under   Royal Irish Academy, Dublin.
Library. Mss. 23P24

The life of Reginald Heber, D.D. Lord Bishop
of Calcutta.
see under   [Heber, Mrs. Amelia (Shipley)]

Life of Rev. Benjamin Woodbury, a home missionary
see under   [Fay, N   T   ]

BX
8495   The life of Rev. James Hervey, M.A., rector of
H4L5   Weston-Favel.   Philadelphia, Presbyterian Board of Publica-
1841   tion, 1841.
240 p. 16cm.

"The life of the Rev. Augustus M. Toplady, Vicar of Broad-
Hembury": p.[163]-240.

1. Hervey, James, 1714-1758. 2. Toplady, Augustus
Montague, 1740-1778.   I. Title: The life of the Rev. Augustus
M   Toplady.

NL 0358295   CSaT OC1W ViU

The life of Rev. James Hervey
see also   The life of the Rev. James Hervey.

Life of Rev. John Bunyan, author of the Pilgrim's
progress ...   N.Y., American tract soc.,
n.d.
12 p.
At head of title: No. 218.
I. American tract society, N.Y.

NL 0358297   MiD-B

PZ161
.B9Z8   The life of Rev. John Bunyan, author of the
1825   Pilgrim's progress. ₍Boston₎ American Tract
Society ₍1825₎
16 p.

1. Bunyan, John, 1628-1688.

NL 0358298   ICU

The life of Rev. John Campbell.
Revised by the committee of publication.
From the London ed. Boston, Massachusetts
Sabbath School society, 1845.
24 p.

NL 0358299   OC1WHi

922.7
F613L   **The life of Rev. John Fletcher: abridged
from authentic sources. By a friend of Sabbath-
schools. New York, Carlton & Porter ₍n.d.₎**
95 p. 15 cm.

1. Fletcher, John William, 1729-1785

NL 0358300   NcD

The life of Rev. John Fletcher
see also   The life of the Rev. John Fletcher.

The life of Rev. Legh Richmond, author of the
Dairyman's of daughter ...
see under   [Wickens, Stephen B.]

Life of Rev. R. Downey Blair...
see under [Hansbrough, Mrs. Lucinda
Victoria (Blair)] 1852-

The life of Rev. Richard Watson ...   Compiled from authentic sources ...   New-York, G. Lane & P. P. Sandford, for
the Methodist Episcopal church, 1841.
312 p. 14½ᵐ.

1. Watson, Richard, 1781-1833.
37-9734
Library of Congress   BX8495.W323L5
₍2₎   922.742

NL 0358304   DLC

Life of Rev. Samuel H. Stearns, late minister of
the Old South church in Boston
see under   [Stearns, William Augustus]
1805-1876.

Life of Rev. Samuel Willard, D.D., A.A.S., of
Deerfield, Mass.
see under   Willard, Samuel, 1776-1859.

The life of Rev. Thos. Boston, late minister of
Ettrick
see under   Boston, Thomas, 1677-1732.

The life of Rev. Thomas Scott La Due ...
see under   La Due, John.

The life of Rev. W.W. Everts, D.D.
see under   [Everts, William Wallace] jr.,
1849-1926.

Life of Rev. William Tennent
see under   [Boudinot, Elias] 1740-1821.

Life of Richard F. Trevellikc...
see under   Hicks, Obadiah.

The life of Richard Nash, of Bath, esq; extracted
principally from his original papers
see under   [Goldsmith,Oliver] 1728-1774.

Rare Book
Collection
HV6248   The life of Richard Turpin, a most notorious
.W5   highwayman; giving an account of all his
A4   daring robberies and burglaries; also his
1829   trial, execution, burial, &c. Embellished
with a steel engraving. London, Printed and
published by W.S. Johnson ₍n.d.₎
1v., unpaged. illus. (col.) 20 cm. (Allman's
edition)

Bound with: The life and death of Jonathon
Wild.

1. Turpin,   Richard, 1706-1739.

NL 0358313   NcU

---

452. The LIFE OF RICHARD TURPIN, the notorious highwayman, containing an account of
his bold adventures, daring robberies, his ex-
pertness in horse-stealing; also his trial, execution, &c. [Woodcut.] Printed and sold by
W. and T. Fordyce, 15, Grey street, Newcastle.
A choice collection of song books and histories
always on hand. n. d.
17 × 9.5 cm. 24 p.
In prose.

NL 0358314   NN

The life of Richard Turpin, the notorious
highwayman; containing an account of his adventures, trial and execution. London, O. Hodgson
₍1740?₎
24 p. fold. col. front. 19cm.

1. Turpin, Richard. 1706-1739.

NL 0358315   NNC

823
L6266   The Life of Richard Turpin, a notorious highwayman: containing a particular account of his
adventures, from his being first put an apprentice to a butcher in Whitechapel, to his
execution at York for horse-stealing. To which
is added, The life of Sawney Beane, the man-
eater.   London, Printed by T. Maiden for A.
Lemoine ₍1807?₎
38p. col.front. 18cm.

Cover title: Tracts.

Continued in next column

VOLUME 332

Continued from preceding column

"The history of Little James": p.₍36₎-38.
Bound with The Eventful life, and wonderful
history of that most notorious character, swindler
and forger, Charles Price. London ₍1810?₎
Douglas and Eleanora. London ₍180-?₎ Arnott,
Samuel. The column, called the Monument. Lon-
don ₍1805₎ Crookenden, Isaac. Berthinia. Lon-
don ₍1802₎ The History of the seven champions of
Christendom. London, 1805. Lebau, Peter. The
English slaves.   London ₍1807₎

NL   0358317   IU

The life of Richard Turpin [1807?]
          see also   The life and trial of Richard
Turpin.

The LIFE of Richard Turpin, the notorious
highwayman, containing an account of his adventu
trial and execution. London,printed for R.
Harrild by Swinborne and Walter, Colchester,
[1810?]

     pp.36. Front. by G.Cruikshank.
     Trial plate inserted.
     This book may be consulted in the room
of the Widener Collection.

NL   0358319   MH OC

---

ar V
3474   The life of Richard Turpin, the noted
          highwayman; containing an account of his
          adventures, and execution.   London,
          Printed by and for Hodgson ₍1826?₎
          24 p. front. 19cm.

          No. 3 in vol. lettered: Tracts.

          1. Turpin, Richard, 1706-1739.

NL   0358320   NIC

The life of Richard Turpin, a most notorious
highwayman; being an account of his daring
robberies and burglaries; with his execution,
burial, &c. Derby:Published by Thomas
Richardson[1830?]
     24p. 18cm.bd. to 20cm.
     [Binder's title: Chap books, I]
     Original wrappers bound in.

NL   0358321   DLC MH

The LIFE of Richard Turpin, a most notorious highwayman. Giving a particular account of all his daring
robberies and burglaries, trial, execution, burial,
&c. Glasgow, Printed for the booksellers [1850?]
     24 p. 16cm.

     Weiss: Chapbooks, 451.
     On t.p.: 117.
     Without covers.

1. Turpin, Richard, 1706-1739.

NL   0358322   NN MnU OC1

The life of Rob Roy MacGregor, the celebrated Scotch freebooter!
containing the cause of the proscription of his name and clan; an
account of his great actions and achievements, and uncommon
prowess in battle; with a view of the manners and customs of the
Scots in the sixteenth and seventeenth centuries...   London:
J. & H. W. Bailey ₍18-₎.   28 p., front.   4. ed.   12°.

1. MacGregor, Robert, called Rob   Roy, 1671-1734.
N. Y. P. L.   March 5, 1917.

NL   0358323   NN

The life of Robert Bruce, king of Scotland.   Edinburgh, Oliver & Boyd, 1810.
     84 p. 14ᶜᵐ.
     Title vignette.

     1. Robert ₁, king of Scotland, 1274-1329. 2. Scotland—Hist.—Robert ₁,
     1306-1329.

                                                          24-18040

Library of Congress   DA783.4.L5

NL   0358324   DLC

The life of Robert Bruce, king of Scotland.
     Edinburgh, Oliver & Boyd, 1812.
     Bound with this are The history of the giants.
     London; and The life of Bamfylde Moore Carew.
     Edinburgh, 1812.
     A chap-book.

NL   0358325   OC1

The life of Robert Burns, the Scots poet. Falkirk, Printed for the booksellers ₍18--₎
     24 p.

     Illus. t.-p.

NL   0358326   ViU

Life of Robert Burns. 1830
          see under   [Lockhart, John Gibson] 1794-
1854.

Life of Robert Burns, 1859
          see under   [Wight, Orlando Williams] ed.

---

40   Life of Robert C. Schenck, [anon.] Published
          under order of union central committee.
          3a Congressional district, Ohio. [Dayton, O.,
          1864?]
               32 p. 1 port. 8°. [Miscellaneous
          pamphlets, v. 451]

NL   0358329   DLC

The life of Robert, earl of Leicester, the
favourite of Queen Elizabeth ...
          see under   [Jebb, Samuel] 1694?-1772.

Life of Robert Gray, bishop of Cape Town and
metropolitan of Africa
          see under   [Lear, Henrietta Louisa (Farrer)]
1824-1896.

Life of Robert Morris, the great financier; with an
engraving and description of the celebrated house, partly
erected in Chestnut street, between Seventh and Eighth,
south side ... ₍Philadelphia₎ Desilver, 1841.
     cover-title, 8 p. fold. pl. 25ᶜᵐ.

     1. Morris, Robert, 1734-1806.
                                                          13-2749
Library of Congress   E302.6.M8L7

NL   0358332   DLC PPAmP PHC PPiU

Life of Robert Owen
     ¬see under   [Packard, Frederick Adolphus]
1794-1867.

Life of Robert Rodolph Suffield

     See *under*

₍Hargrave, Charles₎

Life of Russell Alexander Alger. ₍Park
Place,N.Y., Knapp & company,for Duke's cigarettes, ca.1888₎

     15,₍1₎ p. 7.1cm. (Histories of poor boys
who have become rich,and other famous people)
Portrait on cover.

     1.Curiosa. 2.Miniature books. I.Duke's
cigarettes. II.Title.

NL   0358335   MiU-C

The life of Russell C. Calhoun.
     ₍Essays₎ written in competition for the
prize offered by Mr. Arthur C. Dill₎
n.p.n.p.n.d.

     Manuscript. v.p.

NL   0358336   OO

Life, The, of S. Hahnemann. n. t.-p. ₍Philadelphia: C. L.
Rademacher, 186-₎ 4 p. 8°. (Homœopathic tracts for the
people. no. 1.)

1. Hahnemann, Samuel Christian   Friedrich.
N. Y. P. L.   March 28, 1912.

NL   0358337   NN

Life of S. J. Levick
          see under   Le Vick, Samuel Jones, 1819-
                                                          1885.

...The life of St. Agnes of Rome. Virgin and martyr. Translated from the French. Published with the approbation of the
Right Rev. Bishop of Philadelphia.   Philadelphia: P. F. Cunningham ₍18--?₎ vi, 7-74 p. front. 14cm. (The Saints
and servants of God.)

196820B. 1. Agnes, Saint, 291?–   304?
N. Y. P. L.   August 5, 1943.

NL   0358339   NN

... The life of St. Agnes of Rome. Virgin and martyr,
pub. with the approbation of the Right Rev. Bishop of
Philadelphia. New York, P. J. Kenedy & sons ₍191-₎
vi, 7-74 p. 15½ᶜᵐ. (The saints and servants of God)

     1. Agnes, Saint, 3d cent.
                                                          16-4950

NL   0358340   DLC MBtS Wa

The life of Saint Alexis
          see under   Alexius, Saint. Legend.

Life of St. Alice. [New York?, 194-?] 12 pl.
21 x 29cm.

     Title from binder in which plates are issued.

     1. Adelaide, Saint, consort of Otto I, emperor of
Germany, 931-999, in art.

NL   0358342   NN

VOLUME 332

Case
3A
2420
The LIFE of S. Aloysius Gonzaga, of the Society of Jesus. ₜTranslated from the Frenchₜ Preston, Printed by W. Addison ₜ1761ₜ
155p. port. 17cm.

"Approbatio" dated 1761.
Bound by John Sewel, Preston.

NL 0358343   ICN

The life of S. Aloysius Gonzaga. London, 1867.
see under [De Vere, Aubrey Thomas] 1814-1902.

The life of St. Aloysius Gonzaga, of the Company of Jesus. Philadelphia, 1867
see under [Cepari, Virgilio] 1564?-1631.

Life of St. Aloysius Gonzaga, 1891
see under O'Conor, John Francis Xavier, ed.

The life of St. Alphonsus Ligouri, bishop, confessor, and doctor of the Church, founder of the Congregation of the Most Holy Redeemer
see under [Carroll, Mary Teresa Austin, Mother] d. 1909.

The life of St. Alphonsus Maria de Liguori, bishop of St. Agatha of the Goths, and founder of the congregation of the Most Holy Redeemer
see under [Tannoja, Antonio Maria] d. 1808.

PZ225
.L72
1904
The life of Saint Anthony. ₜThe life of Saint Monica. The life of Saint Augustine. The life of Saint Elizabethₜ New York, Excelsior Catholic Pub. House, 1904.
4 pts. in 1.ports.   (The Young Christians library, no.3)
Binder's title: Lives of eminent saints.

1. Saints. I. Title: Lives of eminent saints.

NL 0358349   ICU

L2035.5
The life of St. Anthony of Padoua with the miracles he wrought both before, and after his death. Written originally in Italian, and now done into English. Printed at Paris, 1660.
ₜ8ₜ 224 p. ₜaₜ⁴, A-I¹², K⁴. (₍aₙ₁, possibly blank, lacking) 12mo.
Translated by John Burbury.

NL 0358350   DFo

The life of Saint Anthony of Padua. 1864, ₜ1865ₜ
see under [Dirks, Servais]

The life of St. Augustine of Canterbury, apostle of the English
see under [Oakeley, Frederick] 1802-1880.

Life of St. Benedict, surnamed "the Moor,"...
see under [Carletti, Giuseppe]

The life of S. Bernardine of Siena
see under Amadio Maria da Venezia, Father.

BV2226
B7
The life of Saint Bridget, "The Mary of Erin" and the special patroness of the dioceses of Kildare and Leighlin, by an Irish priest. New York, P. O'Shea, n.d.

211 p.

1. Brigid, Saint, of Ireland, 451-525.

NL 0358355   MBtS

Life of St. Bridget.   Boston, O'Loughlin & McLaughlin, 1883.

NL 0358356   WaSpG

Life, The, of St. Cajetan, Count of Tiene, founder of the Theatines, and patriarch of clerks regular. [Anon.] Translated from the Italian, by Lady Herbert. With a preface by the Bishop of Salford. Leamington. Art and Book Co. [1887.] xxiv, 260 pp. Portrait. 18 cm., in 8s.

H3544 — Tiene, Gaetano da, St. 1480-1547. — Herbert, Mary Elizabeth, Lady, tr. — Vaughan, Herbert, Cardinal, pref. 1832-1903.

NL 0358357   MB

... The life of S. Camillus of Lellis, founder of the Clerks regular, ministers of the sick ...
see under [Cicatelli, Sanzio]

... The life of St. Cecilia from ms. Asmole 43 & ms. Cotton Tiberius E., VII
see under Dickinson, Bertha Ellen (Lovewell) ed.

The life of St. Charles Borromeo
see under [Thompson, Mrs. Harriet Diana (Calvert)]

Life of St. Columban. [19--?]
see under [Jonas of Bobbio, abbot] d. ca. 665.

W.C.L.
096.1
L722
The Life of Saint Cuthbert, written anonymously about the year A. D. 700 ₜby a monk of Lindisfarne Abbeyₜ With forty-five full-page illuminations from the Lawson Ms., end of twelfth century. Edited by W. Forbes-Leith. Edinburgh, 1888.
xii, 43 p. col. illus. 29 cm.

The translation follows the text edited by J. Stevenson.
1. Cuthbert, Saint d. 687. 2. Illumination of books and manuscripts. Gt. Brit. 3. Miniature painting, English.   I. A monk of Lindisfarne. II. Forbes-Leith, William, 1833-1921, ed. III. British Museum.   Mss. (Additional 33943)

NL 0358362   NcD MH

The life of St. Cuthbert in English verse, c. A. D. 1450. From the original ms. in the library at Castle Howard. Durham ₜEng.ₜ Pub. for the Society by Andrews & co.; ₜetc., etc.ₜ 1891.
3 p. l., ₜvₜ-xvi, ⟨11⟩, ₜ6ₜ 292 p. front. (col. facsim.) 23 cm. (Half-title: The publications of the Surtees society ... vol. LXXXVII)
Edited by J. T. Fowler.
"Earlier life of St. Cuthbert, from the South-English legendary": ⟨11⟩ p.
"Corrigenda, &c.": p. ₜ248ₜ
"Index verborum": p. ₜ249ₜ-278; "Index verborum to short life": p. ₜ279ₜ-281.
1. Cuthbert, Saint, d. 687. 2. English language—Middle English (1100-1500)—Glossaries, vocabularies, etc. I. Fowler, Joseph Thomas, 1833-1924, et

DA20.S9 vol. 87   (942.0062)   C S 35—35

MdBP KU NcD PU MH PPL PP MBr-Z MB
NL 0358363   DLC OU PPPD OC1 PBL WaU-L PPT PBm MiU

The life of Saint David
see under Rhygyfarch, 1056-1099.

The life of St. Dominic, 1170-1221, by a Dominicaness of Headington. London, Burns, Oates & Washbourne, ltd. ₜ1939ₜ
v, 65, ₜ1ₜ p. 16½ᵐ.
"Printed ... 1939."

1. Domingo de Guzmán, Saint, 1170-1221.   I. A Dominicaness of Headington.

Library of Congress   BX4700.D7L5   40-33350
                         ₜ2ₜ   922.246

NL 0358365   DLC ICN

The life of St. Dominic, with a sketch of the Dominican order
see under [Drane, Augusta Theodosia] 1823-1894.

The life of St. Elizabeth of Hungary. By the author of The lives of Sœur Rosalie ... etc. etc. London, Burns and Oates ₜ1859ₜ
iv, 132 p. 16ᵐ.

1. Elizabeth of Hungary, Saint, 1207-1231.

                                            27-17483

Library of Congress   BX4700.E4L5

NL 0358367   DLC

BX4700
.F45L7
Life of Saint Flannan, patron of Killaloe diocese. Tr. and annotated by Very Rev. S. Malone ... Dublin, J. Duffy and co., 1902.
viii, 56 p. 24ᶜᵐ.

1. Flannan, Saint, 7th cent.

NL 0358368   ICU IMunS

The life of S. Francis of Assisi. 1853-54
see under [Chalippe, Candide] 1684-1757.

BV7365
F7A8
A life of Saint Francis of Assisi, with a sketch of the Franciscan order: by a religious order of Poor Clares. Revised and edited by Rev. W. H. Anderdon ... London, Richardson and son, Dublin, John F. Fowler, 1861.

xvi, 413 p. front. 17 cm.

1. Francesco d'Assisi, Saint, 1182-1226. I. Anderdon, William Henry, 1816-1890 ed.

NL 0358370   MBtS IU

VOLUME 332

BX
4700
F6L72
1867
    The life of Saint Francis of Assisi; and a sketch of the Franciscan order, by a religious of the Order of Poor Clares, with emendations and additions by Very Rev. Pamfilo da Magliano. New York, P. O'Shea, 1867.
674 p. 22cm.

1. Francesco d'Assisi, Saint, 1182-1226. I. A religious of the Order of Poor Clares. II. Magliano,   Pamphilo da.

NL 0358371   NIC MoSU CMenSP MBtS MiU DCU ODaU

The life of Saint Francis of Assisi, and a sketch of the Franciscan Order by a religious of the order of Poor Clares. With emendations and additions by Very Rev. Pamfilo da Magliano... New York: P. O'Shea, 1886.   xvi, (1)18-674 p.   New ed.   12°.

"Brief notice of various distinguished members of the Franciscan Order," p. 639-674.

1. Francis of Assisi, saint, 1182-   1226.   2. Franciscans.—History. 3. Magliano, Pamfilo da, editor.
N. Y. P. L.   October 14, 1920.

NL 0358372   NN OCX

     The life of St. Francis of Assisi. *1898, etc.*
        see under   Francesco, d'Assisi, Saint. Legend. Legenda Bonaventurae.

     Life of Saint Francis Solanus, apostle of Peru (1888)
        see under   [Deymann, Clementine, Father] 1844-1896.

     The Life of Saint Gaëtan, founder of the order of Théatins; from a biography of the saint by the Reverend P. de Tracy, published in 1774, and from the Bollandist lives of the saints ... tr. by Lady Herbert. Dublin, C. Smyth, 1873.
     viii, [9]-61 p.   19 cm.

NL 0358375   CU

     The life of St. Gall
        see under   [Walahfrid Strabo] 807?-849.

The life of St. Gregory the Great, by a sister of Notre Dame. New York: P. J. Kenedy & Sons[, 1923].   258 p.   front. (port.) 12°.

     Printed in Ireland.

164400A. 1. Gregory I, the Great,   Saint, pope, ca. 540-604. 2. Sister of Notre Dame.
N. Y. P. L.   April 6, 1925

NL 0358377   NN PRosC PPCCH MBtS

     The LIFE of St. Gregory the Great. By a sister of Notre Dame. Dublin, The Talbot Press, Limited, 1924.

     Port.

NL 0358378   MH OC1

     Life of Saint Hugh of Lincoln
        see under   Thurston, Herbert, 1856-1939.

     ... The life of St. Ignatius Loyola, founder of the Jesuits ...
        see under   [Mariani, Antonio Francesco] 1680-1751.

The life of St. John Berchmans of the Society of Jesus
        see under   [Frizon, Nicolas] d. 1737.

The life of Saint John of the Cross of the Order of Our Lady of Mount Carmel
        see under   [Lewis, David] 1814-1895, ed.

Life of St. John the Baptist, by an Ossory priest. Dublin, James Duffy [n.d.] 195p.

1. John the Baptist, Saint.

NL 0358383   IRivfR

The life of St. Katharine: The tale of the knight and his wife: and an account of the magical manuscript of Dr. Caius. *1845.*
        see under   Halliwell-Phillipps, James Orchard, 1820-1889, ed.

The life of Saint Katharine. 1884.
        see under   Catharina, Saint, of Alexandria. Legend.

The life of St. Louis, king of France
        see under   [Sepet, Marius Cyrille Alphonse] 1845-1925.

The life of Saint Margaret
        see under   Margaret, Saint. Legend.

BX
4700
A37
L513
1927
    Life of Saint Margaret Mary Alacoque, of the order of the Visitation of Holy Mary. Published in French by the Monastery of the Visitation of Paray-le-Monial. Translated into English by the Sisters of the Visitation of Roselands, Walmer, Kent. 2nd. ed. With a preface by Cardinal Bourne. Walmer [Eng.] Visitation Library [1927]
xxiii, 202 p. 19cm.

1. Alacoque, Marguerite Marie, Saint, 1647-1690. 2. Paray-le-Monial, France (Visitation Monastery)

NL 0358388   CMenSP

The life of Saint Margaret, with the lives of Saint Cecilia, Saint Catharino, Saint Agnes, Saint Angela, Saint Elizabeth, Saint Dympna, and Saint Wenefride. And the life of the Blessed Virgin Mary. New York, 1872.
15.5 cm.
On cover: Life of my patron saint.

NL 0358389   CtY

Life of St. Mary Magdalen, translated from the Italian by Bishop McCloskey. Louisville, Ky., The Bradley & Gilbert company, 1900.
2 p. l., iii-viii, [9]-203 p.   19ᶜᵐ.

1. Mary Magdalene, Saint.   I. McCloskey, William George, 1823-1909, tr.

Library of Congress   B82485.M3   1-29755 Revised

NL 0358390   DLC

The life of Saint Mary Magdalen. *1904, 1906.*
        see under   Mary Magdalene, Saint. Legend.

The life of St. Mary Magdalene of Pazzi, a Carmelite nunn
        see under   [Puccini, Vincenzio]

BX4700
.M42C7
    The life of St. Mary of Egypt, the example and model of a true penitent. To which is added, the same in verse, by the late pious Doctor Coyle, bishop of Raphoe ... Dublin, R. Grace & son, 1833.
vi, [7]-105, [2]p.   14½cm.

1. Mary, Saint, of Egypt.

NL 0358393   ICU

The life of Saint Mary of Egypt, the example and model of a true penitent, to which is added the Life of Saint Cecilia and the Life of Saint Bridget. New York, P.J. Kenedy, 1872.

x, 12-178 p.   front.   15 cm.

1. Mary, Saint, of Egypt, 344-421. 2. Cecilia, Saint, 2nd century. 3. Brigid, Saint, of Ireland, ca. 453-ca. 524.   4. Penitents. 5. Saints, Women.

NL 0358394   PLatS

BT
2745
.A78
1891
    The Life of Saint Mary of Egypt, the example and model of a true penitent. To which is added the life of Saint Cecilia and the life of St. Bridget. New York, P. J. Kenedy, 1891.
178 p.   front.   16cm.

1. Mary, Saint, o Egypt, 344-421. 2. Cecilia, Saint. 3. Brigid, Saint, of Ireland, ca. 453-ca. 524.

NL 0358395   DCU

The life of Saint Mary of Egypt; the example and model of a true penitent. New York, P.J. Kenedy and sons [19-]

NL 0358396   MH

Life, The, of St. Mechtildis. [Anon.]
— Rome. The Vatican Press. 1899. 295, (1) pp. Plate. [St. Benedict's series.] 19½ cm, in 8s.

H3910 — S.r. — Matilda, Saint, Abbess of Helfta.

NL 0358397   MB ODaU

Life of St. Nicholas ...
        see under   [Wace] fl. 1170.

VOLUME 332

Life of St. Ninian
    see under   [Barrow, John] 1810-1881.

Life of St.Patrick. Naomh Pádraig, by a Redemptorist father. [Dublin, O'Brien & Ards, printers, pref.1903]

65 p.
Text in Irish and English

NL 0358400   MH

— The life of St. Patrick, with novena prayers and hymns.
Dublin. M. H. Gill & Son, Ltd. 1906. 63 pp. 18½ cm.
Irish and English on opposite pages.
By a Redemptionist father.

M3388 — Patricius, Saint, of Ireland. — Ireland. Lang. Works in Irish.

NL 0358401   MB

The life of Saint Patrick, apostle of Ireland.
(ca. 372-492)   New York, Benziger Brothers
[n. d.]

NL 0358402   RP

BX4700
.P3
.L5   The life of Saint Patrick, apostle of
         Ireland, to which is added the cele-
         brated hymn composed above twelve
         hundred years since by his disciple,
         St. Fiech, comprehending a compendi-
         ous history of his life, also a chron-
         ological table of the archbishops of
         Armagh, Dublin, Cashel, and Tuam,
         from the death of St. Patrick to the
         beginning of the 19th century. Toge-
         ther with the prophecy of St. Malachy,
         describing the   popes of Rome to
         the end of   world.   Balt-

         imore, J. Murphy [18--?]
         191p. front. 19cm.

NL 0358404   NNU

The life of Saint Patrick, apostle of Ireland: to which is added, in the original
Irish character, (with both a Latin and
English translation) the celebrated hymn,
composed about 1200 years since, by his
disciple, Saint Fiech; compending a compendious history of his life. Annexed is
a copious appendix, [containing] a summary
account of the various ecclesiastical institutions, orders, edifices, and establishments
in Ireland, since the introduction of the

Christian religion. Also a chronological
table of the archbishops of Armagh, Dublin,
Cashell and Tuam, from the death of Saint
Patrick till the present year. Together with
an abstract of Irish grammar. Dublin, H.
Fitzpatrick, 1810.

    350,[6] p. 18cm.

    1. Patrick,   Saint, 373?-463?

NL 0358406   FU

The life of Saint Patrick, Apostle of Ireland.
To which is added the celebrated hymn, composed
above twelve hundred years since by his disciple,
St. Fiech; comprehending a compendious history of
his life. Annexed is a copious appendix containing a summary account of the various ecclesiastical institutions, Orders, edifices, and establishments in Ireland, since the introduction of
the Christian Religion. Also a chronological
table of the Archbishops of Armagh, Dublin,
Cashel and Tuam, from the death of St. Patrick
to the present; to-   gether with the prophecy

of St. Malachy, describing the Popes of Rome to
the end of the world.   Baltimore, Fielding
Lucas, Jun'r., 182-

    191p. 20cm.

NL 0358408   PLatS DGU MWA MdW MoSCS

BX
2216
.L6
1825   The life of Saint Patrick, apostle of Ireland;
          to which is added the celebrated hymn, com-
          posed above twelve hundred years since, by
          his disciple, St. Fiech, comprehending a
          compendious history of his life. Annexed
          is a copious appendix, containing a summary
          account of the various ecclesiastical inst-
          itutions, orders, edifices, and establish-
          ments in Ireland ... Also, A chronological
          table of the archbishops ... New York,
          James Costigan, 1825. iii [5] 231 p. front.
          18 cm.
          Parsons, W.   Early Cath. Americana, n.
          864.
          1. Patrick, Saint, 373?-453? 2. Ireland -
          Church History.

NL 0358409   DCU PV

Spec.   The life of Saint Patrick, Apostle of Ireland
Coll.   ... New York, J. M'Loughlin, 1843.
1843   107 p.
.L5

NL 0358410   DGU

282.092
P314Z   The life of Saint Patrick, apostle of Ireland,
          with a copious appendix ... to which are added
          the lives of Saint Bridget, virgin and abbess,
          and Saint Columba, abbot, and apostle of the
          northern Picts.   Baltimore, John Murphy, 1850.
          191. 41p. front. 20cm.
          At head of title: Murphy's enlarged stereotype
          edition.
          Lives of St. Bridget and St. Columba comprise
          41p.
          1. Patrick, Saint, 373?-463? 2. Bridget,
          Saint, of Kildare,   c. 453-523. 3. Columba,
          Saint, 521-597.

NL 0358411   TxDaM CaQML

---

ar V   The Life of Saint Patrick, apostle of Ireland,
10533   with a copious appendix, in which is given
             a summary account of the ecclesiastical
             institutions, &c. in Ireland since the
             introduction of Christianity; a chronologi-
             cal table of the Catholic primates of
             Ireland; the celebrated hymn of St. Fiech,
             on the life of St. Patrick; and the prophecy
             of St. Malachy, describing the popes of Rome
             to the end of the world.   To which are added
             the lives of   Saint Bridget, virgin

             and abbess, and Saint Columba, abbot, and
             apostle of the northern Picts.   Baltimore,
             J. Murphy, 1853.
             191, 41 p. illus. 20cm.

             1. Patrick, Saint, 373?-463? 2. Columba,
             Saint, 521-597.   3. Brigid, Saint, of
             Ireland, ca.   453-ca. 524.

NL 0358413   NIC

... The life of Saint Patrick, apostle of Ireland, with a
copious appendix ... To which are added The lives of Saint
Bridget, Virgin and abbess, and Saint Columba, abbot, and
apostle of the northern Picts.   Baltimore, J. Murphy; [etc.,
etc.] 1854.
    191, [1], 41 p. front. 20cm.
    Murphy's enlarged stereotype edition.

    1. Patrick, Saint, 373?-463? 2. Bridget, Saint, d. 523.   3. Columba, Saint,
521-597.

NL 0358414   ICU MnU

The life of Saint Patrick, apostle of Ireland...
Baltimore, J. Murphy, 1860.

    188, 41 p.   20 cm.

NL 0358415   OrStbM

The life of Saint Patrick, apostle of Ireland, with
a copious appendix ... to which are added the
lives of Saint Bridget, virgin and abbess, and
Saint Columba, abbot and apostle of the northern
Picts. Baltimore, J. Murphy, 1863.
    191, 12, 41 p. front. (port.) (Murphy's
enlarged stereotype edition)
    1. Patrick, Saint, 373?-463? 2. Brigid,
Saint, of Ireland, ca. 453-ca. 524. 3. Columba,
Saint, 521-597.

NL 0358416   ODaU PLatS

BV2226   The life of Saint Patrick, apostle of Ireland,
P3   with a copious appendix, in which is given a
            summary account of the ecclesiastical insti-
            tutions, etc. in Ireland ... a chronological
            table of the Catholic primates of Ireland...
            and the prophecy of Saint Malachy, describi-
            ng the popes of Rome to the end of the world.
            To which are added the lives of Saint Brid-
            get, virgin and abbess, and Saint Columba,
            abbot, and apostle of the Northern Picts.
            Baltimore, John Murphy & co., 1873.

            191, [1], 12, 39, [2] p.   18cm.

            1.Patrick, Saint, bp., 387-493. 2.Brigid,
            Saint, of Ireland, ca.451-ca.525. 3.Columba,
            Saint, 521-597. 4.Ireland-Catholic primates.
            5.Malachy,   Saint, prophecy of.

NL 0358418   MBtS

The life of St. Peter Claver, S.J., the apostle of
    the Negroes [1893]
        see under Slattery, John Richard, 1851-
1926.

... The life of St. Peter of Alcantara ...
    see under [Marchese, Francesco]

... The life of Saint Philip Neri, apostle of Rome,
    and founder of the Congregation of the
    oratory ...
        see under [Bacci, Pietro Giacomo]
fl. 1625.

The life of Saint Pius the Fifth
    see under Dyson, Thomas Austin.

The Life of St. Polycarp, Bishop of Smyrna
    see under   [Cave, William] 1637-1713.

VOLUME 332

Life of St. Rita of Cascia; from the Italian by Very Rev. Richard Connolly . . .   London: R. & T. Washbourne ₁etc., etc.₎ 1903.
vi, 9–272 p.   front.   18½cm.

50737B.   1. Rita da Cascia, Saint,   1381–1457.   I. Connolly, Richard.
N. Y. P. L.   November 18, 1940

NL 0358424   NN MB

Life of St. Rita of Cascia, O. S. A. From the Italian by Very Rev. Richard Connolly.   N. Y., Benziger bros., 1903.
272 p.   front.

NL 0358425   OClND

Life of St. Rita of Cascia, O.S.A. From the Italian by Richard Connolly, O.S.A.... 2d ed. London, Washbourne, 1913.
272p.   illus.

1. Rita, Saint, 1386–1456. I. Connolly, Richard, O.S.A., tr.

NL 0358426   IRivfR ODaU OClJC

Life of St. Rita of Cascia, O.S.A. From the Italian by ... Richard Connolly ... Lond., Burns Oates & Washbourne, ltd. 1925.
272 p., front.

NL 0358427   OCl

... The life of Saint Rose of Lima ...
      -see under   ₍Feuillet, Jean Baptiste₎ 1624?–1687.

271.811
St24-E   The life of St. Stanislaus Kostka, of the Society of Jesus, patron of youth. Tr. from the French. 5th Amer. ed. New York, Christian press association publishing co. ₍n. d.₎
ix, ₍11₎–144 p.   16 cm (On cover: Silver series)
      CONTENTS.--Life of St. Stanislaus Kostka.--A short novena in honour of Saint Stanislaus Kostka.--Litany of Saint Stanislaus.--Three prayers to be recited each day in honor of Saint Stanislaus.--A short novena in honor of St. Stanislaus or Saint Aloysius.--Litany

of Saint Aloysius.--Indulgences, granted by ... Pius VIII.

1. Stanislaus Kostka, Saint, 1550–1568, S. J.

NL 0358430   MoSU

The life of St. Stanislaus Kostka, of the Society of Jesus, patron of novices. Tr. from the French. 1st Amer. ed. Baltimore, J. Murphy & co., 1850.
144 p.   front. 16°.
      CONTENTS.--Life of St. Stanislaus Kostka.--A short novena in honor of Saint Stanislaus Kostka.--Litany of Saint Stanislaus Kostka.--Three prayers to be recited each day in honor of Saint Stanislaus.--A short novena in honor of St. Stanislaus or Saint Aloysius.--Litany of Saint Aloysius.--A favorite devotion of Saint Pius v.--Prayer to recite before the image of Jesus crucified.--Indulgences, granted by ... Pius VIII.--Remarkable epochs in the life of Saint Stanislaus.--Index.

1–6085

NL 0358431   DLC PLatS DCU

Life of Saint Teresa (edited, with a preface, by Henry Edward Manning) (1865)
      see under   ₍Lockhart, Elizabeth₎

Life of Saint Teresa, by the author of Devotions before and after Holy Communion . . . (1875)
      see under   ₍Trench, Maria Marcia Fanny₎

The life of Saint Teresa of the Order of Our Lady of Mount Carmel . . . (1865)
      see under   ₍Lockhart, Elizabeth₎

The life of Saint Teresa. Taken from the French of "A Carmelite nun," by Alice, lady Lovat, with a preface by Mgr. Robert Hugh Benson. London, Herbert & Daniel ₍n. d.₎
2 p. l., vii–xxxi, 629, ₍1₎ p.   front. (port.)   22ᶜᵐ.

1. Teresa, Saint, 1515–1582.   I. Benson, Robert Hugh, 1871–1914.
II. Lovat, Alice Mary (Weld-Blundell) Fraser, baroness, 1846–1938.

A 13–287
Enoch Pratt free library
for Library of Congress   ₍a38b1₎

NL 0358435   MdBE CU WaU CtY-D

The Life of St. Teresa taken from the French of a Carmelite Nun. Simpkin, Marshall, Hamilton, Kent & Co., 1914.

NL 0358436   OCX

BX   The life of Saint Teresa, taken from the french of
4700   "A carmelite nun" by Alice Mary Lovat, with a preface by
T4L5   Robert Hugh Benson. London, Simpkin, Marshall, Hamil-
1920   ton, Kent; St. Louis, B. Herder [1920, c1911]
            629 p. 23cm.

1. Teresa, Saint, 1515–1582.   I. A Carmelite nun.   II.
Lovat, Alice Mary (Weld-Blundell) Frazer, Baroness.

NL 0358437   CMenSP PCC

The life of St. Thomas of Villanova, archbishop of Valentia and Augustinian friar
      see under   ₍Maimbourg, Claude₎

Life of Saint Willibrord, archbishop of Utrecht, and apostle of Holland ₍and The life of St. Lioba, or Love₎ London, Burns and Oates, 1877.
3p.l.,156p.   front.   20cm.

NL 0358439   KAS

PQ1796   The life of Salignac de la Mothe
L4   Fenelon, archbishop of Cambray; author of
          Telemachus, &c., &c.   New York, David
          Longworth, at the Shakspeare-gallery, 1804.
          1p.l.₍7₎–39p.   front.(port.)   21cm.

1. Fénelon, François de Salignac de La Mothe-, 1651–1715.

NL 0358440   NBuG MH CSmH NBu

The life of Sam Houston
      see under   ₍Lester, Charles Edwards₎ 1815–1890.

The life of Samuel Comstock, the bloody mutineer
      see under   ₍Comstock, William₎ fl. 1840.

Life of Samuel Downing, one hundred and four years' old, one of the four soldiers of the revolution now remaining alive. New York, Press of Wynkoop & Hallenbeck, 1865.
19 p.   19ᵐ.
Copyrighted by P. T. Barnum.

1. Downing, Samuel, b. 1761. 2. U. S.—Hist.—Revolution—Personal narratives.   I. Barnum, Phineas Taylor, 1810–1891.

Library of Congress   E275.D73   7–24339

NL 0358443   DLC

The life of Samuel Hebich
      see under   ₍Gundert, Hermann₎ 1814–1893.

PR   The life of Samuel Johnson,LL.D.with occasion-
3533   al remarks on his writings,an   authentic copy
.L72   of his will,and a catalogue of his works. To
            which are added,some papers written by Dr.John-
            son in behalf of a late unfortunate character,
            never before published ...   Dublin ₍₎ Printed
            for R.Moncrieffe ₍etc.₎ 1785.
            vii,₍9₎–240 p.   17½ᶜᵐ.
            London edition printed for G.Kearsley the same year.
            "Postscript" (papers in behalf of Dr.Dodd): p.191–230.
            "A catalogue of Dr.Johnson's works": p.231–240.
            1.Johnson,Samuel,1709–1784. 2.Dodd,William,1729–1777.

NL 0358445   MiU MeWC IEN CSmH MH NjP

The life of Samuel Johnson, LL.D. with occasional remarks on his writings, an authentic copy of his will, and a catalogue of his works. To which are added, some papers written by Dr. Johnson, in behalf of a late unfortunate character, never before published ...   London: Printed for G. Kearsley, 1785.   iv, 144 ₍really 156₎ p.   8°.
      Six leaves between p. 32 and 33 numbered 33*–44*.
      "Attributed to William Cooke."— Johnson, S. Papers written by Dr. Johnson and Dr. Dodd...with notes by R. W. Chapman. Oxford, 1926, p. vi.

      The "papers written by Dr. Johnson, in behalf of a late unfortunate character" were printed, presumably in 1777, with title: Occasional papers by the late William Dodd, LL.D.; "on the day before the intended publication, Mrs. Dodd...conscious they were not her husband's writing...begged they might be suppressed...and the whole impression, consisting of 500 copies, were cancelled, two or there excepted, from one of which they are now reprinted."— cf. "Postscript", p. 128–129.

519284A.   1. Johnson, Samuel, 1709–   1784. 2. Dodd, William, 1729–1777.
I. Cook, William, d. 1824, supposed au.
N. Y. P. L.   April 18, 1931

            ICU NBu CtY
NL 0358447   NN CLU-C CoU IU MH NRU CtY NcD MiEM NNC

*EC75   The life of Samuel Johnson, LL.D. with
J6371   occasional remarks on his writings; an authentic
W785tb   copy of his will; a catalogue of his works,
             and a facsimile of his hand writing. (The
             second edition with considerable additions and
             corrections.) To which is added, Johnsoniana;
             or, A selection of Dr. Johnson's bon-mots,
             observations, &c. most of which were never
             before published ...
             London;Printed for G.Kearsley,no.46,Fleet-
             street.M,DCC,LXXXV. Entered at Stationers-hall.

             iv,209p. front.,fold.facsim. 16.5cm.
             "A catalogue of Dr.Johnson's works":
             p.₍155₎–165.
             Attributed to William Cooke.
             Ms. notes referring to Mrs. Piozzi's
             Anecdotes on p.84 & 86.

NL 0358449   MH MWiW-C IEN NcD NcU

VOLUME 332

The life of Sarah Bernhardt, with her picture, autograph, description of her dresses, and anecdotes of her, on and off the stage ... New York, Russell & co. [1880]
32 p. 15½ᵐᵐ.

1. Bernhardt, Sarah, 1844–

CA 17-1224 Unrev'd
Library of Congress   PN2638.B5L5

NL 0358450   DLC

475
L62   Life of science.

[Kraków] Circle for the Science of Science.

English summaries of articles in Życie
nauki (475 Z9)
Previous to v.6, nr. 35/36, included in
Życie nauki.

NL 0358451   DNAL

Q
141
.L35   The Life of science library. v.1-
New York, H. Schuman, 19 -

1. Scientists-Biog. 2. Scientific societies.

NL 0358452   DAU NBC TxDaM PHC

The life of Sethos
see under [Terrasson, Jean] 1670-1750.

Life of Shakespeare
see under [Halliwell-Phillipps, James
Orchard] 1820-1889.

... The life of Shakespeare and an analysis of his plays.
Girard, Kan., Haldeman-Julius company [1922?]
92 p. 13ᵐᵐ. (Ten cent pocket series no. 266, ed. E. Haldeman-Julius)
List of publications in the series (iv p.) at end.

1. Shakespeare, William. 2. Shakespeare, William—Criticism and interpretation.

24-7004
Library of Congress   PR2899.L5

NL 0358455   DLC

DS
796   The life of Shanghai. [Tokyo, Shobido Print.
.S2   Off., 1934]
L7   4 l., [36] l. of illus.   28 cm.
Cover title.
Date 1934 in manuscript.

1.Shanghai--Descr.--Views.

NL 0358456   MiU

Life of Shishir Kumar Ghosh, founder-editor of
920.5   Amrita bazar patrika; by Wayfarer. Calcutta,
G427LI   T. K. Ghosh [1946]
194 p. facsim., port. 23 cm.

1. Ghosh, Shishir Kumar, 1840-1911.
I. Wayfarer.

NL 0358457   NcD

The life of Sile Doty, 1800-1876
see under Doty, Silas, 1800-1876.

2B2   Life of Simeon Wilhelm, a native of the Susoo
W   country in West Africa ...   Philadelphia,
n.d.

NL 0358459   DLC

Life of Simeon Wilhelm, a native of the Susoo country,
in West Africa: who died at the Church missionary
house, London, Aug. 29, 1817, aged seventeen years.
With an account of some of the West African superstitions. 2d ed. 8000.   Philadelphia, I. Ashmead & co.,
printers [18—]
12 p. illus. 17½ᵐᵐ. (Philadelphia Sunday and adult school union. [Publications] no. 5)
Title vignette.
Subject entries: Wilhelm, Simeon, 1800?-1817.

S- 289

NL 0358460   DLC

The life of Simon William Gabriel Bruté D. D.,
first bishop of Vincennes
see under Bruté de Rémur, Simon
Guillaume Gabriel, Bp., 1779-1839 [supplement]

The life of Sir Francis Bernard, baronet, late
governor of Massachusetts Bay
see under [Bernard, Sir Thomas, bart.]
1750-1818.

LIFE of Sir Henry Vane. [London, 1792]

Port.
The literary and biographical magazine,
and British review, for August, 1792, pp. 81-87.

NL 0358463   MH

The life of Sr. Henry Wotton, sometime provost of
Eaton college
see under [Walton, Izaac] 1593-1683.

The life of Sir Isaac Newton. London,
The Religious Tract Society [n.d.]
192 p. 15cm. (Religious Tract Society.
Monthly volume no. 69)

1. Newton, Sir Isaac, 1642-1727.
I. Religious Tract Society, London.

NL 0358465   CSt

B1299
.N3L5
The life of Sir Isaac Newton. Revised by
Thomas O. Summers.   Nashville, Published by
E. Stevenson & J. E. Evans, Agents, for the
Methodist Episcopal Church, South, 1856.
v, 7-162 p. 16 cm.

1. Newton, Isaac, 1642-1727. I. Summers,
Thomas Osmond, 1812-1882.

NL 0358466   T

The life of Sir Isaac Newton. rev. ed. Nashville,
Pub. House of Methodist Episcopal Church,
South, 1871.

NL 0358467   TU

Life of Sir John Digby (1606-1645) now first printed
from the ms. in the Bibliothèque nationale,
Paris
see under Walsingham, Edward, fl. 1643-
1659.

DA
506   Life of Sir R. Abercromby, containing interesting particulars relating to the eminent ser-
.A1   vices he rendered his country, carried down to
L5   the Battle of Alexandria, where this lamented
hero received his mortal wound; together with
an accurate statement of the campaign of Egypt,
the defeat of the invincibles, and the unexampled courage manifested by the British
troops; furnished from official documents.
By an officer in the army. Ormskirk, J. Fowler, 1806.
252 p.   illus.   22cm.

Contents.- Life of Sir R. Abercromby.- The
life of Marquis Cornwallis.- The life of Sir
William Sidney Smith.

NL 0358470   WU

Life of Sir R. Abercromby
see also Life of Gen. Sir R. Abercromby.

Life of Sir Richard Whittington, knight
four times Lord Mayor of London; comp.
from authentic sources ... London,
Milner & co. n.d.
128 p.   T.

(Bound with, History of Jack, and his
eleven sisters).

NL 0358472   OO

The life of Sir Richard Whittington, knight,
and four times Lord Mayor of London, in the
reigns of Edward III. Richard II and Henry V.
compiled from authentic documents; and containing
many important particulars respecting that
illustrious man, never before published...by the
author of "Memoirs of George Barnwell".
107p., front.(port.)   Harlow, Printed by B. Flower
for M. Jones, 1811.

NL 0358473   OC1

The life of Sir Robert Christison
see under Christison, Sir Robert, bart.
1797-1882.

DA
783.9   The life of Sir Robt. Cochran, prime-minister to King James III. of Scotland.
.M3   London, Printed and sold by A. Dodd, 1734.
L7   55 p.   19 cm.

1.Mar, Robert Cochrane, earl of, d.1482.

NL 0358475   MiU IU MH NjP DLC NcD TxU

---

*EC7   The life of Sir Robt. Cochran, prime-minister
A100   to King James III. of Scotland ...
73462   London: Printed and sold by A. Dodd, and the
booksellers of London and Westminster. 1734.
〈Price one shilling.〉

8°. 55p. 20.5cm.
In this issue line 8, p.42, begins "Force,
they must be"; in another issue it begins
"Force, by Force they must be".
An attack, by implication, on Walpole.

NL 0358476   MH

VOLUME 332

The life of Sir Robt. Cochran, prime-minister to King James III. of Scotland...   London: A. Dodd, 1734.   55 p.   2. ed., rev. 8°.

I. Cochran, Sir Robert, d. 1482.
N. Y. P. L.   January 16, 1925

NL 0358477   NN MdBS-P MnU NjP

AC-L
W357L
L626   The life of Sir Sydney Smith; with a particular account of his confinement in the Temple, and his escape from thence; his defence of Acre against Bonaparte, whom he defeated with the loss of twenty thousand men &c. &c.   Ipswich [Eng.] Printed and sold by J. Raw; and sold also by T. Hurst, London [18--]
36p. incl. front.(port.) 16cm.
        Paper wrappers.
        From the library of Evelyn Waugh.

NL 0358478   TxU

        The life of Sir Sydney Smith, rear admiral of the blue; containing a particular account of his confinement in the Temple, his extraordinary escape, and his defeat of Bonaparte at the siege of St. Jean d'Acre, &c. ... London, T. Tegg (etc.) 1806.
        28 p. front. (port.) 17½ᶜᵐ.

        1. Smith, Sir William Sidney, 1764-1840.
                                                        4-34887 Revised
        Library of Congress   DA87.1.S6L7

NL 0358479   DLC NcD

        The life of Sr Thomas Bobley, the honovrable fovnder of the pvbliqve library in the Vniversity of Oxford
            see under   Bobley, Sir Thomas, 1545-1613.

        The life of Sir Thomas Gresham, founder of the Royal Exchange
            see under   [MacFarlane, Charles] d. 1858.

        The life of Sir Thomas More. London, Burns and Lambert, n.d.

        iv, 147 p. 17 cm.
        Title page engraved.

        1. Thomas More, Saint, 1478-1535.
        2. Great Britain - Church history - 1485-1603.

NL 0358482   PLatS

        The Life of Sir Thomas More. London, Granville mansions: New York, Catholic publication society co. [n.d.]
147 p. 18cm.

        1. More, Sir Thomas, 1478-1535.

NL 0358483   NNF

        The life of Sir Thomas More. 1726
            see under   [More, Cresacre] 1572-1649.

        The life of Sir Walter Ralegh, from his birth ...
            see under   [Oldys, William] 1696-1761.

        The Life of Sir Walter Raleigh.   London, n.d.
        16 p. portr. 8°. [Ward & Lock's penny biographies]
        By G. R. E.

NL 0358486   MB

        The life of Sir Walter Raleigh: containing his adventures by sea and land, and the various discoveries he made; also, An account of his conduct during his apprehension and confinement in the Tower, and the interesting particulars respecting his trial and execution. London, Published by Whittingham and Arliss, 56 Paternoster Row [1811?]
        72 p. ports. 16.5 cm.

NL 0358487   NcU

        Life of Sir Walter Raleigh.
        (In the Living age, Boston, 1855. 22ᶜᵐ.
        (v.45) p.579-614)
        Detached copy.
        A condensed reprint "from the North British review" of an unsigned article appearing in the May issue for 1855, p.315-(353).
        Bibliography precedes text.
        Bibliographical foot-note: p.481.
        1. Raleigh, Sir Walter, 1552?-1618. I. Ser.

NL 0358488   ViU

        The life of Sir Walter Scott, novelist, poet, and historian ...
London, Ward, Locke & Co., [18-?]
p.401-[416]
(Ward and Lock's penny biographical series, no.15)
By I. S. A.
Cover title.

NL 0358489   OO

        Life of Sir William Wallace; or, Scotland five hundred years ago...
            see under   [Hutcheson, Thomas Smith] 1822-1878.

BX4705
M655L5   Life of Sister Mary Paul of the Cross, member of the Order of St. Ursula, Congregation of Paris.   With an introduction by Xavier Sutton.   San Francisco, J. H. Barry, 1917.
177 p. port., plates.

        I. Morrissey, Mary Paul, sister, 1856-1912.

NL 0358491   CU

YA
19336   The life of slavery, or the life of the nation?
YA   Mass meeting of the citizens of New York...
16615   at the Cooper institute, New York, March 6, 1862. [n.p., 18--?]
        11 p.

NL 0358492   DLC Nh

        The Life of slavery, or, The life of the nation? Mass meeting of the citizens of New York, (without distinction of party,) at the Cooper institute, New York, March 6, 1862. Hon. James A. Hamilton in the chair. n.p. (1862)
        6 p.   O

        (In pamphlets on slavery, binder's title, (v. 45))

NL 0358493   OO

        LIFE of Sobieski; translated from the French. New York, 1868

        sm.12°. Front.
        Compiled and translated from the French of N.A. de Salvandy, the Countess Drohojowska, Olympe Chodzko, and other sources." - Translator's note.

NL 0358494   MH

        Life of Sobieski, translated from the French. New York, P. O'Shea (1902?)
        2 p. l., (3)-157 p. front. 15½ᶜᵐ.
        On cover: Sobieski's achievements.

        1. Jan III Sobieski, king of Poland, 1629-1696. I. Title: Sobieski's achievements.
        Library of Congress   DK431.L5   43-27241

NL 0358495   DLC

        The life of Socrates, by Plato, Xenophon &c. his disciples. With many curious and interesting anecdotes of the same, and other celebrated Greek philosophers ... Augusta (Ga.) Printed at the Chronicle office, 1807.
        1 p. l., 34 p. 17½ᶜᵐ.

        1. Socrates.
        Library of Congress   B316.L6   20-11807

NL 0358496   DLC NN

        The life of Sœur Rosalie, of the Daughters of St. Vincent de Paul. Born September 8, 1787; died February 7, 1856.   London, Burns and Lambert, 1858.   v, 86 p. 16cm. (The cheap family and educational library)

        With this was issued and is bound: The life of Mdlle. de Lamourous. London, 1859.

        1. Rosalie, Soeur, originally Jeanne Marie Rendu, 1787-1855. I. The cheap family and educational   library.

NL 0358497   NN

        The life of Sœur Rosalie, of the Daughters of St. Vincent de Paul, born September 8, 1787; died February 7, 1856. Baltimore, J. Murphy & co., 1859.
        vii, (1), (9)-141 p. incl. front. (port.) 15 x 12ᶜᵐ.

        1. Rosalie, sœur, 1787-1856.
                                                        37-17418
        Library of Congress   BX4705.R72L5
                                    (2)   922.244

NL 0358498   DLC

        The life of Soeur Rosalie, author of.
            The life of St. Elizabeth of Hungary
            see under title

        Life of Sogoro
            see under   Sakura gimin den.

        The life of Spencer H. Cone
            see under   [Cone, Edward Winfield] 1814-1871.

VOLUME 332

... **Life** of Sri Ramakrishna, compiled from various authentic sources ... Almora ₍India₎ Advaita ashrama, 1925.

1 p. l., vi p., 1 l., 765, ₍2₎ p. ports. (1 col.) 22½ᵐ. (Himalayan series. no. XLVII)

"Published by Swami Madhavananda."

1. Rāmakṛṣṇa, 1836–1886. I. Madhavananda.

32–29700

Library of Congress   B133.R3L5   921.9

NL   0358502   DLC CtY-D MH NN

Hum
B
133
R3
L5
1928

Life of Sri Ramakrishna, compiled from various authentic sources. ₍2d ed.₎ Calcutta, Advaita Ashrama ₍1928₎ 619p.

Distributed by: Hollywood, California, Vedanta Press.

1. Rāmakṛṣṇa, 1836–1886. I. Pavitrananda, Swami. II.Advaita Ashrama, Mayavati, India.

NL   0358503   FTaSU

Life of Sri Ramakrishna, compiled from various authentic sources. Mayavati, Almora, Himalayas, Advaita Ashrama [1936]

viii, 617 p. ports., plates. 20 cm.
"4th ed."
"Published by Swami Vireswarananda."
"Closely follows the chronology and treatment of the Sri Ramakrishna Lelaprasanga (Discourses of the Life of Sri Ramakrishna) by Swami Saradananda.

NL   0358504   MH

Life of Sri Ramakrishna, comp. from various authentic sources. ₍5th ed.₎ Mayavati, Almora, Himalayas, Advaita Ashrama ₍1943₎

vi, 620 p. col. port. 21 cm.
"Published by Swami Pavitrananda." Originally pub. by Swami Madhavananda.

1. Rāmakṛṣṇa, 1836–1886. I. Pavitrananda, Swami. II. Advaita Ashrama, Mayavati, India.

B133.R3L5 1943   921.9   48–32056*

NL   0358505   DLC OrPR CaBVaU

Life of Sri Ramakrishna, compiled from various authentic sources. ₍6th ed.₎ Mayavati, Almora, Himalayas Advaita Ashrama ₍1948₎

vi, 620 p. col. port. 21 cm.
"Published by Swami Pavitrananda."
Originally published by Swami Madhavananda.

1. Rāmakṛṣṇa, 1836–1886. I. Pavitrananda, Swami. II. Advaita Ashrama, Mayavati, India.

B133.R3L5 1948   921.9   50–26630

NL   0358506   DLC ICU OU CaBVaU

181.4
R141L

LIFE OF Sri Ramakrishna. Compiled from various authentic sources. Calcutta. Advaita Ashrama. 1955. 620p. col.port. geneal.table.

NL   0358507   WaS NjPT NcD MoU ViU FMU

947.085
St16B41

The Life of Stalin; a symposium. New York, Workers' Library Publishers, 1930. 96p. port. 18cm. (Stalin pocket series ₍3₎)
Cover has publisher: Modern Books [London]
CONTENTS.—Introduction.—Stalin, by D.Z. Manuilsky.—Stalin and the party, by L. Kaganovich.—Stalin and the Red Army, by K. Voroshilov.—The "diehard" Bolshevik, by S. Ordzhonikidze.—Leaves from my reminiscences, by A. Yenukidze.

1. Stalin, Iosif, 1879–1953.

NL   0358508   TxU CU NIC CoU NcD

The **Life** of Stalin; a symposium. London, Modern books limited, 1931.

3 p. l., 96 p. 17½ cm. ₍Stalin pocket series. 3₎

"Second edition."

CONTENTS.—Introduction.—Stalin, by D. Z. Manuilsky.—Stalin and the party, by L. Kaganovich.—Stalin and the red army, by K. Voroshilov.—The "diehard" bolshevik, by S. Ordzhonikidze.—Leaves from my reminiscences, by A. Yenukidze.

1. Stalin, Iosif, 1879–

DK268.S8L5 1931   923.247   32—343

NL   0358509   DLC NcD NNC

DK
268
.S8
L5
1932

The life of Stalin; a symposium. London, Modern Books, 1932,1930. 96p. 18cm.

"3d ed."
Contents.– D.Z. Manuilsky: Stalin.– L. Kaganovich: Stalin and the Party.– K. Voroshilov: Stalin and the Red Army.– S. Ordzhonikidze: The "diehard" Bolshevik.– A. Yenukidze: Leaves from my reminiscences.

1. Stalin, Iosif, 1879–1953.

NL   0358510   OrU MH WaU

Life of Stephen A. Douglas, United States senator from Illinois
      see under   [Flint, Henry Martyn] 1829–1868.

The life of Stonewall Jackson
      see under   [Cooke, John Esten] 1830–1886.

181.4
V857yL2

The life of Swami Vivekananda, by his eastern and western disciples. ₍2d ed.₎ Mayavati, Almora, Himalayas, Advaita Ashrama ₍pref. 1933₎ 2v. (927p.) illus., ports.

"Published by Swami Vireswarananda."

1. Vivekananda, Swami, 1863–1902 I. Vireswarananda, Swami. II.° Advaita Ashrama, Mayavati, India.

NL   0358513   NBC ICU

The **life** of Swami Vivekananda, by his eastern and western disciples. ₍3d ed.₎ Mayavati, Almora, Himalayas, Advaita Ashrama ₍1944₎

2 v. (viii, 927 p.) ports. 21 cm.
"Published by Swami Pavitrananda."

1. Vivekānanda, Swami, 1863–1902. I. Pavitrananda, Swami. II. Advaita Ashrama, Mayavati, India.

B133.V5L5 1944   921.9   48–13780*

NL   0358514   DLC CtY OrU

B133
.V5I5
1949

The Life of Swami Vivekananda, by his eastern and western disciples. ₍4th ed.₎ Calcutta, Advaita Ashrama ₍1949₎ viii, 765 p. ports. 22 cm.

"Published by Swami Pavitrananda."

1. Vivekananda, Swami, 1863–1902. I. Pavitrananda, Swami.

NL   0358515   TU NcD ICU ICarbS FTaSU

The life of Swami Vivekananda
      see also   The life of the Swami Vivekananda.

The life of T. P. Atticus ...
      see under   [Nepos, Cornelius]

DC
255
T14
L72

Life of Talleyrand, accompanied with a portrait. Philadelphia, Carey, Lea & Blanchard, 1834. 313 p. front. 23cm.

1. Talleyrand-Périgord, Charles Maurice de, prince de Bénévent, 1754–1838.

NL   0358518   NIC PPL

The life of Tamerlane the Great, with his wars against the great duke of Moso, the king of China, Bajazet the great Turk, the sultan of Egypt, the king of Persia, and some others ...
      see under   [Clarke, Samuel] 1599–1682.

AC901
.T5

Life of Tasso.
      p. xli–xlvi. xix–xlvii. (Thorndike Pamphlets, 54: 7)

NL   0358520   DLC

Life of Teresa Higginson, the teacher mystic. 1845–1905. Rocdale, Orphans' press [1927?] 23 p. illus. (incl. ports.) 18 cm.
"These articles have been reproduced from 'The Catholic times.' "
1. Higginson, Teresa Helena, 1844–1905. I. The Catholic times.

NL   0358521   NN

The life of that eminent comedian Robert Wilks
      see under   [Curll, Edmund] 1675–1747.

MICROFORMS
CENTER
Film
3241

The Life of that eminent physician Herman Boerhaave. [London, T. Davies, 1773?] 208–236p.
In Miscellaneous and fugitive pieces, v. 2. Attributed to Samuel Johnson?
Microfilm (negative) New Haven, Conn., Yale University Library, 1969. 1 reel.
1. Boerhaave, Herman, 1668–1738 I. Johnson, Samuel, 1709–1784

NL   0358523   WU

VOLUME 332

PN2598
.B66L7
Aus-
trian
The life of that excellent tragedian Barton
Booth esq; late one of the managers at the
Theatre-Royal in Drury-Lane ... To which is
added, A poem in his memory. By the author of
A pastoral elegy on the death of Calista.
London, J. Cooper, 1733.
vi, 56 p.

1. Booth,　　　　　Barton, 1681-1733.
I. Pastoral ele-　　gy on the death of Calista, Author of.

NL 0358524　ICU CtY MH DFo CSmH MnHi

The life of that faithful servant of Christ ...
　　see under　Hoskens, Jane (Fenn) 1694-

The LIFE of that heavy man Daniel Lambert
from his birth to the moment of his dissolution, with an account of men noted for their
corpulency. New York, S. Wood, 1814.

24°. pp 44+.
Imperfect:-lacks all after p.44.
An earlier edition was published in
London by J. Drakard.

NL 0358526　MH MWA

The life of that heavy man Daniel Lambert
　　see⁸⁴⁄₄₆ The life of that wonderful and
extraordinarily heavy man, the late Daniel
Lambert.

The life of that incomparable man, Faustus
　　Socinus Senensis
　　see under　[Przýpkowski, Samuel]

Ex
14453
.621
.58
The life of that incomparable princess,
Mary, our late sovereign lady, of ever blessed
memory. Who departed this life, at her royal
pallace at Kensington, the 28th of December,
1694. London, Printed for D. Dring, 1695.
108 p. 16 cm.
Tentatively attributed to Daniel Defoe by W.P. Trent & others.
"Threnodium Britannicum, to the sacred
memory of that most excellent princess, Mary
the Second": p.83-　　　108.

NL 0358529　NjP MB ViW ICN MB

The life of that king of thieves Jonathan
Wild. With anecdotes of Joseph Blake, alias
Blue Skin, one of Wild's pupils. To which is
added, The life of William Nevison, the highwayman. London:Printed by T.Maiden,Sherbourne-
lane, for Ann Lemoine,White-Rose-court,Coleman-
street,and J.Roe,no.90,Houndsditch[1799]
38p. incl.front. 17cm. [Bound with The life
of Mahomet. South Shields,1799]
Frontispiece dated 1799.
Signatures: A-C⁶.

NL 0358530　CtY

The life of that learned antiquary, Sir William Dugdale, kt., garter principal, king of arms. Wherein are
contain'd some passages relating to the civil wars, not
taken notice of by any other historian ... Published from
an original manuscript. London, Printed for E. Cvrli[i]
1713.

1 p. l., 43, [1] p. 19ᶜᵐ.
Brit. mus. Catalogue and Lowndes give publisher as E. Curll.

1. Dugdale, Sir William, 1605-1686.

Library of Congress　　DA3.D8L7　　　　5-5789

NL 0358531　DLC MnU CtY CLU-C

The life of that reverend divine, and learned
historian, Dr. Thomas Fuller
　　see under　[Fell, John, bp. of Oxford]
1625-1686, supposed author.

The life of that wonderful and extraordinarily heavy
man, Daniel Lambert, from his birth to the moment of his
dissolution; with an account of men noted for their corpulency, and other interesting matter. New-York: Printed and sold by Samuel Wood & sons, at the Juvenile book
store, no. 357, Pearl-street. 1815.
46 p. front. (port.) 14ᶜᵐ.

1. Lambert, Daniel, 1770-1809. 2. Corpulence. 3. Chap-books.

Library of Congress　　CT9991.L3L5　　　21-3208

NL 0358533　DLC NN

WZ
270
L722
1818
The LIFE of that wonderful and extraordinarily heavy man, Daniel Lambert,
from his birth to the moment of his
dissolution; with an account of men noted
for their corpulency, and other interesting
matter. New York, Samuel Wood & Sons;
[etc., etc.] 1818.
46 p. incl. front. (port.) 15 cm.
Previously published in New York in
1815.
1. Lambert, Daniel, 1770-1809

NL 0358534　DNLM

... The Life of that wonderful and extraordinary
heavy man, the late Danl. Lambert, from
his birth to the moment of his dissolution,
with an account of men noted for their corpulency, and other interesting matter ...
Stamford, J. Drakard, 1809.
28 p. front. (port.) 20 cm.
At head of title: Drakard's third edition.
Four pages of manuscript regarding Lambert
at end.

NL 0358535　CtY-M

The life of that wonderful and extraordinary
heavy man the late Daniel Lambert, from his
birth to the moment of his dissolution; with
an account of men noted for their corpulency,
and a short but interesting account of General
Tom Thumb ... Stamford, Re-printed by W. & J.
Newcomb for James Dixon, 1859.
36 p. illus.

NL 0358536　NNC

The life of that wonderful ... Daniel Lambert
　　see also　The life of that heavy man Daniel
Lambert.

PR3291
.L762
1668
Mss
room
The life of the afflicted Dorca from her infancy
to ye 50th yeare of her age... Written by an intimate no lesse deare to her then her selfe... 1668.
[7], 113(b.e.97)p. 13½cm.

Pages 61-66,71-80 omitted in numbering.
Manuscript.
With this are "Extracts from Wats' Horae lyricae"
and "Extracts from Norris' Miscelanies"(20 numb.l.)
1. Manuscripts,English.

NL 0358538　ICU

The life of the angelic doctor St. Thomas Aquinas...
　　see under　Dyson, Thomas Austin.

LIFE of the assassin Guiteau. By himself
and others. New York, W.J. Ellis, n. d.

f°. pp.14-. Ports. and other illustr.

NL 0358540　MH

The life of the beautiful and accomplished danseuse,
Mademoiselle Fanny Elssler ... The earlier part of her
life compiled from "Bell's Life in London," and replete
with anecdotes related by an English gentleman ... and
also from a number of the American papers. Selected
and comp. by a lady of this city. Philadelphia, Printed
for the purchaser, and for sale, 65 Walnut st.; New York,
141 Fulton st. [etc. 1840?]
32 p. 21¼ᶜᵐ.

1. Elssler, Fanny, 1810-1884. I. A lady of this city.

　　　　　　　　　　　　　　　　　　　　16-9701
Library of Congress　　GV1785.E4L5

NL 0358541　DLC

The Life of the blessed Julie Billiart
　　see under　Clare, James, 1827-1902.

Life of the Blessed Madeleine Sophie Barat
　　see under　Bannard, Louis, 1826-1919
[supplement]

The life of the Blessed Margaret Mary Alacoque ...
　　see under　[Languet de Villeneuve de Gergy,
Jean Joseph, Abp. of Sens] 1677-1753.

Z
920.92
T367
The life of the blessed martyr, Saynte Thomas.
[London? Rycharde Pynson, n. d.]
[16] l.

Facsimile.

1. Saints. 2. Thomas à Becket, Saint, abp. of
Canterbury, 1118?-1170. 3. Early printed books
- Facsimiles. I. Z sh. cd.

NL 0358545　WaPS

The life of the blessed martyr, Saynte Thomas
　　see also　Here begynneth the lyfe of
the blessed martyr saynte Thomas.

VOLUME 332

BT
1048
.L72
Life of the Blessed Mother; Mater Mea, Fiducia Mea, by a Carmelite of St. Mary Magdalene De' Pazzi. Translation by Sister Joan Mary, D.S.P. [Derby, N.Y.] Daughters of St. Paul [c1954]
188 p.   illus.   22 cm.

1. Mary, Blessed Virgin - Biography.

NL 0358547   DCU

... The life of the Blessed Paul of the
     Cross
          see under   [Strambi, Vincenzo Maria,
     bp.] 1745-1825.

... The life of the Blessed Sebastian of Apparizio
     see under   [Ximenez, Matteo]

Life of the blessed servant of God, the heroic martyr, John Gabriel Perboyre, priest of the Congregation of the mission. Translated from the French by Lady Clare Feilding. Appendix specially prepared for American edition. New Orleans, Finney brothers, 1894.

x p., 1 l., [13]-177 p. front. (port.) pl. 17½ cm.

1. Perboyre, Jean Gabriel, 1802-1840. 2. Vincentians in China.
I. Feilding, Lady Clare, tr.

BX4705.P425V52 1894   922.251   37—14652

NL 0358550   DLC

3A
4356

no. 7
The LIFE of the Blessed Virgin.
     [London, Catholic truth society, 1930]
     32 p. 19 cm.

     Bound in a collection of pamphlets published by the Catholic truth society.

NL 0358551   ICN

The life of the Blessed Virgin Mary.   New
     York, Sadlier [n.d.]
          see under   Orsini, Mathieu, 1802-1875.

The life of the Blessed Virgin Mary, Mother of God, of her Blessed Spouse, St. Joseph, and holy parents, St. Joachim and St. Anne.   New York: E. Dunigan and Brother, 1856.   2 v. in 1.   illus., plates.   4°.

Added eng. t.-p.
Contents: [v. 1] Gentilucci, R. Life of the most Blessed Virgin Mary. [v. 2] Vallejo, J., The life of Saint Joseph, most worthy spouse of the Blessed Virgin Mary, and foster-father of Jesus.

15865A. 1. Mary, Virgin.   2. Joseph, Saint. 3. Joachim,
Saint. 4. Anne, Saint, mother of   Mary the Virgin. 5. Gentilucci,
Romualdo. 6. Vallejo, José Ignacio, 1718-85.
N. Y. P. L.   October 5, 1921.

NL 0358553   NN

The life of the Boston bard
     see under   [Coffin, Robert Stevenson]
     1797-1827.

CT
788
G76
L5
The Life of the celebrated infant Roscius, Master Grossmith, of Reading, Berks, only seven years and a quarter old, by E. C. B. Reading, M. Cowslade, 1825.
30p. 18cm.

1. Grossmith, William Robert, 1818-*1899.*
I. B., E. C.   II. E. C. B.

NL 0358555   WU MH

The life of the celebrated Munroe [!] Edwards, convicted in New-York, before the Court of Oyer and Terminer, June 6, 1842, for forgery and swindling, to the amount of fifty thousand dollars. By a Texian ... Boston, W. White & H. P. Lewis, 1842.

33 p. 19ᶜᵐ.

1. Edwards, Monroe, b. 1808.   I. A Texian.

                                        CA 17-1422 Unrev'd
Library of Congress   HV6698.Z9E32

NL 0358556   DLC TxHU CtY MH NN MWA TxU

Life of the celebrated Regent Moray, patron
     of the Scottish reformation ...
     see under
Lawson, John Parker, d. 1852.

The life of the celebrated Sir Francis Drake
     see under   [Campbell, John] 1708-1775.

Life of the Chicago banker, Geo. W. Green, alias Oliver Gavitt, who was found guilty of poisoning his wife and who committed suicide by hanging in the jail of Cook Co. Chicago, Printed at the Chicago Democrat Office, 45 La Salle St. and published by Mellen & Co., (1855)
     (2), 48 p. illus.   23 cm. Double column.
     A comment on a letter dated in March, 1855 states that pa   of this history had already appeared in   he Chicago Democrat.

NL 0358559   N

Life of the Christ, written by a lawyer for
     his children
          see under   [Walker, Allen W   ]

The life of the church
     see under   Rousselot, Pierre.

The life of the Count Cagliostro
     see under   Barberi,

The life of the Countess de Gondez
     see under   [Lussan, Marguerite de] 1682-
1758.

The life of the Countess Emily Plater
     see under   [Straszewics, Josef] 1801-1838.

The Life of the Dvtches of Svffolke
     see under   [Drue, Thomas] fl. 1631.

---

pE
5
.B 35348
& Co.[1880]
     The LIFE of the Earl of Beaconsfield, K.G.
     By a Londoner journalist.   London, Haughton
     16p. 19cm.

     Cover title.
     Portrait on cover.

NL 0358566   ICN

RA917.8
L723
Life of the emigrant: Great Salt Lake City, and Mormonism at home, by a Georgian. Milledgeville [Ga.] Printed for the author, 1854.
64p. 22cm.

Original blue paper wrappers.
Not in Wagner & Camp.

NL 0358567   OC

The life of the emperor Julian
     see under   La Bletterie, Jean Philippe
     René de, 1696-1752.

LIFE of the Emperor Titus... [Bombay] Bombay Tract and Book Soc., 1852. [80] p. 18cm. (Parsi Gujarati series. no. 7.)

Title-page in English and Gujarati; text and pagination in Gujarati.

868237A. 1. Titus, emperor of Rome, 40?—81. 2. Gujarati language—Texts and translations. I. Bombay Tract and Book Society.

NL 0358569   NN

Life of the Empress Josephine, wife of
     Napoleon I.
          see under   [Hartley, Cecil B   ]

The "life" of the Ettrick shepherd anatomized
     see under   [Browne, James] 1793-1841.

The life of the ever-blessed Virgin from her conception to her assumption proposed as a model to Christian women
     see under   [Hirscher, Johann Baptist
     von, Father] 1788-1865.

The life of the famous Cardinal-Duke de Richlieu
     see under   [Le Clerc, Jean] 1657-1736.

The life of the famous dog Carlo ...
     see under   [Fenwick, Eliza]

The life of the famous John Baptist Colbert
     see under   [Courtilz, Gatien de, sieur de
     Sandras] 1644-1712.

The life of the glorious and blessed virgin and martyr Saincte Katheryne
     see under   Catharina, Saint, of Alexandria.
     Legend.

VOLUME 332

The life of the glorious virgin S. Clare
    see under   Marcos, da Lisboa, Bp.,
    1511-1591.

The life of the great Picus, prince of Mirandula
    see under   [Jesup, Edward] fl. 1723.

The life of the heart; George Sand and her times
    see under   Winwar, Frances, pseud.

The LIFE of the Hon. Chang Chien, with an
account of industrial enterprises inaugurated
by him. Shanghai, printed by the Commercial
press, Ltd., 1915.

Pamphlet.
Portrs., and other illustr.

NL 0358580   MH

The life of the Hon. James Buchanan, as written by himself, and set to music by an old democrat, to the tune of "Poor
old horse let him die!" Price—"Half a Jimmy!" Lancaster,
near Wheatland, 1856.

8 p. 18ᶜᵐ.

1. Buchanan, James, pres. U. S., 1791-1868.
                                                3—7908

NL 0358581   DLC CU-B ICN CtY

Life of the Hon. Neal Dow
    see under   Chubb, Henry Stephen,
    1827-1921.

Life of the Japanese woman of to-day. Compiled from contributions by the teaching staff of the Tokyo Higher Normal School for women. Tokyo, Kenkyusha, 1937.

61 p. illus., port. 23 cm.

1. Women in Japan.   I. Ochanomizu Joshi Daigaku, Tokyo.
HQ1762.L53   72-223164
                                           MARC

NL 0358583   DLC

PR 3991
.A1 L 7   The life of the king of the beggars; or,
Bampfylde Moore Carew.   London, G. Purkess
[18—?]
    300 p.   illus.

Half-title: The king of the beggars.

I. Tc.: The king of the beggars.

NL 0358584   InU

---

x B
H1733t   The life of the Lady Halket.   Edinburgh,
Printed for A. Symson and H. Knox, 1701.
[8], 58, [6]p.   18cm.

Dedication signed: S.C.
"Books written by the Lady Halket": p.[59]-
[64].
Bound with [Halkett, Anne (Murray) lady.
Meditations on the twentieth and fifth Psalm.
Edinburgh, 1701.- Halkett, Anne (Murray) lady.
Meditations and prayers upon the first week.

Continued in next column

Continued from preceding column

Edinburgh, 1701; Halkett, Anne (Murray) lady.
Instructions for youth. Edinburgh, 1701, and
Halkett, Anne (Murray) lady. Meditations upon
the seven gifts of the Holy Spirit. Edinburgh,
1702.

---- ---- Microfilm (negative) Edinburgh,
University of Edinburgh Library, 1967. 1
reel. 35mm.

Filmed with Halkett, Anne (Murray) lady.
Meditations and prayers upon the first week.
Edinburgh, 1701; [Halkett, Anne (Murray) lady;
Meditations on the twentieth and fifth Psalm.
Edinburgh, 1701; and Halkett, Anne (Murray)
lady. Instructions for youth. Edinburgh, 1701.

NL 0358587   IU

The Life of the Lady Halket
    see also The Life of Lady Halket.

The life of the Lady Warner of Parham in Suffolk
    see under   [Carisbrick, Edward]

The life of the late celebrated Mrs. Elizabeth
Wisebourn
    see under   Tanner, Anodyne, M.D.
pseud.

The life of the late earl of Chesterfield:or,The man
of the world. Including his lordship's principal speeches in Parliament;his most admired essays in the paper
called The World;his poems;and the substance of the
system of education,delivered in a series of letters to
his son...   London,Printed for J.Bew,1774.
    2 v.   front.(port.) 17½cm.
    1.Conduct of life.

NL 0358591   ICU ICN CtY IEN CU NjP IU PPL

The life of the late earl of Chesterfield: or, The man of the world.
Lond. 1775.

NL 0358592   PWW

The life of the late Earl of Chesterfield: or, The man of the
world. Including his lordship's principal speeches in Parliament;
his most admired essays in the paper called The World; his poems;
and the substance of the system of education delivered in a series
of letters to his son.   London, Printed: Philadelphia: Re-printed
for R. Marchbank, 1775.   xix p., 1 l., 206 p.   12°.

Evans 14472.

1. Letters, English.   2. Conduct of   life.
N. Y. P. L.   October 27, 1928

NL 0358593   NN MdW PHi PU PPL

The life of the late Earl of Chesterfield: or, The man of
the world. Including his lordship's principal speeches in Parliament; his most admired essays in the paper called the World;
his poems; and the substance of the system of education delivered in a series of letters to his son. London, printed: Philadelphia, re-printed for John Sparhawk. MDCCLXXV.

iv, 388 p. 21 cm.

1. Chesterfield, Philip Dormer Stanhope, 4th earl of, 1694-1773.
I. Chesterfield, Philip Dormer Stanhope, 4th earl of, 1694-1773.

DA501.C5L5   47-39651

NL 0358594   DLC CtY PSt PU NcU TxHU

... The life of the late Emperor Napoleon ...
[London, 1873]
    15 p.   22 cm.   ("Police News" edition)
[In "French political tracts", 13]

NL 0358595   CtY

The life of the late famous comedian, Jo. Hayns
    see under   [Brown, Thomas] 1663-1704.

The life of the late General F. R. Chesney...
    see under   [Chesney, Louisa (Fletcher)]

The life of the late Gen. William Eaton
    see under   Prentiss, Charles, 1774-1820,
comp.

The life of the late Honourable Robert Price, esq.
    see under   Curll, Edmund, 1675-1747,
supposed author.

The life of the late John Howard, esq., with a review of
his travels. To the above work, as confirming Mr. Howard's
ideas of the effects of solitary imprisonment, is annexed the
letter which appeared in the paper of the World, on the case
of Saville, tried at Chelmsford for murder ... London, Printed for the author, and may be had of J. Ridgway, 1790.

vii, 88 p.   21ᶜᵐ.

The "letter" mentioned is by Edward Topham.

1. Howard, John, 1726?-1790.   I. Topham, Edward, 1751-1820.

Library of Congress   HV8978.H8L5   12—36811

NL 0358600   DLC ViU PHi PPL CtY-M

---

*EC8   The life of the late most noble Francis duke
A100   of Bedford, including the speech of the Hon.
802L   Charles James Fox, in the House of commons,
        March 16, 1802. Together with an account of his
        illness, death, and funeral, also many other
        interesting particulars, of that great and
        excellent man.
            London:Published by John Fairburn,146,Minories.
        <Price sixpence.> Printed by C. and W. Galabin,
        Ingram-court. [1802]
            24p. 21.5cm.

NL 0358601   MH IEN

The life of the late Princess Charlotte ... London,
T. Kinnersley, 1818.

iv, 596 p. 5 pl. (incl. front.) 5 port. 22ᶜᵐ.

Preface signed: D. M'I.
Also issued the same year under title: The life and memoirs of Her Royal
Highness Princess Charlotte of Saxe Coburg Saalfeld.

Subject entries: Charlotte Augusta, of Wales, princess, consort of Prince
Leopold of Saxe-Coburg-Saalfeld, 1796-1817.
                                                8-29100

Library of Congress, no.   DA506.A5L72.

NL 0358602   DLC NcD ICN NjR

The life of the late Rev. and learned Dr.
Cotton Mather
    see under   [Mather, Samuel] 1706-1785.

VOLUME 332

The **life** of the late Reverend, learned and pious Mr. Jonathan Edwards, some time minister of the gospel at Northampton, in New-England, and then missionary to the Indians at Stockbridge, and after that president of New-Jersey college, who departed this life at Princeton, March 22 1758, in the 55th. year of his age ... Boston, Printed and sold by S. Kneeland, 1765.

4 p. l., 97 (*i. e.* 98) p. 18 cm.

1. Edwards, Jonathan, 1703–1758.

BX7260.E3L52   S D 18–30

U. S. Dept. of State.   Library
for Library of Congress   [a48b1]†

NL 0358604   DS DLC N

The life of the late reverend Mr. James Hervey A.M. ... Portsmouth, 1764.

NL 0358605   RPJCB

FILM
x B
H578

The **life** of the late Reverend Mr. James Hervey, A.M., rector of Weston-Favell, Northamptonshire. Portsmouth, N.H., Printed by D. and R. Fowle, 1764.

Microfilm copy, made in 1954 by Micro-Copy Service, of the original in the American Antiquarian Society Library. Negative.
Collation of the original: 30p.

1. Hervey, James, 1714–1758.

NL 0358606   IU

By94
57

The **life** of the late Right Honourable George lord Carpenter ... London, Printed for E.Curll, 1736.
1p.l.,49,[2],viiip. front. 19cm.
Port. on t.-p.
"A true copy of the last will and testament of the Right Honourable George lord Carpenter": viiip. at end.

1.Carpenter, George Carpenter, 1st baron, 1657-1732.

NL 0358607   CtY CLU-C

Life of the late Thomas Coutts, esq., banker, in the Strand, with biographical and entertaining anecdotes, of his first wife, Betty [i. e. Susan] Starky, and of the present Mrs. Coutts. By a person of the first respectability. To which is added, an account of the manner in which his immense property has been bequeathed. London: J. Fairburn [1822] 1 p.l., 20 p. front. (port.) 22cm.

"Letter from the Earl of Dundonald [to the editor]", p. 16-18.
Five holograph letters by Thomas Coutts (3 signed: Thomas Coutts & co.) and a bill of exchange, inserted.

With bookplate of Albert M. Cohn.

223951B. 1. Coutts, Thomas, 1735-d. 1815. 3. St. Albans, Harriot 1777?-1837. I. Dundonald, Archi-1831. II. A person of the first N.Y.P.L.

1822. 2. Coutts, Susan (Starkie), (Mellon) Beauclerk, duchess of, bald Cochrane, 9th earl of, 1749?-respectability.
                              September 16, 1943

NL 0358609   NN MH CtY CSmH NjP

Life of the late Thomas Coutts, esq. banker, in the Strand, with biographical...anecdotes, of his first wife, Betty [i. e. Susan] Starky, and of the present Mrs. Coutts. By a person of the first respectability. To which is added, an account of the manner in which his immense property has been bequeathed. London, Printed and published by John Fairburn [1822] 1 p.l., 17 p. 22cm.

With bookplate of Albert M. Cohn, illustrated by George Cruikshank.

——— Biographical and historical addenda...containing numerous . . . anecdotes of . . . Betty [i. e. Susan] Starky; including an official copy...of Mr. Coutts's will, with the codicil...also, the ...letter of the Earl of Dundonald on some statements in the narrative... Embellished with a correct likeness of Mr. Coutts. London, Printed and published by John Fairburn [1822] 20 p. incl. front. (port.) 22cm.

Portrait ascribed to George Cruikshank.—*cf. Cohn 167.*

Continued in next column

Continued from preceding column

Bound with the above.

223951B. 1. Coutts, Thomas, 1735–1822. 2. Coutts, Susan (Starkie), d. 1815. 3. St. Albans, Harriot (Mellon) Beau-   clerk, duchess of, 1777?–1837. I. Dundonald, Archibald Cochrane,   9th earl of, 1749?–1831. II. A person of the first respectability.   III. Title: Biographical and histori-cal addenda to the Life of the late   Thomas Coutts.   *Card revised*

NL 0358612   NN InU DLC NIC IEN ICU MH-BA NcD

The **life** of the late victorious and illustrious prince, John Duke of Marlborough ... By an impartial hand. London, Printed for T. Sanders, 1723.
2 p.l., xvi, [1], 320 [i.e. 294], 22 p., 22 cm.

Error in paging: p. 145-170 omitted in numbering.

1. Marlborough, John Churchill, 1st duke of, 1650-1722.   Augustan Cds.

NL 0358613   InU CSmH NN

The **life** of the learned sir Thomas Smith, etc., 1698
    see under Strype, John, 1643-1737.

The **life** of the Marchioness de Pompadour
    see under [Fauques, Marianne Agnès Pillement, dame de] d. 1773.

Life of the Marlows
    see under Rathmell, William, comp.

The **life** of the martyr, John Brown, of Priest-hill, in the parish of Muirkirk, Ayrshire, who was murdered by Graham of Cleverhouse, near his own house, in 1685; also, an account of his companions in suffering, during the last persecution in Scotland, between the years 1680 and 1688... 24p. Stirling, Printed by W. Macnie, 1828. (In Scottish chap books)

NL 0358617   OC1

Life of the Master. Chicago, 1925
    see under Bible. N. T. English. Selections. 1925.

The **life** of the most eminent and truly illustrious bishop, St.Patrick, the apostle and patron of Ireland. Collected from the most authentick accounts, in print or manuscript; illustrated with several useful notes, historical, chronological, and topographical, and inter-sper'd with suitable reflections... Dublin, Printed for R.Cross...and I.Tisdal, 1743.
    180 p.   14 ᶜᵐ.
1.Patrick, Saint, 373?-463.

NL 0358619   NjP

E
5
.P 27553

The **LIFE** of the most eminent and truly illustrius Bishop, St. Patrick, the apostle and patron of Ireland. Collected from the most authentick accounts ... To which is added, by way of note, an historical account of the antient, ecclesiastical state of the city and diocese of Dublin, the Isle of Man, and several other places ... Dublin, E.Bate,1747.
    127p. 20cm.

NL 0358620   ICN

Life of the most illustrious monarch Almanzor...
    see under

    Luna, Miguel de, fl. 1600.

The **life** of the most learned Father Paul of the order of the Servie. Councellour of state to the most serene republicke of Venice...
    see under [Micanzio, Fulgenzio] 1570-1654.

The **life** of the most learned, reverend and pious Dr. H. Hammond
    See under
    [Fell, John, bp. of Oxford] 1625-1686.

The **life** of the most noble, the Marquis Cornwallis
    see As Great a Man as Nelson

The **life** of the Most Reverend Clement Smyth
    see under [Henry, Mary Gertrude, sister] 1857-

Mhc5
C852X
L62

The **life** of the most reverend Dr. Cranmer, some time Lord Archbishop of Canterbury... the whole including various remarkable events in the history of the Reformation. London, Printed for the editor, 1751.
    74p. illus. 20cm.

1. Cranmer, Thomas, abp. of Canterbury, 1489-1556.

NL 0358626   CtY

The **life** of the Most Reverend Father in God John Tillotson
    see under [Hutchinson, Francis, bp. of Down and Connor] 1660-1739.

The **life** of the most rev. Joseph Dixon, D.D.
    see under [Cusack, Mary Frances] 1830-1899.

Life of the most Reverend Peter Richard Kenrick, archbishop of St. Louis. St. Louis, Missouri. Catholic publishing co., 1891.

    6-65 p. front. (port.) 22 cm.

NL 0358629   PLatS

The **LIFE** of the party.   New York, Rosenfield, [191-?] 51, 55, 54 l. 27cm.

Typescript.
Cover title.
Title changed in ms. from The merry maker.

1. Drama, American.   I. Title: The merry maker.

NL 0358630   NN

VOLUME 332

The LIFE of the princess of Zell, wife of George I, king of England, containing an account of her persecutions, sufferings, and imprisonment for 36 years on a charge of supposed incontinency. To which is added, Ivy castle, or The eve of St. Agnes; being an interesting history of the Wilmington family, including memoirs of Lord Colville & Agnes St. Eustace. Founded on facts. London, printed for the booksellers and for J. Kendrew, [18-].

pp. 36.　Colored fro　nt. (folded).

NL 0358631　MH

The life of the prophet Jeremiah
　　see under　[Alden, Joseph] 1807-1885.

The life of the renowned Peter D'Aubusson
　　see under　Bouhours, Dominique,
　　1628-1702.

BX
8495
.C59
L7
18--
　　The life of the Rev. Adam Clarke ... compiled from authentic documents. By a Wesleyan preacher ... London, T. Allman [18--?]
　　1 p. l., iv, 282 p.　14ᶜᵐ.

1. Clarke, Adam, 1760?-1832.

NL 0358634　MiU

Div. S.
922.7
C597LI
　　The Life of the Rev. Adam Clarke, L.L.D., compiled from authentic documents. By a Wesleyan preacher. London, J. Smith, 1841.
　　iv, 282 p.　12 cm.

1. Clarke, Adam, 1760?-1832. I. A Wesleyan preacher.

NL 0358635　NcD

Life of the Rev. Alex. Mathieson
　　see under　[Croil, James] 1821-1916.

Life of the Rev. Alexander Kilham, formerly a preacher under the Rev. J. Wesley, and one of the founders of the Methodist New Connexion in the year 1797. Including a full account of the disputes which occasioned the separation ... London, R. Groombridge; [etc., etc.,] 1838.

xii, [13,]408p. front. (port.)　19½cm.

Based on a memoir of Mr. Kilham consisting chiefly of extracts from his diary, his published writings, contemporary circulars, and original documents.—*cf.* Pref.

1. Kilham, Alexander, 1762-1798. 2. Methodist New Connexion.

Printed by Wesleyan　　　　University Library

NL 0358637　CtW NjPT NcD TxDaM

The life of the reverend and learned Mr. John Sage
　　see under　[Gillane, John]

Life of the reverend Anthony Horneck, D. D.
　　see under　[Kidder, Richard] bp. of Bath & Wells, cir. 1633-1703.

The **life** of the Rev. Augustus M. Toplady ...
[Philadelphia, Presbyterian board of publication, 1841]
　　p. [163]-240.　15½ᶜᵐ.
　In the life of Rev. James Harvey... Philadelphia, 1841.

1. Toplady, Augustus Montague, 1740-1778. I. Presbyterian church in the U. S. A. Board of publication.

NL 0358640　MiU

The **life** of the Rev. Augustus M. Toplady ...
[Philadelphia, Presbyterian board of publication, 1876?]
　　p. [163]-240.　15½ᶜᵐ.
　In The life of the Rev. James Harvey... Philadelphia [1876]

1. Toplady, Augustus Montague, 1740-1778. I. Presbyterian church in the U. S. A. Board of publication.

NL 0358641　ViU

Life of the Rev. Bernard Gilpin...　London: Religious Tract Soc., 1827.　72 p.　24°.　(Christian biography.)

"The materials for this account...are taken from his Life, written in Latin, by Carleton...and from his Life published by the Rev. William Gilpin."

1. Gilpin, Bernard, 1517-83. 2. Series.
N. Y. P. L.　　　　　　　　　　　　　May 25, 1916.

NL 0358642　NN

Life of the Rev. Bernard Gilpin.　London, Religious Tract Society [1832]
　　72 p.　(Christian Biography)

NL 0358643　OO

266.092
S973Am
　　The life of the Rev. C. F. Swartz, missionary at Trichinopoly and Tanjore, in India.　New York [n.d.]
　　106p.
　　Issued by the American Tract Society.

1. Swartz, Christian Frederick, 1726-1798.

NL 0358644　FTaSU PPLT MWA

BR45
.C4
1850
v.33
no.3
　　The life of the Rev. C. F. Swartz, missionary of Trichinopoly and Tanjore in India.　New York, American Tract Society, 1840.
　　60p. 18cm.　(With Newton, John. The life of the Rev. John Newton. New York [1846?])

At head of title: Christian biography. No.3 (p.[177]-236)
Vol. 33 [no.3] in a set with binder's title: Christian library.

NL 0358645　FMU

The LIFE of the Rev. Dr. Dodd. Also, his Last Sermon, preached in Newgate to His Fellow Prisoners. B. 1850.

pp. 24.
DLC: YA22450

NL 0358646　MH DLC

Life of the Rev. F. Cointet, priest and missionary of the Congregation of holy cross.　Cincinnati, J. P. Walsh, 1855.

82 p.　22½ᵐ.

1. Cointet, François, 1817-1854.

Library of Congress　　　BX4705.C686L5　　37-8471
　　　　　　　　　　　　　　[2]　　　　　　　　　　922.273

NL 0358647　DLC

The **life** of the Reverend Fa. Angel of Ioyevse...
　　see under　[Brousse, Jacques]

Life of the Rev. George Pattrick...　London: Religious Tract Soc. [1835?]　72 p.　24°.　(Christian biography.)

"Abridged from the Memoirs prefixed to his Sermons."

1. Pattrick, George, 1746-1800.　　　2. Series.
N. Y. P. L.　　　　　　　　　　　　　May 29, 1916.

NL 0358649　NN

Div. S.
922.342
T8571
　　Life of the Rev. George Trosse, of Exeter, England. [Philadelphia] Presbyterian Board of Publication, 1840.
　　124 p.　15 cm.

1. Trosse, George, 1631-1713. I. Presbyterian Church in the U. S. A. Board of Publication and Sabbath School Work.

NL 0358650　NcD OClW ViU MWA NWM NNUT

Div. S.
922.7
W591LIF
　　Life of the Rev. George Whitefield.　London, Religious Tract Society [1833]
　　144 p.　14 cm.
　　At head of title: Christian biography.

1. Whitefield, George, 1714-1770. I. Religious Tract Society, London.

NL 0358651　NcD

B
285.8
W586L
　　The life of the Rev. George Whitefield. Abridged from authentic sources, by a Friend of Sabbath schools. Revised by the editors. New York, B. Waugh and T. Mason, for the Sunday School Union of the Methodist Episcopal Church, J. Collard, printer, 1833.
　　59p.　front.　14cm.

NL 0358652　OOxM

Div. S.
922.7
W591LI
　　Life of the Rev. George Whitfield [sic.], A. M. Edinburgh, W. Oliphant; sold by M. Ogle, Glasgow, 1826.
　　322 p.　port.　15 cm.

1. Whitefield, George, 1714-1770.

NL 0358653　NcD PPAmP

The life of the Rev. Herman Norton, to which are added Startling facts, and Signs of danger and of promise, from his pen, while cor. sec. of the American Protestant society. New-York, Published by the American and foreign Christian union, 1853.
　　3 v. in 1.　front. (v.2, fold. map)　15½ᶜᵐ.
Introduction signed: Thomas Dewitt.
"A discourse on the life and character of the Rev. Herman Norton ... by Henry P. Tappan": p.[11]-69.
"Startling facts for American Protestants" and "Signs of danger and of promise" have special title-pages, the former dated 1852.

1. Norton, Herman, 1799-1850. 2. Catholic church—Doctrinal & controversial works—Protestant authors. I. Tappan, Henry Philip, 1805-1881. II. American and foreign Christian union.

NL 0358655　MiU NN ICU NNU

VOLUME 332

BX 5199 P7 L5 Cage
The life of the Reverend Humphrey Prideaux, D.D. Dean of Norwich. With several tracts and letters ... Never before published. London, Printed for J. and P. Knapton, 1748.

[8] 280 p. A[4], B-S[8], T[4], 8vo.

Contents include: An account of the English settlements in the East Indies, Articles for the reformation of the two universities, and letters to Archbishop Tennison, William Lord Archbishop of Canterbury, Charles Townshend, Francis Gwynn, and the Bishop of Worcester.

NL 0358656   DFo MdBP NjPT MH ICN NNUT OU PBL MWA

The life of the Rev. James Hervey ... Philadelphia, Presbyterian board of publication [1876?]
240 p. 15½[cm].

Includes: The life of the Rev. Augustus M. Toplady...; p. [163]-240.

1. Hervey, James, 1714-1758. I. Presbyterian church in the U. S. A. Board of publication.

NL 0358657   ViU

The life of the Rev. James Hervey
    see also   The life of Rev. James Hervey.

The life of the Rev. James Ireland
    see under   Ireland, James, 1748-1806.

The life of the Rev. John Brown of Haddington, Scotland
    see under   Brown, John, 1722-1787.

The life of the Rev. John Fletcher. Abridged from authentic sources. By a friend of Sabbath schools. New York, Published by J. Emory and B. Waugh, for the Sunday school union of the Methodist Episcopal church, 1831.

NL 0358661   GEU

The life of the Rev. John Fletcher
    see also   The life of Rev. John Fletcher.

The life of the Rev. John Janeway
    see under   Janeway, James, 1636?-1674.

Div.S. 922.7 W513Lf
Life of the Rev. John Wesley. London, Religious Tract Society [18--]
144 p. 15 cm.
At head of title: Christian biography.

1. Wesley, John, 1703-1791. I. Religious Tract Society, London.

NL 0358664   NcD

The LIFE of the Rev. John Wesley, compiled from authentic sources. With an appendix, shewing the real character of the Methodist priesthood. [Newcastle-upon-Tyone]. D. France and co., 1842.

pp.20.
"Published for the Newcastle-upon-Tyne Tract Society".

NL 0358665   MH

The Life of the Rev. John Wesley, M.A. Leeds, 1825.
    see under   Whitehead, John, 1740?-1804.

The life of the Rev. Joseph Alleine... [London:] Religious Tract Soc., 1827. 72 p. 24°. (Christian biography.)

"An account of his godly life and practice, and of the course of his ministry in Taunton," by Rev. George Newton. p. 4-10.
"A full narrative of his life, from his being silenced till his death, written by his widow," p. 20-72.

1. Alleine, Joseph, 1634-68. 2. Newton, George, 1602-81. 3. Alleine, Theodosia (Alleine). 4. Series.
N. Y. P. L.   June 1, 1916.

NL 0358667   NN

The life of the Rev. Joseph Benson, abridged from authentic sources, by a friend of Sabbath schools. New York, J. Emory and B. Waugh, 1832.
94 p.

NL 0358668   OC1 NcD

The life of the Reverend Mr. Jonathan Edwards. n.p., n.d.

NL 0358669   RPJCB

BX 8025 .R8 D9 L7
Life of the Rev. Mother Amadeus of the Heart of Jesus, foundress of the Ursuline missions of Montana and Alaska. Sketch taken from convent annals, by an Ursuline of Alaska. For private circulation only. [Missoula, Montana, Press of the Bureau of printing, 1920?]
226 p. front. (port.) illus., ports. 23cm.
At head of title-page: Chronicle of the north land (Kahlekat V.))
1. Dunne, Amadeus of the Heart of Jesus, Mother, 1846-1919. 2. Ursulines. 3. Missions— Alaska. I. Kahlekat V.

NL 0358670   DCU InU

271.974 A481Z1
Life of the Rev. Mother Amadeus of the Heart of Jesus, foundress of the Ursuline Missions of Montana and Alaska. Sketch compiled from convent annals by an Ursuline of Alaska. [Missoula, Mont. The Bureau of Printing, 1923?]
226p. illus. 23cm. (Chronicle of the North land, Kahlekat V.)

1. Amadeus, Mother, 1846-1919. 2. Ursulines. I. Chronicle of the North land (Kahlekat V.)

NL 0358671   MtU

Life of the Rev. Mother Amadeus of the Heart of Jesus, foundress of the Ursuline missions of Montana and Alaska. Sketch compiled from convent annals.
— New York. The Paulist Press. 1923. xiii, 233 pp. Portraits. Plates. 19 cm.

M7259 — Dunne, Sarah Theresa,   1846-1919.— Ursulines.— Roman Catholic Church. Missions. — Roman Catholic Church in Alaska. — Roman Catholic Church in the United States. Montana.

NL 0358672   MB OCX MtU MtHi NjP NBuG PRosC

Life of the Reverend Mother Jeanne Chezard de Matel
    see under   Saint Pierre of Jesus.

Life of the Reverend Mother Julia, foundress and first superior of the Sisters of Notre Dame of Namur. Translated from the French. With the history of the Order in the United States. New York, The Catholic publication society, 1861.

xi, 16-351 p. front. (port.) 18 cm.

1. Julie Billiart, Blessed, 1751-1816.
2. Sisters of Notre Dame de Namur.
3. Sisters of Notre Dame de Namur in the U.S.

NL 0358674   PLatS

Life of the Reverend Mother Julia, foundress and first superior of the Sisters of Notre Dame, of Namur. Translated from the French. With the history of the order in the United States. New York, The Catholic publication society; Boston, P. Donahue; [etc., etc.] 1871.

xi p., 1 l., [15]-351 p. incl. front. (port.) 18½[cm].

1. *Billiart, Julie, 1751-1816. 2. Sisters of Notre Dame de Namur. I. Catholic publication society, New York.
                                              37-8037
Library of Congress   BX4705.B5L5
Copyright 1871: 9896   922.2496

NL 0358675   DLC IdPI MB DCU

BX 7881 .F2 L4 E5 1909
Life of the Reverend Mother Ste.-Marie, Henriette Le Forestier d'Osseville, foundress of the Society of the Faithful Virgin. Translated from the French by F. A. Phillipson. London, Burns & Oates; New York, Benziger, 1909.
xxiii, 279 p. port. 23 cm.

1. Le Forrestier d' Osseville, Henriette, 1803-1858. 2. Daughters of the Faithful Virgin.

NL 0358676   DCU

BX5207 H4L5
The life of the Rev. Oliver Heywood, born 1629 [sic]-died 1702. [London] Religious Tract Society [1832]
72 p. 15 cm. (Christian biography)

1. Heywood, Oliver, 1630-1702.

NL 0358677   MeB

AC901 .M5
Life of the Rev. Samuel Brewer. In the Evangelical magazine, for January 1797.
18 p. (Miscellaneous pamphlets, 412:2)

NL 0358678   DLC

The life of the Rev. Thomas Coke. Abridged from authentic sources. By a friend of Sabbath schools. New York, Emory and Waugh, 1830.
86 p. (Sunday school and youth's library)

Imperfect: p. 33 mutilated; all after p. 86 wanting.

1. Coke, Thomas, 1747-1814.

NL 0358679   NNC NcD GEU

The life of the Rev. Thomas Coke, L.L.D., a clergyman of the Church of England
    see under   Crowther, Jonathan, 1760-1824.

Life of the Rev. Thomas Halyburton
    see under   [Halyburton, Thomas] 1674-1712.

VOLUME 332

Life of the Rev. William Tennent...
    see under   Boudinot, Elias, 1740-1821.

Life of the right honourable and religious lady
    Christian late countess dowager of
    Devonshire
        see under   [Pomfret, Thomas]

---

*EC65   The life of the Right Honourable and Right
C7393   Reverend Dr. Henry Compton late lord bishop of
W714l   London.
              London:Printed for A.Baldwin in Warwick lane,
            [1714?] (Price one shilling)
              8°. 2p.l.,84p. 19.5cm.
              Doubtfully (& erroneously) attributed to
            Nathanael Salmon by BM & DNB.

    NL 0358684   MH InU

---

40   The life of the right honorable Benjamin Disraeli,
          earl of Beaconsfield, New York, Harper &
          brothers, [1878]
              14 p.   4°.   [Franklin square library,
          no. 16]

    NL 0358685   DLC MH

E   The LIFE of the Right Honorable, Charles
5   James Fox, late principal secretary of state
.F 83218 for foreign affairs, &c. &c. comprehending a
          brief view of the times in which he lived; some
          account of his principal cotemporaries; his oc-
          casional verses, and other productions.   [Lon-
          don]J. Oundee,1807.
              367p. ports. 19cm.

    NL 0358686   ICN MiU-C IaU

The life of the right honourable George Canning
    [etc]. with selections from his poems and
    speeches and a narrative of his illness &
    death together with a brief review of his
    premiership.   London, J. Limbirg, 1827.
        30 p.   1 port.   8°.   [Po. Pam. v. 71:9]

    NL 0358687   DLC

Life, The, of the Right Honorable Horatio Lord Viscount Nelson,
baron of the Nile, duke of Bronte, in farther Sicily, &c. &c.   Halifax: J. Hartley, 1839.   vii(i), 344 p, 4 pl.   3. ed.   24°.

1. Nelson (1. viscount), Horatio Nel-   son.
N.Y.P.L.   October 31, 1912.

    NL 0358688   NN

E   The LIFE of the Right Honourable Richard
5   Brinsley Sheridan, containing a comprehensive
.S 552956 review of his abilities as a poet, a statesman,
          an orator, and a dramatist, with the remarks
          of Pitt, Fox, and Burke, on his most celebrated
          speeches, and many curious anecdotes of his par-
          liamentary, literary, and private career; never
          before published: including his monody on Gar-
          rick, verses to Miss Linley, and a collection
          of his fugitive poetry, &c. &c.   London,J.
          Fairburn[1816?]
              38p. 23cm.

    NL 0358689   ICN MH CSmH CtY ICU

The life of the Right Honourable Sir John Holt, knight,
lord chief justice of the Court of King's-bench; containing several arguments touching the rights and liberties of
the people, delivered by his lordship, with great reason
and remarkable courage, upon most important occasions,
during the reigns of Their Majesties, King William the
Third, and Queen Anne; taken from the report of the
Lord Chief Justice Raymond, &c.   And an abstract of
Lord Chief Justice Holt's will, codicils, &c.   Also points
of law, resolved by his lordship, on evidence, at nisi prius.

With a table of references to all his lordship's arguments
and resolutions in the several volumes of reports.   Never
before published ...   By a gentleman of the Inner-Temple.
London, Printed for the author, and sold by J. Worrall,
1764.
    xiii, 154, xi, [31] p.   21cm.
    Introduction signed: J. R.
    1. Holt, Sir John, 1642-1710.   I. R., J.   II. J. R.

                                            24-14569

    NL 0358691   DLC OU N CLL MH TxU OC1 NPV

The life of the Right honourable Sir Robert Peel, bart.   *A new ed*
with alterations and additions.
    London : G. Routledge and co.   1850.   iv, 220 pp.   Sm. 8°.
    ·Portrait wanting.

    NL 0358692   MB MiD

The life of the Right Honourable Sir
    Robert Peel, bart, as subject and citizen,
    as legislator and minister, as patron of
    learning and the arts...new ed. with numer-
    ous alterations and additions.   Lond.
    Routledge, 1853.

    NL 0358693   MA

The Life of the Right Honourable Sir Rob-
    ert Walpole ... Part I. Containing, I.The
    reasons for writing this great man's life. II.
    A survey of the administration of his prede-
    cessors ...   London,E.Curll,1731.
        1p.l.,50p.   19½cm.

    NL 0358694   CtY MnU

The life of the Right Hon. Spencer Perceval
    see under   Fairburn, John, ed.

Life, The, of the right Hon. W. E. Gladstone; a popular biography.
London: George Routledge & Sons, Ltd., 1898.   216 p.   12°.

1. Gladstone, William Ewart.
N.Y.P.L.   July 2, 1912.

    NL 0358696   NN

The life of the Right Honourable William E.
    Gladstone, M.P.   London [1878]
        see under   Stark, Malcolm.

DA   The life of the right honourable William
522   Pitt, by an observer.   London [G.
P6   Thompson, 18--]
L5   28p.   18cm.
            Cover title.

            I. Pitt, William, 1759-1806   I. An
        Observer II. Title

    NL 0358698   WU

The life of the Right Honourable William Pitt,
    late Prime Minister, from the earliest period of
    his life....   London, Printed by W. Glindon,
    [1806?]
        p.[2] [1-3] 4-26. illus.

    Allegorical frontispiece, with explanation.
    Published before his funeral.

    1. Pitt, William,   1759-1806

    NL 0358699   KU

The life of the Rt. Rev. Dr. Doyle; compiled from authentic
    documents: by the author of "The priesthood vindicated" ...
    New York, J. Doyle, 1835.
    288 p.   front. (port.)   15cm.

    1. Doyle, James Warren, bp., 1786-1834.
                                                    37-10805
    Library of Congress   BX4705.D68L5
                                                    922.2415

    NL 0358700   DLC DGU CtY

The life of the Right Reverend Dr. White Kennett,
    late Lord Bishop of Peterborough
        see under   [Newton, William] d. 1744.

The life of the right Reverend Father in
    God, Edw. Rainbow

        see under

    Banks, Jonathan

The life of the Rt. Rev. Gabriel Brute
    see under   Bruté de Rémur, Simon
Guillaume Gabriel, Bp., 1779-1839. [supplement]

941.58   The Life of the Rt. Rev. Jas. Doyle, D.D.
D754   Bishop of Kildare and Leighlin, by the
.YS1   author of "The priesthood vindicated."
1857   New York, D. & J. Sadlier, 1857.
                286 p.   front. (port.)

            1. Doyle, James Warren, bp., 1786-1834

    NL 0358704   CaQML

Life of the Right Reverend Mathias Loras, D.D.,
    first bishop of Dubuque, Iowa, 1792-1858
        see under   [Fleming, Stanislaus, mother]
1854-1932.

The life of the Russian general Suworow;
    with a circumstantial detail of his surprising
    victories; his cruelty to the Turks at Ismail,
    and the Poles at Warsaw; his progress in Italy
    against the French in 1799; his retreat from
    Switzerland,return to Russia,degradation and
    death ...   London, Printed for T.Tegg & co.
    [1795]
        40 p.   front.(port.)   18cm.

    1.Suvorov,Aleksandr Vasil'evich,kniaz' Italiiskii,
1729-1800.

    NL 0358706   MiU DLC

VOLUME 332

Life of the soldier and the airman. v. 1-
₁Mar. 19₎ 1919-
₁Governors Island, N. Y., etc., Recruiting Publicity Bureau,
U. S. Army₎
    v. in   illus., ports., maps. 27-30 cm.
    Frequency varies.
    Vol. 1, no. 1-10 are undated; Dec. 20, 1921-Jan. 1, 1927 issued without vol. numbering.
    Vol. 1, no. 3, 18-v. 2, no. 4 are called "series A."
    Title varies: 1919, The bulletin ₁of the₎ Recruiting Publicity Bureau, U. S. Army.—Jan. 1920-July 1922, June 1923-Dec. 1, 1932, U. S. Army recruiting news.—Aug. 1922-May 1923, Dec. 15, 1932-Apr. 1936,

    Recruiting news.—May 1936-June 1942, United States Army recruiting news.—July 1942-July 1948, Army life and United States Army recruiting news.
    Issues for Mar.–Sept. 1919 published by the Bureau under a variant name: Publicity Bureau, U. S. Army Recruiting Service.

    1. U. S. Army—Period. 2. U. S. Air Force—Period.   I. U. S. Army. Recruiting Publicity Bureau.

UA23.A1A88   War 22-1 rev 2*
U. S. National War   College. Library
for Library of Congress   ₁r54f1₁†

    CoCA NbHi
NL 0358708   DNW DLC I ICJ OrU KMK ICAC OrCS ICRL

Life of the soldier and the airman.
Histories of army posts. Reprinted from "The Recruiting news". ₁Governor's Island, N. Y., U. S. army Recruiting publicity bureau, 1924₎
    1 p. l., 48, ₁1₎ p. incl. illus., port. 26½ᵐᵐ.

    1. Military posts—U. S.   I. Title.

Library of Congress   UA26.A2 1924   24-27323

NL 0358709   DLC DN-Ob WaT KMK IdB WaT MiU NN ICJ ICN

Life of the spirit. v. 1-19 (no. 1-215); July 1946-Aug./Sept. 1964. ₁London, etc.₎ Blackfriars Publications ₁etc.₎
    10 v. 22 cm. monthly.
    Absorbed by New Blackfriars.
    L. C. set incomplete: no. 1-19, 21-26, 102, 203-205, 210 wanting.

    1. Dominicans—Period. 2. Spiritual life—Period.

BX3501.L5   52—66374 rev

NL 0358710   DLC NStBU IMunS MChB-W CStclU MH MdW DCU

Life of the spirit.
    The Christian vision; readings from the first ten years of The Life of the Spirit. Arranged and edited by Mary Ellen Evans...with a foreword by the editor of The Life of the Spirit. London, Blackfriars Publications [1955]
    xv, 311 p.
    1. Evans, Mary Ellen, ed.

NL 0358711   MH-AH

BI33
V44A6   The life of the Swami Vivekananda by his eastern and western disciples, the Advaita Ashrama, Himalayas. The semi-centenary birthday memorial ed. Mayavati, Almora, Himalayas, Published by the Swami Virajananda from the Prabuddha Bharata Office, Advaita Ashrama, 19
    v.   ports. (Himalayan series, no.

    1. Vivekānanda, Swami, 1863-1902. I. Virajananda, Swami, 1874 or 5-   II. Title.

NL 0358712   CU MiD

The life of the Swami Vivekananda ; by his eastern and western disciples, the Advaita Ashrama, Himalayas. The semi-centennial birthday memorial edition. Published by the Swami Virajananda... v. 1 ₁Calcutta: K. C. Ghosh,₎ 1912 v.
    port. 8°. (Himalayan series. no. 23.)

    I. Vivekānanda, Swāmi. 2. Vedanta   philosophy. 3. Advaita Ashrama.
N. Y. P. L.   October 9, 1913.

NL 0358713   NN UU

The life of the Swami Vivekananda, by his Eastern and Western disciples, the Advaita Ashrama, Himalayas. The semi-centenary birthday memorial edition, in three volumes. Published by the swami Virajananda. Mayavati, Almora, Advaita Ashrama, 1912-15.
    3 v. ports. (Himalayan series, XXIII-XXV)

NL 0358714   NNC

    ... The life of the swami Vivekananda by his eastern and western disciples, the Advaita Ashrama, Himalayas... Mayavata, Almora, Himalayas. Pub. by the swami Virajananda from the Prabuddha Bharata office, Advaita Ashrama, 1914-1918.
    4 v. ports (incl. fronts.) 22cm. (Himalayan series. no. 25-27, 37)
    "Semi-centenary birthday memorial ed."
    1. Vivekanan- la, swâmi, 1863-1902.

NL 0358715   MnU

The life of the Swami Vivekananda
    see also The life of Swami Vivekananda.

The life of the valiant & learned Sir Walter Raleigh, knight
    see under [Shirley, John] 1648-1679.

Life of the Venerable Anne of Jesus
    see under [Hardman, Anne] sister.

271.83
P962   The life of the Venerable F. Louis de Ponte, of the Society of Jesus. London and Derby, T. Richardson and son, 1882.
    viii, 244 p. front. (port.) 19½cm.

    1. Puente, Luis de la, 1554-1624. S. J.

NL 0358719   MoSU

The life of the Venerable Father Colin
    see under [Guay, Marcellin]

Life of the venerable M.-M. Dufrost de Lajemmerais...
    see under
    ₁Faillon, Etienne Michel₎ abbé, 1800-1870.

The life of the venerable Madeleine Barat
    see under [Baunard, Louis] 1826-

Life of the Venerable Madeleine Louise Sophie Barat
    see under Baunard, Louis, 1826-1919.
[supplement]

    ... The life of the Venerable Mother Margaret Mary Alacoque
    see under [Languet de la Villeneuve de Gergy, Jean Joseph, abp. of Sens] 1677-1753.

The life of the Venerable Mother Mary of the Incarnation, joint foundress and first superior of the Ursulines of Quebec. London, James Duffy & sons, n.d.

NL 0358725   OClUr

Life, The, of the Venerable Mother Mary of the Incarnation, joint foundress and first Superior of the Ursulines of Quebec. By a religious of the Ursuline community, Blackrock, Cork. Dublin. Duffy. [1880.] x, 9-350 pp. Sm. 8°.

                   June 5,   1902
E4632 — Guyart, Marie. — Ursulines of Quebec.

NL 0358726   MB

    ... The life of the venerable servant of God, Benedict Joseph Labrè ...
    see under [Coltraro, Antonio Maria] d. 1797.

BX
7767   Life of the venerable servant of God, Jean
.P4   Gabriel Perboyre, translated from the French by
F4   Lady Clare Feilding. London, Burns & Oates;
E5   New York, Catholic publication society, 1887.
1887   139 p. port. 18cm.

    1. Perboyre, Jean Gabriel, 1802-1840.

NL 0358728   DCU PV

    Life of the venerable servant of God, Julie Billiart, foundress and first superior general of the Institute of sisters of Notre-Dame, by a member of the same congregation; edited by Father Clare ... London and Leamington, Art and book company; New York, Cincinnati ₁etc.₎ Benziger brothers, 1898.
    xx, 403 p. front., plates, ports. 21cm.
    Bibliographical foot-notes.
    1. Billiart, Julie, 1751-1816. 2. Sisters of Notre Dame de Namur. I. Clare, James, ed.

NL 0358729   DCU MBtS OCX

The life of the Very Reverend and learned Cotton Mather ...
    see under Mather, Samuel, 1706-1785.

---

*N8070 ₁Life of the Virgin. No imprint ₁1908?₎
L4
    65 mount, plates. 30cm.
    Title from binding.

    1. Mary, Virgin.-Art.

NL 0358731   NBuG

The life of Themistocles
    see under [Wilson, Charles]

The life of Theodore Agrippa d'Aubigné
    see under [Scott, Mrs. Sarah (Robinson)] d. 1795.

VOLUME 332

339.5
B665*l*

The LIFE of Thomas Boulter, the noted flying highwayman; convicted at the castle of Winchester, on Friday the 31st of July, 1778, before the Hon. Sir Francis Buller, knt... Together with A short narrative of the life of James Caldwell, his accomplice. Winton, Printed by J. Wilkes, 1778.

    64 p.   21cm.
    1.Boulter, Thomas. 2.Caldwell, James

NL 0358734   MnU ICN

The life of Thomas Carlyle, philosopher, critic and historian. (Signed H. W. D.) London: Ward, Lock & Co. (189–?) p.321–336. 8°. (Ward & Lock's penny books for the people. Biographical series.)

1. Carlyle, Thomas. 2. Title.
N. Y. P. L.   January 20, 1911.

NL 0358735   NN

Life of Thomas Chalmers ... Cincinnati, 1853
    see under [Hanna, William] 1808–1882.

Life of Thomas Chalmers, D. D., LL. D. Written for the Mass. Sabbath school society, and approved by the Committee of publication. Boston, Massachusetts Sabbath school society (1859)

    432 p. 15½ᶜᵐ.

    1. Chalmers, Thomas, 1780–1847.   ɪ. Massachusetts Sabbath school society. Committee of publication.
                                   36–23962
Library of Congress   BX9225.C4L5
                (2)
                          922.541

NL 0358737   DLC

The life of Thomas Cranmer, archbishop of Canterbury, martyred A.D.1556. London, Seeley, Jackson and Halliday, 1856.

    viii, 254 p. port.
    "Based on the...works of Mr. Todd and Mr. Le Bas."

NL 0358738   MH

Life of Thomas Cranmer, the first Protestant archbishop of Canterbury. Lond. Religious tract soc., n.d.

NL 0358739   MA ODW

922
C851*l*

The life of Thomas Cranmer, the first Protestant Archbishop of Canterbury. Philadelphia, American Sunday-School Union (n.d. v.1,192p. 16cm.

    1. Cranmer, Thomas, Abp. of Canterbury, 1489–1556.

NL 0358740   OrU

The life of Thomas Egerton, lord chancellor of England
    see under [Bridgewater, Francis Henry Egerton, 8th earl of] 1756–1829.

1850   Life of Thomas F. Dale, m.d. [Pittsburg, presbyterian banner, 1872]
    7 p.   12°.   (From Presbyterian Banner) [Toner excerpts]

NL 0358742   DLC

The life of Thomas Firmin
    see The life of Mr. Thomas Firmin.

Life of Thomas Geeran
    see under Copleston, Henry Horace [supplement]

Life of Thomas Hawley Canfield; his early efforts to open a route for the transportation of the products of the West to New England, by way of the Great Lakes, St. Lawrence River, and Vermont railroads, and his connection with the early history of the Northern Pacific railroad, from the history of the Red River Valley, North Dakota and park region of northwestern Minnesota ... Burlington, Vt., 1889.

    48 p. front. (port.) 27½ᶜᵐ.

    1. Canfield, Thomas Hawley, 1822–   2. Northern Pacific railroad.
                               15–9240
Library of Congress   HE2754.C25L5

NL 0358745   DLC NN WaU MiU CtY MWA IU OrU CaBViPA

Film
F
851
H5
no.59

Life of Thomas Hawley Canfield; his early efforts to open a route for the transportation of the products of the West to New England, by way of the Great Lakes, St. Lawrence River, and Vermont railroads, and his connection with the early history of the Northern Pacific railroad, from the history of the Red River Valley, North Dakota and park region of northwestern Minnesota ... Burlington, Vt., 1889.

    48 p. front. (port.) 27½ᶜᵐ.

    Microfilm (negative) (History of the Pacific Northwest, no. 59, reel 6)

NL 0358746   UU

The life of Thomas Horace Cleland...
    see under [Cleland, Robert Glass] 1885–

The life of Thomas J. Jackson
    see under McCabe, James Dabney, 1842–1883.

... The life of Thomas Jefferson. 1844
    see under [Simpson, Stephen] 1789–1854.

The life of Thomas Ken, bishop of Bath and Wells
    see under [Anderdon, John Lavicount] 1792–1874.

DA
334
C9
L6
Cage

The life of Thomas L*d* Cromwell, a black-smith's son, born at Putney in Surry, King Henry VIII. first knighted him; then made him Master of the Jewel Office, Privy Counsellor, Master of the Rolls, Knight of the Garter, Earl of Essex (etc.) ... Yet ... he was impeached and attainted in Parliament, and beheaded on Tower-Hill, in ... 1541 ... [London] Printed for J. Roberts, 1715.

    (2) 34 p. A–D⁴, E². 8vo.

NL 0358751   DFo

---

x920.042
L758

The life of Thomas Marquess of Wharton, &c [London, Printed for E. Curll, 1716]
    106p. 20cm. (In The lives and characters of the most illustrious persons, who died in the years, 1713, 1714, and 1715. London, 1716)
    Caption title.
    Probably a reissue, without the top, of Memoirs of the life of the Most Noble Thomas late Marquess of Wharton; with his speeches in Parliament — To which is added, His Lordship's character, by Sir   Richard Steel (sic) London, Printed for   J. Roberts, 1715.

NL 0358752   IU

Case
X
5
.N 267

The LIFE of Tho. Neaves, the noted street-robber, executed at Tyburn, on Friday the seventh of February, 1728–9. for shop-lifting. London, R.Walker[etc.,1729?]
    46p. 20cm.

    Bookplate of Tho.ˢ Jolley, Esq.ʳ F.S.A.

NL 0358753   ICN

The life of Thomas Pain, the author of "Rights of man," with a defence of his writings. By Francis Oldys, A. M. of the University of Pennsylvania (pseud.) [London, 1791]

    124–126, 193–198 p. 21ᶜᵐ.

    Signed: M.
    A review of Chalmers's Life of Paine, detached from the European magazine for August and September, 1791 (v. 20)

    1. Paine, Thomas, 1737–1809. 2. Chalmers, George, 1742–1825. The life of Thomas Paine.
                            4–16005
Library of Congress   JC178.V2L6

NL 0358754   DLC

The life of Thomas Paine. [Edinburgh, 1793]
    see under Mackenzie, Henry] 1745–1831.

The life of Thomas Paine. [n. p.] 1878.

    cover-title, 14 p. 24ᶜᵐ.

    Reprinted from the Lansdale (Pa.) reporter. cf. p. [1]
    Apparently based on Cheetham's Life of Paine.

    1. Paine, Thomas, 1737–1809.   ɪ. Cheetham, James, 1772–1810.
                             4–16043
Library of Congress

NL 0358756   DLC

Life of Thomas Paine. By the editor of "The National".
    see under [Linton, William James] 1812–1897.

The life of Thomas Paine; mover of the "Declaration of independence"
    see under [Blanchard, Calvin]

The life of Thomas Paine, secretary for foreign affairs to Congress in the American war; author of "Common sense," "Rights of man," etc. Interspersed with sundry letters, &c. not before published, and containing his last will and testament, verbatim; with notices of the American and French revolutions. Compiled from authentic documents ... Glasgow, Printed and published by Muir, Gowans, & co., 1833.

    48 p. 21½ᶜᵐ.
    In double columns.
    Almost the whole of this work is copied verbatim from Sherwin's Life of Paine.
    "List of Mr. Paine's   works": p. [47]–48.
    1. Paine, Thomas,   1737–1809. ɪ. Sherwin, W.T. Memoirs of the life of Thomas   Paine.
                            4–16044

NL 0358759   DLC

VOLUME 332

The life of Thomas T. Thomason, missionary
in Calcutta
see under   American Sunday-school union.

Pam.
Coll.   The Life of Thomas W. Gamel. ₍Buff Creek? Tex.,
        1932?₎
31954   32 p. 23 cm.

           Caption title.
           Includes events and stories related by
        Thomas W. Gamel.

           1. Gamel, Thomas W., 1846-   I. Gamel,
        Thomas W., 1846-

NL   0358761   NcD

PR 974   The life of Timothy Benson, a robber,
.G3   quack-doctor, stage player, &c. To which
Vol. 1   is added, Fre! or the heretics revenge.
        A very droll story.   Stirling, Printed by
        M. Randall.
           24 p. 16 cm.   [In Garret, William. A
        right pleasaunt and famous book of histories.
        Newcastle, Vol. 1. no. 18]

NL   0358762   DLC

---

*EC65   The life of Titus Oats from his cradle to his
Oa833   first pilloring for infamous perjury; with a
W685l   true account of his birth and parentage; impar-
        tially set forth for the satisfaction of all
        persons.
           London; Printed by E. Mallet, in Black-Horse
        alley near Fleet-bridge, 1685.
           4p. 28cm.
           Caption title; imprint on p.4.

NL   0358763   MH TxU CtY

        The life of Tom Ellis chronological and
     biographical. Startling and romantic. The
     duel and trial; Ellis' great speech; Last
     letter to the world, etc.   Birmingham,
     Ala., Mills & co., 1888.

NL   0358764   GEU

The life of Tom Thumb. Ornamented with cuts.   Boston:
Printed for N. Coverly, 1822. 16 p. illus. 32°.

   In original wrappers.
   Upper part of title-page cut off.

1. Juvenile literature.
N.Y.P.L.   April 6, 1921.

NL   0358765   NN

The life of Toussaint Louverture
   see under   [Dubroca, Louis]

The Life of Ulricus Zuinylius
   see under   Sime, William.

The life of Venerable Marguerite Bougeoys
        see under   [Butler, Elizabeth F   ]
1857-

The life of Venerable Sister Margaret Bourgeois, foundress
of the Sisters of the congregation of Notre Dame. Established at Montreal, Canada, 1659. Translated from the French
by a religieuse, Cedar Rapids, Iowa. New York, D. & J.
Sadlier & co., 1880.
   v, ₍2₎, 9-233 p. front. (port.)

   1. Bourgeoys, Marguerite, 1620-1700. I. A religieuse, tr.
                                                    37-18221
Library of Congress   BX4705.B73V53
Copyright 1880: 8685   922.271

NL   0358769   DLC

Life of Virginia
   see
Life Insurance Company of Virginia, Richmond.

   The life of Viscount Nelson.   [London, 183-?]
      64 p. 8°.
      First page bears ms. note of writer: "To
   Mr. Southey. From the author, or Borrower?-"
   Southey adds: "Or Thief. R.S."
   In: `C p. v. 1331.
   Only 25 copies printed.
   n. t. p.

NL   0358771   NN

   The life of Voltaire
      see under   [Duvernet, Théophile Imarigeon]
   1734-1796.

   The life of W.J. Fox
      see under   Garnett, Richard, 1835-1906.

   The life of Washington. Batavia ₍N. Y.₎ W A. Seaver,
1840.
      1 p. l., 11 p. front. (port.) 12 x 10ᶜᵐ.
   Cover-title: Child's life of Washington.
   Imprint on cover: Batavia, W. Seaver & son, 1842.

      1. Washington, George, pres. U. S., 1732-1799.   I. Seaver, William A.,
   Batavia, N. Y., pub.
                                                    18-6162
      Library of Congress   E312.L74

NL   0358774   DLC CSmH

1889   The Life of Washington. Chap. X. (From
       Emerson's magazine and Putnam's monthly
       Oct. 1857)
          p. 457-475. 8°. [Toner excerpt. i. e.
       bound lettered)

NL   0358775   DLC

   The life of Washington Irving...   New
York, P.J. Kenedy, 1894.
   1p. l., 9-234p.   front. (port.) 17cm.

NL   0358776   KAS

   Life of Whitenose Woodchuck
      see under   Uncle Faunus [pseud.]

Life of William Allen, with selections from his correspondence. [Re-
view.]
   (In Eclectic Review, April, 1848. New Series, vol. 23, pp. 449-
485.)
   The running title is William Allen: his life and labours.

■627 — Allen. William, English chemist, 1770-1843.

NL   0358778   MB

The Life of William Baker
   see under   Gilpin, William, 1724-1804.

The life of William Bedell
   see under   [Burnet, Gilbert] bp. of Salisbury
1643-1715.

Life of William Caxton
   see under   Stevenson, William, 1772-1829.

The life of William Cobbett. London, Mason,
1835. 422 p.
   see under   Cobbett, William, 1763-1835.

The life of William Cobbett. Dedicated to
his sons. Philadelphia, 1835.
   see under   Cobbett, William, 1763-1835.

   The life of William Cobbett, esq., late M. P. for Oldham.
Including all the memorable events of his extraordinary
life ... with an impartial critique on his public character
... comp. from authentic sources ... London, J. Duncombe & co., 1835.
   216 p. front. (port.) 16ᶜᵐ.

   1. Cobbett, William, 1762-1835.
                                                    10-5908
   Library of Congress   DA522.C5L6

NL   0358784   DLC OkU NcU PPT CSmH NjR NjP

---

x308   The life of William Cobbett, Esq., late
C636   M. P. for Oldham.   Manchester, W. Willis, 1835.
no.183   216p. port. 16cm.

           ₍The Cobbett collection, formed by Arnold
        Muirhead — no.183₎

           1. Cobbett, William, 1763-1835.

NL   0358785   IU

The life of William Cowper, with selections
from his correspondence
   see under   [Seeley, Robert Benton]
1798-1886.

The life of William Cullen Bryant

        see under

₍Hill, David Jayne, 1850-1932.

The life of Wm. Fuller, alias Fullee, alias
Fowler, alias Ellison, &c. by original,
a butcher's son ...
   see under   [Kingston, Richard] fl. 1700,
ascribed author.

The life of William Fuller, by original a butcher's
son ...
   see under   [Kingston, Richard] fl. 1700,
ascribed author.

VOLUME 332

The life of William Fulton
      see under   [Fulton, Sanford Hamilton]
1874–1924.

The life of William H. Seward, including his
      most famous speeches, by a Jeffersonian
      Republican.   Boston, Thayer and Eldridge ...
1850.
          144 p.   front. (port)   19.5 cm.

NL 0358791   NcD CtY

The life of William H. Seward, including his most
famous speeches.   By a Jeffersonian Republican.   Boston, Thayer and Eldridge, 1860.
      144 p.   19ᶜᵐ.

1. Seward, William Henry, 1801–1872.   4-24211

NL 0358792   DLC

The life of William H. Seward with selections
      from his works.   New York, 1855
      see under   Baker, George E., ed.

The Life of William Hawke, the celebrated
highwayman ... containing an account of all
the remarkable robberies he committed ...
with the manner in which he was apprehended,
and his behaviour since conviction.   To which
is added, The swindler's chronicle: containing
a full account of the frauds and forgeries
committed by Thomas Watkinson ... with a
description of the most remarkable swindlers
who now infest this metropolis.   London,
Sold by etc.

NL 0358794   OO

The life of William Henry Harrison, (of Ohio,) the
      people's candidate for the presidency
      see under   [Jackson, Isaac Rand] d. 1843.

                                                        **T.57.421
Life, The, of Wm. Henry West Betty, the celebrated and wonderful
Young Roscius: containing the particulars of his theatrical
career, his education, character, & abilities: . . . with an impartial account of his astonishing performances on the London
theatres . . .
      London.   Fairburn.   [1804.]   36 pp.   Portrait.   17½ cm., in 6s.
Some pages are missing at the end.

J646 — Children. As actors. — Betty, William Henry West. 1791–1874.

NL 0358796   MB MH

The life of William Kain, who was executed at Kingston, Upper Canada,
On the 6th day of September, 1830, for the murder of John Rodolph Couche.
[Kingston, Printed at the Herald office, Quarry street, n.d.]
      16 p.   8vo.   Imprint supplied from colophon, etc.   20.2 x 13 cm.   Front cover
Inscribed: S. Miles.

NL 0358797   CaOTU

... The life of William Kelly; or, The converted drunkard ...   Philadelphia, Sunday and adult school union
[1822?]
      12 p.   19ᶜᵐ.   (Sunday and adult school union.   Tracts, no. 10)
Title vignette.
Has also continuous paging (p. [97]–108)

1. Title: William Kelly.

                                                        26-12098

Library of Congress   BV4510.A1S8 no. 10

NL 0358798   DLC

The life of William Kelly; or, The happy
Christian, an authentic narrative.   20p.   London
Religious tract society [18–]

A chap-book.

NL 0358799   OC1

Life of William M. Richardson, LL.D., late
      chief justice of the Superior court in
      New Hampshire ...
      see under   [Bell, Charles Henry]
1823–1893.

Life of William McKinley and his assassination
      see under   [Halstead, Murat] 1829–1908.

The life of William McKinley, including a genea-
      logical record of the McKinley family
      see under   [Davis, Oscar King] 1866–

The life of William of Waynflete
      see under   Drane, Augusta Theodosia,
1823–1894.

The life of William of Wykeham
      see under   Drane, Augusta Theodosia,
1823–1894.   [supplement]

Life of William Penn.   n.p. [18- ?]

32 p.   port.   18 cm.
Title taken from running title.

NL 0358805   MH

The life of William Penn.   [London: Wetton & Jarvis, 1822.]
      156 p.   front. (port.)   24°.   (Select biography.)
      Caption-title.

1. Penn, William, 1644–1718.
N. Y. P. L.   July 18, 1928

NL 0358806   NN PHC

Life of William Penn.   Boston, 1866.

NL 0358807   PSC-Hi

The life of William Penn, founder of
      Pennsylvania.   Edinburgh, Printed for
      James Robertson & Co., 1828.
          174 p.   front.   15 cm.

NL 0358808   PSC PSC-Hi

The life of William Penn, the founder of Pennsylvania,
with numerous illustrative anecdotes and embellishments.
Philadelphia, Lindsay and Blakiston, 1849.
      x, [11]–210 p.   front., plates, port.   18½ᶜᵐ.
      Attributed to John Frost, but an entirely different work from his "Life
of William Penn, with a sketch of the early history of Pennsylvania," 1839.
An earlier issue, 1848, belongs to the "Young American's library" series.

1. Penn, William, 1644–1718.   1. Frost, John, 1800–1859, supposed
author.
                                                        8—17376

Library of Congress   F152.2.L7

NL 0358809   DLC OrU OC1WHi NcU PSC-Hi PHi PU

... Life of William Penn; with numerous illustrative anecdotes ...   Boston, Lee and Shepard;
New York, Lee, Shepard and Dillingham [18—]
      x, 11–210 p.   front., plates.   18½cm.   (The
young American's library)

NL 0358810   OrSaW

J
L722   ...Life of William Penn with
          numerous illustrative anecdotes...
          Philadelphia, Lindsay [1848]
Educ.   210p.   front., plates, port.   D.   (The young
          American's library)
              Attributed to John Frost, but an entirely
          different work from his "Life of William Penn,
          with a sketch of the early history of Penn-
          sylvania", 1839.

NL 0358811   IaU OC1WHi NjP PSC-Hi OU

Life of William Penn with numerous illustrative
anecdotes.   Boston, Lee and Shepard, 1868.
      210p.   illus.   (The young American's library)

NL 0358812   ICRL

Life of William Penn with numerous illustrative anecdotes.   Phila., Lindsay, 1898.
      210 p.

NL 0358813   PU

Life of William Pitt, late prime minister of Great Britain,
with biographical notices of his principal friends and illustrious cotemporaries ...   Phil., Watts, 1806.
      xl, [5]–242 p.   front. (port.)   18ᶜᵐ.

1. Pitt, William, 1759–1806.

Title from Wells College.   Printed by L. C.   A 33-321

                                              ViU N MH CSmH NN
NL 0358814   NAurW CaBVaU MWA OrPR PPL PHi PPHa CtY

Life of William Pitt, late prime minister of Great Britain,
with biographical notices of his principal friends and illustrious cotemporaries ...   Philadelphia, J. Watts; New
York, J. Osborne, 1806.
      xl, [5]–242 p.   front. (port.)   18ᶜᵐ.

NL 0358815   MiU-C PPL

Life of William Pitt, not published.   Bungay, Childs,
printer, 1816.
      41 p.   20ᶜᵐ.
      No. 1 in a volume of pamphlets lettered: Pitt and Fox.

1. Pitt, William, 1759–1806.

                                                        23-5256

Library of Congress   DA522.P5   1806 c

NL 0358816   DLC

The life of William Pitt, the Great Commoner.
London.   [185–?]   529–544 pp.   Portrait.   [Ward & Lock's
Penny historical series.]   8°.
      By S. I. A.

■2 — S.r. — Pitt, William, the younger, 1759–1806.

NL 0358817   MB

VOLUME 332

Life of William Poole, with a full account of the terrible affray in which he received his death wound ... Official report of the investigation. Verdict. Pursuit of Baker ... with brief biographical notices of James Irwin, Johnny Lyng, Harvey Young, Paugene, *alias* Patrick McLaughlin, and Lewis Baker. Containing also sketches of Tom Hyer, the American champion. James Sullivan and John Morrissey, with portraits. New York, De Witt & Davenport [1855?]

1 p. l., [7]-83 p. front., ports. 23½cm.

1. Poole, William, 1823-1855. 2. Hyer, Thomas, 1819-1864. 3. Ambrose, James, 1813-1856. 4. Morrissey, John, 1831-1878. I. Baker, Lewis, d. 1878, defendant.

24—19407

NL 0358818   DLC GU PPL

Life of William Poole with a full account of the terrible affray in which he received his last words, "I die a true American!" funeral procession. Official report of the investigation. Verdict. Pursuit of Baker. Phrenological character of William Poole, by Messrs. Fowlers and Wells. Examination of his heart, by Dr. Edward H. Dixon. With brief biographical notices of James Irwin, Johnny Lyng, Harvey Young, Paugene alias Patrick McLaughlin and Lewis Baker. Containing also sketches of Tom Hyer, the American champion, James Sullivan and John Morrissey ... New York, De Witt & Daven-   port, 1855.

1 p. l., [7]-83 p. front.,   ports. 24½cm.
1. Poole, William, 1823-   1855. 2. Baker, Lewis.
Library of Congress   HV6534.N5A6 1855   20-18559

NL 0358819   DLC

The **life** of William R. Hearst.   [New York? 1909?]   46 p. illus.   24°.

Caption-title.

1. Hearst, William Randolph,   1863-1951.
N. Y. P. L.   September 19, 1922.

NL 0358820   NN NNC

[The **life** of William Shakespeare, 1791]

NL 0358821   DFo

The **life** of William Shakespeare. London, 1803
  see under Rowe, Nicholas, 1674-1718.

**G.3941.5

Life, The, of William Shakspeare. Interspersed with a variety of authentic and interesting anecdotes.
Dublin. 1822. (1), iii, 40 pp. 14 cm., in 6s.

K2667 — Shakespeare, William. Biog and crit.

NL 0358823   MB

---

q943.08
W648Bℓ

The **life** of William I., Emperor of Germany and king of Prussia. [New York, Harper, 1888]
16p. illus. 41cm. (Harper's Franklin Square library, no.619 extra)

Caption title.

1. Wilhelm I, German emperor, 1797-1888.

NL 0358824   TxU CtY PHi MH PU PPL InU DLC

The **life** of William III. late king of England, and prince of Orange ... Intermixt with very many original papers ... several of which never before printed. Illustrated with divers cuts, medals, &c. London, Printed for S. and J. Sprint [etc.] 1703.

3 p. l., xiii, 648, [8], 32 p. [9 pl., fold. plan. 19½cm.

1. William III, king of Great Britain, 1650-1702. 2. Gt. Brit.—Hist.—William and Mary, 1689-1702.

3—28028

Library of Congress   DA460.L72

NL 0358825   DLC MoU InU PMA NjP ViW DFo

The **life** of William III. late king of England, and prince of Orange. Containing an account of his family, birth, education, accession to the dignity of Stadtholder and Captain-General of Holland, his marriage, expedition to England, and the various steps by which he and his princess ascended the throne, with the history of his reign, enterprizes, and conduct in peace or war. And a relation of his will, death, and funeral. Intermixt with very many original

papers, letters, memoirs, his publick speeches, declarations, treaties, and alliances, several of which never before printed. Illustrated with divers cuts, medals, &c. The second edition corrected. London: Printed for S. and J. Sprint, and J. Nicholson ... James Knapton ... and Benj. Tooke ... 1703.

3 p. l., xiii, 648, [8], 32 p. front., plates, ports., fold. map. 20cm.

Signatures: A⁸, a², B-Q⁸, R⁴, S-Z⁸, Aa-Tt⁸, A-B⁸.
Title within double line border. Marginal notes.
Book-plate of Thos. I. Whitby, 1810.
Bound in old paneled calf.

NL 0358828   CLU-C IU TxU MdBP IEN

---

x942.06
W67Wℓ
1705

The **life** of William III, late King of England, and Prince of Orange ... Intermixt with very many original papers ... several of which never before printed. Illustrated with divers cuts, medals, &c. 3d ed. corr.   London, Printed for S. and J. Sprint, 1705.
xiii, 648, 32p. 20cm.

Title supplied from Brit. Mus. Cat.

Imperfect: t.p. and p.299-300 mutilated.
Pages xi-xiii and 241-256 wanting.
Sometimes attributed to David Jones. Cf.
Dunton. Life and errors. v.1, p.181.

1. William III, King of Great Britain, 1650-1702. I. Jones, David, fl.1676-1720.

NL 0358830   IU NcD OU PBL

The **life** of William III, prince of Orange
    and king of Great Britain and Ireland ...
    see under   Historicus, pseud.

Life of William Wilberforce
    see under   [Wilberforce, Robert Isaac]
    1802-1857.

Ib94
t4
v.1

The **life** of Wolfe, a notorious robber and murderer; who was captain of a desperate gang of thieves inhabiting the haunted castle, in the Black forest; with an account of the singular manner in which he was at last taken for robbing a church, and his full confession at his trial. Derby:Thomas Richardson; and all other booksellers[18--?]
24p. 18cm.bd. to 20cm.
[Binder's title: Chap books, I]
Original wrappers bound in.

NL 0358833   CtY

Life of Zachary Taylor, president of the United
    States
    see under   [Montgomery, Henry]

E
5
Z 12

The **LIFE** of Zæo, "diva dell'aria", and the story of the vigilance persecution, by S.R. With a preface by Captain Molesworth.   London, Universal press agency,1891.
158p. illus.,port. 18cm.

NL 0358835   ICN NNC

The **life** off the 70. archbishopp off Canterbury ...
    see under   Josseline, John, supposed author.

Life office management association.
    Clerical salaries in the life insurance business; being the results of a survey of this and correlated subjects made by the Life office management association. Fort Wayne,Ind., 1932.
3 p.l.,v-xiv,219 p. fold.tables. 22cm.
Bibliography: p.[203]-207.
"Confined to the salaries paid to employees in the home offices of the cooperating companies ... Executive salaries ... the salaries of all officers ... [and] data referring to employees receiving salaries of $5,000 or over ... were ... omitted."—Foreword,signed: William P.Barber [and two others,survey committee]
1.Insurance,Life—   U.S.—Salaries,pensions, etc. I.Title.

NL 0358837   MiU PSt OC1 NN NNC DL CtY

LIFE OFFICE MANAGEMENT ASSOCIATION.
    Directory.
New York.   v.   23cm.

Annual

1. Insurance—Assoc. and org.—Direct. 2. Insurance —Assoc. and org.—U.S.

NL 0358838   NN

Life office management association.
    Index to publications of the Life office management association, 1924 to 1941 ... New York, N. Y. [1942?]
5 p. l., [3]-137 p. 23½cm.
CONTENTS.—Subject index.—Index to contributors.—The Life office management association.

1. Office management—Bibl. 2. Insurance—Bibl.   42-14324
Library of Congress   Z7914.A2L5
    016.3683

NL 0358839   DLC InU MiU OC1 NN

LIFE OFFICE MANAGEMENT ASSOCIATION.
    Index to publications. 1924/54-
New York.   v.   24cm.

Began publication in 1940 with a vol. covering 1924-41. A revised ed., published 1947, covered 1924-46. (Annual supplements also issued). Library's file begins with 1924/54 (also called v.1) which replaces the previous cumulations. Beginning with 1955/57, issued every 5 years

with annual supplements. (Supplements discarded when five year cumulation received.)

1. Management, Insurance company—Bibl. 2. Management, Insurance company—Indexes. 3. Life office management association—Bibl.

NL 0358841   NN

VOLUME 332

Life office management association.
  Life insurance home office buildings; a study of the problems of building construction ... Fort Wayne, Ind., Life office management association, ʿ1933.
    4 p. l., ₃₁-156 p. incl. plates, diagrs. 18½ᶜᵐ.
    Bibliography : p. 83.

      1. Office buildings.   ɪ. Title.
    Library of Congress   NA6230.L5   33–11232
    —— Copy 2.
    Copyright A 61537   ₍2₎   725.23

  NL 0358842   DLC MB

Life Office Management Association.
  Life insurance statements and accounts

  see under

  Wightman, Earl Charles, 1889–

Life office management association.
  Proceedings of the ... annual conference, Life office management association ... 1st–   1924–
  ₍Fort Wayne₎ ʿ1924–
    v. 23ᶜᵐ.

      1. Insurance, Life—Societies. 2. Office management—Societies.
    Library of Congress   HG8754.L5   25–7903

  NL 0358844   DLC IU KyU TxU ICJ

Life office management association.
  Proceedings of the ... Eastern special conference of the Life office management association ... ₍New York₎ Life office management association, ʿ19
    v. 24ᶜᵐ.

      1. Insurance, Life—Societies. 2. Office management—Societies.
    Library of Congress   HG8754.L53   38–22643
    —— 2d set.   ₍3₎   368.3

  NL 0358845   DLC NN

Life office management association.
  Proceedings of the ... special conferences of the Life office management association ...
  New York, N. Y., Life office management association, 19
    v. diagrs., forms. 23½ᶜᵐ.
    19   Eastern special conference, New York, N. Y., Midwestern special conference, Omaha, Nebraska.

      1. Insurance, Life—Societies. 2. Office management—Societies.
    Library of Congress   HG8754.L52   38–5969
    —— 2d set.
    Copyright   ₍3₎   368.306273

  NL 0358846   DLC OU MiU NN

Life Office Management Association.
  Punched card accounting in a life insurance company

  see under

  Batchler, J   L

Life office management association.
  ...Quiz book... Course   ₍New York₎ 194 –
    v.   22cm.
    At head of title: Life office management association institute.
    Course   Rev. ed.

      1. Insurance, Life.
    N. Y. P. L.   April 25, 1951

  NL 0358848   NN

Life office management association.
  Readings in life insurance; a compendium ... 1st ed., 1st impression. New York city, Life office management association, 1934.
    2 v. diagrs., forms. 23½ᶜᵐ.   (*Its* Institute series)
    "Compiled ... by the Life office management association."

      1. Insurance, Life.   ɪ. Title.
    Library of Congress   HG8771.L5   35–8170
                  ₍3₎   368.3082

  NL 0358849   DLC MH OCl MiU

Life office management association.
  Readings in life insurance, a compendium ... 1st ed., 2d impression. New York city, Life office management association, 1936.
    3 v. forms, diagrs. 23½ᶜᵐ.   (*Its* Institute series)
               HG8771.L5 1936
    —— Supplement to Readings in life insurance, volume ɪ. New York, N. Y., Life office management association, 1942.
    2 p. l., 103 p. incl. forms. 23ᶜᵐ.
    1. Insurance, Life.   ɪ. Title.
                          37–22346 Revised
    Library of Congress   HG8771.L5 1936 vol. 1 Suppl.
            ₍r44d2₎   368.3082

  NL 0358850   DLC MB MH

    Life Office Management Association.
      Readings in life insurance, a compendium. 1st ed., 3d. impression. New York, Life Office Management Association 1946–
        v. forms, diagrs. 24 cm. (Its Institute Series)

  NL 0358851   WaSpG

  651
  L62r   Life Office Management Association.
      Records retention and destruction. Report on the survey of member life insurance companies, to determine practices and policies respecting retention and destruction of "ordinary" records. New York, 1950.
      80p. 28cm. (Its Special report, no.32)

      1. Business records. 2. Archives. I. Title.

  NL 0358852   IU

  LIFE OFFICE MANAGEMENT ASSOCIATION.
    Report [of the] Industrial insurance office methods committee. no.1- ; 1954–
    New York.   no.   illus., tables.   23cm.

      Each issue has also a distinctive title: no.1, Peak load problems in industrial operations; no.2, Premium accounting for debit business; etc.
    1. Management, Insurance   company. 2. Office organization and management.

  NL 0358853   NN

  LIFE OFFICE MANAGEMENT ASSOCIATION.
    Roster.
    New York.   no.   23cm.

      1. Management, Insurance   company--Assoc. and org.--U.S

  NL 0358854   NN

Life Office Management Association. *Clerical Salary Study Committee.*
  Clerical salary administration, edited by Leonard W. Ferguson. New York ₍ʿ1948₎
    xv, 220 p. illus. 22 cm.
    Bibliography : p. 197–209.

      1. Job analysis. 2. Clerks—Salaries, pensions, etc. 3. Insurance, Life. ɪ. Ferguson, Leonard W., ed. ɪɪ. Title.
                         A 50–5315
    Temple Univ. Library   HF5549.L49
    for Library of Congress   ₍5₎

  NL 0358855   PPT TxU ICU PU CaBVa OrCS

  HD4926
  .L68   LIFE OFFICE MANAGEMENT ASSOCIATION. Clerical salary study committee.
      Report no.1–   ...
      New York, Life office management association, 1938–
        v. tables,diagrs. 27½cm.

      1.Wages--U.S. 2.Insurance,Life--U.S.--Salaries, pensions,etc. 3.Clerks--U.S.

  NL 0358856   ICU

Life office management association. *Committee on tests.*
  ... The application of psychological tests to the selection, placement, and transfer of clerical employees ... New York, N. Y., Life office management association, 1942.
    4 p. l., 28, ₍1₎ p. diagr. 28 x 21ᶜᵐ. (*Its* Report no. 6)
    Photostat (negative) printed on double leaves, Chinese style.
    Bibliography : p. 27–28.

      1. Clerks. 2. Mental tests. 3. Ability—Testing. ɪ. Title.
                         45–14907
    Library of Congress   HF5549.A2L5 no. 6
            ₍2₎   (658.3115) 658.3115

  NL 0358857   DLC IaU NNC

Life office management association. *Committee on tests.*
  Report₍8₎
  New York, N. Y., 19
    nos. 28ᶜᵐ.
    No. 1 issued in 1940.
    Reproduced from type-written copy.

      1. Clerks. 2. Mental tests. 3. Ability—Testing.
                         45–48513
    Library of Congress   HF5549.A2L5
                     658.3115

  NL 0358858   DLC ICU

    Life Office Management Association. Cost Committee.
      Life office cost analysis
        see under   Benjamin, Roy R., ed.

  q658
  L722s   Life Office Management Association. Office Machinery and Equipment Committee.
      Sorting methods and devices, counting and numbering machines. Prepared by O. D. Seely. New York, 1938.
      15 p. illus. 28cm. (Its Report no.3)

      1. Insurance companies--Records and correspondence. 2. Punched card systems--Business. I. Seely, O   D   II. Title III. Title: Counting and   numbering machines.

  NL 0358860   C

VOLUME 332

q658
L722 Life Office Management Association. Office
Planning and Equipment Committee.
Life company application of visible filing
equipment. Prepared by George A. Parks.
New York, 1941
15 p. illus. 28cm. (Its Report no.14)

1. Insurance companies--Records and correspon-
dence. I. Parks, George A. II. Title
Series: Life Office Management Association.
Office Planning and Equipment Committee.
Reports, no.14.

NL 0358861   C

Film
1664   Life on board a man-of-war; including a
.585   full account of the Battle of Navarino, by
a British seaman. Glasgow, Blackie, 1829.
193 p.

Microfilm (negative) of the original in
Dept. of Printed Books, British Museum. 1
reel.

1. NAVARINO, BATTLE OF, 1827.

NL 0358862   NjP

LIFE on desolate islands; or, Real Robinson Crusoes,
by the author of "Tales of the northern seas," etc.
London, Religious tract society [187-?]   127 p. 15cm.

Published also with title: Real Robinson Crusoes; or, Life on desolate
islands.

1. Castaways. I. Title: Real Robinson Crusoes; or Life on desolate islands.
II. Tales of the northern seas,   Author of.

NL 0358863   NN

Life on the farm;
in amusing rhyme.   N.Y., n.d.
8o. il.   48°

NL 0358864   MWA

Life on the farm; in amusing rhyme.
N.Y., [Kiggins & Kellog, n.d.]
8 p. illus. 8 cm. (First series-No. 4)
Illus. t.p.

NL 0358865   RPB OClWHi

sE
L626   Life on the farm; an amusing rhyme.   New
York, J. S. Redfield [18-]
8p. illus. 8½cm.

On cover: First series._ no.4.

NL 0358866   IU RPB

Life on the Lakes
see under   [Gilman, Chandler Robbins]
1802-1865.

Life on the Mackenzie river.   N.p.n.pub.
1858.
p.145-9, nar.O.

From the National magazine Aug.1858.

NL 0358868   CaBViPA

PS1322
.M451   Life on the Mississippi, by Mark Twain
1870   [pseud.] [book review]
no.67   [1] p. 24cm. [Memoranda and other articles,
no. 67]

Detached from The Nation, Aug. 30, 1883.

1. Clemens, Samuel Langhorne, 1835-1910. Life
on the Mississippi.

NL 0358869   ViU

Life on the plains and among the diggings
see under   Delano, Alonzo.

The life or legend of Gaudama, the Buddha, of the
burmese
see under   Mallalingara-Wouttoo.

Life, or the adventures of William Ramble
see under   Trusler, John, 1735-1820.

The life or the ecclesiasticall historie of S. Thomas
archbishope of Canterbvry
see under   [Baronio, Cesare, cardinal, 1538-
1607.]

Life out of death; a romance...
see under   [Cartwright, Nathaniel]

... Life out of doors, with an introduction by Charles G. D.
Roberts; illustrated by C. M. Relyea. New York, P. F.
Collier & son, 1903.
2 p. L., 615 p. col. front., col. pl. 20½cm. (Added t.-p.: Library for
young people. [vol. IX])
Series title also at head of t.-p.

1. Outdoor life.

Library of Congress   QH50.L72   3—17949
Copyright   [a34b1]

NL 0358875   DLC OrU

The/life, passion, death, and resurrection
of our Lord Jesus Christ ... (H. Formby, ed.)
see under Bible. N.T. Gospels.
English. Harmonies. 18--. Rheims.
Also with dates 1870 and 1873.

*pEB8   The life, persecutions, and death of Queen
C2212   Caroline, the martyr.
Za8212   Printed and published by T.Batchelar,Long
alley.London.[1821]

broadside. 1 illus.(port.) 30.5x23.5cm.

NL 0358877   MH

The life, persecutions, and sufferings, of Sophia Dorothea, princess of Zell, wife of George the First, king of
England, who was imprisoned thirty-six years in the castle of Ahlen in ... Brunswick, on a charge of supposed incontinency. An authentic narrative. London, Printed
and sold by Dean and Munday [ca. 1820]
1 p. L., [5]-30 p. fold. col. front. 17½cm.

1. Sophia Dorothea, consort of George I, king of Great Britain, 1666-
1726.

Library of Congress   DD491.H2753.L7
                                             5—14936†

NL 0358878   DLC ViU NN

Life-pictures; or, By-gone scenes remembered ... Philadelphia, New York [etc.] American Sunday-school union
[1849]
227 p. incl. plates. front. 20cm.
Added t.-p., col. illus.

Library of Congress   PZ3.L6246   7-16052†

NL 0358879   DLC NN

Life-planning institute, Chicago.
The printing trades ... Written expressly for the Life-
planning institute. Chicago, New York [etc., 1921]
cover-title, 52 p. illus., fold. chart. 16½cm. ([Publication] no. 34)

1. Printing as a trade. I. Title.
Library of Congress   Z243.A2L7   21-13874

NL 0358880   DLC

                                             650.8
Life-Planning Institute, Chicago.   18
[Publications] Chicago [etc.] Life-Planning Institute [1921-
no. 1- tables, diagrs. (part fold.) 17cm.
Includes analyses of various occupations.
Bound with no. 1-15: Can one plan one's life? A symposium. Chicago
[1921] 38 p.

NL 0358881   ICJ DLC

HE2741
.L65   Life-planning institute, Chicago.
Transportation; steam and electric railways...
written expressly for the Life-planning institute.
Chicago, c 1922.
cover-title, 1 p.l., 50p.   17cm.
Bibliography: p.49-50.

NL 0358882   DLC

Pam.
Coll.
30315   The life, political career and death of
Sir Robert Peel. Craddock's ed. London, J. G.
Craddock [1850?]
16 p. 23 cm.

1. Peel, Sir Robert, bart., 1788-1850.

NL 0358883   NcD

Life, political career, death and burial of
Sir Robert Peel, bart.; also a concise account
of the death of the Duke of Cambridge, with a
memoir. London, W. S. Johnson [1850?]
15 p.

Volume of pamphlets.

1. Peel, Sir Robert, bart., 1788-1850.

NL 0358884   NNC

E
5
.S 7262   ...The LIFE, predictions, and death of Joanna
Southcott, the Exeter prophetess. Containing an
account of her pretended conception, and her
writings, concerning the coming of Shiloh, the
millenium, and the sealing of the faithful; with
the dissection of her body by Dr. Reece, and
others; the disappointment of her followers, her
burial, &c.   London, Dean and Munday [182-?]
28p.

Bookplate of Lewis Hainsworth.
At head of ti-   tle: A new edition, with
considerable addi- tions.

NL 0358885   ICN

VOLUME 332

...The life preserver. n.p., n.d.
(₍Confederate tract₎ no. 27)
4 p.

At head of title: ₍For the soldiers₎

NL 0358886   OClWHi

The life-preserver. [New York, n.d.]
4p.

(American tract society, no. 431)

YA23635

NL 0358887   DLC

The life- preserver. Founded on fact
see under   [Sargent, Lucius Manlius]
1786-1867.

LIFE preserving almanac. 1861, designed for
farmers, merchants, mechanics, and families;
also some of the evidences of the virtues of Dr.
G.W. Phillips's medicines. St. Louis, Mo. White
Child, & co., [1860?]

pp. 32. Cover-title.

NL 0358889   MH

Life-preserving bed
see under   [Jennings, Henry Constantine]
1731-1819.

Life principles; or, The science of human nature
see under   [Fraser, Walter Pringle] 1872-

Life problem Bible studies...   New York,
Association Press, 1920.
v.   illus.   17 cm.

NL 0358892   DLC

Life prolongation; how you can get well and
keep perfectly well with only pure food
and pure water
see under   [Hebert, Denis C.]

Life publishing co.

Half portions. New York, Life publishing company, 1900.

Life Publishing Company.
Poems from "Life"
see under   Herford, Oliver, 1863-1935, ed.

Life Publishing Company.
The social comedy
see under   Life. New York.

Life record: Harriet Bond Skidmore
see under   [Gracey, Mrs. Annie Ryder]

A life record of "Dr." C. C. O'Donnell.   A fiend's boast.
A wretch who boasted that he cut off the legs of Union soldiers
to prevent them fighting against the South.   A self-convicted
abortionist, who buries his own victims in a grocery box ...
[San Francisco, 1878]
7 p.   illus.   23cm.   [Pamphlets and California biography,
v. 5, no.11]

F860
C2
v. 5:11
x

NL 0358898   CU-B

Life-records of Chaucer ...   London, Pub. for the Chaucer
society by K. Paul, Trench, Trübner & co., 1900.

lviii, 38, xx, 342 p., 1 l.   1 illus., ports.   22½ cm.   (*On cover:*
Chaucer society.   ₍Publications.   2d series, 12, 14, 21, 32;₎

Issued in 4 parts, 1875-1900; each part with special t.-p.

CONTENTS.—pt. I. The robberies of Chaucer by Richard Brerelay
and others at Westminster, and at Hatcham, Surrey, on Tuesday,
Sept. 6, 1390.   Ed. from the contemporary enrolments by W. D.
Selby.—pt. II. Chaucer as valet & squire to Edward III. King Edward
II's household and wardrobe ordinances, A. D. 1323.   English by
Francis Tate in 1601, and ed. from his ms., the Ashmole ms. 1147,
with extracts from Edward IV's household book, by F. J. Furnivall.—
pt. III. Chaucer as page in the household of the Countess of Ulster,
wife of Lional, 3rd son of King Edward III, A. D. 1356-9.   A ms. ed.
by E. A. Bond.   Chaucer as forester of North Petherton, co. Somerset,
A. D. 1390-1400.   By W. D. Selby; with an appendix by Walter Rye
on Chaucer's grandfather, and the poet's connection with Lynn and
Norfolk.—pt. IV. Enrolments and documents from the Public record
office, the Town clerk's office, Guildhall, London, and other sources;
comprising all known records relating to Geoffrey Chaucer.   By
R. E. G. Kirk.

————— Index to the Life-records of Chaucer ₍by₎ Ernest P.
Kuhl ...   ₍Chicago? 1913₎

cover-title, 26 p.   24 cm.

"Reprinted for private circulation from Modern philology, vol. x,
no. 4, April 1913."

PR1901.A3   2d ser., no. 32a

1. Chaucer, Geoffrey, d. 1400.   I. Selby, Walford Dakin, 1845-
1889, ed.   II. Furnivall, Frederick James, 1825-1910, ed.   III. Bond,
Sir Edward Augustus, 1815-1898, ed.   IV. Kirk, Richard Edward
Gent, ed.   V. Kuhl, Ernest Peter.

PR1901.A3   2d ser., no. 12, etc.   14-11922 rev

ViU ICU PBm OrU PU-F CaBVaU
NL 0358901   DLC PBL NIC MH PSC PHC OCl MiU OU NjP

Life (The) register of . . .   96 pp. 12º.   London, West, Newman & Co. 1888.

NL 0358902   DNLM

The life, reign, and death, of His most gracious Majesty, King Geo. IV.   Detailing, from authentic sources, his
birth, education, early habits, pursuits and attachments;
the steps taken by Geo. III. to induce him to marry; his
union with Her late Majesty, and the causes which ended
in their unhappy separation.   With the events which
transpired before and since his succession to the throne,
and the particulars of his last illness and death.   Embellished with a finely-engraven and striking likeness.   London, Dean and Munday ₍1831?₎
24 p.   19ᶜᵐ.
No portrait in L. C. copy.
1. George IV, king of   Great Britain, 1762-1830.

19-19916
Library of Congress   DA542.L5

NL 0358903   DLC

The life, remarkable adventures and pyracies, of
the famous Captain Singleton
see   Defoe, Daniel, 1661?-1731.
The life, adventures and pyracies, of the famous
Captain Singleton.

The life saving appliances of Joseph Francis
see under   [Pond, James L   ] comp.

Life saving benevolent association of New York.
... Copy of the charter, premiums awarded,
list of managers, donors, and a portion of
its correspondence.   New-York, R.C. Root &
Anthony, 1853.
75 p.   27.5 cm.

NL 0358906   CtY

Life Saving Benevolent Association of New York.
Copy of the charter, premiums awarded, list of
managers, donors, and a portion of its correspondence, as published in 1853. New York,
Macgowan & Slipper, 1883.

27 cm.   pp. 74.   Front., plate and charts.

NL 0358907   MH

Life saving devices co.
Mechanical respiration... treating
drowning, electric shock, gas poisoning...
(Chicago, 1915?)
cover-title, 36p. 23 cm.

NL 0358908   DL

Life saving pamphlets. (in French) 1867.

NL 0358909   DN

Life-saving raft company, New York.
The monitor raft.   Prospectus of the Lifesaving raft company
...   New York, H. R. Cooper, 1876.   34 p.   23cm.

1. Rafts.   2. Life saving apparatus.
N. Y. P. L.   March 17, 1949

NL 0358910   NN DN

Life-saving service
see
U. S. Life-saving service.

Life saving society, London.
Handbook, 1893.   (In Pamphlets on physical
education, v. 6)
1. Life-saving.

NL 0358912   CU

Life Saving Society, London.
Handbook of instructions.
101 pp.   24º.   London, 1897.

NL 0358913   DNLM

Life Saving Society, London.   7769a.22
Illustrated handbook for the rescue, release from, and resuscitation
of the drowning, &c.   5th edition.
—   London, 1899.   121 pp.   Illus.   Plates.   24°.

Nov. 12,   1900
*D7220 — Drowning.

NL 0358914   MB

Life Saving Society, London.   614.81 P100
**** Illustrated handbook for the rescue, release from and resuscitation of the drowning, &c., &c., &c.   Sixth edition.   125 p. il.
sq.T.   London 1901.

NL 0358915   ICJ OCU ICRL

VOLUME 332

35   Life scenes. From popular authors. Boston,
D. Lothrop & co. [1877]
48 l. unp. 16°.

NL 0358916   DLC

Life scenes, Written for the Massachusetts
Sabbath School Society, Boston, 1846.
see under   Knight, Helen (Cross)
1814-1906, ed.

Life sciences occasional papers. no. 1-
[Toronto] 1935-
no. illus. 26 cm.
Suspended 1962-67.
Title varies: no. 1-   Occasional papers.
No. 1-   issued by the Royal Ontario Museum of Zoology;
by the Royal Ontario Museum.

1. Biology—Collected works. I. Toronto. Royal Ontario Museum. II. Toronto. Royal Ontario Museum of Zoology. Occasional papers.

QL1.T654   574'.08   41-27336

NL 0358918   DLC KyU ICF

The LIFE, secret confession and execution of Rugg, the
fiend. Murderer of the Maybee family... A full, truthful
and exciting account of Rugg's murders. Free from all
newspaper sensation. Philadelphia, Pa.: Barclay pub.
co., 1885. p. 19-46. illus. 24cm.

Imperfect: t.-p. mutilated.

1. Murder—U.S.—N.Y.—Queens County. 2. Rugg,
Charles Henry, 1858?-1885.

NL 0358919   NN

The life, services and military career of the
noble trio, Ellsworth, Lyon & Baker
see   Burns, Jeremiah
The patriot's offering.

Life sketch and work of evangelist Charles N. Crittenton. Washington, The National Florence Crittenton
mission [1898?]
19 pp. front., pl., port. 8°.
Cover-title.
Subject entries: Crittenton, Charles N.

1-25006—M 1

NL 0358921   DLC

922.23   A life-sketch of Charles Joseph Eugene de Mazenod,
N46   bishop of Marseilles and founder of the Con-
L   gregation of the Oblates of Mary Immaculate.
Jaffna, St. Joseph's Catholic Press, 1929.
ix, 126p front plates ports 21cm

NL 0358922   MnCS

A life sketch of Henry Clay Fish, D. D., by his
children. Preceded by the commemorative
discourse delivered on the twenty-sixth anniversary of his settlement in Newark, by
William Hague, D.D.,   N.Y., Wynkoop &
Hallenbeck, printers [1877?]
4 p. l., 184 p.   port.   21 cm.

NL 0358923   PV MH MH-AH OClWHi IaDuU-S

The **life** sketch of Lydia Mamreoff von
Finkelstein
see under   Mountford, Lydia Mary Olive
(Mamreoff von Finkelstein) 1855-1917.

A **life** sketch of King Azariah Brown... 1898
see under   Brown, Azariah.

CT99   Life-sketch of the Reverend Henry G.
.P463Z8   Perry ... of Chicago, Illinois., together
1889   with the memorials of his parents, Rev.
Gideon B. Perry ... and Abby Brown Perry,
his wife, with their likenesses.   Providence, R. I., 1889.
cover-title, 15 p.   ports.   23½cm.

"Reprinted from the Narragansett historical register. James N. Arnold, editor."

NL 0358926   DLC OClWHi

Life sketches of government officers and members of the legislature of the state of New York...
1858-

Albany: J. Munsell [etc., etc.] 1858-   18 – 21½cm.
v. plates, ports.

Annual (no volumes published for 1869, 1871-72).
1870 called v. 3 on t.-p.
Title varies: 1858-   Biographical sketches of the state officers and members of
the legislature of the state of New York; 1867-68, Life sketches of the state officers,
senators, and members of the assembly of the state of New York; 1870- Life sketches
of government officers and members of the legislature of the state of New York
(slight variations).
Compilers: 1858-   W. D. Murphy; 1867, S. R. Harlow and H. H. Boone;
1868, S. R. Harlow and S. C. Hutchins; 1870, H. H. Boone and T. P. Cook; 1873-
W. H. McElroy and Alexander McBride.
1859-60, 1862/63, 1867-68, 1875 are Ford Collection.

NL 0358928   NN

Life-sketches of Rev. George Henry Clark
see under   [Clark, Uriah]

Life sketches of Zenas Kent and Marvin
Kent ... [Logansport, Ind., A. W. Bowen &
co. [19--?]
[1] p.

Cover title.
From the Portrait and biographical
record of Portage and Summit Counties, Ohio.

NL 0358930   OO

LIFE songs; being original poems, illustrated and illuminated by Louisa, marchioness of Waterford, and the
Countess of Tankerville.   London: J. Nisbet & co., 1884.
21 l. illus. 34cm.

885066A. 1. Poetry, English—Collections.

NL 0358931   NN

... The **life**, speeches, and public services of Abram [!]
Lincoln, together with a sketch of the life of Hannibal Ham-
lin. Republican candidates for the offices of president and
vice-president of the United States. New York, Rudd &
Carleton, 1860.
117 p. incl. front. (port.) 19½ᶜᵐ.
At head of title: The "Wigwam edition".
Portrait on cover.
Deposited for copyright June 8, 1860.

1. Lincoln, Abraham, pres. U. S., 1809-1865. 2. Hamlin, Hannibal,
1809-1891. 3. Campaign literature, 1860—Republican. i. Rudd &
Carleton, pub.

Library of Congress   E457.L728   11—34753

MiU-C NjP DI IaU
NL 0358932   DLC NIC CtY MWA MH NRU OU OClWHi IHi MB

Life, speeches and services of Andrew Johnson, seventeenth president of the United States. With a full history of his life ... speeches on the rebellion ... and services since becoming president ... Philadelphia, T. B.
Peterson & brothers [1865?]
1 p. l., 17-214 p.   front. (port.)   19ᶜᵐ.

1. Johnson, Andrew, pres. U. S., 1808-1875. i. Peterson, T. B., &
brothers, Philadelphia, pub.

11-23202

Library of Congress   E667.J76

NL 0358933   DLC NcU OClWHi NcA-S OOxM TU NcD PP PPT

... The **life,** speeches, and public services of John Bell,
together with a sketch of the life of Edward Everett.
Union candidates for the offices of president and vice-
president of the United States. New York, Rudd &
Carleton, 1860.
118 p. incl. front. (port.)   19ᶜᵐ.
At head of title: The "Union edition."

1. Bell, John, 1797-1869. 2. Everett, Edward, 1794-1865. 3. Campaign
literature, 1860—Constitutional union.

Library of Congress   E415.9.B4L7   7-8629

NL 0358934   DLC MiD MH NIC NcD

Life stories for young people; tr. from the
German by George P. Upton.   Chicago,
A. C. Mc Clurg & Co., 1904-
v.   17 cm.

NL 0358935   DLC

Life stories of dying penitents; or sick-
cells. From the diary of a missionary
priest.   New York, P.J. Kenedy and sons.
[n.d.]
366p.   front.   17½cm.

Published also with title: Household
story book. 1880.

NL 0358936   KAS PP

BT   Life stories of dying penitents; or, sick calls.
2705   From the diary of a missionary priest. New
.L72   York, P.J. Kenedy, 1895.

366 p. 18 cm.

1. Penitents.

NL 0358937   DCU

10F   The life stories of famous Americans.
L72   Boston, DeWolf, Fiske, [c1901.]
176p., (col.)front.,(col.)plates,illus., 17cm.

1. U.S.--Biography. 2. Presidents--U.S.
3. Statesmen, American. I. Title.

NL 0358938   NBuHi MB

...The **life-story** and life-work of General Gordon, R. E., C. B.,
a graphic and faithful account of his extraordinary career as a
Christian soldier and true philanthropist in the Crimea, China,
Abyssinia, the Soudan, and South Africa...   London: E. Appleyard [1884?].   31 p.   port.   8°.

At head of title: "Appleyard's complete edition."

1. Gordon, Charles George, 1833-85.
N. Y. P. L.   November 23, 1922.

NL 0358939   NN PU ICN

Life story magazine
see   Today's woman.

VOLUME 332

RH
B536

The life story of George H. Hodges,
Democratic candidate for governor.
₍n.p., 1910?₎
₍16₎p. port. 20cm.

Cover title.

1. Hodges, George Hartshorn, 1866-1947.
2. Campaign literature, 1910--Democratic--
Kansas.

NL 0358941   KU

The life story of his eminence James Cardinal
Gibbons...
see under   [Thomas, Cornelius Francis] ed.

The life story of James Millikin
see under   [Taylor, Albert Reynolds]
1846-

The life story of Major Harry Webb
Farrington

see under

₍Farrington, Harry Webb₎ 1880-1930.

Life story of Mary Lyon, founder of Mount
Holyoke College
see under   Douglas, Elizabeth Bronson
(Hatch) d. 1905.

The life story of O. P. and M.J. Van
Sweringen. ₍Cleveland, 1937₎
10 p.

NL 0358946   OClWHi

Life story of Pawnee Bill
see under   [Lillie, Gordon William]
1860-1942.

Life story of Rev. Alexander Willbanks, D. D., evangelist,
"the black Billy Sunday". ₍Philadelphia?₎ ⁷1915.
cover-title, 8 p. 23½ᶜᵐ.

1. Willbanks, Alexander.
                                38-4810

Library of Congress   BV3785.W49L5
Copyright A 397415   ₍2₎   922.673

NL 0358948   DLC

The life-story of Simeon Brownell, a man who has played a
prominent part in the history of his time. Whittier, Cal., 1907.
3 p. l., 9-144 p. plates, ports. 20ᶜᵐ.
"Genealogy": p. 135-144.

1. Brownell, Simeon, b. 1826.
                                43-30619

Library of Congress   CT275.B776L5

NL 0358949   DLC NcD NN

E
7
.B 8214

The LIFE-STORY of Simeon Brownell, a man who
has played a prominent part in the history of
his time. Whittier, Cal., 1907.
144p. illus. 20cm.

Xerox copy.

NL 0358950   ICN

The life, strange voyages, and uncommon
adventures of Ambrose Gwinett
see under   [Bickerstaffe, Isaac]
d. 1812? supposed author.

53
A2
792M

The Life, strange voyages, uncommon adventures,
and droll exploits, of Emanuel Mendaci, traveller
... London, W. Bailey, 1792.
58p. front. 19cm.
Fictitious.
Caption title: The surprising adventures, &c.
of Emanuel Mendaci.

NL 0358952   CtY

Life stress and bodily disease
see under   Association for Research in
Nervous and Mental Diseases.

... Life studies from Mother Goose, in wax
works, pantomimes, plays, songs and
tableaux
see under   [Yendes, Lucy A   ]
1851-

Life studies. Supplemented by helpers and
pictures in separate publications.
see under   American Unitarian Association.

Life-study fellowship, *Noroton, Conn.*
"With God all things are possible." Noroton, Conn., Life-
study fellowship, 1944.
1 p. l., 214 p., 1 l. 23½ᶜᵐ.

1. Consolation. 2. Devotional exercises.   I. Title.
                                    44-35143

Library of Congress   ₍BV4905.L49
                ₍2₎   242

NL 0358956   DLC LU NjPT

The life, sufferings, and uncommon vicissitudes of The-
tis, dutchess de Lancy, explaining her birth on an uninhabited island, where she lived till she was sixteen years
of age; the misfortunes and death of her parents, and her
surprising release from that desolate place by the Duke
de Lancy ... London, J. Ker ₍etc., n. d.₎
38 p. incl. front. 18ᶜᵐ.
Fictitious autobiography.
A chap-book.

1. Chap-books.
                                    8-33275†

Library of Congress   PZ3.L6247

NL 0358957   DLC ViU

The Life, surprising adventures, and heroic
actions of Sir William Wallace
see under   [Henry, the Minstrel] fl. 1470-
1492.

... The life, surprising adventures, and most
remarkable escapes of Rinaldo Rinaldini
see under   [Vulpius, Christian August]
1762-1827.

The life, teaching, and works of the Lord
Jesus Christ, arranged as a continuous narrative... London, Frowde, 1886
see under   Bible. N. T. Gospels.
English. Harmonies. 1886. Revised.

The **Life** that never ends; funeral sermons. St. Louis, Concordia Pub. House ₍1949₎
xiv, 168 p. 20 cm.
"Prepared under the auspices of the Literature Board of the
Lutheran Church—Missouri Synod."

1. Funeral sermons. 2. Lutheran Church—Sermons. 3. Sermons,
American.

BV4275.L48   252.9   49-48851*

NL 0358961   DLC PPLT PPWe

Life. The philosophy of its origin and
preservation
see under   [Lee, J   N   ]

Life thoughts.
London, Kegan Paul, Trench & co., 1883.
3 p. l., 73 p. front. 14 cm.
Ms. note by author on fly-leaf signed:
C. F. B. Dresden.
In verse.

NL 0358963   NNUT

Life-time ...
Filed as one word.

...The life, times and adventures of George Barrington, the
celebrated thief & pickpocket, embracing the whole of his history,
and a full account of all his extraordinary feats, which procured
him the name of "the prince of thieves!" His attempted murder
of O'Neill... Embellished with beautiful engravings. London: J. Wilson ₍1820?₎ 73 p. front., plates. 18½cm.

At head of title: Second edition.

NL 0358965   NN NIC PBL

The life, times, and works of Victor Hugo
see under   Barbou, Alfred, 1846-1907.

Life today. v. 1–
Nov. 1948–
₍Concord, N. H.₎
v. in 20 cm.
Monthly, Nov. 1948–Apr. 1949; bimonthly, June 1949–
Title varies: Nov. 1948–June 1949, Life can be beautiful.

AP2.L54822   55-17708

NL 0358967   DLC

The life, travels, and adventures of
Christopher Wagstaff
see under   [Dunton, John] 1659-1733.

VOLUME 332

**D975
.M75**

The life, travels and adventures of Edward
Wortley Montague, son to the most famous
traveller lady Mary Wortley Montague.
Exhibiting his very extraordinary transactions
in England, France, Italy, Turkey, Arabia,
[etc.] Boston, for D. Brewer, [177-]
2 v. in 1 144 p. 16°.

NL 0358969 DLC

**CT788
.M6 M5
1784**

The life, travels and adventures of Edward
Wortley Montague, Esq, son of the most
famous traveller Lady Mary Wortley Montague.
Exhibiting his very extraordinary transactions
in England, France, Italy, Turkey, Arabia,
Egypt, and the Holy land. With remarks on
the manners, and customs of the oriental world.
In two volumes. Boston, Printed by John
West Folsom, for Daniel Brewer of Taunton.
[1784]
2 v. in 1 16 cm.

NL 0358970 DLC PPL

The Life travels and adventures, of Edward
Wortley Montague, esq; son to the most famous
traveller, Lady Mary Wortley Montague, exhib-
iting his very extraordinary transactions in
England, France, Italy, Turkey, Arabia, Egypt,
and the Holy land: . . .
Philadelphia: Printed and sold by Robert
Bell, in Third-Street. M,DCC,LXXIV. 2vols,
in one. pp. 90. 8vo.
Evans 18611.

NL 0358971 N PPL MHi ViLxW

**G226
M65L44**

**in
RareBooks
Room**

The life, travels and adventures of Edward
Wortley Montague, Esq., son to the most
famous traveller Lady Mary Wortley Montague,
exhibiting his very extraordinary transactions in England, France, Italy, Turkey,
Arabia, Egypt, and the Holy Land, with remarks on the manners and customs of the
oriental world. Boston, J. W. Folsom
[179-?]
2 v. in 1 (144 p.) 16cm.

1. Voyages and travels. 2. Montague, Edward Wortley. 1713-1776.

NL 0358972 CoU MWiW

Life, travels and adventures of
Edward Wortley Montagu. Philadelphia:
[1794]
2 v. in 1.

NL 0358973 MWA

Life travels and adventures of Edward Wortley
Montague. Exhibiting his very extraordinary
transactions in England, France, Italy, Turkey,
Arabia, Egypt, and the Holy Land; with remarks
on the manners and customs of the oriental
world. In 2 vols. Boston, 1800.

2 vols. in 1. 144p.

NL 0358974 MB

The life, travels and adventures of Edward
Wortley Montague, esq. Exhibiting his extraordinary transactions in England, France, Italy,
Turkey, Arabia, Egypt and the Holy Land: with
remarks on the manners and customs of the oriental
world... Alexandria: Printed by John Westcott,
for C. Shutz. 1802.
2 v. in 1. 17 cm.

Paged continuously.

Continued in next column

Continued from preceding column

Each volume has special title-page.
Running title: Life and travels of Edward W.
Montague.
For authorship see Evans, American bibliography,
v. 6, no. 18611. Evidently based on "Memoirs of
the late Edw. W--ly M--tague, esq. ... collected
and published from original posthumous papers ...
London, 1777." Some authorities label
this work as in- accurate and partly

fictitious. cf. Library of Congress card; Dictionary of national biography.

NL 0358977 Vi ViW ViU NBu NBuG CSmH PHi

The life, travels and books of Alexander von
Humboldt
see under [Stoddard, Richard Henry]
1825-1903.

The life, travels, and extraordinary adventures
of Elizabeth M'Dougold
see under M'Dougold, Elizabeth, b. 1796.

The life, travels, voyages, and daring engagements of Paul Jones:
containing numerous anecdotes of undaunted courage. To which
is prefixed, The life and adventures of Peter Williamson, who was
kidnapped when an infant from his native place, Aberdeen, and
sold for a slave in America. Albany: Printed by E. & E. Hos-
ford, 1809. 96 p. 24°.

Issued in 1807 under the title: The interesting life, travels, voyages, and daring
engagements of... Paul Jones.
The life and adventures of Peter Williamson, p. [47-[96.

1. Jones, John Paul, 1747-1792. 2. Navy, U. S.—Hist.—Revolution. 3. Williamson, Peter, 1730-1799.
N. Y. P. L. June 15, 1925

NL 0358980 NN ICN PP MH PPL DLC

The life, travels, voyages, and daring
engagements of Paul Jones ... Boston,
Coverly [181-?]
see under [Fanning, Nathaniel] 1755-1805.

The life, travels, voyages, and daring engagements of
Paul Jones: containing numerous anecdotes of undaunted
courage. To which is prefixed the life and adventures
of Peter Williamson, who was kidnapped, when an infant, from his native place, Aberdeen, and sold for a
slave in America. Albany: Printed by H. C. Southwick.
1813.
108 p. 14°°.
Issued in 1807 under title: The interesting life, travels, voyages, and
daring engagements of ... Paul Jones

"Song written on the engagement between the Good man Richard, and
the English frigate Serapis": p. [39]-40.
"Authentic narrative of the life and surprising adventures of Peter Williamson ... Albany. 1813": p. [41]-103.
"Elegy written in a country churchyard. [By] Gray": p. [105]-108.

1. Jones, John Paul, 1747-1792.
Library of Congress E207.J7 I 57 5-5528

NL 0358983 DLC N MWA NjP MiD-B CtY NN

The life, travels, voyages, and daring engagements of Paul
Jones. Containing numerous anecdotes of undaunted courage.
To which is added the life and adventures of Peter Williamson,
who was kidnapped when an infant, from his native place,
Aberdeen, and sold for a slave in America. Hartford: Published by Wm. S. Marsh. John Russell, jr., printer—State
street. 1813.
106 p. 14°°.
Published also under title: The interesting life, travels, voyages, and
daring engagements of ... Paul Jones.
1. Jones, John Paul, 1747-1792. 2. Williamson, Peter, 1730-1799.
45-44207
Library of Congress E207.J7 I 576

NL 0358984 DLC PPRF

The life, travels, voyages, and daring engagements of Paul
Jones. Containing numerous anecdotes of undaunted courage.
To which is added The life and adventures of Peter Williamson,
who was kidnapped when an infant, from his native place,
Aberdeen, and sold for a slave in America. Hartford: Printed
by John Russell, jr.—State street. And for sale, wholesale and
retail. 1813.
106 p. 14°°.
Published in 1807 under title: The interesting life, travels, voyages,
and daring engagements of ... Paul Jones.
"The life and adventures of Peter Williamson": p. [50]-106.
1. Jones, John Paul, 1747-1792. 2. Williamson, Peter, 1730-1799.
14-12725
Library of Congress E207.J7 I 575

NL 0358985 DLC CSmH MH NN Ct

**Cb29
118n**

The life, travels, voyages, and daring
engagements of Paul Jones, containing
numerous anecdotes of undaunted courage.
Woodstock [Vt.]Printed by D.Watson,1823.
72p. 12½cm.
Issued in 1807 under title: The interesting
life, travels, voyages, and daring engagements
of ... Paul Jones.

NL 0358986 CtY

The life, travels, voyages, and daring engagements
of Paul Jones...
see also The interesting life, travels,
voyages and daring engagements of the celebrated
Paul Jones...

Life, travels, voyages, and daring engagements, of that celebrated and justly renowned commodore, Paul Jones. Containing numerous anecdotes of undaunted courage, in the prosecu-
tion of his various enterprises. To which is added, A sketch
of the life of Major General Israel Putnam, comprising a history of some of the most interesting events in the revolutionary
war. Wilmington, Printed and sold by R. Porter. 1814.
106 p. 14°°.
The life of Paul Jones was issued in 1807 under title: The interesting
life, travels, voyages, and daring engagements of Paul Jones ...
"A sketch of the life of Major General Israel Putnam" has special t.-p
1. Jones, John Paul, 1747-1792. 2. Putnam, Israel, 1718-1790.
5-34140
Library of Congress E207.J7 I 6

NL 0358988 DLC MWA

The life, travels, voyages, and daring engagements, of the cele-
brated Paul Jones. To which is added: The life and extraordinary
adventures of Mary Lacy... New-York: Printed for E.
Duyckinck, by G. Bunce, 1809. 108 p. 24°.
Issued in 1807 under the title: The interesting life, travels, voyages, and daring
engagements of ... Paul Jones.
"The female shipwright: or, Life and extraordinary adventures of Mary Lacy
... New-York: E. Duyckinck, 1809." p. [51]-100.
"The life of John Elwes, esq." p. [101]-107.
"The life of Sir R. Arkwright," p. 108.

1. Jones, John Paul, 1747-1792. 2. Navy, U. S.—Hist.—Revolution. 3. Lacy, Mary.
N. Y. P. L. June 15, 1925

NL 0358989 NN DN CSmH MWA N CSt

The life, travels, voyages, and daring
engagements of --- Paul Jones
see also The life of Paul Jones.

... Life, trial, and confession of Frank C. Almy ... Laconia,
N. H., J. J. Lane [1891?]
cover-title, 32 p. illus. (incl. ports.) 22½°°.
Includes an account of the trial of Frank C. Almy, beginning Novem-
ber 16, 1891, in the Grafton county Supreme court, Eastern district of
New Hampshire, for the murder of Christie Warden.

1. Almy, Frank C., 1857-1892? 2. Warden, Christie, d. 1891.
45-31751

NL 0358991 DLC NCH MiD-B Nh NN NNC

VOLUME 332

Bz79
Em64
836*l*

The life, trial and conversations of Robert
Emmet, esq., leader of the Irish insurrection
of 1803; also, the celebrated speech made by
him on that occasion ... Manchester, J. Doherty
[etc., etc.] 1836.
2p.*l*., 100p. front.(port.) 15cm.

1. Emmet, Robert, 1778-1803.

NL 0358992   CtY

The life, trial and conversations of Robert Emmet, esq.,
leader of the Irish insurrection of 1803: also, The celebrated
speech made by him on the occasion ... Stereotyped from
the last Dublin edition. New-York, Published by Robert Coddington, 1845.
132 p. 15ᶜᵐ.

1. Emmet, Robert, 1778-1803.

                   A 34-1440
Title from Portland, Me.,   Pub. Libr. Printed by L. C.

NL 0358993   MeP MH NjP

DA
948
.6
.E5A2x

The life, trial and conversations of
Robert Emmet, esq., leader of the
Irish insurrection of 1803; also,
the celebrated speech made by him on
the occasion...Stereotyped from the
last Dublin edition. New York,
Robert Coddington, 1850.
132 p. 16 cm.
On first page, Emmet's birthdate
given as 1782.

1. Emmet, Robert, 1778-1803.

NL 0358994   OKentU

The life, trial and conversations of Robert
Emmet, esq., leader of the Irish insurrection of
1803; also, the celebrated speech made by him at
his trial... Stereotyped from the Dublin edition.
Boston, Patrick Donahoe, 1852.
132 p.

NL 0358995   PU MB

The Life, trial, and conviction of Captain John Brown,
known as "Old Brown of Ossawatomie," with a full
account of the attempted insurrection at Harper's Ferry.
Compiled from official and authentic sources. New York,
R. M. DeWitt [1859]
100 p. illus., port. 25 cm.
Binder's title: Trial and conviction of John Brown.
John Brown was tried in the Circuit Court of Jefferson County
for treason, for conspiring with slaves to produce insurrection, and
for murder.
1. Brown, John, 1800-1859. 2. Harpers Ferry, W. Va.—John Brown
Raid, 1859. I. DeWitt, Robert M., 1827-1877. II. Virginia. Circuit
Court (Jefferson Co.) III. Title: Trial and conviction of John Brown.

E451.L72   8-12725

      PPL
NL 0358996   DLC OClWHi MB Vi CSaT PHi MdBP MnU-L PPB

Life, trial and conviction of Edward Stokes
    see under   Stokes, Edward S., 1841-
defendant.

The Life, trial, and execution of Captain John Brown,
known as "Old Brown of Ossawatomie," with a full
account of the attempted insurrection at Harper's Ferry.
Compiled from official and authentic sources. Including
Cooke's confession, and all the incidents of the execution.
New York, R. M. DeWitt [*1859]
108 p. illus., p. 26 cm.
On cover: New edition—with additions.
John Brown was tried in the Circuit Court of Jefferson County for
treason, for conspiring with slaves to produce insurrection, and for
murder.
1. Brown, John, 1800-1859. 2. Harpers Ferry, W. Va.—John Brown
Raid, 1859. I. DeWitt, Robert M. II. Virginia. Circuit Court
(Jefferson Co.)

E451.L73 1859   7-13469

    NSyU NcU NNC MiU OClWHi PP OO MB NjP ViW ViHaI
NL 0358998   DLC KU TU MsU ViU PPL NcD MWA MnU-L CLU

Life, trial and execution of Edward H. Ruloff, the perpetrator of eight murders, numerous burglaries and other
crimes; who was recently hanged at Binghamton, N. Y. ...
Philadelphia, Pa., Barclay & co., 1871.
1 p. l., [19]-80 p. incl. plates, ports. 24ᶜᵐ.

1. Ruloff, Edward H., 1819-1871.

Library of Congress   HV6248.R8L5   17-2122

NL 0358999   DLC DI-GS

Life, trial and execution of Edward H.
Ruloff, the perpetrator of eight murders,
numerous burglaries and other crimes who was
recently hanged at Binghamton, N.Y. Philadelphia,
Pa., Barclay, 1872.
80 p.

NL 0359000   PP

942.07
B897
v.25
no.6

The life, trial, and execution of
Joseph Wall for the murder of Benjamin
Armstrong, in the Island of Goree, Africa;
with an account of the various cruelties
committed by him at different periods. By
a Gentleman. London, A. Young and I.
Aldrich, 1802.
36p. front. 24cm. (In Burdett tracts,
v.25, no.6)

NL 0359001   OrU

The life, trial & execution of the famous pirate Robert Kidd...Also the letters of Kidd's
wife to Lord Bellamont and the famous Kidd
letter recently found, enclosed in a bottle, in
a ledge of rocks, in the town of Palmer, Mass.
Palmer, Mass., G. Shaw, 1850.

pp.24. Illustr.

NL 0359002   MH

Life, trial and extraordinary adventures of John H.
Surratt, the conspirator. A correct account and highly
interesting narrative of his doings and adventures from
childhood to the present time. Philadelphia, Barclay &
co. [1867]
1 p. l., 21-24, 37-40, 43-136 p. illus. (incl. ports.) 24ᶜᵐ.
Also published Philadelphia, 1867, under title: Life and extraordinary
adventures of John H. Surratt, the conspirator ...

1. Surratt, John Harrison, 1844-1916. I. Barclay and company, Philadelphia, pub.

Library of Congress   E457.5.L73   19-15072

NL 0359003   DLC NcU DI MH MH-L PHi

... The life, trial and verdict of Oscar
Wilde. London, Published for the proprietors [1895]
cover-title, [2]-15 p. 23ᶜᵐ.

At head of title: Third edition. Complete.
First edition published under title: The
life of Oscar Wilde as prosecutor and prisoner.
Portrait on cover.
Printed on pink paper.

NL 0359004   CLU-C MH

The life, trial, condemnation, and dying address
of the three Thayers
    see under   Thayer, Isaac, d. 1825,
defendant.

Life, trial, confession and conviction of John Hanlon, for
the murder of little Mary Mohrman, containing Judge Ludlow's charge to the jury, and the speeches of the learned counsel on both sides ... Philadelphia, Barclay & co., 1870.
1 p. l., [17]-124 p. incl. plates. 24½ᶜᵐ.

1. Hanlon, John. 2. Mohrman, Mary, 1862?-1868.   45-28553
Library of Congress.   HV6248.H164L5

NL 0359006   DLC CtY GU PP

Life, trial, confession and conviction of John
Hanlon, for the murder of little Mary Mohrman.
Philadelphia, Barclay & Co., 1879.

NL 0359007   DLC

The life, trial, confession and execution of
Albert W. Hicks, the pirate and murderer
    see under   Hicks, Albert W   1820?-1860,
defendant.

Life truths. Philadelphia, The
American Sunday-school union [187-?]
232 p.

NL 0359009   MiU

Life under the Stuarts. London, Falcon Educational Books
[1950]
189 p. plates, ports. 23 cm. (The Falcon histories)
Bibliography: p. 179-189.
CONTENTS.—Introduction, by J. E. Morpurgo.—Constitutional his-
tory and political ideas, by M. Ashley.—Religion, by N. Sykes. The
capital, by T. F. Reddaway.—Country life and economics, by V. M.
Wadsworth.—Education, by T. L. Jarman.—Science, by J. Lindsay.—
Poetry, by D. Grant.—Theatre, by J. C. Trewin.—Prose literature, by
G. Phelps.—Art, by E. Cammaerts.—Architecture, by M. C. Briggs.—
Music, by P. Young.—Sports and pastimes, by S. Carter.—Dress, by
I. Brooke.
1. Gt. Brit.—Hist.—Stuarts, 1603-1714. 2. Gt. Brit.—Civilization—
Hist. 3. Gt. Brit.—Soc. life & cust.

DA380.L5   942.06   51-7502

    NcD MeB AAP IU CaBVa OrP IdPI OrU
NL 0359010   DLC WaWW CaBVaU OrLgE IdPI MH NN ViU NIC

Life under the Tudors. London, Falcon Educational Books
[1950]
226 p. illus., ports., maps. 23 cm. (The Falcon histories)
Bibliography: p. 215-226.

1. Gt. Brit.—Hist.—Tudors, 1485-1603. 2. England—Soc. life &
cust.

DA320.L48   942.05   50-58089

    ICU TxU OKentU OOxM PPD MeB AAP IU CU-S OrP CaOTP
NL 0359011   DLC CaBVa CaBVaU WaT IdPI OrPR OC1W NcD

HG8773
.L74
1952

Life Underwriter Training Council.

Estate creation, conservation and distribution. Book ten, LUTC course, second year.
[5th ed. New York, 1952]
128 p. illus. 28cm.
Cover title.

I. Insurance, Life—Finance. 2. Investments.
I. Title.

NL 0359012   ViU

VOLUME 332

368.3 Life Underwriter Training Council.
L7228ℓ Life Underwriter Training Council course. 6th ed.
₍Hartford₎ 1953-54.
9v. illus.

Book 7-9, 7th ed.
Contents.- Bk.1. Your job.- Bk.2. Your product.- Bk.3.
Your customers.- Bk.4. Your presentation: programming.- Bk.5.
Your presentation: the sales process.- Bk.6. Your market.-
Bk.7. Expanding your business.- Bk.8. Problems of business
ownership - Bk.9. The corporate client.

1. Insurance, Life – Agents.

NL 0359013   FTaSU

Life underwriters association of Canada.

BF131
.B555 Bernhardt, Karl Schofield, 1901–
1943 Elementary psychology, by Karl S. Bernhardt ... Toronto,
Can., The Life underwriters association of Canada ₍ᶜ1943₎

Life underwriters association of Canada.
Life insurance manual; questions and answers concerning life
insurance in Canada. Toronto, The Life underwriters association of Canada, 1944.
₍160₎ p. illus., diagrs. (1 fold.) 18ᵐ.

1. Insurance, Life—Canada.
45-20754
Library of Congress   HG9010.A5L5
368.3

NL 0359015   DLC

Life underwriters association of Canada.
Life insurance manual; questions and answers concerning life
insurance in Canada. Toronto, The Life underwriters association of Canada, 1945.
₍160₎ p. illus., diagrs. (1 fold.) 18ᵐ.

NL 0359016   CaBViP

Life underwriters association of Canada.
HG8751
.L68 Life underwriters news.
Toronto ₍19

LIFE UNDERWRITERS ASSOCIATION OF CANADA.
Official report of the proceedings of the general
meeting. 39th - meeting; 1946-
Toronto. v. 28cm.

Annual.
Prior to 1946, meetings were held jointly with the National association
of life underwriters; for reports on these meetings see: National
association of life underwriters. Proceedings.

1. Insurance, Life--Canada. I. Life underwriters association of Canada.
Proceedings of the general meeting.

NL 0359019   NN

Life Underwriters Association of Canada
The Q and A book; questions and answers
concerning life insurance in Canada. Toronto
1950.
111p. illus.

"Revised edition of the Life insurance
manual, originally published 1944."

NL 0359020   OC1

Life underwriters association of Canada.
Salesman's handbook; based on the
program of the third international
convention of Life underwriters, Toronto,
1922. Toronto, The Assoc., c1922.
149 p. illus.

This book is in loose-leaf form.

NL 0359021   OC1W

Life underwriters' association of Chicago
L. U. A. reports, 1888-1895.
[Chicago, 1895?]

Cover title.

NL 0359022   IChi

Life Underwriters Association of Chicago.
[Programs of meetings] 1895-1896.
23 cm.

NL 0359023   IChi

S368.3 Life underwriters' association of the city of
B216bi Baltimore, inc.
...Bibliography of life insurance books in
the Enoch Pratt free library, comp. and ed. by the
Baltimore life underwriters' association. issued by
The Enoch Pratt free library, 2d ed. [Baltimore,
Maryland] Author. 1939.
54 p. 22 cm.
Mimeographed copy.
Insurance, Life. Bibliography.
1. Enoch Pratt free library, Baltimore

NL 0359024   CoD

830.06
B21 Life underwriter's association of the city
of Baltimore, inc.
Special report, Educational committee, including bibliography of insurance library books ˗
₍and₎ Dean's report, Baltimore institute of
life underwriters. Baltimore, Maryland, 1938.
2 p.l., 50 p. 27½ᵐ.

Reproduction of typewritten copy.

I. Baltimore institute of life underwriting. 1.
Insurance, Life - Bibliography. 2. Insurance, Life
- Education.

NL 0359025   NNC

Life underwriters' association of the city of New York, inc.
"The technique of life insurance selling." A series of fourteen
lectures under the direction of the Educational committee of the
Life underwriters' association of the city of New York, inc., January 17 — May 8, 1936. ₍New York, N. Y.: Consolidated reporting co., 1936₎ 197 p. illus. (ports.) 23cm.

853620A. 1. Insurance, Life. I. Title.
July 1, 1937

NL 0359026   NN OC1 MB

Life underwriters' association of the city of New York, inc.
"The technique of life insurance selling." 1937 edition. A series
of thirteen lectures under the direction of the Educational committee of the Life underwriters' association of the city of New
York, inc. February 4 — April 22, 1937. ₍New York, 1937₎
192 p. 23cm.

918835A. 1. Insurance, Life-Agents —U. S. I. Title.
December 7, 1939

NL 0359027   NN MB

Life underwriters' association of the city of New York, inc.
"The technique of life insurance selling." 1938 edition. A series
of thirteen lectures under the direction of the Educational committee, Life underwriters' association of the city of New York,
inc. New York city: Reported and published by Consolidated
reporting co. ₍1938₎ 193 p. 23cm.

971491A. 1. Insurance, Life— Agents' manuals—U. S.
I. Title.
December 23, 1938

NL 0359028   NN OC1

The Life underwriters' association of the state of Ohio.
Constitution and by-laws of the Life underwriters' association of the state of Ohio; also names of officers and
standing committees, for 1874-5. ₍With circular soliciting
members₎ Cincinnati, R. Clarke & co., 1874.
16, ₍4₎, 4 p. 23ᵐ.
Covers included in paging.

CA 9-1777 Unrev'd
Library of Congress   HG8941.O3A3

NL 0359029   DLC

Life underwriters news.

Toronto ₍19
v. illus. (incl. ports.) 29½ᵐ. monthly.
Official publication of the Life underwriters association of Canada.
Began publication in 1914. cf. Union list of serials.

1. Insurance, Life—Period. I. Life underwriters association of
Canada.
45-46277
Library of Congress   HG8751.L68
368.305

NL 0359030   DLC CaBVaU

Life unfolding ...
see under   Campbell, Elizabeth Anne.

A life unveiled, by a child of the drumlins; with an introduction by John Burroughs ... Garden City, N. Y., Doubleday, Page & company, 1922.
xvi, 335 p. 21½ᵐ.

23—2053
Library of Congress   CT275.Z9L5

NL 0359032   DLC ViU MB GU NN OC1 OCX OkU OKentU CU

...Life versus death
see under   [Congreve, George Thomas] 182ℓ–

268.76 Life victorious; a service for Easter
L72 day, containing "Her Easter choice"
by Margaret Slattery. ₍Boston,
Congregational pub. society, c1915₎
cover-title, 13p. O.

Illustration on cover.
Includes music.

NL 0359034   IaU MB

VOLUME 332

E
5
.C 1847
The LIFE, voyages and adventures of Bampfylde-Moore Carew; commonly called king of the beggars. Being an impartial account of his life, from his leaving Tiverton school, at the age of fifteen, and entering into a society of gypsies, to his death. With a history of his travels twice through great part of America. Collected and amended from his own writings, by Thomas Price. To which is added, A dictionary of the cant language, used by the mendicants.　London, J. Barker [1760?]
212p. front. (port.) 17cm.
Ascribed variously to Thomas Price, Robert Goadby, Mrs. Goadby and Carew himself.

NL 0359035　ICN

The life, voyages and adventures of Bampfylde-Moore Carew; commonly called, king of the beggars. Being an impartial account of his life, from his leaving Tiverton School, at the age of fifteen, and entering into a society of gypsies, to his death...with a history of his travels twice through great part of America. Collected and amended from his own writings, by Thomas Price... To which is added, a dictionary of the cant language, used by the mendicants.　London: Printed for J. Barker; Mr. Brown, Bristol [1785?]　212p.

NL 0359036　NN KMK ICN OC1 MoU CaBVaU

The life, voyages and adventures of Bampfylde-Moore Carew... king of the beggars. Being an impartial account of his life, from his leaving Tiverton school...and entering into a society of gypsies, to his death...with a history of his travels twice through great part of America. Collected and amended from his own writings, by Thomas Price... To which is added, a dictionary of the Cant language, used by the mendicants.　London: J. Barker [, 1810?]. 212 p. front. (port.) 16°.

1. Gipsies—Gt. Br. 2. Carew, Bampfylde Moore, 1693–1770?, supposed author. 3. Price, Thomas, of Poole.

August 16, 1928

NL 0359037　NN ICU OC1

GL20
.C7L7
The Life, voyages, and discoveries of Captain James Cook. 2d ed. London, J.W. Parker, 1840.
220 p. illus.

1. Cook, James, 1728–1779. 2. Voyages around the world. 3. Oceania--Disc. & explor.

NL 0359038　ICU

G
247
A4L62
1844
The Life, voyages, and discoveries, of Captain James Cook. 3d ed. London, J. W. Parker, 1844.
220 p. illus., port.

1. Cook, James, 1728–1779. 2. Oceanica - Discovery and exploration.

NL 0359039　CLU

The LIFE, voyages and discoveries of Captain James Cook. 6th ed. London, J. W. Parker and son, 1859.
viii, [1]-220 p. incl. front., plates, ports.

NL 0359040　WaU

The life voyages and discoveries of Christopher Columbus. London John W. Parker, 1837.
viii 232 p incl front. 13.5 cm.
1. C.C. Life and voyages.

NL 0359041　MiU-C PHi

E
5
.715
The life, voyages, and discoveries of Christopher Columbus. 2d ed. London, 1840.

NL 0359042　ICN

E
111
L72
The life, voyages, and discoveries of Christopher Columbus. 3d ed. London, John W. Parker, 1845.
viii,232 p. illus. 14cm.

1. Colombo, Cristoforo.

NL 0359043　NIC

C13
876l
The life, voyages and discoveries of Christopher Columbus. New ed. London, Longmans, Green, and co., 1876.
viii,232p.incl.front.,illus. 15½cm.

NL 0359044　CtY

The life, voyages, and sea battles of that celebrated pirate, Commodore Paul Jones. London. 1826.

NL 0359045　DN

The life, voyages & sea battles of that celebrated pirate Commodore Paul Jones, still remembered by some of the old inhabitants now living in the coal-trade; in which are contained a variety of important facts, displaying the revolutions of fortune that this naval adventurer underwent. London, Printed by W. Lewis, for T. & J. Allman, 1829.
1 p. L., [5]-28 p. front. (fold. col. pl.) 19½cm.
On cover: Allman's ed.
1. Jones, John Paul, 1747–1792.　I. Allman, T. & J., London, pub.
8—32763
Library of Congress　E207.J7L652

NL 0359046　DLC NjP MiU-C

The life, voyages and sea battles, of that celebrated seaman, Commodore Paul Jones, still remembered by some of the old inhabitants now living in Wapping ... in which are contained a variety of important facts, displaying the revolutions of fortune that this naval adventurer underwent. Derby, Published by Thomas Richardson, 1806?]
24 p.

NL 0359047　MiU-C

Ex
1081
.502
.59
The life, voyages, and sea battles of that celebrated seaman, commodore Paul Jones, still remembered...in which are contained a variety of important facts. Derby, Published by T. Richardson [1820?]
24 p. 18 cm.

1. Jones, John Paul, 1747-1792.

NL 0359048　NjP CtY

The life, voyages, and sea battles, of that celebrated seaman, Commodore Paul Jones, still remembered by some of the old inhabitants now living in Wapping, he being originally in the coal-trade, in which are contained a variety of important facts, displaying the revolutions of fortune that this naval adventurer underwent. Derby, T. Richardson [1830?]
24 p. 18cm.

1. Jones, John Paul, 1747–1792. 2. Chap-books.
45–44205
Library of Congress　E207.J7L73　1830 a

NL 0359049　DLC NcU CSmH

The life, voyages, and sea battles of that celebrated seaman, Commodore Paul Jones, still remembered by some of the old inhabitants now living in Wapping, he being originally in the coal-trade, in which is contained a variety of important facts, displaying the revolutions of fortune that this naval adventurer underwent. Derby, T. Richardson; London, Simpkin, Marshall, and co. [1830?]
24 p. front. (fold. col. pl.) 19 x 11cm.
Another edition, London, 1829, has word "pirate" instead of "seaman" in title and includes scandalous details omitted from the present edition.

Other editions appeared under titles "The interesting life, travels, voyages, and daring engagements of ... Paul Jones ..."; "The life, travels, voyages ... of Paul Jones ..."; "The life of Paul Jones, containing his travels, voyages, and daring engagements ..."; "The life and history of Paul Jones, the English corsair ..."; and other variations.

1. Jones, John Paul, 1747–1792.　I. Richardson, Thomas, Derby, Eng., pub.
17–24576 Revised
Library of Congress　E207.J7 I 653

NL 0359051　DLC ICN NjP CSmH

The life, voyages, and sea battles of that celebrated seaman, Commodore Paul Jones
see also　The life of Paul Jones.

The life, voyages, and surprising adventures of Mary Jane Meadows
see under　Meadows, Mary Jane.

The Life, Voyages, Surprising Incidents, and Sea Battles, of the Famous Commodore Paul Jones, the American Corsair. In which are contained a Variety of Important Facts, Displaying the Revolutions of Fortune that this Naval Adventurer underwent. Accurately compiled from Authentic Documents. London, Printed by T. Maiden ... for Ann Lemoine [1802]
Sm. 8 vo.　Blue-gray boards.
Note. - Harbeck Library, No. 349.
Not in Sabin.

NL 0359054　CSmH

The life-wake of the fine Arkansas gentleman who died before his time. Washington, F. Philp. 1859.
54 p. 23½cm.

1. Pike, Albert, 1809–1891.
35–33265 Revised
Library of Congress　HS511.P6A3

NL 0359055　DLC MB

A life well lived; in memory of Robert Curtis Ogden. [Hampton, Va.], Hampton institute press, 1914]
26 p. front. (port.) 22cm.
Addresses by F. G. Peabody and S. C. Mitchell at the Ogden memorial service, Central Presbyterian church, New York, Oct. 26, 1913; and by W. H. Taft, in the First Presbyterian church, Brooklyn, Nov. 9, 1913.

1. Ogden, Robert Curtis, 1836–1913.　I. Hampton, Va. Normal and agricultural institute.
14–15716 Revised
Library of Congress　LA2317.O5L5

NL 0359056　DLC PU MB

Life with laughter, by "G. P." Illustrated by Alex Gurney. Melbourne, Georgian House [1950]
55 p. illus. 22 cm.

PN6178.A8L5　827.91　51–36595 ‡

NL 0359057　DLC

VOLUME 332

Life with music. v. 1–
Aug. 1948–
₍Hollywood, Calif.₎
v. illus., ports. 24 cm. monthly.

1. Music—Period. 2. Moving-pictures—Period.

ML1.L4   780.5   52-21564

NL 0359058   DLC NN

Life with music

Guide to music and dance in southern
California. Burbank ₍Author₎

Cover title.

NL 0359059   OrP

Life with music.
Guide to music and musicians in
greater Los Angeles and San Diego.
1951 ed. Hollywood,Calif.,°1951.
51p.illus.

NL 0359060   CaBVa DLC

Life with Teena; a Seventeen magazine survey of subscribers
and their mothers. Princeton, N. J., °1945–

v. illus., forms. 29 cm.

Surveys conducted for Triangle Publications.
Vol. 1, general topics, comp. by Benson & Benson; v. 2, food, by
Opinion Research Corporation.
Vol. 2 has subtitle: A Seventeen magazine survey of teen-age girls
and their mothers.

1. Girls. 2. Consumers—U. S. I. Seventeen (Periodical) IV.
Triangle Publications, inc., New York. II. Benson and Benson, inc.,
Princeton, N. J. III. Opinion Research Corporation, Princeton, N. J.

HQ798.L54   658.8   45-10656 rev*

NL 0359061   DLC

308
Z
Box 698   **Life** with the Lincoln;
Dedication number ... Fort Wayne, Ind.;
Lincoln national life insurance co., 1931.
12 p. illus., ports., facsims. (Life with
the Lincoln ... vol. 12, no. 10. February,
1931)

1. Lincoln, Abraham, pres. U. S. - Museums,
relics, etc. I. Lincoln national life
insurance co., Fort Wayne.

NL 0359062   NNC

Life with the Randalls (*Radio program*)
Life with the Randalls, radio dramatic series written by
Rona Finizie ₍and₎ Joe Porter, sponsored by Presbyterian
church, U. S., Committee of religious education and publication, General assembly's Radio committee. ₍Richmond? 1944₎

1 v. 28½ x 22ᶜᵐ.

Reproduced from type-written copy.

1. Radio plays. I. Finizie, Rona. II. Porter, Joseph E. III. Presbyterian church in the U. S. Executive committee of religious education
and publication. IV. Presbyterian church in the U. S. Radio committee.

44-53/64

Library of Congress   PN6120.R2L5

792

NL 0359063   DLC

The **life** within ... Boston. Lothrop publishing company
₍1903₎
4 p. l., 11–385 p. 20ᶜᵐ.
A story of Christian science.

Library of Congress   PZ3.L6248   3–3282
Copyright A 52455

NL 0359064   DLC IdB PBa PPL

Life without money
see under   Begbie, Harold, 1871-1929
₍supplement₎

Life without servants
see under   Begbie, Harold, 1871-1929.
₍supplement₎

The LIFE work of Franz Oppenheimer. n.p.,
₍1914?₎.

17 cm.   pp.8.
Without title-page. Caption title.

NL 0359067   MH

The **Life** work of George Irving; experiences in witnessing
for Christ, edited by David R. Porter. New York, N. Y.,
Association press ₍1945₎

viii, 146 p. front. (port.) 21 cm.
"Copyright ... by the International committee of Young men's
Christian associations."

CONTENTS.—From Prince Edward island to McGill, by Angus Mac-
Leod.—Memories of university life, by C. S. Paterson.—Missionary
mindedness, by J. R. Mott.—The Student association movement, by
D. R. Porter.—The Commission on message and purpose, by W. J.
Hutchins.—The Faith and life seminars, by R. E. Speer.—A unique
group leadership, by O. A. Piper.—High points in a friendship, by

Gale Seaman.—The primary place of evangelism, by S. M. Cavert.—
Letters from friends: A. J. Irving, J. R. Cox, D. S. Cairns ₍and
others₎—Experiences in witnessing for Christ, by George Irving.

1. Irving, George, 1877-1943. 2. Witness bearing (Christianity)
I. Porter, David Richard, 1882–   ed. II. Young men's Christian
associations. International committee.

BV1085.I 7L5   922   46–763

NL 0359069   DLC NRCR

The **life** work of Mrs. Besant; a review and
comments
see under   ₍Gay, Susan Elizabeth₎

The **life** work of the American architect,
Frank Lloyd Wright
see   Wendingen.
Frank Lloyd Wright: The life work of the
American architect.

The **life**, writings, opinions, and times of the Right
Hon. George Gordon Noel Byron, lord Byron; including
... anecdotes, and memoirs of the lives of the most eminent and eccentric, public and noble characters and
courtiers of the ... age and court of His Majesty King
George the Fourth. In the course of the biography is
also separately given, copious recollections of the lately
destroyed ms. originally intended for posthumous publication, and entitled: Memoirs of my own life and times,

Continued in next column

Continued from preceding column

by the Right Hon. Lord Byron ... By an English gentleman, in the Greek military service, and comrade of his
Lordship. Comp. from authentic documents and from
long personal acquaintance ... London, M. Iley, 1825.

3 v. fronts. (v. 1–2, ports.; v. 3, fold. facsim.) 22ᶜᵐ.

1. Byron, George Gordon Noël Byron, 6th baron, 1788-1824.

25-6617

Library of Congress   PR4381.L5 1825

CtY MdBP NRU NcD PPL PPULC PPMoI NIC CU MB PSt
NL 0359073   DLC OKentU MoSW OrU IU CSmH NN TxU CSt

CINEMA
fSP   **Lifeboat** (Motion picture script)
L722   Lifeboat.   Screenplay by Jo Swerling.
1943   Temporary script.   June 17, 1943.
154ℓ. 30cm.

Mimeographed.
Directed by Alfred Hitchcock.
Released, 1944, by Twentieth Century-
Fox.

√I.Swerling, Jo, 1897–   √II.Hitchcock, Alfred, 1899–

NL 0359074   CLSU

Lifela tsa Bakriste. 2d ed. Maseru ₍Basutoland₎ Mazenod
Institute ₍1940₎
332 p. 19 cm.
At head of title: L. J. C. et M. I.

1. Hymns, Sotho.

BV510.S65L5 1940   72–204411

NL 0359075   DLC

Lifela tsa Sione ₍le₎ tsa bohaki le Lipina
tsa tsona. Rokang Jehova, hobane o molema, etsoa
mohau oa hae l hlola ka ha-sa-feleng. -Pesaleme 118.
1. 16th ed. Basutoland, Sesuto book depot, 1918.
440 p.

NL 0359076   PPAN

Lifela tsa sione le tsa bojaki le lipina tsa tsona. 20th ed.
Morija, Basutoland, Morija Sesuto Book Depot, 1943.
503 p. 19 cm.

1. Hymns, Sotho.   I. Morija Sesuto Book Depot.

BV510.S65L54 1943   72–203028

NL 0359077   DLC

Lifela tsa Sekolo ka
Sesutho. Haputsing, 1866.

NL 0359078   PPAN

Lifeline. 1st–
₍Oct.? 1947₎–
₍London₎
no. in   v. illus. 24 cm. quarterly.
Title varies: no. 1–5, Life line.

AP4.L41623   052   52–36289

NL 0359079   DLC NNC IEN

VOLUME 332

D
809
.U5
L72

Lifeline; organ of the American Jewish joint
distribution committee. v.1,no.1-2; Feb.-
July 1941. New York, 1941.

1 v. illus. 27½ cm.

Caption title.
No more published.

1.World war,1939-1945--Jews. I.American
Jewish joint distribution committee.

NL 0359080   MiU OCH ICRL

Lifeline ...
    see also   Life line.

QC23
.D94

Lifermann, J., joint author.

Dumesnil, Georges.
    Sciences physiques; classe de philosophie, programmes du
    18 avril 1947 [par] G. Dumesnil [et] J. Lifermann. **Paris,**
    Librairie Istra [1950]

Lifes and exploits of notorious characters.
    George Barnwell, Richard Turpin, Mary
    The maid of the inn, Doctor Faustus,
    Robert Nixon, The hermit of Windermere,
    James Greenacre, Bamfyeld Moore Carew.
    London, P. Brown [etc.] 1845.
    [181] p. front. 19 cm.
    Each life paged separately.

NL 0359083   CtY

Life's beginnings; wisdom and counsel
for daily guidance; selected by F. J. N.
and C. D. M. London, J. Clarke & co. [1910]
376 p.

NL 0359084   OC1

Life's beginnings; wisdom and counsel for daily
guidance; compiled by F. J. N. and C. D. M.   Boston: Pilgrim Press [1914?].
vii, 376 p.   24°.
    3. impression.

1. Meditations (Religious). 2.   Christian life. 3. N., F. J. 4. M.,
C. D.
                                          June 7, 1915.

NL 0359085   NN

Life's beginnings. Wisdom and counsel for daily
guidance, compiled by F.J.N. and C.D.M. New
York, George H. Doran Company, 1925.
    376 p.

NL 0359086   NRCR

Life's book of animals
    see under   Life. New York.

AP101
.L63

Life's calendar.

[New York, Mitchell & Miller] 18

v.   illus. 25½cm.

Caption title: Life's monthly calendar.
Editor: J. S. Metcalfe.

1. Metcalfe, James Stetson, ed.   CA 7-4055 Unrev'd

NL 0359088   DLC

Life's comedy. 1st–   ser.   New York, C. **Scribner's**
sons, 1897–
    v. illus. 30½cm.
A reissue of "Life's comedy" published quarterly by **Life publishing**
company.

Library of Congress   AP101.L641   98-1990 Revised

NL 0359089   DLC N DSI MB NB PP OC1W OrPS OrP

Life's common way
    see under   [Ellis, J   ] comp.

Life's continuing study of magazine
    audiences
        see   Magazine Audience Group.
    Continuing study of magazine audiences.

Life's Dog Calendar for 1920. N. Y. [1919] folio.   1089

NL 0359092   ViW

Life's evening; or, Thoughts for the aged
    see under   Burnham, Samuel,
    1833-1873. [supplement]

"Life's fitful hours" ...
    see under   [Long, Matthew]

Life's golden stream
    see under   [Brewer, Ferdinand Coffin]

Life's happiest day; or, The little first
    communicant
        see under   [Sylvain, Adrien] 1826-1914.

Life's happy accidents
    see under   [Schneider, William Richard]
1887–   comp.

A life's labours in
South Africa :/the story of the life-work of
Robert Moffat. London, n. d. 12°. —R976

NL 0359098   MdBP

A life's labours in South Africa:
the story of the life-work of Robert
Moffat ...   London, 1871.
161p. front.(photo.)

NL 0359099   IU CaBVaU

Life's lesson. A tale.
    see under   [Thomas, Martha McCannon]
1823–

Life's long battle won
    see under   [Mayo, Mrs. Isabella (Fyvie)]
1843-1914.

Life's lottery; or, Life and its aims
    see under   [Osborne, Elise]

823
L6264

Life's masquerade, a novel.   London, C.
W. Wood, 1867.
    3v. 20cm.

NL 0359103   IU

Life's monthly calendar
    see
Life's calendar.

Life's morning, a special children's day
    services for the Sunday school with **selections**
    for the choir. Chicago, [c1915]
    29 [2] p. 22 cm.
    Cover title.

NL 0359105   RPB

Life's morning; or counsels and encouragements
    for youthful Christians
        see under   Burnham, Samuel, 1833-1873.
[supplement]

'Life's mystery' ...
    see under   [Thornton, William Thomas]
1813-1880.

Life's pages. Los Angeles, Calif., A. Barrett publishing co.,
inc., 1936.
    197 p. incl. plates. 23cm.

Continued in next column

VOLUME 332

Continued from preceding column

1. American poetry (Collections)

Library of Congress   PS586.L47   39–4971

Copyright A 97535   811.0822

NL 0359108   DLC

Life's pathway.   N.Y., n.d.
   [32] p.   col.   illus.   17 cm.

NL 0359109   RPB

Life's possibilities; a book for girls
     see under   Draper, E.A.   [supplement]

Life's prints
   see under   Life. New York.

Life's problems.   Essays; moral, social, and
   psychological
     see under   [Alcock, Sir Rutherford]
   1809–1897.

Life's problems, here and hereafter; an
   autobiography
     see under   [Flanders, George Truesdell]
   1820–1897.

Life's progress through the passions: or, The
   adventures of Natura
     see under   [Haywood, Eliza (Fowler)]
   1693?–1756.

... Life's quiet hours
     see under   [Burnham, Samuel] 1833–1873.

Life's real romance
     see under   Howard, Arthur N.

LIFE'S roses; a volume of selected poems.   London: E.
Nister [etc., etc., 1898]   191 p. incl. col'd front.
illus., plates (part col'd).   23cm.

"Printed in Bavaria."

776794A. 1. Poetry, English—Collections. 2. Poetry,
American—Collections.

NL 0359117   NN RPB PP

Life's security
     see under   [Ramesey, William] fl. 1660.

Life's shop window
     see under   [Clifford, William H.]

Life's song
     see under   [Lowell, James Russell]
   1819–1891.

"Life's true beatitude, " Author of.
   Glimpses in America; or, The new world as we
saw it
     see under title

Life's vagaries, a comedy
     see under   O'Keeffe, John, 1747–1833.

Life's verses

   see under

Life. New York.

823.89
L722   Life's work as it is; or, the emigrant's
   home in Australia... London, Sampson, Low,
   Son, & Marston, 1867.
   vi, 179 p. front.   17½cm.

     1. Australia.   Social life and customs.   I.
Title

NL 0359124   NcD

Lifestream; the psychology magazine for everybody. v. 1,
no. 1–4; spring–Oct./Nov. 1947. [Eastbourne, Eng.] Lifestream Publications.
   1 v. illus., ports. 25 cm. Irregular.
   Edited by B. L. Calmus.
   No more published?

     1. Psychology, Applied—Period.   I. Calmus, Bernard L., ed.

   BF636.A1L5   52–41087

NL 0359125   DLC

A **life-time** collection of 688 recipes for drinks.   London: H.
Jenkins Ltd.[, 1934.]   viii, 11–124 p.   17cm.

729763A.   1. Alcoholic drinks.
                  October 1, 1934

NL 0359126   NN

Life-time hymns. A collection of old and new hymns
   of the Christian church...
     see under   Palmer, Horatio Richmond, 1834–

Lifetime living.   v. 1–
   June 1952–
     [New York]
     v. illus. 29 cm. monthly.
   Editor: June 1952–   M. Gumpert.
   United with Journal of living in May 1955 to
   form Journal of lifetime living.

     1. Retirement—Period.   I. Gumpert, Martin, 1897–1955, ed.

   AP2.L54823   051   54–34883

NL 0359128   DLC

Liff, Abraham Benjamin, 1895–   ed.
                FOR OTHER EDITIONS
Long Beach, *Calif.* **City schools.**   SEE MAIN ENTRY
   Civic education in the Long Beach city schools. A handbook for teachers.   Secondary schools. Long Beach, Calif.,
1936.

LD3907
.E3
1955   Liff, Zanvel Austin, 1927–
.L5   A comparison of interpersonal attitudes to male and female authority
   figures among delinquent and non-
   delinquent institutionalized boys.
   106p. illus.,tables.
   Thesis (Ph.D.) – N.Y.U., School of
   Education, 1955.
   Bibliography: p.92–95.

NL 0359130   NNU

Liff, Zanvel Austin, 1927–
   A comparison of interpersonal attitudes to male and fe-
male authority figures among delinquent and non-delinquent
institutionalized boys.   Ann Arbor, University Microfilms
[1955]
   ([University Microfilms, Ann Arbor, Mich.] Publication no. 13,625)
   Microfilm copy (positive) of typescript.
   Collation of the original, as determined from the film: vii, 106 l.
illus., tables.
   Thesis—New York University.
   Abstracted in Dissertation abstracts, v. 15 (1955) no. 10, p. 1901–
1902.
   Bibliography: leaves 92–95.

     1. Attitude (Psychology)   I. Title: Interpersonal attitudes to
male and female authority figures among delinquent and non-delinquent institutionalized boys.
   Microfilm AC–1 no. 13,625   Mic 55–639

NL 0359132   DLC

Liffa, Aurél, 1872–
   ... Bemerkungen zum stratigraphischen teil der arbeit
Hans v. Staffs: "Beiträge zur stratigraphie und tektonik
des Gerecse-gebirges."   Von dr. Aurel Liffa ... Budapest, Buchdr. des Franklin-vereins, 1907.
   cover-title, 19 p.   25½cm.   (Mitteilungen aus dem Jahrbuche der Königl.
ungarischen geologischen anstalt.   xv. bd., 1. hft.)
   Vom verfasser rev. übertragung aus dem ungarischen original.   (Unga-
risch erschienen im juni 1907)

     1. Staffa, Hans von. Beiträge zur stratigraphie und tektonik des Ge-
recse-gebirges. 2. Geology—Hungary.

                             G S 12–523
   Library, U. S. Geol.   survey (534) B   bd. 16, hft. 1

NL 0359133   DI-GS

Liffa, Aurél, 1872–
   Telkibánya bányaföldtani viszonyai ... Conditions géo-
logiques des gîtes métalliques des environs de Telkibánya.
Budapest, 1955.
   [211,–250 p. fold. map (in pocket) diagrs., tables. 24 cm. (A
Magyar Állami Földtani Intézet évkönyve, 42. köt., 4. füzet)
   Bibliography: p. [250]–251.

     1. Geology—Hungary—Telkibánya. 2. Metals.   (Series: Hun-
gary. Földtani Intézet. A Magyar Állami Földtani Intézet évkönyve,
42. köt., 4. füzet)
   [QE1.H94 köt 42, füzet 4]   G S 56–47
   U. S. Geol. Survey. Libr.
   for Library of Congress   [2]

NL 0359134   DI-GS

VOLUME 332

QE1
.H94
köt. 41,
füzet 3
   Liffa, Aurél, 1872–
     Telkibánya környékének földtana és közettana. **La**
géologie et la pétrographie des environs de Telkibánya.
¡Budapest¿ Nehézipari Könyv- és Folyóiratkiadó Vállalat,
1953.
     78 p. illus., map, diagrs., tables. 24 cm. (A Magyar Állami
Földtani Intézet évkönyve, 41. köt., 3. füzet)
     Part of the illustrative material is folded in pocket.
     Hungarian, French, and Russian.
     "Irodalom" : p. ¡58¿–62.
     1. Geology—Hungary—Telkibánya. 2. Petrology—Hungary—Telki-
bánya.   (Series: Hungary. Földtani Intezet. A Magyar Állami
Földtani Intézet évkönyve, 41. köt., 3. füzet)

                              G S 54–58

U. S. Geol Survey. Libr.
for Library of Congress

   NL   0359135   DI-GS DLC

   Liffa, Aurél, 1872–
   Güll, Wilhelm.
     ... Über die agrogeologischen verhältnisse des Ecsedi
láp. Von Wilhelm Güll, Aurel Liffa und Emerich Tim-
kó. (Mit tafel XVI–XVIII) ... Budapest, Buchdr. des
Franklin-vereins, 1906.

   Liffa, Margit (Sárváry)
     ... Kötés és horgolás
       see under   Feÿér Erzsébet (Kovács)

   Liffers, Hans, 1911–
     Die deutsche verschuldung in den Niederlanden
seit 1924 und ihre liquidierung ... von Hans
Liffers ... Köln, Buchdruckerei Orthen, 1938.
     3 p. l., 5–92 p., 1 l. 21^{cm}.

     Thesis, Köln.
     Bibliography: p. 5–6.

     1. Investments - Germany. 2. Investments -
Netherlands.

   NL   0359138   NNC CtY

   Liffers, Wilhelm, 1910–
     Das warenzeichen als pfändungsobjekt. ...
Berlin, 1936.   47 p.
     Inaug. Diss. - Münster i. W., 1936.
     Lebenslauf.
     Literatur.

   NL   0359139   ICRL

Y
762
.C 8145
   LIFFERT, KARL JOHANNES ARTHUR, 1888–
     Der Einfluss der Quellen auf das dramatische
Schaffen Pierre Corneilles in den ältesten Rö-
mertragödien.   Langensalze, Wendt & Klauwell,
1913.
     132p.   23cm.

     Inaug.-Diss.—Jena.
     Bibliography: p. ¡131¿–132.
     Vita.

   NL   0359140   ICN PBm NN MH CtY ICRL DLC

   LIFFERT, KARL JOHANNES ARTHUR, 1888– .
     Der Einfluss der Quellen auf das dramatische
Schaffen Pierre Corneilles in den ältesten Römertra-
gödien.   Langensalza, Wendt & Klauwell, 1913.
     132 p.   8°.

     Cover title.
     Dissertation
     Lebensabriss.

     "Literatur-Verzeichnis, " p. [131-] 132.
     Film reproduction. Positive.

     1. Corneille, Pierre, 1606-1684.

   NL   0359142   NN

   Liffingwell, William Henry
     see   Leffingwell, William Henry, 1876–1934.

   Liffman, Jeremias Vilhelm, 1809–1854, ed.
   Ivan Lejonriddaren.
     Herr Ivan Lejon-riddaren, en svensk rimmad dikt ifrån
1300-talet, tillhörande sago-kretsen om konung Arthur
och hans runda bord. Efter gamla handskrifter af J. W.
Liffman, och George Stephens, esq. Stockholm, P. A.
Norstedt & söner, kongl. boktryckare ¡1845¿–49.

   Liffman, Jeremias Vilhelm, 1809–1854.
     Remarques sur les temps et les modes de
la langue française; essai de grammaire comparé
... Stockholm, Impr. d'Eckstein, 1842.
     16 p.   23 cm.
     Bibliographical footnotes.
     1. French Language .. Grammar .. Verb

   NL   0359145   NN

   Liffmann, Lucius Abraham.
     *De dysenteria.   Marburgi ... Acad. Nova.
[1798].
     54 p.   12°.

   NL   0359146   NNNAM

   Liffner, Axel Gustaf Adolf, 1919–
     Opus 0,09. Stockholm, Bonnier ¡1947¿
     71 p. 18 cm.

     I. Title.

     PT9875.L52O6   63–38904 ‡

   NL   0359147   DLC MH

   Liffner, Axel Gustaf Adolf, 1919–
     Semikolon. ¡Dikter¿ Stockholm, Bonnier ¡1951¿
     92 p. 18 cm.

     I. Title.

                            A 52–1223

Minnesota. Univ. Libr.
for Library of Congress

   NL   0359148   MnU NN

   Lifförsäkring
     see under   [Engeström, Fredrik von]

---

ar W
5675
   Lifförsäkrings-Aktiebolaget. De förenade
   1933.
     Stockholm, The Life Insurance Com-
pany De Förenade ¡1934¿
     283 p. 25cm.

     1. Insurance, Life--Sweden.

   NL   0359150   NIC PP

16
1274
   Lifford, James Hewitt, 3rd Viscount, 1783-1855.
     Ireland, and the Irish church, its past and
present state.   London, 1842.

   NL   0359151   DLC

283.415
I68
no.1
   Lifford, James Hewitt, **3rd Viscount,** 1783-
1855.
     A plea for Irish landlords; a letter to
Isaac Butt ... by Lord Lifford. Dublin, Hodges,
Smith and co., 1867.
     20 p.   21½cm.

     ¡No. 1¿ in a volume with binder's title:
Irish church.
     1. Landlord and tenant. Ireland 2.
Ireland. History. 1837-1901 I. Butt, Isaac,
1813-1879 II. Title

   NL   0359152   NcD IU

Kress
Room
   Lifford, James Hewitt, 3rd viscount,
     1783-1855.
     Thoughts on the present state of Ireland
... London, J.Murray, 1849.
     30 p. 22 cm.

     Bound with Godley, J.R., An answer to the
question: What is to be done with the unem-
ployed labourers, 1847.

     1.Catholic church in Ireland. 2.Poor -
Ireland. 3.Poor laws - Ireland. I.Title.

   NL   0359153   MH-BA

   Lifford, Ire.   County Donegal historical
     society
     See
   County Donegal historical society.

   Liffort de Buffevent, François
     see
   François de Sainte Marie, *Father.*

   Liffran (Joseph) [1871–]. *Contribution à
l'étude de la leucocythémie aiguë. 116 pp., 1 l.,
1 pl., 2 ch. 4°. Bordeaux, 1893, No. 39.

   NL   0359156   DNLM

---

*EC7
A100
726l
   The Liffy: a fable. In imitation of the
Metamorphosis of Ovid. Addrest to a young
lady. With an epistle dedicatory: in which is
contain'd, An essay upon the Metamorphosis of
Ovid. By ****** **** esq; ...
     Dvblin: Printed by S.Powell, for George Risk, at
the corner of Castle-lane in Dame's-street,
near the horse-guard, 1726.

     8°. xiv(i.e.xvi),[17]-32p. 20cm.
     Page xvi misnumbered xiv.
     In verse.

   NL   0359157   MH NjP CtY DFo

   Lifið. 1.–   árg. Reykjavík, 1936–
     v. in   illus. 20 cm.
     Four no. a year. 1936-37; annual, 1938-
     Editor: 1936–   J. Birkiland.

     I. Birkiland, Jóhánnes, ed.

     AP41.L5   56–4964

   NL   0359158   DLC

VOLUME 332

The Lifilindex for auto- research in personality ...
see under   [Krebs, Stanley Le Fevre]
1864-

Lifiſs, M   M   *ed.*
Экономика советской торговли. Допущено в качестве
учебника для экон. высших учеб. заведений. Москва,
Госторгиздат, 1950.
568 p. 23 cm.
At head of title: Г. Л. Рубинштейн ₍и др.₎

1. Russia—Comm.   I. Rubinshteĭn, G. L.   II. Title.
Title transliterated: Ekonomika sovetskoĭ torgovli.

HF3626.L46   51-30462

NL 0359160   DLC

Lifiſs, M   M
Экономика советской торговли ; учебник для экономиче-
ских вузов. Под ред. М. М. Лифица. Москва, Гос. изд-во
торговой лит-ры, 1955.
512 p. 23 cm.
At head of title: Б. И. Гоголь ... М. М. Лифиц ₍и др.₎

1. Russia—Comm.   I. Gogol', B. I.   II. Title.
Title transliterated: Ekonomika sovetskoĭ torgovli.

HF3626.L463   56-39761

NL 0359161   DLC

HF3626 Lifiſs, M   M   *ed.*
.L72   Die Ökonomik des Sowjethandels, Gesamtredaktion
M. M. Lifiz ₍Übersetzt von W. Fickenscher₎ Ber-
lin, Verlag "Die Wirtschaft" ₍1953₎
640 p.
At head of title: G. L. Rubinstein, B. I.
Gogol, A. G. Kulikow, W. I. Moskwin.
Bibliographical footnotes.

1. Russia—Comm. I. Fickenscher, Wilhelm, tr.
II. Rubinshteĭn, G L   III. Title.

NL 0359162   ICU CU InU WU NIC ViU

Lifiſs, M   M   *ed.*
Планирование хозяйственной деятельности государ-
ственной торговой организации (Торгфинплан торга)
Учеб. пособие для торговых вузов. Москва, Гос. изд-во
торговой лит-ры, 1955.
334 p. 23 cm.
At head of title: Генкина Л. С. ₍и др.₎
On cover: Торгфинплан торга.
1. Retail trade—Russia. 2. Russia—Comm.   I. Genkina, L. S.
II. Title.   III. Title: Torgfinplan torga.
Title transliterated: Planirovanie khozi͡aĭstvennoĭ dei͡a-
tel'nosti gosudarstvennoĭ torgovoĭ organizat͡sii.

HF5349.R9L5   58-16669

NL 0359163   DLC

Lifiſs, M   M
Советская торговля. ₍Москва₎ Гос. изд-во полит.
лит-ры, 1948.
124 p. 20 cm.

1. Russia—Comm.   *Title transliterated:* Sovetskai͡a torgovli͡a.

HF3626.L47   49-21257*

NL 0359164   DLC CaBVaU

Lifiſs, M   M
Советская торговля и ее роль в экономической жизни
страны. ₍Москва₎ Гос. изд-во полит. лит-ры, 1951.
71 p. 20 cm.

1. Russia—Comm.   I. Title.
Title transliterated: Sovetskai͡a torgovli͡a i ee rol'.

HF3626.L472   52-23210

NL 0359165   DLC

Lifiſs, M   M
Советская торговля—-важное средство повышения бла-
госостояния трудящихся. Стенограмма публичной лекции, прочитанной в Москве. Москва, Знание, 1953.
38 p. 22 cm. (Всесоюзное общество по распространению политических и научных знаний. Сер. 2, № 68)

1. Russia—Comm.
Title transliterated: Sovetskai͡a torgovli͡a—vazh-
noe sredstvo povyshenii͡a blagosostoi͡anii͡a.

HF3626.L473   54-20638

NL 0359166   DLC

Lifiſs, M   M   *ed.*
Торгово-финансовый план торга. ₍2. перер. изд.₎ Допущено в качестве учеб. пособия для торгово-экономиче-
ских вузов. Москва, Госторгиздат, 1948.
200 p. 23 cm.
At head of title: Д. В. Гаценко ₍и др.₎
Errata slip inserted.
"'Торгово-финансовый план торга' представляет собой второе,
переработанное издание учебного пособия по курсу 'Экономика
советской торговли,' вышедшего в 1939 г."

1. Russia—Comm.   I. Gat͡senko, D. V.   II. Title.
Title transliterated: Torgovo-finansovyĭ plan torga.

HF3626.L48 1948   50-21304

NL 0359167   DLC

Lifiz, M. M.
see Lifiſs, M. M.

NK9310 Lifka, Bohumír, 1900—   L'Enfant-Jésus de
.D7   Prague.

Drobná, Zoroslava.
Les trésors de la broderie religieuse en Tchécoslovaquie
₍par₎ Zoroslava Drobná. L'Enfant-Jésus de Prague ₍par₎
Bohumír Lifka. ₍Traduit en français par Arnold Wlo-
szczowski₎ Prague, Sfinx, 1950.

CT275   Lifka, Bohumír, 1900-
C277L5 Historiograf české Ameriky Tomáš Čapek. Na paměť
jeho 85. narozenin 6. XII 1946. V Praze, 1947.
10 p. port.

"Zvláštní otisk z Časopisu Rodopisné společnosti československé
v Praze, roc. 17-18."

1. Čapek, Thomas, 1861-

NL 0359170   CU

Lifka, Bohumír, 1900—
Knihovny státních hradů a zámků. ₍Redigovali Hugo
Rokyta a Oldřich J. Blažíček. 1. vyd. V Praze, Státní
tělovýchovné nakl., Skupina kulturní a přírodní památky,
1954₎
26 p. illus. 21 cm. (Publikace Státní památkové správy)

1. Libraries—Czechoslovak Republic. 2. Castles—Czechoslovak Republic. I. Title.

Z795.L53   67-122601 ‡

NL 0359171   DLC MH

₍Lifka, Bohumír, 1900-   , ed.₎
Na paměť F. X. Šaldy; sborník vzpomínání, lásky a
vděčnosti. ₍Red. a vyd. Bohumír Lifka. Kresbou a
dřevorytem vyzdobil Karel Svolinský. V Praze,
1938₎
132 p. illus.

NL 0359172   MH InU

PG 5069 LIFKA, BOHUMÍR, 1900-
.M55 J5   Národní knihovna Čechů a Slováků
zahraničních. ₍V Praze, Marginalie, 1935₎
11 p.

"Zvláštní otisk z "Marginalii", věstníku
Spolku českých bibliofilů, roč. IX, č. 7-8."
Bound with Miniberger, Václav, Jimův Homer
Calvin.

1. Libraries.

NL 0359173   InU

PG 5069 LIFKA, BOHUMÍR, 1900-
.M55 J5   První český tisk v Americe; k výstavě
čs. zahraničního tisku v Praze 1-21. března
1936. ₍V Praze, Marginalie, 1936₎
8 p. facsims.

"Zvláštní otisk z 'Marginalii', věstníku
Spolku českých bibliofilů, roč. X, č. 2-3."
Bound with Miniberger, Václav, Jimův Homer
Calvin.

1. Printing—Hist.—U.S.

NL 0359174   InU MnHi

Lifka, Felix, 1882-
... Vergleichende untersuchungen über die
grösse und form de akarusmilben des hundes,
Beantwortung der Frage, ob es verschiedene
Arten von Akarus Folliculorum Canis gibt und
untersuchungen über das Vorkommen der
Abrusmilben bei gesunden, d.h. Hautreinen
Hunden ... Berlin, 1922.
15 p. 20.5 cm.
Inaug.-Diss. - Tierärztl. Hochshule, Berlin.

NL 0359175   DNAL

Lifka, Franz.
... Entproletarisierung das ziel der Quadragesimo anno. ₍Wien, Typographische anstalt,
1934?₎
16 p. 16 cm.
1. Sociology, Christian. 2.-2a. Catholic
church. Pope, 1922-1939 (Pius XI) Quadragesimo
anno.

NL 0359176   CU

Lifka, Franz.
Ums tägliche Brot. Ein sozialer Roman. Wien, R. M.
Partl ₍1948₎
232 p. 21 cm.

I. Title.

New York. Public Libr.   A 50-3449
for Library of Congress

NL 0359177   NN

The Liflade of St. Julian
see under   Julian, Saint, of Nicomedia.
Legend.

VOLUME 332

Liflíandskiĭ gubernskiĭ statisticheskiĭ komitet
see
Livonia. Gubernskiĭ statisticheskiĭ komitet.

Lifman, Robert
see **Liefmann, Robert,** 1874–1941.

Lifquist, Rosalind Caribelle, 1903–
Food guide for older folks ₍prepared by Rosalind C. Lifquist, Mary Walsh Cashin and Emily C. Davis. Washington, U. S. Govt. Print. Off.,₁ 1952₎
16 p. illus. 24 cm. (U. S. Dept. of Agriculture. Home and garden bulletin no. 17)

1. ₍Old age₎ 2. ₍Diet₎ ₍1, 2. Food for old people₎ I. Title. (Series)
TX7.U6   no. 17   *641.1 613.21   Agr 52–240
U. S. Dept. of Agr. Libr.   1Ag84Hg no. 17
for Library of Congress   ₍5*₎†

NL 0359181   DNAL CaBViP PPD DLC

Lifquist, Rosalind Caribelle, 1903–
Planning food for institutions, by Rosalind C. Lifquist and Edith B. Tate. Washington, U. S. Govt. Print. Off., 1951.
95 p. tables. 26 cm. (U. S. Dept. of Agriculture. Agriculture handbook no. 16)
Contribution from Bureau of Human Nutrition and Home Economics.
"Source material used in compiling tables giving purchase information": p. 90.

1. Cookery for institutions, etc. ₍1. Food for institutions₎ 2. Institution management. I. Tate, Edith (Belcher) 1919– joint author. II. Title. (Series)
TX820.L5   641.57   Agr 51–240
U. S. Dept. of Agr. Libr.   1Ag84Ah no. 16
for Library of Congress   †

NL 0359182   DNAL NNBG AAP WaWW WaT DLC

Lifrustkammaren, Stockholm

see

Stockholm. Livrustkammaren.

Lifs-saga Jóns Jónssonar
see under Jónsson, Jon, 1720–1789.

Lifsábyrgðar- og framfærslustofnunin
See Statsanstalten for Livsforsikring.

NL 0359185   NIC

BR404
.L5   Lifsbilder ur den svenska kyrkans
historia. 1.samlingen. Rock
Island, Ill., Lutheran Augustana Book Concern ₍19--?₎
194 p. 15 cm.

NL 0359186   MnHi

787.207M
L 626 E   Lifschey, Samuel, 1889–
₍Etudes, viola₎

Daily technical studies. New York, G.
Schirmer ₍c1929₎
50 p. 30ᵐ.

Caption title.

NL 0359187   OO PPCI

Lifschey, Samuel, 1889–
Double-stop studies for the viola, by Samuel Lifschey. New York, G. Schirmer, inc. ₍1943₎
31 p. 30 x 23ᵐ.
ublisher's plate no.: 40283.

1. Viola—Studies and exercises.   I. Title.   44–45979
Library of Congress   MT285.L43

NL 0359188   DLC OrP

MT285
.C2
op. 22   **Lifschey, Samuel,** 1889–   ed.
.L5
   Campagnoli, Bartolomeo, 1751–1827.
₍Caprices, viola, op. 22₎
... Forty-one caprices for the viola; study version prepared by Samuel Lifschey. New York, G. Schirmer, inc. ₍1944₎

Lifschey, Samuel, 1889-

Scale and arpeggio studies for the viola.
G. Schirmer ₍c1939₎
v.

Contents

v.2 In all positions.

NL 0359190   OrP OO CLSU

MT285
L5   Lifschey, Samuel, 1899-
Twelve modulatory studies for the viola, by
Samuel Lifschey. New York, G. Schirmer, inc.
₍c1936₎
1 p.l.,25 p. 31cm.

Publisher's no.: 36702.
"These studies are based on the nineteenth of
the Viola caprices, Op.22, by B. Campagnoli." -
pref.

I. Campagnoli, Bartolomeo, 1751-1827. Caprices₎
pour l'alto viola. no.19.

NL 0359191   CU OrP OO PP PPCI

Lifschitz, Abraham Kroll-
see Kroll-Lifschitz, Abraham.

4HF
616   Lifschitz, B
Die schweizerisch-russischen
Handelsbeziehungen. Zürich/New York,
Europa Verlag ₍c1944₎
39 p.

NL 0359193   DLC-P4

LIFSCHITZ, Boris.
Das aussetzungsdelikt in geschichtlicher
darstellung. n.p., 1909.

100 p.
Inaug.-diss, --- Bern.

NL 0359194   MH-L ICRL

Lifschitz, Ch₍aja₎ A₍nna₎.
Wundts Lehre vom Willen. Berlin: W. Pilz, 1910. 64 p.,
1 l. 8°.
Doctoral dissertation, Zürich.
Gift of Carnegie Institution of Washington.

1. Wundt, Wilhelm. 2. Will.   January 13, 1911.

NL 0359195   NN ICRL MH

Lifschitz (Chaja Feiga). *Wird die Wirkung des Pepsins auf das Eiweiss durch das Solenoid begünstigt?* 14 pp. 8°. Zürich, Gebr. Leemann & Co. 1911.

NL 0359196   DNLM

Lifschitz, David, 1903–
A study of the hydrolysis of corn starch ... by David Lifschitz ... New York city, 1931.
24, ₍3₎ p. 23ᵐ.
Thesis (PH. D.)—Columbia university, 1931.
Vita.
"References": p. ₍25–26₎

1. Corn-starch. 2. Hydrolysis.
     32–12535
Library of Congress   QD321.L73 1931
Columbia Univ. Libr.   547.3

NL 0359197   NNC DLC CU OU MiU

HG3361
.P22A725   Lifschitz, Ephraim Baer, 1867-   tr.
Hebraic   Bodenheimer, Max Isidor, 1865–1940.
Sect.   תבנית בית האוצר הלאמי (קולוניאלבנק) משא אשר נשא
בקונגרס השני בבזל. נעתק משפת אשכנז ע״י אפרים דוב
ליפשיץ. ווילנא. תרנ״ם.   Вильна, 1899.

NL 0359199   ICN ICJ

H
3
.825172   LIFSCHITZ, FEITEL, 1875-
Ad. Smiths Methode im Lichte der deutschen
nationalökonomischen Litteratur des XIX. Jahrhunderts. Ein Beitrag zur Geschichte der Methodologie in der Wirtschaftswissenschaft.
Bern, G. Iseli, 1905.
70p. 24cm.

NL 0359199   ICN ICJ

HB103
.S6L7   LIFSCHITZ, FEITEL, 1875-
Ad. Smiths methode im lichte der deutschen nationalökonomischen litteratur des XIX. jahrhunderts. Ein beitrag zur geschichte der methodologie in der wirtschaftswissenschaft... Bern, 1906.
70, ₍1₎ p. 22½cm.
Inaug.-diss.--Bern.
Bibliographical foot-notes.
1. Smith, Adam, 1723-1790. 2. Economics.

NL 0359200   ICU MH-BA KU PU NN

Lifschitz, Feitel.
...Bismarck'sche Kriegsmethoden einst und jetzt. Bern: Der freie Verlag, 1918. 16 p. 8°.
Bibliographical footnotes.

1. European war, 1914- —Causes.   2. Franco-German war, 1870–71.
3. Bismarck-Schoenhausen, Otto   Eduard Leopold, Fürst von, 1815–98.
     February 10, 1920.

NL 0359201   NN

Lifschitz, Feitel.
Deutschlands Stellung zu der Friedensidee und der internationalen Schiedsgerichtsbarkeit. von Dr. F. Lifschitz... "Der Pazifismus ist Unsinn." Engel in "Deutschlands Erneuerung." 1. B. Heft 3. Seite 197. München 1917. "Weiter Kriegsbereit." von Freitag-Loringhoven, "Folgerungen aus dem Weltkriege." Berlin, 1917, Seite 100. Bern: P. Müller-Frey, 1917. 24 p. 12°.
Bibliographical footnotes.

1. Arbitration (International). Ger-   many.
     February 5, 1920.

NL 0359202   NN

VOLUME 332

Lifschitz, Feitel, 1875–
Die historische schule der wirtschaftswissenschaft, von dr.
F. Lifschitz ... Bern, Stämpfli & cie., 1914.
2 p. l., 291 p. 22½ᶜᵐ.

1. Economics—Hist.   ɪ. Title.
34–11531
Library of Congress   HB97.L5   330.154

NL 0359203   DLC KU CU OrU CtY OU NN MH IU ICU MH-BA

₍Lifschitz, Feitel₎ 1875–
Repetitorium der geschichte der nationalökonomie, von dr.
Bernhard Siegfried ₍pseud.₎ 2. aufl. Bern, P. Haupt, 1922.
104 p. 20ᶜᵐ.

1. Economics—Hist. 2. Socialism.   ɪ. Title.
40–22397
Library of Congress   HB75.L5 1922
330.9

NL 0359204   DLC

₍Lifschitz, Feitel₎ 1875–
Repetitorium der National-Ökonomie, von Dr. Bernhard Sieg-
fried ₍pseud.₎ Bern: Akademische Buchhandlung von M.
Drechsel, 1914.   104 p.   18½cm.

671267. 1. Economics.   *Card revised*
April 30, 1942

NL 0359205   NN MoSU

₍Lifschitz, Feitel₎ 1875–
Repetitorium der schweizerischen Volkswirtschaft. von Dr.
Bernhard Siegfried ₍pseud.₎ Zürich: O. Füssli, 1916.   92 p.
20½cm.

784870. 1. Economic history—   Switzerland.   *Card revised*
April 30, 1942

NL 0359206   NN

Lifschitz, Feitel.
La Russia d'oggi. Edizione italiana a cura del Prof. Angelo
Pernice.   Milano: U. Hoepli, 1916.   xi, 260 p.   12°.

At head of title: F. Livchiz.

1. Russia. 2. Pernice. Angelo, trans-   lator.
November 13, 1916.

NL 0359207   NN IU

Lifschitz, Feitel, 1875–
Die russische revolution; eine unparteiische
betrachtung von dr. F. Lifschitz ... Bern,
Akademische buchhandlung von M. Dreschsel,
1917.
cover-title, 15 [1] p.   20.5 cm.

NL 0359208   CSt-H

DK27 **Lifschitz, Feitel,** 1875–
.L5   Russland, von dr. F. Lifschitz ... Zürich, Orell Füssli,
1916.
165 p. 21ᶜᵐ.

1. Russia.

NL 0359209   ICU NSyU DLC CSt-H NN MH NjP

Lifschitz, Feitel.
Russland und Deutschland von dr. F. Lifschitz ...
Bern, P. Müller-Frey, 1917.
36 p. 20½ᶜᵐ.

1. European war, 1914–1918 — Germany. 2. European war, 1914–1918—
Russia.
24–21771
Library of Congress   D515.L585

NL 0359210   DLC

Lifschitz, Feitel.
Separatfrieden zwischen Russland und Deutschland‼
von dr. F. Lifschitz ... Bern, P. Müller-Frey, 1916.
1 p. l., ₍5₎–25 p. 20½ᶜᵐ.

1. European war, 1914–1918—Peace.   ɪ. Title.
24–11751
Library of Congress   D613.L52

NL 0359211   DLC

HB75 **Lifschitz, Feitel,** 1875–
.L59
Über die bedeutung Englands für
die theorie der wirtschaftswissenschaft
mit besonderer berücksichtigung Deutschlands. Bern, Müller ₍1916₎
22 p.   23 ᶜᵐ.

1. Economics - Hist. 2. Economists,
British.

NL 0359212   NjP

DK67.5 **Lifschitz, Feitel,** 1875–
S9L722   Über die schweizerisch-russischen beziehungen, von dr.F.Lifschitz... Zürich, Orell
Füssli, 1916.
19 p.   25½ᶜᵐ.

"Sonderabdruck aus 'Wissen und leben' heft
15 vom 1.mai 1916."

1.Switzerland - Relations (general) with
Russia. 2.Russia - Relations (general) with
Switzerland. I.   Title

NL 0359213   CSt-H

Lifschitz, Feitel.
Untersuchungen über die methodologie der wirtschaftswissenschaft. Von dr. F. Lifschitz ... Leipzig, C. L.
Hirschfeld, 1909.
94 p. 24ᵐᵐ.

1. Economics.
A 10–664
Title from Harvard Univ.   Printed by L. C.

NL 0359214   MH FMU NNC KU CU ICJ

Lifschitz, Feitel, 1875–
Was ist Anarchismus?   Bern: M. Drechsel, 1911.   32 p.
8°.

1. Anarchism.—Theory.
October 5, 1911.

NL 0359215   NN CtY CU

336.494 **Lifschitz, Feitel,** 1875–
L626w   Wertzuwachssteuer; theorie und praxis,
1910   von F. Lifschitz.   Bern, M. Drechsel,
1910.
32p. 22cm.

Includes bibliographical footnotes.

1. Taxation. Switzerland. 2. Switzerland. Economic policy. I. Title.

NL 0359216   KU NIC

Lifschitz, Feitel.
Wie man in Deutschland bereits den nächsten krieg
vorbereitet! von dr. F. Lifschitz ... 2. verm. aufl. ...
Bern, Müller-Frey, 1918.
63 p. 20½ᶜᵐ.

1. European war. 1914–1918—Germany.   ɪ. Title.
24–7416
Library of Congress   D515.L5 1918

NL 0359217   DLC NN

Lifschitz, Feitel, 1875–
Zur Kritik der Boehm-Bawerkschen Werttheorie. Leipzig, W. Engelmann, 1908.
115 p. 23 cm.

1. Value. 2. Böhm von Bawerk, Eugen, Ritter, 1851–1914.
HB205.G3L5   55–46503 ‡

NL 0359218   DLC KU NN CtY ICJ OU

Lifschitz, Ilja, 1900–
Ueber an mundhoehle und genitalien isolierten
lichen ruber planus.
Inaug. diss.   Leipzig, ₍1927₎
Bibl.

NL 0359219   ICRL

Lifschitz, Isaac, 1882–
... Ueber einen   Fall van spinaler progres-
siver Muskelatrophie ...   Berlin [1911]
23 cm.
Inaug.-Diss. - Berlin.
At head of title: Aus der ersten medizinischen
Klinik der Königl. Charité zu Berlin (Geheimrat
Prof. Dr. His).
Lebenslauf.
Literatur: p. [35]–37.

NL 0359220   CtY ICRL DLC DNLM

Lifschitz, Israel, 1888–
Die Aenderungen der Lichtabsorption bei
der Salzbildung organischen Säuren.   Zurich,
1914.
Inaug.-Diss. - Zurich.

NL 0359221   ICRL

Lifschitz, Israel, 1888–
... Die änderungen der lichtabsorption bei der salzbildung organischer säuren, von dr. I. Lifschitz ... mit 15
textabbildungen. Stuttgart, F. Enke, 1914.
cover-title, p. ₍175₎–290. diags. 25½ᶜᵐ. (Sammlung chemischer und
chemisch-technischer vorträge ... xxı. bd., 5./7. hft.)
Contains bibliographies.

1. Absorption of light.
15–4897
Library of Congress   QD1.S2 21. bd., 5./7. hft.

NL 0359222   DLC NcD ViU CoU OU ICJ NN

VOLUME 332

Lifschitz, Israel, 1888–
   ...Der dialektische materialismus und die klinische medizin. ...

   see under

Lifshits, IAkov Isaakovich, 1896–

Lifschitz, Israel, 1888–
   Kurzer abriss der spektroskopie und kolorimetrie. 2. aufl., neu bearb. von dr. I. Lifschitz ... mit 112 abbildungen im text und 1 doppeltafel. Leipzig, J. A. Barth, 1927.

   4 p. l., 324 p., 1 l. illus., double pl., diagrs. 25ᶜᵐ. (*Added t.-p.:* Handbuch der angewandten physikalischen chemie in einzeldarstellungen ... hrsg. von Georg Bredig ... bd. v)

   Bibliographical foot-notes.

   1. Spectrum analysis. 2. Colorimetry.

                                               30–2933

   Library of Congress   QC451.L73 1927

NL 0359224   DLC OU MiU

Lifschitz, Israel, 1888–
   Uber die polychromen salz aus Violursauren. Uber die optischen eigenschaften der Azo- und Diazoverbindungen. Leipzig, A. Hoffmann, 1911.

NL 0359225   OCU

Lifschitz, Jakob Isaakovitsch
   see Lifshits, IAkov Isaakovich, 1896–

Lifschitz, Leon.
   Die Nierenblutung durch Uberanstrengung ... Basel, 1915.
   26 cm.
   Inaug.-Diss. - Basel.

NL 0359227   CtY DNLM MH MiU

LIFSCHITZ, Leon.
Review of the Public Service Commission in the New York Courts.   Typewritten. n.p., 1927.
   (2)-91 p.   228
Thesis -- Law School of Harvard University.

NL 0359228   MH-L

Lifschitz (Louise). *Beobachtung über angeborene idiopathische Herzhypertrophie. 38 pp. 8°. Zürich. 1906.

NL 0359229   DNLM

Lifschitz, Nahum O   **537.838 Q902**
   Die Umformer. Von N. O. Lifschitz, ... Mit 84 Abbildungen. Leipzig, Hachmeister & Thal, [1909].
   viii, 120 p. illus., diagrs. 24ᶜᵐ.

NL 0359230   ICJ

Lifschitz (Raymond) [1894–   ]. *Diagnostic radiographique des tumeurs des os. 98 pp. 8°. Paris. 1925. No. 482.

NL 0359231   DNLM CtY

Lifschitz (Mlle. Rosalie) [1884–   ]. *Contribution à l'étude de la tétanie chez l'adulte et de son origine para-thyroidienne. 79 pp. 8°. Paris. 1914. No. 221.

NL 0359232   DNLM CtY

Lifschitz (S.) *Ueber die Entwicklung der embryonalen Mils. 20 pp., 1 L. 8°. Zürich, I. J. Meier. 1906.

NL 0359233   DNLM

Lifschitz, Samuel.
   ...Vorlesungen über Bauakustik; ins Deutsche übersetzt von L. Zolotnitsky...   Stuttgart: K. Wittwer, 1930.   viii, 119 p. incl. diagrs., tables.   illus. 8°. (Wittwers technische Hilfsbücher.   Bd. 10.)

   Bibliography, p. [118–]119.

501438A. 1. Architectural acoustics.   I. Zolotnitsky, Leo, translator.
                                                        November 28, 1930

NL 0359234   NN

Lifschitz, Samuel Cohen.
   גדול ירקות בארץ־ישראל. חלבות למעשה. יפו, דפוס א. אתין,
   [Jaffa, 1911]
   96 p. 18 cm.

   1. Vegetable gardening—Palestine.
      Title transliterated: Gidul yerakot be-Erets-Yisrael.

   SB319.P3L5   55–55462 ‡

NL 0359235   DLC

Lifschitz, Samuel Cohen.
   הזבלים החיימים. ספר מעבד עפ״י מקורות שונים. יפו, דפוס א.
   אתין, תרע״א [Jaffa, 1910/11]
   45 p. 17 cm.
   Cover title.

   1. Fertilizers and manures.
      Title transliterated: ha-Zevalim ha-ḥimiyim.

   S633.L59   55–55459 ‡

NL 0359236   DLC

Lifschitz (Scheina Sophie). *Ueber die Jodausscheidung nach grossen Jodkaliumdosen und bei kutaner Applikation einiger Jodpräparate. 28 pp. 8°. Bern. 1905.

NL 0359237   DNLM

Lifschitz, Scholom: Eine neue Methode der quantitativen Zuckerbestimmung im Harn. Berlin: Ebering (1913). 25 S. 8°
¶Im Buchh. ebd.
Berlin, Med. Diss. v. 11. Aug. 1913, Ref. Brugsch, Kraus
[Geb. 29. Mai 90 Krutscha; Wohnort: Berlin-Wilmersdorf; Staatsangeh.: Rußland; Vorbildung: 7. G. Petersburg Reife 07; Studium: Berlin 10 S.; Rig. 7. Aug. 13.]
                                                    [U 13. 155#]

NL 0359238   ICRL DNLM CtY

Lifschitz, Zebi Phinehas.
   הלכה פסוקה. משו״ע יורה דעה מסימן א' עד סימן ק״י וחלכות
   נדה ומכ:אות חלק ראשון, עד הלכות מליחה. ווילנא. ברפום י. ל.
   Вильна, 1878. ס״ן. תרל״ח.
   vi, 146 p. 33 cm.
   No more published.

   1. Slaughtering and slaughter-houses—Jews. 2. Jews—Dietary laws.   I. Title.   *Title transliterated:* Halakhah pesukah.

   BM720.S6L5   A 56–6196

   New York. Public Libr.
   for Library of Congress   †

NL 0359239   NN DLC

Lifschitz-Golden, *Mrs.* Manya, 1896–
   Les Juifs dans la littérature française du moyen âge (mystères, miracles, chroniques) by Manya Lifschitz-Golden ... New York, Columbia university [1935].
   2 p. l., 7–211, [1] p. 21 cm. (Publications of the Institute of French studies, inc.)
   Thesis (PH. D.)—Columbia university, 1935.
   Vita.
   Published also without thesis note.
   "Bibliographie": p. 202–211.
   1. Jews in literature. 2. French literature—Old French—Hist. & crit. 3. Mysteries and miracle-plays, French—Hist. & crit. 4. French drama—Medieval—Hist. & crit.   I. Title.

   PQ155.J43L5 1935   840.9   35–14552

NL 0359240   DLC CU IdU

Lifschitz-Golden, *Mrs.* Manya, 1896–
   Les Juifs dans la littérature française du moyen âge (mystères, miracles, chroniques) by Manya Lifschitz-Golden ... New York, Columbia university [1935].
   211 p. 20½ᶜᵐ. (Publications of the Institute of French studies, inc.)
   "Bibliographie": p. 202–211.
   1. Jews in literature. 2. French literature—Old French—Hist. & crit. 3. Mysteries and miracle-plays, French—Hist. & crit.   I. Title.

   Library of Congress   PQ155.J43L5   35–16604

   Copyright A 83930   840.9

NL 0359241   DLC TNJ-R CU PU PPDrop MiU OCU OCH NcU

W 4   LIFSCHITZ SALITA, Wladimiro
C53   Efectos de la estricnina en la
1948   actividad nerviosa superior. [Santiago de Chile] 1948.
             29 p.
             Tesis - Univ. de Chile.
             1. Strychnine

NL 0359242   DNLM

Lifschiz, Ch
   see Lifshits, Kh.

Lifschiz-Trachtenberg (Chaja-Gitel). *Therapie des Nabelschnurvorfalls und ihre Ergebnisse für Mutter und Kind. 35 pp. 8°. Bern. 1910.

NL 0359244   DNLM

LIFSCHÜTZ, Alexander.
Studien uber die bildung der isomeren nitrokörper bei dem nitrierungsprozesse der monosubstituierten benzole.   Dissertation, [kgl. Tech. Hochschule]. München, K. Hofbuchdruckerei Kastner & Callwey, 1910.

   pp. 52.

NL 0359245   MH-C ICRL DLC PU

VOLUME 332

Lifschütz, Alexander, 1890–
Die generalklausel im aktienrecht, von dr. Alexander Lif
schütz ... Mannheim, J. Bensheimer; ₍etc., etc.₎ 1931.
vi p., 1 l., 53 p. 22½ᶜᵐ.

1. Stock companies—Germany. 2. Corporation law—Germany.
I. Title.

35–29896

NL 0359246   DLC OU

Lifschütz, Alexander, 1890–
Sorgen ums Recht; eine Gedankenfolge. Berlin, C. Heymann, 1953.
67 p. 23 cm.

1. Law reform—Germany. 2. Legislation—Germany. 3. Law and
ethics. 4. Punishment—Germany. I. Title.

56–40209 ‡

NL 0359247   DLC MH-L NN NNC

Lifschütz, Alexander, 1890–   Die strafrechtliche
Bekämpfung geistlicher Uebergriffe in weltliches Gebiet.
Breslau: Schletter 1913. 83 S. 8° ¶Auch als: Strafrechtl.
Abhandlungen. H. 177.
Göttingen, Jur. Diss. v. 17. Nov. 1913, Ref. R. v. Hippel
₍Geb. 3. Okt. 90 Berlin-Pankow; Wohnort: Hamburg; Staatsangeh.: Bremen;
Vorbildung: Altes G. Bremen Reife 10; Studium: Göttingen 3, München 1,
Göttingen 2 S.; Rig. 25. Juni 13.₎   [U 13–547

NL 0359248   ICRL

Lifschütz, Alexander, 1890–
Die strafrechtliche bekämpfung geistlicher uebergriffe in
weltliches gebiet. Von dr. jur. A. Lifschütz. Breslau, Schletter, 1913.
2 p. l., 83 p. 23½ᶜᵐ. (*Added t.-p.:* Strafrechtliche abhandlungen ...
hft. 177)
Also issued as inaugural dissertation, Göttingen, 1913.

1. Criminal law—Germany. 2. Ecclesiastical law—Germany.
I. Title.

29–30730

NL 0359249   DLC MiU MH

QD445   **Lifschuetz, Isaac.**
.A6L7   Ueber die einwirkung der concentrirten
schwefelsaeure auf nitroanthrachinone.
Berlin, 1885.
53p.
inaug. diss. Freiburg.

NL 0359250   DLC

Lifschuetz, Isaak, 1882–

see

Lifschitz, Isaac, 1882–

Lifschultz, Burton Benjamin, tr.

Geijerstam, Gustaf af, 1858–1909.
Big and little brother, by Gustav av Geijerstam; translated
for Story-teller's house from the original Swedish, by Burton
Benjamin Lifschultz; drawings by John Dukes McKee. Chicago, Thomas S. Rockwell company, 1930.

Lifschultz, Burton Benjamin, tr.

Sand, George, *pseud. of Mme.* **Dudevant,** 1804–1876.
Wings of courage, by George Sand; translated for Story-
teller's house from the original French, by Burton Benjamin
Lifschultz; drawings by John Dukes McKee. Chicago,
Thomas S. Rockwell company, 1931.

LIFSCHUTZ, E.
Jewish Immigrant Life in American Memoir
Literature. Reprinted from YIVO Annual of
Jewish Social Science, vol.5, 1950, p.216–
231.

1. History–U.S. 2. Immigration.

Originally published in Geshikhte fun der
yiddisher arbeter-bewegung in di faraynigte
shtatn, New York, 1943, vol. 1, ch. VII.

NL 0359254   NNJ

LIFSCHUTZ, E.
Merrymakers and Jesters among
Jews. (Materials for a Lexicon). Reprinted from YIVO Annual, Vol.8, 1952,
p.43–83.
Originally published in Arkhiv far
der Geshikhte fun Yidishn Teater un
Drama (1930).
1. Merrymakers. 2. Customs, Jewish.

NL 0359255   NNJ

PJ5129   **Lifschutz, E.**
.R598Z52   **Rosenfeld, Morris,** 1862–1923.
Hebr   שאריס ראזענפעלדס בריוו. מים אן אריינפיר און דערקלערונגען
פון י. ליפשיץ. בוענאס-איירעס, יידישער וויסנשאפטלעכער אינס-
טיטוט. ייווא. ₍Buenos Aires₎ 1955.

Lifschutz, Harold, 1913–
The counting losses in Geiger-Muller counter circuits and re-
corders, by Harold Lifschutz ... ₍New York, 1938₎
cover-title, 714–725 p. diagrs. 26 x 20ᶜᵐ.
Thesis (PH. D.)—University of Michigan, 1938.
By Harold Lifschutz and O. S. Duffendack.
Running title: Losses in counter recorders.
"Reprinted from the Physical review, vol. 54, no. 9, November 1, 1938."

1. Geiger-Müller counters. I. Duffendack, Ora Stanley, 1890–
joint author. II. Title.

Library of Congress   QC476.L5 1938   39–12911

527 53

NL 0359257   DLC MH

Lifshey, Earl.
Door-to-door selling; the factual story of a little known
but rapidly-growing $7 billion industry. New York, Fair-
child Publications ₍1948₎
64 p. illus., ports. 29 cm.
"Appeared originally as a series of 17 articles in Retailing daily,
beginning March 22, 1948."

1. Canvassing. I. Title.

HF5446.L5   658.847   48–8491*

NL 0359258   MiU OrCS Or CaBVa
DLC OClCC TU MB OU TxU Mi PP PSt FTaSU

070.41   **Lifshey, Earl.**
L722p   Page 1, column 1.   New York, Retailing
Daily ₍1950?₎
60p.

1. Newspapers–Headlines. 2. Journalism.
3. Retail trade. I. Retailing daily.
II. Title.

NL 0359259   ICarbS

Lifshits, Aryeh
see
Lifshitz, Aryeh.

Lifshits, Barukh
see
Lifshitz, Baruch, 1913–

QC670   **Lifshits, Evgeniĭ Mikhaĭlovich,** joint author.
.L313
Landau, Lev Davidovich, 1908–
The classical theory of fields, by L. Landau and E. Lif-
shitz; translated from the Russian by Morton Hamermesh.
Cambridge, Mass., Addison-Wesley Press, 1951.

QA911   **Lifshit͡s, Evgeniĭ Mikhaĭlovich,** joint author.
.L3   **Landau, Lev Davidovich,** 1908–
1954   Механика сплошных сред. Изд. 2., перер. и доп. Москва, Гос. изд-во технико-теорет. лит-ры, 1954.

Lifshits, Evgeniĭ Mikhaĭlovich, joint author.
The rotation of liquid helium

see under

Landau, Lev Davidovich, 1908–

QC175   **Lifshit͡s, Evgeniĭ Mikhaĭlovich,** joint author.
.L32
Landau, Lev Davidovich, 1908–
Statistical physics by L. Landau ... and E. Lifshitz ...
Translated from the Russian, by D. Shoenberg ... Oxford,
The Clarendon press, 1938.

Lifshit͡s, Grigoriĭ Isaakovich.
... Условия труда на строительных работах; с преди-
словием ... Н. М. Исаева. Изд. 2., исправленное и допол
ненное. Москва, Государ. изд-ство Вопросы труда "Гострудиздат", 1929.
81, ₍1₎ p. 20½ᶜᵐ.
At head of title: Г. И. Лифшиц.
Errata slip inserted.
"Приложения" (statutes, etc.) : p. 65–81.

1. Labor laws and legislation—Russia. 2. Building trades—Russia.
I. Russia (1923–   U. S. S. R.) Laws, statutes, etc. II. Title.

34–39019

NL 0359266   DLC

Lifshit͡s, I   I
Цеховый бюджет для массового и серийного производ-
ства в металлопромышленности. Харьков, Гос. республи-
канское об'единение металлообрабатывающей промыш.
Украины, 1930.
271 p. 22 cm.
At head of title: И. И. Лифшиц, Л. И. Рогачевский, В. А. Попова.

1. Machine-shops I. Title.   *Title transliterated:* T͡sekhovyĭ bi͡udzhet.

TJ1135.L5   50–45434

NL 0359267   DLC

VOLUME 332

Lifshiʦ, I   M
The kinetics of the breakdown of superconductivity by a field of high frequency, by I.M. Lifshits and M.I. Kaganov. ₍East Orange, N.J., Associated Technical Services, Inc., 1953₎
4 numb. l. (Associated Technical Services. Translation RJ-1732)

1. Superconductivity. I. Kaganov, M   I joint author. II. Title. III. Series.

NL 0359268   MsSM

Lifshiʦ, I   M
The kinetics of the breakdown of superconductivity by a magnetic field. ₍East Orange, N.J., Associated Technical Services, Inc., 1950₎
9 numb. l. (Associated Technical Services. Translation RJ-1730)

1. Superconductivity. 2. Electromagnetism. I. Title. II. Series.

NL 0359269   MsSM

Lifshiʦ, I   M
The kinetics of the breakdown of superconductivity by an alternating field. ₍East Orange, N.J., Associated Technical Services. Inc. 1953₎
5 numb. l. (Associated Technical Services. Translation RJ-173¹)

1. Superconductivity. I. Title. II. Series.

NL 0359270   MsSM

Lifshiʦ, I͡Akov Isaakovich, 1896–
... Der dialektische materialismus und die klinische medizin. Kharkiw, Medwydaw, 1932.
79, ₍1₎ p. 23½ᵐ.

At head of title: Allukrainische gesellschaft zur förderung der kulturellen verbindungen mit dem auslande.
"Vortrag gehalten auf der III. Allukrainischen tagung der therapeuten am 10. september 1931."

1. Medicine—Philosophy. 2. Medicine, Clinical. 3. Medicine—Russia. I. Title.

Library of Congress   R723.L5
                            ₍734b2₎
                                        33–12346 Revised
                                        610.1

NL 0359271   DLC MiU NN DNLM

Lifshiʦ, I͡Akov Isaakovich, 1896–
Перші підсумки й найближчі перспективи реконструкції медичної науки в УСРР. Харків, Медвидав, 1932.
62 p.

At head of title: Я. І. Ліфшиц.
Microfilm. 1 reel. 35 mm.

1. Medical education—Ukraine. I. Title.
Title romanized: Pershi pidsumky i naĭblyz͡hchi perspektyvy rekonstruktsiï medychnoï nauky v USRR.

Microfilm Slavic 7888 R   Mic 53–525

NL 0359272   DLC

Lifshiʦ, I͡Akov Isaakovich, 1896–
Поворот. За чітку марксистсько-ленінську лінію в теорії та практиці радянської медицини. ₍Хирків, Медвидав, 1932.
Microfilm copy. Negative.
Collation of the original as determined from the film: 117 p.

1. Medicine—Russia. I. Title.   Title transliterated: Povorot.

Microfilm AC–101   Mic 53–360

NL 0359273   DLC

Lifshits, I͡Akov Isaakovich, 1896–
У боротьбі за діялектичний матеріялізм у медицині. ₍Харків, Медвидав₎ 19
Microfilm ₍py. Negative.
Collation .. the original .. 79+.
L. C. copy imperfect: all after p. 79 wanting.

1. Medicine—Philosophy. 2. Dialectical materialism. I. Title.
Title transliterated: U borot'bi za di͡alektychnyĭ materi͡alizm.

Microfilm AC–103   Mic 53–330

NL 0359274   DLC

Lifshits, Jacob ha-Levi
see
Lipschitz, Jacob Lipmann, 1838-1921.

Lifshits, Kh.
Zur wochenbettstatistik der Universitätsfrauenklinik zu Basel während der jahre 1896-1906 ... Basel, 1906.

NL 0359276   MiU CtY

Lifshits, Leon
see Lifschitz, Leon.

Lifshiʦ, Lev Lazarevich.
Единая товарная номенклатура внешней торговли СССР; под ред. Д. Д. Мишустина. Утверждена Наркомвнешторгом СССР 12 дек. 1933 г. Москва, Внешторгиздат, 1936–
v. 25 cm.
At head of title: Научно-исследовательский институт при Всесоюзной академии внешней торговли.
Vol. 2 has added t. p. in French.
Errata slips inserted.
Contents.—₍вып. 1₎ Полный текст на русском языке.—вып. 2. Номенклатура таможенной статистики на русском, французском, английском и немецком языках; перевод под ред. В. А. Соколова.
1. Commercial products—Classification. 2. Commercial products—Russia. I. Moscow. Vsesoi͡uznai͡a akademii͡a vneshneĭ torgovli. Nauchno-issledovatel'skiĭ institut.
Title transliterated: Edinai͡a tovarnai͡a nomenklatura.
HF3621.L5   48–30899 rev*
Library of Congress   ₍r49b2₎

NL 0359278   DLC

Lifshiʦ, Lev Lazarevich.
Товарный химический словарь; русско-немецко-англо-французский. Составлен Л. Лифшицем и Н. Костриц ным. Москва, Внешторгиздат, 1934.
282 p. 18 cm.
At head of title: Всесоюзная торговая палата.

1. Chemistry, Technical—Dictionaries—Polyglot. 2. Dictionaries, Polyglot. I. Kostri͡tsin, N., joint author. II. Vsesoi͡uznai͡a torgovai͡a palata. III. Title.
Title transliterated: Tovarnyĭ khimicheskiĭ slovar'.

TP9.L53   .53–49069

NL 0359279   DLC

Lifshiʦ, M. O.
TX820
.K82
Кулинария. ₍Авторы: П. В. Абатуров и др. Глав. редактор М. О. Лифшиц. Москва, Госторгиздат, 1955.

Lifshiʦ, Mendel' Nakhimovich
see
Lifshits, Mendl.

Lifshits, Mendl. מ͏ים אלעמען צדזאמען. לידער. מינסק, מעלוכע-פֿאַרלאַג פֿון וויײרוסלאנד. ₍Минск₎ 1939.
111 p. 18 cm.

I. Title.   Title transliterated: Mit alemen tsuzamen.

PJ5129.L536M48   57–53803 ‡

NL 0359282   DLC

Lifshits, Mendl. מ͏ים הײסן פֿראַם. מינסק, מעלוכע-פֿאַרלאַג פֿון וויײרוסלאַנד. ₍Minsk₎ 1932.
60 p. 23 cm.
Poems.

I. Title.   Title transliterated: Mit heysn trot.

PJ5129.L536M5   53–47941

NL 0359283   DLC

Lifshits, Mendl. נײע לידער. מינסק, מעלוכע-פֿאַרלאַג׳ פֿון וויײרוסלאַנד. נאצמענקמער. ₍Минск₎ 1936.
92 p. 14 cm.

                      Title transliterated: Naye lider.

PJ5129.L536N3   53–47976

NL 0359284   DLC

Lifshits, Mendl. אונטער אַ מאַזלדיקן שטערן. מעלוכע-פֿאַרלאַג באַם ראַטספֿאַל ₍Минск, 1940₎ קאַם פֿון וומסר₎
155 p. port. 17 cm.
Poems.

I. Title.   Title transliterated: Unter a mazldikn shtern.

PJ5129.L536U55   53–47929

NL 0359285   DLC

Lifshiʦ, Mikhail Aleksandrovich, 1905–   ed.

Lenin, Vladimir Il'ich, 1870–1924.
Ленин о культуре и искусстве; сборник статей и отрывков, составил Мих. Лифшиц. ₍Москва–Ленинград₎ Изогиз, Государственное издательство изобразительных искусств, 1938.

Lifshits, Mikhail Aleksandrovich, 1905–
The philosophy of art of Karl Marx, by Mikhail Lifshitz, translated from the Russian by Ralph B. Winn, edited by Angel Flores. New York, Critics group ₍1938₎
94 p., 1 l. 20ᵐ. (*On cover:* Critics group series, no. 7)
"First printing, February, 1938."

1. Marx, Karl, 1818–1883. 2. Esthetics. I. Winn, Ralph Bubrich, 1895–   tr. II. Flores, Angel, 1900–   ed. III. Title.

BH221.G34M35   701   39–34147 rev

NL 0359287   DLC NcD N OCU TxU TU IU OrPR

BH
221
.G34
M38
L72
1938a
Lifshiʦ, Mikhail Aleksandrovich, 1905–
The philosophy of art of Karl Marx. Translated from the Russian by Ralph B. Winn, edited by Angel Flores. New York, Critics Group ₍1938₎
94 p. (Critics group series, no. 7)
Photocopy. Ann Arbor, University Microfilms, 1972. 94 p. (on double leaves)

1. Marx, Karl, 1818–1883. 2. Aesthetics. I. Flores, Angel, 1900–   ed. II. Title.

NL 0359288   MiU ScU TNJ FMU CLU

VOLUME 332

Lifshits, Mikhail Aleksandrovich, 1905–
 The philosophy of art of Karl Marx, by
Mikhail Lifshitz, translated from the Russian
by Ralph B. Winn, edited by Angel Flores.
New York, Critics group [c1938]
 94 p., 1 l.   20 cm.   (Critics' group
series, no. 7)
 Microfilm.
 "First printing, February, 1938."

NL 0359289   NN

Lifshits, Mikhail Iosifovich, 1888–   ed.

Russia (*1923–   U. S. S. R.*) *Laws, statutes, etc.*
 Единый сельскохозяйственный налог на 1929/30 год.
Текст закона утвержденного 20 февр. 1929 г., с подроб-
ными объяснениями к каждой статье, примерами исчисле-
ния налога и вспомогательными таблицами. Под ред.
М. И. Лифшица. Москва, Крестьянская газета, 1929.

HJ 3536
1928
.L5

Lifshits, Mikhail Iosifovich, ed.
 Итоги и перспективы промыслового обложения в Союзе
ССР (к проекту реформы налога в 1928 году) сборник статей,
с предисловием ... М. И. Фрумкина, под редакцией ... М. И.
Лифшица. Статьи сборника написаны ... А. С. Гордеевым,
Е. А. Доброхотовым, И. Л. Залесским [и др.] Москва, Фи-
нансовое издательство НКФ СССР, 1928.

 144 p.   25ᶜᵐ.

 1. Taxation—Russia—Law. 2. Industrial laws and legislation—Russia.   I. Frumkin, Moisei Il'ich, 1878–   II. Gordeev, Aleksandr Ste-
panovich.   III. Title.

 Library of Congress   HJ3536.1928.L5
                                                       40-15046

NL 0359291   DLC

Law

Lifshits, Mikhail Iosifovich, 1888–   ed.
Buinifskiĭ, P   A
 Налог на сверхприбыль; руководство для налоговых
работников и плательщиков. Постановление ЦИК и
СНК Союза ССР от 18 мая 1927 г. о гос. налоге на сверх-
прибыль, инструкция к нему и раз'яснения. Под ред.
М. О. Лифшица. Москва, Фин. изд-во НКФ СССР, 1927.

Lifshits, Mikhail Iosifovich, 1888–
 Налоговая политика советской власти и новый сельхозналог на 1931 год. Москва, Сельколхозгиз, 1931.

 91 p.   20 cm.

 Author's pseud., М. Ливенский, at head of title.

 1. Agriculture—Taxation—Russia.   I. Title.
       Title transliterated: Nalogovaià politika sovetskoĭ vlasti

                                                    53-54336

NL 0359293   DLC

Lifshits, Mikhail Iosifovich, 1888–
 Новый сельхозналог на 1930–1931 год. Москва, Гос.
изд-во, 1930.

 96 p.   24 cm.

 Author's pseud., М. Ливенский, at head of title.

 1. Agriculture—Taxation—Russia.   I. Title.
       Title transliterated: Novyĭ sel'khoznalog.

                                                    55-50704 ‡

NL 0359294   DLC

Lifshits, Mikhail Iosifovich, 1888–   ed.

HJ4737
.A5
1928a

Russia (*1923–   U. S. S. R.*) *Laws, statutes, etc.*
 Перечень из'ятий и льгот по подоходному налогу с государственных предприятий, кооперативных организа-
ций и акционерных обществ (паевых товариществ) с
участием государственного и кооперативного капитала;
закон и инструкция. Подробное руководство для налоговых органов и плательщиков. Под ред. М. О. Лифшица.
Москва, Финансовое Изд-во НКФ Союза ССР, 1928.

Lifshits, Mikhail Iosifovich, 1888–   ed.

Buinifskiĭ, P   A   *comp.*
 Подоходный налог с рабочих, служащих и госпенсионе-
ров; полное руководство по взиманию подоходного налога
с рабочих, служащих и государственных пенсионеров; под
ред. М. О. Лифшица. Москва, Фин. изд-во НКФ СССР,
1928.

Law

Lifshits, Mikhail Iosifovich, 1888–   ed.
                     FOR OTHER EDITIONS
                      SEE MAIN ENTRY
Russia (*1923–   U. S. S. R.*) *Laws, statutes, etc.*
 Положение о едином сельско-хозяйственном налоге;
полный текст закона, утвержд. правительством Союза
ССР 2 апреля 1927 г., с подробными пояснениями каждой
статьи и примерами. Составил Ф. А. Фотиев, под ред.
М. И. Лифшица. Москва, "Крестьянская газета," 1927.

HJ3539
.A4A5
1928

Lifshits, Mikhail Iosifovich, 1888–   ed.
Russia (*1923–   U. S. S. R.*) *Laws, statutes, etc.*
 Промысловый налог; положение о государственном про-
мысловом налоге от 10 августа 1928 г. с постатейными ком-
ментариями и со всеми дополнениями и разъяснениями на
1 марта 1929 года ... Составили работники Госналога
Наркомфина Союза ССР—   С. И. Осспев, Ф. А.
Фотиев и С. А. Фундман с предисловием и под редакцией
помощника начальника Госналога М. И. Лифшица. Москва, Государственное финансовое издательство, 1929.

HJ2802
.L5

[Lifshits, Mikhail Iosifovich] 1888–
 ... Сельскохозяйственный налог на 1927–1928 год. Москва, Ленинград, Государственное издательство, 1927.

 102 p.   17 x 13ᶜᵐ.

 Author's pseud., М. Ливенский, at head of title.

 1. Taxation—Russia. 2. Agriculture—Economic aspects—Russia.
 I. Title.   *Title transliterated:* Sel'skokhozìaĭstvennyĭ nalog.

                                                    30-15617 Revised
 Library of Congress   HJ2802.L5

NL 0359299   DLC

HJ2802
.L52

[Lifshits, Mikhail Iosifovich] 1888–
 ... Сельскохозяйственный налог на 1928–1929 год; чем он
отличается от налога прошлого года и как будет прово-
диться. Москва, Ленинград, Государственное издательство,
1928.

 128 p.   17ᶜᵐ.

 Author's pseud., М. Ливенский, at head of title.

 1. Taxation—Russia—Law.   I. Title.
       Title transliterated: Sel'skokhozìaĭstvennyĭ nalog

                                                    44-35001

NL 0359300   DLC

Law

Lifshits, Mikhail Iosifovich, 1888–   ed.
Russia (*1923–   U. S. S. R.*) *Laws, statutes, etc.*
 ... Закон о едином сельско-хозяйственном налоге на
1928–29 год. Текст закона, утвержденного правительством Союза ССР 21 апреля 1928 г., с подробными пояснениями каждой статьи, таблицами и примерами исчи-
сления налога. Составил ... С. Л. Любарский; под редакцией ... М. И. Лифшица ... Москва, Издательство
"Крестьянская газета," 1928.

HD5106
.L5

Lifshits, O   L
 Графики сменности. Ред. П. М. Дубиера. Москва, Гос.
социально-экон. изд-во, 1932.

 247 p. 21 cm.

 At head of title: Институт промышленно-экономических иссле-
дований.

 1. Shift systems   2. Hours of labor.   I. Title.
                         Title transliterated: Grafiki smennosti.

 HD5106.L5   51-49129

NL 0359302   DLC

HD57
.Z2

Lifshits, O. L., joint author.

Zabelin, Leonid Viktorovich.
 Вопросы производительности труда. Москва, Центр.
упр. печати ВСНХ СССР, 1926.

Lifshits, Savelii Iosifovich.
 Мартеновское производство стали. Харьков, Гос. науч-
но-техн. изд-во лит-ры по черной и цветной металлургии,
1953.

 210, [2] p. illus. 23 cm.

 Bibliography: p. [211]

 1. Open-hearth process.   I. Title.
                 Title transliterated: Martenovskoe proizvodstvo stali.

 TN740.I.A5   55-21437 rev

NL 0359304   DLC

Lifshits, Semen Iakovlevich.
 ... Hypnoanalyse, von prof. dr. S. Lifshitz ... Mit 3 abbildungen. Stuttgart, F. Enke, 1930.

 122 p. diagrs. 25¼ᶜᵐ. (Abhandlungen aus dem gebiete der psychotherapie und medizinischen psychologie ... 12. hft.)

 1. Hypnotism. 2. Dreams.   A C 33-2778

 Title from John Crerar   Libr. Printed by L. C.

NL 0359305   ICJ OU MiU

Lifshits, Sh
 וועגן שטעטל. כארקאוו. מעלוכע-פארלאג פאר די נאציאנאלע
מינערהייטן אין אוקר׳ר. [Kharkov] 1932.

 67 p. 22 cm.

 At head of title: אינסטיטוט פאר ידיישער פראלעטאריישער קולטור בא
דער אלוקראינישער וויסנשאפטלעכער אקאדעמיע, סאציאל-עקאנאמישער סעקציע.

 1. Jews in Russia—Political and social conditions.   I. Title.
                          Title transliterated: Vegn shtetl.

 DS135.R9L48   58-54025

NL 0359306   DLC MH

Lifshits, Shabbethai
 see
Lipschitz, Shabbethai, 1845–1929.

Lifshits, Vladimir.
 Миллион братьев; стихи. Ленинград, Гос. изд-во
худож. лит-ры, 1943.

 42, [2] p. 14 cm.

 1. World war, 1939–1945—Poetry.   I. Title.
                   Title transliterated: Million brat'ev.

 PG3476.L57M5   49-31668

NL 0359308   DLC

VOLUME 332

Lifshit͡s, Vladimir.
На берегах Невы. Москва, Гос. изд-во детской лит-ры, 1946.
34 p. illus. 20 cm.

   1. World War, 1939–1945—Fiction. I. Title.
   Title transliterated: Na beregakh Nevy.

PZ65.L48   53–20079 ‡

NL 0359309   DLC

Lifshit͡s, Vladimir.
Первокурсники; повесть. ₍Ленинград₎ Ленинградское газетно-журнальное и книжное изд-во, 1951.
218 p. illus. 17 cm.

   I. Title.   *Title transliterated:* Pervokursniki.

PG3476.L57P4   52–24249 ‡

NL 0359310   DLC

Lifshit͡s, Vladimir.
Плечом к плечу; стихотворения. Ленинград, Гос. изд-во худож. лит-ры, 1942.
72, ₍2₎ p. 14 cm.

   1. World war, 1939–1945—Poetry. I. Title.
   Title transliterated: Plechom k plechu.

PG3476.L57P6   49–31667

NL 0359311   DLC

Lifshit͡s, Vladimir.
Семь дней; повесть. ₍Москва₎ Советский писатель, 1948.
155 p. 17 cm.

   1. World War, 1939–1945—Fiction. I. Title.
   Title transliterated: Sem' dnei.

PG3476.L57S4   49–14371*

NL 0359312   DLC

Lifshit͡s, Vladimir.
Стихи и поэмы. Ленинград, Советский писатель, 1950.
135 p. 18 cm.

   Title transliterated: Stikhi i poėmy.
   Library of Congress

PG3476.L57S7   51–16160

NL 0359313   DLC

Lifshit͡s, Y.
   see
Lifschutz, E.

Lifshit͡s, Yeḥezkel
   see
Lipschütz, Ezechiel, 1862–1932.

Lifshit͡s, Z'ak
   see
   Lipchitz, Jacques, 1891–

Lifshitz, Aryeh. הנרימה סאלד. המחנכת בעלית הנוער. ירושלים המחלקה לעלית ילדים ונער. הסוכנות היהודית לארץ ישראל. תשמ"ו.
₍Jerusalem, 1954/55₎
44 p. illus. 20 cm.
Vocalized text.

   1. Szold, Henrietta, 1860–1945.
   Title transliterated: Henriyetah Sold.

DS151.S9L5   58–50168 ‡

NL 0359317   DLC MH

Lifshitz, Aryeh. אורי צבי גרינברג, משורר אדנות האומה. תל־אביב. הוצאת "נחלת" ₍Tel-Aviv, 1945/46₎
85 p. port. 17 cm. (ספרית השקות)

   1. Greenberg, Uri Zvi, 1898–
   Title transliterated: Uri T͡sevi Grinberg.

PJ5053.G68Z75   56–54088

NL 0359318   DLC

Lifshitz, Aryeh Judah Loeb. אבות עטרה לבנים. יכיל: "הסלך הפולני הרב שאול וואהל." "חסר מגוע יטי" ו"נצר מטרשיו" ב"אותות לבית אבות." המחבר: אריה יהודה ליב ליפשיץ. ווארשא. תרפ"ו ₍1926/27₎
210, 39 p. 24 cm.
Photo-offset.
"Printed in Israel."
"שאלות ותשובות": p. 171–210.

   1. Wahl, Saul, 1541–1617. 2. Responsa.
   Title transliterated: Avot 'atarah la-banim.

BM755.W33L5 1926   HE 66–966

NL 0359319   DLC

Lifshitz, Baruch, 1913–
   Bet-She'arim
      see under   Israel Exploration Society.

Lifshitz, E   M
   see
Lifshit͡s, Evgeniĭ Mikhaĭlovich.

Lifshitz, Efraim. אגודת הצרכנים השיתופית. תל־אביב. עם עובד, תשט"ו.
₍Tel-Aviv, 1954/55₎
319 p. 22 cm.
On verso of t. p.: The consumers' co-operative society.

   1. Cooperative societies—Israel.
   Title transliterated: Agudat ha-t͡sarkanim ha-shitufit.

HD3555.P22L5   56–55605

NL 0359322   DLC MH

Lifshitz, Jacob. ספר הבריגדה היהודית; קורות החטיבה הלוחמת והמ־צילה את הגולה, מאת יעקב ליפשיץ. תל־אביב, הוצאת "יבנה," תש"ז.
Tel-Aviv, Yavneh publishing house, 1947.
413 p. illus., ports., maps. 24 cm.
On verso of t. p.: A history of the Jewish infantry brigade group

   1. Gt. Brit. Army. Jewish brigade. I. Title.
   Title transliterated: Sefer ha-brigadah ha-yehudit.

      A 49–4420

   Zionist Archives and   Library
   for Library of Congress

NL 0359323   NNZI

Lifshitz, Jacob. ספר הבריגדה היהודית. קורות החטיבה היהודית הלוחמת. מהדורה ב. תל־אביב. י. שמעוני, תש"י. ₍Tel-Aviv, 1950₎
413 p. illus., ports., maps. 25 cm.
Added t. p.: A history of the Jewish Infantry Brigade Group.

   1. Gt. Brit. Army. Jewish Brigade.
   Title transliterated: Sefer ha-Brigadah ha-Yehudit.

D760.J4L5   56–55553

NL 0359324   DLC MH

Lifshitz, Jacob Lipmann
   see
Lipschitz, Jacob Lipmann, 1838–1921.

Lifshitz, M
Giambattista Vico (1668–1744) Translated from the Russian by Henry F. Mins, Jr. ₍Buffalo, N. Y., 1948₎
391–414 p.

From "Philosophy and phenomenological research", vol. VIII, no. 3, March 1948.

   1. Vico, Giovanni Battista, 1668–1744.
   I. Mins, Henry F   tr.

NL 0359326   NNC

DS117
.D86
Hebraic   **Lifshitz, Maito, tr.**
Sect.   Dubnov, Semen Markovich, 1860–
... די אידישע נעשיכטע פאר שולע און פֿאלק איבער־ זעצט פֿון חיים ליעבערמאן און מיטע לוושיץ ... ניו יארק, מאקם ב. מייועל ₍17₎ מייויעל ₍17₎ 1915.

Lifshitz, Malke
   see   Frumkin, Malke (Lifshitz) 1880–

Lifshitz, Mikhail
      see   Lifshit͡s, Mikhail Aleksandrovich, 1905–

Lifshitz, S.
      see
Lifshit͡s, Semen I͡akovlevich

Lifshitz, Shemariah Isaac, 1828–1872.

Bible. O.T. Proverbs. Hebrew. 1872.
אוצר כל כלי חמדה; או. תורת הנפש. באור על ספר משלי מאתי שמריהו יצחק ליפשיץ. ווילנא. בדפוס ש. י. דווארזעץ. תרל"ב.
Вильна, 1872.

Lifshiz, Chaim Jacob
   see   Lipchitz, Jacques, 1891–

VOLUME 332

Lifshyts, IA   I
   see   Lifshifs, IAkov Isaakovich, 1896–

[Lifsichtz, Clara]
    La clara sombra ... [Buenos Aires, Talleres gráficos "Rinaldi," 1941]
    2 p. l., 776 p., 1 l. 23½ᶜᵐ.
    Author's name on cover.
    Poems.

    I. Title.
                                                        43–38222
    Library of Congress   PQ7797.L49C5
                                                        861.6

NL   0359334   DLC

Lifsichtz, Clara.
    Savia, poesía. Buenos Aires, Ed. Conducta [1947]
    90 p. 21 cm.

    I. Title.
                                                        A 50–214
    New York. Public Libr
    for Library of Congress

NL   0359335   NN

Lifson, Kalman A
    Errors in time-study judgments of industrial work pace. [Washington] American Psychological Association, 1953.
    14 p. diagrs. 26 cm. (Psychological monographs: general and applied, v. 67, no. 5; whole no. 355)
    Cover title.
    "Based upon a thesis submitted to the Graduate School of Purdue University [under title: A psychological approach to pace rating]"
    Bibliography: p. 14.
    1. Time study.   I. Title.   (Series)
    BF1.P8 vol. 67, no. 5   658.5421   53–10722
                                 T60.T5L54

NL   0359336   DLC DNLM OU PBm OCU ViU TxU OOxM

Lifson, Nathan, 1911–
    Studies of osmotic phenomena in biological systems by the Hill-Baldes vapor tension method ... by Nathan Lifson ... [n. p., 1943]
    cover-title, 784–802 p. incl. tab., diagrs. 25ᶜᵐ.
    Thesis (PH. D.)—University of Minnesota, 1943.
    An article reprinted from Gastroenterology. v. 1, no. 8, Aug. 1943, with addition of cover having thesis note and Vita. The article has caption title: The relationship between the total osmotic pressure of gastric juice and its acidity [by] Nathan Lifson ... Richard L. Varco ... and M. B. Visscher ...
    "References": p. 802.
    1. Osmosis. 2. Gastric juice.   I. Varco, Richard Lynn, 1912– joint author. II. Visscher, Maurice Bolkes, 1901– joint author. III. Title: Hill-Baldes vapor   tension method.
    Minnesota. Univ. Libr.   A 45–2920
    for Library of Congress
                          QP198.L45

NL   0359337   MnU DLC

Lifszyc, Deborah
Nkd8C   La fête des semailles en 1935 chez les
+1   Dogon de Sanga, par Deborah Lifszyc et Denise
1936   Paulme ...

         "Extrait du Journal de la Société des
         africanistes, tome VI, 1936."

         I. Paulme, Denise   jt. author

NL   0359338   CtY

Lifszyc, Isaj, 1904–
    Die Agrarfrage in Polen ...   Lodzi [n. d.]
    Dissertation - Zürich.
    "Literaturverzeichnis": p. i–ii.
    Curriculum vitae.

NL   0359339   CtY ICRL DLC

HG9970
.A75L5   Lift. no. 1– ; Feb. 1932–

          New York city, Aviation protection, inc.,
          1932–
          v.   28cm.

NL   0359340   DLC

Lift. (347th college training detachment,
    Macalester college) St. Paul.

NL   0359341   MnHi

A lift for the lazy ...
    see under   [Griffith, H   W   ]

693.5   Lift Slab Inc., San Antonio.
L625   Structural analysis of lift slab design.
         San Antonio [1953]
         45p. (p.19–45 plates) 23cm.

         "A guide to designing a flat plate for
         lifting by use of the Youtz-Slick lift slab
         method."

         1. Concrete construction. 2. Building
         machinery.

NL   0359343   IU

Lift up the glory
    see under   [Hatch, Richard Warren] 1898–

Lift up your eyes
    see under   [Ford motor company, Detroit]

Lift up your hearts; a record of the first
    inter-allied meeting held at St. James's
    Palace, London, June 12, 1941.
        see under   Gt. Brit. Foreign Office.

"Lifted up." The life of Walter Douglas.   3539.8
    Boston. Hoyt. 1872. 138 pp. 16°.

E5369 — Douglas, Walter, Evangelist.

NL   0359347   MB

The lifted veil; or, The hereafter revealed to reform the world, by a psychic. [New York] The International society of applied psychology, 1922.
    viii, 55, [5] p. 19½ᶜᵐ.

    1. Spiritualism.
    Library of Congress   BF1301.L7   23–7564

NL   0359348   DLC

Lifting surfaces in supersonic flow
    see under   Ostrach, Simon.

Lifting the burdens from labor. What the Mills bill is. A comparative table showing the rate of duty now paid, with an estimate of the rate to be collected under the proposed bill ... New York, 1888.
    23 p. tabs. 19 cm.

NL   0359350   RPB

Lifting the veil
    see under   [McLain, Mary Webster]

Liftman, Matilda Schroeder
    How to feed the family. [1918. [New York (city) - Bureau of public health education. Keep well leaflets no. 2)

    Text in English and Yiddish.

NL   0359352   OCl OU

Lifton, Simon L
    Differential diagnosis of mouth diseases
        see under   Columbia university. School of dental and oral surgery.

---

157   Lifton, Walter M, 1918–
L62p   A pilot study to investigate the effect of
        supervision on the empathic ability of coun-
        seling trainees. Project number 15-15, Bureau
        of Educational Research, College of Education,
        University of Illinois.   Urbana, Ill., 1952.
        57, 3l. diagrs. 28cm.

        Cover title.
        Bibliography: leaves 55-57.
        1. Empathy. 2. Counseling. I. Title.

NL   0359354   IU

LD3907
.E3   Lifton, Walter M., 1918–
1950   A study of the changes in self concept
.L5   and content knowledge in students tak-
        ing a course in counseling techniques.
        New York, 1950.
        v, 126 typewritten leaves. forms,
        tables. 29cm.
        Thesis (Ph.D.) - New York University,
        School of Education, 1950.
        Bibliography: p.115-120.

NL   0359355   NNU-W

VOLUME 332

Microfilm
AC-1 Lifton, Walter M   1918–
no. 2187   A study of the changes in self concept and content knowledge in students taking a course in counseling techniques.
Ann Arbor, University Microfilms, 1950 ₁i. e. 1951₎

₁(University Microfilms, Ann Arbor, Mich.₎ Publication no. 2187)
Microfilm copy of typewritten ms. Positive.
Collation of the original: v, 126 l. forms, tables.
Thesis—New York University.
Abstracted in Microfilm abstracts, v. 11 (1951) no. 1, p. 55–56.
Bibliography: leaves 115–120.
1. Counseling. 2. Introspection.
Microfilm AC–1 no. 2187   Mic A 51–17

Michigan. Univ. Libr.
for Library of Congress   †

NL 0359356   MiU DLC FMU

Lifts. Portland, Ore., Hyster co.
      v.

NL 0359357   OrP

Lifvets skiften...
      see under   [Bjorklund, A   P   ]

Liga africanista española.
      Manifiesto de la Liga africanista española. El problema de
Marruecos... ₁Madrid? 1919.₎ 8 p. f°.
      Caption-title.

1. Morocco.—Foreign relations,
tions, Morocco.   Spain. 2. Spain.—Foreign rela-
                                    January 27, 1921.

NL 0359359   NN

Liga africanista española.
      Revista hispano-africana ...
      see under title

Liga agraria de la república de Cuba.

Zayas y Jiménez, Francisco.
      Política agrícola de la república. Nuevo método de siembras
y cultivo de la caña de azúcar, por el dr. Francisco Zayas,
socio de mérito y presidente de honor de la Liga agraria de la
república de Cuba. Habana, Impr. "La Prueba", 1904.

HB9   Liga agrarnykh reform. Petrogradskii otdel.
.A3
      Аграрные вопросы в России. вып. 1–
      Петроградъ, 1917–

Liga ajedrecfstica mexicana por correspondencia.
      "Ajedrez"; organo de la "L. A. M. C."
      see under title

₁Liga aliada de Ciudad-Bolívar.₎
      El festival de las colonias aliadas en Ciudad-Bolívar. Cd-
Bolívar, Venezuela: P. Liccioni & Cia., 1919. 62 p. 8°.

1. European war, 1914– , Armis-   tice. 2. European war, 1914– ,
Venezuela: Ciudad Bolívar.   3. Title.
                                        August 29, 1921.

NL 0359364   NN

Liga Amadores Brasileiros Radio Emissão
      see
Liga de Amadores Brasileiros de Radio Emissão.

Liga antialcohólica de Costa Rica.

Costa Rica. *Secretaría de educación pública.*
      ... Cartilla antialcohólica para uso de las escuelas y colegios
de la república. Escrita por varios maestros y miembros de la
Liga antialcohólica de Costa Rica. San José, Costa Rica, Imprenta nacional, 1929.

Liga antialcohólica de mujeres hondureñas.

Regeneración y prosperidad; revista mensual, órgano de la
Liga antialcohólica de mujeres hondureñas. año 1
mayo 1931–
₁Tegucigalpa, Honduras, C. A., 1931–

HQ   Liga antipornográfica de San Francisco Javier,
471   Manila.
.L73   Al pueblo filipino. Manila, Imprenta de
Santos y Bern₁al₎ 1907.
      12 p.,1 l. 20ᶜᵐ.
      Official report of the Liga antipornografica de San
Francisco Javier.
      Last two letters of publisher's name omitted in print-
ing; indicated by brackets.

NL 0359368   MiU

Liga Antipornográfica de San Francisco Javier,
      Manila.
      ... El apostolado de la buena prensa
            see under   Liga Antipornográfica de
San Francisco Javier, Manila.

HQ   Liga antipornográfica de San Francisco Javier,
471   Manila.
.L72   Catálogo de la Liga antipornográfica de San
Francisco Javier. Manila. Manila, Imprenta de
Santos y Bernal, 1907.
      2 p.l.,iv p.,1 l.,88 p.,1 l. ports. 23ᶜᵐ.

      1.Censorship—Philippine Islands. 2.Art,Immoral.
3.Literature,Immoral.

NL 0359370   MiU MH

BX4700 Liga Antipornográfica de S. Francisco Javier.
F8L5   Certamen artístico literario. Celebrado en el Ateneo de
Manila el 20 de Setiembre de 1908. Manila, Impr. de Santos y
Bernal, 1909.
      288 p. illus.

1. Francisco Xavier, Saint, 1506-1552. I. Title.

NL 0359371   CU MH

HQ   Liga antipornográfica de San Francisco Javier,
935   Manila.
.L72   ... El divorcio ... Manila, Imprenta de
Santos y Bernal, 1911.
      40 p. 19½ᶜᵐ. (Liga antipornográfica de San Francis-
co Javier. Sección de propaganda. Folleto XXXI)
      Pages 29-40,advertising matter.

1.Divorce—Philippine Islands.

NL 0359372   MiU

WF   LIGA Antituberculosa de Damas, Lima
200   ₁Collection of publications₎
qL723   The library has a collection of miscellaneous publications of this organization
kept as received. These publications are
not listed nor bound separately.
      1. Tuberculosis

NL 0359373   DNLM

W 1   LIGA Antituberculosa de Damas, Lima
LI4102   Memoria.
      Lima ₁19–?₎–
            v. illus.

NL 0359374   DNLM

Liga anti-tuberculosa de Puerto Rico.
      ... Algunos consejos contra la tuberculosis. ₁San Juan?
P. R.₎ 1911.
      cover-title, 8 p. 23½ᶜᵐ.
      At head of title: Liga anti-tuberculosa de Puerto Rico.

1. Tuberculosis—Societies. 2. Tuberculosis—Prevention.
                                                    12–21051
Library of Congress   RA644.T7L6

NL 0359375   DLC

Liga anti-tuberculosa de Puerto Rico.
      ... Defiéndase usted y defienda á los demás de la tuber-
culosis. San Juan, P. R., Bureau of supplies, printing,
and transportation, 1911.
      14 p. 20½ᶜᵐ.
      At head of title: Liga anti-tuberculosa de Puerto Rico.

1. Tuberculosis—Societies. 2. Tuberculosis—Prevention.
                                                    12–12080
Library of Congress   RA644.T7L7

NL 0359376   DLC DNLM

W 1   LIGA Anti-Tuberculosa de Puerto Rico
LI411   Informe anual.
      San Juan ₁1906?₎–
            v.
      Report year ends Mar. 31.
      Fifth-sixth reports combined in one
issue.
      Text in Spanish and English.

NL 0359377   DNLM

Liga argentina contra el reumatismo.
      Boletín.
      v.

      Buenos Aires,
            v. illus., tables, diagrs. 25½–26½ᶜᵐ.

      1. Rheumatism - Periodicals. 2. Rheumatism
- Societies.

NL 0359378   NNC

VOLUME 332

Liga argentina contra la tuberculosis.
...Discursos pronunciados en el acto inaugural de la cruzada contra la tuberculosis, Teatro Colón, lunes 29 de julio de 1935. ¡Buenos Aires, 1935¡ 37 p. 18cm.

Cover-title.

888846A. 1. Tuberculosis—Preven-   tion—Argentine Republic.
June 11, 1937

NL 0359379   NN CtY

Liga Argentina contra la Tuberculosis.
La Doble cruz
see under title

W 1   **LIGA** Argentina contra la Tuberculosis
LI418   Memoria.

Buenos Aires. 19
v. illus.

NL 0359381   DNLM

4R-58   Liga Argentina Contra la Tuberculosis, Rosario.
Prof. dr. Clemente Alvarez, 29 enero 1872-22 julio 1948; in memoriam.   [   ]
1949.
95 p.

NL 0359382   DLC-P4

Liga argentina de cultura laica.
Publicaciones...

Buenos Aires.

NL 0359383   NN

LIGA ARGENTINA DE EDUCACION INDUSTRIAL.
Liga Argentina de educacion industrial fundada el 14 de agosto de 1924. Con personeria juridica acordada por el P.E.de la nación con fecha 26 de enero de 1925. Sede Central-Buenos Aires. Buenos Aires,Imp.Obra Cardenal Ferrari Ltda.,[1924].

pp.26. Ports.and map.

NL 0359384   MH

Arg   Liga argentina de educación industrial.
LC1081   Liga argentina de educación industrial
.L3   ... Buenos Aires, Imprenta obra Cardenal Ferrari ltda. [1927?]
26 p. ports.,fold. map.   26 cm.
A statement of the work of the Liga argentina de educación industrial preceding Educación industrial, conferencia pronunciada por el Dr. Alfredo Colmo. A duplicate of the lecture is classed in LC1081 .C6

NL 0359385   DPU

Liga Argentina de Empleados Públicos.
Memoria y balance.

Buenos Aires.
v. 23 cm. annual.
Report year ends May 31.

HD8013.A7L5   51-39863 ‡

NL 0359386   DLC

HD2953   Liga argentina de entidades mutualistas.
.C63   Congreso mutualista argentino.
Congreso mutualista argentino. ¡1st¡–
1942–   Buenos Aires,
Liga argentina de entidades mutualistas, 1943–

Liga argentina de esperanto
see
Argentina esperanto-ligo.

Liga Argentina de la lucha contra el cancer.
... Inauguracion del nuevo pabellon para mujeres donado por Liga Argentina de la lucha contra el cancer. Buenos Aires, Universidad, 1923.
64 p.
At head of title: Instituto de medicina experimental para el estudio y tratamiento del cancer.

NL 0359389   PPC

BV4556   Liga argentina de mujeres interdenominacional.
.A1G8   Guía del hogar ¡revista mensual evangélica interdenominacional¡

¡Buenos Aires, 19

W 1   LIGA Argentina de Profilaxis Social
LI425   Discursos pronunciados con motivo de la ... celebración anual del Día Antivenéreo. 1.– set. 1935-
Buenos Aires.
v. illus., ports.
Title varies slightly.
Each vol. has also a distinctive title.
1. Venereal diseases - Addresses
Title: Día Antivenéreo

NL 0359391   DNLM

W 1   LIGA Argentina de Profilaxis Social
LI425   El Día de la Higiène Social. 1945-47—
Buenos Aires.
v. illus., ports.
Continues the league's ¡Discursos pronunciados con motivo de la¡ ... celebración anual del Día Antivenéreo.
1. Venereal diseases - Addresses
Title

NL 0359392   DNLM

Liga argentina de profilaxis social.
...Hacia la extincion de un flagelo social; discursos pronunciados en el gran acto público efectuado en el Teatro Colón, de Buenos Aires, en la segunda celebración del "Dia antivenéreo," setiembre 7 de 1936. Buenos Aires: Talleres gráficos de la Cia. gral. fabril financiera, 1937. 54 p. illus. 25cm.

1. Venereal diseases—Prevention   —Argentine Republic.
October 10, 1939

NL 0359393   NN

989.207   Liga Argentina por los derechos del Hombre.
M859Yℓ   Paraguay bajo el terror, documentos que acusan. ¡Buenos Aires, Tall. Graficos "Poliglota, 1947¡

1. Morinigo Martinez, Higinio. Pres, Paraguay, 1887-   2. Paraguay--Pol. & govt.   I. Title.

NL 0359394   ICarbS

Liga Argentina por los Derechos del Hombre.
¿Por qué estan detenidos 500 presos políticos desde hace seis meses? 3 años bajo la llamada Ley de "estado de guerra interno." Buenos Aires, 1954.

47 p. illus. 20 cm.

CONTENTS.—El Dr. Samuel Schmerkin, desde la cárcel, asume la defensa de los presos políticos.—Recurso de habeas corpus, por S. Schmerkin.—La justicia de los círculos peronistas gobernantes.—Nómina de los ciudadanos detenidos en las cárceles argentinas al 2 de diciembre de 1954.

1. Political crimes and offenses—Argentine Republic.   I. Schmerkin, Samuel. II. Title.

HV6295.A7L5   60-32741 ‡

NL 0359395   DLC

WM   LIGA Brasileira de Hygiene Mental,
1   Rio de Janeiro
qL723   ¡Collection of publications¡

The library has a collection of miscellaneous publications of this organization kept as received. These publications are not listed nor bound separately.

NL 0359396   DNLM

Liga brasileira pelos alliados, *Rio de Janeiro.*
... Homenagem á Inglaterra: collectanea de publicações relativas ao grande festival realizado no Theatro lyrico do Rio de Janeiro em 5 de agosto de 1917 ... Rio de Janeiro ¡Typ. do Jornal do commercio, de Rodrigues & c.¡ 1918.
68 p. 2 pl. 27½ᶜᵐ.
English text (p. ¡35¡–68) has special t.-p.
CONTENTS.—Saudação á Inglaterra; discurso de Basilio de Magalhães.—Ave, Inglaterra! soneto de Reis Carvalho.—O festival de 5 de agosto; artigos, cartas e photographias.

1. European war, 1914–   —Gt. Brit. 2. European war, 1914–   —Brazil.
19-476

Library of Congress   D517.L5

NL 0359397   DLC CtY

Liga Catholica Internationalis contra Alcoholismum.
Internationale Katholische Liga gegen den Alkoholismus, eine Orientierung von Josef Hermann. Luzern, Generalsekretariat der Internationalen Kathol. Liga gegen den Alkoholismus ¡195-?¡
32 p. 21 cm.

I. Hermann, Josef, ed.

HV5006.L5   56-21139 ‡

NL 0359398   DLC

F1203   Liga Central de Resistencia del Gran Partido
T4L4695   Socialista del Sureste. Departamento Cultural
x   y de Prensa.
Apuntes sobre la organización y trabajos del Partido Socialista del Sureste, formulados por el Secretario compañero Benjamín Carrillo Puerto. Mérida, Tall. Tipográf. del Gobierno del Estado, 1923.
25 p. 14cm. [Terrazas collection]

1. Political parties - Yucatan. 2. Mexico - Pol. & govt. - 1910-1946. I. Carrillo Puerto, Benjamín. II. Title.

NL 0359399   CU-B

VOLUME 332

Liga Central de Resistencia del Gran Partido Socialista
del Sureste. Departamento cultural.
Los lunes rojos. Tomo 1°, epoca 1ª.
Mérida, México, 1923.

"Boletín numero dos, correspondiente a los
meses de febrero, marzo, abril, mayo y junio
del año social de 1923."

NL 0359400   NNC

Liga Central de Resistencia del Gran Partido
Socialista del Sureste. Departamento Cultural.
Programa de trabajos, por el compañero Edmundo Bolfo, jefe
de dicho departamento. Mérida, Tall. "Pluma y lápiz", 1923.
14 p. 15cm. [Terrazas collection]

NL 0359401   CU-B NNC

Liga československých motoristů.
Československo, průvodce pro automobilisty, péčí Ligy
čsl. motoristů. Czechoslovakia, guide for motorists, compiled
under the auspices of the League of Czechoslovak Motorists.
Praha, Z. Janke ¡1933¿

1 v. (unpaged) 25 col. maps. 27 cm.
"Rédaction: A. Tůma; techn. arrangement: F. Rubeš."
Czech, German, French, and English.

1. Czechoslovak Republic—Road maps. 2. Czechoslovak Republic—
Descr. & trav.

G1946.P2L5 1933   Map 51-140

NL 0359402   DLC MiU

Liga českých kněží arcidioecese St. Paulské.
Průvodce po českých katolických osadách v arcidioe-
cesi St. Paulské ve Spojených Státech Severoamerických.
Vydala Liga českých kněží arcidioecese St. Paulské.
Chicago, Ill., Tiskem tiskárny českých benediktinů, 1910.

233 p. incl. plates, ports. 23½cm.
"Předmluva" signed: Rev. Jan Rynda, tajemník Ligy.

1. Catholic church in the U. S. St. Paul, Archdiocese of. 2. Bohemians in Minnesota. 3. Bohemians in U. S. I. Rynda, John. II. Title.

                           19-9832
Library of Congress   BX1417.S3L5

NL 0359403   DLC

W 1   LIGA Chilena contra el Cáncer
LI427   Memoria anual.

         Santiago ¡1938?¿-
             v.
         Report year ends Apr. 26.

NL 0359404   DNLM

---

248   Liga chilena de higiene social.
        Las bases científicas de la profilaxis.

NL 0359405   DPU

---

248   Liga chilena de higiene social.
        Comisión de control del alcohol.

NL 0359406   DPU

---

248   Liga chilena de higiene social.
        Concepto científico moderno de la esclavitud
blanca.

NL 0359407   DPU

---

248   Liga chilena de la higiene social.
        La continencia y la juventud.

NL 0359408   DPU

---

248   Liga chilena de higiene social.
        Declaración de principios y estatutos.

NL 0359409   DPU

355.83
L626
    Liga chilena de higiene social.
       ... La defensa del ejército chileno contra
las enfermedades sociales; con un suplemento
que encierra el informe sobre la aplicación del
plan norte-americano de higiene social en la
escuadra del Pacífico. Santiago, Secretaria y
farmacia ¡1920?¿
       xx, 208 p. diagrs. (part fold.) (Folleto n.
06)

       1. Chile - Army - Sanitary affairs.
       2. Military hygiene.
       3. Hygiene, Sex ual.

NL 0359410   NNC DPU

Liga Chilena de Higiene Social.

    Folleto.

Santiago.
       no. tables, diagrs. 23cm.

       Began publication in 1920 and ceased pub-
lication with no.30, 1925? Cf. Union list
of serials.

       1. Chile - Sanit. affairs. 2. Hygiene,
Public - Chile.   3. Military hygiene.

NL 0359411   TxU

---

248   Liga chilena de higiene social.
        Memorias, 1917-19-

NL 0359412   DPU

---

248   Liga chilena de higiene social.
        Podemos defender al consumo del vino.

NL 0359413   DPU

---

248   Liga chilena de higiene social.
        La transformación de la vinicultura.

NL 0359414   DPU

---

248   Liga chilena de higiene social.
        Verdades modernas sobre el alcohol.

NL 0359415   DPU

F3285
.G3L5
1950
    Liga Chileno-Alemana, Santiago de Chile.
       Los alemanes en Chile en su primer
centenario; resumen historico de la
colonizacion alemana de las provincias del
sur de Chile. Santiago de Chile, 1950.
       207 p. illus., ports. 26cm.

       1. Germans in Chile. 2. Chile—Hist. I. Title.

NL 0359416   ViU DPU

Liga Cívica Pro Evolución Social de P. R.

HN236
.M3
    Mayoral Barnés, Manuel, *ed.*
       Libro segundo de la campaña de la **Liga Cívica Pro Evolución
Social de P. R.**   Ponce, P. R., 1946.

---

252   Liga comercial de Santiago.
       Estado de causas presentado a los señores
socios en 30 de noviembre de 1925. Santiago
de Chile, 1925.

NL 0359418   DPU

Liga contra el alcoholismo de Santiago de
Chile.
           see
Liga nacional contra el alcoholismo, Santiago
de Chile.

---

267   Liga contra el alcoholismo de Valparaíso.
       Memoria anual correspondiente al año de 1924.
ed. 1925.

NL 0359420   DPU

Liga contra el cancer, Chile
      see   Liga chilena contra el cancer.

Liga contra el cancer, Havana.
    Boletin. Edición científica. 1-   1926-

Habana, Instituto del cancer, Hospital "Calixto
Garcia"
       v. illus. 26ᵐ. monthly.

    Caption title.
"Organo de la Sociedad cubana de cancerologia".
Includes bibliographies.
       1. Cancer -   Periodicals. 2. Cancer -
Societies.

DLC
NL 0359422   NNC ICRL CLWM CU-M MnRM DNLM CLM WaU

Liga contra el Cancer. Boletín. Edición
cientifica. Supplement.
       Diagnóstico del cancer incipiente ...
          see under Havana. Instituto del Cancer.

W 1   LIGA Contra el Cáncer, Havana
LI43C   Boletín. Edición social.
       año 1-   enero 1930-
       Habana, Instituto del Cáncer.
          v.
       Issues for 1948?-   lack volume
numbers but constitute año 19-
Supersedes in part the league's Boletín.
Some articles in English.
       1. Neoplasms - period.

NL 0359424   DNLM ICJ

616.994   Liga contra el cáncer, Havana.
L723d   Diagnóstico precoz del cáncer ... Habana ¡Liga
       contra el cáncer¿ 1926.
       156p. pl.

       1. Cancer.

NL 0359425   IU-M DNLM ICJ

VOLUME 332

Liga contra el cáncer, *Havana.*
Diagnóstico y tratamiento del cáncer, editado por la Liga contra el cáncer. Habana, Cuba, Cardenas, la Casa Montalvo, 1932.
4 p. l., 255 p. illus., diagr. 25¼ᵐ.

1. Cancer.   I. Title.
U. S. Surg.-gen. off.   Library
for Library of Congress   RC261.L75   S G 33-30 Revised

NL 0359426   DNLM DLC

Liga contra la tuberculosis en Cuba.
Boletin mensual.
Habana
v. maps, diagrs. 26ᶜᵐ.

1. Tuberculosis—Prevention. 2. Tuberculosis—Cuba.

Library of Congress   RC306.L72   CA 9-2162 Unrev'd

NL 0359427   DLC DNLM

Liga culturaiă
        see   Liga pentru unitatea culturaiă a
tuturor Romămilor.

Liga de Cooperativas de los Estados Unidos
        see
Cooperative League of the U.S.A.

BT
3516   **Liga das Senhoras Católicas, Sao Paulo, Brazil.**
.S23   Relatório. Sao Paulo,
L72   v. illus. 24 cm.
A3
        "Reconhecida pelo decreto 7,053 de 3 de abril
de 1935, do Governo do Estado: Instituicao de
Utilidade Publica".

        1. Catholic Church - Sao Paulo, Brazil -
Charities.

NL 0359430   DCU DPU

Liga de abogados de la república, Mexico.

Law
        García, Luis G
        Inconsistencia de las objeciones del lic. Luis Cabrera al libro segundo del nuevo Código civil ₍por₎ lic. Luis G. García, miembro de la "Liga de abogados de la república." Editado por la propia sociedad. ₍México, 1928₎

Liga de acción política (Mexico)

Edelman, Maurice, 1911–
        ... El arsenal de los Urales, su papel en la guerra contra Hitler; traducción de Víctor Manuel Villaseñor. México, Liga de acción política, 1942.

Liga de Acción Social, *Merida, Mexico.*
Antología de la historia de Yucatán; épocas: prehispánica, conquista, colonial. Prologada por José Esquivel Pren. Epilogada con breves semblanzas de los personajes de esa historia, que dejaron huella en la cultura yucateca, por Gonzalo Cámara Zavala. México, Editorial Cultura, 1951.
334 p. 24 cm.

1. Yucatan—Hist.   I. Title.

F1376.L75   972.6   53-20667 ‡

NL 0359433   DLC NN ICarbS MH PU-Mu WU

B
M7229ℓ   **Liga de Acción Social, Mérida, Mexico.**
        **Biografía del señor licenciado don Olegario
        Molina Solís, publicada por La Liga de Acción
        Social como un homenaje a sus méritos, con
        motivo de la llegada de su cadáver a tierra
        yucateca.** Mérida, México, 1925.
        47p. port., plates(part fold.) 17cm.

        1. Molina Solís, Olegario, 1843-1925.

NL 0359434   IU DLC-P4 DPU NN TxU

LIGA DE ACCION SOCIAL, Mérida, México.
        Biografía del señor licenciado don Olegario
Molina Solís. Mérida, 1925. 47 p. illus.(part fold.),
port. 18cm.

        Film reproduction. Negative.
        Text signed: Dr. Pedro F. Rivas, L.A.S.

        I. Molina, Olegario.   I. Rivas, Pedro F.

NL 0359435   NN

Liga de Acción Social, Mérida, México.
        Celebración del IV centenario de la imprenta
en América
        see its   Memoria de la sesión solemne
celebrada el 17 de noviembre de 1939.

Liga de acción social, Mérida, Mexico.
        Combate; semanario político
        see under title

Liga de Acción Social, *Mérida, Mexico.*
Documentos en defensa del nombre hispanoamericano.
Mérida de Yucatán, 1947.
137 p. 24 cm.

        "En homenaje al cuarto centenario del nacimiento de don Miguel
de Cervantes Saavedra, la Colonia Española de Mérida de Yucatán
coadyuvó con la Liga de Acción Social a la publicación de estos
documentos."

1. Spanish America—Name.   I. Title.

F1408.3.L53   980   49-27175*

NL 0359438   DLC NN CU-B GU

Liga de acción social, *Mérida.*
        ... Memoria de la sesión solemne celebrada el 17 de noviembre
de 1939 para conmemorar el establecimiento de la imprenta en
la Nueva España y en la provincia de Yucatán. ₍Mérida de
Yucatán₎ Imp. Oriente, 1939.
39 p., 1 l. 23½ᵐ.

At head of title: Liga de acción social.
Cover-title: Celebración del IV centenario de la imprenta en América.

1. Printing—Hist.—Mexico. 2. Printing—Hist.—Yucatan.

Library of Congress   Z211.Y9L7   40-30880
                                                655.172

NL 0359439   DLC CU TxU NN DPU

Liga de acción social, *Mérida, Mexico.*
        ... Memoria del IV centenario de la fundación de Mérida de
Yucatán, 6 de enero de 1942. ₍Mérida₎ Imp. Oriente ₍1942₎
136 p., 1 l. incl. illus. (ports.) facsim. group port. 22½ᵐ.

1. Merida, Mexico—Centennial celebrations, etc.   I. Title.

Library of Congress   F1391.M5L5   42-23981
                                                972.6

NL 0359440   DLC DPU NN

Liga de acción social, Merida, Mexico.

Rubio Mañé, Jorge Ignacio.
        ... "Monografía de los Montejos" ... Mérida, Yucatán,
México, Liga de acción social, 1930.

Liga de acción social, *Mérida, Mexico.*
        ... Resumen de la encuesta sobre el monumento a los Montejos.
Mérida, Yucatán, 1931.
cover-title, 45 p. 18ᵐ.

No. ₍81₎ in a collection with binder's title: Biographical pamphlets:
Spanish America.

1. Montejo, Francisco de, ca. 1479-ca. 1548. 2. Montejo y León, Francisco, fl. 1542.
                                                43-26223
                                                Brief cataloging
Library of Congress   F1407.B48 no. 31

NL 0359442   DLC

Liga de acción social, *Mérida, Mexico.*
        ... Síntesis de las respuestas dadas al cuestionario formulado
por la "Liga de acción social" sobre la unificación de la lengua
española en los países hispanoamericanos. Hablemos correctamente, lista de algunas palabras de uso indebido corregidas
conforme al último diccionario de la lengua española. Mérida
de Yucatán, México, Imprenta Oriente, 1943.
23 p. 23ᵐ.
Cover-title: En defensa del idioma.
        1. Spanish language—Provincialisms—Spanish America. 2. Spanish
language—Idioms, corrections, errors.   I. Title: Hablemos correctamente.   II. Title: En defensa del idioma.
                                                46-19240
Library of Congress   PC4821.L47

NL 0359443   DLC

DLC   **Liga de Acción Social, Mérida, México.**
197   Trabajos de la "Liga de Acción So-
        cial" para el establecimiento de las
        escuelas rurales en Yucatan. Merida
        de Yucatan, Impr. "Empresa Editora
        Yucateca", 1913.
                298 p.

NL 0359444   DLC-P4 CU CU-B

527   **Liga de acción social, Mérida, Mexico.**
        Trabajos de la Liga de acción social para el
establecimiento de las escuelas rurales en Yucatán.
México, 1918.

NL 0359445   DPU

S
15   **Liga de Agricultores del Estado de Tlaxcala**
.L5   Bases constitutivas de la Liga de Agricul-
        tores del Estado de Tlaxcala, aprobadas por
        unanimidad en la Asamblea General celebrada
        en Apizaco, el día 22 de marzo de 1912.
        México, Impr. Internacional, 1912.
        13 p. 21cm.

        1. Liga de Agricultores del Estado de
Tlaxcala 2. Agriculture - Mexico - Tlaxcala
(State) - Socie-   ties

NL 0359446   WU

VOLUME 332

4HD   Liga de Agronomos Socialistas, México
1683   El colectivismo agrario en México,
La Comarca Lagunera. México, 1940.
549 p.

(*Its* Publicación no. 15)

NL   0359447   DLC-P4 NN ICarbS InU TxU NcC CU WU

Liga de agrónomos socialistas, Mexico.
... La comarca lagunera
see its   El colectivismo agrario en México.
La Comarca lagunera.

630.7
L723p   Liga de Agrónomos Socialistas, Mexico.
Problemas de la enseñanza agricola.
¡Mexico, D. F., 1936¿
63p.

Contents.--Historia y finalidad de la Escuela Nacional de
Agricultura, por M. Mesa A.--La enseñanza agricola en Mexico,
por M.A. Durán.--La Escuela Regional Campesina como plantel
destinado a lo hijos de los trabajadores del campo, por M. Mesa
A.--La enseñanza agricola frente al articulo tercero constitucional, por M. Mesa A.

1. Agricultural education--Mexico.   I. Title.

NL   0359449   ICarbS

Liga de agrónomos socialistas, *Mexico.*
Proyecto de reformas a la legislación agraria ¡por¿ **Liga de**
agrónomos socialistas. ¡México, D. F., 1938¿
cover-title, 16 p. 22½ᵐ. (*Its* ¡Publicación no.¿ 8)

1. Land tenure—Mexico. 2. Peasantry—Mexico.
43-49456
Library of Congress   HD1289.M6L5

NL   0359450   DLC

G333.0972
L626p
LIGA DE AGRÓNOMOS SOCIALISTAS, *México.*
[Publicaciones] 1-
Mexico, D.F., 1935-
v. 23½cm.

Contents listed on typed cards in Latin
American and public catalogs. L.C. analyticals.

NL   0359451   TxU

Liga de Amadores Brasileiros de Radio Emissão.
TK9956
.Q2
QTC. Revista técnica de rádio.
¡Rio de Janeiro¿

Liga de amigos de la Coruña.

El **centenario** del "Quijote" en Galicia; folleto publicado á
expensas de la Liga de amigos de la Coruña. ¡Coruña, Talleres de fotograbado é imprenta de P. Ferrer, 1905¿

Liga de amigos de los vascos.
DP302
.B46A85
Arte y cultura vasca; exposición de artes plásticas, conferen-
cias, cantos, danzas; homenaje al pueblo uruguayo y a su
presidente, el excmo. señor doctor Juan José de Amézaga
Ibarra; la Liga de amigos de los vascos y el periódico Euzko-
deya de Buenos Aires editan este libro para celebrar el
acontecimiento ... Montevideo ... 1943. ¡Buenos Aires,
Talleres graficos de S. de Amorrortu e hijos, 1943¿

LIGA DE AMIGOS DE LOS VASCOS, Buenos Aires.
Euzko abestiak; cantos populares vascos [por
Liga de amigos de los vascos y Euzko deya.   Buenos
Aires, 1942]   63 p.   music.   18cm.

Microfiche (neg.)   2 sheets.   11 x 15cm.   (NYPL FSN-2966)
Cover title.
Chiefly for 3 voices (SSA or TTB) unaccompanied.
1. Songs, Basque--Collec-   tions. 2. Choral music, Secular
(Men, 3-part)--Unacc.   3. Choral music, Secular (Wom-
en, 3-part)--Unacc. I. Euzko   deya; la voz de los vascos en
America.

NL   0359455   NN

Rare Book
Room
Uzn10
L62C
1876
Liga de Cazadores del Puerto de Santa
María.
Reglamento de la Liga de Cazadores, del
Puerto de Santa María. Discutido en la re-
union celebrada el 4 de Noviembre de 1876
... [Puerto de Santa María]Año de 1876.
Imprenta de D.Manuel del Rio,Palacio 39.
1p.ℓ.,14p. 20cm.

NL   0359456   CtY

LIGA DE COMERCIO DE BARRANQUILLA.
Revista. v. 1, no. 1-2, 5-6, 8-v. 13, no. 120, 122-
v. 16, no. 159, mayo-junio, sept.-oct., dic. 1932-
marzo, mayo, 1942-junio, 1945; no. 160-182, 184, 186,
188-195, julio, 1945-mayo, julio, sept., nov., 1947-
junio, 1948.
Barranquilla.   v.   25cm.

Monthly.
Vols. 1-16, numbered continuously no. 1-159 are also called no. 1-13;
no. 160-195, called año 13-16, lack volume numbering.
Vol. 3, no. 23, v. 7, omitted in numbering.

1. Commerce--Colombia--Barranquilla.   2. Commerce--Per. and soc.
publ.--Colombia.

NL   0359458   NN

HD1491
M6L72
Liga de Comunidades Agrarias del Estado de
Vera Cruz.
Bases y estatutos. Jalapa-Enriquez,
Talleres Gráficas del Gobierno del Estado,
1929.
16 p. 16cm.

1. Agriculture, Cooperative - Vera Cruz,
Mexico (State) -   Societies. I. Title.

NL   0359459   CSt-H TxU

Liga de **communidades** agrarias del estado de Vera Cruz.
... La cuestión agraria y el problema campesino. Puntos
de vista de la Liga de comunidades agrarias del estado de
Veracruz. Jalapa-Enríquez, Ver. ¡Talleres tip. del gobierno
del estado¿ 1924.
81 p. illus. incl. ports. 19½ cm.
At head of title: El agrarismo en México.

1. Agricultural laws and legislation—Mexico. 2. Agricultural laws
and legislation—Vera Cruz, Mexico (State) 3. Agriculture, Cooperative Law and legislation—Mexico. 4. Agriculture, Cooperative—Vera
Cruz, Mexico (State)   I. Title.
34—18782

NL   0359460   DLC CU-B TxU

Liga de Comunidades Agrarias del Estado de
Guanajuato.
Memoria ilustrativa del primer congreso de
la Liga de Comunidades Agrarias del Estado de
Guanajuato, convocado y organizado por la De-
legación de la Comisión Nacional Agraria en
Guanajuato, la Procuraduría de Pueblos de la
Comisión Nacional Agraria en Guanajuato, el
Banco Agrícola Ejidal en Guanajuato, las Co-
munidades Agrarias en el Estado y el ciudada-
no gobernador constitucional del Estado; León

de los Aldamas, junio 7, 8 y 9 de 1930.
[León] Talleres Linotipográficos del Estado
[1930?]
77p. illus.,port. 23cm.
1. Agriculture, Cooperative - Societies. 2.
Agriculture, Co-   operative - Mexico -
Guanajuato.

NL   0359462   TxU

Liga de comunidades agrarias y sindicatos campesinos de Chiapas.
Resolución y antecedentes del problema agrario en la zona del
Soconusco, Chiapas. Editado por la Liga de comunidades agrarias y sindicatos campesinos de Chiapas. Tuxtla Gutierrez,
1942. 44 p. illus. 23cm.

1. Agriculture—Economics—   Mexico—Soconusco. 2. Land-
Mexico—Soconusco.
July 19, 1943

NL   0359463   NN TxU

Liga de comunidades agrarias y sindicatos campesinos de
Yucatán.
Unificación campesina en Yucatán, la Asamblea constituyente
de la Liga de comunidades agrarias y sindicatos campesinos
de Yucatán, agosto de 1938. Mérida, Yucatán, México, Gobierno del estado de Yucatán ¡1938¿
82 p., 1 l. incl. ports., pl.   23ᵐ.

1. Agriculture, Cooperative—Mexico—Yucatan. 2. Sisal hemp.
43-19583
Library of Congress   HD1491.M4Y85
334.6835771

NL   0359464   DLC DPU NN TxU

Liga de Comunidades Agrarias y Sindicatos Campesinos del Estado de México.
Quinto pleno agrario estatal de la Liga de
Comunidades Agrarias y Sindicatos Campesinos
del Edo. de México, C.N.C., celebrado en la
ciudad de Toluca los días 23 y 24 de mayo de
1953. Toluca, 1953.
30p. 22cm.

At head of title: Gobierno del Estado de
México.

NL   0359465   TxU

Liga de comunidades agrarias y sindicatos campesinos del
estado de Tamaulipas.
Primera convención de la Liga de comunidades agrarias y
sindicatos campesinos del estado de Tamaulipas, 1926. ¡México, Editorial "CVLTVRA," 1927¿
292, ¡4¿ p., 1 l.   illus., 2 fold. tab.   23½ᵐ.

1. Agriculture, Cooperative—Societies. 2. Agriculture, Cooperative—
Mexico—Tamaulipas.
42-30691
Library of Congress   HD1491.M4L5 1926

NL   0359466   DLC NNU

Mex
HD
329
.T4L5
1927
Liga de comunidades agrarias y sindicates
campesinos del estado de Tamaulipas.
Segunda convencion de la Liga de comunidades
agrarias y sindicatos campesinos del estado de
Tamaulipas; recopilación del ingeniero Marte R.
Gómez en cumplimiento de acuerdo dictado por el
Sr. Licenciado Emilio Portes Gil ... [n. p.], 1927.
340 p., 1 l., [5] p., 1 l. illus., plates.
fold. tables. 23.5 cm.

NL   0359467   DPU

Liga de comunidades agrarias y sindicatos campesinos del
estado de Tamaulipas.
Segunda convención de la Liga de comunidades agrarias y
sindicatos campesinos del estado de Tamaulipas; recopilación
del ingeniero Marte R. Gómez, en cumplimiento de acuerdo dictado por el sr. licenciado Emilio Portes Gil ... 1927. ¡México,
Editorial "Cvltvra", 1929¿
340 p., 5 l. incl. illus., plates.   fold. tables.   23½ᵐ.

1. Agriculture—Societies.   I. Gómez, Marte R., comp.
38-34398
Library of Congress   S165.L5 1927

NL   0359468   DLC TxU ICarbS

VOLUME 332

334.68
L62c
1928
Liga de Comunidades Agrarias y Sindicatos Campesinos del Estado de Tamaulipas.
Tercera convención de la Liga de Comunidades Agrarias y Sindicatos Campesinos del Estado de Tamaulipas. Recopilación del ingeniero Marte R. Gómez en cumplimiento de acuerdo dictado por Emilio Portes Gil. ‹México, Editorial Cultura, 1930›
371p. illus., ports., fold.tables. 24cm.

1. Agriculture, Cooperative--Societies. 2. Agriculture, Cooperative--Tamaulipas, Mexico.

NL 0359469   IU

Liga de Cooperativas de Puerto Rico.
El Cooperador
see under title

Liga de damas católicas, Argentine republic.
Consejo superior
see   Acción católica argentina. Liga de damas católicas. Consejo superior.

Liga de damas Chilenas.
Estudios sociales ...
see under title

Chi
F
3099
.S9L5
Liga de defensa, Santiago de Chile.
... ¿Subercaseaux traicionó a Chile?
[Santiago, Imp. y lit. Cervantes] 1942.
102 p.   20 cm.

NL 0359473   DPU

Liga de defensa comercial (Argentine Republic)
see   Liga de defensa comercial, Buenos Aires.

Liga de defensa comercial, Buenos Aires.
Informe leído por el Presidente Sr. Antonio León Lanusse en la Asamblea general ordinaria de 29 de diciembre 1914.   Buenos Aires [1914]
93 p.
At head of title: Republica Argentina.

NL 0359475   IU

Liga de defensa comercial, Buenos Aires.
Informe leído por el presidente Sr. Antonio León Lanusse en la Asamblea General Ordinaria de 28 diciembre 1921.   Buenos Aires, Imp. E. L. Frigerio, 1921.
63 p.

NL 0359476   DLC-P4

Liga de defensa comercial, *Buenos Aires.*
Memoria anual.
Buenos Aires,
v. 26½ᶜᵐ.

1. Argentine Republic—Comm. 2. Tariff—Argentine Republic.

CA 18–217 Unrev'd

Library of Congress   HF300.B8

NL 0359477   DLC

Liga de defensa comercial, *Montevideo.*
... Memoria presentada a la ... Asamblea general ordinaria por el Consejo directivo ...
Montevideo,
v. 28½ᶜᵐ.

1. Uruguay—Comm.

CA 31–304 Unrev'd

Library of Congress   HF300.M65   381.0989

NL 0359478   DLC

Liga de defesa paulista.

Coaracy, Vivaldo.
... O caso de São Paulo (publicado pela Liga de defesa paulista) São Paulo, Estabelecimento graphico Irmãos Ferraz, 1931.

Liga de defeza dos interesses publicos.
... Memoria apresentada ao Grande congresso nacional de Lisboa de 1909 ... Lisboa, Officina typographica, 1909.
48 p. map. 22ᶜᵐ.

CONTENTS.—1. pte. Necessidade urgente de estabelecer pórtos-francos ... Relator: Dr. Antonio de Jesus Lopes.—2. pte. Influencia do canal de Panamá no movimento dos pórtos portuguéses. Relator: Antonio Ferreira de Serpa.

1. Free harbors—Portugal. 2. Portugal—Comm. 3. Panama canal. I. Jesus Lopes, Antonio de. II. Ferreira de Serpa, Antonio. III. Congresso nacional, Lisbon, 1909. IV. Title.

18–22921

Library of Congress   HF1418.L5]

NL 0359480   DLC DCU–IA

Liga de escritores revolucionarios
see   Liga de escritores y artistas revolucionarios.

Liga de escritores y artistas revolucionarios.

García Lorca, Federico, 1899–1936.
... Breve antología; poemas seleccionados y presentados por Juan Marinello. México, D. F., Antigua librería Robredo de J. Porrúa e hijos, 1936.

---

q793.31
L62d
Liga de Escritores y artistas revolucionarios
Danzas revolucionarias del trabajo. Proyecto de C. Gutiérrez Cruz. ‹México, 1925›
9+ ℓ. illus. 31cm.

Imperfect: all after leaf 9 wanting.

1. Dancing—Mexico. I. Gutiérrez Cruz, Carlos. II. Ti-   tle.

NL 0359483   IU

Liga de Escritores y Artistas Revolucionarios.
Frente a frente
see under title

Liga de Escritores y Artistas Revolucionarios.
Homenaje a Rubén Romero
see under title

Liga de la defensa nacional centroamericana.
Labor hondureña por la autonomia de Centro-America. Liga de la defensa nacional centro-americana. Comayaguela, Honduras, Impr. "El Sol," 1914.
368 p. plates, ports. 23ᶜᵐ

A protest against a United States protectorate in Nicaragua.

1. Nicaragua—For. rel.—U. S. 2. U. S.—For. rel.—Nicaragua. 3. Central America—For. rel.—U. S. 4. U. S.—For. rel.—Central America. I. Title.

16–7387

Library of Congress   F1438.L72]

NL 0359486   DLC

Liga de las naciones
see
League of nations.

Liga de medianos y pequeños productores de henequén
(*México*)
En defensa de la industria henequenera de Yucatán escrita bajo los auspicios de la Liga de medianos y pequeños productores de henequén. ¿Mérida? Cía. periodística del sureste, s. a.₁ 1931.
87 p. 23½ᶜᵐ.

Reply to "El problema económico de Yucatán" by Enrique Aznar Mendoza.

1. Sisal hemp. 2. Agriculture, Cooperative — Mexico — Yucatan. 3. Aznar Mendoza, Enrique. El problema económico de Yucatán.

43–20745

Library of Congress   HD9156.S8M454   338.1735771

NL 0359488   DLC

Liga de Propaganda Antialcohólica.
El Heraldo antialcohólico
see under title

---

294   Liga de Propietarios Urbanos.
... Estatutos ...   Montevideo perez vila, 1915.

NL 0359490   DPU

---

pF1235
Y9L5
Liga de Resistencia de Albañiles y Constructores. México (Federal District)
¿Quien es Jesús Yurén A. ? [México, 194–?]
8 p. port. 15cm.

1. Yurén, Jesús. 2. Trade-unions - Mexico. I. Title.

NL 0359491   CU–B

Liga de sociedades de la Cruz roja
see   League of Red Cross Societies.

Liga del Sur, Rosario, Argentine Republic (Santa Fé)
La cuestión del dia
see under title

VOLUME 332

4K
Argen. -5
Liga del Sur, Rosario, Argentine Republic (Santa Fé)
Petición de reformas constitucionales y legislativas presentada à la H. Legislatura de la Provincia el 18 de mayo de 1909.   Rosario, Establecimiento Tip. La Capital, 1909.
80 p.

NL 0359494   DLC-P4

Liga democrata antifascista costarricense.
Gavilla, mazo y cerebro; homenaje de la literatura costarricense a España ... ¡San José, Costa Rica¡ Liga democrata antifascista costarricense, 1938.
31 p. 28ᵐ.

No. ¡25¡ in a volume with binder's title: Pamphlets on the Spanish civil war.

43–26413
Brief cataloging

Library of Congress   DP269.P25 no. 25

NL 0359495   DLC

Liga democrática hispanoamericana.

Sáenz, Vicente, 1896–
Guión de historia contemporánea; texto de orientación para profesores y alumnos hispanoamericanos, por Vicente Sáenz ... México, D. F., Liga democrática hispanoamericana, Editorial Rumbos, 1942.

Liga der fremdvölker Russlands.

see

Rysslands undertryckta folkens förbund.

Liga der Rotkreuz-Gesellschaften
see   League of Red Cross Societies.

Liga der Tschechoslowakischen Kraftfahrer
see Liga československých motoristů.

W 6
P3
LIGA Dominicana contra el Cancer
Charlas tabloides de cancerología, especialmente para médicos.   Ciudad Trujillo, Montalvo, 1950.
31 p. (Partido Dominicano. Publicaciones)
1. Neoplasms

NL 0359500   DNLM

ML28
.L63L5
Liga dos Amigos do Canto Gregoriano.
Boletim informativo.
¡Lisboa¡
no. in   v. 23 cm.

ML28.L63L5   783.5'05   74–617725

NL 0359501   DLC

Liga dos Combatentes da Grande Guerra.
Relatório da gerência.

Lisboa.

v. illus. 24 cm. annual.

1. European War, 1914–1918—Societies.

D621.P8L5   52–36760 ‡

NL 0359502   DLC

JL
2415
.1924
L7
Liga dos vinte e um para propaganda da reforma da constituição.
A democracia. Reorganização política da republica dos Estados Unidos do Brasil anno de 1924. Rio de Janeiro, Officinas graphicas do "Jornal do Brasil", 1924.
2 v. 23ᶜᵐ.
Cover-title: ... Exposição de motivos da reforma da constituição do Brasil.
Title varies slightly.
Prepared for the "Liga dos vinte e um" by Taciano Accioli Monteiro, secretario geral. cf. foreword, v.1.
1. Brazil. Constitution. I. Accioli Monteiro Taciano. II. Title.

NL 0359503   MiU

Liga Ecuatoriana Antituberculosa.
Campaña antituberculosa...
see under title

RC
315
.E1
L72
Liga Ecuatoriana Antituberculosa.
Exposición de la Liga Ecuatoriana Antituberculosa al H. Congreso Nacional y documentos anexos. Guayaquil, Litografía e Imprenta La Reforma, 1948.
118 p. illus.

1. Tuberculosis- Prevention. 2. Tuberculosis- Ecuador.

NL 0359505   DPAHO ICarbS

WF
1
qL723i
1951
LIGA Ecuatoriana Antituberculosa. Comité Ejecutivo
Informe presentado por el Dr. Juan Tanca Marengo, presidente del Comité Ejecutivo, al Consejo Supremo de L. E. A. sobre las labores desarrolladas por la Institución durante el período de 1950. Guayaquil, 1951.
13 ℓ.   (Publicaciones de L. E. A.)
1. Liga Ecuatoriana Antituberculosa
I. Tanca Marengo, Juan

NL 0359506   DNLM

Liga Ecuatoriana de Librepensadores.
El Libre examen
see under title

Liga esperantista argentina
see
Argentina esperanto-ligo.

Liga Espiritual de Profesionales Católicos.
Costa Rica un estado católico, por un círculo de abogados de la Liga Espiritual de Profesionales Católicos. San José, Costa Rica, Impr. Nacional, 1955.
XXIV, 202 p. 21 cm.
CONTENT.—Presentación, por F. Volio Sancho.—Introducción, por C. H. Rodríguez Quirós.—Estados teístas y estados ateos, por V. Calvo S.—Interpretación del artículo 76 de la Constitución política de Costa Rica, por J. Rodríguez Ulloa.—Trascendencia de la profesión de fe católica estatal consignada en el artículo 76 de la Constitución política, por E. Odio González.—Antecedentes inmediatos del artículo 76 de la Constitución política y sus antecedents históricos, por L. D. Tinoco Castro.—Antecedentes inmediatos del artículo 76 de la Constitución política de Costa Rica de 7 noviembre de 1949, por R. Carrillo Echeverría.—El artículo 76 de la Constitución política y sus efectos en el derecho de familia, por O. Herrera Mata.—El derecho de los padres en la educación de sus hijos, por R. Odio González.—La educación religiosa como obligación del Estado, por H. Zamora Elizondo.—El artículo 76 de la Constitución política y sus consecuencias en el derecho público, por M. A. Blanco Montero.—Privilegios de la Iglesia Católica en relación de la tributación y otras leyes, por F. Ortiz Céspedes.—Relaciones económicas del Estado Costarricense con la Iglesia Católica, por F. Soto Harrison.—Prohibición de otros cultos opuestos a la moral universal, por H. Zurcher.—Hacia un nuevo concordato, por C. Araya Borge.
1. Ecclesiastical law—Costa Rica. 2. Church and state in Costa Rica. 3. Catholic Church in Costa Rica. I. Title.

57–32535 ‡

NL 0359510   DLC CU-B IEdS

370.1
L626h
Liga Estudiantes Humanistas.
Humanismo y universidad. ¡Buenos Aires¡ 1953.
1v. (unpaged) 19cm.

Includes bibliography.

1. Education, Humanistic. 2. Humanism.

NL 0359511   IU

Liga evangelica de accao missionaria e educacional.

Moreira, Eduardo.
General report of the Rev. Eduardo Moreira's journey in the Portuguese African colonies. London, New York city, World dominion press ¡1935¡

Cos
JL
1447
.A25
.L4
Liga feminista costarricense, San José.
... Programa de educación cívica.
San José, Imp. Borrase hnos. , 1939.
11 p. 19.5 cm.

NL 0359513   DPU

Liga Frailand
see   Freeland League.

Liga für das Arbeitende Palästina in Deutschland.
Für das arbeitende Erez-Israel. Gründungskonferenz der Liga für das Arbeitende Palästina in Deutschland, Berlin, 29. und 30. Dez. 1928. Berlin, 1929.

72 p.

NL 0359515   MH

Liga für Rassenverbesserung
Die geschlechtliche Gesundheitslehre der Frau unter besonderer Berücksichtigung empfängnisverhindernder Mittel. Berlin, Geschäftsstelle: Verlag Plessner [19--?]

8 p.

NL 0359516   MH

VOLUME 332

Liga für Vaterlandsverteidigung der Chinesen in Deutschland.
Chronik der chinesisch-japanischen Beziehungen
see under Hsü, Tao-lin, 1906- ed.

Liga für Vaterlandsverteidigung der Chinesen in Deutschland.
Sino-Japanese relations; historical and juridical survey of the period 1871 to 1931. ₁n. p., 1931?₁ 27 p. 21½cm.

"The present survey is translated from a pamphlet published in German by the 'Liga für Vaterlandsverteidigung der Chinesen in Deutschland.'"

733070A. 1. China—For. rel.—Japan 1871-1931. 2. Japan—For. rel.—China,
1871-1931. I. Title.
N. Y. P. L. October 19, 1934

NL 0359518 NN

LIGA GALLEGA.
Regramento da sociedade Liga gallega na Cruña. Cruña,Carré,1896.

pp.15.

NL 0359519 MH

Liga gegen Imperialismus, gegen Kolonialherrschaft und für Nationale Unabhängigkeit
see League against Imperialism and for National Independence.

Liga Guipuzcoana de Productores.
Circular.

San Sebastian.
no. 24 cm.

1. Guipuzcoa, Spain—Indus.

HC387.G8L5 52–66321 ‡

NL 0359521 DLC

Liga Homoeopathica Internationalis.
Die Bedeutung der Homöopathie für die ärztliche Praxis; zusammengefasste Vorträge...
see under International Homoeopathic Congress. 11th, Berlin, 1937.

WB
1
qL723
LIGA Homoeopathica Internationalis
₁Collection of publications₁
The library has a collection of miscellaneous publications of this organization kept as received. These publications are not listed nor bound separately.

NL 0359523 DNLM

WB
1
GG4
L7s
1934
LIGA Homoeopathica Internationalis
Satzungen, angenommen in der ordentlichen Generalversammlung am 26. Juli 1934 in Arnhem. Leipzig, Schwabe, ₁1934?₁
24 p.

NL 0359524 DNLM

Liga Homoeopathica Internationalis. Congress
see International Homoepathic Congress.

Liga homeopática mexicana.
International homeopathic congress, *Mexico,* 1929.
Programa del Congreso que la Liga internacional homeopática celebra en la ciudad de México del 10 al 16 de agosto de 1929, organizado por la Liga homeopática mexicana y por la Escuela libre de homeopatía de México, bajo el patrocinio de la Secretaría de educación pública ... México, D. F. ₁Imprenta M. León Sánchez, s. a.₁ 1929.

Liga industrial y agrícola, *Santa Clara, Cuba.*
La Liga industrial y agrícola. A society for the advancement of industry, agriculture and commerce. Surveying department. Technical library. Technical and commercial museum. English readin₁ ₁!₁ circle. Santa Clara, Cuba ₁Imp. y pap. El Iris, 1904₁
cover-title, 8 p. 15 cm.

HC157.C9L4 CA 5–1304
Library of Congress ₁a54b1₁

NL 0359527 DLC

Liga Internacional contra la Competencia Desleal
see
Ligue internationale contre la concurrence déloyale.

Liga Internacional de la Enseñanza, de la Educación y de la Cultura Popular
see
Ligue internationale de l'enseignement, de l'éducation et de la culture populaire.

Liga internacional de mujeres ibéricas e hispanoamericanas.
Feminismo internacional; revista mensual ilustrada, órgano de la Liga internacional de mujeres ibéricas e hispanoamericanas. v. 1 (no. 1–11); dic. 1922–nov. 1923. New York city ₁Elena Arizmendi & co., etc.₁ 1922–23.

Pam.
Coll.
33339
Liga Juvenil Comunista de Cuba.
¿Que es la Liga Juvenil Comunista? Porque debe cada joven obrero ingresar en la L. J. C. ₁Habana?₁ Ediciones Juventud Obrera ₁1933₁
16 p. 18 cm.

1. Communism. Cuba. 2. Cuba. Politics and government. I. Title.

NL 0359531 NcD

Liga Kobiet.
Children in People's Poland. Warsaw ₁Książka i Wiedza₁ 1952.
unpaged. illus. 20 x 29 cm.

1. Children in Poland. I. Title.

HQ792.P7L5 362.7 56–17589 rev ‡

NL 0359532 DLC

Liga kobiet, Olkusz.
Jednodniówka pamięci 29 listopada 1830 r. i bitwy pod Krzywopłotami w listopadzie 1914 r.; wydana staraniem "Ligi kobiet w Olkuszu." ₁Olkusz: Liga kobiet, 1915?₁ 10 p. 4°.
Cover-title illus.

1. Poland—Hist.—Revolution, 1830– 1832. 2. European war, 1914–1918
—Campaigns. 3. Title.
N. Y. P. L. August 31, 1926

NL 0359533 NN

AP54
.K6
Liga Kobiet.
Kobieta.
₁Warszawa, "Prasa"₁

AP54
.K63
Liga Kobiet.
Kobieta wiejska.
Warszawa.

Liga Komunistów Jugoslawii
see
Savez komunista Jugoslavije.

TL504
K3
Liga Lotnicza.
Kalendarz lotniczy.
Warszawa.

Liga Lotnicza.
Wyszkolenie lotnicze pierwszego stopnia. ₁Warszawa, 1951₁
101 p. 64 illus. 21 cm.
Errata slip inserted.

1. Aeronautics—Popular works. I. Title.

TL546.7.L5 59–26807

NL 0359538 DLC

Liga Lotnicza
see also
Liga Obrony Kraju.

V5
.L47
Liga maritima brasileira.
₁Rio de Janeiro₁
v. in illus., ports. 32 cm. monthly.
Caption title, 19 –37: Liga maritima; 1938– Revista.
Organ of Liga Maritima Brasileira.
Brazilian

1. Brazil. Armada—Period. I. Liga Maritima Brasileira.

V5.L47 48–36550*‡

NL 0359540 DLC

Liga Maritima Brasileira. Revista
see **Liga maritima brasileira.**

VOLUME 332

273   Liga márítima de Chile.
Anuario de la marina mercante nacional, obsequio de la Liga marítima de Chile, 1922.

NL 0359541   DPU

Liga Maritima de Chile.
Boletín informativo. no. 1-16, 18-19.
Jan. 1925- Jan. 1947, Mar. 1927- Apr. 1947.
Valparaíso.
18 no. in 1 v.
Merged into Mar. after no. 19(?).
1. Merchant marine - Societies, etc.
2. Merchant marine - Chile.

NL 0359542   CU

Liga marítima de Chile.

Yáñez, Eliodoro, 1860–
... Comercio marítimo y marina mercante nacional. Discursos pronunciados por el senador Señor Eliodoro Yáñez en la discusión de las leyes sobre protección a la marina mercante nacional. [Valparaíso] Soc. imprenta y litografía Universo, 1916.

Liga Marítima de Chile.
Instituto Oceanográfico de Valparaíso: su origen, sesión inaugural, primera sesión del Consejo, estatutos. [Valparaíso, Impr. Victoria, 1945]
27 p. illus. 27 cm. (Liga marítima de Chile. Publicación no. 29)
"Publicación no.1 del Instituto Oceanográfico de Valparaíso."

Chi
HE
805
.L52
no.29

NL 0359544   DPU

4F   Liga Maritima de Chile
Chile   Liga Maritima de Chile, XXX aniversario, 1914-1944. [Valparaíso, 1944]
36
1 v. (unpaged)

NL 0359545   DLC-P4

Liga Maritima de Chile.

VK4
.M3   Mar.
[Valparaíso]

Liga maritima de Chile.
Memoria anual del directorio.
[Valparaiso, 19
v. diagrs. 27 cm. (*Its* Publicación no.

1. Merchant marine—Societies. 2. Merchant marine—Chile.
HE805.L5   47-28636

NL 0359547   DLC CLU

Liga Marítima de Chile.
Primer Congreso maritimo nacional
see under   Congreso Marítimo Nacional.

Chi   Liga marítima de Chile. Junta local de Santiago.
HE805   Noticias ... 1936-
.L5Se   Santiago de Chile, 1936-
date   v. illus. 18.5 cm.

NL 0359549   DPU

HE561
.L5   **Liga maritina espanola.**
Boletin oficial de la Liga maritima española...
[Madrid?,   ]

NL 0359550   DLC

Liga Marítima Española.
Estatutos y reglamento. Madrid, est. tip. "Sucesores de Rivadeneyra", 1901.
15 p.

NL 0359551   MH

Liga marítima española.
Información de la Liga marítima española sobre proteccion á las industrias marítimas nacionales. Madrid, M. Romero, impr., 1903.
5 p. l., [3]–365 p. fold. tables. 26½ᶜᵐ.

1. Merchant marine—Spain. 2. Shipping bounties and subsidies—Spain. I. Title.
                    16–13690
Library of Congress   HE743.S8L5

NL 0359552   DLC

Liga marítima española.
Manual de la Liga marítima española, con un retrato de S. M. el rey d. Alfonso XIII ... y un prólogo del excmo. sr. d. Antonio Maura ... Cinco años de labor.—1900-1905. Madrid, Imprenta alemana, 1906.
vii, 294 p., 1 l. port. 21ᶜᵐ.
"Principales publicaciones realizadas por la Junta central de la Liga marítima española desde su fundación, y catálogo de su biblioteca": p. [221]–258.

1. Liga marítima española.
                  35–35641
Library of Congress   HE859.L5
                  387.506246

NL 0359553   DLC

Liga marítima española.

Cervera y Jácome, Juan, 1866–
Páginas marítimas, por J. Cervera y Jácome y J. Cervera y Valderrama ... Madrid, Imprenta alemana, 1911.

Liga Mexicana de Radio Experimentadores.

TK6540
.O56   Onda corta.
[México]

F3315   Liga Minera de Potosí (Honduras)
.4   La minería ante el H. Congreso; memorial de las Ligas Mineras
L5   de Sucre y Potosí. La Paz, 1915.
      10 p. 22cm.
Cover title.
Signed (p. 10): Luis Soux [presidente, Liga Minera de Potosí]
Ricardo Arce [presidente, Liga Minera de Sucre]

NL 0359556   CU-B

Liga Morska
see also
Liga Obrony Kraju.

Liga Morska i Kolonialna.
Informator morski ...
see under Zagórski, Czeslaw, ed.

Liga morska i kolonialna.

Polska na morzu; praca zbiorowa pp. doktora Mieczysława Boguckiego, licencjata Kazimierza Demela, b. wicemarszałka Jana Dębskiego [i. i.] ... pod redakcją J. I. Targa ... Warszawa, Główna księgarnia wojskowa, 1935 [i. e. 1934]

Liga Morska i Kolonialna.
HA1451 Rocznik morski i kolonialny. 1938-
.R6   Warszawa.

.7   Liga Morska i Kolonialna.
.L5   Sprawozdanie z działalności.
Warszawa.
v. illus. 23 cm. annual.
Vols. for 19 issued together.

1. Merchant marine—Poland—Societies, etc.
HE848.7.L5   60–58068

NL 0359561   DLC

Liga Morska i Kolonialna. *Centre d'études*
see Liga Morska i Kolonialna. *Instytut Naukowy.*

Liga Morska i Kolonialna. Instytut Naukowy.
HF37
.S6   **Sprawy** morskie i kolonialne. Revue maritime et coloniale.
Warszawa, Skł. gł.: Biblioteka Polska.

Liga Morska i Kolonialna. *Komisja Terminologiczna*
see
Komisja Terminologiczna Morska.

HE848 Liga Morska i Kolonialna. *Okręg Poznański.*
.7   Sprawozdanie z działalności zarządu.
.L53 W Poznaniu.
v. tables. 23 cm. annual.

1. Merchant marine—Poland—Societies, etc.
HE848.7.L53   60–58067

NL 0359565   DLC

Liga Morska i Rzeczna
see Sea League in America.

VOLUME 332

Liga Morska w Ameryce
see Sea League in America.

Liga municipal dominicana.
Asamblea extraordinaria de la Liga municipal
dominicana ... San Cristóbal, C. B., 27 de
octubre de 1950. ¿San Cristóbal? 1950?¿
cover-title, 1 p.l., 29 numb. l. 27cm. (Its
Boletín núm. 5)
Reproduced from typewritten copy.

NL 0359568   CU-B

JS2055   Liga municipal dominicana.
.C6   **Congreso de municipios dominicanos.** *2d, Santiago de los*
1944 b   *Caballeros,* 1944.
... Reglamento interior, agenda y programa del segundo
Congreso de municipios dominicanos. Sede: Santiago de los
Caballeros. Fecha: del 20 al 25 de agosto de 1944. Ciudad
Trujillo, R. D., La Nación, c. por a., 1944.

Wason   **Liga Muslimin Indonesia.**
BP65   **Piagam, anggaran dasar & anggaran rumah**
I5L72   **tangga dan tafsir asasi.** Djakarta, Dewan
Liga Muslimin Indonesia ¿1952¿
42 p. 21 cm.

1. Mohammedans in Indonesia.

NL 0359570   NIC

Liga, 'n maandelikse oorsig van Volkebondsake. **A monthly**
review of the League of nations. v. 1-2, no. 3; Nov. 1932–
Jan. 1934. ¿Pretoria, 1932-34¿
2 v. in 1. illus. (incl. ports.) 27½ᵐ.
Official organ of South African League of nations union and National
council of women.
No more published. *cf.* Union list of serials.
L. C. set incomplete: v. 1, no. 1, 5-7, 10; v. 2, no. 2-3 wanting.

1. League of nations—Period. 2. International cooperation—Period.
I. South African League of nations union. II. National council of women
of South Africa.

Library of Congress   JX1975.A1L55
                                              44-17697
                                              ᴈII I

NL 0359571   DLC

Liga nacional anticancerosa (*Salvador*)
see
Sociedad beneficencia pública: Liga nacional anticancerosa
(*Salvador*)

Liga nacional campesina (Mexico)

HD1486   **Congreso de unificación de las organizaciones campesinas**
.M4C6   **de la república.** *1st, Mexico,* 1926.
1926   Primer Congreso de unificación de las organizaciones campesinas de la república, celebrado en la ciudad de México, D. F.,
del 15 al 20 de noviembre de 1926. Puebla, S. Loyo, 1927.

G334.6   Liga Nacional Campesina "Ursulo Galván".
L627m   Manifiesto a los campesinos y obreros de la República. ¿Jalapa Enríquez? 1932?¿
28p. illus. 20cm.

947317   1. Mexico - Pol. & govt. - 1910-1946.

NL 0359574   TxU

---

267   Liga nacional contra el alcoholismo, Santiago de Chile.
El deber nacional ante el tributo directo,
el indirecto i el de las bebidas intoxicantes ...
No. 14.

NL 0359575   DPU

---

267   Liga nacional contra el alcoholismo, Santiago de Chile
Declaración de principios y estatutos de la Liga
... ed. 1924. No. 32.

NL 0359576   DPU

Liga nacional contra el alcoholismo, ˅Chile.
Estatutos i folletos de la liga nacional contra
el alcoholismo.
[Santiago de Chile, 1902-13].

HV5397
.L5   analyzed

NL 0359577   DLC

HV5397
.L53   Liga nacional contra 'el alcoholismo, Santiago
de Chile.
La lucha contra el alcoholismo en le ejercito. 1914. Liga nacional contra el alco-
olismo.
Santaigo de Chile, n.d.

Folletos, no.11.

NL 0359578   DLC

HV5397
.L45   Liga nacional contra el alcoholismo,
Santiago de Chile.
...Memoria. 1913-14
[Santiago da Chile], 1914-15.

NL 0359579   DLC

---

267   Liga nacional contra el alcoholismo, Santiago de Chile
Memoria de 1922, ed. 1924. No. 33.

NL 0359580   DPU

HV5397
.L55   Liga nacional contra el alcoholismo, Santiago
de Chile.
El problema del alcoholismo ante la supres-
ion de la autoridad constitucional del
municipio, 1913. Liga naci nal contra el
alcoholismo.
Santiago de Chile, n.d.

Folletos, no.8.

NL 0359581   DLC

HV5060   Liga nacional contra el alcoholismo de la
.H817   república oriental del Uruguay.
Hobson, Richmond Pearson, 1870-1937.
El alcohol y la raza humana, por el capitán Richmond Pear-
son Hobson ... Traducido por la señorita Hortensia de Sal-
terain, revisado por el doctor Joaquín de Salterain ... Buenos
Aires, Talleres gráficos "Damiano," 1924.

1294   Liga nacional contra el alcoholismo de la
república oriental del Uruguay
Constitucion y reglamento Montevideo.
1916.

NL 0359583   DPU

1294   Liga nacional contra el alcoholismo de la
república oriental del Uruguay.
... Nuestra obra mundial ...
Montevideo, 1916.

NL 0359584   DPU

W 1   LIGA Nacional Contra el Cáncer
LI435   Memoria.
Guatemala ¿1953?¿-
v. illus., ports.

NL 0359585   DNLM

Liga Nacional de Asociaciones de Ahorros
Asegurados
see
National League of Insured Savings
Associations.

WC   LIGA Nacional de Higiene y Profilaxia
142   Social, Lima
L723d   El "Día Antivenéreo," 6 de setiembre
1936   de 1936. Lima, 1936.
29 p. illus., ports.
Cover title.
1. Venereal diseases - Prevention

NL 0359587   DNLM

RA644.V4
L62   Liga nacional do higiene y profilaxia social,
Lima.
El "Día antivonéreo", 5 sotiembro do 1937.
Lima, 1937.
45 p. illus. (incl. ports.)

1. Hygiene, Sexual. 2. Sex ... uction., 3.
Venereal diseases - Preven ion.

NL 0359588   NNC

Peru   Liga nacional de higiene y profilaxia social, Lima.
RC 201 ... El "Día antivenéreo", 4 de setiembre de 1938.
.P6L55 Lima, [Imprenta editorial "J. L. C."] 1938.
1938   54, [1] p. facsims. 24 cm.

NL 0359589   DPU

Peru   Liga nacional de higiene y profilaxia social, Lima.
RA 477 ... Estatuto y reglamento. [Lima?]
.L53   Sanmartí y cía., 1933.
1933   cover-title, 15 p. 24 cm.

NL 0359590   DPU

Peru   Liga nacional de higiene y profilaxia social, Lima.
HQ 759 ... Protección a la madre. Algunos aspectos
.L54   de la protección integral a la madre, por el dr.
Carlos A. Bambaren. Seguro social obligatorio
de maternidad, por la dra. Susana Solano. Lima,
1936.
14 p. 24.5 cm.

NL 0359591   DPU

VOLUME 332

Peru   Liga nacional de higiene y profilaxia social, Lima.
HQ 759   ... Refectorio maternal ...   Lima, 1936.
.L55   11 p.   24.5 cm.

NL   0359592   DPU

361   **Liga Nacional de Higiene y Profilaxia Social.**
L623s   Servicio social. Primer ciclo de actuaciones
realizado en el Perú, para propagar la nueva
doctrina asistencial.   Lima, 1932.
34p.   24cm.

Cover title.

1. Public welfare--Peru.   2. Social service.

NL   0359593   IU

Liga nacional de productores, Spain.
[Costa y Martínez, Joaquín] 1846-1911.
Reconstitución y europeización de España; programa
para un partido nacional, publícalo el "directorio" de la Liga
nacional de productores.   Madrid, Imprenta de San Francisco de Sales, 1900.

G178.06
L626e   Liga Nacional de Templanza de la República
Argentina.
Estatutos.   Buenos Aires, 1922.
30p.   14cm.

872996   1. Temperance - Societies, etc.

NL   0359595   TxU

G178.06
L626p   Liga Nacional de Templanza de la República
Argentina.
Programa de la obra social y cultural iniciada
por la Liga Nacional de Templanza de la República
Argentina.   Buenos Aires, 1922.
16p. illus. 18cm.

872995   1. Temperance.

NL   0359596   TxU

1287   Liga Nacional de Tiro.
... Programa ...   Montevideo,
1919.

NL   0359597   DPU

FILM   Liga Nacional Defensora de la Libertad Religio-
F1206   sa, Mexico.
L46   [Selected issues of Mexican newspapers and posters dealing
with the church-state controversy, filmed by Cornejo Franco in
1936 for Dr. Priestley. Guadalajara, etc., México, v.d.]
1 v. (various pagings) illus., ports. On film (Positive)

Microfilm.
2 copies; cop. 2 (Negative)

NL   0359598   CU-B

Liga nacional filipina para la protecion de la
primera infancia, Manila.
Boletín no. 1-5
Manila, 1914-17
5 4. 22½-24cm.

NL   0359599   DL

Liga nacional filipina para la protecion de la
primera infancia, Manila.
... Memoria leida en la enambles general anual
celebrada... septiembre...
Manila, 1913-20
7 v. illus. 23 cm.

NL   0359600   DL

F   Liga Nacional Independiente.
2689   La nueva política; acta-programa de consti-
L543   tución de la Liga Nacional Independiente y
LAC   memoria del presidente del Consejo Directivo.
Asunción, 1930.
29p.   25cm.

1. Paraguay - Pol. & govt. - 1938-
I. Title.

NL   0359601   TxU

Liga Naradów
    see   League of Nations.

Liga Natsiĭ
    see
League of Nations.

Liga Naval Argentina.
Puerto de Buenos Aires; anteproyecto de ley para su
organización.   Buenos Aires, 1937.
193, iv p. illus. 24 cm. (Biblioteca "Liga Naval Argentina."
Publicación nº 1)
"Estudio de la situación del puerto de Buenos Aires, por el ingeniero
F. Kinart": p. [83]-143.
"Informe al gobierno de la República Argentina referente al fun-
cionamiento del puerto de Buenos Aires, por el ingeniero G. P.
Nijhoff": p. [145]-193.

1. Buenos Aires—Harbor.   I. Nijhoff, Gerard Pieter, 1887-
II. Kinart, F.

HE556.B8L5   51-53055

NL   0359604   DLC MB

Liga Naval Brazileira.
Annuario maritimo
see under   *title*

V5
.L5   Liga naval portuguesa.
... Boletim maritimo

Lisboa, 19
v.   illus., (incl. ports.)   26½-27½cm.

1. Naval art and science--Societies.
I. Title.

NL   0359606   DLC

Liga naval portuguesa.
Liga naval portuguesa; breve relação dos seus trabalhos desde
a primeira reunião preliminar até a reunião de 15 de outubro de
1902 para approvação dos novos estatutos. 1900-1902.   Pôrto:
Typ. a vapor da empreza litteraria e typographica, 1902.   189 p.
26cm.

NL   0359607   NN

Liga Obrera de Guatemala.
Liga Obrera de Guatemala. año 1-
dic. 6, 1945-

Guatemala.
v. 30cm. weekly.

1. Labor and laboring classes - Guatemala.
2. Guatemala - Soc. condit. Sp.: Taracena
Flores Collection.

NL   0359608   TxU

Liga obrera unionista

... El Obrero libre; organo de la Liga obrera unionista ...
año 1   15. feb. 1920-
Guatemala, 1920-

UA926
.C95   Liga Obrony Kraju.

Czata.

Warszawa.

TT154   Liga   -Obrony Kraju.
.M58   Modelarz.

[Warszawa, ZG LPŻ]

UA829   Liga   Obrony Kraju.
.P7P75   Przyjaciel żolnierza; magazyn ilustrowany. nr. 1-155; 15/
31 lip. 1953 — 15/31 grudz. 1959. [Warszawa, Wydawn.
MON "Czasopisma Wojskowe"]

Liga obrony powietrznej i przeciw gazowej
panstwa.
Gosiewski, Antoni Henryk, 1900-
... Fotografja i aerofotografja. Warszawa, Nakł. Ligi
obrony powietrznej państwa, 1927.

TL504   Liga obrony powietrznej i przeciw gazowej
.S33   państwa.
Skrzydlata Polska.

[Warszawa, 19

279.9
L62   Liga para a Protocção da Natureza, Lisbon.
Publicações.
Lisboa,

1. Conservation of natural resources.
Portugal.

NL   0359615   DNAL

Liga para asegurar la paz
    see   League to Enforce Peace.

VOLUME 332

Liga patriótica, *Manila.*
... Resolution of the "Liga patriotica", a civil organization of the city of Manila, Philippine islands. Message from the President of the United States transmitting a copy of a resolution, no. 1, of the "Liga patriotica", a civil organization of the city of Manila, Philippine islands, dated May 16, 1935 ... ₁Washington, U. S. Govt. print. off., 1935₁
2 p. 24ᶜᵐ. ₍U. S.₎ 74th Cong., 1st sess. House. Doc. 253)
Referred to the Committee on insular affairs and ordered printed July 29, 1935.
"Resolution no. 1. Resolution expressing the gratitude of the people of the Philippine islands toward the government and people of the United States for the passage of the Tydings-McDuffie law and certification of the constitution of the commonwealth."
1. Philippine islands. Constitution. I. Title.
35–26649
Library of Congress DS685.L588
342.914

NL 0359617 DLC

F
2850
L5
Liga Patriótica Argentina.
Congreso General de Territorios Nacionales celebrado en Río Gallegos, febrero de 1927. Buenos Aires, Tall.Gráf.Argentinos L.J. Rossok, 1927.
234 p. charts (part fold.) (Its Biblioteca)

1. Argentine Republic--Territories and possessions--Congresses. I. Title.

NL 0359618 NSyU

Liga Patriótica Argentina.
Congreso Nacionalista
see Congreso Nacionalista de Trabajadores.

Liga Patriotica Argentina.
Estatutes. Buenos Aires, Imp. Rinaldi Anos, 1919.
35 p. 11cm.
At head of title: La "Liga patriotica argentina" reconoce al Gran pueblo Argentino une e indivisible, con su bandera azul y blanca y suchimo nacinnal.
55714-15

NL 0359620 DL

Liga patriótica de Aguada.
Album histórico de Aguada, P. R.
see under Gonzáles, Eugenio, comp.

Liga patriotica de ensenanza popular.
Memoria. 1st-
1890-
Montevideo, 1890-
1 v. 23½cm.

NL 0359622 DHEW

G342.863
P191cYt
Liga patriótica femenina, Panama.
Recomendaciones de la Liga patriótica femenina al proyecto de Constitución de 1945. Panamá, R. de P. [La Estrella de Panamá, 1945]
27,[1]p. 22cm.

1. Panama (Republic) Constitution.

NL 0359623 TxU

Liga patriótica por Colombia y Antioquia.
. Antioquia por Colombia; documentos relacionados con el proyecto de ferrocarril troncal del Occidente colombiano, recogidos y publicados por la Liga patriótica. Medellin, Impr. oficial, 1925.
300, ii p. illus., map. 24cm.

Below imprint: Encargado de la edición: Tomás Cadavid Restrepo.

312360B. 1. Railways--Colombia-- Projected roads. I. Cadavid Restrepo, Tomás, ed.
April 17, 1946

NL 0359624 NN

WF
1
L724a
1951
LIGA Paulista contra a Tuberculose, São Paulo
Atividades. São Paulo, 1951.
54 p. illus.

NL 0359625 DNLM

Liga paulista contra a tuberculose.
Defesa contra a tisica
see under title

W 1
LI437
LIGA Paulista contra a Tuberculose, São Paulo
Relatório do exercício.
São Paulo ₁19
v.
1948-50 combined in one issue.

NL 0359627 DNLM PPC

Liga Paulista de Hygiene Mental.
Archivos paulistas de hygiene mental
see under title

Wason
HX754
M2L72+
Liga Pembela Demokrasi, Surabaya.
Rakjat menggugat; Pemberontakan Partai Komunis Indonesia c. s. di Madiun, tanggal 18 September 1948. Surabaja, 1953.
10 p. 30 cm.
Cover title.

NL 0359629 NIC

Liga pentru unitatea culturaiă a tuturor Românilor (Liga culturaiă)
Clujul; viata culturală românească. Ed.Ligii culturale, sectiunea Cluj, cu ocazia congresului anual al Ligii culturale, Cluj 22-24 iunie 1929. ₁Cluj?, Ed.Ligii culturale, sectiunea Cluj, Inst. de arte grafice "Ardealul", 1929₁
118 p.,1 ℓ. illus.(incl.ports.) fold. plan. 17ᶜᵐ.
Describes the schools, learned societies, and other cultural institutions of Cluj.
Brief articles on p.₍5₎-50 signed by various authors; p.₍60₎-118 by P.Sergescu (cf.mss.note on cover)

1. Cluj--Intellectual life. I. Sergescu, Pierre.

NL 0359630 MiU

Liga Pernambucana contra a Tuberculose.
Jornal de medicina de Pernambuco
see under title

722
Liga pernambucana contra a tuberculose.
Relatorio apresentado ... 1904 pelo Octavio de Freitas ... Recife, 1904.

NL 0359632 DPU

Liga peruana pro aviación.
... Estatutos de la Liga peruana pro aviacion. Lima, Imp. del Estado, 1910.
8 p. 20½ᵐ.

1. Aeronautics--Societies.
War 12–228
Library, War College Div. General Staff

NL 0359633 DNW

pF1235
F592L5
Liga Política Nacional.
Breves apuntes sobre la vida del c. General Angel Flores, candidato a la presidencia de la república. [México, 1923]
14 p. port. 19cm.
At head of title: 1924-1928.

1. Flores, Angel, 1883-1926. 2. Mexico - Presidents - Election. I. Title.

NL 0359634 CU-B

"Liga," Polski Akademicki Związek Zbliżenia Międzynarodowego
see
Polski Akademicki Związek Zbliżenia Międzynarodowego "Liga."

Liga Pomocy Przemysłowej.
Skorowidz przemysłowo-handlowy Królestwa Galicyi. Lwów, 1906.
xlvi, 544 p. 26 cm.

1. Galicia--Indus.--Direct. 2. Galicia--Comm.--Direct. 3. Galicia--Registers. I. Title.
HC267.G3L5
65–86854

NL 0359636 DLC

₁Liga popierania turystyki₁
Poland. ₁Warsaw, Liga popierania turystyki (League for promotion of tourism) 1937₁
cover-title, 15, ₁1₁ p. illus. (incl. maps) plates. 20ᵐ.

1. Poland--Descr. & trav.--Guide-books.
44–24705
Library of Congress DK403.L5
914.38

NL 0359637 DLC MH

Liga popierania turystyki.
Polska. Pologne. Poland ... ₁Kraków, Drukarnia narodowa, 1938₁
₁20₁ p. illus. (2 col.) map. 33½ᵐ.
"Tourist revue of the League for promotion of tourism and the Polish state railways, summer, 1938."
Polish, French, English and German.
Map and text on p. ₍2₎, text on p. ₍3₎ of cover.
"Redakcja : Dr. H. Szatkowski."

1. Poland--Descr. & trav. 2. Poland--Descr. & trav.--Views. I. Szatkowski, H., ed. II. Title.
A 41–4717
Oberlin college. Library
for Library of Congress

NL 0359638 OO

Liga Popierania Turystyki. *Komisja Studiów.*
Biuletyn. t. 1-
Kraków, 1937-
v. illus., maps (part col.) 24 cm. annual.

1. Tourist trade--Poland--Yearbooks.
G155.P7L5
60–57262

NL 0359639 DLC

VOLUME 332

WC
335
L723a
1951

LIGA Portuguesa de Profilaxia Social,
Oporto
    A acção da Liga Portuguesa de
Profilaxia Social em prol dos leprosos
Portugueses. Porto, Impr. Social, 1951.
    94 p. (Its Cadernos culturais, 11)
    1. Leprosy - Portugal

NL 0359640   DNLM

HQ
1019. P8
L723a
1952

LIGA Portuguesa de Profilaxia Social,
Oporto
    A acção da Liga Portuguesa de
Profilaxia Social em prol do casamento
das enfermeiras dos hospitais civis.
Porto, Impr. Social, 1952.
    92 p. (Cadernos culturais)
    1. Marriage law - Portugal
    2. Nurses - Legal status, laws, etc. -
Portugal

NL 0359641   DNLM

W 1
LI443

LIGA Portuguesa de Profilaxia Social, Oporto
    Boletim. no. 1-2/3; 1929-31. Porto.
    3 no. in 1 v.

NL 0359642   DNLM

309.469
L626c

Liga Portuguesa de Profilaxia Social, Oporto.
    Cadernos culturais; ₍publicações₎
₍no.1₎-
Pôrto, Imprensa Social, 1948-
    v. 19cm.

Some issues lack series title and numbering.
No. 15 issued jointly by the league and the
Sociedade Portuguesa de Ciencias Veterinarias.

NL 0359643   IU

Liga Portuguesa de Profilaxia Social, Oporto.
    O combate às moscas e mosquitos, transmissores de muitas₎
e graves doenças. Porto, Imprensa Social, 1954₎

    97 p. (Cadernos culturais, 13)

NL 0359644   MBCo

Liga Portuguesa de Profilaxia Social, *Oporto.*
    Conferências.
    Pôrto,
        v. illus., ports. 24 cm.
    Began publication in 1933. *cf.* Union list of serials.

    1. Hygiene, Public—Portugal. ₍1. Public health—Portugal₎
2. Social problems.
    RA511.L46   Med 47-3554
    U. S. Army Medical Libr.   ₍W1L I 444₎
    for Library of Congress   ₍a51c1₎†

NL 0359645   DNLM CtY FU ICRL DLC

Liga pro ayuda a Dinamarca, Buenos Aires.

DL101
.D5

Dinamarca, publicación de la "Liga pro ayuda a Dinamarca."
    año ₍1₎-   (no. 1-   ); julio 1940-
    Buenos Aires ₍1940-

308
z
Box 681

Liga protectora de estudiantes pobres, Santiago de Chile.
    La Liga protectora de estudiantes pobres de
Santiago de Chile en su cincuentenario, 1872-
1922₎ su historia y su obra. Antecedentes re-
copilados por el presidente de la institución.
Santiago de Chile, Imparcial, 1940.
    64 p.

NL 0359647   NNC

276

Liga protectora de estudiantes pobres de Rancagua.
    Novena memoria del presidente, 3 de noviembre
de 1912.
    [Binder's title "Education. Miscellaneous v. 3"]

NL 0359648   DPU

Liga protectora de La Serena.

Aguinaldo a la Liga protectora de La Serena ... **año**
1-   1. enero 1876-
Serena ₍Chile₎ Imprenta de la Reforma, 1876-

Liga Przyjaciół Żołnierza.
see
Liga Obrony Kraju.

W 1
LI45

LIGA Puertorriqueña Contra el Cáncer
    Revista. año 1-14, no. 3; nov. 1940-
jun. 1954. San Juan.
    14 v. in   ports.

    Articles in Spanish or English.
    No more published?
    1. Neoplasms - period.

NL 0359651   DNLM ICRL MH

Liga Reformy, *London*
see
Reform League, *London.*

Z
1003
.L5
date

Liga solidaria argentina.
    ... Celebración del día del libro; conferencias
radiofónicas ... 193   [Mendoza?] 19
    v. 19.5 cm.

NL 0359653   DPU

Liga Uruguaya contra el alcoholismo
    see   Liga nacional contra el alcoholismo
de la república oriental del Uruguay.

W 1
LI455

LIGA Uruguaya Contra el Cáncer Genital
    Femenino
    Boletín oficial. año 1-26 (no. 1-91/92);
1926-1./2. trimestre 1952. Montevideo.
    26 v. in
    No more published?
    1. Gynecologic neoplasms - period.

NL 0359655   DNLM ICJ

W 3
LI448
1931

LIGA Uruguaya contra el Cáncer Genital
    Femenino
    Conferencia anticancerosa ₍del Uruguay₎
24 a 30 de Agosto 1930, Montevideo.
Actas y trabajos, exposición científica.
Montevideo, Impr. "El Siglo Ilustrado, "
1931.
    xxiii, 651 p. illus., ports.
    Title: Conferencia anticancerosa
del Uruguay

NL 0359656   DNLM

Liga uruguaya contra la tuberculosis, Montevideo.
    Boletín. no.56-121, Sept./Oct.1946-July/Aug.
1947. Montevideo, 1946-1957.
    1v. illus. bimonthly.

    Incomplete.

NL 0359657   ICRL

W 6
P3

LIGA Uruguaya contra la Tuberculosis
    Cincuentenario de su fundación,
1902-1952. ₍Montevideo, 1952₎
    ₍32₎ p. (chiefly illus., ports.)
    Cover title.

NL 0359658   DNLM

WF
1
qL723

LIGA Uruguaya contra la Tuberculosis
    ₍Collection of publications₎
    The Library has a collection of
miscellaneous publications of this
organization kept as received. These
publications are not listed or bound
separately.
    1. Tuberculosis - Uruguay

NL 0359659   DNLM

HD9506
.S75B6

Liga vizcaína de productores, Bilbao.
    Boletín minero e industrial.

    Bilbao, 19

Liga vizcaína de productores, *Bilbao, Spain.*
    Catálogo de productos metalúrgicos de Vizcaya ... Bilbao,
Liga vizcaína de productores ₍1942₎
    ₍179₎ p. incl. illus., plates, map, tables (1 fold.) diagrs. (1 fold.) 30ᶜᵐ.
    "Segunda edición."—Prólogo.

    1. Steel-works—Vizcaya, Spain.
                         46-40921
    Library of Congress   TS330.V5L5   1942

NL 0359661   DLC NNUN

₍Liga vizcaína de productores, *Bilbao, Spain*₎
    Estadística de precios e índices de primeras materias y pro-
ductos en España de 1913 a 1941. ₍Bilbao, 1943₎
    121 p., 2 l. 21ᶜᵐ. ₍Its Publicación no. 36₎

    1. Raw materials. 2. Spain—Indus.—Stat. ɪ. Title.
                         45-15408
    Library of Congress   HC385.L47

NL 0359662   DLC

VOLUME 332

Liga Vizcaína de Productores, Bilbao, Spain.
   Informes relativos á tratados de comercio,
mejora de os cambios y Ley de huelgas, por
Pablo de Alzola y Minondo, presidente.   Bilbao,
Impr. de la Casa de Misericordia, 1903.
   157 p.   21^{cm}.

HC385
L723

   1.Spain - Commerce.   2.Exchange.   3.Strikes
and lockouts - Spain.   I.Alzola y Minondo,
Pablo de, 1860-1912.   II.Title.

NL 0359663   CSt-H

Liga vyzvolennîâ Ukraïny
   see
League for Ukraine's Liberation.

Liga Walther do Brasil.

   O Jovem luterano ... ano 1-
jan. 1940-
   Porto Alegre, Liga Walther do Brasil [1940-

Liga zashchity deteĭ
   see
League for the Protection of Children.

Liga zum Schutze der Deutschen Kultur.
   Der Kommunismus, sein Wesen und seine Ziele
   see under title

Ligacz, Richard
   Aesops Einfluss auf die deutsche Literatur
des 16.Jahrhunderts.   [Berlin-Steglitz, A.
Hentrich, 1948]
   87 p.

PT123
G74L5

   Inaug.-Diss. - Krakow.
   "Quellennachweis": p.10-12.

   1. Aesopus.   2. German literature - Early
modern (to 1700) - Hist. & crit.

NL 0359668   CU NNC NjP MiU

Ligacz, Richard
   Aesops Einfluss auf die deutsche Literatur des
16.Jahrhunderts.   [Krakau] 1945

NL 0359669   MH

Ligah le-hithkarvuth we-shiṭuf yehudi-'aravi
   see
League for Jewish-Arab rapprochement and understanding
   (*Palestine*)

---

ha-Ligah li-meniʻat kefiyah datit be-Yisrael.   ha-Vaʻad ha
   -poʻel ha-artsi.
                                        ידיעון.
                                        [ירושלים]

   no. in   v.   25-33 cm.
   Issues for   lack title and number.

   1. Religion and state—Israel—Periodicals.   2. Judaism—Israel—
Periodicals.

                           Title romanized: Yediʻon.
   BM390.L53   HE 68-4213

NL 0359671   DLC

The ligaments of the oviduct of the domestic fowl
   see under   [Curtis, Maynie R.]

... Ligan: a collection of tales and essays
   see under   [Duane, William] 1808-1882.

Ligarides, Pantaleon, metropolitan of Gaza.
   Perì tou Katharteriou puròs Katà Barlaam
   see under   Arcudius, Petrus, 1562-1633.

Ligarius, Johannes, 1529-1596.

   Dresdner gesangbuch.   1759.
   Das privilegirte ordentliche und vermehrte Dressdnische
gesang-buch, wie solches so wohl in der churfl. sächsis. schloss-
capelle, als in den andern kirchen bey der churfürstl. sächsischen residentz, nach den lieder-numern an den tafeln, hier-
nächst auch in den gesamten chur- und fürstlich-sächsischen
landen bey öffentlichem gottesdienste gebraucht, und daraus
gesungen zu werden pflegt; darinnen die auserlesensten und
geistreichsten lieder in reicher anzahl zusammen getragen; auf
hohen befehl und vieler verlangen in diesem bequemen formate
mit klarer schrift zum drucke gegeben worden, von einem

   seinem Jesu getreu bleibenden diener ...   Dressden und Leipzig, Verlag der Waltherischen buchhandlung, 1759.

Ligas, Peppino.
   "Rapporto di proporzione"; misure
proporzionate all'altezza ed al torace.
3. ed.   [Torino, Ligas Scuola di Taglio e
Confezione, 195-?]
   1v. (unpaged) tables.   25cm.

I
611
L723 R

   Cover title.

   1. Anatomy, Human   2. Tailoring   I. Ti.

NL 0359677   NB

Ligault (P.-E.)   * De la nature des fièvres inter-
mittentes.   32 pp.   4°.   Paris, 1852, No. 245, v.
548.

NL 0359678   DNLM

Ligda, M   G   H
   Analysis of motion of small precipitation
areas and bands in the hurricane, August
23-28, 1949.   Cambridge, 1955.
   41 p.   illus.   28 cm.   (Massachusetts
Institute of Technology.   Dept of Meteorology.   Weather radar research.   Technical
note no.3)

MO1.81
M414te
no.3

   Cover title.

   Contract DA-36-039 SC-64472.

NL 0359679   DAS

Ligda, M   G   H
   A proposed radar storm warning service for Army combat operations.   Cambridge, Mass., Special Projects Laboratory, Geophysics Research Directorate, Air Force Cambridge
Research Center, 1954.

   v 1., 74 p.   illus.   28 cm.   (Air Force surveys in geophysics, no. 54)
   "AFCRC-TN-54-20."
   Bibliography: p. 72-74.
   1. Radar meteorology.   2. U. S. Air Force.   I. Title: Radar
storm warning service.   (Series: U. S. Air Force.   Cambridge
Research Center.   Geophysics Research Directorate.   Air Force sur-
veys in geophysics, no. 54.   Series: U. S. Air Force.   Cambridge
Research Center.   AFCRC-TN-50-20)

   QC1.U53   no. 54-20   *629.12   629.13245   55-60258
                           QC801.U54   no. 54

NL 0359680   DLC DAS

Ligda, Myron G   H
   Special radar scope cameras.   Cambridge,
Mass., Massachusetts Institute of Technology,
1951.
   41 p.   illus., diagrs.   28cm.   (Massachusetts Institute of Technology.   Dept. of Meteorology.   Weather radar research.   Technical report no.11)

MO1.81
M414w
no.11

   "References": p.41.
   Off-set printing.

NL 0359681   DAS

Ligda, Paul.
   The teaching of elementary algebra, by Paul Ligda ... with
an introduction by John Wesley Young ...   Boston, New York
[etc.] Houghton Mifflin company [*1925]
   xvii, 256 p.   illus., diagrs.   19½^{cm}.

   1. Algebra—Study and teaching.   I. Title.

   Library of Congress   QA159.L5

                                              25—6648

NL 0359682   MtBC OrPR Or PU PPLas PPT NcD CaBVaU ViU ICJ NN MB
             DLC OrU OrSaW WaS CoU FMU KEmT ICJ MtU

Ligdas, Basil, 1901-
   Die zwillingsgeburt mit einer abgestorbenen frucht.
Inaug. diss.   Berlin, 1928.
   Bibl.

NL 0359683   ICRL OU CtY

Ligdas, Nikolas, 1903-
   ... Ueber den Einfluss der Caldwell-Luc-
Operation auf das Zahnsystem ...   Charlotten-
burg [1936]
   Inaug.-Diss. - Berlin.
   Lebenslauf.
   "Literatur": p. [23]-24.

NL 0359684   CtY

Die LIGDRAER; Maandblad van die Ned.
   Geref. Sendingkerk van S.A., Kaapland.
Paarl, N.G.S.-Kerk, 1940-
   v.   22.5cm.
   Monthly.

   Have: v.1(1940)-v.7,no.12 (Feb. 1947);
v.9 (1948)-v.14,no.4 (April, 1953);
v.15, no.3 (March 1954)-

NL 0359685   MH-AH

Lige
   see
Liége.

LIGEARD, H.
   ...La théologie scolastique et la transcendance du
surnaturel, par H.Ligeard...   Paris[etc.]G.Beauchesne
& cie.,1908.
   viii,138,[1]p.   18cm.   (Bibliothèque apologétique,8)

L100
L72

   1.Supernatural.   2.Catholic church--Doctrinal and
controversial works.

NL 0359687   ICU MH IMunS

Ligenza, Henryk, pseud.
   see   Krasiński, Zygmunt, hrabia,
1812-1859.

VOLUME 332

Ligenza, Joseph Raymond, 1924-
   The triiodide ion complexes of amylose and
of the Schardinger dextrins; theoretical and
experimental. ₍New York₎ 1955.
   80 l. diagrs., tables. 29cm.

   Thesis, Columbia University.
   Typescript.
   Bibliographical footnotes.

NL 0359689   NNC

Ligeoix, Maurice.
   ... La question du renvoi en droit international privé ...
Périgueux, Impr. Cassard jeune, 1902.
   ix, ₍1₎, 172 p. 25ᶜᵐ.
   Thèse—Univ. de Poitiers.
   "Bibliographie": p. ₍v₎-ix.

   1. Renvoi.

Library of Congress   JX6650.R5L6   11—7959

NL 0359690   DLC

Ligeoix de la Combe
      see   La Combe, Ligeoix de.

Liger.
   Lettres critiques et dissertation sur le prêt
de commerce
      see   Liger, René.

Liger, A., joint ed.

Luxemburg (Grand duchy) Courts.
   Pasicrisie luxembourgeoise. Recueil de la jurisprudence
luxembourgeoise en matière civile, commerciale, criminelle, de
droit public, fiscal, administratif et notarial ... t. i–
₍1872/1880₎–
Luxembourg. Imprimerie T. Schroell, 1881-19

WC
27950
Liger, Albert, 1854-
   Jeanne d'Arc, épisode de l'histoire de
France. Préface de Georges d'Esparbbès.
Illustrations de l'imagier Andhré Des
Gachons. Orléans, H. Herluison, 1897 [i.e.
1898]
   166 p. illus. 24 cm.

   1. Jeanne d'Arc, Saint, 1412-1431.

NL 0359694   CtY MH NBC

Liger, Charles Louis, 1715-1760, praeses.
   An mutatis meribus Parisinorum, mutataque
medicinae theoria, rarior venae sectio in morbis
acutis?
      see under   Frasne, Joannes Mathaeus de,
respondent.

616.99
L723t
Liger, Charles Louis, 1715-1760.
   Traité de la goutte, dans lequel, après avoir
fait connoître le caractère propre & les
vraies causes de cette maladie, on indique les
moyens les plus sûrs pour la bien traiter &
la guérir radicalement. Par m. Charles-Louis
Liger ... Paris, La veuve Quillau ₍etc.₎
1753.
   2 p.l., ₍vii₎-xxiv, 387, ₍8₎ p. 17ᶜᵐ.

   1. Gout.

NL 0359696   MiU NNNAM DNLM CtY

Liger, Charles Louis, 1715-1760.
   A treatise on the gout: from the French of M. Charles
Louis Liger ... London, R. Griffiths, 1760.
   1 p. l., v-xv, 384 p. 20ᵐᵐ.

   1. Gout.

Library of Congress   RC291.L72   7—34015

NL 0359697   DLC CaBVaU MnU-B CtY DNLM NcD ICJ

526.98
L723s6
1937
Liger, E.
   Guía práctica de topografía usual. Tra-
ducida por José Ma. Mantero. 3.ed.
Barcelona, G.Gili, 1937.
   146p. illus.(part fold.) 20cm.

   Translation of his Sur le terrain, guide
pratique de topographie usuelle.

   1. Topographical surveying. I. Title.

NL 0359698   CLSU

Liger, E
   Sur le terrain; guide pratique de topographie usuelle à
l'usage des élèves-ingénieurs, des élèves-topographes et des
aspirants aux examens et concours des ponts et chaussées.
Paris, H. Dunod et E. Pinat, 1910.
   110 p. illus. 20cm.

NL 0359699   NIC

Liger, E
   Sur le terrain, guide pratique de topographie usuelle à
l'usage des élèves-ingénieurs, des élèves-topographes et des
aspirants aux examens et concours des ponts et chaussées. Par
E. Liger ... 2. éd., par Marcel Gazeau ... Préface de René
Danger ... Paris, Dunod, 1942.
   3 p. l., 115 p. illus., fold. pl., diagrs. 21ᶜᵐ.

   1. Topographical surveying.   I. Gazeau, Marcel, ed. II. Title.
                                                    45—34299
Library of Congress   TA590.L6 1942
                                                    526.9

NL 0359700   DLC NNE CoU IU

Liger, François Joseph, 1819-1907.
   La Cénomanie romaine; ses limites; sa capitale: ses
villes mortes; ses bourgs et villages; ses voies antiques.
Par F. Liger ... Paris, Champion ₍etc.₎; Le Mans, De
Saint-Denis, 1903.
   vi, 390 p. illus., vii plans, 2 fold. maps. 25½ᶜᵐ.
   On cover: 1904.
   "Ouvrages du même auteur": p. ₍388₎-390.

   1. Gaul—Description, geography. 2. Sarthe, France (Dept.)—Antiq.
3. Mans, Le—Antiq. 4. France—Antiquities, Roman.   I. Title.
                                                    20—10938
Library of Congress   DC62.5.L5

NL 0359701   DLC

Joseph
Liger, François₎ 1819-1907.
   Dictionnaire historique et pratique de la
voirie ... Fosses d'aisances, latrines, urinoirs
et vidanges ... Par F. Liger ... Paris, J.
Baudry, 1875.
   vi, 548p. illus., 16 pl., diagrs. 24cm.

   1. Sewerage.

NL 0359702   DP CtY DNLM MdBP

Joseph
Liger, F₍rançois₎, 1819-1907.
   La ferronnerie ancienne et moderne; ou, Monographie du fer
et de la serrurerie. Paris: l'auteur, 1873-75. 2 v. pl. 8°.

   1. Iron.—Manufacture. 2. Iron   COURTLANDT PALMER MEM. COLL.
work.   November 2, 1914.

NL 0359703   NN

Joseph
Liger, François₎ 1819-1907.
   La ferronnerie, ancienne et moderne, ou mono-
graphie du fer et de la serrurerie. Par F.
Liger... Paris, J.Baudry, 1875.
   2 v. illus., 72 pl. 24 1/2cm.
   V.2 has imprint: Paris, Chez l'auteur, 1875.

   1. Iron-founding - History. 2. Locks and keys.
3. Ironwork.

NL 0359704   DP MB MH

WAA
L723f
1875
LIGER, François Joseph, 1819-1907.
   Fosses d'aisances, latrines, urinoirs
et vidanges, historique, construction
ventilation, désinfection études des différents systèmes application à l'agriculture, législation et jurisprudence. Paris,
Baudry, 1875.
   vi, 548 p. illus. (His Dictionnaire
historique et pratique de la voirie de la
construction, de la police municipale et
de la contiguïté)

NL 0359705   DNLM TxU CU

W 4
P23
1953
no. 720
LIGER, François Marie, 1927-
   Sclérodermie et maladie de Paget.
₍Paris, 1953₎
   65 ℓ. (Paris. ₍Université₎ Faculté
de médecine. Thèse, 1953, no. ₍720₎)
   1. Bones - Diseases 2. Scleroderma

NL 0359706   DNLM

Liger, Gaston.
   Aux sources du Rhin. Ne dites plus que la
Suisse est un pays trilingue. Elle a depuis
dimanche, une quatrième langue nationale: le
romanche.

   Cut from L'Epoque, Paris, 22 février, 1938.
Newspaper cuttings.

NL 0359707   MH

Liger, Gaston.
   Renaissance du romanche. Ces rudes vallées
des Grisons où la France recrutait les beaux
régiments suisses de ses rois.

   Cut from l'Epoque, Paris, 23 février, 1938.
Newspaper cuttings.

NL 0359708   MH

Liger, Henri.
   ... La vaccination antidiphtérique dans un
corps de troupes (10ᵉ régiment de dragons à
Montauban), ses indications, sa mise en oeuvre,
ses résultats, ses enseignements ... Toulouse,
1933.
   Thèse - Univ. de Toulouse.
   "Bibliographie": p. [65]-69.

NL 0359709   CtY

VOLUME 332

Liger, Jacques.
... Sur une nouvelle méthode de détermination des courbes tension-courant des électrolytes ... Rouen, 1934.
Thèse - Univ. de Caen.

NL 0359710   CtY

LIGER, Joseph.
Recueil des dispositions pénales dont l'application appartient aux juges de simple police. Luxembourg, 1876.

NL 0359711   MH-L

Bd.w.   Liger, Louis, fl. 1610.
PA   Laudatio funebris piae et felici memoriae
8485   Henrici Magni dedicata. In gymnasio Caluico ...
C84   habita ... Parisiis, Apud Ioan. Libert, 1610.
D4
1602   71 ₍₁₎ p. a⁴, B-I⁴. 8vo.
Cage

NL 0359712   DFo WU

793.71   Liger, Louis, sieur d'Auxerre, 1658-1717.
L62a   Academie des jeux historiques, contenant les jeux de l'histoire de France, de l'histoire romaine, de la fable, du blason, et de la geographie; & les regles pour les joüer. Avec les elemens de ces sciences pour y servir d'introduction
                Ouvrage très-utile à toutes sortes de personnes
                Par le sieur L. Liger.   A Paris, Chez Le Gras 1718.
                358p. front.
                With this is bound: Academie universelle des jeux. Paris, 1718.

NL 0359713   IU

Liger, Louis, *sieur d'Auxerre*, 1658-1717.
Amusemens de la campagne, ou Nouvelles ruses innocentes, qui enseignent la maniere de prendre aux piéges toutes sortes d'oiseaux & de bêtes à quatre pieds; avec les plus beaux secrets de la peche dans les riviers & étangs, & un traité general de toutes les chasses. Le tout divisé en quatre livres. Par le sieur L. Liger ... Paris, chez C. Prudhomme, 1709.
2 v. illus., diagrs. 17ᶜᵐ.
Title in red and black.

1. Trapping.   2. Fishing.   3. Hunting.

                                                    A 18—1506
Harvard Univ. Library
for Library of Congress   ₍a41b1₎

NL 0359714   MH CtY TxDaM-P

SK   Liger, Louis, *sieur d'Auxerre*, 1658-1717
28   Amusemens de la campagne; ou Nouvelles
.L5   ruses innocentes, qui enseignent la maniere de prendre aux piéges toutes sortes d'oiseaux & de bêtes à quatre pieds; avec les plus beaux secrets de la pêche dans les rivieres & étangs & un traité general de toutes les chasses.   Paris, C. Prudhomme, 1734.
          2 v.   illus.   17 cm.

1. Trapping.   2. Fishing.   3. Hunting.

NL 0359715   WU NN MH

Liger, Louis, sieur d'Auxerre, 1658-1717.
Uzn58   Amusemens de la campagne, ou Nouvelles
753ℓ   ruses innocentes, qui enseignent la maniere de prendre aux piéges toutes sortes d'oiseaux & de bêtes ... avec les ... secrets de la pêche ... & un traité general de toutes les chasses ... Par le Sieur L. Liger ... A Paris, au Palais, Chez Saugrain, pere[v.2: fils], Grand'salle, à la Providence[v.2: à la Bonne Foy Couronnée]. 1753.
          2v. illus. 17cm.

NL 0359716   CtY MH

LIGER, Louis, 1658-1717.
Amusemens de la chasse et de la pêche.   1743.

NL 0359717   MH

Liger, Louis, sieur d'Auxerre, 1658-1717.
L'art de toute sorte de chasse et de pêche
see under title

₍Liger, Louis, *sieur d'Auxerre*₎ 1658-1717.
La connoissance parfaite des chevaux; contenant la maniere de les gouverner, nourrir & entretenir en bon corps, & de les conserver en santé dans les voyages. Avec un détail general de toutes leurs maladies, des signes & des causes d'où elles proviennent, des moyens de les prevenir & de les en guerir par des remedes experimentez depuis long-tems & à la portée de tout le monde. Joint à une nouvelle instruction sur le haras ... On trouve aussi dans ce livre l'art de monter à cheval, & de dresser les chevaux de manege, tiré non seulement des meilleurs auteurs qui en ont écrit, mais encore des mémoires manuscrits

de feu monsieur Delcampes ₍sic₎ Le tout enrichi de figures en taille-douce. Paris, P. Ribou, 1712.
9 p. L., 542, ₍10₎ p. front., plates. 19ᶜᵐ.

1. Horses. 2. Horses—Diseases. 3. Horse-training.   I. Delcampe,
——. II. Title.

Library of Congress   SF285.L56   43-29743

NL 0359720   DLC PU-V

₍636.1   ₍Liger Louis, sieur d'Auxerre₎ 1658-1717.
L62c   La connoissance parfaite des chevaux; contenant
1730   la maniere de les gouverner, nourrir & entretenir en bon corps, & de les conserver en santé dans les voyages. Avec un détail general de toutes leurs maladies, des signes & des causes d'où elles proviennent, des moyens de les prevenir & de les en guerir par des remedes experimentez depuis long-tems & à la portée de tout de monde. Joint à une nouvelle instruction sur le haras ... et L'art de monter a cheval et de dresser les che-

vaux de manege, tiré non seulement des meilleurs auteurs qui en ont écrit, mais encore des memoires manuscrits de feu monsieur Descampes ₍sic₎ Le tout enrichi de figures en taille-douce. Paris, La Veuve de P. Ribou, 1730.
          546p. illus. 20cm.

NL 0359722   IU CU

₍Liger, Louis, sieur d'Auxerre₎ 1658-1717.

La connoissance par faite des chevaux, contenant la maniere de les gouverner & de les conserver en santé... Augmenté d'un nouveau dictionnaire de manege... A Paris, Par la Compagnie des libraires, 1741.
          548, 187(i.e. 224)p. illus. 20½ᶜᵐ.

          Pages 209-224 (second pagination) incorrectly numbered 173-187.

NL 0359723   NjP

Liger, Louis, *sieur d'Auxerre*, 1658-1717.
La culture parfaite des jardins fruitiers et potagers, avec des dissertations sur de fausses maximes que plusieurs auteurs ont établies jusqu'icy sur la taille des arbres. Par le sieur Louis Liger, d'Auxerre. Paris, D. Beugnie', 1702.
18 p. L., 448, ₍13₎ p. illus. 17ᶜᵐ.

1. Gardening. ₍I. Horticulture₎ 2. Pruning.

                                                    Agr 25-1457
Library, U. S. Dept. of   Agriculture 90L62

NL 0359724   DNAL

---

634   Liger, Louis, sieur d'Auxerre, 1658-1717.
L62c   Culture parfaite des jardins fruitiers &
1715   potagers, avec des dissertations sur la taille des arbres. Nouv.éd., revûe, corrigée & augmentée de plusieurs novelles expériences. Paris, F. Le Breton, 1714.
          569p. illus. 18cm.

          1. Gardening—Early works to 1800.

NL 0359725   IU

SB99   Liger, Louis, sieur d'Auxerre, 1658-1717.
F715   Culture parfaite des jardins fruitiers
1743   et potagers: avec des dissertations sur la taille des arbres. Nouv. éd., rev., corr., & augm. A Paris, P. du Mesnil, 1743.
          569 p. illus.

          1. Gardening - France. 2. Pruning.

NL 0359726   CU

Liger, Louis, 1658-1717.
Delices (Les) de la campagne; ou Les ruses de la chasse et de la pesche, ou l'on voit comment on prend toutes sortes d'oiseaux & de bêtes à quatre pieds. Avec les plus beaux secrets de la pêche; et la manier de faire les rets & les filets... A Amsterdam: G. Gallet, 1700.   432 p., 61 pl. 3 ed. 12⁰.

Engraved t.-p. also.

NL 0359727   NN NjP MH

₍Liger, Louis₎ sieur d'Auxerre, 1658-1717.
Uzn25   Delices de la campagne en la
732ℓ   chasse et de la pesche ... Augmenté d'un dictionaire, de tous les termes ... Quatrième edition ... augmentée d'un nouveau traité de la grande chasse & de la connoissance des chiens ... A Amsterdam, Chez Michel Charles Le Cene, 1732.
          2v. 90pl.(part fold.) 16cm.
          Added t.-p., engr., in v.1.
          Reissue of Traité de toute sorte de chasse et de pêche, 1714; the t.-p.'s, engr.t.-p.,

and last 6ℓ. of v.2 are new.
          First edition published in 1709 as Amusemens de la campagne. Also published as: Amusemens de la chasse et de la pêche; and l'Art de toute sorte de chasse et de pêche.
          Based on Les ruses innocentes, by F.Fortin.

NL 0359729   CtY NN MH

Liger, Louis, *sieur d'Auxerre*, 1658-1717.
Dictionaire general des termes propres a l'agriculture. Avec leurs definitions et étymologies, pour servir d'instruction à ceux qui souhaiteront se rendre habiles en cet art. Par le sieur Loüis Liger ... Paris, D. Beugnié, 1703.
12 p. L. 377 p. 17ᶜᵐ.

1. Agriculture—Dictionaries.

                                                    Agr 25-97
Library, U. S. Dept. of   Agriculture 30.1L62

NL 0359730   DNAL PCarlD MH-BA

VOLUME 332

Liger, Louis, *sieur d'Auxerre,* 1658–1717.
Dictionaire pratique du bon menager de campagne et de ville, qui apprend generalement la maniere de nourrir, élever & gouverner, tant en santé que malades, toutes sortes de bestiaux, chevaux & volailles, de scavoir mettre à son profit tout ce qui provient de l'agriculture, de faire valoir toutes sortes de terres, prez, vignes & bois ... & faire generalement tout ce qui convient aux jardins d'ornemens. Avec un traité de tout ce concerne la cuisine, les confitures, la patisserie, les liqueurs de toutes sortes, les

chasses differentes, la pêche & autres divertissemens de la campagne ... Par le sieur L. Liger ... Paris, Chez P. Ribou, 1715.
2 v. in 1. 26ᶜᵐ.

1. Agriculture—Dictionaries. 2. Domestic economy—Dictionaries. 3. Fishing—Dictionaries. 4. Cookery—Dictionaries.

A18–1996

Title from Harvard Univ.   Printed by L. C.

NL 0359732   MH NIC ICJ

Liger, Louis, *sieur d'Auxerre,* 1658–1717.
WD 7400
Dictionaire ₍sic₎ pratique du bon menager de campagne et de ville, qui apprend generalement la maniere de nourrir, élever & gouverner, tant en santé que malades, toutes sortes de bestiaux, chevaux & volailles; de scavoir mettre à son profit tout ce qui provient de l'agriculture; de faire valoir toutes sortes de terres, prez, vignes & bois; de cultiver les jardins, tant fruitiers, potagers, que jardins fleuristes ... Avec un traité de tout ce qui concerne la cuisine, les confitures, la pâtisserie, les liqueurs de toutes sortes, les chasses differentes, la pêche, & autres divertis-

semens de la campagne; les mots latins de tout ce qu'on traite dans ce livre ... Par le sieur L. Liger. Nouv. ed., rev., corr. & augm. ... Paris, La veuve de P. Ribou, 1721-22.
2 v. in 1. 25½ x 20ᶜᵐ.
Published also under title: Dictionnaire universel d'agriculture et de jardinage, de fauconnerie, chasse, pêche, cuisine et manège (Paris, 1751) and encyclopedias.

1. Agriculture—Dictionaries.

2. Home economics - Dictionaries and encyclopedias.

NL 0359734   CtY DNAL

S411
.L5
1722
Rare bk.
Coll.
Liger, Louis, *sieur d'Auxerre,* 1658–1717.
Dictionaire ₍sic₎ pratique du bon menager de campagne et de ville, qui apprend generalement la maniere de nourrir, élever & gouverner, tant en santé que malades, toutes sortes de bestiaux, chevaux & volailles; de scavoir mettre à son profit tout ce qui provient de l'agriculture; de faire valoir toutes sortes de terres, prez, vignes & bois; de cultiver les jardins, tant fruitiers, potagers, que jardins fleuristes ... Avec un traité de tout ce qui concerne la cuisine, les confitures, la pâtisserie, les liqueurs de toutes sortes, les chasses differentes, la pêche, & autres divertis-

semens de la campagne; les mots latins de tout ce qu'on traite dans ce livre ... Par le sieur L. Liger. Nouv. ed., rev., corr. & augm. ... Paris, La veuve de P. Ribou, 1722.
2 v. in 1. 25½ x 20ᶜᵐ.
Published also under title: Dictionnaire universel d'agriculture et de jardinage, de fauconnerie, chasse, pêche, cuisine et manège (Paris, 1751)

1. Agriculture—Dictionaries—French. 2. Domestic economy—Dictionaries—French. 3. Cookery—Dictionaries—French.

45–50631

Library of Congress   S411.L5 1722

NL 0359736   DLC ICU MH

₍Liger, Louis, *sieur d'Auxerre*₎ 1658–1717.
Economia general de la casa de campo. Obra mvy vtil de agricvltvra, tr. del idioma francès al castellano, y aumentada considerablemente. Por el doctor don Francisco de la Torre, y Ocòn ... dividesa en tres tomos. t. 1. En que se trata del sitio, y fabrica conveniente à la casa de campo, y sus oficinas, de las aves domesticas, y animales, que en ella se crian para la vtilidad, y del comercio de sus frutos, y esquilmos de sus ganados, mediante la economia ... Madrid, En la imprenta de J. de Ariztia ₍1720?₎
20 p. l., 552, ₍13₎ p. front., 7 pl. (port.). 23½ᶜᵐ.

Continued in next column

Continued from preceding column

Added t.-p., engraved.
Title vignette; head and tail pieces.
No more published.

1. Agriculture—Early works to 1800. 2. Animal industry.   I. Torre y Ocón, Francisco de la, tr.   II. Title.

U. S. Dept. of agr.   Library   33L623E
for Library of Congress   S515.L735   Agr 14–1105 Revised

NL 0359738   DNAL ICU

Liger, Louis, sieur d'Auxerre, 1658–1717.
Historischer und verständiger blumen-gärtner, oder Unterricht von bau- und wartung der blumen, baume und stauden-gewächse, so zur aufputzung eines gartens dienen können ... Diesem sind annoch beygefuget Nützliche unterredungen und gespräche zwischen einem garten-liebhaber und gartner, von anlegung, wartung und pflegung eines baum- und kuchen-gartens ... Mit vielen darzu gehörigen figuren und kupferstichen ausgezieret. Leipzig, J.L.Gleditsch, und M.G.Weidmann, 1715.
5 p.l.,783,₍31₎ p. front.,illus.,XXI pl.(1 feld.) 20 x 17½ᶜᵐ.

A translation of Liger's Le jardinier fleuriste et historiographe and of François Gentil's Le jardinier solitaire.

1.Gardening—Early works to 1800. I.Gentil,François.

NL 0359740   MiU

NAB
1850
Lie 62
Liger, Louis, sieur d'auxerre 1658–1717
Le jardinier fleuriste et historiographie on la culture universalle des fleurs...par le sieur Louis Liger d'Auxere...a Paris, au palais chez damun bengnie...MDCCIV [1704]. 2 vols.

Contents: Instructions in flower gardening; additional sections on planning and embellishing gardens.
12mo. Vol. I: [xxiv]t. p., ded., pref., contents, 1-379 p., text; 11 engr. folding pls.

Vol. II[viii] contents, 1-480 p., text, 7 engr. folding pls. [481-493 index].

Vol. I: a¹², A¹²-Q¹², R⁴
Vol. II: a³, A¹²-V¹², X⁶.

Binding: Mottled calf, gilt tooling on spine, raised bands. Inscribed by G. A. G. Cromber, 1773 at top of t.p. 6-1/2" x 3-9/16".

NL 0359742   DDO

Liger, Louis, *sieur d'Auxerre,* 1658–1717.
Le jardinier fleuriste et historiographe, ou La culture universelle des fleurs, arbres, arbustes & arbrisseaux, servans à l'embellissement des jardins ... Par le Sieur Louis Liger, d'Auxerre ... Amsterdam, E. Roger, 1706.
2 v. illus., fold. plates. 16½ᶜᵐ.
Paged continuously.

1. Floriculture.

Agr 26–151

Library, U. S. Dept. of   Agriculture 97L62

NL 0359743   DNAL MoSB MBH MH-A

Liger, Louis.
Le jardinier fleuriste et historiographe; ou, La culture universelle des fleurs, arbres, arbustes & arbrisseaux servans à l'embellissement des jardins. Nouvelle éd. 2 tom. (paged contin.). Amsterdam. 1708. sm. 12°. pp. ₍24₎, 680, ₍16₎. 15 plates.

NL 0359744   MH-A

Liger, Louis, *sieur d'Auxerre,* 1658–1717.
Le jardinier fleuriste et historiographe. Der historische blumen-gärtner, oder Anweisung zur allgemeinen anbauung der blumen, bäumen und stauden, die zu auszierung eines gartensdienen. Nebst der art allerley lust-stücken, grüne hecken und wände, bosquetten, boulingrin bedeckte gänge ... In französischer sprache mit sonderbahren fleiss verfertiget von herrn Louis Liger ... Leipzig, J. F. Braun, 1716.
15 p. l, 800, ₍4₎, 175, ₍43₎ p. front., illus., plates (part fold.) 17ᶜᵐ.
In 5 parts, pts. 3–5 with special t.-p. 5. th.: Der wohlerfahrne kräutermeister und blumen-gärtner, welcher zeiget eine kurtze anleitung zu gründlicher erkennung der kräuter und blumen ... (175, ₍11₎ p. at end) "Register" to whole   volume after 5. th.
1. Gardening.   ₍1. Horticulture₎

Agr 26–828

Library, U. S. Dept. of   Agriculture 97L62J

NL 0359745   DNAL

Liger, Louis. Le jardinier fleuriste et historiographe ... Paris, Paulus-du-Mesnil, 1748. 2 v.   YA 1151

NL 0359746   DLC

Liger, Louis, *sieur d'Auxerre,* 1658–1717.
Le jardinier fleuriste, ov, La culture universelle des fleurs, arbres, arbustes, arbrisseaux servant à l'embellissement des jardins ... 2. ed., rev., cor. & augm. considerablement ... Par le Sieur L. Liger. Paris, C. Prudhomme, 1717.
12 p. l., 452, ₍16₎ p. illus., 14 pl. (13 fold.) 17½ᶜᵐ.

1. Horticulture.

Agr 11–2198

Library, U. S. Dept. of   Agriculture 97L62

NL 0359747   DNAL

SB406
I5
1742
Liger, Louis, sieur d'Auxerre, 1658–1717.
Le jardinier fleuriste; ou, La culture universelle des fleurs, arbres, arbustes, arbrisseaux servant à l'embellissement des jardins ... Nouv. éd., rev., cor. & augm. considérablement ... Paris, J. Saugrain, 1742.
xiv,514 p. illus.,fold.plates.

1. Floriculture.

NL 0359748   CU MB N

Liger, Louis, *sieur d'Auxerre,* 1658–1717.
Le jardinier fleuriste, ou, La culture universelle des fleurs, arbres, arbustes, arbrisseaux servant à l'embellissement des jardins ... Par le Sieur L. Liger. Nouv. éd., rev., cor. & augm. considérablement ... Paris, Saugrain fils, 1754.
xx, 535 p. illus., fold. plates. 17ᶜᵐ.

1. Floriculture.

Agr 26–152

Library, U. S. Dept. of   Agriculture 97L62

NL 0359749   DNAL ViW MoSB MH-A

635.9
L62
▼
Liger, Louis, sieur d'Auxerre, 1658–1717.
Le jardinier fleuriste, ou, La culture universelle des fleurs, arbres, arbustes, arbrisseaurx servant à l'embellissement des jardins ... Par le Sieur L. Liger. Nouv. éd., rev., cor. & augm. considerablement ... Paris, Saugrain fils, 1754.
xii, 422 p. illus., fold. plates. 17cm.

NL 0359750   ViW

VOLUME 332

Liger, Louis, *sieur d'Auxerre,* 1658–1717.
Le jardinier fleuriste, ou La culture universelle des fleurs, arbres, arbustes, arbrisseaux servant à l'embellissement des jardins ... Par le Sieur L. Liger. Nouv. ed., rev., cor. & augm. considérablement ... Paris, Savoye, 1763.
xxiv, 504 p. fold. plates. 17ᶜᵐ.

1. Floriculture.
Agr 11–1279
Library, U. S. Dept. of Agriculture 97L62

NL 0359751 DNAL MBH MH-A CU

ˣXL
.764
.L62J

Liger, Louis, sieur d'Auxerre, 1658–1717.
Le jardinier fleuriste, ou La culture universelle des fleurs, arbres, arbustes, arbrisseaux servant à l'embellissement des jardins. Contenant plusieurs parterres sur des desseins nouveaux, bosquets, boulingrins, salles, salons, & autres ornemens de jardin ... Par le sieur L. Liger. Nouvelle edition, revûe, corrigée & augmentée considérablement ...
Du fonds de Claude Prudhomme. A Paris, Chez Savoye, rue Saint Jacques, à l'Espérance.

M. DCC. LXIV. Avec approbation & privilège du Roi. [1764]
xxiv, 504 p. illus., 14 fold.pl. 18cm. (8vo)
Page 132 misnumbered 332.

NL 0359753 MB DLC

Liger, Louis, *sieur d'Auxerre,* 1658–1717.
Le jardinier fleuriste; ou, La culture universelle des fleurs, arbres, arbustes, arbrisseaux servant à l'embellissement des jardins ... par le sieur L. Liger. Nouv. éd., rev., cor. & augm. considérablement ... Paris, Saugrain fils, 1768.
xii, 422 p. fold. plates. 17ᶜᵐ.

1. Floriculture.
Agr 11–389
U. S. Dept. of agr. Library 97L62
for Library of Congress [a38b1]

NL 0359754 DNAL MH-A

WA
12507

Liger, Louis, sieur d'Auxerre, 1658–1717.
Le jardinier fleuriste; ou, La culture universelle des fleurs, arbres, arbustes ... Nouv. ed., rev. cor. & augm. considérablement. Paris, Saugrain fils, 1776.
422p. fold. plates.

1. Floriculture.

NL 0359755 CtY MH-A MH

SB 406
L55
1787

Liger, Louis, *sieur d'Auxerre,* 1658–1717.
Le jardinier fleuriste, ou La culture universelle des fleurs, arbres, arbustes, arbrisseaux servant à l'embellissement des jardins ... Par le Sieur L. Liger. Nouv. éd., rev., cor. & augm. considérablement ... Paris, Savoye, 1787.
16, 499 p. illus., fold. plates. 17 cm.

"Trois livres relié."

NL 0359756 OU NN

Liger, Louis, *sieur d'Auxerre,* 1658–1717.
Le jardinier fleuriste, ou La culture universelle des fleurs, arbres, arbustes, arbrisseaux servant à l'embellissement des jardins ... par le sieur L. Liger. Nouv. éd., rev. cor. & augm. considérablement ... Rouen, P. Dumesnil, 1787.
2 pt. in 1 v. illus., fold. plates. 17ᶜᵐ.
Paged continuously: xii, 372 p.

1. Floriculture.
Agr 28–1147
Library, U. S. Dept. of Agriculture 97L62

NL 0359757 DNAL MH-A MB

NP
2750
L72

Liger, Louis, sieur d'Auxerre, 1658–1717.
Le jardinier fleuriste, ou La culture universelle des fleurs, arbres, arbustes, arbrisseaux servant à l'embellissement des jardins ... Nouv. ed., revue, corrigée & augmentée considérablement. Rouen, Veuve de Pierre Dumesnil, 1788.
xii, 419 p. illus. 19cm.

1. Floriculture. I. Title.

NL 0359758 NIC MH-A

Liger, Louis, sieur d'Auxerre, 1658–1717.

Gentil, François.
Le jardinier solitaire, The solitary or Carthusian gard'ner, being dialogues between a gentleman and a gard'ner ... Written in French by Francis Gentil ... Also The compleat florist: or, The universal culture of flowers, trees and shrubs ... By the Sieur Louis Liger d'Auxerre ... Newly done into English. London, B. Tooke, 1706.

Liger, Louis, sieur d'Auxerre, 1658–1717.
Le menage de la ville et des champs, et le jardinier françois accommodez au gout du tems; ou, La maniere facile d'aprêter tout ce qui est necessaire pour l'usage de la vie, & de cultiver parfaitement les jardins fruitiers, potagers & à fleurs. Avec un traité de la chasse & de la pêche. Par le sieur Liger. Bruxelles: J. Leonard, 1712. 12 p.l., 428 p. 16cm.

22765B. 1. Cookery. 2. Gardening. 3. Hunting. 4. Fishing.
January 31, 1940

NL 0359760 NN CU-A

TX719
L52
1714

[Liger, Louis, sieur d'Auxerre] 1658–1717.
Le menage des champs et de la ville; ou, Nouveau cuisinier françois accommodé au goût du temps. Contenant tout ce qu'un parfait chef de cuisine doit sçavoir pour servir toutes sortes de tables ... Paris, Damien Beugnie, 1714.
584 p.

1. Cookery, French. 2. Cookery - To 1800. I. Title.

NL 0359761 CU NNNAM

SB
99
F8
L72

[Liger, Louis, sieur d'Auxerre] 1658–1717.
Le ménage des champs et de la ville, ou Le nouveau jardinier françois accommodé au goust du temps. Enseignant, tout ce qui se doit mettre en pratique pour cultiver parfaitement les jardins fruitiers, potagers, & fleuristes, avec un Traité des orangers, le tout suivy d'un Traité de la chasse & de la pêche. 2. ptie. du Ménage des champs. Paris, D. Beugnié, 1715.
[16], 447, [15] p. illus. 17cm.

NL 0359762 NIC CU MBH

[Liger, Louis, *sieur d'Auxerre*] 1658–1717.
Le ménage des champs et de la ville, ou, Le nouveau jardinier françois accommodé au goust du tems. Enseignant, tout ce qui se doit mettre en pratique pour cultiver parfaitement les jardins fruitiers, potagers, & fleuristes, avec un traité des orangers, le tout suivi d'un traité de la chasse & de la pêche. Seconde partie du Ménage des champs. Paris, Chez C. David, 1737.
8 p. l., 447, [15] p. illus. 17ᶜᵐ.

NL 0359763 ICJ MB NN

[Liger, Louis, *sieur d'Auxerre*] 1658–1717.
Le menage des champs et de la ville; ou, Nouveau cuisinier françois accommodé au goust du tems. Contenant tout ce qu'un parfait chef de cuisine doit sçavoir pour servir toutes sortes de tables ... Paris, Paulus-du-Mesnil, 1732.
6 p. l., 474 p., 8 l. 17ᶜᵐ.

1. Cookery, French. 2. Cookery—Early works to 1800. I. Title.

TX707.L5 47–37213

NL 0359764 DLC

[Liger, Louis, *sieur d'Auxerre*] 1658–1717.
Le menage des champs et de la ville: ou, Nouveau cuisinier françois accomodé au goust du tems, contenant tout ce qu'un parfait chef de cuisine doit sçavoir pour servir toutes sortes de tables, depuis celles des plus grands seigneurs jusqu'à celles des bons bourgeois, avec une instruction pour faire toutes sortes de pâtisseries, confitures séches & liquides, & toutes les différentes liqueurs qui sont aujourd'hui en usage. Premiere partie du Ménage. Paris, Chez Paulus-du-Mesnil, 1738.
6 p. l., 582, [18] p. 17ᶜᵐ.

NL 0359765 ICJ

[Liger, Louis, *sieur d'Auxerre*] 1658–1717.
Le menage des champs et de la ville; ou, Nouveau cuisinier françois, accommodé au goût du tems. Contenant tout ce qu'un parfait chef de cuisine doit sçavoir pour servir toutes sortes de tables ... Nouv. ed. Paris, C. David, 1739.
473 p. 18 cm.

1. Cookery, French. 2. Cookery—Early works to 1800. I. Title.

TX707.L5 1739 48–35439*

NL 0359766 DLC

TX719
L52
1711

[Liger, Louis, sieur d'Auxerre] 1658–1717.
Le menage des champs, et le jardinier françois accomodez au goût du temps ... Paris, Damien Beugnie, 1711.
536 p. plates (part fold.)

1. Cookery, French. 2. Cookery - To 1800. 3. Gardening - To 1800. I. Title.

NL 0359767 CU MH

Liger, Louis, *sieur d'Auxerre,* 1658–1717.
Le menage universel de la ville et des champs, et le jardinier accommodez au gout du tems; ou la maniere facile d'aprêter tout ce qui est necessaire pour l'usage de la vie, & de cultiver parfaitement les jardins fruitiers, potagers, & à fleurs. Avec un traité de la chasse & de la pêche. Nouvelle ed., augm. de l'essentiel du Dictionaire oeconomique. Ouvrage utile à toutes sortes de personnes. Par le sieur Liger. Bruxelles, J. Leonard, 1720.
15 p. l., 416 p. front. 16½ᶜᵐ.

1. Agriculture. 2. Domestic economy.
Agr 28–436
Library, U. S. Dept. of Agriculture 321L62

NL 0359768 DNAL CU MH

VOLUME 332

LIGER, Louis, sieur d'Auxerres, 1658-1717.
Le menage universel de la ville et des
champs, et le jardinier accommode's au gout du
tems; contenant la patisserie, confitures, liqueurs, la cuisine, la fardinage, la chasse et
la peche. secrets du menage, les abeilles, les
chevaux, les etangs, viviers, canaux, fosse's et
marais... Par Mr. de La Ferriere. Nouvelle
ed. augm. Bruxelles, Chez J. Leonard, 1733.

2 p.l., 502, [25] p. front. 19 1/2 cm.

Contains the same material as "Le menage
universel de la ville et des champs" published
under the name of the sieur Liger, at Brussels,
1720, with the addition of "Traité des abeilles"
by De La Ferriere.

NL 0359770   MH

Liger, Louis, *sieur d'Auxerre*, 1658-1717.
Le nouveau theatre d'agriculture et menage des champs,
contenant la maniere de cultiver & faire valoir toutes sortes
de biens à la campagne. Avec une instruction générale sur les
jardins fruitiers, potagers, jardins d'ornemens & botanique, &
sur le commerce de toutes les marchandises qui proviennent de
l'agriculture; le tout suivi d'un traité de la pêche, & de la
chasse : extrait de Foüilloux, & des meilleurs auteurs ... Par le
sieur Liger. Enrichi d'un grand nombre de figures en taille
douce. Paris, Chez M. David, 1713.
10 p. l., 740 p. plates. 25½ᶜᵐ.
With music.
1. Agriculture. 2. Fish-   ing. 3. Hunting.
Harvard univ. Library   A 18-1999
for Library of Congress   [a39b1]

NL 0359771   MH NN MH-A MBH CtY

Liger, Louis, *sieur d'Auxerre*, 1658-1717.
Uxb33   Le nouveau theatre d'agriculture et menage des champs,
723L   contenant la maniere de cultiver & faire valoir toutes sortes
de biens à la campagne. Avec une instruction générale sur les
jardins fruitiers, potagers, jardins d'ornemens & botanique, &
sur le commerce de toutes les marchandises qui proviennent de
l'agriculture; le tout suivi d'un traité de la pêche, & de la
chasse : extrait de Foüilloux, & des meilleurs auteurs ... Par le
sieur Liger. Enrichi d'un grand nombre de figures en taille
douce. Paris, D. Beugnie, 1723.
10 p. l., 740 p. plates. 25½ᶜᵐ.

NL 0359772   CtY MH

Liger, Louis, sieur d'Auxerre, 1658-1717.
La nouvelle maison rustique, ou économie
générale des viens de campagne. [Paris?
17--?]
p.   26.5 cm.

NL 0359773   NNNAM

Liger, Louis, *sieur d'Auxerre*, 1658-1717.
La nouvelle maison rustique, ou, Economie generale de
tous les biens de campagne ; la maniere de les entretenir
& de les multiplier; donnée ci-devant au public par le
sieur Liger. 3. ed., rev., cor., augm., mise en meilleur
ordre, et enrichie de figures en taille-douce. Par M.***
... Paris, Chez C. Prudhomme, 1721.
2 v. front., illus., plates (2 fold.) 26ᶜᵐ.
Title in red and black.

1. Agriculture. 2. Fish-culture.

A 18-1997
Title from Harvard Univ.   Printed by L. C.

NL 0359774   MH IU

Liger, Louis, *sieur d'Auxerre*, 1658-1717.
La nouvelle maison rustique; ou, Économie generale de
tous les biens de campagne : la maniere de les entretenir &
de les multiplier; donnée ci-devant au public par le sieur
Liger. 4. éd., augm. considérablement, & mise en meilleur ordre; avec la vertu des simples, l'apoticairerie &
les décisions du droit-françois sur les matieres rurales;
et enrichie de figures en taille-douce. Par M. * * * ...
Paris, C. Prudhomme, 1732.
2 v. front. (t. 1) illus., plates (1 fold.) 26½ᶜᵐ.
1. Agriculture.

Agr 21-110

Library, U. S. Dept. of   Agriculture 33.17L62

NL 0359775   DNAL CtY

S
515   Liger, Louis, sieur d'Auxerre, 1658-1717.
+L72   La nouvelle maison rustique; ou, Économie
générale de tous les biens de campagne: la
manière de les entretenir & de les multiplier;
donnée ci-devant au public par le sieur Liger.
4. éd., augm. considerablement, & mise en
meilleur ordre; avec la vertu des simples,
l'apoticairerie & les décisions du droit-
françois sur les matières rurales; et enrichie
de figures en taille-douce par M.+++   Paris,
Prudhomme, 1736.
2 v.   illus.   26cm.

NL 0359776   WU

R
50   LIGER, LOUIS, sieur d'Auxerre, 1658-1717.
.508   La nouvelle maison rustique; ou, Économie generale de tous les biens de campagne... 5. édition augmentée considérablement... Avec la vertu des
simples, l'apoticairerie & les décisions du droit
françois sur les matieres rurales.. par M***[Henricus
Besnier]   Paris, Chez la veuve Prudhomme, 1740.
2v.   illus. (part fold.) port.   26cm.

Title page of vol.2 mutilated, part of imprint
missing.
First published in 1700 under title: Œconomie
générale de la campag-   ne, ou Nouvelle maison
rustique.

NL 0359777   ICN

S
515   Liger, Louis, sieur d'Auxerre, 1658-1717.
.L7   La nouvelle maison rustique; ou, Economie generale de tous les
1743   biens de campagne: la maniere de les entretenir & de les multiplier;
donée ci-devant au public par le Sieur Ligier [sic] 5. éd., augmentée considérablement, & mise en meilleur ordre; avec la vertu des
simples, l'apoticairerie & les décisions du droit françois sur les matieres rurales; et enrichie de figures en taille-douce. Par M. ***
[i. e. H. Besnier] ... A Paris, chez la veuve Prudhomme, 1743.
2 v.   illus.   26 1/2 cm.

First published in 1700 under title: Œconomie générale de la
campagne; ou, Nouvelle maison rustique.
Spine title: Maison rustiq.

"Liger" spelled correctly on title page of t. 2.
Imprint dates altered to 1741 by means of slips pasted over the
last two symbols of the Roman numerals.

1. Agriculture - Early works to 1800. I.
Besnier, Henri, ed. II. Title.

NL 0359779   MiEM

S515   Liger, Louis, sieur d'Auxerre, 1658-1717.
L5   La nouvelle maison rustique, ou, Économie générale de tous
1749   les biens de compagne ... 6. éd., augm. considérablement ...
avec la vertu des simples ... Paris, Saugrain, 1749.
2 v.   illus., plates.

First published in 1700 under title: Oeconomie générale de la
compagne.

1. Agriculture - To 1800. I. Title.

NL 0359780   CU MH-A MH KU

Liger, Louis, *sieur d'Auxerre*, 1658-1717.
La nouvelle maison rustique; ou, Économie générale de tous
les biens de campagne, la manière de les entretenir & de les
multiplier; donnée ci-devant au public par le sieur Liger. Sep-
tième edition, augmentée considérablement, & mise en meilleur
ordre, avec la vertu des simples, l'apothicairerie & les décisions
du droit françois sur les matières rurales ... par M*** [H.
Besnier] Tome premier-second. Paris, Chez Saugrain père,
1755.
2 v. front., illus., plates (part fold.) plans. 26 x 19½ᶜᵐ.
First published in 1700 with title: Oeconomie générale de la campagne; ou,
Nouvelle maison rustique.

NL 0359781   ICJ MH-A MB MH-BA NjP

---

630   Liger, Louis, sieur d'Auxerre, 1658-1717.
L62o   La nouvelle maison rustique; ou, Économie
1762   generale de tous les biens de campagne: la
maniere de les entretenir & de les multiplier;
donnée ci-devant au public par le sieur
Liger. 8. éd., augm. considérablement, & mise
en meilleur ordre: avec la vertu des simples,
l'apoticairerie, & les décisions du droit
françois sur les matieres rurales; et enrichie de figures en taille-douce. Par M.***
Paris, Durand, 1762.
2v. illus.

Title for earlier editions: Oeconomie
générale de la campagne, ou Nouvelle maison
rustique.

1. Agriculture. France. I. Title: La
nouvelle maison rustique. II. Title:
Oeconomie générale de la campagne. III.
Title: Economie   rurale, pratique et
générale de tous   les biens de campagne.
0 cd.

NL 0359783   KU MH-A MBH TxHU

Liger, Louis, *sieur d'Auxerre*, 1658-1717.
La nouvelle maison rustique; ou, Économie generale de
tous les biens de campagne: la maniere de les entretenir & de les multiplier; donnée ci-devant au public par le
sieur Liger. 8. éd., augm. considérablement, & mise en
meilleur ordre: avec la vertu des simples, l'apoticairerie, & les décisions du droit françois sur les matieres
rurales; et enrichie de figures en taille-douce. Par
M.*** Paris, Saugrain aîné, 1762.
2 v. front. (t. 1) illus., plates. 26ᶜᵐ.
1. Agriculture. i. Title.

Agr 18-123
Library, U. S. Dept. of   Agriculture 33.17L62

NL 0359784   DNAL TxHU PMA MH

LIGER, Louis, sieur d'Auxerre, 1658-1717.
La nouvelle maison rustique; ou Économie
generale de tous les iens de campagne: la maniere de les entretenir & de les multiplier; donnée ci-devant au public par le sieur Liger.
8. éd., augmentée considérablement, mise en
meilleur ordre: avec la vertu des simples,
l'apoticairerie, & les décisions du droit françois sur les matieres rurales; Par M.***.
Paris, chez Savoye, 1762.

4°. 2 vol. Pl-tes   and other illustr.

NL 0359785   MH

Liger, Louis, sieur d'Auxerre, 1658-1717.
Nouvelle Maison Rustique ... Paris, Chez la
Veuve Savoye, 1766.
2 v.

NL 0359786   PPGi

VOLUME 332

Liger, Louis, *sieur a'Auxerre,* 1658–1717.
La nouvelle maison rustique, ou Économie générale de tous les biens de campagne; la manière de les entretenir & de les multiplier; donnée ci-devant au public par le sieur Liger. Neuvième édition augmentée confidérablement, & mife en meilleur ordre; avec la vertu des fimples, l'apothicairerie; les décifions du droit fur les matières rurales; et enrichie de figures en taille-douce. Par M. *** [Henri Besnier?]. Tome premier–[second]. .... Paris, Chez Samson, 1768.
2 vol. front., illus., plates (1 fold.) 28 x 22ᶜᵐ.
First published in 1700 under title: Œconomie générale de la campagne ou Nouvelle maifon ruftique.

NL 0359787   ICJ CtY CaBVaU CSmH MH-A

Liger, Louis, sieur d'Auxerre, 1658–1717.
La nouvelle maison rustique, ou Economie générale de tous les biens de campagne; la maniere de les entretenir & de les multiplier. 9 éd. augm. considérablement, & mise en meilleur ordre; avec la vertu des simples, l'apothicairerie; les décisions du droit françois sur les matieres rurales. Paris, Savoye, 1768. 2 v. front., illus., plates. 27 cm.

1978-1979. 1. France--Agriculture. 2. Agriculture--Early   works to 1800. 3. Glassware--France/   v.1 p.37,869-870.

NL 0359788   NCorniC MH

Liger, Louis, *sieur d'Auxerre,* 1658–1717.
La nouvelle maison rustique, ou Économie générale de tous les biens de campagne; la maniere de les entretenir et de les multiplier; donnée ci-devant au public par le sieur Liger. 10. éd., augm. considérablement, & mise en meilleur ordre; avec la vertu des simples, l'apothicairerie, les décisions du droit françois sur les matières rurales; et enrichie de figures en taille-douce. Par M. ••• ... Paris, Desaint, 1772.
2 v. front., illus., plates (1 fold.) 26½ x 21ᶜᵐ.

The 5th-9th editions, 1743-1768, were edited by Henri Besnier, also an earlier (unnumbered?) edition in 1721. (*cf.* Catalogue général ... de la Bibliothèque nationale.) The 11th edition, 1790, was edited by La Bretonnerie.
First published in 1700, under title: Œconomie générale de la campagne, ou Nouvelle maison rustique.

1. Agriculture. 1. Besnier, Henri, supposed ed.
12-8092.

Library of Congress   S515.L72

NL 0359790   DLC KMK

Liger, Louis, *sieur d'Auxerre,* 1658–1717.
La nouvelle maison rustique, ou Économie générale de tous les biens de campagne; la maniere de les entretenir & de les multiplier; donnée ci-devant au public par le sieur Liger: 10. éd. augm. considérablement, & mise en meilleur ordre; avec la vertu des simples, l'apothicairerie; les décisions du droit françois sur les matieres rurales; et enrichie de figures en taille-douce, par M ••• ... Paris, Durand, 1775.
2 v. front. (v. 1) illus., plates (2 fold.) 26ᶜᵐ.
1. France. Agriculture.
Agr 10-1899

Library. U. S. Dept. of   Agriculture 33L623

NL 0359791   DNAL ICU

---

630   Liger, Louis, sieur d'Auxerre, 1658–1717.
L620   La nouvelle maison rustique, au Économie
1775   générale de tous les biens de campagne; la maniere de les entretenir & de les multiplier; donnée ci-devant au public par le sieur Liger: 10. éd. augm. considérablement, & mise en meilleur ordre; avec la vertu des simples, l'apothicairerie; les décisions du droit françois sur les matieres rurales; et enrichie de figures en taille-douce, par M.***... Paris, Humblot, 1775.
2v. front.(v.1) illus.,plates (2 fold.) 26cm.

Continued in next column

Continued from preceding column

Title for earlier editions: Oeconomie générale de la campagne, ou Nouvelle maison rustique.

1. Agriculture. France. I. Title: La nouvelle maison rustique. II. Title: Oeconomie générale de   la campagne. 0 cd.

NL 0359793   KU

S515   **Liger, Louis,** *sieur d'Auxerre,* 1658–1717.
L72¦   La nouvelle maison rustique, ou Économie générale de
1775   tous les biens de campagne; la manière de les entretenir et de les multiplier; donnée ci-devant au public par le sieur Liger. 10. éd., augm. considérablement, & mise en meilleur ordre; avec la vertu des simples, l'apothicairerie, les décisions du droit françois sur les matières rurales; et enrichie de figures en taille-douce. Par M. ••• ... Paris, Samson, M. DCC. LXXV. [1775]
2 v. front., illus., plates (1 fold.) 26½ x 21ᶜᵐ

The 5th-9th editions, 1743-1768, were edited by Henri Besnier, also an earlier (unnumbered?) edition in 1721. (*cf.* Catalogue général ... de la Bibliothèque nationale.) The 11th edition, 1790, was edited by La Bretonnerie.
First published in 1700, under title: Œconomie générale de la campagne, ou Nouvelle maison rustique

√ Agriculture   √ 1 Besnier, Henri, supposed ed.

NL 0359795   CU-A

7133 Liger, Louis, sieur d'Auxerre.
La nouvelle maison rustique, ou Économie générale de tous les biens de campagne; la maniere de les entretenir & de les multiplier; donnée ci-devant au public par le sieur Liger: 10. éd. augm. considérablement, & mise en meilleur ordre; avec la vertu des simples, l'apothicairerie; les décisions du droit françois sur les matieres rurales, par M • • • ... Paris, La veuve Savoye, 1775.
2 v. front (v. 1) illus., plates (2 fold.) 26 cm.

NL 0359796   MH

Liger, Louis, *sieur d'Auxerre,* 1658–1717.
WD   La nouvelle maison rustique, ou Économie générale de
7917   tous les biens de campagne; la maniere de les entretenir & de les multiplier; donnée ci-devant au public par le sieur Liger. 11. éd. augm. considérablement, & mise en meilleur ordre; avec la vertu des simples, l'apothicairerie; les décisions du droit françois sur les matieres rurales; et enrichie de figures en taille-douce, par M*** ... Paris, Desaint, 1777.
2 v. front. (v. 1) illus., plates (2 fold.) 26ᶜᵐ.

NL 0359797   CtY CU MH NcD OCl NNC

FILM   Liger, Louis, sieur d'Auxerre, 1658–1717.
Q⁻   La nouvelle maison rustique; ou, Econo-
no.1   mie generale de tous les biens de campagne:
r.26   la maniere de les entretenir & de les
Item 1   multiplier; donnée ci-devant au public par le sieur Liger. 11.éd., augm. considérablement, & mise en meilleur ordre: avec la vertu des simples, l'apothicairerie, & les décisions du droit françois sur les matieres rurales; et enrichie de figures en taille-douce. Par M.*** Paris, Chez   Desaint, 1777.
2v. illus.,   plates.

Microfilm. (Manuscripta. History of science 16th to 19th century, r.26, item 1)

√1.Agriculture - Early works to 1800. √I. Title. √(Series: Manuscripta. History of science 16th   to 19th century)

NL 0359799   CLSU

«Liger, Louis, sieur d'Auxerre, 1658–1717.
Nouvelle maison rustique ou economie generale de tous les biens de campagne ... 9th ed. 1778.

NL 0359800   PPHor

630.944   Liger, Louis, *sieur* d'Auxerre, 1658–1717.
L723o   La nouvelle maison rustique, ou economie
1790   rurale, pratique et générale de tous les biens de campagne; donnée ci-devant au public par Sieur Liger: onzieme edition, revue, corrigée & considérablement augmentée, fondée sur l'experience, & les nouvelles découvertes, les plus sûres & les moins répandues, selon la pratique usuelle, purgée des erreurs anciennes, sans systèmes, avec des observations critiques, neuves & intéressantes. [Seventeen lines] A Paris, Durand, 1790.
2 v. 41 plates   27cm.

RARE BOOK COLLECTION

Edited by La Bretonnerie.
Bound in mottled calf, raised spine, sprinkled green edges, marbled endpapers.
First published in 1700, under title:
OEconomie générale de la campagne...
Brunet v.3, p. 1075.

1. Agriculture - Early works to 1800.
2. France - Agriculture. I. Brétonnerie, de, ed. II. Title.

NL 0359803   FU ViW

Rare   Liger, Louis, sieur d'Auxerre, 1658–1717.
S   La nouvelle maison rustique, ou economie
515   rurale, pratique et générale de tous les biens
L725   de campagne; donnée ci-devant au public par le sieur Liger. 11. éd., revue, corrigée & considérablement augmentée, fondée sur l'experience & les nouvelles découvertes, le plus sûres & les moins répandues, selon la pratique usuelle, purgée des erreurs anciennes, sans systèmes, avec des observations critiques, neuves & intéressantes... Par l'auteur de la Correspondance rurale, & de l'Ecole du jardin fruitier... Paris, Libraires associés, 1790.
2 v. illus.   25 cm.

The 5th-9th editions, 1743-1768, were edited by Henri Besnier, also an earlier (unnumbered?) edition in 1721. (*cf.* Catalogue général ... de la Bibliothèque nationale.) The 11th edition, 1790, was edited by La Brétonnerie.
First published in 1700, under title: Œconomie générale de la campagne, ou Nouvelle maison rustique.

1. Agriculture. I. La Bretonnerie, de, ed. II. Liger, Louis, sieur d'Auxerre, 1658-1717. OEconomie générale de la campagne. III. Title. IV. Title: OEconomie générale de la campagne.

NL 0359805   LU

R   LIGER, LOUIS, sieur d'Auxerre, 1658–1717.
50   La nouvelle maison rustique, ou Economie ru-
.51   rale, pratique et générale de tous les biens de campagne... 11. édition, revue, corrigée & considérablement augmentée… Paris, Merigot, 1790.
2v.

First published in 1700 under title: Œconomie générale de la campagne, ou Nouvelle maison rustique.
Edited by La Brétonnerie.
Vol.2 has im-   print: Paris, Chez les libraires associés,   1790.

NL 0359806   ICN CtY

---

630   Liger, Louis, sieur d'Auxerre, 1658–1717.
L620   La nouvelle maison rustique, ou economie
1790   rurale, pratique et générale de tous les biens de campagne; donnée ci-devant au public par le sieur Liger; 11.ed. revue, corrigée et considérablement augm... Paris, Onfroy, 1790.
2v. front. (v.1) illus.,plates. 26cm.

Title for earlier editions: Oeconomie générale de la campagne, ou Nouvelle maison rustique.

NL 0359807   KU ViW

VOLUME 332

LIGER, Louis, 1658-1717.
La nouvelle maison rustique, ou, Economie
rurale, pratique et générale de tous les biens
de campagne; donnée ci-devant par le sieur Liger. 11.ed., rev., cor.& considérablement augm...
Le tout enrichi de figures,& rendu plus utile...
aux propriétaires des terres... Par l'auteur de
la correspondance rurale,& L'Ecole du jardin
fruitier,[De La Bretonnerie]. Paris,Chez
Samson,1790.

2 v.front.,illus , plates. 26 cm.

NL 0359808   MH

[Liger, Louis, sieur d'Auxerre] 1658-1717.
La nouvelle maison rustique, ou Économie rurale, pratique et
générale de tous les biens de campagne. Nouvelle édition, entièrement refondue, considérablement augmentée, et mise en
ordre, d'après les expériences, les plus sûres, les auteurs les plus
estimés, les mémoires et les procédés de cultivateurs, amateurs et
artistes, chacun dans les parties qui les concernent; par J. F.
Bastien... À Paris: Chez Deterville [etc.] an VI-1798. 3 v.
plans, plates. 26cm.

With bookplate of Charles Atwood Kofoid.
First published in 1700 with title: Œconomie générale de la campagne; ou,
Nouvelle maison rustique.
For further information cf. Graesse, J. G. T. Trésor de livres rares et precieux.

948098-100A. 1. Agriculture.   2. Gardening. 3. Fruit—Culture.
I. Bastien, Jean François, 1747-   1824, ed. II. Title. III. Title: La
maison rustique.
                                                July 18, 1938

    CU MH-A
NL 0359810   NN NIC PKsL NIC PPULC PPGi MH CtY PPHor

Liger, Louis, *sieur d'Auxerre*, 1658-1717.
La nouvelle maison rustique, ou Économie rurale, pratique et générale de tous les biens de campagne. Nouvelle
éd., entièrement refondue, considérablement augm., et
mise en ordre, d'après les expériences les plus sûres ...
par J.-F. Bastien ... Paris, Chez Deterville, an XII—1804.
3 v. illus., 60 pl. (31 fold.) 27cm.

1. Agriculture. 2. Fish-culture.   1. Bastien, Jean François, 1747-1824,
ed.
                                                A 18-1998

Title from Harvard Univ.   Printed by L. C.

NL 0359811   MH MH-A MBH MiDW MiEM CtY

S 515   Liger, Louis, sieur d'Auxerre,
.L7   1658-1717.
1805   La nouvelle maison rustique, ou
(Rare)   économie rurale, pratique et
         générale de tous les biens de
         campagne. Nouv. éd., entièrement
         refondue, considérablement
         augmentée... A Paris, Chez
         Deterville, libraire, 1805.
         3 v. illus.

         1. Agriculture--France. I. Title.

NL 0359812   ICU

LIGER, Louis, 1658-1717.
Oeconomie generale de la campagne, ou,
Nouvelle maison rustique. Par le sieur Louis
Liger... Paris, Chez C.de Sercy, 1700.

2 v.in1. illus . 25 1/2 cm.
Title in red and black.
Title vignette.

NL 0359813   MH

Liger, Louis, *sieur d'Auxerre*, 1658-1717.
Oeconomie générale de la campagne, ou Nouvelle maison
rustique. Par le sieur Louis Liger, d'Auxerre. 2. éd. rev.
& cor. Amsterdam, H. Desbordes, 1701.

2 v. illus. 25½ x 19cm.

1. Agriculture.
                                                Agr 10—1098
U. S. Dept. of agr. Library   30L623
for Library of Congress   [a40b1]

NL 0359814   DNAL MBH MH OC NjP MH

Liger, Louis, *sieur d'Auxerre*, 1658-1717.
Oeconomie generale de la campagne, ou, Nouvelle maison rustique. Par le sieur Louis Liger. 2. ed., rev., cor.
& augm. par l'auteur ... Paris, Chez C. Prudhomme,
1708.

2 v. illus. 26cm.
Title in red and black.

1. Agriculture. 2. Fish-culture.
                                                A 18-2001
Title from Harvard Univ.   Printed by L. C.

NL 0359815   MH MH-A

Liger, Louis, sieur d'Auxerre, 1658-1717.
The retir'd gardener
    see under   Gentil, François.

Mann   Liger, Louis, sieur d'Auxerre, 1658-1717.
SF   [Traité curieux des mouches a miel, et
523   des vers a soye. Paris, C. Prudhomme,
L723   1730?]
         [6], 418 p. 16 cm.

         Mann copy imperfect: t. p. wanting; title
         from caption title.
         Appears to be a reprint of the author's
         La nouvelle maison rustique; ou, Économie

generale de tous les biens de campagne ...
4. éd. Paris, 1730. I. Partie, liv. V, chap.
L. For more information, see notes from
Prof. Frank Phillips in the book.

1. Bees. 2. Silkworms. I. Liger, Louis,
sieur d'Auxer   re, 1658-1717. La
nouvelle mai   son rustique. II. Title.

NL 0359818   NIC

[Liger, Louis, sieur d'Auxerre] 1658-1717.
Traité curieux des mouches a miel, contenant
la maniere de les bien gouverner, pour en tirer
un profit considerable par la récolte de la cire
& du miel, avec un Traité des vers a soye.
Paris, C.Prudhomme, 1734.
418 p. plates. 17cm.

Also in his La nouvelle maison rustique.
8.éd. 1762. v.1. p.350-453.

NL 0359819   DNAL

Liger, Louis, *sieur d'Auxerre*, 1658-1717.
Traité facile pour apprendre a elever des figuiers,
suite de la Culture parfaite des jardins. Par le sieur
Louis Liger, d'Auxerre. Paris, D. Beugnie', 1702.

3 p. l., 81, [3] p. illus. 17cm. [With his La culture parfaite des jardins ... Paris, D. Beugnie', 1702]

1. Fig.
                                                Agr 25-1458
Library, U. S. Dept. of   Agriculture 90L62

NL 0359820   DNAL

[Liger, Louis] sieur d'Auxerre, 1658-1717.
Rare book   Traitté de toute sorte de chasse et de'
Room   pêche ... & un dictionnaire de tous les
Uzn25   termes de filets, de chasse & de pêche,
714l   employez dans ce livre. A Amsterdam,Aux
            dépens d'Estienne Roger,1714.
            2v.in 1. 90pl.(part fold.) 16½cm.
            First edition published in 1709 as
            Amusemens de la campagne, ou Nouvelles ruses
            innocentes. Also published as: Amusemens de
            la chasse et de la pêche; l'Art de toute

sorte de chasse et de pêche; and Délices de la
campagne.
            Based on Les ruses innocentes, by F.
Fortin.

NL 0359822   CtY NN MH

Liger, Marc.
Nouvelles équations approchées pour l'étude des écoule-
ments subsoniques et transsoniques. Chatillon-sous-Bag-
neux, Office national d'études et de recherches aéronautiques,
1953.
48 p. diagrs., tables. 27 cm. (Office national d'études et de
recherches aéronautiques. Publication no 64)
Cover title.
At head of title: O. N. E. R. A.
Bibliography: p. 47-48.
1. Aerodynamics, Transonic. 2. Aerodynamics.   I. Title.
(Series: Office national d'études et de recherches aéronautiques, Paris.
Publication no 64)
                                                A 54-1007
Mass. Inst. of Tech.   Library
for Library of Congress

NL 0359823   MCM NN

---

510   Liger, Pierre
L7d   Dissertation sur la geometrie,avec le
        premier chapitre de nouveaux principes,ou
        elémens des mathematiques. Par M.Liger...
        Paris, C.-P.Gueffier, 1743.
        2 p.ℓ.,108,[4]p. ii diagrs. 16½ cm.
        Bound with this is his Elemens des math-
        ématiques...Seconde partie...[n.p., n.pub.]
        1744.

NL 0359824   MiU

Liger, René
    Dissertation sur le célibat ecclésiastique, ou réponse
aux assertions fausses du Journal ecclésiastique de
septembre et octobre 1790. [P] nd.]
    83 p.

NL 0359825   MH

Liger, René.
    Lettres critiques et dissertation sur le prêt de com-
merce, par M. Liger ... Caen, Impr. de J. C. Pryon, 1774.
233, [1] p., 1 l., 17 p. 17½cm.
"Réponse à la lettre d'un anonyme à l'abbé Liger": 17 p. at end

1. Interest and usury.

Library of Congress   HB535.L7   6-33347†

NL 0359826   DLC ICU NNC

Law   Liger, Renée, ed.

France. *Laws, statutes, etc.*
    Le code de la route; nouveau texte présenté et commenté
par R. Liger. Préf. de A. Rumpler. Paris, A. Michel [1954]

Liger, Renée.
    Dialogues sous l'arbre; essai de caractérologie. Frontis-
pice de Berjole. Paris, Œuvres françaises, 1947.
238 p. illus. 19 cm.

1. Title.

PQ2623.I 49D5   49-21814 rev*

NL 0359828   DLC

MISSISSIPPI

MsG	William Alexander Percy Memorial Library, Greenville.
MsSC*	Mississippi State University, State College.
MsSM	Mississippi State University, State College.
MsU	University of Mississippi, University.

MONTANA

MtBC	Montana State University, Bozeman.
MtBozC*	Montana State University at Bozeman.
MtU	University of Montana, Missoula.

NEW YORK

N	New York State Library, Albany.
NAlU	State University of New York at Albany.
NAurW	Wells College, Aurora.
NB	Brooklyn Public Library, Brooklyn.
NBB	Brooklyn Museum Libraries, Brooklyn.
NBC	Brooklyn College, Brooklyn.
NBM	Medical Research Library of Brooklyn.
NBPol	Polytechnic Institute of Brooklyn, Brooklyn.
NBSU-M	State University of New York, Downstate Medical Center Library, Brooklyn.
NBiSU-H	State University of New York, Harpur College, Binghamton.
NBronSL	Sarah Lawrence College, Bronxville.
NBu	Buffalo and Erie County Public Library, Buffalo.
NBuC	State University of New York, College at Buffalo.
NBuG	Grosvenor Reference Division, Buffalo and Erie County Public Library, Buffalo.
NBuU	State University of New York at Buffalo.
NCH	Hamilton College, Clinton.
NCaS	St. Lawrence University, Canton.
NCorniC	Corning Glass Works Library, Corning. (Includes Corning Museum of Glass Library)
NCoxHi	Greene County Historical Society, Inc., Coxsackie.
NFQC	Queens College Library, Flushing.
NGrnUN*	United Nations Library.
NHC	Colgate University, Hamilton.
NHi	New York Historical Society, New York.
NIC	Cornell University, Ithaca.
NJQ	Queens Borough Public Library, Jamaica.
NL*	Newberry Library, Chicago.
NLC	Not a library symbol.
NN	New York Public Library.
NNAB	American Bible Society, New York.
NNAHI	Augustinian Historical Institute, New York.
NNAJHi	American Jewish Historical Society, New York.
NNB	Association of the Bar of the City of New York, New York.
NNBG	New York Botanical Garden, Bronx Park, New York.
NNC	Columbia University, New York.
NNC-T	— Teachers College Library.
NNCFR	Council on Foreign Relations, New York.
NNCoCi	City College of New York, New York.
NNE	Engineering Societies Library, New York.
NNF	Fordham University, New York.
NNFI	French Institute in the United States, New York.
NNG	General Theological Seminary of the Protestant Episcopal Church. New York.
NNGr	Grolier Club Library, New York.
NNH	Hispanic Society of America, New York.
NNHeb	Hebrew Union College, Jewish Institute of Religion Library, New York.
NNHi	New York Historical Society.
NNJ	Jewish Theological Seminary of America, New York.
NNJIR*	Jewish Institute of Religion, New York.
NNJef	Jefferson School of Social Science, New York. (Library no longer in existence)
NNM	American Museum of Natural History, New York.
NNMM	Metropolitan Museum of Art Library, New York.
NNMor*	Pierpont Morgan Library.
NNNAM	New York Academy of Medicine, New York.
NNNM	New York Medical College, Flower & Fifth Avenue Hospitals, New York.
NNNPsan	New York Psychoanalytic Institute, New York.
NNPM	Pierpont Morgan Library, New York.
NNQ*	Queens Borough Public Library, New York.
NNQC*	Queens College Library, Flushing.
NNRI	Rockefeller Institute for Medical Research, New York.
NNSU-M*	State University of New York College of Medicine at New York City.

NEW YORK continued

NNU	New York University Libraries, New York.
NNU-W	— Washington Square Library.
NNUN	United Nations Library, New York.
NNUN-W	— Woodrow Wilson Memorial Library.
NNUT	Union Theological Seminary, New York.
NNUT-Mc	— McAlpin Collection.
NNWML	Wagner College Library, Staten Island.
NNYI	Yivo Institute for Jewish Research, New York.
NNZI	Zionist Archives and Library of Palestine Foundation, New York.
NNerC	College of New Rochelle, New Rochelle.
NNiaU	Niagara University, Niagara University.
NPV	Vassar College, Poughkeepsie,
NRAB	Samuel Colgate Baptist Historical Library of the American Baptist Historical Society, Rochester.
NRU	University of Rochester, Rochester.
NSchU	Union College, Schenectady.
NSyU	Syracuse University, Syracuse.
NUt	Utica Public Library.
NWM	U.S. Military Academy, West Point.
NYPL*	New York Public Library.
NYhI	International Business Machines Corporation, Thomas J. Watson Research Center, Yorktown Heights.

NEBRASKA

NbOC	Creighton University, Omaha.
NbU	University of Nebraska, Lincoln.

NORTH CAROLINA

Nc	North Carolina State Library, Raleigh.
Nc-Ar	North Carolina State Department of Archives and History, Raleigh.
NcA	Pack Memorial Public Library, Asheville.
NcA-S	— Sondley Reference Library.
NcAS*	Sondley Reference Library, Asheville.
NcC	Public Library of Charlotte & Mecklenburg County, Charlotte.
NcCC	Charlotte College Library, Charlotte.
NcCJ	Johnson C. Smith University, Charlotte.
NcCU	University of North Carolina at Charlotte.
NcD	Duke University, Durham.
NcDurC	North Carolina College at Durham, Durham.
NcGU*	University of North Carolina at Greensboro.
NcGW	University of North Carolina at Greensboro.
NcGuG	Guilford College, Guilford.
NcR	Olivia Raney Public Library, Raleigh.
NcRR	Richard B. Harrison Public Library, Raleigh.
NcRS	North Carolina State University at Raleigh.
NcU	University of North Carolina, Chapel Hill.
NcWfC*	Wake Forest College, Winston-Salem.
NcWfSB	Southeastern Baptist Theological Seminary Library, Wake Forest.
NcWilA	Atlantic Christian College, Wilson.
NcWilC	Carolina Discipliniana Library, Wilson.
NcWsW	Wake Forest College, Winston-Salem.

NORTH DAKOTA

NdFA	North Dakota State University, Fargo. (Formerly North Dakota Agricultural College)
NdHi	State Historical Society of North Dakota, Bismarck.
NdU	University of North Dakota Library, Grand Forks.

NEW HAMPSHIRE

Nh	New Hampshire State Library, Concord.
NhD	Dartmouth College, Hanover.
NhU	University of New Hampshire, Durham.

NEW JERSEY

NjGbS	Glassboro State College, Glassboro.
NjHi	New Jersey Historical Society, Newark.
NjMD	Drew University, Madison.
NjN	Newark Public Library.
NjNBR*	Rutgers–The State University, New Brunswick.
NjNbS	New Brunswick Theological Seminary, New Brunswick.
NjNbT*	New Brunswick Theological Seminary.
NjP	Princeton University, Princeton.
NjPT	Princeton Theological Seminary, Princeton.
NjR	Rutgers–The State University, New Brunswick.
NjT	Trenton Free Library, Trenton.

NEW MEXICO

NmA	Albuquerque Public Library, New Mexico.
NmU	University of New Mexico, Albuquerque.
NmUpU	New Mexico State University, University Park.

NEVADA

NvU	University of Nevada, Reno.

OHIO

O	Ohio State Library, Columbus.
OAU	Ohio University, Athens.
OAkU	University of Akron, Akron.
OBerB	Baldwin-Wallace College, Berea.
OBlC	Bluffton College, Bluffton.
OC	Public Library of Cincinnati and Hamilton County, Cincinnati.
OCH	Hebrew Union College, Cincinnati.
OCHP	Historical and Philosophical Society of Ohio, Cincinnati.
OCLloyd	Lloyd Library and Museum, Cincinnati.
OCU	University of Cincinnati, Cincinnati.
OCX	Xavier University, Cincinnati.
OCl	Cleveland Public Library.
OClCS	Case Institute of Technology, Cleveland.
OClFC	Cleveland State University, Cleveland. (Formerly Fenn College)
OClJC	John Carroll University, Cleveland.
OClMA	Cleveland Museum of Art, Cleveland.
OClSA	Cleveland Institute of Art, Cleveland.
OClW	Case Western Reserve University, Cleveland.
OClWHi	Western Reserve Historical Society, Cleveland.
ODW	Ohio Wesleyan University, Delaware.
ODa	Dayton and Montgomery County Library, Dayton.
ODaStL	St. Leonard College Library, Dayton.
ODaU	University of Dayton, Dayton.
OEac	East Cleveland Public Library.
OFH	Rutherford B. Hayes Library, Fremont.
OGK	Kenyon College, Gambier.
OHi	Ohio State Historical Society, Columbus.
OKentC	Kent State University, Kent.
OO	Oberlin College, Oberlin.
OOxM	Miami University, Oxford.
OSW	Wittenberg University, Springfield.
OTU	University of Toledo, Toledo.
OU	Ohio State University, Columbus.
OWibfU	Wilberforce University, Carnegie Library, Wilberforce.
OWicB	Borromeo Seminary, Wickliffe.
OWoC	College of Wooster, Wooster.
OWorP	Pontifical College Josephinum, Worthington.
OYesA	Antioch College, Yellow Springs.

OKLAHOMA

Ok	Oklahoma State Library, Oklahoma City.
OkEG	Graduate Seminary Library, Enid.
OkS	Oklahoma State University, Stillwater.
OkT	Tulsa Public Library.
OkU	University of Oklahoma, Norman.

OREGON

Or	Oregon State Library, Salem.
OrCS	Oregon State University Library, Corvallis.
OrHi	Oregon Historical Society, Portland.
OrP	Library Association of Portland, Portland.
OrPR	Reed College, Portland.
OrPS	Portland State College, Portland.
OrSaW	Willamette University, Salem.
OrStbM	Mount Angel College, Mount Angel Abbey, Saint Benedict.
OrU	University of Oregon, Eugene.

PENNSYLVANIA

PBL	Lehigh University, Bethlehem.
PBa	Academy of the New Church, Bryn Athyn.
PBm	Bryn Mawr College, Bryn Mawr.
PCA*	Samuel Colgate Baptist Historical Library of the American Baptist Historical Society, Rochester, N. Y.
PCC	Crozer Theological Seminary, Chester.
PCamA	Alliance College, Cambridge Springs.
PCarlD	Dickinson College, Carlisle.
PHC	Haverford College, Haverford.
PHi	Historical Society of Pennsylvania, Philadelphia.
PJA	Abington Library Society, Jenkintown.
PJAlG	Alverthorpe Gallery, Rosenwald Collection, Jenkintown.
PJB	Beaver College, Jenkintown.